HANDBOOK

OF

ENGINEERING FUNDAMENTALS

HANDBOOK

OF

ENGINEERING FUNDAMENTALS

Prepared by a Staff of Specialists
Under the Editorship of

OVID W. ESHBACH

WILEY ENGINEERING
HANDBOOK SERIES

NEW YORK : JOHN WILEY & SONS, INC.
LONDON : CHAPMAN & HALL, LIMITED

PUBLISHER'S PREFACE

In making plans for new editions of our handbooks in mechanical engineering and in electrical engineering, it soon became clear that engineering science and practice had developed to such an extent that handbooks were growing beyond all practical bounds. They had become both bulky and inconvenient and contained much duplicated material. In order to solve the problems presented by these conditions, the editors of our various handbooks were asked to serve as an advisory editorial board.

This board recommended, first, that the fundamental material underlying all engineering be published in a separate volume, and, second, that the existing handbooks as they are revised be issued in several volumes containing material closely related to the specialized branches of engineering. As a result of these recommendations, the Wiley Engineering Handbook Series has been initiated, which in the beginning will comprise the following: Eshbach's "Handbook of Engineering Fundamentals"; Kent's "Mechanical Engineers' Handbook" in two volumes, viz., "Power" and "Design and Shop Practice"; Pender's "Electrical Engineers' Handbook" in two volumes, viz., "Electric Power" and "Communication and Electronics."

This division has also made it possible to devote more space to the various topics so that the entire new series of handbooks contains more complete information on all topics than heretofore has been possible. It is our hope that this new plan will give engineers information that is more useful, more complete, and in more convenient form.

JOHN WILEY & SONS, INC.

EDITOR'S PREFACE

This handbook has been prepared for the purpose of embodying in a single volume those fundamental laws and theories of science which are basic to engineering practice. It is essentially a summary of the principles of mathematics, physics, and chemistry, the properties and uses of engineering materials, the mechanics of solids and fluids, and the commonly used mathematical and physical tables, to which has been added a discussion of contractual relations. Thus, with the exception of the technics of surveying and drawing, there is included the fundamental technology common to nearly all engineering curricula.

It is hoped, that, as a unit in itself, it will be valuable to both student and practicing engineer and, as a companion to any other volume of the Wiley Handbook Series, will give a degree of completeness in scope not previously attainable in this form.

Although each of the contributors as a matter of course checked the technical accuracy of his material, every section has been read by at least two other competent engineers as an additional precaution. The more important tables were checked against at least two independent sources by different individuals.

Appreciation is expressed to all who have cooperated in giving advice and assistance. Among them the editor feels particularly indebted to Mr. H. C. Jennison, Technical Manager, and Mr. W. R. Hibbard, Assistant Metallurgist, of the American Brass Company, who completed the manuscript begun by Mr. W. H. Bassett, deceased; Dr. Lyman J. Briggs, Director of the National Bureau of Standards, Dr. J. W. Finch, Director of the Bureau of Mines, and members of their staffs who reviewed portions of the manuscript and made valuable suggestions; and to editors of other Wiley Handbooks, national societies, corporations, and others for permission to use material previously published by them.

July 1, 1936

OVID W. ESHBACH

LIST OF CONTRIBUTORS

John L. Barnes, S.M., A.M., Ph.D., Department of Mathematics, Tufts College.—*Mathematical and Physical Tables,* and *Mathematics.*

The late W. H. Bassett, The American Brass Co., Waterbury, Conn.—*Copper and Wrought Copper-base Alloys.*

Christopher H. Bierbaum, B.S., M.E., Vice President and Consulting Engineer, Lumen Bearing Co., Buffalo, N. Y.—*Bearing Metals.*

J. G. Brainerd, D.Sc. in E.E., Asst. Prof. Moore School of Elec. Eng., University of Pennsylvania.—*Tables of Conversion Factors—Units of Weights and Measures, Gages,* and *Alignment Charts—Nomograms.*

Carl C. Chambers, D.Sc. in E.E., Moore School of Elec. Eng., University of Pennsylvania.—*Conduction of Electricity in Solids and Fluids.*

W. M. Corse, Metallurgical and Chemical Engineer, Washington, D. C.—*Sand-cast Copper-base Alloys.*

Theodore Crane, C.E., M.A., Professor of Architectural Engineering, School of Fine Arts, Yale University.—*Reinforced Concrete,* and *Cement, Concrete, Lime, Mortar and Plaster.*

Jasper O. Draffin, M.S., Professor of Theoretical and Applied Mechanics, Materials Testing Laboratory, University of Illinois.—*Mechanics of Materials, Testing of Materials,* and *Stone, Brick, and Terra-cotta.*

H. L. Dryden, Ph.D., Chief of the Division of Mechanics and Sound, National Bureau of Standards.—*Wind Pressure on Structures.*

Junius D. Edwards, Asst. Director of Research, Aluminum Research Laboratories, Aluminum Co. of America, New Kensington, Pa.—*Aluminum and Aluminum Alloys.*

Churchill Eisenhart, B.A., M.A., Student at Institute of Applied Statistics, University of London.—*Precision of Measurements.*

Ovid W. Eshbach, E.E., M.S., Personnel Department, Am. Tel. and Tel. Co., New York, N. Y.—*Mathematical and Physical Tables.*

Maurice J. Fish, Ph.D., Instructor in Mathematics, Buffalo Collegiate Center, Buffalo, N. Y.—*Trigonometry, Analytic Geometry, Calculus, Differential Equations, Functions of Complex Variables,* and *Vector Analysis.*

J. C. Fox, B.S. in Chem., Chief Chemist and Metallurgist, Doehler Die Casting Co., Toledo, O.—*Die-Casting Alloys.*

John A. Gann, Ph.D., Chief Metallurgist, The Dow Chemical Co., Midland, Mich.—*Magnesium and Magnesium Alloys.*

E. B. Guenther, M.E., Technical Department, Harbison-Walker Refractories Co., Pittsburgh, Pa.—*Refractories.*

Paul E. Hemke, M.A., Ph.D., Head of the Department of Aeronautical Engineering, Rensselaer Polytechnic Institute.—*Mechanics of Fluids.*

Zay Jeffries, Metallurgical Engineer, Nela Park, Cleveland, O.—*Aluminum and Aluminum Alloys, Tungsten,* and *Molybdenum.*

Robert Thurston Kent, M.E., Consulting Engineer, Verona, N. J.—*Mathematical Tables.*

Paul J. Kiefer, A.B., M.E., Professor of Mechanical Engineering, U. S. Naval Postgraduate School.—*Engineering Thermodynamics.*

Henry C. Knutson, E.E., M.E.E., Asst. Prof., Department of Elec. Eng., Lehigh University.—*Tables on Physical Properties of Materials, Symbols and Abbreviations, Electrical Conductor Materials,* and *Timber.*

R. B. Lindsay, Ph. D., Professor of Theoretical Physics and Chairman of the Department of Physics, Brown University.—*Acoustics.*

Robert J. Martin, B.S., M.A., Ass't Meteorologist, U. S. Weather Bureau, Washington, D. C.—*Meteorology.*

ix

Joseph Mattiello, Ph.D., Technical Director of the Hilo Varnish Corp., Brooklyn, N. Y.—*Chemistry,* and *Paints, Enamels, Varnishes, and Lacquers.*

J. Spotts McDowell, B.S., Research Engineer, Harbison-Walker Refractories Co., Pittsburgh, Pa.—*Refractories.*

D. F. Miner, Manager, Material and Process Engineering Dept., Westinghouse Electric & Manufacturing Co., East Pittsburgh, Pa.—*Welding, Brazing and Soldering Materials, Electrical Conductor Materials, Electric Insulating Materials, Adhesive Materials,* and *Lubricants.*

H. F. Moore, M.E., M.M.E., D.Sc., Research Professor of Engineering Materials, University of Illinois.—*Timber.*

W. M. Peirce, B.S. in Ch.E., M.S., Chief, Metal Research Division, The New Jersey Zinc Co., Palmerton, Pa.—*Zinc and Zinc-base Alloys.*

Janvier M. Rice, E.E., Executive Engineer, Curtiss Aeroplane & Motor Co., Inc., Buffalo, N. Y.—*Arithmetic, Algebra, Geometry,* and *Theoretical Mechanics.*

R. L. Sackett, C.E., Dean of the School of Engineering, Director of the Engineering Experiment Station and of Engineering Extension, Pennsylvania State College.—*Contracts.*

J. B. Seastone, Engineer, Metals Section, Material & Process Engineering Dept., Westinghouse Electric & Manufacturing Co., East Pittsburgh, Pa.—*Magnetic Materials.*

Frank N. Speller, B.A.Sc., D.Sc., Director, Dept. of Metallurgy and Research, National Tube Co. (Subsidiary U. S. Steel Corp.), Pittsburgh, Pa.—*Corrosion of Metals.*

Bradley Stoughton, Ph.B., B.S., Dean of Engineering, Head of Dept. of Metallurgy, Lehigh University.—*General Properties of Metals and Alloys, Iron and Steel,* and *Metal Joining.*

Milton C. Stuart, M.E., Professor of Experimental Mechanical Engineering, Lehigh University.—*Engineering Thermodynamics.*

Irven A. Travis, M.Sc. in E.E., Moore School of Electrical Engineering, University of Pennsylvania.—*Electricity and Magnetism.*

S. B. Tuwiner, B.S., Ch.E., Ph.D., Research Engineer, Phelps Dodge Corp., New York, N. Y.—*Chemistry.*

Ernst Weber, Dr. Phil., Dr. Techn. Ing., Research Professor of Elec. Engr., Polytechnic Institute of Brooklyn.—*Physical Units and Standards,* and *Radiation and Light.*

Charles Weyl, M.Sc. in E.E., Asst. Prof., Moore School of Elec. Eng., University of Pennsylvania.—*Electricity and Magnetism.*

Edgar W. Woolard, Meteorologist, U. S. Weather Bureau, Washington, D. C.—*Meteorology.*

Robert Worthington, 20 Exchange Place, New York, N. Y.—*Nickel and Non-ferrous Nickel Alloys.*

GENERAL TABLE OF CONTENTS

Detailed tables of contents are given at the beginning of each section. An alphabetical index appears following Section 13.

For contents of other handbooks of this series, see pages following Index of this volume.

xi

This book is divided into sections, each section
carrying its independent sequence of page numbers.
For example, 3–15 indicates Section 3, page 15.

SECTION 1

MATHEMATICAL AND PHYSICAL TABLES

BY

O. W. ESHBACH

IN COLLABORATION WITH

J. L. BARNES, J. G. BRAINERD, R. T. KENT, AND H. C. KNUTSON

SYMBOLS AND ABBREVIATIONS

Table 1. Greek Alphabet

A	α	Alpha	H	η	Eta	N	ν	Nu	T	τ	Tau
B	β	Beta	Θ	$\vartheta\ \theta$	Theta	Ξ	ξ	Xi	Υ	υ	Upsilon
Γ	γ	Gamma	I	ι	Iota	O	o	Omicron	Φ	ϕ	Phi
Δ	δ	Delta	K	κ	Kappa	Π	π	Pi	X	χ	Chi
E	ϵ	Epsilon	Λ	λ	Lambda	P	ρ	Rho	Ψ	ψ	Psi
Z	ζ	Zeta	M	μ	Mu	Σ	$\sigma\ s$	Sigma	Ω	ω	Omega

Table 2. Symbols for Mathematical Operations

REFERENCES: American Standard for Mathematical Symbols (AESC Report Z10f). Mathematical Association of America (National Committee Report, 1923, Chapter 8).

Addition and Subtraction

$a + b$, a plus b

$a - b$, a minus b

$a \pm b$, a plus or minus b

$a \mp b$, a minus or plus b

Multiplication and Division

$a \times b$, or $a \cdot b$, or ab, a times b

$a \div b$, or $\dfrac{a}{b}$, or a/b, a divided by b

Symbols of Aggregation

( )   parentheses

[ ]   brackets

{ }   braces

—   vinculum

Equalities and Inequalities

$a = b$, a equals b

$a \approx b$, a approximately equals b

$a \neq b$, a is not equal to b

$a > b$, a is greater than b

$a < b$, a is less than b

$a \geqq b$, a equals or is greater than b

$a \leqq b$, a is less than or equals b

$a \equiv b$, a is identical to b

$a \rightarrow b$, or $a \doteq b$, a approaches b as a limit

Proportion

$a/b = c/d$, or $a : b :: c : d$, a is to b as c is to d

$a \propto b$, a varies directly as b

%, per cent

Powers and Roots

a^2, a squared

a^n, a raised to the nth power

$\sqrt[3]{a}$, cube root of a

$\sqrt[n]{a}$, or $a^{1/n}$, nth root of a

a^{-n}, $1/a^n$

$3.14 \times 10^4 = 31{,}400$

$3.14 \times 10^{-4} = 0.000314$

Miscellaneous

$a!$, $= 1 \cdot 2 \cdot 3 \ldots a$, factorial a

$P(n, r) = n(n-1)(n-2) \ldots (n - r + 1)$

$C(n, r) = \dfrac{P(n,r)}{r!} = \binom{n}{r}$ = binomial coefficients

$|a|$ = absolute value of a

i (or j) $= \sqrt{-1}$, imaginary unit

$\pi = 3.1416$, ratio of the circumference to the diameter of a circle

∞, infinity

Plane Geometry

$\angle$, angle

$\triangle$, triangle

$\parallel$, parallel

$\perp$, perpendicular

$\odot$, circle

$\square$, parallelogram

$\therefore$, therefore

$^{\circ}\,'\,''$, degree, minute, second

$'\,''$, feet, inches

Logarithms

$\log a = \log_{10} a$, common logarithm of a or log of a to the base 10

$\ln a = \log_e a$, natural logarithm of a or log of a to the base $e (e = 2.718)$

$\log^{-1} a$, number whose log is a

Trigonometry

sin, cos, tan

cosec or csc, sec, cot or ctn   } trigonometric functions

vers, covers

$\sin^{-1}, \cos^{-1}$, etc., inverse of the functions

Analytic Geometry

x, y, z; ξ, η, ζ, rectangular coordinates

ρ, s, intrinsic coordinates

ρ, radius of curvature

s, length of arc

r, θ, polar coordinates

ψ, angle from radius vector to tangent

r, θ, ϕ, spherical coordinates

θ, co-latitude

ϕ, longitude

r, θ, z, cylindrical coordinates

e, eccentricity in conics

p, semi latus rectum in conics

$l = \cos\alpha$, $m = \cos\beta$, $n = \cos\gamma$, direction cosines

Calculus

$y = f(x)$, y is a function of x

$y' = f'(x) = \dfrac{dy}{dx} = D_x y$, derivative of $y = f(x)$ with respect to x

$y'' = f''(x) = \dfrac{d(y')}{dx} = D^2{}_x y = \dfrac{d^2 y}{dx^2}$, second derivative of $y = f(x)$ with respect to x

$u = f(x, y)$, u is a function of x and y

$u_x = f_x(x, y) = D_x(u) = \dfrac{\partial u}{\partial x}$, partial derivative of $u = f(x, y)$ with respect to x

$u_{xy} = f_{xy}(x, y) = D_y(D_x u) = \dfrac{\partial^2 u}{\partial y \partial x}$, second partial derivative of $u = f(x, y)$ with respect to x and y

Δy, increment of y

dy, differential of y

δy, variation of y

$\displaystyle\sum_{i=a}^{b}$, summation over i from a to b

$\displaystyle\lim_{x \to a} (y) = b$, $y \to b$ as $x \to a$

$\displaystyle\int$, integral of

$\displaystyle\int_a^b$, definite integral of

Vector Analysis

i, j, k, unit vectors along the axes (right-handed system)

$a \cdot b = (ab) = Sab$, scalar product of a and b

$a \times b = [ab] = Vab$, vector product of a and b

Vectors are indicated in print by **bold**-faced type.

Table 3. Abbreviations for Engineering Terms

NOTE: This list is a selection of American Tentative Standard abbreviations, for scientific and engineering terms, recommended by the American Standards Association. (See ASA, Z10i—1932.)

Absolute	abs
Acre	acre
Alternating-current (as adjective)	a-c
Ampere	amp
Ampere-hour	amp-hr
Angstrom unit	A
Atomic weight	at. wt
Atmosphere	atm
Average	avg
Avoirdupois	avdp
Barometer	bar.
Barrel	bbl
Baumé	Bé
Boiler pressure	bp
Boiling point	bp
Brake horsepower	bhp
Brake horsepower-hour	bhp-hr
Brinell hardness number	Bhn
British thermal unit	Btu or B
Calorie	cal
Candlepower	cp
Centigram	cg
Centiliter	cl
Centimeter	cm
Centimeter-gram-second (system)	cgs
Chemically pure	cp
Circular	cir
Circular mils	cir mils
Coefficient	coef
Cologarithm	colog
Concentrate	conc
Conductivity	cond
Constant	const
Cord	cd
Cosecant	csc
Cosine	cos
Cotangent	ctn
Coulomb	spell out
Counter electromotive force	counter emf
Cubic	cu
Cubic centimeter	cu cm, cm^3, cc
Cubic foot	cu ft
Cubic inch	cu in.
Cubic meter	cu m or m^3
Cubic yard	cu yd
Decibel	db
Degree	deg or °
Degree Centigrade	C
Degree Fahrenheit	F
Degree Kelvin	K
Degree Réaumur	R
Diameter	diam
Direct-current (as adjective)	d-c
Dozen	doz
Dram	dr
Efficiency	eff
Electric	elec
Electromotive force	emf
Equation	eq
External	ext
Farad	spell out
Foot	ft
Foot-candle	ft-c
Foot-Lambert	ft-L
Foot-pound	ft-lb
Foot-pound-second (system)	fps
Freezing point	fp
Frequency	spell out
Fusion point	fnp

Gallon	gal
Grain	spell out
Gram	g
Gram-calory	g-cal
Henry	h
Horsepower	hp
Horsepower-hour	hp-hr
Hour	hr
Hundred	C
Hyperbolic sine	sinh
Hyperbolic cosine	cosh
Hyperbolic tangent	tanh
Inch	in.
Inch-pound	in-lb
Internal	int
Joule	j
Kilocycle	kc
Kilogram	kg
Kilogram-meter	kg-m
Kiloliter	kl
Kilometer	km
Kilovolt	kv
Kilovolt-ampere	kva
Kilowatt	kw
Kilowatthour	kwhr
Lambert	L
Latitude	lat
Linear foot	lin ft
Liter	l
Liquid	liq
Logarithm (common)	log
Logarithm (natural)	log$_e$ or ln
Longitude	long.
Lumen	l
Lumen-hour	l-hr
Magnetomotive force	mmf
Mass	spell out
Mathematics (ical)	math
Maximum	max
Melting point	mp
Meter	m
Meter-kilogram	m-kg
Mho	spell out
Microampere	μa or mu a
Microfarad	μf or mu f
Micromicron	μμ or mu mu
Micron	μ mu
Microwatt	μw or mu w
Mile	spell out
Milliampere	ma
Millifarad	mf
Milligram	mg
Millihenry	mh
Milliliter	ml
Millimeter	mm
Millimicron	mμ or m mu
Million	spell out
Millivolt	mv
Minimum	min
Minute	min
Minute (angular measure)	'
Ohm	spell out
Ounce	oz
Ounce-foot	oz-ft
Ounce-inch	oz-in.
Peck	pk
Pint	pt

Table 3. Abbreviations for Engineering Terms—*Continued*

Potential	spell out
Pound	lb
Pound-foot	lb-ft
Pound-inch	lb-in.
Pounds per square foot	lb per sq ft
Pounds per square inch	lb per sq in.
Power factor	spell out
Quart	qt
Radian	spell out
Reactive kilovolt-ampere	rkva
Reactive volt-ampere	rva
Revolutions per minute	rpm
Revolutions per second	rps
Rod	spell out
Root mean square	rms
Secant	sec
Second	sec
Second (angular measure)	″
Sine	sin
Specific gravity	sp gr
Specific heat	sp ht
Spherical candle power	scp
Square	sq
Square centimeter	sq cm or cm²
Square foot	sq ft
Square inch	sq in.
Square kilometer	sq km or km²
Square meter	sq m or m²
Square root of mean square	rms
Standard	std
Tangent	tan
Temperature	temp
Thousand	M
Ton	spell out
Versed sine	vers
Volt	v
Volt-ampere	va
Watt	w
Watthour	whr
Weight	wt
Yard	yd
Year	yr

Table 4. Symbols for Physical Quantities

NOTE: The most frequently used American Standard and Tentative Standard Symbols are included in this table. Reference to the sources, or publications of the American Standards Association, are indicated by the numbers, in parentheses, which follow the names of the quantities. These numbers correspond to the following:

(1) American Tentative Standard Aeronautical Symbols, ASA, Z10e—1929.
(2) American Institute of Electrical Engineers Standards ASA, Z10g1—1929.
(3) American Tentative Standard Symbols for Heat and Thermodynamics ASA, Z10c—1931.
(4) American Tentative Standard Symbols for Hydraulics ASA, Z10b—1929.
(5) American Standard Symbols for Mechanics, Structural Engineering and Testing Materials, ASA, Z10a—1932.
(6) American Standard Symbols for Photometry and Illumination ASA, Z10d—1930.

Where possible, capital letters denote total quantities and small letters denote specific quantities, or quantities per unit.

NAME OF QUANTITY	SYMBOL
Absorption factor (6)	α
Acceleration, angular (5)	α
Acceleration, linear, general (4) (5)	a
Acceleration due to gravity, general (1) (3) (4) (5)	g
International Adopted Standard (3)	g_o
local (3)	g_L
Adiabatic factor (3)	Y
Admittance (2)	Y, y
Air speed (1)	V
indicated (1)	V_i
Altitude (1)	h
Angle	
of attack (1)	α
between the absolute velocity of the water and the velocity of the runner at any point, measured in degrees (4)	α
between the relative velocity of the water and the velocity of the runner at any point, measured in degrees (4)	β
dihedral (1)	γ
of downwash (1)	ϵ
effective helix (1)	Φ
of pitch (1)	θ
of roll or bank (1)	ϕ
of set of control surface * (1)	δ
of stabilizer setting with reference to lower wing (1)	β
of wing setting (angle between the wing chord and the thrust line) (1)	i_w
of yaw (1)	ψ
Angular	
acceleration (5)	α
displacements	
in roll (1)	ϕ
in pitch (1)	θ
in yaw (1)	ψ
distance (5)	θ
frequency (2)	ω
velocity (1) (2) (3) (4) (5)	ω

Table 4. Symbols for Physical Quantities—*Continued*

NAME OF QUANTITY	SYMBOL
Area (3) (4) (5)	A
Area * (1)	S
Area ratio (1)	$\dfrac{S}{b^2} = \lambda$
Aspect ratio (1)	$\dfrac{b^2}{S}$
Attack, angle of (1)	α
Axes	
of aircraft (left-handed)	
longitudinal (1)	X
lateral (1)	Y
normal (1)	Z
through any point (5)	$X\text{--}X,\ Y\text{--}Y,\ Z\text{--}Z$
Axial breadth or depth of runner entrance (4)	B
Axis, neutral; distance to extreme fiber (5)	c
Bazin's coefficient of roughness (4)	m
Bending moment (5)	M
Breadth (5)	b
Brightness (6)	B
Candlepower (6)	I
mean horizontal (6)	I_h
mean lower hemispherical (6)	I_l
mean spherical (6)	I_s
mean upper hemispherical (6)	I_u
mean zonal (6)	I_z
Capacitance, capacity (2)	C
Ceiling (1)	H
Center of gravity (1)	c.g.
coefficient (with respect to mean chord) (1)	C_g
Center of pressure (1)	c.p.
coefficient of (1)	C_p
Center of rotation (5)	O
Chezy's coefficient (4)	C
Chord length (1)	c
Climb, rate of (1)	r
Coefficient, absolute (1)	C
Concentrated load (5)	F
Concentration (3)	C
Conductance	
electrical (2)	$G,\ g$
thermal (3)	C
thermal, per unit area (3)	C_A
Conductivity	
electrical (2)	γ
thermal (3)	k
Constants (5)	C
Contraction, coefficient of (4)	c_c
Current † (2)	$I,\ i$
Curvature, radius of (5)	ρ
Damping coefficient (1)	λ
Deflection (5)	y
of a panel point of a truss (5)	Δ
Density (3) (5)	$\rho,\ d$
Density (1) (4)	ρ
relative to standard air density (1)	σ
Depth (5)	d
Depth of flow, channels (4)	d
Diameter (1) (3) (4) (5)	D
of runner or impeller (4)	D
of runner or impeller vanes at the middle of entrance space (4)	D_1
of runner or impeller throat (inside diameter of band or shroud ring) (4)	D_{th}
Dielectric	
constant (2)	K or ϵ
flux (2)	Ψ
flux density (2)	D
Difference of potential †‡ (2)	$E,\ e$
Dihedral angle (1)	γ
Discharge	
coefficient of (4)	c_d
rate of; or flow (4)	Q
Displacement, phase (2)	θ or ϕ

Table 4.   Symbols for Physical Quantities—*Continued*

Name of Quantity	Symbol
Displacements	
angular	
in roll (1)	ϕ
in pitch (1)	θ
in yaw (1)	ψ
longitudinal (1)	x
lateral (1)	y
normal (1)	z
Distance	
angular (5)	θ
linear (5)	s
from center of gravity to center of pressure of horizontal tail surface (1)	f
Downwash, angle of (1)	ϵ
Drag	
absolute coefficient of (1)	C_D
coefficient of induced (1)	C_{Di}
coefficient of parasite (1)	C_{Dp}
coefficient of profile (1)	C_{Do}
induced (1)	D_i
parasite (1)	D_p
profile (1)	D_o
Dynamic (or impact) pressure (1)	q
Eccentricity of application of load (5)	e
Efficiency (1) (2) (3)	η
Efficiency (3) (4)	e
hydraulic (4) (5)	e_h
mechanical (4) (5)	e_m
volumetric (5)	e_v
Elasticity	
bulk modulus, of water (4)	K
modulus of (5)	E
Electric potential †‡ (2)	E, e
Electricity, quantity of (2)	Q, q
Electromotive force † (2)	E, e
Electrostatic	
flux (2)	Ψ
flux density (2)	D
Elongation, unit (5)	δ
Energy (2)	W
internal; intrinsic § (3)	U, u
per unit time (power) (4)	P
Enthalpy § (3)	H or h
of dry saturated vapor (3)	h_g
of saturated liquid (3)	h_f
Entropy § (3)	S, s
Expansion, exponent of polytropic (3)	n
Flux	
density	
dielectric; electrostatic (2)	D
magnetic (2)	B
dielectric (2)	Ψ
luminous (6)	F
radiant (6)	Φ
Force (4) (5)	F
in any bar of a framed structure due to a load of unity applied at any point in any direction (5)	u
cross wind (1)	C
cross wind, absolute coefficient (1)	C_c
electromotive † (2)	E, e
magnetomotive (2)	$\mathfrak{F}$
moment of (5)	M
resultant (1)	R
total load (3)	F
Forces (parallel to axes)	
longitudinal (1)	X
lateral (1)	Y
normal (1)	Z
Frequency, angular (2)	ω
Frequency (2)	f
Frequency (harmonic motion) (5)	f or n

Table 4. Symbols for Physical Quantities—*Continued*

NAME OF QUANTITY	SYMBOL
Friction	
coefficient of sliding (5)	f
factor used in expressing pipe-loss (4)	f
Gap (1)	G
Gas constant (3)	R
Gibbs' function, total potential function (3)	z or ζ
Gyration, radius of (5)	k
Head, at any point (4) (5)	H or h
elevation (4)	z
lost * (4)	h
potential (4)	z
pressure (4)	h_p
velocity (4)	h_v
velocity, of approach, weirs (4)	h_0
Heat	
content; enthalpy § (3)	H, h
content of dry saturated vapor; enthalpy of dry saturated vapor (3)	h_g
content of saturated liquid; enthalpy of saturated liquid (3)	h_f
equivalent of work (3)	$\frac{1}{J}$ or A
mechanical equivalent of (3)	J
specific, at constant pressure (3)	c_p
specific, at constant volume (3)	c_v
ratio of specific (3)	κ or k
transfer, overall coefficient of (3)	U
transfer, surface coefficient of (3)	h
of vaporization at constant pressure (3)	L or h_{fg}
Height (5)	h
crest, weirs (4)	Z
Helix, effective angle (1)	Φ
Helmholtz' free energy; internal potential function (3)	ψ
Hydraulic radius (4)	R
Hydraulic slope (4)	S
Illumination (6)	E
Impedance (2)	Z, z
Indraft (inflow velocity) (1)	V'
Inductance (2)	L
mutual (2)	M
self (2)	L
Inertia, moment of	
polar (5)	J
rectangular (5)	I
Joule-Thomson's coefficient (3)	μ
Kutter's coefficient of roughness (4)	n
Length (3) (4) (5)	L
crest, weirs (4)	B
Lift (1)	L
absolute coefficient of (1)	C_L
drag ratio (1)	$\frac{L}{D}$
Light, quantity of (6)	Q
Load	
concentrated (5)	F
eccentricity of application of (5)	e
factor (1)	n
per unit distance (5)	w
total (5)	W
Loading	
specific * (1)	w
power; weight per unit power (1)	w_p
wing; weight per unit area (1)	w_s
Luminous	
flux (6)	F
intensity (candlepower) (6)	I
Magnetic	
intensity (2)	H
flux (2)	Φ
density (2)	B
Magnetomotive force (2)	$\mathfrak{F}$
Mass (3) (5)	m

Table 4.   Symbols for Physical Quantities—*Continued*

NAME OF QUANTITY	SYMBOL
Mechanical equivalent of heat (3)	J
Modulus	
of elasticity (5)	E
bulk, of elasticity of water (4)	K
ratio between, of elasticity of steel and modulus of elasticity of concrete (5)	n
of rupture (5)	R
section (5)	Z or S
Molecular weight (3)	M
Moment	
of any area about a given axis, statical (5)	Q
of force, including bending moment (5)	M
in inch-pounds at any section of a girder due to the moment of 1 in-lb applied to the girder at any point (5)	m
of inertia, polar (5)	J
of inertia, rectangular (5)	I
Moments	
absolute coefficients of	
pitching (1)	C_M
rolling (1)	C_L
yawing (1)	C_N
of inertia about axes	
longitudinal (1)	A
lateral (1)	B
normal (1)	C
pitching (1)	M
rolling (1)	L
yawing (1)	N
Mutual inductance (2)	M
Neutral axis, distance to extreme fiber (5)	c
Number of conductors or turns (2)	N
Number of revolutions per unit of time (5)	n
Period (2) (5)	T
Permeability (2)	μ
Permeance (2)	$\mathcal{P}$
Permittance (2)	C
Permittivity (2)	K or ϵ
Phase displacement (2)	θ or ϕ
Pitch	
angle of (1)	θ
ratio, effective (1)	$\dfrac{V}{ND}$
Potential	
electric †‡ (2)	E, e
function, internal; Helmholtz' free energy (3)	ψ
function, total; Gibbs' function (3)	z or ζ
Power (2)	P, p
Power (1) (3) (4) (5)	P
at brake (4)	P_B
coefficients	
$\dfrac{P}{\rho N^3 D^5}$ (1)	C_P
$\dfrac{P}{\rho V^3 D^2}$ (1)	$C_P{}'$
$\dfrac{P}{\rho V^5/N^2}$ (1)	$C_P{}''$
of turbine under 1-ft head (4)	P_1
from water (4)	P_W
Pressure	
intensity; force per unit area (1) (3) (4) (5)	p
center of (1)	c.p.
coefficient of center of (1)	C_p
dynamic (or impact) (1)	q
mean effective (3)	p_m
saturation (3)	p_f, p_{σ}
Quality of steam (3)	x
Quantity	
of electricity (2)	Q, q
total, of a fluid, water, gas, heat (by volume) (3)	Q
of light (6)	Q
per unit time (3)	q

Table 4. Symbols for Physical Quantities—*Continued*

NAME OF QUANTITY	SYMBOL
Radiant flux (6)	Φ
Radius (3) (5)	r
of curvature (5)	ρ
of gyration (5)	k
hydraulic (4)	R
to any point from center of runner or impeller (4)	r
Ratio	
of the distance from the neutral axis to the outer fiber of a reinforced-concrete beam to the distance from the outer fiber to the point of application of the resultant tensile stress (5)	k
of the lever arm of the resisting couple in a reinforced-concrete beam to the distance between the outer compressive fiber and the point of application of the resultant tensile stress (5)	j
of peripheral speed of runner to $\sqrt{2gH}$ (4)	ϕ
Reactance (2)	X, x
Reactions (5)	R
Reflection factor (6)	ρ
Reluctance (2)	$\mathcal{R}$
Reluctivity (2)	ν
Resistance	
electrical (2)	R, r
thermal (3)	R
Resistivity	
electrical (2)	ρ
thermal (3)	$\dfrac{1}{k}$
Revolutions per minute under 1-ft head (4)	n_1
Revolutions per unit time (3) (4) (5)	n
Reynolds' number (1)	$\rho\,\dfrac{Vl}{\mu}$
Roll or bank, angle of (1)	ϕ
Rotation	
center of (5)	O
rate of, propeller (1)	N
speed of (2)	n
Rupture, modulus of (5)	R
Saturation pressure (3)	p_f, p_g
Saturation temperature (3)	t_f, T_f or t_g, T_g
Section modulus (5)	Z or S
Self-inductance (2)	L
Set of control surfaces, angle of * (1)	δ
Slip-stream velocity (1)	V_s
Slope, hydraulic (4)	S
Span (1)	b
Specific	
heat (3)	c
heat at constant pressure (3)	c_p
heat at constant volume (3)	c_v
heats, ratio of (3)	κ or k
speed or type characteristic (4)	n_s
volume (3)	v
Speed	
air (1)	V
air, indicated (1)	V_i
of rotation (2)	n
specific (4)	n_s
Stabilizer setting with reference to lower wing, angle of (1)	β
Statical moment of any area about a given axis (5)	Q
Steel ratio, in reinforced-concrete beams (5)	p
Stress	
total compressive or total concrete, in reinforced concrete (5)	C
total shear (5)	V
total tensile or total steel in reinforced concrete (5)	T
unit (5)	s
unit compressive (5)	s_c
unit concrete, in reinforced concrete (5)	f_c
unit shear (5)	s_s
unit shear of concrete (5)	v
unit steel, in reinforced concrete (5)	f_s
unit tensile (5)	s_t
Susceptance (2)	b

Table 4. Symbols for Physical Quantities—*Continued*

NAME OF QUANTITY	SYMBOL
Temperature	
absolute ‖ (F abs or K) (3) (5)	T or Θ
ordinary ‖ (F or C) (3) (5)	t or θ
saturation (3)	t_f, T_f or t_g, T_g
Thermal	
conductance (3)	C
conductance per unit area; " unit conductance " (3)	C_A
conductivity (3)	k
resistance (3)	R
resistivity (3)	$\dfrac{1}{k}$
transmission (3)	q
Thickness (5)	d or t
Thrust (1)	T
coefficients	
$\dfrac{T}{\rho N^2 D^4}$ (1)	C_T
$\dfrac{T}{\rho V^2 D^2}$ (1)	$C_T{}'$
$\dfrac{T}{\rho V^4/N^2}$ (1)	$C_T{}''$
Time (4) (5)	t
Time ¶ (3)	t or τ
Torque (1)	Q
coefficients	
$\dfrac{Q}{\rho N^2 D^5}$ (1)	C_Q
$\dfrac{Q}{\rho V^2 D^3}$ (1)	$C_Q{}'$
$\dfrac{Q}{\rho V^5/N^3}$ (1)	$C_Q{}''$
Torque (5)	T
Transmission	
factor (6)	τ
thermal (3)	q
Vaporization, heat of, at constant pressure (3)	L or h_{fg}
Velocity (3) (4)	V
Velocity (5)	V or v
of approach, weirs (4)	v_0
angular (1) (2) (3) (4) (5)	ω
absolute, of the water at any point in a rotating runner or impeller (4)	V
circumferential, of a point on a rotating runner or impeller (4)	u
circumferential or tangential component of absolute, of the water (4)	V_u
coefficient of (4)	c_v
meridional component of the absolute, of the water (4)	V_m
of moving casing (4)	u
radial component of the absolute, of the water (4)	V_r
relative to moving casing (4)	v
relative velocity of the water with respect to the moving runner or impeller (4)	v
slip-stream (1)	V_s
Velocities	
angular	
roll (1)	p
pitch (1)	q
yaw (1)	r
linear	
roll (1)	u
pitch (1)	v
yaw (1)	w
Viscosity	
absolute; coefficient of (1) (3) (4)	μ
kinematic (1) (3) (4)	ν
relative (to absolute viscosity of water) (3)	Z
relative kinematic (3)	use $\dfrac{\nu}{\nu_w}$
Visibility factor (6)	K
Voltage † (2)	E, e

Table 4. Symbols for Physical Quantities—*Continued*

NAME OF QUANTITY	SYMBOL
Volume (5)	V
specific (3)	v
total (3)	V
per unit time (3)	q
Weight	
molecular (3)	M
rate; per unit of power; for unit of time (3)	w
total (1) (3)	W
per unit time (4)	W
per unit time per unit area of cross-section; " mass velocity " (3)	G
per unit volume (4)	w
Width, channel surface (4)	B
Wing setting angle of (angle between the wing chord and the thrust line) (1)	i_w
Work (2) (3) (5)	W
per unit weight (3)	w
heat equivalent of (3),	$\dfrac{1}{J}$ or A
Yaw, angle of (1)	ψ

* Use with appropriate subscript.

† Where distinctions between maximum, instantaneous, effective (root-mean-square), and average values are necessary, $E_m\, I_m\, P_m$ are recommended for maximum values; $e,\ i,\ p$ for instantaneous values; $E,\ I$ for effective (rms) values; and P for average value.

‡ Where a distinction between electromotive force and difference of electric potential is desirable, the symbols $E,\ e,$ and $V,\ v,$ respectively, may be used.

§ Capital letters denote total quantities, and small letters, specific quantities, or quantity per unit.

∥ θ and Θ in source (3) only. θ is preferably used only when t is used for time in the same discussion. Θ is preferably used only when θ is used for ordinary temperature.

¶ τ should be used only when t is used for ordinary temperature in the same discussion.

MATHEMATICAL TABLES

Table 5. Certain Constants Containing e and π

$$e = 2.7182818285 \qquad\qquad M = \log_{10} e = 0.4342944819$$
$$\pi = 3.1415926536 \qquad\qquad M^{-1} = \log_e 10 = 2.3025850930$$

	Powers of e			Multiples of π			Fractions of π	
e^n	Value	Logarithm	$n\pi$	Value	Logarithm	π/n	Value	Logarithm
e	2.718282	0.434294	π	3.141593	0.497150	$\pi/2$	1.570780	0.196120
e^{-1}	0.367879	$\bar{1}.565706$	2π	6.283185	0.798180	$\pi/3$	1.047198	0.020029
e^2	7.389057	0.868589	3π	9.424778	0.974271	$\pi/4$	0.785398	$\bar{1}.895090$
e^{-2}	0.135335	$\bar{1}.131411$	4π	12.566371	1.099210	$\pi/180$	0.017453*	$\bar{2}.241877$
$e^{1/2}$	1.648721	0.217147	5π	15.707963	1.196120			

	Reciprocals of π			Powers of π			Roots of π	
n/π	Value	Logarithm	$\pi^{\pm n}$	Value	Logarithm	$\pi^{\pm 1/n}$	Value	Logarithm
$1/\pi$	0.318310	$\bar{1}.502850$	π^2	9.869604	0.994300	$\sqrt{\pi}$	1.772454	0.248575
$2/\pi$	0.636620	$\bar{1}.803880$	$1/\pi^2$	0.101321	$\bar{1}.005700$	$1/\sqrt{\pi}$	0.564190	$\bar{1}.751425$
$3/\pi$	0.954930	$\bar{1}.979971$	π^3	31.006277	1.491450	$\sqrt[3]{\pi}$	1.464592	0.165717
$180/\pi$	57.295780†	1.758123	$1/\pi^3$	0.032252	$\bar{2}.508550$	$1/\sqrt[3]{\pi}$	0.681784	$\bar{1}.834283$

* Number of radians per degree.   † Number of degrees per radian.

Table 6. Factorials

n	$n! = 1 \cdot 2 \cdot 3 \ldots n$	$1/n!$	n	$n! = 1 \cdot 2 \cdot 3 \ldots n$	$1/n!$
1	1	1.	11	$399{,}168 \times 10^2$	0.250521×10^{-7}
2	2	0.5	12	$479{,}002 \times 10^3$	$.208768 \times 10^{-8}$
3	6	.166667	13	$622{,}702 \times 10^4$	$.160590 \times 10^{-9}$
4	24	$.416667 \times 10^{-1}$	14	$871{,}783 \times 10^5$	$.114707 \times 10^{-10}$
5	120	$.833333 \times 10^{-2}$	15	$130{,}767 \times 10^7$	$.764716 \times 10^{-12}$
6	720	$.138889 \times 10^{-2}$	16	$209{,}228 \times 10^8$	$.477948 \times 10^{-13}$
7	5,040	$.198413 \times 10^{-3}$	17	$355{,}687 \times 10^9$	$.281146 \times 10^{-14}$
8	40,320	$.248016 \times 10^{-4}$	18	$640{,}237 \times 10^{10}$	$.156192 \times 10^{-15}$
9	362,880	$.275573 \times 10^{-5}$	19	$121{,}645 \times 10^{12}$	$.822064 \times 10^{-17}$
10	3,628,800	$.275573 \times 10^{-6}$	20	$243{,}290 \times 10^{13}$	$.411032 \times 10^{-18}$

Table 7

Decimal Equivalents, Squares, Cubes, Square Roots, Cube Roots, Three-halves Powers, Fifth Roots, Reciprocals, Circumference and Area of Circles

Fraction	Decimal	N^2	N^3	$\sqrt{N}$	$\sqrt[3]{N}$	$N^{3/2}$	$\sqrt[5]{N}$	$\dfrac{1}{N}$	Circum.	Area
1/64	.015625	0.000244	$.381\times10^{-5}$	.1250	.2500	.00195	.4353	64.0	.04909	.00019
1/32	.03125	.000977	$.305\times10^{-4}$	.1768	.3150	.00552	.5000	32.0	.09818	.00077
3/64	.046875	.002197	$.103\times10^{-3}$	.2165	.3606	.01015	.5422	18.8235	.14726	.00173
1/16	.0625	.003906	$.244\times10^{-3}$	.2500	.3969	.01563	.5744	16.0	.19635	.00307
5/64	.078125	.006104	$.477\times10^{-3}$	.2795	.4275	.02184	.6006	12.80	.24544	.00479
3/32	.09375	.008789	$.824\times10^{-3}$	.3062	.4543	.02871	.6229	10.6667	.29452	.00690
	.10	.010	.00100	.3162	.4642	.03162	.6310	10.0	.31416	.00785
7/64	.109375	.01196	.001308	.3307	.4782	.03617	.6424	9.1429	.34361	.00939
1/8	.125	.01563	.001953	.3536	.5000	.04419	.6598	8.0	.39270	.01227
9/64	.140625	.01978	.002782	.3750	.5200	.05273	.6755	7.1111	.44179	.01554
5/32	.15625	.02441	.003814	.3953	.5386	.06176	.6899	6.40	.49087	.01917
11/64	.171875	.02954	.005077	.4146	.5560	.07126	.7031	5.8182	.53996	.02320
3/16	.1875	.03516	.006592	.4330	.5724	.08119	.7155	5.3333	.58905	.02761
	.20	.040	.0080	.4472	.5848	.08944	.7248	5.0	.62832	.03142
13/64	.203125	.04126	.008381	.4507	.5878	.09155	.7270	4.9231	.63814	.03241
7/32	.21875	.04785	.01047	.4677	.6025	.10231	.7379	4.5714	.68722	.03758
15/64	.234375	.05493	.01287	.4841	.6166	.11347	.7481	4.2667	.73631	.04314
1/4	.250	.0625	.01563	.5000	.6300	.12500	.7579	4.0	.78540	.04909
17/64	.265625	.07056	.01874	.5154	.6428	.13690	.7671	3.7647	.83448	.05542
9/32	.28125	.07910	.02225	.5303	.6552	.14916	.7759	3.5556	.88357	.06213
19/64	.296875	.08813	.02616	.5449	.6671	.16176	.7844	3.3684	.93266	.06922
	.30	.090	.0270	.5477	.6694	.16432	.7860	3.3333	.94248	.07069
5/16	.3125	.09766	.03052	.5590	.6786	.17469	.7925	3.2000	.98175	.07670
21/64	.328125	.10767	.03533	.5728	.6897	.18796	.8002	3.0476	1.0308	.08456
11/32	.34375	.11816	.04062	.5863	.7005	.20154	.8077	2.9091	1.0799	.09281
23/64	.359375	.12915	.04641	.5995	.7110	.21544	.8149	2.7826	1.1290	.10143
3/8	.375	.14063	.05273	.6124	.7211	.22964	.8219	2.6667	1.1781	.11045
25/64	.390625	.15259	.05961	.6250	.7310	.24414	.8286	2.5600	1.2272	.11984
	.40	.16	.0640	.6325	.7368	.25298	.8326	2.50	1.2566	.12566
13/32	.40625	.16504	.06705	.6374	.7406	.25894	.8351	2.4615	1.2763	.12962
27/64	.421875	.17798	.07508	.6495	.7500	.27402	.8415	2.3704	1.3254	.13979
7/16	.4375	.19141	.08374	.6614	.7592	.28938	.8476	2.2857	1.3744	.15033
29/64	.453125	.20532	.09304	.6732	.7681	.30502	.8536	2.2069	1.4235	.16126
15/32	.46875	.21973	.10300	.6847	.7768	.32093	.8594	2.1333	1.4726	.17257
31/64	.484375	.23462	.11364	.6960	.7854	.33711	.8650	2.0645	1.5217	.18427
1/2	.50	.2500	.12500	.7071	.7937	.35355	.8706	2.0	1.5708	.19635
33/64	.515625	.26587	.13709	.7181	.8019	.37025	.8759	1.9394	1.6199	.20881
17/32	.53125	.28223	.14993	.7289	.8099	.38721	.8812	1.8824	1.6690	.22166
35/64	.546875	.29907	.16355	.7395	.8178	.40442	.8863	1.8286	1.7181	.23489
9/16	.5625	.31641	.17798	.7500	.8255	.42188	.8913	1.7778	1.7671	.24850
37/64	.578125	.33423	.19323	.7604	.8331	.43957	.8962	1.7297	1.8162	.26250
19/32	.59375	.35254	.20932	.7706	.8405	.45751	.9010	1.6842	1.8653	.27688
	.60	.3600	.21600	.7746	.8434	.46476	.9029	1.6667	1.8850	.28274
39/64	.609375	.37134	.22628	.7806	.8478	.47569	.9057	1.6410	1.9144	.29165
5/8	.625	.39063	.24414	.7906	.8550	.49410	.9103	1.6000	1.9635	.30680
41/64	.640625	.41040	.26291	.8004	.8621	.51275	.9148	1.5610	2.0126	.32233
21/32	.65625	.43066	.28262	.8101	.8690	.53162	.9192	1.5238	2.0617	.33824
43/64	.671875	.45142	.30330	.8197	.8759	.55072	.9235	1.4884	2.1108	.35454
11/16	.6875	.47266	.32495	.8297	.8826	.57005	.9278	1.4545	2.1598	.37122
	.70	.4900	.34300	.8367	.8879	.58566	.9312	1.4286	2.1991	.38485
45/64	.703125	.49438	.34761	.8385	.8892	.58959	.9320	1.4222	2.2089	.38829
23/32	.71875	.51660	.37131	.8478	.8958	.60935	.9361	1.3913	2.2580	.40574
47/64	.734375	.53931	.39605	.8570	.9022	.62933	.9401	1.3617	2.3071	.42357
3/4	.750	.56250	.42188	.8660	.9086	.64952	.9441	1.3333	2.3562	.44179
49/64	.765625	.58618	.44879	.8750	.9148	.66992	.9480	1.3061	2.4053	.46038
25/32	.78125	.61035	.47684	.8839	.9210	.69053	.9518	1.2800	2.4544	.47937
51/64	.796875	.63501	.50602	.8927	.9271	.71135	.9556	1.2549	2.5035	.49874
	.80	.6400	.51200	.8944	.9283	.71554	.9564	1.2500	2.5133	.50265
13/16	.8125	.66016	.53638	.9014	.9331	.73238	.9593	1.2308	2.5525	.51849
53/64	.828125	.68579	.56792	.9100	.9391	.75361	.9630	1.2075	2.6016	.53862
27/32	.84375	.71191	.60067	.9186	.9449	.77503	.9666	1.1852	2.6507	.55914
55/64	.859375	.73853	.63467	.9270	.9507	.79666	.9702	1.1636	2.6998	.58004
7/8	.875	.76563	.66992	.9354	.9565	.81849	.9737	1.1429	2.7489	.60132
57/64	.890625	.79321	.70645	.9437	.9621	.84051	.9771	1.1228	2.7980	.62299
	.90	.81000	.72900	.9487	.9655	.85435	.9792	1.1111	2.8274	.63617
29/32	.90625	.82129	.74429	.9520	.9677	.86272	.9805	1.1034	2.8471	.64504
59/64	.921875	.84985	.78346	.9601	.9733	.88513	.9839	1.0847	2.8962	.66747
15/16	.9375	.87891	.82398	.9683	.9787	.90773	.9872	1.0667	2.9452	.69029
61/64	.953125	.90845	.86587	.9763	.9841	.93053	.9905	1.0492	2.9943	.71349
31/32	.96875	.93848	.90915	.9843	.9895	.95349	.9937	1.0323	3.0434	.73708
63/64	.984375	.96899	.95385	.9922	.9948	.97666	.9969	1.0159	3.0925	.76104

Table 7.—*Continued*

N	N^2	N^3	$\sqrt{N}$	$\sqrt[3]{N}$	$N^{3/2}$	$\sqrt[5]{N}$	$\dfrac{1}{N}$	Circle ($N = D$)	
								Circum.	Area
1.	1.0000	1.0000	1.0000	1.0000	1.0000	1.0000	1.0000000	3.1416	.7854
1.125	1.2656	1.4238	1.0606	1.0400	1.1932	1.0238	.88888888	3.5343	.9940
1.25	1.5625	1.9531	1.1180	1.0772	1.3975	1.0456	.80000000	3.9270	1.2272
1.375	1.8906	2.5996	1.1726	1.1120	1.6123	1.0658	.72727272	4.3197	1.4849
1.5	2.25	3.3750	1.2247	1.1447	1.8371	1.0845	.66666666	4.7124	1.7671
1.625	2.6406	4.2910	1.2748	1.1757	2.0715	1.1020	.61538462	5.1051	2.0739
1.75	3.0625	5.3594	1.3229	1.2051	2.3150	1.1186	.57142857	5.4978	2.4053
1.875	3.5156	6.5918	1.3693	1.2331	2.5675	1.1340	.53333333	5.8905	2.7612
2.	4.0000	8.0000	1.4142	1.2599	2.8284	1.1487	.50000000	6.2832	3.1416
2.125	4.5156	9.5957	1.4577	1.2856	3.0977	1.1627	.47058823	6.6759	3.5466
2.25	5.0625	11.3906	1.5000	1.3104	3.3750	1.1761	.44444444	7.0686	3.9761
2.375	5.6406	13.3965	1.5411	1.3342	3.6601	1.1889	.42105263	7.4613	4.4301
2.5	6.2500	15.6250	1.5811	1.3572	3.9529	1.2011	.40000000	7.8540	4.9087
2.625	6.8906	18.0879	1.6202	1.3795	4.2530	1.2129	.38095231	8.2467	5.4119
2.75	7.5625	20.7969	1.6583	1.4011	4.5604	1.2242	.36363636	8.6394	5.9396
2.875	8.2656	23.7637	1.6956	1.4219	4.8748	1.2352	.34782609	9.0321	6.4918
3.	9.000	27.0000	1.7321	1.4422	5.1962	1.2457	.33333333	9.4248	7.0686
3.125	9.7656	30.5176	1.7678	1.4620	5.5243	1.2559	.32000000	9.8175	7.6699
3.25	10.5625	34.3281	1.8028	1.4813	5.8590	1.2658	.30769231	10.2102	8.2958
3.375	11.3906	38.4434	1.8371	1.5000	6.2003	1.2754	.29629629	10.6029	8.9462
3.5	12.2500	42.8750	1.8708	1.5183	6.5479	1.2847	.28571429	10.9956	9.6211
3.625	13.1406	47.6348	1.9039	1.5362	6.9018	1.2938	.27586207	11.3883	10.3206
3.75	14.0625	52.7344	1.9365	1.5536	7.2619	1.3026	.26666666	11.7810	11.0447
3.875	15.0156	58.1856	1.9685	1.5707	7.6279	1.3112	.25806452	12.1737	11.7932
4.	16.0000	64.0000	2.0000	1.5874	8.0000	1.3195	.25000000	12.5664	12.5664
4.125	17.0156	70.1895	2.0310	1.6038	8.3779	1.3277	.24242424	12.9591	13.3640
4.25	18.0625	76.7656	2.0616	1.6198	8.7616	1.3356	.23529412	13.3518	14.1863
4.375	19.1406	83.7402	2.0916	1.6355	9.1510	1.3434	.22857143	13.7445	15.0330
4.5	20.2500	91.1250	2.1213	1.6510	9.5460	1.3510	.22222222	14.1372	15.9043
4.625	21.3906	98.9317	2.1506	1.6661	9.9465	1.3584	.21621622	14.5299	16.8001
4.75	22.5625	107.1719	2.1795	1.6810	10.3524	1.3656	.21052632	14.9226	17.7205
4.875	23.7656	115.8574	2.2079	1.6956	10.7637	1.3728	.20512821	15.3153	18.6655
5.	25.0000	125.0000	2.2361	1.7100	11.1803	1.3799	.20000000	15.7080	19.6350
5.125	26.2656	134.6113	2.2638	1.7241	11.6022	1.3866	.19512195	16.1006	20.6289
5.25	27.5625	144.7031	2.2913	1.7380	12.0293	1.3933	.19047619	16.4933	21.6475
5.375	28.8906	155.2871	2.3184	1.7517	12.4614	1.3998	.18604651	16.8860	22.6906
5.5	30.2500	166.3750	2.3452	1.7652	12.8987	1.4063	.18181818	17.2787	23.7583
5.625	31.6406	177.9785	2.3727	1.7784	13.3409	1.4126	.17777777	17.6714	24.8505
5.75	33.0625	190.1094	2.3979	1.7915	13.7880	1.4188	.17391304	18.0641	25.9672
5.875	34.5156	202.7793	2.4238	1.8044	14.2400	1.4250	.17021277	18.4568	27.1085
6.	36.0000	216.0000	2.4495	1.8171	14.6969	1.4310	.16666666	18.8495	28.2743
6.125	37.5156	229.7832	2.4749	1.8297	15.1586	1.4369	.16326531	19.2422	29.4647
6.25	39.0625	244.1406	2.5000	1.8420	15.6250	1.4427	.16000000	19.6349	30.6796
6.375	40.6406	259.0840	2.5249	1.8542	16.0961	1.4484	.15686275	20.0276	31.9190
6.5	42.2500	274.6250	2.5495	1.8663	16.5718	1.4542	.15384615	20.4203	33.1831
6.625	43.8906	290.7754	2.5739	1.8781	17.0522	1.4596	.15094339	20.8130	34.4716
6.75	45.5625	307.5469	2.5981	1.8899	17.5370	1.4651	.14814815	21.2057	35.7847
6.875	47.2656	324.9512	2.6220	1.9015	18.0264	1.4705	.14545454	21.5984	37.1223
7.	49.0000	343.0000	2.6458	1.9129	18.5203	1.4758	.14285714	21.9911	38.4845
7.125	50.7656	361.7051	2.6693	1.9243	19.0186	1.4810	.14035088	22.3838	39.8712
7.25	52.5625	381.0781	2.6926	1.9354	19.5212	1.4862	.13793103	22.7765	41.2825
7.375	54.3906	401.1309	2.7157	1.9465	20.0283	1.4913	.13559322	23.1692	42.7183
7.5	56.2500	421.8750	2.7386	1.9574	20.5396	1.4963	.13333333	23.5619	44.1786
7.625	58.1406	443.3223	2.7613	1.9683	21.0552	1.5012	.13114754	23.9546	45.6635
7.75	60.0625	465.4844	2.7839	1.9789	21.5751	1.5061	.12903226	24.3473	47.1730
7.875	62.0156	488.3731	2.8063	1.9895	22.0992	1.5110	.12698413	24.7400	48.7069
8.	64.0000	512.0000	2.8284	2.0000	22.6274	1.5157	.12500000	25.1327	50.2655
8.125	66.0156	536.3770	2.8504	2.0104	23.1598	1.5204	.12307692	25.5254	51.8485
8.25	68.0625	561.5156	2.8723	2.0206	23.6963	1.5251	.12121212	25.9181	53.4562
8.375	70.1406	587.4278	2.8940	2.0308	24.2369	1.5297	.11940298	26.3108	55.0883
8.5	72.2500	614.1250	2.9155	2.0408	24.7816	1.5342	.11764706	26.7035	56.7450
8.625	74.3906	641.6192	2.9368	2.0508	25.3301	1.5387	.11594203	27.0962	58.4262
8.75	76.5625	669.9219	2.9580	2.0606	25.8828	1.5431	.11428571	27.4889	60.1320
8.875	78.7656	699.0450	2.9791	2.0704	26.4394	1.5475	.11267605	27.8816	61.8623
9.	81.0000	729.0000	3.0000	2.0801	27.0000	1.5518	.11111111	28.2743	63.6172
9.125	83.2656	759.7989	3.0207	2.0897	27.5645	1.5561	.10958904	28.6670	65.3966
9.25	85.5625	791.4531	3.0414	2.0992	28.1328	1.5604	.10810811	29.0597	67.2006
9.375	87.8906	823.9746	3.0619	2.1086	28.7050	1.5646	.10666666	29.4524	69.0291
9.5	90.2500	857.3750	3.0822	2.1179	29.2810	1.5687	.10526316	29.8451	70.8822
9.625	92.6406	891.6660	3.1024	2.1272	29.8608	1.5728	.10389610	30.2378	72.7597
9.75	95.0625	926.8594	3.1225	2.1363	30.4444	1.5769	.10256410	30.6305	74.6619
9.875	97.5156	962.9668	3.1425	2.1454	31.0317	1.5809	.10126582	31.0232	76.5886

Table 7.—*Continued*

N	N^2	N^3	$\sqrt{N}$	$\sqrt[3]{N}$	$N^{3/2}$	$\sqrt[5]{N}$	$\dfrac{1}{N}$	Circle ($N = D$) Circum.	Area
10	100	1000	3.1623	2.1544	31.623	1.5849	.10000000	31.4159	78.5398
11	121	1331	3.3166	2.2240	36.483	1.6154	.09090909	34.5575	95.0332
12	144	1728	3.4641	2.2894	41.569	1.6438	.08333333	37.6991	113.0973
13	169	2197	3.6056	2.3513	46.873	1.6703	.07692308	40.8407	132.7323
14	196	2744	3.7417	2.4101	52.384	1.6953	.07142857	43.9823	153.9380
15	225	3375	3.8730	2.4662	58.095	1.7188	.06666667	47.1239	176.7146
16	256	4096	4.0000	2.5198	64.000	1.7411	.06250000	50.2654	201.0619
17	289	4913	4.1231	2.5713	70.093	1.7623	.05882353	53.4070	226.9801
18	324	5832	4.2426	2.6207	76.367	1.7826	.05555556	56.5486	254.4690
19	361	6859	4.3589	2.6684	82.819	1.8020	.05263158	59.6902	283.5287
20	400	8000	4.4721	2.7144	89.442	1.8206	.05000000	62.8318	314.1593
21	441	9261	4.5826	2.7589	96.235	1.8384	.04761905	65.9734	346.3606
22	484	10648	4.6904	2.8020	103.19	1.8556	.04545455	69.1150	380.1327
23	529	12167	4.7958	2.8439	110.30	1.8722	.04347826	72.2566	415.4756
24	576	13824	4.8990	2.8845	117.58	1.8882	.04166667	75.3982	452.3893
25	625	15625	5.0000	2.9240	125.00	1.9037	.04000000	78.5398	490.8739
26	676	17576	5.0990	2.9625	132.57	1.9186	.03846154	81.6813	530.9292
27	729	19683	5.1962	3.0000	140.30	1.9332	.03703704	84.8229	572.5553
28	784	21952	5.2915	3.0366	148.16	1.9473	.03571429	87.9645	615.7522
29	841	24389	5.3852	3.0723	156.17	1.9610	.03448276	91.1061	660.5198
30	900	27000	5.4772	3.1072	164.32	1.9744	.03333333	94.2477	706.8583
31	961	29791	5.5678	3.1414	172.60	1.9873	.03225806	97.3893	754.7676
32	1024	32768	5.6569	3.1748	181.02	2.0000	.03125000	100.5309	804.2477
33	1089	35937	5.7446	3.2075	189.57	2.0123	.03030303	103.6725	855.2986
34	1156	39304	5.8310	3.2396	198.25	2.0244	.02941176	106.8141	907.9203
35	1225	42875	5.9161	3.2711	207.06	2.0362	.02857143	109.9557	962.1127
36	1296	46656	6.0000	3.3019	216.00	2.0477	.02777778	113.0972	1017.8760
37	1369	50653	6.0828	3.3322	225.06	2.0589	.02702703	116.2388	1075.2101
38	1444	54872	6.1644	3.3620	234.25	2.0699	.02631579	119.3804	1134.1149
39	1521	59319	6.2450	3.3912	243.56	2.0807	.02564103	122.5220	1194.5906
40	1600	64000	6.3246	3.4200	252.98	2.0913	.02500000	125.6636	1256.6371
41	1681	68921	6.4031	3.4482	262.53	2.1016	.02439024	128.8052	1320.2543
42	1764	74088	6.4807	3.4760	272.19	2.1118	.02380952	131.9468	1385.4424
43	1849	79507	6.5574	3.5034	281.97	2.1218	.02325581	135.0884	1452.2012
44	1936	85184	6.6332	3.5303	291.86	2.1315	.02272727	138.2300	1520.5308
45	2025	91125	6.7082	3.5569	301.87	2.1411	.02222222	141.3716	1590.4313
46	2116	97336	6.7823	3.5830	311.99	2.1506	.02173913	144.5131	1661.9025
47	2209	103823	6.8557	3.6088	322.22	2.1598	.02127660	147.6547	1734.9445
48	2304	110592	6.9282	3.6342	332.55	2.1689	.02083333	150.7963	1809.5574
49	2401	117649	7.0000	3.6593	343.00	2.1779	.02040816	153.9379	1885.7410
50	2500	125000	7.0711	3.6840	353.55	2.1867	.02000000	157.0795	1963.500
51	2601	132651	7.1414	3.7084	364.21	2.1954	.01960784	160.2211	2042.820
52	2704	140608	7.2111	3.7325	374.98	2.2039	.01923077	163.3627	2123.716
53	2809	148877	7.2801	3.7563	385.85	2.2124	.01886792	166.5043	2206.183
54	2916	157464	7.3485	3.7798	396.82	2.2206	.01851852	169.6459	2290.221
55	3025	166375	7.4162	3.8030	407.89	2.2288	.01818182	172.7875	2375.829
56	3136	175616	7.4833	3.8259	419.07	2.2369	.01785714	175.9290	2463.008
57	3249	185193	7.5498	3.8485	430.35	2.2448	.01754386	179.0706	2551.758
58	3364	195112	7.6158	3.8709	441.72	2.2526	.01724138	182.2122	2642.079
59	3481	205379	7.6811	3.8930	453.19	2.2603	.01694915	185.3538	2733.970
60	3600	216000	7.7460	3.9149	464.76	2.2679	.01666667	188.4954	2827.433
61	3721	226981	7.8102	3.9365	476.43	2.2755	.01639344	191.6370	2922.466
62	3844	238328	7.8740	3.9579	488.19	2.2829	.01612903	194.7786	3019.070
63	3969	250047	7.9373	3.9791	500.05	2.2902	.01587302	197.9202	3117.245
64	4096	262144	8.0000	4.0000	512.00	2.2974	.01562500	201.0618	3216.990
65	4225	274625	8.0623	4.0207	524.05	2.3045	.01538462	204.2034	3318.307
66	4356	287496	8.1240	4.0412	536.19	2.3116	.01515152	207.3449	3421.194
67	4489	300763	8.1854	4.0615	548.42	2.3186	.01492537	210.4865	3525.652
68	4624	314432	8.2462	4.0817	560.74	2.3254	.01470588	213.6281	3631.680
69	4761	328509	8.3066	4.1016	573.16	2.3322	.01449275	216.7697	3739.280
70	4900	343000	8.3666	4.1213	585.66	2.3389	.01428571	219.9113	3848.450
71	5041	357911	8.4261	4.1408	598.26	2.3456	.01408451	223.0529	3959.191
72	5184	373248	8.4853	4.1602	610.94	2.3522	.01388889	226.1945	4071.503
73	5329	389017	8.5440	4.1793	623.71	2.3587	.01369863	229.3361	4185.386
74	5476	405224	8.6023	4.1983	636.57	2.3651	.01351351	232.4777	4300.839
75	5625	421875	8.6603	4.2172	649.52	2.3714	.01333333	235.6193	4417.864
76	5776	438976	8.7178	4.2358	662.55	2.3777	.01315789	238.7608	4536.459
77	5929	456533	8.7750	4.2543	675.68	2.3840	.01298701	241.9024	4656.625
78	6084	474552	8.8318	4.2727	688.88	2.3901	.01282051	245.0440	4778.361
79	6241	493039	8.8882	4.2908	702.17	2.3962	.01265823	248.1856	4901.669

Table 7.—*Continued*

N	N^2	N^3	$\sqrt{N}$	$\sqrt[3]{N}$	$N^{3/2}$	$\sqrt[5]{N}$	$\dfrac{1}{N}$	Circle ($N = D$) Circum.	Circle ($N = D$) Area
80	6400	512000	8.9443	4.3089	715.54	2.4022	.01250000	251.327	5026.547
81	6561	531441	9.0000	4.3267	729.00	2.4082	.01234568	254.469	5152.998
82	6724	551368	9.0554	4.3445	742.54	2.4141	.01219512	257.610	5281.016
83	6889	571787	9.1104	4.3621	756.17	2.4200	.01204819	260.752	5410.607
84	7056	592704	9.1652	4.3795	769.88	2.4258	.01190476	263.894	5541.770
85	7225	614125	9.2195	4.3968	783.66	2.4315	.01176471	267.035	5674.501
86	7396	636056	9.2736	4.4140	797.53	2.4372	.01162791	270.177	5808.805
87	7569	658503	9.3274	4.4310	811.49	2.4429	.01149425	273.318	5944.679
88	7744	681472	9.3808	4.4480	825.52	2.4485	.01136364	276.460	6082.124
89	7921	704969	9.4340	4.4647	839.63	2.4540	.01123596	279.602	6221.138
90	8100	729000	9.4868	4.4814	853.82	2.4595	.01111111	282.743	6361.725
91	8281	753571	9.5394	4.4979	868.09	2.4650	.01098901	285.885	6503.882
92	8464	778688	9.5917	4.5144	882.44	2.4705	.01086957	289.026	6647.610
93	8649	804357	9.6437	4.5307	896.86	2.4758	.01075269	292.168	6792.909
94	8836	830584	9.6954	4.5468	911.36	2.4810	.01063830	295.309	6939.778
95	9025	857375	9.7468	4.5629	925.95	2.4863	.01052632	298.451	7088.219
96	9216	884736	9.7980	4.5789	940.61	2.4915	.01041667	301.593	7238.230
97	9409	912673	9.8489	4.5947	955.34	2.4966	.01030928	304.734	7389.812
98	9604	941192	9.8995	4.6104	970.15	2.5018	.01020408	307.876	7542.962
99	9801	970299	9.9499	4.6261	985.04	2.5069	.01010101	311.017	7697.688
100	10000	1000000	10.0000	4.6416	1000.0	2.5119	.01000000	314.159	7853.982
101	10201	1030301	10.0499	4.6570	1015.0	2.5169	.00990099	317.301	8011.85
102	10404	1061208	10.0995	4.6723	1030.1	2.5219	.00980392	320.442	8171.28
103	10609	1092727	10.1489	4.6875	1045.3	2.5268	.00970874	323.584	8332.29
104	10816	1124864	10.1980	4.7027	1060.6	2.5317	.00961538	326.725	8494.87
105	11025	1157625	10.2470	4.7177	1075.9	2.5365	.00952381	329.867	8659.01
106	11236	1191016	10.2956	4.7326	1091.3	2.5413	.00943396	333.009	8824.73
107	11449	1225043	10.3441	4.7475	1106.8	2.5461	.00934579	336.150	8992.02
108	11664	1259712	10.3923	4.7622	1122.4	2.5509	.00925926	339.292	9160.88
109	11881	1295029	10.4403	4.7769	1138.0	2.5556	.00917431	342.433	9331.32
110	12100	1331000	10.4881	4.7914	1153.7	2.5602	.00909091	345.575	9503.32
111	12321	1367631	10.5357	4.8059	1169.5	2.5649	.00900901	348.716	9676.89
112	12544	1404928	10.5830	4.8203	1185.3	2.5695	.00892857	351.858	9852.03
113	12769	1442897	10.6301	4.8346	1201.2	2.5740	.00884956	355.000	10028.75
114	12996	1481544	10.6771	4.8488	1217.2	2.5786	.00877193	358.141	10207.03
115	13225	1520875	10.7238	4.8629	1233.2	2.5831	.00869565	361.283	10386.89
116	13456	1560896	10.7703	4.8770	1249.4	2.5876	.00862069	364.424	10568.32
117	13689	1601613	10.8167	4.8910	1265.5	2.5920	.00854701	367.566	10751.31
118	13924	1643032	10.8628	4.9049	1281.8	2.5964	.00847458	370.708	10935.88
119	14161	1685159	10.9087	4.9187	1298.1	2.6008	.00840336	373.849	11122.02
120	14400	1728000	10.9545	4.9324	1314.5	2.6052	.00833333	376.991	11309.73
121	14641	1771561	11.0000	4.9461	1331.0	2.6095	.00826446	380.132	11499.01
122	14884	1815848	11.0454	4.9597	1347.5	2.6138	.00819672	383.274	11689.86
123	15129	1860867	11.0905	4.9732	1364.1	2.6181	.00813008	386.416	11882.29
124	15376	1906624	11.1355	4.9866	1380.8	2.6223	.00806452	389.557	12076.28
125	15625	1953125	11.1803	5.0000	1397.5	2.6265	.00800000	392.699	12271.84
126	15876	2000376	11.2250	5.0133	1414.4	2.6307	.00793651	395.840	12468.98
127	16129	2048383	11.2694	5.0265	1431.2	2.6349	.00787402	398.982	12667.68
128	16384	2097152	11.3137	5.0397	1448.2	2.6390	.00781250	402.124	12867.96
129	16641	2146689	11.3578	5.0528	1465.2	2.6431	.00775194	405.265	13069.81
130	16900	2197000	11.4018	5.0658	1482.2	2.6472	.00769231	408.407	13273.23
131	17161	2248091	11.4455	5.0788	1499.4	2.6513	.00763359	411.548	13478.22
132	17424	2299968	11.4891	5.0916	1516.6	2.6553	.00757576	414.690	13684.77
133	17689	2352637	11.5326	5.1045	1533.8	2.6593	.00751880	417.831	13892.91
134	17956	2406104	11.5758	5.1172	1551.2	2.6633	.00746269	420.973	14102.61
135	18225	2460375	11.6190	5.1299	1568.6	2.6673	.00740741	424.115	14313.88
136	18496	2515456	11.6619	5.1426	1586.0	2.6712	.00735294	427.256	14526.72
137	18769	2571353	11.7047	5.1551	1603.6	2.6751	.00729927	430.398	14741.14
138	19044	2628072	11.7473	5.1676	1621.1	2.6790	.00724638	433.539	14957.12
139	19321	2685619	11.7898	5.1801	1638.8	2.6829	.00719424	436.681	15174.67
140	19600	2744000	11.8322	5.1925	1656.5	2.6867	.00714286	439.823	15393.80
141	19881	2803221	11.8743	5.2048	1674.3	2.6906	.00709220	442.964	15614.50
142	20164	2863288	11.9164	5.2171	1692.1	2.6944	.00704225	446.106	15836.77
143	20449	2924207	11.9583	5.2293	1710.0	2.6981	.00699301	449.247	16060.60
144	20736	2985984	12.0000	5.2415	1728.0	2.7019	.00694444	452.389	16286.01
145	21025	3048625	12.0416	5.2536	1746.0	2.7057	.00689655	455.531	16512.99
146	21316	3112136	12.0830	5.2656	1764.1	2.7094	.00684932	458.672	16741.54
147	21609	3176523	12.1244	5.2776	1782.2	2.7131	.00680272	461.814	16971.67
148	21904	3241792	12.1655	5.2896	1800.5	2.7168	.00675676	464.955	17203.36
149	22201	3307949	12.2066	5.3015	1818.8	2.7204	.00671141	468.097	17436.62

Table 7.—*Continued*

N	N^2	N^3	$\sqrt{N}$	$\sqrt[3]{N}$	$N^{3/2}$	$\sqrt[5]{N}$	$\dfrac{1}{N}$	Circle ($N = D$)	
								Circum.	Area
150	**22500**	**3375000**	**12.2474**	**5.3133**	**1837.1**	**2.7241**	**.00666667**	**471.239**	**17671.46**
151	22801	3442991	12.2882	5.3251	1855.5	2.7277	.00662252	474.380	17907.86
152	23104	3511808	12.3288	5.3368	1874.0	2.7314	.00657895	477.522	18145.84
153	23409	3581577	12.3693	5.3485	1892.5	2.7349	.00653595	480.663	18385.38
154	23716	3652264	12.4097	5.3601	1911.1	2.7385	.00649351	483.805	18626.50
155	24025	3723875	12.4499	5.3717	1929.7	2.7420	.00645161	486.946	18869.19
156	24336	3796416	12.4900	5.3832	1948.4	2.7455	.00641026	490.088	19113.45
157	24649	3869893	12.5300	5.3947	1967.2	2.7490	.00636943	493.230	19359.28
158	24964	3944312	12.5698	5.4061	1986.0	2.7525	.00632911	496.371	19606.68
159	25281	4019679	12.6095	5.4175	2004.9	2.7560	.00628931	499.513	19855.65
160	**25600**	**4096000**	**12.6491**	**5.4288**	**2023.9**	**2.7595**	**.00625000**	**502.654**	**20106.19**
161	25921	4173281	12.6886	5.4401	2042.9	2.7629	.00621118	505.796	20358.30
162	26244	4251528	12.7279	5.4514	2061.9	2.7663	.00617284	508.938	20611.99
163	26569	4330747	12.7671	5.4626	2081.0	2.7697	.00613497	512.079	20867.24
164	26896	4410944	12.8062	5.4737	2100.2	2.7731	.00609756	515.221	21124.06
165	27225	4492125	12.8452	5.4848	2119.5	2.7765	.00606061	518.362	21382.46
166	27556	4574296	12.8841	5.4959	2138.8	2.7799	.00602410	521.504	21642.43
167	27889	4657463	12.9228	5.5069	2158.1	2.7832	.00598802	524.646	21903.96
168	28224	4741632	12.9615	5.5178	2177.5	2.7865	.00595238	527.787	22167.07
169	28561	4826809	13.0000	5.5288	2197.0	2.7898	.00591716	530.929	22431.75
170	**28900**	**4913000**	**13.0384**	**5.5397**	**2216.5**	**2.7931**	**.00588235**	**534.070**	**22698.00**
171	29241	5000211	13.0767	5.5505	2236.1	2.7964	.00584795	537.212	22965.82
172	29584	5088448	13.1149	5.5613	2255.8	2.7997	.00581395	540.353	23235.21
173	29929	5177717	13.1529	5.5721	2275.5	2.8029	.00578035	543.495	23506.18
174	30276	5268024	13.1909	5.5828	2295.2	2.8061	.00574713	546.637	23778.71
175	30625	5359375	13.2288	5.5934	2315.0	2.8094	.00571429	549.778	24052.81
176	30976	5451776	13.2665	5.6041	2334.9	2.8126	.00568182	552.920	24328.49
177	31329	5545233	13.3041	5.6147	2354.8	2.8158	.00564972	556.061	24605.73
178	31684	5639752	13.3417	5.6252	2374.8	2.8189	.00561798	559.203	24884.55
179	32041	5735339	13.3791	5.6357	2394.9	2.8221	.00558659	562.345	25164.94
180	**32400**	**5832000**	**13.4164**	**5.6462**	**2415.0**	**2.8252**	**.00555556**	**565.486**	**25446.90**
181	32761	5929741	13.4536	5.6567	2435.1	2.8284	.00552486	568.628	25730.42
182	33124	6028568	13.4907	5.6671	2455.3	2.8315	.00549451	571.769	26015.52
183	33489	6128487	13.5277	5.6774	2475.6	2.8346	.00546448	574.911	26302.19
184	33856	6229504	13.5647	5.6877	2495.9	2.8377	.00543478	578.053	26590.43
185	34225	6331625	13.6015	5.6980	2516.3	2.8408	.00540541	581.194	26880.25
186	34596	6434856	13.6382	5.7083	2536.7	2.8438	.00537634	584.336	27171.63
187	34969	6539203	13.6748	5.7185	2557.2	2.8469	.00534759	587.477	27464.58
188	35344	6644672	13.7113	5.7287	2577.7	2.8499	.00531915	590.619	27759.11
189	35721	6751269	13.7477	5.7388	2598.3	2.8529	.00529101	593.761	28055.20
190	**36100**	**6859000**	**13.7840**	**5.7489**	**2619.0**	**2.8560**	**.00526316**	**596.902**	**28352.87**
191	36481	6967871	13.8203	5.7590	2639.7	2.8590	.00523560	600.044	28652.10
192	36864	7077888	13.8564	5.7690	2660.4	2.8619	.00520833	603.185	28952.91
193	37249	7189057	13.8924	5.7790	2681.2	2.8649	.00518135	606.327	29255.29
194	37636	7301384	13.9284	5.7890	2702.1	2.8679	.00515464	609.468	29559.24
195	38025	7414875	13.9642	5.7989	2723.0	2.8708	.00512821	612.610	29864.76
196	38416	7529536	14.0000	5.8088	2744.0	2.8738	.00510204	615.752	30171.85
197	38809	7645373	14.0357	5.8186	2765.0	2.8767	.00507614	618.893	30480.51
198	39204	7762392	14.0712	5.8285	2786.1	2.8796	.00505051	622.035	30790.74
199	39601	7880599	14.1067	5.8383	2807.2	2.8825	.00502513	625.176	31102.55
200	**40000**	**8000000**	**14.1421**	**5.8480**	**2828.4**	**2.8854**	**.00500000**	**628.318**	**31415.93**
201	40401	8120601	14.1774	5.8578	2849.7	2.8883	.00497512	631.460	31730.87
202	40804	8242408	14.2127	5.8675	2871.0	2.8911	.00495050	634.601	32047.39
203	41209	8365427	14.2478	5.8771	2892.3	2.8940	.00492611	637.743	32365.47
204	41616	8489664	14.2829	5.8868	2913.7	2.8968	.00490196	640.884	32685.13
205	42025	8615125	14.3178	5.8964	2935.2	2.8997	.00487805	644.026	33006.36
206	42436	8741816	14.3527	5.9059	2956.7	2.9025	.00485437	647.168	33329.16
207	42849	8869743	14.3875	5.9155	2978.2	2.9053	.00483092	650.309	33653.53
208	43264	8998912	14.4222	5.9250	2999.8	2.9081	.00480769	653.451	33979.47
209	43681	9129329	14.4568	5.9345	3021.5	2.9109	.00478469	656.592	34306.98
210	**44100**	**9261000**	**14.4914**	**5.9439**	**3043.2**	**2.9137**	**.00476190**	**659.734**	**34636.06**
211	44521	9393931	14.5258	5.9533	3065.0	2.9165	.00473934	662.875	34966.71
212	44944	9528128	14.5602	5.9627	3086.8	2.9192	.00471698	666.017	35298.94
213	45369	9663597	14.5945	5.9721	3108.7	2.9220	.00469484	669.159	35632.73
214	45796	9800344	14.6287	5.9814	3130.6	2.9247	.00467290	672.300	35968.09
215	46225	9938375	14.6629	5.9907	3152.5	2.9274	.00465116	675.442	36305.03
216	46656	10077696	14.6969	6.0000	3174.5	2.9302	.00462963	678.583	36643.54
217	47089	10218313	14.7309	6.0092	3196.6	2.9329	.00460829	681.725	36983.61
218	47524	10360232	14.7648	6.0185	3218.7	2.9356	.00458716	684.867	37325.26
219	47961	10503459	14.7986	6.0277	3240.9	2.9383	.00456621	688.008	37668.48

Table 7.—*Continued*

N	N^2	N^3	$\sqrt{N}$	$\sqrt[3]{N}$	$N^{3/2}$	$\sqrt[5]{N}$	$\dfrac{1}{N}$	Circle ($N = D$)	
								Circum.	Area
220	48400	10648000	14.8324	6.0368	3263.1	2.9409	.00454545	691.150	38013.27
221	48841	10793861	14.8661	6.0459	3285.4	2.9436	.00452489	694.291	38359.63
222	49284	10941048	14.8997	6.0550	3307.7	2.9463	.00450450	697.433	38707.56
223	49729	11089567	14.9332	6.0641	3330.1	2.9489	.00448430	700.575	39057.07
224	50176	11239424	14.9666	6.0732	3352.5	2.9516	.00446429	703.716	39408.14
225	50625	11390625	15.0000	6.0822	3375.0	2.9542	.00444444	706.858	39760.78
226	51076	11543176	15.0333	6.0912	3397.5	2.9568	.00442478	709.999	40115.00
227	51529	11697083	15.0665	6.1002	3420.1	2.9594	.00440529	713.141	40470.78
228	51984	11852352	15.0997	6.1091	3442.7	2.9620	.00438596	716.283	40828.14
229	52441	12008989	15.1327	6.1180	3465.4	2.9646	.00436681	719.424	41187.07
230	52900	12167000	15.1658	6.1269	3488.1	2.9672	.00434783	722.566	41547.56
231	53361	12326391	15.1987	6.1358	3510.9	2.9698	.00432900	725.707	41909.63
232	53824	12487168	15.2315	6.1446	3533.7	2.9723	.00431034	728.849	42273.27
233	54289	12649337	15.2643	6.1534	3556.6	2.9749	.00429185	731.990	42638.48
234	54756	12812904	15.2971	6.1622	3579.5	2.9774	.00427350	735.132	43005.26
235	55225	12977875	15.3297	6.1710	3602.5	2.9800	.00425532	738.274	43373.61
236	55696	13144256	15.3623	6.1797	3625.5	2.9825	.00423729	741.415	43743.54
237	56169	13312053	15.3948	6.1885	3648.6	2.9850	.00421941	744.557	44115.03
238	56644	13481272	15.4272	6.1972	3671.7	2.9875	.00420168	747.698	44488.09
239	57121	13651919	15.4596	6.2058	3694.8	2.9900	.00418410	750.840	44862.73
240	57600	13824000	15.4919	6.2145	3718.0	2.9925	.00416667	753.982	45238.93
241	58081	13997521	15.5242	6.2231	3741.3	2.9950	.00414938	757.123	45616.71
242	58564	14172488	15.5563	6.2317	3764.6	2.9975	.00413223	760.265	45996.06
243	59049	14348907	15.5885	6.2403	3788.0	3.0000	.00411523	763.406	46376.98
244	59536	14526784	15.6205	6.2488	3811.4	3.0025	.00409836	766.548	46759.47
245	60025	14706125	15.6525	6.2573	3834.9	3.0049	.00408163	769.690	47143.52
246	60516	14886936	15.6844	6.2658	3858.4	3.0074	.00406504	772.831	47529.16
247	61009	15069223	15.7162	6.2743	3881.9	3.0098	.00404858	775.973	47916.36
248	61504	15252992	15.7480	6.2828	3905.5	3.0122	.00403226	779.114	48305.13
249	62001	15438249	15.7797	6.2912	3929.2	3.0147	.00401606	782.256	48695.47
250	62500	15625000	15.8114	6.2996	3952.9	3.0171	.00400000	785.398	49087.39
251	63001	15813251	15.8430	6.3080	3976.6	3.0195	.00398406	788.539	49480.87
252	63504	16003008	15.8745	6.3164	4000.4	3.0219	.00396825	791.681	49875.92
253	64009	16194277	15.9060	6.3247	4024.2	3.0243	.00395257	794.822	50272.55
254	64516	16387064	15.9374	6.3330	4048.1	3.0267	.00393701	797.964	50670.75
255	65025	16581375	15.9687	6.3413	4072.0	3.0291	.00392157	801.105	51070.52
256	65536	16777216	16.0000	6.3496	4096.0	3.0314	.00390625	804.247	51471.85
257	66049	16974593	16.0312	6.3579	4120.0	3.0338	.00389105	807.389	51874.76
258	66564	17173512	16.0624	6.3661	4144.1	3.0362	.00387597	810.530	52279.24
259	67081	17373979	16.0935	6.3743	4168.2	3.0385	.00386100	813.672	52685.29
260	67600	17576000	16.1245	6.3825	4192.4	3.0418	.00384615	816.813	53092.92
261	68121	17779581	16.1555	6.3907	4216.6	3.0432	.00383142	819.955	53502.11
262	68644	17984728	16.1864	6.3988	4240.8	3.0455	.00381679	823.097	53912.87
263	69169	18191447	16.2173	6.4070	4265.1	3.0478	.00380228	826.238	54325.21
264	69696	18399744	16.2481	6.4151	4289.5	3.0501	.00378788	829.380	54739.11
265	70225	18609625	16.2788	6.4232	4313.9	3.0524	.00377358	832.521	55154.59
266	70756	18821096	16.3095	6.4312	4338.3	3.0547	.00375940	835.663	55571.63
267	71289	19034163	16.3401	6.4393	4362.8	3.0570	.00374532	838.805	55990.25
268	71824	19248832	16.3707	6.4473	4387.3	3.0593	.00373134	841.946	56410.44
269	72361	19465109	16.4012	6.4553	4411.9	3.0616	.00371747	845.088	56832.20
270	72900	19683000	16.4317	6.4633	4436.5	3.0639	.00370370	848.229	57255.53
271	73441	19902511	16.4621	6.4713	4461.2	3.0662	.00369004	851.371	57680.43
272	73984	20123648	16.4924	6.4792	4485.9	3.0684	.00367647	854.512	58106.90
273	74529	20346417	16.5227	6.4872	4510.7	3.0707	.00366300	857.654	58534.94
274	75076	20570824	16.5529	6.4951	4535.5	3.0729	.00364964	860.796	58964.55
275	75625	20796875	16.5831	6.5030	4560.4	3.0752	.00363636	863.937	59395.74
276	76176	21024576	16.6132	6.5108	4585.3	3.0774	.00362319	867.079	59828.49
277	76729	21253933	16.6433	6.5187	4610.2	3.0796	.00361011	870.220	60262.82
278	77284	21484952	16.6733	6.5265	4635.2	3.0818	.00359712	873.362	60698.71
279	77841	21717639	16.7033	6.5343	4660.2	3.0840	.00358423	876.504	61136.18
280	78400	21952000	16.7332	6.5421	4685.3	3.0863	.00357143	879.645	61575.22
281	78961	22188041	16.7631	6.5499	4710.4	3.0885	.00355872	882.787	62015.82
282	79524	22425768	16.7929	6.5577	4735.6	3.0907	.00354610	885.928	62458.00
283	80089	22665187	16.8226	6.5654	4760.8	3.0928	.00353357	889.070	62901.75
284	80656	22906364	16.8523	6.5731	4786.0	3.0950	.00352113	892.212	63347.07
285	81225	23149125	16.8819	6.5808	4811.3	3.0972	.00350877	895.353	63793.97
286	81796	23393656	16.9115	6.5885	4836.7	3.0994	.00349650	898.495	64242.43
287	82369	23639903	16.9411	6.5962	4862.1	3.1015	.00348432	901.636	64692.46
288	82944	23887872	16.9706	6.6039	4887.5	3.1037	.00347222	904.778	65144.07
289	83521	24137569	17.0000	6.6115	4913.0	3.1058	.00346021	907.920	65597.24

MATHEMATICAL AND PHYSICAL TABLES

Table 7.—*Continued*

N	N^2	N^3	$\sqrt{N}$	$\sqrt[3]{N}$	$N^{3/2}$	$\sqrt[5]{N}$	$\dfrac{1}{N}$	Circle ($N = D$) Circum.	Circle ($N = D$) Area
290	84100	24389000	17.0294	6.6191	4938.5	3.1080	.00344828	911.061	66051.99
291	84681	24642171	17.0587	6.6267	4964.1	3.1101	.00343643	914.203	66508.30
292	85264	24897088	17.0880	6.6343	4989.7	3.1123	.00342466	917.344	66966.19
293	85849	25153757	17.1172	6.6419	5015.4	3.1144	.00341297	920.486	67425.65
294	86436	25412184	17.1464	6.6494	5041.1	3.1165	.00340136	923.627	67886.68
295	87025	25672375	17.1756	6.6569	5066.8	3.1186	.00338983	926.769	68349.28
296	87616	25934336	17.2047	6.6644	5092.6	3.1207	.00337838	929.911	68813.45
297	88209	26198073	17.2337	6.6719	5118.4	3.1228	.00336700	933.052	69279.19
298	88804	26463592	17.2627	6.6794	5144.3	3.1249	.00335570	936.194	69746.50
299	89401	26730899	17.2916	6.6869	5170.2	3.1270	.00334448	939.335	70215.38
300	90000	27000000	17.3205	6.6943	5196.2	3.1291	.00333333	942.477	70685.83
301	90601	27270901	17.3494	6.7018	5222.2	3.1312	.00332226	945.619	71157.86
302	91204	27543608	17.3781	6.7092	5248.2	3.1333	.00331126	948.760	71631.45
303	91809	27818127	17.4069	6.7166	5274.3	3.1354	.00330033	951.902	72106.62
304	92416	28094464	17.4356	6.7240	5300.4	3.1374	.00328947	955.043	72583.36
305	93025	28372625	17.4642	6.7313	5326.6	3.1395	.00327869	958.185	73061.66
306	93636	28652616	17.4929	6.7387	5352.8	3.1416	.00326797	961.327	73541.54
307	94249	28934443	17.5214	6.7460	5379.1	3.1436	.00325733	964.468	74022.99
308	94864	29218112	17.5499	6.7533	5405.4	3.1456	.00324675	967.610	74506.01
309	95481	29503629	17.5784	6.7606	5431.7	3.1477	.00323625	970.751	74990.60
310	96100	29791000	17.6068	6.7679	5458.1	3.1497	.00322581	973.893	75476.76
311	96721	30080231	17.6352	6.7752	5484.5	3.1518	.00321543	977.034	75964.50
312	97344	30371328	17.6635	6.7824	5511.0	3.1538	.00320513	980.176	76453.80
313	97969	30664297	17.6918	6.7897	5537.5	3.1558	.00319489	983.318	76944.67
314	98596	30959144	17.7200	6.7969	5564.1	3.1578	.00318471	986.459	77437.12
315	99225	31255875	17.7482	6.8041	5590.7	3.1598	.00317460	989.601	77931.13
316	99856	31554496	17.7764	6.8113	5617.3	3.1618	.00316456	992.742	78426.72
317	100489	31855013	17.8045	6.8185	5644.0	3.1638	.00315457	995.884	78923.88
318	101124	32157432	17.8326	6.8256	5670.7	3.1658	.00314465	999.026	79422.60
319	101761	32461759	17.8606	6.8328	5697.5	3.1678	.00313480	1002.167	79922.90
320	102400	32768000	17.8885	6.8399	5724.3	3.1698	.00312500	1005.309	80424.77
321	103041	33076161	17.9165	6.8470	5751.2	3.1718	.00311526	1008.450	80928.21
322	103684	33386248	17.9444	6.8541	5778.1	3.1737	.00310559	1011.592	81433.22
323	104329	33698267	17.9722	6.8612	5805.0	3.1757	.00309598	1014.734	81939.80
324	104976	34012224	18.0000	6.8683	5832.0	3.1777	.00308642	1017.875	82447.96
325	105625	34328125	18.0278	6.8753	5859.0	3.1796	.00307692	1021.017	82957.68
326	106276	34645976	18.0555	6.8824	5886.1	3.1816	.00306748	1024.158	83468.97
327	106929	34965783	18.0831	6.8894	5913.2	3.1835	.00305810	1027.300	83981.84
328	107584	35287552	18.1108	6.8964	5940.3	3.1855	.00304878	1030.442	84496.28
329	108241	35611289	18.1384	6.9034	5967.5	3.1874	.00303951	1033.583	85012.28
330	108900	35937000	18.1659	6.9104	5994.7	3.1894	.00303030	1036.725	85529.86
331	109561	36264691	18.1934	6.9174	6022.0	3.1913	.00302115	1039.866	86049.01
332	110224	36594368	18.2209	6.9244	6049.3	3.1932	.00301205	1043.008	86569.73
333	110889	36926037	18.2483	6.9313	6076.7	3.1951	.00300300	1046.149	87092.02
334	111556	37259704	18.2757	6.9382	6104.1	3.1970	.00299401	1049.291	87615.88
335	112225	37595375	18.3030	6.9451	6131.5	3.1989	.00298507	1052.433	88141.31
336	112896	37933056	18.3303	6.9521	6159.0	3.2009	.00297619	1055.574	88668.31
337	113569	38272753	18.3576	6.9589	6186.5	3.2028	.00296736	1058.716	89196.88
338	114244	38614472	18.3848	6.9658	6214.1	3.2047	.00295858	1061.857	89727.03
339	114921	38958219	18.4120	6.9727	6241.7	3.2066	.00294985	1064.999	90258.74
340	115600	39304000	18.4391	6.9795	6269.3	3.2085	.00294118	1068.141	90792.03
341	116281	39651821	18.4662	6.9864	6297.0	3.2103	.00293255	1071.282	91326.88
342	116964	40001688	18.4932	6.9932	6324.7	3.2122	.00292398	1074.424	91863.31
343	117649	40353607	18.5203	7.0000	6352.4	3.2141	.00291545	1077.565	92401.31
344	118336	40707584	18.5472	7.0068	6380.2	3.2160	.00290698	1080.707	92940.88
345	119025	41063625	18.5742	7.0136	6408.1	3.2178	.00289855	1083.849	93482.02
346	119716	41421736	18.6011	7.0203	6436.0	3.2197	.00289017	1086.990	94024.73
347	120409	41781923	18.6279	7.0271	6463.9	3.2216	.00288184	1090.132	94569.01
348	121104	42144192	18.6548	7.0338	6491.9	3.2234	.00287356	1093.273	95114.86
349	121801	42508549	18.6815	7.0406	6519.9	3.2253	.00286533	1096.415	95662.28
350	122500	42875000	18.7083	7.0473	6547.9	3.2271	.00285714	1099.557	96211.28
351	123201	43243551	18.7350	7.0540	6576.0	3.2289	.00284900	1102.698	96761.84
352	123904	43614208	18.7617	7.0607	6604.1	3.2308	.00284091	1105.840	97313.97
353	124609	43986977	18.7883	7.0674	6632.3	3.2326	.00283286	1108.981	97867.68
354	125316	44361864	18.8149	7.0740	6660.5	3.2345	.00282486	1112.123	98422.96
355	126025	44738875	18.8414	7.0807	6688.7	3.2363	.00281690	1115.264	98979.80
356	126736	45118016	18.8680	7.0873	6717.0	3.2381	.00280899	1118.406	99538.22
357	127449	45499293	18.8944	7.0940	6745.3	3.2399	.00280112	1121.548	100098.21
358	128164	45882712	18.9209	7.1006	6773.7	3.2417	.00279330	1124.689	100659.77
359	128881	46268279	18.9473	7.1072	6802.1	3.2435	.00278552	1127.831	101222.90

Table 7.—*Continued*

N	N^2	N^3	$\sqrt{N}$	$\sqrt[3]{N}$	$N^{3/2}$	$\sqrt[5]{N}$	$\dfrac{1}{N}$	Circle ($N = D$)	
								Circum.	Area
360	129600	46656000	18.9737	7.1138	6830.5	3.2453	.00277778	1130.972	101787.60
361	130321	47045881	19.0000	7.1204	6859.0	3.2471	.00277008	1134.114	102353.87
362	131044	47437928	19.0263	7.1269	6887.5	3.2489	.00276243	1137.256	102921.72
363	131769	47832147	19.0526	7.1335	6916.1	3.2507	.00275482	1140.397	103491.13
364	132496	48228544	19.0788	7.1400	6944.7	3.2525	.00274725	1143.539	104062.12
365	133225	48627125	19.1050	7.1466	6973.3	3.2543	.00273973	1146.680	104634.67
366	133956	49027896	19.1311	7.1531	7002.0	3.2561	.00273224	1149.822	105208.80
367	134689	49430863	19.1572	7.1596	7030.7	3.2579	.00272480	1152.964	105784.49
368	135424	49836032	19.1833	7.1661	7059.5	3.2597	.00271739	1156.105	106361.76
369	136161	50243409	19.2094	7.1726	7088.3	3.2614	.00271003	1159.247	106940.60
370	136900	50653000	19.2354	7.1791	7117.1	3.2632	.00270270	1162.388	107521.01
371	137641	51064811	19.2614	7.1855	7146.0	3.2650	.00269542	1165.530	108102.99
372	138384	51478848	19.2873	7.1920	7174.9	3.2668	.00268817	1168.671	108686.54
373	139129	51895117	19.3132	7.1984	7203.9	3.2685	.00268097	1171.813	109271.66
374	139876	52313624	19.3391	7.2048	7232.8	3.2702	.00267380	1174.955	109858.35
375	140625	52734375	19.3649	7.2112	7261.8	3.2719	.00266667	1178.096	110446.62
376	141376	53157376	19.3907	7.2177	7290.9	3.2737	.00265957	1181.238	111036.45
377	142129	53582633	19.4165	7.2240	7320.0	3.2754	.00265252	1184.379	111627.86
378	142884	54010152	19.4422	7.2304	7349.2	3.2772	.00264550	1187.521	112220.83
379	143641	54439939	19.4679	7.2368	7378.4	3.2789	.00263852	1190.663	112815.38
380	144400	54872000	19.4936	7.2432	7407.6	3.2807	.00263158	1193.804	113411.49
381	145161	55306341	19.5192	7.2495	7436.8	3.2824	.00262467	1196.946	114009.18
382	145924	55742968	19.5448	7.2558	7466.1	3.2841	.00261780	1200.087	114608.44
383	146689	56181887	19.5704	7.2622	7495.4	3.2858	.00261097	1203.229	115209.27
384	147456	56623104	19.5959	7.2685	7524.8	3.2875	.00260417	1206.371	115811.67
385	148225	57066625	19.6214	7.2748	7554.2	3.2892	.00259740	1209.512	116415.64
386	148996	57512456	19.6469	7.2811	7583.7	3.2909	.00259067	1212.654	117021.18
387	149769	57960603	19.6723	7.2874	7613.2	3.2926	.00258398	1215.795	117628.30
388	150544	58411072	19.6977	7.2936	7642.7	3.2943	.00257732	1218.937	118236.98
389	151321	58863869	19.7231	7.2999	7672.3	3.2960	.00257069	1222.079	118847.24
390	152100	59319000	19.7484	7.3061	7701.9	3.2977	.00256410	1225.220	119459.06
391	152881	59776471	19.7737	7.3124	7731.5	3.2994	.00255754	1228.362	120072.46
392	153664	60236288	19.7990	7.3186	7761.2	3.3011	.00255102	1231.503	120687.42
393	154449	60698457	19.8242	7.3248	7790.9	3.3028	.00254453	1234.645	121303.96
394	155236	61162984	19.8494	7.3310	7820.7	3.3045	.00253807	1237.786	121922.07
395	156025	61629875	19.8746	7.3372	7850.5	3.3061	.00253165	1240.928	122541.75
396	156816	62099136	19.8997	7.3434	7880.3	3.3078	.00252525	1244.070	123163.00
397	157609	62570773	19.9249	7.3496	7910.2	3.3095	.00251889	1247.211	123785.82
398	158404	63044792	19.9499	7.3558	7940.1	3.3111	.00251256	1250.353	124410.21
399	159201	63521199	19.9750	7.3619	7970.0	3.3128	.00250627	1253.494	125036.17
400	160000	64000000	20.0000	7.3681	8000.0	3.3145	.00250000	1256.636	125663.71
401	160801	64481201	20.0250	7.3742	8030.0	3.3161	.00249377	1259.778	126292.81
402	161604	64964808	20.0499	7.3803	8061.1	3.3178	.00248756	1262.919	126923.48
403	162409	65450827	20.0749	7.3864	8090.2	3.3194	.00248139	1266.061	127555.73
404	163216	65939264	20.0998	7.3925	8120.3	3.3211	.00247525	1269.202	128189.55
405	164025	66430125	20.1246	7.3986	8150.5	3.3227	.00246914	1272.344	128824.93
406	164836	66923416	20.1494	7.4047	8180.7	3.3243	.00246305	1275.486	129461.89
407	165649	67419143	20.1742	7.4108	8210.9	3.3260	.00245700	1278.627	130100.42
408	166464	67917312	20.1990	7.4169	8241.2	3.3276	.00245098	1281.769	130740.52
409	167281	68417929	20.2237	7.4229	8271.5	3.3292	.00244499	1284.910	131382.19
410	168100	68921000	20.2485	7.4290	8301.9	3.3308	.00243902	1288.052	132025.43
411	168921	69426531	20.2731	7.4350	8332.3	3.3325	.00243309	1291.194	132670.24
412	169744	69934528	20.2978	7.4410	8362.7	3.3341	.00242718	1294.335	133316.63
413	170569	70444997	20.3224	7.4470	8393.2	3.3357	.00242131	1297.477	133964.58
414	171396	70957944	20.3470	7.4530	8423.7	3.3373	.00241546	1300.618	134614.10
415	172225	71473375	20.3715	7.4590	8454.2	3.3390	.00240964	1303.760	135265.20
416	173056	71991296	20.3961	7.4650	8484.8	3.3406	.00240385	1306.901	135917.86
417	173889	72511713	20.4206	7.4710	8515.4	3.3422	.00239808	1310.043	136572.10
418	174724	73034632	20.4450	7.4770	8546.0	3.3438	.00239234	1313.185	137227.91
419	175561	73560059	20.4695	7.4829	8576.7	3.3454	.00238663	1316.326	137885.29
420	176400	74088000	20.4939	7.4889	8607.4	3.3470	.00238095	1319.468	138544.24
421	177241	74618461	20.5183	7.4948	8638.2	3.3485	.00237530	1322.609	139204.76
422	178084	75151448	20.5426	7.5007	8669.0	3.3501	.00236967	1325.751	139866.85
423	178929	75686967	20.5670	7.5067	8699.8	3.3517	.00236407	1328.893	140530.51
424	179776	76225024	20.5913	7.5126	8730.7	3.3533	.00235849	1332.034	141195.74
425	180625	76765625	20.6155	7.5185	8761.6	3.3559	.00235294	1335.176	141862.54
426	181476	77308776	20.6398	7.5244	8792.5	3.3564	.00234742	1338.317	142530.92
427	182329	77854483	20.6640	7.5302	8823.5	3.3580	.00234192	1341.459	143200.86
428	183184	78402752	20.6882	7.5361	8854.5	3.3596	.00233645	1344.601	143872.38
429	184041	78953589	20.7123	7.5420	8885.6	3.3612	.00233100	1347.742	144545.46

Table 7.—*Continued*

N	N^2	N^3	$\sqrt{N}$	$\sqrt[3]{N}$	$N^{3/2}$	$\sqrt[5]{N}$	$\dfrac{1}{N}$	Circle ($N = D$) Circum.	Area
430	**184900**	**79507000**	**20.7364**	**7.5478**	**8916.7**	**3.3627**	**.00232558**	**1350.884**	**145220.12**
431	185761	80062991	20.7605	7.5537	8947.8	3.3643	.00232019	1354.025	145896.35
432	186624	80621568	20.7846	7.5595	8979.0	3.3659	.00231481	1357.167	146574.15
433	187489	81182737	20.8087	7.5654	9010.1	3.3674	.00230947	1360.308	147253.52
434	188356	81746504	20.8327	7.5712	9041.4	3.3690	.00230415	1363.450	147934.46
435	189225	82312875	20.8567	7.5770	9072.7	3.3705	.00229885	1366.592	148616.97
436	190096	82881856	20.8806	7.5828	9104.0	3.3720	.00229358	1369.733	149301.05
437	190969	83453453	20.9045	7.5886	9135.3	3.3736	.00228833	1372.875	149986.70
438	191844	84027672	20.9284	7.5944	9166.7	3.3752	.00228311	1376.016	150673.92
439	192721	84604519	20.9523	7.6001	9198.1	3.3767	.00227790	1379.158	151362.72
440	**193600**	**85184000**	**20.9762**	**7.6059**	**9229.5**	**3.3783**	**.00227273**	**1382.300**	**152053.08**
441	194481	85766121	21.0000	7.6117	9261.0	3.3798	.00226757	1385.441	152745.02
442	195364	86350888	21.0238	7.6174	9292.5	3.3813	.00226244	1388.583	153438.53
443	196249	86938307	21.0476	7.6232	9324.1	3.3828	.00225734	1391.724	154133.60
444	197136	87528384	21.0713	7.6289	9355.7	3.3844	.00225225	1394.866	154830.25
445	198025	88121125	21.0950	7.6346	9387.3	3.3859	.00224719	1398.008	155528.47
446	198916	88716536	21.1187	7.6403	9419.0	3.3874	.00224215	1401.149	156228.26
447	199809	89314623	21.1424	7.6460	9450.7	3.3889	.00223714	1404.291	156929.62
448	200704	89915392	21.1660	7.6517	9482.4	3.3904	.00223214	1407.432	157632.55
449	201601	90518849	21.1896	7.6574	9514.2	3.3919	.00222717	1410.574	158337.05
450	**202500**	**91125000**	**21.2132**	**7.6631**	**9546.0**	**3.3935**	**.00222222**	**1413.716**	**159043.13**
451	203401	91733851	21.2368	7.6688	9577.8	3.3950	.00221729	1416.857	159750.77
452	204304	92345408	21.2603	7.6744	9609.6	3.3965	.00221239	1419.999	160459.99
453	205209	92959677	21.2838	7.6801	9641.5	3.3980	.00220751	1423.140	161170.77
454	206116	93576664	21.3073	7.6857	9673.5	3.3995	.00220264	1426.282	161883.13
455	207025	94196375	21.3307	7.6914	9705.5	3.4010	.00219780	1429.423	162597.05
456	207936	94818816	21.3542	7.6970	9737.5	3.4025	.00219298	1432.565	163312.55
457	208849	95443993	21.3776	7.7026	9769.5	3.4039	.00218818	1435.707	164029.62
458	209764	96071912	21.4009	7.7082	9801.6	3.4054	.00218341	1438.848	164748.26
459	210681	96702579	21.4243	7.7138	9833.8	3.4069	.00217865	1441.990	165468.47
460	**211600**	**97336000**	**21.4476**	**7.7194**	**9865.9**	**3.4084**	**.00217391**	**1445.131**	**166190.25**
461	212521	97972181	21.4709	7.7250	9898.1	3.4099	.00216920	1448.273	166913.60
462	213444	98611128	21.4942	7.7306	9930.3	3.4113	.00216450	1451.415	167638.52
463	214369	99252847	21.5174	7.7362	9962.6	3.4128	.00215983	1454.556	168365.02
464	215296	99897344	21.5407	7.7418	9994.8	3.4143	.00215517	1457.698	169093.08
465	216225	100544625	21.5639	7.7473	10027.	3.4158	.00215054	1460.839	169822.72
466	217156	101194696	21.5870	7.7529	10060.	3.4173	.00214592	1463.981	170553.92
467	218089	101847563	21.6102	7.7584	10092.	3.4187	.00214133	1467.123	171286.70
468	219024	102503232	21.6333	7.7639	10124.	3.4202	.00213675	1470.264	172021.05
469	219961	103161709	21.6564	7.7695	10157.	3.4217	.00213220	1473.406	172756.96
470	**220900**	**103823000**	**21.6795**	**7.7750**	**10189.**	**3.4231**	**.00212766**	**1476.547**	**173494.45**
471	221841	104487111	21.7025	7.7805	10222.	3.4246	.00212314	1479.689	174233.51
472	222784	105154048	21.7256	7.7860	10255.	3.4260	.00211864	1482.830	174974.14
473	223729	105823817	21.7486	7.7915	10287.	3.4275	.00211416	1485.972	175716.34
474	224676	106496424	21.7715	7.7970	10320.	3.4289	.00210970	1489.114	176460.12
475	225625	107171875	21.7945	7.8025	10352.	3.4304	.00210526	1492.255	177205.46
476	226576	107850176	21.8174	7.8079	10385.	3.4318	.00210084	1495.397	177952.37
477	227529	108531333	21.8403	7.8134	10418.	3.4332	.00209644	1498.538	178700.86
478	228484	109215352	21.8632	7.8188	10450.	3.4347	.00209205	1501.680	179450.91
479	229441	109902239	21.8861	7.8243	10483.	3.4361	.00208768	1504.822	180202.54
480	**230400**	**110592000**	**21.9089**	**7.8297**	**10516.**	**3.4375**	**.00208333**	**1507.965**	**180955.74**
481	231361	111284641	21.9317	7.8352	10549.	3.4390	.00207900	1511.105	181710.50
482	232324	111980168	21.9545	7.8406	10582.	3.4404	.00207469	1514.246	182466.84
483	233289	112678587	21.9773	7.8460	10615.	3.4418	.00207039	1517.388	183224.75
484	234256	113379904	22.0000	7.8514	10648.	3.4433	.00206612	1520.530	183984.23
485	235225	114084125	22.0227	7.8568	10681.	3.4447	.00206186	1523.671	184745.28
486	236196	114791256	22.0454	7.8622	10714.	3.4461	.00205761	1526.813	185507.90
487	237169	115501303	22.0681	7.8676	10747.	3.4475	.00205339	1529.954	186272.10
488	238144	116214272	22.0907	7.8730	10780.	3.4489	.00204918	1533.096	187037.86
489	239121	116930169	22.1133	7.8784	10813.	3.4504	.00204499	1536.238	187805.19
490	**240100**	**117649000**	**22.1359**	**7.8837**	**10847.**	**3.4518**	**.00204082**	**1539.379**	**188574.10**
491	241081	118370771	22.1585	7.8891	10880.	3.4532	.00203666	1542.521	189344.57
492	242064	119095488	22.1811	7.8944	10913.	3.4546	.00203252	1545.662	190116.62
493	243049	119823157	22.2036	7.8998	10946.	3.4560	.00202840	1548.804	190890.24
494	244036	120553784	22.2261	7.9051	10980.	3.4574	.00202429	1551.945	191665.43
495	245025	121287375	22.2486	7.9105	11013.	3.4588	.00202020	1555.087	192442.18
496	246016	122023936	22.2711	7.9158	11046.	3.4602	.00201613	1558.229	193220.51
497	247009	122763473	22.2935	7.9211	11080.	3.4616	.00201207	1561.370	194000.41
498	248004	123505992	22.3159	7.9264	11113.	3.4630	.00200803	1564.512	194781.89
499	249001	124251499	22.3383	7.9317	11147.	3.4643	.00200401	1567.653	195564.93

Table 7.—*Continued*

N	N^2	N^3	$\sqrt{N}$	$\sqrt[3]{N}$	$N^{3/2}$	$\sqrt[5]{N}$	$\dfrac{1}{N}$	Circle ($N = D$)	
								Circum.	Area
500	**250000**	**125000000**	**22.3607**	**7.9370**	**11180**	**3.4657**	**.00200000**	**1570.795**	**196349.54**
501	251001	125751501	22.3830	7.9423	11214	3.4671	.00199601	1573.937	197135.72
502	252004	126506008	22.4054	7.9476	11247	3.4685	.00199203	1577.078	197923.48
503	253009	127263527	22.4277	7.9528	11281	3.4699	.00198807	1580.220	198712.80
504	254016	128024064	22.4499	7.9581	11315	3.4713	.00198413	1583.361	199503.70
505	255025	128787625	22.4722	7.9634	11348	3.4726	.00198020	1586.503	200296.17
506	256036	129554216	22.4944	7.9686	11382	3.4740	.00197628	1589.645	201090.20
507	257049	130323843	22.5167	7.9739	11416	3.4754	.00197239	1592.786	201885.81
508	258064	131096512	22.5389	7.9791	11450	3.4768	.00196850	1595.928	202682.99
509	259081	131872229	22.5610	7.9843	11484	3.4781	.00196464	1599.069	203481.74
510	**260100**	**132651000**	**22.5832**	**7.9896**	**11517**	**3.4795**	**.00196078**	**1602.211**	**204282.06**
511	261121	133432831	22.6053	7.9948	11551	3.4808	.00195695	1605.352	205083.95
512	262144	134217728	22.6274	8.0000	11585	3.4822	.00195313	1608.494	205887.42
513	263169	135005697	22.6495	8.0052	11619	3.4836	.00194932	1611.636	206692.45
514	264196	135796744	22.6716	8.0104	11653	3.4849	.00194553	1614.777	207499.05
515	265225	136590875	22.6936	8.0156	11687	3.4863	.00194175	1617.919	208307.23
516	266256	137388096	22.7156	8.0208	11721	3.4876	.00193798	1621.060	209116.97
517	267289	138188413	22.7376	8.0260	11755	3.4890	.00193424	1624.202	209928.29
518	268324	138991832	22.7596	8.0311	11789	3.4904	.00193050	1627.344	210741.18
519	269361	139798359	22.7816	8.0363	11824	3.4917	.00192678	1630.485	211555.63
520	**270400**	**140608000**	**22.8035**	**8.0415**	**11858**	**3.4930**	**.00192308**	**1633.627**	**212371.66**
521	271441	141420761	22.8254	8.0466	11892	3.4944	.00191939	1636.768	213189.26
522	272484	142236648	22.8473	8.0517	11926	3.4957	.00191571	1639.910	214008.43
523	273529	143055667	22.8692	8.0569	11960	3.4970	.00191205	1643.052	214829.17
524	274576	143877824	22.8910	8.0620	11995	3.4984	.00190840	1646.193	215651.49
525	275625	144703125	22.9129	8.0671	12029	3.4997	.00190476	1649.335	216475.37
526	276676	145531576	22.9347	8.0723	12064	3.5010	.00190114	1652.476	217300.82
527	277729	146363183	22.9565	8.0774	12098	3.5024	.00189753	1655.618	218127.85
528	278784	147197952	22.9783	8.0825	12133	3.5037	.00189394	1658.760	218956.44
529	279841	148035889	23.0000	8.0876	12167	3.5050	.00189036	1661.901	219786.61
530	**280900**	**148877000**	**23.0217**	**8.0927**	**12202**	**3.5064**	**.00188679**	**1665.043**	**220618.34**
531	281961	149721291	23.0434	8.0978	12236	3.5077	.00188324	1668.184	221451.65
532	283024	150568768	23.0651	8.1028	12271	3.5090	.00187970	1671.326	222286.53
533	284089	151419437	23.0868	8.1079	12305	3.5103	.00187617	1674.467	223122.98
534	285156	152273304	23.1084	8.1130	12340	3.5116	.00187266	1677.609	223961.00
535	286225	153130375	23.1301	8.1180	12375	3.5130	.00186916	1680.751	224800.59
536	287296	153990656	23.1517	8.1231	12410	3.5143	.00186567	1683.892	225641.75
537	288369	154854153	23.1733	8.1281	12444	3.5156	.00186220	1687.034	226484.48
538	289444	155720872	23.1948	8.1332	12479	3.5169	.00185874	1690.175	227328.79
539	290521	156590819	23.2164	8.1382	12514	3.5182	.00185529	1693.317	228174.66
540	**291600**	**157464000**	**23.2379**	**8.1433**	**12549**	**3.5195**	**.00185185**	**1696.459**	**229022.10**
541	292681	158340421	23.2594	8.1483	12583	3.5208	.00184843	1699.600	229871.12
542	293764	159220088	23.2809	8.1533	12618	3.5221	.00184502	1702.742	230721.71
543	294849	160103007	23.3024	8.1583	12653	3.5234	.00184162	1705.883	231573.86
544	295936	160989184	23.3238	8.1633	12688	3.5247	.00183824	1709.025	232427.59
545	297025	161878625	23.3452	8.1683	12723	3.5260	.00183486	1712.167	233282.89
546	298116	162771336	23.3666	8.1733	12758	3.5273	.00183150	1715.308	234139.76
547	299209	163667323	23.3880	8.1783	12793	3.5286	.00182815	1718.450	234998.20
548	300304	164566592	23.4094	8.1833	12828	3.5299	.00182482	1721.591	235858.21
549	301401	165469149	23.4307	8.1882	12863	3.5311	.00182149	1724.733	236719.79
550	**302500**	**166375000**	**23.4521**	**8.1932**	**12899**	**3.5324**	**.00181818**	**1727.875**	**237582.94**
551	303601	167284151	23.4734	8.1982	12934	3.5337	.00181488	1731.016	238447.67
552	304704	168196608	23.4947	8.2031	12969	3.5350	.00181159	1734.158	239313.96
553	305809	169112377	23.5160	8.2081	13004	3.5363	.00180832	1737.299	240181.83
554	306916	170031464	23.5372	8.2130	13040	3.5376	.00180505	1740.441	241051.26
555	308025	170953875	23.5584	8.2180	13075	3.5388	.00180180	1743.582	241922.27
556	309136	171879616	23.5797	8.2229	13110	3.5401	.00179856	1746.724	242794.85
557	310249	172808693	23.6008	8.2278	13146	3.5414	.00179533	1749.866	243668.99
558	311364	173741112	23.6220	8.2327	13181	3.5426	.00179211	1753.007	244544.71
559	312481	174676879	23.6432	8.2377	13217	3.5439	.00178891	1756.149	245422.00
560	**313600**	**175616000**	**23.6643**	**8.2426**	**13252**	**3.5451**	**.00178571**	**1759.290**	**246300.86**
561	314721	176558481	23.6854	8.2475	13288	3.5464	.00178253	1762.432	247181.30
562	315844	177504328	23.7065	8.2524	13323	3.5477	.00177936	1765.574	248063.30
563	316969	178453547	23.7276	8.2573	13359	3.5490	.00177620	1768.715	248946.87
564	318096	179406144	23.7487	8.2621	13394	3.5502	.00177305	1771.857	249832.01
565	319225	180362125	23.7697	8.2670	13430	3.5515	.00176991	1774.998	250718.73
566	320356	181321496	23.7908	8.2719	13466	3.5527	.00176678	1778.140	251607.01
567	321489	182284263	23.8118	8.2768	13501	3.5540	.00176367	1781.282	252496.87
568	322624	183250432	23.8328	8.2816	13537	3.5553	.00176056	1784.423	253388.30
569	323761	184220009	23.8537	8.2865	13573	3.5565	.00175747	1787.565	254281.29

Table 7.—*Continued*

N	N^2	N^3	$\sqrt{N}$	$\sqrt[3]{N}$	$N^{3/2}$	$\sqrt[5]{N}$	$\dfrac{1}{N}$	Circle ($N = D$) Circum.	Area
570	324900	185193000	23.8747	8.2913	13609	3.5577	.00175439	1790.706	255175.86
571	326041	186169411	23.8956	8.2962	13644	3.5590	.00175131	1793.848	256072.00
572	327184	187149248	23.9165	8.3010	13680	3.5602	.00174825	1796.989	256969.71
573	328329	188132517	23.9374	8.3059	13716	3.5615	.00174520	1800.131	257868.99
574	329476	189119224	23.9583	8.3107	13752	3.5627	.00174216	1803.273	258769.85
575	330625	190109375	23.9792	8.3155	13788	3.5640	.00173913	1806.414	259672.27
576	331776	191102976	24.0000	8.3203	13824	3.5652	.00173611	1809.556	260576.26
577	332929	192100033	24.0208	8.3251	13860	3.5664	.00173310	1812.697	261481.83
578	334084	193100552	24.0416	8.3300	13896	3.5677	.00173010	1815.839	262388.96
579	335241	194104539	24.0624	8.3348	13932	3.5689	.00172712	1818.981	263297.67
580	336400	195112000	24.0832	8.3396	13968	3.5702	.00172414	1822.122	264207.94
581	337561	196122941	24.1039	8.3443	14004	3.5714	.00172117	1825.264	265119.79
582	338724	197137368	24.1247	8.3491	14040	3.5726	.00171821	1828.405	266033.21
583	339889	198155287	24.1454	8.3539	14077	3.5738	.00171527	1831.547	266948.20
584	341056	199176704	24.1661	8.3587	14113	3.5751	.00171233	1834.689	267864.76
585	342225	200201625	24.1868	8.3634	14149	3.5763	.00170940	1837.830	268782.89
586	343396	201230056	24.2074	8.3682	14186	3.5775	.00170648	1840.972	269702.59
587	344569	202262003	24.2281	8.3730	14222	3.5787	.00170358	1844.113	270623.86
588	345744	203297472	24.2487	8.3777	14258	3.5799	.00170068	1847.255	271546.70
589	346921	204336469	24.2693	8.3825	14295	3.5812	.00169779	1850.397	272471.12
590	348100	205379000	24.2899	8.3872	14331	3.5824	.00169492	1853.538	273397.10
591	349281	206425071	24.3105	8.3919	14368	3.5886	.00169205	1856.680	274324.66
592	350464	207474688	24.3311	8.3967	14404	3.5848	.00168919	1859.821	275253.78
593	351649	208527857	24.3516	8.4014	14440	3.5860	.00168634	1862.963	276184.48
594	352836	209584584	24.3721	8.4061	14477	3.5872	.00168350	1866.104	277116.75
595	354025	210644875	24.3926	8.4108	14514	3.5884	.00168067	1869.246	278050.58
596	355216	211708736	24.4131	8.4155	14550	3.5896	.00167785	1872.388	278985.99
597	356409	212776173	24.4336	8.4202	14587	3.5908	.00167504	1875.529	279922.97
598	357604	213847192	24.4540	8.4249	14624	3.5920	.00167224	1878.671	280861.52
599	358801	214921799	24.4745	8.4296	14660	3.5932	.00166945	1881.812	281801.65
600	360000	216000000	24.4949	8.4343	14697	3.5944	.00166667	1884.954	282743.34
601	361201	217081801	24.5153	8.4390	14734	3.5956	.00166389	1888.096	283686.60
602	362404	218167208	24.5357	8.4437	14770	3.5958	.00166113	1891.237	284631.44
603	363609	219256227	24.5561	8.4484	14807	3.5980	.00165837	1894.379	285577.84
604	364816	220348864	24.5764	8.4530	14844	3.5992	.00165563	1897.520	286525.82
605	366025	221445125	24.5967	8.4577	14881	3.6004	.00165289	1900.662	287475.36
606	367236	222545016	24.6171	8.4623	14918	3.6016	.00165017	1903.804	288426.48
607	368449	223648543	24.6374	8.4670	14955	3.6028	.00164745	1906.945	289379.17
608	369664	224755712	24.6577	8.4716	14992	3.6040	.00164474	1910.087	290333.43
609	370881	225866529	24.6779	8.4763	15029	3.6052	.00164204	1913.228	291289.26
610	372100	226981000	24.6982	8.4809	15066	3.6063	.00163934	1916.370	292246.66
611	373321	228099131	24.7184	8.4856	15103	3.6075	.00163666	1919.511	293205.63
612	374544	229220928	24.7386	8.4902	15140	3.6087	.00163399	1922.653	294166.17
613	375769	230346397	24.7588	8.4948	15177	3.6099	.00163132	1925.795	295128.28
614	376996	231475544	24.7790	8.4994	15214	3.6111	.00162866	1928.936	296091.97
615	378225	232608375	24.7992	8.5040	15252	3.6122	.00162602	1932.078	297057.22
616	379456	233744896	24.8193	8.5086	15289	3.6134	.00162338	1935.219	298024.05
617	380689	234885113	24.8395	8.5132	15326	3.6146	.00162075	1938.361	298992.44
618	381924	236029032	24.8596	8.5178	15363	3.6158	.00161812	1941.503	299962.41
619	383161	237176659	24.8797	8.5224	15400	3.6169	.00161551	1944.644	300933.95
620	384400	238328000	24.8998	8.5270	15437	3.6181	.00161290	1947.786	301907.05
621	385641	239483061	24.9199	8.5316	15475	3.6192	.00161031	1950.927	302881.73
622	386884	240641848	24.9399	8.5362	15513	3.6204	.00160772	1954.069	303857.98
623	388129	241804367	24.9600	8.5408	15550	3.6216	.00160514	1957.211	304835.80
624	389376	242970624	24.9800	8.5453	15588	3.6227	.00160256	1960.352	305815.20
625	390625	244140625	25.0000	8.5499	15625	3.6239	.00160000	1963.494	306796.16
626	391876	245314376	25.0200	8.5544	15663	3.6250	.00159744	1966.635	307778.69
627	393129	246491883	25.0400	8.5590	15700	3.6262	.00159490	1969.777	308762.79
628	394384	247673152	25.0599	8.5635	15738	3.6274	.00159236	1972.919	309748.47
629	395641	248858189	25.0799	8.5681	15775	3.6285	.00158983	1976.060	310735.71
630	396900	250047000	25.0998	8.5726	15813	3.6297	.00158730	1979.202	311724.53
631	398161	251239591	25.1197	8.5772	15850	3.6309	.00158479	1982.343	312714.92
632	399424	252435968	25.1396	8.5817	15888	3.6320	.00158228	1985.485	313706.88
633	400689	253636137	25.1595	8.5862	15926	3.6331	.00157978	1988.626	314700.40
634	401956	254840104	25.1794	8.5907	15964	3.6343	.00157729	1991.768	315695.50
635	403225	256047875	25.1992	8.5952	16002	3.6354	.00157480	1994.910	316692.17
636	404496	257259456	25.2190	8.5997	16040	3.6366	.00157233	1998.051	317690.42
637	405769	258474853	25.2389	8.6043	16077	3.6377	.00156986	2001.193	318690.23
638	407044	259694072	25.2587	8.6088	16115	3.6389	.00156740	2004.334	319691.61
639	408321	260917119	25.2784	8.6132	16153	3.6400	.00156495	2007.476	320694.56

Table 7.—*Continued*

N	N^2	N^3	$\sqrt{N}$	$\sqrt[3]{N}$	$N^{3/2}$	$\sqrt[5]{N}$	$\dfrac{1}{N}$	Circle ($N = D$) Circum.	Circle ($N = D$) Area
640	409600	262144000	25.2982	8.6177	16191	3.6411	.00156250	2010.618	321699.09
641	410881	263374721	25.3180	8.6222	16229	3.6423	.00156006	2013.759	322705.18
642	412164	264609288	25.3377	8.6267	16267	3.6435	.00155763	2016.901	323712.85
643	413449	265847707	25.3574	8.6312	16305	3.6446	.00155521	2020.042	324722.09
644	414736	267089984	25.3772	8.6357	16343	3.6457	.00155280	2023.184	325732.89
645	416025	268336125	25.3969	8.6401	16381	3.6468	.00155039	2026.326	326745.27
646	417316	269586136	25.4165	8.6446	16419	3.6479	.00154799	2029.467	327759.22
647	418609	270840023	25.4362	8.6490	16457	3.6499	.00154560	2032.609	328774.74
648	419904	272097792	25.4558	8.6535	16495	3.6502	.00154321	2035.750	329791.83
649	421201	273359449	25.4755	8.6579	16534	3.6513	.00154083	2038.892	330810.49
650	422500	274625000	25.4951	8.6624	16572	3.6524	.00153846	2042.034	331830.72
651	423801	275894451	25.5147	8.6668	16610	3.6536	.00153610	2045.175	332852.53
652	425104	277167808	25.5343	8.6713	16648	3.6547	.00153374	2048.317	333875.90
653	426409	278445077	25.5539	8.6757	16687	3.6558	.00153139	2051.458	334900.85
654	427716	279726264	25.5734	8.6801	16725	3.6569	.00152905	2054.600	335927.36
655	429025	281011375	25.5930	8.6845	16764	3.6580	.00152672	2057.741	336955.45
656	430336	282300416	25.6125	8.6890	16802	3.6592	.00152439	2060.883	337985.10
657	431649	283593393	25.6320	8.6934	16840	3.6603	.00152207	2064.025	339016.33
658	432964	284890312	25.6515	8.6978	16879	3.6614	.00151976	2067.166	340049.13
659	434281	286191179	25.6710	8.7022	16917	3.6625	.00151745	2070.308	341083.50
660	435600	287496000	25.6905	8.7066	16956	3.6636	.00151515	2073.449	342119.44
661	436921	288804781	25.7099	8.7110	16994	3.6647	.00151286	2076.591	343156.95
662	438244	290117528	25.7294	8.7154	17033	3.6658	.00151057	2079.733	344196.03
663	439569	291434247	25.7488	8.7198	17071	3.6669	.00150830	2082.874	345236.69
664	440896	292754944	25.7682	8.7241	17110	3.6680	.00150602	2086.016	346278.91
665	442225	294079625	25.7876	8.7285	17149	3.6691	.00150376	2089.157	347322.70
666	443556	295408296	25.8070	8.7329	17187	3.6702	.00150150	2092.299	348368.07
667	444889	296740963	25.8263	8.7373	17226	3.6713	.00149925	2095.441	349415.00
668	446224	298077632	25.8457	8.7416	17265	3.6724	.00149701	2098.582	350463.51
669	447561	299418309	25.8650	8.7460	17304	3.6735	.00149477	2101.724	351513.59
670	448900	300763000	25.8844	8.7503	17343	3.6746	.00149254	2104.865	352565.24
671	450241	302111711	25.9037	8.7547	17381	3.6757	.00149031	2108.007	353618.45
672	451584	303464448	25.9230	8.7590	17420	3.6768	.00148810	2111.148	354673.24
673	452929	304821217	25.9422	8.7634	17459	3.6779	.00148588	2114.290	355729.60
674	454276	306182024	25.9615	8.7677	17498	3.6790	.00148368	2117.432	356787.54
675	455625	307546875	25.9808	8.7721	17537	3.6801	.00148148	2120.573	357847.04
676	456976	308915776	26.0000	8.7764	17576	3.6812	.00147929	2123.715	358908.11
677	458329	310288733	26.0192	8.7807	17615	3.6823	.00147710	2126.856	359970.75
678	459684	311665752	26.0384	8.7850	17654	3.6834	.00147493	2129.998	361034.97
679	461041	313046839	26.0576	8.7893	17693	3.6845	.00147275	2133.140	362100.75
680	462400	314432000	26.0768	8.7937	17732	3.6856	.00147059	2136.281	363168.11
681	463761	315821241	26.0960	8.7980	17771	3.6866	.00146843	2139.423	364237.04
682	465124	317214568	26.1151	8.8023	17810	3.6877	.00146628	2142.564	365307.54
683	466489	318611987	26.1343	8.8066	17850	3.6888	.00146413	2145.706	366379.60
684	467856	320013504	26.1534	8.8109	17889	3.6899	.00146199	2148.848	367453.24
685	469225	321419125	26.1725	8.8152	17928	3.6909	.00145985	2151.989	368528.45
686	470596	322828856	26.1916	8.8194	17967	3.6920	.00145773	2155.131	369605.23
687	471969	324242703	26.2107	8.8237	18007	3.6931	.00145560	2158.272	370683.59
688	473344	325660672	26.2298	8.8280	18046	3.6942	.00145349	2161.414	371763.51
689	474721	327082769	26.2488	8.8323	18085	3.6953	.00145138	2164.556	372845.00
690	476100	328509000	26.2679	8.8366	18125	3.6963	.00144928	2167.697	373928.07
691	477481	329939371	26.2869	8.8408	18164	3.6974	.00144718	2170.839	375012.70
692	478864	331373888	26.3059	8.8451	18204	3.6985	.00144509	2173.980	376098.91
693	480249	332812557	26.3249	8.8493	18243	3.6995	.00144300	2177.122	377186.68
694	481636	334255384	26.3439	8.8536	18283	3.7006	.00144092	2180.263	378276.03
695	483025	335702375	26.3629	8.8578	18322	3.7016	.00143885	2183.405	379366.95
696	484416	337153536	26.3818	8.8621	18362	3.7027	.00143678	2186.547	380459.44
697	485809	338608873	26.4008	8.8663	18401	3.7038	.00143472	2189.688	381553.50
698	487204	340068392	26.4197	8.8706	18441	3.7049	.00143266	2192.830	382649.13
699	488601	341532099	26.4386	8.8748	18480	3.7059	.00143062	2195.971	383746.33
700	490000	343000000	26.4575	8.8790	18520	3.7070	.00142857	2199.113	384845.10
701	491401	344472101	26.4764	8.8833	18560	3.7080	.00142653	2202.255	385945.44
702	492804	345948408	26.4953	8.8875	18600	3.7091	.00142450	2205.396	387047.36
703	494209	347428927	26.5141	8.8917	18640	3.7101	.00142248	2208.538	388150.84
704	495616	348913664	26.5330	8.8959	18679	3.7112	.00142045	2211.679	389255.90
705	497025	350402625	26.5518	8.9001	18719	3.7123	.00141844	2214.821	390362.52
706	498436	351895816	26.5707	8.9043	18759	3.7133	.00141643	2217.963	391470.72
707	499849	353393243	26.5895	8.9085	18799	3.7144	.00141443	2221.104	392580.49
708	501264	354894912	26.6083	8.9127	18839	3.7154	.00141243	2224.246	393691.82
709	502681	356400829	26.6271	8.9169	18879	3.7165	.00141044	2227.387	394804.73

Table 7.—Continued

N	N^2	N^3	$\sqrt{N}$	$\sqrt[3]{N}$	$N^{3/2}$	$\sqrt[5]{N}$	$\dfrac{1}{N}$	Circle ($N = D$) Circum.	Area
710	504100	357911000	26.6458	8.9211	18919	3.7175	.00140845	2230.529	395919.21
711	505521	359425431	26.6646	8.9253	18959	3.7185	.00140647	2233.670	397035.26
712	506944	360944128	26.6833	8.9295	18999	3.7196	.00140449	2236.812	398152.89
713	508369	362467097	26.7021	8.9337	19039	3.7206	.00140252	2239.954	399272.08
714	509796	363994344	26.7208	8.9378	19079	3.7217	.00140056	2243.095	400392.84
715	511225	365525875	26.7395	8.9420	19119	3.7227	.00139860	2246.237	401515.18
716	512656	367061696	26.7582	8.9462	19159	3.7238	.00139665	2249.378	402639.08
717	514089	368601813	26.7769	8.9503	19199	3.7248	.00139470	2252.520	403764.56
718	515524	370146232	26.7955	8.9545	19239	3.7258	.00139276	2255.662	404891.60
719	516961	371694959	26.8142	8.9587	19280	3.7269	.00139082	2258.803	406020 22
720	518400	373248000	26.8328	8.9628	19320	3.7279	.00138889	2261.945	407150.41
721	519841	374805361	26.8514	8.9670	19360	3.7290	.00138696	2265.086	408282.17
722	521284	376367048	26.8701	8.9711	19400	3.7300	.00138504	2268.228	409415.50
723	522729	377933067	26.8887	8.9752	19440	3.7310	.00138313	2271.370	410550.40
724	524176	379503424	26.9072	8.9794	19481	3.7321	.00138122	2274.511	411686.87
725	525625	381078125	26.9258	8.9835	19521	3.7331	.00137931	2277.653	412824.91
726	527076	382657176	26.9444	8.9876	19562	3.7341	.00137741	2280.794	413964.52
727	528529	384240583	26.9629	8.9918	19602	3.7351	.00137552	2283.936	415105.71
728	529984	385828352	26.9815	8.9959	19643	3.7362	.00137363	2287.078	416248.46
729	531441	387420489	27.0000	9.0000	19683	3.7372	.00137174	2290.219	417392.79
730	532900	389017000	27.0185	9.0041	19724	3.7382	.00136986	2293.361	418538.68
731	534361	390617891	27.0370	9.0082	19764	3.7392	.00136799	2296.502	419686.15
732	535824	392223168	27.0555	9.0123	19805	3.7403	.00136612	2299.644	420835.19
733	537289	393832837	27.0740	9.0164	19845	3.7413	.00136426	2302.785	421985.79
734	538756	395446904	27.0924	9.0205	19886	3.7423	.00136240	2305.927	423137.97
735	540225	397065375	27.1109	9.0246	19927	3.7433	.00136054	2309.069	424291.72
736	541696	398688256	27.1293	9.0287	19967	3.7443	.00135870	2312.210	425447.04
737	543169	400315553	27.1477	9.0328	20008	3.7454	.00135685	2315.352	426603.94
738	544644	401947272	27.1662	9.0369	20049	3.7464	.00135501	2318.493	427762.40
739	546121	403583419	27.1846	9.0410	20090	3.7474	.00135318	2321.635	428922.43
740	547600	405224000	27.2029	9.0450	20130	3.7484	.00135135	2324.777	430084.03
741	549081	406869021	27.2213	9.0491	20171	3.7494	.00134953	2327.918	431247.21
742	550564	408518488	27.2397	9.0532	20212	3.7504	.00134771	2331.060	432411.95
743	552049	410172407	27.2580	9.0572	20253	3.7514	.00134590	2334.201	433578.27
744	553536	411830784	27.2764	9.0613	20294	3.7524	.00134409	2337.343	434746.16
745	555025	413493625	27.2947	9.0654	20335	3.7534	.00134228	2340.485	435915.62
746	556516	415160936	27.3130	9.0694	20376	3.7545	.00134048	2343.626	437086.64
747	558009	416832723	27.3313	9.0735	20417	3.7555	.00133869	2346.768	438259.24
748	559504	418508992	27.3496	9.0775	20458	3.7565	.00133690	2349.909	439433.41
749	561001	420189749	27.3679	9.0816	20499	3.7575	.00133511	2353.051	440609.16
750	562500	421875000	27.3861	9.0856	20540	3.7585	.00133333	2356.193	441786.47
751	564001	423564751	27.4044	9.0896	20581	3.7595	.00133156	2359.334	442965.35
752	565504	425259008	27.4226	9.0937	20622	3.7605	.00132979	2362.476	444145.80
753	567009	426957777	27.4408	9.0977	20663	3.7615	.00132802	2365.617	445327.83
754	568516	428661064	27.4591	9.1017	20704	3.7625	.00132626	2368.759	446511.42
755	570025	430368875	27.4773	9.1057	20745	3.7635	.00132450	2371.900	447696.59
756	571536	432081216	27.4955	9.1098	20787	3.7645	.00132275	2375.042	448883.32
757	573049	433798093	27.5136	9.1138	20828	3.7655	.00132100	2378.184	450071.63
758	574564	435519512	27.5318	9.1178	20869	3.7665	.00131926	2381.325	451261.51
759	576081	437245479	27.5500	9.1218	20910	3.7675	.00131752	2384.467	452452.96
760	577600	438976000	27.5681	9.1258	20952	3.7685	.00131579	2387.608	453645.98
761	579121	440711081	27.5862	9.1298	20993	3.7694	.00131406	2390.750	454840.57
762	580644	442450728	27.6043	9.1338	21035	3.7704	.00131234	2393.892	456036.73
763	582169	444194947	27.6225	9.1378	21076	3.7714	.00131062	2397.033	457234.46
764	583696	445943744	27.6405	9.1418	21117	3.7724	.00130890	2400.175	458433.77
765	585225	447697125	27.6586	9.1458	21159	3.7734	.00130719	2403.316	459634.64
766	586756	449455096	27.6767	9.1498	21200	3.7744	.00130548	2406.458	460837.08
767	588289	451217663	27.6948	9.1537	21242	3.7754	.00130378	2409.600	462041.10
768	589824	452984832	27.7128	9.1577	21283	3.7764	.00130208	2412.741	463246.69
769	591361	454756609	27.7308	9.1617	21325	3.7774	.00130039	2415.883	464453.84
770	592900	456533000	27.7489	9.1657	21367	3.7784	.00129870	2419.024	465662.57
771	594441	458314011	27.7669	9.1696	21408	3.7793	.00129702	2422.166	466872.87
772	595984	460099648	27.7849	9.1736	21450	3.7803	.00129534	2425.307	468084.74
773	597529	461889917	27.8029	9.1775	21492	3.7813	.00129366	2428.449	469298.18
774	599076	463684824	27.8209	9.1815	21533	3.7822	.00129199	2431.591	470513.19
775	600625	465484375	27.8388	9.1855	21575	3.7832	.00129032	2434.732	471729.77
776	602176	467288576	27.8568	9.1894	21617	3.7842	.00128866	2437.874	472947.92
777	603729	469097433	27.8747	9.1933	21658	3.7852	.00128700	2441.015	474167.65
778	605284	470910952	27.8927	9.1973	21700	3.7861	.00128535	2444.157	475388.94
779	606841	472729139	27.9106	9.2012	21742	3.7871	.00128370	2447.299	476611.81

Table 7.—*Continued*

N	N^2	N^3	$\sqrt{N}$	$\sqrt[3]{N}$	$N^{3/2}$	$\sqrt[5]{N}$	$\dfrac{1}{N}$	Circle ($N = D$)	
								Circum.	Area
780	**608400**	**474552000**	**27.9285**	**9.2052**	**21784**	**3.7881**	**.00128205**	**2450.440**	**477836.24**
781	609961	476379541	27.9464	9.2091	21826	3.7890	.00128041	2453.582	479062.25
782	611524	478211768	27.9643	9.2130	21868	3.7900	.00127877	2456.723	480289.83
783	613089	480048687	27.9821	9.2170	21910	3.7910	.00127714	2459.865	481518.97
784	614656	481890304	28.0000	9.2209	21952	3.7920	.00127551	2463.007	482749.69
785	616225	483736625	28.0179	9.2248	21994	3.7929	.00127389	2466.148	483981.98
786	617796	485587656	28.0357	9.2287	22036	3.7939	.00127226	2469.290	485215.84
787	619369	487443403	28.0535	9.2326	22078	3.7949	.00127065	2472.431	486451.28
788	620944	489303872	28.0713	9.2365	22120	3.7959	.00126904	2475.573	487688.28
789	622521	491169069	28.0891	9.2404	22162	3.7969	.00126743	2478.715	488926.85
790	**624100**	**493039000**	**28.1069**	**9.2443**	**22205**	**3.7978**	**.00126582**	**2481.856**	**490166.99**
791	625681	494913671	28.1247	9.2482	22247	3.7987	.00126422	2484.998	491408.71
792	627264	496793088	28.1425	9.2521	22289	3.7997	.00126263	2488.139	492651.99
793	628849	498677257	28.1603	9.2560	22331	3.8006	.00126103	2491.281	493896.85
794	630436	500566184	28.1780	9.2599	22373	3.8016	.00125945	2494.422	495143.28
795	632025	502459875	28.1957	9.2638	22416	3.8025	.00125786	2497.564	496391.27
796	633616	504358336	28.2135	9.2677	22458	3.8035	.00125628	2500.706	497640.84
797	635209	506261573	28.2312	9.2716	22500	3.8044	.00125471	2503.847	498891.98
798	636804	508169592	28.2489	9.2754	22543	3.8054	.00125313	2506.989	500144.69
799	638401	510082399	28.2666	9.2793	22585	3.8064	.00125156	2510.130	501398.97
800	**640000**	**512000000**	**28.2843**	**9.2832**	**22627**	**3.8073**	**.00125000**	**2513.272**	**502654.82**
801	641601	513922401	28.3019	9.2870	22670	3.8083	.00124844	2516.414	503912.25
802	643204	515849608	28.3196	9.2909	22712	3.8092	.00124688	2519.555	505171.24
803	644809	517781627	28.3373	9.2948	22755	3.8102	.00124533	2522.697	506431.80
804	646416	519718464	28.3549	9.2986	22797	3.8111	.00124378	2525.838	507693.94
805	648025	521660125	28.3725	9.3025	22840	3.8121	.00124224	2528.980	508957.64
806	649636	523606616	28.3901	9.3063	22883	3.8130	.00124069	2532.122	510222.92
807	651249	525557943	28.4077	9.3102	22925	3.8139	.00123916	2535.263	511489.77
808	652864	527514112	28.4253	9.3140	22968	3.8149	.00123762	2538.405	512758.19
809	654481	529475129	28.4429	9.3179	23010	3.8158	.00123609	2541.546	514028.18
810	**656100**	**531441000**	**28.4605**	**9.3217**	**23053**	**3.8168**	**.00123457**	**2544.688**	**515299.74**
811	657721	533411731	28.4781	9.3255	23096	3.8177	.00123305	2547.829	516572.87
812	659344	535387328	28.4956	9.3294	23138	3.8186	.00123153	2550.971	517847.57
813	660969	537367797	28.5132	9.3332	23181	3.8196	.00123001	2554.113	519123.84
814	662596	539353144	28.5307	9.3370	23224	3.8205	.00122850	2557.254	520401.68
815	664225	541343375	28.5482	9.3408	23267	3.8215	.00122699	2560.396	521681.10
816	665856	543338496	28.5657	9.3447	23310	3.8224	.00122549	2563.537	522962.08
817	667489	545338513	28.5832	9.3485	23352	3.8234	.00122399	2566.679	524244.63
818	669124	547343432	28.6007	9.3523	23395	3.8243	.00122249	2569.821	525528.76
819	670761	549353259	28.6182	9.3561	23438	3.8252	.00122100	2572.962	526814.46
820	**672400**	**551368000**	**28.6356**	**9.3599**	**23481**	**3.8262**	**.00121951**	**2576.104**	**528101.73**
821	674041	553387661	28.6531	9.3637	23524	3.8271	.00121803	2579.245	529390.56
822	675684	555412248	28.6705	9.3675	23567	3.8280	.00121655	2582.387	530680.97
823	677329	557441767	28.6880	9.3713	23610	3.8290	.00121507	2585.529	531972.95
824	678976	559476224	28.7054	9.3751	23653	3.8299	.00121359	2588.670	533266.50
825	680625	561515625	28.7228	9.3789	23696	3.8308	.00121212	2591.812	534561.62
826	682276	563559976	28.7402	9.3827	23740	3.8317	.00121065	2594.953	535858.32
827	683929	565609283	28.7576	9.3865	23783	3.8327	.00120919	2598.095	537156.58
828	685584	567663552	28.7750	9.3902	23826	3.8336	.00120773	2601.237	538456.41
829	687241	569722789	28.7924	9.3940	23869	3.8345	.00120627	2604.378	539757.82
830	**688900**	**571787000**	**28.8097**	**9.3978**	**23912**	**3.8355**	**.00120482**	**2607.520**	**541060.79**
831	690561	573856191	28.8271	9.4016	23955	3.8364	.00120337	2610.661	542365.34
832	692224	575930368	28.8444	9.4053	23999	3.8373	.00120192	2613.803	543671.46
833	693889	578009537	28.8617	9.4091	24042	3.8382	.00120048	2616.944	544979.15
834	695556	580093704	28.8791	9.4129	24085	3.8391	.00119904	2620.086	546288.40
835	697225	582182875	28.8964	9.4166	24128	3.8401	.00119760	2623.228	547599.23
836	698896	584277056	28.9137	9.4204	24172	3.8410	.00119617	2626.369	548911.63
837	700569	586376253	28.9310	9.4241	24215	3.8419	.00119474	2629.511	550225.61
838	702244	588480472	28.9482	9.4279	24259	3.8428	.00119332	2632.652	551541.15
839	703921	590589719	28.9655	9.4316	24302	3.8437	.00119190	2635.794	552858.26
840	**705600**	**592704000**	**28.9828**	**9.4354**	**24346**	**3.8446**	**.00119048**	**2638.936**	**554176.94**
841	707281	594823321	29.0000	9.4391	24389	3.8456	.00118906	2642.077	555497.20
842	708964	596947688	29.0172	9.4429	24432	3.8465	.00118765	2645.219	556819.02
843	710649	599077107	29.0345	9.4466	24476	3.8474	.00118624	2648.360	558142.42
844	712336	601211584	29.0517	9.4503	24520	3.8483	.00118483	2651.502	559467.39
845	714025	603351125	29.0689	9.4541	24563	3.8492	.00118343	2654.644	560793.92
846	715716	605495736	29.0861	9.4578	24607	3.8501	.00118203	2657.785	562122.03
847	717409	607645423	29.1033	9.4615	24650	3.8510	.00118064	2660.927	563451.71
848	719104	609800192	29.1204	9.4652	24694	3.8519	.00117925	2664.068	564782.96
849	720801	611960049	29.1376	9.4690	24738	3.8528	.00117786	2667.210	566115.78

Table 7.—*Continued*

N	N^2	N^3	$\sqrt{N}$	$\sqrt[3]{N}$	$N^{3/2}$	$\sqrt[5]{N}$	$\dfrac{1}{N}$	Circle ($N = D$) Circum.	Area
850	**722500**	**614125000**	**29.1548**	**9.4727**	**24782**	**3.8538**	**.00117647**	**2670.352**	**567450.17**
851	724201	616295051	29.1719	9.4764	24825	3.8547	.00117509	2673.493	568786.14
852	725904	618470208	29.1890	9.4801	24869	3.8556	.00117371	2676.635	570123.67
853	727609	620650477	29.2062	9.4838	24913	3.8565	.00117233	2679.776	571462.77
854	729316	622835864	29.2233	9.4875	24957	3.8574	.00117096	2682.918	572803.45
855	731025	625026375	29.2404	9.4912	25000	3.8582	.00116959	2686.059	574145.69
856	732736	627222016	29.2575	9.4949	25044	3.8592	.00116822	2689.201	575489.51
857	734449	629422793	29.2746	9.4986	25088	3.8601	.00116686	2692.343	576834.90
858	736164	631628712	29.2916	9.5023	25132	3.8610	.00116550	2695.484	578181.85
859	737881	633839779	29.3087	9.5060	25176	3.8619	.00116414	2698.626	579530.38
860	**739600**	**636056000**	**29.3258**	**9.5097**	**25220**	**3.8628**	**.00116279**	**2701.767**	**580880.48**
861	741321	638277381	29.3428	9.5134	25264	3.8637	.00116144	2704.909	582232.15
862	743044	640503928	29.3598	9.5171	25308	3.8646	.00116009	2708.051	583585.39
863	744769	642735647	29.3769	9.5207	25352	3.8655	.00115875	2711.192	584940.20
864	746496	644972544	29.3939	9.5244	25396	3.8664	.00115741	2714.334	586296.59
865	748225	647214625	29.4109	9.5281	25440	3.8673	.00115607	2717.475	587654.54
866	749956	649461896	29.4279	9.5317	25485	3.8682	.00115473	2720.617	589014.07
867	751689	651714363	29.4449	9.5354	25529	3.8691	.00115340	2723.759	590375.16
868	753424	653972032	29.4618	9.5391	25573	3.8700	.00115207	2726.900	591737.83
869	755161	656234909	29.4788	9.5427	25617	3.8708	.00115075	2730.042	593102.06
870	**756900**	**658503000**	**29.4958**	**9.5464**	**25661**	**3.8717**	**.00114943**	**2733.183**	**594467.87**
871	758641	660776311	29.5127	9.5501	25706	3.8726	.00114811	2736.325	595835.25
872	760384	663054848	29.5296	9.5537	25750	3.8735	.00114679	2739.466	597204.20
873	762129	665338617	29.5466	9.5574	25794	3.8744	.00114548	2742.608	598574.72
874	763876	667627624	29.5635	9.5610	25839	3.8753	.00114416	2745.750	599946.81
875	765625	669921875	29.5804	9.5647	25883	3.8762	.00114286	2748.891	601320.47
876	767376	672221376	29.5973	9.5683	25927	3.8771	.00114155	2752.033	602695.70
877	769129	674526133	29.6142	9.5719	25972	3.8780	.00114025	2755.174	604072.50
878	770884	676836152	29.6311	9.5756	26016	3.8789	.00113895	2758.316	605450.88
879	772641	679151439	29.6479	9.5792	26061	3.8797	.00113766	2761.458	606830.82
880	**774400**	**681472000**	**29.6648**	**9.5828**	**26105**	**3.8806**	**.00113636**	**2764.599**	**608212.34**
881	776161	683797841	29.6816	9.5865	26150	3.8815	.00113507	2767.741	609595.42
882	777924	686128968	29.6985	9.5901	26194	3.8823	.00113379	2770.882	610980.08
883	779689	688465387	29.7153	9.5937	26239	3.8832	.00113250	2774.024	612366.31
884	781456	690807104	29.7321	9.5973	26283	3.8841	.00113122	2777.166	613754.11
885	783225	693154125	29.7489	9.6010	26328	3.8850	.00112994	2780.307	615143.48
886	784996	695506456	29.7658	9.6046	26373	3.8859	.00112867	2783.449	616534.42
887	786769	697864103	29.7825	9.6082	26417	3.8868	.00112740	2786.590	617926.93
888	788544	700227072	29.7993	9.6118	26462	3.8877	.00112613	2789.732	619321.01
889	790321	702595369	29.8161	9.6154	26507	3.8885	.00112486	2792.874	620716.66
890	**792100**	**704969000**	**29.8329**	**9.6190**	**26551**	**3.8894**	**.00112360**	**2796.015**	**622113.89**
891	793881	707347971	29.8496	9.6226	26596	3.8902	.00112233	2799.157	623512.68
892	795664	709732288	29.8664	9.6262	26641	3.8911	.00112108	2802.298	624913.04
893	797449	712121957	29.8831	9.6298	26686	3.8920	.00111982	2805.440	626314.98
894	799236	714516984	29.8998	9.6334	26730	3.8929	.00111857	2808.581	627718.49
895	801025	716917375	29.9166	9.6370	26775	3.8937	.00111732	2811.723	629123.56
896	802816	719323136	29.9333	9.6406	26820	3.8946	.00111607	2814.865	630530.21
897	804609	721734273	29.9500	9.6442	26865	3.8955	.00111483	2818.006	631938.43
898	806404	724150792	29.9666	9.6477	26910	3.8963	.00111359	2821.148	633348.22
899	808201	726572699	29.9833	9.6513	26955	3.8972	.00111235	2824.289	634759.58
900	**810000**	**729000000**	**30.0000**	**9.6549**	**27000**	**3.8981**	**.00111111**	**2827.431**	**636172.51**
901	811801	731432701	30.0167	9.6585	27045	3.8989	.00110988	2830.573	637587.01
902	813604	733870808	30.0333	9.6620	27090	3.8998	.00110865	2833.714	639003.09
903	815409	736314327	30.0500	9.6656	27135	3.9007	.00110742	2836.856	640420.73
904	817216	738763264	30.0666	9.6692	27180	3.9015	.00110619	2839.997	641839.95
905	819025	741217625	30.0832	9.6727	27225	3.9024	.00110497	2843.139	643260.73
906	820836	743677416	30.0998	9.6763	27270	3.9032	.00110375	2846.281	644683.09
907	822649	746142643	30.1164	9.6799	27316	3.9041	.00110254	2849.422	646107.01
908	824464	748613312	30.1330	9.6834	27361	3.9050	.00110132	2852.564	647532.51
909	826281	751089429	30.1496	9.6870	27406	3.9059	.00110011	2855.705	648959.58
910	**828100**	**753571000**	**30.1662**	**9.6905**	**27451**	**3.9067**	**.00109890**	**2858.847**	**650388.22**
911	829921	756058031	30.1828	9.6941	27497	3.9076	.00109769	2861.988	651818.43
912	831744	758550528	30.1993	9.6976	27542	3.9084	.00109649	2865.130	653250.21
913	833569	761048497	30.2159	9.7012	27587	3.9093	.00109529	2868.272	654683.56
914	835396	763551944	30.2324	9.7047	27632	3.9101	.00109409	2871.413	656118.48
915	837225	766060875	30.2490	9.7082	27678	3.9110	.00109290	2874.555	657554.98
916	839056	768575296	30.2655	9.7118	27723	3.9118	.00109170	2877.696	658993.04
917	840889	771095213	30.2820	9.7153	27769	3.9127	.00109051	2880.838	660432.68
918	842724	773620632	30.2985	9.7188	27814	3.9135	.00108932	2883.980	661873.88
919	844561	776151559	30.3150	9.7224	27859	3.9144	.00108814	2887.121	663316.66

Table 7.–*Continued*

N	N^2	N^3	$\sqrt{N}$	$\sqrt[3]{N}$	$N^{3/2}$	$\sqrt[5]{N}$	$\frac{1}{N}$	Circle (N = D) Circum.	Circle (N = D) Area
920	846400	778688000	30.3315	9.7259	27905	3.9153	.00108696	2890.263	664761.01
921	848241	781229961	30.3480	9.7294	27950	3.9161	.00108578	2893.404	666206.92
922	850084	783777448	30.3645	9.7329	27996	3.9169	.00108460	2896.546	667654.41
923	851929	786330467	30.3809	9.7364	28042	3.9178	.00108342	2899.688	669103.47
924	853776	788889024	30.3974	9.7400	28087	3.9186	.00108225	2902.829	670554.10
925	855625	791453125	30.4138	9.7435	28133	3.9194	.00108108	2905.971	672006.30
926	857476	794022776	30.4302	9.7470	28179	3.9203	.00107991	2909.112	673460.08
927	859329	796597983	30.4467	9.7505	28224	3.9212	.00107875	2912.254	674915.42
928	861184	799178752	30.4631	9.7540	28270	3.9220	.00107759	2915.396	676372.33
929	863041	801765089	30.4795	9.7575	28315	3.9229	.00107643	2918.537	677830.82
930	864900	804357000	30.4959	9.7610	28361	3.9237	.00107527	2921.679	679290.87
931	866761	806954491	30.5123	9.7645	28407	3.9246	.00107411	2924.820	680752.50
932	868624	809557568	30.5287	9.7680	28453	3.9254	.00107296	2927.962	682215.69
933	870489	812166237	30.5450	9.7715	28499	3.9262	.00107181	2931.103	683680.46
934	872356	814780504	30.5614	9.7750	28544	3.9271	.00107066	2934.245	685146.80
935	874225	817400375	30.5778	9.7785	28590	3.9279	.00106952	2937.387	686614.71
936	876096	820025856	30.5941	9.7819	28636	3.9288	.00106838	2940.528	688084.19
937	877969	822656953	30.6105	9.7854	28682	3.9296	.00106724	2943.670	689555.24
938	879844	825293672	30.6268	9.7889	28728	3.9304	.00106610	2946.811	691027.86
939	881721	827936019	30.6431	9.7924	28774	3.9313	.00106496	2949.953	692502.05
940	883600	830584000	30.6594	9.7959	28820	3.9321	.00106383	2953.095	693977.82
941	885481	833237621	30.6757	9.7993	28866	3.9329	.00106270	2956.236	695455.15
942	887364	835896888	30.6920	9.8028	28912	3.9338	.00106157	2959.378	696934.06
943	889249	838561807	30.7083	9.8063	28958	3.9346	.00106045	2962.519	698414.53
944	891136	841232384	30.7246	9.8097	29004	3.9354	.00105932	2965.661	699896.58
945	893025	843908625	30.7409	9.8132	29050	3.9363	.00105820	2968.803	701380.19
946	894916	846590536	30.7571	9.8167	29096	3.9371	.00105708	2971.944	702865.38
947	896809	849278123	30.7734	9.8201	29142	3.9379	.00105597	2975.086	704352.14
948	898704	851971392	30.7896	9.8236	29189	3.9388	.00105485	2978.227	705840.47
949	900601	854670349	30.8058	9.8270	29235	3.9396	.00105374	2981.369	707330.37
950	902500	857375000	30.8221	9.8305	29281	3.9404	.00105263	2984.511	708821.84
951	904401	860085351	30.8383	9.8339	29327	3.9413	.00105152	2987.652	710314.88
952	906304	862801408	30.8545	9.8374	29374	3.9421	.00105042	2990.794	711809.50
953	908209	865523177	30.8707	9.8408	29420	3.9429	.00104932	2993.935	713305.68
954	910116	868250664	30.8869	9.8443	29466	3.9438	.00104822	2997.077	714803.43
955	912025	870983875	30.9031	9.8477	29513	3.9446	.00104712	3000.218	716302.76
956	913936	873722816	30.9192	9.8511	29559	3.9454	.00104603	3003.360	717803.66
957	915849	876467493	30.9354	9.8546	29605	3.9462	.00104493	3006.502	719306.12
958	917764	879217912	30.9516	9.8580	29652	3.9471	.00104384	3009.643	720810.16
959	919681	881974079	30.9677	9.8614	29698	3.9479	.00104275	3012.785	722315.77
960	921600	884736000	30.9839	9.8648	29745	3.9487	.00104167	3015.926	723822.95
961	923521	887503681	31.0000	9.8683	29791	3.9495	.00104058	3019.068	725331.70
962	925444	890277128	31.0161	9.8717	29838	3.9503	.00103950	3022.210	726842.02
963	927369	893056347	31.0322	9.8751	29884	3.9512	.00103842	3025.351	728353.91
964	929296	895841344	31.0483	9.8785	29931	3.9520	.00103734	3028.493	729867.37
965	931225	898632125	31.0644	9.8819	29977	3.9528	.00103627	3031.634	731382.40
966	933156	901428696	31.0805	9.8854	30024	3.9536	.00103520	3034.776	732899.01
967	935089	904231063	31.0966	9.8888	30070	3.9544	.00103413	3037.918	734417.18
968	937024	907039232	31.1127	9.8922	30117	3.9553	.00103306	3041.059	735936.93
969	938961	909853209	31.1288	9.8956	30164	3.9561	.00103199	3044.201	737458.24
970	940900	912673000	31.1448	9.8990	30210	3.9569	.00103093	3047.342	738981.13
971	942841	915498611	31.1609	9.9024	30257	3.9577	.00102987	3050.484	740505.59
972	944784	918330048	31.1769	9.9058	30304	3.9585	.00102881	3053.625	742031.62
973	946729	921167317	31.1929	9.9092	30351	3.9593	.00102775	3056.767	743559.22
974	948676	924010424	31.2090	9.9126	30398	3.9602	.00102669	3059.909	745088.39
975	950625	926859375	31.2250	9.9160	30444	3.9610	.00102564	3063.050	746619.13
976	952576	929714176	31.2410	9.9194	30491	3.9618	.00102459	3066.192	748151.44
977	954529	932574833	31.2570	9.9227	30538	3.9626	.00102354	3069.333	749685.32
978	956484	935441352	31.2730	9.9261	30585	3.9634	.00102249	3072.475	751220.78
979	958441	938313739	31.2890	9.9295	30632	3.9642	.00102145	3075.617	752757.80
980	960400	941192000	31.3050	9.9329	30679	3.9650	.00102041	3078.758	754296.40
981	962361	944076141	31.3209	9.9363	30726	3.9658	.00101937	3081.900	755836.59
982	964324	946966168	31.3369	9.9396	30773	3.9666	.00101833	3085.041	757378.30
983	966289	949862087	31.3528	9.9430	30820	3.9674	.00101729	3088.183	758921.61
984	968256	952763904	31.3688	9.9464	30867	3.9682	.00101626	3091.325	760466.48
985	970225	955671625	31.3847	9.9497	30914	3.9691	.00101523	3094.466	762012.93
986	972196	958585256	31.4006	9.9531	30961	3.9699	.00101420	3097.608	763560.95
987	974169	961504803	31.4166	9.9565	31008	3.9707	.00101317	3100.749	765110.54
988	976144	964430272	31.4325	9.9598	31055	3.9715	.00101215	3103.891	766661.70
989	978121	967361669	31.4484	9.9632	31102	3.9723	.00101112	3107.033	768214.44

Table 7.—*Continued*

N	N^2	N^3	$\sqrt{N}$	$\sqrt[3]{N}$	$N^{3/2}$	$\sqrt[5]{N}$	$\dfrac{1}{N}$	Circle ($N = D$) Circum.	Circle ($N = D$) Area
990	980100	970299000	31.4643	9.9666	31150	3.9731	.00101010	3110.174	769768.74
991	982081	973242271	31.4802	9.9699	31197	3.9739	.00100908	3113.316	771324.61
992	984064	976191488	31.4960	9.9733	31244	3.9747	.00100806	3116.457	772882.06
993	986049	979146657	31.5119	9.9766	31291	3.9755	.00100705	3119.599	774441.07
994	988036	982107784	31.5278	9.9800	31339	3.9763	.00100604	3122.740	776001.66
995	990025	985074875	31.5436	9.9833	31386	3.9771	.00100503	3125.882	777563.82
996	992016	988047936	31.5595	9.9866	31433	3.9779	.00100402	3129.024	779127.54
997	994009	991026973	31.5753	9.9900	31480	3.9787	.00100301	3132.165	780692.84
998	996004	994011992	31.5911	9.9933	31528	3.9795	.00100200	3135.307	782259.71
999	998001	997002999	31.6070	9.9967	31575	3.9803	.00100100	3138.448	783828.15
1000	1000000	1000000000	31.6228	10.0000	31623	3.9811	.00100000	3141.593	785398.16

Table 8. Inches to Decimals of a Foot

In.	Ft.	In.	Ft.	In.	Ft.	In.	Ft.	In.	Ft.	In.	Ft.	In.	Ft.
1/16	.0052	5/16	.0260	9/16	.0469	13/16	.0677	1	.0833	5	.4167	9	.7500
1/8	.0104	3/8	.0313	5/8	.0521	7/8	.0729	2	.1667	6	.5000	10	.8333
3/16	.0156	7/16	.0364	11/16	.0573	15/16	.0781	3	.2500	7	.5833	11	.9167
1/4	.0208	1/2	.0417	3/4	.0625	1	.0833	4	.3333	8	.6667	12	1.0000

Table 9. Circular Arcs, Chords, and Segments

Central Angle in Degrees	Arc R	Height R	Chord R	Height Chord	Area R^2	Central Angle in Degrees	Arc R	Height R	Chord R	Height Chord	Area R^2
1	0.0175	0.0000	0.0175	0.0022	0.00000	31	0.5411	0.0364	0.5345	0.0680	0.01301
2	.0349	.0002	.0349	.0044	.00000	32	.5585	.0387	.5513	.0703	.01429
3	.0524	.0003	.0524	.0066	.00001	33	.5760	.0412	.5680	.0725	.01566
4	.0698	.0006	.0698	.0087	.00003	34	.5934	.0437	.5847	.0747	.01711
5	.0873	.0010	.0872	.0109	.00006	35	.6109	.0463	.6014	.0770	.01864
6	.1047	.0014	.1047	.0131	.00010	36	.6283	.0489	.6180	.0792	.02027
7	.1222	.0019	.1221	.0153	.00015	37	.6458	.0517	.6346	.0814	.02198
8	.1396	.0024	.1395	.0175	.00023	38	.6632	.0545	.6511	.0837	.02378
9	.1571	.0031	.1569	.0196	.00032	39	.6807	.0574	.6676	.0859	.02568
10	.1745	.0038	.1743	.0218	.00044	40	.6981	.0603	.6840	.0882	.02767
11	.1920	.0046	.1917	.0240	.00059	41	.7156	.0633	.7004	.0904	.02976
12	.2094	.0055	.2091	.0262	.00076	42	.7330	.0664	.7167	.0927	.03195
13	.2269	.0064	.2264	.0284	.00097	43	.7505	.0696	.7330	.0949	.03425
14	.2443	.0075	.2437	.0306	.00121	44	.7679	.0728	.7492	.0972	.03664
15	.2618	.0086	.2611	.0328	.00149	45	.7854	.0761	.7654	.0995	.03915
16	.2793	.0097	.2783	.0350	.00181	46	.8029	.0795	.7815	.1017	.04176
17	.2967	.0110	.2956	.0372	.00217	47	.8203	.0829	.7975	.1040	.04448
18	.3142	.0123	.3129	.0394	.00257	48	.8378	.0865	.8135	.1063	.04731
19	.3316	.0137	.3301	.0415	.00302	49	.8552	.0900	.8294	.1086	.05025
20	.3491	.0152	.3473	.0437	.00352	50	8727	.0937	.8452	.1108	.05331
21	.3665	.0167	.3645	.0459	.00408	51	.8901	.0974	.8610	.1131	.05649
22	.3840	.0184	.3816	.0481	.00468	52	.9076	.1012	.8767	.1154	.05978
23	.4014	.0201	.3987	.0503	.00535	53	.9250	.1051	.8924	.1177	.06319
24	.4189	.0219	.4158	.0526	.00607	54	.9425	.1090	.9080	.1200	.06673
25	.4363	.0237	.4329	.0548	.00686	55	.9599	.1130	.9235	.1223	.07039
26	.4538	.0256	.4499	.0570	.00771	56	.9774	.1171	.9389	.1247	.07417
27	.4712	.0276	.4669	.0592	.00862	57	.9948	.1212	.9543	.1270	.07808
28	.4887	.0297	.4838	.0614	.00961	58	1.0123	.1254	.9696	.1293	.08212
29	.5061	.0319	.5008	.0636	.01067	59	1.0297	.1296	.9848	.1316	.08629
30	.5236	.0341	.5176	.0658	.01180	60	1.0472	.1340	1.0000	.1340	.09059

Table 9.—*Continued*

Central Angle in Degrees	Arc R	Height R	Chord R	Height Chord	Area R^2	Central Angle in Degrees	Arc R	Height R	Chord R	Height Chord	Area R^2
61	1.0647	.1384	1.015	.1363	.09502	121	2.1118	.5076	1.741	.2916	.62734
62	1.0821	.1428	1.030	.1387	.09958	122	2.1293	.5152	1.749	.2945	.64063
63	1.0996	.1474	1.045	.1410	.10428	123	2.1468	.5228	1.758	.2975	.65404
64	1.1170	.1520	1.060	.1434	.10911	124	2.1642	.5305	1.766	.3004	.66759
65	1.1345	.1566	1.075	.1457	.11408	125	2.1817	.5383	1.774	.3034	.68125
66	1.1519	.1613	1.089	.1481	.11919	126	2.1991	.5460	1.782	.3064	.69505
67	1.1694	.1661	1.104	.1505	.12443	127	2.2166	.5538	1.790	.3094	.70897
68	1.1868	.1710	1.118	.1529	.12982	128	2.2340	.5616	1.798	.3124	.72301
69	1.2043	.1759	1.133	.1553	.13535	129	2.2515	.5695	1.805	.3155	.73716
70	**1.2217**	**.1808**	**1.147**	**.1576**	**.14102**	**130**	**2.2689**	**.5774**	**1.813**	**.3185**	**.75143**
71	1.2392	.1859	1.161	.1601	.14683	131	2.2864	.5853	1.820	.3216	.76584
72	1.2566	.1910	1.176	.1625	.15279	132	2.3038	.5933	1.827	.3247	.78034
73	1.2741	.1961	1.190	.1649	.15889	133	2.3213	.6013	1.834	.3278	.79497
74	1.2915	.2014	1.204	.1673	.16514	134	2.3387	.6093	1.841	.3309	.80970
75	1.3090	.2066	1.218	.1697	.17154	135	2.3562	.6173	1.848	.3341	.82454
76	1.3265	.2120	1.231	.1722	.17808	136	2.3736	.6254	1.854	.3373	.83949
77	1.3439	.2174	1.245	.1746	.18477	137	2.3911	.6335	1.861	.3404	.85455
78	1.3614	.2229	1.259	.1771	.19160	138	2.4086	.6416	1.867	.3436	.86971
79	1.3788	2284	1.272	.1795	.19859	139	2.4260	.6498	1.873	.3469	.88497
80	**1.3963**	**.2340**	**1.286**	**.1820**	**.20573**	**140**	**2.4435**	**.6580**	**1.879**	**.3501**	**.90034**
81	1.4137	.2396	1.299	.1845	.21301	141	2.4609	.6662	1.885	.3534	.91580
82	1.4312	.2453	1.312	.1869	.22045	142	2.4784	.6744	1.891	.3566	.93135
83	1.4486	.2510	1.325	.1894	.22804	143	2.4958	.6827	1.897	.3599	.94700
84	1.4661	.2569	1.338	.1919	.23578	144	2.5133	.6910	1.902	.3633	.96274
85	1.4835	.2627	1.351	.1944	.24367	145	2.5307	.6993	1.907	.3666	.97858
86	1.5010	.2686	1.364	.1970	.25171	146	2.5482	.7076	1.913	.3700	.99449
87	1.5184	.2746	1.377	.1995	.25990	147	2.5656	.7160	1.918	.3734	1.0105
88	1.5359	.2807	1.389	.2020	.26825	148	2.5831	.7244	1.923	.3768	1.0266
89	1.5533	.2867	1.402	.2046	.27675	149	2.6005	.7328	1.927	.3802	1.0428
90	**1.5708**	**.2929**	**1.414**	**.2071**	**.28540**	**150**	**2.6180**	**.7412**	**1.932**	**.3837**	**1.0590**
91	1.5882	.2991	1.427	.2097	.29420	151	2.6354	.7496	1.936	.3871	1.0753
92	1.6057	.3053	1.439	.2122	.30316	152	2.6529	.7581	1.941	.3906	1.0917
93	1.6232	.3116	1.451	.2148	.31226	153	2.6704	.7666	1.945	.3942	1.1082
94	1.6406	.3180	1.463	.2174	.32152	154	2.6878	.7750	1.949	.3977	1.1247
95	1.6581	.3244	1.475	.2200	.33093	155	2.7053	.7836	1.953	.4013	1.1413
96	1.6755	.3309	1.486	.2226	.34050	156	2.7227	.7921	1.956	.4049	1.1580
97	1.6930	.3374	1.498	.2252	.35021	157	2.7402	.8006	1.960	.4085	1.1747
98	1.7104	.3439	1.509	.2279	.36008	158	2.7576	.8092	1.963	.4122	1.1915
99	1.7279	.3506	1.521	.2305	.37009	159	2.7751	.8178	1.967	.4158	1.2084
100	**1.7453**	**.3572**	**1.532**	**.2332**	**.38026**	**160**	**2.7925**	**.8264**	**1.970**	**.4195**	**1.2253**
101	1.7628	.3639	1.543	.2358	.39058	161	2.8100	.8350	1.973	.4233	1.2422
102	1.7802	.3707	1.554	.2385	.40104	162	2.8274	.8436	1.975	.4270	1.2592
103	1.7977	.3775	1.565	.2412	.41166	163	2.8449	.8522	1.978	.4308	1.2763
104	1.8151	.3843	1.576	.2439	.42242	164	2.8623	.8608	1.981	.4346	1.2934
105	1.8326	.3912	1.587	.2466	.43333	165	2.8798	.8695	1.983	.4385	1.3105
106	1.8500	.3982	1.597	.2493	.44439	166	2.8972	.8781	1.985	.4424	1.3277
107	1.8675	.4052	1.608	.2520	.45560	167	2.9147	.8868	1.987	.4463	1.3449
108	1.8850	.4122	1.618	.2548	.46695	168	2.9322	.8955	1.989	.4502	1.3621
109	1.9024	.4193	1.628	.2575	.47844	169	2.9496	.9042	1.991	.4542	1.3794
110	**1.9199**	**.4264**	**1.638**	**.2603**	**.49008**	**170**	**2.9671**	**.9128**	**1.992**	**.4582**	**1.3967**
111	1.9373	.4336	1.648	.2631	.50187	171	2.9845	.9215	1.994	.4622	1.4140
112	1.9548	.4408	1.658	.2659	.51379	172	3.0020	.9302	1.995	.4663	1.4314
113	1.9722	.4481	1.668	.2687	.52586	173	3.0194	.9390	1.996	.4704	1.4488
114	1.9897	.4554	1.677	.2715	.53807	174	3.0369	.9477	1.997	.4745	1.4662
115	2.0071	.4627	1.687	.2743	.55041	175	3.0543	.9564	1.998	.4786	1.4836
116	2.0246	.4701	1.696	.2772	.56289	176	3.0718	.9651	1.999	.4828	1.5010
117	2.0420	.4775	1.705	.2800	.57551	177	3.0892	.9738	1.999	.4871	1.5184
118	2.0595	.4850	1.714	.2829	.58827	178	3.1067	.9825	2.000	.4914	1.5359
119	2.0769	.4925	1.723	.2858	.60116	179	3.1241	.9913	2.000	.4957	1.5533
120	**2.0944**	**.5000**	**1.732**	**.2887**	**.61418**	**180**	**3.1416**	**1.0000**	**2.000**	**.5000**	**1.5708**

Table 10. Common Logarithms of Numbers

Mantissas in Six Decimal Places

The common logarithm of a number is the index of the power to which the base 10 must be raised in order to equal the number.

The common logarithm of every positive number not an integral power of 10 consists of an *integral* and a *decimal part*. The integral part or whole number is called the *characteristic* and may be either *positive or negative*. The decimal or fractional part is a *positive* number called the *mantissa* and is the same for all numbers which have the same sequential digits.

The characteristic of the logarithm of any positive number greater than one is positive and is one less than the number of digits before the decimal point.

The characteristic of the logarithm of any positive number less than one is negative and is one more than the number of ciphers immediately after the decimal point.

A negative number or number less than zero has no real logarithm.

EXAMPLES: Log_{10} 25400. = 4.404834 Log_{10} 0.0254 = $\bar{2}$.404834 or 8.404834 − 10

The two systems of logarithms in general use are the common or Briggsian logarithms, introduced in 1615 by Henry Briggs, a contemporary of John Napier, the inventor of logarithms, and the natural or less appropriately termed Napierian or hyperbolic logarithms, which developed somewhat accidentally from Napier's original work. The latter have a base denoted by e, an irrational number, which is:

$$\text{Lim}_{u=\infty} \left(1 + \frac{1}{u}\right)^u = 1 + 1 + \frac{1}{2!} + \frac{1}{3!} + \frac{1}{4!} + \ldots = 2.7182818$$

To obtain the natural logarithm, the common logarithm is multiplied by $\log_e 10$ which is 2.302585, or $\log_e N = 2.302585 \log_{10} N$.

N	0	1	2	3	4	5	6	7	8	9
0		000000	301030	477121	602060	698970	778151	845098	903090	954243
1	000000	041393	079181	113943	146128	176091	204120	230449	255273	278754
2	301030	322219	342423	361728	380211	397940	414973	431364	447158	462398
3	477121	491362	505150	518514	531479	544068	556303	568202	579784	591065
4	602060	612784	623249	633468	643453	653213	662758	672098	681241	690196
5	698970	707570	716003	724276	732394	740363	748188	755875	763428	770852
6	778151	785330	792392	799341	806180	812913	819544	826075	832509	838849
7	845098	851258	857332	863323	869232	875061	880814	886491	892095	897627
8	903090	908485	913814	919078	924279	929419	934498	939519	944483	949390
9	954243	959041	963788	968483	973124	977724	982271	986772	991226	995635
10	000000	004321	008600	012837	017033	021189	025306	029384	033424	037426
1	041393	045323	049218	053078	056905	060698	064458	068186	071882	075547
2	079181	082785	086360	089905	093422	096910	100371	103804	107210	110590
3	113943	117271	120574	123852	127105	130334	133539	136721	139879	143015
4	146128	149219	152288	155336	158362	161368	164353	167317	170262	173186
5	176091	178977	181844	184691	187521	190332	193125	195900	198657	201397
6	204120	206826	209515	212188	214844	217484	220108	222716	225309	227887
7	230449	232996	235528	238046	240549	243038	245513	247973	250420	252853
8	255273	257679	260071	262451	264818	267172	269513	271842	274158	276462
9	278754	281033	283301	285557	287802	290035	292256	294466	296665	298853
20	301030	303196	305351	307496	309630	311754	313867	315970	318063	320146
1	322219	324282	326336	328380	330414	332438	334454	336460	338456	340444
2	342423	344392	346353	348305	350248	352183	354108	356026	357935	359835
3	361728	363612	365488	367356	369216	371068	372912	374748	376577	378398
4	380211	382017	383815	385606	387390	389166	390935	392697	394452	396199
5	397940	399674	401401	403121	404834	406540	408240	409933	411620	413300
6	414973	416641	418301	419956	421604	423246	424882	426511	428135	429752
7	431364	432969	434569	436163	437751	439333	440909	442480	444045	445604
8	447158	448706	450249	451786	453318	454845	456366	457882	459392	460898
9	462398	863893	465383	466868	468347	469822	471292	472756	474216	475671
30	477121	478566	480007	481443	482874	484300	485721	487138	488551	489958
1	491362	492760	494155	495544	496930	498311	499687	501059	502427	503791
2	505150	506505	507856	509203	510546	511883	513218	514548	515874	517196
3	518514	519828	521138	522444	523746	525045	526339	527630	528917	530200
4	531479	532754	534026	535294	536558	537819	539076	540329	541579	542825
5	544068	545307	546543	547775	549003	550228	551450	552668	553883	555094

N	0	1	2	3	4	5	6	7	8	9
5	544068	545307	546543	547775	549003	550228	551450	552668	553883	555094
6	556303	557507	558709	559907	561101	562293	563481	564666	565848	567026
7	568202	569374	570543	571709	572872	574031	575188	576341	577492	578639
8	579784	580925	582063	583199	584331	585461	586587	587711	588832	589950
9	591065	592177	593286	594393	595496	596597	597695	598791	599883	600973
40	602060	603144	604226	605305	606381	607455	608526	609594	610660	611723
1	612784	613842	614897	615950	617000	618048	619093	620136	621176	622214
2	623249	624232	625312	626340	627366	628389	629410	630428	631444	632457
3	633468	634477	635484	636488	637490	638489	639486	640481	641474	642465
4	643453	644439	645422	646404	647383	648360	649335	650308	651278	652246
5	653213	654177	655138	656098	657056	658011	658965	659916	660865	661713
6	662758	663701	664642	665581	666518	667453	668386	669317	670246	671173
7	672098	673021	673942	674861	675778	676694	677607	678518	679428	680336
8	681241	682145	683047	683947	684845	685742	686636	687529	688420	689309
9	690196	691081	691965	692847	693727	694605	695482	696356	697229	698100
50	698970	699838	700704	701568	702431	703291	704151	705008	705864	706718
1	707570	708421	709270	710117	710963	711807	712650	713491	714330	715167
2	716003	716838	717671	718502	719331	720159	720986	721811	722634	723456
3	724276	725095	725912	726727	727541	728354	729165	729974	730782	731589
4	732394	733197	733999	734800	735599	736397	737193	737987	738781	739572
5	740363	741152	741939	742725	743510	744293	745075	745855	746634	747412
6	748188	748963	749736	750508	751279	752048	752816	753583	754348	755112
7	755875	756636	757396	758155	758912	759668	760422	761176	761928	762679
8	763428	764176	764923	765669	766413	767156	767898	768638	769377	770115
9	770852	771587	772322	773055	773786	774517	775246	775974	776701	777427
60	778151	778874	779596	780317	781037	781755	782473	783189	783904	784617
1	785330	786041	786751	787460	788168	788875	789581	790285	790988	791691
2	792392	793092	793790	794488	795185	795880	796574	797268	797960	798651
3	799341	800029	800717	801404	802089	802774	803457	804139	804821	805501
4	306180	806858	807535	808211	808886	809560	810233	810904	811575	812245
5	812913	813581	814248	814913	815578	816241	816904	817565	818226	818885
6	819544	820201	820858	821514	822168	822822	823474	824126	824776	825426
7	826075	826723	827369	828015	828660	829304	829947	830589	831230	831870
8	832509	833147	833784	834421	835056	835691	836324	836957	837588	838219
9	838849	839478	840106	840733	841359	841985	842609	843233	843855	844477
70	845098	845718	846337	846955	847573	848189	848805	849419	850033	850646
1	851258	851870	852480	853090	853698	854306	854913	855519	856124	856729
2	857332	857935	858537	859138	859739	860338	860937	861534	862131	862728
3	863323	863917	864511	865104	865696	866287	866878	867467	868056	868644
4	869232	869818	870404	870989	871573	872156	872739	873321	873902	874482
5	875061	875640	876218	876795	877371	877947	878522	879096	879669	880242
6	880814	881385	881955	882525	883093	883661	884229	884795	885361	885926
7	886491	887054	887617	888179	888741	889302	889862	890421	890980	891537
8	892095	892651	893207	893762	894316	894870	895423	895975	896526	897077
9	897627	898176	898725	899273	899821	900367	900913	901458	902003	902547
80	903090	903633	904174	904716	905256	905796	906335	906874	907411	907949
1	908485	909021	909556	910091	910624	911158	911690	912222	912753	913284
2	913814	914343	914872	915400	915927	916454	916980	917506	918030	918555
3	919078	919601	920123	920645	921166	921686	922206	922725	923244	923762
4	924279	924796	925312	925828	926342	926857	927370	927883	928396	928908
5	929419	929930	930440	930949	931458	931966	932474	932981	933487	933993
6	934498	935003	935507	936011	936514	937016	937518	938019	938520	939020
7	939519	940018	940516	941014	941511	942008	942504	943000	943495	943989
8	944483	944976	945469	945961	946452	946943	947434	947924	948413	948902
9	949390	949878	950365	950851	951338	951823	952308	952792	953276	953760
90	954243	954725	955207	955688	956168	956649	957128	957607	958086	958564
1	959041	959518	959995	960471	960946	961421	961895	962369	962843	963316
2	963788	964260	964731	965202	965672	966142	966611	967080	967548	968016
3	968483	968950	969416	969882	970347	970812	971276	971740	972203	972666
4	973128	973590	974051	974512	974972	975432	975891	976350	976808	977266
5	977724	978181	978637	979093	979548	980003	980458	980912	981366	981819
6	982271	982723	983175	983626	984077	984527	984977	985426	985875	986324
7	986772	987219	987666	988113	988559	989005	989450	989895	990339	990783
8	991226	991669	992111	992554	992995	993436	993877	994317	994757	995196
9	995635	996074	996512	996949	997386	997823	998259	998695	999131	999565
100	000000	000434	000868	001301	001734	002166	002598	003029	003461	003891

N	0	1	2	3	4	5	6	7	8	9	Diff.
100	000000	000434	000868	001301	001734	002166	002598	003029	003461	003891	432
1	004321	004751	005181	005609	006038	006466	006894	007321	007748	008174	428
2	008600	009026	009451	009876	010300	010724	011147	011570	011993	012415	424
3	012837	013259	013680	014100	014521	014940	015360	015779	016197	016616	420
4	017033	017451	017868	018284	018700	019116	019532	019947	020361	020775	416
5	021189	021603	022016	022428	022841	023252	023664	024075	024486	024896	412
6	025306	025715	026125	026533	026942	027350	027757	028164	028571	028978	408
7	029384	029789	030195	030600	031004	031408	031812	032216	032619	033021	404
8	033424	033826	034227	034628	035029	035430	035830	036230	036629	037028	400
9	037426	037825	038223	038620	039017	039414	039811	040207	040602	040998	397
110	041393	041787	042182	042576	042969	043362	043755	044148	044540	044932	393
1	045323	045714	046105	046495	046885	047275	047664	048053	048442	048830	390
2	049218	049606	049993	050380	050766	051153	051538	051924	052309	052694	386
3	053078	053463	053846	054230	054613	054996	055378	055760	056142	056524	383
4	056905	057286	057666	058046	058426	058805	059185	059563	059942	060320	379
5	060698	061075	061452	061829	062206	062582	062958	063333	063709	064083	376
6	064458	064832	065206	065580	065953	066326	066699	067071	067443	067815	373
7	068186	068557	068928	069298	069668	070038	070407	070776	071145	071514	370
8	071882	072250	072617	072985	073352	073718	074085	074451	074816	075182	366
9	075547	075912	076276	076640	077004	077368	077731	078094	078457	078819	363
120	079181	079543	079904	080266	080626	080987	081347	081707	082067	082426	360

PROPORTIONAL PARTS

Diff.	1	2	3	4	5	6	7	8	9
434	43.4	86.8	130.2	173.6	217.0	260.4	303.8	347.2	390.6
432	43.2	86.4	129.6	172.8	216.0	259.2	302.4	345.6	388.8
430	43.0	86.0	129.0	172.0	215.0	258.0	301.0	344.0	387.0
428	42.8	85.6	128.4	171.2	214.0	256.8	299.6	342.4	385.2
426	42.6	85.2	127.8	170.4	213.0	255.6	298.2	340.8	383.4
424	42.4	84.8	127.2	169.6	212.0	254.4	296.8	339.2	381.6
422	42.2	84.4	126.6	168.8	211.0	253.2	295.4	337.6	379.8
420	42.0	84.0	126.0	168.0	210.0	252.0	294.0	336.0	378.0
418	41.8	83.6	125.4	167.2	209.0	250.8	292.6	334.4	376.2
416	41.6	83.2	124.8	166.4	208.0	249.6	291.2	332.8	374.4
414	41.4	82.8	124.2	165.6	207.0	248.4	289.8	331.2	372.6
412	41.2	82.4	123.6	164.8	206.0	247.2	288.4	329.6	370.8
410	41.0	82.0	123.0	164.0	205.0	246.0	287.0	328.0	369.0
408	40.8	81.6	122.4	163.2	204.0	244.8	285.6	326.4	367.2
406	40.6	81.2	121.8	162.4	203.0	243.6	284.2	324.8	365.4
404	40.4	80.8	121.2	161.6	202.0	242.4	282.8	323.2	363.6
402	40.2	80.4	120.6	160.8	201.0	241.2	281.4	321.6	361.8
400	40.0	80.0	120.0	160.0	200.0	240.0	280.0	320.0	360.0
398	39.8	79.6	119.4	159.2	199.0	238.8	278.6	318.4	358.2
396	39.6	79.2	118.8	158.4	198.0	237.6	277.2	316.8	356.4
394	39.4	78.8	118.2	157.6	197.0	236.4	275.8	315.2	354.6
392	39.2	78.4	117.6	156.8	196.0	235.2	274.4	313.6	352.8
390	39.0	78.0	117.0	156.0	195.0	234.0	273.0	312.0	351.0
388	38.8	77.6	116.4	155.2	194.0	232.8	271.6	310.4	349.2
386	38.6	77.2	115.8	154.4	193.0	231.6	270.2	308.8	347.4
384	38.4	76.8	115.2	153.6	192.0	230.4	268.8	307.2	345.6
382	38.2	76.4	114.6	152.8	191.0	229.2	267.4	305.6	343.8
380	38.0	76.0	114.0	152.0	190.0	228.0	266.0	304.0	342.0
378	37.8	75.6	113.4	151.2	189.0	226.8	264.6	302.4	340.2
376	37.6	75.2	112.8	150.4	188.0	225.6	263.2	300.8	338.4
374	37.4	74.8	112.2	149.6	187.0	224.4	261.8	299.2	336.6
372	37.2	74.4	111.6	148.8	186.0	223.2	260.4	297.6	334.8
370	37.0	74.0	111.0	148.0	185.0	222.0	259.0	296.0	333.0

N	0	1	2	3	4	5	6	7	8	9	Diff.
120	079181	079543	079904	080266	080626	080987	081347	081707	082067	082426	360
1	082785	083144	083503	083861	084219	084576	084934	085291	085647	086004	357
2	086360	086716	087071	087426	087781	088136	088490	088845	089198	089552	355
3	089905	090258	090611	090963	091315	091667	092018	092370	092721	093071	352
4	093422	093772	094122	094471	094820	095169	095518	095866	096215	096562	349
5	096910	097257	097604	097951	098298	098644	098990	099335	099681	100026	346
6	100371	100715	101059	101403	101747	102091	102434	102777	103119	103462	343
7	103804	104146	104487	104828	105169	105510	105851	106191	106531	106871	341
8	107210	107549	107888	108227	108565	108903	109241	109579	109916	110253	338
9	110590	110926	111263	111599	111934	112270	112605	112940	113275	113609	335
130	113943	114277	114611	114944	115278	115611	115943	116276	116608	116940	333
1	117271	117603	117934	118265	118595	118926	119256	119586	119915	120245	330
2	120574	120903	121231	121560	121888	122216	122544	122871	123198	123525	328
3	123852	124178	124504	124830	125156	125481	125806	126131	126456	126781	325
4	127105	127429	127753	128076	128399	128722	129045	129368	129690	130012	323
5	130334	130655	130977	131298	131619	131939	132260	132580	132900	133219	321
6	133539	133858	134177	134496	134814	135133	135451	135769	136086	136403	318
7	136721	137037	137354	137671	137987	138303	138618	138934	139249	139564	316
8	139879	140194	140508	140822	141136	141450	141763	142076	142389	142702	314
9	143015	143327	143639	143951	144263	144574	144885	145196	145507	145818	311
140	146128	146438	146748	147058	147367	147676	147985	148294	148603	148911	309

PROPORTIONAL PARTS

Diff.	1	2	3	4	5	6	7	8	9
370	37.0	74.0	111.0	148.0	185.0	222.0	259.0	296.0	333.0
368	36.8	73.6	110.4	147.2	184.0	220.8	257.6	294.4	331.2
366	36.6	73.2	109.8	146.4	183.0	219.6	256.2	292.8	329.4
364	36.4	72.8	109.2	145.6	182.0	218.4	254.8	291.2	327.6
362	36.2	72.4	108.6	144.8	181.0	217.2	253.4	289.6	325.8
360	36.0	72.0	108.0	144.0	180.0	216.0	252.0	288.0	324.0
358	35.8	71.6	107.4	143.2	179.0	214.8	250.6	286.4	322.2
356	35.6	71.2	106.8	142.4	178.0	213.6	249.2	284.8	320.4
354	35.4	70.8	106.2	141.6	177.0	212.4	247.8	283.2	318.6
352	35.2	70.4	105.6	140.8	176.0	211.2	246.4	281.6	316.8
350	35.0	70.0	105.0	140.0	175.0	210.0	245.0	280.0	315.0
348	34.8	69.6	104.4	139.2	174.0	208.8	243.6	278.4	313.2
346	34.6	69.2	103.8	138.4	173.0	207.6	242.2	276.8	311.4
344	34.4	68.8	103.2	137.6	172.0	206.4	240.8	275.2	309.6
342	34.2	68.4	102.6	136.8	171.0	205.2	239.4	273.6	307.8
340	34.0	68.0	102.0	136.0	170.0	204.0	238.0	272.0	306.0
338	33.8	67.6	101.4	135.2	169.0	202.8	236.6	270.4	304.2
336	33.6	67.2	100.8	134.4	168.0	201.6	235.2	268.8	302.4
334	33.4	66.8	100.2	133.6	167.0	200.4	233.8	267.2	300.6
332	33.2	66.4	99.6	132.8	166.0	199.2	232.4	265.6	298.8
330	33.0	66.0	99.0	132.0	165.0	198.0	231.0	264.0	297.0
328	32.8	65.6	98.4	131.2	164.0	196.8	229.6	262.4	295.2
326	32.6	65.2	97.8	130.4	163.0	195.6	228.2	260.8	293.4
324	32.4	64.8	97.2	129.6	162.0	194.4	226.8	259.2	291.6
322	32.2	64.4	96.6	128.8	161.0	193.2	225.4	257.6	289.8
320	32.0	64.0	96.0	128.0	160.0	192.0	224.0	256.0	288.0
318	31.8	63.6	95.4	127.2	159.0	190.8	222.6	254.4	286.2
316	31.6	63.2	94.8	126.4	158.0	189.6	221.2	252.8	284.4
314	31.4	62.8	94.2	125.6	157.0	188.4	219.8	251.2	282.6
312	31.2	62.4	93.6	124.8	156.0	187.2	218.4	249.6	280.8
310	31.0	62.0	93.0	124.0	155.0	186.0	217.0	248.0	279.0
308	30.8	61.6	92.4	123.2	154.0	184.8	215.6	246.4	277.2

N	0	1	2	3	4	5	6	7	8	9	Diff.
140	146128	146438	146748	147058	147367	147676	147985	148294	148603	148911	309
1	149219	149527	149835	150142	150449	150756	151063	151370	151676	151982	307
2	152288	152594	152900	153205	153510	153815	154120	154424	154728	155032	305
3	155336	155640	155943	156246	156549	156852	157154	157457	157759	158061	303
4	158362	158664	158965	159266	159567	159868	160168	160469	160769	161068	301
5	161368	161667	161967	162266	162564	162863	163161	163460	163758	164055	299
6	164353	164650	164947	165244	165541	165838	166134	166430	166726	167022	297
7	167317	167613	167908	168203	168497	168792	169086	169380	169674	169968	295
8	170262	170555	170848	171141	171434	171726	172019	172311	172603	172895	293
9	173186	173478	173769	174060	174351	174641	174932	175222	175512	175802	291
150	176091	176381	176670	176959	177248	177536	177825	178113	178401	178689	289
1	178977	179264	179552	179839	180126	180413	180699	180986	181272	181558	287
2	181844	182129	182415	182700	182985	183270	183555	183839	184123	184407	285
3	184691	184975	185259	185542	185825	186108	186391	186674	186956	187239	283
4	187521	187803	188084	188366	188647	188928	189209	189490	189771	190051	281
5	190332	190612	190892	191171	191451	191730	192010	192289	192567	192846	279
6	193125	193403	193681	193959	194237	194514	194792	195069	195346	195623	278
7	195900	196176	196453	196729	197005	197281	197556	197832	198107	198382	276
8	198657	198932	199206	199481	199755	200029	200303	200577	200850	201124	274
9	201397	201670	201943	202216	202488	202761	203033	203305	203577	203848	272
160	204120	204391	204663	204934	205204	205475	205746	206016	206286	206556	271
1	206826	207096	207365	207634	207904	208173	208441	208710	208979	209247	269
2	209515	209783	210051	210319	210586	210853	211121	211388	211654	211921	267
3	212188	212454	212720	212986	213252	213518	213783	214049	214314	214579	266
4	214844	215109	215373	215638	215902	216166	216430	216694	216957	217221	264
5	217484	217747	218010	218273	218536	218798	219060	219323	219585	219846	262
6	220108	220370	220631	220892	221153	221414	221675	221936	222196	222456	261
7	222716	222976	223236	223496	223755	224015	224274	224533	224792	225051	259
8	225309	225568	225826	226084	226342	226600	226858	227115	227372	227630	258
9	227887	228144	228400	228657	228913	229170	229426	229682	229938	230193	256
170	230449	230704	230960	231215	231470	231724	231979	232234	232488	232742	255

PROPORTIONAL PARTS

Diff.	1	2	3	4	5	6	7	8	9
310	31.0	62.0	93.0	124.0	155.0	186.0	217.0	248.0	279.0
308	30.8	61.6	92.4	123.2	154.0	184.8	215.6	246.4	277.2
306	30.6	61.2	91.8	122.4	153.0	183.6	214.2	244.8	275.4
304	30.4	60.8	91.2	121.6	152.0	182.4	212.8	243.2	273.6
302	30.2	60.4	90.6	120.8	151.0	181.2	211.4	241.6	271.8
300	30.0	60.0	90.0	120.0	150.0	180.0	210.0	240.0	270.0
298	29.8	59.6	89.4	119.2	149.0	178.8	208.6	238.4	268.2
296	29.6	59.2	88.8	118.4	148.0	177.6	207.2	236.8	266.4
294	29.4	58.8	88.2	117.6	147.0	176.4	205.8	235.2	264.6
292	29.2	58.4	87.6	116.8	146.0	175.2	204.4	233.6	262.8
290	29.0	58.0	87.0	116.0	145.0	174.0	203.0	232.0	261.0
288	28.8	57.6	86.4	115.2	144.0	172.8	201.6	230.4	259.2
286	28.6	57.2	85.8	114.4	143.0	171.6	200.2	228.8	257.4
284	28.4	56.8	85.2	113.6	142.0	170.4	198.8	227.2	255.6
282	28.2	56.4	84.6	112.8	141.0	169.2	197.4	225.6	253.8
280	28.0	56.0	84.0	112.0	140.0	168.0	196.0	224.0	252.0
278	27.8	55.6	83.4	111.2	139.0	166.8	194.6	222.4	250.2
276	27.6	55.2	82.8	110.4	138.0	165.6	193.2	220.8	248.4
274	27.4	54.8	82.2	109.6	137.0	164.4	191.8	219.2	246.6
272	27.2	54.4	81.6	108.8	136.0	163.2	190.4	217.6	244.8
270	27.0	54.0	81.0	108.0	135.0	162.0	189.0	216.0	243.0
268	26.8	53.6	80.4	107.2	134.0	160.8	187.6	214.4	241.2
266	26.6	53.2	79.8	106.4	133.0	159.6	186.2	212.8	239.4
264	26.4	52.8	79.2	105.6	132.0	158.4	184.8	211.2	237.6

N	0	1	2	3	4	5	6	7	8	9	Diff.
170	230449	230704	230960	231215	231470	231724	231979	232234	232488	232742	255
1	232996	233250	233504	233757	234011	234264	234517	234770	235023	235276	253
2	235528	235781	236033	236285	236537	236789	237041	237292	237544	237795	252
3	238046	238297	238548	238799	239049	239299	239550	239800	240050	240300	250
4	240549	240799	241048	241297	241546	241795	242044	242293	242541	242790	249
5	243038	243286	243534	243782	244030	244277	244525	244772	245019	245266	248
6	245513	245759	246006	246252	246499	246745	246991	247237	247482	247728	246
7	247973	248219	248464	248709	248954	249198	249443	249687	249932	250176	245
8	250420	250664	250908	251151	251395	251638	251881	252125	252368	252610	243
9	252853	253096	253338	253580	253822	254064	254306	254548	254790	255031	242
180	255273	255514	255755	255996	256237	256477	256718	256958	257198	257439	241
1	257679	257918	258158	258398	258637	258877	259116	259355	259594	259833	239
2	260071	260310	260548	260787	261025	261263	261501	261739	261976	262214	238
3	262451	262688	262925	263162	263399	263636	263873	264109	264346	264582	237
4	264818	265054	265290	265525	265761	265996	266232	266467	266702	266937	235
5	267172	267406	267641	267875	268110	268344	268578	268812	269046	269279	234
6	269513	269746	269980	270213	270446	270679	270912	271144	271377	271609	233
7	271842	272074	272306	272538	272770	273001	273233	273464	273696	273927	232
8	274158	274389	274620	274850	275081	275311	275542	275772	276002	276232	230
9	276462	276692	276921	277151	277380	277609	277838	278067	278296	278525	229
190	278754	278982	279211	279439	279667	279895	280123	280351	280578	280806	228
1	281033	281261	281488	281715	281942	282169	282396	282622	282849	283075	227
2	283301	283527	283753	283979	284205	284431	284656	284882	285107	285332	226
3	285557	285782	286007	286232	286456	286681	286905	287130	287354	287578	225
4	287802	288026	288249	288473	288696	288920	289143	289366	289589	289812	223
5	290035	290257	290480	290702	290925	291147	291369	291591	291813	292034	222
6	292256	292478	292699	292920	293141	293363	293584	293804	294025	294246	221
7	294466	294687	294907	295127	295347	295567	295787	296007	296226	296446	220
8	296665	296884	297104	297323	297542	297761	297979	298198	298416	298635	219
9	298853	299071	299289	299507	299725	299943	300161	300378	300595	300813	218
200	301030	301247	301464	301681	301898	302114	302331	302547	302764	302980	217

PROPORTIONAL PARTS

Diff.	1	2	3	4	5	6	7	8	9
262	26.2	52.4	78.6	104.8	131.0	157.2	183.4	209.6	235.8
260	26.0	52.0	78.0	104.0	130.0	156.0	182.0	208.0	234.0
258	25.8	51.6	77.4	103.2	129.0	154.8	180.6	206.4	232.2
256	25.6	51.2	76.8	102.4	128.0	153.6	179.2	204.8	230.4
254	25.4	50.8	76.2	101.6	127.0	152.4	177.8	203.2	228.6
252	25.2	50.4	75.6	100.8	126.0	151.2	176.4	201.6	226.8
250	25.0	50.0	75.0	100.0	125.0	150.0	175.0	200.0	225.0
248	24.8	49.6	74.4	99.2	124.0	148.8	173.6	198.4	223.2
246	24.6	49.2	73.8	98.4	123.0	147.6	172.2	196.8	221.4
244	24.4	48.8	73.2	97.6	122.0	146.4	170.8	195.2	219.6
242	24.2	48.4	72.6	96.8	121.0	145.2	169.4	193.6	217.8
240	24.0	48.0	72.0	96.0	120.0	144.0	168.0	192.0	216.0
238	23.8	47.6	71.4	95.2	119.0	142.8	166.6	190.4	214.2
236	23.6	47.2	70.8	94.4	118.0	141.6	165.2	188.8	212.4
234	23.4	46.8	70.2	93.6	117.0	140.4	163.8	187.2	210.6
232	23.2	46.4	69.6	92.8	116.0	139.2	162.4	185.6	208.8
230	23.0	46.0	69.0	92.0	115.0	138.0	161.0	184.0	207.0
228	22.8	45.6	68.4	91.2	114.0	136.8	159.6	182.4	205.2
226	22.6	45.2	67.8	90.4	113.0	135.6	158.2	180.8	203.4
224	22.4	44.8	67.2	89.6	112.0	134.4	156 8	179.2	201.6
222	22.2	44.4	66.6	88.8	111.0	133.2	155 4	177.6	199.8
220	22.0	44.0	66.0	88.0	110.0	132.0	154.0	176.0	198.0
218	21.8	43.6	65.4	87.2	109.0	130.8	152.6	174.4	196.2
216	21.6	43.2	64.8	86.4	108.0	129.6	151.2	172.8	194.4

N	0	1	2	3	4	5	6	7	8	9	Diff.
200	301030	301247	301464	301681	301898	302114	302331	302547	302764	302980	217
1	303196	303412	303628	303844	304059	304275	304491	304706	304921	305136	216
2	305351	305566	305781	305996	306211	306425	306639	306854	307068	307282	215
3	307496	307710	307924	308137	308351	308564	308778	308991	309204	309417	213
4	309630	309843	310056	310268	310481	310693	310906	311118	311330	311542	212
5	311754	311966	312177	312389	312600	312812	313023	313234	313445	313656	211
6	313867	314078	314289	314499	314710	314920	315130	315340	315551	315760	210
7	315970	316180	316390	316599	316809	317018	317227	317436	317646	317854	209
8	318063	318272	318481	318689	318898	319106	319314	319522	319730	319938	208
9	320146	320354	320562	320769	320977	321184	321391	321598	321805	322012	207
210	322219	322426	322633	322839	323046	323252	323458	323665	323871	324077	206
1	324282	324488	324694	324899	325105	325310	325516	325721	325926	326131	205
2	326336	326541	326745	326950	327155	327359	327563	327767	327972	328176	204
3	328380	328583	328787	328991	329194	329398	329601	329805	330008	330211	203
4	330414	330617	330819	331022	331225	331427	331630	331832	332034	332236	202
5	332438	332640	332842	333044	333246	333447	333649	333850	334051	334253	201
6	334454	334655	334856	335057	335257	335458	335658	335859	336059	336260	201
7	336460	336660	336860	337060	337260	337459	337659	337858	338058	338257	200
8	338456	338656	338855	339054	339253	339451	339650	339849	340047	340246	199
9	340444	340642	340841	341039	341237	341435	341632	341830	342028	342225	198
220	342423	342620	342817	343014	343212	343409	343606	343802	343999	344196	197
1	344392	344589	344785	344981	345178	345374	345570	345766	345962	346157	196
2	346353	346549	346744	346939	347135	347330	347525	347720	347915	348110	195
3	348305	348500	348694	348889	349083	349278	349472	349666	349860	350054	194
4	350248	350442	350636	350829	351023	351216	351410	351603	351796	351989	193
5	352183	352375	352568	352761	352954	353147	353339	353532	353724	353916	192
6	354108	354301	354493	354685	354876	355068	355260	355452	355643	355834	192
7	356026	356217	356408	356599	356790	356981	357172	357363	357554	357744	191
8	357935	358125	358316	358506	358696	358886	359076	359266	359456	359646	190
9	359835	360025	360215	360404	360593	360783	360972	361161	361350	361539	189
230	361728	361917	362105	362294	362482	362671	362859	363048	363236	363424	188
1	363612	363800	363988	364176	364363	364551	364739	364926	365113	365301	
2	365488	365675	365862	366049	366236	366423	366610	366796	366983	367169	187
3	367356	367542	367729	367915	368101	368287	368473	368659	368845	369030	186
4	369216	369401	369587	369772	369958	370143	370328	370513	370698	370883	185
5	371068	371253	371437	371622	371806	371991	372175	372360	372544	372728	184
6	372912	373096	373280	373464	373647	373831	374015	374198	374382	374565	
7	374748	374932	375115	375298	375481	375664	375846	376029	376212	376394	183
8	376577	376759	376942	377124	377306	377488	377670	377852	378034	378216	182
9	378398	378580	378761	378943	379124	379306	379487	379668	379849	380030	181
240	380211	380392	380573	380754	380934	381115	381296	381476	381656	381837	

PROPORTIONAL PARTS

Diff.	1	2	3	4	5	6	7	8	9
216	21.6	43.2	64.8	86.4	108.0	192.6	151.2	172.8	194.4
214	21.4	42.8	64.2	85.6	107.0	128.4	149.8	171.2	192.6
212	21.2	42.4	63.6	84.8	106.0	127.2	148.4	169.6	190.8
210	21.0	42.0	63.0	84.0	105.0	126.0	147.0	168.0	189.0
208	20.8	41.6	62.4	83.2	104.0	124.8	145.6	166.4	187.2
206	20.6	41.2	61.8	82.4	103.0	123.6	144.2	164.8	185.4
204	20.4	40.8	61.2	81.6	102.0	122.4	142.8	163.2	183.6
202	20.2	40.4	60.6	80.8	101.0	121.2	141.4	161.6	181.8
200	20.0	40.0	60.0	80.0	100.0	120.0	140.0	160.0	180.0
198	19.8	39.6	59.4	79.2	99.0	118.8	138.6	158.4	178.2
196	19.6	39.2	58.8	78.4	98.0	117.6	137.2	156.8	176.4
194	19.4	38.8	58.2	77.6	97.0	116.4	135.8	155.2	174.6
192	19.2	38.4	57.6	76.8	96.0	115.2	134.4	153.6	172.8
190	19.0	38.0	57.0	76.0	95.0	114.0	133.0	152.0	171.0
188	18.8	37.6	56.4	75.2	94.0	112.8	131.6	150.4	169.2
186	18.6	37.2	55.8	74.4	93.0	111.6	130.2	148.8	167.4

N	0	1	2	3	4	5	6	7	8	9	Diff.
240	380211	380392	380573	380754	380934	381115	381296	381476	381656	381837	181
1	382017	382197	382377	382557	382737	382917	383097	383277	383456	383636	180
2	383815	383995	384174	384353	384533	384712	384891	385070	385249	385428	179
3	385606	385785	385964	386142	386321	386499	386677	386856	387034	387212	178
4	387390	387568	387746	387924	388101	388279	388456	388634	388811	388989	
5	389166	389343	389520	389698	389875	390051	390228	390405	390582	390759	177
6	390935	391112	391288	391464	391641	391817	391993	392169	392345	392521	176
7	392697	392873	393048	393224	393400	393575	393751	393926	394101	394277	
8	394452	394627	394802	394977	395152	395326	395501	395676	395850	396025	175
9	396199	396374	396548	396722	396896	397071	397245	397419	397592	397766	174
250	397940	398114	398287	398461	398634	398808	398981	399154	399328	399501	173
1	399674	399847	400020	400192	400365	400538	400711	400883	401056	401228	
2	401401	401573	401745	401917	402089	402261	402433	402605	402777	402949	172
3	403121	403292	403464	403635	403807	403978	404149	404320	404492	404663	171
4	404834	405005	405176	405346	405517	405688	405858	406029	406199	406370	
5	406540	406710	406881	407051	407221	407391	407561	407731	407901	408070	170
6	408240	408410	408579	408749	408918	409087	409257	409426	409595	409764	169
7	409933	410102	410271	410440	410609	410777	410946	411114	411283	411451	
8	411620	411788	411956	412124	412293	412461	412629	412796	412964	413132	168
9	413300	413467	413635	413803	413970	414137	414305	414472	414639	414806	167
260	414973	415140	415307	415474	415641	415808	415974	416141	416308	416474	
1	416641	416807	416973	417139	417306	417472	417638	417804	417970	418135	166
2	418301	418467	418633	418798	418964	419129	419295	419460	419625	419791	165
3	419956	420121	420286	420451	420616	420781	420945	421110	421275	421439	
4	421604	421768	421933	422097	422261	422426	422590	422754	422918	423082	164
5	423246	423410	423574	423737	423901	424065	424228	424392	424555	424718	
6	424882	425045	425208	425371	425534	425697	425860	426023	426186	426349	163
7	426511	426674	426836	426999	427161	427324	427486	427648	427811	427973	162
8	428135	428297	428459	428621	428783	428944	429106	429268	429429	429591	
9	429752	429914	430075	430236	430398	430559	430720	430881	431042	431203	161
270	431364	431525	431685	431846	432007	432167	432328	432488	432649	432809	
1	432969	433130	433290	433450	433610	433770	433930	434090	434249	434409	160
2	434569	434729	434888	435048	435207	435367	435526	435685	435844	436004	159
3	436163	436322	436481	436640	436799	436957	437116	437275	437433	437592	
4	437751	437909	438067	438226	438384	438542	438701	438859	439017	439175	158
5	439333	439491	439648	439806	439964	440122	440279	440437	440594	440752	
6	440909	441066	441224	441381	441538	441695	441852	442009	442166	442323	157
7	442480	442637	442793	442950	443106	443263	443419	443576	443732	443889	
8	444045	444201	444357	444513	444669	444825	444981	445137	445293	445449	156
9	445604	445760	445915	446071	446226	446382	446537	446692	446848	447003	155
280	447158	447313	447468	447623	447778	447933	448088	448242	448397	448552	

PROPORTIONAL PARTS

Diff.	1	2	3	4	5	6	7	8	9
184	18.4	36.8	55.2	73.6	92.0	110.4	128.8	147.2	165.6
182	18.2	36.4	54.6	72.8	91.0	109.2	127.4	145.6	163.8
180	18.0	36.0	54.0	72.0	90.0	108.0	126.0	144.0	162.0
178	17.8	35.6	53.4	71.2	89.0	106.8	124.6	142.4	160.2
176	17.6	35.2	52.8	70.4	88.0	105.6	123.2	140.8	158.4
174	17.4	34.8	52.2	69.6	87.0	104.4	121.8	139.2	156.6
172	17.2	34.4	51.6	68.8	86.0	103.2	120.4	137.6	154.8
170	17.0	34.0	51.0	68.0	85.0	102.0	119.0	136.0	153.0
168	16.8	33.6	50.4	67.2	84.0	100.8	117.6	134.4	151.2
166	16.6	33.2	49.8	66.4	83.0	99.6	116.2	132.8	149.4
164	16.4	32.8	49.2	65.6	82.0	98.4	114.8	131.2	147.6
162	16.2	32.4	48.6	64.8	81.0	97.2	113.4	129.6	145.8
160	16.0	32.0	48.0	64.0	80.0	96.0	112.0	128.0	144.0
158	15.8	31.6	47.4	63.2	79.0	94.8	110.6	126.4	142.2
156	15.6	31.2	46.8	62.4	78.0	93.6	109.2	124.8	140.4
154	15.4	30.8	46.2	61.6	77.0	92.4	107.8	123.2	138.6

N	0	1	2	3	4	5	6	7	8	9	Diff.
280	**447158**	**447313**	**447468**	**447623**	**447778**	**447933**	**448088**	**448242**	**448397**	**448552**	
1	448706	448861	449015	449170	449324	449478	449633	449787	449941	450095	154
2	450249	450403	450557	450711	450865	451018	451172	451326	451479	451633	
3	451786	451940	452093	452247	452400	452553	452706	452859	453012	453165	153
4	453318	453471	453624	453777	453930	454082	454235	454387	454540	454692	
5	454845	454997	455150	455302	455454	455606	455758	455910	456062	456214	152
6	456366	456518	456670	456821	456973	457125	457276	457428	457579	457731	
7	457882	458033	458184	458336	458487	458638	458789	458940	459091	459242	151
8	459392	459543	459694	459845	459995	460146	460296	460447	460597	460748	
9	460898	461048	461198	461348	461499	461649	461799	461948	462098	462248	150
290	**462398**	**462548**	**462697**	**462847**	**462997**	**463146**	**463296**	**463445**	**463594**	**463744**	
1	463893	464042	464191	464340	464490	464639	464788	464936	465085	465234	149
2	465383	465532	465680	465829	465977	466126	466274	466423	466571	466719	
3	466868	467016	467164	467312	467460	467608	467756	467904	468052	468200	148
4	468347	468495	468643	468790	468938	469085	469233	469380	469527	469675	
5	469822	469969	470116	470263	470410	470557	470704	470851	470998	471145	147
6	471292	471438	471585	471732	471878	472025	472171	472318	472464	472610	146
7	472756	472903	473049	473195	473341	473487	473633	473779	473925	474071	
8	474216	474362	474508	474653	474799	474944	475090	475235	475381	475526	
9	475671	475816	475962	476107	476252	476397	476542	476687	476832	476976	145
300	**477121**	**477266**	**477411**	**477555**	**477700**	**477844**	**477989**	**478133**	**478278**	**478422**	
1	478566	478711	478855	478999	479143	479287	479431	479575	479719	479863	144
2	480007	480151	480294	480438	480582	480725	480869	481012	481156	481299	
3	481443	481586	481729	481872	482016	482159	482302	482445	482588	482731	143
4	482874	483016	483159	483302	483445	483587	483730	483872	484015	484157	
5	484300	484442	484585	484727	484869	485011	485153	485295	485437	485579	142
6	485721	485863	486005	486147	486289	486430	486572	486714	486855	486997	
7	487138	487280	487421	487563	487704	487845	487986	488127	488269	488410	141
8	488551	488692	488833	488974	489114	489255	489396	489537	489677	489818	
9	489958	490099	490239	490380	490520	490661	490801	490941	491081	491222	140
310	**491362**	**491502**	**491642**	**491782**	**491922**	**492062**	**492201**	**492341**	**492481**	**492621**	
1	492760	492900	493040	493179	493319	493458	493597	493737	493876	494015	139
2	494155	494294	494433	494572	494711	494850	494989	495128	495267	495406	
3	495544	495683	495822	495960	496099	496238	496376	496515	496653	496791	
4	496930	497068	497206	497344	497483	497621	497759	497897	498035	498173	138
5	498311	498448	498586	498724	498862	498999	499137	499275	499412	499550	
6	499687	499824	499962	500099	500236	500374	500511	500648	500785	500922	137
7	501059	501196	501333	501470	501607	501744	501880	502017	502154	502291	
8	502427	502564	502700	502837	502973	503109	503246	503382	503518	503655	136
9	503791	503927	504063	504199	504335	504471	504607	504743	504878	505014	
320	**505150**	**505286**	**505421**	**505557**	**505693**	**505828**	**505964**	**506099**	**506234**	**506370**	
1	506505	506640	506776	506911	507046	507181	507316	507451	507586	507721	135
2	507856	507991	508126	508260	508395	508530	508664	508799	508934	509068	
3	509203	509337	509471	509606	509740	509874	510009	510143	510277	510411	134
4	510545	510679	510813	510947	511081	511215	511349	511482	511616	511750	
5	511883	512017	512151	512284	512418	512551	512684	512818	512951	513084	133
6	513218	513351	513484	513617	513750	513883	514016	514149	514282	514415	
7	514548	514681	514813	514946	515079	515211	515344	515476	515609	515741	
8	515874	516006	516139	516271	516403	516535	516668	516800	516932	517064	132
9	517196	517328	517460	517592	517724	517855	517987	518119	518251	518382	
330	**518514**	**518646**	**518777**	**518909**	**519040**	**519171**	**519303**	**519434**	**519566**	**519697**	131

PROPORTIONAL PARTS

Diff.	1	2	3	4	5	6	7	8	9
154	15.4	30.8	46.2	61.6	77.0	92.4	107.8	123.2	138.6
152	15.2	30.4	45.6	60.8	76.0	91.2	106.4	121.6	136.8
150	15.0	30.0	45.0	60.0	75.0	90.0	105.0	120.0	135.0
148	14.8	29.6	44.4	59.2	74.0	88.8	103.6	118.4	133.2
146	14.6	29.2	43.8	58.4	73.0	87.6	102.2	116.8	131.4
144	14.4	28.8	43.2	57.6	72.0	86.4	100.8	115.2	129.6
142	14.2	28.4	42.6	56.8	71.0	85.2	99.4	113.6	127.8
140	14.0	28.0	42.0	56.0	70.0	84.0	98.0	112.0	126.0
138	13.8	27.6	41.4	55.2	69.0	82.8	96.6	110.4	124.2
136	13.6	27.2	40.8	54.4	68.0	81.6	95.2	108.8	122.4

N	0	1	2	3	4	5	6	7	8	9	Diff.
330	518514	518646	518777	518909	519040	519171	519303	519434	519566	519697	
1	519828	519959	520090	520221	520353	520484	520615	520745	520876	521007	
2	521138	521269	521400	521530	521661	521792	521922	522053	522183	522314	
3	522444	522575	522705	522835	522966	523096	523226	523356	523486	523616	130
4	523746	523876	524006	524136	524266	524396	524526	524656	524785	524915	
5	525045	525174	525304	525434	525563	525693	525822	525951	526081	526210	129
6	526339	526469	526598	526727	526856	526985	527114	527243	527372	527501	
7	527630	527759	527888	528016	528145	528274	528402	528531	528660	528788	
8	528917	529045	529174	529302	529430	529559	529687	529815	529943	530072	128
9	530200	530328	530456	530584	530712	530840	530968	531096	531223	531351	
340	531479	531607	531734	531862	531990	532117	532245	532372	532500	532627	
1	532754	532882	533009	533136	533264	533391	533518	533645	533772	533899	127
2	534026	534153	534280	534407	534534	534661	534787	534914	535041	535167	
3	535294	535421	535547	535674	535800	535927	536053	536180	536306	536432	126
4	536558	536685	536811	536937	537063	537189	537315	537441	537567	537693	
5	537819	537945	538071	538197	538322	538448	538574	538699	538825	538951	
6	539076	539202	539327	539452	539578	539703	539829	539954	540079	540204	125
7	540329	540455	540580	540705	540830	540955	541080	541205	541330	541454	
8	541579	541704	541829	541953	542078	542203	542327	542452	542576	542701	
9	542825	542950	543074	543199	543323	543447	543571	543696	543820	543944	124
350	544068	544192	544316	544440	544564	544688	544812	544936	545060	545183	
1	545307	545431	545555	545678	545802	545925	546049	546172	546296	546419	
2	546543	546666	546789	546913	547036	547159	547282	547405	547529	547652	123
3	547775	547898	548021	548144	548267	548389	548512	548635	548758	548881	
4	549003	549126	549249	549371	549494	549616	549739	549861	549984	550106	
5	550228	550351	550473	550595	550717	550840	550962	551084	551206	551328	122
6	551450	551572	551694	551816	551938	552060	552181	552303	552425	552547	
7	552668	552790	552911	553033	553155	553276	553398	553519	553640	553762	121
8	553883	554004	554126	554247	554368	554489	554610	554731	554852	554973	
9	555094	555215	555336	555457	555578	555699	555820	555940	556061	556182	
360	556303	556423	556544	556664	556785	556905	557026	557146	557267	557387	120
1	557507	557627	557748	557868	557988	558108	558228	558349	558469	558589	
2	558709	558829	558948	559068	559188	559308	559428	559548	559667	559787	
3	559907	560026	560146	560265	560385	560504	560624	560743	560863	560982	119
4	561101	561221	561340	561459	561578	561696	561817	561936	562055	562174	
5	562293	562412	562531	562650	562769	562887	563006	563125	563244	563362	
6	563481	563600	563718	563837	563955	564074	564192	564311	564429	564548	
7	564666	564784	564903	565021	565139	565257	565376	565494	565612	565730	118
8	565848	565966	566084	566202	566320	566437	566555	566673	566791	566909	
9	567026	567144	567262	567379	567497	567614	567732	567849	567967	568084	
370	568202	568319	568436	568554	568671	568788	568905	569023	569140	569257	117
1	569374	569491	569608	569725	569842	569959	570076	570193	570309	570426	
2	570543	570660	570776	570893	571010	571126	571243	571359	571476	571592	
3	571709	571825	571942	572058	572174	572291	572407	572523	572639	572755	116
4	572872	572988	573104	573220	573336	573452	573568	573684	573800	573915	
5	574031	574147	574263	574379	574494	574610	574726	574841	574957	575072	
6	575188	575303	575419	575534	575650	575765	575880	575996	576111	576226	115
7	576341	576457	576572	576687	576802	576917	577032	577147	577262	577377	
8	577492	577607	577722	577836	577951	578066	578181	578295	578410	578525	
9	578639	578754	578868	578983	579097	579212	579326	579441	579555	579669	114
380	579784	579898	580012	580126	580241	580355	580469	580583	580697	580811	

PROPORTIONAL PARTS

Diff.	1	2	3	4	5	6	7	8	9
134	13.4	26.8	40.2	53.6	67.0	80.4	93.8	107.2	120.6
132	13.2	26.4	39.6	52.8	66.0	79.2	92.4	105.6	118.8
130	13.0	26.0	39.0	52.0	65.0	78.0	91.0	104.0	117.0
128	12.8	25.6	38.4	51.2	64.0	76.8	89.6	102.4	115.2
126	12.6	25.2	37.8	50.4	63.0	75.6	88.2	100.8	113.4
124	12.4	24.8	37.2	49.6	62.0	74.4	86.8	99.2	111.6
122	12.2	24.4	36.6	48.8	61.0	73.2	85.4	97.6	109.8
120	12.0	24.0	36.0	48.0	60.0	72.0	84.0	96.0	108.0
118	11.8	23.6	35.4	47.2	59.0	70.8	82.6	94.4	106.2
116	11.6	23.2	34.8	46.4	58.0	69.6	81.2	92.8	104.4
114	11.4	22.8	34.2	45.6	57.0	68.4	79.8	91.2	102.6

N	0	1	2	3	4	5	6	7	8	9	Diff.
380	579784	579898	580012	580126	580241	580355	580469	580583	580697	580811	114
1	580925	581039	581153	581267	581381	581495	581608	581722	581836	581950	
2	582063	582177	582291	582404	582518	582631	582745	582858	582972	583085	
3	583199	583312	583426	583539	583652	583765	583879	583992	584105	584218	
4	584331	584444	584557	584670	584783	584896	585009	585122	585235	585348	113
5	585461	585574	585686	585799	585912	586024	586137	586250	586362	586475	
6	586587	586700	586812	586925	587037	587149	587262	587374	587486	587599	
7	587711	587823	587935	588047	588160	588272	588384	588496	588608	588720	112
8	588832	588944	589056	589167	589279	589391	589503	589615	589727	589838	
9	589950	590061	590173	590284	590396	590507	590619	590730	590842	590953	
390	591065	591176	591237	591399	591510	591621	591732	591843	591955	592066	
1	592177	592288	592399	592510	592621	592732	592843	592954	593064	593175	111
2	593286	593397	593508	593618	593729	593840	593950	594061	594171	594282	
3	594393	594503	594614	594724	594834	594945	595055	595165	595276	595386	
4	595496	595606	595717	595827	595937	596047	596157	596267	596377	596487	110
5	596597	596707	596817	596927	597037	597146	597256	597366	597476	597586	
6	597695	597805	597914	598024	598134	598243	598353	598462	598572	598681	
7	598791	598900	599009	599119	599228	599337	599446	599556	599665	599774	109
8	599883	599992	600101	600210	600319	600428	600537	600646	600755	600864	
9	600973	601082	601191	601299	601408	601517	601625	601734	601843	601951	
400	602060	602169	602277	602386	602494	602603	602711	602819	602928	603036	
1	603144	603253	603361	603469	603577	603686	603794	603902	604010	604118	108
2	604226	604334	604442	604550	604658	604766	604874	604982	605089	605197	
3	605305	605413	605521	605628	605736	605844	605951	606059	606166	606274	
4	606381	606489	606596	606704	606811	606919	607026	607133	607241	607348	107
5	607455	607562	607669	607777	607884	607991	608098	608205	608312	608419	
6	608526	608633	608740	608847	608954	609061	609167	609274	609381	609488	
7	609594	609701	609808	609914	610021	610128	610234	610341	610447	610554	
8	610660	610767	610873	610979	611086	611192	611298	611405	611511	611617	
9	611723	611829	611936	612042	612148	612254	612360	612466	612572	612678	106
410	612784	612890	612996	613102	613207	613313	613419	613525	613630	613736	
1	613842	613947	614053	614159	614264	614370	614475	614581	614686	614792	
2	614897	615003	615108	615213	615319	615424	615529	615634	615740	615845	
3	615950	616055	616160	616265	616370	616476	616581	616686	616790	616895	105
4	617000	617105	617210	617315	617420	617525	617629	617734	617839	617943	
5	618048	618153	618257	618362	618466	618571	618676	618780	618884	618989	
6	619093	619198	619302	619406	619511	619615	619719	619824	619928	620032	
7	620136	620240	620344	620448	620552	620656	620760	620864	620968	621072	104
8	621176	621280	621384	621488	621592	621695	621799	621903	622007	622110	
9	622214	622318	622421	622525	622628	622732	622835	622939	623042	623146	
420	623249	623353	623456	623559	623663	623766	623869	623973	624076	624179	
1	624282	624385	624488	624591	624695	624798	624901	625004	625107	625210	103
2	625312	625415	625518	625621	625724	625827	625929	626032	626135	626238	
3	626340	626443	626546	626648	626751	626853	626956	627058	627161	627263	
4	627366	627468	627571	627673	627775	627878	627980	628082	628185	628287	102
5	628389	628491	628593	628695	628797	628900	629002	629104	629206	629308	
6	629410	629512	629613	629715	629817	629919	630021	630123	630224	630326	
7	630428	630530	630631	630733	630835	630936	631038	631139	631241	631342	
8	631444	631545	631647	631748	631849	631951	632052	632153	632255	632356	
9	632457	632559	632660	632761	632862	632963	633064	633165	633266	633367	
430	633468	633569	633670	633771	633872	633973	634074	634175	634276	634376	101

PROPORTIONAL PARTS

Diff.	1	2	3	4	5	6	7	8	9
114	11.4	22.8	34.2	45.6	57.0	68.4	79.8	91.2	102.6
112	11.2	22.4	33.6	44.8	56.0	67.2	78.4	89.6	100.8
110	11.0	22.0	33.0	44.0	55.0	66.0	77.0	88.0	99.0
108	10.8	21.6	32.4	43.2	54.0	64.8	75.6	86.4	97.2
106	10.6	21.2	31.8	42.4	53.0	63.6	74.2	84.8	95.4
104	10.4	20.8	31.2	41.6	52.0	62.4	72.8	83.2	93.6
102	10.2	20.4	30.6	40.8	51.0	61.2	71.4	81.6	91.8

N	0	1	2	3	4	5	6	7	8	9	Diff.
430	633468	633569	633670	633771	633872	633973	634074	634175	634276	634376	
1	634477	634578	634679	634779	634880	634981	635081	635182	635283	635383	
2	635484	635584	635685	635785	635886	635986	636087	636187	636287	636388	
3	636488	636588	636688	636789	636889	636989	637089	637189	637290	637390	
4	637490	637590	637690	637790	637890	637990	638090	638190	638290	638389	100
5	638489	638589	638689	638789	638888	638988	639088	639188	639287	639387	
6	639486	639586	639686	639785	639885	639984	640084	640183	640283	640382	
7	640481	640581	640680	640779	640879	640978	641077	641177	641276	641375	
8	641474	641573	641672	641771	641871	641970	642069	642168	642267	642366	
9	642465	642563	642662	642761	642860	642959	643058	643156	643255	643354	99
440	643453	643551	643650	643749	643847	643946	644044	644143	644242	644340	
1	644439	644537	644636	644734	644832	644931	645029	645127	645226	645324	
2	645422	645521	645619	645717	645815	645913	646011	646110	646208	646306	
3	646404	646502	646600	646698	646796	646894	646992	647089	647187	647285	98
4	647383	647481	647579	647676	647774	647872	647969	648067	648165	648262	
5	648360	648458	648555	648653	648750	648848	648945	649043	649140	649237	
6	649335	649432	649530	649627	649724	649821	649919	650016	650113	650210	
7	650308	650405	650502	650599	650696	650793	650890	650987	651084	651181	
8	651278	651375	651472	651569	651666	651762	651859	651956	652053	652150	97
9	652246	652343	652440	652536	652633	652730	652826	652923	653019	653116	
450	653213	653309	653405	653502	653598	653695	653791	653888	653984	654080	
1	654177	654273	654369	654465	654562	654658	654754	654850	654946	655042	
2	655138	655235	655331	655427	655523	655619	655715	655810	655906	656002	96
3	656098	656194	656290	656386	656482	656577	656673	656769	656864	656960	
4	657056	657152	657247	657343	657438	657534	657629	657725	657820	657916	
5	658011	658107	658202	658298	658393	658488	658584	658679	658774	658870	
6	658965	659060	659155	659250	659346	659441	659536	659631	659726	659821	
7	659916	660011	660106	660201	660296	660391	660486	660581	660676	660771	95
8	660865	660960	661055	661150	661245	661339	661434	661529	661623	661718	
9	661813	661907	662002	662096	662191	662286	662380	662475	662569	662663	
460	662758	662852	662947	663041	663135	663230	663324	663418	663512	663607	
1	663701	663795	663889	663983	664078	664172	664266	664360	664454	664548	
2	664642	664736	664830	664924	665018	665112	665206	665299	665393	665487	94
3	665581	665675	665769	665862	665956	666050	666143	666237	666331	666424	
4	666518	666612	666705	666799	666892	666986	667079	667173	667266	667360	
5	667453	667546	667640	667733	667826	667920	668013	668106	668199	668293	
6	668386	668479	668572	668665	668759	668852	668945	669038	669131	669224	
7	669317	669410	669503	669596	669689	669782	669875	669967	670060	670153	93
8	670246	670339	670431	670524	670617	670710	670802	670895	670988	671080	
9	671173	671265	671358	671451	671543	671636	671728	671821	671913	672005	
470	672098	672190	672283	672375	672467	672560	672652	672744	672836	672929	
1	673021	673113	673205	673297	673390	673482	673574	673666	673758	673850	
2	673942	674034	674126	674218	674310	674402	674494	674586	674677	674769	92
3	674861	674953	675045	675137	675228	675320	675412	675503	675595	675687	
4	675778	675870	675962	676053	676145	676236	676328	676419	676511	676602	
5	676694	676785	676876	676968	677059	677151	677242	677333	677424	677516	
6	677607	677698	677789	677881	677972	678063	678154	678245	678336	678427	
7	678518	678609	678700	678791	678882	678973	679064	679155	679246	679337	91
8	679428	679519	679610	679700	679791	679882	679973	680063	680154	680245	
9	680336	680426	680517	680607	680698	680789	680879	680970	681060	681151	
480	681241	681332	681422	681513	681603	681693	681784	681874	681964	682055	

PROPORTIONAL PARTS

Diff.	1	2	3	4	5	6	7	8	9
102	10.2	20.4	30.6	40.8	51.0	61.2	71.4	81.6	91.8
100	10.0	20.0	30.0	40.0	50.0	60.0	70.0	80.0	90.0
98	9.8	19.6	29.4	39.2	49.0	58.8	68.6	78.4	88.2
96	9.6	19.2	28.8	38.4	48.0	57.6	67.2	76.8	86.4
94	9.4	18.8	28.2	37.6	47.0	56.4	65.8	75.2	84.6
92	9.2	18.4	27.6	36.8	46.0	55.2	64.4	73.6	82.8
90	9.0	18.0	27.0	36.0	45.0	54.0	63.0	72.0	81.0

N	0	1	2	3	4	5	6	7	8	9	Diff.
480	**681241**	**681332**	**681422**	**681513**	**681603**	**681693**	**681784**	**681874**	**681964**	**682055**	
1	682145	682235	682326	682416	682506	682596	682686	682777	682867	682957	
2	683047	683137	683227	683317	683407	683497	683587	683677	683767	683857	90
3	683947	684037	684127	684217	684307	684396	684486	684576	684666	684756	
4	684845	684935	685025	685114	685204	685294	685383	685473	685563	685652	
5	685742	685831	685921	686010	686100	686189	686279	686368	686458	686547	
6	686636	686726	686815	686904	686994	687083	687172	687261	687351	687440	
7	687529	687618	687707	687796	687886	687975	688064	688153	688242	688331	
8	688420	688509	688598	688687	688776	688865	688953	689042	689131	689220	89
9	689309	689398	689486	689575	689664	689753	689841	689930	690019	690107	
490	**690196**	**690285**	**690373**	**690462**	**690550**	**690639**	**690728**	**690816**	**690905**	**690993**	
1	691081	691170	691258	691347	691435	691524	691612	691700	691789	691877	
2	691965	692053	692142	692230	692318	692406	692494	692583	692671	692759	
3	692847	692935	693023	693111	693199	693287	693375	693463	693551	693639	88
4	693727	693815	693903	693991	694078	694166	694254	694342	694430	694517	
5	694605	694693	694781	694868	694956	695044	695131	695219	695307	695394	
6	695482	695569	695657	695744	695832	695919	696007	696094	696182	696269	
7	696356	696444	696531	696618	696706	696793	696880	696968	697055	697142	
8	697229	697317	697404	697491	697578	697665	697752	697839	697926	698014	87
9	698100	698188	698275	698362	698449	698535	698622	698709	698796	698883	
500	**698970**	**699057**	**699144**	**699231**	**699317**	**699404**	**699491**	**699578**	**699664**	**699751**	
1	699838	699924	700011	700098	700184	700271	700358	700444	700531	700617	
2	700704	700790	700877	700963	701050	701136	701222	701309	701395	701482	
3	701568	701654	701741	701827	701913	701999	702086	702172	702258	702344	
4	702431	702517	702603	702689	702775	702861	702947	703033	703119	703205	
5	703291	703377	703463	703549	703635	703721	703807	703893	703979	704065	86
6	704151	704236	704322	704408	704494	704579	704665	704751	704837	704922	
7	705008	705094	705179	705265	705350	705436	705522	705607	705693	705778	
8	705864	705949	706035	706120	706206	706291	706376	706462	706547	706632	
9	706718	706803	706888	706974	707059	707144	707229	707315	707400	707485	
510	**707570**	**707655**	**707740**	**707826**	**707911**	**707996**	**708081**	**708166**	**708251**	**708336**	
1	708421	708506	708591	708676	708761	708846	708931	709015	709100	709185	85
2	709270	709355	709440	709524	709609	709694	709779	709863	709948	710033	
3	710117	710202	710287	710371	710456	710540	710625	710710	710794	710879	
4	710963	711048	711132	711217	711301	711385	711470	711554	711639	711723	
5	711807	711892	711976	712060	712144	712229	712313	712397	712481	712566	
6	712650	712734	712818	712902	712986	713070	713154	713238	713323	713407	
7	713491	713575	713659	713742	713826	713910	713994	714078	714162	714246	84
8	714330	714414	714497	714581	714665	714749	714833	714916	715000	715084	
9	715167	715251	715335	715418	715502	715586	715669	715753	715836	715920	
520	**716003**	**716087**	**716170**	**716254**	**716337**	**716421**	**716504**	**716588**	**716671**	**716754**	
1	716838	716921	717004	717088	717171	717254	717338	717421	717504	717587	
2	717671	717754	717837	717920	718003	718086	718169	718253	718336	718419	83
3	718502	718585	718668	718751	718834	718917	719000	719083	719165	719248	
4	719331	719414	719497	719580	719663	719745	719828	719911	719994	720077	
5	720159	720242	720325	720407	720490	720573	720655	720738	720821	720903	
6	720986	721068	721151	721233	721316	721398	721481	721563	721646	721728	
7	721811	721893	721975	722058	722140	722222	722305	722387	722469	722552	
8	722634	722716	722798	722881	722963	723045	723127	723209	723291	723374	
9	723456	723538	723620	723702	723784	723866	723948	724030	724112	724194	82
530	**724276**	**724358**	**724440**	**724522**	**724604**	**724685**	**724767**	**724849**	**724931**	**725013**	

PROPORTIONAL PARTS

Diff.	1	2	3	4	5	6	7	8	9
90	9.0	18.0	27.0	36.0	45.0	54.0	63.0	72.0	81.0
88	8.8	17.6	26.4	35.2	44.0	52.8	61.6	70.4	79.2
86	8.6	17.2	25.8	34.4	43.0	51.6	60.2	68.8	77.4
84	8.4	16.8	25.2	33.6	42.0	50.4	58.8	67.2	75.6
82	8.2	16.4	24.6	32.8	41.0	49.2	57.4	65.6	73.8

N	0	1	2	3	4	5	6	7	8	9	Diff.
530	**724276**	**724358**	**724440**	**724522**	**724604**	**724685**	**724767**	**724849**	**724931**	**725013**	
1	725095	725176	725258	725340	725422	725503	725585	725667	725748	725830	
2	725912	725993	726075	726156	726238	726320	726401	726483	726564	726646	
3	726727	726809	726890	726972	727053	727134	727216	727297	727379	727460	
4	727541	727623	727704	727785	727866	727948	728029	728110	728191	728273	
5	728354	728435	728516	728597	728678	728759	728841	728922	729003	729084	
6	729165	729246	729327	729408	729489	729570	729651	729732	729813	729893	81
7	729974	730055	730136	730217	730298	730378	730459	730540	730621	730702	
8	730782	730863	730944	731024	731105	731186	731266	731347	731428	731508	
9	731589	731669	731750	731830	731911	731991	732072	732152	732233	732313	
540	**732394**	**732474**	**732555**	**732635**	**732715**	**732796**	**732876**	**732956**	**733037**	**733117**	
1	733197	733278	733358	733438	733518	733598	733679	733759	733839	733919	
2	733999	734079	734160	734240	734320	734400	734480	734560	734640	734720	80
3	734800	734880	734960	735040	735120	735200	735279	735359	735439	735519	
4	735599	735679	735759	735838	735918	735998	736078	736157	736237	736317	
5	736397	736476	736556	736635	736715	736795	736874	736954	737034	737113	
6	737193	737272	737352	737431	737511	737590	737670	737749	737829	737908	
7	737987	738067	738146	738225	738305	738384	738463	738543	738622	738701	
8	738781	738860	738939	739018	739097	739177	739256	739335	739414	739493	
9	739572	739651	739731	739810	739889	739968	740047	740126	740205	740284	79
550	**740363**	**740442**	**740521**	**740600**	**740678**	**740757**	**740836**	**740915**	**740994**	**741073**	
1	741152	741230	741309	741388	741467	741546	741624	741703	741782	741860	
2	741939	742018	742096	742175	742254	742332	742411	742489	742568	742647	
3	742725	742804	742882	742961	743039	743118	743196	743275	743353	743431	
4	743510	743588	743667	743745	743823	743902	743980	744058	744136	744215	
5	744293	744371	744449	744528	744606	744684	744762	744840	744919	744997	
6	745075	745153	745231	745309	745387	745465	745543	745621	745699	745777	78
7	745855	745933	746011	746089	746167	746245	746323	746401	746479	746556	
8	746634	746712	746790	746868	746945	747023	747101	747179	747256	747334	
9	747412	747489	747567	747645	747722	747800	747878	747955	748033	748110	
560	**748188**	**748266**	**748343**	**748421**	**748498**	**748576**	**748653**	**748731**	**748808**	**748885**	
1	748963	749040	749118	749195	749272	749350	749427	749504	749582	749659	
2	749736	749814	749891	749968	750045	750123	750200	750277	750354	750431	
3	750508	750586	750663	750740	750817	750894	750971	751048	751125	751202	
4	751279	751356	751433	751510	751587	751664	751741	751818	751895	751972	77
5	752048	752125	752202	752279	752356	752433	752509	752586	752663	752740	
6	752816	752893	752970	753047	753123	753200	753277	753353	753430	753506	
7	753583	753660	753736	753813	753889	753966	754042	754119	754195	754272	
8	754348	754425	754501	754578	754654	754730	754807	754883	754960	755036	
9	755112	755189	755265	755341	755417	755494	755570	755646	755722	755799	
570	**755875**	**755951**	**756027**	**756103**	**756180**	**756256**	**756332**	**756408**	**756484**	**756560**	
1	756636	756712	756788	756864	756940	757016	757092	757168	757244	757320	76
2	757396	757472	757548	757624	757700	757775	757851	757927	758003	7₺8079	
3	758155	758230	758306	758382	758458	758533	758609	758685	758761	758836	
4	758912	758988	759063	759139	759214	759290	759366	759441	759517	759592	
5	759668	759743	759819	759894	759970	760045	760121	760196	760272	760347	
6	760422	760498	760573	760649	760724	760799	760875	760950	761025	761101	
7	761176	761251	761326	761402	761477	761552	761627	761702	761778	761853	
8	761928	762003	762078	762153	762228	762303	762378	762453	762529	762604	75
9	762679	762754	762829	762904	762978	763053	763128	763203	763278	763353	
580	**763428**	**763503**	**763578**	**763653**	**763727**	**763802**	**763877**	**763952**	**764027**	**764101**	

PROPORTIONAL PARTS

Diff.	1	2	3	4	5	6	7	8	9
82	8.2	16.4	24.6	32.8	41.0	49.2	57.4	65.6	73.8
80	8.0	16.0	24.0	32.0	40.0	48.0	56.0	64.0	72.0
78	7.8	15.6	23.4	31.2	39.0	46.8	54.6	62.4	70.2
76	7.6	15.2	22.8	30.4	38.0	45.6	53.2	60.8	68.4
74	7.4	14.8	22.2	29.6	37.0	44.4	51.8	59.2	66.6

N	0	1	2	3	4	5	6	7	8	9	Diff.
580	763428	763503	763578	763653	763727	763802	763877	763952	764027	764101	
1	764176	764251	764326	764400	764475	764550	764624	764699	764774	764848	
2	764923	764998	765072	765147	765221	765296	765370	765445	765520	765594	
3	765669	765743	765818	765892	765966	766041	766115	766190	766264	766338	
4	766413	766487	766562	766636	766710	766785	766859	766933	767007	767082	
5	767156	767230	767304	767379	767453	767527	767601	767675	767749	767823	
6	767898	767972	768046	768120	768194	768268	768342	768416	768490	768564	74
7	768638	768712	768786	768860	768934	769008	769082	769156	769230	769303	
8	769377	769451	769525	769599	769673	769746	769820	769894	769968	770042	
9	770115	770189	770263	770336	770410	770484	770557	770631	770705	770778	
590	770852	770926	770999	771073	771146	771220	771293	771367	771440	771514	
1	771587	771661	771734	771808	771881	771955	772028	772102	772175	772248	
2	772322	772395	772468	772542	772615	772688	772762	772835	772908	772981	
3	773055	773128	773201	773274	773348	773421	773494	773567	773640	773713	
4	773786	773860	773933	774006	774079	774152	774225	774298	774371	774444	73
5	774517	774590	774663	774736	774809	774882	774955	775028	775100	775173	
6	775246	775319	775392	775465	775538	775610	775683	775756	775829	775902	
7	775974	776047	776120	776193	776265	776338	776411	776483	776556	776629	
8	776701	776774	776846	776919	776992	777064	777137	777209	777282	777354	
9	777427	777499	777572	777644	777717	777789	777862	777934	778006	778079	
600	778151	778224	778296	778368	778441	778513	778585	778658	778730	778802	
1	778874	778947	779019	779091	779163	779236	779308	779380	779452	779524	
2	779596	779669	779741	779813	779885	779957	780029	780101	780173	780245	
3	780317	780389	780461	780533	780605	780677	780749	780821	780893	780965	72
4	781037	781109	781181	781253	781324	781396	781468	781540	781612	781684	
5	781755	781827	781899	781971	782042	782114	782186	782258	782329	782401	
6	782473	782544	782616	782688	782759	782831	782902	782974	783046	783117	
7	783189	783260	783332	783403	783475	783546	783618	783689	783761	783832	
8	783904	783975	784046	784118	784189	784261	784332	784403	784475	784546	
9	784617	784689	784760	784831	784902	784974	785045	785116	785187	785259	
610	785330	785401	785472	785543	785615	785686	785757	785828	785899	785970	
1	786041	786112	786183	786254	786325	786396	786467	786538	786609	786680	71
2	786751	786822	786893	786964	787035	787106	787177	787248	787319	787390	
3	787460	787531	787602	787673	787744	787815	787885	787956	788027	788098	
4	788168	788239	788310	788381	788451	788522	788593	788663	788734	788804	
5	788875	788946	789016	789087	789157	789228	789299	789369	789440	789510	
6	789581	789651	789722	789792	789863	789933	790004	790074	790144	790215	
7	790285	790356	790426	790496	790567	790637	790707	790778	790848	790918	
8	790988	791059	791129	791199	791269	791340	791410	791480	791550	791620	
9	791691	791761	791831	791901	791971	792041	792111	792181	792252	792322	
620	792392	792462	792532	792602	792672	792742	792812	792882	792952	793022	70
1	793092	793162	793231	793301	793371	793441	793511	793581	793651	793721	
2	793790	793860	793930	794000	794070	794139	794209	794279	794349	794418	
3	794488	794558	794627	794697	794767	794836	794906	794976	795045	795115	
4	795185	795254	795324	795393	795463	795532	795602	795672	795741	795811	
5	795880	795949	796019	796088	796158	796227	796297	796366	796436	796505	
6	796574	796644	796713	796782	796852	796921	796990	797060	797129	797198	
7	797268	797337	797406	797475	797545	797614	797683	797752	797821	797890	
8	797960	798029	798098	798167	798236	798305	798374	798443	798513	798582	
9	798651	798720	798789	798858	798927	798996	799065	799134	799203	799272	69
630	799341	799409	799478	799547	799616	799685	799754	799823	799892	799961	

PROPORTIONAL PARTS

Diff.	1	2	3	4	5	6	7	8	9
76	7.6	15.2	22.8	30.4	38.0	45.6	53.2	60.8	68.4
74	7.4	14.8	22.2	29.6	37.0	44.4	51.8	59.2	66.6
72	7.2	14.4	21.6	28.8	36.0	43.2	50.4	57.6	64.8
70	7.0	14.0	21.0	28.0	35.0	42.0	49.0	56.0	63.0
68	6.8	13.6	20.4	27.2	34.0	40.8	47.6	54.4	61.2

N	0	1	2	3	4	5	6	7	8	9	Diff.
630	799341	799409	799478	799547	799616	799685	799754	799823	799892	799961	
1	800029	800098	800167	800236	800305	800373	800442	800511	800580	800648	
2	800717	800786	800854	800923	800992	801061	801129	801198	801266	801335	
3	801404	801472	801541	801609	801678	801747	801815	801884	801952	802021	
4	802089	802158	802226	802295	802363	802432	802500	802568	802637	802705	
5	802774	802842	802910	802979	803047	803116	803184	803252	803321	803389	
6	803457	803525	803594	803662	803730	803798	803867	803935	804003	804071	
7	804139	804208	804276	804344	804412	804480	804548	804616	804685	804753	
8	804821	804889	804957	805025	805093	805161	805229	805297	805365	805433	68
9	805501	805569	805637	805705	805773	805841	805908	805976	806044	806112	
640	806180	806248	806316	806384	806451	806519	806587	806655	806723	806790	
1	806858	806926	806994	807061	807129	807197	807264	807332	807400	807467	
2	807535	807603	807670	807738	807806	807873	807941	808008	808076	808143	
3	808211	808279	808346	808414	808481	808549	808616	808684	808751	808818	
4	808886	808953	809021	809088	809156	809223	809290	809358	809425	809492	
5	809560	809627	809694	809762	809829	809896	809964	810031	810098	810165	
6	810233	810300	810367	810434	810501	810569	810636	810703	810770	810837	
7	810904	810971	811039	811106	811173	811240	811307	811374	811441	811508	
8	811575	811642	811709	811776	811843	811910	811977	812044	812111	812178	67
9	812245	812312	812379	812445	812512	812579	812646	812713	812780	812847	
650	812913	812980	813047	813114	813181	813247	813314	813381	813448	813514	
1	813581	813648	813714	813781	813848	813914	813981	814048	814114	814181	
2	814248	814314	814381	814447	814514	814581	814647	814714	814780	814847	
3	814913	814980	815046	815113	815179	815246	815312	815378	815445	815511	
4	815578	815644	815711	815777	815843	815910	815976	816042	816109	816175	
5	816241	816308	816374	816440	816506	816573	816639	816705	816771	816838	
6	816904	816970	817036	817102	817169	817235	817301	817367	817433	817499	
7	817565	817631	817698	817764	817830	817896	817962	818028	818094	818160	
8	818226	818292	818358	818424	818490	818556	818622	818688	818754	818820	66
9	818885	818951	819017	819083	819149	819215	819281	819346	819412	819478	
660	819544	819610	819676	819741	819807	819873	819939	820004	820070	820136	
1	820201	820267	820333	820399	820464	820530	820595	820661	820727	820792	
2	820858	820924	820989	821055	821120	821186	821251	821317	821382	821448	
3	821514	821579	821645	821710	821775	821841	821906	821972	822037	822103	
4	822168	822233	822299	822364	822430	822495	822560	822626	822691	822756	
5	822822	822887	822952	823018	823083	823148	823213	823279	823344	823409	
6	823474	823539	823605	823670	823735	823800	823865	823930	823996	824061	
7	824126	824191	824256	824321	824386	824451	824516	824581	824646	824711	
8	824776	824841	824906	824971	825036	825101	825166	825231	825296	825361	65
9	825426	825491	825556	825621	825686	825751	825815	825880	825945	826010	
670	826075	826140	826204	826269	826334	826399	826464	826528	826593	826658	
1	826723	826787	826852	826917	826981	827046	827111	827175	827240	827305	
2	827369	827434	827499	827563	827628	827692	827757	827821	827886	827951	
3	828015	828080	828144	828209	828273	828338	828402	828467	828531	828595	
4	828660	828724	828789	828853	828918	828982	829046	829111	829175	829239	
5	829304	829368	829432	829497	829561	829625	829690	829754	829818	829882	
6	829947	830011	830075	830139	830204	830268	830332	830396	830460	830525	
7	830589	830653	830717	830781	830845	830909	830973	831037	831102	831166	
8	831230	831294	831358	831422	831486	831550	831614	831678	831742	831806	64
9	831870	831934	831998	832062	832126	832189	832253	832317	832381	832445	
680	832509	832573	832637	832700	832764	832828	832892	832956	833020	833083	

PROPORTIONAL PARTS

Diff.	1	2	3	4	5	6	7	8	9
70	7.0	14.0	21.0	28.0	35.0	42.0	49.0	56.0	63.0
68	6.8	13.6	20.4	27.2	34.0	40.8	47.6	54.4	61.2
66	6.6	13.2	19.8	26.4	33.0	39.6	46.2	52.8	59.4
64	6.4	12.8	19.2	25.6	32.0	38.4	44.8	51.2	57.6
62	6.2	12.4	18.6	24.8	31.0	37.2	43.4	49.6	55.8

N	0	1	2	3	4	5	6	7	8	9	Diff.
680	832509	832573	832637	832700	832764	832828	832892	832956	833020	833083	
1	833147	833211	833275	833338	833402	833466	833530	833593	833657	833721	
2	833784	833848	833912	833975	834039	834103	834166	834230	834294	834357	
3	834421	834484	834548	834611	834675	834739	834802	834866	834929	834993	
4	835056	835120	835183	835247	835310	835373	835437	835500	835564	835627	
5	835691	835754	835817	835881	835944	836007	836071	836134	836197	836261	
6	836324	836387	836451	836514	836577	836641	836704	836767	836830	836894	
7	836957	837020	837083	837146	837210	837273	837336	837399	837462	837525	
8	837588	837652	837715	837778	837841	837904	837967	838030	838093	838156	63
9	838219	838282	838345	838408	838471	838534	838597	838660	838723	838786	
690	838849	838912	838975	839038	839101	839164	839227	839289	839352	839415	
1	839478	839541	839604	839667	839729	839792	839855	839918	839981	840043	
2	840106	840169	840232	840294	840357	840420	840482	840545	840608	84067¹	
3	840733	840796	840859	840921	840984	841046	841109	841172	841234	841297	
4	841359	841422	841485	841547	841610	841672	841735	841797	841860	841922	
5	841985	842047	842110	842172	842235	842297	842360	842422	842484	842547	
6	842609	842672	842734	842796	842859	842921	842983	843046	843108	843170	
7	843233	843295	843357	843420	843482	843544	843606	843669	843731	843793	
8	843855	843918	843980	844042	844104	844166	844229	844291	844353	844415	
9	844477	844539	844601	844664	844726	844788	844850	844912	844974	845036	
700	845098	845160	845222	845284	845346	845408	845470	845532	845594	845656	62
1	845718	845780	845842	845904	845966	846028	846090	846151	846213	846275	
2	846337	846399	846461	846523	846585	846646	846708	846770	846832	846894	
3	846955	847017	847079	847141	847202	847264	847326	847388	847449	847511	
4	847573	847634	847696	847758	847819	847881	847943	848004	848066	848128	
5	848189	848251	848312	848374	848435	848497	848559	848620	848682	848743	
6	848805	848866	848928	848989	849051	849112	849174	849235	849297	849358	
7	849419	849481	849542	849604	849665	849726	849788	849849	849911	849972	
8	850033	850095	850156	850217	850279	850340	850401	850462	850524	850585	
9	850646	850707	850769	850830	850891	850952	851014	851075	851136	851197	
710	851258	851320	851381	851442	851503	851564	851625	851686	851747	851809	
1	851870	851931	851992	852053	852114	852175	852236	852297	852358	852419	61
2	852480	852541	852602	852663	852724	852785	852846	852907	852968	853029	
3	853090	853150	853211	853272	853333	853394	853455	853516	853577	853637	
4	853698	853759	853820	853881	853941	854002	854063	854124	854185	854245	
5	854306	854367	854428	854488	854549	854610	854670	854731	854792	854852	
6	854913	854974	855034	855095	855156	855216	855277	855337	855398	855459	
7	855519	855580	855640	855701	855761	855822	855883	855943	856003	856064	
8	856124	856185	856245	856306	856366	856427	856487	856548	856608	856668	
9	856729	856789	856850	856910	856970	857031	857091	857152	857212	857272	
720	857332	857393	857453	857513	857574	857634	857694	857755	857815	857875	
1	857935	857995	858056	858116	858176	858236	858297	858357	858417	858477	
2	858537	858597	858657	858718	858778	858838	858898	858958	859018	859078	
3	859138	859198	859258	859318	859379	859439	859499	859559	859619	859679	60
4	859739	859799	859859	859918	859978	860038	860098	860158	860218	860278	
5	860338	860398	860458	860518	860578	860637	860697	860757	860817	860877	
6	860937	860996	861056	861116	861176	861236	861295	861355	861415	861475	
7	861534	861594	861654	861714	861773	861833	861893	861952	862012	862072	
8	862131	862191	862251	862310	862370	862430	862489	862549	862608	862668	
9	862728	862787	862847	862906	862966	863025	863085	863144	863204	863263	
730	863323	863382	863442	863501	863561	863620	863680	863739	863799	863858	

PROPORTIONAL PARTS

Diff.	1	2	3	4	5	6	7	8	9
64	6.4	12.8	19.2	25.6	32.0	38.4	44.8	51.2	57.6
62	6.2	12.4	18.6	24.8	31.0	37.2	43.4	49.6	55.8
60	6.0	12.0	18.0	24.0	30.0	36.0	42.0	48.0	54.0
58	5.8	11.6	17.4	23.2	29.0	34.8	40.6	46.4	52.2

N	0	1	2	3	4	5	6	7	8	9	Diff.
730	863323	863382	863442	863501	863561	863620	863680	863739	863799	863858	
1	863917	863977	864036	864096	864155	864214	864274	864333	864392	864452	
2	864511	864570	864630	864689	864748	864808	864867	864926	864985	865045	
3	865104	865163	865222	865282	865341	865400	865459	865519	865578	865637	
4	865696	865755	865814	865874	865933	865992	866051	866110	866169	866228	
5	866287	866346	866405	866465	866524	866583	866642	866701	866760	866819	
6	866878	866937	866996	867055	867114	867173	867232	867291	867350	867409	59
7	867467	867526	867585	867644	867703	867762	867821	867880	867939	867998	
8	868056	868115	868174	868233	868292	868350	868409	868468	868527	868586	
9	868644	868703	868762	868821	868879	868938	868997	869056	869114	869173	
740	869232	869290	869349	869408	869466	869525	869584	869642	869701	869760	
1	869818	869877	869935	869994	870053	870111	870170	870228	870287	870345	
2	870404	870462	870521	870579	870638	870696	870755	870813	870872	870930	
3	870989	871047	871106	871164	871223	871281	871339	871398	871456	871515	
4	871573	871631	871690	871748	871806	871865	871923	871981	872040	872098	
5	872156	872215	872273	872331	872389	872448	872506	872564	872622	872681	
6	872739	872797	872855	872913	872972	873030	873088	873146	873204	873262	
7	873321	873379	873437	873495	873553	873611	873669	873727	873785	873844	
8	873902	873960	874018	874076	874134	874192	874250	874308	874366	874424	58
9	874482	874540	874598	874656	874714	874772	874830	874888	874945	875003	
750	875061	875119	875177	875235	875293	875351	875409	875466	875524	875582	
1	875640	875698	875756	875813	875871	875929	875987	876045	876102	876160	
2	876218	876276	876333	876391	876449	876507	876564	876622	876680	876737	
3	876795	876853	876910	876968	877026	877083	877141	877199	877256	877314	
4	877371	877429	877487	877544	877602	877659	877717	877774	877832	877889	
5	877947	878004	878062	878119	878177	878234	878292	878349	878407	878464	
6	878522	878579	878637	878694	878752	878809	878866	878924	878981	879039	
7	879096	879153	879211	879268	879325	879383	879440	879497	879555	879612	
8	879669	879726	879784	879841	879898	879956	880013	880070	880127	880185	
9	880242	880299	880356	880413	880471	880528	880585	880642	880699	880756	
760	880814	880871	880928	880985	881042	881099	881156	881213	881271	881328	
1	881385	881442	881499	881556	881613	881670	881727	881784	881841	881898	
2	881955	882012	882069	882126	882183	882240	882297	882354	882411	882468	57
3	882525	882581	882638	882695	882752	882809	882866	882923	882980	883037	
4	883093	883150	883207	883264	883321	883377	883434	883491	883548	883605	
5	883661	883718	883775	883832	883888	883945	884002	884059	884115	884172	
6	884229	884285	884342	884399	884455	884512	884569	884625	884682	884739	
7	884795	884852	884909	884965	885022	885078	885135	885192	885248	885305	
8	885361'	885418	885474	885531	885587	885644	885700	885757	885813	885870	
9	885926	885983	886039	886096	886152	886209	886265	886321	886378	886434	
770	886491	886547	886604	886660	886716	886773	886829	886885	886942	886998	
1	887054	887111	887167	887223	887280	887336	887392	887449	887505	887561	
2	887617	887674	887730	887786	887842	887898	887955	888011	888067	888123	
3	888179	888236	888292	888348	888404	888460	888516	888573	888629	888685	
4	888741	888797	888853	888909	888965	889021	889077	889134	889190	889246	
5	889302	889358	889414	889470	889526	889582	889638	889694	889750	889806	56
6	889862	889918	889974	890030	890086	890141	890197	890253	890309	890365	
7	890421	890477	890533	890589	890645	890700	890756	890812	890868	890924	
8	890980	891035	891091	891147	891203	891259	891314	891370	891426	891482	
9	891537	891593	891649	891705	891760	891816	891872	891928	891983	892039	
780	892095	892150	892206	892262	892317	892373	892429	892484	892540	892595	

PROPORTIONAL PARTS

Diff.	1	2	3	4	5	6	7	8	9
60	6.0	12.0	18.0	24.0	30.0	36.0	42.0	48.0	54.0
58	5.8	11.6	17.4	23.2	29.0	34.8	40.6	46.4	52.2
56	5.6	11.2	16.8	22.4	28.0	33.6	39.2	44.8	50.4
54	5.4	10.8	16.2	21.6	27.0	32.4	37.8	43.2	48.6

N	0	1	2	3	4	5	6	7	8	9	Diff.
780	892095	892150	892206	892262	892317	892373	892429	892484	892540	892595	
1	892651	892707	892762	892818	892873	892929	892985	893040	893096	893151	
2	893207	893262	893318	893373	893429	893484	893540	893595	893651	893706	
3	893762	893817	893873	893928	893984	894039	894094	894150	894205	894261	
4	894316	894371	894427	894482	894538	894593	894648	894704	894759	894814	
5	894870	894925	894980	895036	895091	895146	895201	895257	895312	895367	
6	895423	895478	895533	895588	895644	895699	895754	895809	895864	895920	
7	895975	896030	896085	896140	896195	896251	896306	896361	896416	896471	
8	896526	896581	896636	896692	896747	896802	896857	896912	896967	897022	
9	897077	897132	897187	897242	897297	897352	897407	897462	897517	897572	
790	897627	897682	897737	897792	897847	897902	897957	898012	898067	898122	55
1	898176	898231	898286	898341	898396	898451	898506	898561	898615	898670	
2	898725	898780	898835	898890	898944	898999	899054	899109	899164	899218	
3	899273	899328	899383	899437	899492	899547	899602	899656	899711	899766	
4	899821	899875	899930	899985	900039	900094	900149	900203	900258	900312	
5	900367	900422	900476	900531	900586	900640	900695	900749	900804	900859	
6	900913	900968	901022	901077	901131	901186	901240	901295	901349	901404	
7	901458	901513	901567	901622	901676	901731	901785	901840	901894	901948	
8	902003	902057	902112	902166	902221	902275	902329	902384	902438	902492	
9	902547	902601	902655	902710	902764	902818	902873	902927	902981	903036	
800	903090	903144	903199	903253	903307	903361	903416	903470	903524	903578	
1	903633	903687	903741	903795	903849	903904	903958	904012	904066	904120	
2	904174	904229	904283	904337	904391	904445	904499	904553	904607	904661	
3	904716	904770	904824	904878	904932	904986	905040	905094	905148	905202	
4	905256	905310	905364	905418	905472	905526	905580	905634	905688	905742	54
5	905796	905850	905904	905958	906012	906066	906119	906173	906227	906281	
6	906335	906389	906443	906497	906551	906604	906658	906712	906766	906820	
7	906874	906927	906981	907035	907089	907143	907196	907250	907304	907358	
8	907411	907465	907519	907573	907626	907680	907734	907787	907841	907895	
9	907949	908002	908056	908110	908163	908217	908270	908324	908378	908431	
810	908485	908539	908592	908646	908699	908753	908807	908860	908914	908967	
1	909021	909074	909128	909181	909235	909289	909342	909396	909449	909503	
2	909556	909610	909663	909716	909770	909823	909877	909930	909984	910037	
3	910091	910144	910197	910251	910304	910358	910411	910464	910518	910571	
4	910624	910678	910731	910784	910838	910891	910944	910998	911051	911104	
5	911158	911211	911264	911317	911371	911424	911477	911530	911584	911637	
6	911690	911743	911797	911850	911903	911956	912009	912063	912116	912169	
7	912222	912275	912328	912381	912435	912488	912541	912594	912647	912700	
8	912753	912806	912859	912913	912966	913019	913072	913125	913178	913231	
9	913284	913337	913390	913443	913496	913549	913602	913655	913708	913761	53
820	913814	913867	913920	913973	914026	914079	914132	914184	914237	914290	
1	914343	914396	914449	914502	914555	914608	914660	914713	914766	914819	
2	914872	914925	914977	915030	915083	915136	915189	915241	915294	915347	
3	915400	915453	915505	915558	915611	915664	915716	915769	915822	915875	
4	915927	915980	916033	916085	916138	916191	916243	916296	916349	916401	
5	916454	916507	916559	916612	916664	916717	916770	916822	916875	916927	
6	916980	917033	917085	917138	917190	917243	917295	917348	917400	917453	
7	917506	917558	917611	917663	917716	917768	917820	917873	917925	917978	
8	918030	918083	918135	918188	918240	918293	918345	918397	918450	918502	
9	918555	918607	918659	918712	918764	918816	918869	918921	918973	919026	
830	919078	919130	919183	919235	919287	919340	919392	919444	919496	919549	
1	919601	919653	919706	919758	919810	919862	919914	919967	920019	920071	
2	920123	920176	920228	920280	920332	920384	920436	920489	920541	920593	
3	920645	920697	920749	920801	920853	920906	920958	921010	921062	921114	52
4	921166	921218	921270	921322	921374	921426	921478	921530	921582	921634	
5	921686	921738	921790	921842	921894	921946	921998	922050	922102	922154	

PROPORTIONAL PARTS

Diff.	1	2	3	4	5	6	7	8	9
56	5.6	11.2	16.8	22.4	28.0	33.6	39.2	44.8	50.4
54	5.4	10.8	16.2	21.6	27.0	32.4	37.8	43.2	48.6
52	5.2	10.4	15.6	20.8	26.0	31.2	36.4	41.6	46.8

N	0	1	2	3	4	5	6	7	8	9	Diff.
835	921686	921738	921790	921842	921894	921946	921998	922050	922102	922154	
6	922206	922258	922310	922362	922414	922466	922518	922570	922622	922674	
7	922725	922777	922829	922881	922933	922985	923037	923089	923140	923192	
8	923244	923296	923348	923399	923451	923503	923555	923607	923658	923710	
9	923762	923814	923865	923917	923969	924021	924072	924124	924176	924228	
840	924279	924331	924383	924434	924486	924538	924589	924641	924693	924744	
1	924796	924848	924899	924951	925003	925054	925106	925157	925209	925261	
2	925312	925364	925415	925467	925518	925570	925621	925673	925725	925776	
3	925828	925879	925931	925982	926034	926085	926137	926188	926240	926291	
4	926342	926394	926445	926497	926548	926600	926651	926702	926754	926805	
5	926857	926908	926959	927011	927062	927114	927165	927216	927268	927319	
6	927370	927422	927473	927524	927576	927627	927678	927730	927781	927832	
7	927883	927935	927986	928037	928088	928140	928191	928242	928293	928345	
8	928396	928447	928498	928549	928601	928652	928703	928754	928805	928857	
9	928908	928959	929010	929061	929112	929163	929215	929266	929317	929368	
850	929419	929470	929521	929572	929623	929674	929725	929776	929827	929879	
1	929930	929981	930032	930083	930134	930185	930236	930287	930338	930389	51
2	930440	930491	930542	930592	930643	930694	930745	930796	930847	930898	
3	930949	931000	931051	931102	931153	931204	931254	931305	931356	931407	
4	931458	931509	931560	931610	931661	931712	931763	931814	931865	931916	
5	931966	932017	932068	932118	932169	932220	932271	932322	932372	932423	
6	932474	932524	932575	932626	932677	932727	932778	932829	932879	932930	
7	932981	933031	933082	933133	933183	933234	933285	933335	933386	933437	
8	933487	933538	933589	933639	933690	933740	933791	933841	933892	933943	
9	933993	934044	934094	934145	934195	934246	934296	934347	934397	934448	
860	934498	934549	934599	934650	934700	934751	934801	934852	934902	934953	
1	935003	935054	935104	935154	935205	935255	935306	935356	935406	935457	
2	935507	935558	935608	935658	935709	935759	935809	935860	935910	935960	
3	936011	936061	936111	936162	936212	936262	936313	936363	936413	936463	
4	936514	936564	936614	936665	936715	936765	936815	936865	936916	936966	
5	937016	937066	937116	937167	937217	937267	937317	937367	937418	937468	
6	937518	937568	937618	937668	937718	937769	937819	937869	937919	937969	
7	938019	938069	938119	938169	938219	938269	938320	938370	938420	938470	50
8	938520	938570	938620	938670	938720	938770	938820	938870	938920	938970	
9	939020	939070	939120	939170	939220	939270	939320	939369	939419	939469	
870	939519	939569	939619	939669	939719	939769	939819	939869	939918	939968	
1	940018	940068	940118	940168	940218	940267	940317	940367	940417	940467	
2	940516	940566	940616	940666	940716	940765	940815	940865	940915	940964	
3	941014	941064	941114	941163	941213	941263	941313	941363	941412	941462	
4	941511	941561	941611	941660	941710	941760	941809	941859	941909	941958	
5	942008	942058	942107	942157	942207	942256	942306	942355	942405	942455	
6	942504	942554	942603	942653	942702	942752	942801	942851	942901	942950	
7	943000	943049	943099	943148	943198	943247	943297	943346	943396	943445	
8	943495	943544	943593	943643	943692	943742	943791	943841	943890	943939	
9	943989	944038	944088	944137	944186	944236	944285	944335	944384	944433	
880	944483	944532	944581	944631	944680	944729	944779	944828	944877	944927	
1	944976	945025	945074	945124	945173	945222	945272	945321	945370	945419	
2	945469	945518	945567	945616	945665	945715	945764	945813	945862	945912	
3	945961	946010	946059	946108	946157	946207	946256	946305	946354	946403	
4	946452	946501	946551	946600	946649	946698	946747	946796	946845	946894	
5	946943	946992	947041	947090	947140	947189	947238	947287	947336	947385	
6	947434	947483	947532	947581	947630	947679	947728	947777	947826	947875	49
7	947924	947973	948022	948070	948119	948168	948217	948266	948315	948364	
8	948413	948462	948511	948560	948608	948657	948706	948755	948804	948853	
9	948902	948951	948999	949048	949097	949146	949195	949244	949292	949341	
890	949390	949439	949488	949536	949585	949634	949683	949731	949780	949829	

PROPORTIONAL PARTS

Diff.	1	2	3	4	5	6	7	8	9
52	5.2	10.4	15.6	20.8	26.0	31.2	36.4	41.6	46.8
50	5.0	10.0	15.0	20.0	25.0	30.0	35.0	40.0	45.0
48	4.8	9.6	14.4	19.2	24.0	28.8	33.6	38.4	43.2

N	0	1	2	3	4	5	6	7	8	9	Diff.
890	949390	949439	949488	949536	949585	949634	949683	949731	949780	949829	
1	949878	949926	949975	950024	950073	950121	950170	950219	950267	950316	
2	950365	950414	950462	950511	950560	950608	950657	950706	950754	950803	
3	950851	950900	950949	950997	951046	951095	951143	951192	951240	951289	
4	951338	951386	951435	951483	951532	951580	951629	951677	951726	951775	
5	951823	951872	951920	951969	952017	952066	952114	952163	952211	952260	
6	952308	952356	952405	952453	952502	952550	952599	952647	952696	952744	
7	952792	952841	952889	952938	952986	953034	953083	953131	953180	953228	
8	953276	953325	953373	953421	953470	953518	953566	953615	953663	953711	
9	953760	953808	953856	953905	953953	954001	954049	954098	954146	954194	
900	954243	954291	954339	954387	954435	954484	954532	954580	954628	954677	
1	954725	954773	954821	954869	954918	954966	955014	955062	955110	955158	
2	955207	955255	955303	955351	955399	955447	955495	955543	955592	955640	
3	955688	955736	955784	955832	955880	955928	955976	956024	956072	956120	
4	956168	956216	956265	956313	956361	956409	956457	956505	956553	956601	
5	956649	956697	956745	956793	956840	956888	956936	956984	957032	957080	48
6	957128	957176	957224	957272	957320	957368	957416	957464	957512	957559	
7	957607	957655	957703	957751	957799	957847	957894	957942	957990	958038	
8	958086	958134	958181	958229	958277	958325	958373	958421	958468	958516	
9	958564	958612	958659	958707	958755	958803	958850	958898	958946	958994	
910	959041	959089	959137	959185	959232	959280	959328	959375	959423	959471	
1	959518	959566	959614	959661	959709	959757	959804	959852	959900	959947	
2	959995	960042	960090	960138	960185	960233	960280	960328	960376	960423	
3	960471	960518	960566	960613	960661	960709	960756	960804	960851	960899	
4	960946	960994	961041	961089	961136	961184	961231	961279	961326	961374	
5	961421	961469	961516	961563	961611	961658	961706	961753	961801	961848	
6	961895	961943	961990	962038	962085	962132	962180	962227	962275	962322	
7	962369	962417	962464	962511	962559	962606	962653	962701	962748	962795	
8	962843	962890	962937	962985	963032	963079	963126	963174	963221	963268	
9	963316	963363	963410	963457	963504	963552	963599	963646	963693	963741	
920	963788	963835	963882	963929	963977	964024	964071	964118	964165	964212	
1	964260	964307	964354	964401	964448	964495	964542	964590	964637	964684	
2	964731	964778	964825	964872	964919	964966	965013	965061	965108	965155	
3	965202	965249	965296	965343	965390	965437	965484	965531	965578	965625	
4	965672	965719	965766	965813	965860	965907	965954	966001	966048	966095	47
5	966142	966189	966236	966283	966329	966376	966423	966470	966517	966564	
6	966611	966658	966705	966752	966799	966845	966892	966939	966986	967033	
7	967080	967127	967173	967220	967267	967314	967361	967408	967454	967501	
8	967548	967595	967642	967688	967735	967782	967829	967875	967922	967969	
9	968016	968062	968109	968156	968203	968249	968296	968343	968390	968436	
930	968483	968530	968576	968623	968670	968716	968763	968810	968856	968903	
1	968950	968996	969043	969090	969136	969183	969229	969276	969323	969369	
2	969416	969463	969509	969556	969602	969649	969695	969742	969789	969835	
3	969882	969928	969975	970021	970068	970114	970161	970207	970254	970300	
4	970347	970393	970440	970486	970533	970579	970626	970672	970719	970765	
5	970812	970858	970904	970951	970997	971044	971090	971137	971183	971229	
6	971276	971322	971369	971415	971461	971508	971554	971601	971647	971693	
7	971740	971786	971832	971879	971925	971971	972018	972064	972110	972157	
8	972203	972249	972295	972342	972388	972434	972481	972527	972573	972619	
9	972666	972712	972758	972804	972851	972897	972943	972989	973035	973082	
940	973128	973174	973220	973266	973313	973359	973405	973451	973497	973543	
1	973590	973636	973682	973728	973774	973820	973866	973913	973959	974005	
2	974051	974097	974143	974189	974235	974281	974327	974374	974420	974466	
3	974512	974558	974604	974650	974696	974742	974788	974834	974880	974926	
4	974972	975018	975064	975110	975156	975202	975248	975294	975340	975386	46
5	975432	975478	975524	975570	975616	975662	975707	975753	975799	975845	

PROPORTIONAL PARTS

Diff.	1	2	3	4	5	6	7	8	9
50	5.0	10.0	15.0	20.0	25.0	30.0	35.0	40.0	45.0
48	4.8	9.6	14.4	19.2	24.0	28.8	33.6	38.4	43.2
46	4.6	9.2	13.8	18.4	23.0	27.6	32.2	36.8	41.4

N	0	1	2	3	4	5	6	7	8	9	Diff.
945	975432	975478	975524	975570	975616	975662	975707	975753	975799	975845	
6	975891	975937	975983	976029	976075	976121	976167	976212	976258	976304	
7	976350	976396	976442	976488	976533	976579	976625	976671	976717	976763	
8	976808	976854	976900	976946	976992	977037	977083	977129	977175	977220	
9	977266	977312	977358	977403	977449	977495	977541	977586	977632	977678	
950	977724	977769	977815	977861	977906	977952	977998	978043	978089	978135	
1	978181	978226	978272	978317	978363	978409	978454	978500	978546	978591	
2	978637	978683	978728	978774	978819	978865	978911	978956	979002	979047	
3	979093	979138	979184	979230	979275	979321	979366	979412	979457	979503	
4	979548	979594	979639	979685	979730	979776	979821	979867	979912	979958	
5	980003	980049	980094	980140	980185	980231	980276	980322	980367	980412	
6	980458	980503	980549	980594	980640	980685	980730	980776	980821	980867	
7	980912	980957	981003	981048	981093	981139	981184	981229	981275	981320	
8	981366	981411	981456	981501	981547	981592	981637	981683	981728	981773	
9	981819	981864	981909	981954	982000	982045	982090	982135	982181	982226	
960	982271	982316	982362	982407	982452	982497	982543	982588	982633	982678	
1	982723	982769	982814	982859	982904	982949	982994	983040	983085	983130	
2	983175	983220	983265	983310	983356	983401	983446	983491	983536	983581	
3	983626	983671	983716	983762	983807	983852	983897	983942	983987	984032	
4	984077	984122	984167	984212	984257	984302	984347	984392	984437	984482	
5	984527	984572	984617	984662	984707	984752	984797	984842	984887	984932	45
6	984977	985022	985067	985112	985157	985202	985247	985292	985337	985382	
7	985426	985471	985516	985561	985606	985651	985696	985741	985786	985830	
8	985875	985920	985965	986010	986055	986100	986144	986189	986234	986279	
9	986324	986369	986413	986458	986503	986548	986593	986637	986682	986727	
970	986772	986817	986861	986906	986951	986996	987040	987085	987130	987175	
1	987219	987264	987309	987353	987398	987443	987488	987532	987577	987622	
2	987666	987711	987756	987800	987845	987890	987934	987979	988024	988068	
3	988113	988157	988202	988247	988291	988336	988381	988425	988470	988514	
4	988559	988604	988648	988693	988737	988782	988826	988871	988916	988960	
5	989005	989049	989094	989138	989183	989227	989272	989316	989361	989405	
6	989450	989494	989539	989583	989628	989672	989717	989761	989806	989850	
7	989895	989939	989983	990028	990072	990117	990161	990206	990250	990294	
8	990339	990383	990428	990472	990516	990561	990605	990650	990694	990738	
9	990783	990827	990871	990916	990960	991004	991049	991093	991137	991182	
980	991226	991270	991315	991359	991403	991448	991492	991536	991580	991625	
1	991669	991713	991758	991802	991846	991890	991935	991979	992023	992067	
2	992111	992156	992200	992244	992288	992333	992377	992421	992465	992509	
3	992554	992598	992642	992686	992730	992774	992819	992863	992907	992951	
4	992995	993039	993083	993127	993172	993216	993260	993304	993348	993392	
5	993436	993480	993524	993568	993613	993657	993701	993745	993789	993833	
6	993877	993921	993965	994009	994053	994097	994141	994185	994229	994273	
7	994317	994361	994405	994449	994493	994537	994581	994625	994669	994713	44
8	994757	994801	994845	994889	994933	994977	995021	995065	995108	995152	
9	995196	995240	995284	995328	995372	995416	995460	995504	995547	995591	
990	995635	995679	995723	995767	995811	995854	995898	995942	995986	996030	
1	996074	996117	996161	996205	996249	996293	996337	996380	996424	996468	
2	996512	996555	996599	996643	996687	996731	996774	996818	996862	996906	
3	996949	996993	997037	997080	997124	997168	997212	997255	997299	997343	
4	997386	997430	997474	997517	997561	997605	997648	997692	997736	997779	
5	997823	997867	997910	997954	997998	998041	998085	998129	998172	998216	
6	998259	998303	998347	998390	998434	998477	998521	998564	998608	998652	
7	998695	998739	998782	998826	998869	998913	998956	999000	999043	999087	
8	999131	999174	999218	999261	999305	999348	999392	999435	999479	999522	
9	999565	999609	999652	999696	999739	999783	999826	999870	999913	999957	
1000	000000	000043	000087	000130	000174	000217	000260	000304	000347	000391	43

PROPORTIONAL PARTS

Diff.	1	2	3	4	5	6	7	8	9
46	4.6	9.2	13.8	18.4	23.0	27.6	32.2	36.8	41.4
44	4.4	8.8	13.2	17.6	22.0	26.4	30.8	35.2	39.6
42	4.2	8.4	12.6	16.8	21.0	25.2	29.4	33.6	37.8

Table 11.   Natural (Napierian) Logarithms of Numbers

The natural logarithm of a number is the index of the power to which the base e ($= 2.7182818$) must be raised in order to equal the number.

EXAMPLE: $\log_e 4.12 = \ln 4.12 = 1.4159$.

The table gives the natural logarithms of numbers from 1.00 to 9.99 directly, and permits the finding of the logarithms of numbers outside of that range by the addition or subtraction of the natural logarithms of powers of 10.

EXAMPLES: $\log_e 679. = \log_e 6.79 + \log_e 10^2 = 1.9155 + 4.6052 = 6.5207$.
$\log_e .0679 = \log_e 6.79 - \log_e 10^2 = 1.9155 - 4.6052 = -2.6897$.

Natural Logarithms of Powers of 10

$\log_e 10 = 2.302\ 585$ $\log_e 10^4 = 9.210\ 340$ $\log_e 10^7 = 16.118\ 096$
$\log_e 10^2 = 4.605\ 170$ $\log_e 10^5 = 11.512\ 925$ $\log_e 10^8 = 18.420\ 681$
$\log_e 10^3 = 6.907\ 755$ $\log_e 10^6 = 13.815\ 511$ $\log_e 10^9 = 20.723\ 266$

To obtain the common logarithm, the natural logarithm is multiplied by $\log_{10} e$, which is 0.434 294, or $\log_{10} N = 0.434\ 294\ \log_e N$.

A negative number or number less than zero has no real logarithm.

N	0	1	2	3	4	5	6	7	8	9
1.0	0.0000	0.0100	0.0198	0.0296	0.0392	0.0488	0.0583	0.0677	0.0770	0.0862
1.1	0.0953	0.1044	0.1133	0.1222	0.1310	0.1398	0.1484	0.1570	0.1655	0.1740
1.2	0.1823	0.1906	0.1989	0.2070	0.2151	0.2231	0.2311	0.2390	0.2469	0.2546
1.3	0.2624	0.2700	0.2776	0.2852	0.2927	0.3001	0.3075	0.3148	0.3221	0.3293
1.4	0.3365	0.3436	0.3507	0.3577	0.3646	0.3716	0.3784	0.3853	0.3920	0.3988
1.5	0.4055	0.4121	0.4187	0.4253	0.4318	0.4383	0.4447	0.4511	0.4574	0.4637
1.6	0.4700	0.4762	0.4824	0.4886	0.4947	0.5008	0.5068	0.5128	0.5188	0.5247
1.7	0.5306	0.5365	0.5423	0.5481	0.5539	0.5596	0.5653	0.5710	0.5766	0.5822
1.8	0.5878	0.5933	0.5988	0.6043	0.6098	0.6152	0.6206	0.6259	0.6313	0.6366
1.9	0.6419	0.6471	0.6523	0.6575	0.6627	0.6678	0.6729	0.6780	0.6831	0.6881
2.0	0.6931	0.6981	0.7031	0.7080	0.7129	0.7178	0.7227	0.7275	0.7324	0.7372
2.1	0.7419	0.7467	0.7514	0.7561	0.7608	0.7655	0.7701	0.7747	0.7793	0.7839
2.2	0.7885	0.7930	0.7975	0.8020	0.8065	0.8109	0.8154	0.8198	0.8242	0.8286
2.3	0.8329	0.8372	0.8416	0.8459	0.8502	0.8544	0.8587	0.8629	0.8671	0.8713
2.4	0.8755	0.8796	0.8838	0.8879	0.8920	0.8961	0.9002	0.9042	0.9083	0.9123
2.5	0.9163	0.9203	0.9243	0.9282	0.9322	0.9361	0.9400	0.9439	0.9478	0.9517
2.6	0.9555	0.9594	0.9632	0.9670	0.9708	0.9746	0.9783	0.9821	0.9858	0.9895
2.7	0.9933	0.9969	1.0006	1.0043	1.0080	1.0116	1.0152	1.0188	1.0225	1.0260
2.8	1.0296	1.0332	1.0367	1.0403	1.0438	1.0473	1.0508	1.0543	1.0578	1.0613
2.9	1.0647	1.0682	1.0716	1.0750	1.0784	1.0818	1.0852	1.0886	1.0919	1.0953
3.0	1.0986	1.1019	1.1053	1.1086	1.1119	1.1151	1.1184	1.1217	1.1249	1.1282
3.1	1.1314	1.1346	1.1378	1.1410	1.1442	1.1474	1.1506	1.1537	1.1569	1.1600
3.2	1.1632	1.1663	1.1694	1.1725	1.1756	1.1787	1.1817	1.1848	1.1878	1.1909
3.3	1.1939	1.1969	1.2000	1.2030	1.2060	1.2090	1.2119	1.2149	1.2179	1.2208
3.4	1.2238	1.2267	1.2296	1.2326	1.2355	1.2384	1.2413	1.2442	1.2470	1.2499
3.5	1.2528	1.2556	1.2585	1.2613	1.2641	1.2669	1.2698	1.2726	1.2754	1.2782
3.6	1.2809	1.2837	1.2865	1.2892	1.2920	1.2947	1.2975	1.3002	1.3029	1.3056
3.7	1.3083	1.3110	1.3137	1.3164	1.3191	1.3218	1.3244	1.3271	1.3297	1.3324
3.8	1.3350	1.3376	1.3403	1.3429	1.3455	1.3481	1.3507	1.3533	1.3558	1.3584
3.9	1.3610	1.3635	1.3661	1.3686	1.3712	1.3737	1.3762	1.3788	1.3813	1.3838
4.0	1.3863	1.3888	1.3913	1.3938	1.3962	1.3987	1.4012	1.4036	1.4061	1.4085
4.1	1.4110	1.4134	1.4159	1.4183	1.4207	1.4231	1.4255	1.4279	1.4303	1.4327
4.2	1.4351	1.4375	1.4398	1.4422	1.4446	1.4469	1.4493	1.4516	1.4540	1.4563
4.3	1.4586	1.4609	1.4633	1.4656	1.4679	1.4702	1.4725	1.4748	1.4770	1.4793
4.4	1.4816	1.4839	1.4861	1.4884	1.4907	1.4929	1.4951	1.4974	1.4996	1.5019
4.5	1.5041	1.5063	1.5085	1.5107	1.5129	1.5151	1.5173	1.5195	1.5217	1.5239
4.6	1.5261	1.5282	1.5304	1.5326	1.5347	1.5369	1.5390	1.5412	1.5433	1.5454
4.7	1.5476	1.5497	1.5518	1.5539	1.5560	1.5581	1.5602	1.5623	1.5644	1.5665
4.8	1.5686	1.5707	1.5728	1.5748	1.5769	1.5790	1.5810	1.5831	1.5851	1.5872
4.9	1.5892	1.5913	1.5933	1.5953	1.5974	1.5994	1.6014	1.6034	1.6054	1.6074

Table 11.—(*Continued*)

N	0	1	2	3	4	5	6	7	8	9
5.0	**1.6094**	**1.6114**	**1.6134**	**1.6154**	**1.6174**	**1.6194**	**1.6214**	**1.6233**	**1.6253**	**1.6273**
5.1	1.6292	1.6312	1.6332	1.6351	1.6371	1.6390	1.6409	1.6429	1.6448	1.6467
5.2	1.6487	1.6506	1.6525	1.6544	1.6563	1.6582	1.6601	1.6620	1.6639	1.6658
5.3	1.6677	1.6696	1.6715	1.6734	1.6752	1.6771	1.6790	1.6808	1.6827	1.6845
5.4	1.6864	1.6882	1.6901	1.6919	1.6938	1.6956	1.6974	1.6993	1.7011	1.7029
5.5	1.7047	1.7066	1.7084	1.7102	1.7120	1.7138	1.7156	1.7174	1.7192	1.7210
5.6	1.7228	1.7246	1.7263	1.7281	1.7299	1.7317	1.7334	1.7352	1.7370	1.7387
5.7	1.7405	1.7422	1.7440	1.7457	1.7475	1.7492	1.7509	1.7527	1.7544	1.7561
5.8	1.7579	1.7596	1.7613	1.7630	1.7647	1.7664	1.7681	1.7699	1.7716	1.7733
5.9	1.7750	1.7766	1.7783	1.7800	1.7817	1.7834	1.7851	1.7867	1.7884	1.7901
6.0	**1.7918**	**1.7934**	**1.7951**	**1.7967**	**1.7984**	**1.8001**	**1.8017**	**1.8034**	**1.8050**	**1.8066**
6.1	1.8083	1.8099	1.8116	1.8132	1.8148	1.8165	1.8181	1.8197	1.8213	1.8229
6.2	1.8245	1.8262	1.8278	1.8294	1.8310	1.8326	1.8342	1.8358	1.8374	1.8390
6.3	1.8405	1.8421	1.8437	1.8453	1.8469	1.8485	1.8500	1.8516	1.8532	1.8547
6.4	1.8563	1.8579	1.8594	1.8610	1.8625	1.8641	1.8656	1.8672	1.8687	1.8703
6.5	1.8718	1.8733	1.8749	1.8764	1.8779	1.8795	1.8810	1.8825	1.8840	1.8856
6.6	1.8871	1.8886	1.8901	1.8916	1.8931	1.8946	1.8961	1.8976	1.8991	1.9006
6.7	1.9021	1.9036	1.9051	1.9066	1.9081	1.9095	1.9110	1.9125	1.9140	1.9155
6.8	1.9169	1.9184	1.9199	1.9213	1.9228	1.9242	1.9257	1.9272	1.9286	1.9301
6.9	1.9315	1.9330	1.9344	1.9359	1.9373	1.9387	1.9402	1.9416	1.9430	1.9445
7.0	**1.9459**	**1.9473**	**1.9488**	**1.9502**	**1.9516**	**1.9530**	**1.9544**	**1.9559**	**1.9573**	**1.9587**
7.1	1.9601	1.9615	1.9629	1.9643	1.9657	1.9671	1.9685	1.9699	1.9713	1.9727
7.2	1.9741	1.9755	1.9769	1.9782	1.9796	1.9810	1.9824	1.9838	1.9851	1.9865
7.3	1.9879	1.9892	1.9906	1.9920	1.9933	1.9947	1.9961	1.9974	1.9988	2.0001
7.4	2.0015	2.0028	2.0042	2.0055	2.0069	2.0082	2.0096	2.0109	2.0122	2.0136
7.5	2.0149	2.0162	2.0176	2.0189	2.0202	2.0215	2.0229	2.0242	2.0255	2.0268
7.6	2.0281	2.0295	2.0308	2.0321	2.0334	2.0347	2.0360	2.0373	2.0386	2.0399
7.7	2.0412	2.0425	2.0438	2.0451	2.0464	2.0477	2.0490	2.0503	2.0516	2.0528
7.8	2.0541	2.0554	2.0567	2.0580	2.0592	2.0605	2.0618	2.0631	2.0643	2.0656
7.9	2.0669	2.0681	2.0694	2.0707	2.0719	2.0732	2.0744	2.0757	2.0769	2.0782
8.0	**2.0794**	**2.0807**	**2.0819**	**2.0832**	**2.0844**	**2.0857**	**2.0869**	**2.0882**	**2.0894**	**2.0906**
8.1	2.0919	2.0931	2.0943	2.0956	2.0968	2.0980	2.0992	2.1005	2.1017	2.1029
8.2	2.1041	2.1054	2.1066	2.1078	2.1090	2.1102	2.1114	2.1126	2.1138	2.1150
8.3	2.1163	2.1175	2.1187	2.1199	2.1211	2.1223	2.1235	2.1247	2.1258	2.1270
8.4	2.1282	2.1294	2.1306	2.1318	2.1330	2.1342	2.1353	2.1365	2.1377	2.1389
8.5	2.1401	2.1412	2.1424	2.1436	2.1448	2.1459	2.1471	2.1483	2.1494	2.1506
8.6	2.1518	2.1529	2.1541	2.1552	2.1564	2.1576	2.1587	2.1599	2.1610	2.1622
8.7	2.1633	2.1645	2.1656	2.1668	2.1679	2.1691	2.1702	2.1713	2.1725	2.1736
8.8	2.1748	2.1759	2.1770	2.1782	2.1793	2.1804	2.1815	2.1827	2.1838	2.1849
8.9	2.1861	2.1872	2.1883	2.1894	2.1905	2.1917	2.1928	2.1939	2.1950	2.1961
9.0	**2.1972**	**2.1983**	**2.1994**	**2.2006**	**2.2017**	**2.2028**	**2.2039**	**2.2050**	**2.2061**	**2.2072**
9.1	2.2083	2.2094	2.2105	2.2116	2.2127	2.2138	2.2148	2.2159	2.2170	2.2181
9.2	2.2192	2.2203	2.2214	2.2225	2.2235	2.2246	2.2257	2.2268	2.2279	2.2289
9.3	2.2300	2.2311	2.2322	2.2332	2.2343	2.2354	2.2364	2.2375	2.2386	2.2396
9.4	2.2407	2.2418	2.2428	2.2439	2.2450	2.2460	2.2471	2.2481	2.2492	2.2502
9.5	2.2513	2.2523	2.2534	2.2544	2.2555	2.2565	2.2576	2.2586	2.2597	2.2607
9.6	2.2618	2.2628	2.2638	2.2649	2.2659	2.2670	2.2680	2.2690	2.2701	2.2711
9.7	2.2721	2.2732	2.2742	2.2752	2.2762	2.2773	2.2783	2.2793	2.2803	2.2814
9.8	2.2824	2.2834	2.2844	2.2854	2.2865	2.2875	2.2885	2.2895	2.2905	2.2915
9.9	2.2925	2.2935	2.2946	2.2956	2.2966	2.2976	2.2986	2.2996	2.3006	2.3016

Table 12. Values of Degrees and Minutes in Radians

Deg	Radians	Deg	Radians	Deg	Radians	Deg	Radians	Deg	Radians	Deg	Radians	Min	Radians	Min	Radians
1	0.01745	31	0.54105	61	1.06465	91	1.58825	121	2.11185	151	2.63545	1	0.00029	31	0.00902
2	.03491	32	.55851	62	1.08210	92	1.60570	122	2.12930	152	2.65290	2	.00058	32	.00931
3	.05236	33	.57596	63	1.09956	93	1.62316	123	2.14676	153	2.67035	3	.00087	33	.00960
4	.06981	34	.59341	64	1.11701	94	1.64061	124	2.16421	154	2.68781	4	.00116	34	.00989
5	.08727	35	.61087	65	1.13446	95	1.65806	125	2.18166	155	2.70526	5	.00145	35	.01018
6	.10472	36	.62832	66	1.15192	96	1.67552	126	2.19912	156	2.72271	6	.00175	36	.01047
7	.12217	37	.64577	67	1.16937	97	1.69297	127	2.21657	157	2.74017	7	.00204	37	.01076
8	.13963	38	.66323	68	1.18682	98	1.71042	128	2.23402	158	2.75762	8	.00233	38	.01105
9	.15708	39	.68068	69	1.20428	99	1.72788	129	2.25148	159	2.77507	9	.00262	39	.01134
10	.17453	40	.69813	70	1.22173	100	1.74533	130	2.26893	160	2.79253	10	.00291	40	.01164
11	.19199	41	.71559	71	1.23918	101	1.76278	131	2.28638	161	2.80998	11	.00320	41	.01193
12	.20944	42	.73304	72	1.25664	102	1.78024	132	2.30384	162	2.82743	12	.00349	42	.01222
13	.22689	43	.75049	73	1.27409	103	1.79769	133	2.32129	163	2.84489	13	.00378	43	.01251
14	.24435	44	.76795	74	1.29154	104	1.81514	134	2.33874	164	2.86234	14	.00407	44	.01280
15	.26180	45	.78540	75	1.30900	105	1.83260	135	2.35620	165	2.87979	15	.00436	45	.01309
16	.27925	46	.80285	76	1.32645	106	1.85005	136	2.37365	166	2.89725	16	.00465	46	.01338
17	.29671	47	.82031	77	1.34390	107	1.86750	137	2.39110	167	2.91470	17	.00495	47	.01367
18	.31416	48	.83776	78	1.36136	108	1.88496	138	2.40856	168	2.93215	18	.00524	48	.01396
19	.33161	49	.85521	79	1.37881	109	1.90241	139	2.42601	169	2.94961	19	.00553	49	.01425
20	.34907	50	.87267	80	1.39626	110	1.91986	140	2.44346	170	2.96706	20	.00582	50	.01454
21	.36652	51	.89012	81	1.41372	111	1.93732	141	2.46092	171	2.98451	21	.00611	51	.01484
22	.38397	52	.90657	82	1.43117	112	1.95477	142	2.47837	172	3.00197	22	.00640	52	.01513
23	.40143	53	.92502	83	1.44862	113	1.97222	143	2.49582	173	3.01942	23	.00669	53	.01542
24	.41888	54	.94248	84	1.46608	114	1.98968	144	2.51328	174	3.03687	24	.00698	54	.01571
25	.43633	55	.95993	85	1.48353	115	2.00713	145	2.53073	175	3.05433	25	.00727	55	.01600
26	.45379	56	.97738	86	1.50098	116	2.02458	146	2.54818	176	3.07178	26	.00756	56	.01629
27	.47124	57	.99484	87	1.51844	117	2.04204	147	2.56564	177	3.08923	27	.00785	57	.01658
28	.48869	58	1.01299	88	1.53589	118	2.05949	148	2.58309	178	3.10669	28	.00814	58	.01687
29	.50615	59	1.02974	89	1.55334	119	2.07694	149	2.60054	179	3.12414	29	.00844	59	.01716
30	.52360	60	1.04720	90	1.57080	120	2.09440	150	2.61800	180	3.14159	30	.00873	60	.01745

Table 13. Values of Radians in Degrees

Rad.	.00 Deg	.01 Deg	.02 Deg	.03 Deg	.04 Deg	.05 Deg	.06 Deg	.07 Deg	.08 Deg	.09 Deg
0.0	0.0000	0.5730	1.1459	1.7189	2.2918	2.8648	3.4377	4.0107	4.5837	5.1566
.1	5.7296	6.3025	6.8755	7.4485	8.0214	8.5944	9.1673	9.7403	10.3132	10.8862
.2	11.4591	12.0321	12.6051	13.1780	13.7510	14.3239	14.8969	15.4699	16.0428	16.6158
.3	17.1887	17.7617	18.3346	18.9076	19.4806	20.0535	20.6265	21.1994	21.7724	22.3454
.4	22.9183	23.4913	24.0642	24.6372	25.2101	25.7831	26.3561	26.9290	27.5020	28.0749
.5	28.6479	29.2208	29.7938	30.3668	30.9397	31.5127	32.0856	32.6586	33.2316	33.8045
.6	34.3775	34.9504	35.5234	36.0963	36.6693	37.2423	37.8152	38.3882	38.9611	39.5341
.7	40.1070	40.6800	41.2530	41.8259	42.3989	42.9718	43.5448	44.1178	44.6907	45.2637
.8	45.8366	46.4096	46.9825	47.5555	48.1285	48.7014	49.2744	49.8473	50.4203	50.9932
.9	51.5662	52.1392	52.7121	53.2851	53.8580	54.4310	55.0039	55.5769	56.1499	56.7228

1 Radian = 57.29578 deg	2 Radians = 114.59156 deg	3 Radians = 171.88734 deg

Table 14. Decimals of a Degree in Minutes and Seconds

Decimal	.00 Min Sec	.01 Min Sec	.02 Min Sec	.03 Min Sec	.04 Min Sec	.05 Min Sec	.06 Min Sec	.07 Min Sec	.08 Min Sec	.09 Min Sec
0.0	0 0	0 36	1 12	1 48	2 24	3 0	3 36	4 12	4 48	5 24
.1	6 0	6 36	7 12	7 48	8 24	9 0	9 36	10 12	10 48	11 24
.2	12 0	12 36	13 12	13 48	14 24	15 0	15 36	16 12	16 48	17 24
.3	18 0	18 36	19 12	19 48	20 24	21 0	21 36	22 12	22 48	23 24
.4	24 0	24 36	25 12	25 48	26 24	27 0	27 36	28 12	28 48	29 24
.5	30 0	30 36	31 12	31 48	32 24	33 0	33 36	34 12	34 48	35 24
.6	36 0	36 36	37 12	37 48	38 24	39 0	39 36	40 12	40 48	41 24
.7	42 0	42 36	43 12	43 48	44 24	45 0	45 36	46 12	46 48	47 24
.8	48 0	48 36	49 12	49 48	50 24	51 0	51 36	52 12	52 48	53 24
.9	54 0	54 36	55 12	55 48	56 24	57 0	57 36	58 12	58 48	59 24

Table 15. Minutes in Decimals of a Degree

Minutes	0 Degrees	1 Degrees	2 Degrees	3 Degrees	4 Degrees	5 Degrees	6 Degrees	7 Degrees	8 Degrees	9 Degrees
0	0.00000	0.01667	0.03333	0.05000	0.06667	0.08333	0.10000	0.11667	0.13333	0.15000
10	.16667	.18333	.20000	.21667	.23333	.25000	.26667	.28333	.30000	.31667
20	.33333	.35000	.36667	.38333	.40000	.41667	.43333	.45000	.46667	.48333
30	.50000	.51667	.53333	.55000	.56667	.58333	.60000	.61667	.63333	.65000
40	.66667	.68333	.70000	.71667	.73333	.75000	.76667	.78333	.80000	.81667
50	.83333	.85000	.86667	.88333	.90000	.91667	.93333	.95000	.96667	.98333

Table 16. Stadia Reductions
Differences in Elevation for 100 ft Inclined Distance

Min-utes	0°	1°	2°	3°	4°	5°	6°	7°	8°	9°	10°	11°	12°
0	0.00	1.74	3.49	5.23	6.96	8.68	10.40	12.10	13.78	15.45	17.10	18.73	20.34
2	0.06	1.80	3.55	5.28	7.02	8.74	10.45	12.15	13.84	15.51	17.16	18.78	20.39
4	0.12	1.86	3.60	5.34	7.07	8.80	10.51	12.21	13.89	15.56	17.21	18.84	20.44
6	0.17	1.92	3.66	5.40	7.13	8.85	10.57	12.26	13.95	15.62	17.26	18.89	20.50
8	0.23	1.98	3.72	5.46	7.19	8.91	10.62	12.32	14.01	15.67	17.32	18.95	20.55
10	0.29	2.04	3.78	5.52	7.25	8.97	10.68	12.38	14.06	15.73	17.37	19.00	20.60
12	0.35	2.09	3.84	5.57	7.30	9.03	10.74	12.43	14.12	15.78	17.43	19.05	20.66
14	0.41	2.15	3.90	5.63	7.36	9.08	10.79	12.49	14.17	15.84	17.48	19.11	20.71
16	0.47	2.21	3.95	5.69	7.42	9.14	10.85	12.55	14.23	15.89	17.54	19.16	20.76
18	0.52	2.27	4.01	5.75	7.48	9.20	10.91	12.60	14.28	15.95	17.59	19.21	20.81
20	0.58	2.33	4.07	5.80	7.53	9.25	10.96	12.66	14.34	16.00	17.65	19.27	20.87
22	0.64	2.38	4.13	5.86	7.59	9.31	11.02	12.72	14.40	16.06	17.70	19.32	20.92
24	0.70	2.44	4.18	5.92	7.65	9.37	11.08	12.77	14.45	16.11	17.76	19.38	20.97
26	0.76	2.50	4.24	5.98	7.71	9.43	11.13	12.83	14.51	16.17	17.81	19.43	21.03
28	0.81	2.56	4.30	6.04	7.76	9.48	11.19	12.88	14.56	16.22	17.86	19.48	21.08
30	0.87	2.62	4.36	6.09	7.82	9.54	11.25	12.94	14.62	16.28	17.92	19.54	21.13
32	0.93	2.67	4.42	6.15	7.88	9.60	11.30	13.00	14.67	16.33	17.97	19.59	21.18
34	0.99	2.73	4.48	6.21	7.94	9.65	11.36	13.05	14.73	16.39	18.03	19.64	21.24
36	1.05	2.79	4.53	6.27	7.99	9.71	11.42	13.11	14.79	16.44	18.08	19.70	21.29
38	1.11	2.85	4.59	6.33	8.05	9.77	11.47	13.17	14.84	16.50	18.14	19.75	21.34
40	1.16	2.91	4.65	6.38	8.11	9.83	11.53	13.22	14.90	16.55	18.19	19.80	21.39
42	1.22	2.97	4.71	6.44	8.17	9.88	11.59	13.28	14.95	16.61	18.24	19.86	21.45
44	1.28	3.02	4.76	6.50	8.22	9.94	11.64	13.33	15.01	16.66	18.30	19.91	21.50
46	1.34	3.08	4.82	6.56	8.28	10.00	11.70	13.39	15.06	16.72	18.35	19.96	21.55
48	1.40	3.14	4.88	6.61	8.34	10.05	11.76	13.45	15.12	16.77	18.41	20.02	21.60
50	1.45	3.20	4.94	6.67	8.40	10.11	11.81	13.50	15.17	16.83	18.46	20.07	21.66
52	1.51	3.26	4.99	6.73	8.45	10.17	11.87	13.56	15.23	16.88	18.51	20.12	21.71
54	1.57	3.31	5.05	6.79	8.51	10.22	11.93	13.61	15.28	16.94	18.57	20.18	21.76
56	1.63	3.37	5.11	6.84	8.57	10.28	11.98	13.67	15.34	16.99	18.62	20.23	21.81
58	1.69	3.43	5.17	6.90	8.63	10.34	12.04	13.73	15.40	17.05	18.68	20.28	21.87
60	1.74	3.49	5.23	6.96	8.68	10.40	12.10	13.78	15.45	17.10	18.73	20.34	21.92
f + c													
.75	0.01	0.02	0.03	0.05	0.06	0.07	0.08	0.10	0.11	0.12	0.14	0.15	0.16
1.00	0.01	0.03	0.04	0.06	0.08	0.09	0.11	0.13	0.15	0.16	0.18	0.20	0.22
1.25	0.02	0.03	0.05	0.08	0.10	0.11	0.14	0.16	0.18	0.21	0.23	0.25	0.27

Corrections to Horizontal Distances

Min-utes	0°	1°	2°	3°	4°	5°	6°	7°	8°	9°	10°	11°	12°
0	......	0.03	0.12	0.27	0.49	0.76	1.09	1.49	1.94	2.45	3.02	3.64	4.32
10	......	0.04	0.14	0.31	0.53	0.81	1.15	1.56	2.02	2.54	3.12	3.75	4.44
20	......	0.05	0.17	0.34	0.57	0.86	1.22	1.63	2.10	2.63	3.22	3.86	4.56
30	0.01	0.07	0.19	0.37	0.62	0.92	1.28	1.70	2.18	2.72	3.32	3.97	4.68
40	0.01	0.08	0.22	0.41	0.66	0.98	1.35	1.78	2.27	2.82	3.42	4.09	4.81
50	0.02	0.10	0.24	0.45	0.71	1.03	1.42	1.86	2.36	2.92	3.53	4.21	4.93

Table 16. Stadia Reductions.—*Continued*

Differences in Elevation for 100 ft Inclined Distance

Min-utes	13°	14°	15°	16°	17°	18°	19°	20°	21°	22°	23°	24°	25°
0	21.92	23.47	25.00	26.50	27.96	29.39	30.78	32.14	33.46	34.73	35.97	37.16	38.30
2	21.97	23.52	25.05	26.55	28.01	29.44	30.83	32.18	33.50	34.77	36.01	37.20	38.34
4	22.02	23.58	25.10	26.59	28.06	29.48	30.87	32.23	33.54	34.82	36.05	37.23	38.38
6	22.08	23.63	25.15	26.64	28.10	29.53	30.92	32.27	33.59	34.86	36.09	37.27	38.41
8	22.13	23.68	25.20	26.69	28.15	29.58	30.97	32.32	33.63	34.90	36.13	37.31	38.45
10	22.18	23.73	25.25	26.74	28.20	29.62	31.01	32.36	33.67	34.94	36.17	37.35	38.49
12	22.23	23.78	25.30	26.79	28.25	29.67	31.06	32.41	33.72	34.98	36.21	37.39	38.53
14	22.28	23.83	25.35	26.84	28.30	29.72	31.10	32.45	33.76	35.02	36.25	37.43	38.56
16	22.34	23.88	25.40	26.89	28.34	29.76	31.15	32.49	33.80	35.07	36.29	37.47	38.60
18	22.39	23.93	25.45	26.94	28.39	29.81	31.19	32.54	33.84	35.11	36.33	37.51	38.64
20	22.44	23.99	25.50	26.99	28.44	29.86	31.24	32.58	33.89	35.15	36.37	37.54	38.67
22	22.49	24.04	25.55	27.04	28.49	29.90	31.28	32.63	33.93	35.19	36.41	37.58	38.71
24	22.54	24.09	25.60	27.09	28.54	29.95	31.33	32.67	33.97	35.23	36.45	37.62	38.75
26	22.60	24.14	25.65	27.13	28.58	30.00	31.38	32.72	34.01	35.27	36.49	37.66	38.78
28	22.65	24.19	25.70	27.18	28.63	30.04	31.42	32.76	34.06	35.31	36.53	37.70	38.82
30	22.70	24.24	25.75	27.23	28.68	30.09	31.47	32.80	34.10	35.36	36.57	37.74	38.86
32	22.75	24.29	25.80	27.28	28.73	30.14	31.51	32.85	34.14	35.40	36.61	37.77	38.89
34	22.80	24.34	25.85	27.33	28.77	30.19	31.56	32.89	34.18	35.44	36.65	37.81	38.93
36	22.85	24.39	25.90	27.38	28.82	30.23	31.60	32.93	34.23	35.48	36.69	37.85	38.97
38	22.91	24.44	25.95	27.43	28.87	30.28	31.65	32.98	34.27	35.52	36.73	37.89	39.00
40	22.96	24.49	26.00	27.48	28.92	30.32	31.69	33.02	34.31	35.56	36.77	37.93	39.04
42	23.01	24.55	26.05	27.52	28.96	30.37	31.74	33.07	34.35	35.60	36.80	37.96	39.08
44	23.06	24.60	26.10	27.57	29.01	30.41	31.78	33.11	34.40	35.64	36.84	38.00	39.11
46	23.11	24.65	26.15	27.62	29.06	30.46	31.83	33.15	34.44	35.68	36.88	38.04	39.15
48	23.16	24.70	26.20	27.67	29.11	30.51	31.87	33.20	34.48	35.72	36.92	38.08	39.18
50	23.22	24.75	26.25	27.72	29.15	30.55	31.92	33.24	34.52	35.76	36.96	38.11	39.22
52	23.27	24.80	26.30	27.77	29.20	30.60	31.96	33.28	34.57	35.80	37.00	38.15	39.26
54	23.32	24.85	26.35	27.81	29.25	30.65	32.01	33.33	34.61	35.85	37.04	38.19	39.29
56	23.37	24.90	26.40	27.86	29.30	30.69	32.05	33.37	34.65	35.89	37.08	38.23	39.33
58	23.42	24.95	26.45	27.91	29.34	30.74	32.09	33.41	34.69	35.93	37.12	38.26	39.36
60	23.47	25.00	26.50	27.96	29.39	30.78	32.14	33.46	34.73	35.97	37.16	38.30	39.40
f + c .75	0.17	0.19	0.20	0.21	0.23	0.24	0.25	0.26	0.27	0.29	0.30	0.31	0.32
1.00	0.23	0.25	0.27	0.28	0.30	0.32	0.33	0.35	0.37	0.38	0.40	0.41	0.43
1.25	0.29	0.31	0.34	0.36	0.38	0.40	0.42	0.44	0.46	0.48	0.50	0.52	0.54

Corrections to Horizontal Distances

Min-utes	13°	14°	15°	16°	17°	18°	19°	20°	21°	22°	23°	24°	25°
0	5.06	5.85	6.70	7.60	8.55	9.55	10.60	11.70	12.84	14.03	15.27	16.54	17.86
10	5.19	5.99	6.84	7.75	8.71	9.72	10.78	11.89	13.04	14.24	15.48	16.76	18.08
20	5.32	6.13	6.99	7.91	8.88	9.89	10.96	12.07	13.23	14.44	15.69	16.98	18.31
30	5.45	6.27	7.14	8.07	9.04	10.07	11.14	12.26	13.43	14.64	15.90	17.20	18.53
40	5.58	6.41	7.29	8.23	9.21	10.24	11.33	12.46	13.63	14.85	16.11	17.42	18.76
50	5.72	6.55	7.44	8.39	9.38	10.42	11.51	12.65	13.83	15.06	16.33	17.64	18.99

Decimals	Minutes	Natural Values				Common Logarithms				Minutes	Decimals
		Sin	Cos	Tan	Cot	Sin	Cos	Tan	Cot		
.00	0	.00000	1.00000	.00000	+∞	−∞	10.000000	−∞	+∞	60	1.00
	1	.00029	1.00000	.00029	3437.75	6.463726	.000000	6.463726	13.536274	59	
	2	.00058	1.00000	.00058	1718.87	.764756	.000000	.764756	.235244	58	
.05	3	.00087	1.00000	.00087	1145.92	.940847	.000000	.940847	.059153	57	.95
	4	.00116	1.00000	.00116	859.436	7.065786	.000000	7.065786	12.934214	56	
	5	.00145	1.00000	.00145	687.549	.162696	.000000	.162696	.837304	55	
.10	6	.00175	1.00000	.00175	572.957	.241877	9.999999	.241878	.758122	54	.90
	7	.00204	1.00000	.00204	491.106	.308824	.999999	.308825	.691175	53	
	8	.00233	1.00000	.00233	429.718	.366816	.999999	.366817	.633183	52	
.15	9	.00262	1.00000	.00262	381.971	.417968	.999999	.417970	.582030	51	.85
	10	.00291	1.00000	.00291	343.774	.463726	.999998	.463727	.536273	50	
	11	.00320	.99999	.00320	312.521	.505118	.999998	.505120	.494880	49	
.20	12	.00349	.99999	.00349	286.478	.542906	.999997	.542909	.457091	48	.80
	13	.00378	.99999	.00378	264.441	.577668	.999997	.577672	.422328	47	
	14	.00407	.99999	.00407	245.552	.609853	.999996	.609857	.390143	46	
.25	15	.00436	.99999	.00436	229.182	.639816	.999996	.639820	.360180	45	.75
	16	.00465	.99999	.00465	214.858	.667845	.999995	.667849	.332151	44	
	17	.00495	.99999	.00495	202.219	.694173	.999995	.694179	.305821	43	
.30	18	.00524	.99999	.00524	190.984	.718997	.999994	.719003	.280997	42	.70
	19	.00553	.99998	.00553	180.932	.742478	.999993	.742484	.257516	41	
	20	.00582	.99998	.00582	171.885	.764754	.999993	.764761	.235239	40	
.35	21	.00611	.99998	.00611	163.700	.785943	.999992	.785951	.214049	39	.65
	22	.00640	.99998	.00640	156.259	.806146	.999991	.806155	.193845	38	
	23	.00669	.99998	.00669	149.465	.825451	.999990	.825460	.174540	37	
.40	24	.00698	99998	.00698	143.237	.843934	.999989	.843944	.156056	36	.60
	25	.00727	.99997	.00727	137.507	.861662	.999989	.861674	.138326	35	
	26	.00756	.99997	.00756	132.219	.878695	.999988	.878708	.121292	34	
.45	27	.00785	.99997	.00785	127.321	.895085	.999987	.895099	.104901	33	.55
	28	.00814	.99997	.00815	122.774	.910879	.999986	.910894	.089106	32	
	29	.00844	.99996	.00844	118.540	.926119	.999985	.926134	.073866	31	
.50	30	.00873	.99996	.00873	114.589	.940842	.999983	.940858	.059142	30	.50
	31	.00902	.99996	.00902	110.892	.955082	.999982	.955100	.044900	29	
	32	.00931	.99996	.00931	107.426	.968870	.999981	.968889	.031111	28	
.55	33	.00960	.99995	.00960	104.171	.982233	.999980	.982253	.017747	27	.45
	34	.00989	.99995	.00989	101.107	−.995198	.999979	.995219	.004781	26	
	35	.01018	.99995	.01018	98.2179	8.007787	.999977	8.007809	11.992191	25	
.60	36	.01047	.99995	.01047	95.4895	.020021	.999976	.020044	.979956	24	.40
	37	.01076	.99994	.01076	92.9085	.031919	.999975	.031945	.968055	23	
	38	.01105	.99994	.01105	90.4633	.043501	.999973	.043527	.956473	22	
.65	39	.01134	.99994	.01135	88.1436	.054781	.999972	.054809	.945191	21	.35
	40	.01164	.99993	.01164	85.9398	.065776	.999971	.065806	.934194	20	
	41	.01193	.99993	.01193	83.8435	.076500	.999969	.076531	.923469	19	
.70	42	.01222	.99993	.01222	81.8470	.086965	.999968	.086997	.913003	18	.30
	43	.01251	.99992	.01251	79.9434	.097183	.999966	.097217	.902783	17	
	44	.01280	.99992	.01280	78.1263	.107167	.999964	.107203	.892797	16	
.75	45	.01309	.99991	.01309	76.3900	.116926	.999963	.116963	.883037	15	.25
	46	.01338	.99991	.01338	74.7292	.126471	.999961	.126510	.873490	14	
	47	.01367	.99991	.01367	73.1390	.135810	.999959	.135851	.864149	13	
.80	48	.01396	.99990	.01396	71.6151	.144953	.999958	.144996	.855004	12	.20
	49	.01425	.99990	.01425	70.1533	.153907	.999956	.153952	.846048	11	
	50	.01454	.99989	.01455	68.7501	.162681	.999954	.162727	.837273	10	
.85	51	.01483	.99989	.01484	67.4019	.171280	.999952	.171328	.828672	9	.15
	52	.01513	.99989	.01513	66.1055	.179713	.999950	.179763	.820237	8	
	53	.01542	.99988	.01542	64.8580	.187985	.999948	.188036	.811964	7	
.90	54	.01571	.99988	.01571	63.6567	.196102	.999946	.196156	.803844	6	.10
	55	.01600	.99987	.01600	62.4992	.204070	.999944	.204126	.795874	5	
	56	.01629	.99987	.01629	61.3829	.211895	.999942	.211953	.788047	4	
.95	57	.01658	.99986	.01658	60.3058	.219581	.999940	.219641	.780359	3	.05
	58	.01687	.99986	.01687	59.2659	.227134	.999938	.227195	.772805	2	
	59	.01716	.99985	.01716	58.2612	.234557	.999936	.234621	.765379	1	
1.00	60	.01745	.99985	.01746	57.2900	8.241855	9.999934	8.241921	11.758079	0	.00
Decimals	Minutes	Cos	Sin	Cot	Tan	Cos	Sin	Cot	Tan	Minutes	Decimals
		Natural Values				Common Logarithms					

Decimals	Minutes	Natural Values				Common Logarithms				Minutes	Decimals
		Sin	Cos	Tan	Cot	Sin	Cos	Tan	Cot		
.00	0	.01745	.99985	.01746	57.2900	8.241855	9.999934	8.241921	11.758079	60	1.00
	1	.01774	.99984	.01775	56.3506	.249033	.999932	.249102	.750898	59	
	2	.01803	.99984	.01804	55.4415	.256094	.999929	.256165	.743835	58	
.05	3	.01832	.99983	.01833	54.5613	.263042	.999927	.263115	.736885	57	.95
	4	.01862	.99983	.01862	53.7086	.269881	.999925	.269956	.730044	56	
	5	.01891	.99982	.01891	52.8821	.276614	.999922	.276691	.723309	55	
.10	6	.01920	.99982	.01920	52.0807	.283243	.999920	.283323	.716677	54	.90
	7	.01949	.99981	.01949	51.3032	.289773	.999918	.289856	.710144	53	
	8	.01978	.99980	.01978	50.5485	.296207	.999915	.296292	.703708	52	
.15	9	.02007	.99980	.02007	49.8157	.302546	.999913	.302634	.697366	51	.85
	10	.02036	.99979	.02036	49.1039	.308794	.999910	.308884	.691116	50	
Γ	11	.02065	.99979	.02066	48.4121	.314954	.999907	.315046	.684954	49	
.20	12	.02094	.99978	.02095	47.7395	.321027	.999905	.321122	.678878	48	.80
	13	.02123	.99977	.02124	47.0853	.327016	.999902	.327114	.672886	47	
	14	.02152	.99977	.02153	46.4489	.332924	.999899	.333025	.666975	46	
.25	15	.02181	.99976	.02182	45.8294	.338753	.999897	.338856	.661144	45	.75
	16	.02211	.99976	.02211	45.2261	.344504	.999894	.344610	.655390	44	
	17	.02240	.99975	.02240	44.6386	.350181	.999891	.350289	.649711	43	
.30	18	.02269	.99974	.02269	44.0661	.355783	.999888	.355895	.644105	42	.70
	19	.02298	.99974	.02298	43.5081	.361315	.999885	.361430	.638570	41	
	20	.02327	.99973	.02328	42.9641	.366777	.999882	.366895	.633105	40	
.35	21	.02356	.99972	.02357	42.4335	.372171	.999879	.372292	.627708	39	.65
	22	.02385	.99972	.02386	41.9158	.377499	.999876	.377622	.622378	38	
	23	.02414	.99971	.02415	41.4106	.382762	.999873	.382889	.617111	37	
.40	24	.02443	.99970	.02444	40.9174	.387962	.999870	.388092	.611908	36	.60
	25	.02472	.99969	.02473	40.4358	.393101	.999867	.393234	.606766	35	
	26	.02501	.99969	.02502	39.9655	.398179	.999864	.398315	.601685	34	
.45	27	.02530	.99968	.02531	39.5059	.403199	.999861	.403338	.596662	33	.55
	28	.02560	.99967	.02560	39.0568	.408161	.999858	.408304	.591696	32	
	29	.02589	.99966	.02589	38.6177	.413068	.999854	.413213	.586787	31	
.50	30	.02618	.99966	.02619	38.1885	.417919	.999851	.418068	.581932	30	.50
	31	.02647	.99965	.02648	37.7686	.422717	.999848	.422869	.577131	29	
	32	.02676	.99964	.02677	37.3579	.427462	.999844	.427618	.572382	28	
.55	33	.02705	.99963	.02706	36.9560	.432156	.999841	.432315	.567685	27	.45
	34	.02734	.99963	.02735	36.5627	.436800	.999838	.436962	.563038	26	
	35	.02763	.99962	.02764	36.1776	.441394	.999834	.441560	.558440	25	
.60	36	.02792	.99961	.02793	35.8006	.445941	.999831	.446110	.553890	24	.40
	37	.02821	.99960	.02822	35.4313	.450440	.999827	.450613	.549387	23	
	38	.02850	.99959	.02851	35.0695	.454893	.999824	.455070	.544930	22	
.65	39	.02879	.99959	.02881	34.7151	.459301	.999820	.459481	.540519	21	.35
	40	.02908	.99958	.02910	34.3678	.463665	.999816	.463849	.536151	20	
	41	.02938	.99957	.02939	34.0273	.467985	.999813	.468172	.531828	19	
.70	42	.02967	.99956	.02968	33.6935	.472253	.999809	.472454	.527546	18	.30
	43	.02996	.99955	.02997	33.3662	.476498	.999805	.476693	.523307	17	
	44	.03025	.99954	.03026	33.0452	.480693	.999801	.480892	.519108	16	
.75	45	.03054	.99953	.03055	32.7303	.484848	.999797	.485050	.514950	15	.25
	46	.03083	.99952	.03084	32.4213	.488963	.999794	.489170	.510830	14	
	47	.03112	.99952	.03114	32.1181	.493040	.999790	.493250	.506750	13	
.80	48	.03141	.99951	.03143	31.8205	.497078	.999786	.497293	.502707	12	.20
	49	.03170	.99950	.03172	31.5284	.501080	.999782	.501298	.498702	11	
	50	.03199	.99949	.03201	31.2416	.505045	.999778	.505267	.494733	10	
.85	51	.03228	.99948	.03230	30.9599	.508974	.999774	.509200	.490800	9	.15
	52	.03257	.99947	.03259	30.6833	.512867	.999769	.513098	.486902	8	
	53	.03286	.99946	.03288	30.4116	.516726	.999765	.516961	.483039	7	
.90	54	.03316	.99945	.03317	30.1446	.520551	.999761	.520790	.479210	6	.10
	55	.03345	.99944	.03346	29.8823	.524343	.999757	.524586	.475414	5	
	56	.03374	.99943	.03376	29.6245	.528102	.999753	.528349	.471651	4	
.95	57	.03403	.99942	.03405	29.3711	.531828	.999748	.532080	.467920	3	.05
	58	.03432	.99941	.03434	29.1220	.535523	.999744	.535779	.464221	2	
	59	.03461	.99940	.03463	28.8771	.539186	.999740	.539447	.460553	1	
1.00	60	.03490	.99939	.03492	28.6363	8.542819	9.999735	8.543084	11.456916	0	.00
Decimals	Minutes	Cos	Sin	Cot	Tan	Cos	Sin	Cot	Tan	Minutes	Decimals
		Natural Values				Common Logarithms					

Decimals	Minutes	Natural Values				Common Logarithms				Minutes	Decimals
		Sin	Cos	Tan	Cot	Sin	Cos	Tan	Cot		
.00	0	.03490	.99939	.03492	28.6363	8.542819	9.999735	8.543084	11.456916	60	1.00
	1	.03519	.99938	.03521	28.3994	.546422	.999731	.546691	.453309	59	
	2	.03548	.99937	.03550	28.1664	.549995	.999726	.550268	.449732	58	
.05	3	.03577	.99936	.03579	27.9372	.553539	.999722	.553817	.446183	57	.95
	4	.03606	.99935	.03609	27.7117	.557054	.999717	.557336	.442664	56	
	5	.03635	.99934	.03638	27.4899	.560540	.999713	.560828	.439172	55	
.10	6	.03664	.99933	.03667	27.2715	.563999	.999708	.564291	.435709	54	.90
	7	.03693	.99932	.03696	27.0566	.567431	.999704	.567727	.432273	53	
	8	.03723	.99931	.03725	26.8450	.570836	.999699	.571137	.428863	52	
.15	9	.03752	.99930	.03754	26.6367	.574214	.999694	.574520	.425480	51	.85
	10	.03781	.99929	.03783	26.4316	.577566	.999689	.577877	.422123	50	
	11	.03810	.99927	.03812	26.2296	.580892	.999685	.581208	.418792	49	
.20	12	.03839	.99926	.03842	26.0307	.584193	.999680	.584514	.415486	48	.80
	13	.03868	.99925	.03871	25.8348	.587469	.999675	.587795	.412205	47	
	14	.03897	.99924	.03900	25.6418	.590721	.999670	.591051	.408949	46	
.25	15	.03926	.99923	.03929	25.4517	.593948	.999665	.594283	.405717	45	.75
	16	.03955	.99922	.03958	25.2644	.597152	.999660	.597492	.402508	44	
	17	.03984	.99921	.03987	25.0798	.600332	.999655	.600677	.399323	43	
.30	18	.04013	.99919	.04016	24.8978	.603489	.999650	.603839	.396161	42	.70
	19	.04042	.99918	.04046	24.7185	.606623	.999645	.606978	.393022	41	
	20	.04071	.99917	.04075	24.5418	.609734	.999640	.610094	.389906	40	
.35	21	.04100	.99916	.04104	24.3675	.612823	.999635	.613189	.386811	39	.65
	22	.04129	.99915	.04133	24.1957	.615891	.999629	.616262	.383738	38	
	23	.04159	.99913	.04162	24.0263	.618937	.999624	.619313	.380687	37	
.40	24	.04188	.99912	.04191	23.8593	.621962	.999619	.622343	.377657	36	.60
	25	.04217	.99911	.04220	23.6945	.624965	.999614	.625352	.374648	35	
	26	.04246	.99910	.04250	23.5321	.627948	.999608	.628340	.371660	34	
.45	27	.04275	.99909	.04279	23.3718	.630911	.999603	.631308	.368692	33	.55
	28	.04304	.99907	.04308	23.2137	.633854	.999597	.634256	.365744	32	
	29	.04333	.99906	.04337	23.0577	.636776	.999592	.637184	.362816	31	
.50	30	.04362	.99905	.04366	22.9038	.639680	.999586	.640093	.359907	30	.50
	31	.04391	.99904	.04395	22.7519	.642563	.999581	.642982	.357018	29	
	32	.04420	.99902	.04424	22.6020	.645428	.999575	.645853	.354147	28	
.55	33	.04449	.99901	.04454	22.4541	.648274	.999570	.648704	.351296	27	.45
	34	.04478	.99900	.04483	22.3081	.651102	.999564	.651537	.348463	26	
	35	.04507	.99898	.04512	22.1640	.653911	.999558	.654352	.345648	25	
.60	36	.04536	.99897	.04541	22.0217	.656702	.999553	.657149	.342851	24	.40
	37	.04565	.99896	.04570	21.8813	.659475	.999547	.659928	.340072	23	
	38	.04594	.99894	.04599	21.7426	.662230	.999541	.662689	.337311	22	
.65	39	.04623	.99893	.04628	21.6056	.664968	.999535	.665433	.334567	21	.35
	40	.04653	.99892	.04658	21.4704	.667689	.999529	.668160	.331840	20	
	41	.04682	.99890	.04687	21.3369	.670393	.999524	.670870	.329130	19	
.70	42	.04711	.99889	.04716	21.2049	.673080	.999518	.673563	.326437	18	.30
	43	.04740	.99888	.04745	21.0747	.675751	.999512	.676239	.323761	17	
	44	.04769	.99886	.04774	20.9460	.678405	.999506	.678900	.321100	16	
.75	45	.04798	.99885	.04803	20.8188	.681043	.999500	.681544	.318456	15	.25
	46	.04827	.99883	.04833	20.6932	.683665	.999493	.684172	.315828	14	
	47	.04856	.99882	.04862	20.5691	.686272	.999487	.686784	.313216	13	
.80	48	.04885	.99881	.04891	20.4465	.688863	.999481	.689331	.310619	12	.20
	49	.04914	.99879	.04920	20.3253	.691438	.999475	.691963	.308037	11	
	50	.04943	.99878	.04949	20.2056	.693998	.999469	.694529	.305471	10	
.85	51	.04972	.99876	.04978	20.0872	.696543	.999463	.697081	.302919	9	.15
	52	.05001	.99875	.05007	19.9702	.699073	.999456	.699617	.300383	8	
	53	.05030	.99873	.05037	19.8546	.701589	.999450	.702139	.297861	7	
.90	54	.05059	.99872	.05066	19.7403	.704090	.999443	.704646	.295354	6	.10
	55	.05088	.99870	.05095	19.6273	.706577	.999437	.707140	.292860	5	
	56	.05117	.99869	.05124	19.5156	.709049	.999431	.709618	.290382	4	
.95	57	.05146	.99867	.05153	19.4051	.711507	.999424	.712083	.287917	3	.05
	58	.05175	.99866	.05182	19.2959	.713952	.999418	.714534	.285466	2	
	59	.05205	.99864	.05212	19.1879	.716383	.999411	.716972	.283028	1	
1.00	60	.05234	.99863	.05241	19.0811	8.718800	9.999404	8.719396	11.280604	0	.00
Decimals	Minutes	Cos	Sin	Cot	Tan	Cos	Sin	Cot	Tan	Minutes	Decimals
		Natural Values				Common Logarithms					

Decimals	Minutes	Natural Values				Common Logarithms				Minutes	Decimals
		Sin	Cos	Tan	Cot	Sin	Cos	.Tan	Cot		
.00	0	.05234	.99863	.05241	19.0811	8.718800	9.999404	8.719396	11.280604	60	1.00
	1	.05263	.99861	.05270	18.9755	.721204	.999398	.721806	.278194	59	
	2	.05292	.99860	.05299	18.8711	.723595	.999391	.724204	.275796	58	
.05	3	.05321	.99858	.05328	18.7678	.725972	.999384	.726588	.273412	57	.95
	4	.05350	.99857	.05357	18.6656	.728337	.999378	.728959	.271041	56	
	5	.05379	.99855	.05387	18.5645	.730688	.999371	.731317	.268683	55	
.10	6	.05408	.99854	.05416	18.4645	.733027	.999364	.733663	.266337	54	.90
	7	.05437	.99852	.05445	18.3655	.735354	.999357	.735996	.264004	53	
	8	.05466	.99851	.05474	18.2677	.737667	.999350	.738317	.261683	52	
.15	9	.05495	.99849	.05503	18.1708	.739969	.999343	.740626	.259374	51	.85
	10	.05524	.99847	.05533	18.0750	.742259	.999336	.742922	.257078	50	
	11	.05553	.99846	.05562	17.9802	.744536	.999329	.745207	.254793	49	
.20	12	.05582	.99844	.05591	17.8863	.746802	.999322	.747479	.252521	48	.80
	13	.05611	.99842	.05620	17.7934	.749055	.999315	.749740	.250260	47	
	14	.05640	.99841	.05649	17.7015	.751297	.999308	.751989	.248011	46	
.25	15	.05669	.99839	.05678	17.6106	.753528	.999301	.754227	.245773	45	.75
	16	.05698	.99838	.05708	17.5205	.755747	.999294	.756453	.243547	44	
	17	.05727	.99836	.05737	17.4314	.757955	.999287	.758668	.241332	43	
.30	18	.05756	.99834	.05766	17.3432	.760151	.999279	.760872	.239128	42	.70
	19	.05785	.99833	.05795	17.2558	.762337	.999272	.763065	.236935	41	
	20	.05814	.99831	.05824	17.1693	.764511	.999265	.765246	.234754	40	
.35	21	.05844	.99829	.05854	17.0837	.766675	.999257	.767417	.232583	39	.65
	22	.05873	.99827	.05883	16.9990	.768828	.999250	.769578	.230422	38	
	23	.05902	.99826	.05912	16.9150	.770970	.999242	.771727	.228273	37	
.40	24	.05931	.99824	.05941	16.8319	.773101	.999235	.773866	.226134	36	.60
	25	.05960	.99822	.05970	16.7496	.775223	.999227	.775995	.224005	35	
	26	.05989	.99821	.05999	16.6681	.777333	.999220	.778114	.221886	34	
.45	27	.06018	.99819	.06029	16.5874	.779434	.999212	.780222	.219778	33	.55
	28	.06047	.99817	.06058	16.5075	.781524	.999205	.782320	.217680	32	
	29	.06076	.99815	.06087	16.4283	.783605	.999197	.784408	.215592	31	
.50	30	.06105	.99813	.06116	16.3499	.785675	.999189	.786486	.213514	30	.50
	31	.06134	.99812	.06145	16.2722	.787736	.999181	.788554	.211446	29	
	32	.06163	.99810	.06175	16.1952	.789787	.999174	.790613	.209387	28	
.55	33	.06192	.99808	.06204	16.1190	.791828	.999166	.792662	.207338	27	.45
	34	.06221	.99806	.06233	16.0435	.793859	.999158	.794701	.205299	26	
	35	.06250	.99804	.06262	15.9687	.795881	.999150	.796731	.203269	25	
.60	36	.06279	.99803	.06291	15.8945	.797894	.999142	.798752	.201248	24	.40
	37	.06308	.99801	.06321	15.8211	.799897	.999134	.800763	.199237	23	
	38	.06337	.99799	.06350	15.7483	.801892	.999126	.802765	.197235	22	
.65	39	.06366	.99797	.06379	15.6762	.803876	.999118	.804758	.195242	21	.35
	40	.06395	.99795	.06408	15.6048	.805852	.999110	.806742	.193258	20	
	41	.06424	.99793	.06437	15.5340	.807819	.999102	.808717	.191283	19	
.70	42	.06453	.99792	.06467	15.4638	.809777	.999094	.810683	.189317	18	.30
	43	.06482	.99790	.06496	15.3943	.811726	.999086	.812641	.187359	17	
	44	.06511	.99788	.06525	15.3254	.813667	.999077	.814589	.185411	16	
.75	45	.06540	.99786	.06554	15.2571	.815599	.999069	.816529	.183471	15	.25
	46	.06569	.99784	.06584	15.1893	.817522	.999061	.818461	.181539	14	
	47	.06598	.99782	.06613	15.1222	.819436	.999053	.820384	.179616	13	
.80	48	.06627	.99780	.06642	15.0557	.821343	.999044	.822298	.177702	12	.20
	49	.06656	.99778	.06671	14.9898	.823240	.999036	.824205	.175795	11	
	50	.06685	.99776	.06700	14.9244	.825130	.999027	.826103	.173897	10	
.85	51	.06714	.99774	.06730	14.8596	.827011	.999019	.827992	.172008	9	.15
	52	.06743	.99772	.06759	14.7954	.828884	.999010	.829874	.170126	8	
	53	.06773	.99770	.06788	14.7317	.830749	.999002	.831748	.168252	7	
.90	54	.06802	.99768	.06817	14.6685	.832607	.998993	.833613	.166387	6	.10
	55	.06831	.99766	.06847	14.6059	.834456	.998984	.835471	.164529	5	
	56	.06860	.99764	.06876	14.5438	.836297	.998976	.837321	.162679	4	
.95	57	.06889	.99762	.06905	14.4823	.838130	.998967	.839163	.160837	3	.05
	58	.06918	.99760	.06934	14.4212	.839956	.998958	.840998	.159002	2	
	59	.06947	.99758	.06963	14.3607	.841774	.998950	.842825	.157175	1	
1.00	60	.06976	.99756	.06993	14.3007	8.843585	9.998941	8.844644	11.155356	0	.00
		Cos	Sin	Cot	Tan	Cos	Sin	Cot	Tan		
Decimals	Minutes	Natural Values				Common Logarithms				Minutes	Decimals

Decimals	Minutes	Natural Values				Common Logarithms				Minutes	Decimals
		Sin	Cos	Tan	Cot	Sin	Cos	Tan	Cot		
.00	0	.06976	.99756	.06993	14.3007	8.843585	9.998941	8.844644	11.155356	60	1.00
	1	.07005	.99754	.07022	14.2411	.845387	.998932	.846455	.153545	59	
	2	.07034	.99752	.07051	14.1821	.847183	.998923	.848260	.151740	58	
.05	3	.07063	.99750	.07080	14.1235	.848971	.998914	.850057	.149943	57	.95
	4	.07092	.99748	.07110	14.0655	.850751	.998905	.851846	.148154	56	
	5	.07121	.99746	.07139	14.0079	.852525	.998896	.853628	.146372	55	
.10	6	.07150	.99744	.07168	13.9507	.854291	.998887	.855403	.144597	54	.90
	7	.07179	.99742	.07197	13.8940	.856049	.998878	.857171	.142829	53	
	8	.07208	.99740	.07227	13.8378	.857801	.998869	.858932	.141068	52	
.15	9	.07237	.99738	.07256	13.7821	.859546	.998860	.860686	.139314	51	.85
	10	.07266	.99736	.07285	13.7267	.861283	.998851	.862433	.137567	50	
	11	.07295	.99734	.07314	13.6719	.863014	.998841	.864173	.135827	49	
.20	12	.07324	.99731	.07344	13.6174	.864738	.998832	.865906	.134094	48	.80
	13	.07353	.99729	.07373	13.5634	.866455	.998823	.867632	.132368	47	
	14	.07382	.99727	.07402	13.5098	.868165	.998813	.869351	.130649	46	
.25	15	.07411	.99725	.07431	13.4566	.869868	.998804	.871064	.128936	45	.75
	16	.07440	.99723	.07461	13.4039	.871565	.998795	.872770	.127230	44	
	17	.07469	.99721	.07490	13.3515	.873255	.998785	.874469	.125531	43	
.30	18	.07498	.99719	.07519	13.2996	.874938	.998776	.876162	.123838	42	.70
	19	.07527	.99716	.07548	13.2480	.876615	.998766	.877849	.122151	41	
	20	.07556	.99714	.07578	13.1969	.878285	.998757	.879529	.120471	40	
.35	21	.07585	.99712	.07607	13.1461	.879949	.998747	.881202	.118798	39	.65
	22	.07614	.99710	.07636	13.0958	.881607	.998738	.882869	.117131	38	
	23	.07643	.99708	.07665	13.0458	.883258	.998728	.884530	.115470	37	
.40	24	.07672	.99705	.07695	12.9962	.884903	.998718	.886185	.113815	36	.60
	25	.07701	.99703	.07724	12.9469	.886542	.998708	.887833	.112167	35	
	26	.07730	.99701	.07753	12.8981	.888174	.998699	.889476	.110524	34	
.45	27	.07759	.99699	.07782	12.8496	.889801	.998689	.891112	.108888	33	.55
	28	.07788	.99696	.07812	12.8014	.891421	.998679	.892742	.107258	32	
	29	.07817	.99694	.07841	12.7536	.893035	.998669	.894366	.105634	31	
.50	30	.07846	.99692	.07870	12.7062	.894643	.998659	.895984	.104016	30	.50
	31	.07875	.99689	.07899	12.6591	.896246	.998649	.897596	.102404	29	
	32	.07904	.99687	.07929	12.6124	.897842	.998639	.899203	.100797	28	
.55	33	.07933	.99685	.07958	12.5660	.899432	.998629	.900803	.099197	27	.45
	34	.07962	.99683	.07987	12.5199	.901017	.998619	.902398	.097602	26	
	35	.07991	.99680	.08017	12.4742	.902596	.998609	.903987	.096013	25	
.60	36	.08020	.99678	.08046	12.4288	.904169	.998599	.905570	.094430	24	.40
	37	.08049	.99676	.08075	12.3838	.905736	.998589	.907147	.092853	23	
	38	.08078	.99673	.08104	12.3390	.907297	.998578	.908719	.091281	22	
.65	39	.08107	.99671	.08134	12.2946	.908853	.998568	.910285	.089715	21	.35
	40	.08136	.99668	.08163	12.2505	.910404	.998558	.911846	.088154	20	
	41	.08165	.99666	.08192	12.2067	.911949	.998548	.913401	.086599	19	
.70	42	.08194	.99664	.08221	12.1632	.913488	.998537	.914951	.085049	18	.30
	43	.08223	.99661	.08251	12.1201	.915022	.998527	.916495	.083505	17	
	44	.08252	.99659	.08280	12.0772	.916550	.998516	.918034	.081966	16	
.75	45	.08281	.99657	.08309	12.0346	.918073	.998506	.919568	.080432	15	.25
	46	.08310	.99654	.08339	11.9923	.919591	.998495	.921096	.078904	14	
	47	.08339	.99652	.08368	11.9504	.921103	.998485	.922619	.077381	13	
.80	48	.08368	.99649	.08397	11.9087	.922610	.998474	.924136	.075864	12	.20
	49	.08397	.99647	.08427	11.8673	.924112	.998464	.925649	.074351	11	
	50	.08426	.99644	.08456	11.8262	.925609	.998453	.927156	.072844	10	
.85	51	.08455	.99642	.08485	11.7853	.927100	.998442	.928658	.071342	9	.15
	52	.08484	.99639	.08514	11.7448	.928587	.998431	.930155	.069845	8	
	53	.08513	.99637	.08544	11.7045	.930068	.998421	.931647	.068353	7	
.90	54	.08542	.99635	.08573	11.6645	.931544	.998410	.933134	.066866	6	.10
	55	.08571	.99632	.08602	11.6248	.933015	.998399	.934616	.065384	5	
	56	.08600	.99630	.08632	11.5853	.934481	.998388	.936093	.063907	4	
.95	57	.08629	.99627	.08661	11.5461	.935942	.998377	.937565	.062435	3	.05
	58	.08658	.99625	.08690	11.5072	.937398	.998366	.939032	.060968	2	
	59	.08687	.99622	.08720	11.4685	.938850	.998355	.940494	.059506	1	
1.00	60	.08716	.99619	.08749	11.4301	8.940296	9.998344	8.941952	11.058048	0	.00
Decimals	Minutes	Cos	Sin	Cot	Tan	Cos	Sin	Cot	Tan	Minutes	Decimals
		Natural Values				Common Logarithms					

Decimals	Minutes	Natural Values				Common Logarithms				Minutes	Decimals
		Sin	Cos	Tan	Cot	Sin	Cos	Tan	Cot		
.00	0	.08716	.99619	.08749	11.4301	8.940296	9.998344	8.941952	11.058048	60	1.00
	1	.08745	.99617	.08778	11.3919	.941738	.998333	.943404	.056596	59	
	2	.08774	.99614	.08807	11.3540	.943174	.998322	.944852	.055148	58	
.05	3	.08803	.99612	.08837	11.3163	.944606	.998311	.946295	.053705	57	.95
	4	.08831	.99609	.08866	11.2789	.946034	.998300	.947734	.052266	56	
	5	.08860	.99607	.08895	11.2417	.947456	.998289	.949168	.050832	55	
.10	6	.08889	.99604	.08925	11.2048	.948874	.998277	.950597	.049403	54	.90
	7	.08918	.99602	.08954	11.1681	.950287	.998266	.952021	.047979	53	
	8	.08947	.99599	.08983	11.1316	.951696	.998255	.953441	.046559	52	
.15	9	.08976	.99596	.09013	11.0954	.953100	.998243	.954856	.045144	51	.85
	10	.09005	.99594	.09042	11.0594	.954499	.998232	.956267	.043733	50	
	11	.09034	.99591	.09071	11.0237	.955894	.998220	.957674	.042326	49	
.20	12	.09063	.99588	.09101	10.9882	.957284	.998209	.959075	.040925	48	.80
	13	.09092	.99586	.09130	10.9529	.958670	.998197	.960473	.039527	47	
	14	.09121	.99583	.09159	10.9178	.960052	.998186	.961866	.038134	46	
.25	15	.09150	.99580	.09189	10.8829	.961429	.998174	.963255	.036745	45	.75
	16	.09179	.99578	.09218	10.8483	.962801	.998163	.964639	.035361	44	
	17	.09208	.99575	.09247	10.8139	.964170	.998151	.966019	.033981	43	
.30	18	.09237	.99572	.09277	10.7797	.965534	.998139	.967394	.032606	42	.70
	19	.09266	.99570	.09306	10.7457	.966893	.998128	.968766	.031234	41	
	20	.09295	.99567	.09335	10.7119	.968249	.998116	.970133	.029867	40	
.35	21	.09324	.99564	.09365	10.6783	.969600	.998104	.971496	.023504	39	.65
	22	.09353	.99562	.09394	10.6450	.970947	.998092	.972855	.027145	38	
	23	.09382	.99559	.09423	10.6118	.972289	.998080	.974209	.025791	37	
.40	24	.09411	.99556	.09453	10.5789	.973628	.998068	.975560	.024440	36	.60
	25	.09440	.99553	.09482	10.5462	.974962	.998056	.976906	.023094	35	
	26	.09469	.99551	.09511	10.5136	.976293	.998044	.978248	.021752	34	
.45	27	.09498	.99548	.09541	10.4813	.977619	.998032	.979586	.020414	33	.55
	28	.09527	.99545	.09570	10.4491	.978941	.998020	.980921	.019079	32	
	29	.09556	.99542	.09600	10.4172	.980259	.998008	.982251	.017749	31	
.50	30	.09585	.99540	.09629	10.3854	.981573	.997996	.983577	.016423	30	.50
	31	.09614	.99537	.09658	10.3538	.982883	.997984	.984899	.015101	29	
	32	.09642	.99534	.09688	10.3224	.984189	.997972	.986217	.013783	28	
.55	33	.09671	.99531	.09717	10.2913	.985491	.997959	.987532	.012468	27	.45
	34	.09700	.99528	.09746	10.2602	.986789	.997947	.988842	.011158	26	
	35	.09729	.99526	.09776	10.2294	.988083	.997935	.990149	.009851	25	
.60	36	.09758	.99523	.09805	10.1988	.989374	.997922	.991451	.008549	24	.40
	37	.09787	.99520	.09834	10.1683	.990660	.997910	.992750	.007250	23	
	38	.09816	.99517	.09864	10.1381	.991943	.997897	.994045	.005955	22	
.65	39	.09845	.99514	.09893	10.1080	.993222	.997885	.995337	.004663	21	.35
	40	.09874	.99511	.09923	10.0780	.994497	.997872	.996624	.003376	20	
	41	.09903	.99508	.09952	10.0483	.995768	.997860	.997908	.002092	19	
.70	42	.09932	.99506	.09981	10.0187	.997036	.997847	.999188	.000812	18	.30
	43	.09961	.99503	.10011	9.98931	.998299	.997835	9.000465	10.999535	17	
	44	.09990	.99500	.10040	9.96007	.999560	.997822	.001738	.998262	16	
.75	45	.10019	.99497	.10069	9.93101	9.000816	.997809	.003007	.996993	15	.25
	46	.10048	.99494	.10099	9.90211	.002069	.997797	.004272	.995728	14	
	47	.10077	.99491	.10128	9.87338	.003318	.997784	.005534	.994466	13	
.80	48	.10106	.99488	.10158	9.84482	.004563	.997771	.006792	.993208	12	.20
	49	.10135	.99485	.10187	9.81641	.005805	.997758	.008047	.991953	11	
	50	.10164	.99482	.10216	9.78817	.007044	.997745	.009298	.990702	10	
.85	51	.10192	.99479	.10246	9.76009	.008278	.997732	.010546	.989454	9	.15
	52	.10221	.99476	.10275	9.73217	.009510	.997719	.011790	.988210	8	
	53	.10250	.99473	.10305	9.70441	.010737	.997706	.013031	.986969	7	
.90	54	.10279	.99470	.10334	9.67680	.011962	.997693	.014268	.985732	6	.10
	55	.10308	.99467	.10363	9.64935	.013182	.997680	.015502	.984498	5	
	56	.10337	.99464	.10393	9.62205	.014400	.997667	.016732	.983268	4	
.95	57	.10366	.99461	.10422	9.59490	.015613	.997654	.017959	.982041	3	.05
	58	.10395	.99458	.10452	9.56791	.016824	.997641	.019183	.980817	2	
	59	.10424	.99455	.10481	9.54106	.018031	.997628	.020403	.979597	1	
1.00	60	.10453	.99452	.10510	9.51436	9.019235	9.997614	9.021320	10.978380	0	.00
Decimals	Minutes	Cos	Sin	Cot	Tan	Cos	Sin	Cot	Tan	Minutes	Decimals
		Natural Values				Common Logarithms					

Decimals	Minutes	Natural Values				Common Logarithms				Minutes	Decimals
		Sin	Cos	Tan	Cot	Sin	Cos	Tan	Cot		
.00	0	.10453	.99452	.10510	9.51436	9.019235	9.997614	9.021620	10.978380	60	1.00
	1	.10482	.99449	.10540	9.48781	.020435	.997601	.022834	.977166	59	
	2	.10511	.99446	.10569	9.46141	.021632	.997588	.024044	.975956	58	
.05	3	.10540	.99443	.10599	9.43515	.022825	.997574	.025251	.974749	57	.95
	4	.10569	.99440	.10628	9.40904	.024016	.997561	.026455	.973545	56	
	5	.10597	.99437	.10657	9.38307	.025203	.997547	.027655	.972345	55	
.10	6	.10626	.99434	.10687	9.35724	.026386	.997534	.028852	.971148	54	.90
	7	.10655	.99431	.10716	9.33155	.027567	.997520	.030046	.969954	53	
	8	.10684	.99428	.10746	9.30599	.028744	.997507	.031237	.968763	52	
.15	9	.10713	.99424	.10775	9.28058	.029918	.997493	.032425	.967575	51	.85
	10	.10742	.99421	.10805	9.25530	.031089	.997480	.033609	.966391	50	
	11	.10771	.99418	.10834	9.23016	.032257	.997466	.034791	.965209	49	
.20	12	.10800	.99415	.10863	9.20516	.033421	.997452	.035969	.964031	48	.80
	13	.10829	.99412	.10893	9.18028	.034582	.997439	.037144	.962856	47	
	14	.10858	.99409	.10922	9.15554	.035741	.997425	.038316	.961684	46	
.25	15	.10887	.99406	.10952	9.13093	.036896	.997411	.039485	.960515	45	.75
	16	.10916	.99402	.10981	9.10646	.038048	.997397	.040651	.959349	44	
	17	.10945	.99399	.11011	9.08211	.039197	.997383	.041813	.958187	43	
.30	18	.10973	.99396	.11040	9.05789	.040342	.997369	.042973	.957027	42	.70
	19	.11002	.99393	.11070	9.03379	.041485	.997355	.044130	.955870	41	
	20	.11031	.99390	.11099	9.00983	.042625	.997341	.045284	.954716	40	
.35	21	.11060	.99386	.11128	8.98598	.043762	.997327	.046434	.953566	39	.65
	22	.11089	.99383	.11158	8.96227	.044895	.997313	.047582	.952418	38	
	23	.11118	.99380	.11187	8.93867	.046026	.997299	.048727	.951273	37	
.40	24	.11147	.99377	.11217	8.91520	.047154	.997285	.049869	.950131	36	.60
	25	.11176	.99374	.11246	8.89185	.048279	.997271	.051008	.948992	35	
	26	.11205	.99370	.11276	8.86862	.049400	.997257	.052144	.947856	34	
.45	27	.11234	.99367	.11305	8.84551	.050519	.997242	.053277	.946723	33	.55
	28	.11263	.99364	.11335	8.82252	.051635	.997228	.054407	.945593	32	
	29	.11291	.99360	.11364	8.79964	.052749	.997214	.055535	.944465	31	
.50	30	.11320	.99357	.11394	8.77689	.053859	.997199	.056659	.943341	30	.50
	31	.11349	.99354	.11423	8.75425	.054966	.997185	.057781	.942219	29	
	32	.11378	.99351	.11452	8.73172	.056071	.997170	.058900	.941100	28	
.55	33	.11407	.99347	.11482	8.70931	.057172	.997156	.060016	.939984	27	.45
	34	.11436	.99344	.11511	8.68701	.058271	.997141	.061130	.938870	26	
	35	.11465	.99341	.11541	8.66482	.059367	.997127	.062240	.937760	25	
.60	36	.11494	.99337	.11570	8.64275	.060460	.997112	.063348	.936652	24	.40
	37	.11523	.99334	.11600	8.62078	.061551	.997098	.064453	.935547	23	
	38	.11552	.99331	.11629	8.59893	.062639	.997083	.065556	.934444	22	
.65	39	.11580	.99327	.11659	8.57718	.063724	.997068	.066655	.933345	21	.35
	40	.11609	.99324	.11688	8.55555	.064806	.997053	.067752	.932248	20	
	41	.11638	.99320	.11718	8.53402	.065885	.997039	.068846	.931154	19	
.70	42	.11667	.99317	.11747	8.51259	.066962	.997024	.069938	.930062	18	.30
	43	.11696	.99314	.11777	8.49128	.068036	.997009	.071027	.928973	17	
	44	.11725	.99310	.11806	8.47007	.069107	.996994	.072113	.927887	16	
.75	45	.11754	.99307	.11836	8.44896	.070176	.996979	.073197	.926803	15	.25
	46	.11783	.99303	.11865	8.42795	.071242	.996964	.074278	.925722	14	
	47	.11812	.99300	.11895	8.40705	.072306	.996949	.075356	.924644	13	
.80	48	.11840	.99297	.11924	8.38625	.073366	.996934	.076432	.923568	12	.20
	49	.11869	.99293	.11954	8.36555	.074424	.996919	.077505	.922495	11	
	50	.11898	.99290	.11983	8.34496	.075480	.996904	.078576	.921424	10	
.85	51	.11927	.99286	.12013	8.32446	.076533	.996889	.079644	.920356	9	.15
	52	.11956	.99283	.12042	8.30406	.077583	.996874	.080710	.919290	8	
	53	.11985	.99279	.12072	8.28376	.078631	.996858	.081773	.918227	7	
.90	54	.12014	.99276	.12101	8.26355	.079676	.996843	.082833	.917167	6	.10
	55	.12043	.99272	.12131	8.24345	.080719	.996828	.083891	.916109	5	
	56	.12071	.99269	.12160	8.22344	.081759	.996812	.084947	.915053	4	
.95	57	.12100	.99265	.12190	8.20352	.082797	.996797	.086000	.914000	3	.05
	58	.12129	.99262	.12219	8.18370	.083832	.996782	.087050	.912950	2	
	59	.12158	.99258	.12249	8.16398	.084864	.996766	.088098	.911902	1	
1.00	60	.12187	.99255	.12278	8.14435	9.085894	9.996751	9.089144	10.910856	0	.00
		Cos	Sin	Cot	Tan	Cos	Sin	Cot	Tan		
Decimals	Minutes	Natural Values				Common Logarithms				Minutes	Decimals

Decimals	Minutes	Natural Values				Common Logarithms				Minutes	Decimals
		Sin	Cos	Tan	Cot	Sin	Cos	Tan	Cot		
.00	0	.12187	.99255	.12278	8.14435	9.085894	9.996751	9.089144	10.910856	60	1.00
	1	.12216	.99251	.12308	8.12481	.086922	.996735	.090187	.909813	59	
	2	.12245	.99248	.12338	8.10536	.087947	.996720	.091228	.908772	58	
.05	3	.12274	.99244	.12367	8.08600	.088970	.996704	.092266	.907734	57	.95
	4	.12302	.99240	.12397	8.06674	.089990	.996688	.093302	.906698	56	
	5	.12331	.99237	.12426	8.04756	.091008	.996673	.094336	.905664	55	
.10	6	.12360	.99233	.12456	8.02848	.092024	.996657	.095367	.904633	54	.90
	7	.12389	.99230	.12485	8.00948	.093037	.996641	.096395	.903605	53	
	8	.12418	.99226	.12515	7.99058	.094047	.996625	.097422	.902578	52	
.15	9	.12447	.99222	.12544	7.97176	.095056	.996610	.098446	.901554	51	.85
	10	.12476	.99219	.12574	7.95302	.096062	.996594	.099468	.900532	50	
	11	.12504	.99215	.12603	7.93438	.097065	.996578	.100487	.899513	49	
.20	12	.12533	.99211	.12633	7.91582	.098066	.996562	.101504	.898496	48	.80
	13	.12562	.99208	.12662	7.89734	.099065	.996546	.102519	.897481	47	
	14	.12591	.99204	.12692	7.87895	.100062	.996530	.103532	.896468	46	
.25	15	.12620	.99200	.12722	7.86064	.101055	.996514	.104542	.895458	45	.75
	16	.12649	.99197	.12751	7.84242	.102048	.996498	.105550	.894450	44	
	17	.12678	.99193	.12781	7.82428	.103037	.996482	.106556	.893444	43	
.30	18	.12706	.99189	.12810	7.80622	.104025	.996465	.107559	.892441	42	.70
	19	.12735	.99186	.12840	7.78825	.105010	.996449	.108560	.891440	41	
	20	.12764	.99182	.12869	7.77035	.105992	.996433	.109559	.890441	40	
.35	21	.12793	.99178	.12899	7.75254	.106973	.996417	.110556	.889444	39	.65
	22	.12822	.99175	.12929	7.73480	.107951	.996400	.111551	.888449	38	
	23	.12851	.99171	.12958	7.71715	.108927	.996384	.112543	.887457	37	
.40	24	.12880	.99167	.12988	7.69957	.109901	.996368	.113533	.886467	36	.60
	25	.12908	.99163	.13017	7.68208	.110873	.996351	.114521	.885479	35	
	26	.12937	.99160	.13047	7.66466	.111842	.996335	.115507	.884493	34	
.45	27	.12966	.99156	.13076	7.64732	.112809	.996318	.116491	.883509	33	.55
	28	.12995	.99152	.13106	7.63005	.113774	.996302	.117472	.882528	32	
	29	.13024	.99148	.13136	7.61287	.114737	.996285	.118452	.881548	31	
.50	30	.13053	.99144	.13165	7.59575	.115698	.996269	.119429	.880571	30	.50
	31	.13081	.99141	.13195	7.57872	.116656	.996252	.120404	.879596	29	
	32	.13110	.99137	.13224	7.56176	.117613	.996235	.121377	.878623	28	
.55	33	.13139	.99133	.13254	7.54487	.118567	.996219	.122348	.877652	27	.45
	34	.13168	.99129	.13284	7.52806	.119519	.996202	.123317	.876683	26	
	35	.13197	.99125	.13313	7.51132	.120469	.996185	.124284	.875716	25	
.60	36	.13226	.99122	.13343	7.49465	.121417	.996168	.125249	.874751	24	.40
	37	.13254	.99118	.13372	7.47806	.122362	.996151	.126211	.873789	23	
	38	.13283	.99114	.13402	7.46154	.123306	.996134	.127172	.872828	22	
.65	39	.13312	.99110	.13432	7.44509	.124248	.996117	.128130	.871870	21	.35
	40	.13341	.99106	.13461	7.42871	.125187	.996100	.129087	.870913	20	
	41	.13370	.99102	.13491	7.41240	.126125	.996083	.130041	.869959	19	
.70	42	.13399	.99098	.13521	7.39616	.127060	.996066	.130994	.869006	18	.30
	43	.13427	.99094	.13550	7.37999	.127993	.996049	.131944	.868056	17	
	44	.13456	.99091	.13580	7.36389	.128925	.996032	.132893	.867107	16	
.75	45	.13485	.99087	.13609	7.34786	.129854	.996015	.133839	.866161	15	.25
	46	.13514	.99083	.13639	7.33190	.130781	.995998	.134784	.865216	14	
	47	.13543	.99079	.13669	7.31600	.131706	.995980	.135726	.864274	13	
.80	48	.13572	.99075	.13698	7.30018	.132630	.995963	.136667	.863333	12	.20
	49	.13600	.99071	.13728	7.28442	.133551	.995946	.137605	.862395	11	
	50	.13629	.99067	.13758	7.26873	.134470	.995928	.138542	.861458	10	
.85	51	.13658	.99063	.13787	7.25310	.135387	.995911	.139476	.860524	9	.15
	52	.13687	.99059	.13817	7.23754	.136303	.995894	.140409	.859591	8	
	53	.13716	.99055	.13846	7.22204	.137216	.995876	.141340	.858660	7	
.90	54	.13744	.99051	.13876	7.20661	.138128	.995859	.142269	.857731	6	.10
	55	.13773	.99047	.13906	7.19125	.139037	.995841	.143196	.856804	5	
	56	.13802	.99043	.13935	7.17594	.139944	.995823	.144121	.855879	4	
.95	57	.13831	.99039	.13965	7.16071	.140850	.995806	.145044	.854956	3	.05
	58	.13860	.99035	.13995	7.14553	.141754	.995788	.145966	.854034	2	
	59	.13889	.99031	.14024	7.13042	.142655	.995771	.146885	.853115	1	
1.00	60	.13917	.99027	.14054	7.11537	9.143555	9.995753	9.147803	10.852197	0	.00
Decimals	Minutes	Cos	Sin	Cot	Tan	Cos	Sin	Cot	Tan	Minutes	Decimals
		Natural Values				Common Logarithms					

Decimals	Minutes	Natural Values				Common Logarithms				Minutes	Decimals
		Sin	Cos	Tan	Cot	Sin	Cos	Tan	Cot		
.00	0	.13917	.99027	.14054	7.11537	9.143555	9.995753	9.147803	10.852197	60	1.00
	1	.13946	.99023	.14084	7.10038	.144453	.995735	.148718	.851282	59	
	2	.13975	.99019	.14113	7.08546	.145349	.995717	.149632	.850368	58	
.05	3	.14004	.99015	.14143	7.07059	.146243	.995699	.150544	.849456	57	.95
	4	.14033	.99011	.14173	7.05579	.147136	.995681	.151454	.848546	56	
	5	.14061	.99006	.14202	7.04105	.148026	.995664	.152363	.847637	55	
.10	6	.14090	.99002	.14232	7.02637	.148915	.995646	.153269	.846731	54	.90
	7	.14119	.98998	.14262	7.01174	.149802	.995628	.154174	.845826	53	
	8	.14148	.98994	.14291	6.99718	.150686	.995610	.155077	.844923	52	
.15	9	.14177	.98990	.14321	6.98268	.151569	.995591	.155978	.844022	51	.85
	10	.14205	.98986	.14351	6.96823	.152451	.995573	.156877	.843123	50	
	11	.14234	.98982	.14381	6.95385	.153330	.995555	.157775	.842225	49	
.20	12	.14263	.98978	.14410	6.93952	.154208	.995537	.158671	.841329	48	.80
	13	.14292	.98973	.14440	6.92525	.155083	.995519	.159565	.840435	47	
	14	.14320	.98969	.14470	6.91104	.155957	.995501	.160457	.839543	46	
.25	15	.14349	.98965	.14499	6.89388	.156830	.995482	.161347	.838653	45	.75
	16	.14378	.98961	.14529	6.88278	.157700	.995464	.162236	.837764	44	
	17	.14407	.98957	.14559	6.86874	.158569	.995446	.163123	.836877	43	
.30	18	.14436	.98953	.14588	6.85475	.159435	.995427	.164008	.835992	42	.70
	19	.14464	.98948	.14618	6.84082	.160301	.995409	.164892	.835108	41	
	20	.14493	.98944	.14648	6.82694	.161164	.995390	.165774	.834226	40	
.35	21	.14522	.98940	.14678	[6.81312	.162025	.995372	.166654	.833346	39	.65
	22	.14551	.98936	.14707	6.79936	.162885	.995353	.167532	.832468	38	
	23	.14580	.98931	.14737	6.78564	.163743	.995334	.168409	.831591	37	
.40	24	.14608	.98927	.14767	6.77199	.164600	.995316	.169284	.830716	36	.60
	25	.14637	.98923	.14796	6.75838	.165454	.995297	.170157	.829843	35	
	26	.14666	.98919	.14826	6.74483	.166307	.995278	.171029	.828971	34	
.45	27	.14695	.98914	.14856	6.73133	.167159	.995260	.171899	.828101	33	.55
	28	.14723	.98910	.14886	6.71789	.168008	.995241	.172767	.827233	32	
	29	.14752	.98906	.14915	6.70450	.168856	.995222	.173634	.826366	31	
.50	30	.14781	.98902	.14945	6.69116	.169702	.995203	.174499	.825501	30	.50
	31	.14810	.98897	.14975	6.67787	.170547	.995184	.175362	.824638	29	
	32	.14838	.98893	.15005	6.66463	.171389	.995165	.176224	.823776	28	
.55	33	.14867	.98889	.15034	6.65144	.172230	.995146	.177084	.822916	27	.45
	34	.14896	.98884	.15064	6.63831	.173070	.995127	.177942	.822058	26	
	35	.14925	.98880	.15094	6.62523	.173908	.995108	.178799	.821201	25	
.60	36	.14954	.98876	.15124	6.61219	.174744	.995089	.179655	.820345	24	.40
	37	.14982	.98871	.15153	6.59921	.175578	.995070	.180508	.819492	23	
	38	.15011	.98867	.15183	6.58627	.176411	.995051	.181360	.818640	22	
.65	39	.15040	.98863	.15213	6.57339	.177242	.995032	.182211	.817789	21	.35
	40	.15069	.98858	.15243	6.56055	.178072	.995013	.183059	.816941	20	
	41	.15097	.98854	.15272	6.54777	.178900	.994993	.183907	.816093	19	
.70	42	.15126	.98849	.15302	6.53503	.179726	.994974	.184752	.815248	18	.30
	43	.15155	.98845	.15332	6.52234	.180551	.994955	.185597	.814403	17	
	44	.15184	.98841	.15362	6.50970	.181374	.994935	.186439	.813561	16	
.75	45	.15212	.98836	.15391	6.49710	.182196	.994916	.187280	.812720	15	.25
	46	.15241	.98832	.15421	6.48456	.183016	.994896	.188120	.811880	14	
	47	.15270	.98827	.15451	6.47206	.183834	.994877	.188958	.811042	13	
.80	48	.15299	.98823	.15481	6.45961	.184651	.994857	.189794	.810206	12	.20
	49	.15327	.98818	.15511	6.44720	.185466	.994838	.190629	.809371	11	
	50	.15356	.98814	.15540	6.43484	.186280	.994818	.191462	.808538	10	
.85	51	.15385	.98809	.15570	6.42253	.187092	.994798	.192294	.807706	9	.15
	52	.15414	.98805	.15600	6.41026	.187903	.994779	.193124	.806876	8	
	53	.15442	.98800	.15630	6.39804	.188712	.994759	.193953	.806047	7	
.90	54	.15471	.98796	.15660	6.38587	.189519	.994739	.194780	.805220	6	.10
	55	.15500	.98791	.15689	6.37374	.190325	.994720	.195606	.804394	5	
	56	.15529	.98787	.15719	6.36165	.191130	.994700	.196430	.803570	4	
.95	57	.15557	.98782	.15749	6.34961	.191933	.994680	.197253	.802747	3	.05
	58	.15586	.98778	.15779	6.33761	.192734	.994660	.198074	.801926	2	
	59	.15615	.98773	.15809	6.32566	.193534	.994640	.198894	.801106	1	
1.00	60	.15643	.98769	.15838	6.31375	9.194332	9.994620	9.199713	10.800287	0	.00
Decimals	Minutes	Cos	Sin	Cot	Tan	Cos	Sin	Cot	Tan	Minutes	Decimals
		Natural Values				Common Logarithms					

Decimals	Minutes	Natural Values				Common Logarithms				Minutes	Decimals
		Sin	Cos	Tan	Cot	Sin	Cos	Tan	Cot		
.00	0	.15643	.98769	.15838	6.31375	9.194332	9.994620	9.199713	10.800287	60	1.00
	1	.15672	.98764	.15868	6.30189	.195129	.994600	.200529	.799471	59	
	2	.15701	.98760	.15898	6.29007	.195925	.994580	.201345	.798655	58	
.05	3	.15730	.98755	.15928	6.27829	.196719	.994560	.202159	.797841	57	.95
	4	.15758	.98751	.15958	6.26655	.197511	.994540	.202971	.797029	56	
	5	.15787	.98746	.15988	6.25486	.198302	.994519	.203782	.796218	55	
.10	6	.15816	.98741	.16017	6.24321	.199091	.994499	.204592	.795408	54	.90
	7	.15845	.98737	.16047	6.23160	.199879	.994479	.205400	.794600	53	
	8	.15873	.98732	.16077	6.22003	.200666	.994459	.206207	.793793	52	
.15	9	.15902	.98728	.16107	6.20851	.201451	.994438	.207013	.792987	51	.85
	10	.15931	.98723	.16137	6.19703	.202234	.994418	.207817	.792183	50	
	11	.15959	.98718	.16167	6.18559	.203017	.994398	.208619	.791381	49	
.20	12	.15988	.98714	.16196	6.17419	.203797	.994377	.209420	.790580	48	.80
	13	.16017	.98709	.16226	6.16283	.204577	.994357	.210220	.789780	47	
	14	.16046	.98704	.16256	6.15151	.205354	.994336	.211018	.788982	46	
.25	15	.16074	.98700	.16286	6.14023	.206131	.994316	.211815	.788185	45	.75
	16	.16103	.98695	.16316	6.12899	.206906	.994295	.212611	.787389	44	
	17	.16132	.98690	.16346	6.11779	.207679	.994274	.213405	.786595	43	
.30	18	.16160	.98686	.16376	6.10664	.208452	.994254	.214198	.785802	42	.70
	19	.16189	.98681	.16405	6.09552	.209222	.994233	.214989	.785011	41	
	20	.16218	.98676	.16435	6.08444	.209992	.994212	.215780	.784220	40	
.35	21	.16246	.98671	.16465	6.07340	.210760	.994191	.216568	.783432	39	.65
	22	.16275	.98667	.16495	6.06240	.211526	.994171	.217356	.782644	38	
	23	.16304	.98662	.16525	6.05143	.212291	.994150	.218142	.781858	37	
.40	24	.16333	.98657	.16555	6.04051	.213055	.994129	.218926	.781074	36	.60
	25	.16361	.98652	.16585	6.02962	.213818	.994108	.219710	.780290	35	
	26	.16390	.98648	.16615	6.01878	.214579	.994087	.220492	.779508	34	
.45	27	.16419	.98643	.16645	6.00797	.215338	.994066	.221272	.778728	33	.55
	28	.16447	.98638	.16674	5.99720	.216097	.994045	.222052	.777948	32	
	29	.16476	.98633	.16704	5.98646	.216854	.994024	.222830	.777170	31	
.50	30	.16505	.98629	.16734	5.97576	.217609	.994003	.223607	.776393	30	.50
	31	.16533	.98624	.16764	5.96510	.218363	.993982	.224382	.775618	29	
	32	.16562	.98619	.16794	5.95448	.219116	.993960	.225156	.774844	28	
.55	33	.16591	.98614	.16824	5.94390	.219868	.993939	.225929	.774071	27	.45
	34	.16620	.98609	.16854	5.93333	.220618	.993918	.226700	.773300	26	
	35	.16648	.98604	.16884	5.92283	.221367	.993897	.227471	.772529	25	
.60	36	.16677	.98600	.16914	5.91236	.222115	.993875	.228239	.771761	24	.40
	37	.16706	.98595	.16944	5.90191	.222861	.993854	.229007	.770993	23	
	38	.16734	.98590	.16974	5.89151	.223606	.993832	.229773	.770227	22	
.65	39	.16763	.98585	.17004	5.88114	.224349	.993811	.230539	.769461	21	.35
	40	.16792	.98580	.17033	5.87080	.225092	.993789	.231302	.768698	20	
	41	.16820	.98575	.17063	5.86051	.225833	.993768	.232065	.767935	19	
.70	42	.16849	.98570	.17093	5.85024	.226573	.993746	.232826	.767174	18	.30
	43	.16878	.98565	.17123	5.84001	.227311	.993725	.233586	.766414	17	
	44	.16906	.98561	.17153	5.82982	.228048	.993703	.234345	.765655	16	
.75	45	.16935	.98556	.17183	5.81966	.228784	.993681	.235103	.764897	15	.25
	46	.16964	.98551	.17213	5.80953	.229518	.993660	.235859	.764141	14	
	47	.16992	.98546	.17243	5.79944	.230252	.993638	.236614	.763386	13	
.80	48	.17021	.98541	.17273	5.78938	.230984	.993616	.237368	.762632	12	.20
	49	.17050	.98536	.17303	5.77936	.231715	.993594	.238120	.761880	11	
	50	.17078	.98531	.17333	5.76937	.232444	.993572	.238872	.761128	10	
.85	51	.17107	.98526	.17363	5.75941	.233172	.993550	.239622	.760378	9	.15
	52	.17136	.98521	.17393	5.74949	.233899	.993528	.240371	.759629	8	
	53	.17164	.98516	.17423	5.73960	.234625	.993506	.241118	.758882	7	
.90	54	.17193	.98511	.17453	5.72974	.235349	.993484	.241865	.758135	6	.10
	55	.17222	.98506	.17483	5.71992	.236073	.993462	.242610	.757390	5	
	56	.17250	.98501	.17513	5.71013	.236795	.993440	.243354	.756646	4	
.95	57	.17279	.98496	.17543	5.70037	.237515	.993418	.244097	.755903	3	.05
	58	.17308	.98491	.17573	5.69064	.238235	.993396	.244839	.755161	2	
	59	.17336	.98486	.17603	5.68094	.238953	.993374	.245579	.754421	1	
1.00	60	.17365	.98481	.17633	5.67123	9.239670	9.993351	9.246319	10.753681	0	.00
Decimals	Minutes	Cos	Sin	Cot	Tan	Cos	Sin	Cot	Tan	Minutes	Decimals
		Natural Values				Common Logarithms					

80°

Decimals	Minutes	Natural Values				Common Logarithms				Minutes	Decimals
		Sin	Cos	Tan	Cot	Sin	Cos	Tan	Cot		
.00	0	.17365	.98481	.17633	5.67128	9.239670	9.993351	9.246319	10.753681	60	1.00
	1	.17393	.98476	.17663	5.66165	.240386	.993329	.247057	.752943	59	
	2	.17422	.98471	.17693	5.65205	.241101	.993307	.247794	.752206	58	
.05	3	.17451	.98466	.17723	5.64248	.241814	.993284	.248530	.751470	57	.95
	4	.17479	.98461	.17753	5.63295	.242526	.993262	.249264	.750736	56	
	5	.17508	.98455	.17783	5.62344	.243237	.993240	.249998	.750002	55	
.10	6	.17537	.98450	.17813	5.61397	.243947	.993217	.250730	.749270	54	.90
	7	.17565	.98445	.17843	5.60452	.244656	.993195	.251461	.748539	53	
	8	.17594	.98440	.17873	5.59511	.245363	.993172	.252191	.747809	52	
.15	9	.17623	.98435	.17903	5.58573	.246069	.993149	.252920	.747080	51	.85
	10	.17651	.98430	.17933	5.57638	.246775	.993127	.253648	.746352	50	
	11	.17680	.98425	.17963	5.56706	.247478	.993104	.254374	.745626	49	
.20	12	.17708	.98420	.17993	5.55777	.248181	.993081	.255100	.744900	48	.80
	13	.17737	.98414	.18023	5.54851	.248883	.993059	.255824	.744176	47	
	14	.17766	.98409	.18053	5.53927	.249583	.993036	.256547	.743453	46	
.25	15	.17794	.98404	.18083	5.53007	.250282	.993013	.257269	.742731	45	.75
	16	.17823	.98399	.18113	5.52090	.250980	.992990	.257990	.742010	44	
	17	.17852	.98394	.18143	5.51176	.251677	.992967	.258710	.741290	43	
.30	18	.17880	.98389	.18173	5.50264	.252373	.992944	.259429	.740571	42	.70
	19	.17909	.98383	.18203	5.49356	.253067	.992921	.260146	.739854	41	
	20	.17937	.98378	.18233	5.48451	.253761	.992898	.260863	.739137	40	
.35	21	.17966	.98373	.18263	5.47548	.254453	.992875	.261578	.738422	39	.65
	22	.17995	.98368	.18293	5.46648	.255144	.992852	.262292	.737708	38	
	23	.18023	.98362	.18323	5.45751	.255834	.992829	.263005	.736995	37	
.40	24	.18052	.98357	.18353	5.44857	.256523	.992806	.263717	.736283	36	.60
	25	.18081	.98352	.18384	5.43966	.257211	.992783	.264428	.735572	35	
	26	.18109	.98347	.18414	5.43077	.257898	.992759	.265138	.734862	34	
.45	27	.18138	.98341	.18444	5.42192	.258583	.992736	.265847	.734153	33	.55
	28	.18166	.98336	.18474	5.41309	.259268	.992713	.266555	.733445	32	
	29	.18195	.98331	.18504	5.40429	.259951	.992690	.267261	.732739	31	
.50	30	.18224	.98325	.18534	5.39552	.260633	.992666	.267967	.732033	30	.50
	31	.18252	.98320	.18564	5.38677	.261314	.992643	.268671	.731329	29	
	32	.18281	.98315	.18594	5.37805	.261994	.992619	.269375	.730625	28	
.55	33	.18309	.98310	.18624	5.36936	.262673	.992596	.270077	.729923	27	.45
	34	.18338	.98304	.18654	5.36070	.263351	.992572	.270779	.729221	26	
	35	.18367	.98299	.18684	5.35206	.264027	.992549	.271479	.728521	25	
.60	36	.18395	.98294	.18714	5.34345	.264703	.992525	.272178	.727822	24	.40
	37	.18424	.98288	.18745	5.33487	.265377	.992501	.272876	.727124	23	
	38	.18452	.98283	.18775	5.32631	.266051	.992478	.273573	.726427	22	
.65	39	.18481	.98277	.18805	5.31778	.266723	.992454	.274269	.725731	21	.35
	40	.18509	.98272	.18835	5.30928	.267395	.992430	.274964	.725036	20	
	41	.18538	.98267	.18865	5.30080	.268065	.992406	.275658	.724342	19	
.70	42	.18567	.98261	.18895	5.29235	.268734	.992382	.276351	.723649	18	.30
	43	.18595	.98256	.18925	5.28393	.269402	.992359	.277043	.722957	17	
	44	.18624	.98250	.18955	5.27553	.270069	.992335	.277734	.722266	16	
.75	45	.18652	.98245	.18986	5.26715	.270735	.992311	.278424	.721576	15	.25
	46	.18681	.98240	.19016	5.25880	.271400	.992287	.279113	.720887	14	
	47	.18710	.98234	.19046	5.25048	.272064	.992263	.279801	.720199	13	
.80	48	.18738	.98229	.19076	5.24218	.272726	.992239	.280488	.719512	12	.20
	49	.18767	.98223	.19106	5.23391	.273388	.992214	.281174	.718826	11	
	50	.18795	.98218	.19136	5.22566	.274049	.992190	.281858	.718142	10	
.85	51	.18824	.98212	.19166	5.21744	.274708	.992166	.282542	.717458	9	.15
	52	.18852	.98207	.19197	5.20925	.275367	.992142	.283225	.716775	8	
	53	.18881	.98201	.19227	5.20107	.276025	.992118	.283907	.716093	7	
.90	54	.18910	.98196	.19257	5.19293	.276681	.992093	.284588	.715412	6	.10
	55	.18938	.98190	.19287	5.18480	.277337	.992069	.285268	.714732	5	
	56	.18967	.98185	.19317	5.17671	.277991	.992044	.285947	.714053	4	
.95	57	.18995	.98179	.19347	5.16863	.278645	.992020	.286624	.713376	3	.05
	58	.19024	.98174	.19378	5.16058	.279297	.991996	.287301	.712699	2	
	59	.19052	.98168	.19408	5.15256	.279948	.991971	.287977	.712023	1	
1.00	60	.19081	.98163	.19438	5.14455	9.280599	9.991947	9.288652	10.711348	0	.00
Decimals	Minutes	Cos	Sin	Cot	Tan	Cos	Sin	Cot	Tan	Minutes	Decimals
		Natural Values				Common Logarithms					

Decimals	Minutes	Natural Values				Common Logarithms				Minutes	Decimals
		Sin	Cos	Tan	Cot	Sin	Cos	Tan	Cot		
.00	0	.19081	.98163	.19438	5.14455	9.280599	9.991947	9.288652	10.711348	60	1.00
	1	.19109	.98157	.19468	5.13658	.281248	.991922	.289326	.710674	59	
	2	.19138	.98152	.19498	5.12862	.281897	.991897	.289999	.710001	58	
.05	3	.19167	.98146	.19529	5.12069	.282544	.991873	.290671	.709329	57	.95
	4	.19195	.98140	.19559	5.11279	.283190	.991848	.291342	.708658	56	
	5	.19224	.98135	.19589	5.10490	.283836	.991823	.292013	.707987	55	
.10	6	.19252	.98129	.19619	5.09704	.284480	.991799	.292682	.707318	54	.90
	7	.19281	.98124	.19649	5.08921	.285124	.991774	.293350	.706650	53	
	8	.19309	.98118	.19680	5.08139	.285766	.991749	.294017	.705983	52	
.15	9	.19338	.98112	.19710	5.07360	.286408	.991724	.294684	.705316	51	.85
	10	.19366	.98107	.19740	5.06584	.287048	.991699	.295349	.704651	50	
	11	.19395	.98101	.19770	5.05809	.287688	.991674	.296013	.703987	49	
.20	12	.19423	.98096	.19801	5.05037	.288326	.991649	.296677	.703323	48	.80
	13	.19452	.98090	.19831	5.04267	.288964	.991624	.297339	.702661	47	
	14	.19481	.98084	.19861	5.03499	.289600	.991599	.298001	.701999	46	
.25	15	.19509	.98079	.19891	5.02734	.290236	.991574	.298662	.701338	45	.75
	16	.19538	.98073	.19921	5.01971	.290870	.991549	.299322	.700678	44	
	17	.19566	.98067	.19952	5.01210	.291504	.991524	.299980	.700020	43	
.30	18	.19595	.98061	.19982	5.00451	.292137	.991498	.300638	.699362	42	.70
	19	.19623	.98056	.20012	4.99695	.292768	.991473	.301295	.698705	41	
	20	.19652	.98050	.20042	4.98940	.293399	.991448	.301951	.698049	40	
.35	21	.19680	.98044	.20073	4.98188	.294029	.991422	.302607	.697393	39	.65
	22	.19709	.98039	.20103	4.97438	.294658	.991397	.303261	.696739	38	
	23	.19737	.98033	.20133	4.96690	.295286	.991372	.303914	.696086	37	
.40	24	.19766	.98027	.20164	4.95945	.295913	.991346	.304567	.695433	36	.60
	25	.19794	.98021	.20194	4.95201	.296539	.991321	.305218	.694782	35	
	26	.19823	.98016	.20224	4.94460	.297164	.991295	.305869	.694131	34	
.45	27	.19851	.98010	.20254	4.93721	.297788	.991270	.306519	.693481	33	.55
	28	.19880	.98004	.20285	4.92984	.298412	.991244	.307168	.692832	32	
	29	.19908	.97998	.20315	4.92249	.299034	.991218	.307816	.692184	31	
.50	30	.19937	.97992	.20345	4.91516	.299655	.991193	.308463	.691537	30	.50
	31	.19965	.97987	.20376	4.90785	.300276	.991167	.309109	.690891	29	
	32	.19994	.97981	.20406	4.90056	.300895	.991141	.309754	.690246	28	
.55	33	.20022	.97975	.20436	4.89330	.301514	.991115	.310399	.689601	27	.45
	34	.20051	.97969	.20466	4.88605	.302132	.991090	.311042	.688958	26	
	35	.20079	.97963	.20497	4.87882	.302748	.991064	.311685	.688315	25	
60	36	.20108	.97958	.20527	4.87162	.303364	.991038	.312327	.687673	24	.40
	37	.20136	.97952	.20557	4.86444	.303979	.991012	.312968	.687032	23	
	38	.20165	.97946	.20588	4.85727	.304593	.990986	.313608	.686392	22	
.65	39	.20193	.97940	.20618	4.85013	.305207	.990960	.314247	.685753	21	.35
	40	.20222	.97934	.20648	4.84300	.305819	.990934	.314885	.685115	20	
	41	.20250	.97928	.20679	4.83590	.306430	.990908	.315523	.684477	19	
.70	42	.20279	.97922	.20709	4.82882	.307041	.990882	.316159	.683841	18	.30
	43	.20307	.97916	.20739	4.82175	.307650	.990855	.316795	.683205	17	
	44	.20336	.97910	.20770	4.81471	.308259	.990829	.317430	.682570	16	
75	45	.20364	.97905	.20800	4.80769	.308867	.990803	.318064	.681936	15	.25
	46	.20393	.97899	.20830	4.80068	.309474	.990777	.318697	.681303	14	
	47	.20421	.97893	.20861	4.79370	.310080	.990750	.319330	.680670	13	
.80	48	.20450	.97887	.20891	4.78673	.310685	.990724	.319961	.680039	12	.20
	49	.20478	.97881	.20921	4.77978	.311289	.990697	.320592	.679408	11	
	50	.20507	.97875	.20952	4.77286	.311893	.990671	.321222	.678778	10	
.85	51	.20535	.97869	.20982	4.76595	.312495	.990645	.321851	.678149	9	.15
	52	.20563	.97863	.21013	4.75906	.313097	.990618	.322479	.677521	8	
	53	.20592	.97857	.21043	4.75219	.313698	.990591	.323106	.676894	7	
.90	54	.20620	.97851	.21073	4.74534	.314297	.990565	.323733	.676267	6	.10
	55	.20649	.97845	.21104	4.73851	.314897	.990538	.324358	.675642	5	
	56	.20677	.97839	.21134	4.73170	.315495	.990511	.324983	.675017	4	
.95	57	.20706	.97833	.21164	4.72490	.316092	.990485	.325607	.674393	3	.05
	58	.20734	.97827	.21195	4.71813	.316689	.990458	.326231	.673769	2	
	59	.20763	.97821	.21225	4.71137	.317284	.990431	.326853	.673147	1	
1.00	60	.20791	.97815	.21256	4.70463	9.317879	9.990404	9.327475	10.672525	0	.00
Decimals	Minutes	Cos	Sin	Cot	Tan	Cos	Sin	Cot	Tan	Minutes	Decimals
		Natural Values				Common Logarithms					

Decimals	Minutes	Natural Values Sin	Cos	Tan	Cot	Common Logarithms Sin	Cos	Tan	Cot	Minutes	Decimals
.00	0	.20791	.97815	.21256	4.70463	9.317879	9.990404	9.327475	10.672525	60	1.00
	1	.20820	.97809	.21286	4.69791	.318473	.990378	.328095	.671905	59	
	2	.20848	.97803	.21316	4.69121	.319066	.990351	.328715	.671285	58	
.05	3	.20877	.97797	.21347	4.68452	.319658	.990324	.329334	.670666	57	.95
	4	.20905	.97791	.21377	4.67786	.320249	.990297	.329953	.670047	56	
	5	.20933	.97784	.21408	4.67121	.320840	.990270	.330570	.669430	55	
.10	6	.20962	.97778	.21438	4.66458	.321430	.990243	.331187	.668813	54	.90
	7	.20990	.97772	.21469	4.65797	.322019	.990215	.331803	.668197	53	
	8	.21019	.97766	.21499	4.65138	.322607	.990188	.332418	.667582	52	
.15	9	.21047	.97760	.21529	4.64480	.323194	.990161	.333033	.666967	51	.85
	10	.21076	.97754	.21560	4.63825	.323780	.990134	.333646	.666354	50	
	11	.21104	.97748	.21590	4.63171	.324366	.990107	.334259	.665741	49	
.20	12	.21132	.97742	.21621	4.62518	.324950	.990079	.334871	.665129	48	.80
	13	.21161	.97735	.21651	4.61868	.325534	.990052	.335482	.664518	47	
	14	.21189	.97729	.21682	4.61219	.326117	.990025	.336093	.663907	46	
.25	15	.21218	.97723	.21712	4.60572	.326700	.989997	.336702	.663298	45	.75
	16	.21246	.97717	.21743	4.59927	.327281	.989970	.337311	.662689	44	
	17	.21275	.97711	.21773	4.59283	.327862	.989942	.337919	.662081	43	
.30	18	.21303	.97705	.21804	4.58641	.328442	.989915	.338527	.661473	42	.70
	19	.21331	.97698	.21834	4.58001	.329021	.989887	.339133	.660867	41	
	20	.21360	.97692	.21864	4.57363	.329599	.989860	.339739	.660261	40	
.35	21	.21388	.97686	.21895	4.56726	.330176	.989832	.340344	.659656	39	.65
	22	.21417	.97680	.21925	4.56091	.330753	.989804	.340948	.659052	38	
	23	.21445	.97673	.21956	4.55458	.331329	.989777	.341552	.658448	37	
.40	24	.21474	.97667	.21986	4.54826	.331903	.989749	.342155	.657845	36	.60
	25	.21502	.97661	.22017	4.54196	.332478	.989721	.342757	.657243	35	
	26	.21530	.97655	.22047	4.53568	.333051	.989693	.343358	.656642	34	
.45	27	.21559	.97648	.22078	4.52941	.333624	.989665	.343958	.656042	33	.55
	28	.21587	.97642	.22108	4.52316	.334195	.989637	.344558	.655442	32	
	29	.21616	.97636	.22139	4.51693	.334767	.989610	.345157	.654843	31	
.50	30	.21644	.97630	.22169	4.51071	.335337	.989582	.345755	.654245	30	.50
	31	.21672	.97623	.22200	4.50451	.335906	.989553	.346353	.653647	29	
	32	.21701	.97617	.22231	4.49832	.336475	.989525	.346949	.653051	28	
.55	33	.21729	.97611	.22261	4.49215	.337043	.989497	.347545	.652455	27	.45
	34	.21758	.97604	.22292	4.48600	.337610	.989469	.348141	.651859	26	
	35	.21786	.97598	.22322	4.47986	.338176	.989441	.348735	.651265	25	
.60	36	.21814	.97592	.22353	4.47374	.338742	.989413	.349329	.650671	24	.40
	37	.21843	.97585	.22383	4.46764	.339307	.989385	.349922	.650078	23	
	38	.21871	.97579	.22414	4.46155	.339871	.989356	.350514	.649486	22	
.65	39	.21899	.97573	.22444	4.45548	.340434	.989328	.351106	.648894	21	.35
	40	.21928	.97566	.22475	4.44942	.340996	.989300	.351697	.648303	20	
	41	.21956	.97560	.22505	4.44338	.341558	.989271	.352287	.647713	19	
.70	42	.21985	.97553	.22536	4.43735	.342119	.989243	.352876	.647124	18	.30
	43	.22013	.97547	.22567	4.43134	.342679	.989214	.353465	.646535	17	
	44	.22041	.97541	.22597	4.42534	.343239	.989186	.354053	.645947	16	
.75	45	.22070	.97534	.22628	4.41936	.343797	.989157	.354640	.645360	15	.25
	46	.22098	.97528	.22658	4.41340	.344355	.989128	.355227	.644773	14	
	47	.22126	.97521	.22689	4.40745	.344912	.989100	.355813	.644187	13	
.80	48	.22155	.97515	.22719	4.40152	.345469	.989071	.356398	.643602	12	.20
	49	.22183	.97508	.22750	4.39560	.346024	.989042	.356982	.643018	11	
	50	.22212	.97502	.22781	4.38969	.346579	.989014	.357566	.642434	10	
.85	51	.22240	.97496	.22811	4.38381	.347134	.988985	.358149	.641851	9	.15
	52	.22268	.97489	.22842	4.37793	.347687	.988956	.358731	.641269	8	
	53	.22297	.97483	.22872	4.37207	.348240	.988927	.359313	.640687	7	
.90	54	.22325	.97476	.22903	4.36623	.348792	.988898	.359893	.640107	6	.10
	55	.22353	.97470	.22934	4.36040	.349343	.988869	.360474	.639526	5	
	56	.22382	.97463	.22964	4.35459	.349893	.988840	.361053	.638947	4	
.95	57	.22410	.97457	.22995	4.34879	.350443	.988811	.361632	.638368	3	.05
	58	.22438	.97450	.23026	4.34300	.350992	.988782	.362210	.637790	2	
	59	.22467	.97444	.23056	4.33723	.351540	.988753	.362787	.637213	1	
1.00	60	.22495	.97437	.23087	4.33148	9.352088	9.988724	9.363364	10.636636	0	.00

Decimals	Minutes	Cos	Sin	Cot	Tan	Cos	Sin	Cot	Tan	Minutes	Decimals
		Natural Values				Common Logarithms					

Decimals	Minutes	Natural Values				Common Logarithms				Minutes	Decimals
		Sin	Cos	Tan	Cot	Sin	Cos	Tan	Cot		
.00	0	.22495	.97437	.23087	4.33148	9.352088	9.988724	9.363364	10.636636	60	1.00
	1	.22523	.97430	.23117	4.32573	.352635	.988695	.363940	.636060	59	
	2	.22552	.97424	.23148	4.32001	.353181	.988666	.364515	.635485	58	
.05	3	.22580	.97417	.23179	4.31430	.353726	.988636	.365090	.634910	57	.95
	4	.22608	.97411	.23209	4.30860	.354271	.988607	.365664	.634336	56	
	5	.22637	.97404	.23240	4.30291	.354815	.988578	.366237	.633763	55	
.10	6	.22665	.97398	.23271	4.29724	.355358	.988548	.366810	.633190	54	.90
	7	.22693	.97391	.23301	4.29159	.355901	.988519	.367382	.632618	53	
	8	.22722	.97384	.23332	4.28595	.356443	.988489	.367953	.632047	52	
.15	9	.22750	.97378	.23363	4.28032	.356984	.988460	.368524	.631476	51	.85
	10	.22778	.97371	.23393	4.27471	.357524	.988430	.369094	.630906	50	
	11	.22807	.97365	.23424	4.26911	.358064	.988401	.369663	.630337	49	
.20	12	.22835	.97358	.23455	4.26352	.358603	.988371	.370232	.629768	48	.80
	13	.22863	.97351	.23485	4.25795	.359141	.988342	.370799	.629201	47	
	14	.22892	.97345	.23516	4.25239	.359678	.988312	.371367	.628633	46	
.25	15	.22920	.97338	.23547	4.24685	.360215	.988282	.371933	.628067	45	.75
	16	.22948	.97331	.23578	4.24132	.360752	.988252	.372499	.627501	44	
	17	.22977	.97325	.23608	4.23580	.361287	.988223	.373064	.626936	43	
.30	18	.23005	.97318	.23639	4.23030	.361822	.988193	.373629	.626371	42	.70
	19	.23033	.97311	.23670	4.22481	.362356	.988163	.374193	.625807	41	
	20	.23062	.97304	.23700	4.21933	.362889	.988133	.374756	.625244	40	
.35	21	.23090	.97298	.23731	4.21387	.363422	.988103	.375319	.624681	39	.65
	22	.23118	.97291	.23762	4.20842	.363954	.988073	.375881	.624119	38	
	23	.23146	.97284	.23793	4.20298	.364485	.988043	.376442	.623558	37	
.40	24	.23175	.97278	.23823	4.19756	.365016	.988013	.377003	.622997	36	.60
	25	.23203	.97271	.23854	4.19215	.365546	.987983	.377563	.622437	35	
	26	.23231	.97264	.23885	4.18675	.366075	.987953	.378122	.621878	34	
.45	27	.23260	.97257	.23916	4.18137	.366604	.987922	.378681	.621319	33	.55
	28	.23288	.97251	.23946	4.17600	.367131	.987892	.379239	.620761	32	
	29	.23316	.97244	.23977	4.17064	.367659	.987862	.379797	.620203	31	
.50	30	.23345	.97237	.24008	4.16530	.368185	.987832	.380354	.619646	30	.50
	31	.23373	.97230	.24039	4.15997	.368711	.987801	.380910	.619090	29	
	32	.23401	.97223	.24069	4.15465	.369236	.987771	.381466	.618534	28	
.55	33	.23429	.97217	.24100	4.14934	.369761	.987740	.382020	.617980	27	.45
	34	.23458	.97210	.24131	4.14405	.370285	.987710	.382575	.617425	26	
	35	.23486	.97203	.24162	4.13377	.370808	.987679	.383129	.616871	25	
.60	36	.23514	.97196	.24193	4.13350	.371330	.987649	.383682	.616318	24	.40
	37	.23542	.97189	.24223	4.12825	.371852	.987618	.384234	.615766	23	
	38	.23571	.97182	.24254	4.12301	.372373	.987588	.384786	.615214	22	
.65	39	.23599	.97176	.24285	4.11778	.372894	.987557	.385337	.614663	21	.35
	40	.23627	.97169	.24316	4.11256	.373414	.987526	.385888	.614112	20	
	41	.23656	.97162	.24347	4.10736	.373933	.987496	.386438	.613562	19	
.70	42	.23684	.97155	.24377	4.10216	.374452	.987465	.386987	.613013	18	.30
	43	.23712	.97148	.24408	4.09699	.374970	.987434	.387536	.612464	17	
	44	.23740	.97141	.24439	4.09182	.375487	.987403	.388084	.611916	16	
.75	45	.23769	.97134	.24470	4.08666	.376003	.987372	.388631	.611369	15	.25
	46	.23797	.97127	.24501	4.08152	.376519	.987341	.389178	.610822	14	
	47	.23825	.97120	.24532	4.07639	.377035	.987310	.389724	.610276	13	
.80	48	.23853	.97113	.24562	4.07127	.377549	.987279	.390270	.609730	12	.20
	49	.23882	.97106	.24593	4.06616	.378063	.987248	.390815	.609185	11	
	50	.23910	.97100	.24624	4.06107	.378577	.987217	.391360	.608640	10	
.85	51	.23938	.97093	.24655	4.05599	.379089	.987186	.391903	.608097	9	.15
	52	.23966	.97086	.24686	4.05092	.379601	.987155	.392447	.607553	8	
	53	.23995	.97079	.24717	4.04586	.380113	.987124	.392989	.607011	7	
.90	54	.24023	.97072	.24747	4.04081	.380624	.987092	.393531	.606469	6	.10
	55	.24051	.97065	.24778	4.03578	.381134	.987061	.394073	.605927	5	
	56	.24079	.97058	.24809	4.03076	.381643	.987030	.394614	.605386	4	
.95	57	.24108	.97051	.24840	4.02574	.382152	.986998	.395154	.604846	3	.05
	58	.24136	.97044	.24871	4.02074	.382661	.986967	.395694	.604306	2	
	59	.24164	.97037	.24902	4.01576	.383168	.986936	.396233	.603767	1	
1.00	60	.24192	.97030	.24933	4.01078	9.383675	9.986904	9.396771	10.603229	0	.00

Decimals	Minutes	Cos	Sin	Cot	Tan	Cos	Sin	Cot	Tan	Minutes	Decimals
		Natural Values				Common Logarithms					

Decimals	Minutes	Natural Values				Common Logarithms				Minutes	Decimals
		Sin	Cos	Tan	Cot	Sin	Cos	Tan	Cot		
.00	0	.24192	.97030	.24933	4.01078	9.383675	9.986904	9.396771	10.603229	60	1.00
	1	.24220	.97023	.24964	4.00582	.384182	.986873	.397309	.602691	59	
	2	.24249	.97015	.24995	4.00086	.384687	.986841	.397846	.602154	58	
.05	3	.24277	.97008	.25026	3.99592	.385192	.986809	.398383	.601617	57	.95
	4	.24305	.97001	.25056	3.99099	.385697	.986778	.398919	.601081	56	
	5	.24333	.96994	.25087	3.98607	.386201	.986746	.399455	.600545	55	
.10	6	.24362	.96987	.25118	3.98117	.386704	.986714	.399990	.600010	54	.90
	7	.24590	.96980	.25149	3.97627	.387207	.986683	.400524	.599476	53	
	8	.24418	.96973	.25180	3.97139	.387709	.986651	.401058	.598942	52	
.15	9	.24446	.96966	.25211	3.96651	.388210	.986619	.401591	.598409	51	.85
	10	.24474	.96959	.25242	3.96165	.388711	.986587	.402124	.597876	50	
	11	.24503	.96952	.25273	3.95680	.389211	.986555	.402656	.597344	49	
.20	12	.24531	.96945	.25304	3.95196	.389711	.986523	.403187	.596813	48	.80
	13	.24559	.96937	.25335	3.94713	.390210	.986491	.403718	.596282	47	
	14	.24587	.96930	.25366	3.94232	.390708	.986459	.404249	.595751	46	
.25	15	.24615	.96923	.25397	3.93751	.391206	.986427	.404778	.595222	45	.75
	16	.24644	.96916	.25428	3.93271	.391703	.986395	.405308	.594692	44	
	17	.24672	.96909	.25459	3.92793	.392199	.986363	.405836	.594164	43	
.30	18	.24700	.96902	.25490	3.92316	.392695	.986331	.406364	.593636	42	.70
	19	.24728	.96894	.25521	3.91839	.393191	.986299	.406892	.593108	41	
	20	.24756	.96887	.25552	3.91364	.393685	.986266	.407419	.592581	40	
.35	21	.24784	.96880	.25583	3.90890	.394179	.986234	.407945	.592055	39	.65
	22	.24813	.96873	.25614	3.90417	.394673	.986202	.408471	.591529	38	
	23	.24841	.96866	.25645	3.89945	.395166	.986169	.408996	.591004	37	
.40	24	.24869	.96858	.25676	3.89474	.395658	.986137	.409521	.590479	36	.60
	25	.24897	.96851	.25707	3.89004	.396150	.986104	.410045	.589955	35	
	26	.24925	.96844	.25738	3.88536	.396641	.986072	.410569	.589431	34	
.45	27	.24954	.96837	.25769	3.88068	.397132	.986039	.411092	.588908	33	.55
	28	.24982	.96829	.25800	3.87601	.397621	.986007	.411615	.588385	32	
	29	.25010	.96822	.25831	3.87136	.398111	.985974	.412137	.587863	31	
.50	30	.25038	.96815	.25862	3.86671	.398600	.985942	.412658	.587342	30	.50
	31	.25066	.96807	.25893	3.86208	.399088	.985909	.413179	.586821	29	
	32	.25094	.96800	.25924	3.85745	.399575	.985876	.413699	.586301	28	
.55	33	.25122	.96793	.25955	3.85284	.400062	.985843	.414219	.585781	27	.45
	34	.25151	.96786	.25986	3.84824	.400549	.985811	.414738	.585262	26	
	35	.25179	.96778	.26017	3.84364	.401035	.985778	.415257	.584743	25	
.60	36	.25207	.96771	.26048	3.83906	.401520	.985745	.415775	.584225	24	.40
	37	.25235	.96764	.26079	3.83449	.402005	.985712	.416293	.583707	23	
	38	.25263	.96756	.26110	3.82992	.402489	.985679	.416810	.583190	22	
.65	39	.25291	.96749	.26141	3.82537	.402972	.985646	.417326	.582674	21	.35
	40	.25320	.96742	.26172	3.82083	.403455	.985613	.417842	.582158	20	
	41	.25348	.96734	.26203	3.81630	.403938	.985580	.418358	.581642	19	
.70	42	.25376	.96727	.26235	3.81177	.404420	.985547	.418873	.581127	18	.30
	43	.25404	.96719	.26266	3.80726	.404901	.985514	.419387	.580613	17	
	44	.25432	.96712	.26297	3.80276	.405382	.985480	.419901	.580099	16	
.75	45	.25460	.96705	.26328	3.79827	.405862	.985447	.420415	.579585	15	.25
	46	.25488	.96697	.26359	3.79378	.406341	.985414	.420927	.579073	14	
	47	.25516	.96690	.26390	3.78931	.406820	.985381	.421440	.578560	13	
.80	48	.25545	.96682	.26421	3.78485	.407299	.985347	.421952	.578048	12	.20
	49	.25573	.96675	.26452	3.78040	.407777	.985314	.422463	.577537	11	
	50	.25601	.96667	.26483	3.77595	.408254	.985280	.422974	.577026	10	
.85	51	.25629	.96660	.26515	3.77152	.408731	.985247	.423484	.576516	9	.15
	52	.25657	.96653	.26546	3.76709	.409207	.985213	.423993	.576007	8	
	53	.25685	.96645	.26577	3.76268	.409682	.985180	.424503	.575497	7	
.90	54	.25713	.96638	.26608	3.75828	.410157	.985146	.425011	.574989	6	.10
	55	.25741	.96630	.26639	3.75388	.410632	.985113	.425519	.574481	5	
	56	.25769	.96623	.26670	3.74950	.411106	.985079	.426027	.573973	4	
.95	57	.25798	.96615	.26701	3.74512	.411579	.985045	.426534	.573466	3	.05
	58	.25826	.96608	.26733	3.74075	.412052	.985011	.427041	.572959	2	
	59	.25854	.96600	.26764	3.73640	.412524	.984978	.427547	.572453	1	
1.00	60	.25882	.96593	.26795	3.73205	9.412996	9.984944	9.428052	10.571948	0	.00
Decimals	Minutes	Cos	Sin	Cot	Tan	Cos	Sin	Cot	Tan	Minutes	Decimals
		Natural Values				Common Logarithms					

Decimals	Minutes	Natural Values				Common Logarithms				Minutes	Decimals
		Sin	Cos	Tan	Cot	Sin	Cos	Tan	Cot		
.00	0	.25882	.96593	.26795	3.73205	9.412996	9.984944	9.428052	10.571948	60	1.00
	1	.25910	.96585	.26826	3.72771	.413467	.984910	.428558	.571442	59	
	2	.25938	.96578	.26857	3.72338	.413938	.984876	.429062	.570938	58	
.05	3	.25966	.96570	.26888	3.71907	.414408	.984842	.429566	.570434	57	.95
	4	.25994	.96562	.26920	3.71476	.414878	.984808	.430070	.569930	56	
	5	.26022	.96555	.26951	3.71046	.415347	.984774	.430573	.569427	55	
.10	6	.26050	.96547	.26982	3.70616	.415815	.984740	.431075	.568925	54	.90
	7	.26079	.96540	.27013	3.70188	.416283	.984706	.431577	.568423	53	
	8	.26107	.96532	.27044	3.69761	.416751	.984672	.432079	.567921	52	
.15	9	.26135	.96524	.27076	3.69335	.417217	.984638	.432580	.567420	51	.85
	10	.26163	.96517	.27107	3.68909	.417684	.984603	.433080	.566920	50	
	11	.26191	.96509	.27138	3.68485	.418150	.984569	.433580	.566420	49	
.20	12	.26219	.96502	.27169	3.68061	.418615	.984535	.434080	.565920	48	.80
	13	.26247	.96494	.27201	3.67638	.419079	.984500	.434579	.565421	47	
	14	.26275	.96486	.27232	3.67217	.419544	.984466	.435078	.564922	46	
.25	15	.26303	.96479	.27263	3.66796	.420007	.984432	.435576	.564424	45	.75
	16	.26331	.96471	.27294	3.66376	.420470	.984397	.436073	.563927	44	
	17	.26359	.96463	.27326	3.65957	.420933	.984363	.436570	.563430	43	
.30	18	.26387	.96456	.27357	3.65538	.421395	.984328	.437067	.562933	42	.70
	19	.26415	.96448	.27388	3.65121	.421857	.984294	.437563	.562437	41	
	20	.26443	.96440	.27419	3.64705	.422318	.984259	.438059	.561941	40	
.35	21	.26471	.96433	.27451	3.64289	.422778	.984224	.438554	.561446	39	.65
	22	.26500	.96425	.27482	3.63874	.423238	.984190	.439048	.560952	38	
	23	.26528	.96417	.27513	3.63461	.423697	.984155	.439543	.560457	37	
.40	24	.26556	.96410	.27545	3.63048	.424156	.984120	.440036	.559964	36	.60
	25	.26584	.96402	.27576	3.62636	.424615	.984085	.440529	.559471	35	
	26	.26612	.96394	.27607	3.62224	.425073	.984050	.441022	.558978	34	
.45	27	.26640	.96386	.27638	3.61814	.425530	.984015	.441514	.558486	33	.55
	28	.26668	.96379	.27670	3.61405	.425987	.983981	.442006	.557994	32	
	29	.26696	.96371	.27701	3.60996	.426443	.983946	.442497	.557503	31	
.50	30	.26724	.96363	.27732	3.60588	.426899	.983911	.442988	.557012	30	.50
	31	.26752	.96355	.27764	3.60181	.427354	.983875	.443479	.556521	29	
	32	.26780	.96347	.27795	3.59775	.427809	.983840	.443968	.556032	28	
.55	33	.26808	.96340	.27826	3.59370	.428263	.983805	.444458	.555542	27	.45
	34	.26836	.96332	.27858	3.58966	.428717	.983770	.444947	.555053	26	
	35	.26864	.96324	.27889	3.58562	.429170	.983735	.445435	.554565	25	
.60	36	.26892	.96316	.27921	3.58160	.429623	.983700	.445923	.554077	24	.40
	37	.26920	.96308	.27952	3.57758	.430075	.983664	.446411	.553589	23	
	38	.26948	.96301	.27983	3.57357	.430527	.983629	.446898	.553102	22	
.65	39	.26976	.96293	.28015	3.56957	.430978	.983594	.447384	.552616	21	.35
	40	.27004	.96285	.28046	3.56557	.431429	.983558	.447870	.552130	20	
	41	.27032	.96277	.28077	3.56159	.431879	.983523	.448356	.551644	19	
.70	42	.27060	.96269	.28109	3.55761	.432329	.983487	.448841	.551159	18	.30
	43	.27088	.96261	.28140	3.55364	.432778	.983452	.449326	.550674	17	
	44	.27116	.96253	.28172	3.54968	.433226	.983416	.449810	.550190	16	
.75	45	.27144	.96246	.28203	3.54573	.433675	.983381	.450294	.549706	15	.25
	46	.27172	.96238	.28234	3.54179	.434122	.983345	.450777	.549223	14	
	47	.27200	.96230	.28266	3.53785	.434569	.983309	.451260	.548740	13	
.80	48	.27228	.96222	.28297	3.53393	.435016	.983273	.451743	.548257	12	.20
	49	.27256	.96214	.28329	3.53001	.435462	.983238	.452225	.547775	11	
	50	.27284	.96206	.28360	3.52609	.435908	.983202	.452706	.547294	10	
.85	51	.27312	.96198	.28391	3.52219	.436353	.983166	.453187	.546813	9	.15
	52	.27340	.96190	.28423	3.51829	.436798	.983130	.453668	.546332	8	
	53	.27368	.96182	.28454	3.51441	.437242	.983094	.454148	.545852	7	
.90	54	.27396	.96174	.28486	3.51053	.437686	.983058	.454628	.545372	6	.10
	55	.27424	.96166	.28517	3.50666	.438129	.983022	.455107	.544893	5	
	56	.27452	.96158	.28549	3.50279	.438572	.982986	.455586	.544414	4	
.95	57	.27480	.96150	.28580	3.49894	.439014	.982950	.456064	.543936	3	.05
	58	.27508	.96142	.28612	3.49509	.439456	.982914	.456542	.543458	2	
	59	.27536	.96134	.28643	3.49125	.439897	.982878	.457019	.542981	1	
1.00	60	.27564	.96126	.28675	3.48741	9.440338	9.982842	9.457496	10.542504	0	.00
Decimals	Minutes	Cos	Sin	Cot	Tan	Cos	Sin	Cot	Tan	Minutes	Decimals
		Natural Values				Common Logarithms					

Decimals	Minutes	Natural Values				Common Logarithms				Minutes	Decimals
		Sin	Cos	Tan	Cot	Sin	Cos	Tan	Cot		
.00	0	.27564	.96126	.28675	3.48741	9.440338	9.982842	9.457496	10.542504	60	1.00
	1	.27592	.96118	.28706	3.48359	.440778	.982805	.457973	.542027	59	
	2	.27620	.96110	.28738	3.47977	.441218	.982769	.458449	.541551	58	
.05	3	.27648	.96102	.28769	3.47596	.441658	.982733	.458925	.541075	57	.95
	4	.27676	.96094	.28800	3.47216	.442096	.982696	.459400	.540600	56	
	5	.27704	.96086	.28832	3.46837	.442535	.982660	.459875	.540125	55	
.10	6	.27731	.96078	.28864	3.46458	.442973	.982624	.460349	.539651	54	.90
	7	.27759	.96070	.28895	3.46080	.443410	.982587	.460823	.539177	53	
	8	.27787	.96062	.28927	3.45703	.443847	.982551	.461297	.538703	52	
.15	9	.27815	.96054	.28958	3.45327	.444284	.982514	.461770	.538230	51	.85
	10	.27843	.96046	.28990	3.44951	.444720	.982477	.462242	.537758	50	
	11	.27871	.96037	.29021	3.44576	.445155	.982441	.462715	.537285	49	
.20	12	.27899	.96029	.29053	3.44202	.445590	.982404	.463186	.536814	48	.80
	13	.27927	.96021	.29084	3.43829	.446025	.982367	.463658	.536342	47	
	14	.27955	.96013	.29116	3.43456	.446459	.982331	.464128	.535872	46	
.25	15	.27983	.96005	.29147	3.43084	.446893	.982294	.464599	.535401	45	.75
	16	.28011	.95997	.29179	3.42713	.447326	.982257	.465069	.534931	44	
	17	.28039	.95989	.29210	3.42343	.447759	.982220	.465539	.534461	43	
.30	18	.28067	.95981	.29242	3.41973	.448191	.982183	.466008	.533992	42	.70
	19	.28095	.95972	.29274	3.41604	.448623	.982146	.466477	.533523	41	
	20	.28123	.95964	.29305	3.41236	.449054	.982109	.466945	.533055	40	
.35	21	.28150	.95956	.29337	3.40869	.449485	.982072	.467413	.532587	39	.65
	22	.28178	.95948	.29368	3.40502	.449915	.982035	.467880	.532120	38	
	23	.28206	.95940	.29400	3.40136	.450345	.981998	.468347	.531653	37	
.40	24	.28234	.95931	.29432	3.39771	.450775	.981961	.468814	.531186	36	.60
	25	.28262	.95923	.29463	3.39406	.451204	.981924	.469280	.530720	35	
	26	.28290	.95915	.29495	3.39042	.451632	.981886	.469746	.530254	34	
.45	27	.28318	.95907	.29526	3.38679	.452060	.981849	.470211	.529789	33	.55
	28	.28346	.95898	.29558	3.38317	.452488	.981812	.470676	.529324	32	
	29	.28374	.95890	.29590	3.37955	.452915	.981774	.471141	.528859	31	
.50	30	.28402	.95882	.29621	3.37594	.453342	.981737	.471605	.528395	30	.50
	31	.28429	.95874	.29653	3.37234	.453768	.981700	.472069	.527931	29	
	32	.28457	.95865	.29685	3.36875	.454194	.981662	.472532	.527468	28	
.55	33	.28485	.95857	.29716	3.36516	.454619	.981625	.472995	.527005	27	.45
	34	.28513	.95849	.29748	3.36158	.455044	.981587	.473457	.526543	26	
	35	.28541	.95841	.29780	3.35800	.455469	.981549	.473919	.526081	25	
.60	36	.28569	.95832	.29811	3.35443	.455893	.981512	.474381	.525619	24	.40
	37	.28597	.95824	.29843	3.35087	.456316	.981474	.474842	.525158	23	
	38	.28625	.95816	.29875	3.34732	.456739	.981436	.475303	.524697	22	
.65	39	.28652	.95807	.29906	3.34377	.457162	.981399	.475763	.524237	21	.35
	40	.28680	.95799	.29938	3.34023	.457584	.981361	.476223	.523777	20	
	41	.28708	.95791	.29970	3.33670	.458006	.981323	.476683	.523317	19	
.70	42	.28736	.95782	.30001	3.33317	.458427	.981285	.477142	.522858	18	.30
	43	.28764	.95774	.30033	3.32965	.458848	.981247	.477601	.522399	17	
	44	.28792	.95766	.30065	3.32614	.459268	.981209	.478059	.521941	16	
.75	45	.28820	.95757	.30097	3.32264	.459688	.981171	.478517	.521483	15	.25
	46	.28847	.95749	.30128	3.31914	.460108	.981133	.478975	.521025	14	
	47	.28875	.95740	.30160	3.31565	.460527	.981095	.479432	.520568	13	
.80	48	.28903	.95732	.30192	3.31216	.460946	.981057	.479889	.520111	12	.20
	49	.28931	.95724	.30224	3.30868	.461364	.981019	.480345	.519655	11	
	50	.28959	.95715	.30255	3.30521	.461782	.980981	.480801	.519199	10	
.85	51	.28987	.95707	.30287	3.30174	.462199	.980942	.481257	.518743	9	.15
	52	.29015	.95698	.30319	3.29829	.462616	.980904	.481712	.518288	8	
	53	.29042	.95690	.30351	3.29483	.463032	.980866	.482167	.517833	7	
.90	54	.29070	.95681	.30382	3.29139	.463448	.980827	.482621	.517379	6	.10
	55	.29098	.95673	.30414	3.28795	.463864	.980789	.483075	.516925	5	
	56	.29126	.95664	.30446	3.28452	.464279	.980750	.483529	.516471	4	
.95	57	.29154	.95656	.30478	3.28109	.464694	.980712	.483982	.516018	3	.05
	58	.29182	.95647	.30509	3.27767	.465108	.980673	.484435	.515565	2	
	59	.29209	.95639	.30541	3.27426	.465522	.980635	.484887	.515113	1	
1.00	60	.29237	.95630	.30573	3.27085	9.465935	9.930596	9.485339	10.514661	0	.00

Decimals	Minutes	Cos	Sin	Cot	Tan	Cos	Sin	Cot	Tan	Minutes	Decimals
		Natural Values				Common Logarithms					

Decimals	Minutes	Natural Values				Common Logarithms				Minutes	Decimals
		Sin	Cos	Tan	Cot	Sin	Cos	Tan	Cot		
.00	0	.29237	.95630	.30573	3.27085	9.465935	9.980596	9.485339	10.514661	60	1.00
	1	.29265	.95622	.30605	3.26745	.466348	.980558	.485791	.514209	59	
	2	.29293	.95613	.30637	3.26406	.466761	.980519	.486242	.513758	58	
.05	3	.29321	.95605	.30669	3.26067	.467173	.980480	.486693	.513307	57	.95
	4	.29348	.95596	.30700	3.25729	.467585	.980442	.487143	.512857	56	
	5	.29376	.95588	.30732	3.25392	.467996	.980403	.487593	.512407	55	
.10	6	.29404	.95579	.30764	3.25055	.468407	.980364	.488043	.511957	54	.90
	7	.29432	.95571	.30796	3.24719	.468817	.980325	.488492	.511508	53	
	8	.29460	.95562	.30828	3.24383	.469227	.980286	.488941	.511059	52	
.15	9	.29487	.95554	.30860	3.24049	.469637	.980247	.489390	.510610	51	.85
	10	.29515	.95545	.30891	3.23714	.470046	.980208	.489838	.510162	50	
	11	.29543	.95536	.30923	3.23381	.470455	.980169	.490286	.509714	49	
.20	12	.29571	.95528	.30955	3.23048	.470863	.980130	.490733	.509267	48	.80
	13	.29599	.95519	.30987	3.22715	.471271	.980091	.491180	.508820	47	
	14	.29626	.95511	.31019	3.22384	.471679	.980052	.491627	.508373	46	
.25	15	.29654	.95502	.31051	3.22053	.472086	.980012	.492073	.507927	45	.75
	16	.29682	.95493	.31083	3.21722	.472492	.979973	.492519	.507481	44	
	17	.29710	.95485	.31115	3.21392	.472898	.979934	.492965	.507035	43	
.30	18	.29737	.95476	.31147	3.21063	.473304	.979895	.493410	.506590	42	.70
	19	.29765	.95467	.31178	3.20734	.473710	.979855	.493854	.506146	41	
	20	.29793	.95459	.31210	3.20406	.474115	.979816	.494299	.505701	40	
.35	21	.29821	.95450	.31242	3.20079	.474519	.979776	.494743	.505257	39	.65
	22	.29849	.95441	.31274	3.19752	.474923	.979737	.495186	.504814	38	
	23	.29876	.95433	.31306	3.19426	.475327	.979697	.495630	.504370	37	
.40	24	.29904	.95424	.31338	3.19100	.475730	.979658	.496073	.503927	36	.60
	25	.29932	.95415	.31370	3.18775	.476133	.979618	.496515	.503485	35	
	26	.29960	.95407	.31402	3.18451	.476536	.979579	.496957	.503043	34	
.45	27	.29987	.95398	.31434	3.18127	.476938	.979539	.497399	.502601	33	.55
	28	.30015	.95389	.31466	3.17804	.477340	.979499	.497841	.502159	32	
	29	.30043	.95380	.31498	3.17481	.477741	.979459	.498282	.501718	31	
.50	30	.30071	.95372	.31530	3.17159	.478142	.979420	.498722	.501278	30	.50
	31	.30098	.95363	.31562	3.16838	.478542	.979380	.499163	.500837	29	
	32	.30126	.95354	.31594	3.16517	.478942	.979340	.499603	.500397	28	
.55	33	.30154	.95345	.31626	3.16197	.479342	.979300	.500042	.499958	27	.45
	34	.30182	.95337	.31658	3.15877	.479741	.979260	.500481	.499519	26	
	35	.30209	.95328	.31690	3.15558	.480140	.979220	.500920	.499080	25	
.60	36	.30237	.95319	.31722	3.15240	.480539	.979180	.501359	.498641	24	.40
	37	.30265	.95310	.31754	3.14922	.480937	.979140	.501797	.498203	23	
	38	.30292	.95301	.31786	3.14605	.481334	.979100	.502235	.497765	22	
.65	39	.30320	.95293	.31818	3.14288	.481731	.979059	.502672	.497328	21	.35
	40	.30348	.95284	.31850	3.13972	.482128	.979019	.503109	.496891	20	
	41	.30376	.95275	.31882	3.13656	.482525	.978979	.503546	.496454	19	
.70	42	.30403	.95266	.31914	3.13341	.482921	.978939	.503982	.496018	18	.30
	43	.30431	.95257	.31946	3.13027	.483316	.978898	.504418	.495582	17	
	44	.30459	.95248	.31978	3.12713	.483712	.978858	.504854	.495146	16	
.75	45	.30486	.95240	.32010	3.12400	.484107	.978817	.505289	.494711	15	.25
	46	.30514	.95231	.32042	3.12087	.484501	.978777	.505724	.494276	14	
	47	.30542	.95222	.32074	3.11775	.484895	.978737	.506159	.493841	13	
.80	48	.30570	.95213	.32106	3.11464	.485289	.978696	.506593	.493407	12	.20
	49	.30597	.95204	.32139	3.11153	.485682	.978655	.507027	.492973	11	
	50	.30625	.95195	.32171	3.10842	.486075	.978615	.507460	.492540	10	
.85	51	.30653	.95186	.32203	3.10532	.486467	.978574	.507893	.492107	9	.15
	52	.30680	.95177	.32235	3.10223	.486860	.978533	.508326	.491674	8	
	53	.30708	.95168	.32267	3.09914	.487251	.978493	.508759	.491241	7	
.90	54	.30736	.95159	.32299	3.09606	.487643	.978452	.509191	.490809	6	.10
	55	.30763	.95150	.32331	3.09298	.488034	.978411	.509622	.490378	5	
	56	.30791	.95142	.32363	3.08991	.488424	.978370	.510054	.489946	4	
.95	57	.30819	.95133	.32396	3.08685	.488814	.978329	.510485	.489515	3	.05
	58	.30846	.95124	.32428	3.08379	.489204	.978288	.510916	.489084	2	
	59	.30874	.95115	.32460	3.08073	.489593	.978247	.511346	.488654	1	
1.00	60	.30902	.95106	.32492	3.07768	9.489982	9.978206	9.511776	10.488224	0	.00

Decimals	Minutes	Cos	Sin	Cot	Tan	Cos	Sin	Cot	Tan	Minutes	Decimals
		Natural Values				Common Logarithms					

Decimals	Minutes	Natural Values				Common Logarithms				Minutes	Decimals
		Sin	Cos	Tan	Cot	Sin	Cos	Tan	Cot		
.00	0	.30902	.95106	.32492	3.07768	9.489982	9.978206	9.511776	10.488224	60	1.00
	1	.30929	.95097	.32524	3.07464	.490371	.978165	.512206	.487794	59	
	2	.30957	.95088	.32556	3.07160	.490759	.978124	.512635	.487365	58	
.05	3	.30985	.95079	.32588	3.06857	.491147	.978083	.513064	.486936	57	.95
	4	.31012	.95070	.32621	3.06554	.491535	.978042	.513493	.486507	56	
	5	.31040	.95061	.32653	3.06252	.491922	.978001	.513921	.486079	55	
.10	6	.31068	.95052	.32685	3.05950	.492308	.977959	.514349	.485651	54	.90
	7	.31095	.95043	.32717	3.05649	.492695	.977918	.514777	.485223	53	
	8	.31123	.95033	.32749	3.05349	.493081	.977877	.515204	.484796	52	
.15	9	.31151	.95024	.32782	3.05049	.493466	.977835	.515631	.484369	51	.85
	10	.31178	.95015	.32814	3.04749	.493851	.977794	.516057	.483943	50	
	11	.31206	.95006	.32846	3.04450	.494236	.977752	.516484	.483516	49	
.20	12	.31233	.94997	.32878	3.04152	.494621	.977711	.516910	.483090	48	.80
	13	.31261	.94988	.32911	3.03854	.495005	.977669	.517335	.482665	47	
	14	.31289	.94979	.32943	3.03556	.495388	.977628	.517761	.482239	46	
.25	15	.31316	.94970	.32975	3.03260	.495772	.977586	.518186	.481814	45	.75
	16	.31344	.94961	.33007	3.02963	.496154	.977544	.518610	.481390	44	
	17	.31372	.94952	.33040	3.02667	.496537	.977503	.519034	.480966	43	
.30	18	.31399	.94943	.33072	3.02372	.496919	.977461	.519458	.480542	42	.70
	19	.31427	.94933	.33104	3.02077	.497301	.977419	.519882	.480118	41	
	20	.31454	.94924	.33136	3.01783	.497682	.977377	.520305	.479695	40	
.35	21	.31482	.94915	.33169	3.01489	.498064	.977335	.520723	.479272	39	.65
	22	.31510	.94906	.33201	3.01196	.498444	.977293	.521151	.478849	38	
	23	.31537	.94897	.33233	3.00903	.498825	.977251	.521573	.478427	37	
.40	24	.31565	.94888	.33266	3.00611	.499204	.977209	.521995	.478005	36	.60
	25	.31593	.94878	.33298	3.00319	.499584	.977167	.522417	.477583	35	
	26	.31620	.94869	.33330	3.00028	.499963	.977125	.522838	.477162	34	
.45	27	.31648	.94860	.33363	2.99738	.500342	.977083	.523259	.476741	33	.55
	28	.31675	.94851	.33395	2.99447	.500721	.977041	.523680	.476320	32	
	29	.31703	.94842	.33427	2.99158	.501099	.976999	.524100	.475900	31	
.50	30	.31730	.94832	.33460	2.98868	.501476	.976957	.524520	.475480	30	.50
	31	.31758	.94823	.33492	2.98580	.501854	.976914	.524940	.475060	29	
	32	.31786	.94814	.33524	2.98292	.502231	.976872	.525359	.474641	28	
.55	33	.31813	.94805	.33557	2.98004	.502607	.976830	.525778	.474222	27	.45
	34	.31841	.94795	.33589	2.97717	.502984	.976787	.526197	.473803	26	
	35	.31868	.94786	.33621	2.97430	.503360	.976745	.526615	.473385	25	
.60	36	.31896	.94777	.33654	2.97144	.503735	.976702	.527033	.472967	24	.40
	37	.31923	.94768	.33686	2.96858	.504110	.976660	.527451	.472549	23	
	38	.31951	.94758	.33718	2.96573	.504485	.976617	.527868	.472132	22	
.65	39	.31979	.94749	.33751	2.96288	.504860	.976574	.528285	.471715	21	.35
	40	.32006	.94740	.33783	2.96004	.505234	.976532	.528702	.471298	20	
	41	.32034	.94730	.33816	2.95721	.505608	.976489	.529119	.470881	19	
.70	42	.32061	.94721	.33848	2.95437	.505981	.976446	.529535	.470465	18	.30
	43	.32089	.94712	.33881	2.95155	.506354	.976404	.529951	.470049	17	
	44	.32116	.94702	.33913	2.94872	.506727	.976361	.530366	.469634	16	
.75	45	.32144	.94693	.33945	2.94591	.507099	.976318	.530781	.469219	15	.25
	46	.32171	.94684	.33978	2.94309	.507471	.976275	.531196	.468804	14	
	47	.32199	.94674	.34010	2.94028	.507843	.976232	.531611	.468389	13	
.80	48	.32227	.94665	.34043	2.93748	.508214	.976189	.532025	.467975	12	.20
	49	.32254	.94656	.34075	2.93468	.508585	.976146	.532439	.467561	11	
	50	.32282	.94646	.34108	2.93189	.508956	.976103	.532853	.467147	10	
.85	51	.32309	.94637	.34140	2.92910	.509326	.976060	.533266	.466734	9	.15
	52	.32337	.94627	.34173	2.92632	.509696	.976017	.533679	.466321	8	
	53	.32364	.94618	.34205	2.92354	.510065	.975974	.534092	.465908	7	
.90	54	.32392	.94609	.34238	2.92076	.510434	.975930	.534504	.465496	6	.10
	55	.32419	.94599	.34270	2.91799	.510803	.975887	.534916	.465084	5	
	56	.32447	.94590	.34303	2.91523	.511172	.975844	.535328	.464672	4	
.95	57	.32474	.94580	.34335	2.91246	.511540	.975800	.535739	.464261	3	.05
	58	.32502	.94571	.34368	2.90971	.511907	.975757	.536150	.463850	2	
	59	.32529	.94561	.34400	2.90696	.512275	.975714	.536561	.463439	1	
1.00	60	.32557	.94552	.34433	2.90421	9.512642	9.975670	9.536972	10.463028	0	.00
Decimals	Minutes	Cos	Sin	Cot	Tan	Cos	Sin	Cot	Tan	Minutes	Decimals
		Natural Values				Common Logarithms					

Decimals	Minutes	Natural Values				Common Logarithms				Minutes	Decimals
		Sin	Cos	Tan	Cot	Sin	Cos	Tan	Cot		
.00	0	.32557	.94552	.34433	2.90421	9.512642	9.975670	9.536972	10.463028	60	1.00
	1	.32584	.94542	.34465	2.90147	.513009	.975627	.537382	.462618	59	
	2	.32612	.94533	.34498	2.89873	.513375	.975583	.537792	.462208	58	
.05	3	.32639	.94523	.34530	2.89600	.513741	.975539	.538202	.461798	57	.95
	4	.32667	.94514	.34563	2.89327	.514107	.975496	.538611	.461389	56	
	5	.32694	.94504	.34596	2.89055	.514472	.975452	.539020	.460980	55	
.10	6	.32722	.94495	.34628	2.88783	.514837	.975408	.539429	.460571	54	.90
	7	.32749	.94485	.34661	2.88511	.515202	.975365	.539837	.460163	53	
	8	.32777	.94476	.34693	2.88240	.515566	.975321	.540245	.459755	52	
.15	9	.32804	.94466	.34726	2.87970	.515930	.975277	.540653	.459347	51	.85
	10	.32832	.94457	.34758	2.87700	.516294	.975233	.541061	.458939	50	
	11	.32859	.94447	.34791	2.87430	.516657	.975189	.541468	.458532	49	
.20	12	.32887	.94438	.34824	2.87161	.517020	.975145	.541875	.458125	48	.80
	13	.32914	.94428	.34856	2.86892	.517382	.975101	.542281	.457719	47	
	14	.32942	.94418	.34889	2.86624	.517745	.975057	.542688	.457312	46	
.25	15	.32969	.94409	.34922	2.86356	.518107	.975013	.543094	.456906	45	.75
	16	.32997	.94399	.34954	2.86089	.518468	.974969	.543499	.456501	44	
	17	.33024	.94390	.34987	2.85822	.518829	.974925	.543905	.456095	43	
.30	18	.33051	.94380	.35020	2.85555	.519190	.974880	.544310	.455690	42	.70
	19	.33079	.94370	.35052	2.85289	.519551	.974836	.544715	.455285	41	
	20	.33106	.94361	.35085	2.85023	.519911	.974792	.545119	.454881	40	
.35	21	.33134	.94351	.35118	2.84758	.520271	.974748	.545524	.454476	39	.65
	22	.33161	.94342	.35150	2.84494	.520631	.974703	.545928	.454072	38	
	23	.33189	.94332	.35183	2.84229	.520990	.974659	.546331	.453669	37	
.40	24	.33216	.94322	.35216	2.83965	.521349	.974614	.546735	.453265	36	.60
	25	.33244	.94313	.35248	2.83702	.521707	.974570	.547138	.452862	35	
	26	.33271	.94303	.35281	2.83439	.522066	.974525	.547540	.452460	34	
.45	27	.33298	.94293	.35314	2.83176	.522424	.974481	.547943	.452057	33	.55
	28	.33326	.94284	.35346	2.82914	.522781	.974436	.548345	.451655	32	
	29	.33353	.94274	.35379	2.82653	.523138	.974391	.548747	.451253	31	
.50	30	.33381	.94264	.35412	2.82391	.523495	.974347	.549149	.450851	30	.50
	31	.33408	.94254	.35445	2.82130	.523852	.974302	.549550	.450450	29	
	32	.33436	.94245	.35477	2.81870	.524208	.974257	.549951	.450049	28	
.55	33	.33463	.94235	.35510	2.81610	.524564	.974212	.550352	.449648	27	.45
	34	.33490	.94225	.35543	2.81350	.524920	.974167	.550752	.449248	26	
	35	.33518	.94215	.35576	2.81091	.525275	.974122	.551153	.448847	25	
.60	36	.33545	.94206	.35608	2.80833	.525630	.974077	.551552	.448448	24	.40
	37	.33573	.94196	.35641	2.80574	.525984	.974032	.551952	.448048	23	
	38	.33600	.94186	.35674	2.80316	.526339	.973987	.552351	.447649	22	
.65	39	.33627	.94176	.35707	2.80059	.526693	.973942	.552750	.447250	21	.35
	40	.33655	.94167	.35740	2.79802	.527046	.973897	.553149	.446851	20	
	41	.33682	.94157	.35772	2.79545	.527400	.973852	.553548	.446452	19	
.70	42	.33710	.94147	.35805	2.79289	.527753	.973807	.553946	.446054	18	.30
	43	.33737	.94137	.35838	2.79033	.528105	.973761	.554344	.445656	17	
	44	.33764	.94127	.35871	2.78778	.528458	.973716	.554741	.445259	16	
.75	45	.33792	.94118	.35904	2.78523	.528810	.973671	.555139	.444861	15	.25
	46	.33819	.94108	.35937	2.78269	.529161	.973625	.555536	.444464	14	
	47	.33846	.94098	.35969	2.78014	.529513	.973580	.555933	.444067	13	
.80	48	.33874	.94088	.36002	2.77761	.529864	.973535	.556329	.443671	12	.20
	49	.33901	.94078	.36035	2.77507	.530215	.973489	.556725	.443275	11	
	50	.33929	.94068	.36068	2.77254	.530565	.973444	.557121	.442879	10	
.85	51	.33956	.94058	.36101	2.77002	.530915	.973398	.557517	.442483	9	.15
	52	.33983	.94049	.36134	2.76750	.531265	.973352	.557913	.442087	8	
	53	.34011	.94039	.36167	2.76498	.531614	.973307	.558308	.441692	7	
.90	54	.34038	.94029	.36199	2.76247	.531963	.973261	.558703	.441297	6	.10
	55	.34065	.94019	.36232	2.75996	.532312	.973215	.559097	.440903	5	
	56	.34093	.94009	.36265	2.75746	.532661	.973169	.559491	.440509	4	
.95	57	.34120	.93999	.36298	2.75496	.533009	.973124	.559885	.440115	3	.05
	58	.34147	.93989	.36331	2.75246	.533357	.973078	.560279	.439721	2	
	59	.34175	.93979	.36364	2.74997	.533704	.973032	.560673	.439327	1	
1.00	60	.34202	.93969	.36397	2.74748	9.534052	9.972986	9.561066	10.438934	0	.00

Decimals	Minutes	Cos	Sin	Cot	Tan	Cos	Sin	Cot	Tan	Minutes	Decimals
		Natural Values				Common Logarithms					

70°

20°   VALUES AND LOGARITHMS OF TRIGONOMETRIC FUNCTIONS

Decimals	Minutes	\ Natural Values — Sin	Cos	Tan	Cot	Common Logarithms — Sin	Cos	Tan	Cot	Minutes	Decimals
.00	0	.34202	.93969	.36397	2.74748	9.534052	9.972986	9.561066	10.438934	60	1.00
	1	.34229	.93959	.36430	2.74499	.534399	.972940	.561459	.438541	59	
	2	.34257	.93949	.36463	2.74251	.534745	.972894	.561851	.438149	58	
.05	3	.34284	.93939	.36496	2.74004	.535092	.972848	.562244	.437756	57	.95
	4	.34311	.93929	.36529	2.73756	.535438	.972802	.562636	.437364	56	
	5	.34339	.93919	.36562	2.73509	.535783	.972755	.563028	.436972	55	
.10	6	.34366	.93909	.36595	2.73263	.536129	.972709	.563419	.436581	54	.90
	7	.34393	.93899	.36628	2.73017	.536474	.972663	.563811	.436189	53	
	8	.34421	.93889	.36661	2.72771	.536818	.972617	.564202	.435798	52	
.15	9	.34448	.93879	.36694	2.72526	.537163	.972570	.564593	.435407	51	.85
	10	.34475	.93869	.36727	2.72281	.537507	.972524	.564983	.435017	50	
	11	.34503	.93859	.36760	2.72036	.537851	.972478	.565373	.434627	49	
.20	12	.34530	.93849	.36793	2.71792	.538194	.972431	.565763	.434237	48	.80
	13	.34557	.93839	.36826	2.71548	.538538	.972385	.566153	.433847	47	
	14	.34584	.93829	.36859	2.71305	.538880	.972338	.566542	.433458	46	
.25	15	.34612	.93819	.36892	2.71062	.539223	.972291	.566932	.433068	45	.75
	16	.34639	.93809	.36925	2.70819	.539565	.972245	.567320	.432680	44	
	17	.34666	.93799	.36958	2.70577	.539907	.972198	.567709	.432291	43	
.30	18	.34694	.93789	.36991	2.70335	.540249	.972151	.568098	.431902	42	.70
	19	.34721	.93779	.37024	2.70094	.540590	.972105	.568486	.431514	41	
	20	.34748	.93769	.37057	2.69853	.540931	.972058	.568873	.431127	40	
.35	21	.34775	.93759	.37090	2.69612	.541272	.972011	.569261	.430739	39	.65
	22	.34803	.93748	.37123	2.69371	.541613	.971964	.569648	.430352	38	
	23	.34830	.93738	.37157	2.69131	.541953	.971917	.570035	.429965	37	
.40	24	.34857	.93728	.37190	2.68892	.542293	.971870	.570422	.429578	36	.60
	25	.34884	.93718	.37223	2.68653	.542632	.971823	.570809	.429191	35	
	26	.34912	.93708	.37256	2.68414	.542971	.971776	.571195	.428805	34	
.45	27	.34939	.93698	.37289	2.68175	.543310	.971729	.571581	.428419	33	.55
	28	.34966	.93688	.37322	2.67937	.543649	.971682	.571967	.428033	32	
	29	.34993	.93677	.37355	2.67700	.543987	.971635	.572352	.427648	31	
.50	30	.35021	.93667	.37388	2.67462	.544325	.971588	.572738	.427262	30	.50
	31	.35048	.93657	.37422	2.67225	.544663	.971540	.573123	.426877	29	
	32	.35075	.93647	.37455	2.66989	.545000	.971493	.573507	.426493	28	
.55	33	.35102	.93637	.37488	2.66752	.545338	.971446	.573892	.426108	27	.45
	34	.35130	.93626	.37521	2.66516	.545674	.971398	.574276	.425724	26	
	35	.35157	.93616	.37554	2.66281	.546011	.971351	.574660	.425340	25	
.60	36	.35184	.93606	.37588	2.66046	.546347	.971303	.575044	.424956	24	.40
	37	.35211	.93596	.37621	2.65811	.546683	.971256	.575427	.424573	23	
	38	.35239	.93585	.37654	2.65576	.547019	.971208	.575810	.424190	22	
.65	39	.35266	.93575	.37687	2.65342	.547354	.971161	.576193	.423807	21	.35
	40	.35293	.93565	.37720	2.65109	.547689	.971113	.576576	.423424	20	
	41	.35320	.93555	.37754	2.64875	.548024	.971066	.576959	.423041	19	
.70	42	.35347	.93544	.37787	2.64642	.548359	.971018	.577341	.422659	18	.30
	43	.35375	.93534	.37820	2.64410	.548693	.970970	.577723	.422277	17	
	44	.35402	.93524	.37853	2.64177	.549027	.970922	.578104	.421896	16	
.75	45	.35429	.93514	.37887	2.63945	.549360	.970874	.578486	.421514	15	.25
	46	.35456	.93503	.37920	2.63714	.549693	.970827	.578867	.421133	14	
	47	.35484	.93493	.37953	2.63483	.550026	.970779	.579248	.420752	13	
.80	48	.35511	.93483	.37986	2.63252	.550359	.970731	.579629	.420371	12	.20
	49	.35538	.93472	.38020	2.63021	.550692	.970683	.580009	.419991	11	
	50	.35565	.93462	.38053	2.62791	.551024	.970635	.580389	.419611	10	
.85	51	.35592	.93452	.38086	2.62561	.551356	.970586	.580769	.419231	9	.15
	52	.35619	.93441	.38120	2.62332	.551687	.970538	.581149	.418851	8	
	53	.35647	.93431	.38153	2.62103	.552018	.970490	.581528	.418472	7	
.90	54	.35674	.93420	.38186	2.61874	.552349	.970442	.581907	.418093	6	.10
	55	.35701	.93410	.38220	2.61646	.552680	.970394	.582286	.417714	5	
	56	.35728	.93400	.38253	2.61418	.553010	.970345	.582665	.417335	4	
.95	57	.35755	.93389	.38286	2.61190	.553341	.970297	.583044	.416956	3	.05
	58	.35782	.93379	.38320	2.60963	.553670	.970249	.583422	.416578	2	
	59	.35810	.93368	.38353	2.60736	.554000	.970200	.583800	.416200	1	
1.00	60	.35837	.93358	.38386	2.60509	9.554329	9.970152	9.584177	10.415823	0	.00

Decimals	Minutes	Cos	Sin	Cot	Tan	Cos	Sin	Cot	Tan	Minutes	Decimals
		\ Natural Values				Common Logarithms					

1–77

69°

Decimals	Minutes	Natural Values Sin	Cos	Tan	Cot	Common Logarithms Sin	Cos	Tan	Cot	Minutes	Decimals
.00	0	.35837	.93358	.38386	2.60509	9.554329	9.970152	9.584177	10.415823	60	1.00
	1	.35864	.93348	.38420	2.60283	.554658	.970103	.584555	.415445	59	
	2	.35891	.93337	.38453	2.60057	.554987	.970055	.584932	.415068	58	
.05	3	.35918	.93327	.38487	2.59831	.555315	.970006	.585309	.414691	57	.95
	4	.35945	.93316	.38520	2.59606	.555643	.969957	.585686	.414314	56	
	5	.35973	.93306	.38553	2.59381	.555971	.969909	.586062	.413938	55	
.10	6	.36000	.93295	.38587	2.59156	.556299	.969860	.586439	.413561	54	.90
	7	.36027	.93285	.38620	2.58932	.556626	.969811	.586815	.413185	53	
	8	.36054	.93274	.38654	2.58708	.556953	.969762	.587190	.412810	52	
.15	9	.36081	.93264	.38687	2.58484	.557280	.969714	.587566	.412434	51	.85
	10	.36108	.93253	.38721	2.58261	.557606	.969665	.587941	.412059	50	
	11	.36135	.93243	.38754	2.58038	.557932	.969616	.588316	.411684	49	
.20	12	.36162	.93232	.38787	2.57815	.558258	.969567	.588691	.411309	48	.80
	13	.36190	.93222	.38821	2.57593	.558583	.969518	.589066	.410934	47	
	14	.36217	.93211	.38854	2.57371	.558909	.969469	.589440	.410560	46	
.25	15	.36244	.93201	.38888	2.57150	.559234	.969420	.589814	.410186	45	.75
	16	.36271	.93190	.38921	2.56928	.559558	.969370	.590188	.409812	44	
	17	.36298	.93180	.38955	2.56707	.559883	.969321	.590562	.409438	43	
.30	18	.36325	.93169	.38988	2.56487	.560207	.969272	.590935	.409065	42	.70
	19	.36352	.93159	.39022	2.56266	.560531	.969223	.591308	.408692	41	
	20	.36379	.93148	.39055	2.56046	.560855	.969173	.591681	.408319	40	
.35	21	.36406	.93137	.39089	2.55827	.561178	.969124	.592054	.407946	39	.65
	22	.36434	.93127	.39122	2.55608	.561501	.969075	.592426	.407574	38	
	23	.36461	.93116	.39156	2.55389	.561824	.969025	.592799	.407201	37	
.40	24	.36488	.93106	.39190	2.55170	.562146	.968976	.593171	.406829	36	.60
	25	.36515	.93095	.39223	2.54952	.562468	.968926	.593542	.406458	35	
	26	.36542	.93084	.39257	2.54734	.562790	.968877	.593914	.406086	34	
.45	27	.36569	.93074	.39290	2.54516	.563112	.968827	.594285	.405715	33	.55
	28	.36596	.93063	.39324	2.54299	.563433	.968777	.594656	.405344	32	
	29	.36623	.93052	.39357	2.54082	.563755	.968728	.595027	.404973	31	
.50	30	.36650	.93042	.39391	2.53865	.564075	.968678	.595398	.404602	30	.50
	31	.36677	.93031	.39425	2.53648	.564396	.968628	.595768	.404232	29	
	32	.36704	.93020	.39458	2.53432	.564716	.968578	.596138	.403862	28	
.55	33	.36731	.93010	.39492	2.53217	.565036	.968528	.596508	.403492	27	.45
	34	.36758	.92999	.39526	2.53001	.565356	.968479	.596878	.403122	26	
	35	.36785	.92988	.39559	2.52786	.565676	.968429	.597247	.402753	25	
.60	36	.36812	.92978	.39593	2.52571	.565995	.968379	.597616	.402384	24	.40
	37	.36839	.92967	.39626	2.52357	.566314	.968329	.597985	.402015	23	
	38	.36867	.92956	.39660	2.52142	.566632	.968278	.598354	.401646	22	
.65	39	.36894	.92945	.39694	2.51929	.566951	.968228	.598722	.401278	21	.35
	40	.36921	.92935	.39727	2.51715	.567269	.968178	.599091	.400909	20	
	41	.36948	.92924	.39761	2.51502	.567587	.968128	.599459	.400541	19	
.70	42	.36975	.92913	.39795	2.51289	.567904	.968078	.599827	.400173	18	.30
	43	.37002	.92902	.39829	2.51076	.568222	.968027	.600194	.399806	17	
	44	.37029	.92892	.39862	2.50864	.568539	.967977	.600562	.399438	16	
.75	45	.37056	.92881	.39896	2.50652	.568856	.967927	.600929	.399071	15	.25
	46	.37083	.92870	.39930	2.50440	.569172	.967876	.601296	.398704	14	
	47	.37110	.92859	.39963	2.50229	.569488	.967826	.601663	.398337	13	
.80	48	.37137	.92849	.39997	2.50018	.569804	.967775	.602029	.397971	12	.20
	49	.37164	.92838	.40031	2.49807	.570120	.967725	.602395	.397605	11	
	50	.37191	.92827	.40065	2.49597	.570435	.967674	.602761	.397239	10	
.85	51	.37218	.92816	.40098	2.49386	.570751	.967624	.603127	.396873	9	.15
	52	.37245	.92805	.40132	2.49177	.571066	.967573	.603493	.396507	8	
	53	.37272	.92794	.40166	2.48967	.571380	.967522	.603858	.396142	7	
.90	54	.37299	.92784	.40200	2.48758	.571695	.967471	.604223	.395777	6	.10
	55	.37326	.92773	.40234	2.48549	.572009	.967421	.604588	.395412	5	
	56	.37353	.92762	.40267	2.48340	.572323	.967370	.604953	.395047	4	
.95	57	.37380	.92751	.40301	2.48132	.572636	.967319	.605317	.394683	3	.05
	58	.37407	.92740	.40335	2.47924	.572950	.967268	.605682	.394318	2	
	59	.37434	.92729	.40369	2.47716	.573263	.967217	.606046	.393954	1	
1.00	60	.37461	.92718	.40403	2.47509	9.573575	9.967165	9.606410	10.393590	0	.00

Decimals	Minutes	Cos	Sin	Cot	Tan	Cos	Sin	Cot	Tan	Minutes	Decimals
		Natural Values				Common Logarithms					

Decimals	Minutes	Natural Values				Common Logarithms				Minutes	Decimals
		Sin	Cos	Tan	Cot	Sin	Cos	Tan	Cot		
.00	0	.37461	.92718	.40403	2.47509	9.573575	9.967166	9.606410	10.393590	60	1.00
	1	.37488	.92707	.40436	2.47302	.573888	.967115	.606773	.393227	59	
	2	.37515	.92697	.40470	2.47095	.574200	.967064	.607137	.392863	58	
.05	3	.37542	.92686	.40504	2.46888	.574512	.967013	.607500	.392500	57	.95
	4	.37569	.92675	.40538	2.46682	.574824	.966961	.607863	.392137	56	
	5	.37595	.92664	.40572	2.46476	.575136	.966910	.608225	.391775	55	
.10	6	.37622	.92653	.40606	2.46270	.575447	.966859	.608588	.391412	54	.90
	7	.37649	.92642	.40640	2.46065	.575758	.966808	.608950	.391050	53	
	8	.37676	.92631	.40674	2.45860	.576069	.966756	.609312	.390688	52	
.15	9	.37703	.92620	.40707	2.45655	.576379	.966705	.609674	.390326	51	.85
	10	.37730	.92609	.40741	2.45451	.576689	.966653	.610036	.389964	50	
	11	.37757	.92598	.40775	2.45246	.576999	.966602	.610397	.389603	49	
.20	12	.37784	.92587	.40809	2.45043	.577309	.966550	.610759	.389241	48	.80
	13	.37811	.92576	.40843	2.44839	.577618	.966499	.611120	.388880	47	
	14	.37838	.92565	.40877	2.44636	.577927	.966447	.611480	.388520	46	
.25	15	.37865	.92554	.40911	2.44433	.578236	.966395	.611841	.388159	45	.75
	16	.37892	.92543	.40945	2.44230	.578545	.966344	.612201	.387799	44	
	17	.37919	.92532	.40979	2.44027	.578853	.966292	.612561	.387439	43	
.30	18	.37946	.92521	.41013	2.43825	.579162	.966240	.612921	.387079	42	.70
	19	.37973	.92510	.41047	2.43623	.579470	.966188	.613281	.386719	41	
	20	.37999	.92499	.41081	2.43422	.579777	.966136	.613641	.386359	40	
.35	21	.38026	.92488	.41115	2.43220	.580085	.966085	.614000	.386000	39	.65
	22	.38053	.92477	.41149	2.43019	.580392	.966033	.614359	.385641	38	
	23	.38080	.92466	.41183	2.42819	.580699	.965981	.614718	.385282	37	
.40	24	.38107	.92455	.41217	2.42618	.581005	.965929	.615077	.384923	36	.60
	25	.38134	.92444	.41251	2.42418	.581312	.965876	.615435	.384565	35	
	26	.38161	.92432	.41285	2.42218	.581618	.965824	.615793	.384207	34	
.45	27	.38188	.92421	.41319	2.42019	.581924	.965772	.616151	.383849	33	.55
	28	.38215	.92410	.41353	2.41819	.582229	.965720	.616509	.383491	32	
	29	.38241	.92399	.41387	2.41620	.582535	.965668	.616867	.383133	31	
.50	30	.38268	.92388	.41421	2.41421	.582840	.965615	.617224	.382776	30	.50
	31	.38295	.92377	.41455	2.41223	.583145	.965563	.617582	.382418	29	
	32	.38322	.92366	.41490	2.41025	.583449	.965511	.617939	.382061	28	
.55	33	.38349	.92355	.41524	2.40827	.583754	.965458	.618295	.381705	27	.45
	34	.38376	.92343	.41558	2.40629	.584058	.965406	.618652	.381348	26	
	35	.38403	.92332	.41592	2.40432	.584361	.965353	.619008	.380992	25	
.60	36	.38430	.92321	.41626	2.40235	.584665	.965301	.619364	.380636	24	.40
	37	.38456	.92310	.41660	2.40038	.584968	.965248	.619720	.380280	23	
	38	.38483	.92299	.41694	2.39841	.585272	.965195	.620076	.379924	22	
.65	39	.38510	.92287	.41728	2.39645	.585574	.965143	.620432	.379568	21	.35
	40	.38537	.92276	.41763	2.39449	.585877	.965090	.620787	.379213	20	
	41	.38564	.92265	.41797	2.39253	.586179	.965037	.621142	.378858	19	
.70	42	.38591	.92254	.41831	2.39058	.586482	.964984	.621497	.378503	18	.30
	43	.38617	.92243	.41865	2.38863	.586783	.964931	.621852	.378148	17	
	44	.38644	.92231	.41899	2.38668	.587085	.964879	.622207	.377793	16	
.75	45	.38671	.92220	.41933	2.38473	.587386	.964826	.622561	.377439	15	.25
	46	.38698	.92209	.41968	2.38279	.587688	.964773	.622915	.377085	14	
	47	.38725	.92198	.42002	2.38084	.587989	.964720	.623269	.376731	13	
.80	48	.38752	.92186	.42036	2.37891	.588289	.964666	.623623	.376377	12	.20
	49	.38778	.92175	.42070	2.37697	.588590	.964613	.623976	.376024	11	
	50	.38805	.92164	.42105	2.37504	.588890	.964560	.624330	.375670	10	
.85	51	.38832	.92152	.42139	2.37311	.589190	.964507	.624683	.375317	9	.15
	52	.38859	.92141	.42173	2.37118	.589489	.964454	.625036	.374964	8	
	53	.38886	.92130	.42207	2.36925	.589789	.964400	.625388	.374612	7	
.90	54	.38912	.92119	.42242	2.36733	.590088	.964347	.625741	.374259	6	.10
	55	.38939	.92107	.42276	2.36541	.590387	.964294	.626093	.373907	5	
	56	.38966	.92096	.42310	2.36349	.590686	.964240	.626445	.373555	4	
.95	57	.38993	.92085	.42345	2.36158	.590984	.964187	.626797	.373203	3	.05
	58	.39020	.92073	.42379	2.35967	.591282	.964133	.627149	.372851	2	
	59	.39046	.92062	.42413	2.35776	.591580	.964080	.627501	.372499	1	
1.00	60	.39073	.92050	.42447	2.35585	9.591878	9.964026	9.627852	10.372148	0	.00
Decimals	Minutes	Cos	Sin	Cot	Tan	Cos	Sin	Cot	Tan	Minutes	Decimals
		Natural Values				Common Logarithms					

67°

Decimals	Minutes	Natural Values				Common Logarithms				Minutes	Decimals
		Sin	Cos	Tan	Cot	Sin	Cos	Tan	Cot		
.00	0	.39073	.92050	.42447	2.35585	9.591878	9.964026	9.627852	10.372148	60	1.00
	1	.39100	.92039	.42482	2.35395	.592176	.963972	.628203	.371797	59	
	2	.39127	.92028	.42516	2.35205	.592473	.963919	.628554	.371446	58	
.05	3	.39153	.92016	.42551	2.35015	.592770	.963865	.628905	.371095	57	.95
	4	.39180	.92005	.42585	2.34825	.593067	.963811	.629255	.370745	56	
	5	.39207	.91994	.42619	2.34636	.593363	.963757	.629606	.370394	55	
.10	6	.39234	.91982	.42654	2.34447	.593659	.963704	.629956	.370044	54	.90
	7	.39260	.91971	.42688	2.34258	.593955	.963650	.630306	.369694	53	
	8	.39287	.91959	.42722	2.34069	.594251	.963596	.630656	.369344	52	
.15	9	.39314	.91948	.42757	2.33881	.594547	.963542	.631005	.368995	51	.85
	10	.39341	.91936	.42791	2.33693	.594842	.963488	.631355	.368645	50	
	11	.39367	.91925	.42826	2.33505	.595137	.963434	.631704	.368296	49	
.20	12	.39394	.91914	.42860	2.33317	.595432	.963379	.632053	.367947	48	.80
	13	.39421	.91902	.42894	2.33130	.595727	.963325	.632402	.367598	47	
	14	.39448	.91891	.42929	2.32943	.596021	.963271	.632750	.367250	46	
.25	15	.39474	.91879	.42963	2.32756	.596315	.963217	.633099	.366901	45	.75
	16	.39501	.91868	.42998	2.32570	.596609	.963163	.633447	.366553	44	
	17	.39528	.91856	.43032	2.32383	.596903	.963108	.633795	.366205	43	
.30	18	.39555	.91845	.43067	2.32197	.597196	.963054	.634143	.365857	42	.70
	19	.39581	.91833	.43101	2.32012	.597490	.962999	.634490	.365510	41	
	20	.39608	.91822	.43136	2.31826	.597783	.962945	.634838	.365162	40	
.35	21	.39635	.91810	.43170	2.31641	.598075	.962890	.635185	.364815	39	.65
	22	.39661	.91799	.43205	2.31456	.598368	.962836	.635532	.364468	38	
	23	.39688	.91787	.43239	2.31271	.598660	.962781	.635879	.364121	37	
.40	24	.39715	.91775	.43274	2.31086	.598952	.962727	.636226	.363774	36	.60
	25	.39741	.91764	.43308	2.30902	.599244	.962672	.636572	.363428	35	
	26	.39768	.91752	.43343	2.30718	.599536	.962617	.636919	.363081	34	
.45	27	.39795	.91741	.43378	2.30534	.599827	.962562	.637265	.362735	33	.55
	28	.39822	.91729	.43412	2.30351	.600118	.962508	.637611	.362389	32	
	29	.39848	.91718	.43447	2.30167	.600409	.962453	.637956	.362044	31	
.50	30	.39875	.91706	.43481	2.29984	.600700	.962398	.638302	.361698	30	.50
	31	.39902	.91694	.43516	2.29801	.600990	.962343	.638647	.361353	29	
	32	.39928	.91683	.43550	2.29619	.601280	.962288	.638992	.361008	28	
.55	33	.39955	.91671	.43585	2.29437	.601570	.962233	.639337	.360663	27	.45
	34	.39982	.91660	.43620	2.29254	.601860	.962178	.639682	.360318	26	
	35	.40008	.91648	.43654	2.29073	.602150	.962123	.640027	.359973	25	
.60	36	.40035	.91636	.43689	2.28891	.602439	.962067	.640371	.359629	24	.40
	37	.40062	.91625	.43724	2.28710	.602728	.962012	.640716	.359284	23	
	38	.40088	.91613	.43758	2.28528	.603017	.961957	.641060	.358940	22	
.65	39	.40115	.91601	.43793	2.28348	.603305	.961902	.641404	.358596	21	.35
	40	.40141	.91590	.43828	2.28167	.603594	.961846	.641747	.358253	20	
	41	.40168	.91578	.43862	2.27987	.603882	.961791	.642091	.357909	19	
.70	42	.40195	.91566	.43897	2.27806	.604170	.961735	.642434	.357566	18	.30
	43	.40221	.91555	.43932	2.27626	.604457	.961680	.642777	.357223	17	
	44	.40248	.91543	.43966	2.27447	.604745	.961624	.643120	.356880	16	
.75	45	.40275	.91531	.44001	2.27267	.605032	.961569	.643463	.356537	15	.25
	46	.40301	.91519	.44036	2.27088	.605319	.961513	.643806	.356194	14	
	47	.40328	.91508	.44071	2.26909	.605606	.961458	.644148	.355852	13	
.80	48	.40355	.91496	.44105	2.26730	.605892	.961402	.644490	.355510	12	.20
	49	.40381	.91484	.44140	2.26552	.606179	.961346	.644832	.355168	11	
	50	.40408	.91472	.44175	2.26374	.606465	.961290	.645174	.354826	10	
.85	51	.40434	.91461	.44210	2.26196	.606751	.961235	.645516	.354484	9	.15
	52	.40461	.91449	.44244	2.26018	.607036	.961179	.645857	.354143	8	
	53	.40488	.91437	.44279	2.25840	.607322	.961123	.646199	.353801	7	
.90	54	.40514	.91425	.44314	2.25663	.607607	.961067	.646540	.353460	6	.10
	55	.40541	.91414	.44349	2.25486	.607892	.961011	.646881	.353119	5	
	56	.40567	.91402	.44384	2.25309	.608177	.960955	.647222	.352778	4	
.95	57	.40594	.91390	.44418	2.25132	.608461	.960899	.647562	.352438	3	.05
	58	.40621	.91378	.44453	2.24956	.608745	.960843	.647903	.352097	2	
	59	.40647	.91366	.44488	2.24780	.609029	.960786	.648243	.351757	1	
1.00	60	.40674	.91355	.44523	2.24604	9.609313	9.960730	9.648583	10.351417	0	.00
Decimals	Minutes	Cos	Sin	Cot	Tan	Cos	Sin	Cot	Tan	Minutes	Decimals
		Natural Values				Common Logarithms					

Decimals	Minutes	Natural Values				Common Logarithms				Minutes	Decimals
		Sin	Cos	Tan	Cot	Sin	Cos	Tan	Cot		
.00	0	.40674	.91355	.44523	2.24604	9.609313	9.960730	9.648583	10.351417	60	1.00
	1	.40700	.91343	.44558	2.24428	.609597	.960674	.648923	.351077	59	
	2	.40727	.91331	.44593	2.24252	.609880	.960618	.649263	.350737	58	
.05	3	.40753	.91319	.44627	2.24077	.610164	.960561	.649602	.350398	57	.95
	4	.40780	.91307	.44662	2.23902	.610447	.960505	.649942	.350058	56	
	5	.40806	.91295	.44697	2.23727	.610729	.960448	.650281	.349719	55	
.10	6	.40833	.91283	.44732	2.23553	.611012	.960392	.650620	.349380	54	.90
	7	.40860	.91272	.44767	2.23378	.611294	.960335	.650959	.349041	53	
	8	.40886	.91260	.44802	2.23204	.611576	.960279	.651297	.348703	52	
.15	9	.40913	.91248	.44837	2.23030	.611858	.960222	.651636	.348364	51	.85
	10	.40939	.91236	.44872	2.22857	.612140	.960165	.651974	.348026	50	
	11	.40966	.91224	.44907	2.22683	.612421	.960109	.652312	.347688	49	
.20	12	.40992	.91212	.44942	2.22510	.612702	.960052	.652650	.347350	48	.80
	13	.41019	.91200	.44977	2.22337	.612983	.959995	.652988	.347012	47	
	14	.41045	.91188	.45012	2.22164	.613264	.959938	.653326	.346674	46	
.25	15	.41072	.91176	.45047	2.21992	.613545	.959882	.653663	.346337	45	.75
	16	.41098	.91164	.45082	2.21819	.613825	.959825	.654000	.346000	44	
	17	.41125	.91152	.45117	2.21647	.614105	.959768	.654337	.345663	43	
.30	18	.41151	.91140	.45152	2.21475	.614385	.959711	.654674	.345326	42	.70
	19	.41178	.91128	.45187	2.21304	.614665	.959654	.655011	.344989	41	
	20	.41204	.91116	.45222	2.21132	.614944	.959596	.655348	.344652	40	
.35	21	.41231	.91104	.45257	2.20961	.615223	.959539	.655684	.344316	39	.65
	22	.41257	.91092	.45292	2.20790	.615502	.959482	.656020	.343980	38	
	23	.41284	.91080	.45327	2.20619	.615781	.959425	.656356	.343644	37	
.40	24	.41310	.91068	.45362	2.20449	.616060	.959368	.656692	.343308	36	.60
	25	.41337	.91056	.45397	2.20278	.616338	.959310	.657028	.342972	35	
	26	.41363	.91044	.45432	2.20108	.616616	.959253	.657364	.342636	34	
.45	27	.41390	.91032	.45467	2.19938	.616894	.959195	.657699	.342301	33	.55
	28	.41416	.91020	.45502	2.19769	.617172	.959138	.658034	.341966	32	
	29	.41443	.91008	.45538	2.19599	.617450	.959080	.658369	.341631	31	
.50	30	.41469	.90996	.45573	2.19430	.617727	.959023	.658704	.341296	30	.50
	31	.41496	.90984	.45608	2.19261	.618004	.958965	.659039	.340961	29	
	32	.41522	.90972	.45643	2.19092	.618281	.958908	.659373	.340627	28	
.55	33	.41549	.90960	.45678	2.18923	.618558	.958850	.659708	.340292	27	.45
	34	.41575	.90948	.45713	2.18755	.618834	.958792	.660042	.339958	26	
	35	.41602	.90936	.45748	2.18587	.619110	.958734	.660376	.339624	25	
.60	36	.41628	.90924	.45784	2.18419	.619386	.958677	.660710	.339290	24	.40
	37	.41655	.90911	.45819	2.18251	.619662	.958619	.661043	.338957	23	
	38	.41681	.90899	.45854	2.18084	.619938	.958561	.661377	.338623	22	
.65	39	.41707	.90887	.45889	2.17916	.620213	.958503	.661710	.338290	21	.35
	40	.41734	.90875	.45924	2.17749	.620488	.958445	.662043	.337957	20	
	41	.41760	.90863	.45960	2.17582	.620763	.958387	.662376	.337624	19	
.70	42	.41787	.90851	.45995	2.17416	.621038	.958329	.662709	.337291	18	.30
	43	.41813	.90839	.46030	2.17249	.621313	.958271	.663042	.336958	17	
	44	.41840	.90826	.46065	2.17083	.621587	.958213	.663375	.336625	16	
.75	45	.41866	.90814	.46101	2.16917	.621861	.958154	.663707	.336293	15	.25
	46	.41892	.90802	.46136	2.16751	.622135	.958096	.664039	.335961	14	
	47	.41919	.90790	.46171	2.16585	.622409	.958038	.664371	.335629	13	
.80	48	.41945	.90778	.46206	2.16420	.622682	.957979	.664703	.335297	12	.20
	49	.41972	.90766	.46242	2.16255	.622956	.957921	.665035	.334965	11	
	50	.41998	.90753	.46277	2.16090	.623229	.957863	.665366	.334634	10	
.85	51	.42024	.90741	.46312	2.15925	.623502	.957804	.665698	.334302	9	.15
	52	.42051	.90729	.46348	2.15760	.623774	.957746	.666029	.333971	8	
	53	.42077	.90717	.46383	2.15596	.624047	.957687	.666360	.333640	7	
.90	54	.42104	.90704	.46418	2.15432	.624319	.957628	.666691	.333309	6	.10
	55	.42130	.90692	.46454	2.15268	.624591	.957570	.667021	.332979	5	
	56	.42156	.90680	.46489	2.15104	.624863	.957511	.667352	.332648	4	
.95	57	.42183	.90668	.46525	2.14940	.625135	.957452	.667682	.332318	3	.05
	58	.42209	.90655	.46560	2.14777	.625406	.957393	.668013	.331987	2	
	59	.42235	.90643	.46595	2.14614	.625677	.957335	.668343	.331657	1	
1.00	60	.42262	.90631	.46631	2.14451	9.625948	9.957276	9.668673	10.331327	0	.00
Decimals	Minutes	Cos	Sin	Cot	Tan	Cos	Sin	Cot	Tan	Minutes	Decimals
		Natural Values				Common Logarithms					

Decimals	Minutes	Natural Values				Common Logarithms				Minutes	Decimals
		Sin	Cos	Tan	Cot	Sin	Cos	Tan	Cot		
.00	0	.42262	.90631	.46631	2.14451	9.625943	9.957276	9.668673	10.331327	60	1.00
	1	.42288	.90618	.46666	2.14288	.626219	.957217	.669002	.330998	59	
	2	.42315	.90606	.46702	2.14125	.626490	.957158	.669332	.330668	58	
.05	3	.42341	.90594	.46737	2.13963	.626760	.957099	.669661	.330339	57	.95
	4	.42367	.90582	.46772	2.13801	.627030	.957040	.669991	.330009	56	
	5	.42394	.90569	.46808	2.13639	.627300	.956981	.670320	.329680	55	
.10	6	.42420	.90557	.46843	2.13477	.627570	.956921	.670649	.329351	54	.90
	7	.42446	.90545	.46879	2.13316	.627840	.956862	.670977	.329023	53	
	8	.42473	.90532	.46914	2.13154	.628109	.956803	.671306	.328694	52	
.15	9	.42499	.90520	.46950	2.12993	.628378	.956744	.671635	.328365	51	.85
	10	.42525	.90507	.46985	2.12832	.628647	.956684	.671963	.328037	50	
	11	.42552	.90495	.47021	2.12671	.628916	.956625	.672291	.327709	49	
.20	12	.42578	.90483	.47056	2.12511	.629185	.956566	.672619	.327381	48	.80
	13	.42604	.90470	.47092	2.12350	.629453	.956506	.672947	.327053	47	
	14	.42631	.90458	.47128	2.12190	.629721	.956447	.673274	.326726	46	
.25	15	.42657	.90446	.47163	2.12030	.629939	.956387	.673602	.326398	45	.75
	16	.42683	.90433	.47199	2.11871	.630257	.956327	.673929	.326071	44	
	17	.42709	.90421	.47234	2.11711	.630524	.956268	.674257	.325743	43	
.30	18	.42736	.90408	.47270	2.11552	.630792	.956208	.674584	.325416	42	.70
	19	.42762	.90396	.47305	2.11392	.631059	.956148	.674911	.325089	41	
	20	.42788	.90383	.47341	2.11233	.631326	.956089	.675237	.324763	40	
.35	21	.42815	.90371	.47377	2.11075	.631593	.956029	.675564	.324436	39	.65
	22	.42841	.90358	.47412	2.10916	.631859	.955969	.675890	.324110	38	
	23	.42867	.90346	.47448	2.10758	.632125	.955909	.676217	.323783	37	
.40	24	.42894	.90334	.47483	2.10600	.632392	.955849	.676543	.323457	36	.60
	25	.42920	.90321	.47519	2.10442	.632658	.955789	.676869	.323131	35	
	26	.42946	.90309	.47555	2.10284	.632923	.955729	.677194	.322806	34	
.45	27	.42972	.90296	.47590	2.10126	.633189	.955669	.677520	.322480	33	.55
	28	.42999	.90284	.47626	2.09969	.633454	.955609	.677846	.322154	32	
	29	.43025	.90271	.47662	2.09811	.633719	.955548	.678171	.321829	31	
.50	30	.43051	.90259	.47698	2.09654	.633984	.955488	.678496	.321504	30	.50
	31	.43077	.90246	.47733	2.09498	.634249	.955428	.678821	.321179	29	
	32	.43104	.90233	.47769	2.09341	.634514	.955368	.679146	.320854	28	
.55	33	.43130	.90221	.47805	2.09184	.634778	.955307	.679471	.320529	27	.45
	34	.43156	.90208	.47840	2.09028	.635042	.955247	.679795	.320205	26	
	35	.43182	.90196	.47876	2.08872	.635306	.955186	.680120	.319880	25	
.60	36	.43209	.90183	.47912	2.08716	.635570	.955126	.680444	.319556	24	.40
	37	.43235	.90171	.47948	2.08560	.635834	.955065	.680768	.319232	23	
	38	.43261	.90158	.47984	2.08405	.636097	.955005	.681092	.318908	22	
.65	39	.43287	.90146	.48019	2.08250	.636360	.954944	.681416	.318584	21	.35
	40	.43313	.90133	.48055	2.08094	.636623	.954883	.681740	.318260	20	
	41	.43340	.90120	.48091	2.07939	.636886	.954823	.682063	.317937	19	
.70	42	.43366	.90103	.48127	2.07785	.637148	.954762	.682387	.317613	18	.30
	43	.43392	.90095	.48163	2.07630	.637411	.954701	.682710	.317290	17	
	44	.43418	.90082	.48198	2.07476	.637673	.954640	.683033	.316967	16	
.75	45	.43445	.90070	.48234	2.07321	.637935	.954579	.683356	.316644	15	.25
	46	.43471	.90057	.48270	2.07167	.638197	.954518	.683679	.316321	14	
	47	.43497	.90045	.48306	2.07014	.638458	.954457	.684001	.315999	13	
.80	48	.43523	.90032	.48342	2.06860	.638720	.954396	.684324	.315676	12	.20
	49	.43549	.90019	.48378	2.06706	.638981	.954335	.684646	.315354	11	
	50	.43575	.90007	.48414	2.06553	.639242	.954274	.684968	.315032	10	
.85	51	.43602	.89994	.48450	2.06400	.639503	.954213	.685290	.314710	9	.15
	52	.43628	.89981	.48486	2.06247	.639764	.954152	.685612	.314388	8	
	53	.43654	.89968	.48521	2.06094	.640024	.954090	.685934	.314066	7	
.90	54	.43680	.89956	.48557	2.05942	.640284	.954029	.686255	.313745	6	.10
	55	.43706	.89943	.48593	2.05790	.640544	.953968	.686577	.313423	5	
	56	.43733	.89930	.48629	2.05637	.640804	.953906	.686898	.313102	4	
.95	57	.43759	.89918	.48665	2.05485	.641064	.953845	.687219	.312781	3	.05
	58	.43785	.89905	.48701	2.05333	.641324	.953783	.687540	.312460	2	
	59	.43811	.89892	.48737	2.05182	.641583	.953722	.687861	.312139	1	
1.00	60	.43837	.89879	.48773	2.05030	9.641842	9.953660	9.688182	10.311818	0	.00
Decimals	Minutes	Cos	Sin	Cot	Tan	Cos	Sin	Cot	Tan	Minutes	Decimals
		Natural Values				Common Logarithms					

Decimals	Minutes	Natural Values				Common Logarithms				Minutes	Decimals
		Sin	Cos	Tan	Cot	Sin	Cos	Tan	Cot		
.00	0	.43837	.89879	.48773	2.05030	9.641342	9.953660	9.688182	10.311818	60	1.00
	1	.43863	.89867	.48809	2.04879	.642101	.953599	.688502	.311498	59	
	2	.43889	.89854	.48845	2.04728	.642360	.953537	.688823	.311177	58	
.05	3	.43916	.89841	.48881	2.04577	.642618	.953475	.689143	.310857	57	.95
	4	.43942	.89828	.48917	2.04426	.642877	.953413	.689463	.310537	56	
	5	.43968	.89816	.48953	2.04276	.643135	.953352	.689783	.310217	55	
.10	6	.43994	.89803	.48989	2.04125	.643393	.953290	.690103	.309897	54	.90
	7	.44020	.89790	.49026	2.03975	.643650	.953228	.690423	.309577	53	
	8	.44046	.89777	.49062	2.03825	.643908	.953166	.690742	.309258	52	
.15	9	.44072	.89764	.49098	2.03675	.644165	.953104	.691062	.308938	51	.85
	10	.44098	.89752	.49134	2.03526	.644423	.953042	.691381	.308619	50	
	11	.44124	.89739	.49170	2.03376	.644680	.952980	.691700	.308300	49	
.20	12	.44151	.89726	.49206	2.03227	.644936	.952918	.692019	.307981	48	.80
	13	.44177	.89713	.49242	2.03078	.645193	.952855	.692338	.307662	47	
	14	.44203	.89700	.49278	2.02929	.645450	.952793	.692656	.307344	46	
.25	15	.44229	.89687	.49315	2.02780	.645706	.952731	.692975	.307025	45	.75
	16	.44255	.89674	.49351	2.02631	.645962	.952669	.693293	.306707	44	
	17	.44281	.89662	.49387	2.02483	.646218	.952606	.693612	.306388	43	
.30	18	.44307	.89649	.49423	2.02335	.646474	.952544	.693930	.306070	42	.70
	19	.44333	.89636	.49459	2.02187	.646729	.952481	.694248	.305752	41	
	20	.44359	.89623	.49495	2.02039	.646984	.952419	.694566	.305434	40	
.35	21	.44385	.89610	.49532	2.01891	.647240	.952356	.694883	.305117	39	.65
	22	.44411	.89597	.49568	2.01743	.647494	.952294	.695201	.304799	38	
	23	.44437	.89584	.49604	2.01596	.647749	.952231	.695518	.304482	37	
.40	24	.44464	.89571	.49640	2.01449	.648004	.952168	.695836	.304164	36	.60
	25	.44490	.89558	.49677	2.01302	.648258	.952106	.696153	.303847	35	
	26	.44516	.89545	.49713	2.01155	.648512	.952043	.696470	.303530	34	
.45	27	.44542	.89532	.49749	2.01008	.648766	.951980	.696787	.303213	33	.55
	28	.44568	.89519	.49786	2.00862	.649020	.951917	.697103	.302897	32	
	29	.44594	.89506	.49822	2.00715	.649274	.951854	.697420	.302580	31	
.50	30	.44620	.89493	.49858	2.00569	.649527	.951791	.697736	.302264	30	.50
	31	.44646	.89480	.49894	2.00423	.649781	.951723	.698053	.301947	29	
	32	.44672	.89467	.49931	2.00277	.650034	.951665	.698369	.301631	28	
.55	33	.44698	.89454	.49967	2.00131	.650287	.951602	.698685	.301315	27	.45
	34	.44724	.89441	.50004	1.99986	.650539	.951539	.699001	.300999	26	
	35	.44750	.89428	.50040	1.99841	.650792	.951476	.699316	.300684	25	
.60	36	.44776	.89415	.50076	1.99695	.651044	.951412	.699632	.300368	24	.40
	37	.44802	.89402	.50113	1.99550	.651297	.951349	.699947	.300053	23	
	38	.44828	.89389	.50149	1.99406	.651549	.951286	.700263	.299737	22	
.65	39	.44854	.89376	.50185	1.99261	.651800	.951222	.700578	.299422	21	.35
	40	.44880	.89363	.50222	1.99116	.652052	.951159	.700893	.299107	20	
	41	.44906	.89350	.50258	1.98972	.652304	.951096	.701208	.298792	19	
.70	42	.44932	.89337	.50295	1.98828	.652555	.951032	.701523	.298477	18	.30
	43	.44958	.89324	.50331	1.98684	.652806	.950968	.701837	.298163	17	
	44	.44984	.89311	.50368	1.98540	.653057	.950905	.702152	.297848	16	
.75	45	.45010	.89298	.50404	1.98396	.653308	.950841	.702466	.297534	15	.25
	46	.45036	.89285	.50441	1.98253	.653558	.950778	.702781	.297219	14	
	47	.45062	.89272	.50477	1.98110	.653808	.950714	.703095	.296905	13	
.80	48	.45088	.89259	.50514	1.97966	.654059	.950650	.703409	.296591	12	.20
	49	.45114	.89245	.50550	1.97823	.654309	.950586	.703722	.296278	11	
	50	.45140	.89232	.50587	1.97681	.654558	.950522	.704036	.295964	10	
.85	51	.45166	.89219	.50623	1.97538	.654808	.950458	.704350	.295650	9	.15
	52	.45192	.89206	.50660	1.97395	.655058	.950394	.704663	.295337	8	
	53	.45218	.89193	.50696	1.97253	.655307	.950330	.704976	.295024	7	
.90	54	.45243	.89180	.50733	1.97111	.655556	.950266	.705290	.294710	6	.10
	55	.45269	.89167	.50769	1.96969	.655805	.950202	.705603	.294397	5	
	56	.45295	.89153	.50806	1.96827	.656054	.950138	.705916	.294084	4	
.95	57	.45321	.89140	.50843	1.96685	.656302	.950074	.706228	.293772	3	.05
	57	.45347	.89127	.50879	1.96544	.656551	.950010	.706541	.293459	2	
	59	.45373	.89114	.50916	1.96402	.656799	.949945	.706854	.293146	1	
1.00	60	.45399	.89101	.50953	1.96261	9.657047	9.949881	9.707166	10.292834	0	.00

Decimals	Minutes	Cos	Sin	Cot	Tan	Cos	Sin	Cot	Tan	Minutes	Decimals
		Natural Values				Common Logarithms					

Decimals	Minutes	Natural Values				Common Logarithms				Minutes	Decimals
		Sin	Cos	Tan	Cot	Sin	Cos	Tan	Cot		
.00	0	.45399	.89101	.50953	1.96261	9.657047	9.949831	9.707166	10.292834	60	1.00
	1	.45425	.89087	.50989	1.96120	.657295	.949816	.707478	.292522	59	
	2	.45451	.89074	.51026	1.95979	.657542	.949752	.707790	.292210	58	
.05	3	.45477	.89061	.51063	1.95838	.657790	.949688	.708102	.291898	57	.95
	4	.45503	.89048	.51099	1.95698	.658037	.949623	.708414	.291586	56	
	5	.45529	.89035	.51136	1.95557	.658284	.949558	.708726	.291274	55	
.10	6	.45554	.89021	.51173	1.95417	.658531	.949494	.709037	.290963	54	.90
	7	.45580	.89008	.51209	1.95277	.658778	.949429	.709349	.290651	53	
	8	.45606	.88995	.51246	1.95137	.659025	.949364	.709660	.290340	52	
.15	9	.45632	.88981	.51283	1.94997	.659271	.949300	.709971	.290029	51	.85
	10	.45658	.88968	.51319	1.94858	.659517	.949235	.710282	.289718	50	
	11	.45684	.88955	.51356	1.94718	.659763	.949170	.710593	.289407	49	
.20	12	.45710	.88942	.51393	1.94579	.660009	.949105	.710904	.289096	48	.80
	13	.45736	.88928	.51430	1.94440	.660255	.949040	.711215	.288785	47	
	14	.45762	.88915	.51467	1.94301	.660501	.948975	.711525	.288475	46	
.25	15	.45787	.88902	.51503	1.94162	.660746	.948910	.711836	.288164	45	.75
	16	.45813	.88888	.51540	1.94023	.660991	.948845	.712146	.287854	44	
	17	.45839	.88875	.51577	1.93885	.661236	.948780	.712456	.287544	43	
.30	18	.45865	.88862	.51614	1.93746	.661481	.948715	.712766	.287234	42	.70
	19	.45891	.88848	.51651	1.93608	.661726	.948650	.713076	.286924	41	
	20	.45917	.88835	.51688	1.93470	.661970	.948584	.713386	.286614	40	
.35	21	.45942	.88822	.51724	1.93332	.662214	.948519	.713696	.286304	39	.65
	22	.45968	.88808	.51761	1.93195	.662459	.948454	.714005	.285995	38	
	23	.45994	.88795	.51798	1.93057	.662703	.948388	.714314	.285686	37	
.40	24	.46020	.88782	.51835	1.92920	.662946	.948323	.714624	.285376	36	.60
	25	.46046	.88768	.51872	1.92782	.663190	.948257	.714933	.285067	35	
	26	.46072	.88755	.51909	1.92645	.663433	.948192	.715242	.284758	34	
.45	27	.46097	.88741	.51946	1.92508	.663677	.948126	.715551	.284449	33	.55
	28	.46123	.88728	.51983	1.92371	.663920	.948060	.715860	.284140	32	
	29	.46149	.88715	.52020	1.92235	.664163	.947995	.716168	.283832	31	
.50	30	.46175	.88701	.52057	1.92098	.664406	.947929	.716477	.283523	30	.50
	31	.46201	.88688	.52094	1.91962	.664648	.947863	.716785	.283215	29	
	32	.46226	.88674	.52131	1.91826	.664891	.947797	.717093	.282907	28	
.55	33	.46252	.88661	.52168	1.91690	.665133	.947731	.717401	.282599	27	.45
	34	.46278	.88647	.52205	1.91554	.665375	.947665	.717709	.282291	26	
	35	.46304	.88634	.52242	1.91418	.665617	.947600	.718017	.281983	25	
.60	36	.46330	.88620	.52279	1.91282	.665859	.947533	.718325	.281675	24	.40
	37	.46355	.88607	.52316	1.91147	.666100	.947467	.718633	.281367	23	
	38	.46381	.88593	.52353	1.91012	.666342	.947401	.718940	.281060	22	
.65	39	.46407	.88580	.52390	1.90876	.666583	.947335	.719248	.280752	21	.35
	40	.46433	.88566	.52427	1.90741	.666824	.947269	.719555	.280445	20	
	41	.46458	.88553	.52464	1.90607	.667065	.947203	.719862	.280138	19	
.70	42	.46484	.88539	.52501	1.90472	.667305	.947136	.720169	.279831	18	.30
	43	.46510	.88526	.52538	1.90337	.667546	.947070	.720476	.279524	17	
	44	.46536	.88512	.52575	1.90203	.667786	.947004	.720783	.279217	16	
.75	45	.46561	.88499	.52613	1.90068	.668027	.946937	.721089	.278911	15	.25
	46	.46587	.88485	.52650	1.89935	.668267	.946871	.721396	.278604	14	
	47	.46613	.88472	.52687	1.89801	.668506	.946804	.721702	.278298	13	
.80	48	.46639	.88458	.52724	1.89667	.668746	.946738	.722009	.277991	12	.20
	49	.46664	.88445	.52761	1.89533	.668986	.946671	.722315	.277685	11	
	50	.46690	.88431	.52798	1.89400	.669225	.946604	.722621	.277379	10	
.85	51	.46716	.88417	.52836	1.89266	.669464	.946538	.722927	.277073	9	.15
	52	.46742	.88404	.52873	1.89133	.669703	.946471	.723232	.276768	8	
	53	.46767	.88390	.52910	1.89000	.669942	.946404	.723538	.276462	7	
.90	54	.46793	.88377	.52947	1.88867	.670181	.946337	.723844	.276156	6	.10
	55	.46819	.88363	.52985	1.88734	.670419	.946270	.724149	.275851	5	
	56	.46844	.88349	.53022	1.88602	.670658	.946203	.724454	.275546	4	
.95	57	.46870	.88336	.53059	1.88469	.670896	.946136	.724760	.275240	3	.05
	58	.46896	.88322	.53096	1.88337	.671134	.946069	.725065	.274935	2	
	59	.46921	.88308	.53134	1.88205	.671372	.946002	.725370	.274630	1	
1.00	60	.46947	.88295	.53171	1.88073	9.671609	9.945935	9.725674	10.274326	0	.00
Decimals	Minutes	Cos	Sin	Cot	Tan	Cos	Sin	Cot	Tan	Minutes	Decimals
		Natural Values				Common Logarithms					

62°

Decimals	Minutes	Natural Values				Common Logarithms				Minutes	Decimals
		Sin	Cos	Tan	Cot	Sin	Cos	Tan	Cot		
.00	0	.46947	.88295	.53171	1.88073	9.671609	9.945935	9.725674	10.274326	60	1.00
	1	.46973	.88281	.53208	1.87941	.671847	.945868	.725979	.274021	59	
	2	.46999	.88267	.53246	1.87809	.672084	.945800	.726284	.273716	58	
.05	3	.47024	.88254	.53283	1.87677	.672321	.945733	.726588	.273412	57	.95
	4	.47050	.88240	.53320	1.87546	.672558	.945666	.726892	.273108	56	
	5	.47076	.88226	.53358	1.87415	.672795	.945598	.727197	.272803	55	
.10	6	.47101	.88213	.53395	1.87283	.673032	.945531	.727501	.272499	54	.90
	7	.47127	.88199	.53432	1.87152	.673268	.945464	.727805	.272195	53	
	8	.47153	.88185	.53470	1.87021	.673505	.945396	.728109	.271891	52	
.15	9	.47178	.88172	.53507	1.86891	.673741	.945328	.728412	.271588	51	.85
	10	.47204	.88158	.53545	1.86760	.673977	.945261	.728716	.271284	50	
	11	.47229	.88144	.53582	1.86630	.674213	.945193	.729020	.270980	49	
.20	12	.47255	.88130	.53620	1.86499	.674448	.945125	.729323	.270677	48	.80
	13	.47281	.88117	.53657	1.86369	.674684	.945058	.729626	.270374	47	
	14	.47306	.88103	.53694	1.86239	.674919	.944990	.729929	.270071	46	
.25	15	.47332	.88089	.53732	1.86109	.675155	.944922	.730233	.269767	45	.75
	16	.47358	.88075	.53769	1.85979	.675390	.944854	.730535	.269465	44	
	17	.47383	.88062	.53807	1.85850	.675624	.944786	.730838	.269162	43	
.30	18	.47409	.88048	.53844	1.85720	.675859	.944718	.731141	.268859	42	.70
	19	.47434	.88034	.53882	1.85591	.676094	.944650	.731444	.268556	41	
	20	.47460	.88020	.53920	1.85462	.676328	.944582	.731746	.268254	40	
.35	21	.47486	.88006	.53957	1.85333	.676562	.944514	.732048	.267952	39	.65
	22	.47511	.87993	.53995	1.85204	.676796	.944446	.732351	.267649	38	
	23	.47537	.87979	.54032	1.85075	.677030	.944377	.732653	.267347	37	
.40	24	.47562	.87965	.54070	1.84946	.677264	.944309	.732955	.267045	36	.60
	25	.47588	.87951	.54107	1.84818	.677498	.944241	.733257	.266743	35	
	26	.47614	.87937	.54145	1.84689	.677731	.944172	.733558	.266442	34	
.45	27	.47639	.87923	.54183	1.84561	.677964	.944104	.733860	.266140	33	.55
	28	.47665	.87909	.54220	1.84433	.678197	.944036	.734162	.265838	32	
	29	.47690	.87896	.54258	1.84305	.678430	.943967	.734463	.265537	31	
.50	30	.47716	.87882	.54296	1.84177	.678663	.943899	.734764	.265236	30	.50
	31	.47741	.87868	.54333	1.84049	.678895	.943830	.735066	.264934	29	
	32	.47767	.87854	.54371	1.83922	.679128	.943761	.735367	.264633	28	
.55	33	.47793	.87840	.54409	1.83794	.679360	.943693	.735668	.264332	27	.45
	34	.47818	.87826	.54446	1.83667	.679592	.943624	.735969	.264031	26	
	35	.47844	.87812	.54484	1.83540	.679824	.943555	.736269	.263731	25	
.60	36	.47869	.87798	.54522	1.83413	.680056	.943486	.736570	.263430	24	.40
	37	.47895	.87784	.54560	1.83286	.680288	.943417	.736870	.263130	23	
	38	.47920	.87770	.54597	1.83159	.680519	.943348	.737171	.262829	22	
.65	39	.47946	.87756	.54635	1.83033	.680750	.943279	.737471	.262529	21	.35
	40	.47971	.87743	.54673	1.82906	.680982	.943210	.737771	.262229	20	
	41	.47997	.87729	.54711	1.82780	.681213	.943141	.738071	.261929	19	
.70	42	.48022	.87715	.54748	1.82654	.681443	.943072	.738371	.261629	18	.30
	43	.48048	.87701	.54786	1.82528	.681674	.943003	.738671	.261329	17	
	44	.48073	.87687	.54824	1.82402	.681905	.942934	.738971	.261029	16	
.75	45	.48099	.87673	.54862	1.82276	.682135	.942864	.739271	.260729	15	.25
	46	.48124	.87659	.54900	1.82150	.682365	.942795	.739570	.260430	14	
	47	.48150	.87645	.54938	1.82025	.682595	.942726	.739870	.260130	13	
.80	48	.48175	.87631	.54975	1.81899	.682825	.942656	.740169	.259831	12	.20
	49	.48201	.87617	.55013	1.81774	.683055	.942587	.740468	.259532	11	
	50	.48226	.87603	.55051	1.81649	.683284	.942517	.740767	.259233	10	
.85	51	.48252	.87589	.55089	1.81524	.683514	.942448	.741066	.258934	9	.15
	52	.48277	.87575	.55127	1.81399	.683743	.942378	.741365	.258635	8	
	53	.48303	.87561	.55165	1.81274	.683972	.942308	.741664	.258336	7	
.90	54	.48328	.87546	.55203	1.81150	.684201	.942239	.741962	.258038	6	.10
	55	.48354	.87532	.55241	1.81025	.684430	.942169	.742261	.257739	5	
	56	.48379	.87518	.55279	1.80901	.684658	.942099	.742559	.257441	4	
.95	57	.48405	.87504	.55317	1.80777	.684887	.942029	.742858	.257142	3	.05
	58	.48430	.87490	.55355	1.80653	.685115	.941959	.743156	.256844	2	
	59	.48456	.87476	.55393	1.80529	.685343	.941889	.743454	.256546	1	
1.00	60	.48481	.87462	.55431	1.80405	9.685571	9.941819	9.743752	10.256248	0	.00
Decimals	Minutes	Cos	Sin	Cot	Tan	Cos	Sin	Cot	Tan	Minutes	Decimals
		Natural Values				Common Logarithms					

Decimals	Minutes	Natural Values				Common Logarithms				Minutes	Decimals
		Sin	Cos	Tan	Cot	Sin	Cos	Tan	Cot		
.00	0	.48481	.87462	.55431	1.80405	9.685571	9.941819	9.743752	10.256248	60	1.00
	1	.48506	.87448	.55469	1.80281	.685799	.941749	.744050	.255950	59	
	2	.48532	.87434	.55507	1.80158	.686027	.941679	.744348	.255652	58	
.05	3	.48557	.87420	.55545	1.80034	.686254	.941609	.744645	.255355	57	.95
	4	.48583	.87406	.55583	1.79911	.686482	.941539	.744943	.255057	56	
	5	.48608	.87391	.55621	1.79788	.686709	.941469	.745240	.254760	55	
.10	6	.48634	.87377	.55659	1.79665	.686936	.941398	.745538	.254462	54	.90
	7	.48659	.87363	.55697	1.79542	.687163	.941328	.745835	.254165	53	
	8	.48684	.87349	.55736	1.79419	.687389	.941258	.746132	.253868	52	
.15	9	.48710	.37335	.55774	1.79296	.687616	.941187	.746429	.253571	51	.85
	10	.48735	.87321	.55812	1.79174	.687843	.941117	.746726	.253274	50	
	11	.48761	.87306	.55850	1.79051	.688069	.941046	.747023	.252977	49	
.20	12	.48786	.87292	.55888	1.78929	.688295	.940975	.747319	.252681	48	.80
	13	.48811	.87278	.55926	1.78807	.688521	.940905	.747616	.252384	47	
	14	.48837	.87264	.55964	1.78685	.688747	.940834	.747913	.252087	46	
.25	15	.48862	.87250	.56003	1.78563	.688972	.940763	.748209	.251791	45	.75
	16	.48888	.87235	.56041	1.78441	.689198	.940693	.748505	.251495	44	
	17	.48913	.87221	.56079	1.78319	.689423	.940622	.748801	.251199	43	
.30	18	.48938	.87207	.56117	1.78198	.689648	.940551	.749097	.250903	42	.70
	19	.48964	.87193	.56156	1.78077	.689873	.940480	.749393	.250607	41	
	20	.48989	.87178	.56194	1.77955	.690098	.940409	.749689	.250311	40	
.35	21	.49014	.87164	.56232	1.77834	.690323	.940338	.749985	.250015	39	.65
	22	.49040	.87150	.56270	1.77713	.690548	.940267	.750281	.249719	38	
	23	.49065	.87136	.56309	1.77592	.690772	.940196	.750576	.249424	37	
.40	24	.49090	.87121	.56347	1.77471	.690996	.940125	.750872	.249128	36	.60
	25	.49116	.87107	.56385	1.77351	.691220	.940054	.751167	.248833	35	
	26	.49141	.87093	.56424	1.77230	.691444	.939982	.751462	.248538	34	
.45	27	.49166	.87079	.56462	1.77110	.691668	.939911	.751757	.248243	33	.55
	28	.49192	.87064	.56501	1.76990	.691892	.939840	.752052	.247948	32	
	29	.49217	.87050	.56539	1.76869	.692115	.939768	.752347	.247653	31	
.50	30	.49242	.87036	.56577	1.76749	.692339	.939697	.752642	.247358	30	.50
	31	.49268	.87021	.56616	1.76629	.692562	.939625	.752937	.247063	29	
	32	.49293	.87007	.56654	1.76510	.692785	.939554	.753231	.246769	28	
.55	33	.49318	.86993	.56693	1.76390	.693008	.939482	.753526	.246474	27	.45
	34	.49344	.86978	.56731	1.76271	.693231	.939410	.753820	.246180	26	
	35	.49369	.86964	.56769	1.76151	.693453	.939339	.754115	.245885	25	
.60	36	.49394	.86949	.56808	1.76032	.693676	.939267	.754409	.245591	24	.40
	37	.49419	.86935	.56846	1.75913	.693898	.939195	.754703	.245297	23	
	38	.49445	.86921	.56885	1.75794	.694120	.939123	.754997	.245003	22	
.65	39	.49470	.86906	.56923	1.75675	.694342	.939052	.755291	.244709	21	.35
	40	.49495	.86892	.56962	1.75556	.694564	.938980	.755585	.244415	20	
	41	.49521	.86878	.57000	1.75437	.694786	.938908	.755878	.244122	19	
.70	42	.49546	.86863	.57039	1.75319	.695007	.938836	.756172	.243828	18	.30
	43	.49571	.86849	.57078	1.75200	.695229	.938763	.756465	.243535	17	
	44	.49596	.86834	.57116	1.75082	.695450	.938691	.756759	.243241	16	
.75	45	.49622	.86820	.57155	1.74964	.695671	.938619	.757052	.242948	15	.25
	46	.49647	.86805	.57193	1.74846	.695892	.938547	.757345	.242655	14	
	47	.49672	.86791	.57232	1.74728	.696113	.938475	.757638	.242362	13	
.80	48	.49697	.86777	.57271	1.74610	.696334	.938402	.757931	.242069	12	.20
	49	.49723	.86762	.57309	1.74492	.696554	.938330	.758224	.241776	11	
	50	.49748	.86748	.57348	1.74375	.696775	.938258	.758517	.241483	10	
.85	51	.49773	.86733	.57386	1.74257	.696995	.938185	.758810	.241190	9	.15
	52	.49798	.86719	.57425	1.74140	.697215	.938113	.759102	.240898	8	
	53	.49824	.86704	.57464	1.74022	.697435	.938040	.759395	.240605	7	
.90	54	.49849	.86690	.57503	1.73905	.697654	.937967	.759687	.240313	6	.10
	55	.49874	.86675	.57541	1.73788	.697874	.937895	.759979	.240021	5	
	56	.49899	.86661	.57580	1.73671	.698094	.937822	.760272	.239728	4	
.95	57	.49924	.86646	.57619	1.73555	.698313	.937749	.760564	.239436	3	.05
	58	.49950	.86632	.57657	1.73438	.698532	.937676	.760856	.239144	2	
	59	.49975	.86617	.57696	1.73321	.698751	.937604	.761148	.238852	1	
1.00	60	.50000	.86603	.57735	1.73205	9.698970	9.937531	9.761439	10.238561	0	.00
Decimals	Minutes	Cos	Sin	Cot	Tan	Cos	Sin	Cot	Tan	Minutes	Decimals
		Natural Values				Common Logarithms					

Decimals	Minutes	Natural Values				Common Logarithms				Minutes	Decimals
		Sin	Cos	Tan	Cot	Sin	Cos	Tan	Cot		
.00	0	.50000	.86603	.57735	1.73205	9.698970	9.937531	9.761439	10.238561	60	1.00
	1	.50025	.86588	.57774	1.73089	.699189	.937458	.761731	.238269	59	
	2	.50050	.86573	.57813	1.72973	.699407	.937385	.762023	.237977	58	
.05	3	.50076	.86559	.57851	1.72857	.699626	.937312	.762314	.237686	57	.95
	4	.50101	.86544	.57890	1.72741	.699844	.937238	.762606	.237394	56	
	5	.50125	.86530	.57929	1.72625	.700062	.937165	.762897	.237103	55	
.10	6	.50151	.86515	.57968	1.72509	.700280	.937092	.763188	.236812	54	.90
	7	.50176	.86501	.58007	1.72393	.700498	.937019	.763479	.236521	53	
	8	.50201	.86486	.58046	1.72278	.700716	.936946	.763770	.236230	52	
.15	9	.50227	.86471	.58085	1.72163	.700933	.936872	.764061	.235939	51	.85
	10	.50252	.86457	.58124	1.72047	.701151	.936799	.764352	.235648	50	
	11	.50277	.86442	.58162	1.71932	.701368	.936725	.764643	.235357	49	
.20	12	.50302	.86427	.58201	1.71817	.701585	.936652	.764933	.235067	48	.80
	13	.50327	.86413	.58240	1.71702	.701802	.936578	.765224	.234776	47	
	14	.50352	.86398	.58279	1.71588	.702019	.936505	.765514	.234486	46	
.25	15	.50377	.86384	.58318	1.71473	.702236	.936431	.765805	.234195	45	.75
	16	.50403	.86369	.58357	1.71358	.702452	.936357	.766095	.233905	44	
	17	.50428	.86354	.58396	1.71244	.702669	.936284	.766385	.233615	43	
.30	18	.50453	.86340	.58435	1.71129	.702885	.936210	.766675	.233325	42	.70
	19	.50478	.86325	.58474	1.71015	.703101	.936136	.766965	.233035	41	
	20	.50503	.86310	.58513	1.70901	.703317	.936062	.767255	.232745	40	
.35	21	.50528	.86295	.58552	1.70787	.703533	.935988	.767545	.232455	39	.65
	22	.50553	.86281	.58591	1.70673	.703749	.935914	.767834	.232166	38	
	23	.50578	.86266	.58631	1.70560	.703964	.935840	.768124	.231876	37	
.40	24	.50603	.86251	.58670	1.70446	.704179	.935766	.768414	.231586	36	.60
	25	.50628	.86237	.58709	1.70332	.704395	.935692	.768703	.231297	35	
	26	.50654	.86222	.58748	1.70219	.704610	.935618	.768992	.231008	34	
.45	27	.50679	.86207	.58787	1.70106	.704825	.935543	.769281	.230719	33	.55
	28	.50704	.86192	.58826	1.69992	.705040	.935469	.769571	.230429	32	
	29	.50729	.86178	.58865	1.69879	.705254	.935395	.769860	.230140	31	
.50	30	.50754	.86163	.58905	1.69766	.705469	.935320	.770148	.229852	30	.50
	31	.50779	.86148	.58944	1.69653	.705683	.935246	.770437	.229563	29	
	32	.50804	.86133	.58983	1.69541	.705898	.935171	.770726	.229274	28	
.55	33	.50829	.86119	.59022	1.69428	.706112	.935097	.771015	.228985	27	.45
	34	.50854	.86104	.59061	1.69316	.706326	.935022	.771303	.228697	26	
	35	.50879	.86089	.59101	1.69203	.706539	.934948	.771592	.228408	25	
.60	36	.50904	.86074	.59140	1.69091	.706753	.934873	.771880	.228120	24	.40
	37	.50929	.86059	.59179	1.68979	.706967	.934798	.772168	.227832	23	
	38	.50954	.86045	.59218	1.68866	.707180	.934723	.772457	.227543	22	
.65	39	.50979	.86030	.59258	1.68754	.707393	.934649	.772745	.227255	21	.35
	40	.51004	.86015	.59297	1.68643	.707606	.934574	.773033	.226967	20	
	41	.51029	.86000	.59336	1.68531	.707819	.934499	.773321	.226679	19	
.70	42	.51054	.85985	.59376	1.68419	.708032	.934424	.773608	.226392	18	.30
	43	.51079	.85970	.59415	1.68308	.708245	.934349	.773896	.226104	17	
	44	.51104	.85956	.59454	1.68196	.708458	.934274	.774184	.225816	16	
.75	45	.51129	.85941	.59494	1.68085	.708670	.934199	.774471	.225529	15	.25
	46	.51154	.85926	.59533	1.67974	.708882	.934123	.774759	.225241	14	
	47	.51179	.85911	.59573	1.67863	.709094	.934048	.775046	.224954	13	
.80	48	.51204	.85896	.59612	1.67752	.709306	.933973	.775333	.224667	12	.20
	49	.51229	.85881	.59651	1.67641	.709518	.933898	.775621	.224379	11	
	50	.51254	.85866	.59691	1.67530	.709730	.933822	.775908	.224092	10	
.85	51	.51279	.85851	.59730	1.67419	.709941	.933747	.776195	.223805	9	.15
	52	.51304	.85836	.59770	1.67309	.710153	.933671	.776482	.223518	8	
	53	.51329	.85821	.59809	1.67198	.710364	.933596	.776768	.223232	7	
.90	54	.51354	.85806	.59849	1.67088	.710575	.933520	.777055	.222945	6	.10
	55	.51379	.85792	.59888	1.66978	.710786	.933445	.777342	.222658	5	
	56	.51404	.85777	.59928	1.66867	.710997	.933369	.777628	.222372	4	
.95	57	.51429	.85762	.59967	1.66757	.711208	.933293	.777915	.222085	3	.05
	58	.51454	.85747	.60007	1.66647	.711419	.933217	.778201	.221799	2	
	59	.51479	.85732	.60046	1.66538	.711629	.933141	.778488	.221512	1	
1.00	60	.51504	.85717	.60086	1.66428	9.711839	9.933066	9.778774	10.221226	0	.00
Decimals	Minutes	Cos	Sin	Cot	Tan	Cos	Sin	Cot	Tan	Minutes	Decimals
		Natural Values				Common Logarithms					

Decimals	Minutes	Natural Values				Common Logarithms				Minutes	Decimals
		Sin	Cos	Tan	Cot	Sin	Cos	Tan	Cot		
.00	0	.51504	.85717	.60086	1.66428	9.711839	9.933066	9.778774	10.221226	60	1.00
	1	.51529	.85702	.60126	1.66318	.712050	.932990	.779060	.220940	59	
	2	.51554	.85687	.60165	1.66209	.712260	.932914	.779346	.220654	58	
.05	3	.51579	.85672	.60205	1.66099	.712469	.932838	.779632	.220368	57	.95
	4	.51604	.85657	.60245	1.65990	.712679	.932762	.779918	.220082	56	
	5	.51628	.85642	.60284	1.65881	.712889	.932685	.780203	.219797	55	
.10	6	.51653	.85627	.60324	1.65772	.713098	.932609	.780489	.219511	54	.90
	7	.51678	.85612	.60364	1.65663	.713308	.932533	.780775	.219225	53	
	8	.51703	.85597	.60403	1.65554	.713517	.932457	.781060	.218940	52	
.15	9	.51728	.85582	.60443	1.65445	.713726	.932380	.781346	.218654	51	.85
	10	.51753	.85567	.60483	1.65337	.713935	.932304	.781631	.218369	50	
	11	.51778	.85551	.60522	1.65228	.714144	.932228	.781916	.218084	49	
.20	12	.51803	.85536	.60562	1.65120	.714352	.932151	.782201	.217799	48	.80
	13	.51828	.85521	.60602	1.65011	.714561	.932075	.782486	.217514	47	
	14	.51852	.85506	.60642	1.64903	.714769	.931998	.782771	.217229	46	
.25	15	.51877	.85491	.60681	1.64795	.714978	.931921	.783056	.216944	45	.75
	16	.51902	.85476	.60721	1.64687	.715186	.931845	.783341	.216659	44	
	17	.51927	.85461	.60761	1.64579	.715394	.931768	.783626	.216374	43	
.30	18	.51952	.85446	.60801	1.64471	.715602	.931691	.783910	.216090	42	.70
	19	.51977	.85431	.60841	1.64363	.715809	.931614	.784195	.215805	41	
	20	.52002	.85416	.60881	1.64256	.716017	.931537	.784479	.215521	40	
.35	21	.52026	.85401	.60921	1.64148	.716224	.931460	.784764	.215236	39	.65
	22	.52051	.85385	.60960	1.64041	.716432	.931383	.785048	.214952	38	
	23	.52076	.85370	.61000	1.63934	.716639	.931306	.785332	.214668	37	
.40	24	.52101	.85355	.61040	1.63826	.716846	.931229	.785616	.214384	36	.60
	25	.52126	.85340	.61080	1.63719	.717053	.931152	.785900	.214100	35	
	26	.52151	.85325	.61120	1.63612	.717259	.931075	.786184	.213816	34	
.45	27	.52175	.85310	.61160	1.63505	.717466	.930998	.786468	.213532	33	.55
	28	.52200	.85294	.61200	1.63398	.717673	.930921	.786752	.213248	32	
	29	.52225	.85279	.61240	1.63292	.717879	.930843	.787036	.212964	31	
.50	30	.52250	.85264	.61280	1.63185	.718085	.930766	.787319	.212681	30	.50
	31	.52275	.85249	.61320	1.63079	.718291	.930688	.787603	.212397	29	
	32	.52299	.85234	.61360	1.62972	.718497	.930611	.787886	.212114	28	
.55	33	.52324	.85218	.61400	1.62866	.718703	.930533	.788170	.211830	27	.45
	34	.52349	.85203	.61440	1.62760	.718909	.930456	.788453	.211547	26	
	35	.52374	.85188	.61480	1.62654	.719114	.930378	.788736	.211264	25	
.60	36	.52399	.85173	.61520	1.62548	.719320	.930300	.789019	.210981	24	.40
	37	.52423	.85157	.61561	1.62442	.719525	.930223	.789302	.210698	23	
	38	.52448	.85142	.61601	1.62336	.719730	.930145	.789585	.210415	22	
.65	39	.52473	.85127	.61641	1.62230	.719935	.930067	.789868	.210132	21	.35
	40	.52498	.85112	.61681	1.62125	.720140	.929989	.790151	.209849	20	
	41	.52522	.85096	.61721	1.62019	.720345	.929911	.790434	.209566	19	
.70	42	.52547	.85081	.61761	1.61914	.720549	.929833	.790716	.209284	18	.30
	43	.52572	.85066	.61801	1.61808	.720754	.929755	.790999	.209001	17	
	44	.52597	.85051	.61842	1.61703	.720958	.929677	.791281	.208719	16	
.75	45	.52621	.85035	.61882	1.61598	.721162	.929599	.791563	.208437	15	.25
	46	.52646	.85020	.61922	1.61493	.721366	.929521	.791846	.208154	14	
	47	.52671	.85005	.61962	1.61388	.721570	.929442	.792128	.207872	13	
.80	48	.52696	.84989	.62003	1.61283	.721774	.929364	.792410	.207590	12	.20
	49	.52720	.84974	.62043	1.61179	.721978	.929286	.792692	.207308	11	
	50	.52745	.84959	.62083	1.61074	.722181	.929207	.792974	.207026	10	
.85	51	.52770	.84943	.62124	1.60970	.722385	.929129	.793256	.206744	9	.15
	52	.52794	.84928	.62164	1.60865	.722588	.929050	.793538	.206462	8	
	53	.52819	.84913	.62204	1.60761	.722791	.928972	.793819	.206181	7	
.90	54	.52844	.84897	.62245	1.60657	.722994	.928893	.794101	.205899	6	.10
	55	.52869	.84882	.62285	1.60553	.723197	.928815	.794383	.205617	5	
	56	.52893	.84866	.62325	1.60449	.723400	.928736	.794664	.205336	4	'
.95	57	.52918	.84851	.62365	1.60345	.723603	.928657	.794946	.205054	3	.05
	58	.52943	.84836	.62406	1.60241	.723805	.928578	.795227	.204773	2	
	59	.52967	.84820	.62446	1.60137	.724007	.928499	.795508	.204492	1	
1.00	60	.52992	.84805	.62487	1.60033	9.724210	9.928420	9.795789	10.204211	0	.00
Decimals	Minutes	Cos	Sin	Cot	Tan	Cos	Sin	Cot	Tan	Minutes	Decimals
		Natural Values				Common Logarithms					

Decimals	Minutes	Natural Values				Common Logarithms				Minutes	Decimals
		Sin	Cos	Tan	Cot	Sin	Cos	Tan	Cot		
.00	0	.52992	.84805	.62487	1.60033	9.724210	9.928420	9.795789	10.204211	60	1.00
	1	.53017	.84789	.62527	1.59930	.724412	.928342	.796070	.203930	59	
	2	.53041	.84774	.62568	1.59826	.724614	.928263	.796351	.203649	58	
.05	3	.53066	.84759	.62608	1.59723	.724816	.928183	.796632	.203368	57	.95
	4	.53091	.84743	.62649	1.59620	.725017	.928104	.796913	.203087	56	
	5	.53115	.84728	.62689	1.59517	.725219	.928025	.797194	.202806	55	
.10	6	.53140	.84712	.62730	1.59414	.725420	.927946	.797474	.202526	54	.90
	7	.53164	.84697	.62770	1.59311	.725622	.927867	.797755	.202245	53	
	8	.53189	.84681	.62811	1.59208	.725823	.927787	.798036	.201964	52	
.15	9	.53214	.84666	.62852	1.59105	.726024	.927708	.798316	.201684	51	.85
	10	.53238	.84650	.62892	1.59002	.726225	.927629	.798596	.201404	50	
	11	.53263	.84635	.62933	1.58900	.726426	.927549	.798877	.201123	49	
.20	12	.53288	.84619	.62973	1.58797	.726626	.927470	.799157	.200843	48	.80
	13	.53312	.84604	.63014	1.58695	.726827	.927390	.799437	.200563	47	
	14	.53337	.84588	.63055	1.58593	.727027	.927310	.799717	.200283	46	
.25	15	.53361	.84573	.63095	1.58490	.727228	.927231	.799997	.200003	45	.75
	16	.53386	.84557	.63136	1.58388	.727428	.927151	.800277	.199723	44	
	17	.53411	.84542	.63177	1.58286	.727628	.927071	.800557	.199443	43	
.30	18	.53435	.84526	.63217	1.58184	.727828	.926991	.800836	.199164	42	.70
	19	.53460	.84511	.63258	1.58083	.728027	.926911	.801116	.198884	41	
	20	.53484	.84495	.63299	1.57981	.728227	.926831	.801396	.198604	40	
.35	21	.53509	.84480	.63340	1.57879	.728427	.926751	.801675	.198325	39	.65
	22	.53534	.84464	.63380	1.57778	.728626	.926671	.801955	.198045	38	
	23	.53558	.84448	.63421	1.57676	.728825	.926591	.802234	.197766	37	
.40	24	.53583	.84433	.63462	1.57575	.729024	.926511	.802513	.197487	36	.60
	25	.53607	.84417	.63503	1.57474	.729223	.926431	.802792	.197208	35	
	26	.53632	.84402	.63544	1.57372	.729422	.926351	.803072	.196928	34	
.45	27	.53656	.84386	.63584	1.57271	.729621	.926270	.803351	.196649	33	.55
	28	.53681	.84370	.63625	1.57170	.729820	.926190	.803630	.196370	32	
	29	.53705	.84355	.63666	1.57069	.730018	.926110	.803909	.196091	31	
.50	30	.53730	.84339	.63707	1.56969	.730217	.926029	.804187	.195813	30	.50
	31	.53754	.84324	.63748	1.56868	.730415	.925949	.804466	.195534	29	
	32	.53779	.84308	.63789	1.56767	.730613	.925868	.804745	.195255	28	
.55	33	.53804	.84292	.63830	1.56667	.730811	.925788	.805023	.194977	27	.45
	34	.53828	.84277	.63871	1.56566	.731009	.925707	.805302	.194698	26	
	35	.53853	.84261	.63912	1.56466	.731206	.925626	.805580	.194420	25	
.60	36	.53877	.84245	.63953	1.56366	.731404	.925545	.805859	.194141	24	.40
	37	.53902	.84230	.63994	1.56265	.731602	.925465	.806137	.193863	23	
	38	.53926	.84214	.64035	1.56165	.731799	.925384	.806415	.193585	22	
.65	39	.53951	.84198	.64076	1.56065	.731996	.925303	.806693	.193307	21	.35
	40	.53975	.84182	.64117	1.55966	.732193	.925222	.806971	.193029	20	
	41	.54000	.84167	.64158	1.55866	.732390	.925141	.807249	.192751	19	
.70	42	.54024	.84151	.64199	1.55766	.732587	.925060	.807527	.192473	18	.30
	43	.54049	.84135	.64240	1.55666	.732784	.924979	.807805	.192195	17	
	44	.54073	.84120	.64281	1.55567	.732980	.924897	.808083	.191917	16	
.75	45	.54097	.84104	.64322	1.55467	.733177	.924816	.808361	.191639	15	.25
	46	.54122	.84088	.64363	1.55368	.733373	.924735	.808638	.191362	14	
	47	.54146	.84072	.64404	1.55269	.733569	.924654	.808916	.191084	13	
.80	48	.54171	.84057	.64446	1.55170	.733765	.924572	.809193	.190807	12	.20
	49	.54195	.84041	.64487	1.55071	.733961	.924491	.809471	.190529	11	
	50	.54220	.84025	.64528	1.54972	.734157	.924409	.809748	.190252	10	
.85	51	.54244	.84009	.64569	1.54873	.734353	.924328	.810025	.189975	9	.15
	52	.54269	.83994	.64610	1.54774	.734549	.924246	.810302	.189698	8	
	53	.54293	.83978	.64652	1.54675	.734744	.924164	.810580	.189420	7	
.90	54	.54317	.83962	.64693	1.54576	.734939	.924083	.810857	.189143	6	.10
	55	.54342	.83946	.64734	1.54478	.735135	.924001	.811134	.188866	5	
	56	.54366	.83930	.64775	1.54379	.735330	.923919	.811410	.188590	4	
.95	57	.54391	.83915	.64817	1.54281	.735525	.923837	.811687	.188313	3	.05
	58	.54415	.83899	.64858	1.54183	.735719	.923755	.811964	.188036	2	
	59	.54440	.83883	.64899	1.54085	.735914	.923673	.812241	.187759	1	
1.00	60	.54464	.83867	.64941	1.53986	9.736109	9.923591	9.812517	10.187483	0	.00
Decimals	Minutes	Cos	Sin	Cot	Tan	Cos	Sin	Cot	Tan	Minutes	Decimals
		Natural Values				Common Logarithms					

Decimals	Minutes	Natural Values				Common Logarithms				Minutes	Decimals
		Sin	Cos	Tan	Cot	Sin	Cos	Tan	Cot		
.00	0	.54464	.83867	.64941	1.53986	9.736109	9.923591	9.812517	10.187483	60	1.00
	1	.54488	.83851	.64982	1.53888	.736303	.923509	.812794	.187206	59	
	2	.54513	.83835	.65024	1.53791	.736498	.923427	.813070	.186930	58	
.05	3	.54537	.83819	.65065	1.53693	.736692	.923345	.813347	.186653	57	.95
	4	.54561	.83804	.65106	1.53595	.736886	.923263	.813623	.186377	56	
	5	.54586	.83788	.65148	1.53497	.737080	.923181	.813899	.186101	55	
.10	6	.54610	.83772	.65189	1.53400	.737274	.923098	.814176	.185824	54	.90
	7	.54635	.83756	.65231	1.53302	.737467	.923016	.814452	.185548	53	
	8	.54659	.83740	.65272	1.53205	.737661	.922933	.814728	.185272	52	
.15	9	.54683	.83724	.65314	1.53107	.737855	.922851	.815004	.184996	51	.85
	10	.54708	.83708	.65355	1.53010	.738048	.922768	.815280	.184720	50	
	11	.54732	.83692	.65397	1.52913	.738241	.922686	.815555	.184445	49	
.20	12	.54756	.83676	.65438	1.52816	.738434	.922603	.815831	.184169	48	.80
	13	.54781	.83660	.65480	1.52719	.738627	.922520	.816107	.183893	47	
	14	.54805	.83645	.65521	1.52622	.738820	.922438	.816382	.183618	46	
.25	15	.54829	.83629	.65563	1.52525	.739013	.922355	.816658	.183342	45	.75
	16	.54854	.83613	.65604	1.52429	.739206	.922272	.816933	.183067	44	
	17	.54878	.83597	.65646	1.52332	.739398	.922189	.817209	.182791	43	
.30	18	.54902	.83581	.65688	1.52235	.739590	.922106	.817484	.182516	42	.70
	19	.54927	.83565	.65729	1.52139	.739783	.922023	.817759	.182241	41	
	20	.54951	.83549	.65771	1.52043	.739975	.921940	.818035	.181965	40	
.35	21	.54975	.83533	.65813	1.51946	.740167	.921857	.818319	.181693	39	.65
	22	.54999	.83517	.65854	1.51850	.740359	.921774	.818585	.181415	38	
	23	.55024	.83501	.65896	1.51754	.740550	.921691	.818860	.181140	37	
.40	24	.55048	.83485	.65938	1.51658	.740742	.921607	.819135	.180865	36	.60
	25	.55072	.83469	.65980	1.51562	.740934	.921524	.819410	.180590	35	
	26	.55097	.83453	.66021	1.51466	.741125	.921441	.819684	.180316	34	
.45	27	.55121	.83437	.66063	1.51370	.741316	.921357	.819959	.180041	33	.55
	28	.55145	.83421	.66105	1.51275	.741508	.921274	.820234	.179766	32	
	29	.55169	.83405	.66147	1.51179	.741699	.921190	.820508	.179492	31	
.50	30	.55194	.83389	.66189	1.51084	.741889	.921107	.820783	.179217	30	.50
	31	.55218	.83373	.66230	1.50988	.742080	.921023	.821057	.178943	29	
	32	.55242	.83356	.66272	1.50893	.742271	.920939	.821332	.178668	28	
.55	33	.55266	.83340	.66314	1.50797	.742462	.920856	.821606	.178394	27	.45
	34	.55291	.83324	.66356	1.50702	.742652	.920772	.821880	.178120	26	
	35	.55315	.83308	.66398	1.50607	.742842	.920688	.822154	.177846	25	
.60	36	.55339	.83292	.66440	1.50512	.743033	.920504	.822429	.177571	24	.40
	37	.55363	.83276	.66482	1.50417	.743223	.920520	.822703	.177297	23	
	38	.55388	.83260	.66524	1.50322	.743413	.920436	.822977	.177023	22	
.65	39	.55412	.83244	.66566	1.50223	.743602	.920352	.823251	.176749	21	.35
	40	.55436	.83228	.66608	1.50133	.743792	.920268	.823524	.176476	20	
	41	.55460	.83212	.66650	1.50038	.743982	.920184	.823798	.176202	19	
.70	42	.55484	.83195	.66692	1.49944	.744171	.920099	.824072	.175928	18	.30
	43	.55509	.83179	.66734	1.49849	.744361	.920015	.824345	.175655	17	
	44	.55533	.83163	.66776	1.49755	.744550	.919931	.824619	.175381	16	
.75	45	.55557	.83147	.66818	1.49661	.744739	.919845	.824893	.175107	15	.25
	46	.55581	.83131	.66860	1.49566	.744928	.919762	.825166	.174834	14	
	47	.55605	.83115	.66902	1.49472	.745117	.919677	.825439	.174561	13	
.80	48	.55630	.83098	.66944	1.49378	.745306	.919593	.825713	.174287	12	.20
	49	.55654	.83082	.66986	1.49284	.745494	.919508	.825986	.174014	11	
	50	.55678	.83066	.67028	1.49190	.745683	.919424	.826259	.173741	10	
.85	51	.55702	.83050	.67071	1.49097	.745871	.919339	.826532	.173468	9	.15
	52	.55726	.83034	.67113	1.49003	.746060	.919254	.826805	.173195	8	
	53	.55750	.83017	.67155	1.48909	.746248	.919169	.827078	.172922	7	
.90	54	.55775	.83001	.67197	1.48816	.746436	.919085	.827351	.172649	6	.10
	55	.55799	.82985	.67239	1.48722	.746624	.919000	.827624	.172376	5	
	56	.55823	.82969	.67282	1.48629	.746812	.918915	.827897	.172103	4	
.95	57	.55847	.82953	.67324	1.48536	.746999	.918830	.828170	.171830	3	.05
	58	.55871	.82936	.67366	1.48442	.747187	.918745	.828442	.171558	2	
	59	.55895	.82920	.67409	1.48349	.747374	.918659	.828715	.171285	1	
1.00	60	.55919	.82904	.67451	1.48256	9.747562	9.918574	9.828987	10.171013	0	.00

Decimals	Minutes	Cos	Sin	Cot	Tan	Cos	Sin	Cot	Tan	Minutes	Decimals
		Natural Values				Common Logarithms					

Decimals	Minutes	Natural Values				Common Logarithms				Minutes	Decimals
		Sin	Cos	Tan	Cot	Sin	Cos	Tan	Cot		
.00	0	.55919	.82904	.67451	1.48256	9.747562	9.918574	9.828987	10.171013	60	1.00
	1	.55943	.82887	.67493	1.48163	.747749	.918489	.829260	.170740	59	
	2	.55968	.82871	.67536	1.48070	.747936	.918404	.829532	.170468	58	
.05	3	.55992	.82855	.67578	1.47977	.748123	.918318	.829805	.170195	57	.95
	4	.56016	.82839	.67620	1.47885	.748310	.918233	.830077	.169923	56	
	5	.56040	.82822	.67663	1.47792	.748497	.918147	.830349	.169651	55	
.10	6	.56064	.82806	.67705	1.47699	.748683	.918062	.830621	.169379	54	.90
	7	.56088	.82790	.67748	1.47607	.748870	.917976	.830893	.169107	53	
	8	.56112	.82773	.67790	1.47514	.749056	.917891	.831165	.168835	52	
.15	9	.56136	.82757	.67832	1.47422	.749243	.917805	.831437	.168563	51	.85
	10	.56160	.82741	.67875	1.47330	.749429	.917719	.831709	.168291	50	
	11	.56184	.82724	.67917	1.47238	.749615	.917634	.831981	.168019	49	
.20	12	.56208	.82708	.67960	1.47146	.749801	.917548	.832253	.167747	48	.80
	13	.56232	.82692	.68002	1.47053	.749987	.917462	.832525	.167475	47	
	14	.56256	.82675	.68045	1.46962	.750172	.917376	.832796	.167204	46	
.25	15	.56280	.82659	.68088	1.46870	.750358	.917290	.833068	.166932	45	.75
	16	.56305	.82643	.68130	1.46778	.750543	.917204	.833339	.166661	44	
	17	.56329	.82626	.68173	1.46686	.750729	.917118	.833611	.166389	43	
.30	18	.56353	.82610	.68215	1.46595	.750914	.917032	.833882	.166118	42	.70
	19	.56377	.82593	.68258	1.46503	.751099	.916946	.834154	.165846	41	
	20	.56401	.82577	.68301	1.46411	.751284	.916859	.834425	.165575	40	
.35	21	.56425	.82561	.68343	1.46320	.751469	.916773	.834696	.165304	39	.65
	22	.56449	.82544	.68386	1.46229	.751654	.916687	.834967	.165033	38	
	23	.56473	.82528	.68429	1.46137	.751839	.916600	.835238	.164762	37	
.40	24	.56497	.82511	.68471	1.46046	.752023	.916514	.835509	.164491	36	.60
	25	.56521	.82495	.68514	1.45955	.752208	.916427	.835780	.164220	35	
	26	.56545	.82478	.68557	1.45864	.752392	.916341	.836051	.163949	34	
.45	27	.56569	.82462	.68600	1.45773	.752576	.916254	.836322	.163678	33	.55
	28	.56593	.82446	.68642	1.45682	.752760	.916167	.836593	.163407	32	
	29	.56617	.82429	.68685	1.45592	.752944	.916081	.836864	.163136	31	
.50	30	.56641	.82413	.68728	1.45501	.753128	.915994	.837134	.162866	30	.50
	31	.56665	.82396	.68771	1.45410	.753312	.915907	.837405	.162595	29	
	32	.56689	.82380	.68814	1.45320	.753495	.915820	.837675	.162325	28	
.55	33	.56713	.82363	.68857	1.45229	.753679	.915733	.837946	.162054	27	.45
	34	.56736	.82347	.68900	1.45139	.753862	.915646	.838216	.161784	26	
	35	.56760	.82330	.68942	1.45049	.754046	.915559	.838487	.161513	25	
.60	36	.56784	.82314	.68985	1.44958	.754229	.915472	.838757	.161243	24	.40
	37	.56808	.82297	.69028	1.44868	.754412	.915385	.839027	.160973	23	
	38	.56832	.82281	.69071	1.44778	.754595	.915297	.839297	.160703	22	
.65	39	.56856	.82264	.69114	1.44688	.754778	.915210	.839568	.160432	21	.35
	40	.56880	.82248	.69157	1.44598	.754960	.915123	.839838	.160162	20	
	41	.56904	.82231	.69200	1.44508	.755143	.915035	.840108	.159892	19	
.70	42	.56928	.82214	.69243	1.44418	.755326	.914948	.840378	.159622	18	.30
	43	.56952	.82198	.69286	1.44329	.755508	.914860	.840648	.159352	17	
	44	.56976	.82181	.69329	1.44239	.755690	.914773	.840917	.159083	16	
.75	45	.57000	.82165	.69372	1.44149	.755872	.914685	.841187	.158813	15	.25
	46	.57024	.82148	.69416	1.44060	.756054	.914598	.841457	.158543	14	
	47	.57047	.82132	.69459	1.43970	.756236	.914510	.841727	.158273	13	
.80	48	.57071	.82115	.69502	1.43881	.756413	.914422	.841996	.158004	12	.20
	49	.57095	.82098	.69545	1.43792	.756600	.914334	.842266	.157734	11	
	50	.57119	.82082	.69588	1.43703	.756782	.914246	.842535	.157465	10	
.85	51	.57143	.82065	.69631	1.43614	.756963	.914158	.842805	.157195	9	.15
	52	.57167	.82048	.69675	1.43525	.757144	.914070	.843074	.156926	8	
	53	.57191	.82032	.69718	1.43436	.757326	.913982	.843343	.156657	7	
.90	54	.57215	.82015	.69761	1.43347	.757507	.913894	.843612	.156388	6	.10
	55	.57238	.81999	.69804	1.43258	.757688	.913806	.843882	.156118	5	
	56	.57262	.81982	.69847	1.43169	.757869	.913718	.844151	.155849	4	
.95	57	.57286	.81965	.69891	1.43080	.758050	.913630	.844420	.155580	3	.05
	58	.57310	.81949	.69934	1.42992	.758230	.913541	.844689	.155311	2	
	59	.57334	.81932	.69977	1.42903	.758411	.913453	.844958	.155042	1	
1.00	60	.57358	.81915	.70021	1.42815	9.758591	9.913365	9.845227	10.154773	0	.00

Decimals	Minutes	Cos	Sin	Cot	Tan	Cos	Sin	Cot	Tan	Minutes	Decimals
		Natural Values				Common Logarithms					

Decimals	Minutes	Natural Values				Common Logarithms				Minutes	Decimals
		Sin	Cos	Tan	Cot	Sin	Cos	Tan	Cot		
.00	0	.57358	.81915	.70021	1.42815	9.758591	9.913365	9.845227	10.154773	60	1.00
	1	.57381	.81899	.70064	1.42726	.758772	.913276	.845496	.154504	59	
	2	.57405	.81882	.70170	1.42638	.758952	.913187	.845764	.154236	58	
.05	3	.57429	.81865	.70151	1.42550	.759132	.913099	.846033	.153967	57	.95
	4	.57453	.81848	.70194	1.42462	.759312	.913010	.846302	.153698	56	
	5	.57477	.81832	.70238	1.42374	.759492	.912922	.846570	.153430	55	
.10	6	.57501	.81815	.70281	1.42286	.759672	.912833	.846839	.153161	54	.90
	7	.57524	.81798	.70325	1.42198	.759852	.912744	.847108	.152892	53	
	8	.57548	.81782	.70368	1.42110	.760031	.912655	.847376	.152624	52	
.15	9	.57572	.81765	.70412	1.42022	.760211	.912566	.847644	.152356	51	.85
	10	.57596	.81748	.70455	1.41934	.760390	.912477	.847913	.152087	50	
	11	.57619	.81731	.70499	1.41847	.760569	.912388	.848181	.151819	49	
.20	12	.57643	.81714	.70542	1.41759	.760748	.912299	.848449	.151551	48	.80
	13	.57667	.81698	.70586	1.41672	.760927	.912210	.848717	.151283	47	
	14	.57691	.81681	.70629	1.41584	.761106	.912121	.848986	.151014	46	
.25	15	.57715	.81664	.70673	1.41497	.761285	.912031	.849254	.150746	45	.75
	16	.57738	.81647	.70717	1.41409	.761464	.911942	.849522	.150478	44	
	17	.57762	.81631	.70760	1.41322	.761642	.911853	.849790	.150210	43	
.30	18	.57786	.81614	.70804	1.41235	.761821	.911763	.850057	.149943	42	.70
	19	.57810	.81597	.70848	1.41148	.761999	.911674	.850325	.149675	41	
	20	.57833	.81580	.70891	1.41061	.762177	.911584	.850593	.149407	40	
.35	21	.57857	.81563	.70935	1.40974	.762356	.911495	.850861	.149139	39	.65
	22	.57881	.81546	.70979	1.40887	.762534	.911405	.851129	.148871	38	
	23	.57904	.81530	.71023	1.40800	.762712	.911315	.851396	.148604	37	
.40	24	.57928	.81513	.71066	1.40714	.762889	.911226	.851664	.148336	36	.60
	25	.57952	.81496	.71110	1.40627	.763067	.911136	.851931	.148069	35	
	26	.57976	.81479	.71154	1.40540	.763245	.911046	.852199	.147801	34	
.45	27	.57999	.81462	.71198	1.40454	.763422	.910956	.852466	.147534	33	.55
	28	.58023	.81445	.71242	1.40367	.763600	.910866	.852733	.147267	32	
	29	.58047	.81428	.71285	1.40281	.763777	.910776	.853001	.146999	31	
.50	30	.58070	.81412	.71329	1.40195	.763954	.910686	.853268	.146732	30	.50
	31	.58094	.81395	.71373	1.40109	.764131	.910596	.853535	.146465	29	
	32	.58118	.81378	.71417	1.40022	.764308	.910506	.853802	.146198	28	
.55	33	.58141	.81361	.71461	1.39936	.764485	.910415	.854069	.145931	27	.45
	34	.58165	.81344	.71505	1.39850	.764662	.910325	.854336	.145664	26	
	35	.58189	.81327	.71549	1.39764	.764838	.910235	.854603	.145397	25	
.60	36	.58212	.81310	.71593	1.39679	.765015	.910144	.854870	.145130	24	.40
	37	.58236	.81293	.71637	1.39593	.765191	.910054	.855137	.144863	23	
	38	.58260	.81276	.71681	1.39507	.765367	.909963	.855404	.144596	22	
.65	39	.58283	.81259	.71725	1.39421	.765544	.909873	.855671	.144329	21	.35
	40	.58307	.81242	.71769	1.39336	.765720	.909782	.855938	.144062	20	
	41	.58330	.81225	.71813	1.39250	.765896	.909691	.856204	.143796	19	
.70	42	.58354	.81208	.71857	1.39165	.766072	.909601	.856471	.143529	18	.30
	43	.58378	.81191	.71901	1.39079	.766247	.909510	.856737	.143263	17	
	44	.58401	.81174	.71946	1.38994	.766423	.909419	.857004	.142996	16	
.75	45	.58425	.81157	.71990	1.38909	.766598	.909328	.857270	.142730	15	.25
	46	.58449	.81140	.72034	1.38824	.766774	.909237	.857537	.142463	14	
	47	.58472	.81123	.72078	1.38738	.766949	.909146	.857803	.142197	13	
.80	48	.58496	.81106	.72122	1.38653	.767124	.909055	.858069	.141931	12	.20
	49	.58519	.81089	.72167	1.38568	.767300	.908964	.858335	.141664	11	
	50	.58543	.81072	.72211	1.38484	.767475	.908873	.858602	.141398	10	
.85	51	.58567	.81055	.72255	1.38399	.767649	.908781	.858868	.141132	9	.15
	52	.58590	.81038	.72299	1.38314	.767824	.908690	.859134	.140866	8	
	53	.58614	.81021	.72344	1.38229	.767999	.908599	.859400	.140600	7	
.90	54	.58637	.81004	.72388	1.38145	.768173	.908507	.859666	.140334	6	.10
	55	.58661	.80987	.72432	1.38060	.768348	.908416	.859932	.140068	5	
	56	.58684	.80970	.72477	1.37976	.768522	.908324	.860198	.139802	4	
.95	57	.58708	.80953	.72521	1.37891	.768697	.908233	.860464	.139536	3	.05
	58	.58731	.80936	.72565	1.37807	.768871	.908141	.860730	.139270	2	
	59	.58755	.80919	.72610	1.37722	.769045	.908049	.860995	.139005	1	
1.00	60	.58779	.80902	.72654	1.37638	9.769219	9.907958	9.861261	10.138739	0	.00
Decimals	Minutes	Cos	Sin	Cot	Tan	Cos	Sin	Cot	Tan	Minutes	Decimals
		Natural Values				Common Logarithms					

Decimals	Minutes	Natural Values				Common Logarithms				Minutes	Decimals
		Sin	Cos	Tan	Cot	Sin	Cos	Tan	Cot		
.00	0	.58779	.80902	.72654	1.37638	9.769219	9.907958	9.861261	10.138739	60	1.00
	1	.58802	.80885	.72699	1.37554	.769393	.907866	.861527	.138473	59	
	2	.58826	.80867	.72743	1.37470	.769566	.907774	.861792	.138208	58	
.05	3	.58849	.80850	.72788	1.37386	.769740	.907682	.862058	.137942	57	.95
	4	.58873	.80833	.72832	1.37302	.769913	.907590	.862323	.137677	56	
	5	.58896	.80816	.72877	1.37218	.770087	.907498	.862589	.137411	55	
.10	6	.58920	.80799	.72921	1.37134	.770260	.907405	.862854	.137146	54	.90
	7	.58943	.80782	.72966	1.37050	.770433	.907314	.863119	.136881	53	
	8	.58967	.80765	.73010	1.36967	.770606	.907222	.863385	.136615	52	
.15	9	.58990	.80748	.73055	1.36883	.770779	.907129	.863650	.136350	51	.85
	10	.59014	.80730	.73100	1.36800	.770952	.907037	.863915	.136085	50	
	11	.59037	.80713	.73144	1.36716	.771125	.906945	.864180	.135820	49	
.20	12	.59061	.80696	.73189	1.36633	.771298	.906852	.864445	.135555	48	.80
	13	.59084	.80679	.73234	1.36549	.771470	.906760	.864710	.135290	47	
	14	.59108	.80662	.73278	1.36466	.771643	.906667	.864975	.135025	46	
.25	15	.59131	.80644	.73323	1.36383	.771815	.906575	.865240	.134760	45	.75
	16	.59154	.80627	.73368	1.36300	.771987	.906482	.865505	.134495	44	
	17	.59178	.80610	.73413	1.36217	.772159	.906389	.865770	.134230	43	
.30	18	.59201	.80593	.73457	1.36134	.772331	.906296	.866035	.133965	42	.70
	19	.59225	.80576	.73502	1.36051	.772503	.906204	.866300	.133700	41	
	20	.59248	.80558	.73547	1.35968	.772675	.906111	.866564	.133436	40	
.35	21	.59272	.80541	.73592	1.35885	.772847	.906018	.866829	.133171	39	.65
	22	.59295	.80524	.73637	1.35802	.773018	.905925	.867094	.132906	38	
	23	.59318	.80507	.73681	1.35719	.773190	.905832	.867358	.132642	37	
.40	24	.59342	.80489	.73726	1.35637	.773361	.905739	.867623	.132377	36	.60
	25	.59365	.80472	.73771	1.35554	.773533	.905645	.867887	.132113	35	
	26	.59389	.80455	.73816	1.35472	.773704	.905552	.868152	.131848	34	
.45	27	.59412	.80438	.73861	1.35389	.773875	.905459	.868416	.131584	33	.55
	28	.59436	.80420	.73906	1.35307	.774046	.905366	.868680	.131320	32	
	29	.59459	.80403	.73951	1.35224	.774217	.905272	.868945	.131055	31	
.50	30	.59482	.80386	.73996	1.35142	.774388	.905179	.869209	.130791	30	.50
	31	.59506	.80368	.74041	1.35060	.774558	.905085	.869473	.130527	29	
	32	.59529	.80351	.74086	1.34978	.774729	.904992	.869737	.130263	28	
.55	33	.59552	.80334	.74131	1.34896	.774899	.904898	.870001	.129999	27	.45
	34	.59576	.80316	.74176	1.34814	.775070	.904804	.870265	.129735	26	
	35	.59599	.80299	.74221	1.34732	.775240	.904711	.870529	.129471	25	
.60	36	.59622	.80282	.74267	1.34650	.775410	.904617	.870793	.129207	24	.40
	37	.59646	.80264	.74312	1.34568	.775580	.904523	.871057	.128943	23	
	38	.59669	.80247	.74357	1.34487	.775750	.904429	.871321	.128679	22	
.65	39	.59693	.80230	.74402	1.34405	.775920	.904335	.871585	.128415	21	.35
	40	.59716	.80212	.74447	1.34323	.776090	.904241	.871849	.128151	20	
	41	.59739	.80195	.74492	1.34242	.776259	.904147	.872112	.127888	19	
.70	42	.59763	.80178	.74538	1.34160	.776429	.904053	.872376	.127624	18	.30
	43	.59786	.80160	.74583	1.34079	.776598	.903959	.872640	.127360	17	
	44	.59809	.80143	.74628	1.33998	.776768	.903864	.872903	.127097	16	
.75	45	.59832	.80125	.74674	1.33916	.776937	.903770	.873167	.126833	15	.25
	46	.59856	.80108	.74719	1.33835	.777106	.903676	.873430	.126570	14	
	47	.59879	.80091	.74764	1.33754	.777275	.903581	.873694	.126306	13	
.80	48	.59902	.80073	.74810	1.33673	.777444	.903487	.873957	.126043	12	.20
	49	.59926	.80056	.74855	1.33592	.777613	.903392	.874220	.125780	11	
	50	.59949	.80038	.74900	1.33511	.777781	.903298	.874484	.125516	10	
.85	51	.59972	.80021	.74946	1.33430	.777950	.903203	.874747	.125253	9	.15
	52	.59995	.80003	.74991	1.33349	.778119	.903108	.875010	.124990	8	
	53	.60019	.79986	.75037	1.33268	.778287	.903014	.875273	.124727	7	
.90	54	.60042	.79968	.75082	1.33187	.778455	.902919	.875537	.124463	6	.10
	55	.60065	.79951	.75128	1.33107	.778624	.902824	.875800	.124200	5	
	56	.60089	.79934	.75173	1.33026	.778792	.902729	.876063	.123937	4	
.95	57	.60112	.79916	.75219	1.32946	.778960	.902634	.876326	.123674	3	.05
	58	.60135	.79899	.75264	1.32865	.779128	.902539	.876589	.123411	2	
	59	.60158	.79881	.75310	1.32785	.779295	.902444	.876852	.123148	1	
1.00	60	.60182	.79864	.75355	1.32704	9.779463	9.902349	9.877114	10.122886	0	.00
Decimals	Minutes	Cos	Sin	Cot	Tan	Cos	Sin	Cot	Tan	Minutes	Decimals
		Natural Values				Common Logarithms					

Decimals	Minutes	Natural Values Sin	Cos	Tan	Cot	Common Logarithms Sin	Cos	Tan	Cot	Minutes	Decimals
.00	0	.60182	.79864	.75355	1.32704	9.779463	9.902349	9.877114	10.122886	60	1.00
	1	.60205	.79846	.75401	1.32624	.779631	.902253	.877377	.122623	59	
	2	.60228	.79829	.75447	1.32544	.779798	.902158	.877640	.122360	58	
.05	3	.60251	.79811	.75492	1.32464	.779966	.902063	.877903	.122097	57	.95
	4	.60274	.79793	.75538	1.32384	.780133	.901967	.878165	.121835	56	
	5	.60298	.79776	.75584	1.32304	.780300	.901872	.878428	.121572	55	
.10	6	.60321	.79758	.75629	1.32224	.780467	.901776	.878691	.121309	54	.90
	7	.60344	.79741	.75675	1.32144	.780634	.901681	.878953	.121047	53	
	8	.60367	.79723	.75721	1.32064	.780801	.901585	.879216	.120784	52	
.15	9	.60390	.79706	.75767	1.31984	.780968	.901490	.879478	.120522	51	.85
	10	.60414	.79688	.75812	1.31904	.781134	.901394	.879741	.120259	50	
	11	.60437	.79671	.75858	1.31825	.781301	.901298	.880003	.119997	49	
.20	12	.60460	.79653	.75904	1.31745	.781468	.901202	.880265	.119735	48	.80
	13	.60483	.79635	.75950	1.31666	.781634	.901106	.880528	.119472	47	
	14	.60506	.79618	.75996	1.31586	.781800	.901010	.880790	.119210	46	
.25	15	.60529	.79600	.76042	1.31507	.781966	.900914	.881052	.118948	45	.75
	16	.60553	.79583	.76088	1.31427	.782132	.900818	.881314	.118686	44	
	17	.60576	.79565	.76134	1.31348	.782298	.900722	.881577	.118423	43	
.30	18	.60599	.79547	.76180	1.31269	.782464	.900626	.881839	.118161	42	.70
	19	.60622	.79530	.76226	1.31190	.782630	.900529	.882101	.117899	41	
	20	.60645	.79512	.76272	1.31110	.782796	.900433	.882363	.117637	40	
.35	21	.60668	.79494	.76318	1.31031	.782961	.900337	.882625	.117375	39	.65
	22	.60691	.79477	.76364	1.30952	.783127	.900240	.882887	.117113	38	
	23	.60714	.79459	.76410	1.30873	.783292	.900144	.883148	.116852	37	
.40	24	.60738	.79441	.76456	1.30795	.783458	.900047	.883410	.116590	36	.60
	25	.60761	.79424	.76502	1.30716	.783623	.899951	.883672	.116328	35	
	26	.60784	.79406	.76548	1.30637	.783788	.899854	.883934	.116066	34	
.45	27	.60807	.79388	.76594	1.30558	.783953	.899757	.884196	.115804	33	.55
	28	.60830	.79371	.76640	1.30480	.784118	.899660	.884457	.115543	32	
	29	.60853	.79353	.76686	1.30401	.784282	.899564	.884719	.115281	31	
.50	30	.60876	.79335	.76733	1.30323	.784447	.899467	.884980	.115020	30	.50
	31	.60899	.79318	.76779	1.30244	.784612	.899370	.885242	.114758	29	
	32	.60922	.79300	.76825	1.30166	.784776	.899273	.885504	.114496	28	
.55	33	.60945	.79282	.76871	1.30087	.784941	.899176	.885765	.114235	27	.45
	34	.60968	.79264	.76918	1.30009	.785105	.899078	.886026	.113974	26	
	35	.60991	.79247	.76964	1.29931	.785269	.898981	.886288	.113712	25	
.60	36	.61015	.79229	.77010	1.29853	.785433	.898884	.886549	.113451	24	.40
	37	.61038	.79211	.77057	1.29775	.785597	.898787	.886811	.113189	23	
	38	.61061	.79193	.77103	1.29696	.785761	.898689	.887072	.112928	22	
.65	39	.61084	.79176	.77149	1.29618	.785925	.898592	.887333	.112667	21	.35
	40	.61107	.79158	.77196	1.29541	.786089	.898494	.887594	.112406	20	
	41	.61130	.79140	.77242	1.29463	.786252	.898397	.887855	.112145	19	
.70	42	.61153	.79122	.77289	1.29385	.786416	.898299	.888116	.111884	18	.30
	43	.61176	.79105	.77335	1.29307	.786579	.898202	.888378	.111622	17	
	44	.61199	.79087	.77382	1.29229	.786742	.898104	.888639	.111361	16	
.75	45	.61222	.79069	.77428	1.29152	.786906	.898006	.888900	.111100	15	.25
	46	.61245	.79051	.77475	1.29074	.787069	.897908	.889161	.110839	14	
	47	.61268	.79033	.77521	1.28997	.787232	.897810	.889421	.110579	13	
.80	48	.61291	.79016	.77563	1.28919	.787395	.897712	.889682	.110318	12	.20
	49	.61314	.78998	.77615	1.28842	.787557	.897614	.889943	.110057	11	
	50	.61337	.78980	.77661	1.28764	.787720	.897516	.890204	.109796	10	
.85	51	.61360	.78962	.77708	1.28687	.787883	.897418	.890465	.109535	9	.15
	52	.61383	.78944	.77754	1.28610	.788045	.897320	.890725	.109275	8	
	53	.61406	.78926	.77801	1.28533	.788208	.897222	.890986	.109014	7	
.90	54	.61429	.78908	.77848	1.28456	.788370	.897123	.891247	.108753	6	.10
	55	.61451	.78891	.77895	1.28379	.788532	.897025	.891507	.108493	5	
	56	.61474	.78873	.77941	1.28302	.788694	.896926	.891768	.108232	4	
.95	57	.61497	.78855	.77988	1.28225	.788856	.896828	.892023	.107972	3	.05
	58	.61520	.78837	.78035	1.28148	.789018	.896729	.892289	.107711	2	
	59	.61543	.78819	.78082	1.28071	.789180	.896631	.892549	.107451	1	
1.00	60	.61566	.78801	.78129	1.27994	9.789342	9.896532	9.892810	10.107190	0	.00

Decimals	Minutes	Cos	Sin	Cot	Tan	Cos	Sin	Cot	Tan	Minutes	Decimals
		Natural Values				Common Logarithms					

Decimals	Minutes	Natural Values				Common Logarithms				Minutes	Decimals
		Sin	Cos	Tan	Cot	Sin	Cos	Tan	Cot		
.00	0	.61566	.78801	.78129	1.27994	9.789342	9.896532	9.892810	10.107190	60	1.00
	1	.61589	.78783	.78175	1.27917	.789504	.896433	.893070	.106930	59	
	2	.61612	.78765	.78222	1.27841	.789665	.896335	.893331	.106669	58	
.05	3	.61635	.78747	.78269	1.27764	.789827	.896236	.893591	.106409	57	.95
	4	.61658	.78729	.78316	1.27688	.789988	.896137	.893851	.106149	56	
	5	.61681	.78711	.78363	1.27611	.790149	.896038	.894111	.105889	55	
.10	6	.61704	.78694	.78410	1.27535	.790310	.895939	.894372	.105628	54	.90
	7	.61726	.78676	.78457	1.27458	.790471	.895840	.894632	.105368	53	
	8	.61749	.78658	.78504	1.27382	.790632	.895741	.894892	.105108	52	
.15	9	.61772	.78640	.78551	1.27306	.790793	.895641	.895152	.104848	51	.85
	10	.61795	.78622	.78598	1.27230	.790954	.895542	.895412	.104588	50	
	11	.61818	.78604	.78645	1.27153	.791115	.895443	.895672	.104328	49	
.20	12	.61841	.78586	.78692	1.27077	.791275	.895343	.895932	.104068	48	.80
	13	.61864	.78568	.78739	1.27001	.791436	.895244	.896192	.103808	47	
	14	.61887	.78550	.78786	1.26925	.791596	.895145	.896452	.103548	46	
.25	15	.61909	.78532	.78834	1.26849	.791757	.895045	.896712	.103288	45	.75
	16	.61932	.78514	.78881	1.26774	.791917	.894945	.896971	.103029	44	
	17	.61955	.78496	.78928	1.26698	.792077	.894846	.897231	.102769	43	
.30	18	.61978	.78478	.78975	1.26622	.792237	.894745	.897491	.102509	42	.70
	19	.62001	.78460	.79022	1.26546	.792397	.894646	.897751	.102249	41	
	20	.62024	.78442	.79070	1.26471	.792557	.894546	.898010	.101990	40	
.35	21	.62046	.78424	.79117	1.26395	.792716	.894446	.898270	.101730	39	.65
	22	.62069	.78405	.79164	1.26319	.792876	.894346	.898530	.101470	38	
	23	.62092	.78387	.79212	1.26244	.793035	.894246	.898789	.101211	37	
.40	24	.62115	.78369	.79259	1.26169	.793195	.894146	.899049	.100951	36	.60
	25	.62138	.78351	.79306	1.26093	.793354	.894046	.899308	.100692	35	
	26	.62160	.78333	.79354	1.26018	.793514	.893946	.899568	.100432	34	
.45	27	.62183	.78315	.79401	1.25943	.793573	.893846	.899827	.100173	33	.55
	28	.62206	.78297	.79449	1.25867	.793832	.893745	.900087	.099913	32	
	29	.62229	.78279	.79496	1.25792	.793991	.893645	.900346	.099654	31	
.50	30	.62251	.78261	.79544	1.25717	.794150	.893544	.900605	.099395	30	.50
	31	.62274	.78243	.79591	1.25642	.794308	.893444	.900864	.099136	29	
	32	.62297	.78225	.79639	1.25567	.794467	.893343	.901124	.098876	28	
.55	33	.62320	.78206	.79686	1.25492	.794626	.893243	.901383	.098617	27	.45
	34	.62342	.78188	.79734	1.25417	.794784	.893142	.901642	.098358	26	
	35	.62365	.78170	.79781	1.25343	.794942	.893041	.901901	.098099	25	
.60	36	.62388	.78152	.79829	1.25268	.795101	.892940	.902160	.097840	24	.40
	37	.62411	.78134	.79877	1.25193	.795259	.892839	.902420	.097580	23	
	38	.62433	.78116	.79924	1.25118	.795417	.892739	.902679	.097321	22	
.65	39	.62456	.78098	.79972	1.25044	.795575	.892638	.902938	.097062	21	.35
	40	.62479	.78079	.80020	1.24969	.795733	.892536	.903197	.096803	20	
	41	.62502	.78061	.80067	1.24895	.795891	.892435	.903456	.096544	19	
.70	42	.62524	.78043	.80115	1.24820	.796049	.892334	.903714	.096286	18	.30
	43	.62547	.78025	.80163	1.24746	.796206	.892233	.903973	.096027	17	
	44	.62570	.78007	.80211	1.24672	.796364	.892132	.904232	.095768	16	
.75	45	.62592	.77988	.80258	1.24597	.796521	.892030	.904491	.095509	15	.25
	46	.62615	.77970	.80306	1.24523	.796679	.891929	.904750	.095250	14	
	47	.62638	.77952	.80354	1.24449	.796836	.891827	.905008	.094992	13	
.80	48	.62660	.77934	.80402	1.24375	.796993	.891726	.905267	.094733	12	.20
	49	.62683	.77916	.80450	1.24301	.797150	.891624	.905526	.094474	11	
	50	.62706	.77897	.80498	1.24227	.797307	.891523	.905785	.094215	10	
.85	51	.62728	.77879	.80546	1.24153	.797464	.891421	.906043	.093957	9	.15
	52	.62751	.77861	.80594	1.24079	.797621	.891319	.906302	.093698	8	
	53	.62774	.77843	.80642	1.24005	.797777	.891217	.906560	.093440	7	
.90	54	.62796	.77824	.80690	1.23931	.797934	.891115	.906819	.093181	6	.10
	55	.62819	.77806	.80738	1.23858	.798091	.891013	.907077	.092923	5	
	56	.62842	.77788	.80786	1.23784	.798247	.890911	.907336	.092664	4	
.95	57	.62864	.77769	.80834	1.23710	.798403	.890809	.907594	.092406	3	.05
	58	.62887	.77751	.80882	1.23637	.798560	.890707	.907853	.092147	2	
	59	.62909	.77733	.80930	1.23563	.798716	.890605	.908111	.091889	1	
1.00	60	.62932	.77715	.80978	1.23490	9.798872	9.890503	9.908369	10.091631	0	.00
Decimals	Minutes	Cos	Sin	Cot	Tan	Cos	Sin	Cot	Tan	Minutes	Decimals
		Natural Values				Common Logarithms					

Decimals	Minutes	Natural Values				Common Logarithms				Minutes	Decimals
		Sin	Cos	Tan	Cot	Sin	Cos	Tan	Cot		
.00	0	.62932	.77715	.80978	1.23490	9.798872	9.890503	9.908369	10.091631	60	1.00
	1	.62955	.77696	.81027	1.23416	.799028	.890400	.908628	.091372	59	
	2	.62977	.77678	.81075	1.23343	.799184	.890298	.908886	.091114	58	
.05	3	.63000	.77660	.81123	1.23270	.799399	.890195	.909144	.090856	57	.95
	4	.63022	.77641	.81171	1.23196	.799495	.890093	.909402	.090598	56	
	5	.63045	.77623	.81220	1.23123	.799651	.889990	.909660	.090340	55	
.10	6	.63068	.77605	.81268	1.23050	.799806	.889888	.909918	.090082	54	.90
	7	.63090	.77586	.81316	1.22977	.799962	.889785	.910177	.089823	53	
	8	.63113	.77568	.81364	1.22904	.800117	.889682	.910435	.089565	52	
.15	9	.63135	.77550	.81413	1.22831	.800272	.889579	.910693	.089307	51	.85
	10	.63158	.77531	.81461	1.22758	.800427	.889477	.910951	.089049	50	
	11	.63180	.77513	.81510	1.22685	.800582	.889374	.911209	.088791	49	
.20	12	.63203	.77494	.81558	1.22612	.800737	.889271	.911467	.088533	48	.80
	13	.63225	.77476	.81606	1.22539	.800892	.889168	.911725	.088275	47	
	14	.63248	.77458	.81655	1.22467	.801047	.889064	.911982	.088018	46	
.25	15	.63271	.77439	.81703	1.22394	.801201	.888961	.912240	.087760	45	.75
	16	.63293	.77421	.81752	1.22321	.801356	.888858	.912498	.087502	44	
	17	.63316	.77402	.81800	1.22249	.801511	.888755	.912756	.087244	43	
.30	18	.63338	.77384	.81849	1.22176	.801665	.888651	.913014	.086986	42	.70
	19	.63361	.77366	.81898	1.22104	.801819	.888548	.913271	.086729	41	
	20	.63383	.77347	.81946	1.22031	.801973	.888444	.913529	.086471	40	
.35	21	.63406	.77329	.81995	1.21959	.802128	.888341	.913787	.086213	39	.65
	22	.63428	.77310	.82044	1.21886	.802282	.888237	.914044	.085956	38	
	23	.63451	.77292	.82092	1.21814	.802436	.888134	.914302	.085698	37	
.40	24	.63473	.77273	.82141	1.21742	.802589	.888030	.914560	.085440	36	.60
	25	.63496	.77255	.82190	1.21670	.802743	.887926	.914817	.085183	35	
	26	.63518	.77236	.82238	1.21598	.802897	.887822	.915075	.084925	34	
.45	27	.63540	.77218	.82287	1.21526	.803050	.887718	.915332	.084668	33	.55
	28	.63563	.77199	.82336	1.21454	.803204	.887614	.915590	.084410	32	
	29	.63585	.77181	.82385	1.21382	.803357	.887510	.915847	.084153	31	
.50	30	.63608	.77162	.82434	1.21310	.803511	.887406	.916104	.083896	30	.50
	31	.63630	.77144	.82483	1.21238	.803664	.887302	.916362	.083638	29	
	32	.63653	.77125	.82531	1.21166	.803817	.887198	.916619	.083381	28	
.55	33	.63675	.77107	.82580	1.21094	.803970	.887093	.916877	.083123	27	.45
	34	.63698	.77088	.82629	1.21023	.804123	.886989	.917134	.082866	26	
	35	.63720	.77070	.82678	1.20951	.804276	.886885	.917391	.082609	25	
.60	36	.63742	.77051	.82727	1.20879	.804428	.886780	.917648	.082352	24	.40
	37	.63765	.77033	.82776	1.20808	.804581	.886676	.917906	.082094	23	
	38	.63787	.77014	.82825	1.20736	.804734	.886571	.918163	.081837	22	
.65	39	.63810	.76996	.82874	1.20665	.804886	.886466	.918420	.081580	21	.35
	40	.63832	.76977	.82923	1.20593	.805039	.886362	.918677	.081323	20	
	41	.63854	.76959	.82972	1.20522	.805191	.886257	.918934	.081066	19	
.70	42	.63877	.76940	.83022	1.20451	.805343	.886152	.919191	.080809	18	.30
	43	.63899	.76921	.83071	1.20379	.805495	.886047	.919448	.080552	17	
	44	.63922	.76903	.83120	1.20308	.805647	.885942	.919705	.080295	16	
.75	45	.63944	.76884	.83169	1.20237	.805799	.885837	.919962	.080038	15	.25
	46	.63966	.76866	.83218	1.20166	.805951	.885732	.920219	.079781	14	
	47	.63989	.76847	.83268	1.20095	.806103	.885627	.920476	.079524	13	
.80	48	.64011	.76828	.83317	1.20024	.806254	.885522	.920733	.079267	12	.20
	49	.64033	.76810	.83366	1.19953	.806406	.885416	.920990	.079010	11	
	50	.64056	.76791	.83415	1.19882	.806557	.885311	.921247	.078753	10	
.85	51	.64078	.76772	.83465	1.19811	.806709	.885205	.921503	.078497	9	.15
	52	.64100	.76754	.83514	1.19740	.806860	.885100	.921760	.078240	8	
	53	.64123	.76735	.83564	1.19669	.807011	.884994	.922017	.077983	7	
.90	54	.64145	.76717	.83613	1.19599	.807163	.884889	.922274	.077726	6	.10
	55	.64167	.76698	.83662	1.19528	.807314	.884783	.922530	.077470	5	
	56	.64190	.76679	.83712	1.19457	.807465	.884677	.922787	.077213	4	
.95	57	.64212	.76661	.83761	1.19387	.807615	.884572	.923044	.076956	3	.05
	58	.64234	.76642	.83811	1.19316	.807766	.884466	.923300	.076700	2	
	59	.64256	.76623	.83860	1.19246	.807917	.884360	.923557	.076443	1	
1.00	60	.64279	.76604	.83910	1.19175	9.803067	9.884254	9.923814	10.076186	0	.00
Decimals	Minutes	Cos	Sin	Cot	Tan	Cos	Sin	Cot	Tan	Minutes	Decimals
		Natural Values				Common Logarithms					

Decimals	Minutes	Natural Values				Common Logarithms				Minutes	Decimals
		Sin	Cos	Tan	Cot	Sin	Cos	Tan	Cot		
.00	0	.64279	.76604	.83910	1.19175	9.808067	9.884254	9.923814	10.076186	60	1.00
	1	.64301	.76586	.83960	1.19105	.808218	.884148	.924070	.075930	59	
	2	.64323	.76567	.84009	1.19035	.808368	.884042	.924327	.075673	58	
.05	3	.64346	.76548	.84059	1.18964	.808519	.883936	.924583	.075417	57	.95
	4	.64368	.76530	.84108	1.18894	.808669	.883829	.924840	.075160	56	
	5	.64390	.76511	.84158	1.18824	.808819	.883723	.925096	.074904	55	
.10	6	.64412	.76492	.84208	1.18754	.808969	.883617	.925352	.074648	54	.90
	7	.64435	.76473	.84258	1.18684	.809119	.883510	.925609	.074391	53	
	8	.64457	.76455	.84307	1.18614	.809269	.883404	.925865	.074135	52	
.15	9	.64479	.76436	.84357	1.18544	.809419	.883297	.926122	.073878	51	.85
	10	.64501	.76417	.84407	1.18474	.809569	.883191	.926378	.073622	50	
	11	.64524	.76398	.84457	1.18404	.809718	.883084	.926634	.073366	49	
.20	12	.64546	.76380	.84507	1.18334	.809868	.882977	.926890	.073110	48	.80
	13	.64568	.76361	.84556	1.18264	.810017	.882871	.927147	.072853	47	
	14	.64590	.76342	.84606	1.18194	.810167	.882764	.927403	.072597	46	
.25	15	.64612	.76323	.84656	1.18125	.810316	.882657	.927659	.072341	45	.75
	16	.64635	.76304	.84706	1.18055	.810465	.882550	.927915	.072085	44	
	17	.64657	.76286	.84756	1.17986	.810614	.882443	.928171	.071829	43	
.30	18	.64679	.76267	.84806	1.17916	.810763	.882336	.928427	.071573	42	.70
	19	.64701	.76248	.84856	1.17846	.810912	.882229	.928684	.071316	41	
	20	.64723	.76229	.84906	1.17777	.811061	.882121	.928940	.071060	40	
.35	21	.64746	.76210	.84956	1.17708	.811210	.882014	.929196	.070804	39	.65
	22	.64768	.76192	.85006	1.17638	.811358	.881907	.929452	.070548	38	
	23	.64790	.76173	.85057	1.17569	.811507	.881799	.929708	.070292	37	
.40	24	.64812	.76154	.85107	1.17500	.811655	.881692	.929964	.070036	36	.60
	25	.64834	.76135	.85157	1.17430	.811804	.881584	.930220	.069780	35	
	26	.64856	.76116	.85207	1.17361	.811952	.881477	.930475	.069525	34	
.45	27	.64878	.76097	.85257	1.17292	.812100	.881369	.930731	.069269	33	.55
	28	.64901	.76078	.85308	1.17223	.812248	.881261	.930987	.069013	32	
	29	.64923	.76059	.85358	1.17154	.812396	.881153	.931243	.068757	31	
.50	30	.64945	.76041	.85408	1.17085	.812544	.881046	.931499	.068501	30	.50
	31	.64967	.76022	.85458	1.17016	.812692	.880938	.931755	.068245	29	
	32	.64989	.76003	.85509	1.16947	.812840	.880830	.932010	.067990	28	
.55	33	.65011	.75984	.85559	1.16878	.812988	.880722	.932266	.067734	27	.45
	34	.65033	.75965	.85609	1.16809	.813135	.880613	.932522	.067478	26	
	35	.65055	.75946	.85660	1.16741	.813283	.880505	.932778	.067222	25	
.60	36	.65077	.75927	.85710	1.16672	.813430	.880397	.933033	.066967	24	.40
	37	.65100	.75908	.85761	1.16603	.813578	.880289	.933289	.066711	23	
	38	.65122	.75889	.85811	1.16535	.813725	.880180	.933545	.066455	22	
.65	39	.65144	.75870	.85862	1.16466	.813872	.880072	.933800	.066200	21	.35
	40	.65166	.75851	.85912	1.16398	.814019	.879963	.934056	.065944	20	
	41	.65188	.75832	.85963	1.16329	.814166	.879855	.934311	.065689	19	
.70	42	.65210	.75813	.86014	1.16261	.814313	.879746	.934567	.065433	18	.30
	43	.65232	.75794	.86064	1.16192	.814460	.879637	.934822	.065178	17	
	44	.65254	.75775	.86115	1.16124	.814607	.879529	.935078	.064922	16	
.75	45	.65276	.75756	.86166	1.16056	.814753	.879420	.935333	.064667	15	.25
	46	.65298	.75738	.86216	1.15987	.814900	.879311	.935589	.064411	14	
	47	.65320	.75719	.86267	1.15919	.815046	.879202	.935844	.064156	13	
.80	48	.65342	.75700	.86318	1.15851	.815193	.879093	.936100	.063900	12	.20
	49	.65364	.75680	.86368	1.15783	.815339	.878984	.936355	.063645	11	
	50	.65386	.75661	.86419	1.15715	.815485	.878875	.936611	.063389	10	
.85	51	.65408	.75642	.86470	1.15647	.815632	.878766	.936866	.063134	9	.15
	52	.65430	.75623	.86521	1.15579	.815778	.878656	.937121	.062879	8	
	53	.65452	.75604	.86572	1.15511	.815924	.878547	.937377	.062623	7	
.90	54	.65474	.75585	.86623	1.15443	.816069	.878438	.937632	.062368	6	.10
	55	.65496	.75566	.86674	1.15375	.816215	.878328	.937887	.062113	5	
	56	.65518	.75547	.86725	1.15308	.816361	.878219	.938142	.061858	4	
.95	57	.65540	.75528	.86776	1.15240	.816507	.878109	.938398	.061602	3	.05
	58	.65562	.75509	.86827	1.15172	.816652	.877999	.938653	.061347	2	
	59	.65584	.75490	.86878	1.15104	.816798	.877890	.938908	.061092	1	
1.00	60	.65606	.75471	.86929	1.15037	9.816943	9.877780	9.939163	10.060837	0	.00
Decimals	Minutes	Cos	Sin	Cot	Tan	Cos	Sin	Cot	Tan	Minutes	Decimals
		Natural Values				Common Logarithms					

49°

Decimals	Minutes	Natural Values Sin	Cos	Tan	Cot	Common Logarithms Sin	Cos	Tan	Cot	Minutes	Decimals
.00	0	.65606	.75471	.86929	1.15037	9.816943	9.877780	9.939163	10.060837	60	1.00
	1	.65628	.75452	.86980	1.14969	.817088	.877670	.939418	.060582	59	
	2	.65650	.75433	.87031	1.14902	.817233	.877560	.939673	.060327	58	
.05	3	.65672	.75414	.87082	1.14834	.817379	.877450	.939928	.060072	57	.95
	4	.65694	.75395	.87133	1.14767	.817524	.877340	.940183	.059817	56	
	5	.65716	.75375	.87184	1.14699	.817668	.877230	.940439	.059561	55	
.10	6	.65738	.75356	.87236	1.14632	.817813	.877120	.940694	.059306	54	.90
	7	.65759	.75337	.87287	1.14565	.817958	.877010	.940949	.059051	53	
	8	.65781	.75318	.87338	1.14498	.818103	.876899	.941204	.058796	52	
.15	9	.65803	.75299	.87389	1.14430	.818247	.876789	.941459	.058541	51	.85
	10	.65825	.75280	.87441	1.14363	.818392	.876678	.941713	.058287	50	
	11	.65847	.75261	.87492	1.14296	.818536	.876568	.941968	.058032	49	
.20	12	.65869	.75241	.87543	1.14229	.818681	.876457	.942223	.057777	48	.80
	13	.65891	.75222	.87595	1.14162	.818825	.876347	.942478	.057522	47	
	14	.65913	.75203	.87646	1.14095	.818969	.876236	.942733	.057267	46	
.25	15	.65935	.75184	.87698	1.14028	.819113	.876125	.942988	.057012	45	.75
	16	.65956	.75165	.87749	1.13961	.819257	.876014	.943243	.056757	44	
	17	.65978	.75146	.87801	1.13894	.819401	.875904	.943498	.056502	43	
.30	18	.66000	.75126	.87852	1.13828	.819545	.875793	.943752	.056248	42	.70
	19	.66022	.75107	.87904	1.13761	.819689	.875682	.944007	.055993	41	
	20	.66044	.75088	.87955	1.13694	.819832	.875571	.944262	.055738	40	
.35	21	.66066	.75069	.88007	1.13627	.819976	.875459	.944517	.055483	39	.65
	22	.66088	.75050	.88059	1.13561	.820120	.875348	.944771	.055229	38	
	23	.66109	.75030	.88110	1.13494	.820263	.875237	.945026	.054974	37	
.40	24	.66131	.75011	.88162	1.13428	.820406	.875126	.945281	.054719	36	.60
	25	.66153	.74992	.88214	1.13361	.820550	.875014	.945535	.054465	35	
	26	.66175	.74973	.88265	1.13295	.820693	.874903	.945790	.054210	34	
.45	27	.66197	.74953	.88317	1.13228	.820836	.874791	.946045	.053955	33	.55
	28	.66218	.74934	.88369	1.13162	.820979	.874680	.946299	.053701	32	
	29	.66240	.74915	.88421	1.13096	.821122	.874568	.946554	.053446	31	
.50	30	.66262	.74896	.88473	1.13029	.821265	.874456	.946808	.053192	30	.50
	31	.66284	.74876	.88524	1.12963	.821407	.874344	.947063	.052937	29	
	32	.66306	.74857	.88576	1.12897	.821550	.874232	.947318	.052682	28	
.55	33	.66327	.74838	.88628	1.12831	.821693	.874121	.947572	.052428	27	.45
	34	.66349	.74818	.88680	1.12765	.821835	.874009	.947827	.052173	26	
	35	.66371	.74799	.88732	1.12699	.821977	.873896	.948081	.051919	25	
.60	36	.66393	.74780	.88784	1.12633	.822120	.873784	.948335	.051665	24	.40
	37	.66414	.74760	.88836	1.12567	.822262	.873672	.948590	.051410	23	
	38	.66436	.74741	.88888	1.12501	.822404	.873560	.948844	.051156	22	
.65	39	.66458	.74722	.88940	1.12435	.822546	.873448	.949099	.050901	21	.35
	40	.66480	.74703	.88992	1.12369	.822688	.873335	.949353	.050647	20	
	41	.66501	.74683	.89045	1.12303	.822830	.873223	.949608	.050392	19	
.70	42	.66523	.74664	.89097	1.12238	.822972	.873110	.949862	.050138	18	.30
	43	.66545	.74644	.89149	1.12172	.823114	.872998	.950116	.049884	17	
	44	.66566	.74625	.89201	1.12106	.823255	.872885	.950371	.049629	16	
.75	45	.66588	.74606	.89253	1.12041	.823397	.872772	.950625	.049375	15	.25
	46	.66610	.74586	.89306	1.11975	.823539	.872659	.950879	.049121	14	
	47	.66632	.74567	.89358	1.11909	.823680	.872547	.951133	.048867	13	
.80	48	.66653	.74548	.89410	1.11844	.823821	.872434	.951388	.048612	12	.20
	49	.66675	.74528	.89463	1.11778	.823963	.872321	.951642	.048358	11	
	50	.66697	.74509	.89515	1.11713	.824104	.872208	.951896	.048104	10	
.85	51	.66718	.74489	.89567	1.11648	.824245	.872095	.952150	.047850	9	.15
	52	.66740	.74470	.89620	1.11582	.824386	.871981	.952405	.047595	8	
	53	.66762	.74451	.89672	1.11517	.824527	.871868	.952659	.047341	7	
.90	54	.66783	.74431	.89725	1.11452	.824668	.871755	.952913	.047087	6	.10
	55	.66805	.74412	.89777	1.11387	.824808	.871641	.953167	.046833	5	
	56	.66827	.74392	.89830	1.11321	.824949	.871528	.953421	.046579	4	
.95	57	.66848	.74373	.89883	1.11256	.825090	.871414	.953675	.046325	3	.05
	58	.66870	.74353	.89935	1.11191	.825230	.871301	.953929	.046071	2	
	59	.66891	.74334	.89988	1.11126	.825371	.871187	.954183	.045817	1	
1.00	60	.66913	.74314	.90040	1.11061	9.825511	9.871073	9.954437	10.045563	0	.00

Decimals	Minutes	Cos	Sin	Cot	Tan	Cos	Sin	Cot	Tan	Minutes	Decimals
		Natural Values				Common Logarithms					

Decimals	Minutes	Natural Values				Common Logarithms				Minutes	Decimals
		Sin	Cos	Tan	Cot	Sin	Cos	Tan	Cot		
.00	0	.66913	.74314	.90040	1.11061	9.825511	9.871073	9.954437	10.045563	60	1.00
	1	.66935	.74295	.90093	1.10996	.825651	.870960	.954691	.045309	59	
	2	.66956	.74276	.90146	1.10931	.825791	.870846	.954946	.045054	58	
.05	3	.66978	.74256	.90199	1.10867	.825931	.870732	.955200	.044800	57	.95
	4	.66999	.74237	.90251	1.10802	.826071	.870618	.955454	.044546	56	
	5	.67021	.74217	.90304	1.10737	.826211	.870504	.955708	.044292	55	
.10	6	.67043	.74198	.90357	1.10672	.826351	.870390	.955961	.044039	54	.90
	7	.67064	.74178	.90410	1.10607	.826491	.870276	.956215	.043785	53	
	8	.67086	.74159	.90463	1.10543	.826631	.870161	.956469	.043531	52	
.15	9	.67107	.74139	.90516	1.10478	.826770	.870047	.956723	.043277	51	.85
	10	.67129	.74120	.90569	1.10414	.826910	.869933	.956977	.043023	50	
	11	.67151	.74100	.90621	1.10349	.827049	.869818	.957231	.042769	49	
.20	12	.67172	.74080	.90674	1.10285	.827189	.869704	.957485	.042515	48	.80
	13	.67194	.74061	.90727	1.10220	.827328	.869589	.957739	.042261	47	
	14	.67215	.74041	.90781	1.10156	.827467	.869474	.957993	.042007	46	
.25	15	.67237	.74022	.90834	1.10091	.827606	.869360	.958247	.041753	45	.75
	16	.67258	.74002	.90887	1.10027	.827745	.869245	.958500	.041500	44	
	17	.67280	.73983	.90940	1.09963	.827884	.869130	.958754	.041246	43	
.30	18	.67301	.73963	.90993	1.09899	.828023	.869015	.959008	.040992	42	.70
	19	.67323	.73944	.91046	1.09834	.828162	.868900	.959262	.040738	41	
	20	.67344	.73924	.91099	1.09770	.828301	.868785	.959516	.040484	40	
.35	21	.67366	.73904	.91153	1.09706	.828439	.868670	.959769	.040231	39	.65
	22	.67387	.73885	.91206	1.09642	.828578	.868555	.960023	.039977	38	
	23	.67409	.73865	.91259	1.09578	.828716	.868440	.960277	.039723	37	
.40	24	.67430	.73846	.91313	1.09514	.828855	.868324	.960530	.039470	36	.60
	25	.67452	.73826	.91366	1.09450	.828993	.868209	.960784	.039216	35	
	26	.67473	.73806	.91419	1.09386	.829131	.868093	.961038	.038962	34	
.45	27	.67495	.73787	.91473	1.09322	.829269	.867978	.961292	.038708	33	.55
	28	.67516	.73767	.91526	1.09258	.829407	.867862	.961545	.038455	32	
	29	.67538	.73747	.91580	1.09195	.829545	.867747	.961799	.038201	31	
.50	30	.67559	.73728	.91633	1.09131	.829683	.867631	.962052	.037948	30	.50
	31	.67580	.73708	.91687	1.09067	.829821	.867515	.962306	.037694	29	
	32	.67602	.73688	.91740	1.09003	.829959	.867399	.962560	.037440	28	
.55	33	.67623	.73669	.91794	1.08940	.830097	.867283	.962813	.037187	27	.45
	34	.67645	.73649	.91847	1.08876	.830234	.867167	.963067	.036933	26	
	35	.67666	.73629	.91901	1.08813	.830372	.867051	.963320	.036680	25	
.60	36	.67688	.73610	.91955	1.08749	.830509	.866935	.963574	.036426	24	.40
	37	.67709	.73590	.92008	1.08686	.830646	.866819	.963828	.036172	23	
	38	.67730	.73570	.92062	1.08622	.830784	.866703	.964081	.035919	22	
.65	39	.67752	.73551	.92116	1.08559	.830921	.866586	.964335	.035665	21	.35
	40	.67773	.73531	.92170	1.08496	.831058	.866470	.964588	.035412	20	
	41	.67795	.73511	.92224	1.08432	.831195	.866353	.964842	.035158	19	
.70	42	.67816	.73491	.92277	1.08369	.831332	.866237	.965095	.034905	18	.30
	43	.67837	.73472	.92331	1.08306	.831469	.866120	.965349	.034651	17	
	44	.67859	.73452	.92385	1.08243	.831606	.866004	.965602	.034398	16	
.75	45	.67880	.73432	.92439	1.08179	.831742	.865887	.965855	.034145	15	.25
	46	.67901	.73413	.92493	1.08116	.831879	.865770	.966109	.033891	14	
	47	.67923	.73393	.92547	1.08053	.832015	.865653	.966362	.033638	13	
.80	48	.67944	.73373	.92601	1.07990	.832152	.865536	.966616	.033384	12	.20
	49	.67965	.73353	.92655	1.07927	.832288	.865419	.966869	.033131	11	
	50	.67987	.73333	.92709	1.07864	.832425	.865302	.967123	.032877	10	
.85	51	.68008	.73314	.92763	1.07801	.832561	.865185	.967376	.032624	9	.15
	52	.68029	.73294	.92817	1.07738	.832697	.865068	.967629	.032371	8	
	53	.68051	.73274	.92872	1.07676	.832833	.864950	.967883	.032117	7	
.90	54	.68072	.73254	.92926	1.07613	.832969	.864833	.968136	.031864	6	.10
	55	.68093	.73234	.92980	1.07550	.833105	.864716	.968389	.031611	5	
	56	.68115	.73215	.93034	1.07487	.833241	.864598	.968643	.031357	4	
.95	57	.68136	.73195	.93088	1.07425	.833377	.864481	.968896	.031104	3	.05
	58	.68157	.73175	.93143	1.07362	.833512	.864363	.969149	.030851	2	
	59	.68179	.73155	.93197	1.07299	.833648	.864245	.969403	.030597	1	
1.00	60	.68200	.73135	.93252	1.07237	9.833783	9.864127	9.969656	10.030344	0	.00
Decimals	Minutes	Cos	Sin	Cot	Tan	Cos	Sin	Cot	Tan	Minutes	Decimals
		Natural Values				Common Logarithms					

47°

Decimals	Minutes	Sin	Cos	Tan	Cot	Sin	Cos	Tan	Cot	Minutes	Decimals
		Natural Values				Common Logarithms					
.00	0	.68200	.73135	.93252	1.07237	9.833783	9.864127	9.969656	10.030344	60	1.00
	1	.68221	.73116	.93306	1.07174	.833919	.864010	.969909	.030091	59	
	2	.68242	.73096	.93360	1.07112	.834054	.863892	.970162	.029838	58	
.05	3	.68264	.73076	.93415	1.07049	.834189	.863774	.970416	.029584	57	.95
	4	.68285	.73056	.93469	1.06987	.834325	.863656	.970669	.029331	56	
	5	.68306	.73036	.93524	1.06925	.834460	.863538	.970922	.029078	55	
.10	6	.68327	.73016	.93578	1.06862	.834595	.863419	.971175	.028825	54	.90
	7	.68349	.72996	.93633	1.06800	.834730	.863301	.971429	.028571	53	
	8	.68370	.72976	.93688	1.06738	.834865	.863183	.971682	.028318	52	
.15	9	.68391	.72957	.93742	1.06676	.834999	.863064	.971935	.028065	51	.85
	10	.68412	.72937	.93797	1.06613	.835134	.862946	.972188	.027812	50	
	11	.68434	.72917	.93852	1.06551	.835269	.862827	.972441	.027559	49	
.20	12	.68455	.72897	.93906	1.06489	.835403	.862709	.972695	.027305	48	.80
	13	.68476	.72877	.93961	1.06427	.835538	.862590	.972948	.027052	47	
	14	.68497	.72857	.94016	1.06365	.835672	.862471	.973201	.026799	46	
.25	15	.68518	.72837	.94071	1.06303	.835807	.862353	.973454	.026546	45	.75
	16	.68539	.72817	.94125	1.06241	.835941	.862234	.973707	.026293	44	
	17	.68561	.72797	.94180	1.06179	.836075	.862115	.973960	.026040	43	
.30	18	.68582	.72777	.94235	1.06117	.836209	.861996	.974213	.025787	42	.70
	19	.68603	.72757	.94290	1.06056	.836343	.861877	.974466	.025534	41	
	20	.68624	.72737	.94345	1.05994	.836477	.861758	.974720	.025280	40	
.35	21	.68645	.72717	.94400	1.05932	.836611	.861638	.974973	.025027	39	.65
	22	.68666	.72697	.94455	1.05870	.836745	.861519	.975226	.024774	38	
	23	.68688	.72677	.94510	1.05809	.836878	.861400	.975479	.024521	37	
.40	24	.68709	.72657	.94565	1.05747	.837012	.861280	.975732	.024268	36	.60
	25	.68730	.72637	.94620	1.05685	.837146	.861161	.975985	.024015	35	
	26	.68751	.72617	.94676	1.05624	.837279	.861041	.976238	.023762	34	
.45	27	.68772	.72597	.94731	1.05562	.837412	.860922	.976491	.023509	33	.55
	28	.68793	.72577	.94786	1.05501	.837546	.860802	.976744	.023256	32	
	29	.68814	.72557	.94841	1.05439	.837679	.860682	.976997	.023003	31	
.50	30	.68835	.72537	.94896	1.05378	.837812	.860562	.977250	.022750	30	.50
	31	.68857	.72517	.94952	1.05317	.837945	.860442	.977503	.022497	29	
	32	.68878	.72497	.95007	1.05255	.838078	.860322	.977756	.022244	28	
.55	33	.68899	.72477	.95062	1.05194	.838211	.860202	.978009	.021991	27	.45
	34	.68920	.72457	.95118	1.05133	.838344	.860082	.978262	.021738	26	
	35	.68941	.72437	.95173	1.05072	.838477	.859962	.978515	.021485	25	
.60	36	.68962	.72417	.95229	1.05010	.838610	.859842	.978768	.021232	24	.40
	37	.68983	.72397	.95284	1.04949	.838742	.859721	.979021	.020979	23	
	38	.69004	.72377	.95340	1.04888	.838875	.859601	.979274	.020726	22	
.65	39	.69025	.72357	.95395	1.04827	.839007	.859480	.979527	.020473	21	.35
	40	.69046	.72337	.95451	1.04766	.839140	.859360	.979780	.020220	20	
	41	.69067	.72317	.95506	1.04705	.839272	.859239	.980033	.019967	19	
.70	42	.69088	.72297	.95562	1.04644	.839404	.859119	.980286	.019714	18	.30
	43	.69109	.72277	.95618	1.04583	.839536	.858998	.980538	.019462	17	
	44	.69130	.72257	.95673	1.04522	.839668	.858877	.980791	.019209	16	
.75	45	.69151	.72236	.95729	1.04461	.839800	.858756	.981044	.018956	15	.25
	46	.69172	.72216	.95785	1.04401	.839932	.858635	.981297	.018703	14	
	47	.69193	.72196	.95841	1.04340	.840064	.858514	.981550	.018450	13	
.80	48	.69214	.72176	.95897	1.04279	.840196	.858393	.981803	.018197	12	.20
	49	.69235	.72156	.95952	1.04218	.840328	.858272	.982056	.017944	11	
	50	.69256	.72136	.96008	1.04158	.840459	.858151	.982309	.017691	10	
.85	51	.69277	.72116	.96064	1.04097	.840591	.858029	.982562	.017438	9	.15
	52	.69298	.72095	.96120	1.04036	.840722	.857908	.982814	.017186	8	
	53	.69319	.72075	.96176	1.03976	.840854	.857786	.983067	.016933	7	
.90	54	.69340	.72055	.96232	1.03915	.840985	.857665	.983320	.016680	6	.10
	55	.69361	.72035	.96288	1.03855	.841116	.857543	.983573	.016427	5	
	56	.69382	.72015	.96344	1.03794	.841247	.857422	.983826	.016174	4	
.95	57	.69403	.71995	.96400	1.03734	.841378	.857300	.984079	.015921	3	.05
	58	.69424	.71974	.96457	1.03674	.841509	.857178	.984332	.015668	2	
	59	.69445	.71954	.96513	1.03613	.841640	.857056	.984584	.015416	1	
1.00	60	.69466	.71934	.96569	1.03553	9.841771	9.856934	9.984837	10.015163	0	.00

Decimals	Minutes	Cos	Sin	Cot	Tan	Cos	Sin	Cot	Tan	Minutes	Decimals
		Natural Values				Common Logarithms					

Decimals	Minutes	Natural Values				Common Logarithms				Minutes	Decimals
		Sin	Cos	Tan	Cot	Sin	Cos	Tan	Cot		
.00	0	.69466	.71934	.96569	1.03553	9.841771	9.856934	9.984837	10.015163	60	1.00
	1	.69487	.71914	.96625	1.03493	.841902	.856812	.985090	.014910	59	
	2	.69508	.71894	.96681	1.03433	.842033	.856690	.985343	.014657	58	
.05	3	.69529	.71873	.96738	1.03372	.842163	.856568	.985596	.014404	57	.95
	4	.69549	.71853	.96794	1.03312	.842294	.856446	.985848	.014152	56	
	5	.69570	.71833	.96850	1.03252	.842424	.856323	.986101	.013899	55	
.10	6	.69591	.71813	.96907	1.03192	.842555	.856201	.986354	.013646	54	.90
	7	.69612	.71792	.96963	1.03132	.842685	.856078	.986607	.013393	53	
	8	.69633	.71772	.97020	1.03072	.842815	.855956	.986860	.013140	52	
.15	9	.69654	.71752	.97076	1.03012	.842946	.855833	.987112	.012888	51	.85
	10	.69675	.71732	.97133	1.02952	.843076	.855711	.987365	.012635	50	
	11	.69696	.71711	.97189	1.02892	.843206	.855588	.987618	.012382	49	
.20	12	.69717	.71691	.97246	1.02832	.843336	.855465	.987871	.012129	48	.80
	13	.69737	.71671	.97302	1.02772	.843466	.855342	.988123	.011877	47	
	14	.69758	.71650	.97359	1.02713	.843595	.855219	.988376	.011624	46	
.25	15	.69779	.71630	.97416	1.02653	.843725	.855096	.988629	.011371	45	.75
	16	.69800	.71610	.97472	1.02593	.843855	.854973	.988882	.011118	44	
	17	.69821	.71590	.97529	1.02533	.843984	.854850	.989134	.010866	43	
.30	18	.69842	.71569	.97586	1.02474	.844114	.854727	.989387	.010613	42	.70
	19	.69862	.71549	.97643	1.02414	.844243	.854603	.989640	.010360	41	
	20	.69883	.71529	.97700	1.02355	.844372	.854480	.989893	.010107	40	
.35	21	.69904	.71508	.97756	1.02295	.844502	.854356	.990145	.009855	39	.65
	22	.69925	.71488	.97813	1.02236	.844631	.854233	.990398	.009602	38	
	23	.69946	.71468	.97870	1.02176	.844760	.854109	.990651	.009349	37	
.40	24	.69966	.71447	.97927	1.02117	.844889	.853986	.990903	.009097	36	.60
	25	.69987	.71427	.97984	1.02057	.845018	.853862	.991156	.008844	35	
	26	.70008	.71407	.98041	1.01998	.845147	.853738	.991409	.008591	34	
.45	27	.70029	.71386	.98098	1.01939	.845276	.853614	.991662	.008338	33	.55
	28	.70049	.71366	.98155	1.01879	.845405	.853490	.991914	.008086	32	
	29	.70070	.71345	.98213	1.01820	.845533	.853366	.992167	.007833	31	
.50	30	.70091	.71325	.98270	1.01761	.845662	.853242	.992420	.007580	30	.50
	31	.70112	.71305	.98327	1.01702	.845790	.853118	.992672	.007328	29	
	32	.70132	.71284	.98384	1.01642	.845919	.852994	.992925	.007075	28	
.55	33	.70153	.71264	.98441	1.01583	.846047	.852869	.993178	.006822	27	.45
	34	.70174	.71243	.98499	1.01524	.846175	.852745	.993431	.006569	26	
	35	.70195	.71223	.98556	1.01465	.846304	.852620	.993683	.006317	25	
.60	36	.70215	.71203	.98613	1.01406	.846432	.852496	.993936	.006064	24	.40
	37	.70236	.71182	.98671	1.01347	.846560	.852371	.994189	.005811	23	
	38	.70257	.71162	.98728	1.01288	.846688	.852247	.994441	.005559	22	
.65	39	.70277	.71141	.98786	1.01229	.846816	.852122	.994694	.005306	21	.35
	40	.70298	.71121	.98843	1.01170	.846944	.851997	.994947	.005053	20	
	41	.70319	.71100	.98901	1.01112	.847071	.851872	.995199	.004801	19	
.70	42	.70339	.71080	.98958	1.01053	.847199	.851747	.995452	.004548	18	.30
	43	.70360	.71059	.99016	1.00994	.847327	.851622	.995705	.004295	17	
	44	.70381	.71039	.99073	1.00935	.847454	.851497	.995957	.004043	16	
.75	45	.70401	.71019	.99131	1.00876	.847582	.851372	.996210	.003790	15	.25
	46	.70422	.70998	.99189	1.00818	.847709	.851246	.996463	.003537	14	
	47	.70443	.70978	.99247	1.00759	.847836	.851121	.996715	.003285	13	
.80	48	.70463	.70957	.99304	1.00701	.847964	.850996	.996968	.003032	12	.20
	49	.70484	.70937	.99362	1.00642	.848091	.850870	.997221	.002779	11	
	50	.70505	.70916	.99420	1.00583	.848218	.850745	.997473	.002527	10	
.85	51	.70525	.70896	.99478	1.00525	.848345	.850619	.997726	.002274	9	.15
	52	.70546	.70875	.99536	1.00467	.848472	.850493	.997979	.002021	8	
	53	.70567	.70855	.99594	1.00408	.848599	.850368	.998231	.001769	7	
.90	54	.70587	.70834	.99652	1.00350	.848726	.850242	.998484	.001516	6	.10
	55	.70608	.70813	.99710	1.00291	.848852	.850116	.998737	.001263	5	
	56	.70628	.70793	.99768	1.00233	.848979	.849990	.998989	.001011	4	
.95	57	.70649	.70772	.99826	1.00175	.849106	.849864	.999242	.000758	3	.05
	58	.70670	.70752	.99884	1.00116	.849232	.849738	.999495	.000505	2	
	59	.70690	.70731	.99942	1.00058	.849359	.849611	.999747	.000253	1	
1.00	60	.70711	.70711	1.00000	1.00000	9.849485	9.849485	10.000000	10.000000	0	.00
Decimals	Minutes	Cos	Sin	Cot	Tan	Cos	Sin	Cot	Tan	Minutes	Decimals
		Natural Values				Common Logarithms					

Table 18.　Values and Logarithms of Exponentials and Hyperbolic Functions

The following tables give values of e^x, e^{-x}, sinh x, cosh x and tanh x for values of x from 0.00 to 6.00 in intervals of 0.01.

To facilitate computations involving multiplication, the common logarithms of e^x, sinh x, cosh x, and tanh x are also given.

For values of x greater than 6: e^x may be computed from the relationship $e^x = \log^{-1}(x \log_{10} e) = \log^{-1} 0.43429x$; e^{-x} approaches zero; sinh x and cosh x are approximately equal and become $0.5\, e^x$; and tanh x and coth x have values approximately equal to unity.

Where more accurate values of the exponentials and functions are required they may be computed from the following relationships.

$$e = 2.71828\ 18285 \qquad\qquad \frac{1}{e} = 0.36787\ 94412$$

$$M = \log_{10} e = 0.43429\ 44819 \qquad\qquad \frac{1}{M} = \log_e 10 = 2.30258\ 50930$$

$$e^x = \log^{-1} Mx \qquad\qquad e^{-x} = \log^{-1} - Mx$$

$$\text{Sinh } x = \frac{e^x - e^{-x}}{2} \qquad \cosh x = \frac{e^x + e^{-x}}{2} \qquad \tanh x = \frac{e^x - e^{-x}}{e^x + e^{-x}}$$

$$\text{csch } x = \frac{1}{\sinh x} \qquad \text{sech } x = \frac{1}{\cosh x} \qquad \coth x = \frac{1}{\tanh x}$$

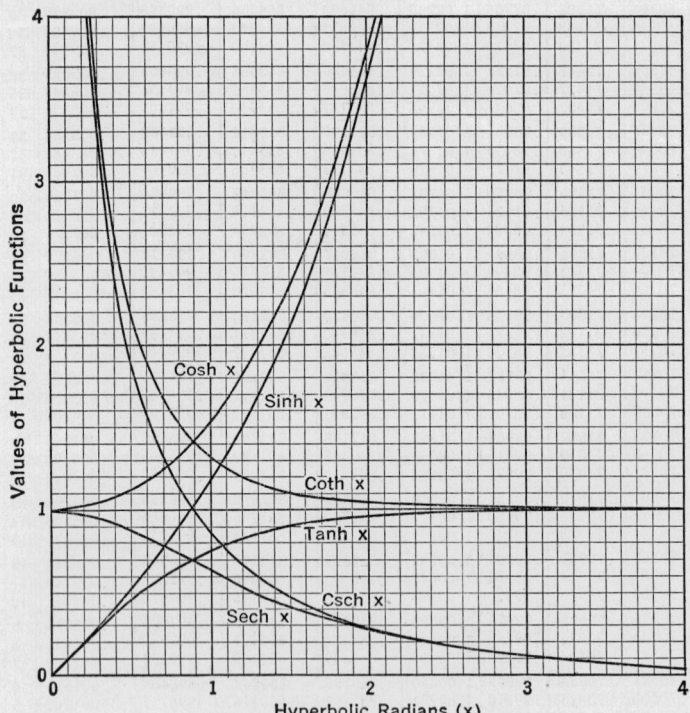

Chart of the Hyperbolic Functions.

x	Natural Values					Common Logarithms			
	e^x	e^{-x}	Sinh x	Cosh x	Tanh x	e^x	Sinh x	Cosh x	Tanh x
0.00	1.0000	1.0000	0.0000	1.0000	.00000	0.00000	− ∞	0.00000	− ∞
0.01	1.0101	.99005	0.0100	1.0001	.01000	.00434	$\bar{2}$.00001	.00002	$\bar{3}$.99999
0.02	1.0202	.98020	0.0200	1.0002	.02000	.00869	.30106	.00009	$\bar{2}$.30097
0.03	1.0305	.97045	0.0300	1.0005	.02999	.01303	.47719	.00020	.47699
0.04	1.0408	.96079	0.0400	1.0008	.03998	.01737	.60218	.00035	.60183
0.05	1.0513	.95123	0.0500	1.0013	.04996	.02171	.69915	.00054	.69861
0.06	1.0618	.94176	0.0600	1.0018	.05993	.02606	.77841	.00078	.77763
0.07	1.0725	.93239	0.0701	1.0025	.06989	.03040	.84545	.00106	.84439
0.08	1.0833	.92312	0.0801	1.0032	.07983	.03474	.90355	.00139	.90216
0.09	1.0942	.91393	0.0901	1.0041	.08976	.03909	.95483	.00176	.95307
0.10	1.1052	.90484	0.1002	1.0050	.09967	0.04343	$\bar{1}$.00072	0.00217	$\bar{2}$.99856
0.11	1.1163	.89583	0.1102	1.0061	.10956	.04777	.04227	.00262	$\bar{1}$.03965
0.12	1.1275	.88692	0.1203	1.0072	.11943	.05212	.08022	.00312	.07710
0.13	1.1388	.87810	0.1304	1.0085	.12927	.05646	.11517	.00366	.11151
0.14	1.1503	.86936	0.1405	1.0098	.13909	.06080	.14755	.00424	.14330
0.15	1.1618	.86071	0.1506	1.0113	.14889	.06514	.17772	.00487	.17285
0.16	1.1735	.85214	0.1607	1.0128	.15865	.06949	.20597	.00554	.20044
0.17	1.1853	.84366	0.1708	1.0145	.16838	.07383	.23254	.00625	.22629
0.18	1.1972	.83527	0.1810	1.0162	.17808	.07817	.25762	.00700	.25062
0.19	1.2092	.82696	0.1911	1.0181	.18775	.08252	.28136	.00779	.27357
0.20	1.2214	.81873	0.2013	1.0201	.19738	0.08685	$\bar{1}$.30392	0.00863	$\bar{1}$.29529
0.21	1.2337	.81058	0.2115	1.0221	.20697	.09120	.32541	.00951	.31590
0.22	1.2461	.80252	0.2218	1.0243	.21652	.09554	.34592	.01043	.33549
0.23	1.2586	.79453	0.2320	1.0266	.22603	.09989	.36555	.01139	.35416
0.24	1.2712	.78663	0.2423	1.0289	.23550	.10423	.38437	.01239	.37198
0.25	1.2840	.77880	0.2526	1.0314	.24492	.10857	.40245	.01343	.38902
0.26	1.2969	.77105	0.2629	1.0340	.25430	.11292	.41986	.01452	.40534
0.27	1.3100	.76338	0.2733	1.0367	.26362	.11726	.43663	.01564	.42099
0.28	1.3231	.75578	0.2837	1.0395	.27291	.12160	.45282	.01681	.43601
0.29	1.3364	.74826	0.2941	1.0423	.28213	.12595	.46847	.01801	.45046
0.30	1.3499	.74082	0.3045	1.0453	.29131	0.13029	1.48362	0.01926	$\bar{1}$.46436
0.31	1.3634	.73345	0.3150	1.0484	.30044	.13463	.49830	.02054	.47775
0.32	1.3771	.72615	0.3255	1.0516	.30951	.13897	.51254	.02107	.49067
0.33	1.3910	.71892	0.3360	1.0549	.31852	.14332	.52637	.02323	.50314
0.34	1.4049	.71177	0.3466	1.0584	.32748	.14766	.53981	.02463	.51518
0.35	1.4191	.70469	0.3572	1.0619	.33638	.15200	.55290	.02607	.52682
0.36	1.4333	.69768	0.3678	1.0655	.34521	.15635	.56564	.02755	.53809
0.37	1.4477	.69073	0.3785	1.0692	.35399	.16069	.57807	.02907	.54899
0.38	1.4623	.68386	0.3892	1.0731	.36271	.16503	.59019	.03063	.55956
0.39	1.4770	.67706	0.4000	1.0770	.37136	.16937	.60202	.03222	.56980
0.40	1.4918	.67032	0.4108	1.0811	.37995	0.17372	$\bar{1}$.61358	0.03385	$\bar{1}$.57973
0.41	1.5068	.66365	0.4216	1.0852	.38847	.17806	.62488	.03552	.58936
0.42	1.5220	.65705	0.4325	1.0895	.39693	.18240	.63594	.03723	.59871
0.43	1.5373	.65051	0.4434	1.0939	.40532	.18675	.64677	.03897	.60780
0.44	1.5527	.64404	0.4543	1.0984	.41364	.19109	.65738	.04075	.61663
0.45	1.5683	.63763	0.4653	1.1030	.42190	.19543	.66777	.04256	.62521
0.46	1.5841	.63128	0.4764	1.1077	.43008	.19978	.67797	.04441	.63355
0.47	1.6000	.62500	0.4875	1.1125	.43820	.20412	.68797	.04630	.64167
0.48	1.6161	.61878	0.4986	1.1174	.44624	.20846	.69779	.04822	.64957
0.49	1.6323	.61263	0.5098	1.1225	.45422	.21280	.70744	.05018	.65726
0.50	1.6487	.60653	0.5211	1.1276	.46212	0.21715	1.71692	0.05217	1.66475
0.51	1.6653	.60050	0.5324	1.1329	.46995	.22149	.72624	.05419	.67205
0.52	1.6820	.59452	0.5438	1.1383	.47770	.22583	.73540	.05625	.67916
0.53	1.6989	.58860	0.5552	1.1438	.48538	.23018	.74442	.05834	.68608
0.54	1.7160	.58275	0.5666	1.1494	.49299	.23452	.75330	.06046	.69284
0.55	1.7333	.57695	0.5782	1.1551	.50052	.23886	.76204	.06262	.69942
0.56	1.7507	.57121	0.5897	1.1609	.50798	.24320	.77065	.06481	.70584
0.57	1.7683	.56553	0.6014	1.1669	.51536	.24755	.77914	.06703	.71211
0.58	1.7860	.55990	0.6131	1.1730	.52267	.25189	.78751	.06929	.71822
0.59	1.8040	.55433	0.6248	1.1792	.52990	.25623	.79576	.07157	.72419
0.60	1.8221	.54881	0.6367	1.1855	.53705	0.26058	$\bar{1}$.80390	0.07389	$\bar{1}$.73001

x	e^x	e^{-x}	Sinh x	Cosh x	Tanh x	e^x	Sinh x	Cosh x	Tanh x
			Natural Values				Common Logarithms		
0.60	1.8221	.54881	0.6367	1.1855	.53705	0.26058	$\bar{1}$.80390	0.07389	$\bar{1}$.73001
0.61	1.8404	.54335	0.6485	1.1919	.54413	.26492	.81194	.07624	.73570
0.62	1.8589	.53794	0.6605	1.1984	.55113	.26926	.81987	.07861	.74125
0.63	1.8776	.53259	0.6725	1.2051	.55805	.27361	.82770	.08102	.74667
0.64	1.8965	.52729	0.6846	1.2119	.56490	.27795	.83543	.08346	.75197
0.65	1.9155	.52205	0.6967	1.2188	.57167	.28229	.84308	.08593	.75715
0.66	1.9348	.51685	0.7090	1.2258	.57836	.28663	.85063	.08843	.76220
0.67	1.9542	.51171	0.7213	1.2330	.58498	.29098	.85809	.09095	.76714
0.68	1.9739	.50662	0.7336	1.2402	.59152	.29532	.86548	.09351	.77197
0.69	1.9937	.50158	0.7461	1.2476	.59798	.29966	.87278	.09609	.77669
0.70	2.0138	.49659	0.7586	1.2552	.60437	0.30401	$\bar{1}$.88000	0.09870	$\bar{1}$.78130
0.71	2.0340	.49164	0.7712	1.2628	.61068	.30835	.88715	.10134	.78581
0.72	2.0544	.48675	0.7838	1.2706	.61691	.31269	.89423	.10401	.79022
0.73	2.0751	.48191	0.7966	1.2785	.62307	.31704	.90123	.10670	.79453
0.74	2.0959	.47711	0.8094	1.2865	.62915	.32138	.90817	.10942	.79875
0.75	2.1170	.47237	0.8223	1.2947	.63515	.32572	.91504	.11216	.80288
0.76	2.1383	.46767	0.8353	1.3030	.64108	.33006	.92185	.11493	.80691
0.77	2.1598	.46301	0.8484	1.3114	.64693	.33441	.92859	.11773	.81086
0.78	2.1815	.45841	0.8615	1.3199	.65271	.33875	.93527	.12055	.81472
0.79	2.2034	.45384	0.8748	1.3286	.65841	.34309	.94190	.12340	.81850
0.80	2.2255	.44933	0.8881	1.3374	.66404	0.34744	$\bar{1}$.94846	0.12627	1.82219
0.81	2.2479	.44486	0.9015	1.3464	.66959	.35178	.95498	.12917	.82581
0.82	2.2705	.44043	0.9150	1.3555	.67507	.35612	.96144	.13209	.82935
0.83	2.2933	.43605	0.9286	1.3647	.68048	.36046	.96784	.13503	.83281
0.84	2.3164	.43171	0.9423	1.3740	.68581	.36481	.97420	.13800	.83620
0.85	2.3396	.42741	0.9561	1.3835	.69107	.36915	.98051	.14099	.83952
0.86	2.3632	.42316	0.9700	1.3932	.69626	.37349	.98677	.14400	.84277
0.87	2.3869	.41895	0.9840	1.4029	.70137	.37784	.99299	.14704	.84595
0.88	2.4109	.41478	0.9981	1.4128	.70642	.38218	.99916	.15009	.84906
0.89	2.4351	.41066	1.0122	1.4229	.71139	.38652	0.00528	.15317	.85211
0.90	2.4596	.40657	1.0265	1.4331	.71630	0.39087	0.01137	0.15627	$\bar{1}$.85509
0.91	2.4843	.40252	1.0409	1.4434	.72113	.39521	.01741	.15939	.85801
0.92	2.5093	.39852	1.0554	1.4539	.72590	.39955	.02341	.16254	.86088
0.93	2.5345	.39455	1.0700	1.4645	.73059	.40389	.02937	.16570	.86368
0.94	2.5600	.39063	1.0847	1.4753	.73522	.40824	.03530	.16888	.86642
0.95	2.5857	.38674	1.0995	1.4862	.73978	.41258	.04119	.17208	.86910
0.96	2.6117	.38289	1.1144	1.4973	.74428	.41692	.04704	.17531	.87173
0.97	2.6379	.37908	1.1294	1.5085	.74870	.42127	.05286	.17855	.87431
0.98	2.6645	.37531	1.1446	1.5199	.75307	.42561	.05864	.18181	.87683
0.99	2.6912	.37158	1.1598	1.5314	.75736	.42995	.06439	.18509	.87930
1.00	2.7183	.36788	1.1752	1.5431	.76159	0.43429	0.07011	0.18839	$\bar{1}$.88172
1.01	2.7456	.36422	1.1907	1.5549	.76576	.43864	.07580	.19171	.88409
1.02	2.7732	.36059	1.2063	1.5669	.76987	.44298	.08146	.19504	.88642
1.03	2.8011	.35701	1.2220	1.5790	.77391	.44732	.08708	.19839	.88869
1.04	2.8292	.35345	1.2379	1.5913	.77789	.45167	.09268	.20176	.89092
1.05	2.8577	.34994	1.2539	1.6038	.78181	.45601	.09825	.20515	.89310
1.06	2.8864	.34646	1.2700	1.6164	.78566	.46035	.10379	.20855	.89524
1.07	2.9154	.34301	1.2862	1.6292	.78946	.46470	.10930	.21197	.89733
1.08	2.9447	.33960	1.3025	1.6421	.79320	.46904	.11479	.21541	.89938
1.09	2.9743	.33622	1.3190	1.6552	.79688	.47338	.12025	.21886	.90139
1.10	3.0042	.33287	1.3356	1.6685	.80050	0.47772	0.12569	0.22233	$\bar{1}$.90336
1.11	3.0344	.32956	1.3524	1.6820	.80406	.48207	.13111	.22582	.90529
1.12	3.0649	.32628	1.3693	1.6956	.80757	.48641	.13649	.22931	.90718
1.13	3.0957	.32303	1.3863	1.7093	.81102	.49075	.14186	.23283	.90903
1.14	3.1268	.31982	1.4035	1.7233	.81441	.49510	.14720	.23636	.91085
1.15	3.1582	.31664	1.4208	1.7374	.81775	.49944	.15253	.23990	.91262
1.16	3.1899	.31349	1.4382	1.7517	.82104	.50378	.15783	.24346	.91436
1.17	3.2220	.31037	1.4558	1.7662	.82427	.50812	.16311	.24703	.91607
1.18	3.2544	.30728	1.4735	1.7808	.82745	.51247	.16836	.25062	.91774
1.19	3.2871	.30422	1.4914	1.7957	.83058	.51681	.17360	.25422	.91938
1.20	3.3201	.30119	1.5095	1.8107	.83365	0.52115	0.17882	0.25784	$\bar{1}$.92099

x	Natural Values					Common Logarithms			
	e^x	e^{-x}	Sinh x	Cosh x	Tanh x	e^x	Sinh x	Cosh x	Tanh x
1.20	3.3201	.30119	1.5095	1.8107	.83365	0.52115	0.17882	0.25784	1.92099
1.21	3.3535	.29820	1.5276	1.8258	.83668	.52550	.18402	.26146	.92256
1.22	3.3872	.29523	1.5460	1.8412	.83965	.52984	.18920	.26510	.92410
1.23	3.4212	.29229	1.5645	1.8568	.84258	.53418	.19437	.26876	.92561
1.24	3.4556	.28938	1.5831	1.8725	.84546	.53853	.19951	.27242	.92709
1.25	3.4903	.28650	1.6019	1.8884	.84828	.54287	.20464	.27610	.92854
1.26	3.5254	.28365	1.6209	1.9045	.85106	.54721	.20975	.27979	.92996
1.27	3.5609	.28083	1.6400	1.9208	.85380	.55155	.21485	.28349	.93135
1.28	3.5966	.27804	1.6593	1.9373	.85648	.55590	.21993	.28721	.93272
1.29	3.6328	.27527	1.6788	1.9540	.85913	.56024	.22499	.29093	.93406
1.30	3.6693	.27253	1.6984	1.9709	.86172	0.56458	0.23004	0.29467	1.93537
1.31	3.7062	.26982	1.7182	1.9880	.86428	.56893	.23507	.29842	.93665
1.32	3.7434	.26714	1.7381	2.0053	.86678	.57327	.24009	.30217	.93791
1.33	3.7810	.26448	1.7583	2.0228	.86925	.57761	.24509	.30594	.93914
1.34	3.8190	.26185	1.7786	2.0404	.87167	.58195	.25008	.30972	.94035
1.35	3.8574	.25924	1.7991	2.0583	.87405	.58630	.25505	.31352	.94154
1.36	3.8962	.25666	1.8198	2.0764	.87639	.59064	.26002	.31732	.94270
1.37	3.9354	.25411	1.8406	2.0947	.87869	.59498	.26496	.32113	.94384
1.38	3.9749	.25158	1.8617	2.1132	.88095	.59933	.26990	.32495	.94495
1.39	4.0149	.24908	1.8829	2.1320	.88317	.60367	.27482	.32878	.94604
1.40	4.0552	.24660	1.9043	2.1509	.88535	0.60801	0.27974	0.33262	1.94712
1.41	4.0960	.24414	1.9259	2.1700	.88749	.61236	.28464	.33647	.94817
1.42	4.1371	.24171	1.9477	2.1894	.88960	.61670	.28952	.34033	.94919
1.43	4.1787	.23931	1.9697	2.2090	.89167	.62104	.29440	.34420	.95020
1.44	4.2207	.23693	1.9919	2.2288	.89370	.62538	.29926	.34807	.95119
1.45	4.2631	.23457	2.0143	2.2488	.89569	.62973	.30412	.35196	.95216
1.46	4.3060	.23224	2.0369	2.2691	.89765	.63407	.30896	.35585	.95311
1.47	4.3492	.22993	2.0597	2.2896	.89958	.63841	.31379	.35976	.95404
1.48	4.3929	.22764	2.0827	2.3103	.90147	.64276	.31862	.36367	.95495
1.49	4.4371	.22537	2.1059	2.3312	.90332	.64710	.32343	.36759	.95584
1.50	4.4817	.22313	2.1293	2.3524	.90515	0.65144	0.32823	0.37151	1.95672
1.51	4.5267	.22091	2.1529	2.3738	.90694	.65578	.33303	.37545	.95758
1.52	4.5722	.21871	2.1768	2.3955	.90870	.66013	.33781	.37939	.95842
1.53	4.6182	.21654	2.2008	2.4174	.91042	.66447	.34258	.38334	.95924
1.54	4.6646	.21438	2.2251	2.4395	.91212	.66881	.34735	.38730	.96005
1.55	4.7115	.21225	2.2496	2.4619	.91379	.67316	.35211	.39126	.96084
1.56	4.7588	.21014	2.2743	2.4845	.91542	.67750	.35686	.39524	.96162
1.57	4.8066	.20805	2.2993	2.5073	.91703	.68184	.36160	.39921	.96238
1.58	4.8550	.20598	2.3245	2.5305	.91860	.68619	.36633	.40320	.96313
1.59	4.9037	.20393	2.3499	2.5538	.92015	.69053	.37105	.40719	.96386
1.60	4.9530	.20190	2.3756	2.5775	.92167	0.69487	0.37577	0.41119	1.96457
1.61	5.0028	.19989	2.4015	2.6013	.92316	.69921	.38048	.41520	.96528
1.62	5.0531	.19790	2.4276	2.6255	.92462	.70356	.38518	.41921	.96597
1.63	5.1039	.19593	2.4540	2.6499	.92606	.70790	.38987	.42323	.96664
1.64	5.1552	.19398	2.4806	2.6746	.92747	.71224	.39456	.42725	.96730
1.65	5.2070	.19205	2.5075	2.6995	.92886	.71659	.39923	.43129	.96795
1.66	5.2593	.19014	2.5346	2.7247	.93022	.72093	.40391	.43532	.96858
1.67	5.3122	.18825	2.5620	2.7502	.93155	.72527	.40857	.43937	.96921
1.68	5.3656	.18637	2.5896	2.7760	.93286	.72961	.41323	.44341	.96982
1.69	5.4195	.18452	2.6175	2.8020	.93415	.73396	.41788	.44747	.97042
1.70	5.4739	.18268	2.6456	2.8283	.93541	0.73830	0.42253	0.45153	1.97100
1.71	5.5290	.18087	2.6740	2.8549	.93665	.74264	.42717	.45559	.97158
1.72	5.5845	.17907	2.7027	2.8818	.93786	.74699	.43180	.45966	.97214
1.73	5.6407	.17728	2.7317	2.9090	.93906	.75133	.43643	.46374	.97269
1.74	5.6973	.17552	2.7609	2.9364	.94023	.75567	.44105	.46782	.97323
1.75	5.7546	.17377	2.7904	2.9642	.94138	.76002	.44567	.47191	.97376
1.76	5.8124	.17204	2.8202	2.9922	.94250	.76436	.45028	.47600	.97428
1.77	5.8709	.17033	2.8503	3.0206	.94361	.76870	.45488	.48009	.97479
1.78	5.9299	.16864	2.8806	3.0492	.94470	.77304	.45948	.48419	.97529
1.79	5.9895	.16696	2.9112	3.0782	.94576	.77739	.46408	.48830	.97578
1.80	6.0496	.16530	2.9422	3.1075	.94681	0.78173	0.46867	0.49241	1.97626

x	Natural Values					Common Logarithms			
	e^x	e^{-x}	Sinh x	Cosh x	Tanh x	e^x	Sinh x	Cosh x	Tanh x
1.80	**6.0496**	**.16530**	**2.9422**	**3.1075**	**.94681**	**0.78173**	**0.46867**	**0.49241**	**$\bar{1}$.97626**
1.81	6.1104	.16365	2.9734	3.1371	.94783	.78607	.47325	.49652	.97673
1.82	6.1719	.16203	3.0049	3.1669	.94884	.79042	.47783	.50064	.97719
1.83	6.2339	.16041	3.0367	3.1972	.94983	.79476	.48241	.50476	.97764
1.84	6.2965	.15882	3.0689	3.2277	.95080	.79910	.48698	.50889	.97809
1.85	6.3598	.15724	3.1013	3.2585	.95175	.80344	.49154	.51302	.97852
1.86	6.4237	.15567	3.1340	3.2897	.95268	.80779	.49610	.51716	.97895
1.87	6.4883	.15412	3.1671	3.3212	.95359	.81213	.50066	.52130	.97936
1.88	6.5535	.15259	3.2005	3.3530	.95449	.81647	.50521	.52544	.97977
1.89	6.6194	.15107	3.2341	3.3852	.95537	.82082	.50976	.52959	.98017
1.90	**6.6859**	**.14957**	**3.2682**	**3.4177**	**.95624**	**0.82516**	**0.51430**	**0.53374**	**$\bar{1}$.98057**
1.91	6.7531	.14808	3.3025	3.4506	.95709	.82950	.51884	.53789	.98095
1.92	6.8210	.14661	3.3372	3.4838	.95792	.83385	.52338	.54205	.98133
1.93	6.8895	.14515	3.3722	3.5173	.95873	.83819	.52791	.54621	.98170
1.94	6.9588	.14370	3.4075	3.5512	.95953	.84253	.53244	.55038	.98206
1.95	7.0287	.14227	3.4432	3.5855	.96032	.84687	.53696	.55455	.98242
1.96	7.0993	.14086	3.4792	3.6201	.96109	.85122	.54148	.55872	.98272
1.97	7.1707	.13946	3.5156	3.6551	.96185	.85556	.54600	.56290	.98311
1.98	7.2427	.13807	3.5523	3.6904	.96259	.85990	.55051	.56707	.98344
1.99	7.3155	.13670	3.5894	3.7261	.96331	.86425	.55502	.57126	.98377
2.00	**7.3891**	**.13534**	**3.6269**	**3.7622**	**.96403**	**0.86859**	**0.55953**	**0.57544**	**$\bar{1}$.98409**
2.01	7.4633	.13399	3.6647	3.7987	.96473	.87293	.56403	.57963	.98440
2.02	7.5383	.13266	3.7028	3.8355	.96541	.87727	.56853	.58382	.98471
2.03	7.6141	.13134	3.7414	3.8727	.96609	.88162	.57303	.58802	.98502
2.04	7.6906	.13003	3.7803	3.9103	.96675	.88596	.57753	.59221	.98531
2.05	7.7679	.12873	3.8196	3.9483	.96740	.89030	.58202	.59641	.98560
2.06	7.8460	.12745	3.8593	3.9867	.96803	.89465	.58650	.60061	.98589
2.07	7.9248	.12619	3.8993	4.0255	.96865	.89899	.59099	.60482	.98617
2.08	8.0045	.12493	3.9398	4.0647	.96926	.90333	.59547	.60903	.98644
2.09	8.0849	.12369	3.9806	4.1043	.96986	.90768	.59995	.61324	.98671
2.10	**8.1662**	**.12246**	**4.0219**	**4.1443**	**.97045**	**0.91202**	**0.60443**	**0.61745**	**$\bar{1}$.98697**
2.11	8.2482	.12124	4.0635	4.1847	.97103	.91636	.60890	.62167	.98723
2.12	8.3311	.12003	4.1056	4.2256	.97159	.92070	.61337	.62589	.98748
2.13	8.4149	.11884	4.1480	4.2669	.97215	.92505	.61784	.63011	.98773
2.14	8.4994	.11765	4.1909	4.3085	.97269	.92939	.62231	.63433	.98798
2.15	8.5849	.11648	4.2342	4.3507	.97323	.93373	.62677	.63856	.98821
2.16	8.6711	.11533	4.2779	4.3932	.97375	.93808	.63123	.64278	.98845
2.17	8.7583	.11418	4.3221	4.4362	.97426	.94242	.63569	.64701	.98868
2.18	8.8463	.11304	4.3666	4.4797	.97477	.94676	.64015	.65125	.98890
2.19	8.9352	.11192	4.4116	4.5236	.97526	.95110	.64460	.65548	.98912
2.20	**9.0250**	**.11080**	**4.4571**	**4.5679**	**.97574**	**0.95545**	**0.64905**	**0.65972**	**$\bar{1}$.98934**
2.21	9.1157	.10970	4.5030	4.6127	.97622	.95979	.65350	.66396	.98955
2.22	9.2073	.10861	4.5494	4.6580	.97668	.96413	.65795	.66820	.98975
2.23	9.2999	.10753	4.5962	4.7037	.97714	.96848	.66240	.67244	.98996
2.24	9.3933	.10646	4.6434	4.7499	.97759	.97282	.66684	.67668	.99016
2.25	9.4877	.10540	4.6912	4.7966	.97803	.97716	.67128	.68093	.99035
2.26	9.5831	.10435	4.7394	4.8437	.97846	.98151	.67572	.68518	.99054
2.27	9.6794	.10331	4.7880	4.8914	.97888	.98585	.68016	.68943	.99073
2.28	9.7767	.10228	4.8372	4.9395	.97929	.99019	.68459	.69368	.99091
2.29	9.8749	.10127	4.8868	4.9881	.97970	.99453	.68903	.69794	.99109
2.30	**9.9742**	**.10026**	**4.9370**	**5.0372**	**.98010**	**0.99888**	**0.69346**	**0.70219**	**$\bar{1}$.99127**
2.31	10.074	.09926	4.9876	5.0868	.98049	1.00322	.69789	.70645	.99144
2.32	10.176	.09827	5.0387	5.1370	.98087	.00756	.70232	.71071	.99161
2.33	10.278	.09730	5.0903	5.1876	.98124	.01191	.70675	.71497	.99178
2.34	10.381	.09633	5.1425	5.2388	.98161	.01625	.71117	.71923	.99194
2.35	10.486	.09537	5.1951	5.2905	.98197	.02059	.71559	.72349	.99210
2.36	10.591	.09442	5.2483	5.3427	.98233	.02493	.72002	.72776	.99226
2.37	10.697	.09348	5.3020	5.3954	.98267	.02928	.72444	.73203	.99241
2.38	10.805	.09255	5.3562	5.4487	.98301	.03362	.72885	.73630	.99256
2.39	10.913	.09163	5.4109	5.5026	.98335	.03796	.73327	.74056	.99271
2.40	**11.023**	**.09072**	**5.4662**	**5.5569**	**.98367**	**1.04231**	**0.73769**	**0.74484**	**$\bar{1}$.99285**

x	Natural Values					Common Logarithms			
	e^x	e^{-x}	Sinh x	Cosh x	Tanh x	e^x	Sinh x	Cosh x	Tanh x
2.40	11.023	.09072	5.4662	5.5569	.98367	1.04231	0.73769	0.74484	$\overline{1}$.99285
2.41	11.134	.08982	5.5221	5.6119	.98400	.04665	.74210	.74911	.99299
2.42	11.246	.08892	5.5785	5.6674	.98431	.05099	.74652	.75338	.99313
2.43	11.359	.08804	5.6354	5.7235	.98462	.05534	.75093	.75766	.99327
2.44	11.473	.08716	5.6929	5.7801	.98492	.05968	.75534	.76194	.99340
2.45	11.588	.08629	5.7510	5.8373	.98522	.06402	.75975	.76621	.99353
2.46	11.705	.08543	5.8097	5.8951	.98551	.06836	.76415	.77049	.99366
2.47	11.822	.08458	5.8689	5.9535	.98579	.07271	.76856	.77477	.99379
2.48	11.941	.08374	5.9288	6.0125	.98607	.07705	.77296	.77906	.99391
2.49	12.061	.08291	5.9892	6.0721	.98635	.08139	.77737	.78334	.99403
2.50	12.182	.08208	6.0502	6.1323	.98661	1.08574	0.78177	0.78762	$\overline{1}$.99415
2.51	12.305	.08127	6.1118	6.1931	.98688	.09008	.78617	.79191	.99426
2.52	12.429	.08046	6.1741	6.2545	.98714	.09442	.79057	.79619	.99438
2.53	12.554	.07966	6.2369	6.3166	.98739	.09877	.79497	.80048	.99449
2.54	12.680	.07887	6.3004	6.3793	.98764	.10311	.79937	.80477	.99460
2.55	12.807	.07808	6.3645	6.4426	.98788	.10745	.80377	.80906	.99470
2.56	12.936	.07730	6.4293	6.5066	.98812	.11179	.80816	.81335	.99480
2.57	13.066	.07654	6.4946	6.5712	.98835	.11614	.81256	.81764	.99491
2.58	13.197	.07577	6.5607	6.6365	.98858	.12048	.81695	.82194	.99501
2.59	13.330	.07502	6.6274	6.7024	.98881	.12482	.82134	.82623	.99511
2.60	13.464	.07427	6.6947	6.7690	.98903	1.12917	0.82573	0.83052	$\overline{1}$.99521
2.61	13.599	.07353	6.7628	6.8363	.98924	.13351	.83012	.83482	.99530
2.62	13.736	.07280	6.8315	6.9043	.98946	.13785	.83451	.83912	.99540
2.63	13.874	.07208	6.9008	6.9729	.98966	.14219	.83890	.84341	.99549
2.64	14.013	.07136	6.9709	7.0423	.98987	.14654	.84329	.84771	.99558
2.65	14.154	.07065	7.0417	7.1123	.99007	.15088	.84768	.85201	.99566
2.66	14.296	.06995	7.1132	7.1831	.99026	.15522	.85206	.85631	.99575
2.67	14.440	.06925	7.1854	7.2546	.99045	.15957	.85645	.86061	.99583
2.68	14.585	.06856	7.2583	7.3268	.99064	.16391	.86083	.86492	.99592
2.69	14.732	.06788	7.3319	7.3998	.99083	.16825	.86522	.86922	.99600
2.70	14.880	.06721	7.4063	7.4735	.99101	1.17260	0.86960	0.87352	$\overline{1}$.99608
2.71	15.029	.06654	7.4814	7.5479	.99118	.17694	.87398	.87783	.99615
2.72	15.180	.06587	7.5572	7.6231	.99136	.18128	.87836	.88213	.99623
2.73	15.333	.06522	7.6338	7.6991	.99153	.18562	.88274	.88644	.99631
2.74	15.487	.06457	7.7112	7.7758	.99170	.18997	.88712	.89074	.99638
2.75	15.643	.06393	7.7894	7.8533	.99186	.19431	.89150	.89505	.99645
2.76	15.800	.06329	7.8683	7.9316	.99202	.19865	.89588	.89936	.99652
2.77	15.959	.06266	7.9480	8.0106	.99218	.20300	.90026	.90367	.99659
2.78	16.119	.06204	8.0285	8.0905	.99233	.20734	.90463	.90798	.99666
2.79	16.281	.06142	8.1098	8.1712	.99248	.21168	.90901	.91229	.99672
2.80	16.445	.06081	8.1919	8.2527	.99263	1.21602	0.91339	0.91660	$\overline{1}$.99679
2.81	16.610	.06020	8.2749	8.3351	.99278	.22037	.91776	.92091	.99685
2.82	16.777	.05961	8.3586	8.4182	.99292	.22471	.92213	.92522	.99691
2.83	16.945	.05901	8.4432	8.5022	.99306	.22905	.92651	.92953	.99698
2.84	17.116	.05843	8.5287	8.5871	.99320	.23340	.93088	.93385	.99704
2.85	17.288	.05784	8.6150	8.6728	.99333	.23774	.93525	.93816	.99709
2.86	17.462	.05727	8.7021	8.7594	.99346	.24208	.93963	.94247	.99715
2.87	17.637	.05670	8.7902	8.8469	.99359	.24643	.94400	.94679	.99721
2.88	17.814	.05613	8.8791	8.9352	.99372	.25077	.94837	.95110	.99726
2.89	17.993	.05558	8.9689	9.0244	.99384	.25511	.95274	.95542	.99732
2.90	18.174	.05502	9.0596	9.1146	.99396	1.25945	0.95711	0.95974	$\overline{1}$.99737
2.91	18.357	.05448	9.1512	9.2056	.99408	.26380	.96148	.96405	.99742
2.92	18.541	.05393	9.2437	9.2976	.99420	.26814	.96584	.96837	.99747
2.93	18.728	.05340	9.3371	9.3905	.99431	.27248	.97021	.97269	.99752
2.94	18.916	.05287	9.4315	9.4844	.99443	.27683	.97458	.97701	.99757
2.95	19.106	.05234	9.5268	9.5791	.99454	.28117	.97895	.98133	.99762
2.96	19.298	.05182	9.6231	9.6749	.99464	.28551	.98331	.98565	.99767
2.97	19.492	.05130	9.7203	9.7716	.99475	.28985	.98768	.98997	.99771
2.98	19.688	.05079	9.8185	9.8693	.99485	.29420	.99205	.99429	.99776
2.99	19.886	.05029	9.9177	9.9680	.99496	.29854	.99641	.99861	.99780
3.00	20.086	.04979	10.018	10.063	.99505	1.30288	1.00078	1.00293	$\overline{1}$.99785

x	Natural Values					Common Logarithms			
	e^x	e^{-x}	Sinh x	Cosh x	Tanh x	e^x	Sinh x	Cosh x	Tanh x
3.00	20.086	.04979	10.018	10.068	.99505	1.30288	1.00078	1.00293	$\bar{1}$.99785
3.01	20.287	.04929	10.119	10.168	.99515	.30723	.00514	.00725	.99789
3.02	20.491	.04880	10.221	10.270	.99525	.31157	.00950	.01157	.99793
3.03	20.697	.04832	10.325	10.373	.99534	.31591	.01387	.01589	.99797
3.04	20.905	.04783	10.429	10.477	.99543	.32026	.01823	.02022	.99801
3.05	21.115	.04736	10.534	10.581	.99552	.32460	.02259	.02454	.99805
3.06	21.328	.04689	10.640	10.687	.99561	.32894	.02696	.02886	.99809
3.07	21.542	.04642	10.748	10.794	.99570	.33328	.03132	.03319	.99813
3.08	21.758	.04596	10.856	10.902	.99578	.33763	.03568	.03751	.99817
3.09	21.977	.04550	10.966	11.011	.99587	.34197	.04004	.04184	.99820
3.10	22.198	.04505	11.077	11.122	.99595	1.34631	1.04440	1.04616	$\bar{1}$.99824
3.11	22.421	.04460	11.188	11.233	.99603	.35066	.04876	.05049	.99827
3.12	22.646	.04416	11.301	11.345	.99611	.35500	.05312	.05481	.99831
3.13	22.874	.04372	11.415	11.459	.99618	.35934	.05748	.05914	.99834
3.14	23.104	.04328	11.530	11.574	.99626	.36368	.06184	.06347	.99837
3.15	23.336	.04285	11.647	11.689	.99633	.36803	.06620	.06779	.99841
3.16	23.571	.04243	11.764	11.807	.99641	.37237	.07056	.07212	.99844
3.17	23.807	.04200	11.883	11.925	.99648	.37671	.07492	.07645	.99847
3.18	24.047	.04159	12.003	12.044	.99655	.38106	.07927	.08078	.99850
3.19	24.288	.04117	12.124	12.165	.99662	.38540	.08363	.08510	.99853
3.20	24.533	.04076	12.246	12.287	.99668	1.38974	1.08799	1.08943	$\bar{1}$.99856
3.21	24.779	.04036	12.369	12.410	.99675	.39409	.09235	.09376	.99859
3.22	25.028	.03996	12.494	12.534	.99681	.39843	.09670	.09809	.99861
3.23	25.280	.03956	12.620	12.660	.99688	.40277	.10106	.10242	.99864
3.24	25.534	.03916	12.747	12.786	.99694	.40711	.10542	.10675	.99867
3.25	25.790	.03877	12.876	12.915	.99700	.41146	.10977	.11108	.99869
3.26	26.050	.03839	13.006	13.044	.99706	.41580	.11413	.11541	.99872
3.27	26.311	.03801	13.137	13.175	.99712	.42014	.11849	.11974	.99875
3.28	26.576	.03763	13.269	13.307	.99717	.42449	.12284	.12407	.99877
3.29	26.843	.03725	13.403	13.440	.99723	.42883	.12720	.12840	.99879
3.30	27.113	.03688	13.538	13.575	.99728	1.43317	1.13155	1.13273	$\bar{1}$.99882
3.31	27.385	.03652	13.674	13.711	.99734	43751	.13591	.13706	.99884
3.32	27.660	.03615	13.812	13.848	.99739	.44186	.14026	.14139	.99886
3.33	27.938	.03579	13.951	13.987	.99744	.44620	.14461	.14573	.99889
3.34	28.219	.03544	14.092	14.127	.99749	.45054	.14897	.15006	.99891
3.35	28.503	.03508	14.234	14.269	.99754	.45489	.15332	.15439	.99893
3.36	28.789	.03474	14.377	14.412	.99759	.45923	.15768	.15872	.99895
3.37	29.079	.03439	14.522	14.556	.99764	.46357	.16203	.16306	.99897
3.38	29.371	.03405	14.668	14.702	.99768	.46792	.16638	.16739	.99899
3.39	29.666	.03371	14.816	14.850	.99773	.47226	.17073	.17172	.99901
3.40	29.964	.03337	14.965	14.999	.99777	1.47660	1.17509	1.17605	$\bar{1}$.99903
3.41	30.265	.03304	15.116	15.149	.99782	.48094	.17944	.18039	.99905
3.42	30.569	.03271	15.268	15.301	.99786	.48529	.18379	.18472	.99907
3.43	30.877	.03239	15.422	15.455	.99790	.48963	.18814	.18906	.99909
3.44	31.187	.03206	15.577	15.610	.99795	.49397	.19250	.19339	.99911
3.45	31.500	.03175	15.734	15.766	.99799	.49832	.19685	.19772	.99912
3.46	31.817	.03143	15.893	15.924	.99803	.50266	.20120	.20206	.99914
3.47	32.137	.03112	16.053	16.084	.99807	.50700	.20555	.20639	.99916
3.48	32.460	.03081	16.215	16.245	.99810	.51134	.20990	.21073	.99918
3.49	32.786	.03050	16.378	16.408	.99814	.51569	.21425	.21506	.99919
3.50	33.115	.03020	16.543	16.573	.99818	1.52003	1.21860	1.21940	$\bar{1}$.99921
3.51	33.448	.02990	16.709	16.739	.99821	.52437	.22296	.22373	.99922
3.52	33.784	.02960	16.877	16.907	.99825	.52872	.22731	.22807	.99924
3.53	34.124	.02930	17.047	17.077	.99828	.53306	.23166	.23240	.99925
3.54	34.467	.02901	17.219	17.248	.99832	.53740	.23601	.23674	.99927
3.55	34.813	.02872	17.392	17.421	.99835	.54175	.24036	.24107	.99928
3.56	35.163	.02844	17.567	17.596	.99838	.54609	.24471	.24541	.99930
3.57	35.517	.02816	17.744	17.772	.99842	.55043	.24906	.24975	.99931
3.58	35.874	.02788	17.923	17.951	.99845	.55477	.25341	.25408	.99933
3.59	36.234	.02760	18.103	18.131	.99848	.55912	.25776	.25842	.99934
3.60	36.598	.02732	18.285	18.313	.99851	1.56346	1.26211	1.26275	$\bar{1}$.99935

x	Natural Values					Common Logarithms			
	e^x	e^{-x}	Sinh x	Cosh x	Tanh x	e^x	Sinh x	Cosh x	Tanh x
3.60	36.598	.02732	18.285	18.313	.99851	1.56346	1.26211	1.26275	1̄.99935
3.61	36.966	.02705	18.470	18.497	.99854	.56780	.26646	.26709	.99936
3.62	37.338	.02678	18.655	18.682	.99857	.57215	.27080	.27143	.99938
3.63	37.713	.02652	18.843	18.870	.99859	.57649	.27515	.27576	.99939
3.64	38.092	.02625	19.033	19.059	.99862	.58083	.27950	.28010	.99940
3.65	38.475	.02599	19.224	19.250	.99865	.58517	.28385	.28444	.99941
3.66	38.861	.02573	19.418	19.444	.99868	.58952	.28820	.28878	.99942
3.67	39.252	.02548	19.613	19.639	.99870	.59386	.29255	.29311	.99944
3.68	39.646	.02522	19.811	19.836	.99873	.59820	.29690	.29745	.99945
3.69	40.045	.02497	20.010	20.035	.99875	.60255	.30125	.30179	.99946
3.70	40.447	.02472	20.211	20.236	.99878	1.60689	1.30559	1.30612	1̄.99947
3.71	40.854	.02448	20.415	20.439	.99880	.61123	.30994	.31046	.99948
3.72	41.264	.02423	20.620	20.644	.99883	.61558	.31429	.31480	.99949
3.73	41.679	.02399	20.828	20.852	.99885	.61992	.31864	.31914	.99950
3.74	42.098	.02375	21.037	21.061	.99887	.62426	.32299	.32348	.99951
3.75	42.521	.02352	21.249	21.272	.99889	.62860	.32733	.32781	.99952
3.76	42.948	.02328	21.463	21.486	.99892	.63295	.33168	.33215	.99953
3.77	43.380	.02305	21.679	21.702	.99894	.63729	.33603	.33649	.99954
3.78	43.816	.02282	21.897	21.919	.99896	.64163	.34038	.34083	.99955
3.79	44.256	.02260	22.117	22.140	.99898	.64598	.34472	.34517	.99956
3.80	44.701	.02237	22.339	22.362	.99900	1.65032	1.34907	1.34951	1̄.99957
3.81	45.150	.02215	22.564	22.586	.99902	.65466	.35342	.35384	.99957
3.82	45.604	.02193	22.791	22.813	.99904	.65900	.35777	.35818	.99958
3.83	46.063	.02171	23.020	23.042	.99906	.66335	.36211	.36252	.99959
3.84	46.525	.02149	23.252	23.274	.99908	.66769	.36646	.36686	.99960
3.85	46.993	.02128	23.486	23.507	.99909	.67203	.37081	.37120	.99961
3.86	47.465	.02107	23.722	23.743	.99911	.67638	.37515	.37554	.99961
3.87	47.942	.02086	23.961	23.982	.99913	.68072	.37950	.37988	.99962
3.88	48.424	.02065	24.202	24.222	.99915	.68506	.38385	.38422	.99963
3.89	48.911	.02045	24.445	24.466	.99916	.68941	.38819	.38856	.99964
3.90	49.402	.02024	24.691	24.711	.99918	1.69375	1.39254	1.39290	1̄.99964
3.91	49.899	.02004	24.939	24.960	.99920	.69809	.39689	.39724	.99965
3.92	50.400	.01984	25.190	25.210	.99921	.70243	.40123	.40158	.99966
3.93	50.907	.01964	25.444	25.463	.99923	.70678	.40558	.40591	.99966
3.94	51.419	.01945	25.700	25.719	.99924	.71112	.40993	.41025	.99967
3.95	51.935	.01925	25.958	25.977	.99926	.71546	.41427	.41459	.99968
3.96	52.457	.01906	26.219	26.238	.99927	.71981	.41862	.41893	.99968
3.97	52.985	.01887	26.483	26.502	.99929	.72415	.42296	.42327	.99969
3.98	53.517	.01869	26.749	26.768	.99930	.72849	.42731	.42761	.99970
3.99	54.055	.01850	27.018	27.037	.99932	.73284	.43166	.43195	.99970
4.00	54.598	.01832	27.290	27.308	.99933	1.73718	1.43600	1.43629	1̄.99971
4.01	55.147	.01813	27.564	27.583	.99934	.74152	.44035	.44063	.99971
4.02	55.701	.01795	27.842	27.860	.99936	.74586	.44469	.44497	.99972
4.03	56.261	.01777	28.122	28.139	.99937	.75021	.44904	.44931	.99973
4.04	56.826	.01760	28.404	28.422	.99938	.75455	.45339	.45365	.99973
4.05	57.397	.01742	28.690	28.707	.99939	.75889	.45773	.45799	.99974
4.06	57.974	.01725	28.979	28.996	.99941	.76324	.46208	.46233	.99974
4.07	58.557	.01708	29.270	29.287	.99942	.76758	.46642	.46668	.99975
4.08	59.145	.01691	29.564	29.581	.99943	.77192	.47077	.47102	.99975
4.09	59.740	.01674	29.862	29.878	.99944	.77626	.47511	.47536	.99976
4.10	60.340	.01657	30.162	30.178	.99945	1.78061	1.47946	1.47970	1̄.99976
4.11	60.947	.01641	30.465	30.482	.99946	.78495	.48380	.48404	.99977
4.12	61.559	.01624	30.772	30.788	.99947	.78929	.48815	.48838	.99977
4.13	62.178	.01608	31.081	31.097	.99948	.79364	.49249	.49272	.99978
4.14	62.803	.01592	31.393	31.409	.99949	.79798	.49684	.49706	.99978
4.15	63.434	.01576	31.709	31.725	.99950	.80232	.50118	.50140	.99978
4.16	64.072	.01561	32.028	32.044	.99951	.80667	.50553	.50574	.99979
4.17	64.715	.01545	32.350	32.365	.99952	.81101	.50987	.51008	.99979
4.18	65.366	.01530	32.675	32.691	.99953	.81535	.51422	.51442	.99980
4.19	66.023	.01515	33.004	33.019	.99954	.81969	.51856	.51876	.99980
4.20	66.686	.01500	33.336	33.351	.99955	1.82404	1.52291	1.52310	1̄.99980

x	Natural Values					Common Logarithms			
	e^x	e^{-x}	Sinh x	Cosh x	Tanh x	e^x	Sinh x	Cosh x	Tanh x
4.20	66.686	.01500	33.336	33.351	.99955	1.82404	1.52291	1.52310	$\bar{1}$.99980
4.21	67.357	.01485	33.671	33.686	.99956	.82838	.52725	.52745	.99981
4.22	68.033	.01470	34.009	34.024	.99957	.83272	.531 0	.53179	.99981
4.23	68.717	.01455	34.351	34.366	.99958	.83707	.53594	.53613	.99982
4.24	69.408	.01441	34.697	34.711	.99958	.84141	.54029	.54047	.99982
4.25	70.105	.01426	35.046	35.060	.99959	.84575	.54463	.54481	.99982
4.26	70.810	.01412	35.398	35.412	.99960	.85009	.54898	.54915	.99983
4.27	71.522	.01398	35.754	35.768	.99961	.85444	.55332	.55349	.99983
4.28	72.240	.01384	36.113	36.127	.99962	.85878	.55767	.55783	.99983
4.29	72.966	.01370	36.476	36.490	.99962	.86312	.56201	.56217	.99984
4.30	73.700	.01357	36.843	36.857	.99963	1.86747	1.56636	1.56652	$\bar{1}$.99984
4.31	74.440	.01343	37.214	37.227	.99964	.87181	.57070	.57086	.99984
4.32	75.189	.01330	37.588	37.601	.99965	.87615	.57505	.57520	.99985
4.33	75.944	.01317	37.966	37.979	.99965	.88050	.57939	.57954	.99985
4.34	76.708	.01304	38.347	38.360	.99966	.88484	.58373	.58388	.99985
4.35	77.478	.01291	38.733	38.746	.99967	.88918	.58808	.58822	.99986
4.36	78.257	.01278	39.122	39.135	.99967	.89352	.59242	.59256	.99986
4.37	79.044	.01265	39.515	39.528	.99968	.89787	.59677	.59691	.99986
4.38	79.838	.01253	39.913	39.925	.99969	.90221	.60111	.60125	.99986
4.39	80.640	.01240	40.314	40.326	.99969	.90655	.60546	.60559	.99987
4.40	81.451	.01228	40.719	40.732	.99970	1.91090	1.60980	1.60993	$\bar{1}$.99987
4.41	82.269	.01216	41.129	41.141	.99970	.91524	.61414	.61427	.99987
4.42	83.096	.01203	41.542	41.554	.99971	.91958	.61849	.61861	.99987
4.43	83.931	.01191	41.960	41.972	.99972	.92392	.62283	.62296	.99988
4.44	84.775	.01180	42.382	42.393	.99972	.92827	.62718	.62730	.99988
4.45	85.627	.01168	42.808	42.819	.99973	.93261	.63152	.63164	.99988
4.46	86.488	.01156	43.238	43.250	.99973	.93695	.63587	.63598	.99988
4.47	87.357	.01145	43.673	43.684	.99974	.94130	.64021	.64032	.99989
4.48	88.235	.01133	44.112	44.123	.99974	.94564	.64455	.64467	.99989
4.49	89.121	.01122	44.555	44.566	.99975	.94998	.64890	.64901	.99989
4.50	90.017	.01111	45.003	45.014	.99975	1.95433	1.65324	1.65335	$\bar{1}$.99989
4.51	90.922	.01100	45.455	45.466	.99976	.95867	.65759	.65769	.99989
4.52	91.836	.01089	45.912	45.923	.99976	.96301	.66193	.66203	.99990
4.53	92.759	.01078	46.374	46.385	.99977	.96735	.66627	.66637	.99990
4.54	93.691	.01067	46.840	46.851	.99977	.97170	.67062	.67072	.99990
4.55	94.632	.01057	47.311	47.321	.99978	.97604	.67496	.67506	.99990
4.56	95.583	.01046	47.787	47.797	.99978	.98038	.67931	.67940	.99990
4.57	96.544	.01036	48.267	48.277	.99979	.98473	.68365	.68374	.99991
4.58	97.514	.01025	48.752	48.762	.99979	.98907	.68799	.68808	.99991
4.59	98.494	.01015	49.242	49.252	.99979	.99341	.69234	.69243	.99991
4.60	99.484	.01005	49.737	49.747	.99980	1.99775	1.69668	1.69677	$\bar{1}$.99991
4.61	100.48	.00995	50.237	50.247	.99980	2.00210	.70102	.70111	.99991
4.62	101.49	.00985	50.742	50.752	.99981	.00644	.70537	.70545	.99992
4.63	102.51	.00975	51.252	51.262	.99981	.01078	.70971	.70979	.99992
4.64	103.54	.00966	51.767	51.777	.99981	.01513	.71406	.71414	.99992
4.65	104.58	.00956	52.288	52.297	.99982	.01947	.71840	.71848	.99992
4.66	105.64	.00947	52.813	52.823	.99982	.02381	.72274	.72282	.99992
4.67	106.70	.00937	53.344	53.354	.99982	.02816	.72709	.72716	.99993
4.68	107.77	.00928	53.880	53.890	.99983	.03250	.73143	.73151	.99993
4.69	108.85	.00919	54.422	54.431	.99983	.03684	.73577	.73585	.99993
4.70	109.95	.00910	54.969	54.978	.99983	2.04118	1.74012	1.74019	$\bar{1}$.99993
4.71	111.05	.00900	55.522	55.531	.99984	.04553	.74446	.74453	.99993
4.72	112.17	.00892	56.080	56.089	.99984	.04987	.74881	.74887	.99993
4.73	113.30	.00883	56.643	56.652	.99984	.05421	.75315	.75322	.99993
4.74	114.43	.00874	57.213	57.222	.99985	.05856	.75749	.75756	.99993
4.75	115.58	.00865	57.788	57.796	.99985	.06290	.76184	.76190	.99993
4.76	116.75	.00857	58.369	58.377	.99985	.06724	.76618	.76624	.99994
4.77	117.92	.00848	58.955	58.964	.99986	.07158	.77052	.77059	.99994
4.78	119.10	.00840	59.548	59.556	.99986	.07593	.77487	.77493	.99994
4.79	120.30	.00831	60.147	60.155	.99986	.08027	.77921	.77927	.99994
4.80	121.51	.00823	60.751	60.759	.99986	2.08461	1.78355	1.78361	$\bar{1}$.99994

x	Natural Values					Common Logarithms			
	e^x	e^{-x}	Sinh x	Cosh x	Tanh x	e^x	Sinh x	Cosh x	Tanh x
4.80	121.51	.00823	60.751	60.760	.99986	2.08461	1.78355	1.78361	1̄.99994
4.81	122.73	.00815	61.362	61.370	.99987	.08896	.78790	.78796	.99994
4.82	123.97	.00807	61.979	61.987	.99987	.09330	.79224	.79230	.99994
4.83	125.21	.00799	62.601	62.609	.99987	.09764	.79658	.79664	.99994
4.84	126.47	.00791	63.231	63.239	.99987	.10199	.80093	.80098	.99995
4.85	127.74	.00783	63.866	63.874	.99988	.10633	.80527	.80532	.99995
4.86	129.02	.00775	64.508	64.516	.99988	.11067	.80962	.80967	.99995
4.87	130.32	.00767	65.157	65.164	.99988	.11501	.81396	.81401	.99995
4.88	131.63	.00760	65.812	65.819	.99988	.11936	.81830	.81835	.99995
4.89	132.95	.00752	66.473	66.481	.99989	.12370	.82265	.82269	.99995
4.90	134.29	.00745	67.141	67.149	.99989	2.12804	1.82699	1.82704	1̄.99995
4.91	135.64	.00737	67.816	67.823	.99989	.13239	.83133	.83138	.99995
4.92	137.00	.00730	68.498	68.505	.99989	.13673	.83568	.83572	.99995
4.93	138.38	.00723	69.186	69.193	.99990	.14107	.84002	.84006	.99995
4.94	139.77	.00715	69.882	69.889	.99990	.14541	.84436	.84441	.99996
4.95	141.17	.00708	70.584	70.591	.99990	.14976	.84871	.84875	.99996
4.96	142.59	.00701	71.293	71.300	.99990	.15410	.85305	.85309	.99996
4.97	144.03	.00694	72.010	72.017	.99990	.15844	.85739	.85743	.99996
4.98	145.47	.00687	72.734	72.741	.99991	.16279	.86174	.86178	.99996
4.99	146.94	.00681	73.465	73.472	.99991	.16713	.86608	.86612	.99996
5.00	148.41	.00674	74.203	74.210	.99991	2.17147	1.87042	1.87046	1̄.99996
5.01	149.90	.00667	74.949	74.956	.99991	.17582	.87477	.87480	.99996
5.02	151.41	.00660	75.702	75.710	.99991	.18016	.87911	.87915	.99996
5.03	152.93	.00654	76.463	76.470	.99991	.18450	.88345	.88349	.99996
5.04	154.47	.00647	77.232	77.238	.99992	.18884	.88780	.88783	.99996
5.05	156.02	.00641	78.008	78.014	.99992	.19319	.89214	.89217	.99996
5.06	157.59	.00635	78.792	78.798	.99992	.19753	.89648	.89652	.99997
5.07	159.17	.00628	79.584	79.590	.99992	.20187	.90083	.90086	.99997
5.08	160.77	.00622	80.384	80.390	.99992	.20622	.90517	.90520	.99997
5.09	162.39	.00616	81.192	81.198	.99992	.21056	.90951	.90955	.99997
5.10	164.02	.00610	82.008	82.014	.99993	2.21490	1.91386	1.91389	1̄.99997
5.11	165.67	.00604	82.832	82.838	.99993	.21924	.91820	.91823	.99997
5.12	167.34	.00598	83.665	83.671	.99993	.22359	.92254	.92257	.99997
5.13	169.02	.00592	84.506	84.512	.99993	.22793	.92689	.92692	.99997
5.14	170.72	.00586	85.355	85.361	.99993	.23227	.93123	.93126	.99997
5.15	172.43	.00580	86.213	86.219	.99993	.23662	.93557	.93560	.99997
5.16	174.16	.00574	87.079	87.085	.99993	.24096	.93992	.93994	.99997
5.17	175.91	.00568	87.955	87.960	.99994	.24530	.94426	.94429	.99997
5.18	177.68	.00563	88.839	88.844	.99994	.24965	.94860	.94863	.99997
5.19	179.47	.00557	89.732	89.737	.99994	.25399	.95294	.95297	.99997
5.20	181.27	.00552	90.633	90.639	.99994	2.25833	1.95729	1.95731	1̄.99997
5.21	183.09	.00546	91.544	91.550	.99994	.26267	.96163	.96166	.99997
5.22	184.93	.00541	92.464	92.470	.99994	.26702	.96597	.96600	.99997
5.23	186.79	.00535	93.394	93.399	.99994	.27136	.97032	.97034	.99998
5.24	188.67	.00530	94.332	94.338	.99994	.27570	.97466	.97469	.99998
5.25	190.57	.00525	95.281	95.286	.99994	.28005	.97900	.97903	.99998
5.26	192.48	.00520	96.238	96.243	.99995	.28439	.98335	.98337	.99998
5.27	194.42	.00514	97.205	97.211	.99995	.28873	.98769	.98771	.99998
5.28	196.37	.00509	98.182	98.188	.99995	.29307	.99203	.99206	.99998
5.29	198.34	.00504	99.169	99.174	.99995	.29742	.99638	.99640	.99998
5.30	200.34	.00499	100.17	100.17	.99995	2.30176	2.00072	2.00074	1̄.99998
5.31	202.35	.00494	101.17	101.18	.99995	.30610	.00506	.00508	.99998
5.32	204.38	.00489	102.19	102.19	.99995	.31045	.00941	.00943	.99998
5.33	206.44	.00484	103.22	103.22	.99995	.31479	.01375	.01377	.99998
5.34	208.51	.00480	104.25	104.26	.99995	.31913	.01809	.01811	.99998
5.35	210.61	.00475	105.30	105.31	.99995	.32348	.02244	.02246	.99998
5.36	212.72	.00470	106.36	106.36	.99996	.32782	.02678	.02680	.99998
5.37	214.86	.00465	107.43	107.43	.99996	.33216	.03112	.03114	.99998
5.38	217.02	.00461	108.51	108.51	.99996	.33650	.03547	.03548	.99998
5.39	219.20	.00456	109.60	109.60	.99996	.34085	.03981	.03983	.99998
5.40	221.41	.00452	110.70	110.71	.99996	2.34519	2.04415	2.04417	1̄.99998

x	Natural Values					Common Logarithms			
	e^x	e^{-x}	Sinh x	Cosh x	Tanh x	e^x	Sinh x	Cosh x	Tanh x
5.40	**221.41**	**.00452**	**110.70**	**110.71**	**.99996**	**2.34519**	**2.04415**	**2.04417**	**1̄.99998**
5.41	223.63	.00447	111.81	111.82	.99996	.34953	.04849	.04851	.99998
5.42	225.88	.00443	112.94	112.94	.99996	.35388	.05284	.05285	.99998
5.43	228.15	.00438	114.07	114.08	.99996	.35822	.05718	.05720	.99998
5.44	230.44	.00434	115.22	115.22	.99996	.36256	.06152	.06154	.99998
5.45	232.76	.00430	116.38	116.38	.99996	.36690	.06587	.06588	.99998
5.46	235.10	.00425	117.55	117.55	.99996	.37125	.07021	.07023	.99998
5.47	237.46	.00421	118.73	118.73	.99996	.37559	.07455	.07457	.99998
5.48	239.85	.00417	119.92	119.93	.99997	.37993	.07890	.07891	.99998
5.49	242.26	.00413	121.13	121.13	.99997	.38428	.08324	.08325	.99999
5.50	**244.69**	**.00409**	**122.34**	**122.35**	**.99997**	**2.38862**	**2.08758**	**2.08760**	**1̄.99999**
5.51	247.15	.00405	123.57	123.58	.99997	.39296	.09193	.09194	.99999
5.52	249.64	.00401	124.82	124.82	.99997	.39731	.09627	.09628	.99999
5.53	252.14	.00397	126.07	126.07	.99997	.40165	.10061	.10063	.99999
5.54	254.68	.00393	127.34	127.34	.99997	.40599	.10495	.10497	.99999
5.55	257.24	.00389	128.62	128.62	.99997	.41033	.10930	.10931	.99999
5.56	259.82	.00385	129.91	129.91	.99997	.41468	.11364	.11365	.99999
5.57	262.43	.00381	131.22	131.22	.99997	.41902	.11798	.11800	.99999
5.58	265.07	.00377	132.53	132.54	.99997	.42336	.12233	.12234	.99999
5.59	267.74	.00374	133.87	133.87	.99997	.42771	.12667	.12668	.99999
5.60	**270.43**	**.00370**	**135.21**	**135.22**	**.99997**	**2.43205**	**2.13101**	**2.13103**	**1̄.99999**
5.61	273.14	.00366	136.57	136.57	.99997	.43639	.13536	.13537	.99999
5.62	275.89	.00362	137.94	137.95	.99997	.44074	.13970	.13971	.99999
5.63	278.66	.00359	139.33	139.33	.99997	.44508	.14404	.14405	.99999
5.64	281.46	.00355	140.73	140.73	.99997	.44942	.14839	.14840	.99999
5.65	284.29	.00352	142.14	142.15	.99998	.45376	.15273	.15274	.99999
5.66	287.15	.00348	143.57	143.58	.99998	.45811	.15707	.15708	.99999
5.67	290.03	.00345	145.02	145.02	.99998	.46245	.16141	.16142	.99999
5.68	292.95	.00341	146.47	146.48	.99998	.46679	.16576	.16577	.99999
5.69	295.89	.00338	147.95	147.95	.99998	.47114	.17010	.17011	.99999
5.70	**298.87**	**.00335**	**149.43**	**149.44**	**.99998**	**2.47548**	**2.17444**	**2.17445**	**1̄.99999**
5.71	301.87	.00331	150.93	150.94	.99998	.47982	.17879	.17880	.99999
5.72	304.90	.00328	152.45	152.45	.99998	.48416	.18313	.18314	.99999
5.73	307.97	.00325	153.98	153.99	.99998	.48851	.18747	.18748	.99999
5.74	311.06	.00321	155.53	155.53	.99998	.49285	.19182	.19182	.99999
5.75	314.19	.00318	157.09	157.10	.99998	.49719	.19616	.19617	.99999
5.76	317.35	.00315	158.67	158.68	.99998	.50154	.20050	.20051	.99999
5.77	320.54	.00312	160.27	160.27	.99998	.50588	.20484	.20485	.99999
5.78	323.76	.00309	161.88	161.88	.99998	.51022	.20919	.20920	.99999
5.79	327.01	.00306	163.51	163.51	.99998	.51457	.21353	.21354	.99999
5.80	**330.30**	**.00303**	**165.15**	**165.15**	**.99998**	**2.51891**	**2.21787**	**2.21788**	**1̄.99999**
5.81	333.62	.00300	166.81	166.81	.99998	.52325	.22222	.22222	.99999
5.82	336.97	.00297	168.48	168.49	.99998	.52759	.22656	.22657	.99999
5.83	340.36	.00294	170.18	170.18	.99998	.53194	.23090	.23091	.99999
5.84	343.78	.00291	171.89	171.89	.99998	.53628	.23525	.23525	.99999
5.85	347.23	.00288	173.62	173.62	.99998	.54062	.23959	.23960	.99999
5.86	350.72	.00285	175.36	175.36	.99998	.54497	.24393	.24394	.99999
5.87	354.25	.00282	177.12	177.13	.99998	.54931	.24828	.24828	.99999
5.88	357.81	.00279	178.90	178.91	.99998	.55365	.25262	.25262	.99999
5.89	361.41	.00277	180.70	180.70	.99998	.55799	.25696	.25697	.99999
5.90	**365.04**	**.00274**	**182.52**	**182.52**	**.99998**	**2.56234**	**2.26130**	**2.26131**	**1̄.99999**
5.91	368.71	.00271	184.35	184.35	.99999	.56668	.26565	.26565	.99999
5.92	372.41	.00269	186.20	186.21	.99999	.57102	.26999	.27000	.99999
5.93	376.15	.00266	188.08	188.08	.99999	.57537	.27433	.27434	.99999
5.94	379.93	.00263	189.97	189.97	.99999	.57971	.27868	.27868	.99999
5.95	383.75	.00261	191.88	191.88	.99999	.58405	.28302	.28303	.99999
5.96	387.61	.00258	193.80	193.81	.99999	.58840	.28736	.28737	.99999
5.97	391.51	.00255	195.75	195.75	.99999	.59274	.29171	.29171	.99999
5.98	395.44	.00253	197.72	197.72	.99999	.59708	.29605	.29605	.99999
5.99	399.41	.00250	199.71	199.71	.99999	.60142	.30039	.30040	.99999
6.00	**403.43**	**.00248**	**201.71**	**201.72**	**.99999**	**2.60577**	**2.30473**	**2.30474**	**1̄.99999**

Table 19. Table of Integrals

Elementary Indefinite Integrals

1. $\int a\,dx = ax + c$

2. $\int (u + v + w + \ldots)dx = \int u\,dx + \int v\,dx + \int w\,dx + \ldots$

3. $\int u\,dv = uv - \int v\,du$, integration by parts

4. $\int f(x)\,dx = \int f[\phi(y)]\phi'(y)dy$, $x = \phi(y)$, change of variable

5. $\int x^n\,dx = \dfrac{x^{n+1}}{n+1} + c$, $(n \neq -1)$

6. $\int \dfrac{dx}{x} = \log_e x + c = \log_e c_1 x$, $[\log_e x = \log_e(-x) + (2k+1)\pi i]$

7. $\int e^{ax}\,dx = \dfrac{1}{a}e^{ax} + c$

8. $\int a^x\,dx = \dfrac{a^x}{\log_e a} + c$

9. $\int a^x \log_e a\,dx = a^x + c$

10. $\int \sin ax\,dx = -\dfrac{1}{a}\cos ax + c$

11. $\int \cos ax\,dx = \dfrac{1}{a}\sin ax + c$

12. $\int \tan ax\,dx = -\dfrac{1}{a}\log_e \cos ax + c = \dfrac{1}{a}\log_e \sec ax + c$

13. $\int \cot ax\,dx = \dfrac{1}{a}\log_e \sin ax + c = -\dfrac{1}{a}\log_e \csc ax + c$

14. $\int \sec ax\,dx = \dfrac{1}{a}\log_e(\sec ax + \tan ax) + c = \dfrac{1}{a}\log_e \tan\left(\dfrac{ax}{2} + \dfrac{\pi}{4}\right) + c$

15. $\int \csc ax\,dx = \dfrac{1}{a}\log_e(\csc ax - \cot ax) + c = \dfrac{1}{a}\log_e \tan\dfrac{ax}{2} + c$

16. $\int \dfrac{dx}{\sqrt{a^2 - x^2}} = \sin^{-1}\dfrac{x}{a} + c = -\cos^{-1}\dfrac{x}{a} + c$ $(x^2 < a^2)$

17. $\int \dfrac{dx}{a^2 + x^2} = \dfrac{1}{a}\tan^{-1}\dfrac{x}{a} + c = -\dfrac{1}{a}\cot^{-1}\dfrac{x}{a} + c$

18. $\int \sinh ax\,dx = \dfrac{1}{a}\cosh ax + c$

19. $\int \cosh ax\,dx = \dfrac{1}{a}\sinh ax + c$

20. $\int \tanh ax\,dx = \dfrac{1}{a}\log_e(\cosh ax) + c$

21. $\int \coth ax\,dx = \dfrac{1}{a}\log_e(\sinh ax) + c$

22. $\int \operatorname{sech} ax\,dx = \dfrac{1}{a}\sin^{-1}(\tanh ax) + c$

23. $\int \operatorname{csch} ax\,dx = \dfrac{1}{a}\log_e\left(\tanh\dfrac{ax}{2}\right) + c$

24. $\int \sin^2 ax\,dx = \dfrac{1}{2}x - \dfrac{1}{2a}\sin ax \cos ax + c = \dfrac{1}{2}x - \dfrac{1}{4a}\sin 2ax + c$

25. $\int \cos^2 ax\,dx = \dfrac{1}{2}x + \dfrac{1}{2a}\sin ax \cos ax + c = \dfrac{1}{2}x + \dfrac{1}{4a}\sin 2ax + c$

26. $\int \tan^2 ax\,dx = \dfrac{1}{a}\tan ax - x + c$

27. $\int \cot^2 ax\,dx = -\dfrac{1}{a}\cot ax - x + c$

Elementary Indefinite Integrals—*Continued*

28. $\int \sec^2 ax \, dx = \dfrac{1}{a} \tan ax + c$

29. $\int \csc^2 ax \, dx = -\dfrac{1}{a} \cot ax + c$

30. $\int \sin^{-1} ax \, dx = x \sin^{-1} ax + \dfrac{1}{a} \sqrt{1 - a^2 x^2} + c$

31. $\int \cos^{-1} ax \, dx = x \cos^{-1} ax - \dfrac{1}{a} \sqrt{1 - a^2 x^2} + c$

32. $\int \tan^{-1} ax \, dx = x \tan^{-1} ax - \dfrac{1}{2a} \log_e (1 + a^2 x^2) + c$

33. $\int \cot^{-1} ax \, dx = x \cot^{-1} ax + \dfrac{1}{2a} \log_e (1 + a^2 x^2) + c$

34. $\int \sec^{-1} ax \, dx = x \sec^{-1} ax - \dfrac{1}{a} \log_e (ax + \sqrt{a^2 x^2 - 1}) + c$

35. $\int \csc^{-1} ax \, dx = x \csc^{-1} ax + \dfrac{1}{a} \log_e (ax + \sqrt{a^2 x^2 - 1}) + c$

Integrals Involving $(ax + b)$

36. $\int (ax + b)^n \, dx = \dfrac{1}{a(n + 1)} (ax + b)^{n+1} \quad (n \neq -1)$

37. $\int \dfrac{dx}{ax + b} = \dfrac{1}{a} \log_e (ax + b)$

38. $\int x(ax + b)^n \, dx = \dfrac{1}{a^2(n + 2)} (ax + b)^{n+2} - \dfrac{b}{a^2(n + 1)} (ax + b)^{n+1} (n \neq -1, -2)$

39. $\int \dfrac{x \, dx}{ax + b} = \dfrac{x}{a} - \dfrac{b}{a^2} \log_e (ax + b)$

40. $\int \dfrac{x \, dx}{(ax + b)^2} = \dfrac{b}{a^2(ax + b)} + \dfrac{1}{a^2} \log_e (ax + b)$

41. $\int \dfrac{x^2 \, dx}{ax + b} = \dfrac{1}{a^3} \left[\dfrac{1}{2}(ax + b)^2 - 2b(ax + b) + b^2 \log_e (ax + b) \right]$

42. $\int \dfrac{x^2 \, dx}{(ax + b)^2} = \dfrac{1}{a^3} \left[(ax + b) - 2b \log_e (ax + b) - \dfrac{b^2}{ax + b} \right]$

43. $\int \dfrac{x^2 \, dx}{(ax + b)^3} = \dfrac{1}{a^3} \left[\log_e (ax + b) + \dfrac{2b}{ax + b} - \dfrac{b^2}{2(ax + b)^2} \right]$

44. $\int \dfrac{dx}{x(ax + b)} = \dfrac{1}{b} \log_e \dfrac{x}{ax + b}$

45. $\int \dfrac{dx}{x^2 (ax + b)} = -\dfrac{1}{bx} + \dfrac{a}{b^2} \log_e \dfrac{ax + b}{x}$

46. $\int \dfrac{dx}{x(ax + b)^2} = \dfrac{1}{b(ax + b)} - \dfrac{1}{b^2} \log_e \dfrac{ax + b}{x}$

47. $\int \dfrac{dx}{x^2 (ax + b)^2} = -\dfrac{b + 2ax}{b^2 x(ax + b)} + \dfrac{2a}{b^3} \log_e \dfrac{ax + b}{x}$

48. $\int \dfrac{dx}{x \sqrt{ax + b}} = \dfrac{1}{\sqrt{b}} \log_e \dfrac{\sqrt{ax + b} - \sqrt{b}}{\sqrt{ax + b} + \sqrt{b}} \qquad (b \text{ positive})$

49. $\int \dfrac{dx}{x \sqrt{ax + b}} = \dfrac{2}{\sqrt{-b}} \tan^{-1} \sqrt{\dfrac{ax + b}{-b}} \qquad (b \text{ negative})$

50. $\int \dfrac{\sqrt{ax + b}}{x} \, dx = 2 \sqrt{ax + b} + \sqrt{b} \log_e \dfrac{\sqrt{ax + b} - \sqrt{b}}{\sqrt{ax + b} + \sqrt{b}} \qquad (b \text{ positive})$

51. $\int \dfrac{\sqrt{ax + b}}{x} \, dx = 2 \sqrt{ax + b} - 2 \sqrt{-b} \tan^{-1} \sqrt{\dfrac{ax + b}{-b}} \qquad (b \text{ negative})$

Integrals Involving $(ax + b)$—*Continued*

52. $\displaystyle \int \frac{dx}{x^2 \sqrt{ax + b}} = -\frac{\sqrt{ax + b}}{bx} - \frac{a}{2b\sqrt{b}} \log_e \frac{\sqrt{ax + b} - \sqrt{b}}{\sqrt{ax + b} + \sqrt{b}}$ (b positive)

53. $\displaystyle \int \frac{dx}{x^2 \sqrt{ax + b}} = -\frac{\sqrt{ax + b}}{bx} - \frac{a}{b\sqrt{-b}} \tan^{-1} \sqrt{\frac{ax + b}{-b}}$ (b negative)

54. $\displaystyle \int \frac{ax + b}{fx + g} dx = \frac{ax}{f} + \frac{bf - ag}{f^2} \log_e (fx + g)$

55. $\displaystyle \int \frac{dx}{(ax + b)(fx + g)} = \frac{1}{bf - ag} \log_e \left(\frac{fx + g}{ax + b}\right)$ ($ag \neq bf$)

56. $\displaystyle \int \frac{x \, dx}{(ax + b)(fx + g)} = \frac{1}{bf - ag}\left[\frac{b}{a} \log_e (ax + b) - \frac{g}{f} \log_e (fx + g)\right]$ ($ag \neq bf$)

57. $\displaystyle \int \frac{dx}{(ax + b)^2(fx + g)} = \frac{1}{bf - ag}\left(\frac{1}{ax + b} + \frac{f}{bf - ag} \log_e \frac{fx + g}{ax + b}\right)$ ($ag \neq bf$)

Integrals Involving $(ax^n + b)$

58. $\displaystyle \int (ax^2 + b)^n x \, dx = \frac{1}{2a} \frac{(ax^2 + b)^{n+1}}{n + 1}$ ($n \neq -1$)

59. $\displaystyle \int \frac{dx}{ax^2 + b} = \frac{1}{\sqrt{ab}} \tan^{-1}\left(x\sqrt{\frac{a}{b}}\right)$ (a and b positive)

60. $\displaystyle \int \frac{dx}{ax^2 + b} = \frac{1}{2\sqrt{-ab}} \log_e \frac{x\sqrt{a} - \sqrt{-b}}{x\sqrt{a} + \sqrt{-b}}$ (a positive, b negative)

$\displaystyle \qquad\qquad = \frac{1}{2\sqrt{-ab}} \log_e \frac{\sqrt{b} + x\sqrt{-a}}{\sqrt{b} - x\sqrt{-a}}$ (a negative, b positive)

61. $\displaystyle \int \frac{dx}{x(ax^2 + b)} = \frac{1}{2b} \log_e \frac{x^2}{ax^2 + b}$

62. $\displaystyle \int \frac{dx}{(ax^2 + b)^n} = \frac{1}{2(n - 1)b} \frac{x}{(ax^2 + b)^{n-1}} + \frac{2n - 3}{2(n - 1)b}\int \frac{dx}{(ax^2 + b)^{n-1}}$ (n integer > 1)

63. $\displaystyle \int \frac{x^2 \, dx}{ax^2 + b} = \frac{x}{a} - \frac{b}{a}\int \frac{dx}{ax^2 + b}$

64. $\displaystyle \int \frac{x^2 \, dx}{(ax^2 + b)^n} = -\frac{1}{2(n - 1)a} \frac{x}{(ax^2 + b)^{n-1}} + \frac{1}{2(n - 1)a}\int \frac{dx}{(ax^2 + b)^{n-1}}$ (n integer > 1)

65. $\displaystyle \int \frac{dx}{x^2(ax^2 + b)^n} = \frac{1}{b}\int \frac{dx}{x^2(ax^2 + b)^{n-1}} - \frac{a}{b}\int \frac{dx}{(ax^2 + b)^n}$ ($n =$ positive integer)

66. $\displaystyle \int \sqrt{ax^2 + b} \, dx = \frac{x}{2} \sqrt{ax^2 + b} + \frac{b}{2\sqrt{a}} \log_e (x\sqrt{a} + \sqrt{ax^2 + b})$ (a positive)

67. $\displaystyle \int \sqrt{ax^2 + b} \, dx = \frac{x}{2} \sqrt{ax^2 + b} + \frac{b}{2\sqrt{-a}} \sin^{-1}\left(x\sqrt{-\frac{a}{b}}\right)$ (a negative)

68. $\displaystyle \int \frac{dx}{\sqrt{ax^2 + b}} = \frac{1}{\sqrt{a}} \log_e (x\sqrt{a} + \sqrt{ax^2 + b})$ (a positive)

69. $\displaystyle \int \frac{dx}{\sqrt{ax^2 + b}} = \frac{1}{\sqrt{-a}} \sin^{-1}\left(x\sqrt{-\frac{a}{b}}\right)$ (a negative)

70. $\displaystyle \int \frac{x \, dx}{\sqrt{ax^2 + b}} = \frac{1}{a} \sqrt{ax^2 + b}$

71. $\displaystyle \int \frac{\sqrt{ax^2 + b}}{x} dx = \sqrt{ax^2 + b} + \sqrt{b} \log_e \frac{\sqrt{ax^2 + b} - \sqrt{b}}{x}$ (b positive)

72. $\displaystyle \int \frac{\sqrt{ax^2 + b}}{x} dx = \sqrt{ax^2 + b} - \sqrt{-b} \tan^{-1} \frac{\sqrt{ax^2 + b}}{\sqrt{-b}}$ (b negative)

73. $\displaystyle \int x \sqrt{ax^2 + b} \, dx = \frac{1}{3a} (ax^2 + b)^{3/2}$

Integrals Involving $(ax^n + b)$—Continued

74. $\displaystyle\int x^2 \sqrt{ax^2+b}\ dx = \frac{x}{4a}(ax^2+b)^{3/2} - \frac{bx}{8a}\sqrt{ax^2+b} - \frac{b^2}{8a\sqrt{a}}\log_e\left(x\sqrt{a}+\sqrt{ax^2+b}\right)$
   (a positive)

75. $\displaystyle\int x^2 \sqrt{ax^2+b}\ dx = \frac{x}{4a}(ax^2+b)^{3/2} - \frac{bx}{8a}\sqrt{ax^2+b} - \frac{b^2}{8a\sqrt{-a}}\sin^{-1}\left(x\sqrt{\frac{-a}{b}}\right)$
   (a negative)

76. $\displaystyle\int \frac{dx}{x\sqrt{ax^2+b}} = \frac{1}{\sqrt{b}}\log_e\frac{\sqrt{ax^2+b}-\sqrt{b}}{x}$ (b positive)

77. $\displaystyle\int \frac{dx}{x\sqrt{ax^2+b}} = \frac{1}{\sqrt{-b}}\sec^{-1}\left(x\sqrt{-\frac{a}{b}}\right)$ (b negative)

78. $\displaystyle\int \frac{x^2\,dx}{\sqrt{ax^2+b}} = \frac{x}{2a}\sqrt{ax^2+b} - \frac{b}{2a\sqrt{a}}\log_e\left(x\sqrt{a}+\sqrt{ax^2+b}\right)$ (a positive)

79. $\displaystyle\int \frac{x^2\,dx}{\sqrt{ax^2+b}} = \frac{x}{2a}\sqrt{ax^2+b} - \frac{b}{2a\sqrt{-a}}\sin^{-1}\left(x\sqrt{-\frac{a}{b}}\right)$ (a negative)

80. $\displaystyle\int \frac{\sqrt{ax^2+b}}{x^2}\,dx = -\frac{\sqrt{ax^2+b}}{x} + \sqrt{a}\log_e\left(x\sqrt{a}+\sqrt{ax^2+b}\right)$ (a positive)

81. $\displaystyle\int \frac{\sqrt{ax^2+b}}{x^2}\,dx = -\frac{\sqrt{ax^2+b}}{x} - \sqrt{-a}\sin^{-1}\left(x\sqrt{-\frac{a}{b}}\right)$ (a negative)

82. $\displaystyle\int \frac{dx}{x(ax^n+b)} = \frac{1}{bn}\log_e\frac{x^n}{ax^n+b}$

83. $\displaystyle\int \frac{dx}{x\sqrt{ax^n+b}} = \frac{1}{n\sqrt{b}}\log_e\frac{\sqrt{ax^n+b}-\sqrt{b}}{\sqrt{ax^n+b}+\sqrt{b}}$ (b positive)

84. $\displaystyle\int \frac{dx}{x\sqrt{ax^n+b}} = \frac{2}{n\sqrt{-b}}\sec^{-1}\sqrt{-\frac{ax^n}{b}}$ (b negative)

Integrals Involving $(ax^2 + bx + d)$

85. $\displaystyle\int \frac{dx}{ax^2+bx+d} = \frac{1}{\sqrt{b^2-4ad}}\log_e\frac{2ax+b-\sqrt{b^2-4ad}}{2ax+b+\sqrt{b^2-4ad}}$ ($b^2>4ad$)

86. $\displaystyle\int \frac{dx}{ax^2+bx+d} = \frac{2}{\sqrt{4ad-b^2}}\tan^{-1}\frac{2ax+b}{\sqrt{4ad-b^2}}$ ($b^2<4ad$)

87. $\displaystyle\int \frac{dx}{ax^2+bx+d} = -\frac{2}{2ax+b}$ ($b^2=4ad$)

88. $\displaystyle\int \frac{dx}{\sqrt{ax^2+bx+d}} = \frac{1}{\sqrt{a}}\log_e\left(2ax+b+2\sqrt{a(ax^2+bx+d)}\right)$ (a positive)

89. $\displaystyle\int \frac{dx}{\sqrt{ax^2+bx+d}} = \frac{1}{\sqrt{-a}}\sin^{-1}\frac{-2ax-b}{\sqrt{b^2-4ad}}$ (a negative)

90. $\displaystyle\int \frac{x\,dx}{ax^2+bx+d} = \frac{1}{2a}\log_e(ax^2+bx+d) - \frac{b}{2a}\int\frac{dx}{ax^2+bx+d}$

91. $\displaystyle\int \frac{x\,dx}{\sqrt{ax^2+bx+d}} = \frac{\sqrt{ax^2+bx+d}}{a} - \frac{b}{2a}\int\frac{dx}{\sqrt{ax^2+bx+d}}$

92. $\displaystyle\int \frac{dx}{x\sqrt{ax^2+bx+d}} = -\frac{1}{\sqrt{d}}\log_e\left(\frac{\sqrt{ax^2+bx+d}+\sqrt{d}}{x}+\frac{b}{2\sqrt{d}}\right)$ (d positive)

93. $\displaystyle\int \frac{dx}{x\sqrt{ax^2+bx+d}} = \frac{1}{\sqrt{-d}}\sin^{-1}\frac{bx+2d}{x\sqrt{b^2-4ad}}$ (d negative)

94. $\displaystyle\int \frac{dx}{x\sqrt{ax^2+bx}} = -\frac{2}{bx}\sqrt{ax^2+bx}$

Integrals Involving $(ax^2 + bx + d)$—*Continued*

95. $\int \sqrt{ax^2 + bx + d}\, dx = \dfrac{2\,ax + b}{4a} \sqrt{ax^2 + bx + d} + \dfrac{4\,ad - b^2}{8a} \int \dfrac{dx}{\sqrt{ax^2 + bx + d}} =$

96. $\int x \sqrt{ax^2 + bx + d}\, dx = \dfrac{(ax^2 + bx + d)^{3/2}}{3a} - \dfrac{b}{2a} \int \sqrt{ax^2 + bx + d}\, dx$

Integrals Involving $\sin^n ax$

97. $\int \sin^3 ax\, dx = -\dfrac{1}{a} \cos ax + \dfrac{1}{3a} \cos^3 ax$

98. $\int \sin^4 ax\, dx = \dfrac{3}{8} x - \dfrac{1}{4a} \sin 2\,ax + \dfrac{1}{32\,a} \sin 4\,ax$

99. $\int \sin^n ax\, dx = -\dfrac{\sin^{n-1} ax \cos ax}{na} + \dfrac{n-1}{n} \int \sin^{n-2} ax\, dx$ (n = positive integer)

100. $\int x \sin ax\, dx = \dfrac{\sin ax}{a^2} - \dfrac{x \cos ax}{a}$

101. $\int x^2 \sin ax\, dx = \dfrac{2x}{a^2} \sin ax - \left(\dfrac{x^2}{a} - \dfrac{2}{a^3}\right) \cos ax$

102. $\int x^3 \sin ax\, dx = \left(\dfrac{3x^2}{a^2} - \dfrac{6}{a^4}\right) \sin ax - \left(\dfrac{x^3}{a} - \dfrac{6x}{a^3}\right) \cos ax$

103. $\int x^n \sin ax\, dx = -\dfrac{x^n}{a} \cos ax + \dfrac{n}{a} \int x^{n-1} \cos ax\, dx$ ($n > 0$)

104. $\int \dfrac{\sin ax}{x^n}\, dx = -\dfrac{1}{n-1} \dfrac{\sin ax}{x^{n-1}} + \dfrac{a}{n-1} \int \dfrac{\cos ax}{x^{n-1}}\, dx$

105. $\int \dfrac{dx}{\sin^n ax} = -\dfrac{1}{a(n-1)} \dfrac{\cos ax}{\sin^{n-1} ax} + \dfrac{n-2}{n-1} \int \dfrac{dx}{\sin^{n-2} ax}$ (n integer > 1)

106. $\int \dfrac{x\, dx}{\sin^2 ax} = -\dfrac{x}{a} \cot ax + \dfrac{1}{a^2} \log_e \sin ax$

107. $\int \dfrac{dx}{1 + \sin ax} = -\dfrac{1}{a} \tan\left(\dfrac{\pi}{4} - \dfrac{ax}{2}\right)$

108. $\int \dfrac{dx}{1 - \sin ax} = \dfrac{1}{a} \cot\left(\dfrac{\pi}{4} - \dfrac{ax}{2}\right)$

109. $\int \dfrac{x\, dx}{1 + \sin ax} = -\dfrac{x}{a} \tan\left(\dfrac{\pi}{4} - \dfrac{ax}{2}\right) + \dfrac{2}{a^2} \log_e \cos\left(\dfrac{\pi}{4} - \dfrac{ax}{2}\right)$

110. $\int \dfrac{x\, dx}{1 - \sin ax} = \dfrac{x}{a} \cot\left(\dfrac{\pi}{4} - \dfrac{ax}{2}\right) + \dfrac{2}{a^2} \log_e \sin\left(\dfrac{\pi}{4} - \dfrac{ax}{2}\right)$

111. $\int \dfrac{dx}{b + d \sin ax} = \dfrac{-2}{a \sqrt{b^2 - d^2}} \tan^{-1}\left[\sqrt{\dfrac{b-d}{b+d}} \tan\left(\dfrac{\pi}{4} - \dfrac{ax}{2}\right)\right]$ ($b^2 > d^2$)

112. $\int \dfrac{dx}{b + d \sin ax} = \dfrac{-1}{a \sqrt{d^2 - b^2}} \log_e \dfrac{d + b \sin ax + \sqrt{d^2 - b^2} \cos ax}{b + d \sin ax}$ ($d^2 > b^2$)

113. $\int \sin ax \sin bx\, dx = \dfrac{\sin (a-b)x}{2(a-b)} - \dfrac{\sin (a+b)x}{2(a+b)}$ ($a^2 \neq b^2$)

Integrals Involving $\cos^n ax$

114. $\int \cos^3 ax\, dx = \dfrac{1}{a} \sin ax - \dfrac{1}{3a} \sin^3 ax$

115. $\int \cos^4 ax\, dx = \dfrac{3}{8} x + \dfrac{1}{4a} \sin 2\,ax + \dfrac{1}{32a} \sin 4\,ax$

116. $\int \cos^n ax\, dx = \dfrac{\cos^{n-1} ax \sin ax}{na} + \dfrac{n-1}{n} \int \cos^{n-2} ax\, dx$ (n = positive integer)

117. $\int x \cos ax\, dx = \dfrac{\cos ax}{a^2} + \dfrac{x \sin ax}{a}$

Integrals Involving $\cos^n ax$—Continued

118. $\displaystyle\int x^2 \cos ax\, dx = \frac{2x}{a^2}\cos ax + \left(\frac{x^2}{a} - \frac{2}{a^3}\right)\sin ax$

119. $\displaystyle\int x^3 \cos ax\, dx = \left(\frac{3x^2}{a^2} - \frac{6}{a^4}\right)\cos ax + \left(\frac{x^3}{a} - \frac{6x}{a^3}\right)\sin ax$

120. $\displaystyle\int x^n \cos ax\, dx = \frac{x^n \sin ax}{a} - \frac{n}{a}\int x^{n-1}\sin ax\, dx \quad (n > 0)$

121. $\displaystyle\int \frac{\cos ax}{x^n}\, dx = -\frac{1}{n-1}\frac{\cos ax}{x^{n-1}} - \frac{a}{n-1}\int \frac{\sin ax}{x^{n-1}}\, dx$

122. $\displaystyle\int \frac{dx}{\cos^n ax} = \frac{1}{a(n-1)}\frac{\sin ax}{\cos^{n-1} ax} + \frac{n-2}{n-1}\int \frac{dx}{\cos^{n-2} ax} \quad (n \text{ integer} > 1)$

123. $\displaystyle\int \frac{x\, dx}{\cos^2 ax} = \frac{x}{a}\tan ax + \frac{1}{a^2}\log_e \cos ax$

124. $\displaystyle\int \frac{dx}{1 + \cos ax} = \frac{1}{a}\tan \frac{ax}{2}$

125. $\displaystyle\int \frac{dx}{1 - \cos ax} = -\frac{1}{a}\cot \frac{ax}{2}$

126. $\displaystyle\int \frac{x\, dx}{1 + \cos ax} = \frac{x}{a}\tan \frac{ax}{2} + \frac{2}{a^2}\log_e \cos \frac{ax}{2}$

127. $\displaystyle\int \frac{x\, dx}{1 - \cos ax} = -\frac{x}{a}\cot \frac{ax}{2} + \frac{2}{a^2}\log_e \sin \frac{ax}{2}$

128. $\displaystyle\int \frac{dx}{b + d\cos ax} = \frac{2}{a\sqrt{b^2 - d^2}}\tan^{-1}\left(\sqrt{\frac{b-d}{b+d}}\tan \frac{ax}{2}\right) \quad (b^2 > d^2)$

129. $\displaystyle\int \frac{dx}{b + d\cos ax} = \frac{1}{a\sqrt{d^2 - b^2}}\log_e \frac{d + b\cos ax + \sqrt{d^2 - b^2}\sin ax}{b + d\cos ax} \quad (d^2 > b^2)$

130. $\displaystyle\int \cos ax \cos bx\, dx = \frac{\sin (a-b)x}{2(a-b)} + \frac{\sin (a+b)x}{2(a+b)} \quad (a^2 \neq b^2)$

Integrals Involving $\sin^n ax$, $\cos^n ax$

131. $\displaystyle\int \sin ax \cos bx\, bx = -\frac{1}{2}\left[\frac{\cos (a-b)x}{a-b} + \frac{\cos (a+b)x}{a+b}\right] \quad (a^2 \neq b^2)$

132. $\displaystyle\int \sin^2 ax \cos^2 ax\, dx = \frac{x}{8} - \frac{\sin 4ax}{32a}$

133. $\displaystyle\int \sin^n ax \cos ax\, dx = \frac{1}{a(n+1)}\sin^{n+1} ax \quad (n \neq -1)$

134. $\displaystyle\int \sin ax \cos^n ax\, dx = -\frac{1}{a(n+1)}\cos^{n+1} ax \quad (n \neq -1)$

135. $\displaystyle\int \sin^n ax \cos^m ax\, dx = -\frac{\sin^{n-1} ax \cos^{m+1} ax}{a(n+m)} + \frac{n-1}{n+m}\int \sin^{n-2} ax \cos^m ax\, dx \quad (m, n \text{ pos})$

136. $\displaystyle\int \frac{\sin^n ax}{\cos^m ax}\, dx = \frac{\sin^{n+1} ax}{a(m-1)\cos^{m-1} ax} - \frac{n-m+2}{m-1}\int \frac{\sin^n ax}{\cos^{m-2} ax}\, dx \quad (m, n \text{ pos}, m \neq 1)$

137. $\displaystyle\int \frac{\cos^m ax}{\sin^n ax}\, dx = \frac{-\cos^{m+1} ax}{a(n-1)\sin^{n-1} ax} + \frac{n-m-2}{(n-1)}\int \frac{\cos^m ax}{\sin^{n-2} ax}\, dx \quad (m, n \text{ pos}, n \neq 1)$

138. $\displaystyle\int \frac{dx}{\sin ax \cos ax} = \frac{1}{a}\log_e \tan ax$

139. $\displaystyle\int \frac{dx}{b\sin ax + d\cos ax} = \frac{1}{a\sqrt{b^2 + d^2}}\log_e \tan \tfrac{1}{2}\left(ax + \tan^{-1}\frac{d}{b}\right)$

140. $\displaystyle\int \frac{\sin ax}{b + d\cos ax}\, dx = -\frac{1}{ad}\log_e (b + d\cos ax)$

141. $\displaystyle\int \frac{\cos ax}{b + d\sin ax}\, dx = \frac{1}{ad}\log_e (b + d\sin ax)$

Integrals Involving $\tan^n ax$, $\cot^n ax$, $\sec^n ax$, $\csc^n ax$

142. $\int \tan^n ax\, dx = \dfrac{1}{a(n-1)} \tan^{n-1} ax - \int \tan^{n-2} ax\, dx$ (n integer > 1)

143. $\int \cot^n ax\, dx = -\dfrac{1}{a(n-1)} \cot^{n-1} ax - \int \cot^{n-2} ax\, dx$ (n integer > 1)

144. $\int \sec^n ax\, dx = \dfrac{1}{a(n-1)} \dfrac{\sin ax}{\cos^{n-1} ax} + \dfrac{n-2}{n-1} \int \sec^{n-2} ax\, dx$ (n integer > 1)

145. $\int \csc^n ax\, dx = -\dfrac{1}{a(n-1)} \dfrac{\cos ax}{\sin^{n-1} ax} + \dfrac{n-2}{n-1} \int \csc^{n-2} ax\, dx$ (n integer > 1)

146. $\int \dfrac{dx}{b + d\tan ax} = \dfrac{1}{b^2 + d^2} \left[bx + \dfrac{d}{a} \log_e (b\cos ax + d\sin ax) \right]$

147. $\int \dfrac{dx}{\sqrt{b + d\tan^2 ax}} = \dfrac{1}{a\sqrt{b-d}} \sin^{-1} \left[\sqrt{\dfrac{b-d}{b}} \sin ax \right]$ (b pos, $b^2 > d^2$)

148. $\int \tan ax \sec ax\, dx = \dfrac{1}{a} \sec ax$

149. $\int \tan^n ax \sec^2 ax\, dx = \dfrac{1}{a(n+1)} \tan^{n+1} ax$ ($n \neq -1$)

150. $\int \dfrac{\sec^2 ax\, dx}{\tan ax} = \dfrac{1}{a} \log_e \tan ax$

151. $\int \cot ax \csc ax\, dx = -\dfrac{1}{a} \csc ax$

152. $\int \cot^n ax \csc^2 ax\, dx = -\dfrac{1}{a(n+1)} \cot^{n+1} ax$ ($n \neq -1$)

153. $\int \dfrac{\csc^2 ax}{\cot ax}\, dx = -\dfrac{1}{a} \log_e \cot ax$

Integrals Involving b^{ax}, e^{ax}, $\sin bx$, $\cos bx$

154. $\int x b^{ax}\, dx = \dfrac{x b^{ax}}{a \log_e b} - \dfrac{b^{ax}}{a^2 (\log_e b)^2}$

155. $\int x e^{ax}\, dx = \dfrac{e^{ax}}{a^2} (ax - 1)$

156. $\int x^n b^{ax}\, dx = \dfrac{x^n b^{ax}}{a \log_e b} - \dfrac{n}{a \log_e b} \int x^{n-1} b^{ax}\, dx$ (n positive)

157. $\int x^n e^{ax}\, dx = \dfrac{1}{a} x^n e^{ax} - \dfrac{n}{a} \int x^{n-1} e^{ax}\, dx$ (n positive)

158. $\int \dfrac{dx}{b + de^{ax}} = \dfrac{1}{ab} \left[ax - \log_e (b + de^{ax}) \right]$

159. $\int \dfrac{e^{ax}\, dx}{b + de^{ax}} = \dfrac{1}{ad} \log_e (b + de^{ax})$

160. $\int \dfrac{dx}{be^{ax} + de^{-ax}} = \dfrac{1}{a\sqrt{bd}} \tan^{-1} \left(e^{ax} \sqrt{\dfrac{b}{d}} \right)$ (b and d positive)

161. $\int \dfrac{e^{ax}}{x}\, dx = \log_e x + ax + \dfrac{(ax)^2}{2 \cdot 2!} + \dfrac{(ax)^3}{3 \cdot 3!} + \cdots$

162. $\int \dfrac{e^{ax}}{x^n}\, dx = \dfrac{1}{n-1} \left(-\dfrac{e^{ax}}{x^{n-1}} + a\int \dfrac{e^{ax}}{x^{n-1}}\, dx \right)$ (n integer > 1)

163. $\int e^{ax} \sin bx\, dx = \dfrac{e^{ax}}{a^2 + b^2} (a \sin bx - b \cos bx)$

164. $\int e^{ax} \cos bx\, dx = \dfrac{e^{ax}}{a^2 + b^2} (a \cos bx + b \sin bx)$

165. $\int x e^{ax} \sin bx\, dx = \dfrac{x e^{ax}}{a^2 + b^2} (a \sin bx - b \cos bx)$
$$- \dfrac{e^{ax}}{(a^2 + b^2)^2} [(a^2 - b^2) \sin bx - 2ab \cos bx]$$

166. $\int x e^{ax} \cos bx\, dx = \dfrac{x e^{ax}}{a^2 + b^2} (a \cos bx + b \sin bx)$
$$- \dfrac{e^{ax}}{(a^2 + b^2)^2} \left[(a^2 - b^2) \cos bx + 2ab \sin bx \right]$$

Some Definite Integrals

1. $\displaystyle\int_0^a \sqrt{a^2 - x^2}\, dx = \frac{\pi a^2}{4}$

2. $\displaystyle\int_0^a \sqrt{2\,ax - x^2}\, dx = \frac{\pi a^2}{4}$

3. $\displaystyle\int_0^\infty \frac{dx}{a + bx^2} = \frac{\pi}{2\sqrt{ab}}$ (a and b positive)

4. $\displaystyle\int_0^{\sqrt{a/b}} \frac{dx}{a + bx^2}\, dx = \int_{\sqrt{a/b}}^\infty \frac{dx}{a + bx^2} = \frac{\pi}{4\sqrt{ab}}$ (a and b positive)

5. $\displaystyle\int_0^{\sqrt{a/b}} \frac{dx}{\sqrt{a - bx^2}} = \frac{\pi}{2\sqrt{b}}$ (a and b positive)

6. $\displaystyle\int_0^\infty \frac{\sin bx}{x}\, dx = \frac{\pi}{2}$ $(b > 0)$
$$= 0 \qquad (b = 0)$$
$$= -\frac{\pi}{2} \qquad (b < 0)$$

7. $\displaystyle\int_0^\infty \frac{\tan x}{x}\, dx = \frac{\pi}{2}$

8. $\displaystyle\int_0^{\pi/2} \sin^{2\,n+1} x\, dx = \int_0^{\pi/2} \cos^{2n+1} x\, dx = \frac{2 \cdot 4 \cdot 6 \cdot \,\ldots\, \cdot 2n}{3 \cdot 5 \cdot 7 \cdot \,\ldots\, \cdot (2\,n + 1)}$ $(n > 0)$

9. $\displaystyle\int_0^{\pi/2} \sin^{2n} x\, dx = \int_0^{\pi/2} \cos^{2n} x\, dx = \frac{1 \cdot 3 \cdot 5 \cdot \,\ldots\, \cdot (2\,n - 1)}{2 \cdot 4 \cdot 6 \cdot \,\ldots\, \cdot 2n} \cdot \frac{\pi}{2}$ $(n > 0)$

10. $\displaystyle\int_0^\pi \sin ax \sin bx\, dx = \int_0^\pi \cos ax \cos bx\, dx = 0$ $(a \neq b)$

11. $\displaystyle\int_0^\pi \sin^2 ax\, dx = \int_0^\pi \cos^2 ax\, dx = \frac{\pi}{2}$

12. $\displaystyle\int_0^{\pi/2} \log_e \cos x\, dx = \int_0^{\pi/2} \log_e \sin x\, dx = -\frac{\pi}{2} \log_e 2$

13. $\displaystyle\int_0^\infty e^{-ax^2}\, dx = \frac{1}{2}\sqrt{\frac{\pi}{a}}$

14. $\displaystyle\int_0^\infty x^n\, e^{-ax}\, dx = \frac{n!}{a^{n+1}}$ $(a > 0,\ n = 1, 2, 3, \ldots)$

15. $\displaystyle\int_0^1 \frac{\log_e x}{1 - x}\, dx = -\frac{\pi^2}{6}$

16. $\displaystyle\int_0^1 \frac{\log_e x}{1 + x}\, dx = -\frac{\pi^2}{12}$

17. $\displaystyle\int_0^1 \frac{\log_e x}{1 - x^2}\, dx = \frac{\pi^2}{8}$

PHYSICAL PROPERTIES OF MATERIALS

By H. C. Knutson

Table 20. Properties of Gases

(All properties are at a pressure equivalent to 760 mm of mercury unless otherwise stated)

Name	Formula	Density (0° C) G per l	Density (0° C) Lb per cu ft	Molecular Weight	Melting Point, deg cent	Latent Heat of Fusion, g-cal per g	Boiling Point, deg cent	Latent Heat of Vaporization, g-cal per g	Specific Heat Constant Pressure, C_p	Specific Heat Temp, deg cent	Mean Ratio, $\frac{C_p}{C_v}$	Mean Ratio Temp, deg cent	Thermal Coeff. Constant Volume	Thermal Coeff. CV Temp, deg cent	Thermal Coeff. Constant Pressure	Thermal Coeff. CP Temp, deg cent	Viscosity Poises* ×10^6	Viscosity Temp, deg cent
Acetylene	C_2H_2	1.173	0.07323	26.016	− 81.3		− 83.6		0.3832	15	1.26	15					93.5	0
Air		1.2929	.08071	28.952				51.0	0.2377	−30−+10	1.401	20	0.003665	0–100	0.003671		181.2	20.2
Ammonia	NH_3	0.7710	.04813	17.031	− 75	108.0	− 33.5	327.1	0.5202	23–100	1.3172	0					102	20
Argon	A	1.7837	.11135	39.944	−189.2	6.71	−185.7	37.7	0.1233	20– 90	1.668	15	.003668 (517 mm)				224.1	17.9
Arsine	AsH_3	3.48	.217	77.95	−113.5		− 54.8										114.0	15
Butane-iso	C_4H_{10}	2.637	.1669	58.08	−145.0		− 10.2	87.4									75.5	23
Butane-n	C_4H_{10}	2.519 (710 mm)	.1572 (710 mm)	58.08	−135.0		− 0.6	91.5			1.11	15					83.3	16.0
Carbon dioxide	CO_2	1.9769 (710 mm)	.12341 (710 mm)	44.000	− 57	45.3	− 80 Subl.	137.9	0.2025	15–100	1.3003	0	.0036981	0–100	.003707 (518 mm)	0–100	145.7	15.0
Carbon monoxide	CO	1.2504	.07807	28.000	−207	8.00	−191.5	50.4	0.2425	23– 99	1.403	0	.003667 (518 mm)		.003669		184.0	20
Carbon oxychloride (phosgene)	$COCl_2$	4.531	.283	98.91	−118		8.3											
Carbon oxysulfide	COS	2.72	.170	66.06	−138		− 48										119.0	15
Chlorine	Cl_2	3.214	.2006	70.914	−101.6	23.0	− 34.7	81	0.1125	16–343	1.336	0					137	20
Chlorine monoxide	Cl_2O	3.89	.243	86.91	− 20		3.8 (explodes)										129	12.7
Cyanogen	C_2N_2	2.335	.146	52.02	− 27.90		− 21.17		0.4095	15	1.256	15					107	20
Ethane	C_2H_6	1.3566	.08469	30.05	−172.0		− 88.3	258.0	0.3861	15	1.22	15					101	20
Ethyl chloride	C_2H_5Cl	2.870	.1793	64.50	−138.7		12.2	92.5	0.2750	10–170	1.19	16					105	20
Ethylene	C_2H_4	1.2604	.07868	28.031	−169.4		−103.8		0.399	15–100	1.18	100					109.0	20
Fluorine	F_2	1.696	.1059	38.00	−223		−187	40.5	0.182	0								
Helium	He	0.1784	.01114	4.002	−272		−268.94	5.97	1.25	−180	1.660	−180					196.9	15.3
Hydrogen	H_2	0.08988	.005611	2.0156	−259.14	14.0	−252.8	106.7	3.409	12–198	1.4080	4–16	.003665 (567 mm) / .0036504 (764 mm)	0–100	.0036600 (1000 mm)	0–100	88.9	15

* Dyne sec per sq cm.

Table 20. Properties of Gases.—Continued

(All properties are at a pressure equivalent to 760 mm of mercury unless otherwise stated)

Name	Formula	Density (0 °C)		Molecular Weight	Melting Point, deg cent	Latent Heat of Fusion, g-cal per g	Boiling Point, deg cent	Latent Heat of Vaporization, g-cal per g	Specific Heat g-cal per g or Btu per lb				Thermal Coefficient of Expansion per deg cent				Viscosity	
		G per l	Lb per cu ft						Constant Pressure, C_p	Temp, deg cent	Mean Ratio, $\frac{C_p}{C_v}$	Temp, deg cent	Constant Volume	Temp, deg cent	Constant Pressure	Temp, deg cent	Poises* $\times 10^6$	Temp, deg cent
Hydrogen bromide	HBr	3.6445	.22752	80.92	−86.7	7.67	−68.1	48.7	0.082	11–100	1.42	20					181.9	18.7
Hydrogen chloride	HCl	1.6392	.10233	36.465	−111.3	13.4	−83.1	105.9	0.194	13–100	1.389	20					140	20
Hydrogen fluoride	HF	0.922	.0576	20.01	−92.3		−36.7 (755 mm)		0.343	0							185.7	20.6
Hydrogen iodide	HI	5.789	.3614	127.93	−51.3	5.68	−35.7 (755 mm)	33.92	0.06	0	1.40	20–100						
Hydrogen selenide	H2Se	3.670	.229	81.22	−64		−42											
Hydrogen sulfide	H2S	1.539	.09608	34.08	−86		−62	131.9	0.2451	20–206	1.324						130	20
Hydrogen telluride	H2Te	5.803	.363	129.5	−48		−1.8											
Krypton	Kr	3.708	.2315	82.9	−169		−151.8	28			1.666	19					246	15
Methane	CH4	0.717	.0448	16.0317	−182.5	14.53	−161.4	138	0.5929	18–208	1.316	11–30					120.1	20
Methyl chloride	CH3Cl	2.3076	.14406	50.4804	−103.6		23.73	102.3	0.24		1.20						116	20
Methyl ether	(CH3)2O	2.1098	.13171	46.05	−138		−24.9				1.11	6–30						
Methyl fluoride	CH3F	1.5452	.09646	34.02			−78.0											
Monomethylamine	CH3NH2	1.396	.08715	31.05	−92.5		−6.8											
Neon	Ne	0.9004	.05621	20.183	−248.67	2.84	−245.9				1.642	19					312	15
Nitric oxide	NO	1.3402	.08367	30.008	−167		−153		0.232	10–180	1.40	15					179	0
Nitrogen	N2	1.2506	.07807	28.016	−209.86	18.4	−195.8	47.8	0.2438	0–200	1.41		.0036682				170.7	10.9
Nitrosyl chloride	NOCl	2.992	.1868	65.47	−64.5	6.1	−5.5											
Nitrous oxide	N2O	1.978	.1235	44.016	−102.4		−89.8		0.2126	26–103	1.311	0	.003676		.003719		138	0
Oxygen	O2	1.42904	.089212	32.0000	−218.4	3.33	−183.0	51	0.2175	13–207	1.3977	5–14	.003668 (75.9 cm)				195.7	15.4
Phosphine	PH3	1.529	.0955	34.04	−133.5		−87.4										112.0	15
Propane	C3H8	2.020	.1261	44.06	−189.9		−44.5											
Silicon tetrafluoride	SiF4	4.68	.292	104.06			−68										129	20
Sulfur dioxide	SO2	2.9269	.18272	64.06	−76		−10	94.8	0.1544	16–202	1.256	16–34	.003845		.003903		222	15
Xenon	X	5.85	.365	130.2	−140	3.73	−109.1	24.4			1.666	19						

* Dyne sec per sq cm.

Table 21. Properties of Liquids

(Normal compounds only)

Name	Density G per cu cm	Density Temp,* deg cent	Melting Point, deg cent	Latent Heat of Fusion, g-cal per g	Boiling Point (760 mm), deg cent	Latent Heat of Vaporization, g-cal per g	Viscosity Poises †	Viscosity Temp, deg cent	Specific Heat G-cal per g or Btu per lb	Specific Heat Temp,* deg cent
Acetaldehyde (aldehyde)	0.806	0	−120.0	...	20.8	136.0	0.00231	20	...	...
Acetic acid	1.05	20	16.7	43.2	118.5	96.8	0.01222	20	0.522	26–95
Acetone	0.792	20	94.6	19.6	56.1	124.5	0.0031	20	0.506	0
Allyl alcohol	0.847	25	−129.0	...	97.0	163.0	0.01363	20	0.665	21–96
Amyl alcohol	0.817	20	−78.5	...	137.9	120.2	...	...	...	...
Aniline	1.035	0	−6.24	20.95	183.9	110.0	0.04467	20	0.512	8–82
Benzene (benzol)	0.879	20	5.56	30.34	80.12	94.2	0.00654	20	0.340	10
Bromine	3.187	0	−7.2	16.2	58.8	48.0	0.01005	20	0.107	13–45
Butyl alcohol	0.810	20	−89.8	30.0	117.7	141.0	0.02948	20	0.687	21–115
Butyric acid	0.954	25	−5.55	30.10	163.5	114.0	0.01540	20	0.515	20–100
Carbolic acid (phenol)	1.07	25	41	29.03	182.2	...	0.1274	18.3	0.561	14–26
Carbon disulfide	1.293	0	−111.8	...	46.26	84.1	0.00376	20	0.240	20
Carbon tetrachloride	1.594	20	−22.8	41.57	76.75	46.4	0.00975	20	0.201	20
Castor oil	0.9603	...	...	...	...	...	9.86	20	0.434	...
Chloroform	1.489	20	−63.5	...	61.2	59.0	0.00571	20	0.226	15
Decane	0.747	20	−32.0	...	174.0	...	0.0077	22.3	0.500	0–50
Di-ethyl ether	0.714	20	−116.3	...	34.5	83.9	0.00245	20	0.529	0
Ethyl acetate	0.899	20	−83.6	...	77.1	...	0.0045	20	0.457	20
Ethyl alcohol	0.789	20	−114.6	24.89	78.32	204.3	0.012	20	0.548	0
Ethyl bromide	1.45	15	−119.0	...	38.4	59.9	0.00402	20	0.215	15–20
Ethyl chloride	0.918	8	−138.7	...	12.2	92.5	...	...	0.367	0
Ethyl iodide	1.944	14	−108.5	...	72.1	45.6	0.00592	20	0.161	20
Ethylene bromide	2.17	...	10.01	...	131.7	46.2	0.01721	20	0.173	20
Ethylene chloride	1.246	...	−35.3	...	83.7	77.33	0.00838	20	0.299	20
Formic acid	1.22	20	8.4	58.89	100.8	119.9	0.01784	20	0.525	20–100
Gasoline	0.66–0.69	...	...	...	70.0–90.0	...	...	...	0.5	0–100
Glycerin	1.261	20	18.1	47.5	290.0	...	8.30	20.3	0.576	15–50

*Where the temperature is not given, ordinary temperature is understood.   † Dyne sec per sq cm.

Formula column:
Acetaldehyde (aldehyde) — C_2H_4O;
Acetic acid — $C_2H_4O_2$;
Acetone — C_3H_6O;
Allyl alcohol — C_3H_6O;
Amyl alcohol — $C_5H_{12}O$;
Aniline — $C_6H_5NH_2$;
Benzene (benzol) — C_6H_6;
Bromine — Br;
Butyl alcohol — $C_4H_{10}O$;
Butyric acid — $C_4H_8O_2$;
Carbolic acid (phenol) — C_6H_6O;
Carbon disulfide — CS_2;
Carbon tetrachloride — CCl_4;
Chloroform — $CHCl_3$;
Decane — $C_{10}H_{22}$;
Di-ethyl ether — $C_4H_{10}O$;
Ethyl acetate — $C_4H_8O_2$;
Ethyl alcohol — C_2H_6O;
Ethyl bromide — C_2H_5Br;
Ethyl chloride — C_2H_5Cl;
Ethyl iodide — C_2H_5I;
Ethylene bromide — C_2H_4Br;
Ethylene chloride — C_2H_4Cl;
Formic acid — CH_2O_2;
Glycerin — $C_3H_8O_3$.

Table 21.   Properties of Liquids.—Continued

(Normal compounds only)

Name	Formula	Density		Melting Point, deg cent	Latent Heat of Fusion, g-cal per g	Boiling Point (760 mm), deg cent	Latent Heat of Vaporization, g-cal per g	Viscosity		Specific Heat	
		G per cu cm	Temp,* deg cent					Poises †	Temp, deg cent	G-cal per g or Btu per lb	Temp,* deg cent
Heptane	C_7H_{16}	0.684	20	—90.7		98.4	76.3	0.00416	20	0.490	20
Hexane	C_6H_{14}	0.660	20	—95.4		68.7	79.3	0.00326	20	0.600	20
Kerosene		0.78–0.82								0.5	0–100
Linseed oil		0.934	15.5			287.0		0.331	30		
Methyl acetate	$C_3H_6O_2$	0.927	20	—98.1	22.0	57.1	98.1	0.00388	20	0.468	15
Methyl alcohol	CH_4O	0.792	15	—97.8		64.7	262.8	0.00596	20	0.601	15–20
Methyl iodide	CH_3I	2.285	15	—64.0		42.3	45.9	0.00500	20		
Naphthalene	$C_{10}H_8$	1.152		80.2	35.6	218.0	75.5	0.040	20	0.396	80–85
Neatsfoot oil		0.913–0.917									
Nitric acid (100%)	HNO_3	1.513	20	—47	9.53	86.0	114.9	0.021	20	0.350	14
Nitrobenzene	$C_6H_5O_2N$	1.212	7.5	5.85	22.5	210.9	79.1	0.0062	22.3	0.503	0–50
Nonane	C_9H_{20}	0.718	20	—51.0		150.6		0.00542	20	0.578	20–123
Octane	C_8H_{18}	0.707	17	—56.9		124.6	70.95			0.471	6.6
Olive oil		0.918	15	—20±		300±		0.840	20		
Pentane	C_5H_{12}	0.631	20	—129.9		36.0		0.0024	20	0.511	21–58
Petroleum		0.878	0							0.560	20–137
Propionic acid	$C_3H_6O_2$	0.99		—20.8		141.1	98.8	0.01102	20	0.57	20
Propyl alcohol	C_3H_8O	0.804	20	—127.0		97.5	164.4	0.02256	20		
Rapeseed oil		0.913	15	3.5				1.18	30		
Soya bean oil		0.919	30					0.406	15.6		
Sperm oil		0.88	25					0.420	15.6		
Sulfuric acid (100%)	H_2SO_4	1.831	20	10.49	24.03	(98.3%) 330.0	122.08	0.50	20.0	0.344	20
Tallow		0.94	15	27–41				0.176	66		
Toluene	C_7H_8	0.882	0	—95.0		110.3	86.53	0.00590	20	0.440	12–99
Turpentine		0.873	16	—10		160.0	68.6	0.01487	20	0.411	0
Water	H_2O	1.00000‡	4	0	79.70	100.0	539.44	0.010050	20	1.000	16
Xylene O	$C_6H_4(CH_3)_2$	0.863	20	—27.1		142.0	82.9	0.00881	13.88	0.411	30

* Where the temperature is not given, ordinary temperature is understood.   † Dyne sec per sq cm.   ‡ 8 ⅓ lb per gal, 62 ½ lb per cu ft (approx.).

Table 22. Physical Properties of Metals

(For properties of alloys, see Sec. 11, Metallic Materials)

Name	Atomic Weight	Density, G per cu cm	Density, Temp* deg cent	Melting Point, deg cent	Latent Heat of Fusion, g-cal per g	Boiling Point, deg cent	Latent Heat of Vaporization, g-cal per g	Specific Heat, G-cal per g or Btu per lb	Specific Heat, Temp deg cent	Thermal Coeff of Linear Expansion, ×10⁴ per deg cent	TCLE, Temp deg cent	Thermal Conductivity, G-cal per sec per sq cm per deg cent per cm	Therm Cond, Temp deg cent	Electrical Resistivity, Microhm-cm	Elec Res, Temp* deg cent	Temp Coefficient of Resistivity, Temp Coefficient	TCR, Temp deg cent
Aluminum	26.97	2.70	20	659.8	93.0	1800	1950–2000	0.226	0–100	0.257	20–300	0.480	18	2.688	20	0.00403	20
Antimony	121.76	6.618	20	630.5	39.0	1380	373	0.0504	20–100	∥0.136 ⊥0.080	20	0.0442	0	39.1	0	0.0036	20
Arsenic	74.93	5.73	14	Volatilizes		615 Sublimes	74	0.078	18	0.05	20			35	0	0.0042	20
Barium	137.36	3.5	20	850		1140	628	0.068	−185 to +20					9.8	20	0.0033	20
Beryllium	9.02	1.8	20	1350	318	1500		0.425	0–100	0.122	20			10.1	20		
Bismuth	209.00	9.781	20	271.3	12.5	1450	221	0.0294	20	∥0.140 ⊥0.103	20	0.0194	18	119.0	18	0.004	20
Cadmium	112.41	8.648	20	320.9	12.8	766	227.5	0.0552	27.9	∥0.54 ⊥0.20	0	0.222	18	7.54	18	0.0042	0
Calcium	40.08	1.55	20	810	78	1170		0.149	0–100	0.25	0–21			4.59	20	0.00364	0–600
Cerium	140.13	6.90	20	640	64	1400		0.0511	20–100					78	20		
Cesium	132.81	1.873	20	26.0	3.78	670	131.4	0.0482	0–26	0.97	0–26			19	0	0.00478	−80 to +25
Chromium	52.01	6.93	25	1765	70	2200	14.71	0.111	18–100	0.068	20–100			2.6	0		
Cobalt	58.94	8.71	21	1480	64	3000		0.1001	20	0.123	20			9.7	20	0.00658	0–100
Copper	63.57	8.89	20	1083	49.3	2300	1756	0.0928	18–100	0.162	20	0.918	18	1.724	20	0.00393	20
Gold	197.2	19.3	20	1063	15.9	2600	446	0.0312	18	0.143	17–100	0.705	17	2.44	0	0.0034	20
Iridium	193.1	22.42	17	2454±3	26.1	4800	340	0.0323	18–100	0.065	20	0.141	17	6.10	20	0.00411	20
Iron (99.97%)	55.84	7.87	20	1535	65	3200	1110	0.1075	20	0.119	0–100	0.18	0	9.8	20	0.0065	0–100
Lead	207.22	11.342	20	327.4	6	1620	323	0.0297	0	0.291	20–100	0.083	18	22.0	20	0.0039	20
Lithium	6.940	0.534	20	186	120.5	1200		0.96	50	0.512	0–178	0.167	0	8.55	0	0.0047	0
Magnesium	24.32	1.74	20	651	70	1097	1300–1500	0.249	0–100	0.283	20–300	0.376	0–100	4.4611	20	0.0040	20
Manganese	54.93	7.2	20	1260		1900	1044	0.1211	20–100	0.228	0–100			5.0±			

*Where the temperature is not given, ordinary temperature is understood.

†$\dfrac{1}{v}\dfrac{dv}{dt} = 182.0 \times 10^{-6}$ at 20 deg cent.

Table 22. Physical Properties of Metals.—Continued

(For properties of alloys, see Sec. 11, Metallic Materials)

Name	Atomic Weight	Density G per cu cm	Density Temp* deg cent	Melting Point, deg cent	Latent Heat of Fusion, g-cal per g	Boiling Point, deg cent	Latent Heat of Vaporization, g-cal per g	Specific Heat G-cal per g or Btu per lb	Specific Heat Temp, deg cent	Thermal Coeff of Linear Expansion ×10⁴ per deg cent	Thermal Coeff of Linear Expansion Temp, deg cent	Thermal Conductivity G-cal per sec per sq cm per deg cent per cm	Thermal Conductivity Temp, deg cent	Electrical Resistivity Microhm-cm	Electrical Resistivity Temp* deg cent	Temp Coefficient of Resistivity Temp Coefficient	Temp Coefficient of Resistivity Temp, deg cent
Mercury	200.61	13.546	20	−38.87	2.776	356.9	71	0.0333	17	†	…	0.0148	0	95.783	20	0.00089	20
Molybdenum	96.0	10.2	…	2620	…	3700	176.8	0.0589	0	0.049	25–100	0.346	17	5.08	20	0.0047	0–100
Nickel	58.69	8.85	20	1440	73	2900	1010	0.1032	0	0.132	25–100	0.14	0–100	7.8	20	0.00537	20–100
Osmium	190.8	22.48	20	2700	…	5300	350	0.0311	19.98	0.066	40	…	…	9.5	20	…	…
Palladium	106.7	12.0	20	1553	35.93	2200	610	0.0538	0	0.1173	20	0.1683	18	11	0	0.0033	20
Platinum	195.23	21.37	20	1773.5	26.9	4300	637	0.0319	20–100	0.0893	20	0.1664	18	9.83	0	0.003	20
Potassium	39.10	0.870	20	62.3	14.6	760	513	0.177	3.4	0.83	0–50	0.236	0	6.1	0	0.0055	0
Rhodium	102.91	12.44	20	1966	…	>2500	620	0.058	10–97	0.0876	6–21	1.006	18	5.11	0	0.0043	0
Silver	107.880	10.5	20	960.5	25.9	1950	551.6	0.0557	0	0.197	0–100	0.365	0	1.629	18	0.0038	20
Sodium	22.997	0.9712	20	97.5	27	880	1170	0.283	0	0.622	−190 to −17	…	…	4.3	0	0.0054	20
Strontium	87.63	2.60	…	800	…	1150	1045	0.0735	15	…	…	…	…	24.8	20	…	…
Tantalum	181.4	16.6	…	2850	…	>4100	159	0.036	58	0.0655	0–100	0.130	17	15.5	20	0.0031	20
Tellurium	127.5	6.25	20	452	7.3	1390	…	0.0483	15–100	‖0.016 ⊥0.272	20	0.0143	45	200,000	19.6	…	…
Thallium	204.39	11.95	20	303.5	…	1650	220	0.0326	20–100	0.302	40	0.093	0	17.6	0	0.0040	0
Thorium	232.12	11.00	17	1845	…	>3000	…	0.0276	0–100	‖0.305 ⊥0.155	20	…	…	18	20	0.0021	20–1800
Tin	118.70	7.29±	…	231.89	14.4	2260	655	0.0548	25	…	…	0.155	0	11.5	20	0.0042	20
Titanium	47.90	4.5	18	1800	…	>3000	1320	0.1125	0–100	…	…	…	…	3.0	20	…	…
Tungsten	184.0	19.0±	…	3382	…	5900	1183	0.032	100	0.0444	27	0.476	17	5.50	20	0.0047	0–100
Uranium	238.14	18.7	13	<1850	…	…	…	0.0280	0–98	…	…	…	…	60±18	20	…	…
Vanadium	50.95	5.6	…	1710	…	3000	…	0.1153	0–100	…	…	…	…	…	…	0.0037	20
Zinc	65.38	7.14±	…	419.45	26.6	905±2	426.8	0.0931	20–100	‖0.639 ⊥0.141	20–100	0.2653	18	5.75	0	…	…
Zirconium	91.22	6.53	…	1900	…	>2900	…	0.066	0–100	…	…	…	…	170±	0	0.00116	−80 to +30

* Where the temperature is not given, ordinary temperature is understood.

† $\dfrac{1}{v}\dfrac{dv}{dt} = 182.0 \times 10^{-6}$ at 20 deg cent.

Table 23. Mechanical Properties of Metals *
(For properties of alloys, see Sec. 11, Metallic Materials)

Name	Tensile Strength, lb per sq in.	Elongation, per cent	Reduction of Area, per cent	Modulus of Elasticity, lb per sq in.	Modulus of Rigidity (Shearing Modulus), lb per sq in.	Brinell Hardness, Diam of Ball and Load	Poisson's Ratio
Aluminum	9,000 W	60% in 2 in.		10,000,000	3,870,000 W	15; 10 mm, 500 kg	0.33
Antimony †	1,560			11,300,000 W	2,860,000		
Arsenic							
Cadmium	12,000 C	52%	80%	10,000,000 C	3,500,000 C	147; 10 mm, 1000 kg C	0.30
Calcium	8,700 C	6% in 5 cm				21–24; 10 mm, 500 kg C	
Cerium						42; 10 mm, 500 kg C	
Chromium						28; 5 mm, 90 kg	
Cobalt	34,000 C; 37,000 A; 96,000 DW	5% DW	8% DW			91; 10 mm, 500 kg; 124; 10 mm, 1600 kg; 48; 10 mm, 500 kg A	
Copper	51,000 HS; 60,000 HW	4% in 2 in.; 3% in 10 in.		16,000,000		103; 10 mm, 500 kg	0.35 RA
Gold	25,000 C; 37,000 D	25% in 2 in. C		11,400,000 D	3,700,000	25; 10 mm, 500 kg RA	0.42 RA
Iridium	40,000 C			75,000,000 DH		172; C	
Iron (99.97%)		40% in 2 in.	80%	29,700,000	10,000,000	50–90; 10 mm, 500 kg	0.28
Lead ‡	1,780 R; 3,000			2,130,000–2,400,000 R; 2,550,000 A	780,000	4.2 C	0.43
Magnesium	27,000 AS	15% in 2 in. AS		6,250,000	2,400,000	37; 10 mm, 500 kg	
Molybdenum	255,000–312,000 DW	43% S				147; 10 mm, 500 kg AS	0.21
Nickel	70,000–85,000 R	43–53% in 2 in. R	65–75% R	30,000,000 D	10,000,000 D	85–105; 10 mm, 500 kg R	0.39
Palladium	39,000 DH	18% in 2 in. DH		17,000,000 D	6,400,000	49; D	0.38
Platinum	53,000 DH; 34,100 A	50% in 2 in. A		24,200,000 D	9,300,000	13; 10 mm, 500 kg; 24; 10 mm, 500 kg A	
Potassium						0.037; 10 mm, 1.6 kg D	
Rhodium				42,500,000		139	
Silver	15,400 T; 41,200 RH; 44,100–51,200 DH	41% in 2 in.	37.7%	11,240,000 DH	3,800,000	42; 10 mm, 500 kg T; 59; 10 mm, 500 kg DH	0.37 DA
Sodium						0.07; 10 mm, 3.2 kg	
Tantalum	132,000 DHW; 80,000 DW			27,000,000			
Thorium	4,000 C			4,000,000 C			
Tin	5,000 R; 10,000 D	35% in 2 in. C		5,700,000–7,800,000 R	2,400,000	14; 10 mm, 500 kg C	0.33
Tungsten (99.2%)	215,000 DHW§; 590,000 DHW‖	4% in 2 in. G§	28% G§; 65% DHW‖	51,400,000 DW	21,400,000 DW		0.17
Zinc	18,000–35,000 R			12,000,000	5,000,000	39	

* Values given are in most cases representative only. Considerable variations may be expected relative to size, shape, and treatment.
† Wire diameter 0.36 mm.
‡ Compressive stress 2120 lb per sq in. $\Delta l = -32\%\, l_0$.
§ Swaged rod 0.03 in. diameter.
‖ Hard drawn wire 0.00114 in. diameter.

A Annealed	R Rolled
C Cast	S Sheet
D Drawn	T Sand cast
G Swaged	W Wire
H Hard	

Table 24. Density of Miscellaneous Non-metallic Solids

Name	g per cu cm	lb per cu ft
Agate	2.5–2.7	156–168
Amber	1.06–1.11	66–69
Asbestos	2.0–2.8	125–175
Asphalt	1.1–1.5	69–94
Basalt	2.4–3.1	150–193
Bauxite	2.55	159
Beeswax	0.96–0.97	60–61
Biotite	2.7–3.1	168–193
Borax	1.7–1.8	106–112
Brick, soft	1.6	100
common	1.79	112
hard	2.0	125
pressed	2.16	135
fire	2.24–2.4	140–150
sand lime	2.18	136
Brickwork		
mortar	1.6	100
cement	1.79	112
Carbon, diamond	3.52	220
graphite	2.25	140
Cement, natural	2.8–3.2	175–200
Portland	3.05–3.15	190–197
loose	1.44	90
barreled	1.84	115
slag	1.9–2.3	119–144
Chalk	1.9–2.8	119–175
Charcoal, oak	0.57	35
pine	0.28–0.44	17–27
Clay	1.8–2.6	112–162
Coal, anthracite	1.4–1.8	87–112
bituminous	1.2–1.6	75–100
charcoal	0.27–0.58	17–36
lignite	1.1–1.4	69–87
Coke	1.0–1.7	62–106
Concrete†		144
Corundum	3.9–4.0	244–250
Dolomite	2.84	177
Earth		
dry, loose	1.2	75
packed	1.5	94
moist, loose	1.3	81
packed	1.6	100
mud, flowing	1.7	106
packed	1.8	112
Emery	4.0	250
Feldspar	2.55–2.75	159–172
Flint	2.63	164
Garnet	3.15–4.3	197–268
Gas carbon	1.88	117
Gelatin	1.27	80
Glass, common	2.5–2.75	156–172
crystal	2.90–3.00	181–187
flint	3.2–4.7	200–294
plate	2.45–2.72	153–170
Glue	1.27	80
Gneiss	2.4–2.7	150–169
Granite	2.65–2.7	165–169
Gravel, dry, loose	1.4–1.7	87–106
packed	1.6–1.9	100–119
wet	1.9	119
Gypsum	2.31–2.33	144–145
Hematite	4.9–5.3	306–330
Hornblende	3.0	187
Iodine	4.94	308
Ivory	1.83–1.92	114–120

Name	g per cu cm	lb per cu ft
Lava, basaltic	2.8–3.0	175–187
trachytic	2.0–2.7	125–168
Leather	.86–1.02	54–64
Lime, mortar	1.65–1.78	103–111
quick (in bulk)	0.8–0.96	50–60
slaked	1.3–1.4	81–87
Limestone	2.00–2.9	125–181
Litharge		
(artificial)	9.3–9.4	580–587
natural	7.8–8.0	487–499
Magnesia		
carbonate	2.4	150
Magnetite	4.9–5.2	306–324
Marble	2.6–2.84	162–177
Masonry, dry		
rubble	2.24–2.56	140–160
dressed	2.24–2.88	140–180
Mica	2.6–3.2	162–200
Muscovite	2.76–3.00	172–187
Oligoclase	2.65–2.67	165–167
Orthoclase	2.58–2.61	161–163
Paper	0.7–1.15	44–72
Pitch	1.07	67
Plaster-of-Paris	1.5–1.8	94–112
Porcelain	2.3–2.5	143–156
Porphyry	2.6–2.9	162–181
Pumice	0.37–0.90	23–56
Pyrite	4.95–5.1	309–318
Quartz	2.65	165
Quartzite	2.73	170
Resin	1.07	67
Riprap		
limestone	1.3–1.4	81–87
sandstone	1.4	87
shale	1.7	106
Rock salt	2.18	136
Rubber		
caoutchouc	0.92–0.96	57–60
manufactured	1.0–2.0	62–125
Salt	0.78–1.25	49–78
Sand, dry	1.44–1.76	90–110
wet	1.89–2.07	118–129
Selenium	4.82	301
Serpentine	2.50–2.65	156–165
Shale	2.6–2.9	162–181
Silicon	2.42	151
Slag, bank	1.1–1.2	69–75
bank screenings	1.5–1.9	94–119
furnace	2.0–3.9	125–244
machine	1.5	94
sand	0.8–0.9	50–56
Slate	2.6–3.3	162–205
Soapstone	2.6–2.8	162–175
Starch	1.53	95
Stone, various	2.16–3.4	135–212
crushed	1.6	100
Sugar	1.61	100
Sulfur	2.0–2.1	125–131
Talc	2.7–2.8	168–175
Tar, bituminous	1.20	75
Terracotta	1.9	119
Tile	1.76–1.92	110–120
Tourmaline	3.0–3.2	187–200
Traprock	2.72–3.4	170–212
Wood	see Sec. 12	see Sec. 12

* Ordinary temperatures understood.

† See p. 12-09 for light-weight concrete.

Table 25. Specific Heat of Miscellaneous Non-metallic Solids

Name	Temp, deg cent	Specific heat, g-cal per g or Btu per lb	Name	Temp, deg cent	Specific heat, g-cal per g or Btu per lb
Asbestos..........	20–98	0.195	Granite..........	12–100	.192
Bakelite..........	.....	.3–.4	Ice..............	−20	.465
Basalt............	20–100	.20		0	.487
Carbon, graphite...	−76–0	.126	India rubber, Para	?–100	.481
	26–76	.165	Limestone.......	.....	.22
diamond........	0	.1044	Marble..........	18	.21
Calcspar..........	0–100	.2005	Mica............	20	.10
Cellulose..........	.....	.35	Paraffin..........	0–20	.694
Chalk............	20–99	.214	Porcelain........	15–950	.26
Clay.............	20–100	.22	Quartz..........	0	.17
Coal.............	.....	.3	Rock salt........	12–100	.188
Coke.............	21–400	.265	Sand............	.....	.19
Concrete..........	70–312	.156	Selenium........	20.5	.077
Ebonite..........	20–100	.40	Silicon..........	18.2–99.1	.181
Glass			Sulfur, rhombic...	15–96	.176
normal thermometer 16III......	19–100	.1988	monoclinic......	0–52	.181
crown..........	10–50	.161	Woods, general....	.....	.3–.7
flint............	10–50	.117			

Table 26. Thermal Coefficient of Linear Expansion of Miscellaneous Non-metallic Solids*

Name	Temp, deg cent	Thermal Coefficient of Expansion, per deg cent ($\times 10^4$)	Name	Temp, deg cent	Thermal Coefficient of Expansion, per deg cent ($\times 10^4$)
Amber............	0–30	0.50	Quartz glass......	16–1000	0.0058
Bakelite, bleached..	20–60	0.22	Rock salt.........	40	0.4040
Caoutchouc.......	16.7–25.3	0.770	Rubber, hard.....	0	0.691
Carbon, diamond...	50	0.012	Rubber, hard.....	−160	0.300
graphite........	50	0.06	Selenium.........	0–100	0.660
Celluloid..........	20.–80.	1.0	Silicon...........	−3 to + 18	0.0249
Ebonite...........	25.3–35.4	0.842	Tourmaline:		
Fluorspar: CaF₂....	0–100	0.1950	‖ to longitudinal		
Glass, tube........	0–100	0.0833	axis........	0–100	0.0937
plate...........	0–100	0.0891	‖ to horizontal		
crown (mean)....	0–100	0.0897	axis........	0–100	0.0773
flint............	50–60	0.0788	Vulcanite........	0–18	0.6360
Jena thermometer 16III			Wedgwood Ware..	0–100	0.0890
normal........	0–100	0.081	Wood ‖ to fiber		
Jena thermometer 56III	0–100	0.058	ash...........	0–100	0.0951
			beech..........	2.34	0.0257
Jena thermometer 59III..........	−191 to+16	0.424	chestnut.......	2.34	0.0649
			elm...........	2.34	0.0565
Gutta percha......	20	1.983	mahogany......	2.34	0.0361
Ice..............	−20 to −1	0.51	maple.........	2.34	0.0638
Iceland spar:			oak...........	2.34	0.0492
‖ to axis........	0–80	0.2631	pine...........	2.34	0.0541
⊥ to axis........	0–80	0.0544	walnut.........	2.34	0.0658
Limestone.........	25–100	0.09	Wood:		
Marble...........	15–100	0.117	⊥ to fiber		
Paraffin...........	0–16	1.0662	beech..........	2.34	0.614
Paraffin...........	16–38	1.3030	chestnut.......	2.34	0.325
Porcelain..........	20–790	0.0413	elm...........	2.34	0.443
Bayeux.........	1000–1400	0.0553	mahogany......	2.34	0.404
Quartz:			maple.........	2.34	0.484
‖ to axis........	0–80	0.0797	oak...........	2.34	0.544
‖ to axis........	−190 to+16	0.0521	pine...........	2.34	0.341
⊥ to axis........	0–80	0.1337	walnut.........	2.34	0.484
Quartz glass.......	−190 to+16	−0.0026	Wax, white.......	10–26	2.300
Quartz glass.......	16–500	0.0057	Wax, white.......	26–31	3.120

* The coefficient of cubical expansion may be taken as three times the linear coefficient.

TABLES OF CONVERSION FACTORS, UNITS OF WEIGHTS AND MEASURES

By J. G. Brainerd

Table 27. Length [L]

Multiply Number of → / to Obtain ↓ by	Centimeters	Feet	Inches	Kilometers	Nautical miles	Meters	Mils	Miles	Millimeters	Yards
Centimeters	1	30.48	2.540	10^5	1.853×10^5	100	2.540×10^{-3}	1.609×10^5	0.1	91.44
Feet	3.281×10^{-2}	1	8.333×10^{-2}	3281	6080.27	3.281	8.333×10^{-5}	5280	3.281×10^{-3}	3
Inches	0.3937	12	1	3.937×10^4	7.296×10^4	39.37	0.001	6.336×10^4	3.937×10^{-2}	36
Kilometers	10^{-5}	3.048×10^{-4}	2.540×10^{-5}	1	1.853	0.001	2.540×10^{-8}	1.609	10^{-6}	9.144×10^{-4}
Nautical miles		1.645×10^{-4}		0.5396	1	5.396×10^{-4}		0.8684		4.934×10^{-4}
Meters	0.01	0.3048	2.540×10^{-2}	1000	1853	1		1609	0.001	0.9144
Mils	393.7	1.2×10^4	1000	3.937×10^7		3.937×10^4	1		39.37	3.6×10^4
Miles	6.214×10^{-6}	1.894×10^{-4}	1.578×10^{-5}	0.6214	1.1516	6.214×10^{-4}		1	6.214×10^{-7}	5.682×10^{-4}
Millimeters	10	304.8	25.40	10^6		1000	2.540×10^{-2}		1	914.4
Yards	1.094×10^{-2}	0.3333	2.778×10^{-2}	1094	2027	1.094	2.778×10^{-5}	1760	1.094×10^{-3}	1

Metric Multiples

10^6 microns $= 10^3$ millimeters $= 10^2$ centimeters $= 10$ decimeters $= 1$ meter $= 10^{-1}$ dekameter $= 10^{-2}$ hectometer $= 10^{-3}$ kilometer $= 10^{-4}$ myriameter $= 10^{-6}$ megameter $= 10^{10}$ Angstrom Units.

Land Measure

7.92 inches = 1 link
25 links = 1 rod = 16.5 feet = 5.5 yards (1 rod = 1 pole = 1 perch)
4 rods = 1 chain (Gunther's) = 66 feet = 22 yards = 100 links
10 chains = 1 furlong = 660 feet = 220 yards = 1000 links = 40 rods
8 furlongs = 1 mile = 5280 feet = 1760 yards = 8000 links = 320 rods = 80 chains

Ropes and Cables

2 yards = 1 fathom   120 fathoms = 1 cable's length

Nautical Measure

6080.27 feet = 1 nautical mile = 1.15156 statute miles
3 nautical miles = 1 league (U. S.)   3 statute miles = 1 league (Gr. Britain)

(NOTE. A nautical mile is the length of a minute of longitude of the earth at the equator at sea level. The British Admiralty uses the round figure of 6080 feet. The word "knot" is used to denote "nautical miles per hour.")

Miscellaneous

3 inches = 1 palm   9 inches = 1 span
4 inches = 1 hand   2 1/2 feet = 1 military pace

Table 28. Area [L^2]

to Obtain ↓ / Multiply Number of → by	Acres	Circular mils	Square centimeters	Square feet	Square inches	Square kilometers	Square meters	Square miles	Square millimeters	Square yards
Acres	1			2.296×10^{-5}		247.1	2.471×10^{-4}	640		2.066×10^{-4}
Circular mils		1	1.973×10^{5}	1.833×10^{8}	1.273×10^{6}		1.973×10^{9}		1973	
Square centimeters	5.067×10^{-6}		1	929.0	6.452	10^{10}	10^{4}	2.590×10^{10}	0.01	8361
Square feet	4.356×10^{4}		1.076×10^{-3}	1	6.944×10^{-3}	1.076×10^{7}	10.76	2.788×10^{7}	1.076×10^{-5}	9
Square inches	6,272,640	7.854×10^{-7}	0.1550	144	1	1.550×10^{9}	1550	4.015×10^{9}	1.550×10^{-3}	1296
Square kilometers	4.047×10^{-3}		10^{-10}	9.290×10^{-8}	6.452×10^{-10}	1	10^{-6}	2.590	10^{-12}	8.361×10^{-7}
Square meters	4047		0.0001	9.290×10^{-2}	6.452×10^{-4}	10^{-6}	1	2.590×10^{6}	10^{-6}	0.8361
Square miles	1.562×10^{-3}		3.861×10^{-11}	3.587×10^{-8}		0.3861	3.861×10^{-7}	1	3.861×10^{-13}	3.228×10^{-7}
Square millimeters		5.067×10^{-4}	100	9.290×10^{4}	645.2	10^{12}	10^{6}		1	8.361×10^{5}
Square yards	4840		1.196×10^{-4}	0.1111	7.716×10^{-4}	1.196×10^{6}	1.196	3.098×10^{6}	1.196×10^{-6}	1

Land Measure

$30\ 1/4$ square yards = 1 square rod = $272\ 1/4$ square feet
16 square rods = 1 square chain = 484 square yards = 4356 square feet
$2\ 1/2$ square chains = 1 rood = 40 square rods = 1210 square yards
4 roods = 1 acre = 10 square chains = 160 square rods
640 acres = 1 square mile = 2560 roods = 102,400 square rods
1 section of land = 1 square mile; 1 quarter section = 160 acres

Architect's Measure

100 square feet = 1 square

Circular Inch and Circular Mil

A circular inch is the area of a circle 1 inch in diameter = 0.7854 square inch
1 square inch = 1.2732 circular inches
A circular mil is the area of a circle 1 mil (or 0.001 inch) in diameter = 0.7854 square mil
1 square mil = 1.2732 circular mils
1 circular inch = 10^6 circular mils = 0.7854×10^6 square mils
1 square inch = 1.2732×10^6 circular mils = 10^6 square mils

Metric Multiples

1 square meter = 1 centiare = 10^{-2} are = 10^{-4} hectare
= 10^{-6} square kilometer = 10^{-8} square myriameter

Table 29.   Volume $[L^3]$

Multiply Number of → / to Obtain ↓	Bushels (dry)	Cubic centimeters	Cubic feet	Cubic inches	Cubic meters	Cubic yards	Gallons (liquid)	Liters	Pints (liquid)	Quarts (liquid)
Bushels (dry)	1		0.8036	4.651×10^{-4}	28.38			2.838×10^{-2}		
Cubic centimeters	3.524×10^4	1	2.832×10^4	16.39	10^6	7.646×10^5	3785	1000	473.2	946.4
Cubic feet	1.2445	3.531×10^{-5}	1	5.787×10^{-4}	35.31	27	0.1337	3.531×10^{-2}	1.671×10^{-2}	3.342×10^{-2}
Cubic inches	2150.4	6.102×10^{-2}	1728	1	6.102×10^4	46,656	231	61.02	28.87	57.75
Cubic meters	3.524×10^{-2}	10^{-6}	2.832×10^{-2}	1.639×10^{-5}	1	0.7646	3.785×10^{-3}	0.001	4.732×10^{-4}	9.464×10^{-4}
Cubic yards		1.308×10^{-6}	3.704×10^{-2}	2.143×10^{-5}	1.308	1	4.951×10^{-3}	1.308×10^{-3}	6.189×10^{-4}	1.238×10^{-3}
Gallons (liquid)		2.642×10^{-4}	7.481	4.329×10^{-3}	264.2	202.0	1	0.2642	0.125	0.25
Liters	35.24	0.001	28.32	1.639×10^{-2}	1000	764.6	3.785	1	0.4732	0.9464
Pints (liquid)		2.113×10^{-3}	59.84	3.463×10^{-2}	2113	1616	8	2.113	1	2
Quarts (liquid)......		1.057×10^{-3}	29.92	1.732×10^{-2}	1057	807.9	4	1.057	0.5	1

Metric Multiples

10 milliliters	= 1 centiliter	= 0.338 fluid ounce
10 centiliters	= 1 deciliter	= 0.845 liquid gill
10 deciliters	= 1 liter	= 1.0567 liquid quarts
10 liters	= 1 dekaliter	= 2.6417 liquid gallons
10 dekaliters	= 1 hectoliter	= 2.8375 U. S. bushels
10 hectoliters	= 1 kiloliter (or stere)	= 28.375 U. S. bushels

Cubic Measure

1 cord of wood = a pile cut 4 feet long, piled 4 feet high and 8 feet on the ground = 128 cubic feet

1 perch of stone = a quantity 1 1/2 feet thick, 1 foot high and 16 1/2 feet long = 24 3/4 cubic feet

(NOTE.—A perch of stone is, however, often computed differently in different localities; thus, in most if not all of the States and Territories west of the Mississippi, stone-masons figure rubble by the perch of 16 1/2 cubic feet. In Philadelphia, 22 cubic feet are called a perch. In Chicago, stone is measured by the cord of 100 cubic feet. Check should be made against local practice.)

Board Measure

In board measure, boards are assumed to be one inch in thickness. Therefore, feet board measure of a stick of square timber = length in feet × breadth in feet × thickness in inches.

Shipping Measure

For register tonnage or measurement of the entire internal capacity of a vessel, it is arbitrarily assumed, to facilitate computation, that:

100 cubic feet = 1 register ton

For the measurement of cargo:

40 cubic feet = 1 U. S. shipping ton = 32.143 U. S. bushels
42 cubic feet = 1 British shipping ton = 32.703 Imperial bushels

Dry Measure

One U. S. Winchester bushel contains 1.2445 cubic feet or 2150.42 cubic inches. It holds 77.601 pounds distilled water at 62° F.

(Note.—The above is a *struck* bushel. A *heaped* bushel in general equals 1 1/4 struck bushels, although for apples and pears it contains 1.2731 struck bushels = 2737.72 cubic inches.)

One U. S. gallon (dry measure) = 1/8 bushel and contains 268.8 cubic inches.

(Note.—This is not a legal U. S. *dry measure* and therefore is given for comparison only.)

One British Imperial bushel contains 1.2843 cubic feet or 2219.36 cubic inches. It holds 80 pounds distilled water at 62° F.

One British Imperial gallon = 1/8 Imperial bushel and contains 277.42 cubic inches.

1 Winchester bushel = 0.9694 Imperial bushel
1 Imperial bushel   = 1.032 Winchester bushels

Same relations as above maintain for gallons (dry measure)

(Note.—1 U. S. gallon (dry) = 1.164 U. S. gallons (liquid)).

U. S. Units

2 pints	= 1 quart			=	67.2 cubic inches
4 quarts	= 1 gallon *	= 8 pints		=	268.8 cubic inches
2 gallons*	= 1 peck	= 16 pints	= 8 quarts	=	537.6 cubic inches
4 pecks	= 1 bushel	= 64 pints	= 32 quarts = 8 gallons*	=	2150.42 cubic inches

1 cubic foot contains 6.428 gallons (dry measure)*

Liquid Measure

One U. S. gallon (liquid measure) contains 231 cubic inches. It holds 8.336 pounds distilled water at 62° F.

One British Imperial gallon contains 277.42 cubic inches. It holds 10 pounds distilled water at 62° F.

1 U. S. gallon (liquid) = 0.8327 Imperial gallon
1 Imperial gallon   = 1.201 U. S. gallons (liquid)

(Note.—1 U. S. gallon (liquid) = 0.8594 U. S. gallon (dry)).

U. S. Units

4 gills	= 1 pint	=	16 fluid ounces
2 pints	= 1 quart = 8 gills	=	32 fluid ounces
4 quarts	= 1 gallon = 32 gills = 8 pints	=	128 fluid ounces

1 cubic foot contains 7.4805 gallons (liquid measure)

Apothecaries' Fluid Measure

60 minims = 1 fluid drachm.   8 drachms = 1 fluid ounce

In the U. S. a fluid ounce is the 128th part of a U. S. gallon, or 1.805 cu in. or 29.58 cu cm. It contains 455.8 grains of water at 62° F. In Great Britain the fluid ounce is 1.732 cu in. and contains 1 ounce avoirdupois (or 437.5 grains) of water at 62° F.

---

* The *gallon* is not a U. S. legal *dry measure*.

Table 30.   Plane Angle [No Dimensions]

Multiply Number of → / to Obtain ↓ by	Degrees	Minutes	Quadrants	Radians *	Revolutions * (Circumferences)	Seconds
Degrees	1	1.667×10^{-2}	90	57.30	360	2.778×10^{-4}
Minutes	60	1	5400	3438	2.16×10^{4}	1.667×10^{-2}
Quadrants	1.111×10^{-2}	1.852×10^{-4}	1	0.6366	4	3.087×10^{-6}
Radians *	1.745×10^{-2}	2.909×10^{-4}	1.571	1	6.283	4.848×10^{-6}
Revolutions * (Circumferences)	2.778×10^{-3}	4.630×10^{-5}	0.25	0.1591	1	7.716×10^{-7}
Seconds	3600	60	3.24×10^{5}	2.063×10^{5}	1.296×10^{6}	1

* 2π radians = 1 circumference = 360 degrees by definition.

Table 31.   Solid Angle [No Dimensions]

Multiply Number of → / to Obtain ↓ by	Hemispheres	Spheres *	Spherical right angles	Steradians †
Hemispheres	1	2	0.25	0.1592
Spheres *	0.5	1	0.125	7.958×10^{-2}
Spherical right angles	4	8	1	0.6366
Steradians †	6.283	12.57	1.571	1

* A sphere is the total solid angle about a point.   † 4π steradians = 1 sphere by definition.

Table 32.   Time [T]

Multiply Number of → / to Obtain ↓ by	Days	Hours	Minutes	Months (average)*	Seconds	Weeks
Days	1	4.167×10^{-2}	6.944×10^{-4}	30.42	1.157×10^{-5}	7
Hours	24	1	1.667×10^{-2}	730.0	2.778×10^{-4}	168
Minutes	1440	60	1	4.380×10^{4}	1.667×10^{-2}	1.008×10^{4}
Months (average) *	3.288×10^{-2}	1.370×10^{-3}	2.283×10^{-5}	1	3.806×10^{-7}	0.2302
Seconds	8.64×10^{4}	3600	60	2.628×10^{6}	1	6.048×10^{5}
Weeks	0.1429	5.952×10^{-3}	9.921×10^{-5}	4.344	1.654×10^{-6}	1

* One common year = 365 days; one leap year = 366 days; one average month = $\frac{1}{12}$ of a common year.

Table 33.　Linear Velocity [LT^{-1}]

Multiply Number of → / to Obtain ↓	Centimeters per second	Feet per minute	Feet per second	Kilometers per hour	Kilometers per minute	Knots *	Meters per minute	Meters per second	Miles per hour	Miles per minute
Centimeters per second	1	0.5080	30.48	27.78	1667	51 48	1.667	100	44.70	2682
Feet per minute	1.969	1	60	54.68	3281	101.3	3.281	196.8	88	5280
Feet per second	3.281×10^{-2}	1.667×10^{-2}	1	0.9113	54.68	1.689	5.468×10^{-2}	3.281	1.467	88
Kilometers per hour	0.036	1.829×10^{-2}	1.097	1	60	1.853	0.06	3.6	1.609	96.54
Kilometers per minute	0.0006	3.048×10^{-4}	1.829×10^{-2}	1.667×10^{-2}	1	3.088×10^{-2}	0.001	0.06	2.682×10^{-2}	1.609
Knots *	1.943×10^{-2}	9.868×10^{-3}	0.5921	0.5396	32.38	1	3.238×10^{-2}	1.943	0.8684	52.10
Meters per minute	0.6	0.3048	18.29	16.67	1000	30.88	1	60	26.82	1609
Meters per second	0.01	5.080×10^{-3}	0.3048	0.2778	16.67	0.5148	1.667×10^{-2}	1	0.4770	26.82
Miles per hour	2.237×10^{-2}	1.136×10^{-2}	0.6818	0.6214	37.28	1.152	3.728×10^{-2}	2.237	1	60
Miles per minute	3.728×10^{-4}	1.892×10^{-4}	1.136×10^{-2}	1.036×10^{-2}	0.6214	1.919×10^{-2}	6.214×10^{-4}	3.728×10^{-2}	1.667×10^{-2}	1

* Nautical miles per hour.

The Miner's Inch
(Used in Measuring Flow of Water)

An Act of the California legislature, May 23, 1901, makes the standard miner's inch 1.5 cu ft per minute, measured through any aperture or orifice.

The term Miner's Inch is more or less indefinite, for the reason that California water companies do not all use the same head above the center of the aperture, and the inch varies from 1.36 to 1.73 cu ft per minute, but the most common measurement is through an aperture 2 in. high and whatever length is required, and through a plank 1 1/4 in. thick. The lower edge of the aperture should be 2 in. above the bottom of the measuring-box, and the plank 5 in. high above the aperture, thus making a 6-in. head above the center of the stream. Each square inch of this opening represents a miner's inch, which is equal to a flow of 1.5 cu ft per minute.

Table 34. Angular Velocity $[T^{-1}]$

to Obtain ↓ / Multiply Number of → by	Degrees per second	Radians per second	Revolutions per minute	Revolutions per second
Degrees per second	1	57.30	6	360
Radians per second	1.745×10^{-2}	1	0.1047	6.283
Revolutions per minute	0.1667	9.549	1	60
Revolutions per second	2.778×10^{-3}	0.1592	1.667×10^{-2}	1

Table 35. Linear Acceleration * $[LT^{-2}]$

to Obtain ↓ / Multiply Number of → by	Centimeters per second per second	Feet per second per second	Kilometers per hour per second	Meters per second per second	Miles per hour per second
Centimeters per second per second	1	30.48	27.78	100	44.70
Feet per second per second	3.281×10^{-2}	1	0.9113	3.281	1.467
Kilometers per hour per second	0.036	1.097	1	3.6	1.609
Meters per second per second	0.01	0.3048	0.2778	1	0.4470
Miles per hour per second	2.237×10^{-2}	0.6818	0.6214	2.237	1

* The (standard) acceleration due to gravity (g_0) = 980.7 cm per sec per sec, = 32.17 feet per sec per sec = 35.30 km per hour per sec = 9.807 meters per sec per sec = 21.94 miles per hour per sec.

Table 36. Angular Acceleration $[T^{-2}]$

to Obtain ↓ / Multiply Number of → by	Radians per second per second	Revolutions per minute per minute	Revolutions per minute per second	Revolutions per second per second
Radians per second per second	1	1.745×10^{-3}	0.1047	6.283
Revolutions per minute per minute	573.0	1	60	3600
Revolutions per minute per second	9.549	1.667×10^{-2}	1	60
Revolutions per second per second	0.1592	2.778×10^{-4}	1.667×10^{-2}	1

Table 37.   Mass [M] and Weight *

Multiply Number of → — to Obtain ↓ — by	Grains	Grams	Kilograms	Milligrams	Ounces †	Pounds †	Tons (long)	Tons (metric)	Tons (short)
Grains	1	15.43	1.543×10^4	1.543×10^{-2}	437.5	7000			
Grams	6.481×10^{-2}	1	1000	0.001	28.35	453.6	1.016×10^6	10^6	$9.072 \ 10^5$
Kilograms	6.481×10^{-5}	0.001	1	10^{-6}	2.835×10^{-2}	0.4536	1016	1000	907.2
Milligrams	64.81	1000	10^6	1	2.835×10^4	4.536×10^5	1.016×10^9	10^9	9.072×10^8
Ounces †	2.286×10^{-3}	3.527×10^{-2}	35.27	3.527×10^{-5}	1	16	3.584×10^4	3.527×10^4	3.2×10^4
Pounds †	1.429×10^{-4}	2.205×10^{-3}	2.205	2.205×10^{-6}	6.250×10^{-2}	1	2240	2205	2000
Tons (long)		9.842×10^{-7}	9.842×10^{-4}	9.842×10^{-10}	2.790×10^{-5}	4.464×10^{-4}	1	0.9842	0.8929
Tons (metric)		10^{-6}	0.001	10^{-9}	2.835×10^{-5}	4.536×10^{-4}	1.016	1	0.9072
Tons (short)		1.102×10^{-6}	1.102×10^{-3}	1.102×10^{-9}	3.125×10^{-5}	0.0005	1.120	1.102	1

* These same conversion factors apply to the *gravitational* units of force having the corresponding names. The dimensions of these units when used as gravitational units of force are MLT^{-2}; see table for *Force*.

† Avoirdupois pounds and ounces.

Metric Multiples

10^6 micrograms $= 10^3$ milligrams $= 10^2$ centigrams $= 10$ decigrams $= 1$ gram $= 10^{-1}$ dekagram $= 10^{-2}$ hectogram $= 10^{-3}$ kilogram $= 10^{-4}$ myriagram $= 10^{-6}$ megagram

Avoirdupois Weight

(Used Commercially)

27.343 grains	= 1 drachm
16 drachms	= 1 ounce (oz) = 437.5 grains
16 ounces	= 1 pound (lb) = 7000 grains
28 pounds	= 1 quarter (qr)
4 quarters	= 1 hundredweight (cwt) = 112 pounds
20 hundredweight	= 1 gross or long ton *
2000 pounds	= 1 net or short ton

(* NOTE.—The long ton is used by the U. S. custom-houses in collecting duties upon foreign goods. It is also used in freighting coal and selling it wholesale.)

14 pounds   = 1 stone; 100 pounds = 1 quintal

Troy Weight

(Used in weighing gold or silver)

24 grains	= 1 pennyweight (dwt)
20 pennyweights	= 1 ounce (oz) = 480 grains
12 ounces	= 1 pound (lb) = 5760 grains

The grain is the same in Avoirdupois, Troy and Apothecaries' weights. A carat, for weighing diamonds = 3.086 grains = 0.200 gram. (International Standard, 1913.)

1 pound troy   = .8229 pound avoirdupois
1 pound avoirdupois = 1.2153 pounds troy

Apothecaries' Weight

(Used in compounding medicines)

20 grains = 1 scruple (℈)
3 scruples = 1 drachm (℥) = 60 grains
8 drachms = 1 ounce (℥) = 480 grains
12 ounces = 1 pound (lb) = 5760 grains

The grain is the same in Avoirdupois, Troy and Apothecaries' weights.

1 pound apothecaries = 0.82286 pound avoirdupois
1 pound avoirdupois = 1.2153 pounds apothecaries

Table 38.   Density or Mass per Unit Volume $[ML^{-3}]$

to Obtain ↓ \ Multiply Number of → by	Grams per cubic centimeter	Kilograms per cubic meter	Pounds per cubic foot	Pounds per cubic inch
Grams per cubic centimeter	1	0.001	1.602×10^{-2}	27.68
Kilograms per cubic meter	1000	1	16.02	2.768×10^{4}
Pounds per cubic foot	62.43	6.243×10^{-2}	1	1728
Pounds per cubic inch	3.613×10^{-2}	3.613×10^{-5}	5.787×10^{-4}	1
Pounds per mil foot *	3.405×10^{-7}	3.405×10^{-10}	5.456×10^{-9}	9.425×10^{-6}

* Unit of volume is a volume one foot long and one circular mil in cross-section area.

Table 39.   Force * $[MLT^{-2}]$ or $[F]$

to Obtain ↓ \ Multiply Number of → by	Dynes	Grams	Joules per cm	Joules per meter	Kilograms	Pounds	Poundals
Dynes	1	980.7	10^{7}	10^{5}	9.807×10^{5}	4.448×10^{5}	1.383×10^{4}
Grams	1.020×10^{-3}	1	1.020×10^{4}	102.0	1000	453.6	14.10
Joules per cm	10^{-7}	9.807×10^{-5}	1	.01	9.807×10^{-2}	4.448×10^{-2}	1.383×10^{-3}
Joules per meter	10^{-5}	9.807×10^{-3}	100	1	9.807	4.448	0.1383
Kilograms	1.020×10^{-6}	0.001	10.20	0.1020	1	0.4536	1.410×10^{-2}
Pounds	2.248×10^{-6}	2.205×10^{-3}	22.48	0.2248	2.205	1	3.108×10^{-2}
Poundals	7.233×10^{-5}	7.093×10^{-2}	723.3	7.233	70.93	32.17	1

* Conversion factors between absolute and gravitational units apply only under standard acceleration due to gravity conditions. (See Sec. 3.)

Table 40. Torque or Moment of Force $[ML^2T^{-2}]$ or $[FL]$ *

Multiply Number of → to Obtain ↓	Dyne-centimeters	Gram-centimeters	Kilogram-meters	Pound-feet
Dyne-centimeters	1	980.7	9.807×10^7	1.356×10^7
Gram-centimeters	1.020×10^{-3}	1	10^5	1.383×10^4
Kilogram-meters	1.020×10^{-8}	10^{-5}	1	0.1383
Pound-feet	7.376×10^{-8}	7.233×10^{-5}	7.233	1

* Same dimensions as energy.

Table 41. Pressure or Force per Unit Area $[ML^{-1}T^{-2}]$ or $[FL^{-2}]$

Multiply Number of → to Obtain ↓	Atmospheres *	Baryes or dynes per square centimeter †	Centimeters of mercury at 0° C ‡	Inches of mercury at 0° C ‡	Inches of water at 4° C	Feet of water at 4° C	Kilograms per square meter §	Pounds per square foot	Pounds per square inch	Tons (short) per square foot
Atmospheres *	1	9.869×10^{-7}	1.316×10^{-2}	3.342×10^{-2}	2.458×10^{-3}	2.950×10^{-2}	9.678×10^{-5}	4.725×10^{-4}	6.804×10^{-2}	0.9450
Baryes or dynes per square centimeter †		1					98.07	478.8	6.895×10^4	9.576×10^5
Centimeters of mercury at 0° C ‡	76.00	7.501×10^{-5}	1	2.540	0.1868	2.232	7.356×10^{-3}	3.591×10^{-2}	5.171	71.83
Inches of mercury at 0° C ‡	29.92	2.953×10^{-5}	0.3937	1	7.355×10^{-2}	0.8826	2.896×10^{-3}	1.414×10^{-2}	2.036	28.28
Inches of water at 4° C	406.8	4.015×10^{-4}	5.354	13.60	1	12	3.937×10^{-2}	0.1922	27.68	384.5
Feet of water at 4° C	33.90	3.346×10^{-5}	0.4460	1.133	8.333×10^{-2}	1	3.281×10^{-3}	1.602×10^{-2}	2.307	32.04
Kilograms per square meter §	1.033×10^4	1.020×10^{-2}	136.0	345.3	25.40	304.8	1	4.882	703.1	9765
Pounds per square foot	2117	2.089×10^{-3}	27.85	70.73	5.204	62.43	0.2048	1	144	2000
Pounds per square inch	14.70	1.450×10^{-5}	0.1934	0.4912	3.613×10^{-2}	0.4335	1.422×10^{-3}	6.944×10^{-3}	1	13.89
Tons (short) per square foot	1.058							0.0005	0.072	1

* Definition: One atmosphere (standard) = 76 cm of mercury at 0° C.
† Sometimes called a bar.
‡ To convert height h of a column of mercury at t degrees Centigrade to the equivalent height h_o at 0° C. use $h_o = h \left\{ 1 - \dfrac{(m - l)t}{1 + mt} \right\}$ where $m = 0.0001818$ and $l = 18.4 \times 10^{-6}$ if the scale is engraved on brass; $l = 8.5 \times 10^{-6}$ if on glass. This assumes the scale is correct at 0° C; for other cases (any liquid) see International Critical Tables, vol. 1, p. 68.
§ 1 gram per sq cm = 10 kilograms per sq m.

Table 42.   Energy, Work and Heat * $[ML^2T^{-2}]$ or $[FL]$

Multiply Number of → / to Obtain ↓ by	British thermal units †	Centimeter-grams	Ergs or centimeter-dynes	Foot-pounds	Horsepower-hours	Joules ‡ or watt-seconds	Kilogram-calories †	Kilowatt-hours	Meter-kilograms	Watt-hours
British thermal units †	1	9.297×10^{-8}	9.480×10^{-11}	1.285×10^{-3}	2545	9.480×10^{-4}	3.969	3413	9.297×10^{-3}	3.413
Centimeter-grams	1.076×10^{7}	1	1.020×10^{-3}	1.383×10^{4}	2.737×10^{10}	1.020×10^{4}	4.269×10^{7}	3.671×10^{10}	10^{5}	3.671×10^{7}
Ergs or centimeter-dynes	1.055×10^{10}	980.7	1	1.356×10^{7}	2.684×10^{13}	10^{7}	4.186×10^{10}	3.6×10^{13}	9.807×10^{7}	3.6×10^{10}
Foot-pounds	778.3	7.233×10^{-5}	7.367×10^{-8}	1	1.98×10^{6}	0.7376	3087	2.655×10^{6}	7.233	2655
Horsepower-hours	3.929×10^{-4}	3.654×10^{-11}	3.722×10^{-14}	5.050×10^{-7}	1	3.722×10^{-7}	1.559×10^{-3}	1.341	3.653×10^{-6}	1.341×10^{-3}
Joules ‡ or watt-seconds	1054.8	9.807×10^{-5}	10^{-7}	1.356	2.684×10^{6}	1	4186	3.6×10^{6}	9.807	3600
Kilogram-calories †	0.2520	2.343×10^{-8}	2.389×10^{-11}	3.239×10^{-4}	641.3	2.389×10^{-4}	1	860.0	2.343×10^{-3}	0.8600
Kilowatt-hours	2.930×10^{-4}	2.724×10^{-11}	2.778×10^{-14}	3.766×10^{-7}	0.7457	2.778×10^{-7}	1.163×10^{-3}	1	2.724×10^{-6}	0.001
Meter-kilograms	107.6	10^{-5}	1.020×10^{-8}	0.1383	2.737×10^{5}	0.1020	426.9	3.671×10^{5}	1	367.1
Watt-hours	0.2930	2.724×10^{-8}	2.778×10^{-11}	3.766×10^{-4}	745.7	2.778×10^{-4}	1.163	1000	2.724×10^{-3}	1

* See note at the bottom of Table 43.

† Mean calorie and Btu used throughout.   One gram-calorie = 0.001 kilogram-calorie; one Ostwald calorie = 0.01 kilogram-calorie.

The IT cal, 1000 international steam-table calories, has been defined as the 1/860th part of the international kilowatthour (see *Mechanical Engineering*, Nov., 1935, p. 710).   Its value is very nearly equal to the mean kilogram-calorie, 1 IT cal = 1.00037 kilogram-calories (mean). 1 Btu = 251.996 IT cal.

‡ Absolute joule, defined as 10^7 ergs.   The international joule, based on the international ohm and ampere, equals 1.0003 absolute joules.

Table 43. Power or Rate of Doing Work * $[ML^2T^{-3}]$ or $[FLT^{-1}]$

Multiply Number of → / to Obtain ↓	British thermal units per minute	Ergs per second	Foot-pounds per minute	Foot-pounds per second	Horsepower *	Kilogram-calories per minute	Kilowatts	Metric horsepower	Watts
British thermal units per minute	1	5.689×10^{-9}	1.285×10^{-3}	7.712×10^{-2}	42.41	3.969	56.89	41.83	5.689×10^{-2}
Ergs per second	1.758×10^8	1	2.259×10^5	1.356×10^7	7.457×10^9	6.977×10^8	10^{10}	7.355×10^9	10^7
Foot-pounds per minute	778.0	4.426×10^{-6}	1	60	3.3×10^4	3087	4.426×10^4	3.255×10^4	44.26
Foot-pounds per second	12.97	7.376×10^{-8}	1.667×10^{-2}	1	550	51.44	737.6	542.5	0.7376
Horsepower *	2.357×10^{-2}	1.341×10^{-10}	3.030×10^{-5}	1.818×10^{-3}	1	9.355×10^{-2}	1.341	0.9863	1.341×10^{-3}
Kilogram-calories per minute	0.2520	1.433×10^{-9}	3.239×10^{-4}	1.943×10^{-2}	10.69	1	14.33	10.54	1.433×10^{-2}
Kilowatts	1.758×10^{-2}	10^{-10}	2.260×10^{-5}	1.356×10^{-3}	0.7457	6.977×10^{-2}	1	0.7355	10^{-3}
Metric horsepower	2.390×10^{-2}	1.360×10^{-10}	3.072×10^{-5}	1.843×10^{-3}	1.014	9.485×10^{-2}	1.360	1	1.360×10^{-3}
Watts	17.58	10^{-7}	2.260×10^{-2}	1.356	745.7	69.77	1000	735.5	1

1 Cheval-vapeur = 75 kilogram-meters per second
1 Poncelet   = 100 kilogram-meters per second

* The "horsepower" used in these tables is equal to 550 foot-pounds per second by definition. Other definitions are one horsepower equals 746 watts (U. S. and Great Britain) and one horsepower equals 736 watts (continental Europe). Neither of these latter definitions is equivalent to the first; the "horsepowers" defined in these latter definitions are widely used in the rating of electrical machinery.

Table 44. Quantity of Electricity and Dielectric Flux $[Q]$

Multiply Number of → / to Obtain ↓	Abcoulombs	Ampere-hours	Coulombs	Faradays	Stat-coulombs
Abcoulombs	1	360	0.1	9649	3.335×10^{-11}
Ampere-hours	2.778×10^{-3}	1	2.778×10^{-4}	26.80	9.259×10^{-14}
Coulombs	10	3600	1	9.649×10^4	3.335×10^{-10}
Faradays	1.036×10^{-4}	3.731×10^{-2}	1.036×10^{-5}	1	3.457×10^{-15}
Statcoulombs	2.998×10^{10}	1.080×10^{13}	2.998×10^9	2.893×10^{14}	1

Table 45. Charge per Unit Area and Dielectric Flux Density [QL^{-2}]

Multiply Number of → / to Obtain ↓ by	Abcoulombs per square centimeter	Coulombs per square centimeter	Coulombs per square inch	Statcoulombs per square centimeter
Abcoulombs per square centimeter	1	0.1	1.550×10^{-2}	3.335×10^{-11}
Coulombs per square centimeter	10	1	0.1550	3.335×10^{-10}
Coulombs per square inch	64.52	6.452	1	2.151×10^{-9}
Statcoulombs per square centimeter	2.998×10^{10}	2.998×10^{9}	4.647×10^{8}	1

Table 46. Electric Current [QT^{-1}]

Multiply Number of → / to Obtain ↓ by	Abamperes	Amperes	Statamperes
Abamperes	1	0.1	3.335×10^{-11}
Amperes	10	1	3.335×10^{-10}
Statamperes	2.998×10^{10}	2.998×10^{9}	1

Table 47. Current Density [$QT^{-1}L^{-2}$]

Multiply Number of → / to Obtain ↓ by	Abamperes per square centimeter	Amperes per square centimeter	Amperes per square inch	Statamperes per square centimeter
Abamperes per square centimeter	1	0.1	1.550×10^{-2}	3.335×10^{-11}
Amperes per square centimeter	10	1	0.1550	3.335×10^{-10}
Amperes per square inch	64.52	6.452	1	2.151×10^{-9}
Statamperes per square centimeter	2.998×10^{10}	2.998×10^{9}	4.647×10^{8}	1

Table 48. Electric Potential and Electromotive Force $[MQ^{-1}L^2T^{-2}]$ or $[FQ^{-1}L]$

Multiply Number of → to Obtain ↓	Abvolts	Microvolts	Millivolts	Statvolts	Volts
Abvolts	1	100	10^5	2.998×10^{10}	10^8
Microvolts	0.01	1	1000	2.998×10^8	10^6
Millivolts	10^{-5}	0.001	1	2.998×10^5	1000
Statvolts	3.335×10^{-11}	3.335×10^{-9}	3.335×10^{-6}	1	3.335×10^{-3}
Volts	10^{-8}	10^{-6}	0.001	299.8	1

Table 49. Electric Field Intensity and Potential Gradient $[MQ^{-1}LT^{-2}]$ or $[FQ^{-1}]$

Multiply Number of → to Obtain ↓	Abvolts per centimeter	Microvolts per meter	Millivolts per meter	Statvolts per centimeter	Volts per centimeter	Kilovolts per centimeter	Volts per millimeter	Volts per inch	Volts per mil
Abvolts per centimeter	1	1	1000	2.998×10^{10}	10^8	10^{11}	10^9	3.937×10^7	3.937×10^{10}
Microvolts per meter	1	1	1000	2.998×10^{10}	10^8	10^{11}	10^9	3.937×10^7	3.937×10^{10}
Millivolts per meter	0.001	0.001	1	2.998×10^7	10^5	10^8	10^6	3.937×10^4	3.937×10^7
Statvolts per centimeter	3.335×10^{-11}	3.335×10^{-11}	3.335×10^{-8}	1	3.335×10^{-3}	3.335	3.335×10^{-2}	1.313×10^{-3}	1.313
Volts per centimeter	10^{-8}	10^{-8}	10^{-5}	299.8	1	1000	10	0.3937	393.7
Kilovolts per centimeter	10^{-11}	10^{-11}	10^{-8}	0.2998	0.001	1	0.01	3.937×10^{-4}	0.3937
Volts per millimeter	10^{-9}	10^{-9}	10^{-6}	29.98	0.1	100	1	3.937×10^{-2}	39.37
Volts per inch	2.540×10^{-8}	2.540×10^{-8}	2.540×10^{-5}	761.6	2.540	2540	25.40	1	1000
Volts per mil	2.540×10^{-11}	2.540×10^{-11}	2.540×10^{-8}	0.7616	2.540×10^{-3}	2.540	2.540×10^{-2}	0.001	1

Table 50. Electric Resistance $[MQ^{-2}L^2T^{-1}]$ or $[FQ^{-2}LT]$

Multiply Number of → / to Obtain ↓	Abohms	Megohms	Microhms	Ohms	Statohms
Abohms	1	10^{15}	1000	10^9	8.988×10^{20}
Megohms	10^{-15}	1	10^{-12}	10^{-6}	8.988×10^5
Microhms	0.001	10^{12}	1	10^6	8.988×10^{17}
Ohms	10^{-9}	10^6	10^{-6}	1	8.988×10^{11}
Statohms	1.112×10^{-21}	1.112×10^{-6}	1.112×10^{-18}	1.112×10^{-12}	1

Electrical Conductance $[F^{-1}QL^{-1}T^{-1}]$

1 mho = 1 ohm^{-1} = 10^{-6} megmho = 10^6 micromho

Table 51. Electric Resistivity * $[MQ^{-2}L^3T^{-1}]$ or $[FQ^{-2}L^2T]$

Multiply Number of → / to Obtain ↓	Abohm-centimeters	Microhm-centimeters	Microhm-inches	Ohms (mil, foot)	Ohms (meter, gram) †
Abohm-centimeters	1	1000	2540	166.2	$\dfrac{10^5}{\delta}$
Microhm-centimeters	0.001	1	2.540	0.1662	$\dfrac{100}{\delta}$
Microhm-inches	3.937×10^{-4}	0.3937	1	6.545×10^{-2}	$\dfrac{39.37}{\delta}$
Ohms (mil, foot)	6.015×10^{-3}	6.015	15.28	1	$\dfrac{601.5}{\delta}$
Ohms (meter, gram) †	$10^{-5}\delta$	0.01δ	$2.540 \times 10^{-2}\delta$	$1.662 \times 10^{-3}\delta$	1

* In this table δ is density in grams per cm.^{3} The following names, corresponding respectively to those at the tops of columns, are sometimes used:| abohms per cm cube; microhms per cm cube; microhms per inch cube; ohms per mil-foot; ohms per meter-gram. The first four columns are headed by units of *volume* resistivity, the last by a unit of *mass* resistivity. The dimensions of the latter are $Q^{-2}L^6T^{-1}$; not these given in the heading of the table.

† One ohm (meter, gram) = 5710 ohms (mile, pound).

Table 52. Electric Conductivity * $[M^{-1}Q^2L^{-3}T]$ or $[F^{-1}Q^2L^{-2}T^{-1}]$

to Obtain ↓ / Multiply Number of → by	Abmhos per cm	Mhos (mil, foot)	Mhos (meter, gram)	Micromhos per cm	Micromhos per inch
Abmhos per cm	1	6.015×10^3	$10^{-5}\delta$	0.001	3.937×10^{-4}
Mhos (mil, foot)	166.2	1	$1.662 \times 10^{-3}\delta$	0.1662	6.524×10^{-2}
Mhos (meter, gram)	$10^5/\delta$	$601.5/\delta$	1	$100/\delta$	$39.37/\delta$
Micromhos per cm	1000	6.015	0.01δ	1	0.3937
Micromhos per inch	2540	15.28	$2.540 \times 10^{-2}\delta$	2.540	1

* See footnote of Table 51, Electric Resistivity. Names sometimes used are abmho per cm cube, mho per mil-foot, etc. Dimensions of mass conductivity are $Q^2L^{-6}T$.

Table 53. Capacitance $[M^{-1}Q^2L^{-2}T^2]$ or $[F^{-1}Q^2L^{-1}]$

to Obtain ↓ / Multiply Number of → by	Abfarads	Farads	Microfarads	Statfarads
Abfarads	1	10^{-9}	10^{-15}	1.112×10^{-21}
Farads	10^9	1	10^{-6}	1.112×10^{-12}
Microfarads	10^{15}	10^6	1	1.112×10^{-6}
Statfarads	8.988×10^{20}	8.988×10^{11}	8.988×10^5	1

Table 54. Inductance $[MQ^{-2}L^2]$ or $[FQ^{-2}LT^2]$

to Obtain ↓ / Multiply Number of → by	Abhenries *	Henries	Microhenries	Millihenries	Stathenries
Abhenries *	1	10^9	1000	10^6	8.988×10^{20}
Henries	10^{-9}	1	10^{-6}	0.001	8.988×10^{11}
Microhenries	0.001	10^6	1	1000	8.988×10^{17}
Millihenries	10^{-6}	1000	0.001	1	8.988×10^{14}
Stathenries	1.112×10^{-21}	1.112×10^{-12}	1.112×10^{-18}	1.112×10^{-15}	1

* An abhenry is sometimes called a "centimeter." See footnote to Table 56 on "Magnetic Flux Density."

Table 55. Magnetic Flux $[MQ^{-1}L^2T^{-1}]$ or $[FQ^{-1}LT]$

to Obtain ↓	Multiply Number of → Kilolines	Maxwells (or lines)	Webers
Kilolines	1	0.001	10^5
Maxwells (or lines)	1000	1	10^8
Webers	10^{-5}	10^{-8}	1

Table 56. Magnetic Flux Density $[MQ^{-1}T^{-1}]$ or $[FQ^{-1}L^{-1}T]$

to Obtain ↓	Multiply Number of → Gausses (or lines per square centimeter)	Lines per square inch	Webers per square centimeter	Webers per square inch
Gausses * (or lines per square centimeter)	1	0.1550	10^8	1.550×10^7
Lines per square inch	6.452	1	6.452×10^8	10^8
Webers per square centimeter	10^{-8}	$1.550 \times ^{-9}$	1	0.1550
Webers per square inch	6.452×10^{-8}	10^{-8}	6.452	1

* The name "gauss" is sometimes used for the unit of magnetic field intensity (1 gauss = 1 gilbert per cm). Since flux density = permeability × field intensity ($B = \mu H$) these two quantities have the same units if μ is considered dimensionless, just as 1 abhenry = $\mu \times 1$ cm; hence the occasional name centimeter for an abhenry. The A.I.E.E. sanctions "gauss" for both B and H; physicists usually do not. In 1930 the International Electrotechnical Commission, of which the U. S. National Committee is the electrical standards committee of the American Standards Association, adopted the following names for units in the cgs electromagnetic system: Magnetomotive force, gilbert; magnetizing force, oersted; magnetic flux, maxwell; magnetic flux density, gauss. The name oersted has been used for a unit of reluctance in the U. S.

Table 57. Magnetic Potential and Magnetomotive Force $[QT^{-1}]$

to Obtain ↓	Multiply Number of → Abampere-turns	Ampere-turns	Gilberts
Abampere-turns	1	0.1	7.958×10^{-2}
Ampere-turns	10	1	0.7958
Gilberts	12.57	1.257	1

Table 58. Magnetic Field Intensity, Potential Gradient and Magnetizing Force $[QL^{-1}T^{-1}]$

to Obtain ↓ / Multiply Number of → / by	Abampere-turns per centimeter	Ampere-turns per centimeter	Ampere-turns per inch	Gilberts per centimeter *
Abampere-turns per centimeter	1	0.1	3.937×10^{-2}	7.958×10^{-2}
Ampere-turns per centimeter	10	1	0.3937	0.7958
Ampere-turns per inch	25.40	2.540	1	2.021
Gilberts per centimeter	12.57	1.257	0.4950	1

* Called "oersteds" by the I.E.C. (1930). See footnote of Table 56 on "Magnetic Flux Density."

Table 59. Specific Heat $[L^2T^{-2}t^{-1}]$

(t = temperature)

To change specific heat in gram-calories per gram per degree Centigrade to the units given in any line of the following table, multiply by the factor in the last column.

Unit of Heat or Energy	Unit of Mass	Temperature Scale *	Factor
Gram-calories...................	Gram	Centigrade	1
Kilogram-calories...............	Kilogram	Centigrade	1
British thermal units..............	Pound	Centigrade	1.800
British thermal units.............	Pound	Fahrenheit	1.000
Joules........................	Gram	Centigrade	4.186
Joules........................	Pound	Fahrenheit	1055.
Kilowatt-hours.................	Kilogram	Centigrade	1.163×10^{-3}
Kilowatt-hours.................	Pound	Fahrenheit	2.930×10^{-4}

* Temperature conversion formulas:
t_c = temperature in Centigrade degrees.
t_f = temperature in Fahrenheit degrees.
1 deg fahr = (5/9) deg cent.
$t_c = \frac{5}{9}(t_f - 32)$
$t_f = \frac{9}{5}t_c + 32$

Table 60. Thermal Conductivity $[MLT^{-3}t^{-1}]$

(t = temperature)

To convert thermal conductivity, in gram-calories transmitted per second from one face of a cube 1 cm on edge to the opposite face per degree Centigrade temperature difference between these faces, to the units given in any line of the following table, multiply by the factor in the last column.

Units of				Temperature Scale	Factor
Heat	Area	Thickness	Time		
Gram-calories.............	cm²	cm	second	Centigrade	1
Kilogram-calories.........	m²	cm	hour	Centigrade	3.6×10^4
British thermal units.......	ft²	inch	hour	Fahrenheit	2903.
Joules....................	cm²	cm	second	Centigrade	4.186
Joules....................	ft²	inch	second	Fahrenheit	850.6
Kilowatt-hours............	m²	cm	hour	Centigrade	41.86
Kilowatt-hours	ft²	inch	hour	Fahrenheit	0.8506

GAGES

By J. G. Brainerd

Sheet Metal Gages

The important sheet metal gages in use in the United States are: the United States Standard Gage for sheet and plate iron and steel, the American Wire Gage (also called the Brown and Sharpe W.G.) for copper, aluminum, and brass and other non-ferrous alloys, the Tin Plate Gage, the Galvanized Sheet Gage, the American Zinc Gage, and the Birmingham Wire (or Stubs' Iron Wire) Gage. In Canada and England the Birmingham Gage (different from the Birmingham Wire Gage) and the Imperial Standard Wire Gage (S.W.G.) are used. Still other gages are used elsewhere. In Japan standard thickness of sheet metal is denoted by the thickness in millimeters. A standard Decimal Gage, in which the standard thicknesses are denoted by decimal parts of an inch and not by gage numbers, has been used in the United States. Copper sheets may be obtained with thicknesses any integral multiple of $1/16$ of an inch up to 2 inches. Heavy copper sheets may be obtained in definite weights per square foot. Each ounce of weight is equivalent to approximately 0.001352 inch thickness. Lead is usually ordered in this manner, each pound being equivalent to approximately 0.017 inch thickness.

The United States Standard Gage for sheet iron and steel (Act of Congress, March 3, 1893; formerly the legal standard for duties) is a *weight* gage based on a density for wrought iron of 480 pounds per cubic foot. Since 1893, steel (density of 489.6 lb per cu ft) has come into general use. A given gage number of this gage represents a fixed weight per unit area, hence a steel sheet will have a smaller thickness than a wrought iron sheet of the same gage number (but monel metal sheets are rolled to the thickness given for wrought iron without regard to weight, which is about 552.2 lb per cu ft). Practice among steel manufacturers is irregular, some keeping the *thickness* constant for a given gage number irrespective of weight. If this practice is followed, the weight per square foot and per square meter given in the second and third columns of Table 61 will vary, whereas thickness will remain that given for wrought iron.

The American Wire Gage specifies thicknesses without regard to weight. For the basis of this gage see the next section (Wire Gages), where are also given the Birmingham W.G. and the S.W.G.

Tables of Thickness and Weight corresponding to United States Standard gage and American Wire gage numbers are shown in Tables 61 and 62. These tables are taken from Circular No. 391 of the Bureau of Standards, in which are given all the gages mentioned above and the tolerances customary in commerce. A committee of the American Standards Association is now working (1936) on the standardization of sheet metal gages.

Table 61. United States Standard Gage * for Sheet and Plate Iron and Steel, and Its Extension †

Gage No.	Weight per square foot		Weight per square meter	Approximate thickness			
				Wrought iron 480 lb/ft³		Steel and open-hearth iron 489.6 lb/ft³	
	Ounces	Pounds	kg	Inch	mm	Inch	mm
0000000.....	320	20.00	97.65	0.500	12.70	0.490	12.45
000000......	300	18.75	91.55	.469	11.91	.460	11.67
00000.......	280	17.50	85.44	.438	11.11	.429	10.90
0000........	260	16.25	79.34	.406	10.32	.398	10.12
000.........	240	15.00	73.24	.375	9.52	.368	9.34
00..........	220	13.75	67.13	.344	8.73	.337	8.56
0...........	200	12.50	61.03	.312	7.94	.306	7.78
1...........	180	11.25	54.93	.2812	7.14	.2757	7.00
2...........	170	10.62	51.88	.2656	6.75	.2604	6.62
3...........	160	10.00	48.82	.2500	6.35	.2451	6.23
4...........	150	9.375	45.77	.2344	5.95	.2298	5.84
5...........	140	8.750	42.72	.2188	5.56	.2145	5.45
6...........	130	8.125	39.67	.2031	5.16	.1991	5.06
7...........	120	7.500	36.62	.1875	4.76	.1838	4.67
8...........	110	6.875	33.57	.1719	4.37	.1685	4.28
9...........	100	6.250	30.52	.1562	3.97	.1532	3.89
10..........	90	5.625	27.46	.1406	3.57	.1379	3.50
11..........	80	5.000	24.41	.1250	3.18	.1225	3.11
12..........	70	4.375	21.36	.1094	2.778	.1072	2.724
13..........	60	3.750	18.31	.0938	2.381	.0919	2.335
14..........	50	3.125	15.26	.0781	1.984	.0766	1.946
15..........	45	2.812	13.73	.0703	1.786	.0689	1.751
16..........	40	2.500	12.21	.0625	1.588	.0613	1.557
17..........	36	2.250	10.99	.0562	1.429	.0551	1.400
18..........	32	2.000	9.765	.0500	1.270	.0490	1.245
19..........	28	1.750	8.544	.0438	1.111	.0429	1.090
20..........	24	1.500	7.324	.0375	.952	.0368	.934
21..........	22	1.375	6.713	.0344	.873	.0337	.856
22..........	20	1.250	6.103	.0312	.794	.0306	.778
23..........	18	1.125	5.493	.0281	.714	.0276	.700
24..........	16	1.000	4.882	.0250	.635	.0245	.623
25..........	14	.8750	4.272	.0219	.556	.0214	.545
26..........	12	.7500	3.662	.0188	.476	.0184	.467
27..........	11	.6875	3.357	.0172	.437	.0169	.428
28..........	10	.6250	3.052	.0156	.397	.0153	.389
29..........	9	.5625	2.746	.0141	.357	.0138	.350
30..........	8	.5000	2.441	.0125	.318	.0123	.311
31..........	7	.4375	2.136	.0109	.278	.0107	.272
32..........	6 1/2	.4062	1.983	.0102	.258	.0100	.253
33..........	6	.3750	1.831	.0094	.238	.0092	.233
34..........	5 1/2	.3438	1.678	.0086	.218	.0084	.214
35..........	5	.3125	1.526	.0078	.198	.0077	.195
36..........	4 1/2	.2812	1.373	.0070	.179	.0069	.175
37..........	4 1/4	.2656	1.297	.0066	.169	.0065	.165
38..........	4	.2500	1.221	.0062	.159	.0061	.156
39..........	3 3/4	.2344	1.144	.0059	.149	.0057	.146
40..........	3 1/2	.2188	1.068	.0055	.139	.0054	.136
41..........	3 3/8	.2109	1.030	.0053	.134	.0052	.131
42..........	3 1/4	.2031	.9917	.0051	.129	.0050	.126
43..........	3 1/8	.1953	.9536	.0049	.124	.0048	.122
44..........	3	.1875	.9155	.0047	.119	.0046	.117

* For the Galvanized Sheet Gage, add 2.5 ounces to the weight per square foot as given in the table. Gage numbers below 8 and above 34 are not used in the Galvanized Sheet Gage.
† Gage numbers greater than 38 were not in the standard as set up by law, but are in general use.

Table 62. American Wire Gage—Weights of Copper, Aluminum and Brass Sheets and Plates

Gage No.	Thickness		Approximate weight * per sq ft in lb		
	Inch	mm	Copper	Aluminum	Commercial (high) brass
0000.............	0.4600	11.68	21.27	6.49	20.27
000..............	.4096	10.40	18.94	5.78	18.05
00...............	.3648	9.266	16.87	5.14	16.07
0................	.3249	8.252	15.03	4.58	14.32
1................	.2893	7.348	13.38	4.08	12.75
2................	.2576	6.544	11.91	3.632	11.35
3................	.2294	5.827	10.61	3.234	10.11
4................	.2043	5.189	9.45	2.880	9.00
5................	.1819	4.621	8.41	2.565	8.01
6................	.1620	4.115	7.49	2.284	7.14
7................	.1443	3.665	6.67	2.034	6.36
8................	.1285	3.264	5.94	1.812	5.66
9................	.1144	2.906	5.29	1.613	5.04
10...............	.1019	2.588	4.713	1.437	4.490
11...............	.0907	2.305	4.195	1.279	3.996
12...............	.0808	2.053	3.737	1.139	3.560
13...............	.0720	1.828	3.330	1.015	3.172
14...............	.0641	1.628	2.965	0.904	2.824
15...............	.0571	1.450	2.641	.805	2.516
16...............	.0508	1.291	2.349	.716	2.238
17...............	.0453	1.150	2.095	.639	1.996
18...............	.0403	1.024	1.864	.568	1.776
19...............	0.0359	0.9116	1.660	.506	1.582
20...............	.0320	.8118	1.480	.451	1.410
21...............	.0285	.7230	1.318	.402	1.256
22...............	.0253	.6438	1.170	.3567	1.115
23...............	.0226	.5733	1.045	.3186	0.996
24...............	.0201	.5106	0.930	.2834	.886
25...............	.0179	.4547	.828	.2524	.789
26...............	.0159	.4049	.735	.2242	.701
27...............	.0142	.3606	.657	.2002	.626
28...............	.0126	.3211	.583	.1776	.555
29...............	.0113	.2859	.523	.1593	.498
30...............	.0100	.2546	.4625	.1410	.4406
31...............	.00893	.2268	.4130	.1259	.3935
32...............	.00795	.2019	.3677	.1121	.3503
33...............	.00708	.1798	.3274	.0998	.3119
34...............	.00630	.1601	.2914	.0888	.2776
35...............	.00561	.1426	.2595	.0791	.2472
36...............	.00500	.1270	.2312	.0705	.2203
37...............	.00445	.1131	.2058	.0627	.1961
38...............	.00397	.1007	.1836	.0560	.1749
39...............	.00353	.0897	.1633	.0498	.1555
40...............	.00314	.0799	.1452	.0443	.1383

* Assumed specific gravities or densities in grams per cubic centimeter; Copper, 8.89; Aluminum, 2.71; brass, 8.47.

Wire Gages

The sizes of wires having a diameter less than $1/2$ inch are usually stated in terms of certain arbitrary scales called "gages." The size or gage number of a solid wire refers to the cross-section of the wire perpendicular to its length; the size or gage number of a stranded wire refers to the total cross-section of the constituent wires, irrespective of the pitch of the spiraling. Larger wires are usually described in terms of their area expressed in circular mils. A circular mil is the area of a circle 1 mil in diameter, and the area of any circle in circular mils is equal to the square of its diameter in mils.

There are a number of wire gages in use, the principal ones being the following:

American or Brown and Sharpe Wire Gage.—This gage is the one commonly used in the United States for copper, aluminum and resistance wires. The gage is designated by either of the abbreviations A.W.G. or B. & S.

Basis of the A.W.G. or B. & S. Gage.—The diameters of wires having successive numbers on this gage are in the ratio of $\sqrt[39]{92}$ (= 1.1229 approx.) to 1, and the No. 36 wire has a diameter of 5 mils. No. 35 A.W.G., therefore, has a diameter of 5×1.1229 = 5.61 mils and so on until No. 0000 is reached, having a diameter of 460 mils.

The ratio $\sqrt[39]{92}$ is approximately equal to $\sqrt[6]{2}$, which is 1.1225. This circumstance makes it possible to have a group of wires of regular gage size with an aggregate area approximately equal to that of another regular gage size. For example, a reduction of three gage numbers (as from gage No. 36 to No. 33) results in a new gage number representing a diameter approximately $\sqrt{2}$ times that represented by the original gage number—or an area approximately two times as great.

The following approximate relations are also useful:

An increase of 1 in the number increases the resistance 25 per cent.
An increase of 2 in the number increases the resistance 60 per cent.
An increase of 3 in the number increases the resistance 100 per cent.
An increase of 10 in the number increases the resistance 10 times.

A No. 10 A.W.G. copper wire has the following approximate characteristics:

Ohms per 1000 feet 1
Circular mils area 10,000
Weight, pounds per 1000 feet 32

A No. 10 A.W.G. aluminum wire has the following approximate characteristics:

Ohms per 1000 feet 1.6
Circular mils area 10,000
Weight, pounds per 1000 feet 9.5

Remembering these rules it is easy to find the approximate size, resistance, area, or weight of any size wire. For example, a No. 12 A.W.G. copper wire has a resistance of 1 plus 60 per cent = 1.6 ohms per 1000 ft approximately. Its area, being inversely as its resistance, is 10,000/1.6 = 6250 circular mils; its diameter is therefore $\sqrt{6250}$ = 79 mils and its weight, 32/1.6 = 20 pounds per 1000 feet.

U. S. Steel Wire Gage.—This gage, known also as the "Washburn and Moen," "Roebling," "American Steel and Wire Co.'s gage," is the one usually employed in the United States for steel and iron wire. It is frequently abbreviated "S.W.G.," but to avoid confusion with the British Standard Wire Gage (*see below*) it should be abbreviated "Stl. W.G." or "A. (steel) W.G."

Birmingham (or Stubs' Iron) Wire Gage.—This gage is still used in the United States for some purposes, e.g., to designate the size of brass wire, and is also employed to a limited extent in Great Britain. It is usually abbreviated "B.W.G." It is sometimes referred to as the "Stubs' Iron Wire Gage," but it should not be confused with the Stubs' Steel Wire Gage.

British Standard Wire Gage.—This gage, usually called simply the "Standard Wire Gage," and abbreviated "S.W.G." is also known as the "New British Standard" (abbreviated "N.B.S."), the English Legal Standard, or the Imperial Wire Gage, and is the legal standard of Great Britain for all wires, as fixed by order in Council, August 23, 1883. It was constructed by modifying the Birmingham Wire Gage, so that the differences between successive diameters were the same for short ranges, i.e., so that a graph representing the diameters consists of a series of a few straight lines.

Edison Wire Gage.—The size of a wire on this gage is equal to its cross-sectional area in circular mils divided by 1000. For example, a solid wire 0.2 inch in diameter has the number $(200)^2/1000$ = 40. This gage is now rarely used.

Metric Wire Gage.—The gage number is ten times the diameter in millimeters.

Other Gages.—In addition wire sizes are sometimes specified in terms of the "Old English Wire Gage," known also as the "London Gage," and the "Stubs' Steel Wire Gage." The Old English Wire Gage is the same as B.W.G. for all gage numbers under 20.

Comparison of Wire Gages.—A comparison of the different gages, in terms of the diameters (in mils or thousandths of an inch) of solid wires corresponding to the various numbers, is given in Table 63. The cross-section in circular mils is the square of the diameter in mils.

Table 63.   Comparison of Wire Gage Diameters in Mils

(Bureau of Standards, Circulars No. 31 and No. 67)

Gage No.	American wire gage (B. & S.)	Steel wire gage	Birmingham wire gage (Stubs')	Old English wire gage (London)	Stubs' steel wire gage	(British) Standard wire gage	Metric gage *	Gage No.
7–0	....	490.0	....	....	....	500	....	7–0
6–0	....	461.5	....	....	....	464	....	6–0
5–0	....	430.5	....	....	....	432	....	5–0
4–0	460	393.8	454	454	....	400	....	4–0
3–0	410	362.5	425	425	....	372	....	3–0
2–0	365	331.0	380	380	....	348	....	2–0
0	325	306.5	340	340	....	324	....	0
1	289	283.0	300	300	227	300	3.94	1
2	258	262.5	284	284	219	276	7.87	2
3	229	243.7	259	259	212	252	11.8	3
4	204	225.3	238	238	207	232	15.7	4
5	182	207.0	220	220	204	212	19.7	5
6	162	192.0	203	203	201	192	23.6	6
7	144	177.0	180	180	199	176	27.6	7
8	128	162.0	165	165	197	160	31.5	8
9	114	148.3	148	148	194	144	35.4	9
10	102	135.0	134	134	191	128	39.4	10
11	91	120.5	120	120	188	116	....	11
12	81	105.5	109	109	185	104	47.2	12
13	72	91.5	95	95	182	92	....	13
14	64	80.0	83	83	180	80	55.1	14
15	57	72.0	72	72	178	72	....	15
16	51	62.5	65	65	175	64	63.0	16
17	45	54.0	58	58	172	56	....	17
18	40	47.5	49	49	168	48	70.9	18
19	36	41.0	42	42	164	40	....	19
20	32	34.8	35	35	161	36	78.7	20
21	28.5	31.7	32	31.5	157	32	....	21
22	25.3	28.6	28	29.5	155	28	....	22
23	22.6	25.8	25	27.0	153	24	....	23
24	20.1	23.0	22	25.0	151	22	....	24
25	17.9	20.4	20	23.0	148	20	98.4	25
26	15.9	18.1	18	20.5	146	18	....	26
27	14.2	17.3	16	18.75	143	16.4	....	27
28	12.6	16.2	14	16.50	139	14.8	....	28
29	11.3	15.0	13	15.50	134	13.6	....	29
30	10.0	14.0	12	13.75	127	12.4	118	30
31	8.9	13.2	10	12.25	120	11.6	....	31
32	8.0	12.8	9	11.25	115	10.8	....	32
33	7.1	11.8	8	10.25	112	10.0	....	33
34	6.3	10.4	7	9.50	110	9.2	....	34
35	5.6	9.5	5	9.00	108	8.4	138	35
36	5.0	9.0	4	7.50	106	7.6	....	36
37	4.5	8.5	....	6.50	103	6.8	....	37
38	4.0	8.0	....	5.75	101	6.0	....	38
39	3.5	7.5	....	5.00	99	5.2	....	39
40	3.1	7.0	....	4.50	97	4.8	157	40
41	....	6.6	....	....	95	4.4	....	41
42	....	6.2	....	....	92	4.0	....	42
43	....	6.0	....	....	88	3.6	....	43
44	....	5.8	....	....	85	3.2	....	44
45	....	5.5	....	....	81	2.8	177	45
46	....	5.2	....	....	79	2.4	....	46
47	....	5.0	....	....	77	2.0	....	47
48	....	4.8	....	....	75	1.6	....	48
49	....	4.6	....	....	72	1.2	....	49
50	....	4.4	....	....	69	1.0	197	50

* For diameters corresponding to metric gage numbers, 1.2, 1.4, 1.6, 1.8, 2.5, 3.5, and 4.5, divide those of 12, 14, etc., by ten.

STANDARD STRUCTURAL SIZES

Steel Sections. Tables 64 to 70 give the dimensions, weights, and properties of *rolled steel* structural sections, including wide-flange sections, American standard beams, channels, angles, tees, and zees. The values for the various structural forms, taken from the January 1934 edition of "Steel Construction," by the kind permission of the publisher, the American Institute of Steel Construction, give the section specifications required in designing steel structures. The theory of design is covered in Section 5.

Most of the sections can be supplied promptly by the Bethlehem, Carnegie, and Illinois Steel Company mills. Owing to variations in the rolling practice of the different mills, their products are not identical, although their divergence from the values given in the tables is practically negligible. For standardization, only the lesser values are given, and therefore they are on the side of safety.

Further information on sections listed in the tables, together with information on other products and on the requirements for placing orders, may be gathered from mill catalogs.

Aluminum Sections. Tables 64 to 70 for structural-steel sections are roughly applicable to aluminum sections with the following reservations:

(a) Aluminum wide-flange beams are not readily available in the large variety of sizes given for steel sections. The aluminum beams coming closest to the wide flange steel beams are a short series of "H" beams in sizes 4×4, 5×5, 6×6, and 8×8. For the specifications of this series see the catalog of any aluminum rolling mill.

(b) In the other shapes of beams, sizes approximating the following steel sizes are available in aluminum.

1. American standard beams; $12 \times 5 \, 1/4$, 12×5, and $10 \times 4 \, 3/4$.
2. Channels; 12×3, $10 \times 2 \, 5/8$, $9 \times 2 \, 1/2$, and $8 \times 2 \, 1/4$.
3. Angles with equal legs; most sizes up to and including 6×6, in thicknesses up to $3/4$ in.
4. Angles with unequal legs; most sizes up to and including 6×4, in thicknesses up to $3/4$ in.
5. Tees; almost all sizes.
6. Zees; almost all sizes.

(c) The tabulated values for steel sections, with the exception of weight, may be used in approximate calculations for aluminum sections since there is usually less than 2 per cent difference between the aluminum and steel values. In most cases the aluminum value is slightly higher and therefore on the safe side. On the average, the weights of the aluminum sections are 0.356 the weights of the corresponding steel sections.

For information about other standard aluminum sections and for more accurate values than those corresponding to the steel tables see the catalog of any aluminum rolling mill.

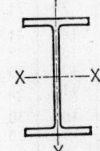

Table 64.

Properties of Wide Flange Sections

Nominal Size, in.	Wt per Foot, lb	Area of Section, in.²	Depth of Section, in.	Flange Width, in.	Flange Thickness, in.	Web Thickness, in.	Axis X–X I, in.⁴	Axis X–X S, in.³	Axis X–X k, in.	Axis Y–Y I, in.⁴	Axis Y–Y S, in.³	Axis Y–Y k, in.
36 × 16 1/2	300	88.17	36.72	16.655	1.680	0.945	20290.2	1105.1	15.17	1225.2	147.1	3.73
	280	82.32	36.50	16.595	1.570	.885	18819.3	1031.2	15.12	1127.5	135.9	3.70
	260	76.56	36.24	16.555	1.440	.845	17233.8	951.1	15.00	1020.6	123.3	3.65
	250	73.49	36.12	16.525	1.380	.815	16465.9	911.7	14.97	969.6	117.4	3.63
	240	70.60	36.00	16.500	1.320	.790	15724.0	873.6	14.92	920.1	111.5	3.61
	230	67.73	35.88	16.475	1.260	.765	14988.4	835.5	14.88	870.9	105.7	3.59
36 × 12	194	57.11	36.48	12.117	1.260	.770	12103.4	663.6	14.56	355.4	58.7	2.49
	182	53.54	36.32	12.072	1.180	.725	11281.5	621.2	14.52	327.7	54.3	2.47
	170	49.98	36.16	12.027	1.100	.680	10470.0	579.1	14.47	300.6	50.0	2.45
	160	47.09	36.00	12.000	1.020	.653	9738.8	541.0	14.38	275.4	45.9	2.42
	150	44.16	35.84	11.972	.940	.625	9012.1	502.9	14.29	250.4	41.8	2.38

Table 64. Properties of Wide Flange Sections—*Continued*

Nominal Size, in.	Wt. per Foot, lb.	Area of Section, in.²	Depth of Section, in.	Flange Width, in.	Flange Thickness, in.	Web Thickness, in.	Axis X–X I, in.⁴	Axis X–X S, in.³	Axis X–X k, in.	Axis Y–Y I, in.⁴	Axis Y–Y S, in.³	Axis Y–Y k, in.
33 × 15 3/4	240	70.52	33.50	15.865	1.400	.830	13585.1	811.1	13.88	874.3	110.2	3.52
	220	64.73	33.25	15.810	1.275	.775	12312.1	740.6	13.79	782.4	99.0	3.48
	210	61.78	33.12	15.783	1.210	.748	11664.5	704.4	13.74	735.6	93.2	3.45
	200	58.79	33.00	15.750	1.150	.715	11048.2	669.6	13.71	691.7	87.8	3.43
33 × 11 1/2	152	44.71	33.50	11.565	1.055	.635	8147.6	486.4	13.50	256.1	44.3	2.39
	141	41.51	33.31	11.535	.960	.605	7442.2	446.8	13.39	229.7	39.8	2.35
	132	38.84	33.15	11.510	.880	.580	6856.8	413.7	13.29	207.8	36.1	2.31
	125	36.78	33.00	11.500	.805	.570	6354.7	385.1	13.14	188.2	32.7	2.26
30 × 15	210	61.78	30.38	15.105	1.315	.775	9872.4	649.9	12.64	707.9	93.7	3.38
	200	58.76	30.25	15.070	1.250	.740	9340.5	617.6	12.61	665.7	88.3	3.37
	190	55.90	30.12	15.040	1.185	.710	8825.9	586.1	12.57	624.6	83.1	3.34
	180	52.89	30.00	15.000	1.125	.670	8328.2	555.2	12.55	585.6	78.1	3.33
	172	50.65	29.88	14.985	1.065	.655	7891.5	528.2	12.48	550.1	73.4	3.30
30 × 10 1/2	132	38.83	30.30	10.551	1.000	.615	5753.1	379.7	12.17	185.0	35.1	2.18
	124	36.45	30.16	10.521	.930	.585	5347.1	354.6	12.11	169.7	32.3	2.16
	116	34.13	30.00	10.500	.850	.564	4919.1	327.9	12.00	153.2	29.2	2.12
	108	31.77	29.82	10.484	.760	.548	4461.0	299.2	11.85	135.1	25.8	2.06
27 × 14	177	52.10	27.31	14.090	1.190	.725	6728.6	492.8	11.36	518.9	73.7	3.16
	163	47.93	27.12	14.035	1.095	.670	6141.5	452.9	11.32	468.7	66.8	3.13
	154	45.30	27.00	14.000	1.035	.635	5775.8	427.8	11.29	437.6	62.5	3.11
	145	42.68	26.88	13.965	.975	.600	5414.3	402.9	11.26	406.9	58.3	3.09
27 × 10	114	33.53	27.28	10.070	.932	.570	4080.5	299.2	11.03	149.6	29.7	2.11
	106	31.17	27.14	10.035	.862	.535	3761.2	277.2	10.98	136.1	27.1	2.09
	98	28.82	27.00	10.000	.792	.500	3446.5	255.3	10.94	122.9	24.6	2.07
	91	26.77	26.84	9.983	.712	.483	3129.2	233.2	10.81	109.0	21.8	2.02
24 × 14	160	47.04	24.72	14.091	1.135	.656	5110.3	413.5	10.42	492.6	69.9	3.23
	150	44.10	24.56	14.063	1.055	.628	4733.5	385.5	10.36	452.5	64.3	3.20
	140	41.16	24.41	14.029	.980	.594	4376.1	358.6	10.31	414.5	59.1	3.17
	130	38.21	24.25	14.000	.900	.565	4009.5	330.7	10.24	375.2	53.6	3.13
24 × 12	120	35.29	24.31	12.088	.930	.556	3635.3	299.1	10.15	254.0	42.0	2.68
	110	32.36	24.16	12.042	.855	.510	3315.0	274.4	10.12	229.1	38.0	2.66
	100	29.43	24.00	12.000	.775	.468	2987.3	248.9	10.08	203.5	33.9	2.63
24 × 9	94	27.63	24.29	9.061	.872	.516	2683.0	220.9	9.85	102.2	22.6	1.92
	87	25.58	24.16	9.025	.807	.480	2467.8	204.3	9.82	92.9	20.6	1.91
	80	23.54	24.00	9.000	.727	.455	2229.7	185.8	9.73	82.4	18.3	1.87
	74	21.77	23.87	8.975	.662	.430	2033.8	170.4	9.67	73.8	16.5	1.84
21 × 13	142	41.76	21.46	13.132	1.095	.659	3403.1	317.2	9.03	385.9	58.8	3.04
	132	38.81	21.31	13.087	1.020	.614	3141.6	294.8	9.00	353.8	54.1	3.02
	122	35.85	21.16	13.040	.945	.567	2883.2	272.5	8.97	322.1	49.4	3.00
	112	32.93	21.00	13.000	.865	.527	2620.6	249.6	8.92	289.7	44.6	2.96
21 × 9	103	30.27	21.29	9.071	1.010	0.608	2268.0	213.1	8.66	119.9	26.4	1.99
	96	28.21	21.14	9.038	0.935	.575	2088.9	197.6	8.60	109.3	24.2	1.97
	89	26.15	21.00	9.000	.865	.537	1919.2	182.8	8.57	99.4	22.1	1.95
	82	24.10	20.86	8.962	.795	.499	1752.4	168.0	8.53	89.6	20.0	1.93
21 × 8 1/4	73	21.46	21.24	8.295	.740	.455	1600.3	150.7	8.64	66.2	16.0	1.76
	68	20.02	21.13	8.270	.685	.430	1478.3	139.9	8.59	60.4	14.6	1.74
	63	18.52	21.00	8.250	.620	.410	1343.6	128.0	8.52	53.8	13.0	1.70
	59	17.36	20.91	8.230	.575	.390	1246.8	119.3	8.47	49.2	12.0	1.68
18 × 11 3/4	124	36.45	18.64	11.889	1.071	.651	2227.1	239.0	7.82	281.9	47.4	2.78
	114	33.51	18.48	11.833	.991	.595	2033.8	220.1	7.79	255.6	43.2	2.76
	105	30.86	18.32	11.792	.911	.554	1852.5	202.2	7.75	231.0	39.2	2.73
	96	28.22	18.16	11.750	.831	.512	1674.7	184.4	7.70	206.8	35.2	2.71
18 × 8 3/4	85	24.97	18.32	8.838	.911	.526	1429.9	156.1	7.57	99.4	22.5	2.00
	77	22.63	18.16	8.787	.831	.475	1286.8	141.7	7.54	88.6	20.2	1.98
	70	20.56	18.00	8.750	.751	.438	1153.9	128.2	7.49	78.5	17.9	1.95
	64	18.80	17.87	8.715	.686	.403	1045.8	117.0	7.46	70.3	16.1	1.93
18 × 7 1/2	55	16.19	18.12	7.532	.630	.390	889.9	98.2	7.41	42.0	11.1	1.61
	50	14.71	18.00	7.500	.570	.358	800.6	89.0	7.38	37.2	9.9	1.59
	47	13.81	17.90	7.492	.520	.350	736.4	82.3	7.30	33.5	9.0	1.56

Table 64.   Properties of Wide Flange Sections—*Continued*

Nominal Size, in.	Wt. per Foot, lb.	Area of Section, in.^{2}	Depth of Section, in.	Flange Width, in.	Flange Thickness, in.	Web Thickness, in.	Axis X-X I, in.^{4}	Axis X-X S, in.^{3}	Axis X-X k, in.	Axis Y-Y I, in.^{4}	Axis Y-Y S, in.^{3}	Axis Y-Y k, in.
16 × 11 1/2	114	33.51	16.64	11.629	1.035	.631	1642.6	197.4	7.00	254.6	43.8	2.76
	105	30.87	16.48	11.582	.955	.584	1497.5	181.7	6.96	230.7	39.8	2.73
	96	28.22	16.32	11.533	.875	.535	1355.1	166.1	6.93	207.2	35.9	2.71
	88	25.87	16.16	11.502	.795	.504	1222.6	151.3	6.87	185.2	32.2	2.67
16 × 8 1/2	78	22.92	16.32	8.586	.875	.529	1042.6	127.8	6.74	87.5	20.4	1.95
	71	20.86	16.16	8.543	.795	.486	936.9	115.9	6.70	77.9	18.2	1.93
	64	18.80	16.00	8.500	.715	.443	833.8	104.2	6.66	68.4	16.1	1.91
	58	17.04	15.86	8.464	.645	.407	746.4	94.1	6.62	60.5	14.3	1.88
16 × 7	50	14.70	16.25	7.073	.628	.380	655.4	80.7	6.68	34.8	9.8	1.54
	45	13.24	16.12	7.039	.563	.346	583.3	72.4	6.64	30.5	8.7	1.52
	40	11.77	16.00	7.000	.503	.307	515.5	64.4	6.62	26.5	7.6	1.50
	36	10.59	15.85	6.992	.428	.299	446.3	56.3	6.49	22.1	6.3	1.45
14 × 16	426	125.25	18.69	16.695	3.033	1.875	6610.3	707.4	7.26	2359.5	282.7	4.34
	412	121.15	18.50	16.645	2.938	1.825	6309.7	682.1	7.22	2264.9	272.1	4.32
	398	116.98	18.31	16.590	2.843	1.770	6013.7	656.9	7.17	2169.7	261.6	4.31
	384	112.93	18.12	16.540	2.748	1.720	5727.5	632.2	7.12	2078.1	251.3	4.29
	370	108.78	17.94	16.475	2.658	1.655	5454.2	608.1	7.08	1986.0	241.1	4.27
	356	104.68	17.75	16.420	2.563	1.600	5179.4	583.6	7.03	1895.7	230.9	4.26
	342	100.59	17.56	16.365	2.468	1.545	4911.5	559.4	6.99	1806.9	220.8	4.24
	328	96.43	17.38	16.295	2.378	1.475	4656.1	535.8	6.95	1718.5	210.9	4.22
	314	92.30	17.19	16.235	2.283	1.415	4399.4	511.9	6.90	1631.4	201.0	4.20
	300	88.20	17.00	16.175	2.188	1.355	4149.5	488.2	6.86	1546.0	191.2	4.19
	287	84.37	16.81	16.130	2.093	1.310	3912.1	465.5	6.81	1466.5	181.8	4.17
	273	80.22	16.62	16.065	1.998	1.245	3673.2	442.0	6.77	1382.9	172.2	4.15
	264	77.63	16.50	16.025	1.938	1.205	3526.0	427.4	6.74	1331.2	166.1	4.14
	255	74.98	16.37	15.990	1.873	1.170	3372.6	412.0	6.71	1278.1	159.9	4.13
	246	72.33	16.25	15.945	1.813	1.125	3228.9	397.4	6.68	1226.6	153.9	4.12
	237	69.69	16.12	15.910	1.748	1.090	3080.9	382.2	6.65	1174.8	147.7	4.11
	228	67.06	16.00	15.865	1.688	1.045	2942.4	367.8	6.62	1124.8	141.8	4.10
	219	64.36	15.87	15.825	1.623	1.005	2798.2	352.6	6.59	1073.2	135.6	4.08
	211	62.07	15.75	15.800	1.563	.980	2671.4	339.2	6.56	1028.6	130.2	4.07
	202	59.39	15.63	15.750	1.503	.930	2538.8	324.9	6.54	979.7	124.4	4.06
	193	56.73	15.50	15.710	1.438	.890	2402.4	310.0	6.51	930.1	118.4	4.05
	184	54.07	15.38	15.660	1.378	.840	2274.8	295.8	6.49	882.7	112.7	4.04
	176	51.73	15.25	15.640	1.313	.820	2149.6	281.9	6.45	837.9	107.1	4.02
	167	49.09	15.12	15.600	1.248	.780	2020.8	267.3	6.42	790.2	101.3	4.01
	158	46.47	15.00	15.550	1.188	.730	1900.6	253.4	6.40	745.0	95.8	4.00
	150	44.08	14.88	15.515	1.128	.695	1786.9	240.2	6.37	702.5	90.6	3.99
	142	41.85	14.75	15.500	1.063	.680	1672.2	226.7	6.32	660.1	85.2	3.97
	*320	94.12	16.81	16.710	2.093	1.890	4141.7	492.8	6.63	1635.1	195.7	4.17
14 × 14 1/2	136	39.98	14.75	14.740	1.063	.660	1593.0	216.0	6.31	567.7	77.0	3.77
	127	37.33	14.62	14.690	.998	.610	1476.7	202.0	6.29	527.6	71.8	3.76
	119	34.99	14.50	14.650	.938	.570	1373.1	189.4	6.26	491.8	67.1	3.75
14 × 14 1/2	111	32.65	14.37	14.620	0.873	0.540	1266.5	176.3	6.23	454.9	62.2	3.73
	103	30.26	14.25	14.575	.813	.495	1165.8	163.6	6.21	419.7	57.6	3.72
	95	27.94	14.12	14.545	.748	.465	1063.5	150.6	6.17	383.7	52.8	3.71
	87	25.56	14.00	14.500	.688	.420	966.9	138.1	6.15	349.7	48.2	3.70
14 × 12	84	24.71	14.18	12.023	.778	.451	928.4	130.9	6.13	225.5	37.5	3.02
	78	22.94	14.06	12.000	.718	.428	851.2	121.1	6.09	206.9	34.5	3.00
14 × 10	74	21.76	14.19	10.072	.783	.450	796.8	112.3	6.05	133.5	26.5	2.48
	68	20.00	14.06	10.040	.718	.418	724.1	103.0	6.02	121.2	24.1	2.46
	61	17.94	13.91	10.000	.643	.378	641.5	92.2	5.98	107.3	21.5	2.45
14 × 8	58	17.06	14.06	8.098	.718	.406	597.9	85.0	5.92	63.7	15.7	1.93
	53	15.59	13.94	8.062	.658	.370	542.1	77.8	5.90	57.5	14.3	1.92
	48	14.11	13.81	8.031	.593	.339	484.9	70.2	5.86	51.3	12.8	1.91
	43	12.65	13.68	8.000	.528	.308	429.0	62.7	5.82	45.1	11.3	1.89
14 × 6 3/4	42	12.34	14.24	6.801	.573	.338	432.2	60.7	5.92	28.1	8.3	1.51
	38	11.17	14.12	6.776	.513	.313	385.3	54.6	5.87	24.6	7.3	1.49
	34	10.00	14.00	6.750	.453	.287	339.2	48.5	5.83	21.3	6.3	1.46
	30	8.81	13.86	6.733	.383	.270	289.6	41.8	5.73	17.5	5.2	1.41

* Core column section.

Table 64. Properties of Wide Flange Sections—*Continued*

Nominal Size, in.	Wt. per Foot, lb.	Area of Section, in.²	Depth of Section, in.	Flange Width, in.	Flange Thickness, in.	Web Thickness, in.	Axis X-X I, in.⁴	Axis X-X S, in.³	Axis X-X k, in.	Axis Y-Y I, in.⁴	Axis Y-Y S, in.³	Axis Y-Y k, in.
12 × 12	190	55.86	14.38	12.670	1.736	1.060	1892.5	263.2	5.82	589.7	93.1	3.25
	176	51.79	14.12	12.615	1.606	1.005	1712.5	242.6	5.75	538.4	85.4	3.22
	161	47.38	13.88	12.515	1.486	.905	1541.8	222.2	5.70	486.2	77.7	3.20
	147	43.24	13.62	12.450	1.356	.840	1374.4	201.8	5.64	436.8	70.2	3.18
	133	39.11	13.38	12.365	1.236	.755	1221.2	182.5	5.59	389.9	63.1	3.16
	120	35.31	13.12	12.320	1.106	.710	1071.7	163.4	5.51	345.1	56.0	3.13
	106	31.19	12.88	12.230	.986	.620	930.7	144.5	5.46	300.9	49.2	3.11
	99	29.09	12.75	12.190	.921	.580	858.5	134.7	5.43	278.2	45.7	3.09
	92	27.06	12.62	12.155	.856	.545	788.9	125.0	5.40	256.4	42.2	3.08
	85	24.98	12.50	12.105	.796	.495	723.3	115.7	5.38	235.5	38.9	3.07
	79	23.22	12.38	12.080	.736	.470	663.0	107.1	5.34	216.4	35.8	3.05
	72	21.16	12.25	12.040	.671	.430	597.4	97.5	5.31	195.3	32.4	3.04
	65	19.11	12.12	12.000	.606	.390	533.4	88.0	5.28	174.6	29.1	3.02
12 × 10	64	18.83	12.31	10.060	.701	.405	528.3	85.8	5.29	119.0	23.7	2.51
	58	17.06	12.19	10.014	.641	.359	476.1	78.1	5.28	107.4	21.4	2.51
	53	15.59	12.06	10.000	.576	.345	426.2	70.7	5.23	96.1	19.2	2.48
12 × 8	50	14.71	12.19	8.077	.641	.371	394.5	64.7	5.18	56.4	14.0	1.96
	45	13.24	12.06	8.042	.576	.336	350.8	58.2	5.15	50.0	12.4	1.94
	40	11.77	11.94	8.000	.516	.294	310.1	51.9	5.13	44.1	11.0	1.94
12 × 6 1/2	36	10.59	12.24	6.565	.540	.305	280.8	45.9	5.15	23.7	7.2	1.50
	32	9.41	12.12	6.533	.480	.273	246.8	40.7	5.12	20.6	6.3	1.48
	28	8.23	12.00	6.500	.420	.240	213.5	35.6	5.09	17.5	5.4	1.46
	25	7.39	11.87	6.500	.355	.240	183.4	30.9	4.98	14.5	4.5	1.40
10 × 10	136	40.03	11.88	10.575	1.498	.915	917.2	154.4	4.79	295.9	56.0	2.72
	124	36.46	11.62	10.505	1.368	.845	813.1	139.9	4.72	264.8	50.4	2.69
	112	32.92	11.38	10.415	1.248	.755	718.7	126.3	4.67	235.4	45.2	2.67
	100	29.43	11.12	10.345	1.118	.685	625.0	112.4	4.61	206.6	39.9	2.65
	89	26.19	10.88	10.275	.998	.615	542.4	99.7	4.55	180.6	35.2	2.63
	77	22.67	10.62	10.195	.868	.535	457.2	86.1	4.49	153.4	30.1	2.60
	72	21.18	10.50	10.170	.808	.510	420.7	80.1	4.46	141.8	27.9	2.59
	66	19.41	10.38	10.117	.748	.457	382.5	73.7	4.44	129.2	25.5	2.58
	60	17.66	10.25	10.075	.683	.415	343.7	67.1	4.41	116.5	23.1	2.57
	54	15.88	10.12	10.028	.618	.368	305.7	60.4	4.39	103.9	20.7	2.56
	49	14.40	10.00	10.000	.558	.340	272.9	54.6	4.35	93.0	18.6	2.54
10 × 8	45	13.24	10.12	8.022	.618	.350	248.6	49.1	4.33	53.2	13.3	2.00
	41	12.06	10.00	8.000	.558	.328	222.4	44.5	4.29	47.7	11.9	1.99
	37	10.88	9.88	7.978	.498	.306	196.9	39.9	4.25	42.2	10.6	1.97
	33	9.71	9.75	7.964	.433	.292	170.9	35.0	4.20	36.5	9.2	1.94
10 × 5 3/4	29	8.53	10.22	5.799	.500	.289	157.3	30.8	4.29	15.2	5.2	1.34
	26	7.65	10.12	5.769	.450	.259	139.7	27.6	4.27	13.4	4.6	1.32
	23	6.77	10.00	5.750	.390	.240	120.6	24.1	4.22	11.3	3.9	1.29
	21	6.19	9.90	5.750	.340	.240	106.3	21.5	4.14	9.7	3.4	1.25
8 × 8	67	19.70	9.00	8.287	0.933	0.575	271.8	60.4	3.71	88.6	21.4	2.12
	58	17.06	8.75	8.222	.808	.510	227.3	52.0	3.65	74.9	18.2	2.10
	48	14.11	8.50	8.117	.683	.405	183.7	43.2	3.61	60.9	15.0	2.08
	40	11.76	8.25	8.077	.558	.365	146.3	35.5	3.53	49.0	12.1	2.04
	35	10.30	8.12	8.027	.493	.315	126.5	31.1	3.50	42.5	10.6	2.03
	33	9.70	8.06	8.012	.463	.300	117.9	29.3	3.49	39.7	9.9	2.02
	31	9.12	8.00	8.000	.433	.288	109.7	27.4	3.47	37.0	9.2	2.01
8 × 6 1/2	27	7.93	8.03	6.528	.448	.273	94.1	23.4	3.44	20.8	6.4	1.62
	24	7.06	7.93	6.500	.398	.245	82.5	20.8	3.42	18.2	5.6	1.61
8 × 5 1/4	21	6.18	8.19	5.272	.403	.252	73.8	18.0	3.45	9.13	3.5	1.22
	19	5.59	8.09	5.264	.353	.244	64.7	16.0	3.40	7.87	3.0	1.19
	17	5.00	8.00	5.250	.308	.230	56.4	14.1	3.36	6.72	2.6	1.16

Table 65.
Properties of American Standard Beams

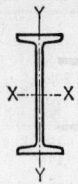

Nominal Size, in.	Weight per Foot, lb.	Area of Section, in.²	Depth of Section, in.	Width of Flange, in.	Web Thickness, in.	Axis X–X			Axis Y–Y		
						I in.⁴	S in.³	k in.	I in.⁴	S in.³	k in.
24 × 7 7/8	120.0	35.13	24.00	8.048	0.798	3010.8	250.9	9.26	84.9	21.1	1.56
	115.0	33.67	24.00	7.987	.737	2940.5	245.0	9.35	82.8	20.7	1.57
	110.0	32.18	24.00	7.925	.675	2869.1	239.1	9.44	80.6	20.3	1.58
	105.9	30.98	24.00	7.875	.625	2811.5	234.3	9.53	78.9	20.0	1.60
24 × 7	100.0	29.25	24.00	7.247	.747	2371.8	197.6	9.05	48.4	13.4	1.29
	95.0	27.79	24.00	7.186	.686	2301.5	191.8	9.08	47.0	13.0	1.30
	90.0	26.30	24.00	7.124	.624	2230.1	185.8	9.21	45.5	12.8	1.32
	85.0	24.84	24.00	7.063	.563	2159.8	180.0	9.33	44.2	12.5	1.33
	79.9	23.33	24.00	7.000	.500	2087.2	173.9	9.46	42.9	12.2	1.36
20 × 7	100.0	29.20	20.00	7.273	.873	1648.3	164.8	7.51	52.4	14.4	1.34
	95.0	27.74	20.00	7.200	.800	1599.7	160.0	7.59	50.5	14.0	1.35
	90.0	26.26	20.00	7.126	.726	1550.3	155.0	7.68	48.7	13.7	1.36
	85.0	24.80	20.00	7.053	.653	1501.7	150.2	7.78	47.0	13.3	1.38
	81.4	23.74	20.00	7.000	.600	1466.3	146.6	7.86	45.8	13.1	1.39
20 × 6 1/4	75.0	21.90	20.00	6.391	.641	1263.5	126.3	7.60	30.1	9.4	1.17
	70.0	20.42	20.00	6.317	.567	1214.2	121.4	7.71	28.9	9.2	1.19
	65.4	19.08	20.00	6.250	.500	1169.5	116.9	7.83	27.9	8.9	1.21
18 × 6	70.0	20.46	18.00	6.251	.711	917.5	101.9	6.70	24.5	7.8	1.09
	65.0	18.98	18.00	6.169	.629	877.7	97.5	6.80	23.4	7.6	1.11
	60.0	17.50	18.00	6.087	.547	837.8	93.1	6.92	22.3	7.3	1.13
	54.7	15.94	18.00	6.000	.460	795.5	88.4	7.07	21.2	7.1	1.15
15 × 6	75.0	21.85	15.00	6.278	.868	687.2	91.6	5.61	30.6	9.8	1.18
	70.0	20.38	15.00	6.180	.770	659.6	87.9	5.69	28.8	9.3	1.19
	65.0	18.91	15.00	6.082	.672	632.1	84.3	5.78	27.2	8.9	1.20
	60.8	17.68	15.00	6.000	.590	609.0	81.2	5.87	26.0	8.7	1.21
15 × 5 1/2	55.0	16.06	15.00	5.738	.648	508.7	67.8	5.63	17.0	5.9	1.03
	50.0	14.59	15.00	5.640	.550	481.1	64.2	5.74	16.0	5.7	1.05
	45.0	13.12	15.00	5.542	.452	453.6	60.5	5.88	15.0	5.4	1.07
	42.9	12.49	15.00	5.500	.410	441.8	58.9	5.95	14.6	5.3	1.08
12 × 5 1/4	55.0	16.04	12.00	5.600	.810	319.3	53.2	4.46	17.3	6.2	1.04
	50.0	14.57	12.00	5.477	.687	301.6	50.3	4.55	16.0	5.8	1.05
	45.0	13.10	12.00	5.355	.565	284.1	47.3	4.66	14.8	5.5	1.06
	40.8	11.84	12.00	5.250	.460	268.9	44.8	4.77	13.8	5.3	1.08
12 × 5	35.0	10.20	12.00	5.078	.428	227.0	37.8	4.72	10.0	3.9	.99
	31.8	9.26	12.00	5.000	.350	215.8	36.0	4.83	9.5	3.8	1.01
10 × 4 3/4	40.0	11.69	10.00	5.091	.741	158.0	31.6	3.68	9.4	3.7	.90
	35.0	10.22	10.00	4.944	.594	145.8	29.2	3.78	8.5	3.4	.91
	30.0	8.75	10.00	4.797	.447	133.5	26.7	3.91	7.6	3.2	.93
	25.4	7.38	10.00	4.660	.310	122.1	24.4	4.07	6.9	3.0	.97
8 × 4	25.5	7.43	8.00	4.262	.532	68.1	17.0	3.03	4.7	2.2	.80
	23.0	6.71	8.00	4.171	.441	64.2	16.0	3.09	4.4	2.1	.81
	20.5	5.97	8.00	4.079	.349	60.2	15.1	3.18	4.0	2.0	.82
	18.4	5.34	8.00	4.000	.270	56.9	14.2	3.26	3.8	1.9	.84
7 × 3 3/4	20.0	5.83	7.00	3.860	.450	41.9	12.0	2.68	3.1	1.6	.74
	17.5	5.09	7.00	3.755	.345	38.9	11.1	2.77	2.9	1.6	.76
	15.3	4.43	7.00	3.660	.250	36.2	10.4	2.86	2.7	1.5	.78
6 × 3 3/8	17.25	5.02	6.00	3.565	.465	26.0	8.7	2.28	2.3	1.3	.68
	14.75	4.29	6.00	3.443	.343	23.8	7.9	2.36	2.1	1.2	.69
	12.5	3.61	6.00	3.330	.230	21.8	7.3	2.46	1.8	1.1	.72
5 × 3	14.75	4.29	5.00	3.284	.494	15.0	6.0	1.87	1.7	1.0	.63
	12.25	3.56	5.00	3.137	.347	13.5	5.4	1.95	1.4	.91	.63
	10.0	2.87	5.00	3.000	.210	12.1	4.8	2.05	1.2	.82	.65
4 × 2 3/4	10.5	3.05	4.00	2.870	.400	7.1	3.5	1.52	1.0	.70	.57
	9.5	2.76	4.00	2.796	.326	6.7	3.3	1.56	.91	.65	.58
	8.5	2.46	4.00	2.723	.253	6.3	3.2	1.60	.83	.61	.58
	7.7	2.21	4.00	2.660	.190	6.0	3.0	1.64	.77	.58	.59
3 × 2 3/8	7.5	2.17	3.00	2.509	.349	2.9	1.9	1.15	.59	.47	.52
	6.5	1.88	3.00	2.411	.251	2.7	1.8	1.19	.51	.43	.52
	5.7	1.64	3.00	2.330	.170	2.5	1.7	1.23	.46	.40	.53

Table 66.

Properties of American Standard Channels

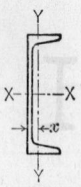

Nominal Size, in.	Wt. per Foot, lb.	Area of Section, in.²	Depth of Section, in.	Width of Flange, in.	Web Thickness, in.	Axis X-X			Axis Y-Y			
						I, in.⁴	S, in.³	k, in.	I, in.⁴	S, in.³	k, in.	X in.
*18 × 4	58.0	16.98	18.00	4.200	0.700	670.7	74.5	6.29	18.5	5.6	1.04	.88
	51.9	15.18	18.00	4.100	.600	622.1	69.1	6.40	17.1	5.3	1.06	.87
	45.8	13.38	18.00	4.000	.500	573.5	63.7	6.55	15.8	5.1	1.09	.89
	42.7	12.48	18.00	3.950	.450	549.2	61.0	6.64	15.0	4.9	1.10	.90
15 × 3 1/2	55.0	16.11	15.00	3.814	.814	429.0	57.2	5.16	12.1	4.1	.87	.82
	50.0	14.64	15.00	3.716	.716	401.4	53.6	5.24	11.2	3.8	.87	.80
	45.0	13.17	15.00	3.618	.618	373.9	49.8	5.33	10.3	3.6	.88	.79
	40.0	11.70	15.00	3.520	.520	346.3	46.2	5.44	9.3	3.4	.89	.78
	35.0	10.23	15.00	3.422	.422	318.7	42.5	5.58	8.4	3.2	.91	.79
	33.9	9.90	15.00	3.400	.400	312.6	41.7	5.62	8.2	3.2	.91	.79
12 × 3	40.0	11.73	12.00	3.415	.755	196.5	32.8	4.09	6.6	2.5	.75	.72
	35.0	10.26	12.00	3.292	.632	178.8	29.8	4.18	5.9	2.3	.76	.69
	30.0	8.79	12.00	3.170	.510	161.2	26.9	4.28	5.2	2.1	.77	.63
	25.0	7.32	12.00	3.047	.387	143.5	23.9	4.43	4.5	1.9	.79	.68
	20.7	6.03	12.00	2.940	.280	128.1	21.4	4.61	3.9	1.7	.81	.70
10 × 2 5/8	35.0	10.27	10.00	3.180	.820	115.2	23.0	3.34	4.6	1.9	.67	.69
	30.0	8.80	10.00	3.033	.673	103.0	20.6	3.42	4.0	1.7	.67	.65
	25.0	7.33	10.00	2.886	.526	90.7	18.1	3.52	3.4	1.5	.68	.62
	20.0	5.86	10.00	2.739	.379	78.5	15.7	3.66	2.8	1.3	.70	.61
	15.3	4.47	10.00	2.600	.240	66.9	13.4	3.87	2.3	1.2	.72	.64
9 × 2 1/2	25.0	7.33	9.00	2.812	.612	70.5	15.7	3.10	3.0	1.4	.64	.61
	20.0	5.86	9.00	2.648	.448	60.6	13.5	3.22	2.4	1.2	.65	.59
	15.0	4.39	9.00	2.485	.285	50.7	11.3	3.40	1.9	1.0	.67	.59
	13.4	3.89	9.00	2.430	.230	47.3	10.5	3.49	1.8	.97	.67	.61
8 × 2 1/4	21.25	6.23	8.00	2.619	.579	47.6	11.9	2.77	2.2	1.1	.60	.59
	18.75	5.49	8.00	2.527	.487	43.7	10.9	2.82	2.0	1.0	.60	.57
	16.25	4.76	8.00	2.435	.395	39.8	9.9	2.89	1.8	.94	.61	.56
	13.75	4.02	8.00	2.343	.303	35.8	9.0	2.99	1.5	.86	.62	.56
	11.5	3.36	8.00	2.260	.220	32.3	8.1	3.10	1.3	.79	.63	.58
7 × 2 1/8	19.75	5.79	7.00	2.509	.629	33.1	9.4	2.39	1.8	.96	.56	.58
	17.25	5.05	7.00	2.404	.524	30.1	8.6	2.44	1.6	.86	.56	.55
	14.75	4.32	7.00	2.299	.419	27.1	7.7	2.51	1.4	.79	.57	.53
	12.25	3.58	7.00	2.194	.314	24.1	6.9	2.59	1.2	.71	.58	.53
	9.8	2.85	7.00	2.090	.210	21.1	6.0	2.72	.98	.63	.59	.55
6 × 2	15.5	4.54	6.00	2.279	.559	19.5	6.5	2.07	1.3	.73	.53	.55
	13.0	3.81	6.00	2.157	.437	17.3	5.8	2.13	1.1	.65	.53	.52
	10.5	3.07	6.00	2.034	.314	15.1	5.0	2.22	.87	.57	.53	.50
	8.2	2.39	6.00	1.920	.200	13.0	4.3	2.34	.70	.50	.54	.52
5 × 1 3/4	11.5	3.36	5.00	2.032	.472	10.4	4.1	1.76	.82	.54	.49	.51
	9.0	2.63	5.00	1.885	.325	8.8	3.5	1.83	.64	.45	.49	.48
	6.7	1.95	5.00	1.750	.190	7.4	3.0	1.95	.48	.38	.50	.49
4 × 1 5/8	7.25	2.12	4.00	1.720	.320	4.5	2.3	1.47	.44	.35	.46	.46
	6.25	1.82	4.00	1.647	.247	4.1	2.1	1.50	.38	.32	.45	.46
	5.4	1.56	4.00	1.580	.180	3.8	1.9	1.56	.32	.29	.45	.46
3 × 1 1/2	6.0	1.75	3.00	1.596	.356	2.1	1.4	1.08	.31	.27	.42	.46
	5.0	1.46	3.00	1.498	.258	1.8	1.2	1.12	.25	.24	.41	.44
	4.1	1.19	3.00	1.410	1.70	1.6	1.1	1.17	.20	.21	.41	.44

* Car and Shipbuilding Channel; not an American Standard.

Table 67.

Properties of Angles with Equal Legs

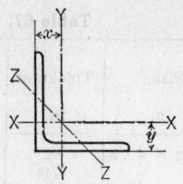

| Size, in. | Thickness, in. | Weight per Foot, lb. | Area of Section, in.² | Axis X–X and Axis Y–Y | | | | Axis Z–Z |
				I, in.⁴	S, in.³	k, in.	x or y, in.	k, in.
8 × 8	1 1/8	56.9	16.73	98.0	17.5	2.42	2.41	1.56
	1 1/16	54.0	15.87	93.5	16.7	2.43	2.39	1.56
	1	51.0	15.00	89.0	15.8	2.44	2.37	1.56
	15/16	48.1	14.12	84.3	14.9	2.44	2.34	1.56
	7/8	45.0	13.23	79.6	14.0	2.45	2.32	1.57
	13/16	42.0	12.34	74.7	13.1	2.46	2.30	1.57
	3/4	38.9	11.44	69.7	12.2	2.47	2.28	1.57
	11/16	35.8	10.53	64.6	11.3	2.48	2.25	1.58
	5/8	32.7	9.61	59.4	10.3	2.49	2.23	1.58
	9/16	29.6	8.68	54.1	9.3	2.50	2.21	1.58
	1/2	26.4	7.75	48.6	8.4	2.50	2.19	1.59
6 × 6	1	37.4	11.00	35.5	8.6	1.80	1.86	1.17
	15/16	35.3	10.37	33.7	8.1	1.80	1.84	1.17
	7/8	33.1	9.73	31.9	7.6	1.81	1.82	1.17
	13/16	31.0	9.09	30.1	7.2	1.82	1.80	1.17
	3/4	28.7	8.44	28.2	6.7	1.83	1.78	1.17
	11/16	26.5	7.78	26.2	6.2	1.83	1.75	1.17
	5/8	24.2	7.11	24.2	5.7	1.84	1.73	1.18
	9/16	21.9	6.43	22.1	5.1	1.85	1.71	1.18
	1/2	19.6	5.75	19.9	4.6	1.86	1.68	1.18
	7/16	17.2	5.06	17.7	4.1	1.87	1.66	1.19
	3/8	14.9	4.36	15.4	3.5	1.88	1.64	1.19
5 × 5	1	30.6	9.00	19.6	5.8	1.48	1.61	.97
	15/16	28.9	8.50	18.7	5.5	1.48	1.59	.97
	7/8	27.2	7.98	17.8	5.2	1.49	1.57	.97
	13/16	25.4	7.46	16.8	4.9	1.50	1.55	.97
	3/4	23.6	6.94	15.7	4.5	1.51	1.52	.97
	11/16	21.8	6.40	14.7	4.2	1.51	1.50	.98
	5/8	20.0	5.86	13.6	3.9	1.52	1.48	.98
	9/16	18.1	5.31	12.4	3.5	1.53	1.46	.98
	1/2	16.2	4.75	11.3	3.2	1.54	1.43	.98
	7/16	14.3	4.18	10.0	2.8	1.55	1.41	.98
	3/8	12.3	3.61	8.7	2.4	1.56	1.39	.99
4 × 4	3/4	18.5	5.44	7.7	2.8	1.19	1.27	.78
	11/16	17.1	5.03	7.2	2.6	1.19	1.25	.78
	5/8	15.7	4.61	6.7	2.4	1.20	1.23	.78
	9/16	14.3	4.18	6.1	2.2	1.21	1.21	.78
	1/2	12.8	3.75	5.6	2.0	1.22	1.18	.78
	7/16	11.3	3.31	5.0	1.8	1.23	1.16	.78
	3/8	9.8	2.86	4.4	1.5	1.23	1.14	.79
	5/16	8.2	2.40	3.7	1.3	1.24	1.12	.79
	1/4	6.6	1.94	3.0	1.1	1.25	1.09	.80
3 1/2 × 3 1/2	3/4	16.0	4.69	5.0	2.1	1.03	1.15	.68
	11/16	14.8	4.34	4.7	2.0	1.04	1.12	.68
	5/8	13.6	3.98	4.3	1.8	1.04	1.10	.68
	9/16	12.4	3.62	4.0	1.7	1.05	1.08	.68
	1/2	11.1	3.25	3.6	1.5	1.06	1.06	.68
	7/16	9.8	2.87	3.3	1.3	1.07	1.04	.68
	3/8	8.5	2.48	2.9	1.2	1.07	1.01	.69
	5/16	7.2	2.09	2.5	.98	1.08	.99	.69
	1/4	5.8	1.69	2.0	.79	1.09	.97	.69
3 × 3	5/8	11.5	3.36	2.6	1.3	.88	.98	.58
	9/16	10.4	3.06	2.4	1.2	.89	.95	.58
	1/2	9.4	2.75	2.2	1.1	.90	.93	.58
	7/16	8.3	2.43	2.0	.95	.91	.91	.58
	3/8	7.2	2.11	1.8	.83	.91	.89	.58
	5/16	6.1	1.78	1.5	.71	.92	.87	.59
	1/4	4.9	1.44	1.2	.58	.93	.84	.59

Table 67. Properties of Angles with Equal Legs—*Continued*

Size, in.	Thickness, in.	Weight per Foot, lb.	Area of Section, in.²	Axis X–X and Axis Y–Y				Axis Z–Z
				I, in.⁴	S, in.³	k, in.	x or y, in.	k, in.
2 1/2 × 2 1/2	1/2	7.7	2.25	1.2	.72	.74	.81	.49
	7/16	6.8	2.00	1.1	.65	.75	.78	.49
	3/8	5.9	1.73	.98	.57	.75	.76	.49
	5/16	5.0	1.47	.85	.48	.76	.74	.49
	1/4	4.1	1.19	.70	.39	.77	.72	.49
	3/16	3.07	.90	.55	.30	.78	.69	.49
2 × 2	7/16	5.3	1.56	.54	.40	.59	.66	.39
	3/8	4.7	1.36	.48	.35	.59	.64	.39
	5/16	3.92	1.15	.42	.30	.60	.61	.39
	1/4	3.19	.94	.35	.25	.61	.59	.39
	3/16	2.44	.71	.27	.19	.62	.57	.39
	1/8	1.65	.48	.19	.13	.63	.55	.40
1 3/4 × 1 3/4	3/8	3.99	1.17	.31	.26	.51	.57	.34
	5/16	3.39	1.00	.27	.23	.52	.55	.34
	1/4	2.77	.81	.23	.19	.53	.53	.34
	3/16	2.12	.62	.18	.14	.54	.51	.34
	1/8	1.44	.42	.13	.10	.55	.48	.35
1 1/2 × 1 1/2	5/16	2.86	.84	.16	.16	.44	.49	.29
	1/4	2.34	.69	.14	.13	.45	.47	.29
	3/16	1.80	.53	.11	.10	.46	.44	.29
	1/8	1.23	.36	.08	.07	.47	.42	.30
1 1/4 × 1 1/4	5/16	2.33	.68	.09	.11	.36	.42	.24
	1/4	1.92	.56	.08	.09	.37	.40	.24
	3/16	1.48	.43	.06	.07	.38	.38	.24
	1/8	1.01	.30	.04	.05	.38	.36	.25
1 × 1	1/4	1.49	.44	.04	.06	.29	.34	.20
	3/16	1.16	.34	.03	.04	.30	.32	.19
	1/8	.80	.23	.02	.03	.30	.30	.20

Table 68.

Properties of Angles with Unequal Legs

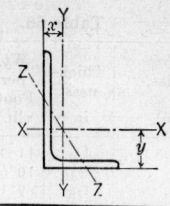

Size, in.	Thickness, in.	Wt. per Foot, lb.	Area of Section, in.²	Axis X–X I, in.⁴	S, in.³	k, in.	y, in.	Axis Y–Y I, in.⁴	S, in.³	k, in.	x, in.	Axis Z–Z k, in.
8 × 6	1 1/8	49.3	14.48	88.9	16.8	2.48	2.70	42.5	9.9	1.71	1.70	1.28
	1 1/16	46.8	13.75	84.9	15.9	2.48	2.68	40.7	9.4	1.72	1.68	1.28
	1	44.2	13.00	80.8	15.1	2.49	2.65	38.8	8.9	1.73	1.65	1.28
	15/16	41.7	12.25	76.6	14.3	2.50	2.63	36.9	8.4	1.73	1.63	1.28
	7/8	39.1	11.48	72.3	13.4	2.51	2.61	34.9	7.9	1.74	1.61	1.28
	13/16	36.5	10.72	67.9	12.6	2.52	2.59	32.8	7.4	1.75	1.59	1.28
	3/4	33.8	9.94	63.4	11.7	2.53	2.56	30.7	6.9	1.76	1.56	1.29
	11/16	31.2	9.15	58.8	10.8	2.54	2.54	28.6	6.4	1.77	1.54	1.29
	5/8	28.5	8.36	54.1	9.9	2.54	2.52	26.3	5.9	1.77	1.52	1.29
	9/16	25.7	7.56	49.3	9.0	2.55	2.50	24.0	5.3	1.78	1.50	1.30
	1/2	23.0	6.75	44.3	8.0	2.56	2.47	21.7	4.8	1.79	1.47	1.30
	7/16	20.2	5.93	39.2	7.1	2.57	2.45	19.3	4.2	1.80	1.45	1.31
8 × 4	1	37.4	11.00	69.6	14.1	2.52	3.05	11.6	3.9	1.03	1.05	.85
	15/16	35.3	10.37	66.1	13.3	2.52	3.02	11.1	3.7	1.03	1.02	.85
	7/8	33.1	9.73	62.5	12.5	2.53	3.00	10.5	3.5	1.04	1.00	.85
	13/16	31.0	9.09	58.7	11.7	2.54	2.98	10.0	3.3	1.05	.98	.85
	3/4	28.7	8.44	54.9	10.9	2.55	2.95	9.4	3.1	1.05	.95	.85
	11/16	26.5	7.78	51.0	10.1	2.56	2.93	8.7	2.9	1.06	.93	.85
	5/8	24.2	7.11	46.9	9.2	2.57	2.91	8.1	2.6	1.07	.91	.86
	9/16	21.9	6.43	42.8	8.4	2.58	2.88	7.4	2.4	1.07	.88	.86
	1/2	19.6	5.75	38.5	7.5	2.59	2.86	6.7	2.2	1.08	.86	.86
	7/16	17.2	5.06	34.1	6.6	2.60	2.83	6.0	1.9	1.09	.83	.87
7 × 4	1	34.0	10.00	47.7	10.9	2.18	2.60	11.2	3.9	1.06	1.10	.85
	15/16	32.1	9.43	45.4	10.3	2.19	2.58	10.7	3.7	1.07	1.08	.86
	7/8	30.2	8.86	42.9	9.7	2.20	2.55	10.2	3.5	1.07	1.05	.86
	13/16	28.2	8.28	40.4	9.0	2.21	2.53	9.6	3.2	1.08	1.03	.86
	3/4	26.2	7.69	37.8	8.4	2.22	2.51	9.1	3.0	1.09	1.01	.86
	11/16	24.2	7.09	35.1	7.8	2.23	2.49	8.5	2.8	1.09	.99	.86
	5/8	22.1	6.48	32.4	7.1	2.24	2.46	7.8	2.6	1.10	.96	.86
	9/16	20.0	5.87	29.6	6.5	2.24	2.44	7.2	2.4	1.11	.94	.87
	1/2	17.9	5.25	26.7	5.8	2.25	2.42	6.5	2.1	1.11	.92	.87
	7/16	15.8	4.62	23.7	5.1	2.26	2.39	5.8	1.9	1.12	.89	.88
	3/8	13.6	3.98	20.6	4.4	2.27	2.37	5.1	1.6	1.13	.87	.88
6 × 4	1	30.6	9.00	30.8	8.0	1.85	2.17	10.8	3.8	1.09	1.17	.86
	15/16	28.9	8.50	29.3	7.6	1.86	2.14	10.3	3.6	1.10	1.14	.86
	7/8	27.2	7.98	27.7	7.2	1.86	2.12	9.8	3.4	1.11	1.12	.86
	13/16	25.4	7.47	26.2	6.7	1.87	2.10	9.2	3.2	1.11	1.10	.86
	3/4	23.6	6.94	24.5	6.3	1.88	2.08	8.7	3.0	1.12	1.08	.86
	11/16	21.8	6.40	22.8	5.8	1.89	2.06	8.1	2.8	1.13	1.06	.86
	5/8	20.0	5.86	21.1	5.3	1.90	2.03	7.5	2.5	1.13	1.03	.86
	9/16	18.1	5.31	19.3	4.8	1.90	2.01	6.9	2.3	1.14	1.01	.87
	1/2	16.2	4.75	17.4	4.3	1.91	1.99	6.3	2.1	1.15	.99	.87
	7/16	14.3	4.18	15.5	3.8	1.92	1.96	5.6	1.9	1.16	.96	.87
	3/8	12.3	3.61	13.5	3.3	1.93	1.94	4.9	1.6	1.17	.94	.88
5 × 3 1/2	3/4	19.8	5.81	13.9	4.3	1.55	1.75	5.6	2.2	.98	1.00	.75
	11/16	18.3	5.37	13.0	4.0	1.56	1.72	5.2	2.1	.98	.97	.75
	5/8	16.8	4.92	12.0	3.7	1.56	1.70	4.8	1.9	.99	.95	.75
	9/16	15.2	4.47	11.0	3.3	1.57	1.68	4.5	1.7	1.00	.93	.75
	1/2	13.6	4.00	10.0	3.0	1.58	1.66	4.1	1.6	1.01	.91	.75
	7/16	12.0	3.53	8.9	2.6	1.59	1.63	3.6	1.4	1.01	.88	.76
	3/8	10.4	3.05	7.8	2.3	1.60	1.61	3.2	1.2	1.02	.86	.76
	5/16	8.7	2.56	6.6	1.9	1.61	1.59	2.7	1.0	1.03	.84	.77
4 × 3 1/2	3/4	17.3	5.06	7.3	2.8	1.20	1.34	5.2	2.2	1.01	1.09	.72
	11/16	16.0	4.68	6.9	2.6	1.21	1.32	4.9	2.0	1.02	1.07	.72
	5/8	14.7	4.30	6.4	2.4	1.22	1.29	4.5	1.8	1.03	1.04	.72
	9/16	13.3	3.90	5.9	2.2	1.23	1.27	4.2	1.7	1.03	1.02	.72

Table 68.   Properties of Angles with Unequal Legs—*Continued*

Size, in.	Thickness, in.	Wt. per Foot, lb.	Area of Section, in.^{2}	Axis X–X				Axis Y–Y				Axis Z–Z
				I, in.^{4}	S, in.^{3}	k, in.	y, in.	I, in.^{4}	S, in.^{3}	k, in.	x, in.	k, in.
4 × 3½	1/2	11.9	3.50	5.3	1.9	1.23	1.25	3.8	1.5	1.04	1.00	.72
	7/16	10.6	3.09	4.8	1.7	1.24	1.23	3.4	1.4	1.05	.98	.72
	3/8	9.1	2.67	4.2	1.5	1.25	1.21	3.0	1.2	1.06	.96	.73
	5/16	7.7	2.25	3.6	1.3	1.26	1.18	2.6	1.0	1.07	.93	.73
4 × 3	3/4	16.0	4.69	6.9	2.7	1.22	1.42	3.3	1.6	.84	.92	.64
	11/16	14.8	4.34	6.5	2.5	1.22	1.39	3.1	1.5	.84	.89	.64
	5/8	13.6	3.98	6.0	2.3	1.23	1.37	2.9	1.4	.85	.87	.64
	9/16	12.4	3.62	5.6	2.1	1.24	1.35	2.7	1.2	.86	.85	.64
	1/2	11.1	3.25	5.1	1.9	1.25	1.33	2.4	1.1	.86	.83	.64
	7/16	9.8	2.87	4.5	1.7	1.25	1.30	2.2	1.0	.87	.80	.64
	3/8	8.5	2.48	4.0	1.5	1.26	1.28	1.9	.87	.88	.78	.64
	5/16	7.2	2.09	3.4	1.2	1.27	1.26	1.7	.73	.89	.76	.65
	1/4	5.8	1.69	2.8	1.0	1.28	1.24	1.4	.60	.90	.74	.65
3½ × 3	3/4	14.7	4.31	4.7	2.1	1.04	1.21	3.2	1.5	.85	.96	.62
	11/16	13.6	4.00	4.4	1.9	1.05	1.19	3.0	1.4	.86	.94	.62
	5/8	12.5	3.67	4.1	1.8	1.06	1.17	2.8	1.3	.87	.92	.62
	9/16	11.4	3.34	3.8	1.6	1.07	1.15	2.6	1.2	.87	.90	.62
	1/2	10.2	3.00	3.5	1.5	1.07	1.13	2.3	1.1	.88	.88	.62
	7/16	9.1	2.65	3.1	1.3	1.08	1.10	2.1	.98	.89	.85	.62
	3/8	7.9	2.30	2.7	1.1	1.09	1.08	1.9	.85	.90	.83	.62
	5/16	6.6	1.93	2.3	.95	1.10	1.06	1.6	.72	.90	.81	.63
	1/4	5.4	1.56	1.9	.78	1.11	1.04	1.3	.59	.91	.79	.63
3 × 2½	1/2	8.5	2.50	2.1	1.0	.91	1.00	1.3	.74	.72	.75	.52
	7/16	7.6	2.21	1.9	.93	.92	.98	1.2	.66	.73	.73	.52
	3/8	6.6	1.92	1.7	.81	.93	.96	1.0	.58	.74	.71	.52
	5/16	5.6	1.62	1.4	.69	.94	.93	.90	.49	.74	.68	.53
	1/4	4.5	1.31	1.2	.56	.95	.91	.74	.40	.75	.66	.53
2½ × 2	1/2	6.8	2.00	1.1	.70	.75	.88	.64	.46	.56	.63	.42
	7/16	6.1	1.78	1.0	.62	.76	.85	.58	.41	.57	.60	.42
	3/8	5.3	1.55	.91	.55	.77	.83	.51	.36	.58	.58	.42
	5/16	4.5	1.31	.79	.47	.78	.81	.45	.31	.58	.56	.42
	1/4	3.62	1.06	.65	.38	.78	.79	.37	.25	.59	.54	.42
	3/16	2.75	.81	.51	.29	.79	.76	.29	.20	.60	.51	.43
2 × 1½	3/8	3.99	1.17	.43	.34	.61	.71	.21	.20	.42	.46	.32
	5/16	3.39	1.00	.38	.29	.62	.69	.18	.17	.42	.44	.32
	1/4	2.77	.81	.32	.24	.62	.66	.15	.14	.43	.41	.32
	3/16	2.12	.62	.25	.18	.63	.64	.12	.11	.44	.39	.32
	1/8	1.44	.42	.17	.13	.64	.62	.09	.08	.45	.37	.33
1¾ × 1¼	1/4	2.34	.69	.20	.18	.54	.60	.09	.10	.35	.35	.27
	3/16	1.80	.53	.16	.14	.55	.58	.07	.08	.36	.33	.27
	1/8	1.23	.36	.11	.09	.56	.56	.05	.05	.37	.31	.27

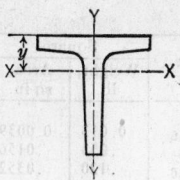

Table 69.

Properties and Dimensions of Tees

Nominal Size, in.	Wt. per Foot, lb	Area of Section, in.²	Depth of Section, in.	Width of Flange, in.	Minimum Thickness Flange, in.	Minimum Thickness Stem, in.	Axis X–X I, in.⁴	S, in.³	k, in.	y, in.	Axis Y–Y I, in.⁴	S, in.³	k, in.
6½ × 6½	19.8	5.80	6½	6½	3/8	7/16	23.5	5.0	2.01	1.76	10.1	3.1	1.32
4 × 4	13.5	3.97	4	4	1/2	1/2	5.7	2.0	1.20	1.18	2.8	1.4	.84
4 × 4	10.5	3.09	4	4	3/8	3/8	4.5	1.6	1.21	1.13	2.1	1.1	.83
3½ × 3½	11.7	3.44	3½	3½	1/2	1/2	3.73	1.53	1.04	1.05	1.91	1.09	.74
3½ × 3½	9.2	2.70	3½	3½	3/8	3/8	3.0	1.20	1.05	1.00	1.39	.80	.72
3 × 3	7.8	2.29	3	3	3/8	3/8	1.84	.86	.89	.88	.89	.60	.63
3 × 3	6.7	1.97	3	3	5/16	5/16	1.61	.74	.90	.85	.75	.50	.62
2½ × 2½	6.4	1.87	2½	2½	3/8	3/8	1.0	.59	.74	.76	.52	.42	.53
2½ × 2½	4.6	1.33	2½	2½	1/4	1/4	.74	.42	.75	.71	.34	.27	.51
2¼ × 2¼	4.9	1.43	2¼	2¼	5/16	5/16	.65	.41	.67	.68	.33	.29	.48
2¼ × 2¼	4.1	1.19	2¼	2¼	1/4	1/4	.52	.32	.66	.65	.25	.22	.46
2 × 2	4.3	1.26	2	2	5/16	5/16	.44	.31	.59	.61	.23	.23	.43
2 × 2	3.56	1.05	2	2	1/4	1/4	.37	.26	.59	.59	.18	.18	.42

Tee sections are seldom used as structural framing members. When so used they are generally employed on short spans in flexure. In these tables are listed a few selected sizes, the range of whose section moduli will cover all ordinary conditions. For sizes not listed, the catalogs of the respective rolling mills should be consulted.

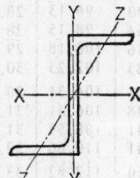

Table 70.

Properties and Dimensions of Zees

Nominal Size, in.	Weight per Foot, lb	Area of Section, in.²	Depth of Section, in.	Width of Flange, in.	Thickness, in.	Axis X–X I, in.⁴	S, in.³	k, in.	Axis Y–Y I, in.⁴	S, in.³	k, in.	Axis Z–Z k, in.
6 × 3½	34.6	10.17	6⅛	3 5/8	7/8	50.2	16.4	2.22	19.2	6.0	1.37	.83
	29.4	8.63	6	3½	3/4	42.1	14.0	2.21	15.4	4.9	1.34	.81
	25.4	7.46	6 1/16	3 9/16	5/8	38.9	12.8	2.28	14.4	4.4	1.39	.82
	21.1	6.19	6⅛	3 5/8	1/2	34.4	11.2	2.36	12.9	3.8	1.44	.84
	18.4	5.39	6 1/16	3 9/16	7/16	29.8	9.8	2.35	11.0	3.3	1.43	.83
	15.7	4.59	6	3½	3/8	25.3	8.4	2.35	9.1	2.8	1.41	.83
5 × 3¼	14.0	4.10	5 1/16	3 5/16	3/8	16.2	6.4	1.99	7.7	2.5	1.37	.76
	11.6	3.40	5	3¼	5/16	13.4	5.3	1.98	6.2	2.0	1.35	.75
4 × 3 1/16	10.3	3.03	4 1/16	3⅛	5/16	7.9	3.9	1.62	5.5	1.8	1.34	.68
	8.2	2.41	4	3 1/16	1/4	6.3	3.1	1.62	4.2	1.4	1.33	.67
3 × 2 11/16	6.7	1.97	3	2 11/16	1/4	2.9	1.9	1.21	2.8	1.1	1.19	.55

Zee sections are seldom used as structural framing members. When so used they are generally employed on short spans in flexure. In these tables are listed a few selected sizes, the range of whose section moduli will cover all ordinary conditions. For sizes not listed, the catalogs of the respective rolling mills should be consulted.

Table 71. Square and Round Bars

Size, in.	Square Weight, lb	Square Area, sq in.	Round Weight, lb	Round Area, sq in.	Size, in.	Square Weight, lb	Square Area, sq in.	Round Weight, lb	Round Area, sq in.
0					4	54.40	16.000	42.73	12.566
1/16	0.013	0.0039	0.010	0.0031	1/16	56.11	16.504	44.07	12.962
1/8	.053	.0156	.042	.0123	1/8	57.85	17.016	45.44	13.364
3/16	.120	.0352	.094	.0276	3/16	59.62	17.535	46.83	13.772
1/4	.213	.0625	.167	.0491	1/4	61.41	18.063	48.23	14.186
5/16	.332	.0977	.261	.0767	5/16	63.23	18.598	49.66	14.607
3/8	.478	.1406	.376	.1105	3/8	65.08	19.141	51.11	15.033
7/16	.651	.1914	.511	.1503	7/16	66.95	19.691	52.58	15.466
1/2	.850	.2500	.668	.1963	1/2	68.85	20.250	54.07	15.904
9/16	1.076	.3164	.845	.2485	9/16	70.78	20.816	55.59	16.349
5/8	1.328	.3906	1.043	.3068	5/8	72.73	21.391	57.12	16.800
11/16	1.607	.4727	1.262	.3712	11/16	74.71	21.973	58.67	17.257
3/4	1.913	.5625	1.502	.4418	3/4	76.71	22.563	60.25	17.721
13/16	2.245	.6602	1.763	.5185	13/16	78.74	23.160	61.85	18.190
7/8	2.603	.7656	2.044	.6013	7/8	80.80	23.766	63.46	18.665
15/16	2.988	.8789	2.347	.6903	15/16	82.89	24.379	65.10	19.147
1	3.400	1.0000	2.670	.7854	5	85.00	25.000	66.76	19.635
1/16	3.838	1.1289	3.015	.8866	1/16	87.14	25.629	68.44	20.129
1/8	4.303	1.2656	3.380	.9940	1/8	89.30	26.266	70.14	20.629
3/16	4.795	1.4102	3.766	1.1075	3/16	91.49	26.910	71.86	21.135
1/4	5.313	1.5625	4.172	1.2272	1/4	93.71	27.563	73.60	21.648
5/16	5.857	1.7227	4.600	1.3530	5/16	95.96	28.223	75.36	22.166
3/8	6.428	1.8906	5.049	1.4849	3/8	98.23	28.891	77.15	22.691
7/16	7.026	2.0664	5.518	1.6230	7/16	100.53	29.566	78.95	23.221
1/2	7.650	2.2500	6.008	1.7671	1/2	102.85	30.250	80.78	23.758
9/16	8.301	2.4414	6.519	1.9175	9/16	105.20	30.941	82.62	24.301
5/8	8.978	2.6406	7.051	2.0739	5/8	107.58	31.641	84.49	24.850
11/16	9.682	2.8477	7.604	2.2365	11/16	109.98	32.348	86.38	25.406
3/4	10.413	3.0625	8.178	2.4053	3/4	112.41	33.063	88.29	25.967
13/16	11.170	3.2852	8.773	2.5802	13/16	114.87	33.785	90.22	26.535
7/8	11.953	3.5156	9.388	2.7612	7/8	117.35	34.516	92.17	27.109
15/16	12.763	3.7539	10.024	2.9483	15/16	119.86	35.254	94.14	27.688
2	13.600	4.0000	10.681	3.1416	6	122.40	36.000	96.13	28.274
1/16	14.463	4.2539	11.359	3.3410	1/16	124.96	36.754	98.15	28.866
1/8	15.353	4.5156	12.058	3.5466	1/8	127.55	37.516	100.18	29.465
3/16	16.270	4.7852	12.778	3.7583	3/16	130.17	38.285	102.23	30.069
1/4	17.213	5.0625	13.519	3.9761	1/4	132.81	39.063	104.31	30.680
5/16	18.182	5.3477	14.280	4.2000	5/16	135.48	39.848	106.41	31.296
3/8	19.178	5.6406	15.062	4.4301	3/8	138.18	40.641	108.53	31.919
7/16	20.201	5.9414	15.866	4.6664	7/16	140.90	41.441	110.66	32.548
1/2	21.250	6.2500	16.690	4.9087	1/2	143.65	42.250	112.82	33.183
9/16	22.326	6.5664	17.534	5.1572	9/16	146.43	43.066	115.00	33.824
5/8	23.428	6.8906	18.400	5.4119	5/8	149.23	43.891	117.20	34.472
11/16	24.557	7.2227	19.287	5.6727	11/16	152.06	44.723	119.43	35.125
3/4	25.713	7.5625	20.195	5.9396	3/4	154.91	45.563	121.67	35.785
13/16	26.895	7.9102	21.123	6.2126	13/16	157.79	46.410	123.93	36.450
7/8	28.103	8.2656	22.072	6.4918	7/8	160.70	47.266	126.22	37.122
15/16	29.338	8.6289	23.042	6.7771	15/16	163.64	48.129	128.52	37.800
3	30.60	9.000	24.03	7.069	7	166.60	49.000	130.85	38.485
1/16	31.89	9.379	25.05	7.366	1/16	169.59	49.879	133.19	39.175
1/8	33.20	9.766	26.08	7.670	1/8	172.60	50.766	135.56	39.871
3/16	34.54	10.160	27.13	7.980	3/16	175.64	51.660	137.95	40.574
1/4	35.91	10.563	28.21	8.296	1/4	178.71	52.563	140.36	41.282
5/16	37.31	10.973	29.30	8.618	5/16	181.81	53.473	142.79	41.997
3/8	38.73	11.391	30.42	8.946	3/8	184.93	54.391	145.24	42.718
7/16	40.18	11.816	31.55	9.281	7/16	188.07	55.316	147.71	43.445
1/2	41.65	12.250	32.71	9.621	1/2	191.25	56.250	150.21	44.179
9/16	43.15	12.691	33.89	9.968	9/16	194.45	57.191	152.72	44.918
5/8	44.68	13.141	35.09	10.321	5/8	197.68	58.141	155.26	45.664
11/16	46.23	13.598	36.31	10.680	11/16	200.93	59.098	157.81	46.415
3/4	47.81	14.063	37.55	11.045	3/4	204.21	60.063	160.39	47.173
13/16	49.42	14.535	38.81	11.416	13/16	207.52	61.035	162.99	47.937
7/8	51.05	15.016	40.10	11.793	7/8	210.85	62.016	165.60	48.707
15/16	52.71	15.504	41.40	12.177	15/16	214.21	63.004	168.24	49.483
4	54.40	16.000	42.73	12.566	8	217.60	64.000	170.90	50.265

Table 72. Pipe

(Steel Construction, 1934, A.I.S.C.)

	Dimensions					Threads per inch	Couplings			Properties		
Nom. Diam., in.	Outside Diam., in.	Inside Diam., in.	Thickness, in.	Weight per Foot, lb Plain Ends	Weight per Foot, lb Thread and Coupling		Outside Diam., in.	Length, in.	Weight, lb	I, in.^{4}	A, in.^{2}	k, in.

						Standard						
1/8	0.405	0.269	0.068	0.24	0.25	27	0.562	7/8	0.03	0.001	0.072	0.12
1/4	0.540	0.364	0.088	0.42	0.43	18	0.685	1	0.04	0.003	0.125	0.16
3/8	0.675	0.493	0.091	0.57	0.57	18	0.848	1 1/8	0.07	0.007	0.167	0.21
1/2	0.840	0.622	0.109	0.85	0.85	14	1.024	1 3/8	0.12	0.017	0.250	0.26
3/4	1.050	0.824	0.113	1.13	1.13	14	1.281	1 5/8	0.21	0.037	0.333	0.33
1	1.315	1.049	0.133	1.68	1.68	11 1/2	1.576	1 7/8	0.35	0.087	0.494	0.42
1 1/4	1.660	1.380	0.140	2.27	2.28	11 1/2	1.950	2 1/8	0.55	0.195	0.669	0.54
1 1/2	1.900	1.610	0.145	2.72	2.73	11 1/2	2.218	2 3/8	0.76	0.310	0.799	0.62
2	2.375	2.067	0.154	3.65	3.68	11 1/2	2.760	2 5/8	1.23	0.666	1.075	0.79
2 1/2	2.875	2.469	0.203	5.79	5.82	8	3.276	2 7/8	1.76	1.530	1.704	0.95
3	3.500	3.068	0.216	7.58	7.62	8	3.948	3 1/8	2.55	3.017	2.228	1.16
3 1/2	4.000	3.548	0.226	9.11	9.20	8	4.591	3 5/8	4.33	4.788	2.680	1.34
4	4.500	4.026	0.237	10.79	10.89	8	5.091	3 5/8	5.41	7.233	3.174	1.51
5	5.563	5.047	0.258	14.62	14.81	8	6.296	4 1/8	9.16	15.16	4.300	1.88
6	6.625	6.065	0.280	18.97	19.19	8	7.358	4 1/8	10.82	28.14	5.581	2.25
8	8.625	8.071	0.277	24.70	25.00	8	9.420	4 5/8	15.84	63.35	7.265	2.95
8	8.625	7.981	0.322	28.55	28.81	8	9.420	4 5/8	15.84	72.49	8.399	2.94
10	10.750	10.192	0.279	31.20	32.00	8	11.721	6 1/8	33.92	125.4	9.178	3.70
10	10.750	10.136	0.307	34.24	35.00	8	11.721	6 1/8	33.92	137.4	10.07	3.69
10	10.750	10.020	0.365	40.48	41.13	8	11.721	6 1/8	33.92	160.7	11.91	3.67
12	12.750	12.090	0.330	43.77	45.00	8	13.958	6 1/8	48.27	248.5	12.88	4.39
12	12.750	12.000	0.375	49.56	50.71	8	13.958	6 1/8	48.27	279.3	14.38	4.38

						Extra Strong						
1/8	0.405	0.215	0.095	0.31	0.32	27	0.582	1 1/8	0.05	0.001	0.093	0.12
1/4	0.540	0.302	0.119	0.54	0.54	18	0.724	1 3/8	0.07	0.004	0.157	0.16
3/8	0.675	0.423	0.126	0.74	0.75	18	0.898	1 5/8	0.13	0.009	0.217	0.20
1/2	0.840	0.546	0.147	1.09	1.10	14	1.085	1 7/8	0.22	0.020	0.320	0.25
3/4	1.050	0.742	0.154	1.47	1.49	14	1.316	2 1/8	0.33	0.045	0.433	0.32
1	1.315	0.957	0.179	2.17	2.20	11 1/2	1.575	2 3/8	0.47	0.106	0.639	0.41
1 1/4	1.660	1.278	0.191	3.00	3.05	11 1/2	2.054	2 7/8	1.04	0.242	0.881	0.52
1 1/2	1.900	1.500	0.200	3.63	3.69	11 1/2	2.294	2 7/8	1.17	0.391	1.068	0.61
2	2.375	1.939	0.218	5.02	5.13	11 1/2	2.870	3 5/8	2.17	0.868	1.477	0.77
2 1/2	2.875	2.323	0.276	7.66	7.83	8	3.389	4 1/8	3.43	1.924	2.254	0.92
3	3.500	2.900	0.300	10.25	10.46	8	4.014	4 1/8	4.13	3.894	3.016	1.14
3 1/2	4.000	3.364	0.318	12.51	12.82	8	4.628	4 5/8	6.29	6.280	3.678	1.31
4	4.500	3.826	0.337	14.98	15.39	8	5.233	4 5/8	8.16	9.610	4.407	1.48
5	5.563	4.813	0.375	20.78	21.42	8	6.420	5 1/8	12.87	20.67	6.112	1.84
6	6.625	5.761	0.432	28.57	29.33	8	7.482	5 1/8	15.18	40.49	8.405	2.20
8	8.625	7.625	0.500	43.39	44.72	8	9.596	6 1/8	26.63	105.7	12.76	2.88
10	10.750	9.750	0.500	54.74	56.94	8	11.958	6 5/8	44.16	211.9	16.10	3.63
12	12.750	11.750	0.500	65.42	68.02	8	13.958	6 5/8	51.99	361.5	19.24	4.34

						Double—Extra Strong						
1/2	0.840	0.252	0.294	1.71	1.73	14	1.085	1 7/8	0.22	0.024	0.504	0.22
3/4	1.050	0.434	0.308	2.44	2.46	14	1.316	2 1/8	0.33	0.058	0.718	0.28
1	1.315	0.599	0.358	3.66	3.68	11 1/2	1.575	2 3/8	0.47	0.140	1.076	0.36
1 1/4	1.660	0.896	0.382	5.21	5.27	11 1/2	2.054	2 7/8	1.04	0.341	1.534	0.47
1 1/2	1.900	1.100	0.400	6.41	6.47	11 1/2	2.294	2 7/8	1.17	0.568	1.885	0.55
2	2.375	1.503	0.436	9.03	9.14	11 1/2	2.870	3 5/8	2.17	1.311	2.656	0.70
2 1/2	2.875	1.771	0.552	13.70	13.87	8	3.389	4 1/8	3.43	2.871	4.028	0.84
3	3.500	2.300	0.600	18.58	18.79	8	4.014	4 1/8	4.13	5.992	5.466	1.05
3 1/2	4.000	2.728	0.636	22.85	23.16	8	4.628	4 5/8	6.29	9.848	6.721	1.21
4	4.500	3.152	0.674	27.54	27.95	8	5.233	4 5/8	8.16	15.28	8.101	1.37
5	5.563	4.063	0.750	38.55	39.20	8	6.420	5 1/8	12.87	33.64	11.34	1.72
6	6.625	4.897	0.864	53.16	53.92	8	7.482	5 1/8	15.18	66.33	15.64	2.06
8	8.625	6.875	0.875	72.42	73.76	8	9.596	6 1/8	26.63	162.0	21.30	2.76

Large O. D. Pipe

Pipe 14″ and larger is sold by actual O. S. diameter and thickness.
Sizes 14″, 15″, and 16″ are available regularly in thicknesses varying by 1/16″ from 1/4″ to 1″, inclusive.
All pipe is furnished random length unless otherwise ordered, viz: 12 to 22 ft with privilege of furnishing 5 per cent in 6 to 12 ft lengths. Pipe railing is most economically detailed with slip joints and random lengths between couplings.

Table 73. Standard Screw Threads

Number or Diameter	Nominal or Major Diameter	Coarse Series			Fine Series			S.A.E. Extra Fine Series	
		Threads per inch	Minor Diameter	Area at Root	Threads per inch	Minor Diameter	Area at Root	Threads per inch	Minor Diameter
1/4	0.2500	20	0.1850	0.0269	28	0.2036	0.0326	36	0.2139
5/16	0.3125	18	0.2403	0.0454	24	0.2584	0.0524	32	0.2719
3/8	0.3750	16	0.2938	0.0678	24	0.3209	0.0809	32	0.3344
7/16	0.4375	14	0.3447	0.0933	20	0.3725	0.1090	28	0.3911
1/2	0.5000	13	0.4001	0.1257	20	0.4350	0.1486	28	0.4536
9/16	0.5625	12	0.4542	0.1620	18	0.4903	0.1888	24	0.5084
5/8	0.6250	11	0.5069	0.2018	18	0.5528	0.2400	24	0.5709
3/4	0.7500	10	0.6201	0.3020	16	0.6688	0.3513	20	0.6850
7/8	0.8750	9	0.7307	0.4193	14	0.7822	0.4805	20	0.8100
1	1.0000	8	0.8376	0.5510	14	0.9072	0.6464	20	0.9350
1 1/8	1.1250	7	0.9394	0.6931	12	1.0167	0.8118	18	1.0528
1 1/4	1.2500	7	1.0644	0.8898	12	1.1417	1.0238	18	1.1778
1 3/8	1.3750	6	1.1585	1.0541	12	1.2667	1.2602		
1 1/2	1.5000	6	1.2835	1.2938	12	1.3917	1.5212	18	1.4278
1 3/4	1.7500	5	1.4902	1.7441	....	....	....	16	1.6778
2	2.0000	4 1/2	1.7113	2.3001	....	....	....	16	1.9278
2 1/4	2.2500	4 1/2	1.9613	3.0212	....	....	....	16	2.1778
2 1/2	2.5000	4	2.1752	3.7161	....	....	....	16	2.4278
2 3/4	2.7500	4	2.4252	4.6194	....	....	....	16	2.6778
3	3.0000	4	2.6752	5.6209	....	....	....	16	2.9278
3 1/4	3.2500	4	2.9252	6.7205	....	....	....		
3 1/2	3.5000	4	3.1752	7.9183	....	....	....	16	3.4278
3 3/4	3.7500	4	3.4252	9.2143	....	....	....		
4	4.0000	4	3.6752	10.6084	....	....	....	16	3.9278

Table 74. A.S.A. Standard Bolts and Nuts

Nominal Size	Unfinished and Semi-finished Bolt Heads					Finished Bolt Heads			Thickness of Nuts		
	Across Flats	Across Square Corners	Across Hex Corners	Thickness Unfinished Head	Thickness Semifinished Head	Across Flats	Across Hex Corners	Thickness Finished Head	Unfinished	Semifinished	Finished
1/4	3/8	0.498	0.414	11/64	5/32	7/16	0.488	3/16	7/32	13/64	7/32
5/16	1/2	0.665	0.552	13/64	3/16	9/16	0.629	15/64	17/64	1/4	17/64
3/8	9/16	0.747	0.620	1/4	15/64	5/8	0.699	9/32	21/64	5/16	21/64
7/16	5/8	0.828	0.687	19/64	9/32	3/4	0.840	21/64	3/8	23/64	3/8
1/2	3/4	0.995	0.827	21/64	19/64	13/16	0.911	3/8	7/16	27/64	7/16
9/16	7/8	1.163	0.966	3/8	11/32	7/8	0.982	27/64	1/2	15/32	1/2
5/8	15/16	1.244	1.033	27/64	25/64	1	1.123	15/32	35/64	17/32	35/64
3/4	1 1/8	1.494	1.240	1/2	15/32	1 1/8	1.263	9/16	21/32	41/64	21/32
7/8	1 5/16	1.742	1.447	19/32	9/16	1 5/16	1.474	21/32	49/64	3/4	49/64
1	1 1/2	1.991	1.653	21/32	19/32	1 1/2	1.686	3/4	7/8	55/64	7/8
1 1/8	1 11/16	2.239	1.859	3/4	11/16	1 11/16	1.898	27/64	1	31/32	1
1 1/4	1 7/8	2.489	2.067	27/32	25/32	1 7/8	2.109	15/16	1 1/32	1 1/32	1 3/32
1 3/8	2 1/16	2.738	2.273	29/32	27/32	2 1/16	2.321	1 1/32	1 13/64	1 9/64	1 13/64
1 1/2	2 1/4	2.986	2.480	1	15/16	2 1/4	2.533	1 1/8	1 5/16	1 1/4	1 5/16
1 5/8	2 7/16	3.235	2.686	1 3/32	1 1/32	2 7/16	2.744	1 7/32	1 27/64	1 23/64	1 27/64
1 3/4	2 5/8	3.485	2.893	1 5/32	1 3/32	2 5/8	2.956	1 5/16	1 17/32	1 15/32	1 17/32
1 7/8	2 13/16	3.733	3.100	1 1/4	1 3/16	2 13/16	3.168	1 13/32	1 41/64	1 37/64	1 41/64
2	3	3.982	3.306	1 11/32	1 7/32	3	3.379	1 1/2	1 3/4	1 11/16	1 3/4
2 1/4	3 3/8	4.480	3.720	1 1/2	1 3/8	3 3/8	3.802	1 11/16	1 31/32	1 29/32	1 31/32
2 1/2	3 3/4	4.977	4.133	1 21/32	1 17/32	3 3/4	4.226	1 7/8	2 3/16	2 3/32	2 3/16
2 3/4	4 1/8	5.476	4.546	1 53/64	1 11/16	4 1/8	4.649	2 1/16	2 13/32	2 5/16	2 13/32
3	4 1/2	5.973	4.959	2	1 7/8	4 1/2	5.072	2 1/4	2 5/8	2 17/32	2 5/8

Table 75. Properties of American Standard Yard Lumber and Timber Sizes

Nominal Size in inches	American Standard Dressed Size, inches	Area of Section, A, sq in.	Weight per lin ft,* W, lb	Moment of Inertia, I, in.^{4}	Section-Modulus, S, in.^{3}
2 × 4	1 5/8 × 3 5/8	5.89	1.6	6.45	3.56
2 × 6	1 5/8 × 5 5/8	9.14	2.5	24.10	8.57
2 × 8	1 5/8 × 7 1/2	12.19	3.4	57.13	15.32
2 × 10	1 5/8 × 9 1/2	15.44	4.3	116.09	24.44
2 × 12	1 5/8 × 11 1/2	18.69	5.2	205.94	35.82
2 × 14	1 5/8 × 13 1/2	23.62	6.5	333.15	49.36
2 × 16	1 5/8 × 15 1/2	25.18	7.0	504.24	65.07
2 × 18	1 5/8 × 17 1/2	28.43	7.9	725.71	82.94
2 × 20	1 5/8 × 19 1/2	31.69	8.8	1,004.05	102.98
3 × 4	2 5/8 × 3 5/8	9.51	2.6	10.42	5.75
3 × 6	2 5/8 × 5 5/8	14.76	4.2	38.93	13.84
3 × 8	2 5/8 × 7 1/2	19.68	5.7	92.28	24.60
3 × 10	2 5/8 × 9 1/2	24.93	7.2	187.55	39.48
3 × 12	2 5/8 × 11 1/2	30.18	8.8	332.69	57.86
3 × 14	2 5/8 × 13 1/2	35.43	10.3	538.21	79.73
3 × 16	2 5/8 × 15 1/2	40.68	11.3	814.60	105.11
3 × 18	2 5/8 × 17 1/2	45.94	12.8	1,172.36	133.98
3 × 20	2 5/8 × 19 1/2	51.19	14.21	1,622.00	166.36
4 × 4	3 5/8 × 3 5/8	13.14	3.6	14.38	7.94
4 × 6	3 5/8 × 5 5/8	20.39	5.7	53.76	19.11
4 × 8	3 5/8 × 7 1/2	27.18	7.5	127.44	33.98
4 × 10	3 5/8 × 9 1/2	34.43	9.6	258.99	54.52
4 × 12	3 5/8 × 11 1/2	41.68	11.6	459.42	79.90
4 × 14	3 5/8 × 13 1/2	48.93	13.6	743.23	110.11
4 × 16	3 5/8 × 15 1/2	56.18	15.6	1,124.90	145.15
4 × 18	3 5/8 × 17 1/2	63.43	17.6	1,618.96	185.02
4 × 20	3 5/8 × 19 1/2	70.69	19.6	2,239.88	229.73
6 × 6	5 1/2 × 5 1/2	30.25	8.4	76.25	27.73
6 × 8	5 1/2 × 7 1/2	41.25	11.4	193.35	51.56
6 × 10	5 1/2 × 9 1/2	52.25	14.5	329.96	82.73
6 × 12	5 1/2 × 11 1/2	63.25	17.5	697.06	121.23
6 × 14	5 1/2 × 13 1/2	74.25	20.6	1,127.66	167.06
6 × 16	5 1/2 × 15 1/2	85.25	23.6	1,706.76	220.22
6 × 18	5 1/2 × 17 1/2	96.25	26.7	2,456.36	280.73
6 × 20	5 1/2 × 19 1/2	107.25	29.8	3,398.46	348.53
6 × 22	5 1/2 × 21 1/2	118.25	32.8	4,555.05	423.76
8 × 8	7 1/2 × 7 1/2	56.25	15.6	263.67	70.31
8 × 10	7 1/2 × 9 1/2	71.25	19.8	535.85	112.81
8 × 12	7 1/2 × 11 1/2	86.25	23.9	950.55	165.31
8 × 14	7 1/2 × 13 1/2	101.25	28.0	1,537.73	227.81
8 × 16	7 1/2 × 15 1/2	116.25	32.0	2,327.42	300.31
8 × 18	7 1/2 × 17 1/2	131.25	36.4	3,349.60	382.81
8 × 20	7 1/2 × 19 1/2	146.25	40.6	4,634.30	475.31
8 × 22	7 1/2 × 21 1/2	161.25	44.8	6,211.48	577.81
8 × 24	7 1/2 × 23 1/2	176.25	48.9	8,111.17	690.31
10 × 10	9 1/2 × 9 1/2	90.25	25.0	678.75	142.89
10 × 12	9 1/2 × 11 1/2	109.25	30.3	1,204.01	209.39
10 × 14	9 1/2 × 13 1/2	128.25	35.6	1,947.78	288.56
10 × 16	9 1/2 × 15 1/2	147.25	40.9	2,948.04	380.39
10 × 18	9 1/2 × 17 1/2	166.25	46.1	4,242.80	484.89

* Based on assumed average weight of 40 lb per cu ft

Table 75.   Properties of American Standard Yard Lumber and Timber Sizes—*Continued*

Nominal Size in inches	American Standard Dressed Size, inches	Area of Section, A, sq in.	Weight per lin ft,* W, lb	Moment of Inertia, I, in.^{4}	Section-Modulus, S, in.^{3}
10 × 20	9 1/2 × 19 1/2	185.25	51.4	5,870.05	602.06
10 × 22	9 1/2 × 21 1/2	204.25	56.7	7,867.81	731.89
10 × 24	9 1/2 × 23 1/2	223.25	62.0	10,274.06	874.39
10 × 26	9 1/2 × 25 1/2	242.25	67.3	13,126.81	1029.56
10 × 28	9 1/2 × 27 1/2	261.25	72.5	16,465.24	1197.39
10 × 30	9 1/2 × 29 1/2	280.25	77.8	20,323.79	1377.89
12 × 12	11 1/2 × 11 1/2	132.25	36.7	1,457.50	253.47
12 × 14	11 1/2 × 13 1/2	155.25	43.1	2,357.85	349.31
12 × 16	11 1/2 × 15 1/2	178.25	49.5	3,568.70	460.48
12 × 18	11 1/2 × 17 1/2	201.25	55.9	5,136.49	586.98
12 × 20	11 1/2 × 19 1/2	224.25	62.3	7,105.90	728.81
12 × 22	11 1/2 × 21 1/2	247.25	68.7	9,524.24	885.98
12 × 24	11 1/2 × 23 1/2	270.25	75.0	12,437.08	1058.47
12 × 26	11 1/2 × 25 1/2	293.25	81.4	15,890.42	1246.31
12 × 28	11 1/2 × 27 1/2	316.25	87.8	19,932.58	1449.47
12 × 30	11 1/2 × 29 1/2	339.25	94.2	24,602.61	1667.97
14 × 14	13 1/2 × 13 1/2	182.25	50.6	2,767.92	410.06
14 × 16	13 1/2 × 15 1/2	209.25	58.1	4,189.36	540.56
14 × 18	13 1/2 × 17 1/2	236.25	65.6	6,029.29	689.06
14 × 20	13 1/2 × 19 1/2	263.25	73.1	8,341.73	855.56
14 × 22	13 1/2 × 21 1/2	290.25	80.6	11,180.67	1040.06
14 × 24	13 1/2 × 23 1/2	317.25	88.1	14,600.10	1242.56
14 × 26	13 1/2 × 25 1/2	344.25	95.6	18,654.04	1463.06
14 × 28	13 1/2 × 27 1/2	371.25	103.1	23,398.73	1701.56
14 × 30	13 1/2 × 29 1/2	398.25	110.6	28,881.42	1958.06
16 × 16	15 1/2 × 15 1/2	240.25	66.7	4,809.98	620.64
16 × 18	15 1/2 × 17 1/2	271.25	75.3	6,922.49	791.14
16 × 20	15 1/2 × 19 1/2	302.25	83.9	9,577.50	982.31
16 × 22	15 1/2 × 21 1/2	333.25	92.5	12,837.00	1194.14
16 × 24	15 1/2 × 23 1/2	364.25	101.2	16,763.00	1426.64
16 × 26	15 1/2 × 25 1/2	395.25	109.8	21,417.50	1679.81
16 × 28	15 1/2 × 27 1/2	426.25	118.4	26,863.78	1953.64
16 × 30	15 1/2 × 29 1/2	457.25	127.0	33,159.98	2248.14
18 × 18	17 1/2 × 17 1/2	306.25	85.0	7,815.73	893.23
18 × 20	17 1/2 × 19 1/2	341.25	94.8	10,813.33	1109.06
18 × 22	17 1/2 × 21 1/2	376.25	104.5	14,493.43	1348.23
18 × 24	17 1/2 × 23 1/2	411.25	114.2	18,926.02	1610.72
18 × 26	17 1/2 × 25 1/2	446.25	123.9	24,181.11	1896.56
18 × 28	17 1/2 × 27 1/2	481.25	133.7	30,331.62	2205.72
18 × 30	17 1/2 × 29 1/2	516.25	143.4	37,438.79	2538.22
20 × 20	19 1/2 × 19 1/2	380.25	105.6	12,049.49	1235.81
20 × 22	19 1/2 × 21 1/2	419.25	116.4	16,149.86	1502.31
20 × 24	19 1/2 × 23 1/2	458.25	127.3	21,089.04	1794.81
20 × 26	19 1/2 × 25 1/2	497.25	138.1	26,944.73	2113.31
20 × 28	19 /2 × 27 1/2	536.25	148.9	33,798.17	2457.81
20 × 30	19 1/2 × 29 1/2	575.25	159.8	41,717.61	2828.31
24 × 24	23 1/2 × 23 1/2	552.25	153.4	25,414.96	2162.97
24 × 26	23 1/2 × 25 1/2	599.25	166.4	32,471.80	2546.81
24 × 28	23 1/2 × 27 1/2	646.25	179.5	40,731.06	2916.97
24 × 30	23 1/2 × 29 1/2	693.25	192.5	50,274.98	3408.47

* Based on assumed average weight of 40 lb per cu ft

SECTION 2

MATHEMATICS

BY

J. L. BARNES

IN COLLABORATION WITH

J. G. BRAINERD, C. EISENHART, M. J. FISH, AND J. M. RICE

The authors and editor gratefully acknowledge the kindness of the editors of previous handbooks, published by John Wiley and Sons, in permitting the use of illustrations and material from those issues.

MATHEMATICS

Notation

A Symbol is a letter or sign used to represent a mathematical entity such as a numerical value or an operation. The *notation* for symbols used in this section follows in general the American Standard for Mathematical Symbols (A.E.S.C. report Z 10 f) and (for elementary subjects) the recommendations of the Math. Assoc. of America (Report of Nat. Com., 1923, Chapter 8). The names of letters taken from the Greek alphabet may be found in Table 1, Section 1, and standard mathematical symbols in Table 2, Section 1.

An Abbreviation, as distinguished from a symbol, is a shortened expression for a name or a unit. Abbreviations for engineering terms may be found in Table 3, Section 1. (See also A.S.A. report Z 10 i.)

ARITHMETIC

By Janvier M. Rice

1. NUMBER NOTATION

Notation. Numbers are expressed by *words* and represented by *figure* or *letter* characters. The *figure notation* in common use is the *Arabic,* so called because it was first introduced into Europe by the Arabs. The common *letter notation* is named from the ancient Romans who used it.

Numeration of Arabic Numbers. Any method of naming numbers is called *numeration*. The method in common use is a decimal system in which the figures or *digits* are separated by commas into groups of three figures each, called periods. For example, the number 1,211,024,006,357.089 is read, " one *trillion,* two hundred eleven *billion,* twenty-four *million,* six *thousand,* three hundred fifty-seven, and eighty-nine *thousandths.*"

A whole number is called an *integer.* A number expressed by an *integer* and *fraction* is a *mixed number.*

Roman Notation uses seven letters and a bar; a letter with a bar placed over it represents a thousand times as much as it does without the bar. The letters and rules for combining them to represent numbers are as follows:

I	V	X	L	C	D	M	$\overline{\text{L}}$
1	5	10	50	100	500	1000	50,000

Rule 1. If no letter precedes a letter of greater value, add the numbers represented by the letters.

Example: XXX represents 30; VI represents 6.

Rule 2. If a letter precedes a letter of greater value, subtract the smaller from the greater; add the remainder or remainders thus obtained to the numbers represented by the other letters.

Example: IV represents 4; XL represents 40; CXLV represents 145.

Other Illustrations:

IX	XIII	XIV	LV	XLII	XCVI	MDCI	$\overline{\text{IV}}$CCXL
9	13	14	55	42	96	1601	4240

2. FUNDAMENTAL PROCESSES AND TERMS

Addition is indicated by the sign +, which is read *plus.* The numbers added are called *addends.* The result is called the *sum.*

Subtraction is indicated by the sign −, which is read *minus.* The number subtracted is called the *subtrahend,* and the number from which it is subtracted the *minuend.* The result is called the *remainder* or *difference.*

Multiplication is indicated by the sign $\times$, which is read *times* or *multiplied by*. The number multiplied is called the *multiplicand*, and the number by which it is multiplied, the *multiplier*. The result is called the *product*.

Division is indicated by the sign $\div$, which is read *divided by*. The number divided is called the *dividend*, and the number by which it is divided the *divisor*. The result is called the *quotient*.

The process of division may be indicated also by a *fraction*, the *numerator* of which is the dividend and the *denominator* the divisor.

If the quotient is an *integer* the division is *exact*. If the division is not exact, the part of the dividend that is left is called the *remainder*.

Reciprocals. The reciprocal of a number is 1 divided by the number and, unless the division is exact, may be expressed as a fraction, decimal, or mixed number. Thus the reciprocal of 4 is $1/4$ or 0.25. If tables are available, use of reciprocals saves the labor of division if long divisors are involved, as the same result can be obtained by multiplying the dividend by the reciprocal of the divisor. Reciprocals of numbers may be found in Table 7, Section 1.

Percentage. *Per cent* means " by the hundred." To determine the per cent change in a quantity, divide the change in number of units by the original number of units and multiply by 100. For example, if an article costing 80 cents is sold for one dollar, the profit is 20 cents, or 25 per cent of the cost; if it is sold instead for 68 cents, the loss is 12 cents or 15 per cent of the cost.

Combination of Processes. If either $\times$ or $\div$ occurs in an expression in connection with $+$, $-$, or both, the indicated *multiplications* or *divisions* are to be performed first. If both $\times$ and $\div$ occur and are succeeding signs in any expression, the indicated multiplications and divisions are performed in order from the left. For example:

$$3 + 10 \div 2 \times 4 - 1 = 3 + 5 \times 4 - 1 = 3 + 20 - 1 = 22$$

To avoid confusion, *parentheses* ( ), *brackets* [ ], *braces* {}, and the *vinculum* $\overline{}$, are used as *signs of aggregation* in grouping expressions. Each group being regarded as a single number, operations within groups should be performed first. For example:

$$2 \times \{[10 \div (3 - 1)] + 4 \div \overline{3 - 1}\} = 2 \times \{5 + 4 \div 2\} = 2 \times 7 = 14$$

Factors and Divisors. Integers that multiplied together produce a given number are called *factors* of the number. A whole number that has no factors other than 1 and the number itself is a *prime number.* A number that has factors other than 1 and itself is called a *composite number.*

Integers which are factors of an integer are also called *exact divisors.*

The process of separating a number into its factors is called *factoring.*

Factorials. The multiple product $n(n - 1)(n - 2) \ldots 3 \times 2 \times 1$ is called *factorial n* and written $n!$ Values of $n!$ up to those of 20! are given in Table 6, Section 1.

Greatest Common Divisor. If two or more numbers are divisible by the same number, they are said to have a *common divisor.* The greatest number that will exactly divide all of them is called their greatest common divisor (G.C.D.).

Least Common Multiple. A number that is divisible by each of two or more numbers is a *common multiple* of those numbers. The least number satisfying this condition of divisibility is the *least common multiple* of the numbers (L.C.M.).

Fractions having the same denominator are called *similar* fractions, and those having different denominators *dissimilar* fractions. In adding dissimilar fractions, find the L.C.M. of the denominators, called the *least common denominator*, and change the given fractions to similar fractions having this denominator.

Powers and Roots. A *power* of a number is a product obtained by using the number a certain number of times as a factor. The number of times the number occurs as a factor is called the exponent, and is written at the right of the number and a little above. For example, the second power or square of 3 is 9 and is written $3^2 = 9$. Likewise, the third power or cube of 3 is 27 and is written $3^3 = 27$.

One of the equal factors of a number is called the *root* of the number. In the example above, 3 is the *square root* of 9 and the *cube root* of 27.

The process of finding the root of a number may be indicated by the radical sign or by a fractional exponent of the number.

Example: $9^{1/2} = \sqrt{9} = 3$, $8^{1/3} = \sqrt[3]{8} = 2.$

3. SQUARE ROOT AND CUBE ROOT

To Extract the Square Root. (1) Point off the given number into periods of two figures each, starting at the decimal point and going both ways.

(2) Find the largest square in the left-hand period and use its root as the first digit of the result; subtract the square from the left-hand period and to the remainder annex the next period for a new dividend.

(3) Double the root already found and annex one zero for a trial-divisor; determine how many times it will go into the dividend, and put the number in the result and also in place of the zero in the divisor. Multiply this completed divisor by the number just placed in the result, subtract the product from the dividend, and to the remainder bring down the next period for a new dividend and proceed as before.

(4) If at any time the product of a new figure in the result by the " completed " divisor is greater than the dividend, erase the new figure from both the result and the divisor, substituting a figure just small enough to make the product of the new figure of the result by the divisor less than or equal to the dividend. If at any time a divisor is not contained in the dividend even once, bring down the next period for a new dividend, annex another zero to the trial divisor, put a zero in the quotient and proceed in the regular manner.

Example:

$$\begin{array}{r|l}
& 3'02.'98'06'52' \underline{|\ 17.406\ +} \\
& 1 \\ \hline
27 & 202 \\
& 189 \\ \hline
344 & 1398 \\
& 1376 \\ \hline
34806 & 220652 \\
& 208836
\end{array}$$

To Extract the Cube Root. (1) Point off the given number into periods of three figures, each starting at the decimal point and going both ways.

(2) Find the largest cube in the left-hand period and use its root as the first digit of the result; subtract the cube from the left-hand period and to the remainder annex the next period for a new dividend; square the root already found and multiply by 300 for a trial divisor. Find how many times this trial divisor is contained in the dividend and write the number in the root.

(3) Add together the trial divisor, 30 times the product of the first figure of the root by the second, and the square of the second figure in the root; multiply the sum (which is the completed divisor) by the last figure in the root, and subtract from the dividend.

(4) To the remainder annex the next period and proceed as before to find the third figure of the root—that is, square the two figures of the root already found, multiply by 300 for a trial divisor, etc.

(5) If at any time the product of a new figure in the root by the " completed" divisor is greater than the dividend, erase the new figure from the result and from wherever it appeared in obtaining the divisor, substituting a figure just small enough to make the product of the new figure of the result by the divisor less than or equal to the dividend. If at any time a divisor does not go into the dividend even once, write a zero in the root, annex the next period to the dividend, and proceed in the regular manner.

Example:

$$\begin{array}{r|l}
& 158'252'.632'929 \underline{|\ 54.09} \\
5^3 = & 125 \\ \hline
300 \times 5^2 = 7500 & 33252 \\
30 \times 5 \times 4 = 600 & \\
4^2 = 16 & \\ \hline
8116 & 32464 \\ \hline
300 \times 540^2 = 87480000 & 788632929 \\
30 \times 540 \times 9 = 145800 & \\
9^2 = 81 & \\ \hline
87625881 & 788632929
\end{array}$$

Tables of Square Roots and Cube Roots, as well as squares and cubes, of integers from 1 to 1000 are given in Table 7, Section 1.

To Extract Any Root other than the square root or cube root (and frequently for the latter), logarithms are generally employed. See p. 2–10.

4. APPROXIMATE COMPUTATIONS

Significant Figures

Numerical engineering data are subject to errors of various kinds and should be written so that no ambiguity can exist as to the significance of the figures. In the number 0.002953 it would naturally be understood that four *significant figures*, 2, 9, 5, 3, are intended. In 2,953,000, however, it should be made clear whether the three zeros are in doubt or not. Frequently powers of 10 are used as factors to bring significant figures into prominence. Thus 2,953,000 might be written 2953×10^3; however, this notation does not *necessarily* imply that only the four digits at the left are significant, as this method is sometimes used only to conserve space.

Addition and Subtraction. A doubtful figure in any of the numbers makes the sum or difference in the column in which it lies doubtful. Retain significant figures in the result for only those columns in which all figures are significant. In the example, doubtful figures are indicated by the symbol x.

2.953xx
0.8942x
0.06483
3.912xx

Multiplication. It is convenient to arrange the work so that the figures of the multiplier are used from left to right, since doubtful figures are thus displayed prominently to the right of the vertical line. It is unnecessary to write the doubtful figures. The operation may be abbreviated by dropping the right-hand figures of the multiplicand one by one as multiplication is completed by successive figures of the multiplier, making proper allowance for so doing in the products.

2,953	
4,128	
11,812	
295	3
59	06
23	624
12,19x	xxx

Division. Work may be much abbreviated for numbers with limited significant figures by cutting off one figure of the divisor at each division, instead of adding a doubtful zero from the dividend to the remainder. This method gives rise to no loss in accuracy, and leads quickly to the desired result.

```
4128) 12190 (2
      8256
 413)  3934 (9
       3717
  41)   217 (5
        205
   4)    12 (3
```

Errors

A definite number of significant figures is usually implied in a numerical table. The last right-hand digit may be in error as much as half a unit. Therefore, in adding numbers taken from a table, errors may accumulate. The last right-hand digit may thus be in error several units, and this fact should be noted carefully in any computation. Similar observations apply to other operations of arithmetic. In general, the result obtained by computing with numerical tables of, say, four significant figures cannot be depended upon beyond three significant figures. Hence to reach a desired degree of accuracy it is essential to carry along one extra figure up to the last step.

The Absolute Error in any approximation is the actual difference between the approximate and the exact value. The limits between which the absolute error lies are usually all that is known of its magnitude. Thus if we take $\sqrt{7} = 2.646$, absolute error lies between $- 0.0005$ and $+ 0.0005$ (inclusive), i.e., is numerically $\leqq 0.0005$.

The Relative Error is the ratio of absolute error to exact value. Usually in any given case an upper limit only of the relative error is known. Thus, the relative error in $\sqrt{7} = 2.646$ is less than or equal to " 1 part in 2×2646."

The Probable Error is that error which is equally likely to be, or not to be, exceeded. Thus for the tabular value of $\sqrt{7} = 2.646$ with an absolute error lying numerically between 0 and 0.0005, the probable error is 0.00025. An interpolated value has a greater probable error owing to the inaccuracy of the fundamental assumption for interpolation (see below).

Simple Theorems on Errors.

(1) In a sum or difference, the absolute error of the result is not greater than the sum of the absolute errors of the given terms.

(2) In a product or quotient, the relative error of the result is not greater than the sum of the relative errors of the terms (practically).

Interpolation in Tables

It is often convenient to consult tables for values which are not directly given, but which may be found by *interpolation by first differences*, as illustrated below. The principle is the same, regardless of the nature of the data involved.

Example: Table 7, Section 1, gives $\sqrt{160} = 12.6491$ and $\sqrt{161} = 12.6886$. Suppose $\sqrt{160.3}$ to be desired. The square root has increased 0.0395 for an increase of 1 unit in the number. Interpolation is based on the *assumption* (not strictly correct) that a change in the number amounting to a fraction of a unit changes its function (in this case the square root) by the same fractional amount of its corresponding total change.* On this basis, $\sqrt{160.3} = 12.6491 + (0.0395 \times 0.3) = 12.6610$.

ALGEBRA

By Janvier M. Rice

5. NUMBERS

Classification of Numbers. The following are examples of number classifications: *positive integers*, 1, 2, 3; *negative integers*, -1, -2, -3; *integers*, all positive and negative integers and zero; *fractions*, $1/3$, $-5/2$; *rational numbers*, i.e., those which can be expressed as the quotient of two integers, as $3/5$, $\sqrt[3]{-1/27}$; *irrational numbers*, i.e., those which cannot be expressed as the quotient of two integers, as $\sqrt{2}$, π; *real numbers*, i.e., those which are not complex or purely imaginary (see below); *imaginary numbers*, i.e., even roots of negative numbers, as $\sqrt[4]{-3}$, $\sqrt{-1}$ (the symbol i is used for $\sqrt{-1}$) †; *complex numbers* i.e., combinations of real and imaginary numbers, as $(2 + 3\sqrt{-1}) = (2 + 3i)$.

The Absolute Value of a Number is its numerical value without regard to sign, as absolute value of -3 is 3 and is written $|-3|$.

6. FUNDAMENTAL OPERATIONS

Symbols of Operation and Grouping are the same in algebra as in arithmetic except that the omission of a symbol in algebra indicates multiplication whereas in arithmetic it indicates addition. Thus $2\,a/b$ means $2 \times a/b$, whereas $2\,3/7$ means $2 + 3/7$.

Grouping. If an expression within parentheses is preceded by a plus sign, the parentheses may be removed. If an expression within parentheses is preceded by a minus sign, the parentheses may be removed if the sign of every term within them is changed. Thus, $2 + (a - b) = 2 + a - b$; and $2 - (a - b) = 2 - a + b$. If parentheses occur within parentheses, these may be removed, in succession, by removing first the innermost parentheses; next, the innermost of all that remain, and so on. Thus:

$$a - [6 + c - (d + 3)] = a - [6 + c - d - 3] = a - [3 + c - d] = a - 3 - c + d$$

Parentheses may be introduced, if desired, by reversing the process.

Addition and Subtraction. Like terms should be combined; the others are simply repeated, preceded by their proper signs. Thus:

$$- 2\,ax + 4\,z - (c - 5\,ax + 3\,z) = 3\,ax + z - c$$

Similarly, polynomials are added or subtracted by combining their respective terms.

Thus, to add $m^5 - 3\,m^4n - 6\,m^3n^2$, $+ m^3n^2 + m^2n^3 - 5\,m^4n$, and $- n^5 + 2\,m^5 + 7\,m^4n$, write:

$$
\begin{array}{l}
+ \quad m^5 - 3\,m^4n - 6\,m^3n^2 \\
\quad\quad\quad - 5\,m^4n + \quad m^3n^2 + m^2n^3 \\
\underline{+ 2\,m^5 + 7\,m^4n \quad\quad\quad\quad\quad\quad - n^5} \\
+ 3\,m^5 - \quad m^4n - 5\,m^3n^2 + m^2n^3 - n^5
\end{array}
$$

Or for subtraction:

$$(a^3x^2 + 2\,a^2x^3 - 4\,ax^4) - (a^5 + 4\,a^3x^2 - 3\,a^2x^3 - 4\,ax^4) =$$
$$a^3x^2 + 2\,a^2x^3 - 4\,ax^4 - a^5 - 4\,a^3x^2 + 3\,a^2x^3 + 4\,ax^4 = - a^5 - 3\,a^3x^2 + 5\,a^2x^3$$

---

* This procedure is known as "interpolation by first differences." If a more accurate result is necessary, and the accuracy of the tabulated data so warrants, "interpolation by differences of higher order" may be employed. (See Smithsonian Mathematical Tables or an advanced algebra book.)

† Electrical engineers generally use j instead of i for $\sqrt{-1}$ to avoid confusion with use of i for current.

Powers and Roots. The notation a^n denotes the nth power of a, even if the exponent n is negative or fractional. If no exponent is shown, 1 is understood. Rules for powers are: $(+a)^n = +a^n$; $(-a)^n = +a^n$ if n is an even integer and $-a^n$ if n is odd; $(a^m)^n = a^{mn}$; $a^{-n} = 1/a^n$; $a^0 = 1$; $0^a = 0$; $a^m \times a^n = a^{m+n}$; $a^m/a^n = a^{m-n}$; $(ab)^n = a^n b^n$; $\left(\dfrac{a}{b}\right)^n = \dfrac{a^n}{b^n}$.

The notation $a^{1/n}$ or $\sqrt[n]{a}$ denotes the nth root of a; n is called the index of the root. An even real root of a positive number is positive or negative, and an odd real root is positive; an odd real root of a negative number is negative, and all even roots are complex or purely imaginary. Also $a^{m/n} = \left(\sqrt[n]{a}\right)^m = \sqrt[n]{a^m}$.

Operations with radicals are performed by changing to exponents.

Example: $\sqrt{2} \times \sqrt[3]{3} = 2^{1/2} \times 3^{1/3} = 2^{3/6} \times 3^{2/6} = (2^3)^{1/6} \times (3^2)^{1/6} = 8^{1/6} \times 9^{1/6} = 72^{1/6} = \sqrt[6]{72}$.

Division by radicals may be avoided by *rationalizing*.

Example: To compute $\dfrac{\sqrt{3} + \sqrt{2}}{\sqrt{5} - \sqrt{3}}$, multiply numerator and denominator by $\sqrt{5} + \sqrt{3}$. This rationalizes the denominator, for $(\sqrt{5} - \sqrt{3})(\sqrt{5} + \sqrt{3}) = 5 - 3 = 2$, hence the value $1/2$ $(\sqrt{3} + \sqrt{2})(\sqrt{5} + \sqrt{3}) = 1/2\,(3 + \sqrt{6} + \sqrt{10} + \sqrt{15})$.

The symbol i denotes $\sqrt{-1}$, which is the imaginary unit. If a is positive and n even, then $(-a)^{1/n} = a^{1/n}i$. Powers of i are $i^2 = -1$, $i^3 = -\sqrt{-1}$, $i^4 = +1$, etc. A complex quantity is the sum of a real and an imaginary quantity, as $a + ib$.

Multiplication. To find the product of monomials, multiply the product of the literal factors by the product of the numerical factors. The product is positive if all the factors are positive or if an even number of them are negative; it is negative if an odd number of them are negative.

Thus: $4\,a \times 3\,c = +12\,ac$; $4\,a \times (-3\,c) = -12\,ac$; $-4\,a \times (-3\,c) = +12\,ac$; $a^2 \times a^3 = a^5$; $4\,a^2c \times ac^3 = 4\,a^3c^4$; $6\,ab^2y^3 \times 2\,b^3y^3 \times (-5a^2y) = -60\,a^3b^5y^7$.

To multiply two polynomials, multiply each term of one factor by each term of the other factor and add the partial products.

Thus, to multiply $(-a^3 + 2\,a^2b - b^3)$ by $(+4\,a^2 + 8\,ab)$, the operation may be arranged and carried out thus:

$$
\begin{array}{l}
\quad -a^3 + 2\,a^2b - b^3 \\
\quad\ 4\,a^2 + 8\,ab \\
\hline
-4\,a^5 + 8\,a^4b - 4\,a^2b^3 \\
\quad\ -8\,a^4b \qquad\qquad + 16\,a^3b^2 - 8\,ab^4 \\
\hline
-4\,a^5 \qquad\quad -4\,a^2b^3 + 16\,a^3b^2 - 8\,ab^4
\end{array}
$$

If $ab = 0$, either a or b or both $= 0$.

Division. To find the quotient of monomials, multiply the quotient of the literal factors by the quotient of the numerical factors. The quotient is positive if dividend and divisor have like signs; it is negative if dividend and divisor have unlike signs.

Thus: $\dfrac{-12\,ac}{4a} = -3c$; $\dfrac{a^5}{a^2} = a^3$; $\dfrac{-60\,a^3b^5y^7}{-5a^2y} = 12\,ab^5y^6$.

To divide a polynomial by a polynomial, arrange both dividend and divisor according to ascending or descending powers of some common letter, and keep this order throughout the operation. Arrange the computation thus: Dividend$\left|\dfrac{\text{Divisor}}{\text{Quotient}}\right.$. Divide the first term of the dividend by the first term of the divisor and write the result as the first term of the quotient. Multiply all terms of the divisor by the first term of the quotient. Subtract the product from the dividend. If there is a remainder, consider it as a new dividend and proceed as before.

Thus: $(22\,a^2b^2 + 15\,b^4 + 3\,a^4 - 10\,a^3b - 22\,ab^3) \div (a^2 + 3\,b^2 - 2\,ab)$

$$
\begin{array}{l}
3\,a^4 - 10\,a^3b + 22\,a^2b^2 - 22\,ab^3 + 15\,b^4 \quad\big|\ a^2 - 2\,ab + 3\,b^2 \\
3\,a^4 -\ 6\,a^3b +\ 9\,a^2b^2 \qquad\qquad\qquad\qquad \overline{\ 3\,a^2 - 4\,ab + 5\,b^2} \\
\hline
\quad -4\,a^3b + 13\,a^2b^2 - 22\,ab^3 \\
\quad -4\,a^3b +\ 8\,a^2b^2 - 12\,ab^3 \\
\hline
\qquad\qquad\ 5\,a^2b^2 - 10\,ab^3 + 15\,b^4 \\
\qquad\qquad\ 5\,a^2b^2 - 10\,ab^3 + 15\,b^4
\end{array}
$$

The quotient is $(3\,a^2 - 4\,ab + 5\,b^2)$.

Division by 0 is not permissible, and care must be exercised in algebraic computations that this error has not been unwittingly committed.

Useful Identities * obtained by multiplication or division include:

$(a \pm b)^2 = a^2 \pm 2\,ab + b^2$

$(a + b)(a - b) = a^2 - b^2$

$(a + b)(x + y) = ax + ay + bx + by$

$(a + b + c)^2 = a^2 + b^2 + c^2 + 2\,ab + 2\,ac + 2\,bc$

$(a^n - b^n) \div (a - b) = a^{n-1} + a^{n-2}b + a^{n-3}b^2 + \ldots + a\,b^{n-2} + b^{n-1}$ (if $a \neq b$)

$(a^n + b^n) \div (a + b) = a^{n-1} - a^{n-2}b + a^{n-3}b^2 - \ldots - a\,b^{n-2} + b^{n-1}$ (if n is odd)

$(a^n - b^n) \div (a + b) = a^{n-1} - a^{n-2}b + a^{n-2}b^2 - \ldots + a\,b^{n-2} - b^{n-1}$ (if n is even)

Factoring is the process of finding two or more expressions the product of which is equal to a given expression. The general procedure in factoring polynomials is first to factor out any monomial common to each term and then to treat the remaining polynomial by such processes as:

(1) Comparison with known identities such as those listed above.

Example: $x^2y - 4\,y^3 = y\,(x^2 - 4\,y^2) = y\,(x + 2\,y)(x - 2\,y)$.

(2) Use of the theorem: $x^2 + bx + c = (x + p)(x + q)$ if p and q are two numbers the sum of which is b and the product c.

Example: Given $x^2 - x - 6$. Since $(-3) + (2) = -1$ and $(-3) \times (2) = -6$, $p = -3$ and $q = 2$; hence $x^2 - x - 6 = (x - 3)(x + 2)$.

(3) Use of the theorem: If r is a root of $f(x) = 0$ (see p. 2–14), $(x - r)$ is a factor of $f(x)$.

Example: Given $2\,x^2 - 2\,x - 12$. By formula (p. 2–13), the roots of $2\,x^2 - 2\,x - 12 = 0$ are 3 and (-2); therefore $(x - 3)$ and $(x + 2)$ are factors and $2x^2 - 2x - 12 = 2\,(x - 3)(x + 2)$.

7. RATIONAL FRACTIONS

Fundamental Laws applying to fractions are illustrated by the following equalities:

Signs. $+\dfrac{a}{b} = \dfrac{-a}{-b} = -\dfrac{-a}{b} = -\dfrac{a}{-b}$.

Addition and Subtraction. $\dfrac{a}{c} \pm \dfrac{b}{d} = \dfrac{ad \pm bc}{cd}$; $\dfrac{a}{c} \pm \dfrac{b}{c} = \dfrac{a \pm b}{c}$; $\dfrac{a}{c} \pm \dfrac{a}{d} = \dfrac{a(d \pm c)}{cd}$. To combine several fractions, use their least common denominator. Thus:

$$\frac{a}{def} + \frac{b}{e^3g} - \frac{c}{df^2} = \frac{ae^2fg + bdf^2 - ce^3g}{de^3f^2g}.$$

Multiplication. $\dfrac{a}{b} \times \dfrac{c}{d} = \dfrac{ac}{bd}$; $\dfrac{a}{b} = \dfrac{ac}{bc}$.

Division. $\dfrac{a}{b} \div \dfrac{c}{d} = \dfrac{a}{b} \times \dfrac{d}{c} = \dfrac{ad}{bc}$; $\dfrac{a}{b} = \dfrac{a \div c}{b \div c}$.

Powers and Roots. $\dfrac{a^n}{b^n} = \left(\dfrac{a}{b}\right)^n = \left(\dfrac{b}{a}\right)^{-n} = \dfrac{b^{-n}}{a^{-n}}$ (whether n is an integer or fraction);

$\left(\dfrac{a}{b}\right)^{m/n} = \left(\sqrt[n]{\dfrac{a}{b}}\right)^m = \sqrt[n]{\left(\dfrac{a}{b}\right)^m}$.

Partial Fractions

Decomposition of a Proper Fraction † into its simplest partial fractions can be accomplished by application of the following rule, where the denominator of the given fraction contains factors prime to each other (except that one or more of them may be repeated).

Rule: Set up partial fractions in accordance with the procedure given under the appropriate case (or cases) below. These partial fractions contain unknown constants. Since the equality between the given fraction and the partial fractions is an identity, the constants can be determined by equating coefficients of like powers of the variable appearing in the two members (i.e., using the method of undetermined coefficients). The latter step can sometimes be simplified by short-cut substitution methods.

---

* An *identity* is an identical equality of two expressions; that is, an equality which holds true for *all* values of the symbols.

† A *proper fraction* is one in which the numerator is of lower degree than the denominator. An *improper fraction* (for which the reverse is true) may readily be reduced, by dividing the numerator by the denominator, to give the sum of an integral part and a proper fraction.

Case I: If the denominator can be resolved into real linear factors $(P, Q, R \ldots)$, all of which are different, let $\dfrac{\text{Num}}{PQR\ldots} = \dfrac{A}{P} + \dfrac{B}{Q} + \dfrac{C}{R} + \ldots$

Example: $\dfrac{6x^2 - x + 1}{x^3 - x} = \dfrac{A}{x} + \dfrac{B}{x-1} + \dfrac{C}{x+1}$. Clearing of fractions,

$$6x^2 - x + 1 = A(x-1)(x+1) + Bx(x+1) + Cx(x-1)$$

As this equality is an identity, it is true for all values of x. Letting $x = 0$, $A = -1$; letting $x = 1$, $B = 3$; letting $x = -1$, $C = 4$. Hence, $\dfrac{6x^2 - x + 1}{x^3 - x} = -\dfrac{1}{x} + \dfrac{3}{x-1} + \dfrac{4}{x+1}$.

Or, using the method of undetermined coefficients, the identity may be written:
$$6x^2 - x + 1 = (A + B + C)x^2 + (B - C)x - A.$$
Then, $A + B + C = 6$; $B - C = -1$; $-A = 1$, and solving simultaneously, $A = -1$, $B = 3$, $C = 4$, as before.

Case II: If the denominator can be resolved into real linear factors $(P, Q \ldots)$, one or more of which are repeated, let $\dfrac{\text{Num}}{P^2 Q^3 \ldots} = \dfrac{A}{P} + \dfrac{B}{P^2} + \dfrac{C}{Q} + \dfrac{D}{Q^2} + \dfrac{E}{Q^3} + \ldots$

Example: $\dfrac{x+1}{x(x-1)^3} = \dfrac{A}{x} + \dfrac{B}{x-1} + \dfrac{C}{(x-1)^2} + \dfrac{D}{(x-1)^3}$. Clearing of fractions,
$$x + 1 = A(x-1)^3 + Bx(x-1)^2 + Cx(x-1) + Dx$$
Determine the constants by methods illustrated in the example under *Case I*. Constants A and D can be obtained quickly by the substitution method, but for B and C the method of undetermined coefficients should be used after simplifying the identity by substituting the numerical values of A and D, collecting terms, etc.

Case III: If the denominator contains quadratic factors $(P, Q \ldots)$ which cannot be separated into real linear factors and all of which are different, let

$$\dfrac{\text{Num}}{PQ\ldots} = \dfrac{Ax + B}{P} + \dfrac{Cx + D}{Q} + \ldots$$

Example: $\dfrac{3x^2 - 2}{(x^2 + x + 1)(x + 1)} = \dfrac{Ax + B}{x^2 + x + 1} + \dfrac{C}{x + 1}$. Clearing of fractions,
$$3x^2 - 2 = (Ax + B)(x + 1) + C(x^2 + x + 1)$$
$$= (A + C)x^2 + (A + B + C)x + (B + C)$$
Equate coefficients of like powers of x to determine the constants. (See example under *Case I*.)

Case IV: If the denominator contains quadratic factors $(P, Q \ldots)$ which cannot be separated into real linear factors and one or more of which are repeated, let
$$\dfrac{\text{Num}}{P^2 Q^3 \ldots} = \dfrac{Ax + B}{P} + \dfrac{Cx + D}{P^2} + \dfrac{Ex + F}{Q} + \dfrac{Gx + H}{Q^2} + \dfrac{Ix + J}{Q^3} + \ldots$$

Example: $\dfrac{5x^2 - 4x + 16}{(x-3)(x^2 - x + 1)^2} = \dfrac{A}{x-3} + \dfrac{Bx + C}{x^2 - x + 1} + \dfrac{Dx + E}{(x^2 - x + 1)^2}$. Clearing of fractions,
$$5x^2 - 4x + 16 = A(x^2 - x + 1)^2 + (Bx + C)(x-3)(x^2 - x + 1) + (Dx + E)(x - 3)$$
Proceed from here on by method similar to that discussed in example under *Case II*.

8. RATIO AND PROPORTION

Laws of Ratio and Proportion are stated in the following theorems, in which the symbols have finite values and division by zero is excluded:

(a) If $\dfrac{a}{b} = \dfrac{c}{d}$ then: $\dfrac{a}{c} = \dfrac{b}{d}$; $ad = bc$; $\dfrac{ma + nb}{pa + qb} = \dfrac{mc + nd}{pc + qd}$; $\left(\dfrac{a}{b}\right)^n = \left(\dfrac{c}{d}\right)^n$. If also $\dfrac{e}{f} = \dfrac{g}{h}$, then: $\dfrac{ae}{bf} = \dfrac{cg}{dh}$.

(b) If $\dfrac{a}{b} = \dfrac{c}{d} = \dfrac{e}{f} = \ldots$, then: $\dfrac{a}{b} = \dfrac{c}{d} = \dfrac{e}{f} = \ldots = \dfrac{pa + qc + re + \ldots}{pb + qd + rf + \ldots}$.

Variation.

If $y = kx$, y varies directly as x; i.e., y is directly proportional to x.

If $y = \dfrac{k}{x}$, y varies inversely as x; i.e., y is inversely proportional to x.

If $y = kxz$, y varies jointly as x and z.

If $y = k\dfrac{x}{z}$, y varies directly as x and inversely as z.

The symbol k is called the constant factor of proportionality.

9. INEQUALITIES

Laws of Inequalities are stated in the following theorems, in which the symbols have *finite positive values* and *division by zero* is excluded:

(a) If $a > b$, then: $a + c > b + c$ $b < a$

$$a - c > b - c \qquad\qquad c - a < c - b$$

$$ac > bc \qquad\qquad\qquad -ca < -cb$$

$$\frac{a}{c} > \frac{b}{c} \qquad\qquad\qquad \frac{c}{a} < \frac{c}{b}$$

Corollary: If $a - c > b$, then $a > b + c$.

(b) If $a > b$ and $c > d$, then: $a + c > b + d$; $ac > bd$;
but $a - c$ may be $>$ or $=$ or $< b - d$; a/c may be $>$ or $=$ or $< b/d$.

10. LOGARITHMS

The Logarithm of a given number is the power to which a fixed number called the base must be raised to produce the given number. In $y = b^x$, b is the base, x the logarithm to this base, and y the number which is produced. For common, or Briggs, logarithms the base is 10. The only other system in frequent use is the Napierian, natural, or hyperbolic system, for which the base $e = 2.71828$ (to five decimal places). The abbreviation *log* means the logarithm of a number to the base 10. The notation ln 6 or $\log_e$ 6 means the logarithm of 6 to the base e; log 6 means the logarithm of 6 to the base 10. Thus, log 100 = 2, because $100 = 10^2$; log 10 = 1, because $10 = 10^1$; log 1 = 0, because $1 = 10^0$; log 0.1 $= -1$, because $0.1 = 10^{-1}$. Any number > 1 has a positive logarithm, and any number < 1 has a negative logarithm (provided the base > 1). A number which is not a whole power of 10 results from raising 10 to some mixed-numbered, fractional, or irrational power. The integral part of the power is called the *characteristic* and may be either positive, zero, or negative; the decimal part, called the *mantissa*, is always positive and may be obtained from a table of logarithms. Since 10 is larger than e (2.71828), it takes a higher power of e to produce a given number than it does of 10. This means that the logarithm of a number to base e is larger than that to base 10. Relation between the two systems of logarithms is:

$$\log_e n = \log_{10} n \div \log_{10} e$$

or
$$\log_e n = \log_{10} n \div 0.4343 = \log_{10} n \times 2.303$$

Numerical Value of the *mantissa* for base 10 is taken from Table 10, Section 1, disregarding for the moment the decimal point in the number whose logarithm is being determined. The *characteristic* is determined by the following rules. If the given number is greater than 1, the characteristic of its logarithm is positive and is one less than the number of figures preceding the decimal point; thus,

$$\log 6.54 = 0.815578; \ \log 65.4 = 1.815578; \ \log 654 = 2.815578; \ \log 6540 = 3.815578$$

If the given number is less than 1, the characteristic of its logarithm is negative and is numerically one greater than the number of zeros immediately following the decimal point; thus the four-place logarithm of 6 is 0.7782, and

$$\log 0.6 = \bar{1}.7782; \ \log 0.06 = \bar{2}.7782; \ \log 0.006 = \bar{3}.7782; \ \log 0.0006 = \bar{4}.7782$$

The mantissa is always positive, so $\bar{2}.7782$ is the same as $-2 + 0.7782$ and may be written $8.7782 - 10$. If the given number is an integral power of 10, the mantissa is zero.

To determine a number whose logarithm is given, the above procedure is reversed.

The *cologarithm* of a number is the logarithm of its reciprocal. Hence, colog $N = \log 1/N = \log 1 - \log N = -\log N$. Cologarithms are useful (if tables of them are available) in dealing with fractions, since cologarithms of factors in the denominator may be *added* to logarithms of factors in the numerator.

Multiplication and Division of numbers may be performed by logarithms and the use of the following rules:

To multiply a by b, $\log a + \log b = \log ab$

To divide a by b, $\log a - \log b = \log a/b$

Here log a and log b are obtained from Table 10 and the above rules for the characteristic; then the number corresponding to log ab or log a/b is found from Table 10. For example, to multiply 68.31 by 0.2754, log 68.31 = 1.834484, log 0.2754 = 9.439964 - 10, the sum of the logs is 1.274448, and its corresponding number is 18.813, the last digit being possibly one unit in error.

Powers and Roots of numbers are most conveniently computed by logarithms and the use of the following rules:

To raise a to the nth power, $\qquad n \log a = \log a^n$

To extract the nth root of a, $\qquad \dfrac{1}{n} \log a = \log a^{1/n}$

For example, to raise 0.6831 to the 1.53 power: $1.53 \times \bar{1}.834484 = 1.53(-1 + .834484)$ $= -1.53 + 1.276761 = -1 - 0.53 + 1.276761 = \bar{1}.746761$, which is log of 0.55816. To find the fifth root of 0.6831: one-fifth of $\bar{1}.834484$ is $\tfrac{1}{5}(-5 + 4.834484) = \bar{1}.966897$, which is log of 0.92661.

Simple exponential equations may be solved by a variation of the above principle. Thus, given $a^x = b$, write

$$x \log a = \log b, \text{ whence } x = \frac{\log b}{\log a} \text{ and } \log x = \log (\log b) - \log (\log a).$$

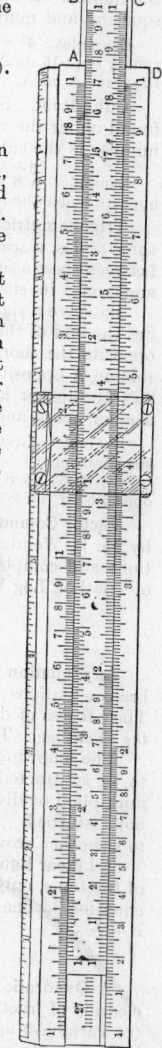

Theory of the Slide Rule

A Slide Rule is an instrument for mechanical computation based on the use of logarithms. With it the operations of multiplication, division, the finding of powers, and the extraction of roots can be performed rapidly and with an accuracy sufficient for most engineering work. With a good 10-inch Mannheim rule the results obtained are accurate to approximately $\frac{1}{10}$ of 1 per cent.

The Simple Mannheim Rule consists of a fixed and a sliding part both of which are ruled with logarithmic scales, i.e., with divisions at distances equal to the logarithms of the numbers marking the division points. Since the logarithm of the product of two numbers is the sum of the logarithms of the numbers and the logarithm of the quotient of two numbers is the difference of their logarithms, multiplication or division of the numbers can be effected by moving the slide to the right or left to add or subtract the logarithms. The scales on the fixed part of the rule are called the A and D scales, and those on the slide the B and C scales. The A and B scales are each divided into two parts, each part being a half-size reproduction of the C and D scale. A "runner," which consists of a glass plate with a fine vertical line on it, is used to facilitate some of the operations. Since 0 is the logarithm of 1 the numbering on each scale begins with the figure 1. In using the scale the figures 1, 2, 3, etc., are to be taken either as representing these numbers, or as 10, 20, 30, etc., or 100, 200, 300, etc., or 0.1, 0.2, 0.3, etc.; that is, the numbers multiplied or divided by 10, 100, etc., as may be most convenient for the solution of a given problem.

Use of the Simple Mannheim Slide Rule

The following examples illustrate the use of the slide rule.

Proportion. Set the first term of a proportion on the C scale opposite the second term on the D scale; then opposite the third term on the C scale read the fourth term on the D scale.

Example: Find the fourth term in the proportion 12 : 21 :: 30 : x. Move the slide to the right until 12 on C is opposite 21 on D, then opposite 30 on C read x on D, = 52.5.

Multiplication. Set 1 on the C scale opposite one of the factors on D. Under the other factor on the C scale read the product on the D scale.

Example: 25×3. Move the slide to the right until the left 1 on C is opposite 25 on D. Under 3 on C is found the product on D, = 75.

Example: 25×5. If the slide is moved to the right as above, the 5 on C will be beyond the end of D. In this case move the slide to the left until the right 1 on C is opposite 25 on D. Under 5 on C is found the product on D, = 125.

Division. Place the divisor on C opposite the dividend on D, and the quotient is found on D under 1 on C.

Example: $750 \div 25$. Move the slide until 25 on C is opposite 750 on D. Under 1 on C is found the quotient on D, = 30.

FIG. 1

Combined Multiplication and Division. Arrange the numbers to be multiplied and divided in the form of a fraction with one more factor in the numerator than in the denominator, supplying the factor 1 if necessary. Then perform alternate division and multiplication, using the runner to indicate partial results.

Example: $\dfrac{4 \times 5 \times 8}{3 \times 6} = 8.9$ nearly. Set 3 on C over 4 on D, set runner to 5 on C, then set 6 on C under the runner, and read under 8 on C the result 8.9 — on D.

Powers and Roots. The numbers on scales A and B are the squares of the opposite numbers on scales C and D, and the numbers on scales C and D the square roots of the opposite numbers on scales A and B. In extracting square roots, if the number of digits is odd, take the number on the left-hand scale of A; if the number of digits is even, take the number on the right-hand scale of A. To cube a number, perform the operations of squaring and multiplication.

Examples: $4^2 = 16$. Set the runner over 4 on D and read 16 on A. $\sqrt{16} = 4$. Set the runner over 16 on A and read 4 on D. $2^3 = 8$. Set 1 on C over 2 on D, and above 2 on B read the result 8 on A.

Cube Root. Set the runner over the number on A; then move the slide until there is found under the runner on B the same number which is found under 1 on C on D; this number is the cube root desired.

Example: $\sqrt[3]{8} = 2$. Set the runner over 8 on A, move the slide along until the same number appears under the runner on B and under 1 on C on D; this is the number 2.

Trigonometric Computations. On the under side of the slide (which is reversible) are three scales, a scale of natural sines marked S, a scale of natural tangents marked T, and between these a scale of equal parts. To use these scales, turn the slide over. Opposite an angle on S its sine is found on A, and opposite an angle on T is found its tangent on D.

To solve a right triangle in which the two arms are given, use the T and D scales. Set the end of the T scale opposite the longer arm on D and find the smaller angle on T opposite the shorter arm on D. In all other cases use the A and S scales. Set a given side on A opposite its opposite angle on S. With this setting the hypotenuse is opposite 90°, the longer arm opposite the larger acute angle, and the shorter arm opposite the smaller acute angle.

Example: Given, shorter arm = 24, opposite angle = 35.5°. Find the remaining parts of the triangle.
Set 35.5° on S opposite 24 on A. Opposite 54.5° on S read the longer arm 33.6 on A and opposite 90° on S the hypotenuse 41.3 on A.

Vector Computations. Scales for circular and hyperbolic functions have been designed by M. P. Weinbach and A. F. Puchstein to facilitate computations involving these functions and complex numbers. For detailed instructions in their use consult the manual of The Log Log Vector Slide Rule published by Keuffel and Esser Co.

11. EQUATIONS

An Equation is a statement of conditional equality between two expressions. Algebraic equations contain one or more letter symbols representing *unknown* quantities. The process of determining values of unknowns satisfying the equations is called *solving the equations.* The solutions of an equation in one unknown are called its *roots.*

The following theorem is of fundamental importance: If the same quantity is added to, or subtracted from, both sides (i.e., *members*) of an equation, or if both members are multiplied or divided by the same quantity (excluding division by zero), the equality is not disturbed. It follows that any term may be *transposed* from one side of an equation to the other provided its sign is changed.

A Linear Equation is an equation of the first degree; that is, one in which, after clearing of fractions, only terms of the first degree in the variable (or variables) appear. A linear equation in one unknown has only one root. Example: Given, $3x + 2 = 0$. Solution: $x = -\,2/3$.

Quadratic Equation

A Quadratic Equation is an equation of the second degree; that is, one in which, after clearing of fractions, one or more terms of the second degree (as x^2 or xy) in the variable (or variables) appear, but none of higher degree. A quadratic equation in one unknown has two roots which are either both real or both complex. The roots may be determined by any one of the following methods:

Solution by Factoring. Given the equation $ax^2 + bx + c = 0$ (abbreviated $f(x) = 0$). If $(x - r)$ is a factor of $f(x)$, then r is a root of $f(x) = 0$. Factors can sometimes be written by inspection. (See p. 2-14.) Example: Given: $x^2 - x - 6 = 0$. This may be written $(x - 3)(x + 2) = 0$. Hence, the roots are 3 and -2.

Solution by Completing the Square. The equation $ax^2 + bx + c = 0$ may be written in the form $x^2 + \dfrac{b}{a} x = -\dfrac{c}{a}$. Add $\left(\dfrac{b}{2a}\right)^2$ to both members. Then

$$x^2 + \frac{b}{a} x + \left(\frac{b}{2a}\right)^2 = -\frac{c}{a} + \left(\frac{b}{2a}\right)^2 \quad \text{or} \quad \left(x + \frac{b}{2a}\right)^2 = \frac{b^2 - 4ac}{4a^2}$$

whence $\left(x + \dfrac{b}{2a}\right) = \pm \dfrac{\sqrt{b^2 - 4ac}}{2a}$ or $x = \dfrac{-b \pm \sqrt{b^2 - 4ac}}{2a} =$ the roots

Example: Given, $2x^2 + x - 3 = 0$. This may be written $x^2 + 1/2\, x = 3/2$. Add $(1/4)^2$ to both members. Then $x^2 + 1/2\, x + (1/4)^2 = 3/2 + (1/4)^2$, or $(x + 1/4)^2 = 25/16$, whence $(x + 1/4)$ $= \pm\, 5/4$ and $x = 1$ or $-3/2 =$ the roots.

Solution by Formula. The symbolic solution of $ax^2 + bx + c = 0$ is

$$x = \frac{-b \pm \sqrt{b^2 - 4ac}}{2a},$$

as shown above. This solution may be used as a general formula. Thus, in the previous example of $2x^2 + x - 3 = 0$, the coefficients are $a = 2$, $b = 1$, $c = -3$. Substituting these values into the formula, $x = \dfrac{-1 \pm \sqrt{(1)^2 - 4(2)(-3)}}{2 \times 2} = \dfrac{-1 \pm 5}{4} = 1$ or $-\dfrac{3}{2}$, as before.

The **Discriminant** of the equation $ax^2 + bx + c = 0$ is the quantity $b^2 - 4ac$. If $b^2 - 4ac > 0$, the roots are real and unequal; if $b^2 - 4ac = 0$, the roots are real and equal; if $b^2 - 4ac < 0$, the roots are complex and unequal. If $b^2 - 4ac$ is a positive perfect square, or zero, the roots are rational. If $b = 0$, the roots are equal in absolute value but opposite in sign; if $c = 0$, one root is zero.

Cubic Equation

A **Cubic Equation** is an equation of the third degree; that is, one in which, after clearing of fractions, one or more terms of the third degree in the variable (or variables) appear, but none of higher degree. A cubic equation in one unknown has three roots, of which either all are real or one real and two complex.

Algebraic Solution. Write the equation in the form $ax^3 + 3bx^2 + 3cx + d = 0$. Let

$$q = ac - b^2 \quad \text{and} \quad r = 1/2\,(3abc - a^2d) - b^3.$$

Also let $\qquad s_1 = \left(r + \sqrt{q^3 + r^2}\right)^{1/3}$ and $s_2 = \left(r - \sqrt{q^3 + r^2}\right)^{1/3}$.

Then the roots are:

$$x_1 = [(s_1 + s_2) - b] \div a$$

$$x_2 = \left[-\frac{1}{2}(s_1 + s_2) + \frac{\sqrt{-3}}{2}(s_1 - s_2) - b\right] \div a$$

$$x_3 = \left[-\frac{1}{2}(s_1 + s_2) - \frac{\sqrt{-3}}{2}(s_1 - s_2) - b\right] \div a$$

If $q^3 + r^2 > 0$, there are one real root and a pair of complex roots. If $q^3 + r^2 = 0$, all three roots are real and at least two are equal. If $q^3 + r^2 < 0$, all three roots are real but the numerical solution leads to the extraction of the cube roots of complex quantities, and therefore the algebraic forms are *irreducible*. In such a case the trigonometric solution should be employed.

Example: Given the equation $x^3 + 12x^2 + 45x + 54 = 0$.
Here $a = 1$, $b = 4$, $c = 15$, $d = 54$. $q = 15 - 16 = -1$; $r = 1/2\,(180 - 54) - 64 = -1$; $q^3 + r^2 = -1 + 1 = 0$, $s_1 = s_2 = (-1)^{1/3} = -1$. $s_1 + s_2 = -2$; $s_1 - s_2 = 0$.
Hence the roots are $x_1 = (-2 - 4) = -6$; $x_2 = x_3 = [-1/2\,(-2) - 4] = -3$.

Trigonometric Solution. Write the equation in the form $ax^3 + 3bx^2 + 3cx + d = 0$. Let $q = ac - b^2$ and $r = 1/2\,(3abc - a^2d) - b^3$ (as in algebraic solution). Then the roots are:

$$x_1 = (y_1 - b) \div a$$
$$x_2 = (y_2 - b) \div a$$
$$x_3 = (y_3 - b) \div a$$

where y_1, y_2, and y_3 have the following values (upper of alternative signs being used when r is $+$ and the lower when r is $-$):

Case I: If q is $-$ and $q^3 + r^2 \leqq 0$:

$$y_1 = \pm\, 2\,\sqrt{-q}\,\cos\left[\frac{1}{3}\cos^{-1}\frac{\pm r}{\sqrt{-q^3}}\right]$$

$$y_2 = \pm\, 2\,\sqrt{-q}\,\cos\left[\frac{1}{3}\cos^{-1}\frac{\pm r}{\sqrt{-q^3}}+\frac{2\pi}{3}\right]$$

$$y_3 = \pm\, 2\,\sqrt{-q}\,\cos\left[\frac{1}{3}\cos^{-1}\frac{\pm r}{\sqrt{-q^3}}+\frac{4\pi}{3}\right]$$

Case II: If q is $-$ and $q^3 + r^2 \geqq 0$:

$$y_1 = \pm\, 2\,\sqrt{-q}\,\cosh\left[\frac{1}{3}\cosh^{-1}\frac{\pm r}{\sqrt{-q^3}}\right]$$

$$y_2 = \mp\,\sqrt{-q}\,\cosh\left[\frac{1}{3}\cosh^{-1}\frac{\pm r}{\sqrt{-q^3}}\right] + i\,\sqrt{-3\,q}\,\sinh\left[\frac{1}{3}\cosh^{-1}\frac{\pm r}{\sqrt{-q^3}}\right]$$

$$y_3 = \mp\,\sqrt{-q}\,\cosh\left[\frac{1}{3}\cosh^{-1}\frac{\pm r}{\sqrt{-q^3}}\right] - i\,\sqrt{-3\,q}\,\sinh\left[\frac{1}{3}\cosh^{-1}\frac{\pm r}{\sqrt{-q^3}}\right]$$

Case III: If q is $+$:

$$y_1 = \pm\, 2\,\sqrt{q}\,\sinh\left[\frac{1}{3}\sinh^{-1}\frac{\pm r}{\sqrt{q^3}}\right]$$

$$y_2 = \mp\,\sqrt{q}\,\sinh\left[\frac{1}{3}\sinh^{-1}\frac{\pm r}{\sqrt{q^3}}\right] + i\,\sqrt{3\,q}\,\cosh\left[\frac{1}{3}\sinh^{-1}\frac{\pm r}{\sqrt{q^3}}\right]$$

$$y_3 = \mp\,\sqrt{q}\,\sinh\left[\frac{1}{3}\sinh^{-1}\frac{\pm r}{\sqrt{q^3}}\right] - i\,\sqrt{3\,q}\,\cosh\left[\frac{1}{3}\sinh^{-1}\frac{\pm r}{\sqrt{q^3}}\right]$$

Example: Given the equation $x^3 + 6\,x^2 - 9\,x - 54 = 0$.
Here $a = 1$, $b = 2$, $c = -3$, $d = -54$; $q = -3 - 4 = -7$; $r = 1/2\,(-18 + 54) - 8 = 10$; $q^3 + r^2 = -343 + 100 = -243$. Note that q is $-$; $q^3 + r^2 < 0$; r is $+$.
Therefore use *Case I* with upper signs.

$$y_1 = 2\,\sqrt{7}\,\cos\left[\frac{1}{3}\cos^{-1}\frac{10}{\sqrt{343}}\right] = 2\,\sqrt{7}\,\cos 19.1° = 5$$

Hence, one root is $x_1 = 5 - 2 = 3$. The other roots can be similarly determined.

Biquadratic Equation

Method of Solution.　Given the equation $x^4 + a x^3 + b x^2 + c x + d = 0$.　First find any real root y_1 of the cubic equation:

$$8\,y^3 - 4\,b y^2 + 2\,(ac - 4\,d)\,y - [c^2 + d\,(a^2 - 4\,b)] = 0$$

Then the four roots of the biquadratic equation are given by the roots of the following two quadratic equations:

$$x^2 + \left[\frac{a}{2} - \sqrt{\frac{a^2}{4} + 2\,y_1 - b}\,\right]x + \left(y_1 + \sqrt{y_1{}^2 - d}\,\right) = 0$$

$$x^2 + \left[\frac{a}{2} + \sqrt{\frac{a^2}{4} + 2\,y_1 - b}\,\right]x + \left(y_1 - \sqrt{y_1{}^2 - d}\,\right) = 0$$

Nth Degree Equation

Fundamental Theorems of importance in the solution of nth degree equations in one unknown are given below.　$f(x)$ represents an nth degree polynomial written in descending integral powers of x with all terms considered present even though some may have zero coefficients.

Theorem I: If $f(x)$ is divided by $(x - r)$, the remainder is the value of $f(x)$ resulting if r is substituted for x, which value is designated by $f(r)$. This is known as the *remainder theorem*.

Theorem II: If, and only if, $f(x)$ is exactly divisible by $(x - r)$, will r be a root of $f(x) = 0$. An nth degree equation has n such factors and consequently n roots.

Theorem III: In the equation $f(x) = 0$, if the coefficient of the first term is unity, then the coefficient of the second term with sign changed equals the sum of all the roots; the coefficient of the third term equals the sum of all products formed from two of the roots at a time; the coefficient of the fourth term with sign changed equals the sum of all the products formed from three of the roots at a time; etc. If the degree is even, the last coefficient equals the product of all roots; if odd, the last coefficient, with sign changed, equals the product of all roots.

Theorem IV: In the equation $f(x) = 0$, if all coefficients are integral, every integral root is a factor of the last term of $f(x)$.

Theorem V: In the equation $f(x) = 0$, if the coefficient of the first term is unity, and the other coefficients are integral, there cannot be a fractional † root.

Theorem VI: In the equation $f(x) = 0$, if x is replaced by y/m, the roots of the resulting equation $\phi(y) = 0$ are m times corresponding roots of $f(x) = 0$.

Theorem VII: In the equation $f(x) = 0$, if x is replaced by $(-y)$, the roots of the resulting equation $\phi(y) = 0$ are equal in absolute value but opposite in sign to corresponding roots of $f(x) = 0$.

Theorem VIII: In the equation $f(x) = 0$, if x is replaced by $(y + h)$, the roots of the resulting equation $\phi(y) = 0$ are less by h than corresponding roots of $f(x) = 0$.

Theorem IX: If two consecutive coefficients of $f(x)$ have unlike signs, a *variation of sign* is said to occur. In the equation $f(x) = 0$, the number of positive roots cannot exceed the number of variations of sign of $f(x)$, and the number of negative roots cannot exceed the number of variations of sign of $f(-x)$. This is known as *Decartes' rule of signs*.

Theorem X: In the equation $f(x) = 0$, if two real numbers a and b, when substituted for x, give numerical values for $f(x)$ [designated $f(a)$ and $f(b)$] differing in sign, then an odd number of roots lie between $x = a$ and $x = b$. This is known as the *location theorem*.*

Synthetic Division is a useful aid in the application of certain of the above theorems. To divide $f(x)$ by $(x - r)$, proceed as illustrated by the following example:

To divide $3x^3 + 4x^2 - 6x + 5$ by $(x - 2)$: The number $2 (= r)$ is bracketed to the right of the line of coefficients. The first coefficient 3 is written down below the original ones. Multiply it by 2 and add the product $(3 \times 2 = 6)$ to the second coefficient 4. Multiply the sum $(4 + 6 = 10)$ by 2, and add the product $(10 \times 2 = 20)$ to the third coefficient $- 6$. Continuing, the last sum 33 is the remainder, and the preceding

Solution:
$$\begin{array}{r} 3 + 4 - 6 + 5 \underline{|2} \\ \underline{+ 6 + 20 + 28} \\ \underbrace{3 + 10 + 14} + 33 = \text{Remainder} \end{array}$$

Coefficients of quotient, $3x^2 + 10x + 14.$

sums, 3, 10, and 14, are successive coefficients of the quotient $3x^2 + 10x + 14.$

If powers of x are missing in the given polynomial, their places are to be supplied by zero coefficients.

Imaginary Roots. If the coefficients in the equation $f(x) = 0$ are real, then any imaginary roots occur only in conjugate pairs of the general form $(a + bi)$ and $(a - bi)$, where $i = \sqrt{-1}$. Existence of imaginary roots may often be established by *Theorem IX*, since if the total possible number of positive and negative roots does not equal the degree of the equation, the difference (plus 1 if it is odd) represents the *minimum* number of imaginary roots.

Integral Roots. The method of determining integral roots is illustrated by example. To find the roots of $x^4 - x^3 - 9x^2 + 11x + 6 = 0$. From *Theorem IV*, possible integral roots are ± 1, ± 2, ± 3, ± 6. From *Theorem V*, there can be no fractional roots. From *Theorem IX*, there can be not more than two positive roots and not more than two negative roots (but there need not be that many of either). Whether or not there are irrational or imaginary roots is not yet known.

Try $+1$ and -1 as roots by direct substitution. Neither is a root. Applying *Theorem II*, try $+2$ as a root, using synthetic division. It is found to be a root. The equation now may be written $(x - 2)(x^3 + x^2 - 7x - 3) = 0$.

$$\begin{array}{r} 1 - 1 - 9 + 11 + 6 \underline{|2} \\ \underline{+ 2 + 2 - 14 - 6} \\ 1 + 1 - 7 - 3 0 \end{array}$$

The second factor shows that only $+ 3$ or $- 3$ need be tried. Try $- 3$. It is a root. Equation now is $(x - 2)(x + 3)(x^2 - 2x - 1) = 0$. Solving for roots of the quadratic factor by formula (p. 2–13), they are found to be $1 \pm \sqrt{2}$. Hence the roots of the given equation are 2, $- 3$, $1 + \sqrt{2}$, $1 - \sqrt{2}$.

$$\begin{array}{r} 1 + 1 - 7 - 3 \underline{|-3} \\ \underline{- 3 + 6 + 3} \\ 1 - 2 - 1 0 \end{array}$$

Fractional Roots. The method of determining fractional roots is illustrated by example. To find the roots of $36x^4 - 55x^2 - 35x - 6 = 0$. From *Theorem IV*, possible integral roots are ± 1, ± 2, ± 3, ± 6. *Theorem V* shows that fractional roots may exist. From *Theorem IX*, there can be not more than one positive and not more than three negative roots (but there need not be that many of either). Whether or not there are irrational or imaginary roots is not yet known.

Employing the method for determining integral roots, none is found. To check for fractional roots, the given equation should be replaced by one satisfying the conditions of *Theorem V* (and therefore having no fractional roots) by employing *Theorem VI*. Divide the members of the given equation by 36 (the coefficient of x^4); then let $x = y/m$ throughout; and finally multiply both members of this new equation by m^4 (which procedure does not affect the values of its roots). The last two steps may be performed more quickly

---

* *Sturm's theorem* gives a method for determining the exact number of real roots lying between a and b. (See any advanced algebra book.)

† In this section *fractional* means *rational fractional*.

by simply replacing x by y and multiplying the second term by m; the third term by m^2; etc. (assuming no terms missing). This gives $y^4 - \frac{55}{36} m^2 y^2 - \frac{35}{36} m^3 y - \frac{1}{6} m^4 = 0$. Now let m equal the smallest number which will clear of fractions; this is 6. The result is $y^4 - 55 y^2 - 210 y - 216 = 0$. This equation is found to have the integral roots -2, -3, -4, 9. Hence, by *Theorem VI*, the roots of the original equation are $-\frac{1}{3}$, $-\frac{1}{2}$, $-\frac{2}{3}$ and $\frac{3}{2}$.

Irrational Roots. A method of determining positive irrational roots, known as *Horner's method*,* is illustrated by example. To find the real roots of $x^4 - 2 x^3 + 4 x^2 - 15 x + 14 = 0$. First depress the equation by removing any rational roots. By a method previously discussed, $+2$ is found to be the only integral root. The depressed equation (using synthetic division) becomes $x^3 + 4 x - 7 = 0$. This has no integral roots, and by *Theorem V* it has no fractional roots. From *Theorem IX*, there can be not more than one positive root and no negative roots. Therefore there must be a pair of imaginary roots. By the same process of elimination, the remaining root must be irrational.

By direct substitution, or by synthetic division (noting *Theorem I*), or by plotting $f(x) = x^3 + 4 x - 7$ (see *Graphical Solution*, below), $f(x)$ is found to change sign between $+1$ and $+2$. Therefore, by *Theorem X*, the irrational root lies between these two values. Using *Theorem VIII*, let $x = y + 1$ in order to diminish the irrational root of $f(x) = 0$ by 1, thus making the corresponding root of $\phi(y) = 0$ lie between 0 and 1. This is very easily accomplished by synthetic division by dividing $f(x)$ by $(x - 1)$; then dividing the new quotient by $(x - 1)$; etc., the remainders furnishing coefficients of the transformed equation.† The numerical work is illustrated at the right.

$$\begin{array}{rrrr|l}
1 + 0 & + 4 & - 7 & \underline{1} \\
+ 1 & + 1 & + 5 & \\
\hline
1 + 1 & + 5 & - 2 & \\
+ 1 & + 2 & & \\
\hline
1 + 2 & + 7 & & \\
+ 1 & & & \\
\hline
1 + 3 & & &
\end{array}$$

The first transformed equation becomes $\phi(y) = y^3 + 3 y^2 + 7 y - 2 = 0$ and has a root between 0 and 1. By plotting $\phi(y)$ to large scale, the root is found to lie between 0.2 and 0.3. Therefore the corresponding root of the original equation lies between 1.2 and 1.3.

Next diminish the irrational root of $\phi(y) = 0$ by 0.2 to obtain an equation with roots between 0 and 0.1. The second transformed equation becomes $\psi(z) = z^3 + 3.6 z^2 + 8.32 z - 0.472 = 0$ and has a root between 0 and 0.1. By plotting (or more simply, by neglecting higher powers of z and putting $8.32 z = 0.472$),‡ it is found to lie between 0.05 and 0.06. Therefore the corresponding root of the original equation lies between 1.25 and 1.26. Continuing in like manner, the irrational root may be found to any required number of decimal places.

$$\begin{array}{rrr|l}
1 + 3 & + 7 & - 2 & \underline{0.2} \\
+ 0.2 & + 0.64 & + 1.528 & \\
\hline
1 + 3.2 & + 7.64 & - 0.472 & \\
+ 0.2 & + 0.68 & & \\
\hline
1 + 3.4 & + 8.32 & & \\
+ 0.2 & & & \\
\hline
1 + 3.6 & & &
\end{array}$$

Negative Irrational Roots of $f(x) = 0$ are obtained by replacing x by $(-y)$; finding corresponding positive irrational roots of the transformed equation $\phi(y) = 0$; and then, by *Theorem VII*, changing the signs of the roots thus determined.

Graphical Solution is frequently employed when the degree of an equation is higher than 2, or only approximate values of the roots are required, or fractional or irrational exponents appear, or transcendental functions are involved. Assume the given equation to be $f(x) = 0$. Plot the graph of $y = f(x)$; then the abscissas of the intersections of the graph with the x axis are roots of $f(x) = 0$. Or break up $f(x)$ into the difference of two functions of x as $f_1(x)$ and $f_2(x)$, and plot the graphs of $y = f_1(x)$ and $y = f_2(x)$; then the abscissas of the intersections of the two graphs are roots of $f(x) = 0$.

12. DETERMINANTS

A Determinant of the nth order is a square array of n^2 elements represented by

$$\Delta = \begin{vmatrix}
a_1 & b_1 & c_1 & \ldots & l_1 \\
a_2 & b_2 & c_2 & \ldots & l_2 \\
a_3 & b_3 & c_3 & \ldots & l_3 \\
\multicolumn{5}{c}{\cdots\cdots\cdots\cdots} \\
\multicolumn{5}{c}{\cdots\cdots\cdots\cdots} \\
a_n & b_n & c_n & \ldots & l_n
\end{vmatrix}$$

and having a value determined by its *expansion* (or *development*) into $n!$ *terms* forming the algebraic sum of all the different products obtainable by using as factors one and only one *element* from each column and each row of the array, with sign affixed to each term (or product) in accordance with a general rule given below. The *principal diagonal* consists of the elements $a_1 b_2 c_3 \ldots l_n$.

---

* Other approximation methods known as Newton's method and Graeffe's method can be found in advanced algebra books.

† For proof of the theorem upon which this procedure is based, see any advanced algebra book.

‡ Caution must be used with this short-cut method. In this connection, an error may sometimes be caught later by noting that after a single root has been isolated between two limits, the first remainder after each synthetic division (which represents the last term in the new transformed equation) must never change sign. This fact follows from graphical considerations.

Evaluation of Determinants

Simple Cases. A second order determinant is expanded thus:

$$\Delta = \begin{vmatrix} a_1 & b_1 \\ a_2 & b_2 \end{vmatrix} = a_1 b_2 - a_2 b_1.$$ In the case of a **third order determinant**, the first and second columns are rewritten, for convenience, to the right of the determinant; then the diagonals running down from left to right give the positive terms and those running up from left to right give the negative terms. (*Caution: This method cannot be applied to higher order determinants.*) Thus:

$$\Delta = \begin{vmatrix} a_1 & b_1 & c_1 \\ a_2 & b_2 & c_2 \\ a_3 & b_3 & c_3 \end{vmatrix} \begin{matrix} a_1 & b_1 \\ a_2 & b_2 \\ a_3 & b_3 \end{matrix} = \left\{ \begin{matrix} a_1 b_2 c_3 + b_1 c_2 a_3 + c_1 a_2 b_3 \\ -a_3 b_2 c_1 - b_3 c_2 a_1 - c_3 a_2 b_1 \end{matrix} \right\}$$

General Case. The *first minor* of any element, as c_k, is the determinant formed of the elements remaining after suppressing the column and row to which c_k belongs; it may be designated C_k. Any determinant may be expressed in terms of the elements of a column (or row) and their first minors as follows:

Rule: Form the product of each element in a column (or row) by its corresponding minor. Give each product thus formed a positive or a negative sign according as the sum of the number of the column and the number of the row containing the element is even or odd. Keep repeating the process on the determinants formed by the minors until determinants can be expanded easily. The algebraic sum of the final resulting terms is the value of the determinant.

$$\text{Thus,} \quad \begin{vmatrix} a_1 & b_1 & c_1 \\ a_2 & b_2 & c_2 \\ a_3 & b_3 & c_3 \end{vmatrix} = a_1 \begin{vmatrix} b_2 & c_2 \\ b_3 & c_3 \end{vmatrix} - a_2 \begin{vmatrix} b_1 & c_1 \\ b_3 & c_3 \end{vmatrix} + a_3 \begin{vmatrix} b_1 & c_1 \\ b_2 & c_2 \end{vmatrix}$$

$$= a_1 (b_2 c_3 - b_3 c_2) - a_2 (b_1 c_3 - b_3 c_1) + a_3 (b_1 c_2 - b_2 c_1).$$

Properties of Determinants

Simplification of the work involved in evaluating a determinant may often be accomplished by consideration of certain general properties of determinants. The most important of these are given by the following theorems:

Theorem I: A determinant vanishes if:
(a) It has two identical rows (or columns).
(b) Corresponding elements of two rows (or columns) have a constant ratio.
(c) The ratio of the differences of corresponding elements in one pair of rows (or columns) to the differences of corresponding elements in a second pair of rows (or columns) is constant.

Theorem II: A determinant is not changed in value by:
(a) Interchanging all corresponding rows and columns.
(b) Adding to each element of a row (or column) the corresponding element of another row (or column) multiplied by a constant factor.

Theorem III: A determinant is not changed in absolute value but is changed in sign if two rows (or columns) are interchanged.

Theorem IV: A determinant having the sum of two or more terms appearing in each element of a given row (or column) is equal to the sum of two or more determinants having for elements of that row (or column), the separate terms of that row (or column) of the given determinant.

Theorem V: A determinant is multiplied by a given factor if each element of a row (or column) is multiplied by the same factor.

Example:

$$\Delta = \begin{vmatrix} 2 & 9 & 9 & 4 \\ 2 & -3 & 12 & 8 \\ 4 & 8 & 3 & -5 \\ 1 & 2 & 6 & 4 \end{vmatrix} = \begin{vmatrix} 2 & 5 & 9 & 4 \\ 2 & -7 & 12 & 8 \\ 4 & 0 & 3 & -5 \\ 1 & 0 & 6 & 4 \end{vmatrix} = 3 \begin{vmatrix} 2 & 5 & 3 & 4 \\ 2 & -7 & 4 & 8 \\ 4 & 0 & 1 & -5 \\ 1 & 0 & 2 & 4 \end{vmatrix}$$
$$\text{(Theorem II}b) \qquad\qquad \text{(Theorem V)}$$

$$= 3 \times (-5) \begin{vmatrix} 2 & 4 & 8 \\ 4 & 1 & -5 \\ 1 & 2 & 4 \end{vmatrix} + 3 \times (-7) \begin{vmatrix} 2 & 3 & 4 \\ 4 & 1 & -5 \\ 1 & 2 & 4 \end{vmatrix} = 0 \quad -21 \begin{vmatrix} 1 & 1 & 0 \\ 4 & 1 & -5 \\ 1 & 2 & 4 \end{vmatrix}$$
$$\text{(Expanding)} \qquad\qquad\qquad \text{(Theorem I}b) \quad \text{(Theorem II}b)$$

$$= -21 \begin{vmatrix} 1 & -5 \\ 2 & 4 \end{vmatrix} - (-21) \begin{vmatrix} 4 & -5 \\ 1 & 4 \end{vmatrix} = -21 \left[(4 + 10) - (16 + 5) \right] = +147$$
$$\text{(Expanding)} \qquad\qquad\qquad \text{(Expanding)}$$

13. SYSTEMS OF LINEAR EQUATIONS
General Considerations

Two linear equations in two unknowns are **independent** if they express *different* relations between the unknowns; otherwise, they are **dependent**. The equations are **compati-**

ble if there is at least one set of values of the unknowns which satisfies both equations; otherwise, the equations are **incompatible** (or **inconsistent**). They are called **simultaneous equations** if the letter symbols are considered as representing values which satisfy both equations. **Solving** the equations simultaneously consists of finding these values. The two equations considered together form a **system** of equations.

Similar definitions apply if the system contains more than two equations and any number of unknowns. Not all the unknowns need appear in any one equation. A system of linear equations containing the same number of unknowns as independent equations gives one and only one set of values which satisfy all the equations simultaneously, that is, one solution. A system containing more unknowns than independent equations has an infinite number of solutions. A system containing fewer unknowns than independent equations has no solution as it is incompatible.

An equation is **homogeneous** if all its terms are of the same degree in the variables; otherwise, it is **non-homogeneous**. It follows that a homogeneous equation can contain no constant term (other than zero).

Methods of Solution

Two or Three Independent Linear Equations in as many unknowns can usually be solved simultaneously most quickly by a process of *elimination of unknowns*. Distinction is sometimes made between elimination by *addition and/or subtraction*, by *substitution*, and by *comparison*, but basically all three methods are closely related. The following example illustrates elimination by addition and subtraction:

$$\text{Solve:} \quad \begin{cases} 2x + y + 3z = 9 & (1) \\ x - 2y + z = -2 & (2) \\ 3x + 2y + 2z = 7 & (3) \end{cases}$$

$$(2) + (3) \text{ gives:} \quad 4x + 3z = 5 \qquad (4)$$
$$2 \times (1) + (2) \text{ gives:} \quad 5x + 7z = 16 \qquad (5)$$
$$5 \times (4) - 4 \times (5) \text{ gives:} \quad -13z = -39 \text{ or } z = 3$$

Putting $z = 3$ in (4) or (5): $x = -1$
Then from (1), (2), or (3): $y = 2$

Any Number of Independent Linear Equations in an equal number of unknowns can be solved simultaneously by the above process, but if more than three *non-homogeneous* equations are involved, the computations can usually be greatly facilitated by the aid of determinants. (To condense the explanation, however, a system of only three equations will be used.)

Consider the equations: $2x + y + 3z = 9$ (Note that all constants are
$\qquad\qquad\qquad\qquad\qquad\quad x - 2y + z = -2$ placed in the right-hand mem-
$\qquad\qquad\qquad\qquad\qquad\quad 3x + 2y + 2z = 7$ bers.)

The determinant of the coefficients, $\Delta = \begin{vmatrix} 2 & 1 & 3 \\ 1 & -2 & 1 \\ 3 & 2 & 2 \end{vmatrix}$ is called the *determinant of the system.*

Rule: Any unknown is equal to a fraction whose denominator is the determinant of the system and whose numerator is the same determinant except for replacement of each coefficient of the unknown sought by the constant term in the same equation.

Thus in the above example:

$$x = \frac{\begin{vmatrix} 9 & 1 & 3 \\ -2 & -2 & 1 \\ 7 & 2 & 2 \end{vmatrix}}{\begin{vmatrix} 2 & 1 & 3 \\ 1 & -2 & 1 \\ 3 & 2 & 2 \end{vmatrix}} = \frac{\begin{vmatrix} 9 & 1 & 3 \\ -2 & -2 & 1 \\ 5 & 0 & 3 \end{vmatrix}}{\begin{vmatrix} 2 & 1 & 3 \\ 1 & -2 & 1 \\ 4 & 0 & 3 \end{vmatrix}} = \frac{\begin{vmatrix} 9 & 1 & 3 \\ 16 & 0 & 7 \\ 5 & 0 & 3 \end{vmatrix}}{\begin{vmatrix} 2 & 1 & 3 \\ 5 & 0 & 7 \\ 4 & 0 & 3 \end{vmatrix}} = \frac{-(48 - 35)}{-(15 - 28)} = -1$$

If there are n non-homogeneous linear equations in $(n - 1)$ unknowns, and any one equation is not independent of the rest, there are in effect $(n - 1)$ independent equations in $(n - 1)$ unknowns, and the determinant of the coefficients (with the constant terms used for the last column) must equal zero.

Any number of independent *homogeneous* linear equations in an equal number of unknowns has the single solution consisting of zero values for all unknowns. However, if not all the equations are independent, there is an infinite number of solutions and the determinant of the system must equal zero.

14. SPECIAL SYSTEMS OF NTH DEGREE EQUATIONS

Two Quadratic Equations, or one quadratic and one linear equation, in two unknowns, can be solved by a process of elimination. Obtain a third equation containing only one of the unknowns; solve it; then substitute in the given linear equation, or one of the given quadratic equations, to obtain corresponding values of the other unknown. Numerous special methods which facilitate the work of solving in certain cases are discussed in standard algebra books. Fundamentally, however, all of them are based on a process of elimination of one variable.

A pair of quadratic equations has four sets of values (including imaginary solutions) which satisfy them simultaneously; a quadratic equation and a linear equation have two simultaneous solutions.

A Graphical Method of solution applicable to simultaneous equations *of any degree in two unknowns* is of particular value if the equations are not linear. (See page 2–16).

15. SPECIAL SERIES

A Series is an expression indicating the summation of a sequence of terms. If a series ends with some particular term, it is a *finite series*; but if the terms are formed according to some fixed law and their number is infinite, the result is an *infinite series*. A *convergent series* is one in which, if the number of terms is indefinitely increased, the sum approaches some finite value as a limit; a *divergent series* is one whose sum, thus taken, increases indefinitely or oscillates. Many series are convergent for values of the variable lying within a certain range (or ranges) and divergent for values in another range (or ranges).

Binomial Theorem

The Binomial Theorem gives a method of writing a power of a binomial as a series. It is:

$$(a \pm b)^n = a^n \pm na^{n-1}b + \frac{n(n-1)}{2!}a^{n-2}b^2 \pm \frac{n(n-1)(n-2)}{3!}a^{n-3}b^3 + \cdots$$

$$(\pm 1)^{r-1}\frac{n(n-1)\cdots(n-r+2)}{(r-1)!}a^{n-r+1}b^{r-1}\cdots$$

where the last term shown is the rth term.

If n is a positive integer, the series is finite; it has $(n+1)$ terms, the last being b^n; and the equality is true for all finite values of a and b. However, if n is fractional or negative, the series is infinite; it is convergent only for $|b| < |a|$ (see p. 2–80); and therefore the equality is true only for values of a and b thus related.

The coefficients n, $\frac{n(n-1)}{2!}$, ... are called *binomial coefficients*. For convenience, the symbol $\binom{n}{r}$ is frequently used to represent the quantity $\frac{n(n-1)\cdots(n-r+1)}{r!}$. This is the coefficient of the $(r+1)$th term. Thus $\binom{n}{3} = \frac{n(n-1)(n-2)}{3!}$. If n is a positive integer, the coefficients of the rth term from the beginning and the rth from the end are equal.

The binomial $(a \pm b)^n$ may be written as $a^n(1 \pm x)^n$, where $x = b/a$. It is often more convenient to expand the second form than the first. The following special forms can be used if n is any positive integer; and for any negative or fractional value of n, if x lies between 0 and 1:

$$(1 \pm x)^n = 1 \pm nx + \frac{n(n-1)}{1\cdot 2}x^2 \pm \frac{n(n-1)(n-2)}{1\cdot 2\cdot 3}x^3 + \frac{n(n-1)(n-2)(n-3)}{1\cdot 2\cdot 3\cdot 4}x^4 \pm \cdots$$

$$\frac{1}{1 \pm x} = (1 \pm x)^{-1} = 1 \mp x + x^2 \mp x^3 + x^4 \mp x^5 + \cdots$$

$$\sqrt{1 \pm x} = (1 \pm x)^{1/2} = 1 \pm \frac{1}{2}x - \frac{1}{2\cdot 4}x^2 \pm \frac{1\cdot 3}{2\cdot 4\cdot 6}x^3 - \frac{1\cdot 3\cdot 5}{2\cdot 4\cdot 6\cdot 8}x^4 \pm \frac{1\cdot 3\cdot 5\cdot 7}{2\cdot 4\cdot 6\cdot 8\cdot 10}x^5 - \cdot$$

$$\frac{1}{\sqrt{1 \pm x}} = (1 \pm x)^{-1/2} = 1 \mp \frac{1}{2}x + \frac{1\cdot 3}{2\cdot 4}x^2 \mp \frac{1\cdot 3\cdot 5}{2\cdot 4\cdot 6}x^3 + \cdots$$

Common Progression Series

A Progression is a sequence of terms which proceed according to some fixed law. *A series* may be formed by writing an expression indicating the summation of the terms appearing in a progression.

An **Arithmetic Progression** is a sequence of terms each of which differs from the preceding by the same number d, called the *common difference*. If n = number of terms, a = first term, l = last term, s = sum of n terms, then $l = a + (n - 1)d$, and $s = \dfrac{n}{2}(a + l)$. The arithmetic mean of two numbers is the number which placed between them would make with them an arithmetic progression. Thus, the arithmetic mean of m, n is $(m + n)/2$.

Example: Given the series $3 + 5 + 7 + \ldots$ to 10 terms. Here $n = 10$; $a = 3$; $d = 2$; hence $l = 3 + (10 - 1) \times 2 = 21$, and $s = (10/2)(3 + 21) = 120$.

A **Geometric Progression** is a sequence of terms each of which is obtained from the preceding by multiplying it by a fixed number r, called the *ratio*. If n = number of terms, a = first term, l = last term, s = sum of n terms, then $l = ar^{n-1}$, $s = (rl - a)/(r - 1)$ $= a(1 - r^n)/(1 - r)$. The geometric mean of two numbers is the number which placed between them would make with them a geometric progression. Thus, the geometric mean of m, n is $\sqrt{mn}$.

Example: Given the series $3 + 6 + 12 + \ldots$ to 6 terms. Here $n = 6$; $a = 3$; $r = 2$; hence $l = 3 \times 2^{(6-1)} = 96$, and $s = (2 \times 96 - 3)/(2 - 1)$, or $= 3(1 - 2^6)/(1 - 2) = 189$.

If $|r| < 1$ and the number of terms is increased indefinitely, $s \to a/(1 - r)$ as $n \to \infty$.

Example: Given the infinite series $1/2 + 1/4 + 1/8 + \ldots$. Here $a = 1/2$ and $r = 1/2$; hence $s \to (1/2)/(1 - 1/2) = 1$ as $n \to \infty$.

An **Harmonic Progression** is a sequence of terms whose reciprocals form an arithmetic progression. The harmonic mean of two numbers is the number which placed between them would make with them an harmonic progression. Thus, the harmonic mean of m, n is $2mn/(m + n)$.

The **Relation between Arithmetic, Geometric, and Harmonic Means** of two numbers is expressed by the equality $G^2 = AH$, where G = geometric mean, A = arithmetic mean, and H = harmonic mean.

Other Series

1. $1 + 2 + 3 + 4 + \ldots + (n - 1) + n = n(n + 1)/2$.
2. $p + (p + 1) + (p + 2) + \ldots + (q - 1) + q = (q + p)(q - p + 1)/2$.
3. $2 + 4 + 6 + 8 + \ldots + (2n - 2) + 2n = n(n + 1)$.
4. $1 + 3 + 5 + 7 + \ldots + (2n - 3) + (2n - 1) = n^2$.
5. $1^2 + 2^2 + 3^2 + 4^2 + \ldots + (n - 1)^2 + n^2 = n(n + 1)(2n + 1)/6$.
6. $1^3 + 2^3 + 3^3 + 4^3 + \ldots + (n - 1)^3 + n^3 = n^2(n + 1)^2/4$.

7. $\dfrac{1 + 2 + 3 + 4 + 5 \ldots + n}{n^2} \to \dfrac{1}{2}$

8. $\dfrac{1 + 2^2 + 3^2 + 4^2 + \ldots + n^2}{n^3} \to \dfrac{1}{3}$ } as $n \to \infty$.

9. $\dfrac{1 + 2^3 + 3^3 + 4^3 + \ldots + n^3}{n^4} \to \dfrac{1}{4}$

16. APPROXIMATE FORMULAS

The **Approximate Formulas** listed below are sufficiently accurate to be satisfactory in the solution of many practical problems. Care must be taken, however, to use them only under the conditions specified.

(a) If $|x|$ and $|y|$ are small compared with 1:

1. $(1 \pm x)^2 = 1 \pm 2x$.

2. $(1 \pm x)^{1/2} = 1 \pm \dfrac{x}{2}$.

3. $\dfrac{1}{1 \pm x} = 1 \mp x$.

4. $(1 + x)(1 + y) = 1 + x + y$.

5. $(1 + x)(1 - y) = 1 + x - y$.

6. $e^x = 1 + x + \dfrac{x^2}{2}$ (where $e = 2.71828$).

7. $\log_e(1 \pm x) = \pm x - \dfrac{x^2}{2} \pm \dfrac{x^3}{3}$. } (Last term often may be omitted).

8. $\log_e\left(\dfrac{1 + x}{1 - x}\right) = 2\left(x + \dfrac{x^3}{3} + \dfrac{x^5}{5}\right)$.

(b) If $|x|$ is small compared with a and $a > 0$:

9. $a^x = 1 + x \log_e a + \dfrac{x^2}{2} (\log_e a)^2$.   (Last term often may be omitted.)

(c) If a and b are nearly equal and both > 0:

10. $\sqrt{ab} = \dfrac{a + b}{2}$.

(d) If b is small compared with a and both > 0:

11. $\sqrt{a^2 \pm b} = a \pm \dfrac{b}{2\,a}$.

12. $\sqrt{a^3 \pm b} = a \pm \dfrac{b}{3\,a^2}$.

13. $\sqrt{a^2 + b^2} = 0.960\,a + 0.398\,b$. This is within 4 per cent of the true value if $a > b$. A closer approximation is $\sqrt{a^2 + b^2} = 0.9938\,a + 0.0703\,b + 0.3567\,\dfrac{b^2}{a}$.

14. $\sqrt{a^2 + b^2 + c^2} = 0.939\,a + 0.389\,b + 0.297\,c$. This is within 6 per cent of the true value if $a > b > c$. For instance, for the numbers 43, 42, and 41, the error < 5.2 per cent.

(e) If $|x|$ is less than $\dfrac{\pi}{18}$:

15. $\sin x = x - \dfrac{x^3}{6}$.

16. $\cos x = 1 - \dfrac{x^2}{2}$.   (Last term often may be omitted.)

17. $\tan x = x + \dfrac{x^3}{3}$.

(Note: If $x = 8° = \dfrac{8\pi}{180} = 0.13963$, $\sin x = x - \frac{1}{6}\,x^3 = 0.13918$, which is one unit in error in the fifth decimal place. If the absolute value of the angle is less than 5°, the values of x and $\sin x$ do not differ more than one unit in the fourth decimal place.)

(f) If $|y|$ is less than $\dfrac{\pi}{36}$ and small compared with $|x|$:

18. $\sin (x \pm y) = \sin x \pm y \cos x$.

19. $\cos (x \pm y) = \cos x \mp y \sin x$.

20. $\tan (x \pm y) = \tan x \pm \dfrac{y}{\cos^2 x}$.

17. PERMUTATIONS AND COMBINATIONS

A Permutation of n things is any *arrangement* of any number of them in a definite order. The possible number of *different* arrangements of n things taken r at a time is designated $_nP_r$.

For n things all different:

$$_nP_r = n(n - 1)(n - 2) \ldots (n - r + 1) = \frac{n!}{(n - r)!}$$

(Particular cases: $_nP_1 = n$; $_nP_n = n!$.)

Example: How many different arrangements of the letters in the word "black" can be made, using three at a time? Solution: $_5P_3 = 5 \times 4 \times 3 = 60$.

For n things taken all at a time of which n_1 are alike, n_2 others are alike, etc.:

$$_nP_n = \frac{n!}{n_1!\, n_2!\, n_3! \ldots}$$

Example: How many different arrangements can be made of the letters in the word "level"? Solution: $P = \dfrac{5!}{2!\,2!} = 30$.

A Combination of n things is any *group* of any number of them without reference to their order within the group. The possible number of *different* groups of n things taken r at a time is designated $_nC_r$.

For n things all different:

$$_nC_r = \frac{_nP_r}{r!} = \frac{n(n - 1)(n - 2) \ldots (n - r + 1)}{r!} = \frac{n!}{r!(n - r)!}$$

$$= \frac{n(n - 1)(n - 2) \ldots (r + 1)}{(n - r)!} = \frac{_nP_{n-r}}{(n - r)!} = {_nC_{n-r}}$$

(Particular cases: $_nC_1 = n$; $_nC_n = 1$.)

Example: In how many ways can 9 books be selected from a set of 11?

Solution: $_{11}C_9 = {}_{11}C_2 = \dfrac{11 \times 10}{2!} = 55.$

For n things all different, the total number of combinations taken any number at a time is:

$$_nC_1 + {}_nC_2 + \ldots + {}_nC_{n-1} + {}_nC_n = 2^n - 1.$$

Example: How many different sums can be formed from a penny, a nickel, a dime, a quarter, and a half dollar?   Solution: $2^5 - 1 = 31.$

For two groups of m and n things, respectively, all different, the number of combinations of $(r + s)$ things, r from the first group and s from the second group, is:

$$_mC_r \cdot {}_nC_s = \frac{m!\,n!}{r!\,s!\,(m-r)!\,(n-s)!}$$

18. PROBABILITY

The Probability *that an event will happen* is the ratio of the number of favorable cases to the entire number of possible cases, provided all cases are *equally likely* to occur.   The *probability of failure* is unity minus the probability of happening.   The *odds* in favor of the event are given by the ratio of probability of happening to probability of failure.

Example: From an urn containing 5 black and 4 white balls, 3 balls are drawn at random. What is the probability that 2 will be black and 1 white?   Solution: From 9 balls, 3 may be drawn in $_9C_3 = 9 \times 8 \times 7 \div 3! = 84$ ways.   The number of favorable cases is $_5C_2 \cdot {}_4C_1 = (5 \times 4/2) \times 4 = 40$.   Hence the required probability is $^{40}/_{84} = {}^{10}/_{21}$, i.e., 10 chances in 21.

Events of a set are *independent* if the occurrence of any one of them does not affect the occurrence of others; otherwise, they are *dependent*.   Events of a set are *mutually exclusive* if the occurrence of any one of them on a particular occasion excludes the occurrence of any other on that occasion.

The probability of *simultaneous occurrence* of two *independent events* whose respective probabilities are a and b is ab.   The probability of *occurrence of one or the other* of two *mutually exclusive* events whose respective probabilities are a and b is $a + b$.

Example: The probability of drawing a jack from a full pack of cards is $^1/_{13}$.   The probability of drawing a spade is $^1/_4$.   Hence the probability of drawing the jack of spades is $(^1/_{13}) \times (^1/_4) = {}^1/_{52}$.   The probability of drawing a jack or an ace is $^1/_{13} + {}^1/_{13} = {}^2/_{13}$.

MATHEMATICS OF FINANCE

By J. L. Barnes

19. INTEREST AND DISCOUNT

Interest is *money* paid for the use of *capital* during a period of time.   The capital or sum of money borrowed is called the *principal*.

The Rate of Interest is the ratio of the interest earned *in a unit time* to the principal. It is usually expressed as the per cent paid for the use of the principal for *one year*.

Simple Interest, I, is computed by the relation

$$I = Pit \qquad (1)$$

where P is the principal, i the rate of interest, and t the time in years.

The *sum*, S, due at the end of the interval of time, t, is,

$$S = P + I \qquad (2)$$

In Ordinary Simple Interest calculations, a month is regarded as 30 days, and a year as 12 months, or 360 days.   Thus, if d denotes the time in days

$$I = Pi\,\frac{d}{360} \qquad (3)$$

Exact Simple Interest.   Simple interest computed by taking the exact number of days or 365 days for the year is called *exact simple interest.*   Thus

$$I_e = Pi\,\frac{d}{365} \qquad (4)$$

where I_e is the exact simple interest.   To facilitate calculation Table I shows the number of days between two dates, a year or less apart, and Table II the exact simple interest on $1000 for the number of days indicated.

Example: To obtain the number of days between April 13, and December 4, determine the number of days *from* April *to* December, 244, subtract 13, and add 4.   Thus, $244 - 13 + 4 = 235$ days.

Table I.   Days between the Same Dates of Different Months

(Leap year adds one day in February.)

To → From ↓	Jan.	Feb.	March	April	May	June	July	Aug.	Sept.	Oct.	Nov.	Dec.
Jan.....	365	31	59	90	120	151	181	212	243	273	304	334
Feb.....	334	365	28	59	89	120	150	181	212	242	273	303
March..	306	337	365	31	61	92	122	153	184	214	245	275
April....	275	306	334	365	30	61	91	122	153	183	214	244
May....	245	276	304	335	365	31	61	92	123	153	184	214
June....	214	245	273	304	333	365	30	61	92	122	153	183
July....	184	215	243	274	304	335	365	31	62	92	123	153
Aug....	153	184	212	243	273	304	334	365	31	61	92	122
Sept....	122	153	181	212	242	273	303	334	365	30	61	91
Oct.....	92	123	151	182	212	243	273	304	335	365	31	61
Nov....	61	92	120	151	181	212	242	273	304	334	365	30
Dec.....	31	62	90	121	151	182	212	243	274	304	335	365

Table II.   Exact Simple Interest on $1000

$$I_e = 1000\, i\, \frac{d}{365}$$

d	2 1/2%	3%	3 1/2%	4%	4 1/2%	5%	5 1/2%	6%	7%	8%
1	0.06849	0.08219	0.09589	0.10959	0.12329	0.13699	0.15069	0.16438	0.19178	0.21918
2	0.13699	0.16438	0.19178	0.21918	0.24658	0.27397	0.30137	0.32877	0.38356	0.43836
3	0.20548	0.24658	0.28767	0.32877	0.36986	0.41096	0.45206	0.49315	0.57534	0.65753
4	0.27397	0.32877	0.38356	0.43836	0.49315	0.54795	0.60274	0.65753	0.76712	0.87671
5	0.34247	0.41096	0.47945	0.54795	0.61644	0.68493	0.75342	0.82192	0.95890	1.09589
6	0.41096	0.49315	0.57534	0.65754	0.73973	0.82192	0.90411	0.98630	1.15068	1.31507
7	0.47945	0.57534	0.67123	0.76712	0.86301	0.95890	1.05479	1.15068	1.34247	1.53425
8	0.54795	0.65753	0.76712	0.87671	0.98630	1.09589	1.20548	1.31507	1.53425	1.75342
9	0.61644	0.73973	0.86301	0.98630	1.10959	1.23288	1.35616	1.47945	1.72603	1.97260
10	0.68493	0.82192	0.95890	1.09589	1.23288	1.36986	1.50685	1.64384	1.91781	2.19178
20	1.36986	1.64384	1.91781	2.19178	2.46575	2.73973	3.01370	3.28767	3.83562	4.38356
30	2.05480	2.46575	2.87671	3.28767	3.69863	4.10959	4.52055	4.93151	5.75342	6.57534
40	2.73973	3.28767	3.83561	4.38357	4.93151	5.47945	6.02740	6.57534	7.67123	8.76712
50	3.42466	4.10958	4.79452	5.47946	6.16438	6.84932	7.53425	8.21918	9.58904	10.9589
60	4.10959	4.93151	5.75342	6.57535	7.39726	8.21918	9.04110	9.86301	11.5068	13.1507
70	4.79452	5.75342	6.71233	7.67124	8.63017	9.58904	10.5479	11.5068	13.4247	15.3425
80	5.47945	6.57534	7.67123	8.76713	9.86301	10.9589	12.0548	13.1507	15.3425	17.5342
90	6.16438	7.39726	8.63014	9.86302	11.0959	12.3288	13.5616	14.7945	17.2603	19.7260
100	6.84932	8.21918	9.58904	10.9589	12.3288	13.6986	15.0685	16.4384	19.1781	21.9178
110	7.53425	9.04110	10.5479	12.0548	13.5616	15.0685	16.5753	18.0822	21.0959	24.1096
120	8.21918	9.86301	11.5068	13.1507	14.7945	16.4384	18.0822	19.7260	23.0137	26.3014
130	8.90414	10.6849	12.4658	14.2466	16.0274	17.8082	19.5890	21.3699	24.9315	28.4932
140	9.58904	11.5068	13.4246	15.3425	17.2603	19.1781	21.0959	23.0137	26.8493	30.6849
150	10.2740	12.3288	14.3836	16.4384	18.4932	20.5479	22.6027	24.6575	28.7671	32.8767
160	10.9589	13.1507	15.3425	17.5343	19.7260	21.9178	24.1096	26.3014	30.6849	35.0685
170	11.6438	13.9726	16.3014	18.6302	20.9589	23.2877	25.6164	27.9452	32.6027	37.2603
180	12.3288	14.7945	17.2603	19.7260	22.1918	24.6575	27.1233	29.5890	34.5205	39.4521
190	13.0137	15.6164	18.2192	20.8219	23.4247	26.0274	28.6301	31.2329	36.4384	41.6438
200	13.6986	16.4384	19.1781	21.9178	24.6575	27.3973	30.1370	32.8767	38.3562	43.8356
210	14.3836	17.2603	20.1370	23.0137	25.8904	28.7671	31.6438	34.5205	40.2740	46.0274
220	15.0685	18.0822	21.0959	24.1096	27.1233	30.1370	33.1507	36.1644	42.1918	48.2192
230	15.7534	18.9041	22.0548	25.2055	28.3562	31.5068	34.6575	37.8082	44.1096	50.4110
240	16.4383	19.7260	23.0137	26.3014	29.5890	32.8767	36.1644	39.4521	46.0274	52.6027
250	17.1233	20.5479	23.9726	27.3973	30.8219	34.2466	37.6712	41.0959	47.9452	54.7945
260	17.8082	21.3699	24.9315	28.4932	32.0548	35.6164	39.1781	42.7397	49.8630	56.9863
270	18.4931	22.1918	25.8904	29.5891	33.2877	36.9863	40.6849	44.3836	51.7808	59.1781
280	19.1781	23.0137	26.8493	30.6850	34.5205	38.3562	42.1918	46.0274	53.6986	61.3699
290	19.8630	23.8356	27.8082	31.7809	35.7534	39.7260	43.6986	47.6712	55.6164	63.5616
300	20.5479	24.6575	28.7671	32.8767	36.9863	41.0959	45.2055	49.3151	57.5342	65.7534
310	21.2329	25.4795	29.7260	33.9726	38.2192	42.4658	46.7123	50.9589	59.4521	67.9452
320	21.9178	26.3014	30.6849	35.0685	39.4521	43.8356	48.2192	52.6027	61.3699	70.1370
330	22.6027	27.1233	31.6438	36.1644	40.6849	45.2055	49.7260	54.2466	63.2877	72.3288
340	23.2876	27.9452	32.6027	37.2603	41.9178	46.5753	51.2329	55.8904	65.2055	74.5205
350	23.9726	28.7671	33.5616	38.3562	43.1507	47.9452	52.7397	57.5342	67.1233	76.7123
360	24.6575	29.5890	34.5205	39.4521	44.3836	49.3151	54.2466	59.1781	69.0411	78.9041

Compound Interest is the interest on the principal and its unpaid interest combined at regular intervals. The sum S, or amount to which P will accumulate in n equal conversion periods or time units, is,

$$S = P(1 + i)^n \tag{5}$$

If there are m conversion periods per year, n years, and j is the nominal or quoted interest rate per year,

$$S = P\left(1 + \frac{j}{m}\right)^{mn} \tag{6}$$

Values of the sum, S, if $P = 1$ (amount of one) may be obtained from Table III for values of n from 1 to 50 at different rates, i. The value of S may also be calculated with the aid of logarithms, thus

$$\log S = \log P + n \log(1 + i) \tag{7}$$

Table III.   Amount of 1 (Compound Interest)

$$s = (1 + i)^n$$

n	2 1/2%	3%	3 1/2%	4%	4 1/2%	5%	5 1/2%	6%	7%	8%
1	1.02500	1.03000	1.03500	1.04000	1.04500	1.05000	1.05500	1.06000	1.07000	1.08000
2	1.05062	1.06090	1.07122	1.08160	1.09203	1.10250	1.11303	1.12360	1.14490	1.16640
3	1.07689	1.09273	1.10872	1.12486	1.14117	1.15763	1.17424	1.19102	1.22504	1.25971
4	1.10381	1.12551	1.14752	1.16986	1.19252	1.21551	1.23882	1.26248	1.31080	1.36049
5	1.13141	1.15927	1.18769	1.21665	1.24618	1.27628	1.30696	1.33823	1.40255	1.46933
6	1.15969	1.19405	1.22926	1.26532	1.30226	1.34010	1.37884	1.41852	1.50073	1.58687
7	1.18869	1.22987	1.27228	1.31593	1.36086	1.40710	1.45468	1.50363	1.60578	1.71382
8	1.21840	1.26677	1.31681	1.36857	1.42210	1.47746	1.53469	1.59385	1.71819	1.85093
9	1.24886	1.30477	1.36290	1.42331	1.48610	1.55133	1.61909	1.68948	1.83846	1.99900
10	1.28008	1.34392	1.41060	1.48024	1.55297	1.62889	1.70814	1.79085	1.96715	2.15892
11	1.31209	1.38423	1.45997	1.53945	1.62285	1.71034	1.80209	1.89830	2.10485	2.33164
12	1.34489	1.42576	1.51107	1.60103	1.69588	1.79586	1.90121	2.01220	2.25219	2.51817
13	1.37851	1.46853	1.56396	1.66507	1.77220	1.88565	2.00577	2.13293	2.40985	2.71962
14	1.41297	1.51259	1.61869	1.73168	1.85194	1.97993	2.11609	2.26090	2.57853	2.93719
15	1.44830	1.55797	1.67535	1.80094	1.93528	2.07893	2.23248	2.39656	2.75903	3.17217
16	1.48451	1.60471	1.73399	1.87298	2.02237	2.18287	2.35526	2.54035	2.95216	3.42594
17	1.52162	1.65285	1.79467	1.94790	2.11338	2.29202	2.48480	2.69277	3.15882	3.70002
18	1.55966	1.70243	1.85749	2.02582	2.20848	2.40662	2.62147	2.85434	3.37993	3.99602
19	1.59865	1.75351	1.92250	2.10685	2.30786	2.52695	2.76565	3.02560	3.61653	4.31570
20	1.63862	1.80611	1.98979	2.19112	2.41171	2.65330	2.91776	3.20714	3.86968	4.66096
21	1.67958	1.86029	2.05943	2.27877	2.52024	2.78596	3.07823	3.39956	4.14056	5.03383
22	1.72157	1.91610	2.13151	2.36992	2.63365	2.92526	3.24754	3.60354	4.43040	5.43654
23	1.76461	1.97359	2.20611	2.46472	2.75217	3.07152	3.42615	3.81975	4.74053	5.87146
24	1.80873	2.03279	2.28333	2.56330	2.87601	3.22510	3.61459	4.04893	5.07237	6.34118
25	1.85394	2.09378	2.36324	2.66584	3.00543	3.38635	3.81339	4.29187	5.42743	6.84848
26	1.90029	2.15659	2.44596	2.77247	3.14068	3.55567	4.02313	4.54938	5.80735	7.39635
27	1.94780	2.22129	2.53157	2.88337	3.28201	3.73346	4.24440	4.82235	6.21387	7.98806
28	1.99650	2.28793	2.62017	2.99870	3.42970	3.92013	4.47784	5.11169	6.64884	8.62711
29	2.04640	2.35657	2.71188	3.11865	3.58404	4.11614	4.72412	5.41839	7.11426	9.31727
30	2.09757	2.42726	2.80679	3.24340	3.74532	4.32194	4.98395	5.74349	7.61226	10.0627
31	2.15000	2.50008	2.90503	3.37313	3.91386	4.53804	5.25807	6.08810	8.14511	10.8677
32	2.20376	2.57508	3.00671	3.50806	4.08998	4.76491	5.54726	6.45339	8.71527	11.7371
33	2.25885	2.65234	3.11194	3.64838	4.27403	5.00319	5.85236	6.84059	9.32534	12.6701
34	2.31532	2.73191	3.22086	3.79432	4.46636	5.25335	6.17424	7.25103	9.97811	13.6901
35	2.37321	2.81386	3.33359	3.94609	4.66735	5.51602	6.51383	7.68609	10.6766	14.7853
36	2.43254	2.89828	3.45027	4.10393	4.87738	5.79182	6.87209	8.14725	11.4239	15.9682
37	2.49335	2.98523	3.57103	4.26809	5.09686	6.08141	7.25005	8.63609	12.2236	17.2456
38	2.55568	3.07478	3.69601	4.43881	5.32622	6.38548	7.64880	9.15425	13.0793	18.6253
39	2.61957	3.16703	3.82537	4.61637	5.56590	6.70475	8.06949	9.70351	13.9948	20.1153
40	2.68506	3.26204	3.95926	4.80102	5.81636	7.03999	8.51331	10.2857	14.9745	21.7245
41	2.75219	3.35990	4.09783	4.99306	6.07810	7.39199	8.98154	10.9029	16.0227	23.4625
42	2.82100	3.46070	4.24126	5.19278	6.35161	7.76159	9.47553	11.5570	17.1443	25.3395
43	2.89152	3.56452	4.38970	5.40050	6.63744	8.14967	9.99668	12.2505	18.3444	27.3666
44	2.96381	3.67145	4.54334	5.61652	6.93612	8.55715	10.5465	12.9855	19.6285	29.5560
45	3.03790	3.78160	4.70236	5.84118	7.24825	8.98501	11.1266	13.7646	21.0025	31.9205
46	3.11385	3.89504	4.86694	6.07482	7.57442	9.43426	11.7385	14.5905	22.4726	34.4741
47	3.19169	4.01190	5.03728	6.31782	7.91527	9.90597	12.3841	15.4659	24.0457	37.2320
48	3.27149	4.13225	5.21359	6.57053	8.27145	10.4013	13.0653	16.3939	25.7289	40.2106
49	3.35328	4.25622	5.39606	6.83335	8.64367	10.9213	13.7838	17.3775	27.5299	43.4274
50	3.43711	4.38391	5.58493	7.10668	9.03264	11.4674	14.5420	18.4202	29.4570	46.9016

Example: To find the amount of \$3900 at 3 1/2 per cent compounded annually for 29 years proceed in this way. (a) Enter the table at the column headed 3 1/2 per cent and opposite $n = 29$ read 2.71188 .. , the amount of 1. (b) Multiply this tabular value by 3900 to obtain the result. To use the table for a value of time not given use the relation that the amount of 1 for $n_1 + n_2$ years is equal to the amount for n_1 years times the amount for n_2 years. Thus if the table extends to only 50 periods of time, the amount of 1 for 67 periods at the rate 0.04 is $(1.04)^{67} = (1.04)^{50} \cdot (1.04)^{17}$, and the two factors of the second member can be read from the table.

The Present Value of a sum S due in n years is defined as the principal P which drawing a given rate of (compound) interest i will in n years amount to S, or in which $v = (1 + i)^{-1}$

$$P = S (1 + i)^{-n} = Sv^n, \tag{8}$$

Values of P or v^n for $S = 1$, may be obtained from Table IV.

Table IV.   Present Value of 1
$$v^n = (1 + i)^{-n}$$

n	2 1/2%	3%	3 1/2%	4%	4 1/2%	5%	5 1/2%	6%	7%	8%
1	0.97561	0.97087	0.96618	0.96154	0.95694	0.95238	0.94787	0.94340	0.93458	0.92593
2	0.95181	0.94260	0.93351	0.92456	0.91573	0.90703	0.89845	0.89000	0.87344	0.85734
3	0.92860	0.91514	0.90194	0.88900	0.87630	0.86384	0.85161	0.83962	0.81630	0.79383
4	0.90595	0.88849	0.87144	0.85480	0.83856	0.82270	0.80722	0.79209	0.76290	0.73503
5	0.88385	0.86261	0.84197	0.82193	0.80245	0.78353	0.76513	0.74726	0.71299	0.68058
6	0.86230	0.83748	0.81350	0.79031	0.76790	0.74622	0.72525	0.70496	0.66634	0.63017
7	0.84127	0.81309	0.78599	0.75992	0.73483	0.71068	0.68744	0.66506	0.62275	0.58349
8	0.82075	0.78941	0.75941	0.73069	0.70319	0.67684	0.65160	0.62741	0.58201	0.54027
9	0.80073	0.76642	0.73373	0.70259	0.67290	0.64461	0.61763	0.59190	0.54393	0.50025
10	0.78120	0.74409	0.70892	0.67556	0.64393	0.61391	0.58543	0.55839	0.50835	0.46319
11	0.76214	0.72242	0.68495	0.64958	0.61620	0.58468	0.55491	0.52679	0.47509	0.42888
12	0.74356	0.70138	0.66178	0.62460	0.58966	0.55684	0.52598	0.49697	0.44401	0.39711
13	0.72542	0.68095	0.63940	0.60057	0.56427	0.53032	0.49856	0.46884	0.41496	0.36770
14	0.70773	0.66112	0.61778	0.57748	0.53997	0.50507	0.47257	0.44230	0.38782	0.34046
15	0.69047	0.64186	0.59689	0.55526	0.51672	0.48102	0.44793	0.41727	0.36245	0.31524
16	0.67363	0.62317	0.57671	0.53391	0.49447	0.45811	0.42458	0.39365	0.33873	0.29189
17	0.65720	0.60502	0.55720	0.51337	0.47318	0.43630	0.40245	0.37136	0.31657	0.27027
18	0.64117	0.58739	0.53836	0.49363	0.45280	0.41552	0.38147	0.35034	0.29586	0.25025
19	0.62553	0.57029	0.52016	0.47464	0.43330	0.39573	0.36158	0.33051	0.27651	0.23171
20	0.61027	0.55368	0.50257	0.45639	0.41464	0.37689	0.34273	0.31180	0.25842	0.21455
21	0.59539	0.53755	0.48557	0.43883	0.39679	0.35894	0.32486	0.29416	0.24151	0.19866
22	0.58086	0.52189	0.46915	0.42196	0.37970	0.34185	0.30793	0.27751	0.22571	0.18394
23	0.56670	0.50669	0.45329	0.40573	0.36335	0.32557	0.29187	0.26180	0.21095	0.17032
24	0.55288	0.49193	0.43796	0.39012	0.34770	0.31007	0.27666	0.24698	0.19715	0.15770
25	0.53939	0.47761	0.42315	0.37512	0.33273	0.29530	0.26223	0.23300	0.18425	0.14602
26	0.52623	0.46369	0.40884	0.36069	0.31840	0.28124	0.24856	0.21981	0.17220	0.13520
27	0.51340	0.45019	0.39501	0.34682	0.30469	0.26785	0.23560	0.20737	0.16093	0.12519
28	0.50088	0.43708	0.38165	0.33348	0.29157	0.25509	0.22332	0.19563	0.15040	0.11591
29	0.48866	0.42435	0.36875	0.32065	0.27901	0.24295	0.21168	0.18456	0.14056	0.10733
30	0.47674	0.41199	0.35628	0.30832	0.26700	0.23138	0.20064	0.17411	0.13137	0.09938
31	0.46511	0.39999	0.34423	0.29646	0.25550	0.22036	0.19018	0.16425	0.12277	0.09202
32	0.45377	0.38834	0.33259	0.28506	0.24450	0.20987	0.18027	0.15496	0.11474	0.08520
33	0.44270	0.37703	0.32134	0.27409	0.23397	0.19987	0.17087	0.14619	0.10723	0.07889
34	0.43191	0.36604	0.31048	0.26355	0.22390	0.19035	0.16196	0.13791	0.10022	0.07305
35	0.42137	0.35538	0.29998	0.25342	0.21425	0.18129	0.15352	0.13011	0.09366	0.06763
36	0.41109	0.34503	0.28983	0.24367	0.20503	0.17266	0.14552	0.12274	0.08754	0.06262
37	0.40107	0.33498	0.28003	0.23430	0.19620	0.16444	0.13793	0.11579	0.08181	0.05799
38	0.39128	0.32523	0.27056	0.22529	0.18775	0.15661	0.13074	0.10924	0.07646	0.05369
39	0.38174	0.31575	0.26141	0.21662	0.17967	0.14915	0.12392	0.10306	0.07146	0.04971
40	0.37243	0.30656	0.25257	0.20829	0.17193	0.14205	0.11746	0.09722	0.06678	0.04603
41	0.36335	0.29763	0.24403	0.20028	0.16453	0.13528	0.11134	0.09172	0.06241	0.04262
42	0.35448	0.28896	0.23578	0.19257	0.15744	0.12884	0.10554	0.08653	0.05833	0.03946
43	0.34584	0.28054	0.22781	0.18517	0.15066	0.12270	0.10003	0.08163	0.05451	0.03654
44	0.33740	0.27237	0.22010	0.17805	0.14417	0.11686	0.09482	0.07701	0.05095	0.03383
45	0.32917	0.26444	0.21266	0.17120	0.13796	0.11130	0.08988	0.07265	0.04761	0.03133
46	0.32115	0.25674	0.20547	0.16461	0.13202	0.10600	0.08519	0.06854	0.04450	0.02901
47	0.31331	0.24926	0.19852	0.15828	0.12634	0.10095	0.08075	0.06466	0.04159	0.02686
48	0.30567	0.24200	0.19181	0.15219	0.12090	0.09614	0.07654	0.06100	0.03887	0.02487
49	0.29822	0.23495	0.18532	0.14634	0.11569	0.09156	0.07255	0.05755	0.03632	0.02303
50	0.29094	0.22811	0.17905	0.14071	0.11071	0.08720	0.06877	0.05429	0.03395	0.02132

Example: The present value of \$3900 due in 17 years with the (compound) interest rate 3 1/2 per cent is found in the following way: (a) Enter the table at the column headed 3 1/2 per cent and opposite $n = 17$ read $0.55720\ldots$, the present value of 1. (b) Multiply this tabular value by 3900 to obtain the result.

Discount is the money paid at the beginning of an interval of time for the use of capital during that interval. Denote the rate of interest by i, and the *rate of discount* by d. Then

$$d = \frac{i}{1+i} \tag{9}$$

In place of the type of discount just defined, which can be called *compound discount*, it is usual practice for the banker to give for each unit of the bill an amount $1 - d/m$, in which d is the rate of discount per year and $1/m$ indicates the fractional part of a year. For fractional parts of a year, then, the banker uses what is called *simple discount*.

The Average Due Time for a number of sums, due at different times, is the time at which they may all be paid with due regard to the equities involved. Denote by $S_1, S_2, \ldots, S_r$ the sums due at the ends of $n_1, n_2, \ldots, n_r$ years, respectively, and the average due time by T. On the assumption that money is worth a (compound) rate of interest i,

$$T = \frac{\log \sum_{k=1}^{r} S_k - \log \sum_{k=1}^{r} \frac{S_k}{(1+i)^{n_k}}}{\log (1+i)} \tag{10}$$

If the times are small, the following approximate relation may be employed:

$$T \approx \frac{\sum_{k=1}^{r} n_k S_k}{\sum_{k=1}^{r} S_k} \tag{11}$$

20. ANNUITIES AND SINKING FUNDS

An Annuity Certain is a succession of periodic payments for a definite (certain) term of years. The first payment of an annuity is supposed to be made at the end of the first period. The sum or amount to which the payments accumulate is called the *amount of the annuity*. Ordinarily the nominal rate of interest j and the number m of conversion intervals per year are known, so the effective rate i can be determined. It is given by

$$i = \left(1 + \frac{j}{m}\right)^m - 1 \tag{12}$$

Denote the amount of an annuity of 1 per year payable annually for n years by $s_{\overline{n}|}$. Then

$$s_{\overline{n}|} = \frac{(1+i)^n - 1}{i} \tag{13}$$

The yearly payment of an annuity is called the *annual rent*. Denote the annual rent of an annuity by R, and the amount for n years by S. Then

$$S = R s_{\overline{n}|} = \frac{R[(1+i)^n - 1]}{i} \tag{14}$$

This relation may be solved for n,

$$n = \frac{\log (Si + R) - \log R}{\log (1+i)}, \tag{15}$$

a relation which is exact if n is an integer and approximate if n is not an integer.

The Present Value of an Annuity Certain is the sum of the present values of all the future payments. Denote the present value of an annuity certain of 1 per year for n years by $a_{\overline{n}|}$ and the effective rate of interest by i. Then

$$a_{\overline{n}|} = \frac{1 - (1+i)^{-n}}{i} \tag{16}$$

Denote the present value of an annuity certain of R per year by A. Then

$$A = R a_{\overline{n}|} = \frac{R[1 - (1+i)^{-n}]}{i} \tag{17}$$

As in the preceding paragraph,

$$i = \left(1 + \frac{j}{m}\right)^{m} - 1 \tag{18}$$

Table V. Amount of 1 per Annum

$$s_{\overline{n}|} = \frac{(1 + i)^{n} - 1}{i}$$

n	2 1/2%	3%	3 1/2%	4%	4 1/2%	5%	5 1/2%	6%	7%	8%
1	1.00000	1.00000	1.00000	1.00000	1.00000	1.00000	1.00000	1.00000	1.00000	1.00000
2	2.02500	2.03000	2.03500	2.04000	2.04500	2.05000	2.05500	2.06000	2.07000	2.08000
3	3.07562	3.09090	3.10623	3.12160	3.13702	3.15250	3.16803	3.18360	3.21490	3.24640
4	4.15252	4.18363	4.21494	4.24646	4.27819	4.31013	4.34227	4.37462	4.43994	4.50611
5	5.25633	5.30914	5.36247	5.41632	5.47071	5.52563	5.58109	5.63709	5.75074	5.86660
6	6.38774	6.46841	6.55015	6.63298	6.71689	6.80191	6.88805	6.97532	7.15329	7.33593
7	7.54743	7.66246	7.77941	7.89829	8.01915	8.14201	8.26689	8.39384	8.65402	8.92280
8	8.73612	8.89234	9.05169	9.21423	9.38001	9.54911	9.72157	9.89747	10.2598	10.6366
9	9.95452	10.1591	10.3685	10.5828	10.8021	11.0266	11.2563	11.4913	11.9780	12.4876
10	11.2034	11.4639	11.7314	12.0061	12.2882	12.5779	12.8754	13.1808	13.8165	14.4866
11	12.4835	12.8078	13.1420	13.4864	13.8412	14.2068	14.5835	14.9716	15.7836	16.6455
12	13.7956	14.1920	14.6020	15.0258	15.4640	15.9171	16.3856	16.8699	17.8885	18.9771
13	15.1404	15.6178	16.1130	16.6268	17.1599	17.7130	18.2868	18.8821	20.1406	21.4953
14	16.5190	17.0863	17.6770	18.2919	18.9321	19.5986	20.2926	21.0151	22.5505	24.2149
15	17.9319	18.5989	19.2957	20.0236	20.7840	21.5786	22.4087	23.2760	25.1290	27.1521
16	19.3802	20.1569	20.9710	21.8245	22.7193	23.6575	24.6411	25.6725	27.8881	30.3243
17	20.8647	21.7616	22.7050	23.6975	24.7417	25.8404	26.9964	28.2129	30.8402	33.7502
18	22.3864	23.4144	24.4997	25.6454	26.8551	28.1324	29.4812	30.9057	33.9990	37.4502
19	23.9460	25.1169	26.3572	27.6712	29.0636	30.5390	32.1027	33.7600	37.3790	41.4463
20	25.5447	26.8704	28.2797	29.7781	31.3714	33.0660	34.8683	36.7856	40.9955	45.7620
21	27.1833	28.6765	30.2695	31.9692	33.7831	35.7193	37.7861	39.9927	44.8652	50.4229
22	28.8629	30.5368	32.3289	34.2480	36.3034	38.5052	40.8644	43.3923	49.0057	55.4568
23	30.5844	32.4529	34.4604	36.6179	38.9370	41.4305	44.1118	46.9958	53.4361	60.8933
24	32.3490	34.4265	36.6665	39.0826	41.6892	44.5020	47.5380	50.8156	58.1767	66.7648
25	34.1578	36.4593	38.9499	41.6459	44.5652	47.7271	51.1526	54.8645	63.2490	73.1059
26	36.0117	38.5530	41.3131	44.3117	47.5706	51.1135	54.9660	59.1564	68.6765	79.9544
27	37.9120	40.7096	43.7591	47.0842	50.7113	54.6691	58.9891	63.7058	74.4838	87.3508
28	39.8598	42.9309	46.2906	49.9676	53.9933	58.4026	63.2335	68.5281	80.6977	95.3388
29	41.8563	45.2189	48.9108	52.9663	57.4230	62.3227	67.7114	73.6398	87.3465	103.966
30	43.9027	47.5754	51.6227	56.0849	61.0071	66.4389	72.4355	79.0582	94.4608	113.283
31	46.0003	50.0027	54.4295	59.3283	64.7524	70.7608	77.4194	84.8017	102.073	123.346
32	48.1503	52.5028	57.3345	62.7015	68.6662	75.2988	82.6774	90.8898	110.218	134.214
33	50.3540	55.0778	60.3412	66.2095	72.7562	80.0638	88.2248	97.3432	118.933	145.951
34	52.6129	57.7302	63.4532	69.8579	77.0303	85.0670	94.0771	104.184	128.259	158.627
35	54.9282	60.4621	66.6740	73.6522	81.4966	90.3203	100.251	111.435	138.237	172.317
36	57.3014	63.2759	70.0076	77.5983	86.1640	95.8363	106.765	119.121	148.913	187.102
37	59.7340	66.1742	73.4579	81.7023	91.0413	101.628	113.637	127.268	160.337	203.070
38	62.2273	69.1595	77.0289	85.9703	96.1382	107.710	120.887	135.904	172.561	220.316
39	64.7830	72.2342	80.7249	90.4092	101.464	114.095	128.536	145.058	185.640	238.941
40	67.4026	75.4013	84.5503	95.0255	107.030	120.800	136.606	154.762	199.635	259.057
41	70.0876	78.6633	88.5095	99.8265	112.847	127.840	145.119	165.048	214.610	280.781
42	72.8398	82.0232	92.6074	104.820	118.925	135.232	154.100	175.951	230.632	304.244
43	75.6608	85.4839	96.8486	110.012	125.276	142.993	163.576	187.508	247.777	329.583
44	78.5523	89.0484	101.238	115.413	131.914	151.143	173.573	199.758	266.121	356.950
45	81.5161	92.7199	105.782	121.029	138.850	159.700	184.119	212.744	285.749	386.506
46	84.5540	96.5015	110.484	126.871	146.098	168.685	195.246	226.508	306.752	418.426
47	87.6679	100.397	115.351	132.945	153.673	178.119	206.984	241.099	329.224	452.900
48	90.8596	104.408	120.388	139.263	161.588	188.025	219.368	256.565	353.270	490.132
49	94.1311	108.541	125.602	145.834	169.859	198.427	232.434	272.958	378.999	530.343
50	97.4844	112.797	130.998	152.667	178.503	209.348	246.217	290.336	406.529	573.770

Example: The amount of an annuity certain yielding an annual rent of $400 for 10 years with effective interest at 4 per cent may be found in the following way: (a) Enter the table in the column headed 4 per cent and opposite n = 10 read 12.0061 . ., the amount of 1. (b) Multiply this tabular value by 400 to obtain the result.

Table VI.   Present Value of 1 per Annum

$$a_{\overline{n}|} = \frac{1 - (1+i)^{-n}}{i}$$

n	2 1/2%	3%	3 1/2%	4%	4 1/2%	5%	5 1/2%	6%	7%	8%
1	0.97561	0.97087	0.96618	0.96154	0.95694	0.95238	0.94787	0.94340	0.93458	0.92593
2	1.92742	1.91347	1.89969	1.88609	1.87267	1.85941	1.84632	1.83339	1.80802	1.78326
3	2.85602	2.82861	2.80164	2.77509	2.74896	2.72325	2.69793	2.67301	2.62432	2.57710
4	3.76197	3.71710	3.67308	3.62990	3.58753	3.54595	3.50515	3.46511	3.38721	3.31213
5	4.64583	4.57971	4.51505	4.45182	4.38998	4.32948	4.27028	4.21236	4.10020	3.99271
6	5.50812	5.41719	5.32855	5.24214	5.15787	5.07569	4.99553	4.91732	4.76654	4.62288
7	6.34939	6.23028	6.11454	6.00205	5.89270	5.78637	5.68297	5.58238	5.38929	5.20637
8	7.17014	7.01969	6.87396	6.73275	6.59589	6.46321	6.33457	6.20979	5.97130	5.74664
9	7.97087	7.78611	7.60769	7.43533	7.26879	7.10782	6.95220	6.80169	6.51523	6.24689
10	8.75206	8.53020	8.31661	8.11090	7.91272	7.72173	7.53763	7.36009	7.02358	6.71008
11	9.51421	9.25262	9.00155	8.76048	8.52892	8.30641	8.09254	7.88687	7.49867	7.13896
12	10.2578	9.95400	9.66333	9.38507	9.11858	8.86325	8.61852	8.38384	7.94269	7.53608
13	10.9832	10.6350	10.3027	9.98565	9.68285	9.39357	9.11708	8.85268	8.35765	7.90378
14	11.6909	11.2961	10.9205	10.5631	10.2228	9.89864	9.58965	9.29498	8.74547	8.24424
15	12.3814	11.9379	11.5174	11.1184	10.7396	10.3797	10.0376	9.71225	9.10791	8.55948
16	13.0550	12.5611	12.0941	11.6523	11.2340	10.8378	10.4622	10.1059	9.44665	8.85137
17	13.7122	13.1661	12.6513	12.1657	11.7072	11.2741	10.8646	10.4773	9.76322	9.12164
18	14.3534	13.7535	13.1897	12.6593	12.1600	11.6896	11.2461	10.8276	10.0591	9.37189
19	14.9789	14.3238	13.7098	13.1339	12.5933	12.0853	11.6077	11.1581	10.3356	9.60360
20	15.5892	14.8775	14.2124	13.5903	13.0079	12.4622	11.9504	11.4699	10.5940	9.81815
21	16.1846	15.4150	14.6980	14.0292	13.4047	12.8212	12.2752	11.7641	10.8355	10.0168
22	16.7654	15.9369	15.1671	14.4511	13.7844	13.1630	12.5832	12.0416	11.0612	10.2007
23	17.3321	16.4436	15.6204	14.8568	14.1478	13.4886	12.8750	12.3034	11.2722	10.3711
24	17.8850	16.9355	16.0584	15.2470	14.4955	13.7986	13.1517	12.5504	11.4693	10.5288
25	18.4244	17.4132	16.4815	15.6221	14.8282	14.0939	13.4139	12.7834	11.6536	10.6748
26	18.9506	17.8768	16.8904	15.9828	15.1466	14.3752	13.6625	13.0032	11.8258	10.8100
27	19.4640	18.3270	17.2854	16.3296	15.4513	14.6430	13.8981	13.2105	11.9867	10.9352
28	19.9649	18.7641	17.6670	16.6631	15.7429	14.8981	14.1214	13.4062	12.1371	11.0511
29	20.4536	19.1885	18.0358	16.9837	16.0219	15.1411	14.3331	13.5907	12.2777	11.1584
30	20.9303	19.6004	18.3921	17.2920	16.2889	15.3725	14.5337	13.7648	12.4090	11.2578
31	21.3954	20.0004	18.7363	17.5885	16.5444	15.5928	14.7239	13.9291	12.5318	11.3498
32	21.8492	20.3888	19.0689	17.8736	16.7889	15.8027	14.9042	14.0840	12.6466	11.4350
33	22.2919	20.7658	19.3902	18.1477	17.0229	16.0026	15.0751	14.2302	12.7538	11.5139
34	22.7238	21.1318	19.7007	18.4112	17.2468	16.1929	15.2370	14.3681	12.8540	11.5869
35	23.1452	21.4872	20.0007	18.6646	17.4610	16.3742	15.3906	14.4983	12.9477	11.6546
36	23.5563	21.8323	20.2905	18.9083	17.6660	16.5469	15.5361	14.6210	13.0352	11.7172
37	23.9573	22.1672	20.5705	19.1426	17.8622	16.7113	15.6740	14.7368	13.1170	11.7752
38	24.3486	22.4925	20.8411	19.3679	18.0500	16.8679	15.8047	14.8460	13.1935	11.8289
39	24.7303	22.8082	21.1025	19.5845	18.2297	17.0170	15.9287	14.9491	13.2649	11.8786
40	25.1028	23.1148	21.3551	19.7928	18.4016	17.1591	16.0461	15.0463	13.3317	11.9246
41	25.4661	23.4124	21.5991	19.9931	18.5661	17.2944	16.1575	15.1380	13.3941	11.9672
42	25.8206	23.7014	21.8348	20.1856	18.7236	17.4232	16.2630	15.2245	13.4525	12.0067
43	26.1665	23.9819	22.0627	20.3708	18.8742	17.5459	16.3630	15.3062	13.5070	12.0432
44	26.5039	24.2543	22.2828	20.5488	19.0184	17.6628	16.4579	15.3832	13.5579	12.0771
45	26.8330	24.5187	22.4955	20.7200	19.1564	17.7741	16.5477	15.4558	13.6055	12.1084
46	27.1542	24.7755	22.7009	20.8847	19.2884	17.8801	16.6329	15.5244	13.6500	12.1374
47	27.4675	25.0247	22.8994	21.0429	19.4147	17.9810	16.7137	15.5890	13.6916	12.1643
48	27.7732	25.2667	23.0913	21.1951	19.5356	18.0772	16.7902	15.6500	13.7305	12.1891
49	28.0714	25.5017	23.2766	21.3415	19.6513	18.1687	16.8628	15.7076	13.7668	12.2122
50	28.3623	25.7298	23.4556	21.4822	19.7620	18.2559	16.9315	15.7619	13.8008	12.2335

Example: The present value of $39 per year for 20 years with an effective interest rate of 5 per cent is found in the following way: (a) Enter the table at the column headed 5 per cent and opposite $n = 20$ read 12.4622 . . , the present value of 1 per year. (b) Multiply the tabular value by 39 to obtain the result.

The Annuity Which 1 Will Purchase is the annuity whose present value is 1. Denote the annual rent of such an annuity by r. Then

$$r = \frac{1}{a_{\overline{n}|}} \qquad (19)$$

If the purchase price is A, the annual rent is

$$R = rA = \frac{A}{a_{\overline{n}|}} = \frac{Ai}{1 - (1+i)^{-n}} \qquad (20)$$

Table VII. Annuity Which 1 Will Purchase

$$\frac{1}{a_{\overline{n}|}} = \frac{i}{1 - (1+i)^{-n}}, \quad \text{or} \quad \frac{1}{s_{\overline{n}|}} + i$$

n	2 1/2%	3%	3 1/2%	4%	4 1/2%	5%	5 1/2%	6%	7%	8%
1	1.025000	1.030000	1.035000	1.040000	1.045000	1.050000	1.055000	1.060000	1.070000	1.080000
2	0.518827	0.522611	0.526401	0.530196	0.533998	0.537805	0.541618	0.545437	0.553092	0.560769
3	0.350137	0.353530	0.356934	0.360349	0.363773	0.367209	0.370654	0.374110	0.381052	0.388033
4	0.265818	0.269027	0.272251	0.275490	0.278744	0.282012	0.285295	0.288591	0.295228	0.301921
5	0.215247	0.218355	0.221481	0.224627	0.227792	0.230975	0.234176	0.237396	0.243891	0.250456
6	0.181550	0.184598	0.187668	0.190762	0.193878	0.197018	0.200179	0.203363	0.209796	0.216315
7	0.157495	0.160506	0.163545	0.166610	0.169702	0.172820	0.175964	0.179135	0.185553	0.192072
8	0.139467	0.142456	0.145477	0.148528	0.151610	0.154722	0.157864	0.161036	0.167468	0.174015
9	0.125457	0.128434	0.131446	0.134493	0.137575	0.140690	0.143840	0.147022	0.153487	0.160079
10	0.114259	0.117231	0.120241	0.123291	0.126379	0.129505	0.132668	0.135868	0.142378	0.149029
11	0.105106	0.108077	0.111092	0.114149	0.117248	0.120389	0.123571	0.126793	0.133357	0.140076
12	0.097487	0.100462	0.103484	0.106552	0.109666	0.112825	0.116029	0.119277	0.125902	0.132695
13	0.091048	0.094030	0.097062	0.100144	0.103275	0.106456	0.109684	0.112960	0.119651	0.126522
14	0.085537	0.088526	0.091571	0.094669	0.097820	0.101024	0.104279	0.107585	0.114345	0.121297
15	0.080767	0.083767	0.086825	0.089941	0.093114	0.096342	0.099626	0.102963	0.109795	0.116829
16	0.076599	0.079611	0.082685	0.085820	0.089015	0.092270	0.095583	0.098952	0.105858	0.112977
17	0.072928	0.075953	0.079043	0.082199	0.085418	0.088699	0.092042	0.095445	0.102425	0.109629
18	0.069670	0.072709	0.075817	0.078993	0.082237	0.085546	0.088920	0.092357	0.099413	0.106702
19	0.066761	0.069814	0.072940	0.076139	0.079407	0.082745	0.086150	0.089621	0.096753	0.104128
20	0.064147	0.067216	0.070361	0.073582	0.076876	0.080243	0.083679	0.087185	0.094393	0.101852
21	0.061787	0.064872	0.068037	0.071280	0.074601	0.077996	0.081465	0.085005	0.092289	0.099832
22	0.059647	0.062747	0.065932	0.069199	0.072546	0.075971	0.079471	0.083046	0.090406	0.098032
23	0.057696	0.060814	0.064019	0.067309	0.070683	0.074137	0.077670	0.081279	0.088714	0.096422
24	0.055913	0.059047	0.062273	0.065587	0.068987	0.072471	0.076036	0.079679	0.087189	0.094978
25	0.054276	0.057428	0.060674	0.064012	0.067439	0.070953	0.074549	0.078227	0.085811	0.093679
26	0.052769	0.055938	0.059205	0.062567	0.066021	0.069564	0.073193	0.076904	0.084561	0.092507
27	0.051377	0.054564	0.057852	0.061239	0.064720	0.068292	0.071952	0.075697	0.083426	0.091448
28	0.050088	0.053293	0.056603	0.060013	0.063521	0.067123	0.070814	0.074593	0.082392	0.090489
29	0.048891	0.052115	0.055445	0.058880	0.062415	0.066046	0.069769	0.073580	0.081449	0.089618
30	0.047778	0.051019	0.054371	0.057830	0.061392	0.065051	0.068805	0.072649	0.080586	0.088827
31	0.046739	0.049999	0.053372	0.056855	0.060443	0.064132	0.067917	0.071792	0.079797	0.088107
32	0.045768	0.049047	0.052442	0.055949	0.059563	0.063280	0.067095	0.071002	0.079073	0.087451
33	0.044859	0.048156	0.051572	0.055104	0.058745	0.062490	0.066335	0.070273	0.078408	0.086852
34	0.044007	0.047322	0.050760	0.054315	0.057982	0.061755	0.065630	0.069598	0.077797	0.086304
35	0.043206	0.046539	0.049999	0.053577	0.057270	0.061072	0.064975	0.068974	0.077234	0.085803
36	0.042452	0.045804	0.049284	0.052887	0.056606	0.060435	0.064366	0.068395	0.076715	0.085345
37	0.041741	0.045112	0.048613	0.052240	0.055984	0.059840	0.063800	0.067857	0.076237	0.084924
38	0.041070	0.044459	0.047982	0.051632	0.055402	0.059284	0.063272	0.067358	0.075795	0.084539
39	0.040436	0.043844	0.047388	0.051061	0.054856	0.058765	0.062780	0.066894	0.075387	0.084185
40	0.039836	0.043262	0.046827	0.050524	0.054343	0.058278	0.062320	0.066462	0.075009	0.083860
41	0.039268	0.042712	0.046298	0.050017	0.053862	0.057822	0.061891	0.066059	0.074660	0.083562
42	0.038729	0.042192	0.045798	0.049540	0.053409	0.057395	0.061489	0.065683	0.074336	0.083287
43	0.038217	0.041698	0.045325	0.049090	0.052982	0.056993	0.061113	0.065333	0.074036	0.083034
44	0.037730	0.041230	0.044878	0.048665	0.052581	0.056616	0.060761	0.065006	0.073758	0.082802
45	0.037268	0.040785	0.044453	0.048263	0.052202	0.056262	0.060431	0.064701	0.073500	0.082587
46	0.036827	0.040363	0.044051	0.047882	0.051845	0.055928	0.060122	0.064415	0.073260	0.082390
47	0.036407	0.039961	0.043669	0.047522	0.051507	0.055614	0.059831	0.064148	0.073037	0.082208
48	0.036006	0.039578	0.043307	0.047181	0.051189	0.055318	0.059559	0.063898	0.072831	0.082040
49	0.035624	0.039213	0.042962	0.046857	0.050887	0.055040	0.059302	0.063664	0.072639	0.081886
50	0.035258	0.038866	0.042634	0.046550	0.050602	0.054777	0.059062	0.063444	0.072460	0.081743

Example: The annual rent for 10 years which $3900 will purchase at an effective interest rate of 5 per cent is found in the following way: (a) Enter the table at the column headed 5 per cent and opposite n = 10 read 0.129505 . ., the rent purchased by 1. (b) Multiply the tabular value by 3900 to obtain the result.

A Sinking or Amortization Fund is a fund set aside to provide a definite sum (usually for canceling a debt) at a certain time; it is usually created by equal and regular contributions and their interest earnings, compounded; that is, by an annuity and its interest earnings. Denote the annual instalment or rent required by R, the amount of the sinking fund by S, the number of years for its creation by n, and the effective rate of interest by i. Then

$$R = \frac{S}{s_{\overline{n}|}} = \frac{Si}{(1+i)^n - 1} \tag{21}$$

Table VIII.　Annuity Which Will Amount to 1 (Sinking Fund)

$$\frac{1}{s_{\overline{n}|}} = \frac{i}{(1+i)^n - 1} \quad \text{or} \quad \frac{1}{a_{\overline{n}|}} - i$$

n	2 1/2%	3%	3 1/2%	4%	4 1/2%	5%	5 1/2%	6%	7%	8%
1	1.000000	1.000000	1.000000	1.000000	1.000000	1.000000	1.000000	1.000000	1.000000	1.000000
2	0.493827	0.492611	0.491400	0.490196	0.488997	0.487805	0.486618	0.485437	0.483092	0.480769
3	0.325137	0.323530	0.321934	0.320349	0.318773	0.317209	0.315654	0.314110	0.311052	0.308033
4	0.240818	0.239027	0.237251	0.235490	0.233744	0.232012	0.230295	0.228591	0.225228	0.221921
5	0.190247	0.188355	0.186481	0.184627	0.182792	0.180975	0.179176	0.177396	0.173891	0.170456
6	0.156550	0.154598	0.152668	0.150762	0.148878	0.147017	0.145179	0.143363	0.139796	0.136315
7	0.132495	0.130506	0.128544	0.126610	0.124701	0.122820	0.120964	0.119135	0.115553	0.112072
8	0.114467	0.112456	0.110477	0.108528	0.106609	0.104722	0.102864	0.101036	0.097468	0.094015
9	0.100457	0.098434	0.096446	0.094493	0.092575	0.090690	0.088840	0.087022	0.083486	0.080079
10	0.089259	0.087231	0.085241	0.083291	0.081379	0.079505	0.077668	0.075868	0.072377	0.069029
11	0.080106	0.078077	0.076092	0.074149	0.072248	0.070389	0.068571	0.066793	0.063357	0.060076
12	0.072487	0.070462	0.068484	0.066552	0.064666	0.062825	0.061029	0.059277	0.055902	0.052695
13	0.066048	0.064030	0.062062	0.060144	0.058275	0.056456	0.054684	0.052960	0.049651	0.046522
14	0.060536	0.058526	0.056571	0.054669	0.052820	0.051024	0.049279	0.047585	0.044345	0.041297
15	0.055766	0.053767	0.051825	0.049941	0.048114	0.046342	0.044626	0.042963	0.039795	0.036829
16	0.051599	0.049611	0.047685	0.045820	0.044015	0.042270	0.040582	0.038952	0.035858	0.032977
17	0.047928	0.045953	0.044043	0.042199	0.040418	0.038699	0.037042	0.035445	0.032425	0.029629
18	0.044670	0.042709	0.040817	0.038993	0.037237	0.035546	0.033920	0.032357	0.029413	0.026702
19	0.041760	0.039814	0.037940	0.036139	0.034407	0.032745	0.031150	0.029621	0.026753	0.024128
20	0.039147	0.037216	0.035361	0.033582	0.031876	0.030243	0.028679	0.027185	0.024393	0.021852
21	0.036787	0.034872	0.033037	0.031280	0.029601	0.027996	0.026465	0.025005	0.022289	0.019832
22	0.034646	0.032747	0.030932	0.029199	0.027546	0.025971	0.024471	0.023046	0.020406	0.018032
23	0.032696	0.030814	0.029019	0.027309	0.025682	0.024137	0.022670	0.021278	0.018714	0.016422
24	0.030913	0.029047	0.027273	0.025587	0.023987	0.022471	0.021036	0.019679	0.017189	0.014978
25	0.029276	0.027428	0.025674	0.024012	0.022439	0.020952	0.019549	0.018227	0.015811	0.013679
26	0.027768	0.025938	0.024205	0.022567	0.021021	0.019564	0.018193	0.016904	0.014561	0.012507
27	0.026377	0.024564	0.022852	0.021239	0.019719	0.018292	0.016952	0.015697	0.013426	0.011448
28	0.025088	0.023293	0.021603	0.020013	0.018521	0.017123	0.015814	0.014593	0.012392	0.010489
29	0.023891	0.022115	0.020445	0.018880	0.017415	0.016046	0.014769	0.013580	0.011449	0.009618
30	0.022777	0.021019	0.019371	0.017830	0.016392	0.015051	0.013805	0.012649	0.010586	0.008827
31	0.021739	0.019999	0.018372	0.016855	0.015443	0.014132	0.012917	0.011792	0.009797	0.008107
32	0.020768	0.019047	0.017442	0.015949	0.014563	0.013280	0.012095	0.011002	0.009073	0.007451
33	0.019859	0.018156	0.016572	0.015104	0.013745	0.012490	0.011335	0.010273	0.008408	0.006852
34	0.019007	0.017322	0.015760	0.014315	0.012982	0.011755	0.010630	0.009598	0.007797	0.006304
35	0.018205	0.016539	0.014998	0.013577	0.012270	0.011072	0.009975	0.008974	0.007234	0.005803
36	0.017451	0.015804	0.014284	0.012887	0.011606	0.010434	0.009366	0.008395	0.006715	0.005345
37	0.016741	0.015112	0.013613	0.012240	0.010984	0.009840	0.008800	0.007857	0.006237	0.004924
38	0.016070	0.014459	0.012982	0.011632	0.010402	0.009284	0.008272	0.007358	0.005795	0.004539
39	0.015436	0.013844	0.012388	0.011061	0.009856	0.008765	0.007780	0.006894	0.005387	0.004185
40	0.014836	0.013262	0.011827	0.010523	0.009343	0.008278	0.007320	0.006462	0.005009	0.003860
41	0.014268	0.012712	0.011298	0.010017	0.008862	0.007822	0.006891	0.006059	0.004660	0.003562
42	0.013728	0.012192	0.010798	0.009540	0.008409	0.007395	0.006489	0.005683	0.004336	0.003287
43	0.013217	0.011698	0.010325	0.009090	0.007982	0.006993	0.006113	0.005333	0.004036	0.003034
44	0.012730	0.011230	0.009878	0.008665	0.007581	0.006616	0.005761	0.005006	0.003758	0.002802
45	0.012267	0.010785	0.009453	0.008262	0.007202	0.006262	0.005431	0.004701	0.003499	0.002587
46	0.011826	0.010363	0.009051	0.007882	0.006845	0.005928	0.005122	0.004415	0.003260	0.002390
47	0.011407	0.009961	0.008669	0.007522	0.006507	0.005614	0.004831	0.004148	0.003037	0.002208
48	0.011006	0.009578	0.008306	0.007181	0.006189	0.005318	0.004559	0.003898	0.002831	0.002040
49	0.010623	0.009213	0.007962	0.006857	0.005887	0.005040	0.004302	0.003664	0.002639	0.001886
50	0.010258	0.008866	0.007634	0.006550	0.005602	0.004777	0.004062	0.003444	0.002460	0.001743

Example: The annual instalment required to create a fund of $22,000 in 25 years at 4 per cent may be found in the following way: (a) Enter the table at the column headed 4 per cent and opposite n = 25 read 0.024012 . . , the annual instalment to accumulate 1. (b) Multiply this tabular value by 22,000 to obtain the result.

A **Life Annuity** * is one whose payments continue only during the lifetime of the recipient. Its cost and present value depend not only upon the rate of interest but also upon the *probability of living* and differs in this respect from an annuity certain.

* For the theory of life insurance computations see Mathematical Theory of Finance, by Putnam, John Wiley & Sons, Inc.

Mortality tables (Table IX) are constructed from the experience of agencies such as insurance companies to indicate the probable deaths occurring in each succeeding year from a chosen initial group. Denote the age of the group by x, the number living by l_x, the number dying in the year interval from x to $x + 1$ by d_x, the probability of living during the year x by p_x, and the probability of dying within the year by q_x, then:

$$d_x = l_x - l_{x+1} \tag{22}$$

$$p_x = \frac{l_{x+1}}{l_x} \tag{23}$$

$$q_x = \frac{d_x}{l_x} = 1 - p_x \tag{24}$$

The probability of a person age x living n years is:

$$_np_x = \frac{l_{x+n}}{l_x} \tag{25}$$

and of not living n years is: $\quad |\ _nq_x = 1 - {}_np_x \tag{26}$

Table IX. American Experience Table of Mortality

Age x	Number living l_x	Number of deaths d_x	Yearly probability of dying q_x	Yearly probability of living p_x	Age x	Number living l_x	Number of deaths d_x	Yearly probability of dying q_x	Yearly probability of living p_x
10	100,000	749	0.007 490	0.992 510	53	66,797	1,091	0.016 333	0.983 667
11	99,251	746	0.007 516	0.992 484	54	65,706	1,143	0.017 396	0.982 604
12	98,505	743	0.007 543	0.992 457	55	64,563	1,199	0.018 571	0.981 429
13	97,762	740	0.007 569	0.992 431	56	63,364	1,260	0.019 885	0.980 115
14	97,022	737	0.007 596	0.992 404	57	62,104	1,325	0.021 335	0.978 665
15	96,285	735	0.007 634	0.992 366	58	60,779	1,394	0.022 936	0.977 064
16	95,550	732	0.007 661	0.992 339	59	59,385	1,468	0.024 720	0.975 280
17	94,818	729	0.007 688	0.992 312	60	57,917	1,546	0.026 693	0.973 307
18	94,089	727	0.007 727	0.992 273	61	56,371	1,628	0.028 880	0.971 120
19	93,362	725	0.007 765	0.992 235	62	54,743	1,713	0.031 292	0.968 708
20	92,637	723	0.007 805	0.992 195	63	53,030	1,800	0.033 943	0.966 057
21	91,914	722	0.007 855	0.992 145	64	51,230	1,889	0.036 873	0.963 127
22	91,192	721	0.007 906	0.992 094	65	49,341	1,980	0.040 129	0.959 871
23	90,471	720	0.007 958	0.992 042	66	47,361	2,070	0.043 707	0.956 293
24	89,751	719	0.008 011	0.991 989	67	45,291	2,158	0.047 647	0.952 353
25	89,032	718	0.008 065	0.991 935	68	43,133	2,243	0.052 002	0.947 998
26	88,314	718	0.008 130	0.991 870	69	40,890	2,321	0.056 762	0.943 238
27	87,596	718	0.008 197	0.991 803	70	38,569	2,391	0.061 993	0.938 007
28	86,878	718	0.008 264	0.991 736	71	36,178	2,448	0.067 665	0.932 335
29	86,160	719	0.008 345	0.991 655	72	33,730	2,487	0.073 733	0.926 267
30	85,441	720	0.008 427	0.991 573	73	31,243	2,505	0.080 178	0.919 822
31	84,721	721	0.008 510	0.991 490	74	28,738	2,501	0.087 028	0.912 972
32	84,000	723	0.008 607	0.991 393	75	26,237	2,476	0.094 371	0.905 629
33	83,277	726	0.008 718	0.991 282	76	23,761	2,431	0.102 311	0.897 689
34	82,551	729	0.008 831	0.991 169	77	21,330	2,369	0.111 064	0.888 936
35	81,822	732	0.008 946	0.991 054	78	18,961	2,291	0.120 827	0.879 173
36	81,090	737	0.009 089	0.990 911	79	16,670	2,196	0.131 734	0.868 266
37	80,353	742	0.009 234	0.990 766	80	14,474	2,091	0.144 466	0.855 534
38	79,611	749	0.009 408	0.990 592	81	12,383	1,964	0.158 605	0.841 395
39	78,862	756	0.009 586	0.990 414	82	10,419	1,816	0.174 297	0.825 703
40	78,106	765	0.009 794	0.990 206	83	8,603	1,648	0.191 561	0.808 439
41	77,341	774	0.010 008	0.989 992	84	6,955	1,470	0.211 359	0.788 641
42	76,567	785	0.010 252	0.989 748	85	5,485	1,292	0.235 552	0.764 448
43	75,782	797	0.010 517	0.989 483	86	4,193	1,114	0.265 681	0.734 319
44	74,985	812	0.010 829	0.989 171	87	3,079	933	0.303 020	0.696 980
45	74,173	828	0.011 163	0.988 837	88	2,146	744	0.346 692	0.653 308
46	73,345	848	0.011 562	0.988 438	89	1,402	555	0.395 863	0.604 137
47	72,497	870	0.012 000	0.988 000	90	847	385	0.454 545	0.545 455
48	71,627	896	0.012 509	0.987 491	91	462	246	0.532 466	0.467 534
49	70,731	927	0.013 106	0.986 894	92	216	137	0.634 259	0.365 741
50	69,804	962	0.013 781	0.986 219	93	79	58	0.734 177	0.265 823
51	68,842	1,011	0.014 541	0.985 459	94	21	18	0.857 143	0.142 857
52	67,841	1,044	0.015 389	0.984 611	95	3	3	1.000 000	0.000 000

Present Value of a Life Annuity. If p is the probability of receiving a certain sum of money S, the value of the *expectation* is pS and the present value of S due in n years is,

$$pS(1 + i)^{-n} = pSv^n \tag{27}$$

The present value of the expectation of a person, x years of age, who is to receive 1 if he lives n more years is called the *n-year pure endowment of 1* denoted by $_nE_x$.

$$_nE_x = {_np_x} \cdot v^n \tag{28}$$

Similarly, the present value of a *life annuity* of 1 beginning at age $x + m$ to a person of age x is,

$$a_{x+m} = \sum_{n=m}^{95-x} {_nE_x,} \tag{29}$$

since 95 is the upper bound of age in the American Experience Table of Mortality.

GEOMETRY

By Janvier M. Rice

21.　GEOMETRIC CONCEPTS

Definitions and fundamental properties of important geometric figures and geometric relations are given below. In general, very common and well-known terms (as point, line, radius, etc.) are not discussed.

Plane Angles

A **Plane Angle** measures the extent or degree to which two straight lines deviate in direction. Straight lines that have the same direction do not meet or intersect in finite distances and are called *parallel lines*. Two straight lines that are not parallel but lie in the same plane intersect. The point of intersection of non-parallel lines is the *vertex* of the angle between them. The *size of the angle* is the extent of the opening between the lines and is independent of their length. The size of an angle generated by a revolving line varies from zero to one *complete revolution* as the line is rotated about a vertex to its original position.

A **Degree** (°) is $1/360$ of a revolution (or *perigon*) and is divided into 60 units called *minutes* (′) which in turn are divided into 60 units called *seconds* (″).

A **Radian** is a *central angle* which intercepts a *circular arc* equal to its *radius*. One radian, therefore, equals $360/2\pi$ degrees or 57.295779513°, and 1° = 0.017453293 radian.

An **Angle** of 90° is called a *right angle*, and the lines that form it are said to be *perpendicular*. An angle less than a right angle is called *acute*. An angle greater than a right angle but less than 180° is called *obtuse*. If the sum of two angles equals 90°, they are said to be *complementary* to each other, and if their sum is 180°, *supplementary* to each other.

Polygons

A **Polygon**, or *plane rectilinear figure*, is a portion of a plane bounded by straight lines.

A **Triangle** is a polygon of three sides. It is *isosceles* if two sides (and their opposite angles) are equal; it is *equilateral* if all three sides (and all three angles) are equal.

A **Quadrilateral** is a polygon of four sides. This classification includes the *trapezium* having no two sides parallel; the *trapezoid* having two opposite sides parallel (*isosceles trapezoid* if the non-parallel sides are equal); and the *parallelogram* having both pairs of opposite sides parallel and equal. The parallelogram includes the *rhomboid* having no right angles and, in general, adjacent sides not equal; the *rhombus* having no right angles but all sides equal; the *rectangle* having only right angles and, in general, adjacent sides not equal; and the *square* having only right angles, and all sides equal.

Similar Polygons have their respective angles equal and their corresponding sides proportional.

A **Regular Polygon** has all sides equal and all angles equal. An *equilateral triangle* and a *square* are regular polygons.

Other Polygons classified according to number of sides are: (5) *pentagon*; (6) *hexagon*; (7) *heptagon*; (8) *octagon*; (9) *enneagon* or *nonagon*; (10) *decagon*; (12) *dodecagon*. Two regular polygons of the same number of sides are *similar*.

Properties of Triangles.

General Triangle. The sum of the angles equals 180°. $\angle XAB$ (Fig. 1) is an *exterior angle* of $\triangle ABC$ and equals the sum of the opposite *interior angles* (i.e., $\angle XAB = \angle B + \angle C$). A *median* of a triangle is a line joining a vertex to the mid-point of the opposite side. The three medians meet at the *center of gravity*, G, and G trisects each median (i.e., $AG = 2/3\,AD$, etc.) *Bisectors of angles* of a triangle (Fig. 2) meet in a point M equidistant from all sides. M is the center of the *inscribed circle* (tangent to all sides), or the *incenter* of the triangle. An angle bisector divides the opposite side into segments

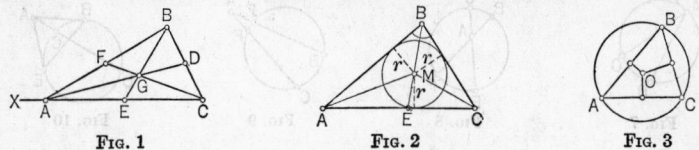

| FIG. 1 | FIG. 2 | FIG. 3 |

proportional to the adjacent sides of the angle (i.e., $AE/EC = AB/BC$, etc.). An *altitude* of a triangle is a perpendicular from a vertex to the opposite side. The three altitudes meet in a point called the *orthocenter*. The *perpendicular bisectors* of the sides of a triangle (Fig. 3) meet in a point O equidistant from all vertices. O is the center of the *circumscribed circle* (passing through all vertices), or the *circumcenter* of the triangle. The longest side of a triangle is opposite the largest angle, and vice versa. The line joining the mid-points of two sides of a triangle is parallel to the third side and half its length. If two triangles are mutually equiangular, they are *similar*, and their corresponding sides are proportional.

Orthogonal Projection. In Figs. 4 and 5, AE is the orthogonal projection of AB on AC, BE being perpendicular to AC. The square of the side opposite an acute angle equals the sum of the squares of the other two sides diminished by twice the product of one of those sides by the orthogonal projection of the other side upon it. In Fig. 4, $a^2 = b^2 + c^2 - 2b \cdot AE$. The square of the side opposite an obtuse angle equals the sum of the squares of the other two sides increased by twice the product of one of those sides by the orthogonal projection of the other side upon it. In Fig. 5, $a^2 = b^2 + c^2 + 2b \cdot AE$.

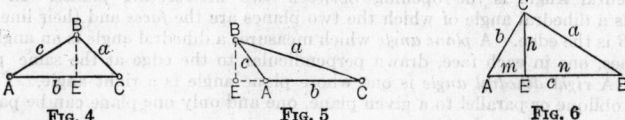

| FIG. 4 | FIG. 5 | FIG. 6 |

Right Triangle. In Fig. 6, let h be the *altitude* drawn from the vertex of right angle C to the *hypotenuse* c. Then $\angle A + \angle B = 90°$; $c^2 = a^2 + b^2$; $h^2 = mn$; $b^2 = cm$; $a^2 = cn$; median from $C = c/2$.

Isosceles Triangle. Two sides are equal and their opposite angles are equal. If a straight line from the vertex at which the equal sides meet bisects the base, it also bisects the vertical angle and is perpendicular to the base. .

Plane Curvilinear Figures

An *arc* is a part of a curve. A *chord* is a straight line joining two points on a curve (i.e., joining the extremities of an arc). A *segment* of a curve is that portion of its plane included between a concave arc and its chord. An angle *intercepts* an arc cut off by its sides; the arc *subtends* the angle. Two curves are *tangent* to each other at a point if, in passing the point, they touch each other. If one of the "curves" is a straight line, the line itself is called a *tangent* to the curve.

A **Circle** is a closed plane curve (or the surface bounded by the curve), all the points of which are equidistant from a *center* point within. A *central angle* is one whose vertex is at the center and whose sides are two radii. A *sector* of a circle is the part of its plane which is included between an arc and two radii drawn to its extremities. A *secant* of a circle is a straight line intersecting it in two points. Parallel secants (or tangents) intercept equal arcs. A tangent line meets a circle in only one point and is perpendicular to the radius to that point. If a radius is perpendicular to a chord, it bisects both the chord and the arc intercepted by the chord. If two circles are tangent to each other, the line of centers passes through the point of contact; if the circles intersect, the line of centers bisects the common chord at right angles. In Fig. 8, the product of linear segments AC and AE equals the product of linear segments AB and AF. In Fig. 9, the product of the whole secant AB and its external segment AE equals the product of the whole secant AC and its external segment AF. In Fig. 10, the product of the whole secant AD and its external segment AC equals the square of tangent AB (or AE). Also $\angle\ ABE = \angle\ AEB$.

Angle Measurement. Considering the arc of a circle to be expressed in terms of the central angle which it subtends, the arc may be said to contain a certain number of degrees

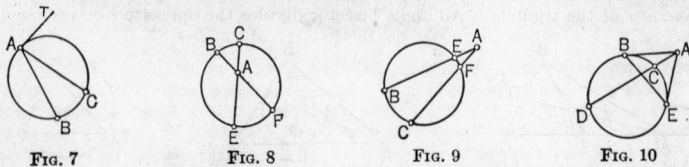

FIG. 7   FIG. 8   FIG. 9   FIG. 10

and hence be used to express the measurement of other angles related to the circle. On this basis, an entire circle equals 360°. The *inscribed angle* formed by two chords intersecting on a circle equals half the arc intercepted by it. Thus, in Fig. 7, $\angle\ BAC = 1/2$ arc BC. An angle inscribed in a semicircle is a right angle. The angle formed by a tangent to a circle and a chord having one extremity at the point of contact equals half the arc intercepted by the chord. In Fig. 7, $\angle\ BAT = 1/2$ arc BCA. The angle formed by two chords intersecting within a circle equals half the sum of the intercepted arcs. In Fig. 8, $\angle\ BAC$ (or $\angle\ EAF$) $= 1/2$ (arc $BC +$ arc EF), and $\angle\ BAE$ (or $\angle\ CAF$) $= 1/2$ (arc $BE +$ arc CF). The angle formed by two secants, or two tangents, or a secant and a tangent, intersecting outside a circle, equals half the difference of the intercepted arcs. In Fig. 9, $\angle\ BAC = 1/2$ (arc $BC -$ arc EF). In Fig. 10, $\angle\ BAE = 1/2$ (arc $BDE -$ arc BCE), and $\angle\ BAD = 1/2$ (arc $BD -$ arc BC).

Other Plane Curves appearing in the mensuration table on pp. 2-38 to 2-40 are defined and discussed in the section on analytic geometry.

Non-Planar Angles

A **Dihedral Angle** is the opening between two intersecting planes. In Fig. 11, $P-BD-Q$ is a dihedral angle of which the two planes are the *faces* and their line of intersection DB is the edge. A *plane angle* which measures a dihedral angle is an angle formed by two lines, one in each face, drawn perpendicular to the edge at the same point (as $\angle\ ABC$). A *right dihedral angle* is one whose plane angle is a right angle. Through a given line oblique or parallel to a given plane, one and only one plane can be passed per-

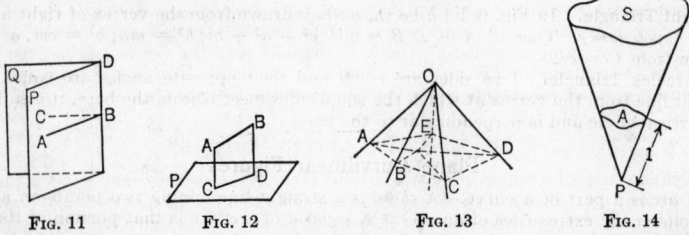

FIG. 11   FIG. 12   FIG. 13   FIG. 14

pendicular to the given plane. The line of intersection CD (Fig. 12) is the *orthogonal projection* of line AB upon plane P. The *angle between a line and a plane* is the angle that the line (produced if necessary) makes with its orthogonal projection on the plane. This angle is the least angle which the line makes with any line in the plane.

A **Polyhedral Angle** is the opening of three or more planes which meet in a common point. In Fig. 13, $O-ABCDE$ is a polyhedral angle of which the intersections of the planes, as OA, OB, etc., are the *edges*; the portions of the planes lying between the edges are the *faces*; and the common point O is the *vertex*. Angles formed by adjacent edges, as angles AOB, BOC, etc., are *face angles*. A polyhedral angle is called a *trihedral angle* if it has three faces; a *tetrahedral angle* if it has four faces; and so on.

A **Solid Angle** measures the opening between surfaces, either planar or non-planar, which meet in a common point. The polyhedral angle is a special case. In Fig. 14 the solid angle at any point P, subtended by any surface S, is equal numerically to the portion

A of the surface of a sphere of unit radius which is cut out by a conical surface with vertex at P and having the perimeter of S for base. The *unit solid angle* is the *steradian* and equals the central solid angle which intercepts a spherical area (of any shape) equal to the (radius)^2. The total solid angle about a point equals 4π steradians.

A **Spherical Angle** is the opening between two arcs of great circles drawn from the same point (*vertex*), and is measured by the plane angle formed by tangents to its sides at its vertex. If the planes of the great circles are perpendicular, the angle is a *right spherical angle*.

Polyhedrons

A **Polyhedron** is a solid bounded by plane surfaces.

A **Prism** is a polyhedron of which two faces (the *bases*) are congruent polygons in parallel planes and the other (*lateral*) faces are parallelograms whose planes intersect in the *lateral edges*. Prisms are *triangular, rectangular, quadrangular*, and so on, according as their bases are triangles, rectangles, quadrilaterals, and so on. A *right prism* has its lateral edges perpendicular to its bases. A prism whose bases are parallelograms is a *parallelepiped*; if in addition the edges are perpendicular to the bases, it is a *right parallelepiped*. A *rectangular parallelepiped* is a *right* parallelepiped whose bases are rectangles. A *cube* is a parallelepiped whose six faces are squares. A *truncated prism* is that part of a prism included between a base and a section made by a plane oblique to the base. A *right section* of a prism is a section made by a plane which cuts all the lateral edges and is perpendicular to them.

A **Prismatoid** is a polyhedron of which two faces (the *bases*) are polygons in parallel planes and the other (*lateral*) faces are triangles or trapezoids with one side common with one base and the opposite vertex or side common with the other base.

A **Pyramid** is a polyhedron of which one face (the *base*) is a polygon and the other (*lateral*) faces are triangles meeting in a common point called the *vertex* of the pyramid and intersecting one another in its *lateral edges*. Pyramids are *triangular, quadrangular*, and so on, according as their bases are triangles, quadrilaterals, and so on. A *regular pyramid* (or *right pyramid*) has for its base a regular polygon whose center coincides with the foot of the perpendicular dropped from the vertex to the base. A *frustum of a pyramid* is the portion of a pyramid included between its base and a section parallel to the base. If the section is not parallel to the base, a *truncated pyramid* results.

A **Regular Polyhedron** has all faces formed of congruent regular polygons and all polyhedral angles equal. The only regular polyhedrons possible are the five types discussed in the mensuration table, p. 2–41.

A **Tetrahedron** is a polyhedron of four faces. It may be described also as a triangular pyramid, and any one of its four triangular faces may be considered as the base. The four perpendiculars erected at circumcenters of the four faces meet in a point equidistant from all vertices, which is the center of the circumscribed sphere. The four *medians*, joining each vertex with the center of gravity of the opposite face, meet in a point, which is the *center of gravity* of the tetrahedron. This point is three-fourths of the distance from each vertex along a median. The four altitudes meet in a point, called the *orthocenter* of the tetrahedron. The six planes bisecting the six dihedral angles meet in a point equidistant from all faces, this being the center of the inscribed sphere.

Solids Having Curved Surfaces

A **Cylinder** is a solid bounded by two parallel plane surfaces (the *bases*) and a cylindrical *lateral* surface. A *cylindrical surface* is a surface generated by the movement of a straight line (the *generatrix*) which constantly is parallel to a fixed straight line and touches a fixed curve (the *directrix*) not in the plane of the fixed straight line. The generatrix in any position is an *element* of the cylindrical surface. A *circular cylinder* is one having circular bases. A *right cylinder* is one whose elements are perpendicular to its bases. A *truncated cylinder* is the part of a cylinder included between a base and a section made by a plane oblique to the base. A *right section* of a cylinder is a section made by a plane which cuts all the elements and is perpendicular to them.

A **Cone** is a solid bounded by a conic *lateral* surface and a plane (the *base*) which cuts all the elements of the conic surface. A *conic surface* is a surface generated by the movement of a straight line (the *generatrix*) which constantly touches a fixed plane curve (the *directrix*) and passes through a fixed point (the *vertex*) not in the plane of the fixed curve. The generatrix in any position is an *element* of the conic surface. A *circular cone* is one having a circular base. A *right cone* is a circular cone whose center of the base coincides with the foot of the perpendicular dropped from the vertex to the base. A *frustum of a cone* is the portion of a cone included between its base and a section parallel to the base.

A **Sphere** is a solid bounded by a surface all points of which are equidistant from a point within called the *center*. Every plane section of a sphere is a circle. This circle is a *great circle* if its plane passes through the center of the sphere; otherwise, it is a *small circle*. *Poles* of such a circle are the extremities of the diameter of the sphere which is perpendicular to the plane of the circle. Through two points on a spherical surface, not extremities of a diameter, one great circle can be passed. The shortest line that can be drawn on the surface of a sphere between two such points is an arc of a great circle less than a semicircumference joining those points. If two spherical surfaces intersect, their line of intersection is a circle whose plane is perpendicular to the line of centers, and whose center lies on this line.

A **Spherical Sector** is the portion of a sphere generated by the revolution of a circular sector about a diameter of the circle of which the sector is a part. A *hemisphere* is half of a sphere.

A **Spherical Segment** is the portion of a sphere contained between two parallel plane sections (the *bases*), one of which may be tangent to the sphere (in which case there is only one base). The term "segment" also is applied in an analogous manner to various solids of revolution, the planes in such cases being perpendicular to an axis. A *zone* is the portion of a spherical surface included between two parallel planes.

A **Spherical Polygon** is a figure on a spherical surface bounded by three or more arcs of great circles. The sum of the angles of a spherical triangle (polygon of three sides) is greater than two right angles and less than six right angles.

Other Solids appearing in the mensuration table on pp. 2–41 to 2–44, if not sufficiently defined by their figures, may be found discussed in the section on analytic geometry.

22. MENSURATION

Mensuration treats of the measurement of lines, surfaces, and solids, in terms of length, area, and volume, respectively. Table I furnishes important mensuration formulas for the more common plane figures and solids. In addition to these formulas, useful data on circumferences and areas of circles, length of their arcs, and various properties of their segments, as well as data on volumes of spheres, may be found in Tables 7 of Section 1. The area of the surface of a sphere may be obtained by multiplying the area of a great circle (Table 7) by 4.

Perimeters (or Circumferences) of Similar Figures are to each other as their respective linear dimensions. Thus, the perimeter of a quadrilateral having a side $2a$ has twice the length of the perimeter of a similar quadrilateral whose corresponding side is a; the circumference of a circle of radius $2r$ is twice that of one of radius r; and so on.

Areas of Similar Figures are to each other as the squares of their respective linear dimensions. Thus, the area of a triangle having a side $2a$ is four times the area of a similar triangle whose corresponding side is a; the area of the surface of a sphere of radius $2r$ is four times the area of one of radius r; and so on.

Volumes of Similar Solids are to each other as the cubes of their respective linear dimensions. Thus, the volume of a right regular pyramid of altitude $2h$ is eight times the volume of a similar pyramid of altitude h; the volume of a sphere of radius $2r$ is eight times the volume of one of radius r; and so on.

Table I.　Mensuration Formulas

Approximate Decimal Equivalents (for reference):

$$\pi = 3.1416 \qquad \frac{1}{\pi} = 0.318 \qquad \sqrt{2} = 1.414$$

$$\frac{\pi}{2} = 1.5708 \qquad \frac{1}{2\pi} = 0.159 \qquad \sqrt{3} = 1.732$$

$$\frac{\pi}{4} = 0.7854 \qquad \frac{1}{4\pi} = 0.080 \qquad \frac{1}{\sqrt{2}} = 0.707$$

$$\frac{\pi}{180} = 0.01745 \qquad \frac{180}{\pi} = 57.296 \qquad \frac{1}{\sqrt{3}} = 0.577$$

$$\frac{\pi}{360} = 0.00873 \qquad \frac{360}{\pi} = 114.591$$

Ia. Plane Rectilinear Figures

Notation. Lines, a, b, c, ...; angles, α, β, γ, ...; altitude (perpendicular height), h; side, s; diagonals, d, d_1, ...; perimeter, p; radius of inscribed circle, r; radius of circumscribed circle, R; area, A.

---

1. Right Triangle

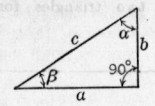

(One angle 90°)

$p = a + b + c$; $c^2 = a^2 + b^2$;

$A = \dfrac{ab}{2} = \dfrac{a^2}{2}\tan\beta = \dfrac{c^2}{4}\sin 2\beta = \dfrac{c^2}{4}\sin 2\alpha$.

For additional formulas, see *General Triangle* below, and also trigonometry.

---

2. General Triangle (and Equilateral Triangle)

For General Triangle:

$p = a + b + c$. Let $s = \frac{1}{2}(a + b + c)$.

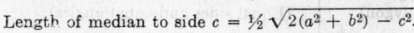

$r = \dfrac{\sqrt{s(s-a)(s-b)(s-c)}}{s}$; $R = \dfrac{a}{2\sin\alpha} = \dfrac{abc}{4rs}$;

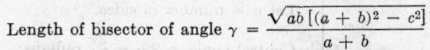

$A = \dfrac{ah}{2} = \dfrac{ab}{2}\sin\gamma = \dfrac{b^2\sin\gamma\sin\alpha}{2\sin\beta} = rs = \dfrac{abc}{4\,R}$.

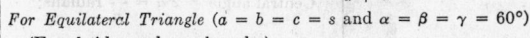

Length of median to side $c = \frac{1}{2}\sqrt{2(a^2 + b^2) - c^2}$.

Length of bisector of angle $\gamma = \dfrac{\sqrt{ab[(a+b)^2 - c^2]}}{a+b}$.

For Equilateral Triangle ($a = b = c = s$ and $\alpha = \beta = \gamma = 60°$):

(Equal sides and equal angles)

$p = 3s$; $r = \dfrac{s}{2\sqrt{3}}$; $R = \dfrac{s}{\sqrt{3}} = 2r$;

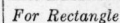

$h = \dfrac{s\sqrt{3}}{2}$; $s = \dfrac{2h}{\sqrt{3}}$; $A = \dfrac{s^2\sqrt{3}}{4}$.

For additional formulas, see trigonometry.

---

3. Rectangle (and Square)

For Rectangle:

$p = 2(a + b)$; $d = \sqrt{a^2 + b^2}$; $A = ab$.

For Square ($a = b = s$):

$p = 4s$; $d = s\sqrt{2}$; $s = \dfrac{d}{\sqrt{2}}$; $A = s^2 = \dfrac{d^2}{2}$.

---

4. General Parallelogram (Rhomboid) (and Rhombus)

For General Parallelogram (Rhomboid):

(Opposite sides parallel)

$p = 2(a + b)$; $d_1 = \sqrt{a^2 + b^2 - 2ab\cos\gamma}$;

$d_2 = \sqrt{a^2 + b^2 + 2ab\cos\gamma}$; $d_1^2 + d_2^2 = 2(a^2 + b^2)$;

$A = ah = ab\sin\gamma$.

For Rhombus ($a = b = s$):

(Opposite sides parallel and all sides equal)

$p = 4s$; $d_1 = 2s\sin\dfrac{\gamma}{2}$; $d_2 = 2s\cos\dfrac{\gamma}{2}$; $d_1^2 + d_2^2 = 4s^2$;

$d_1 d_2 = 2s^2\sin\gamma$; $A = sh = s^2\sin\gamma = \dfrac{d_1 d_2}{2}$.

---

5. General Trapezoid (and Isosceles Trapezoid)

Let mid-line bisecting non-parallel sides $= m$. Then $m = \dfrac{a+b}{2}$.

For General Trapezoid:

(Only one pair of opposite sides parallel)

$p = a + b + c + d$; $A = \dfrac{(a+b)h}{2} = mh$.

For Isosceles Trapezoid ($d = c$):

(Non-parallel sides equal)

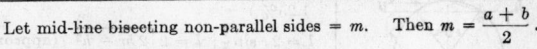

$A = \dfrac{(a+b)h}{2} = mh = \dfrac{(a+b)\,c\sin\gamma}{2}$

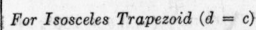

$= (a - c\cos\gamma)\,c\sin\gamma = (b + c\cos\gamma)\,c\sin\gamma$.

Ia. Plane Rectilinear Figures—*Continued*

6. General Quadrilateral (Trapezium)

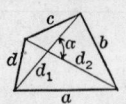

(No sides parallel)

$p = a + b + c + d$

$A = \frac{1}{2} d_1 d_2 \sin \alpha$ = sum of areas of the two triangles formed by either diagonal and the four sides.

---

7. Quadrilateral Inscribed in Circle

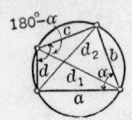

(Sum of opposite angles = 180°)

$ac + bd = d_1 d_2.$

Let $s = \frac{1}{2}(a + b + c + d) = \frac{p}{2}$ and α = angle between sides a and b.

$A = \sqrt{(s - a)(s - b)(s - c)(s - d)} = 1/2\,(ab + cd) \sin \alpha.$

---

8. Regular Polygon (and General Polygon)

For Regular Polygon:

(Equal sides and equal angles)

Let n = number of sides.

Central angle $= 2\,\alpha = \dfrac{2\pi}{n}$ radians;

Vertex angle $= \beta = \dfrac{(n - 2)}{n}\,\pi$ radians.

$p = ns; \quad s = 2\,r \tan \alpha = 2\,R \sin \alpha;$

$r = \dfrac{s}{2} \cot \alpha; \quad R = \dfrac{s}{2} \csc \alpha;$

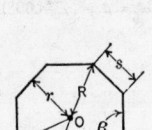

$A = \dfrac{nsr}{2} = nr^2 \tan \alpha = \dfrac{n\,R^2}{2} \sin 2\,\alpha = \dfrac{ns^2}{4} \cot \alpha$ = sum of areas of the n equal triangles such as OAB.

For General Polygon:

A = sum of areas of constituent triangles into which it can be divided.

Ib. Plane Curvilinear Figures

Notation.   Lines, $a, b, \ldots$; radius, r; diameter, d; perimeter, p; circumference, c; central angle in radians, θ; arc, s; chord of arc (s), l; chord of half arc $(s/2)$, l'; rise, h; area, A.

---

9. Circle (and Circular Arc)

For Circle:

$$d = 2\,r; \quad c = 2\pi r = \pi d; \quad A = \pi r^2 = \frac{\pi d^2}{4} = \frac{c^2}{4\pi}.$$

For Circular Arc:

Let arc $PAQ = s$; and chord $PA = \left(\text{chord of } \dfrac{s}{2}\right) = l'$. Then,

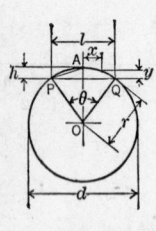

$s = r\,\theta = \dfrac{d\theta}{2}; \quad s = \dfrac{8l' - l}{3}.$ (The latter equation is Huyghen's approximate formula. For θ small, error is very small; for $\theta = 120°$, error equals about 1 part in 400; for $\theta = 180°$, error is less than 1.25%.)

$l = 2\,r \sin \dfrac{\theta}{2}; \quad l = 2\sqrt{2\,hr - h^2}$ (approximate formula)

$r = \dfrac{s}{\theta} = \dfrac{l}{2 \sin \dfrac{\theta}{2}}; \quad r = \dfrac{4\,h^2 + l^2}{8\,h}$ (approximate formula)

$h = r \mp \sqrt{r^2 - \dfrac{l^2}{4}}$ (− if $\theta \leq 180°$; + if $\theta \geq 180°$) $= r\left(1 - \cos \dfrac{\theta}{2}\right)$

$\quad = r \operatorname{versin} \dfrac{\theta}{2} = 2\,r \sin^2 \dfrac{\theta}{4} = \dfrac{l}{2} \tan \dfrac{\theta}{4} = r + y - \sqrt{r^2 - x^2}.$

Side ordinate $y = h - r + \sqrt{r^2 - x^2}.$

Ib. Plane Curvilinear Figures—*Continued*

10. Circular Sector (and Semicircle)

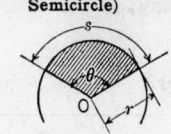

For Circular Sector:

$$A = \frac{\theta r^2}{2} = \frac{sr}{2}.$$

For Semicircle:

$$A = \frac{\pi r^2}{2}.$$

---

11. Circular Segment

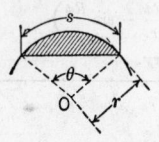

$$A = \frac{r^2}{2}(\theta - \sin \theta)$$

$$= 1/2 \left[sr \mp l\,(r - h) \right] \; (- \text{ if } h \leqq r; \; + \text{ if } h \geqq r).$$

$$A = \frac{2lh}{3} \text{ or } \frac{h}{15}(8l' + 6l). \text{ (Approximate formulas. For } h \text{ small compared with } r, \text{ error is very small; for } h = \frac{r}{4}, \text{ first formula}$$
errs about 3.5% and second less than 1.0%.)

---

12. Annulus

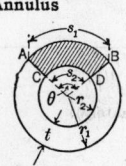

(Surface between two concentric circles)

$$A = \pi(r_1{}^2 - r_2{}^2) = \pi(r_1 + r_2)(r_1 - r_2);$$

$$A \text{ of sector } ABCD = \frac{\theta}{2}(r_1{}^2 - r_2{}^2) = \frac{\theta}{2}(r_1 + r_2)(r_1 - r_2)$$

$$= \frac{t}{2}(s_1 + s_2).$$

---

13. Ellipse

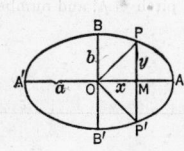

$$p = \pi(a + b)\left(1 + \frac{R^2}{4} + \frac{R^4}{64} + \frac{R^6}{256} + \dots \right) \text{ where } R = \frac{a - b}{a + b}.$$

$$p = \pi(a + b)\frac{64 - 3\,R^4}{64 - 16\,R^2} \text{ (approximate formula).}$$

$$A = \pi ab; \; A \text{ of quadrant } AOB = \frac{\pi\,ab}{4};$$

$$A \text{ of sector } AOP = \frac{ab}{2}\cos^{-1}\frac{x}{a}; \; A \text{ of sector } POB = \frac{ab}{2}\sin^{-1}\frac{x}{a};$$

$$A \text{ of section } BPP'B' = xy + ab\sin^{-1}\frac{x}{a};$$

$$A \text{ of segment } PAP'P = -xy + ab\cos^{-1}\frac{x}{a}.$$

For additional formulas, see analytic geometry.

---

14. Parabola

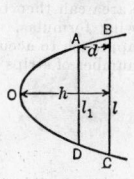

$$\text{Arc } BOC = s = 1/2\sqrt{l^2 + 16\,h^2} + \frac{l^2}{8h}\log_e\frac{4\,h + \sqrt{l^2 + 16\,h^2}}{l}.$$

Let $R = \frac{h}{l}$. Then,

$$s = l\left(1 + \frac{8\,R^2}{3} - \frac{32\,R^4}{5} + \dots\right) \text{ (approximate formula).}$$

$$d = \frac{h}{l^2}(l^2 - l_1{}^2); \; l_1 = l\sqrt{\frac{h - d}{h}}; \; h = \frac{dl^2}{l^2 - l_1{}^2};$$

$$A \text{ of segment } BOC = \frac{2\,hl}{3};$$

$$A \text{ of section } ABCD = \frac{2}{3}d\left(\frac{l^3 - l_1{}^3}{l^2 - l_1{}^2}\right).$$

For additional formulas, see analytic geometry.

---

15. Hyperbola

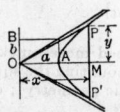

$$A \text{ of figure } OPAP'O = ab\log_e\left(\frac{x}{a} + \frac{y}{b}\right) = ab\cosh^{-1}\frac{x}{a};$$

$$A \text{ of segment } PAP' = xy - ab\log_e\left(\frac{x}{a} + \frac{y}{b}\right) = xy - ab\cosh^{-1}\frac{x}{a}.$$

For additional formulas, see analytic geometry.

Ib. Plane Curvilinear Figures—*Continued*

---

16. Cycloid

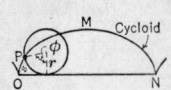

Arc $OP = s = 4\,r\left(1 - \cos\dfrac{\phi}{2}\right)$;   Arc $OMN = 8\,r$;

A under curve $OMN = 3\,\pi\,r^2$.

For additional formulas, see analytic geometry.

---

17. Epicycloid

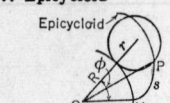

Arc $MP = s = \dfrac{4\,r}{R}\,(R + r)\left(1 - \cos\dfrac{R\phi}{2\,r}\right)$;

Area $MOP = A = \dfrac{r}{2\,R}\,(R + r)(R + 2\,r)\left(\dfrac{R\phi}{r} - \sin\dfrac{R\phi}{r}\right)$.

For additional formulas, see analytic geometry.

---

18. Hypocycloid

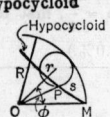

Arc $MP = s = \dfrac{4\,r}{R}\,(R - r)\left(1 - \cos\dfrac{R\phi}{2\,r}\right)$;

Area $MOP = A = \dfrac{r}{2\,R}\,(R - r)(R - 2\,r)\left(\dfrac{R\phi}{r} - \sin\dfrac{R\phi}{r}\right)$.

For additional formulas, see analytic geometry.

---

19. Catenary

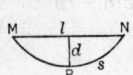

If d is small compared with l:

Arc $MPN = s = l\left[1 + \dfrac{2}{3}\left(\dfrac{2d}{l}\right)^2\right]$ (approximately).

For additional formulas, see analytic geometry.

---

20. Helix

Let length of helix $= s$; radius of coil ($=$ radius of cylinder in figure) $= r$; distance advanced in one revolution $=$ pitch $= h$; and number of revolutions $= n$. Then,

$$s = n\sqrt{(2\pi r)^2 + h^2}.$$

---

21. Spiral of Archimedes

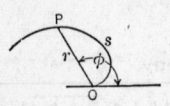

Let $a = \dfrac{r}{\phi}$. Then,

Arc $OP = s = \dfrac{a}{2}\left[\phi\sqrt{1 + \phi^2} + \log_e\left(\phi + \sqrt{1 + \phi^2}\right)\right]$.

For additional formulas, see analytic geometry.

---

22. Irregular Figure

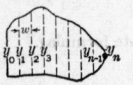

Divide the figure into an *even* number, n, of strips by means of $(n + 1)$ ordinates, y_i, spaced equal distances, w. The area can then be determined approximately by any of the following formulas, which are presented in the order of usual increasing approach to accuracy. In any of the first three cases, the greater the number of strips used, the more nearly accurate will be the result.

(Approximate Formulas)

Trapezoidal Rule......... $A = w\left[\dfrac{y_0 + y_n}{2} + y_1 + y_2 + \ldots + y_{n-1}\right]$;

Durand's Rule.......... $A = w\left[0.4(y_0 + y_n) + 1.1(y_1 + y_{n-1}) + y_2 + y_3 + \ldots + y_{n-2}\right]$;

Simpson's Rule.......... $A = \dfrac{w}{3}\left[(y_0 + y_n) + 4\,(y_1 + y_3 + \ldots + y_{n-1}) + \right.$
(n *must* be even) $\left. 2\,(y_2 + y_4 + \ldots + y_{n-2})\right]$;

Weddle's Rule.......... $A = \dfrac{3w}{10}\left[5(y_1 + y_5) + 6\,y_3 + y_0 + y_2 + y_4 + y_6\right]$.
(for 6 strips only)

Areas of irregular surfaces can often be determined more quickly by such methods as plotting on squared paper and counting the squares; graphical coordinate representation (see analytic geometry); or use of a planimeter.

Ic. Solids Having Plane Surfaces

Notation. Lines, $a, b, c, \ldots$; altitude (perpendicular height), h; slant height, s; perimeter of base, p_b or p_B; perimeter of a right section, p_r; area of base, A_b or A_B; area of a right section, A_r; total area of lateral surfaces, A_l; total area of all surfaces, A_t; volume, V.

---

23. Wedge (and Right Triangular Prism)

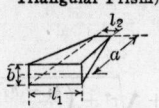

For Wedge:

(Narrow-side rectangular); $V = \dfrac{ab}{6}(2l_1 + l_2)$.

For Right Triangular Prism (or wedge having parallel triangular bases perpendicular to sides) $l_2 = l_1 = l$:

$V = \dfrac{abl}{2}$.

---

24. Rectangular Prism (or Rectangular Parallelepiped) (and Cube)

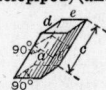

For Rectangular Prism or Rectangular Parallelepiped:

$A_l = 2c(a + b)$; $A_t = 2(de + ac + bc)$;

$V = A_r c = abc$.

For Cube (letting $b = c = a$):

$A_t = 6a^2$; $V = a^3$;   Diagonal $= a\sqrt{3}$.

---

25. General Prism

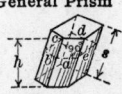

$A_l = hp_b = sp_r = s(a + b + \ldots + n)$;

$V = hA_b = sA_r$.

---

26. General Truncated Prism (and Truncated Triangular Prism)

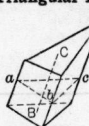

For General Truncated Prism:

$V = A_r \cdot$ (length of line BC joining centers of gravity of bases).

For Truncated Triangular Prism:

$V = \dfrac{A_r}{3}(a + b + c)$.

---

27. Prismatoid

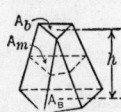

Let area of mid-section $= A_m$.

$V = \dfrac{h}{6}(A_B + A_b + 4A_m)$.

---

28. Right Regular Pyramid (and Frustum of Right Regular Pyramid)

For Right Regular Pyramid:

$A_l = \dfrac{sp_B}{2}$; $V = \dfrac{hA_B}{3}$.

For Frustum of Right Regular Pyramid:

$A_l = \dfrac{s}{2}(p_B + p_b)$; $V = \dfrac{h}{3}\left(A_B + A_b + \sqrt{A_B A_b}\right)$.

---

29. General Pyramid (and Frustum of Pyramid)

For General Pyramid:

$V = \dfrac{hA_B}{3}$

For Frustum of General Pyramid:

$V = \dfrac{h}{3}\left(A_B + A_b + \sqrt{A_B A_b}\right)$.

---

30. Regular Polyhedrons

Tetrahedron   Cube   Octahedron

Dodecahedron   Icosahedron

Let edge $= a$, and radius of inscribed sphere $= r$. Then,

$r \approx \dfrac{3V}{A_t}$, and:

Number of Faces	Form of Faces	Total Area A_t	Volume V
4	Equilateral triangle	$1.7321\,a^2$	$0.1179\,a^3$
6	Square	$6.0000\,a^2$	$1.0000\,a^3$
8	Equilateral triangle	$3.4641\,a^2$	$0.4714\,a^3$
12	Regular pentagon	$20.6457\,a^2$	$7.6631\,a^3$
20	Equilateral triangle	$8.6603\,a^2$	$2.1817\,a^3$

(Factors shown only to four decimal places.)

Id. Solids Having Curved Surfaces

Notation. Lines, a, b, c, . . . ; altitude (perpendicular height), h, h_1, . . . ; slant height, s; radius, r; perimeter of base, p_b; perimeter of a right section, p_r; angle in radians, ϕ; arc, s; chord of segment, l; rise, h; area of base, A_b or A_B; area of a right section, A_r; total area of convex surface, A_l; total area of all surfaces, A_t; volume, V.

---

31. Right Circular Cylinder (and Truncated Right Circular Cylinder)

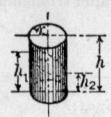

For Right Circular Cylinder:

$A_l = 2\pi rh;\quad A_t = 2\pi r\,(r + h);$

$V = \pi r^2 h.$

For Truncated Right Circular Cylinder:

$$A_l = \pi r\,(h_1 + h_2);\quad A_t = \pi r\left[h_1 + h_2 + r + \sqrt{r^2 + \left(\frac{h_1 - h_2}{2}\right)^2}\,\right];$$

$$V = \frac{\pi r^2}{2}\,(h_1 + h_2).$$

---

32. Ungula (Wedge) of Right Circular Cylinder

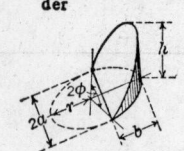

$A_l = \dfrac{2\,rh}{b}\,[a + (b - r)\phi];$

$V = \dfrac{h}{3b}\,[a\,(3r^2 - a^2) + 3\,r^2\,(b - r)\phi]$

$\quad = \dfrac{hr^3}{b}\left[\sin\phi - \dfrac{\sin^3\phi}{3} - \phi\cos\phi\right].$

For Semicircular Base (letting $a = b = r$):

$A_l = 2\,rh;\quad V = \dfrac{2\,r^2 h}{3}.$

---

33. General Cylinder

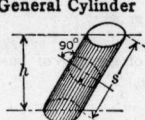

$A_l = p_b h = p_r s;$

$V = A_b h = A_r s.$

---

34. Right Circular Cone (and Frustum of Right Circular Cone)

For Right Circular Cone:

$A_l = \pi r_B s = \pi r_B \sqrt{r_B^2 + h^2};\quad A_t = \pi r_B\,(r_B + s);$

$V = \dfrac{\pi r_B^2 h}{3}.$

For Frustum of Right Circular Cone:

$s = \sqrt{h_1^2 + (r_B - r_b)^2};\quad A_l = \pi s\,(r_B + r_b);$

$V = \dfrac{\pi h_1}{3}\,(r_B^2 + r_b^2 + r_B\,r_b).$

---

35. General Cone (and Frustum of General Cone)

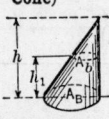

For General Cone:

$V = \dfrac{A_B h}{3}.$

For Frustum of General Cone:

$V = \dfrac{h_1}{3}\,(A_B + A_b + \sqrt{A_B A_b}\,).$

---

36. Sphere

Let diameter $= d$.

$A_t = 4\pi r^2 = \pi d^2;$

$V = \dfrac{4\pi r^3}{3} = \dfrac{\pi d^3}{6}.$

---

37. Spherical Sector (and Hemisphere)

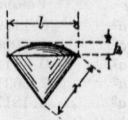

For Spherical Sector:

$A_t = \dfrac{\pi r}{2}\,(4h + l);\quad V = \dfrac{2\pi r^2 h}{3}.$

For Hemisphere (letting $h = \dfrac{l}{2} = r$):

$A_t = 3\pi r^2;\quad V = \dfrac{2\pi r^3}{3}.$

Id.   Solids Having Curved Surfaces—*Continued*

38. Spherical Zone (and Spherical Segment)

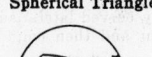
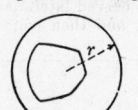

For Spherical Zone Bounded by Two Planes:

$$A_l = 2\pi rh; \quad A_t = \frac{\pi}{4}(8\,rh + a^2 + b^2).$$

For Spherical Zone Bounded by One Plane (b = 0):

$$A_l = 2\pi rh = \frac{\pi}{4}(4\,h^2 + a^2);$$

$$A_t = \frac{\pi}{4}(8\,rh + a^2) = \frac{\pi}{2}(2\,h^2 + a^2).$$

For Spherical Segment with Two Bases:

$$V = \frac{\pi h}{24}(3\,a^2 + 3\,b^2 + 4\,h^2).$$

For Spherical Segment with One Base (b = 0):

$$V = \frac{\pi h}{24}(3\,a^2 + 4\,h^2) = \pi h^2\left(r - \frac{h}{3}\right).$$

39. Spherical Polygon (and Spherical Triangle)

For Spherical Polygon:

Let sum of angles in radians = θ and number of sides = n.

$$A = [\theta - (n - 2)\pi]r^2$$

(The quantity $[\theta - (n - 2)\pi]$ is called "spherical excess.")

For Spherical Triangle (n = 3):

$$A = (\theta - \pi)\,r^2$$

For additional formulas, see trigonometry.

40. Torus

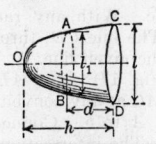

$$A_l = 4\pi^2\,Rr;$$

$$V = 2\pi^2\,Rr^2.$$

41. Ellipsoid (and Spheroids)

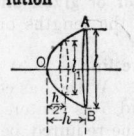

For Ellipsoid:

$$V = \frac{4}{3}\pi abc.$$

For Prolate Spheroid:

Let $c = b$ and $\dfrac{\sqrt{a^2 - b^2}}{a} = e$.

$$A_t = 2\pi b^2 + 2\pi ab\,\frac{\sin^{-1} e}{e}; \quad V = \frac{4}{3}\pi ab^2.$$

For Oblate Spheroid:

Let $c = a$ and $\dfrac{\sqrt{a^2 - b^2}}{a} = e$.

$$A_t = 2\pi a^2 + \frac{\pi b^2}{e}\,ln\left(\frac{1 + e}{1 - e}\right); \quad V = \frac{4}{3}\pi a^2 b.$$

42. Paraboloid of Revolution

$$A_l \text{ of segment } DOC = \frac{2\pi l}{3h^2}\left[\left(\frac{l^2}{16} + h^2\right)^{3/2} - \left(\frac{l}{4}\right)^3\right].$$

For Paraboloidal Segment with Two Bases:

$$V \text{ of } ABCD = \frac{\pi d}{8}(l^2 + l_1^2).$$

For Paraboloidal Segment with One Base (l₁ = 0 and d = h):

$$V \text{ of } DOC = \frac{\pi h l^2}{8}.$$

43. Hyperboloid of Revolution

$$V \text{ of segment } AOB = \frac{\pi h}{24}(l^2 + 4l_1^2).$$

Id. Solids Having Curved Surfaces—*Continued*

44. Surface and Solid of Revolution 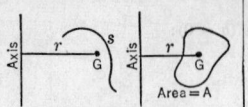	Let perpendicular distance from axis to center of gravity (G) of curve (or surface) = r. Curve (or surface) must not cross axis. Then, *Area of Surface* generated by curve revolving about axis: $A_l = 2\pi rs.$ *Volume of Solid* generated by surface revolving about axis: $V = 2\pi rA.$
45. Irregular Solid 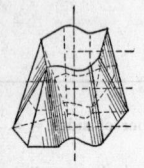	One of the following methods can often be employed to determine the volume of an irregular solid with a reasonable approach to accuracy: (a) Divide the solid into prisms, cylinders, etc., and sum their individual volumes. (b) Divide one surface into triangles, after replacing curved lines by straight ones and curved surfaces by plane ones. Then multiply the area of each triangle by the mean depth of the section beneath it (which generally approximates the average of the depths at its corners). Sum the volumes thus obtained. (c) If two surfaces are parallel, replace any curved lateral surfaces by plane surfaces best suited to the contour and then employ the prismatoidal formula.

23. CONSTRUCTIONS

Typical Constructions applicable to the graphical solution of common elementary geometrical problems are presented in the following paragraphs. If two or more methods of solution are possible but almost equally simple under all circumstances, only one method, in general, is given.

Lines

1. To draw a line parallel to a given line.

Case 1. At a given distance from the given line (Fig. 15a).

With the given distance as radius and with any centers m and n on the given line AB, describe arcs xy and zw, respectively. Draw CD touching these arcs. CD is the required parallel line.

Case 2. Through a given point (Fig. 15b). Let C be the given point and D be any point on the given line AB. Draw CD. With equal radii draw arcs bf and ce with D and C, respectively, as centers. With radius equal to chord bf and with c as center draw an arc cutting arc ce at E. CE is the required parallel line.

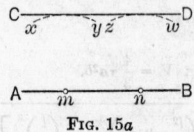

FIG. 15a

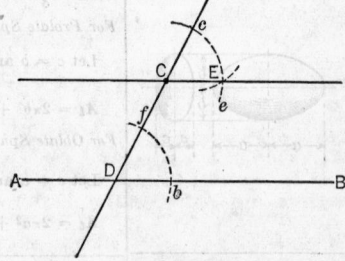

FIG. 15b

2. To bisect a given line (Fig. 16). Let AB be the given line. With any radius greater than 0.5 AB describe two arcs with A and B as centers. The line CD, through points of intersection of the arcs, is the perpendicular bisector of the given line.

3. To divide a given line into a given number of equal parts (Fig. 17). Let AB be the given line and let the number of equal parts be five. Draw line AC at any convenient angle with AB, and step off with dividers five equal lengths from A to b. Connect b with B, and draw parallels to Bb through the other points in AC. The intersections of these parallels with AB determine the required equal parts on the given line.

4. To divide a given line into segments proportional to a number of given unequal parts. Follow the same procedure as under 3 above except make the lengths on AC equal to (or proportional to) the lengths of the given unequal parts.

5. To erect a perpendicular to a given line at a given point in the line.

Case 1. Point C is at or near the middle of the line AB (Fig. 18). With C as center, describe arcs of equal radii intersecting AB at a and b. With a and b as centers, and any radius greater than Ca, describe arcs intersecting at D. CD is the required perpendicular.

Case 2. Point C is at or near the extremity of the line AB (Fig. 19). With any point O, as center, and radius OC, describe an arc intersecting AB at a. Extend aO to intersect the arc at D. CD is the required perpendicular.

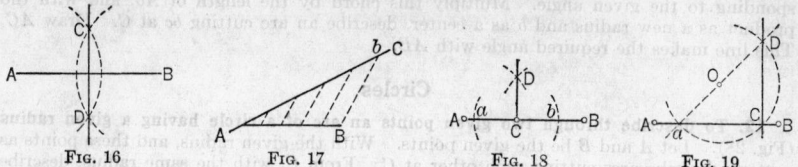

FIG. 16   FIG. 17   FIG. 18   FIG. 19

6. To erect a perpendicular to a given line through a given point outside the line.

Case 1. Point C is opposite, or nearly opposite, the middle of the line AB (Fig. 20). With C as center, describe an arc intersecting AB at a and b. With a and b as centers, describe arcs of equal radii intersecting at D. CD is the required perpendicular.

Case 2. Point C is opposite, or nearly opposite, the extremity of the line AB (Fig. 21). Through C, draw any line intersecting AB at a. Divide

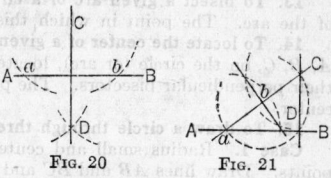

FIG. 20   FIG. 21

line Ca into two equal parts, ab and bC (method given above). With b as center, and radius bC, describe an arc intersecting AB at D. CD is the required perpendicular.

Angles

7. To bisect a given angle.

Case 1. Vertex B is accessible (Fig. 22). Let ABC be the given angle. With B as center, and a large radius, describe an arc intersecting AB and BC at a and c respectively. With a and c as centers, describe arcs of equal radii intersecting at D. DB is the required bisector.

Case 2. The vertex is inaccessible (Fig. 23). Let the given angle be that between lines AB and BC. Draw lines ab and bc parallel to the given lines, and at equal distances

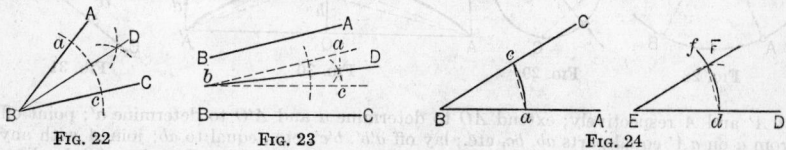

FIG. 22   FIG. 23   FIG. 24

from them, intersecting at b. Construct Db bisecting angle abc (method given above). Db is the required bisector.

8. To construct an angle equal to a given angle if one new side and the new vertex are given (Fig. 24). Let ABC be the given angle; DE the new side; and E the new vertex. With center B and a convenient radius, describe arc ac. With the same radius and center E, draw arc df. With radius equal to chord ac and with center d draw an arc cutting the arc df at F. Draw EF. Then DEF is the required angle.

9. To construct angles of 60° and 30° (Fig. 25). About any point A on a line AB, describe with a convenient radius the arc bc. From b, using an equal radius, describe an arc cutting the former one at C. Draw AC, and drop a perpendicular CD from C to line AB. Then CAD is a 60° angle and ACD is a 30° angle.

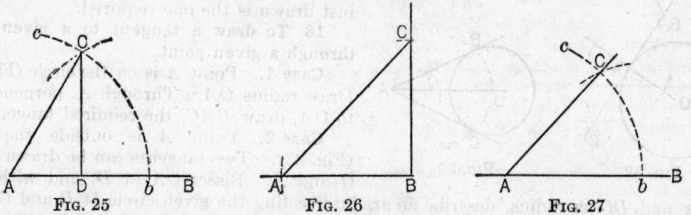

FIG. 25   FIG. 26   FIG. 27

10. To construct an angle of 45° (Fig. 26). Set off any distance AB; draw BC perpendicular and equal to AB; and join CA. Angles CAB and ACB are each 45°.

11. To draw a line making a given angle with a given line (Fig. 27). Let AB be the given line. With A as the center and with as large a radius as convenient, describe arc bc. Determine from Table 9, Section 1, the length of chord to radius one, corresponding to the given angle. Multiply this chord by the length of Ab, and with the product as a new radius and b as a center, describe an arc cutting bc at C. Draw AC. This line makes the required angle with AB.

Circles

12. To describe through two given points an arc of a circle having a given radius (Fig. 28). Let A and B be the given points. With the given radius, and these points as centers, describe arcs cutting each other at C. From C, with the same radius, describe arc AB, which is the required arc.

13. To bisect a given arc of a circle. Draw the perpendicular bisector of the chord of the arc. The point in which this bisector meets the arc is the required mid-point.

14. To locate the center of a given circle or circular arc (Fig. 29). Select three points, A, B, C, on the circle (or arc), located well apart. Draw chords AB and BC and erect their perpendicular bisectors. The point O, where the bisectors intersect, is the required center.

15. To draw a circle through three given points not in the same straight line.

Case 1. Radius small and center accessible (Fig. 29). Let A, B, C, be the given points. Draw lines AB and BC and erect their perpendicular bisectors. From point O, where the bisectors intersect, describe a circle of radius OA which is the required circle.

Case 2. Radius very long or center inaccessible (Fig. 30). Let A, O, A', be the given points (O not necessarily mid-point of AOA'). Draw arcs Aa' and $A'a$ with centers

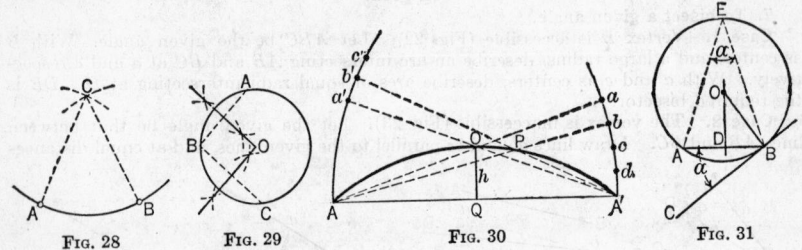

FIG. 28   FIG. 29   FIG. 30   FIG. 31

at A' and A respectively; extend AO to determine a and $A'O$ to determine a'; point off from a on aA' equal parts ab, bc, etc.; lay off $a'b'$, $b'c'$, etc., equal to ab; join A with any point as b and A' with the corresponding point b'; the intersection P of these joining lines is a point on the required circle.

16. To lay out a circular arc without locating the center of the circle, having given the chord and the rise (Fig. 30). Let AA' be the chord and QO the rise. (In this case, O is mid-point of AOA'.) The arc can be constructed through the points A, O, A', as under 15, Case 2, above.

17. To construct, upon a given chord, a circle in which a given angle can be inscribed (Fig. 31). Let AB be the given line, and α the given angle. Construct angle ABC equal to angle α. Bisect line AB by the perpendicular at D. Draw a perpendicular to BC from point B. With O, the point of intersection of the perpendiculars, as center, and OB as radius, describe a circle. The angle AEB, with vertex E located anywhere on the arc AEB, equals α, and therefore the circle just drawn is the one required.

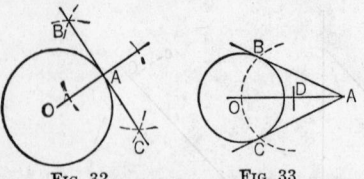

FIG. 32   FIG. 33

18. To draw a tangent to a given circle through a given point.

Case 1. Point A is on the circle (Fig. 32). Draw radius OA. Through A, perpendicular to OA, draw BAC, the required tangent.

Case 2. Point A is outside the circle (Fig. 33). Two tangents can be drawn. Join O and A. Bisect OA at D, and with D as center and DO as radius, describe an arc intersecting the given circle at B and C. BA and CA are the required tangents.

19. To draw a common tangent to two given circles. Let the circles have centers O and O' and corresponding radii r and r' $(r > r')$.

Case 1. Common internal tangents (when circles do not intersect) (Fig. 34). Construct a circle having the same center O as the larger circle and a radius equal to the sum of the radii of the given circles $(r + r')$. Construct a tangent $O'P$ from center O' of the smaller circle to this circle. Construct $O'N$ perpendicular to this tangent. Draw OP. The line MN joining the extremities of the radii OM and $O'N$ is a common tangent. The figure shows two such common internal tangents.

Case 2. Common external tangents (Fig. 35). Construct a circle having the same center O as the larger circle and radius equal to the difference of the radii $(r - r')$. Construct a tangent to this circle from the center of the smaller circle. The line joining the extremities M, N, of the radii of the given circles perpendicular to this tangent is a required common tangent. There are two such tangents.

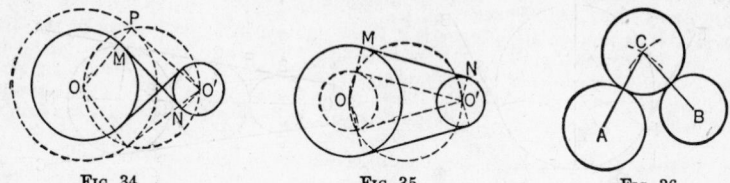

FIG. 34   FIG. 35   FIG. 36

20. To draw a circle with a given radius that will be tangent to two given circles (Fig. 36). Let R be the given radius and A and B the given circles. About center of circle A with radius equal to R plus radius of A, and about center of B with radius equal to R plus radius of B, draw two arcs cutting each other in C, which is the center of the required circle.

21. To describe a circular arc touching two given circles, one of them at a given point (Fig. 37). Let AB, FG be the given circles and F the given point. Draw the radius EF, and produce it both ways. Set off FH equal to the radius AC of the other circle; join CH, and bisect it by the perpendicular LT, cutting EF at T. About center T, with radius TF, describe arc FA as required.

22. To draw a circular arc that will be tangent to two given lines inclined to one another, one tangential point being given (Fig. 38). Let AB and CD be the given lines and E the given point. Draw the line GH, bisecting the angle formed by AB and CD. From E draw EF at right angles to AB; then F, its intersection with GH, is the center of the required circular arc.

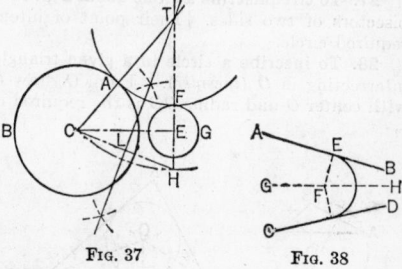

FIG. 37   FIG. 38

23. To connect two given parallel lines by a reversed curve composed of two circular arcs of equal radius, the curve being tangent to the lines at given points (Fig. 39). Let AD and BE be the given lines and A and B the given points. Join A and B, and bisect the connecting line at C. Bisect CA and CB by perpendiculars. At A and B erect

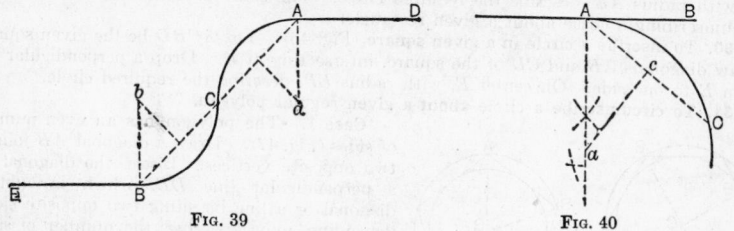

FIG. 39   FIG. 40

perpendiculars to the given lines, and the intersections a and b are the centers of the arcs composing the required curve.

24. To describe a circular arc which will be tangent to a given line at a given point, and pass through another given point outside the line (Fig. 40). Let AB be the given line, A the given point on the line, and C the given point outside it. Draw from A a line perpendicular to the given line. Connect A and C by a straight line, and bisect this line by the perpendicular *ca*. The point *a* where these two perpendiculars intersect is the center of the required circular arc.

25. To draw a circular arc joining two given relatively inclined lines, tangent to the lines, and passing through a given point on the line bisecting their included angle (Fig. 41). Let *AB* and *DE* be the given lines and *F* the given point on the line *FC* which bisects their included angle. Through *F* draw *DA* at right angles to *FC*; bisect the angles *A* and *D* by lines intersecting at *C*, and about *C* as a center, with radius *CF*, draw the arc *HFG* required.

26. To draw a series of circles between two given relatively inclined lines, touching the lines, and touching each other (Fig. 42). Let *AB* and *CD* be the given lines. Bisect

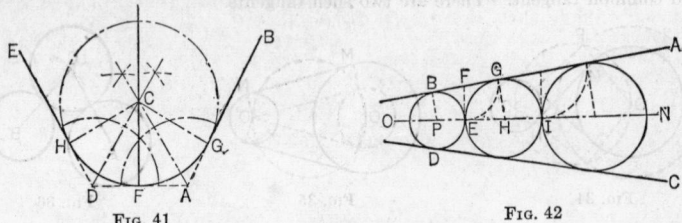

FIG. 41   FIG. 42

their included angle by the line *NO*. From a point *P* in this line draw the perpendicular *PB* to the line *AB*, and on *P* describe the circle *BD*, touching the given lines and cutting the center line at *E*. From *E* draw *EF* perpendicular to the center line, cutting *AB* at *F*; and about *F* as a center describe an arc *EG*, cutting *AB* at *G*. Draw *GH* parallel to *BP*, giving *H*, the center of the next circle, to be described with the radius *HE*; and so on for the next circle *IN*.

27. To circumscribe a circle about a given triangle (Fig. 43). Construct perpendicular bisectors of two sides. Their point of intersection *O* is the center (*circumcenter*) of the required circle.

28. To inscribe a circle in a given triangle (Fig. 44). Draw bisectors of two angles, intersecting in *O* (*incenter*). From *O* draw *OD* perpendicular to *BC*. Then the circle with center *O* and radius *OD* is the required circle.

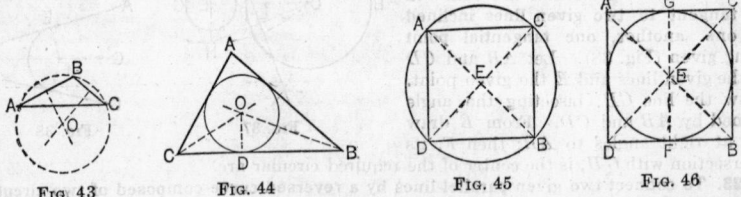

FIG. 43   FIG. 44   FIG. 45   FIG. 46

29. To circumscribe a circle about a given square (Fig. 45). Let *ACBD* be the given square. Draw diagonals *AB* and *CD* of the square, intersecting at *E*. On center *E*, with radius *AE*, describe the required circle. The same procedure can be used for circumscribing a circle about a given rectangle.

30. To inscribe a circle in a given square (Fig. 46). Let *ACBD* be the given square. Draw diagonals *AB* and *CD* of the square, intersecting at *E*. Drop a perpendicular *EF* from *E* to one side. On center *E*, with radius *EF*, describe the required circle.

31. To circumscribe a circle about a given regular polygon.

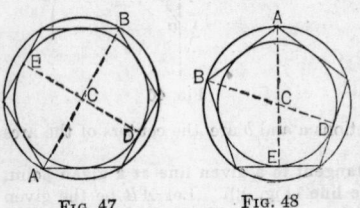

FIG. 47   FIG. 48

Case 1. The polygon has an even number of sides (Fig. 47). Draw a diagonal *AB* joining two opposite vertices. Bisect the diagonal by a perpendicular line *DE*, which is another diagonal or a line bisecting two opposite sides, depending upon whether the number of sides is, or is not, divisible by 4. With the mid-point *C* as the center, and radius *CA*, describe the required circle.

Case 2. The polygon has an odd number of sides (Fig. 48). Bisect two of the sides at *D* and *E* by the perpendicular lines *DB* and *EA* which pass through the respective opposite vertices and intersect at a point C. With C as the center, and radius CA, describe the required circle.

32. To inscribe a circle in a given regular polygon (Figs. 47, 48). Locate the center, C, as in 31 above. With C as center, and radius CD, describe the required circle.

Polygons

33. To construct a triangle on a given base, the lengths of the sides being given (Fig. 49). Let AB be the given base and a, b, the given lengths of sides. With A and B as centers, and b and a as respective radii, describe arcs intersecting at C. Draw AC and BC to complete the required triangle.

34. To construct a rectangle of given base and given height (Fig. 50). Let AB be the base and c the height. Erect the perpendicular AC equal to c. With C and B as centers, and AB and c as respective radii, describe arcs intersecting at D. Draw BD and CD to complete the required rectangle.

35. To construct a square with a given diagonal (Fig. 51). Let AC be the given diagonal. Draw a circle on AC as diameter and erect the diameter BD perpendicular to AC. Then $ABCD$ is the required square.

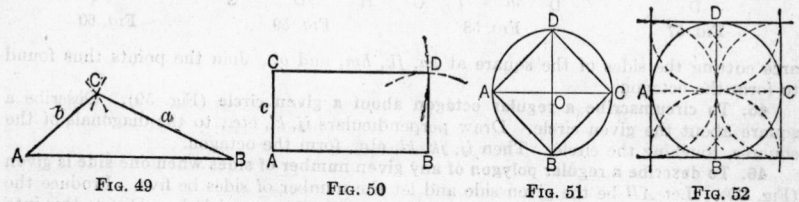

FIG. 49   FIG. 50   FIG. 51   FIG. 52

36. To inscribe a square in a given circle (Fig. 51). Draw perpendicular diameters. AC and BD. Their extremities are the vertices of an inscribed square.

37. To circumscribe a square about a given circle (Fig. 52). Draw perpendicular diameters AC and BD. With A, B, C, D, as centers, and the radius of the circle as radius, describe the four semicircular arcs shown. Their outer intersections are the vertices of the required square.

38. To inscribe a regular pentagon in a given circle (Fig. 53). Draw perpendicular diameters AC and BD intersecting at O. Bisect AO at E and with E as center, and EB as radius, draw an arc cutting AC at F. With B as center and BF as radius, draw an arc cutting the circle at G and H; also with the same radius, step around the circle to I and K. Join the points thus found to form the pentagon.

39. To inscribe a regular hexagon in a given circle (Fig. 54). Step around the circle with compasses set to the radius and join consecutive divisions thus marked off.

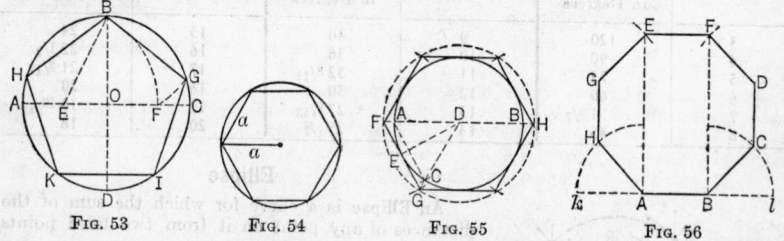

FIG. 53   FIG. 54   FIG. 55   FIG. 56

40. To circumscribe a regular hexagon about a given circle (Fig. 55). Draw a diameter ADB and with center A and radius AD, describe an arc cutting the circle at C. Draw AC and bisect it with the radius DE. Through E, draw FG parallel to AC, cutting diameter AB extended at F. With center D and radius DF, describe the circumscribing circle FH; and within this circle inscribe a regular hexagon as under 39 above. This hexagon circumscribes the given circle, as required.

41. To construct a regular hexagon having a side of given length (Fig. 54). Draw a circle with radius equal to the given length of side and inscribe a regular hexagon (see 39 above).

42. To construct a regular octagon having a side of given length (Fig. 56). Let AB be the given side. Produce AB in both directions, and draw perpendiculars AE and BF.

Bisect the external angles at A and B by the lines AH and BC, making them equal to AB. Draw CD and HG parallel to AE, and equal to AB; from the centers G, D, with the radius AB, draw arcs cutting the perpendiculars at E, F, and draw EF to complete the octagon.

43. To inscribe a regular octagon in a given circle (Fig. 57). Draw perpendicular diameters AC and BD. Bisect arcs AB, BC, etc., and join Ae, eB, etc., to form the octagon.

44. To inscribe a regular octagon in a given square (Fig. 58). Draw diagonals of the given square, intersecting at O. With A, B, C, D, as centers, and AO as radius, describe

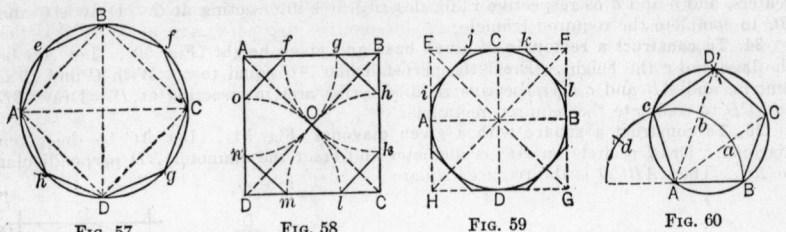

FIG. 57　　　　　　FIG. 58　　　　　　FIG. 59　　　　　　FIG. 60

arcs cutting the sides of the square at gn, fk, hm, and ol. Join the points thus found to form the octagon.

45. To circumscribe a regular octagon about a given circle (Fig. 59). Describe a square about the given circle. Draw perpendiculars ij, kl, etc., to the diagonals of the squares, touching the circle. Then ij, jk, kl, etc., form the octagon.

46. To describe a regular polygon of any given number of sides when one side is given (Fig. 60). Let AB be the given side and let the number of sides be five. Produce the line AB, and with A as center and AB as radius, describe a semicircle. Divide this into as many equal parts as there are to be sides of the polygon—in this case, five. Draw lines from A through the division points a, b, and c (omitting the last). With B and c as centers, and AB as radius, cut Aa at C and Ab at D. Draw cD, DC, and CB, to complete the polygon.

47. To inscribe a regular polygon of a given number of sides in a given circle. Determine the central angle subtended by any side by dividing 360° by the number of sides (see Table II). Lay off this angle successively round the center of the circle by means of a protractor. The radii thus drawn intersect the circle at vertices of the required polygon.

Table II.　Table of Polygonal Angles

Number of Sides	Angle at Center in Degrees	Number of Sides	Angle at Center in Degrees	Number of Sides	Angle at Center in Degrees
3	120	9	40	15	24
4	90	10	36	16	22 1/2
5	72	11	32 8/11	17	21 3/17
6	60	12	30	18	20
7	51 3/7	13	27 9/13	19	18 18/19
8	45	14	25 5/7	20	18

Ellipse

An **Ellipse** is a curve for which the sum of the distances of any point on it from two fixed points (the *foci*) is constant.

48. To describe an ellipse for which the axes are given (Fig. 61). Let AB be the *major* and RS the *minor* axis $(AB > RS)$. With O as center, and OB and OR as radii, describe circles. From O draw any radial line intersecting the circles at M and N. Through M draw a line parallel to OR, and through N a line parallel to OB. These lines intersect at H, a point on the ellipse. Repeat the construction to obtain other points.

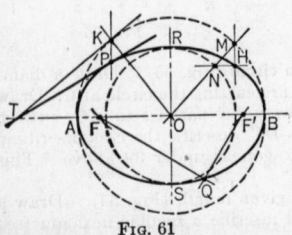

FIG. 61

49. To locate the foci of an ellipse, having given the axes (Fig. 61). With R as center, and radius equal to AO, describe arcs intersecting AB at F and F', the required foci.

50. To describe an ellipse mechanically, having given an axis and the foci (Fig. 61). A cord of length equal to the major axis is pinned or fixed at its ends to the foci F and F'. With a pencil inside the loop, keeping the cord taut so as to guide the pencil point, trace the outline of the ellipse (Q represents the pencil point and length FQF' the cord). If the minor axis RS is given rather than the major axis AB, the length AB (for the cord) is readily determined as $FR + RF'$.

51. To draw a tangent to a given ellipse through a given point.

Case 1. Point P is on the curve (Fig. 61). With O as center, and OB as radius, describe a circle. Through P draw a line parallel to OR, intersecting the circle at K. Through K draw a tangent to the circle, intersecting the major axis at T. PT is the required tangent.

Case 2. Point P is not on the curve (Fig. 62). With P as center, and radius PF', describe an arc. With F as center, and radius AB, describe an arc intersecting the first

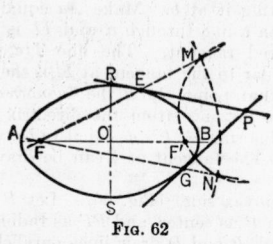

FIG. 62

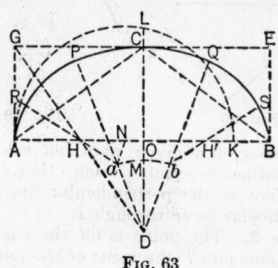

FIG. 63

arc at M and N. Draw FM and FN, intersecting the ellipse at E and G. PE and PG are the required tangents.

52. To describe an ellipse approximately by means of circular arcs of three radii (Fig. 63). On the major axis AB draw the rectangle BG of altitude equal to half the minor axis, OC; to the diagonal AC draw the perpendicular GHD; set off OK equal to OC, and describe a semicircle on AK; produce OC to L; set off OM equal to CL, and from D describe an arc with radius DM; from A, with radius OL, draw an arc cutting AB at N; from H, with radius HN, draw an arc cutting arc ab at a. Thus the five centers H, a, D, b, H', are found, from which the arcs AR, RP, PQ, QS, SB, are described. The part of the ellipse below axis AB can be constructed in like manner.

Parabola

A **Parabola** is a curve for which the distance of any point on it from a fixed line (the *directrix*) is equal to its distance from a fixed point (the *focus*). For a general discussion of its properties, see the section on analytic geometry.

53. To describe a parabola for which the vertex, the axis, and a point of the curve are given (Fig. 64). Let A be the given vertex, AB the given axis, and M the given point. Construct the rectangle $ABMC$. Divide MC and CA into the same number of equal parts (say four), numbering the divisions consecutively in the manner shown. Connect $A1$, $A2$, and $A3$. Through $1'$, $2'$, $3'$, draw parallels to the axis AB. The intersections I, II, and III, of these lines are points on the required curve. A similar construction below the axis will give the other symmetrical branch of the curve.

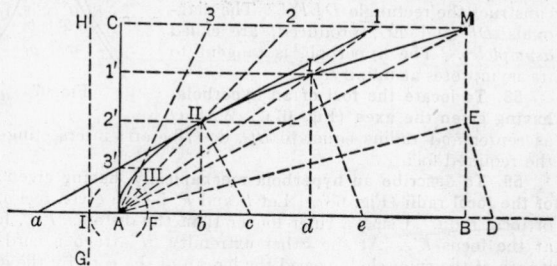

FIG. 64

54. To locate the focus and directrix of a parabola, having given the vertex, the axis, and a point of the curve (Fig. 64). Let A be the given vertex, AB the given axis, and M the given point. Drop the perpendicular MB from M to AB. Bisect it at E and draw AE. Draw ED perpendicular to AE at E and intersecting the axis at D. With A as center and BD as radius, describe arcs cutting the axis at F and I. Then F is the focus, and the line GH, perpendicular to the axis through I, is the directrix.

55. To describe a parabola mechanically, having given the focus and directrix (Fig. 65). Let F be the given focus and EN the given directrix. Place a straight-edge to the directrix EN, and apply to it a square, LEG. Fasten to the end G one end of a cord equal in length to the edge EG, and attach the other end to the focus F; slide the square along the straight-edge, holding the cord taut against the edge of the square by a pencil D, by which the parabolic curve is described.

56. To draw a tangent to a given parabola through a given point.

Case 1. The point is on the curve (Fig. 64). Let II be the given point. Drop a perpendicular from II to the axis, cutting it at b. Make Aa equal to Ab. Then a line through a and II is the required tangent. The line IIc perpendicular to the tangent at II is the *normal* at that point; bc is the *subnormal*. All

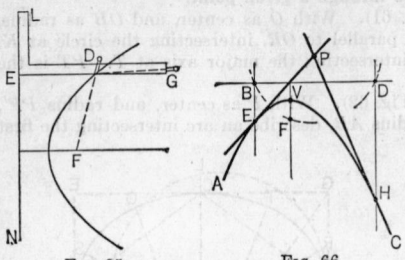

FIG. 65   FIG. 66

subnormals of a given parabola are equal to the distance from the directrix to the focus and hence equal to each other. Thus the subnormal at I is de equal to bc, where d is the foot of the perpendicular dropped from I. The tangent at I can be drawn as a perpendicular to Ie through I.

Case 2. The point is off the curve (on the convex side) (Fig. 66). Let P be the given point and F the focus of the parabola. With P as center, and PF as radius, draw arcs intersecting the directrix at B and D. Through B and D draw lines parallel to the axis, intersecting the parabola at E and H. PE and PH are the required tangents.

Hyperbola

An **Hyperbola** is a curve for which the difference of the distances of any point on it from two fixed points (the *foci*) is constant. It has two distinct branches.

57. To describe an hyperbola for which the foci and the difference of the focal radii are given (Fig. 67). Let F and F' be the given foci and AOB the given difference of the focal radii. Lay out AOB (the transverse axis) so that $AF = F'B$ and $AO = OB$. A and B are points on the required curve. With centers F and F', and any radius greater than FB or $F'A$, describe arcs aa. With the same centers, and radius equal to the difference between the first radius and the transverse axis AOB, describe arcs bb, intersecting arcs aa at P, Q, R, and S, points on the required curve. Repeat the construction for additional points. Make $BC = BC' = OF = OF'$, and construct the rectangle $DEFG$. The diagonals DF and EG, produced, are called *asymptotes*. The hyperbola is tangent to its asymptotes at infinity.

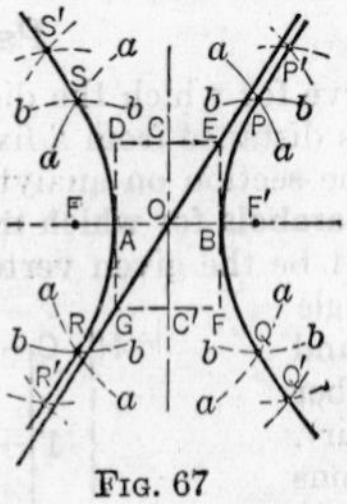

58. To locate the foci of an hyperbola, having given the axes (Fig. 67). With O

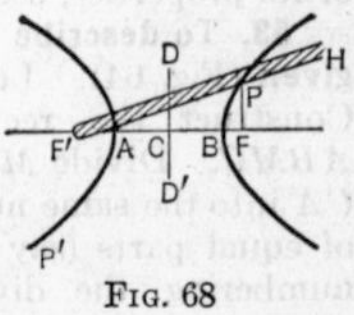

FIG. 67   FIG. 68

as center and radius equal to BC, describe arcs intersecting AB extended, at F and F', the required foci.

59. To describe an hyperbola mechanically, having given the foci and the difference of the focal radii (Fig. 68). Let F and F' be the given foci and AB the given difference of focal radii. Using a ruler longer than the distance $F'F$, fasten one of its extremities at the focus F'. At the other extremity H attach a cord of such a length that the length of the ruler shall exceed the length of the cord by the given distance AB. Attach the other extremity of the cord at the focus F. Press a pencil P against the ruler, and keep the cord constantly taut while the ruler is turned around F' as a center. The point of the pencil will describe one branch of the curve, and the other can be obtained in like manner.

60. To draw a tangent to a given hyperbola through a given point.

Case 1. Point P is on the curve (Fig. 69). Draw lines connecting P with the foci. Bisect the angle $F'PF$. The bisecting line TP is the required tangent.

Case 2. Point P is off the curve on the convex side (Fig. 70). With P as center and radius PF', describe an arc. With F as center, and radius AB, describe an arc intersecting the first arc at M and N. Produce lines FM and FN to intersect the curve at E and G. PE and PG are the required tangents.

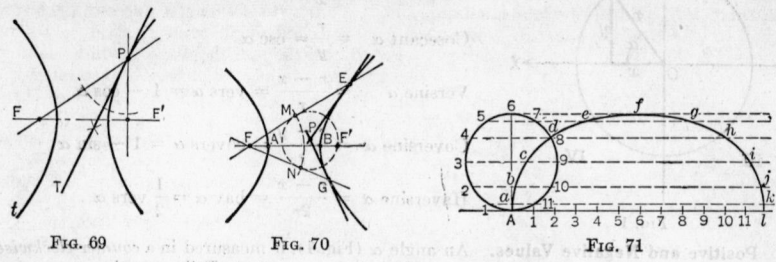

FIG. 69   FIG. 70   FIG. 71

Cycloid

A **Cycloid** is a curve generated by a point on a circle rolling on a straight line.

61. To describe a cycloid for which the generating circle is given (Fig. 71). Let A be the generating point. Divide the circumference of the generating circle into an even number of equal arcs, as $A1$, 1–2, etc., and set off the rectified arcs on the base. Through the points 1, 2, 3, etc., on the circle, draw horizontal lines, and on them set off distances $1a = A1$, $2b = A2$, $3c = A3$, etc. The points A, a, b, c, etc., are points of the cycloid.

An **Epicycloid** is a curve generated by a point on one circle rolling on the *outside* of another circle. An **Hypocycloid** is a curve generated by the point if the generating circle rolls on the *inside* of the second circle.

Involute of a Circle

An **Involute of a Circle** is a curve generated by the free end of a taut string as it is unwound from a circle.

62. To describe an involute of a given circle (Fig. 72). Let AB be the given circle. Through B draw Bb perpendicular to AB. Make Bb equal in length to half the circumference of the circle. Divide Bb and the semi-circumference into the same number of equal parts, say six. From each point of division 1, 2, 3, etc., of the circumference, draw lines to the center C of the circle. Then draw $1a_1$ perpendicular to $C1$; $2a_2$ perpendicular to $C2$; and so on. Make $1a_1$ equal to bb_1; $2a_2$ equal to bb_2; $3a_3$ equal to bb_3; and so on. Join the points A, a_1, a_2, a_3, etc., by a curve; this curve is the required involute.

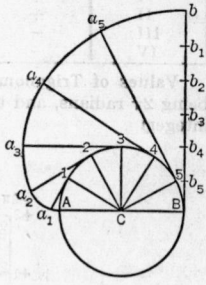

FIG. 72

TRIGONOMETRY

By M. J. Fish

24. CIRCULAR FUNCTIONS OF PLANE ANGLES

Definitions and Values

Trigonometric Functions. The angle α in Fig. 1, is measured in degrees or radians, as defined in Art. 21. The ratio of any two of the quantities x, y, or r determines the extent of the opening between the lines OP and OX. Since these ratios are functions of the angle they may be used to measure or construct it. The definitions and terms used to designate the functions are as follows:

$$\text{Sine } \alpha \quad = \frac{y}{r} = \sin \alpha$$

$$\text{Cosine } \alpha \quad = \frac{x}{r} = \cos \alpha$$

$$\text{Tangent } \alpha \quad = \frac{y}{x} = \tan \alpha$$

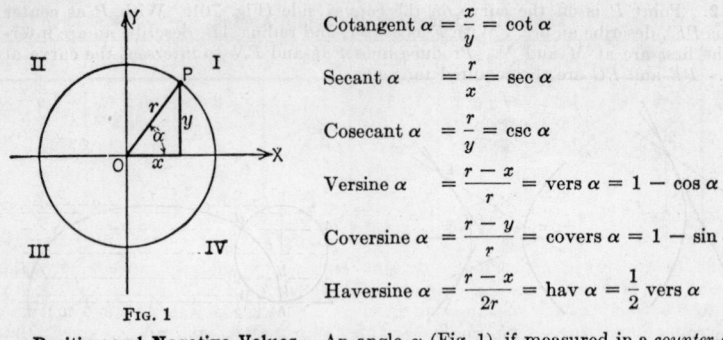

FIG. 1

$$\text{Cotangent } \alpha = \frac{x}{y} = \cot \alpha$$

$$\text{Secant } \alpha \quad = \frac{r}{x} = \sec \alpha$$

$$\text{Cosecant } \alpha \; = \frac{r}{y} = \csc \alpha$$

$$\text{Versine } \alpha \quad = \frac{r-x}{r} = \text{vers } \alpha = 1 - \cos \alpha$$

$$\text{Coversine } \alpha \; = \frac{r-y}{r} = \text{covers } \alpha = 1 - \sin \alpha$$

$$\text{Haversine } \alpha \; = \frac{r-x}{2r} = \text{hav } \alpha = \frac{1}{2} \text{ vers } \alpha$$

Positive and Negative Values. An angle α (Fig. 1), if measured in a *counter-clockwise* direction, is said to be *positive*; if measured *clockwise, negative*. Following the convention that x is positive if measured along OX to the right of the OY axis and negative if measured to the left, and similarly, y is positive if measured along OY above the OX axis and negative if measured below, the signs of the trigonometric functions are different for angles in the quadrants I, II, III, and IV. The signs of the six most common functions are tabulated in Table I.

Table I. Signs of Trigonometric Functions

Quadrant	sin	cos	tan	cot	sec	csc
I	+	+	+	+	+	+
II	+	−	−	−	−	+
III	−	−	+	+	−	−
IV	−	+	−	−	+	−

Values of Trigonometric Functions are periodic, the period of the sin, cos, sec, csc being 2π radians, and that of the tan and cot, π radians. For example, in Fig. 2, (n an integer)

$$\sin (\alpha + 2\pi n) = \sin \alpha$$
$$\tan (\alpha + \pi n) \; = \tan \alpha$$

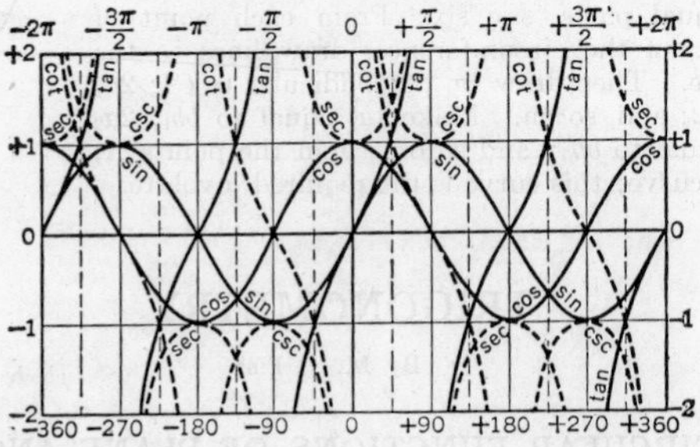

FIG. 2

Functions of angles in any quadrant (Fig. 1) in terms of angles in the first quadrant, and values of the functions for certain angles are given in Tables II and III, respectively. Values of the functions for angles in increments of one minute and five hundredths of a degree may be obtained from Section 1, Table 17. Combined with this table is a table of common logarithms of the functions.

Table II. Functions of Angles in Any Quadrant in Terms of Angles in the First Quadrant

	$-\alpha$	$90° \pm \alpha$	$180° \pm \alpha$	$270° \pm \alpha$	$360° \pm \alpha$
sin	$-\sin \alpha$	$+\cos \alpha$	$\mp \sin \alpha$	$-\cos \alpha$	$\pm \sin \alpha$
cos	$+\cos \alpha$	$\mp \sin \alpha$	$-\cos \alpha$	$\pm \sin \alpha$	$+\cos \alpha$
tan	$-\tan \alpha$	$\mp \cot \alpha$	$\pm \tan \alpha$	$\mp \cot \alpha$	$\pm \tan \alpha$
cot	$-\cot \alpha$	$\mp \tan \alpha$	$\pm \cot \alpha$	$\mp \tan \alpha$	$\pm \cot \alpha$
sec	$+\sec \alpha$	$\mp \csc \alpha$	$-\sec \alpha$	$\pm \csc \alpha$	$+\sec \alpha$
csc	$-\csc \alpha$	$+\sec \alpha$	$\mp \csc \alpha$	$-\sec \alpha$	$\pm \csc \alpha$

Table III. Functions of Certain Angles

	0°	30°	45°	60°	90°	180°	270°	360°
sin	0	$1/2$	$1/2\sqrt{2}$	$1/2\sqrt{3}$	1	0	-1	0
cos	1	$1/2\sqrt{3}$	$1/2\sqrt{2}$	$1/2$	0	-1	0	1
tan	0	$1/3\sqrt{3}$	1	$\sqrt{3}$	∞	0	∞	0
cot	∞	$\sqrt{3}$	1	$1/3\sqrt{3}$	0	∞	0	∞
sec	1	$2/3\sqrt{3}$	$\sqrt{2}$	2	∞	-1	∞	1
csc	∞	2	$\sqrt{2}$	$2/3\sqrt{3}$	1	∞	-1	∞

Inverse, or Anti-functions. The symbol $\sin^{-1} x$ means the angle whose sine is x, and is read inverse sine of x, anti-sine of x, or arc sine x. Similarly for $\cos^{-1} x$, $\tan^{-1} x$, $\cot^{-1} x$, $\sec^{-1} x$, $\csc^{-1} x$, $\text{vers}^{-1} x$, the last meaning an angle α such that $(1 - \cos\alpha) = x$. While the direct functions (sine, etc.) are single valued, the indirect are many valued; thus $\sin 30° = 0.5$, but $\sin^{-1} 0.5 = 30°,\ 150°,\ ..$

Functional Relationships, Identities

Table IV. Functions of an Angle in Terms of Each of the Others

	$\sin\alpha = a$	$\cos\alpha = a$	$\tan\alpha = a$	$\cot\alpha = a$	$\sec\alpha = a$	$\csc\alpha = a$
sin	a	$\sqrt{1-a^2}$	$\dfrac{a}{\sqrt{1+a^2}}$	$\dfrac{1}{\sqrt{1+a^2}}$	$\dfrac{\sqrt{a^2-1}}{a}$	$\dfrac{1}{a}$
cos	$\sqrt{1-a^2}$	a	$\dfrac{1}{\sqrt{1+a^2}}$	$\dfrac{a}{\sqrt{1+a^2}}$	$\dfrac{1}{a}$	$\dfrac{\sqrt{a^2-1}}{a}$
tan	$\dfrac{a}{\sqrt{1-a^2}}$	$\dfrac{\sqrt{1-a^2}}{a}$	a	$\dfrac{1}{a}$	$\sqrt{a^2-1}$	$\dfrac{1}{\sqrt{a^2-1}}$
cot	$\dfrac{\sqrt{1-a^2}}{a}$	$\dfrac{a}{\sqrt{1-a^2}}$	$\dfrac{1}{a}$	a	$\dfrac{1}{\sqrt{a^2-1}}$	$\sqrt{a^2-1}$
sec	$\dfrac{1}{\sqrt{1-a^2}}$	$\dfrac{1}{a}$	$\sqrt{1+a^2}$	$\dfrac{\sqrt{1+a^2}}{a}$	a	$\dfrac{a}{\sqrt{a^2-1}}$
csc	$\dfrac{1}{a}$	$\dfrac{1}{\sqrt{1-a^2}}$	$\dfrac{\sqrt{1+a^2}}{a}$	$\sqrt{1+a^2}$	$\dfrac{a}{\sqrt{a^2-1}}$	a

Note: The sign of the radical is to be determined by the quadrant.

Functions of the Sum and Difference of Two Angles.

$$\sin(\alpha \pm \beta) = \sin\alpha\cos\beta \pm \cos\alpha\sin\beta$$
$$\cos(\alpha \pm \beta) = \cos\alpha\cos\beta \mp \sin\alpha\sin\beta$$
$$\tan(\alpha \pm \beta) = (\tan\alpha \pm \tan\beta)/(1 \mp \tan\alpha\tan\beta)$$
$$\cot(\alpha \pm \beta) = (\cot\beta\cot\alpha \mp 1)/(\cot\beta \pm \cot\alpha).$$

If x is small, say 3° or 4°, then the following are close approximations, in which the quantity x is to be expressed in radians (1° = 0.01745 radian).

$$\sin\alpha \approx \alpha, \qquad \cos\alpha \approx 1, \qquad \tan\alpha \approx \alpha$$
$$\sin(\alpha \pm x) \approx \sin\alpha \pm x\cos\alpha, \qquad \cos(\alpha \pm x) \approx \cos\alpha \mp x\sin\alpha$$

Functions of Half Angles.

$$\sin \tfrac{1}{2}\alpha = \sqrt{\tfrac{1}{2}(1-\cos\alpha)} = \tfrac{1}{2}\sqrt{1+\sin\alpha} - \tfrac{1}{2}\sqrt{1-\sin\alpha}$$
$$\cos \tfrac{1}{2}\alpha = \sqrt{\tfrac{1}{2}(1+\cos\alpha)} = \tfrac{1}{2}\sqrt{1+\sin\alpha} + \tfrac{1}{2}\sqrt{1-\sin\alpha}$$
$$\tan \tfrac{1}{2}\alpha = \sqrt{(1-\cos\alpha)/(1+\cos\alpha)} = (1-\cos\alpha)/\sin\alpha = \sin\alpha/(1+\cos\alpha)$$
$$\cot \tfrac{1}{2}\alpha = \sqrt{(1+\cos\alpha)/(1-\cos\alpha)} = (1+\cos\alpha)/\sin\alpha = \sin\alpha/(1-\cos\alpha)$$

Functions of Multiples of Angles.

$$\sin 2\alpha = 2\sin\alpha\cos\alpha,$$
$$\tan 2\alpha = 2\tan\alpha/(1-\tan^2\alpha)$$
$$\cos 2\alpha = 2\cos^2\alpha - 1 = 1 - 2\sin^2\alpha$$
$$\cot 2\alpha = (\cot^2\alpha - 1)/2\cot\alpha$$

$$\sin 3\alpha = 3\sin\alpha - 4\sin^3\alpha \qquad\qquad \cos 3\alpha = 4\cos^3\alpha - 3\cos\alpha$$
$$\sin 4\alpha = 8\cos^3\alpha\sin\alpha - 4\cos\alpha\sin\alpha \qquad \cos 4\alpha = 8\cos^4\alpha - 8\cos^2\alpha + 1$$

Products and Powers of Functions.

$$\sin\alpha\sin\beta = \tfrac{1}{2}\cos(\alpha-\beta) - \tfrac{1}{2}\cos(\alpha+\beta)$$
$$\cos\alpha\cos\beta = \tfrac{1}{2}\cos(\alpha-\beta) + \tfrac{1}{2}\cos(\alpha+\beta)$$
$$\sin\alpha\cos\beta = \tfrac{1}{2}\sin(\alpha-\beta) + \tfrac{1}{2}\sin(\alpha+\beta)$$
$$\tan\alpha\cot\alpha = \sin\alpha\csc\alpha = \cos\alpha\sec\alpha = 1$$
$$\sin^2\alpha = \tfrac{1}{2}(1 - \cos 2\alpha); \qquad \cos^2\alpha = \tfrac{1}{2}(1 + \cos 2\alpha)$$
$$\sin^3\alpha = \tfrac{1}{4}(3\sin\alpha - \sin 3\alpha); \quad \cos^3\alpha = \tfrac{1}{4}(\cos 3\alpha + 3\cos\alpha)$$

Sums and Differences of Functions.

$$\sin\alpha + \sin\beta = 2\sin\tfrac{1}{2}(\alpha+\beta)\cos\tfrac{1}{2}(\alpha-\beta)$$
$$\sin\alpha - \sin\beta = 2\cos\tfrac{1}{2}(\alpha+\beta)\sin\tfrac{1}{2}(\alpha-\beta)$$
$$\cos\alpha + \cos\beta = 2\cos\tfrac{1}{2}(\alpha+\beta)\cos\tfrac{1}{2}(\alpha-\beta)$$
$$\cos\alpha - \cos\beta = -2\sin\tfrac{1}{2}(\alpha+\beta)\sin\tfrac{1}{2}(\alpha-\beta)$$
$$\tan\alpha + \tan\beta = \frac{\sin(\alpha+\beta)}{\cos\alpha\cos\beta}; \qquad \cot\alpha + \cot\beta = \frac{\sin(\alpha+\beta)}{\sin\alpha\sin\beta}$$
$$\tan\alpha - \tan\beta = \frac{\sin(\alpha-\beta)}{\cos\alpha\cos\beta}; \qquad \cot\alpha - \cot\beta = -\frac{\sin(\alpha-\beta)}{\sin\alpha\sin\beta}$$
$$\sin^2\alpha - \sin^2\beta = \sin(\alpha+\beta)\sin(\alpha-\beta)$$
$$\cos^2\alpha - \cos^2\beta = -\sin(\alpha+\beta)\sin(\alpha-\beta)$$
$$\cos^2\alpha - \sin^2\beta = \cos(\alpha+\beta)\cos(\alpha-\beta)$$

Anti-Trigonometric or Inverse Functional Relations.

In the following formulas the periodic constant is omitted.

$$\sin^{-1}x = -\sin^{-1}(-x) = \frac{\pi}{2} - \cos^{-1}x = \cos^{-1}\sqrt{1-x^2} = \tan^{-1}\frac{x}{\sqrt{1-x^2}} = \cot^{-1}\frac{\sqrt{1-x^2}}{x}$$
$$= \csc^{-1}\frac{1}{x} = \sec^{-1}\frac{1}{\sqrt{1-x^2}}$$

$$\cos^{-1}x = \pi - \cos^{-1}(-x) = \frac{\pi}{2} - \sin^{-1}x = \tfrac{1}{2}\cos^{-1}(2x^2-1) = \sin^{-1}\sqrt{1-x^2}$$
$$= \tan^{-1}\frac{\sqrt{1-x^2}}{x} = \cot^{-1}\frac{x}{\sqrt{1-x^2}} = \sec^{-1}\frac{1}{x} = \csc^{-1}\frac{1}{\sqrt{1-x^2}}$$

$$\tan^{-1}x = -\tan^{-1}(-x) = \frac{\pi}{2} - \cot^{-1}x = \sin^{-1}\frac{x}{\sqrt{1+x^2}} = \cos^{-1}\frac{1}{\sqrt{1+x^2}} = \cot^{-1}\frac{1}{x}$$
$$= \sec^{-1}\sqrt{1+x^2} = \csc^{-1}\frac{\sqrt{1+x^2}}{x}$$

$$\cot^{-1}x = \tan^{-1}\frac{1}{x}; \quad \sec^{-1}x = \cos^{-1}\frac{1}{x}; \quad \csc^{-1}x = \sin^{-1}\frac{1}{x}$$

$$\sin^{-1}x \pm \sin^{-1}y = \sin^{-1}\{x\sqrt{1-y^2} \pm y\sqrt{1-x^2}\}$$
$$\cos^{-1}x \pm \cos^{-1}y = \cos^{-1}\{xy \mp \sqrt{(1-x^2)(1-y^2)}\}$$
$$\sin^{-1}x \pm \cos^{-1}y = \sin^{-1}\{xy \pm \sqrt{(1-x^2)(1-y^2)}\} = \cos^{-1}\{y\sqrt{1-x^2} \mp x\sqrt{1-y^2}\}$$
$$\tan^{-1}x \pm \tan^{-1}y = \tan^{-1}\frac{x \pm y}{1 \mp xy}$$
$$\tan^{-1}x \pm \cot^{-1}y = \tan^{-1}\frac{xy \pm 1}{y \mp x} = \cot^{-1}\frac{y \mp x}{xy \pm 1}$$

25. SOLUTION OF TRIANGLES

Relations Between Angles and Sides of Plane Triangles. Let a, b, c = sides of triangle; α, β, γ = angles opposite a, b, c, respectively; A = area of triangle; $s = \tfrac{1}{2}(a+b+c)$.

$$\frac{a}{\sin\alpha} = \frac{b}{\sin\beta} = \frac{c}{\sin\gamma} \qquad \text{(Law of Sines)}$$

$$a^2 = b^2 + c^2 - 2bc \cos \alpha \quad \text{(Law of Cosines)}$$

$$\frac{a - b}{a + b} = \frac{\tan \frac{1}{2} (\alpha - \beta)}{\tan \frac{1}{2} (\alpha + \beta)} \quad \text{(Law of Tangents)}$$

$$\alpha + \beta + \gamma = 180°$$

$$a = b \cos \gamma + c \cos \beta; \; b = c \cos \alpha + a \cos \gamma; \; c = a \cos \beta + b \cos \alpha$$

$$A = \sqrt{s(s - a)(s - b)(s - c)}$$

$$\sin \alpha = \frac{2}{bc} A; \; \sin \beta = \frac{2}{ca} A; \; \sin \gamma = \frac{2}{ab} A$$

$$\sin \frac{\alpha}{2} = \sqrt{\frac{(s - b)(s - c)}{bc}}; \; \sin \frac{\beta}{2} = \sqrt{\frac{(s - c)(s - a)}{ca}}; \; \sin \frac{\gamma}{2} = \sqrt{\frac{(s - a)(s - b)}{ab}}$$

$$\cos \frac{\alpha}{2} = \sqrt{\frac{s(s - a)}{bc}}; \; \cos \frac{\beta}{2} = \sqrt{\frac{s(s - b)}{ca}}; \; \cos \frac{\gamma}{2} = \sqrt{\frac{s(s - c)}{ab}}$$

$$\tan \frac{\alpha}{2} = \sqrt{\frac{(s - b)(s - c)}{s(s - a)}}; \; \tan \frac{\beta}{2} = \sqrt{\frac{(s - c)(s - a)}{s(s - b)}}; \; \tan \frac{\gamma}{2} = \sqrt{\frac{(s - a)(s - b)}{s(s - c)}}$$

Solution of Plane Oblique Triangles.

Given $a, b, c.$ (If logarithms are to be used, use 1.)

1. $r = \sqrt{\dfrac{(s - a)(s - b)(s - c)}{s}}; A = \sqrt{s(s - a)(s - b)(s - c)} = rs;$

$$\tan \frac{\alpha}{2} = \frac{r}{s - a}; \; \tan \frac{\beta}{2} = \frac{r}{s - b}; \; \tan \frac{\gamma}{2} = \frac{r}{s - c}.$$

2. $\cos \alpha = \dfrac{b^2 + c^2 - a^2}{2bc}; \; \cos \beta = \dfrac{a^2 + c^2 - b^2}{2ac};$

$$\cos \gamma = \frac{a^2 + b^2 - c^2}{2ab}, \text{ or } \gamma = 180° - (\alpha + \beta).$$

Given $a, b, \alpha.$

$\sin \beta = \dfrac{b \sin \alpha}{a}$ (if $a > b$, $\beta < \dfrac{\pi}{2}$ and has only one value; if $b > a$, β has two values, β_1 and $\beta_2 = 180° - \beta_1$); $\gamma = 180° - (\alpha + \beta); c = \dfrac{a \sin \gamma}{\sin \alpha}; A = \frac{1}{2} ab \sin \gamma.$

Given $a, \alpha, \beta.$

$$b = \frac{a \sin \beta}{\sin \alpha}; \gamma = 180° - (\alpha + \beta); c = \frac{a \sin \gamma}{\sin \alpha}; A = \frac{1}{2} ab \sin \gamma.$$

Given $a, b, \gamma.$ (If logarithms are to be used, use 1.)

1. $\tan \frac{1}{2} (\alpha - \beta) = \dfrac{a - b}{a + b} \cot \frac{1}{2} \gamma; \frac{1}{2} (\alpha + \beta) = 90° - \frac{1}{2} \gamma; c = \dfrac{a \sin \gamma}{\sin \alpha}$

$A = \frac{1}{2} ab \sin \gamma.$

2. $c = \sqrt{a^2 + b^2 - 2 ab \cos \gamma}; \; \sin \alpha = \dfrac{a \sin \gamma}{c}; \; \beta = 180° - (\alpha + \gamma).$

3. $\tan \alpha = \dfrac{a \sin \gamma}{b - a \cos \gamma}; \; \beta = 180° - (\alpha + \gamma); c = \dfrac{a \sin \gamma}{\sin \alpha}.$

Solution of Plane Right Triangles. Let $\gamma = 90°$ and c be the hypotenuse. Given any two sides or one side and an acute angle α.

$$a = \sqrt{c^2 - b^2} = \sqrt{(c + b)(c - b)} = b \tan \alpha = c \sin \alpha.$$

$$b = \sqrt{c^2 - a^2} = \sqrt{(c + a)(c - a)} = \frac{a}{\tan \alpha} = c \cos \alpha.$$

$$c = \sqrt{a^2 + b^2} = \frac{a}{\sin \alpha} = \frac{b}{\cos \alpha}.$$

$$\alpha = \sin^{-1} \frac{a}{c} = \cos^{-1} \frac{b}{c} = \tan^{-1} \frac{a}{b}; \; \beta = 90° - \alpha.$$

$$A = \frac{ab}{2} = \frac{a^2}{2 \tan \alpha} = \frac{b^2 \tan \alpha}{2} = \frac{c^2 \sin 2\alpha}{4}.$$

26. SPHERICAL TRIGONOMETRY

Spherical Trigonometry. Let O be the center of the sphere and a, b, c the sides of a triangle on the surface with opposite angles α, β, γ, respectively, the sides being measured by the angle subtended at the center of the sphere. Let $s = \frac{1}{2}(a + b + c)$, $\sigma = \frac{1}{2}(\alpha + \beta + \gamma)$, $E = \alpha + \beta + \gamma - 180°$, the spherical excess. The following formulas are valid usually only for triangles of which the sides and angles are all between $0°$ and $180°$. To each such triangle there is a polar triangle, whose sides are $180° - \alpha$, $180° - \beta$, $180° - \gamma$, and whose angles are $180° - a$, $180° - b$, $180° - c$.

General Formulas.

$$\frac{\sin a}{\sin \alpha} = \frac{\sin b}{\sin \beta} = \frac{\sin c}{\sin \gamma} \text{ (Law of Sines)}$$

$$\cos a = \cos b \cos c + \sin b \sin c \cos \alpha \text{ (Law of Cosines)}$$

$$\cos \alpha = - \cos \beta \cos \gamma + \sin \beta \sin \gamma \cos a \text{ (Law of Cosines)}$$

$$\cos a \sin b = \sin a \cos b \cos \gamma + \sin c \cos \alpha$$

$$\cot a \sin b = \sin \gamma \cot \alpha + \cos \gamma \cos b$$

$$\cos \alpha \sin \beta = \sin \gamma \cos \alpha - \sin \alpha \cos \beta \cos c$$

$$\cot \alpha \sin \beta = \sin c \cot a - \cos c \cos \beta$$

$$\sin \frac{a}{2} = \sqrt{\frac{- \cos \sigma \cos (\sigma - \alpha)}{\sin \beta \sin \gamma}} \; ; \; \sin \frac{\alpha}{2} = \sqrt{\frac{\sin(s - b) \sin (s - c)}{\sin b \sin c}} :$$

$$\cos \frac{a}{2} = \sqrt{\frac{\cos (\sigma - \beta) \cos (\sigma - \gamma)}{\sin \beta \sin \gamma}} \; ; \; \cos \frac{\alpha}{2} = \sqrt{\frac{\sin s \sin (s - a)}{\sin b \sin c}}$$

$$\tan \frac{a}{2} = \sqrt{\frac{- \cos \sigma \cos (\sigma - \alpha)}{\cos (\sigma - \beta) \cos (\sigma - \gamma)}} \; ; \; \tan \frac{\alpha}{2} = \sqrt{\frac{\sin (s - b) \sin (s - c)}{\sin s \sin (s - a)}}$$

$$\tan \frac{E}{4} = \sqrt{\tan \frac{s}{2} \tan \frac{(s - a)}{2} \tan \frac{(s - b)}{2} \tan \frac{(s - c)}{2}} \; ; \; \cot \frac{E}{2} = \frac{\cot \frac{a}{2} \cot \frac{b}{2} + \cos \gamma}{\sin \gamma}$$

$$\tan \left(\frac{a + b}{2}\right) = \frac{\cos \left(\dfrac{\alpha - \beta}{2}\right)}{\cos \left(\dfrac{\alpha + \beta}{2}\right)} \tan \frac{c}{2} \; ; \; \tan \left(\frac{a - b}{2}\right) = \frac{\sin \left(\dfrac{\alpha - \beta}{2}\right)}{\sin \left(\dfrac{\alpha + \beta}{2}\right)} \tan \frac{c}{2}$$

$$\tan \left(\frac{\alpha + \beta}{2}\right) = \frac{\cos \left(\dfrac{a - b}{2}\right)}{\cos \left(\dfrac{a + b}{2}\right)} \cot \frac{\gamma}{2} \; ; \; \tan \left(\frac{\alpha - \beta}{2}\right) = \frac{\sin \left(\dfrac{a - b}{2}\right)}{\sin \left(\dfrac{a + b}{2}\right)} \cot \frac{\gamma}{2}$$

$$\cos \left(\frac{\alpha + \beta}{2}\right) \cos \frac{c}{2} = \cos \left(\frac{a + b}{2}\right) \sin \frac{\gamma}{2} \; ; \; \sin \left(\frac{\alpha + \beta}{2}\right) \cos \frac{c}{2} = \cos \left(\frac{a - b}{2}\right) \cos \frac{\gamma}{2}$$

$$\cos \left(\frac{\alpha - \beta}{2}\right) \sin \frac{c}{2} = \sin \left(\frac{a + b}{2}\right) \sin \frac{\gamma}{2} \; ; \; \sin \left(\frac{\alpha - \beta}{2}\right) \sin \frac{c}{2} = \sin \left(\frac{a - b}{2}\right) \cos \frac{\gamma}{2}$$

The Right Spherical Triangle Let $\gamma = 90°$ and c be the hypotenuse.

$$\cos c = \cos a \cos b = \cot \alpha \cot \beta; \; \cos a = \frac{\cos \alpha}{\sin \beta}; \; \cos b = \frac{\cos \beta}{\sin \alpha}; \; \sin \alpha = \frac{\sin a}{\sin c}; \; \cos \alpha = \frac{\tan b}{\tan c};$$

$$\tan \alpha = \frac{\tan a}{\sin b}$$

27. HYPERBOLIC TRIGONOMETRY

Hyperbolic Angles are defined in a manner similar to circular angles but with reference to an *equilateral hyperbola*. The comparative relations are shown in Figs. 3 and 4. A *circular angle* is a central angle measured in radians by the ratio s/r or the ratio $2A/r^2$, where A is the area of the sector included by the angle α and the arc s (Fig. 3). For the *hyperbola* the radius ρ is not constant and only the value of the *differential hyperbolic angle* $d\theta$ is defined by the ratio ds/ρ. Thus, $\theta = \int ds/\rho = 2A/a^2$, where A represents the shaded area in Fig. 4. If both s and ρ are measured in the same units the angle is expressed in *hyperbolic radians*.

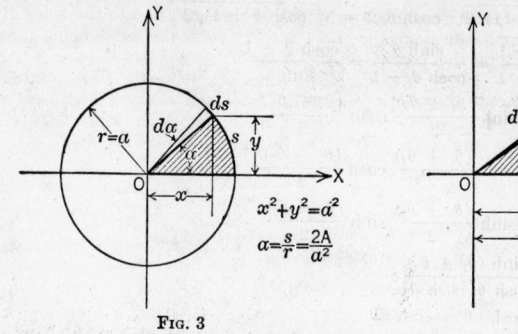

$$x^2 + y^2 = a^2$$
$$\alpha = \frac{s}{r} = \frac{2A}{a^2}$$

FIG. 3

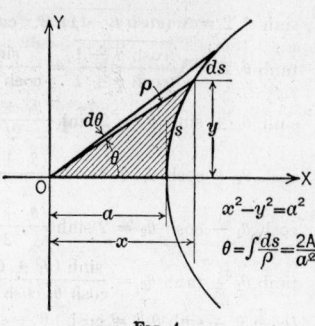

$$x^2 - y^2 = a^2$$
$$\theta = \int \frac{ds}{\rho} = \frac{2A}{a^2}$$

FIG. 4

Hyperbolic Functions are defined by ratios similar to those defining functions of circular angles and also named similarly. Their names and abbreviations are:

Hyperbolic sine θ $\quad = \dfrac{y}{a} = \sinh \theta$

Hyperbolic cosine θ $\quad = \dfrac{x}{a} = \cosh \theta$

Hyperbolic tangent θ $\quad = \dfrac{y}{x} = \tanh \theta$

Hyperbolic cotangent $\theta = \dfrac{x}{y} = \coth \theta$

Hyperbolic secant $\quad \theta = \dfrac{a}{x} = \operatorname{sech} \theta$

Hyperbolic cosecant $\quad \theta = \dfrac{a}{y} = \operatorname{csch} \theta$

Values and Exponential Equivalents. The values of hyperbolic functions may be computed from their exponential equivalents. The graphs are shown in Fig. 5. Values for increments of 0.01 radian are given in Section 1, Table 18.

$$\sinh \theta = \frac{e^\theta - e^{-\theta}}{2} \; ; \; \cosh \theta = \frac{e^\theta + e^{-\theta}}{2} \; ; \; \tanh \theta = \frac{e^\theta - e^{-\theta}}{e^\theta + e^{-\theta}}$$

If θ is extremely small, $\sinh \theta \approx \theta$, $\cosh \theta \approx 1$, and $\tanh \theta \approx \theta$. For large values of θ, $\sinh \theta \approx \cosh \theta$, and $\tanh \theta \approx \coth \theta \approx 1$.

Fundamental Identities.

$$\operatorname{csch} \theta = \frac{1}{\sinh \theta} \; ; \; \operatorname{sech} \theta = \frac{1}{\cosh \theta} \; ; \; \coth \theta = \frac{1}{\tanh \theta}$$

$$\cosh^2 \theta - \sinh^2 \theta = 1; \; \operatorname{sech}^2 \theta = 1 - \tanh^2 \theta;$$
$$\operatorname{csch}^2 \theta = \coth^2 \theta - 1$$

$$\cosh \theta + \sinh \theta = e^\theta; \; \cosh \theta - \sinh \theta = e^{-\theta}$$

$$\sinh (-\theta) = -\sinh \theta; \; \cosh (-\theta) = \cosh \theta$$

$$\tanh (-\theta) = -\tanh \theta; \; \coth (-\theta) = -\coth \theta$$

$$\sinh (\theta_1 \pm \theta_2) = \sinh \theta_1 \cosh \theta_2 \pm \cosh \theta_1 \sinh \theta_2$$

$$\cosh (\theta_1 \pm \theta_2) = \cosh \theta_1 \cosh \theta_2 \pm \sinh \theta_1 \sinh \theta_2$$

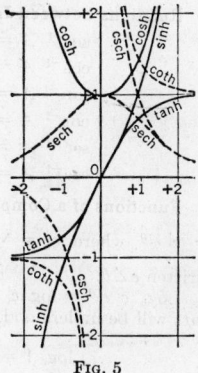

FIG. 5

$$\tanh (\theta_1 \pm \theta_2) = \frac{\tanh \theta_1 \pm \tanh \theta_2}{1 \pm \tanh \theta_1 \tanh \theta_2} \; ; \; \coth (\theta_1 \pm \theta_2) = \frac{1 \pm \coth \theta_1 \coth \theta_2}{\coth \theta_1 \pm \coth \theta_2}$$

$$\sinh 2\theta = 2 \sinh \theta \cosh \theta = \frac{2 \tanh \theta}{1 - \tanh^2 \theta}$$

$$\cosh 2\theta = \sinh^2 \theta + \cosh^2 \theta = 1 + 2 \sinh^2 \theta = 2 \cosh^2 \theta - 1 = \frac{1 + \tanh^2 \theta}{1 - \tanh^2 \theta}$$

$$\tanh 2\theta = \frac{2\tanh\theta}{1+\tanh^2\theta}\ ;\quad \coth 2\theta = \frac{1+\coth^2\theta}{2\coth\theta}$$

$$\sinh\theta/2 = \sqrt{(\cosh\theta-1)/2};\quad \cosh\theta/2 = \sqrt{(\cosh\theta+1)/2}$$

$$\tanh\theta/2 = \sqrt{\frac{\cosh\theta-1}{\cosh\theta+1}} = \frac{\sinh\theta}{\cosh\theta+1} = \frac{\cosh\theta-1}{\sinh\theta}$$

$$\sinh\theta_1 \pm \sinh\theta_2 = 2\sinh\frac{(\theta_1\pm\theta_2)}{2}\cosh\frac{(\theta_1\mp\theta_2)}{2}$$

$$\cosh\theta_1 + \cosh\theta_2 = 2\cosh\frac{(\theta_1+\theta_2)}{2}\cosh\frac{(\theta_1-\theta_2)}{2}$$

$$\cosh\theta_1 - \cosh\theta_2 = 2\sinh\frac{(\theta_1+\theta_2)}{2}\sinh\frac{(\theta_1-\theta_2)}{2}$$

$$\tanh\theta_1 \pm \tanh\theta_2 = \frac{\sinh(\theta_1\pm\theta_2)}{\cosh\theta_1\cosh\theta_2}:$$

$$(\cosh\theta \pm \sinh\theta)^n = \cosh n\theta \pm \sinh n\theta$$

Anti-hyperbolic or Inverse Functions. The angle whose hyperbolic sine is u is written: $\sinh^{-1}u$. Values of the angles in hyperbolic radians, corresponding to the several functions, may be computed from their logarithmic equivalents.

$$\sinh^{-1}u = \log_e(u + \sqrt{u^2+1});\quad \cosh^{-1}u = \log_e(u + \sqrt{u^2-1})$$

$$\tanh^{-1}u = {}^1/_2\log_e\frac{1+u}{1-u}\ ;\quad \coth^{-1}u = {}^1/_2\log_e\frac{u+1}{u-1}$$

28. FUNCTIONS OF IMAGINARY AND COMPLEX ANGLES

Relation of Hyperbolic to Circular Functions. By comparison of the exponential equivalents of hyperbolic and circular functions the following identities are established $(i = \sqrt{-1})$:

$$\sin\alpha = -i\sinh i\alpha \qquad\qquad \sinh\beta = -i\sin i\beta$$
$$\cos\alpha = \cosh i\alpha \qquad\qquad\quad \cosh\beta = \cos i\beta$$
$$\tan\alpha = -i\tanh i\alpha \qquad\qquad \tanh\beta = -i\tan i\beta$$
$$\cot\alpha = i\coth i\alpha \qquad\qquad\quad \coth\beta = i\cot i\beta$$
$$\sec\alpha = \operatorname{sech} i\alpha \qquad\qquad\quad \operatorname{sech}\beta = \sec i\beta$$
$$\csc\alpha = i\operatorname{csch} i\alpha \qquad\qquad\quad \operatorname{csch}\beta = i\csc i\beta$$

Relations between Inverse Functions.

$$\sin^{-1}A = -i\sinh^{-1}iA \qquad\qquad \sinh^{-1}B = -i\sin^{-1}iB$$
$$\cos^{-1}A = -i\cosh^{-1}A \qquad\qquad \cosh^{-1}B = i\cos^{-1}B$$
$$\tan^{-1}A = -i\tanh^{-1}iA \qquad\qquad \tanh^{-1}B = -i\tan^{-1}iB$$
$$\cot^{-1}A = i\coth^{-1}iA \qquad\qquad \coth^{-1}B = i\cot^{-1}iB$$
$$\sec^{-1}A = -i\operatorname{sech}^{-1}A \qquad\qquad \operatorname{sech}^{-1}B = i\sec^{-1}B$$
$$\csc^{-1}A = i\operatorname{csch}^{-1}iA \qquad\qquad \operatorname{csch}^{-1}B = i\csc^{-1}iB$$

Functions of a Complex Angle. In complex notation $c = a + ib = |c|(\cos\theta + i\sin\theta) = |c|\,e^{i\theta}$, where $|c| = \sqrt{a^2+b^2}$, $i = \sqrt{-1}$, and $\theta = \tan^{-1}\dfrac{b}{a}$. $|c|\,e^{i\theta}$, is frequently written $c\angle\theta$.

$\log_e|c|\,e^{i\theta} = \log|c| + i(\theta + 2k\pi)$ and is infinitely many valued. By its principal part will be understood $\log_e|c| + i\theta$. Some convenient identities are:

$$\log_e 1 = 0;\ \log_e(-1) = i\pi;\ \log_e i = i\frac{\pi}{2};\ \log_e(-i) = i\frac{3\pi}{2}$$

$$(\cos\theta \pm i\sin\theta)^n = \cos n\theta \pm i\sin n\theta;\ \sqrt[n]{\cos\theta \pm i\sin\theta} = \cos\frac{\theta+2\pi k}{n} \pm i\sin\frac{\theta+2\pi k}{n}$$

The use of complex angles occurs frequently in electric circuit problems where it is often necessary to express the functions of them as a complex number.

$$\sin(\alpha \pm i\beta) = \sin\alpha\cosh\beta \pm i\cos\alpha\sinh\beta = \sqrt{\cosh^2\beta - \cos^2\alpha}\ e^{\pm i\theta}$$

where $\theta = \tan^{-1}\cot\alpha\tanh\beta$.

$$\cos(\alpha \pm i\beta) = \cos\alpha\cosh\beta \mp i\sin\alpha\sinh\beta = \sqrt{\cosh^2\beta - \sin^2\alpha}\; e^{\pm i\theta}$$

where $\theta = \tan^{-1}\tan\alpha\tanh\beta$.

$$\sinh(\alpha \pm i\beta) = \sinh\alpha\cos\beta \pm i\cosh\alpha\sin\beta = \sqrt{\sinh^2\alpha + \sin^2\beta}\; e^{\pm i\theta} = \sqrt{\cosh^2\alpha - \cos^2\beta}\; e^{\pm i\theta}$$

where $\theta = \tan^{-1}\coth\alpha\tan\beta$.

$$\cosh(\alpha \pm i\beta) = \cosh\alpha\cos\beta \pm i\sinh\alpha\sin\beta = \sqrt{\sinh^2\alpha + \cos^2\beta}\; e^{\pm i\theta} = \sqrt{\cosh^2\alpha - \sin^2\beta}\; e^{\pm i\theta}$$

where $\theta = \tan^{-1}\tanh\alpha\tan\beta$.

$$\tan(\alpha \pm i\beta) = \frac{\sin 2\alpha \pm i\sinh 2\beta}{\cos 2\alpha + \cosh 2\beta}; \qquad \tanh(\alpha \pm i\beta) = \frac{\sinh 2\alpha \pm i\sin 2\beta}{\cosh 2\alpha + \cos 2\beta}$$

The hyperbolic sine and cosine have the period $2\pi i$; the hyperbolic tangent has the period πi.

$$\sinh(\alpha + 2k\pi i) = \sinh\alpha; \quad \cosh(\alpha + 2k\pi i) = \cosh\alpha$$
$$\tanh(\alpha + k\pi i) = \tanh\alpha; \quad \coth(\alpha + k\pi i) = \coth\alpha$$

Inverse Functions of Complex Numbers.

$$\sin^{-1}(A \pm iB) = \sin^{-1}\left[\frac{\sqrt{B^2 + (1+A)^2} - \sqrt{B^2 + (1-A)^2}}{2}\right]$$

$$\pm\, i\cosh^{-1}\left[\frac{\sqrt{B^2 + (1+A)^2} + \sqrt{B^2 + (1-A)^2}}{2}\right]$$

$$\cos^{-1}(A \pm iB) = \cos^{-1}\left[\frac{\sqrt{B^2 + (1+A)^2} - \sqrt{B^2 + (1-A)^2}}{2}\right]$$

$$\mp\, i\cosh^{-1}\left[\frac{\sqrt{B^2 + (1+A)^2} + \sqrt{B^2 + (1-A)^2}}{2}\right]$$

$$\tan^{-1}(A \pm iB) = \left[\frac{\pi - \tan^{-1}\dfrac{A}{\pm B - 1} + \tan^{-1}\dfrac{A}{\pm B + 1}}{2}\right]$$

$$\pm\, i\,\tfrac{1}{4}\log_e \frac{A^2 + (1 \pm B)^2}{A^2 + (1 \mp B)^2}$$

$$\sinh^{-1}(A \pm iB) = \cosh^{-1}\left[\frac{\sqrt{A^2 + (1+B)^2} + \sqrt{A^2 + (1-B)^2}}{2}\right]$$

$$\pm\, i\sin^{-1}\left[\frac{\sqrt{A^2 + (1+B)^2} - \sqrt{A^2 + (1-B)^2}}{2}\right]$$

$$\cosh^{-1}(A \pm iB) = \cosh^{-1}\left[\frac{\sqrt{B^2 + (1+A)^2} + \sqrt{B^2 + (1-A)^2}}{2}\right]$$

$$\pm\, i\cos^{-1}\left[\frac{\sqrt{B^2 + (1+A)^2} - \sqrt{B^2 + (1-A)^2}}{2}\right]$$

$$\tanh^{-1}(A \pm iB) = \tfrac{1}{2}\tanh^{-1}\frac{2A}{1 + A^2 + B^2} + i\,\tfrac{1}{2}\tan^{-1}\frac{\pm 2B}{1 - A^2 - B^2}$$

PLANE ANALYTIC GEOMETRY

By M. J. Fish

29. POINT AND LINE

Coordinates. The position of a point P_1 in a plane is determined if its distance and direction from each of two lines or axes OX and OY, which are perpendicular to each other, are known. The distances x and y (Fig. 1) perpendicular to the axes are called the *cartesian* or *rectangular coordinates* of the point. The directions to the right of OY and above OX are called *positive*, and opposite directions *negative*. The point O of intersection of OY and OX is called the *origin*.

The position of a point P is also given by its radial distance r from the origin and the angle θ between the radius r and the horizontal axis OX (Fig. 2). These coordinates r, θ, are called *polar coordinates*.

The functional relation between the coordinates of any point on a line is the equation of the line and defines its character.

The distance s between two points P_1 (x_1, y_1) and P_2 (x_2, y_2) on a straight line is

$$s = \sqrt{(x_2 - x_1)^2 + (y_2 - y_1)^2} \tag{1}$$

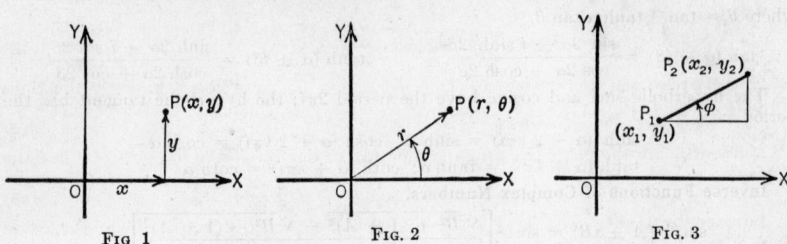

| FIG 1 | FIG. 2 | FIG. 3 |

The slope m of the line P_1P_2 is defined as the tangent of the angle ϕ, which the line makes with OX.

$$m = \tan \phi = \frac{y_2 - y_1}{x_2 - x_1} \tag{2}$$

If expressed in polar coordinates

$$s = \sqrt{r_1{}^2 + r_2{}^2 - 2r_1 r_2 \cos (\theta_2 - \theta_1)} \tag{3}$$

where r_1, r_2 and θ_1, θ_2 are the radius vectors and vectorial angles of the points P_1 and P_2.

The **Equation of a Straight Line** in cartesian coordinates is of the first degree and is expressed as follows:

$$Ax + By + C = 0 \tag{4}$$

where A, B, and C are constants.

Other forms of the equation are:
$$y = mx + b \tag{5}$$

where m is the slope and b is the y intercept;

$$y - y_1 = m (x - x_1) \tag{6}$$

where m is the slope and (x_1, y_1) is a point on the line;

$$\frac{x - x_1}{y - y_1} = \frac{x_1 - x_2}{y_1 - y_2} \tag{7}$$

where (x_1, y_1) and (x_2, y_2) are two points on the line;

$$\frac{x}{a} + \frac{y}{b} = 1 \tag{8}$$

where a and b are the x and y intercepts, respectively;

$$x \cos \alpha + y \sin \alpha - p = 0 \tag{9}$$

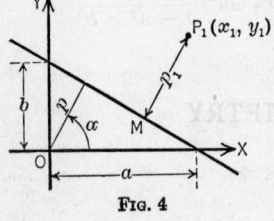

FIG. 4

where α is the angle between OX and the perpendicular from the origin to the line and p is the length of the perpendicular (Fig. 4). This is called the *perpendicular form* and is obtained by dividing the general form $Ax + By + C = 0$ by $\pm \sqrt{A^2 + B^2}$. The sign before the radical is taken opposite to that of C if $C \neq 0$ and the same as that of B if $C = 0$.

The **Perpendicular Distance of a Point** P_1 (x_1, y_1) (Fig. 4) from the line $Ax + By + C = 0$ is

$$p_1 = \frac{Ax_1 + By_1 + C}{\pm \sqrt{A^2 + B^2}} \tag{10}$$

where the sign before the radical is opposite to that of C if $C \neq 0$, and the same as B if $C = 0$.

Parallel Lines. The two lines $Ax + By + C = 0$, $A_1x + B_1y + C_1 = 0$ are parallel if

$$\frac{A}{A_1} = \frac{B}{B_1} \tag{11}$$

A line through the point (x_1, y_1) and parallel to the line $Ax + By + C = 0$ has the equation

$$A(x - x_1) + B(y - y_1) = 0 \tag{12}$$

If the two equations are written as $y = m_1x + b_1$, $y = m_2x + b_2$, the lines are parallel if $m_1 = m_2$.

Perpendicular Lines. The two lines $y = m_1x + b_1$ and $y = m_2x + b_2$ are perpendicular if

$$m_1 = -\frac{1}{m_2} \tag{13}$$

If the equations are written as $Ax + By + C = 0$, $A_1x + B_1y + C_1 = 0$, the lines are perpendicular if

$$AA_1 + BB_1 = 0 \tag{14}$$

A line through the point (x_1, y_1) perpendicular to the line $Ax + By + C = 0$ has the equation

$$B(x - x_1) - A(y - y_1) = 0 \tag{15}$$

Intersecting Lines. Let $Ax + By + C = 0$ and $A_1x + B_1y + C_1 = 0$ be the equations of two intersecting lines and λ an arbitrary constant. Then

$$(Ax + By + C) + \lambda(A_1x + B_1y + C_1) = 0 \tag{16}$$

represents the system of lines through the point of intersection.

The three lines $Ax + By + C = 0$, $A_1x + B_1y + C_1 = 0$, $A_2x + B_2y + C_2 = 0$ meet in a point if

$$\begin{vmatrix} A & B & C \\ A_1 & B_1 & C_1 \\ A_2 & B_2 & C_2 \end{vmatrix} = 0 \tag{17}$$

The Angle θ between Two Lines with equations $A_1x + B_1y + C_1 = 0$ and $A_2x + B_2y + C_2 = 0$ can be found from

$$\sin\theta = \frac{A_1B_2 - A_2B_1}{\sqrt{(A_1{}^2 + B_1{}^2)(A_2{}^2 + B_2{}^2)}}, \quad \cos\theta = \frac{A_1A_2 + B_1B_2}{\sqrt{(A_1{}^2 + B_1{}^2)(A_2{}^2 + B_2{}^2)}}, \quad \tan\theta = \frac{A_1B_2 - A_2B_1}{A_1A_2 + B_1B_2} \tag{18}$$

The signs of $\tan\theta$ and $\cos\theta$ determine whether the acute or obtuse angle is meant. If the equations are in the form $y = m_1x + b_1$, $y = m_2x + b_2$, then

$$\sin\theta = \frac{m_2 - m_1}{\sqrt{(1 + m_1{}^2)(1 + m_2{}^2)}}, \quad \cos\theta = \frac{1 + m_1m_2}{\sqrt{(1 + m_1{}^2)(1 + m_2{}^2)}}, \quad \tan\theta = \frac{m_2 - m_1}{1 + m_1m_2} \tag{19}$$

30. TRANSFORMATION OF COORDINATES

Change of Origin O to O'. Let x, y denote the coordinates of a point P with respect to the old axes, and x', y' the coordinates with respect to the new axes (Fig. 5). Then, if the coordinates of the new origin O' with respect to the old axes are $x = h$, $y = k$, the relations between the old and the new coordinates are

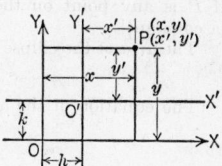

Fig. 5

$$\left.\begin{array}{l} x = x' + h, \\ y = y' + k \end{array}\right\} \tag{20}$$

Rotation of Axes about the Origin. Let θ (Fig. 6) be the angle through which the axes are rotated. Then

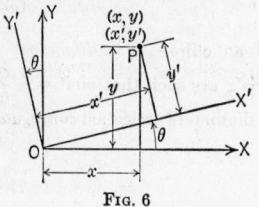

Fig. 6

$$\left.\begin{array}{l} x = x'\cos\theta - y'\sin\theta \\ y = x'\sin\theta + y'\cos\theta \end{array}\right\} \tag{21}$$

If the axes are both translated and rotated,

$$\left.\begin{array}{l} x = x'\cos\theta - y'\sin\theta + h \\ y = x'\sin\theta + y'\cos\theta + k \end{array}\right\} \tag{22}$$

Coordinate Transformation. The relations between the rectangular coordinates x, y and the polar coordinates r, θ are

$$x = r\cos\theta, \quad y = r\sin\theta, \quad r = \sqrt{x^2 + y^2}, \quad \theta = \tan^{-1}\frac{y}{x} \tag{23}$$

$$x + iy = r\,e^{i\theta}, \quad x - iy = r\,e^{-i\theta} \tag{24}$$

$(i = \sqrt{-1},\ e = 2.7183,$ the base of the natural logarithms$)$

31. CONIC SECTIONS

A Conic Section is a curve traced by a point P moving in a plane so that the distance PF of the point from a fixed point (*focus*) is in constant ratio to the distance PM of the point from a fixed line (*directrix*) in the plane of the curve. The ratio, $e = \dfrac{PF}{PM}$, is called the *eccentricity*. If $e < 1$, the curve is an *ellipse*; $e = 1$, a *parabola*; $e > 1$, an *hyperbola*; and $e = 0$, a *circle*, which is a special case of an ellipse.

The Circle. The equation is

$$(x - x_0)^2 + (y - y_0)^2 = r^2 \tag{25}$$

where (x_0, y_0) is the center and r the radius. If $x_0 = 0$, $y_0 = 0$, that is, if the center is at the origin,

$$x^2 + y^2 = r^2 \tag{26}$$

If the point $P_1(x_1, y_1)$ is on the circle $x^2 + y^2 + 2gx + 2fy + c = 0$, then the equation of the tangent to the circle at $P_1(x_1, y_1)$ is

$$xx_1 + yy_1 + g(x + x_1) + f(y + y_1) + c = 0 \tag{27}$$

The Ellipse (Fig. 7). The equation is

$$\frac{(x - x_0)^2}{a^2} + \frac{(y - y_0)^2}{b^2} = 1 \tag{28}$$

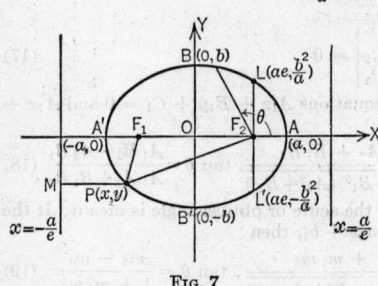

where (x_0, y_0) is the center, a = semi-major axis, b = semi-minor axis. In Fig. 7, $(x_0, y_0) = (0, 0)$.

Coordinates of *foci* are $F_1 = (-ae, 0)$, $F_2 = (ae, 0)$; $e^2 = \dfrac{(F_1 P)^2}{(MP)^2} = 1 - \dfrac{b^2}{a^2} < 1$;

and the *directrices* are the lines $x = -\dfrac{a}{e}$, $x = \dfrac{a}{e}$.

The chord LL' through F is called the *latus rectum* and has the length $\dfrac{2b^2}{a} = 2a\,(1 - e^2)$.

Fig. 7

If P is any point on the ellipse, $F_1 P = a - ex$, $F_2 P = a + ex$, and $F_1 P + F_2 P = 2a$ (a constant).

The *area* of the ellipse with semi-axes a and b is

$$A = \pi a b \tag{29}$$

The equation of the *tangent* to the ellipse at the point (x_1, y_1) is

$$\frac{xx_1}{a^2} + \frac{yy_1}{b^2} = 1; \tag{30}$$

the equation of the tangent with slope m is

$$y = mx \pm \sqrt{a^2 m^2 + b^2} \tag{31}$$

The equation of the *normal* to the ellipse at the point (x_1, y_1) is

$$(x - x_1)\frac{y_1}{b^2} - (y - y_1)\frac{x_1}{a^2} = 0 \tag{32}$$

Conjugate Diameters. A line through the center of an ellipse is a *diameter*; if the slopes m and m' of the two diameters $y = mx$ and $y = m'x$ are such that $mm' = -\dfrac{b^2}{a^2}$ each diameter bisects all chords parallel to the other and the diameters are called *conjugate*.

Other Forms of the Equation of the Ellipse.

$$\frac{x^2}{a^2} + \frac{y^2}{a^2(1 - e^2)} = 1 \tag{33}$$

$$ax^2 + by^2 + 2gx + 2fy + c = 0 \tag{34}$$

If a, b, and $\left(\dfrac{g^2}{a} + \dfrac{f^2}{b} - c\right)$ have the same sign, (34) is an ellipse whose axes are parallel to the coordinate axes.

The polar form of the equation with F_2 as pole and F_2A as the polar axis is

$$r = \frac{a(1 - e^2)}{1 - e \cos \theta} \qquad (35)$$

The parametric form is
$$x = a \cos \phi, \; y = b \sin \phi \qquad (36)$$

The Hyperbola (Fig. 8). The equation is

$$\frac{(x - x_0)^2}{a^2} - \frac{(y - y_0)^2}{b^2} = 1 \qquad (37)$$

where (x_0, y_0) is the center, $AA' = 2a$ is the transverse axis, $BB' = 2b$ is the conjugate axis. In Fig. 8, $(x_0, y_0) = (0, 0)$.

$e^2 = \dfrac{(F_1 P)^2}{(PM)^2} = 1 + \dfrac{b^2}{a^2} > 1;$ the coordinates of the *foci*, $F_1 = (-ae, \; 0)$, $F_2 = (ae, 0)$; and the *directrices* are the lines $x = -\dfrac{a}{e}, \; x = \dfrac{a}{e}.$

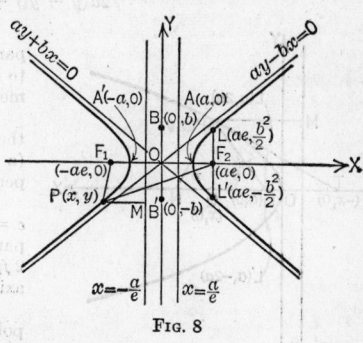

Fig. 8

The chord LL' through F is called the *latus rectum* and has the length $\dfrac{2b^2}{a}$. If P is any point on the curve, $F_1 P = ex - a$, $F_2 P = ex + a$, and $|F_2 P - F_1 P| = 2a$ (a constant).

The equation of the *tangent* to the hyperbola at the point (x_1, y_1) is

$$\frac{xx_1}{a^2} - \frac{yy_1}{b^2} = 1 \qquad (38)$$

The equation of the tangent whose slope is m is

$$y = mx \pm \sqrt{a^2 m^2 - b^2} \qquad (39)$$

The equation of the *normal* to the hyperbola at the point (x_1, y_1) is
$$a^2 y_1 (x - x_1) + b^2 x_1 (y - y_1) = 0 \qquad (40)$$

Conjugate Hyperbolas and Diameters. The two hyperbolas $\dfrac{x^2}{a^2} - \dfrac{y^2}{b^2} = 1$ and $\dfrac{y^2}{b^2} - \dfrac{x^2}{a^2} = 1$ are conjugate. The transverse axis of each is the conjugate axis of the other.

If the slopes of the two lines $y = mx$ and $y = m_1 x$ through the center O are connected by the relation $mm_1 = \dfrac{b^2}{a^2}$, each of these lines bisects all chords of the hyperbola which are parallel to the other line. Two such lines are called *conjugate diameters*. The equation of the hyperbola referred to its conjugate diameters as oblique axes is

$$\frac{x'^2}{a_1^2} - \frac{y'^2}{b_1^2} = 1 \qquad (41)$$

where $2a_1$ and $2b_1$ are the conjugate axes.

The Asymptotes. The lines $y = \dfrac{b}{a} x$ and $y = -\dfrac{b}{a} x$ are the *asymptotes* of the hyperbola $\dfrac{x^2}{a^2} - \dfrac{y^2}{b^2} = 1$. The asymptotes are two tangents whose points of contact with the curve are at an infinite distance from the center. The equation of the hyperbola when referred to its asymptotes as oblique axes is

$$4x'y' = a^2 + b^2 \qquad (42)$$

If $a = b$, the asymptotes are the perpendicular lines $y = x$, $y = -x$; the corresponding hyperbola

$$x^2 - y^2 = a^2 \qquad (43)$$

is called the *rectangular* or *equilateral hyperbola*.

The Parabola (Fig. 9). The equation of the parabola is

$$y^2 = 4ax \qquad (44)$$

The *focus* F is on OX, called the *axis of the parabola*, and has the coordinates $(a, 0)$; the *eccentricity* $e = \dfrac{FP}{PM} = 1$; and the *directrix* is $x = -a$. The chord LL' through F is the *latus rectum* and has the length $4a$.

The *tangent* to the parabola $y^2 = 4\,ax$ at the point (x_1, y_1) is

$$yy_1 = 2a(x + x_1) \tag{45}$$

The equation of the tangent whose slope is m is

$$y = mx + \frac{a}{m} \tag{46}$$

The *normal* to the parabola at the point (x_1, y_1) is

$$2a(y - y_1) + y_1(x - x_1) = 0 \tag{47}$$

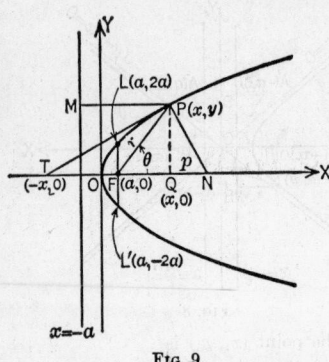

FIG. 9

A *diameter* of the curve is a straight line parallel to the axis. It bisects all chords parallel to the tangent at the point where the diameter meets the parabola.

If P_1T is tangent to the curve at (x_1, y_1), then $TQ = 2x_1$ is the *subtangent*, and $QN = 2a$ (a constant) is the *subnormal*, where P_1N is perpendicular to P_1T.

The equation of the form $y^2 + 2\,gx + 2\,fy + c = 0$, where $g \neq 0$, is a parabola whose axis is parallel to OX; and the equation $x^2 + 2\,gx + 2\,fy + c = 0$, where $f \neq 0$, is a parabola whose axis is parallel to OY.

The polar equation of the parabola with F as pole and FO as polar axis is

$$r = \frac{p}{1 - \cos\theta} \tag{48}$$

where p is one-half the latus rectum ($p = 2a$ in Fig. 9).

The parabola referred to the tangents at the extremities of its latus rectum as axes of coordinates is

$$x^{1/2} \pm y^{1/2} = b^{1/2} \tag{49}$$

where b is the distance from the origin to each point of tangency.

The General Equation of a Conic Section has the form

$$ax^2 + 2\,hxy + by^2 + 2\,gx + 2\,fy + c = 0 \tag{50}$$

$$\text{Let } D = \begin{vmatrix} a & h & g \\ h & b & f \\ g & f & c \end{vmatrix}; \quad d = \begin{vmatrix} a & h \\ h & b \end{vmatrix} \tag{51}$$

Then the following is a classification of conic sections.

1. Two parallel lines, for $D = 0$, $d = 0$.
2. Two intersecting lines, for $D = 0$, $d \neq 0$.
3. A parabola, for $D \neq 0$, $d = 0$.
4. An ellipse, for $D \neq 0$, $d > 0$ (central conic).
5. An hyperbola, for $D \neq 0$, $d < 0$ (central conic).

Let $A + B = a + b$, $AB = ab - h^2 = d$, and $A - B$ have the same sign as h. Let $c' = D/d$; then the equation of the conic referred to its axes is

$$\frac{x^2}{-\dfrac{c'}{A}} + \frac{y^2}{-\dfrac{c'}{B}} = 1 \tag{52}$$

To find the center (x_0, y_0) of the conic solve the equations

$$\left.\begin{array}{l} ax_0 + hy_0 + g = 0 \\ hx_0 + by_0 + f = 0 \end{array}\right\} \tag{53}$$

To remove the term in xy from (50), rotate the axes about the origin through an angle θ such that $\tan 2\theta = \dfrac{2\,h}{a - b}$.

32. HIGHER PLANE CURVES

Plane Curves. The point (x, y) describes a plane curve if x and y are continuous functions of a variable t (parameter), as $x = x(t)$, $y = y(t)$. The elimination of t from the two equations gives $F(x, y) = 0$ or in explicit form $y = f(x)$. The angle τ which the tangent to the curve makes with OX can be found from

$$\sin \tau = \frac{dy}{ds}, \ \cos \tau = \frac{dx}{ds}, \ \tan \tau = \frac{dy}{dx} = y' \tag{54}$$

where ds is the element of arc length:

$$ds = \sqrt{dx^2 + dy^2} = \sqrt{1 + y'^2} \, dx > 0 \tag{55}$$

In polar coordinates,

$$ds = \sqrt{dr^2 + r^2 d\theta^2} = \sqrt{\left(\frac{dr}{d\theta}\right)^2 + r^2} \, d\theta \tag{56}$$

From Fig. 10, it may be seen that

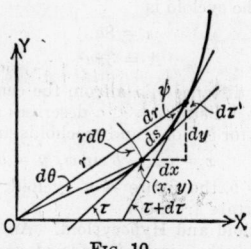

Fɪɢ. 10

$$\sin \psi = \frac{rd\theta}{ds}, \ \cos \psi = \frac{dr}{ds}, \ \tan \psi = \frac{rd\theta}{dr} \tag{57}$$

The equation of the *tangent* to the curve $F(x, y) = 0$ at the point (x_1, y_1) is

$$\left(\frac{\partial F}{\partial x}\right)_{x = x_1, \, y = y_1} (x - x_1) + \left(\frac{\partial F}{\partial y}\right)_{x = x_1, \, y = y_1} (y - y_1) = 0 \tag{58}$$

The equation of the *normal* to the curve $F(x, y) = 0$ at the point (x_1, y_1) is

$$\left(\frac{\partial F}{\partial y}\right)_{x = x_1, \, y = y_1} (x - x_1) - \left(\frac{\partial F}{\partial x}\right)_{x = x_1, \, y = y_1} (y - y_1) = 0 \tag{59}$$

The *radius of curvature* of the curve at the point (x, y) is

$$\rho = \frac{ds}{d\tau} = \frac{\left[1 + \left(\frac{dy}{dx}\right)^2\right]^{3/2}}{\frac{d^2y}{dx^2}} = \frac{[1 + y'^2]^{3/2}}{y''} \tag{60}$$

The reciprocal $1/\rho$ is called the *curvature of the curve* at (x, y).

The coordinates (x_0, y_0) of the center of curvature for the point (x, y) on the curve (the center of the circle of curvature tangent to the curve at (x, y) and of radius ρ) can be found from the equations

$$\left. \begin{array}{l} x_0 = x - \rho \dfrac{dy}{ds} = x - y' \dfrac{[1 + y'^2]}{y''} \\[3mm] y_0 = y + \rho \dfrac{dx}{ds} = y + \dfrac{[1 + y'^2]}{y''} \end{array} \right\} \tag{61}$$

A curve has a *singular point* if simultaneously,

$$F(x, y) = 0, \ \frac{\partial F}{\partial x} = 0, \ \frac{\partial F}{\partial y} = 0 \tag{62}$$

Let

$$D = \left(\frac{\partial^2 F}{\partial x \partial y}\right)^2 - \frac{\partial^2 F}{\partial x^2} \frac{\partial^2 F}{\partial y^2} \tag{63}$$

Then for $D > 0$, the curve has a *double point* with two real different tangents.
For $D = 0$, the curve has a *cusp* with two coincident tangents.
For $D < 0$, the curve has an *isolated point* with no real tangent.

Cycloid and Trochoid. A *cycloid* is a curve traced by a point P on the circumference of a circle which rolls without slipping on a straight line (Fig. 11). The parametric equations are

$$x = OD = a \, (\phi - \sin \phi), \ y = DP = a \, (1 - \cos \phi) \tag{64}$$

In rectangular coordinates

$$x = a \cos^{-1} \frac{(a - y)}{a} \pm \sqrt{(2a - y)y} \qquad (65)$$

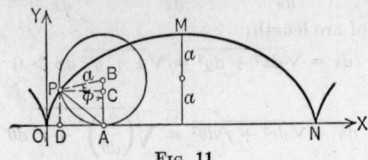

Fig. 11

The length of one arch of the cycloid is

$$s = 8a \qquad (66)$$

and its area

$$A = 3\pi a^2 \qquad (67)$$

A point on the radius at a distance $b > a$ from the center describes a *prolate trochoid*. A point at a distance $b < a$ describes a *curtate trochoid*. The general equations for cycloids and trochoids are

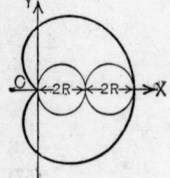

$$x = a\phi - b \sin \phi, \quad y = b(1 - \cos \phi) \qquad (68)$$

If $a = b$, the figure is a cycloid; if $b > a$, prolate trochoid; if $b < a$, curtate trochoid.

Epicycloid and Hypocycloid. An *epicycloid* is a curve traced by a point on the circumference of a circle of radius r which rolls without slipping on the outside of a fixed circle of radius R. If the moving circle rolls without slipping on the inside of the fixed circle, the curve is an *hypocycloid*.

Fig. 12

An epicycloid has the equations

$$\left.\begin{array}{l} x = (R + r) \cos\phi - r \cos \dfrac{R + r}{r}\phi \\[2mm] y = (R + r) \sin\phi - r \sin \dfrac{R + r}{r}\phi \end{array}\right\} \qquad (69)$$

For $r = R$, the epicycloid becomes a *cardioid* (Fig. 12) with the equation

$$(x^2 + y^2 - 2Rx)^2 = 4R^2(x^2 + y^2) \qquad (70)$$

or in polar coordinates

$$r = 2R (1 + \cos \theta) \qquad (71)$$

An hypocycloid has the equations

$$\left.\begin{array}{l} x = (R - r) \cos\phi + r \cos \dfrac{R - r}{r}\phi \\[2mm] y = (R - r) \sin\phi - r \sin \dfrac{R - r}{r}\phi \end{array}\right\} \qquad (72)$$

For $r = \frac{1}{4} R$, the rolling circle makes four revolutions in passing around the fixed circle forming the *astroid* or hypocycloid of four cusps with equation

$$x^{2/3} + y^{2/3} = R^{2/3} \qquad (73)$$

An **Epitrochoid** is a curve traced by a point on the radius of the outer rolling circle at a fixed distance b from its center. The equations of the curve are

$$\left.\begin{array}{l} x = (R + r) \cos\phi - b \cos \dfrac{R + r}{r}\phi \\[2mm] y = (R + r) \sin\phi - b \sin \dfrac{R + r}{r}\phi \end{array}\right\} \qquad (74)$$

An **Hypotrochoid** is a curve traced by a point on the radius of the inner rolling circle at a fixed distance b from its center. The equations are

$$\left.\begin{array}{l} x = (R - r) \cos\phi + b \cos \dfrac{R - r}{r}\phi \\[2mm] y = (R - r) \sin\phi - b \sin \dfrac{R - r}{r}\phi \end{array}\right\} \qquad (75)$$

If $R = 2r$, the hypotrochoid is an ellipse.

An **Involute of a Circle** is a curve traced by the end of a taut string wrapped around a fixed circle and unwinding (Fig. 13). If it begins to unwind at A, the arc AP of the involute is traced when the string has unwound as far as B, and the part unwound is BP. BP is tangent to the circle at B and $BP = \text{arc } BA = r\phi$. The parametric equations are

$$\left. \begin{array}{l} x = R \cos\phi + R\,\phi \sin\phi \\ y = R \sin\phi - R\,\phi \cos\phi \end{array} \right\} \tag{76}$$

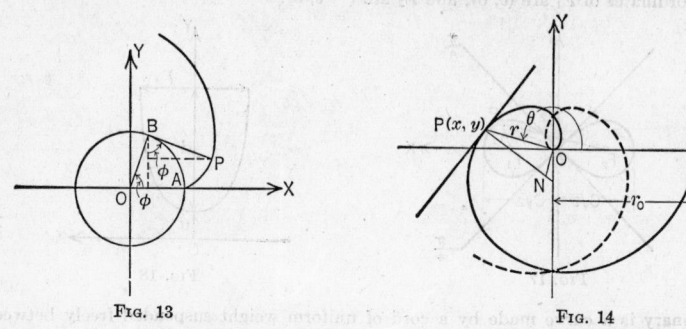

FIG. 13   FIG. 14

A **Spiral of Archimedes** is the locus of a point P whose distance from the origin O is proportional to the angle which the radius vector OP makes with a fixed initial position (Fig. 14). Another method of finding the curve is to consider it generated by a point P moving at a constant speed in a given straight line OP, which at the same time rotates at constant speed about a fixed point O on the line. The equation is

$$r = a\theta \tag{77}$$

where $a = ON$ (a constant), the polar subnormal.

After one complete turn of OP, the length OP is $r_0 = 2\pi a$, and after $1/n$ turns, its length is $r = r_0/n$. The length of the arc OP is

$$s = \tfrac{1}{2} a\left[\theta \sqrt{1 + \theta^2} + \sinh^{-1}\theta\right] \tag{77}$$

For many turns it is approximately

$$s \approx \tfrac{1}{2} a\,\theta^2 \tag{78}$$

An **Hyperbolic Spiral** has the equation

$$r\theta = a \tag{79}$$

where $OT = -a$ (a constant), the polar subtangent (Fig. 15). If $\theta \to \infty$, then $r \to 0$. Therefore, the origin is an asymptotic point about which the curve winds an infinite number of times but which it never actually reaches.

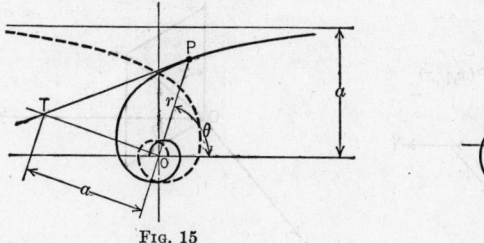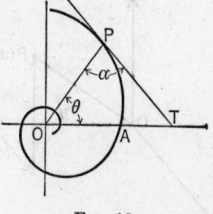

FIG. 15   FIG. 16

If $\theta \to 0$, $r \to \infty$. Therefore, a line parallel to the polar axis at a distance a is an asymptote of the curve.

A **Logarithmic or Equiangular Spiral** is a curve that makes a constant angle with the radius vectors (Fig. 16.). Its polar equation is

$$r = ae^{m\theta} \qquad (m > 0) \tag{80}$$

For $\theta = 0$, $r = OA = a$; $m = \cot\alpha$, α being the constant angle.

As $\theta \to -\infty$, $r \to 0$. Therefore, the origin is an asymptotic point, which, for decreasing θ, the spiral approaches but never actually reaches.

A **Lemniscate** is the locus of a point P, the product of whose distances r_1 and r_2 from two fixed points F_1 and F_2 is a constant (Fig. 17). Let $r_1{}^2 \cdot r_2{}^2 = c^4$; then the equation of the lemniscate is

$$(x^2 + y^2)^2 + 2\,c^2(y^2 - x^2) = 0 \tag{81}$$

or in polar coordinates

$$r^2 = 2\,c^2 \cos 2\theta \tag{82}$$

The coordinates of F_1 are $(c, 0)$, and F_2 are $(-c, 0)$.

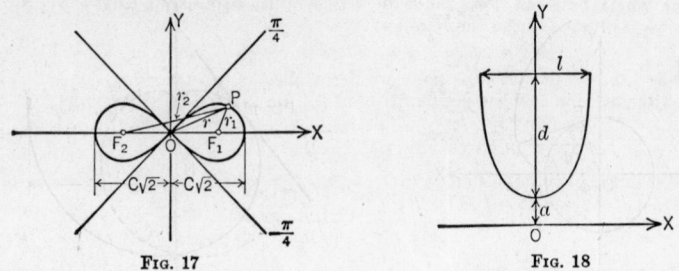

Fig. 17   Fig. 18

A **Catenary** is a curve made by a cord of uniform weight suspended freely between two points at the same level (Fig. 18). Its equation is

$$y = \frac{a}{2}\,(e^{x/a} + e^{-x/a}) \tag{83}$$

The length of arc s is approximately equal to $l\left[\,1 + \dfrac{2}{3}\left(\dfrac{2d}{l}\right)^2\,\right]$, for l large in comparison to d.

SOLID ANALYTIC GEOMETRY
By M. J. Fish

33. POINT, LINE, AND PLANE

Coordinates. In a right-hand orthogonal cartesian coordinate system the position of a point P (Fig. 1) is fixed by its distance and direction from each of three planes which are perpendicular to each other. Thus the coordinates of the point P (x, y, z) are the perpendicular distances to the planes zy, xz, and xy, respectively.

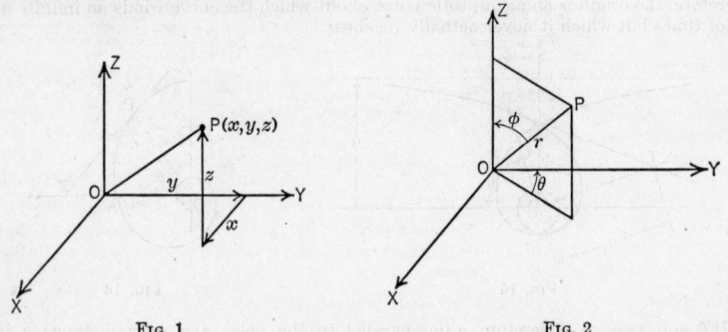

Fig. 1   Fig. 2

The position of a point in space is also determined by its distance and direction from some fixed point. In Fig. 2 the distance from the origin O is r, and the direction of r is fixed by the angles θ and ϕ. The three quantities, r, θ, ϕ, are called the *spherical* or *polar* coordinates, where r is the *radius vector* of the point and the angles θ and ϕ are the *vectorial angles*.

The **Distance between Two Points**, P_1 (x_1, y_1, z_1) and P_2 (x_2, y_2, z_2) is

$$s = \sqrt{(x_2 - x_1)^2 + (y_2 - y_1)^2 + (z_2 - z_1)^2} \tag{1}$$

The angles α, β, γ, which the line $P_1 P_2$ makes with the coordinate directions X, Y, Z, respectively, are called the *direction angles* of $P_1 P_2$.

The cosines,

$$\cos \alpha = \frac{x_2 - x_1}{s}, \quad \cos \beta = \frac{y_2 - y_1}{s}, \quad \cos \gamma = \frac{z_2 - z_1}{s} \tag{2}$$

are called the *direction cosines* of $P_1 P_2$, and

$$\cos^2 \alpha + \cos^2 \beta + \cos^2 \gamma = 1 \tag{3}$$

The Angle between Two Lines in terms of their direction angles α_1, β_1, γ_1, and α_2, β_2, γ_2, is obtained from the relation:

$$\cos \theta = \cos \alpha_1 \cos \alpha_2 + \cos \beta_1 \cos \beta_2 + \cos \gamma_1 \cos \gamma_2 \tag{4}$$

If $\cos \theta = 0$, $\theta = 90°$ and the lines are perpendicular to each other.

A Straight Line in Space is represented by the first degree equations,

$$\left. \begin{array}{l} y = m_1 x + b_1 \\ z = m_2 x + b_2 \end{array} \right\} \tag{5}$$

If the line goes through a point $P_1(x_1, y_1, z_1)$ and has the direction angles α, β, γ, then

$$\frac{x - x_1}{\cos \alpha} = \frac{y - y_1}{\cos \beta} = \frac{z - z_1}{\cos \gamma} \tag{6}$$

and $m_1 = \dfrac{\cos \beta}{\cos \alpha}$, $m_2 = \dfrac{\cos \gamma}{\cos \alpha}$

The equations of a line through two points (x_1, y_1, z_1) and (x_2, y_2, z_2) are

$$\frac{x - x_1}{x_2 - x_1} = \frac{y - y_1}{y_2 - y_1} = \frac{z - z_1}{z_2 - z_1} \tag{7}$$

The Equation of a Plane may be expressed as follows:

$$Ax + By + Cz + D = 0 \tag{8}$$

where A, B, C, and D are constants.

$Ax + By + D = 0$, is a plane parallel to the z axis.

$Ax + Cz + D = 0$, is a plane parallel to the y axis.

$By + Cz + D = 0$, is a plane parallel to the x axis.

$Ax + By + Cz = 0$, is a plane passing through the origin O.

A plane through three points $P_1 (x_1, y_1, z_1)$, $P_2 (x_2, y_2, z_2)$, $P_3 (x_3, y_3, z_3)$ has the equation

$$\begin{vmatrix} x & y & z & 1 \\ x_1 & y_1 & z_1 & 1 \\ x_2 & y_2 & z_2 & 1 \\ x_3 & y_3 & z_3 & 1 \end{vmatrix} = 0 \tag{9}$$

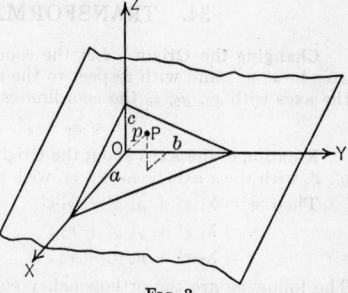

FIG. 3

The equation of a plane whose x, y, z intercepts are respectively a, b, c (Fig. 3) is

$$\frac{x}{a} + \frac{y}{b} + \frac{z}{c} = 1 \tag{10}$$

The perpendicular form of the equation of a plane, where $OP = p$ is the perpendicular distance of the plane from the origin O and has the direction angles α, β, γ, is

$$x \cos \alpha + y \cos \beta + z \cos \gamma - p = 0 \tag{11}$$

To bring the general form $Ax + By + Cz + D = 0$ into the perpendicular form, divide it by $\pm \sqrt{A^2 + B^2 + C^2}$, where the sign before the radical is opposite to that of D.

The coefficients A, B, C are proportional to the direction cosines λ, μ, ν of a line perpendicular to the plane. Therefore,

$$A(x - x_1) + B(y - y_1) + C(z - z_1) = 0 \tag{12}$$

is a plane through $P_1 (x_1, y_1, z_1)$ and perpendicular to a line with direction cosines λ, μ, ν proportional to A, B, C.

The Perpendicular Distance of a Point P_1 from a Plane $Ax + By + Cz + D = 0$ is given by

$$PP_1 = \frac{Ax_1 + By_1 + Cz_1 + D}{\pm \sqrt{A^2 + B^2 + C^2}} \tag{13}$$

where the sign before the radical is opposite to that of D.

A Line through a Point P_1 Perpendicular to a Plane $Ax + By + Cz + D = 0$ has the equations

$$\frac{x - x_1}{A} = \frac{y - y_1}{B} = \frac{z - z_1}{C} \tag{14}$$

Parallel Planes. Two planes $A_1x + B_1y + C_1z + D_1 = 0$ and $A_2x + B_2y + C_2z + D_2 = 0$ are parallel if $A_1 : B_1 : C_1 = A_2 : B_2 : C_2$.

$$A(x - x_1) + B(y - y_1) + C(z - z_1) = 0 \tag{15}$$

is a plane through the point P_1 (x_1, y_1, z_1) and parallel to the plane $Ax + By + Cz + D = 0$.

The Angle θ between Two Planes $Ax + By + Cz + D = 0$ and $A_1x + B_1y + C_1z + D_1 = 0$ is the angle between two intersecting lines, each perpendicular to one of the planes:

$$\cos\theta = \frac{AA_1 + BB_1 + CC_1}{\pm\sqrt{(A^2 + B^2 + C^2)(A_1^2 + B_1^2 + C_1^2)}} \tag{16}$$

The two planes are perpendicular if $AA_1 + BB_1 + CC_1 = 0$.

Line of Intersection of Two Planes. The direction cosines λ, μ, ν of the line of intersection of two planes $Ax + By + Cz + D = 0$ and $A_1x + B_1y + C_1z + D_1 = 0$ are found from the ratios

$$\lambda : \mu : \nu = \begin{vmatrix} B & C \\ B_1 & C_1 \end{vmatrix} : \begin{vmatrix} C & A \\ C_1 & A_1 \end{vmatrix} : \begin{vmatrix} A & B \\ A_1 & B_1 \end{vmatrix} \tag{17}$$

Four Points, P_k (x_k, y_k, z_k) $(k = 1, 2, 3, 4)$, lie in the same plane if

$$\begin{vmatrix} 1 & x_1 & y_1 & z_1 \\ 1 & x_2 & y_2 & z_2 \\ 1 & x_3 & y_3 & z_3 \\ 1 & x_4 & y_4 & z_4 \end{vmatrix} = 0 \tag{18}$$

Four Planes $A_k x + B_k y + C_k z + D_k = 0$ $(k = 1, 2, 3, 4)$ pass through the same point if

$$\begin{vmatrix} A_1 & B_1 & C_1 & D_1 \\ A_2 & B_2 & C_2 & D_2 \\ A_3 & B_3 & C_3 & D_3 \\ A_4 & B_4 & C_4 & D_4 \end{vmatrix} = 0 \tag{19}$$

34. TRANSFORMATION OF COORDINATES

Changing the Origin. Let the coordinates of a point P with respect to the original axes be x, y, z and with respect to the new axes x', y', z'. For a parallel displacement of the axes with x_0, y_0, z_0 the coordinates of the new origin

$$x = x_0 + x', \quad y = y_0 + y', \quad z = z_0 + z' \tag{20}$$

Rotation of the Axes about the Origin. Let the cosines of the angles of the new axes x', y', z', with the x axis be λ_1, μ_1, ν_1, with the y axis be λ_2, μ_2, ν_2, with the z axis be λ_3, μ_3, ν_3.

Then
$$\left.\begin{aligned} x &= \lambda_1 x' + \mu_1 y' + \nu_1 z' \\ y &= \lambda_2 x' + \mu_2 y' + \nu_2 z' \\ z &= \lambda_3 x' + \mu_3 y' + \nu_3 z' \end{aligned}\right. \qquad \left.\begin{aligned} x' &= \lambda_1 x + \lambda_2 y + \lambda_3 z \\ y' &= \mu_1 x + \mu_2 y + \mu_3 z \\ z' &= \nu_1 x + \nu_2 y + \nu_3 z \end{aligned}\right\} \tag{21}$$

The following are the orthogonality conditions:

(1) $\lambda_1^2 + \mu_1^2 + \nu_1^2 = 1$
$\quad\lambda_2^2 + \mu_2^2 + \nu_2^2 = 1$
$\quad\lambda_3^2 + \mu_3^2 + \nu_3^2 = 1$

(2) $\lambda_1^2 + \lambda_2^2 + \lambda_3^2 = 1$
$\quad\mu_1^2 + \mu_2^2 + \mu_3^2 = 1$
$\quad\nu_1^2 + \nu_2^2 + \nu_3^2 = 1$

(3) $\lambda_1\lambda_2 + \mu_1\mu_2 + \nu_1\nu_2 = 0$
$\quad\lambda_2\lambda_3 + \mu_2\mu_3 + \nu_2\nu_3 = 0$
$\quad\lambda_3\lambda_1 + \mu_3\mu_1 + \nu_3\nu_1 = 0$

(4) $\lambda_1\mu_1 + \lambda_2\mu_2 + \lambda_3\mu_3 = 0$
$\quad\mu_1\nu_1 + \mu_2\nu_2 + \mu_3\nu_3 = 0$
$\quad\nu_1\lambda_1 + \nu_2\lambda_2 + \nu_3\lambda_3 = 0$

(5) $\lambda_1 = \mu_2\nu_3 - \nu_2\mu_3$
$\quad\mu_1 = \nu_2\lambda_3 - \lambda_2\nu_3$
$\quad\nu_1 = \lambda_2\mu_3 - \mu_2\lambda_3$

(6) $\lambda_2 = \nu_1\mu_3 - \mu_1\nu_3$
$\quad\mu_2 = \lambda_1\nu_3 - \nu_1\lambda_3$
$\quad\nu_2 = \mu_1\lambda_3 - \lambda_1\mu_3$

(7) $\lambda_3 = \mu_1\nu_2 - \nu_1\mu_2$
$\quad\mu_3 = \nu_1\lambda_2 - \lambda_1\nu_2$
$\quad\nu_3 = \lambda_1\mu_2 - \mu_1\lambda_2$

(8) $\begin{vmatrix} \lambda_1 & \mu_1 & \nu_1 \\ \lambda_2 & \mu_2 & \nu_2 \\ \lambda_3 & \mu_3 & \nu_3 \end{vmatrix} = 1$

For a combination of displacement and rotation, apply the corresponding equations simultaneously.

Spherical or Polar Coordinates. The relations between the rectangular coordinates x, y, z of a point P and its spherical coordinates r, θ, ϕ (Fig. 2), are

$$x = r \sin \phi \sin \theta, \quad y = r \sin \phi \cos \theta, \quad z = r \cos \phi$$

$$r^2 = x^2 + y^2 + z^2, \quad \theta = \tan^{-1} \frac{x}{y}, \quad \phi = \tan^{-1} \frac{\sqrt{x^2 + y^2}}{z} \tag{22}$$

35. QUADRIC SURFACES

The General Form of the Equation of a Surface of the Second Degree is

$$F(x, y, z) \equiv a_{11} x^2 + 2a_{12} xy + 2a_{13} xz + a_{22} y^2 + 2a_{23} yz$$
$$+ a_{33} z^2 + 2a_{14} x + 2a_{24} y + 2a_{34} z + a_{44} = 0 \tag{23}$$

where the a_{ik} are constants, and $a_{ik} = a_{ki}$, i.e., $a_{12} = a_{21}$, etc.

$$\text{Let } D = \begin{vmatrix} a_{11} & a_{12} & a_{13} & a_{14} \\ a_{21} & a_{22} & a_{23} & a_{24} \\ a_{31} & a_{32} & a_{33} & a_{34} \\ a_{41} & a_{42} & a_{43} & a_{44} \end{vmatrix}, \quad d = \begin{vmatrix} a_{11} & a_{12} & a_{13} \\ a_{21} & a_{22} & a_{23} \\ a_{31} & a_{32} & a_{33} \end{vmatrix}$$

Let $I \equiv a_{11} + a_{22} + a_{33}$ and $J \equiv a_{22} a_{33} + a_{33} a_{11} + a_{11} a_{22} - a_{23}{}^2 - a_{13}{}^2 - a_{12}{}^2$. I and J are invariant under coordinate transformation. The following is a classification of the quadratic surfaces, so far as they are real and do not degenerate into curves in one plane:

Ellipsoid, for $D < 0$, $d > 0$, $J > 0$.
Hyperboloid of two sheets, for $D < 0$, Id and J not both > 0.
Hyperboloid of one sheet, for $D > 0$, Id and J not both > 0.
Cone, for $D = 0$, $d \neq 0$, Id and J not both > 0.
Elliptic paraboloid, for $D < 0$, $d = 0$, $J > 0$.
Hyperbolic paraboloid, for $D > 0$, $d = 0$, $J < 0$.
Cylinder, for $D = 0$, $d = 0$.

Ellipsoid and Hyperboloids. Consider the center of the quadric as the origin and the principal axes of the quadric as the orthogonal coordinate axes. Then

$$\frac{x^2}{a^2} + \frac{y^2}{b^2} + \frac{z^2}{c^2} = 1 \text{ is an } ellipsoid \text{ (Fig. 4)} \tag{24}$$

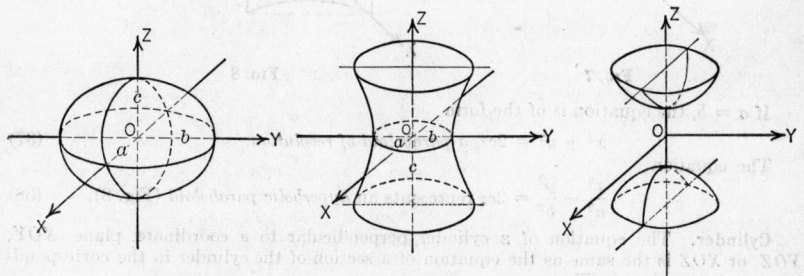

FIG. 4   FIG. 5   FIG. 6

$$\frac{x^2}{a^2} + \frac{y^2}{b^2} - \frac{z^2}{c^2} = 1 \text{ is an } hyperboloid \text{ of one sheet (Fig. 5)} \tag{25}$$

$$\frac{x^2}{a^2} + \frac{y^2}{b^2} - \frac{z^2}{c^2} = -1 \text{ is an } hyperboloid \text{ of two sheets (Fig. 6)} \tag{26}$$

where a, b, c are the semi-axes.
The length of the semi-axes is found from

$$a^2 = -\frac{D}{\lambda_1 d}, \quad b^2 = -\frac{D}{\lambda_2 d}, \quad c^2 = -\frac{D}{\lambda_3 d}, \tag{27}$$

where λ_1, λ_2, λ_3 are the real roots of the following cubic equation:

$$\begin{vmatrix} a_{11} - \lambda & a_{12} & a_{13} \\ a_{12} & a_{22} - \lambda & a_{23} \\ a_{13} & a_{23} & a_{33} - \lambda \end{vmatrix} = 0 \tag{28}$$

Cone. The equation

$$ax^2 + by^2 + cz^2 + 2hxy + 2gxz + 2fyz = 0 \tag{29}$$

represents a cone with vertex at the origin. If the cross-section of the cone is an ellipse with axes $2a$ and $2b$, whose plane is parallel to OZ and at a distance c from the origin, then the equation of the cone with vertex at the origin is

$$\frac{x^2}{a^2} + \frac{y^2}{b^2} - \frac{z^2}{c^2} = 0 \tag{30}$$

If $a = b$, the cross-section is circular, and the cone is a cone of revolution.

Sphere. An equation of the form

$$x^2 + y^2 + z^2 + ax + by + cz + d = 0 \tag{31}$$

represents a sphere with radius

$$r = 1/2 \sqrt{a^2 + b^2 + c^2 - 4d} \tag{32}$$

and center

$$x_0 = -1/2\, a, \ y_0 = -1/2\, b, \ z_0 = -1/2\, c \tag{33}$$

If (x_0, y_0, z_0) are the coordinates of the center and r is the radius, then the equation of the sphere is

$$(x - x_0)^2 + (y - y_0)^2 + (z - z_0)^2 = r^2 \tag{34}$$

If $x_0 = 0$, $y_0 = 0$, $z_0 = 0$, then the equation is

$$x^2 + y^2 + z^2 = r^2 \tag{35}$$

Paraboloids. The equation

$$\frac{x^2}{a^2} + \frac{y^2}{b^2} = 2cz \tag{36}$$

represents an *elliptic paraboloid* (Fig. 7).

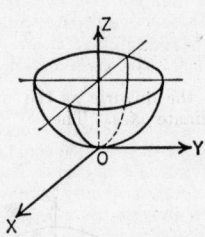 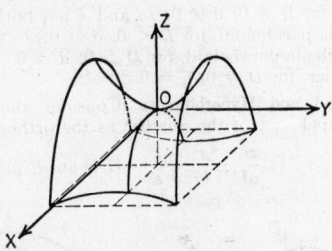

FIG. 7   FIG. 8

If $a = b$, the equation is of the form

$$x^2 + y^2 = 2cz, \text{ a paraboloid of revolution.} \tag{37}$$

The equation

$$\frac{x^2}{a^2} - \frac{y^2}{b^2} = 2cz \text{ represents an } hyperbolic\ paraboloid \text{ (Fig. 8).} \tag{38}$$

Cylinder. The equation of a cylinder perpendicular to a coordinate plane XOY, YOZ, or XOZ is the same as the equation of a section of the cylinder in the corresponding coordinate plane. Thus

$$\frac{x^2}{a^2} + \frac{y^2}{b^2} = 1 \tag{39}$$

$$\frac{x^2}{a^2} - \frac{y^2}{b^2} = 1 \tag{40}$$

$$y^2 = 4ax \tag{41}$$

are *elliptic*, *hyperbolic*, and *parabolic* cylinders respectively with elements or generators parallel to OZ.

Tangent Plane. The equation of the tangent plane to any quadric

$$F(x, y, z) \equiv a_{11}\, x^2 + 2a_{12}\, xy + 2a_{13}\, xz + a_{22}\, y^2 + 2a_{23}\, yz + a_{33}\, z^2 + 2a_{14}\, x$$
$$+ 2a_{24}\, y + 2a_{34}\, z + a_{44} = 0 \tag{42}$$

at the point (x_1, y_1, z_1) is

$$\left(\frac{\partial F}{\partial x}\right)_{x=x_1,\, y=y_1,\, z=z_1} (x - x_1) + \left(\frac{\partial F}{\partial y}\right)_{x=x_1,\, y=y_1,\, z=z_1} (y - y_1) + \left(\frac{\partial F}{\partial z}\right)_{x=x_1,\, y=y_1,\, z=z_1} (z - z_1) = 0 \tag{43}$$

Example. Find the tangent plane to the hyperboloid of one sheet at point (x_1, y_1, z_1).

Given $\dfrac{x^2}{a^2} + \dfrac{y^2}{b^2} - \dfrac{z^2}{c^2} = 1$

Then $\left(\dfrac{\partial F}{\partial x}\right)_{x=x_1,\,y=y_1,\,z=z_1} (x-x_1) + \left(\dfrac{\partial F}{\partial y}\right)_{x=x_1,\,y=y_1,\,z=z_1} (y-y_1) + \left(\dfrac{\partial F}{\partial z}\right)_{x=x_1,\,y=y_1,\,z=z_1} (z-z_1)$

$$= \dfrac{2x_1(x-x_1)}{a^2} + \dfrac{2y_1(y-y_1)}{b^2} - \dfrac{2z_1(z-z_1)}{c^2} = 0.$$

$\dfrac{xx_1}{a^2} + \dfrac{yy_1}{b^2} - \dfrac{zz_1}{c^2} - \dfrac{x_1^2}{a^2} - \dfrac{y_1^2}{b^2} + \dfrac{z_1^2}{c^2} = \dfrac{xx_1}{a^2} + \dfrac{yy_1}{b^2} - \dfrac{zz_1}{c^2} - 1 = 0$ is the tangent plane.

The Normal. The line through a point P_1 on a surface and perpendicular to the tangent plane at P_1 is called the *normal* to the surface at P_1.

The equations of the normal to the surface $F(x, y, z) = 0$ at the point (x_1, y_1, z_1) are

$$\dfrac{x-x_1}{\left(\dfrac{\partial F}{\partial x}\right)_{x=x_1,\,y=y_1,\,z=z_1}} = \dfrac{y-y_1}{\left(\dfrac{\partial F}{\partial y}\right)_{x=x_1,\,y=y_1,\,z=z_1}} = \dfrac{z-z_1}{\left(\dfrac{\partial F}{\partial z}\right)_{x=x_1,\,y=y_1,\,z=z_1}} \tag{44}$$

DIFFERENTIAL CALCULUS
By M. J. Fish

36. FUNCTIONS AND DERIVATIVES

Definition of a Function. A variable y is said to be a function of a variable x if the value of y is determined when the value of x is given. In this definition, x is called the independent variable and y the dependent variable. The symbols $F(x), f(x), \phi(x)$, etc., are used to represent various functions of x, while the symbol $f(a)$ represents the value of $f(x)$ when $x = a$.

Limit, Derivative, Differential, Continuity. The *constant a* is said to be the *limit of a variable x*, if, as the variable changes its value, the numerical difference between the variable and constant becomes and remains less than any small positive constant which may be assigned. The symbol $x \to a$ or $\lim x = a$ is used for this definition. An example of a variable becoming equal to its limit is a swinging pendulum finally coming to rest. An illustration of a variable never reaching its limit is a polygon of n sides inscribed in a circle. No matter how large n is taken, the circumference or area of the polygon never equals that of the circle.

x becomes *infinitely large*, $x \to \infty$, means that the value of x becomes *larger* than any assigned *positive* number. $x \to -\infty$ means that the value of x becomes *smaller* than any assigned *negative* number.

Usually a change in x causes a change in y. A change in x is called an *increment* of x and is denoted by Δx. Similarly a change in y is denoted by Δy. If

$$\lim_{\Delta x \to 0} \dfrac{f(x + \Delta x) - f(x)}{\Delta x}$$

has a *definite* value, it is called the *derivative* of y with respect to x and is denoted by $\dfrac{dy}{dx}$ or $f'(x)$.

The geometric interpretation of $f'(x)$ is

$$f'(x) = \dfrac{dy}{dx} = \tan \theta \tag{1}$$

or $f'(x)$ is equal to the slope of the tangent to the curve $y = f(x)$ at the point of contact $P(x, y)$ (Fig. 1).

$$\lim_{PR \to 0} \dfrac{RQ}{PR} = \lim_{\Delta x \to 0} \dfrac{\Delta y}{\Delta x} = \dfrac{f(x + \Delta x) - f(x)}{\Delta x} = \dfrac{dy}{dx} = f'(x) = \tan \theta \tag{2}$$

The differentials of x and y, respectively, are

$$dx = \Delta x$$
$$dy = f'(x)dx$$

Continuity of a Function in an Interval. A function is called *continuous* at $x = b$ if it has a definite value at b and approaches that value as a limit whenever x approaches b as a limit. The notion of continuity at a point suggests that the graph of the function is a smooth curve in the neighborhood of the point. The analytic conditions that $f(x)$ be continuous at b are that $f(b)$ have a definite value and that

$$|f(x) - f(b)| < \epsilon \text{ for } |x - b| < \delta \ (\epsilon) \tag{3}$$

where ϵ is any positive number which can be chosen as small as desired, while $\delta(\epsilon)$ depends on ϵ. The bars outside of $|f(x) - f(b)|$ show that the *absolute value* or value without the algebraic sign is to be taken; thus $|2 - 5| = |5 - 2| = 3$. A function which is continuous at each point of an interval is said to be continuous in that interval. An example of a continuous function is $f(x) = x^2$. The function $\phi(x) = \dfrac{1}{x - a}$ is continuous for all values of x other than $x = a$, at which point it becomes infinite. Every differentiable function is continuous, although the reverse is not always true.

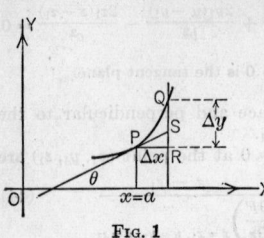

Fig. 1

If, in the above definition of continuity, the number δ can be chosen the same for all points in the interval, the function is said to be *uniformly continuous* in that interval.

Derivatives of Higher Order. The *derivative* of the *first derivative* of y with respect to x is called the *second derivative of y with respect to x* and is denoted by

$$\frac{d}{dx}\left(\frac{dy}{dx}\right) = \frac{d^2 y}{dx^2} \quad \text{or} \quad f''(x) \tag{4}$$

$$\frac{d^3 y}{dx^3} \quad \text{or} \quad f'''(x) \tag{5}$$

is the third derivative of y with respect to x. If $y = f(x)$, the second differential of $f(x)$ is

$$d^2 f = f''(x) dx^2 \tag{6}$$

Indeterminate Forms

If a function $f(x)$ for $x = a$ (where a can also be ∞) has no determined value but appears in one of the meaningless forms

$$\frac{0}{0}, \frac{\infty}{\infty}, \ 0 \cdot \infty, \ \infty - \infty, \ 0^0, \ \infty^0, \ 0^\infty, \ 1^\infty$$

then it may happen that the $\lim\limits_{x \to a} f(x)$ has a definite value. For the determination of this limiting value, if it exists, the following rules can be used:

$\dfrac{0}{0}$. If $f(x) = \dfrac{\phi(x)}{\psi(x)}$, $\phi(a) = 0$, and $\psi(a) = 0$, then

$$\lim_{x \to a} f(x) = \lim_{x \to a} \frac{\phi'(x)}{\psi'(x)} \qquad \text{(L'Hospital's rule)} \tag{7}$$

If, however, $\phi'(a) = 0$ and $\psi'(a) = 0$, the rule is applied again, with the result

$$\lim_{x \to a} \frac{\phi(x)}{\psi(x)} = \lim_{\xi \to a} \frac{\phi'(\xi)}{\psi'(\xi)} = \frac{\phi''(a)}{\psi''(a)} \tag{8}$$

unless $\phi''(a) = 0$ and $\psi''(a) = 0$. In this case, the rule is applied again.

Example. Find the value of $\dfrac{\sin x}{x}$ for $x = 0$.

$$\lim_{x \to 0} \frac{\sin x}{x} = \lim_{x \to 0} \frac{\cos x}{1} = 1.$$

$\dfrac{\infty}{\infty}$. If $f(x) = \dfrac{\phi(x)}{\psi(x)}$, $\phi(a) = \infty$, and $\psi(a) = \infty$, then

$$\lim_{x \to a} \frac{\phi(x)}{\psi(x)} = \lim_{x \to a} \frac{\phi'(x)}{\psi'(x)} \tag{9}$$

as before. $0 \cdot \infty$. If $f(x) = \phi(x) \cdot \psi(x)$, $\phi(a) = 0$, and $\psi(a) = \infty$, then place $\dfrac{1}{\psi(x)} = \omega(x)$ and obtain the previous case $\dfrac{0}{0}$.

$\infty - \infty$. If $f(x) = \phi(x) - \psi(x)$, $\phi(a) = \infty$, and $\psi(a) = \infty$, then place $\phi(x) = \dfrac{1}{u(x)}$, $\psi(x) = \dfrac{1}{v(x)}$ and obtain

$$f(x) = \frac{v(x) - u(x)}{u(x)v(x)} \tag{10}$$

which takes the form $\dfrac{0}{0}$.

$0^{0},\ \infty^{0},\ 0^{\infty},\ 1^{\infty}$. An expression of the type $[\psi(x)]^{\phi(x)}$ may, for $x = a$, give rise to the forms $0^{0},\ \infty^{0},\ 0^{\infty},\ 1^{\infty}$.

Such an expression may be reduced to a type $\dfrac{0}{0}$ or $\dfrac{\infty}{\infty}$ by the use of logarithms. Thus,

$$\left. \begin{aligned} u &= [\psi(x)]^{\phi(x)} \\ \log_e u &= \phi(x)\cdot\log_e \psi(x) \end{aligned} \right\} \tag{11}$$

If $\lim\limits_{x \to a} \phi(x)\cdot\log_e \psi(x)$ can be found by the previous methods, the limit approached by u can be found.

Example. $u = (1 - x)^{1/x}$ for $x = 0$

$$\log_e u = \frac{\log_e (1 - x)}{x}$$

$$\lim_{x \to 0} \frac{\log_e (1 - x)}{x} = -1$$

Therefore $\lim\limits_{x \to 0} \log_e u = -1$ and $\lim\limits_{x \to 0} u = e^{-1}$.

37. DIFFERENTIATION FORMULAS

Table I. Differentiation Formulas

Let $u, v, w, \ldots$ be functions of x; a and n be constants; and e be the base of the natural or Napierian logarithms. Then $e = 2.7183^{-}$.

$\dfrac{d}{dx}\, a = 0$

$\dfrac{d}{dx}(u + v + w + \ldots) = \dfrac{du}{dx} + \dfrac{dv}{dx} + \dfrac{dw}{dx} + \ldots$

$\dfrac{d}{dx}\, au = a\dfrac{du}{dx}$

$\dfrac{d}{dx}\, uv = u\dfrac{dv}{dx} + v\dfrac{du}{dx}$

$\dfrac{d}{dx}(uvw..) = \left(\dfrac{1}{u}\dfrac{du}{dx} + \dfrac{1}{v}\dfrac{dv}{dx} + \dfrac{1}{w}\dfrac{dw}{dx} + \ldots\right)(uvw \ldots)$

$\dfrac{d}{dx}\left(\dfrac{u}{v}\right) = \dfrac{v\dfrac{du}{dx} - u\dfrac{dv}{dx}}{v^2}$

$\dfrac{d}{dx}\, u^n = nu^{n-1}\dfrac{du}{dx}$

$\dfrac{d}{dx}\, \log_e u = \dfrac{1}{u}\dfrac{du}{dx}$

$\dfrac{d}{dx}\, \log_{10} u = \dfrac{1}{u}\dfrac{du}{dx}\log_{10} e = (0.4343)\dfrac{1}{u}\dfrac{du}{dx}$

$\dfrac{d}{dx}\, e^u = e^u\dfrac{du}{dx}$

$\dfrac{d}{dx}\, u^v = vu^{v-1}\dfrac{du}{dx} + u^v\dfrac{dv}{dx}\log_e u$

$\dfrac{d}{dx}\, f(u) = \dfrac{df(u)}{du}\cdot\dfrac{du}{dx}$

$\dfrac{d^2 f(u)}{dx^2} = \dfrac{df(u)}{du}\cdot\dfrac{d^2 u}{dx^2} + \dfrac{d^2 f(u)}{du^2}\left(\dfrac{du}{dx}\right)^2$

$\dfrac{d}{dx}\, \sin u = \cos u\dfrac{du}{dx}$

$\dfrac{d}{dx}\, \cos u = -\sin u\dfrac{du}{dx}$

$\dfrac{d}{dx}\, \tan u = \sec^2 u\dfrac{du}{dx}$

$\dfrac{d}{dx}\, \cot u = -\csc^2 u\dfrac{du}{dx}$

$\dfrac{d}{dx}\, \sec u = \sec u \tan u\dfrac{du}{dx}$

$\dfrac{d}{dx}\, \csc u = -\csc u \cot u\dfrac{du}{dx}$

$\dfrac{d}{dx}\, \sin^{-1} u = \dfrac{1}{\sqrt{1 - u^2}}\dfrac{du}{dx}\ \left(-\dfrac{\pi}{2} \leqq \sin^{-1} u \leqq \dfrac{\pi}{2}\right)$

$\dfrac{d}{dx}\, \cos^{-1} u = -\dfrac{1}{\sqrt{1 - u^2}}\dfrac{du}{dx}\ (0 \leqq \cos^{-1} u \leqq \pi)$

$\dfrac{d}{dx}\, \tan^{-1} u = \dfrac{1}{1 + u^2}\dfrac{du}{dx}$

$\dfrac{d}{dx}\, \cot^{-1} u = -\dfrac{1}{1 + u^2}\dfrac{du}{dx}$

$\dfrac{d}{dx}\, \sec^{-1} u = \dfrac{1}{u\sqrt{u^2 - 1}}\dfrac{du}{dx}$ *

$\dfrac{d}{dx}\, \csc^{-1} u = -\dfrac{1}{u\sqrt{u^2 - 1}}\dfrac{du}{dx}$ *

$\dfrac{d}{dx}\, \sinh u = \cosh u\dfrac{du}{dx}$

$\dfrac{d}{dx}\, \cosh u = \sinh u\dfrac{du}{dx}$

$\dfrac{d}{dx}\, \tanh u = \operatorname{sech}^2 u\dfrac{du}{dx}$

$\dfrac{d}{dx}\, \coth u = -\operatorname{csch}^2 u\dfrac{du}{dx}$

$\dfrac{d}{dx}\, \operatorname{sech} u = -\operatorname{sech} u \tanh u\dfrac{du}{dx}$

$\dfrac{d}{dx}\, \operatorname{csch} u = -\operatorname{csch} u \coth u\dfrac{du}{dx}$

$\dfrac{d}{dx}\, \sinh^{-1} u = \dfrac{1}{\sqrt{u^2 + 1}}\dfrac{du}{dx}$

$\dfrac{d}{dx}\, \cosh^{-1} u = \dfrac{1}{\sqrt{u^2 - 1}}\dfrac{du}{dx}$

$\dfrac{d}{dx}\, \tanh^{-1} u = \dfrac{1}{1 - u^2}\dfrac{du}{dx}$

$\dfrac{d}{dx}\, \coth^{-1} u = \dfrac{1}{1 - u^2}\dfrac{du}{dx}$

$\dfrac{d}{dx}\, \operatorname{sech}^{-1} u = -\dfrac{1}{u\sqrt{1 - u^2}}\dfrac{du}{dx}$

$\dfrac{d}{dx}\, \operatorname{csch}^{-1} u = -\dfrac{1}{u\sqrt{u^2 + 1}}\dfrac{du}{dx}$

* For angles in the first and third quadrants. Use the opposite sign in the second and fourth quadrants.

38. PARTIAL DERIVATIVES

Functions of Two Variables and Partial Derivatives. A quantity $f(x, y)$ is a function of two variables, if the value of f is determined when the values of x and y are given. If x is considered as the only variable while y is taken as constant, then the derivative of $f(x, y)$ with respect to x is called the *partial derivative* of f with respect to x and is denoted by

$$\frac{\partial f}{\partial x} = f_x = \lim_{\Delta x \to 0} \frac{f(x + \Delta x, y) - f(x, y)}{\Delta x} \tag{12}$$

Likewise, the partial derivative of f with respect to y is obtained by considering x to be constant while y varies:

$$\frac{\partial f}{\partial y} = f_y = \lim_{\Delta y \to 0} \frac{f(x, y + \Delta y) - f(x, y)}{\Delta y} \tag{13}$$

If $\dfrac{\partial f}{\partial x}$ and $\dfrac{\partial f}{\partial y}$ are again differentiable, the partial derivatives of the second order may be found.

$$\frac{\partial}{\partial x}\left(\frac{\partial f}{\partial x}\right) = \frac{\partial^2 f}{\partial x^2} = f_{xx} \qquad \frac{\partial}{\partial y}\left(\frac{\partial f}{\partial y}\right) = \frac{\partial^2 f}{\partial y^2} = f_{yy}$$

$$\frac{\partial}{\partial x}\left(\frac{\partial f}{\partial y}\right) = \frac{\partial^2 f}{\partial x \partial y} = f_{yx} \qquad \frac{\partial}{\partial y}\left(\frac{\partial f}{\partial x}\right) = \frac{\partial^2 f}{\partial y \partial x} = f_{xy} \tag{14}$$

But under the conditions that $\dfrac{\partial f}{\partial x}$ and $\dfrac{\partial f}{\partial y}$ are continuous functions,

$$\frac{\partial^2 f}{\partial y \partial x} = \frac{\partial^2 f}{\partial x \partial y} \tag{15}$$

which means that the order of differentiation for the second partial derivatives is interchangeable.

Similarly, the third partial derivatives of $f(x,y)$ are four in number:

$$\frac{\partial}{\partial x}\left(\frac{\partial^2 f}{\partial x^2}\right) = \frac{\partial^3 f}{\partial x^3} \qquad \frac{\partial}{\partial x}\left(\frac{\partial^2 f}{\partial y^2}\right) = \frac{\partial}{\partial y}\left(\frac{\partial^2 f}{\partial x \partial y}\right) = \frac{\partial^2}{\partial y^2}\left(\frac{\partial f}{\partial x}\right) = \frac{\partial^3 f}{\partial x \partial y^2}$$

$$\frac{\partial}{\partial y}\left(\frac{\partial^2 f}{\partial y^2}\right) = \frac{\partial^3 f}{\partial y^3} \qquad \frac{\partial}{\partial y}\left(\frac{\partial^2 f}{\partial x^2}\right) = \frac{\partial}{\partial x}\left(\frac{\partial^2 f}{\partial x \partial y}\right) = \frac{\partial^2}{\partial x^2}\left(\frac{\partial f}{\partial y}\right) = \frac{\partial^3 f}{\partial x^2 \partial y} \tag{16}$$

The formulas above may be generalized to the case where f is a function of more than two variables; $f(x, y, z, \ldots)$ is determined if values for $x, y, z, \ldots$ are given. If the increments $\Delta x, \Delta y, \Delta z, \ldots$ are assigned to $x, y, z, \ldots$ in $f(x, y, z, \ldots)$, the following is obtained:

The total increment of f is

$$\Delta f = f(x + \Delta x, y + \Delta y, z + \Delta z, \ldots) - f(x, y, z, \ldots) \tag{17}$$

The total differential of f is

$$df = \frac{\partial f}{\partial x} dx + \frac{\partial f}{\partial y} dy + \frac{\partial f}{\partial z} dz + \ldots \tag{18}$$

The second total differential of f is

$$d^2 f = \frac{\partial^2 f}{\partial x^2}(dx)^2 + \frac{\partial^2 f}{\partial y^2}(dy)^2 + \frac{\partial^2 f}{\partial z^2}(dz)^2 + \ldots + 2\frac{\partial^2 f}{\partial x \partial y} dx dy + \ldots \tag{19}$$

In general, $d^n f = \left(\dfrac{\partial f}{\partial x} dx + \dfrac{\partial f}{\partial y} dy + \dfrac{\partial f}{\partial z} dz + \ldots\right)^n$ ⠀⠀⠀⠀⠀⠀ (20)

where after the development ∂f^n is to be replaced by $\partial^n f$.

Exact Differential. In order for the expression $P(x, y)dx + Q(x, y)\,dy$ to be the *exact* or *complete* differential of a function of two variables, it is necessary and sufficient that

$$\frac{\partial Q}{\partial x} = \frac{\partial P}{\partial y} \quad \text{(integrability condition)} \tag{21}$$

For three variables, $P\,dx + Q\,dy + R\,dz$, the corresponding conditions are

$$\frac{\partial Q}{\partial z} = \frac{\partial R}{\partial y}, \; \frac{\partial R}{\partial x} = \frac{\partial P}{\partial z}, \; \frac{\partial P}{\partial y} = \frac{\partial Q}{\partial x} \tag{22}$$

Differentiation of Composite Functions. If $u = f(x, y, z, \ldots w)$, and $x, y, z, \ldots w$ are functions of a single variable t, then

$$\frac{du}{dt} = \frac{\partial u}{\partial x}\frac{dx}{dt} + \frac{\partial u}{\partial y}\frac{dy}{dt} + \ldots + \frac{\partial u}{\partial w}\frac{dw}{dt} \tag{23}$$

which is the total derivative of u with respect to t.

Example. Given: $u = x^2 + y^2 + 3xy$, $x = t^2$, $y = \dfrac{1}{t}$.

Then
$$\frac{dx}{dt} = 2t, \quad \frac{dy}{dt} = -\frac{1}{t^2}$$

and
$$\frac{du}{dt} = \left(2t^2 + \frac{3}{t}\right)2t - \left(\frac{2}{t} + 3t^2\right)\frac{1}{t^2}$$

The equation reduces to
$$\frac{du}{dt} = 4t^3 + 3 - \frac{2}{t^3}$$

which expresses the rate of change of u with respect to t as a function of t.

Implicit Functions. The equation $F(x, y) = 0$ defines y as an *implicit* function of x, and x as an implicit function of y. If the equation is solved for y in terms of x, $y = f(x)$, then y is called an *explicit* function of x. An example of an elementary case of $F(x, y) = 0$ which can be solved for $y = f(x)$ is

$$x^2 + y^2 - r^2 = 0 \text{ which gives } y = \sqrt{r^2 - x^2} \tag{24}$$

To find $\dfrac{dy}{dx}$, either differentiate $y = f(x)$ or use

$$\frac{dy}{dx} = -\frac{\dfrac{\partial F}{\partial x}}{\dfrac{\partial F}{\partial y}} \qquad \left(\frac{\partial F}{\partial y} \neq 0\right) \tag{25}$$

$$\frac{d^2 y}{dx^2} = -\frac{\dfrac{\partial^2 F}{\partial x^2}\left(\dfrac{\partial F}{\partial y}\right)^2 - 2\dfrac{\partial^2 F}{\partial x \partial y}\dfrac{\partial F}{\partial x}\dfrac{\partial F}{\partial y} + \dfrac{\partial^2 F}{\partial y^2}\left(\dfrac{\partial F}{\partial x}\right)^2}{\left(\dfrac{\partial F}{\partial y}\right)^3} \qquad \left(\frac{\partial F}{\partial y} \neq 0\right) \tag{26}$$

39. SERIES EXPANSION OF FUNCTIONS

Mean Value Theorem. If $f(x)$ is *single valued, continuous* in the interval $a \leqq x \leqq b$, and has a derivative for all values of x between a and b, then

$$f(b) - f(a) = (b - a)f'(\xi) \tag{27}$$

where ξ is a value of x between a and b; if

$$\xi = x + \theta h, \ 0 < \theta < 1 \tag{28}$$

another form is

$$f(x + h) = f(x) + h f'(\xi) \tag{29}$$

Taylor's Formula. If $f(x)$ and all its derivatives are continuous in the neighborhood of the point $x = a$, then $f(x)$ can be developed into a power series arranged according to ascending powers of $x - a$. The series is:

$$f(x) = f(a) + \frac{f'(a)}{1!}(x - a) + \frac{f''(a)}{2!}(x - a)^2 + \ldots + \frac{f^{(n-1)}(a)}{(n-1)!}(x - a)^{n-1} + R_n \tag{30}$$

where $n! = n(n - 1)(n - 2) \ldots 2 \cdot 1$, and is called factorial n, and

$$R_n = \frac{f^n(\xi)}{n!}(x - a)^n \tag{31}$$

is the *remainder* after n terms of the series and

$$\xi = a + \theta(x - a), \ 0 < \theta < 1 \tag{32}$$

Another form:

$$f(x + h) = f(x) + \frac{h}{1!}f'(x) + \frac{h^2}{2!}f''(x) + \ldots + \frac{h^{n-1}}{(n-1)!}f^{(n-1)}(x) + R_n \tag{33}$$

where
$$R_n = \frac{h^n}{n!}f^n(\xi), \ \xi = x + \theta h, \ 0 < \theta < 1 \tag{34}$$

Maclaurin's Form of Taylor's Formula (for $a = 0$).

$$f(x) = f(0) + \frac{f'(0)}{1!}x + \frac{f''(0)}{2!}x^2 + \ldots + \frac{f^{(n-1)}(0)}{(n-1)!}x^{n-1} + R_n \tag{35}$$

where
$$R_n = \frac{f^n(\xi)}{n!}x^n, \ \xi = \theta x, \ 0 < \theta < 1 \tag{36}$$

Care must be exercised in using these formulas that the *series converges*, that is, $\lim_{n \to \infty} R_n$ $= 0$. If Taylor's series converges rapidly, the sum of the first few terms gives a good approximation to $f(x)$ for values of x near $x = a$. If Maclaurin's series converges rapidly, the sum of the first few terms gives a good approximation to $f(x)$ for values of x near $x = 0$. That not all functions can be expanded into Maclaurin's series is shown by the examples; $f(x) = \dfrac{1}{x}; \dfrac{1}{x^2}; \sqrt{x}, \dfrac{1}{\sqrt{x}}; \log_e x; \cot x;$ etc.

Example. Expand e^{nx} into a series of ascending powers of x.

$$f(x) = e^{nx}, \qquad f(0) = 1$$
$$f'(x) = ne^{nx}, \qquad f'(0) = n$$
$$f''(x) = n^2 e^{nx}, \qquad f''(0) = n^2$$
$$f'''(x) = n^3 e^{nx}, \qquad f'''(0) = n^3$$
$$f^{IV}(x) = n^4 e^{nx}, \qquad f^{IV}(0) = n^4$$

$$e^{nx} = 1 + \frac{n}{1!} x + \frac{n^2}{2!} x^2 + \frac{n^3}{3!} x^3 + \dots$$

If x and n are less than unity, this series converges rapidly.

Taylor's Formula for Two Variables.

$$f(x + h,\, y + k) = f(x, y) + \frac{1}{1!}\left(h\frac{\partial}{\partial x} + k\frac{\partial}{\partial y}\right)^{(1)} f(x, y) + \frac{1}{2!}\left(h\frac{\partial}{\partial x} + k\frac{\partial}{\partial y}\right)^{(2)} f(x, y) + \dots$$

$$\dots + \frac{1}{(n-1)!}\left(h\frac{\partial}{\partial x} + k\frac{\partial}{\partial y}\right)^{(n-1)} f(x, y) + R_n \tag{37}$$

where
$$R_n = \frac{1}{n!}\left(h\frac{\partial}{\partial x} + k\frac{\partial}{\partial y}\right)^{(n)} f(x + \theta h,\, y + \theta k),\ 0 < \theta < 1 \tag{38}$$

Infinite Series. The expression

$$a_0 + a_1 x + a_2 x^2 + a_3 x^3 + \dots + a_n x^n + \dots \tag{39}$$

is a *power series*. If the number of terms is finite, the power series is a polynomial; if infinite, the power series is an *infinite* series. The series above is said to *converge* for a given value $x = b$, if the sum of the first n terms approaches a limit L as n is indefinitely increased; $s_n \to L$ as $n \to \infty$. The limit L is called the *value* of the series. The geometric series is an example of a power series:

$$1 + x + x^2 + x^3 + \dots x^n + \dots \tag{40}$$

From algebra, the sum of the first n terms of this series is

$$\frac{1 - x^n}{1 - x} = \frac{1}{1 - x} - \frac{x^n}{1 - x} \tag{41}$$

If $|x| < 1$, the last fraction above approaches zero as $n \to \infty$, and s_n, the sum of the first n terms, approaches the limit $\dfrac{1}{1 - x}$. Hence, the geometric series converges for any value of x in the interval $-1 < x < 1$.

A series which does not converge is called *divergent*. An example is the harmonic series

$$1 + \frac{1}{2} + \frac{1}{3} + \frac{1}{4} + \dots + \frac{1}{n} + \dots \tag{42}$$

Absolute Convergence. If in the series (39) each term is replaced by its absolute value and if the new series

$$|a_0| + |a_1 x| + |a_2 x^2| + |a_3 x^2| + \dots + |a_n x^n| + \dots \tag{43}$$

converges for a given value of x, then series (39) is called *absolutely convergent* for that value of x. If series (43) is convergent, then so is series (39). The determination of the convergence of series (43) is then the determination of the convergence of a series of positive terms. Series, which though convergent are not so absolutely, are called *conditionally convergent*.

Tests for Convergence

Comparison Test. If no term of a series of positive numbers is greater than the corresponding term of a known convergent series, then the first series converges. If no term of a given series is less than the corresponding term of a known divergent series of positive numbers, then the first series diverges.

Ratio Test. If, in a series of positive numbers, the ratio of the $(n + 1)$st term to the nth term approaches a limit L as $n \to \infty$, and if $L < 1$, the series converges; if $D > 1$, the series diverges: if $L = 1$, the test fails.

Raabe's Test. A series of positive functions of x,

$$u_0(x) + u_1(x) + u_2(x) + \ldots + u_n(x) + \ldots \tag{44}$$

is convergent, if there is a sufficiently large N such that for all $n > N$, k being a constant > 1

$$\frac{u_n}{u_{n+1}} \geqq 1 + \frac{k}{n} \tag{45}$$

On the contrary, the series is divergent if

$$\frac{u_n}{u_{n+1}} \leqq 1 + \frac{1}{n} \tag{46}$$

In particular, the series is convergent or divergent according to whether the expression $n\left(\dfrac{u_n}{u_{n+1}} - 1\right)$ has a limit > 1 or < 1, respectively.

One of the above tests may indicate the convergence or divergence of the series in cases where the other tests give no information.

Conditional Convergence. If, in a series of alternately positive and negative terms, each term is less in absolute value than the preceding term, and the absolute value of the nth term approaches zero as a limit as $n \to \infty$, the series converges.

For example, the series:

$$a_0 - a_1 + a_2 - a_3 + \ldots + (-1)^n a_n + \ldots \tag{47}$$

in which the a's are positive numbers with $a_{n+1} < a_n$ and $\lim_{n \to \infty} a_n = 0$, converges.

Region of Convergence of Power Series. Given the power series

$$a_0 + a_1 x + a_2 x^2 + \ldots + a_n x^n + \ldots \tag{48}$$

If the ratio $\dfrac{|a_{n+1}|}{|a_n|}$ approaches a limit L as $n \to \infty$, then the ratio $\dfrac{|a_{n+1}|}{|a_n|} |x|$ approaches a limit $L |x|$ which is less than 1 if $|x| < \dfrac{1}{L}$ and greater than 1 if $|x| > \dfrac{1}{L}$. The region of convergence is then determined as the interval $-\dfrac{1}{L} < x < \dfrac{1}{L}$.

Example. Find the region of convergence of the power series

$$2 + 4x + 6x^2 + \ldots + 2nx^{n-1} + 2(n+1)x^n + \ldots$$

$$\frac{|a_{n+1}|}{|a_n|} |x| = \frac{|2(n+1)|}{|2n|} |x| = \frac{n+1}{n} |x|$$

As $n \to \infty$, this latter approaches the limit Lx which, in this case, equals x. The region of convergence is $-1 < x < 1$.

Uniform Convergence. The relation of uniform convergence to that of convergence is somewhat like that of uniform continuity to that of continuity of a function. Consider a series of functions of a variable x

$$f(x) = u_0(x) + u_1(x) + u_2(x) + \ldots + u_n(x) + R_n(x) \tag{49}$$

where $R_n(x)$ is the remainder after n terms. Given ϵ, a positive quantity which can be made as small as desired. If $|R_n(x)| < \epsilon$ for all the indices n larger than a given number N, which is independent of the value of x in the interval $a < x < b$, then the series is uniformly convergent in that interval. Note that once N is determined it is valid for all values of x in that interval. If the power series

$$a_0 + a_1 x + a_2 x^2 + \ldots + a_n x^n + \ldots \tag{50}$$

has the interval of convergence $-R < x < R$, then the series (50) is uniformly convergent in any interval within this interval. If series (49) is a uniformly convergent series of continuous functions, then $f(x)$, the limit of the sum of the $u_n(x)$, is a continuous function. It is this property which allows such a series to be differentiated or integrated term by term.

Weierstrass' Test for the Uniform Convergence of a Series in an Interval. If series (49) above is given such that, for all values of x in an interval, the absolute values of the terms of the series are respectively less than the corresponding terms in a convergent series of positive constant terms $T = M_1 + M_2 + M_3 + \ldots + M_n + \ldots$, then the series (49) is uniformly convergent in this interval.

Example. The series $\cos x + \dfrac{1}{2^2} \cos^2 x + \dfrac{1}{3^2} \cos^3 x + \ldots$ is uniformly convergent for all values of x because the absolute values of its terms are not greater than the corresponding terms of the convergent series

$$1 + \frac{1}{2^2} + \frac{1}{3^2} + \ldots$$

Operations with Series. A uniformly convergent series of continuous functions may be differentiated term by term. Given the series (49) above uniformly convergent in $a < x < b$ where the $u_n(x)$ are continuous. Then

$$f'(x) = u_0'(x) + u_1'(x) + \ldots + u_n'(x) + \ldots \qquad (51)$$

which converges in the same interval as $f(x)$. If, in turn, $f'(x)$ is uniformly convergent in this same interval

$$f''(x) = u_0''(x) + u_1''(x) + \ldots + u_n''(x) + \ldots \qquad (52)$$

which converges in the same interval. The reasoning above can be repeated. In particular, a power series may be differentiated term by term.

A uniformly convergent series of continuous functions may be integrated term by term. Given

$$f(x) = u_0(x) + u_1(x) + u_2(x) + \ldots + u_n(x) + \ldots \qquad (53)$$

uniformly convergent in $a < x < b$ where the $u_n(x)$ are continuous. Then

$$\int_a^b f(x)dx = \int_a^b u_0(x)dx + \int_a^b u_1(x)dx + \ldots + \int_a^b u_n(x)dx + \ldots \qquad (54)$$

In particular, this is true if $f(x)$ defines a power series.

Two power series may be added, multiplied together, or divided one by the other, and the result is a power series which converges when both of the first do and represents the sum, product, or quotient, respectively, of the two series.

Trigonometric or Fourier Series

If the infinite series

$$\frac{a_0}{2} + \sum_{n=1}^{\infty} (a_n \cos nx + b_n \sin nx) = \frac{1}{2}a_0 + a_1 \cos x + a_2 \cos 2x$$
$$+ a_3 \cos 3x + \ldots + b_1 \sin x + b_2 \sin 2x + b_3 \sin 3x + \ldots \qquad (55)$$

converges over an interval of length 2π in x, say $0 \leqq x < 2\pi$ or $-\pi < x \leqq \pi$, the series converges for all values of x and defines a periodic function $f(x + 2\pi) = f(x)$ of period 2π. To determine the coefficients, use the formulas

$$a_0 = \frac{1}{\pi}\int_0^{2\pi} f(x)dx, \ a_k = \frac{1}{\pi}\int_0^{2\pi} f(x) \cos k\,x\,dx, \ b_k = \frac{1}{\pi}\int_0^{2\pi} f(x) \sin k\,x\,dx \qquad (56)$$

Conversely, if $f(x)$ is a function, single-valued and finite in an interval of length 2π, and continuous except for a finite number of discontinuities (jumps) in the interval, the numbers a_0, a_k, b_k may be computed as above and the series constructed. If the series converges to the value of $f(x)$, there has been found an expansion of $f(x)$ over the interval from 0 to 2π in a Fourier series. For questions of convergence and term-by-term differentiation and integration consult a book on Fourier series.

Example. Develop e^x in the interval 0 to 2π.

$$a_0 = \frac{1}{\pi}\int_0^{2\pi} e^x\,dx = \frac{1}{\pi}(e^{2\pi} - 1), \ a_k = \frac{1}{\pi}\int_0^{2\pi} e^x \cos k\,x\,dx = \frac{e^{2\pi} - 1}{\pi(k^2 + 1)}, \ b_k = -\frac{k(e^{2\pi} - 1)}{\pi(k^2 + 1)}$$

Hence

$$e^x = \frac{1}{\pi}(e^{2\pi} - 1)\left[\frac{1}{2} + \frac{1}{1^2 + 1}\cos x + \frac{1}{2^2 + 1}\cos 2x + \frac{1}{3^2 + 1}\cos 3x + \ldots\right]$$
$$- \frac{1}{\pi}(e^{2\pi} - 1)\left[\frac{1}{1^2 + 1}\sin x + \frac{2}{2^2 + 1}\sin 2x + \frac{3}{3^2 + 1}\sin 3x + \ldots\right] \qquad (57)$$

The expansion is valid only in the interval from 0 to 2π; outside that interval the series repeats itself owing to the periodic property of $\sin kx$ and $\cos kx$. It may be remarked that the expansion does not give the value of the function for 0 or 2π but gives the point midway in the jump. If series (57) were differentiated the coefficients of the cosine terms (after differentiation) would be $1 + \frac{1}{k^2}$ and would not approach 0 when k became infinite, so that the series would evidently oscillate.

The Fourier Series with Sines or Cosines Only. If $f(x) = f(-x)$, it is called an *even* function; if $f(-x) = -f(x)$, it is called an *odd* function. If $f(x)$ is even, so is $f(x) \cos kx$, while $f(x) \sin kx$ is odd. Then

$$a_k = \frac{1}{\pi}\int_{-\pi}^{\pi} f(x) \cos kx\,dx = \frac{2}{\pi}\int_0^{\pi} f(x) \cos kx\,dx \quad \text{(also holds for } k = 0\text{)} \quad (58a)$$

$$b_k = \frac{1}{\pi}\int_{-\pi}^{\pi} f(x) \sin kx\,dx = 0 \qquad (58b)$$

Hence an even function may be expanded into a series of cosines in the interval $-\pi < x < \pi$ and the coefficients computed as in (58a) and (58b).

If $f(x)$ is an odd function, so is $f(x)$ cos kx, while $f(x)$ sin kx is even. Then

$$a_k = \frac{1}{\pi} \int_{-\pi}^{\pi} f(x) \cos kx \, dx = 0 \qquad (59a)$$

$$b_k = \frac{1}{\pi} \int_{-\pi}^{\pi} f(x) \sin kx \, dx = \frac{2}{\pi} \int_{0}^{\pi} f(x) \sin kx \, dx \qquad (59b)$$

Hence an odd function may be expanded into a series of sines in the interval $-\pi < x < \pi$, and the coefficients computed as in (59a) and (59b).

It follows that any function $f(x)$ of the type which may be expanded into a Fourier series can be expanded into a series of sines only or a series of cosines only. For a function $\phi(x)$ may be defined equal to $f(x)$ between 0 and π and $\phi(-x) = -f(x)$. Then $\phi(x)$ is an odd function and can be expanded into a sine series. Or, for a cosine series, $\phi(x)$ may be defined as equal to $f(x)$ between 0 and π and $\phi(-x) = f(x)$. Then $\phi(x)$ is an even function and can be expanded into a cosine series.

Example. Expand $f(x) = x$ into a cosine series in the interval $(0, \pi)$.

Here

$$\frac{1}{2} a_0 = \frac{1}{\pi} \int_0^{\pi} x \, dx = \frac{\pi}{2}$$

$$a_k = \frac{2}{\pi} \int_0^{\pi} x \cos k \, x \, dx = \frac{2}{\pi} \left\{ \left[\frac{x \sin kx}{k} \right]_0^{\pi} - \int_0^{\pi} \frac{\sin kx}{k} \, dx \right\}$$

$$= \frac{2}{\pi} \left[\frac{1}{k^2} \cos kx \right]_0^{\pi} = \frac{2}{\pi k^2} (\cos k\pi - 1)$$

Therefore

$$x = \frac{\pi}{2} - \frac{4}{\pi} \left[\cos x + \frac{\cos 3x}{3^2} + \frac{\cos 5x}{5^2} + \dots \right] (0 < x < \pi)$$

If $x = 0$, the sum of the series is zero, if $x = \pi$, the sum of the series is π.

Table II. Functions Expanded into Series
(log = $\log_e$)

$$(a + x)^n = a^n + na^{n-1} x + \frac{n(n-1)}{2!} a^{n-2} x^2 + \frac{n(n-1)(n-2)}{3!} a^{n-3} x^3 + \dots \qquad (x^2 < a^2)$$

$$e^x = 1 + x + \frac{x^2}{2!} + \frac{x^3}{3!} + \frac{x^4}{4!} + \dots \qquad (-\infty < x < \infty)$$

$$a^x = 1 + x \log a + \frac{(x \log a)^2}{2!} + \frac{(x \log a)^3}{3!} + \dots \qquad (-\infty < x < \infty)$$

$$e^{-x^2} = 1 - x^2 + \frac{x^4}{2!} - \frac{x^6}{3!} + \frac{x^8}{4!} - \dots \qquad (-\infty < x < \infty)$$

$$e^{\sin x} = 1 + x + \frac{x^2}{2!} - \frac{3x^4}{4!} - \frac{8x^5}{5!} - \frac{3x^6}{6!} + \frac{56x^7}{7!} + \dots \qquad (-\infty < x < \infty)$$

$$e^{\cos x} = e \left(1 - \frac{x^2}{2!} + \frac{4x^4}{4!} - \frac{31x^6}{6!} + \dots \right) \qquad (-\infty < x < \infty)$$

$$e^{\tan x} = 1 + x + \frac{x^2}{2!} + \frac{3x^3}{3!} + \frac{9x^4}{4!} + \frac{37x^5}{5!} + \dots \qquad \left(-\frac{\pi}{2} < x < \frac{\pi}{2} \right)$$

$$\log x = \frac{x-1}{x} + \frac{1}{2} \left(\frac{x-1}{x} \right)^2 + \frac{1}{3} \left(\frac{x-1}{x} \right)^3 + \dots \qquad \left(x > \frac{1}{2} \right)$$

$$\log x = 2 \left[\frac{x-1}{x+1} + \frac{1}{3} \left(\frac{x-1}{x+1} \right)^3 + \frac{1}{5} \left(\frac{x-1}{x+1} \right)^5 + \dots \right] \qquad (x > 0)$$

$$\log (1 + x) = x - \frac{x^2}{2} + \frac{x^3}{3} - \frac{x^4}{4} + \dots \qquad (-1 < x < 1)$$

$$\log \left(\frac{1+x}{1-x} \right) = 2 \left[x + \frac{x^3}{3} + \frac{x^5}{5} + \frac{x^7}{7} + \dots \right] \qquad (-1 < x < 1)$$

$$\log \left(\frac{x+1}{x-1} \right) = 2 \left[\frac{1}{x} + \frac{1}{3} \left(\frac{1}{x} \right)^3 + \frac{1}{5} \left(\frac{1}{x} \right)^5 + \dots \right] \qquad (-1 < x < 1)$$

$$\log \sin x = \log x - \frac{x^2}{6} - \frac{x^4}{180} - \frac{x^6}{2835} - \dots \qquad (-\pi < x < \pi)$$

Table II. Functions Expanded into Series (*Continued*)

$$\log \cos x = -\frac{x^2}{2} - \frac{x^4}{12} - \frac{x^6}{45} - \frac{17x^8}{2520} - \cdots \qquad \left(-\frac{\pi}{2} < x < \frac{\pi}{2}\right)$$

$$\log \tan x = \log x + \frac{x^2}{3} + \frac{7x^4}{90} + \frac{62x^6}{2835} + \cdots \qquad \left(-\frac{\pi}{2} < x < \frac{\pi}{2}\right)$$

$$\sin x = x - \frac{x^3}{3!} + \frac{x^5}{5!} - \frac{x^7}{7!} + \cdots \qquad (-\infty < x < \infty)$$

$$\cos x = 1 - \frac{x^2}{2!} + \frac{x^4}{4!} - \frac{x^6}{6!} + \cdots \qquad (-\infty < x < \infty)$$

$$\tan x = x + \frac{x^3}{3} + \frac{2x^5}{15} + \frac{17x^7}{315} + \frac{62x^9}{2835} + \cdots \qquad \left(-\frac{\pi}{2} < x < \frac{\pi}{2}\right)$$

$$\cot x = \frac{1}{x} - \frac{x}{3} - \frac{x^3}{45} - \frac{2x^5}{945} - \frac{x^7}{4725} - \cdots \qquad (-\pi < x < \pi)$$

$$\sec x = 1 + \frac{x^2}{2!} + \frac{5x^4}{4!} + \frac{61x^6}{6!} + \cdots \qquad \left(-\frac{\pi}{2} < x < \frac{\pi}{2}\right)$$

$$\csc x = \frac{1}{x} + \frac{x}{3!} + \frac{7x^3}{3\cdot5!} + \frac{31x^5}{3\cdot7!} + \cdots \qquad (-\pi < x < \pi)$$

$$\sin^{-1} x = x + \frac{x^3}{2\cdot3} + \frac{3x^5}{2\cdot4\cdot5} + \frac{3\cdot5x^7}{2\cdot4\cdot6\cdot7} + \cdots \qquad (-1 < x < 1)$$

$$\cos^{-1} x = \frac{\pi}{2} - \sin^{-1} x$$

$$\tan^{-1} x = \frac{\pi}{2} - \frac{1}{x} + \frac{1}{3x^3} - \frac{1}{5x^5} + \cdots \qquad (-1 > x > 1)$$

$$\cot^{-1} x = \frac{\pi}{2} - \tan^{-1} x$$

$$\sec^{-1} x = \frac{\pi}{2} - \frac{1}{x} - \frac{1}{6x^3} - \frac{3}{2\cdot4\cdot5x^5} - \frac{3\cdot5}{2\cdot4\cdot6\cdot7x^7} - \cdots \qquad (-1 > x > 1)$$

$$\csc^{-1} x = \frac{\pi}{2} - \sec^{-1} x$$

$$\sinh x = x + \frac{x^3}{3!} + \frac{x^5}{5!} + \frac{x^7}{7!} + \cdots \qquad (-\infty < x < \infty)$$

$$\cosh x = 1 + \frac{x^2}{2!} + \frac{x^4}{4!} + \frac{x^6}{6!} + \frac{x^8}{8!} + \cdots \qquad (-\infty < x < \infty)$$

$$\tanh x = x - \frac{x^3}{3} + \frac{2x^5}{15} - \frac{17x^7}{315} + \cdots \qquad \left(-\frac{\pi}{2} < x < \frac{\pi}{2}\right)$$

$$\coth x = \frac{1}{x} + \frac{x}{3} - \frac{x^3}{45} + \frac{2x^5}{945} - \frac{x^7}{4725} + \cdots \qquad (-\pi < x < \pi)$$

$$\operatorname{sech} x = 1 - \frac{x^2}{2!} + \frac{5x^4}{4!} - \frac{61x^6}{6!} + \frac{1385x^8}{8!} - \cdots \qquad \left(-\frac{\pi}{2} < x < \frac{\pi}{2}\right)$$

$$\operatorname{csch} x = \frac{1}{x} - \frac{x}{6} + \frac{7x^3}{360} - \frac{31x^5}{15120} + \cdots \qquad (-\pi < x < \pi)$$

$$\sinh^{-1} x = x - \frac{x^3}{2\cdot3} + \frac{3x^5}{2\cdot4\cdot5} - \frac{3\cdot5x^7}{2\cdot4\cdot6\cdot7} + \cdots \qquad (-1 < x < 1)$$

$$\sinh^{-1} x = \log 2x + \frac{1}{2\cdot2x^2} - \frac{3}{2\cdot4\cdot4x^4} + \frac{3\cdot5}{2\cdot4\cdot6\cdot6x^6} + \cdots \qquad (x > 1)$$

$$\cosh^{-1} x = \pm\left(\log 2x - \frac{1}{2\cdot2x^2} - \frac{1\cdot3}{2\cdot4\cdot4x^4} - \frac{1\cdot3\cdot5}{2\cdot4\cdot6\cdot6x^6} - \cdots\right) \qquad (x > 1)$$

$$\tanh^{-1} x = x + \frac{x^3}{3} + \frac{x^5}{5} + \frac{x^7}{7} + \cdots \qquad (-1 < x < 1)$$

$$\coth^{-1} x = \frac{1}{x} + \frac{1}{3x^3} + \frac{1}{5x^5} + \frac{1}{7x^7} + \cdots \qquad (-1 > x > 1)$$

$$\operatorname{sech}^{-1} x = \pm\left(\log \frac{2}{x} - \frac{1}{2\cdot2}x^2 - \frac{1\cdot3}{2\cdot4\cdot4}x^4 - \frac{1\cdot3\cdot5}{2\cdot4\cdot6\cdot6}x^6 - \cdots\right) \qquad (0 < x < 1)$$

$$\operatorname{csch}^{-1} x = \frac{1}{x} - \frac{1}{2\cdot3x^3} + \frac{3}{2\cdot4\cdot5x^5} - \frac{3\cdot5}{2\cdot4\cdot6\cdot7x^7} + \cdots \qquad (-1 > x > 1)$$

40. MAXIMA AND MINIMA

Function of a Single Variable. If a continuous function of x ceases to increase and begins to decrease (Fig. 2), it is said to have a *maximum* value; if the function ceases to decrease and begins to increase (Fig. 3), it is said to have a *minimum* value. A maximum point of a curve is one whose ordinate is algebraically greater than the ordinate of any other point in the immediate neighborhood. A minimum point of a curve is one whose ordinate is algebraically less than the ordinate of any other point in the immediate neighborhood. To find the values of x which give maximum or minimum

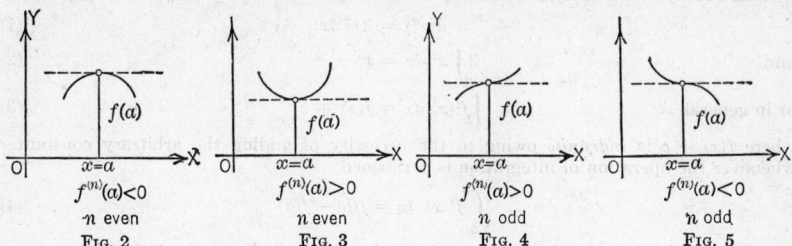

$f^{(n)}(a) < 0$	$f^{(n)}(a) > 0$	$f^{(n)}(a) > 0$	$f^{(n)}(a) < 0$
n even	n even	n odd	n odd
Fig. 2	Fig. 3	Fig. 4	Fig. 5

values of $f(x)$, note that the tangent to the curve at the extreme value is parallel to the OX axis. Then simply solve the equation $f'(x) = 0$.

If $x = a$ is a solution of this equation, it must be tested to see if it gives a maximum or minimum. To do this, compute the higher derivatives of $f(x)$ until one is found which does not vanish at $x = a$, $f^{(n)}(a) \neq 0$. If its order, n, is an even number, then there is a minimum if $f^{(n)}(a) > 0$, and a maximum if it is < 0. If n is odd, then there is neither a maximum nor minimum, but an inflection point (Figs. 4 and 5). Often, the physical interpretation of the problem will tell whether there is a maximum or minimum when $f'(a) = 0$, and further tests are unnecessary.

Example. A piece of wire of length 30 in. is bent into a rectangle. Find the maximum area. Let $x = $ the length of the base, then $1/2(30 - 2x) = $ the length of the altitude. The area, $A = x(15 - x) = 15x - x^2$.

For a maxima or minima, $\dfrac{dA}{dx} = 15 - 2x = 0$, $x = 7.5$.

Then $A = 7.5(15 - 7.5) = 56.25$ sq in.

To find whether the area is maxima or minima, $\dfrac{d^2 A}{dx^2} = -2$ which is less than 0, and therefore the area 56.25 sq in. is a maximum.

Functions of Two or More Independent Variables. The function $f(x, y)$ has a maximum value at (a, b) if $f(a + h, b + k) < f(a, b)$ for all values of $|h|$ and $|k|$ sufficiently small. Likewise, if $f(a + h, b + k) > f(a, b)$, then $f(x, y)$ has a minimum at (a, b). If the function is represented graphically by the surface $z = f(x, y)$, then z has a maximum or minimum value when the tangent plane of the surface is parallel to the XOY plane. Hence, it is necessary that

$$\frac{\partial f}{\partial x} = \frac{\partial f}{\partial y} = 0 \qquad (60)$$

If, in addition,

$$\frac{\partial^2 f}{\partial x^2} \frac{\partial^2 f}{\partial y^2} - \left(\frac{\partial^2 f}{\partial x \partial y}\right)^2 > 0 \qquad (61)$$

$f(x, y)$ has a maximum value if

$$\frac{\partial^2 f}{\partial x^2} \text{ or } \frac{\partial^2 f}{\partial y^2} < 0 \qquad (62)$$

and a minimum value if

$$\frac{\partial^2 f}{\partial x^2} \text{ or } \frac{\partial^2 f}{\partial y^2} > 0 \qquad (63)$$

If

$$\frac{\partial^2 f}{\partial x^2} \frac{\partial^2 f}{\partial y^2} - \left(\frac{\partial^2 f}{\partial x \partial y}\right)^2 < 0, \qquad (64)$$

then $f(x, y)$ has neither maxima nor minima, and if the expression equals 0, it is doubtful. For a function of several variables $f(x, y, z, \ldots)$, necessary conditions for a maxima or minima are

$$\frac{\partial f}{\partial x} = \frac{\partial f}{\partial y} = \frac{\partial f}{\partial z} = \ldots = 0 \qquad (65)$$

INTEGRAL CALCULUS

By M. J. Fish

41. ELEMENTARY PRINCIPLES

Integration is the inverse operation of differentiation. It is indicated by the symbol $\int$ followed by the differential function to be integrated. For example,

$$d(x^3) = 3x^2\,dx \tag{1}$$

and

$$3\int x^2\,dx = x^3 + c \tag{2}$$

or in general

$$\int f'(x)\,dx = f(x) + c \tag{3}$$

where $f(x) + c$ is *indefinite* owing to the necessity of adding the arbitrary constant c whenever the operation of integration is performed.

$$\int_a^b f'(x)\,dx = f(b) - f(a) \tag{4}$$

is called the *definite integral*, where $f'(x)$ is continuous in the interval a to b or has at most a finite number of finite discontinuities in the interval.

Fundamental Forms. Since integration is an anti-differentiation operation, facility in integrating depends upon the ability to recognize the forms of the derivatives of elementary functions and also the knowledge of how to transform a given function into an elementary form. Table I is a list of fundamental forms to which many integrals may be reduced by simple transformation. The constant of integration has been omitted in the tabulation. The integrals of other frequently occurring forms are given in Table 19, Section 1.

Integration by Parts is a method frequently employed if it is advantageous to consider the integral of a function as the integral of the product of a function by the differential of another function; then

$$\int u\,dv = uv - \int v\,du \tag{5}$$

since

$$d(uv) = u\,dv + v\,du \tag{6}$$

where u and v are both functions of a variable x.

Integration of Rational Fractions. If the degree of the numerator is not less than that of the denominator in the equation

$$R(x) = \frac{\phi(x)}{f(x)}$$

where $\phi(x)$ and $f(x)$ are rational polynomials, $R(x)$ can be put in the form of a polynomial and a remainder by performing the division indicated. The remainder may then be represented by partial fractions, see Art. 7, page 2–08, and both the polynomial and remainder integrated directly by application of formulas 1, 2, 15, and 16 in Table I.

Integration of Irrational Functions may frequently be accomplished by reducing them to rational integrals by changing the variable. The method is called integration by rationalization or integration by substitution.

For example, integrals containing the following forms may be rationalized by the substitutions indicated:

Form	Substitution
$f[(ax+b)^{p/q}]\,dx$	let $ax + b = y^q$
$f[(ax+b)^{p/q}(ax+b)^{r/s}]\,dx$	let $ax + b = y^n$, where n is the L.C.M. of q, s
$f[x, \sqrt{x^2 + ax + b}]\,dx$	let $\sqrt{x^2 + ax + b} = y - x$
$f[x, \sqrt{-x^2 + ax + b}]\,dx$	let $\sqrt{-x^2 + ax + b} = \sqrt{(\alpha - x)(\beta + x)}$
	$= (\alpha - x)y$ or $= (\beta + x)y$
$f[\sin x, \cos x]\,dx$	let $\tan \dfrac{x}{2} = y$
$f[x, \sqrt{a^2 - x^2}]\,dx$	let $x = a \sin y$
$f[x, \sqrt{x^2 - a^2}]\,dx$	let $x = a \sec y$ or $x = a \cosh y$
$f[x, \sqrt{x^2 + a^2}]\,dx$	let $x = a \tan y$ or $x = a \sinh y$

Table I. Fundamental Integrals

1. $\int u^n \, du = \dfrac{u^{n+1}}{n+1}$.

2. $\int \dfrac{du}{u} = \log u$.

3. $\int a^u \, du = \dfrac{a^u}{\log a}$.

4. $\int e^u \, du = e^u$.

5. $\int \cos u \, du = \sin u$.

6. $\int \sin u \, du = -\cos u$.

7. $\int \sec^2 u \, du = \tan u$.

8. $\int \csc^2 u \, du = -\cot u$.

9. $\int \sec u \tan u \, du = \sec u$.

10. $\int \csc u \cot u \, du = -\csc u$.

11. $\int \tan u \, du = \log \sec u$.
$= -\log \cos u$

12. $\int \cot u \, du = \log \sin u$.
$= -\log \csc u$.

13. $\int \sec u \, du = \log(\sec u + \tan u)$
$= \log \tan\left(\dfrac{\pi}{4} + \dfrac{u}{2}\right)$.

14. $\int \csc u \, du = \log(\csc u - \cot u)$
$= \log \tan \dfrac{u}{2}$.

15. $\int \dfrac{du}{u^2 + a^2} = \dfrac{1}{a} \tan^{-1} \dfrac{u}{a}$,
$= -\dfrac{1}{a} \cot^{-1} \dfrac{u}{a}$.

16. $\int \dfrac{du}{u^2 - a^2} = \dfrac{1}{2a} \log \dfrac{u-a}{u+a}$,
$= \dfrac{1}{2a} \log \dfrac{a-u}{a+u}$
$= -\dfrac{1}{a} \tanh^{-1} \dfrac{u}{a}$ $\qquad (u < a)$
$= -\dfrac{1}{a} \coth^{-1} \dfrac{u}{a}$ $\qquad (u > a)$.

17. $\int \dfrac{du}{\sqrt{a^2 - u^2}} = \sin^{-1} \dfrac{u}{a}$,
$= -\cos^{-1} \dfrac{u}{a}$.

18. $\int \dfrac{du}{\sqrt{u^2 \pm a^2}} = \log(u + \sqrt{u^2 \pm a^2})$
$\int \dfrac{du}{\sqrt{u^2 + a^2}} = \sinh^{-1} \dfrac{u}{a}$
$\int \dfrac{du}{\sqrt{u^2 - a^2}} = \cosh^{-1} \dfrac{u}{a}$.

19. $\int \dfrac{du}{u\sqrt{u^2 - a^2}} = \dfrac{1}{a} \sec^{-1} \dfrac{u}{a}$,
$= -\dfrac{1}{a} \csc^{-1} \dfrac{u}{a}$.

20. $\int \dfrac{du}{\sqrt{2au - u^2}} = \text{vers}^{-1} \dfrac{u}{a}$.

21. $\int \sinh u \, du = \cosh u$.

22. $\int \cosh u \, du = \sinh u$.

23. $\int \tanh u \, du = \log \cosh u$.

24. $\int \coth u \, du = \log \sinh u$.

25. $\int \text{sech} \, u \, du = 2 \tan^{-1} e^u$.

26. $\int \text{csch} \, u \, du = \log \tanh \dfrac{u}{2}$.

In general, with the exception of the square root of polynomials of the second degree, integrals containing fractional powers of polynomials above the first degree cannot be rationalized or integrated in terms of the elementary integral forms.

Elliptic Integrals.* An elliptic integral has the form

$$\int R[x, \sqrt{f(x)}] \, dx$$

where R represents a rational function and $f(x) = a + bx + cx^2 + dx^3 + ex^4$, an algebraic function of the third or fourth degree.

Elliptic Integral of the First Kind.

$$F(\phi, k) = \int_0^x \frac{dx}{\sqrt{(1-x^2)(1-k^2 x^2)}} = \int_0^\phi \frac{d\phi}{\sqrt{1-k^2 \sin^2 \phi}} \ (k^2 < 1, \ x = \sin \phi) \qquad (8)$$

Elliptic Integral of the Second Kind.

$$B(\phi, k) = \int_0^x \frac{\sqrt{1-k^2 x^2}}{\sqrt{1-x^2}} \, dx = \int_0^\phi \sqrt{1-k^2 \sin^2 \phi} \, d\phi \ (k^2 < 1, \ x = \sin \phi) \qquad (9)$$

Elliptic Integral of the Third Kind.

$$E(\phi, k) = \int_0^x \frac{dx}{(x^2 - a)\sqrt{(1-x^2)(1-k^2 x^2)}} = \int_0^\phi \frac{d\phi}{(\sin^2 \phi - a)\sqrt{1-k^2 \sin^2 \phi}} \qquad (10)$$
$$(k^2 < 1, \ x = \sin \phi)$$

* Reference: Smithsonian Mathematical Formulae and Tables of Elliptic Functions by E. P. Adams and R. L. Hippisley. 1922, Washington, D. C.

The "complete" integrals are

$$K = F\left(\frac{\pi}{2}, k\right), \qquad E = E\left(\frac{\pi}{2}, k\right)$$

$$K' = F\left(\frac{\pi}{2}, \sqrt{1 - k^2}\right), \qquad E' = E\left(\frac{\pi}{2}, \sqrt{1 - k^2}\right) \tag{11}$$

where $K = F\left(\dfrac{\pi}{2}, k\right) = \displaystyle\int_0^1 \frac{dx}{\sqrt{(1 - x^2)(1 - k^2 x^2)}} = \int_0^{\pi/2} \frac{d\phi}{\sqrt{1 - k^2 \sin^2 \phi}}$

and

$$KE + EK' - KK' = \frac{\pi}{2}$$

$$K = \frac{\pi}{2}\left[1 + \left(\frac{1}{2}\right)^2 k^2 + \left(\frac{3}{2 \cdot 4}\right)^2 k^4 + \left(\frac{3 \cdot 5}{2 \cdot 4 \cdot 6}\right)^3 k^6 + \dots\right] \tag{12}$$

$$E = \frac{\pi}{2}\left[1 - \left(\frac{1}{2^2}\right) k^2 - \left(\frac{3}{2^2 \cdot 4^2}\right) k^4 - \left(\frac{3^2 \cdot 5}{2^2 \cdot 4^2 \cdot 6^2}\right) k^6 - \dots\right] \tag{13}$$

The inverse function of $u = F(\phi, k)$ is $\phi = $ am u, (am = amplitude)

$$x \equiv \sin \phi \equiv \text{sn } u = u - (1 + k^2)\frac{u^3}{3!} + (1 + 14k^2 + k^4)\frac{u^5}{5!} - \dots \tag{14}$$

$$\cos \phi \equiv \text{cn } u = 1 - \frac{u^2}{2!} + (1 + 4k^2)\frac{u^4}{4!} - (1 + 44k^2 + 16k^4)\frac{u^6}{6!} + \dots \tag{15}$$

$$\sqrt{1 - k^2 x^2} \equiv \Delta\phi \equiv \text{dn } u = 1 - k^2\frac{u^2}{2!} + k^2(4 + k^2)\frac{u^4}{4!} - k^2(16 + 44k^2 + k^4)\frac{u^6}{6!} + \dots \tag{16}$$

42. DEFINITE INTEGRALS

Definite Integral. The definite integral is denoted by

$$\int_a^b f(x)\, dx \tag{17}$$

and represents the

$$\lim_{n \to \infty} \sum_{\nu = 1}^{n} f(\xi_\nu)\, \Delta x_\nu \tag{18}$$

that is, the limit of the sum of

$$f(\xi_1)\Delta x_1 + f(\xi_2)\Delta x_2 + \dots + f(\xi_n)\Delta x_n \text{ as } n \to \infty \text{ and } \Delta x_\nu \to 0. \tag{19}$$

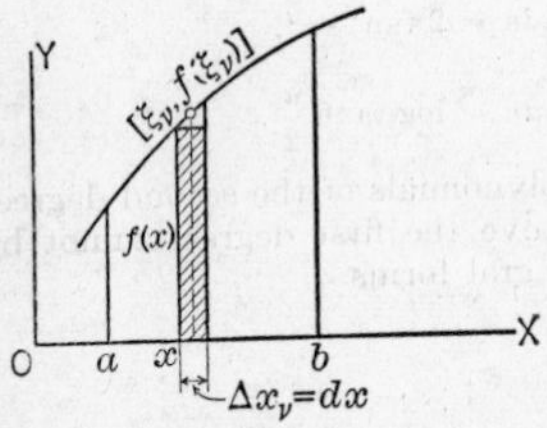

FIG. 1

The interval of integration $a \leqq x \leqq b$ is partitioned into n arbitrary parts $\Delta x_1, \Delta x_2, \dots, \Delta x_n$, so that $\Delta x_1 + \Delta x_2 + \dots + \Delta x_n = b - a$. ξ_ν represents an arbitrary value of x in the interval Δx_ν; the limit is to be taken as $n \to \infty$ and $\Delta x_\nu \to 0$.

The geometric interpretation of the definite integral is the area under the curve $y = f(x)$, if $f(x) \geqq 0$, between the x axis and the ordinates at $x = a$ and $x = b$. $f(x)\, dx$ represents the area of a parallelogram of height $f(x)$ and width dx (Fig. 1). If $f(x)$ is a continuous function or has only a finite number of finite discontinuities (jumps), the integral above exists and

$$\frac{d}{dx}\int_a^x f(x)\, dx = \frac{d}{dx}\int_a^x f(u)\, du = f(x) \tag{20}$$

For the purposes of evaluating a definite integral,

if $F(x) = \displaystyle\int f(x)\, dx$, then $\displaystyle\int_a^b f(x)\, dx = F(b) - F(a)$ \qquad (21)

For example, $\displaystyle\int_3^5 x^2\, dx = \left[\frac{x^3}{3}\right]_3^5 = \frac{125}{3} - 9 = \frac{98}{3}$.

Some Fundamental Theorems.

$$\int_a^b [f_1(x) + f_2(x) + \dots + f_n(x)]\, dx = \int_a^b f_1(x)\, dx + \int_a^b f_2(x)\, dx + \dots + \tag{22}$$

$$\int_a^b f_n(x)\, dx$$

$$\int_a^b f(x)\, dx = -\int_b^a f(x)\, dx \tag{23}$$

$$\int_a^b f(x)\, dx = \int_a^c f(x)\, dx + \int_c^b f(x)\, dx \qquad (a \leqq c \leqq b) \quad (24)$$

$$\int_a^b f(x)\, dx = (b-a)f(\xi) \text{ where } \xi \text{ is some value between } a \text{ and } b \text{ (mean value theorem)} \tag{25}$$

Simpson's Rule for Approximate Integration. This is a method for obtaining the approximate value of the definite integral of a continuous function when the integral can not be evaluated in elementary functions.

Given the integral $\int_a^b f(x)\, dx$ which is to be evaluated.

Plot the curve $f(x)$, and divide the interval into n equal parts (n = even), erecting the ordinates $y_0, y_1, \ldots, y_n$ as shown (Fig. 2). Then *Simpson's rule* states that

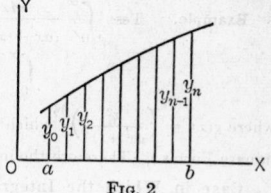

FIG. 2

$$\int_a^b f(x)\, dx = \frac{b-a}{3n}\,(y_0 + 4y_1 + 2y_2 + 4y_3 + 2y_4 + \ldots + 4y_{n-1} + y_n) \tag{26}$$

Multiple Integrals. Given a region R in the XOY plane and let it be divided into rectangles by the lines

$$\begin{aligned} x &= x_i & (i = 0, 1, 2, \ldots, n) \\ y &= y_k & (k = 0, 1, 2, \ldots, m) \end{aligned} \left.\right\} \tag{27}$$

Consider any rectangle, with dimensions $x_{i+1} - x_i$ and $y_{k+1} - y_k$, which lies either wholly or partly in R, and let (ξ_i, η_k) be any point in this rectangle or in R if the rectangle extends outside of R. Let $f(x, y)$ be any function which is continuous in R. Then the limit of the double sum

$$\sum_{i=0}^n \sum_{k=0}^m f(\xi_i, \eta_k)(x_{i+1} - x_i)(y_{k-1} - y_k) \tag{28}$$

as n and m both $\to \infty$ and each of the differences $x_{i+1} - x_i$ and $y_{k+1} - y_k \to 0$ is expressed by the formula

$$\iint_R f(x, y)\, dx\, dy \tag{29}$$

which may be written as

$$\iint_R f(x, y)\, dA, \tag{30}$$

where dA is the element of area.

In case polar coordinates (r, θ) are used instead of (x, y), then $f(x, y)$ is replaced by $F(r, \theta)$ and $dA = dx\, dy$ by $r\, d\theta\, dr$.

The analogous triple integral in space is

$$\iiint_R f(x, y, z)\, dx\, dy\, dz \tag{31}$$

which may be written as

$$\iiint_R f(x, y, z)\, dV \tag{32}$$

where dV is the element of volume.

If spherical coordinates (r, θ, ϕ) are used instead of (x, y, z), then $f(x, y, z)$ is replaced by $F(r, \theta, \phi)$ and $dV = dx\, dy\, dz$ by $r^2 \sin \phi\, d\theta\, d\phi\, dr$. If cylindrical coordinates (r, θ, z) are used instead of (x, y, z), then $f(x, y, z)$ is replaced by $G(r, \theta, z)$ and $dx\, dy\, dz$ by $r\, d\theta\, dr\, dz$.

Improper Integrals. It may happen that the interval of integration becomes *infinite*, that the integral itself becomes infinite at certain points, or that both occur. In such cases the integral may have a definition.

Case in Which One of the Limits is Infinite. By definition,

$$\int_a^\infty f(x)\, dx = \lim_{b \to \infty} \int_a^b f(x)\, dx$$

If the expression on the right has a definite value, then so does the expression on the left which is then said to converge. A rule to determine when this is so is as follows: if the integral $\int_a^\infty f(x)dx$ is written in the form

$$\int_a^\infty \frac{g(x)}{x^k} \, dx, \tag{33}$$

then if $|g(x)| < M$, a constant, for arbitrarily large values of x and $k > 1$, the integral *converges*; however, if $|g(x)| > m$, an arbitrary positive constant, for sufficiently large values of x and $k \leqq 1$, the integral *diverges*.

Example. Test $\int_0^\infty \frac{xdx}{(ax+x^2)^{3/2}}$ for convergence or divergence.

$$\int_0^\infty \frac{xdx}{(ax+x^2)^{3/2}} = \int_0^\infty \left(\frac{x^2}{ax+x^2}\right)^{3/2} \frac{dx}{x^2},$$

where $g(x) = \left(\dfrac{x^2}{ax+x^2}\right)^{3/2}$ which approaches the limit 1 as $x \to \infty$, and $k = 2 > 1$. (See Indeterminate Forms.) Therefore the integral converges.

Case in Which the Integrand Is Infinite. Consider the case in which the integrand becomes infinite at the upper limit. For, if the integrand becomes infinite at the lower limit, the limits may be reversed by a change of sign; and if the integrand becomes infinite at an intermediate point, the formula (24)

$$\int_a^b f(x)dx = \int_a^c f(x)dx + \int_c^b f(x)dx \qquad (a < c < b) \quad (34)$$

may be used. Then, if $f(b) \to \infty$, by definition,

$$\int_a^b f(x)dx = \lim_{\epsilon \to 0} \int_a^{b-\epsilon} f(x)dx \tag{35}$$

where ϵ is a small positive quantity. If the limit exists, the integral is said to converge. A rule to determine when this is so, is as follows: if the integral $\int_a^b f(x)dx$ is written in the form

$$\int_a^b \frac{g(x)}{(b-x)^k} \, dx \tag{36}$$

then for values of x sufficiently near b, if $|g(x)| < M$, a constant, and $k < 1$, the integral converges; however, for values of x sufficiently near b, if $|g(x)| > m$, a constant, and $k \geqq 1$, the integral diverges.

Example. Test $\int_0^1 \log_e x \, dx$ for convergence or divergence.

The integrand is infinite at $x = 0$. Let $\int_0^1 \log_e x \, dx = \int_0^1 \frac{x^{1/2}\log_e x}{x^{1/2}} \, dx$, where $g(x) = x^{1/2}\log_e x$ which tends to zero as $x \to 0$. Since $k = 1/2 < 1$, the integral converges.

Integrals Containing a Parameter. Consider

$$\phi(\alpha) = \int_{x_0}^{x_1} f(x, \alpha)dx, \tag{37}$$

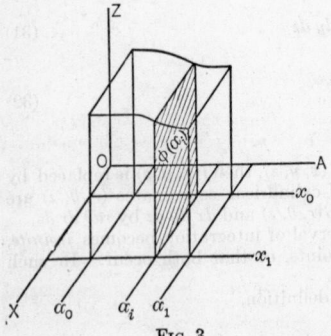

FIG 3

a definite integral in which the integrand contains the parameter α. As an example,

$$\int_0^{\pi/2} \cos \alpha x \, dx = \left[\frac{1}{\alpha} \sin \alpha x\right]_0^{\pi/2} = \frac{1}{\alpha} \tag{38}$$

The indefinite integral is a function of x and α, while the definite integral is a function of α alone. The function $f(x, \alpha)$ may be plotted as the surface $z = f(x, \alpha)$ over the rectangle of values of x where $x_0 \leqq x \leqq x_1$ and $\alpha_0 \leqq \alpha \leqq \alpha_1$. The value $\phi(\alpha_i)$ of the function when $\alpha = \alpha_i$ is then the area of the section shown made by the plane $\alpha = \alpha_i$ (Fig. 3). The function $\phi(\alpha)$ is continuous if $f(x, \alpha)$ is continuous in the two variables x and α. In case the limits of the integral are functions of α, as

$$\phi(\alpha) = \int_{x_0 = g_0(\alpha)}^{x_1 = g_1(\alpha)} f(x, \alpha)dx, \qquad \alpha_0 \leqq \alpha \leqq \alpha_1 \qquad (39)$$

the function $\phi(\alpha)$ is continuous if $f(x, \alpha)$ is continuous over the region bounded by the lines $\alpha = \alpha_0$, $\alpha = \alpha_1$ and the curves $x_0 = g_0(\alpha)$, $x_1 = g_1(\alpha)$, and if the functions $g_0(\alpha)$ and $g_1(\alpha)$ are continuous.

Uniform Convergence of Integrals. An integral is uniformly convergent if, for a positive number ϵ, which can be made arbitrarily small, there corresponds another number L, such that

$$\left| \int_l^\infty f(x, \alpha)d\alpha \right| < \epsilon \qquad (40)$$

provided that $l \geqq L$ where the number L is the same for every value of α in the interval $\alpha_0 \leqq \alpha \leqq \alpha_1$.

Differentiation under the Integral Sign. If $f(x)$ is a continuous function of x for $x = a$ or $x = b$, then

$$\frac{\partial}{\partial b} \int_a^b f(x)dx = f(b), \quad \frac{\partial}{\partial a} \int_a^b f(x)dx = - f(a) \qquad (41)$$

If $\phi(\alpha) = \int_a^b f(x, \alpha)dx$, then $\dfrac{d\phi}{d\alpha} = \int_a^b \dfrac{\partial f(x, \alpha)}{\partial \alpha} dx$, where $f(x, \alpha)$ is a continuous function of x and α between the limits $a \leqq x \leqq b$, $\alpha_0 \leqq \alpha \leqq \alpha_1$, and in addition $\dfrac{\partial f}{\partial \alpha}$ exists and is continuous. In case the limits of the integral are functions of α, as

$$\phi(\alpha) = \int_{x_0 = g_0(\alpha)}^{x_1 = g_1(\alpha)} f(x, \alpha)dx \qquad (42)$$

then $\qquad \dfrac{d\phi}{d\alpha} = \displaystyle\int_{g_0(\alpha)}^{g_1(\alpha)} \dfrac{\partial f(x, \alpha)}{\partial \alpha} dx - f(g_0, \alpha) \dfrac{dg_0}{d\alpha} + f(g_1, \alpha) \dfrac{dg_1}{d\alpha} \qquad (43)$

where $\dfrac{\partial f}{\partial \alpha}$ exists and is continuous and where $g_0(\alpha)$, $g_1(\alpha)$ are differentiable. The formula for differentiation under the integral sign can be applied where the integral obtained is uniformly convergent in the interval of definition; that is, if

$$\phi(\alpha) = \int_a^b f(x, \alpha) \, dx, \qquad \alpha_0 \leqq \alpha \leqq \alpha_1 \qquad (44)$$

and in addition $\qquad\qquad \dfrac{d\phi}{d\alpha} = \displaystyle\int_a^b \dfrac{\partial f(x, \alpha)}{\partial \alpha} dx \qquad (45)$

is uniformly convergent. The process of differentiating under the integral sign is sometimes of use in evaluating the function $\phi(\alpha)$.

Example. Given $\phi(\alpha) = \displaystyle\int_0^1 \dfrac{x^\alpha - 1}{\log_e x} dx$.

$\dfrac{d\phi}{d\alpha} = \displaystyle\int_0^1 \dfrac{x^\alpha \log_e x}{\log_e x} dx = \int_0^1 x^\alpha \, dx = \left[\dfrac{1}{\alpha + 1} x^{\alpha+1} \right]_0^1 = \dfrac{1}{\alpha + 1}$ and $\phi(\alpha) = \log_e (\alpha + 1) + C.$

But $\phi(0) = \displaystyle\int_0^1 0 \, dx = 0$, and $\phi(0) = \log_e 1 + C.$ Therefore $C = 0$.

Hence $\qquad\qquad \phi(\alpha) = \displaystyle\int_0^1 \dfrac{x^\alpha - 1}{\log_e x} dx = \log_e (\alpha + 1).$

Integration under the Integral Sign. Let $f(x, \alpha)$ be a function of two variables, continuous in the region defined by $a \leqq x \leqq b$, $\alpha_0 \leqq \alpha \leqq \alpha_1$, where a, b, α_0, α_1 are constants. The inversion of the order of integration

$$\int_a^b dx \int_{\alpha_0}^{\alpha_1} f(x, \alpha)d\alpha = \int_{\alpha_0}^{\alpha_1} d\alpha \int_a^b f(x, \alpha) \, dx \qquad (46)$$

is the formula for integration under the integral sign and is valid under the conditions stated above.

The case of integration under the integral sign with infinite limits is valid if the integral $\int_a^{+\infty} f(x, \alpha)dx$ is uniformly convergent in $\alpha_0 \leqq \alpha \leqq \alpha_1$, and the formula is

$$\int_a^{+\infty} dx \int_{\alpha_0}^{\alpha_1} f(x, \alpha)d\alpha = \int_{\alpha_0}^{\alpha_1} d\alpha \int_a^{+\infty} f(x, \alpha)dx \qquad (47)$$

The method of integration under the integral sign is sometimes useful for evaluating definite integrals.

Example. Consider $\int_0^1 x^\alpha \, dx = \dfrac{1}{\alpha + 1} \ (\alpha + 1 > 0)$.

Multiply by $d\alpha$ and integrate between the limits c and d.

$$\int_c^d d\alpha \int_0^1 x^\alpha \, dx = \int_c^d \frac{d\alpha}{\alpha + 1} = \log_e \frac{d + 1}{c + 1}$$

but $\qquad \int_0^1 dx \int_c^d x^\alpha \, d\alpha = \int_0^1 \dfrac{x^d - x^c}{\log_e x} \, dx;$ therefore $\int_0^1 \dfrac{x^d - x^c}{\log_e x} \, dx = \log_e \dfrac{d + 1}{c + 1}$

Example. Consider $f(x, \ y) = \dfrac{x^2 - y^2}{(x^2 + y^2)^2}$.

Applying the formula above $\int_0^1 dx \int_0^1 \dfrac{x^2 - y^2}{(x^2 + y^2)^2} \, dy = \int_0^1 dy \int_0^1 \dfrac{x^2 - y^2}{(x^2 + y^2)^2} \, dx.$

A first integration for the expression on the left, $\int_0^1 \dfrac{x^2 - y^2}{(x^2 + y^2)^2} \, dy = \left[\dfrac{y}{x^2 + y^2} \right]_0^1 = \dfrac{1}{1 + x^2}.$

Then $\qquad\qquad \int_0^1 \dfrac{dx}{1 + x^2} = \left[\tan^{-1} x \right]_0^1 = \dfrac{\pi}{4}$

In integrating the expression on the right $\int_0^1 \dfrac{x^2 - y^2}{(x^2 + y^2)^2} \, dx = \left[-\dfrac{x}{x^2 + y^2} \right]_0^1 = -\dfrac{1}{1 + y^2};$

$-\int_0^1 \dfrac{dy}{1 + y^2} = -\dfrac{\pi}{4}$. The results are not equal since the function $\dfrac{x^2 - y^2}{(x^2 + y^2)^2}$ is discontinuous at $x = 0$, $y = 0$.

43. LINE, SURFACE, AND VOLUME INTEGRALS

Line Integrals. Consider a plane curve C, defined by the two parametric equations $x = f(t)$, $y = \phi(t)$. By varying t from a to b, a certain arc AB of this curve is obtained. Suppose that $a < b$, and take between a and b a sequence of increasing numbers $(a = t_0 < t_1 < t_2 < \dots t_{n-1} < t_n = b)$, and in each partial interval $(t_{i-1}, \ t_i)$ take any value θ_i such that $t_{i-1} \leqq \theta_i \leqq t_i$. Let (x_i, y_i) be the coordinates of the point of C which corresponds to the value t_i of the parameter; let (ξ_i, η_i) be the coordinates of the point which corresponds to the value θ_i. Let $P(x, y)$ be a function of the two variables x and y which is continuous along the arc AB.

Consider the sum

$$\sum_{i=1}^n P(\xi_i, \eta_i)(x_i - x_{i-1}) \equiv P(\xi_1, \eta_1)(x_1 - x_0) + P(\xi_2, \eta_2)(x_2 - x_1) + \dots + P(\xi_n, \eta_n)(x_n - x_{n-1}) \quad (48)$$

extended to all the partial intervals. If the number n of the subdivisions increases

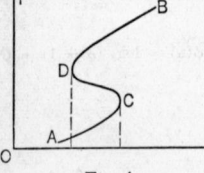

indefinitely in such a manner that the largest of the differences $t_i - t_{i-1}$ tends toward zero, the preceding sum tends toward a limit, which is called the line integral of the function $P(x, y)$ along the arc AB and is represented by the symbol

$$\int_{(AB)} P(x, y) \, dx \quad (49)$$

Fig. 4

Suppose that the curve is one as $ACDB$ in Fig. 4 on which are found two points C and D where the abscissa is a maximum or minimum. Then each of the arcs AC, CD, DB satisfies the preceding conditions, and

$$\int_{(ACDB)} P(x, y) dx = \int_{(AC)} P(x, y) dx + \int_{(CD)} P(x, y) dx + \int_{(DB)} P(x, y) dx \quad (50)$$

A discussion similar to that above can be made for the line integral $\int_{(AB)} Q(x, y) dy$, but it is more common to find line integrals occurring in the form

$$\int_{\substack{a, \, b \\ (C)}}^{x, \, y} [P(x, y) dx + Q(x, y) dy] \quad (51)$$

where $y = f(x)$. This is the line integral along the curve C or $y = f(x)$ from the point (a, b) to the point (x, y).

As an example of the application of the line integral, consider the work done by a force on a particle. By definition, the work done by a constant force F acting on a particle which moves a distance s along a straight line inclined at an angle θ to the force is $W = Fs \cos \theta$. If the path is curvilinear and the force variable, the differential of work is $dW = F \cos \theta \, ds$, where ds is the infinitesimal arc. Hence

$$W = \int dW = \int_{a,\,b}^{x,\,y} F \cos \theta \, ds \tag{52}$$

where the path must be known to evaluate the integral (Fig. 5).

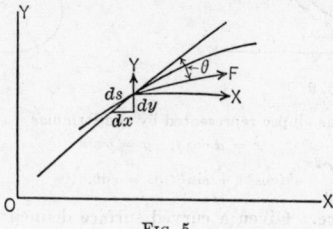

Fig. 5

Example. Find the value of $\int_{0,\,0}^{1,\,3} [y^2 \, dx + (xy - x^2)dy]$ along the paths (a) $y = 3x$, (b) $y^2 = 9x$.

(a) Substitute $y = 3x$, $dy = 3dx$ and obtain $\int_0^1 [9x^2 + (3x^2 - x^2)3] \, dx = \int_0^1 15x^2 = 5$.

(b) Substitute $y^2 = 9x$, $2y \, dy = 9dx$ and obtain $\int_0^3 \left[\dfrac{2}{9}y^3 + \left(\dfrac{y^3}{9} - \dfrac{y^4}{81} \right) \right] dy = \left[\dfrac{1}{12}y^4 - \dfrac{y^5}{405} \right]_0^3$
$= 6\,^3/_{20}$.

Connectivity of Regions. A region is called simply connected if every closed curve or surface in the region can be shrunk to a point without passing outside of the region. In the section of a plane between two concentric circles a curve surrounding the inner curve cannot be shrunk to a point. Such a region is called multiply connected.

A multiply connected region can be made simply connected by the following procedure. Suppose that, in the region in Fig. 7, a line is drawn connecting the two bounding circles and it is agreed that no curve shall cross this line. Then the entire region would be surrounded by a single boundary, part of which would be counted twice. In like manner, the region in Fig. 8 can be made simply connected by two such

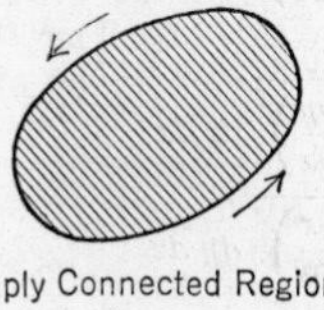

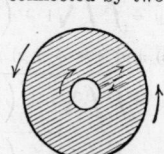

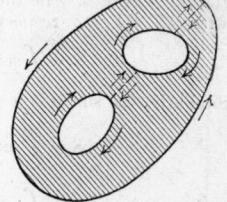

Simply Connected Region
Fig. 6

Doubly Connected Region
Fig. 7

Triply Connected Region
Fig. 8

lines or cuts as they are called. The number of cuts which is necessary to reduce the region to two simply connected regions is called the connectivity. Thus, in Fig. 7, two cuts would make two simply connected regions out of the original region.

In using line integrals about closed curves, in order to distinguish between the two directions in which a curve may be traversed, it is customary to say that the positive direction is that in which a person walking about the curve would have the region on his left. In Figs. 6, 7, 8, the arrows show the positive direction.

Area Expressed as a Line Integral. Given a region of area A bounded by a closed curve C, such that a line parallel to OX or OY meets the region in two points or not at all (points of tangency to be counted twice). Then

$$A = \tfrac{1}{2} \int (x \, dy - y \, dx) \tag{53}$$

where the line integral is to be taken around the boundary of the area. The formula is also true for areas which can be cut up into areas of the simple type shown in Fig. 9. Thus the area of a region as shown in Fig. 10 or that of a multiply connected region can be reduced to the above type.

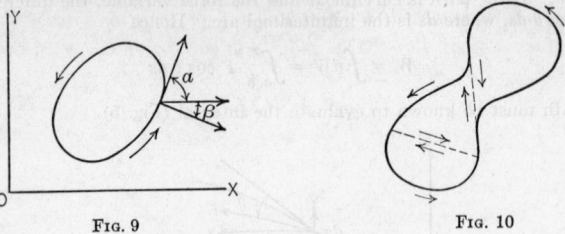

FIG. 9　　　　　　　　　　　　FIG. 10

Example. The area of the ellipse represented by the formulas

$$x = a \cos t, \quad y = b \sin t$$

has the expression $A = \frac{1}{2} \int_0^{2\pi} ab(\cos^2 t + \sin^2 t)dt = \pi ab$.

Area of Curved Surface. Given a curved surface defined by the equations

$$x = \phi(u, v), \; y = \psi(u, v), \; z = f(u, v) \tag{54}$$

The area of any portion of the surface is defined as the integral

$$S = \int \int \sqrt{EG - F^2} \, du \, dv \tag{55}$$

the integration to be extended over values of u and v corresponding to the portion of the surface considered. In the above formula

$$E = \left(\frac{\partial x}{\partial u}\right)^2 + \left(\frac{\partial y}{\partial u}\right)^2 + \left(\frac{\partial z}{\partial u}\right)^2, \; F = \frac{\partial x}{\partial u}\frac{\partial x}{\partial v} + \frac{\partial y}{\partial u}\frac{\partial y}{\partial v} + \frac{\partial z}{\partial u}\frac{\partial z}{\partial v}, \; G = \left(\frac{\partial x}{\partial v}\right)^2 + \left(\frac{\partial y}{\partial v}\right)^2 + \left(\frac{\partial z}{\partial v}\right)^2 \tag{56}$$

Example. A sphere of radius r is defined by the equations

$$x = r \cos \theta \sin \phi, \; y = r \sin \theta \sin \phi, \; z = r \cos \phi$$

in spherical coordinates. Then

$$E = r^2 \sin^2 \phi, F = 0, G = r^2 \text{ and } S = \int_0^{2\pi} \int_0^{2\pi} r^2 \sin \phi d\phi d\theta = 4\pi r^2$$

A surface $z = f(x, y)$ is the special case of (54) in which $x = u$, $y = v$, $z = f(u, v) = f(x,y)$. Let α, β, γ be the angles made by the normal to the surface at the point (x, y, z) with OX, OY, OZ, respectively. Then

$$S = \int \sec \gamma \, dx \, dy = \int \int \sqrt{1 + \left(\frac{\partial z}{\partial x}\right)^2 + \left(\frac{\partial z}{\partial y}\right)^2} \, dx \, dy \tag{57}$$

Similarly, the surfaces $y = \psi(z, x)$ and $x = \phi(y, z)$ give

$$S = \int \sec \beta \, dz \, dx = \int \int \sqrt{1 + \left(\frac{\partial y}{\partial z}\right)^2 + \left(\frac{\partial y}{\partial x}\right)^2} \, dz \, dx \tag{58}$$

and

$$S = \int \sec \alpha \, dy \, dz = \int \int \sqrt{1 + \left(\frac{\partial x}{\partial y}\right)^2 + \left(\frac{\partial x}{\partial z}\right)^2} \, dy \, dz \tag{59}$$

Example. Find the area of the surface cut from the cylinder $y^2 + z^2 = a^2$ by the cylinder $x^2 + y^2 = a^2$.

$$z = \sqrt{a^2 - y^2}, \frac{\partial z}{\partial x} = p = 0, \frac{\partial z}{\partial y} = q = -\frac{y}{\sqrt{a^2 - y^2}}$$

The element of surface $dS = \sqrt{1 + p^2 + q^2} dx \, dy = \frac{a}{\sqrt{a^2 - y^2}} \, dx \, dy$

$$S = 8 \int_0^a \int_0^{\sqrt{a^2 - y^2}} \frac{a}{\sqrt{a^2 - y^2}} \, dx \, dy = 8 \int_0^a a \, dy = 8a^2$$

where the limits are taken over one-eighth of the surface cut out.

Surface Integrals. A surface integral may be defined in a similar manner to the line integral; if a surface $z = f(x, y)$ is divided into elements of area ΔS_i and the value of the function $F(x, y, z)$ is taken at any point (ξ_i, η_i, ζ_i) of the element, and the sum $\Sigma F(\xi_i, \eta_i, \zeta_i)\Delta S_i$ is extended over all the elements, the limit of the sum of elements, as the number n of elements increases indefinitely and the elements become small in every direction, is defined as the surface integral of the function F over the surface.

This may be written

$$\lim_{n \to \infty} \sum_{i=1}^{n} F(\xi_i, \eta_i, \zeta_i) \Delta S_i = \int F dS = \iint F(x, y, z) \sqrt{1 + \left(\frac{\partial z}{\partial x}\right)^2 + \left(\frac{\partial z}{\partial y}\right)^2} \, dx \, dy \quad (60)$$

Since $dS = \sec \alpha \, dy \, dz = \sec \beta \, dz \, dx = \sec \gamma \, dx \, dy$, (60) can be written

$$\iint F(x, y, z) \sec \alpha \, dy \, dz, \iint F(x, y, z) \sec \beta \, dz \, dx, \text{ or } \iint F(x, y, z) \sec \gamma \, dx \, dy \quad (60a)$$

If we set $F(x, y, z) \sec \alpha = P(x, y, z)$, $F(x, y, z) \sec \beta = Q(x, y, z)$, $F(x, y, z) \sec \gamma = R(x, y, z)$, we have

$$\iint P(x, y, z) \, dy \, dz, \iint Q(x, y, z) dz \, dx, \text{ or } \iint R(x, y, z) \, dx \, dy \quad (60b)$$

In applications, it is common to find surface integrals occurring in the form $\iint (P \, dy \, dz + Q \, dx \, dz + R dx \, dy)$ which is equal to $\iint (P \cos \alpha + Q \cos \beta + R \cos \gamma) dS$.

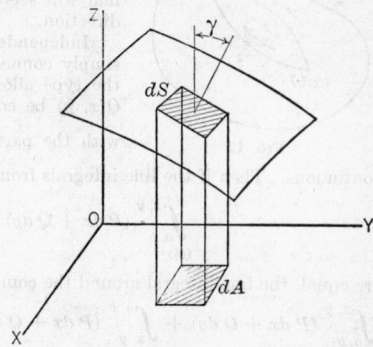

Green's Theorem. This is a method whereby a line integral around a closed curve may be stepped up into a surface integral which spans the curve, or a surface integral may be stepped up into a volume integral. Consider a simply connected region R bounded by a closed curve C of the type allowed for line integrals and let $P(x, y)$ and $Q(x, y)$ be continuous functions of x, y with continuous partial derivatives $\dfrac{\partial P}{\partial y}$ and $\dfrac{\partial Q}{\partial x}$ over this region. Then

FIG. 11

$$\iint_{(R)} \left(\frac{\partial P}{\partial y} - \frac{\partial Q}{\partial x}\right) dx \, dy = -\int_{(C)} (P dx + Q dy) \quad (61)$$

This result can be extended to regions of more complicated form. Green's theorem is sometimes found written in other forms. Referring to Fig. 9, let α be the angle made with OX by the positive direction of C, and β be the angle made with OX by the normal drawn outward. Then if F is a function of (x, y) and $\dfrac{dF}{dn}$ is its derivative in the direction of the outward normal,

$$\frac{dF}{dn} = \frac{\partial F}{\partial x}\frac{dy}{ds} - \frac{\partial F}{\partial y}\frac{dx}{ds} = \frac{\partial F}{\partial x} \cos \beta + \frac{dF}{dy} \sin \beta \quad (62)$$

where s is the arc length of the curve.

Let $P = \dfrac{\partial F}{\partial y}$, $Q = -\dfrac{\partial F}{\partial x}$, then (61) may be written as

$$\iint_{(R)} \left(\frac{\partial^2 F}{\partial x^2} + \frac{\partial^2 F}{\partial y^2}\right) dx \, dy = \int_{(C)} \left(\frac{\partial F}{\partial x} dy - \frac{\partial F}{\partial y} dx\right) = \int_{(C)} \frac{dF}{dn} ds \quad (63)$$

In space, the analogous formulas are

$$\iiint_{(V)} \left[\frac{\partial P(x, y, z)}{\partial x} + \frac{\partial Q(x, y, z)}{\partial y} + \frac{\partial R(x, y, z)}{\partial z}\right] dx \, dy \, dz$$

$$= \iint_{(S)} (P \cos \alpha + Q \cos \beta + R \cos \gamma) \, dS = \iint_{(S')} (P \, dy \, dz + Q \, dz \, dx + R \, dx \, dy) \quad (64)$$

where the triple integral is to be taken over the volume V of the region, the first double integral over the bounding surface S of the region, and the second double integral is taken over the projections of the bounding surface on the planes YOZ, XOZ, XOY, respectively. The signs of the cosines are to be determined as is customary, with the outward normal as the positive direction.

Example. Apply Green's theorem to $\iint (x \, dy \, dz + y \, dz \, dx + z \, dx \, dy)$ over the cylinder

$$x^2 + y^2 = a^2, \quad z = \pm b.$$

Since $\qquad P = x, \quad Q = y, \quad R = z; \quad \dfrac{\partial P}{\partial x} = 1, \dfrac{\partial Q}{\partial y} = 1, \dfrac{\partial R}{\partial z} = 1,$

and $\qquad \displaystyle\int_{-a}^{a} \int_{-\sqrt{a^2-x^2}}^{\sqrt{a^2-x^2}} \int_{-b}^{+b} 3 \, dx \, dy \, dz = 6\pi a^2 b.$

Stokes' Theorem. This theorem is a method of expressing the integral around a closed curve in space as an integral over a surface having that curve as a boundary; namely,

$$\int_{(C)} [P(x, y, z)\, dx + Q(x, y, z)\, dy + R(x, y, z)\, dz]$$

$$= -\int\int_{(S)} \left[\left(\frac{\partial Q}{\partial z} - \frac{\partial R}{\partial y}\right) \cos \alpha + \left(\frac{\partial R}{\partial x} - \frac{\partial P}{\partial z}\right) \cos \beta + \left(\frac{\partial P}{\partial y} - \frac{\partial Q}{\partial x}\right) \cos \gamma \right] dS \quad (65)$$

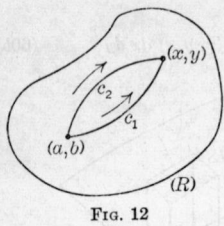

FIG. 12

where C is the space curve and S is the surface which it bounds. The signs are such that an observer standing with his feet on the surface and head in the direction of the normal will see the integration around C taken in the positive direction.

Independence of Path and Exact Differential. Given a simply connected region R, bounded by a closed curve of the type allowed for line integrals, and let $P(x, y)$ and $Q(x, y)$ be continuous functions of (x, y) over this region with the partial differentials $\frac{\partial P}{\partial y}$ and $\frac{\partial Q}{\partial x}$, single valued and continuous. Then if the line integrals from (a, b) to (x, y) along the two paths

$$\int_{a,\, b}^{x,\, y}{}_{(c_1)} (P\, dx + Q\, dy) = \int_{a,\, b}^{x,\, y}{}_{(c_2)} (P\, dx + Q\, dy) \quad (66)$$

are equal, the line integral around the combined path c

$$\int_{a,\, b}^{x,\, y}{}_{(c_1)} (P\, dx + Q\, dy) + \int_{x,\, y}^{a,\, b}{}_{(c_2)} (P\, dx + Q\, dy)$$

$$= \int_{(c)} (P\, dx + Q\, dy) = 0 \text{ vanishes (Fig. 12)}. \quad (67)$$

By making use of Green's theorem, it may be stated that, in a simply connected region in which P, Q, and their first partial derivatives are continuous, a necessary and sufficient condition that the integral $\int (P\, dx + Q\, dy)$ around any closed path should be zero and that the integral along a path connecting the two points be independent of the path is $\frac{\partial P}{\partial y} = \frac{\partial Q}{\partial x}$. In three dimensions, similar conditions for

$$\int_{a,\, b,\, c}^{x,\, y,\, z} (P\, dx + Q\, dy + R\, dz) \quad (68)$$

are that

$$\frac{\partial P}{\partial y} = \frac{\partial Q}{\partial x}, \ \frac{\partial Q}{\partial z} = \frac{\partial R}{\partial y}, \ \frac{\partial R}{\partial x} = \frac{\partial P}{\partial z}. \quad (69)$$

The condition $\frac{\partial P}{\partial y} = \frac{\partial Q}{\partial x}$ is a necessary and sufficient condition that $P\, dx + Q\, dy$ be the exact differential of some function $\phi(x, y)$ as well as that the line integral $\int_{a,\, b}^{x,\, y}{}_{(c_1)} d\phi$ be independent of the path.

Example. Consider $\int \left[\frac{2x - y}{x^2 + y^2} dx + \frac{2y + x}{x^2 + y^2} dy \right]$.

Here $\frac{\partial P}{\partial y} = \frac{\partial Q}{\partial x} = \frac{y^2 - 4xy - x^2}{(x^2 + y^2)^2}$, and the condition is met, but P and Q and their derivatives are discontinuous at the origin and hence the theorem may be applied only to simply connected regions which do not contain the origin. That is, the integrals along any two paths which do not enclose the origin are the same, but the integrals along two paths which do enclose the origin are not necessarily the same.

44. SOME APPLICATIONS OF INTEGRATION

Length of Arc of a Curve. The length s of the arc of a plane curve $y = f(x)$ from the point (a, b) to the point (c, d) is

$$s = \int_a^c \sqrt{1 + \left(\frac{dy}{dx}\right)^2}\, dx = \int_b^d \sqrt{1 + \left(\frac{dx}{dy}\right)^2}\, dy \quad (70)$$

If the equation of the curve is in polar coordinates, $r = f(\theta)$, then the length of the arc from the point (r_1, θ_1) to the point (r_2, θ_2) is

$$s = \int_{\theta_1}^{\theta_2} \sqrt{r^2 + \left(\frac{dr}{d\theta}\right)^2}\, d\theta = \int_{r_1}^{r_2} \sqrt{1 + r^2 \left(\frac{d\theta}{dr}\right)^2}\, dr \tag{71}$$

If the curve is in three dimensions, represented by the equations $y = f_1(x)$, $z = f_2(x)$, the length of arc from $x_1 = a$ to $x_2 = b$ is

$$s = \int_a^b \sqrt{1 + \left(\frac{dy}{dx}\right)^2 + \left(\frac{dz}{dx}\right)^2}\, dx \tag{72}$$

Plane Area. The area bounded by the curve $y = f(x)$, the axis OX, and the ordinates at $x = a$, $x = b$ is

$$A = \int_a^b f(x)\, dx \tag{73}$$

where y has the same sign for all values of x between a and b.

In polar coordinates, the area bounded by the curve $r = f(\theta)$, and the two radii $\theta = \alpha$, $\theta = \beta$ is

$$A = \frac{1}{2} \int_\alpha^\beta r^2\, d\theta \tag{74}$$

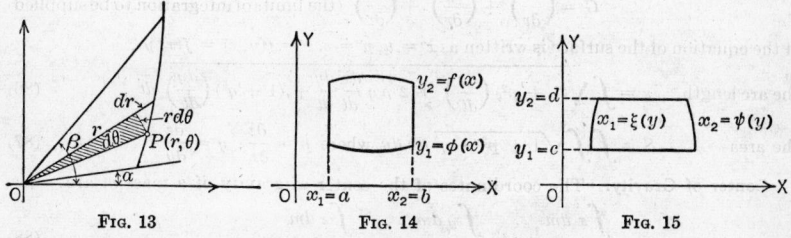

FIG. 13   FIG. 14   FIG. 15

In rectangular coordinates, if the area is bounded by the two curves $y_2 = f(x)$, $y_1 = \phi(x)$, and the lines $x_2 = b$, $x_1 = a$, then

$$A = \int_a^b dx \int_{\phi(x)}^{f(x)} dy \tag{75}$$

If the area is bounded by the two curves $x_2 = \psi(y)$, $x_1 = \xi(y)$, and the lines $y_2 = d$, $y_1 = c$, then

$$A = \int_c^d dy \int_{\xi(y)}^{\psi(y)} dx \tag{76}$$

If expressed in polar coordinates, the area by double integration is

$$A = \int_{\theta_1}^{\theta_2} d\theta \int_{r_1 = f_1(\theta)}^{r_2 = f_2(\theta)} r\, dr \quad \text{or} \quad \int_{r_1}^{r_2} r\, dr \int_{\theta_1 = \phi_1(r)}^{\theta_2 = \phi_2(r)} d\theta \tag{77}$$

Area of a Surface of Revolution. The area of the surface of a solid of revolution generated by revolving the curve $y = f(x)$ between $x = a$ and $x = b$:

About the x axis is

$$2\pi \int_a^b y \sqrt{1 + \left(\frac{dy}{dx}\right)^2}\, dx \tag{78}$$

About the y axis is

$$2\pi \int_c^d x \sqrt{1 + \left(\frac{dx}{dy}\right)^2}\, dy \tag{79}$$

where $c = f(a)$ and $d = f(b)$.

Volume. By triple integration:

Rectangular coordinates

$$V = \int \int \int dx\, dy\, dz \tag{80}$$

Spherical coordinates

$$V = \int \int \int r^2 \sin \phi\, d\theta\, d\phi\, dr \tag{81}$$

Cylindrical coordinates

$$V = \int \int \int r\, dr\, d\theta\, dz \tag{82}$$

(the limits of integration to be supplied)

Volume of a Solid of Revolution. The volume of a solid of revolution generated by revolving that portion of the curve $y = f(x)$ between $x = a$ and $x = b$:

about the x axis is

$$\pi \int_a^b y^2 \, dx \tag{83a}$$

about the y axis is

$$\pi \int_c^d x^2 \, dy \tag{83b}$$

where $c = f(a)$ and $d = f(b)$.

Surfaces. If the equation of a surface is written in the parametric form $x = f_1(u, v)$, $y = f_2(u, v)$, $z = f_3(u, v)$ where $u = u(t)$, $v = v(t)$, the length of arc of a curve on the surface is

$$s = \int \sqrt{E\left(\frac{du}{dt}\right)^2 + 2F\frac{du}{dt}\frac{dv}{dt} + G\left(\frac{dv}{dt}\right)^2} \, dt \tag{84}$$

The area S of a portion of the surface is

$$S = \iint \sqrt{EG - F^2} \, du \, dv \tag{85}$$

where

$$E = \left(\frac{\partial x}{\partial u}\right)^2 + \left(\frac{\partial y}{\partial u}\right)^2 + \left(\frac{\partial z}{\partial u}\right)^2$$

$$F = \frac{\partial x}{\partial u}\frac{\partial x}{\partial v} + \frac{\partial y}{\partial u}\frac{\partial y}{\partial v} + \frac{\partial z}{\partial u}\frac{\partial z}{\partial v}$$

$$G = \left(\frac{\partial x}{\partial v}\right)^2 + \left(\frac{\partial y}{\partial v}\right)^2 + \left(\frac{\partial z}{\partial v}\right)^2 \text{(the limits of integration to be supplied)}$$

If the equation of the surface is written as $x = u, y = v, z = f(u, v) = f(x, y)$,

the arc length

$$s = \int \sqrt{(1 + p^2)\left(\frac{dx}{dt}\right)^2 + 2\,p\,q\,\frac{dx}{dt}\frac{dy}{dt} + (1 + q^2)\left(\frac{dy}{dt}\right)^2} \, dt \tag{86}$$

the area

$$S = \iint \sqrt{1 + p^2 + q^2} \, dx \, dy \text{ where } p = \frac{\partial z}{\partial x}, \quad q = \frac{\partial z}{\partial y} \tag{87}$$

Center of Gravity. The coordinates of the center of gravity of a mass m are

$$x = \frac{\int x \, dm}{\int dm}, \quad y = \frac{\int y \, dm}{\int dm}, \quad z = \frac{\int z \, dm}{\int dm} \tag{88}$$

(the limits of integration to be supplied)

Moment. The moment of a mass m

about the plane YOZ, $\quad M_{yz} = \int x \, dm;$

about the plane XOZ, $\quad M_{xz} = \int y \, dm;$ $\qquad\qquad$ (89)

about the plane XOY, $\quad M_{xy} = \int z \, dm$

(the limits of integration to be supplied)

Moment of Inertia. The moments of inertia, I, are

for a plane curve about the X axis, $\quad I_x = \int y^2 \, ds$

for a plane curve about the Y axis, $\quad I_y = \int x^2 \, ds$ $\qquad\qquad$ (90)

for a plane curve about the origin, $\quad I_0 = \int (x^2 + y^2) \, ds$

for a plane area about the x axis, $\quad I_x = \int y^2 \, dA$

for a plane area about the y axis, $\quad I_y = \int x^2 \, dA$ $\qquad\qquad$ (91)

for a plane area about the origin, $\quad I_0 = \int (x^2 + y^2) \, dA$

for a solid of mass m about the YOZ plane, $I_{yz} = \int x^2 \, dm$

for a solid of mass m about the XOZ plane, $I_{xz} = \int y^2 \, dm$ $\qquad\qquad$ (92)

for a solid of mass m about the XOY plane, $I_{xy} = \int z^2 \, dm$

for a solid of mass m about the x axis, $\quad I_x = I_{xz} + I_{xy}$, etc.

(the limits of integration to be supplied)

Pressure. The pressure p against an area vertical to the surface of the liquid and between the depths a and b is

$$P = \int_{y=a}^{y=b} \rho y dA \tag{93}$$

where ρ is the weight of the liquid per unit volume, y is the depth beneath the surface of the liquid of a horizontal element of area, and dA is the area of a horizontal element of area expressed in terms of y.

Center of Pressure. The depth $\bar{y}$ of the center of pressure against an area vertical to the surface of the liquid and between the depths a and b is

$$\bar{y} = \frac{\int_{y=a}^{y=b} \rho y dA}{\int_{y=a}^{y=b} \rho dA} \tag{94}$$

Work. The work W done in moving a particle from $s = a$ to $s = b$ against a force whose component expressed as a function of s in the direction of motion is $F(s)$ is

$$W = \int_{s=a}^{s=b} F(s)\, ds \tag{95}$$

DIFFERENTIAL EQUATIONS
By M. J. Fish

45. FUNDAMENTAL TYPES

Definition. Any equation containing a function of a set of variables and its derivatives is a *differential equation*. If the equation has derivatives with respect to one variable only, it is called an *ordinary differential equation*, otherwise it is a *partial differential equation*.

Examples.

$$\frac{d^2 y}{dx^2} + k^2 y = 0 \tag{1}$$

$$\frac{d^2 y}{dx^2} = \sqrt{1 + y^2 + \frac{dy}{dx}} \tag{2}$$

$$y \frac{\partial^2 z}{\partial x^2} + z x \frac{\partial^2 z}{\partial x \partial y} - \frac{\partial z}{\partial y} = xyz \tag{3}$$

$$y - x \frac{dy}{dx} + 3 \frac{dx}{dy} = 0 \tag{4}$$

Equations (1), (2), (4) are ordinary differential equations, and (3) is a partial differential equation.

The Order of the differential equation is the order of the highest derivative involved. Thus in (1), (2), (3), the order is two; in (4), the order is one.

The Degree of a differential equation is the exponent of the highest order appearing in the equation after it is completely rationalized and cleared of fractions. The degree of (1), (3), (4) is one; that of (2) is two.

A Solution or Integral of a differential equation is a relation between the variables which satisfies the equation identically.

A General Solution of an ordinary differential equation of the nth order is one that contains n arbitrary constants. Thus, $y = \sin x + c$, where c is an arbitrary constant, is a general solution of the equation $\frac{dy}{dx} = \cos x$.

Particular Solution. A solution which is derivable from a general solution by assigning fixed values to the arbitrary constants is called a *particular solution*. Thus, $y_1 = \sin x$, $y_2 = \sin x + 4$ are two particular solutions of the above equation.

46. ORDINARY DIFFERENTIAL EQUATIONS OF THE FIRST ORDER

Separation of Variables. A differential equation of the first order

$$f\left(x, y, \frac{dy}{dx}\right) = 0 \tag{5}$$

can be brought into the form

$$P(x, y) \, dx + Q(x, y) \, dy = 0 \qquad (6)$$

For the special case where P is a function of x only and Q a function of y only,

$$P(x) \, dx + Q(y) \, dy = 0 \qquad (7)$$

and the variables are separated. The solution of this is

$$\int P(x) \, dx + \int Q(y) \, dy = c \qquad (8)$$

where c is an arbitrary constant.

Example. Solve, $\dfrac{dy}{dx} = -\dfrac{x}{y}$.

This can be written as $x\,dx + y\,dy = 0$ and has the solution $\int x\,dx + \int y\,dy = \dfrac{x^2}{2} + \dfrac{y^2}{2} = c$,

and if $c = \dfrac{k}{2}$, $x^2 + y^2 = k$, which represents a set of concentric circles. There are an infinite number of solutions depending on the value for k. A definite circle of the set goes through each point (a, b) such that $a^2 + b^2 = k$.

Homogeneous Equations. A function $f(x, y)$ is said to be homogeneous of the nth degree in x and y, if, when x and y are replaced by $k\,x$ and $k\,y$, respectively, the function is multiplied by k^n, regardless of the value of k, that is, $f(k\,x, k\,y) = k^n f(x, y)$. An equation

$$P(x, y) \, dx + Q\,(x, y) \, dy = 0 \qquad (9)$$

is said to be homogeneous if the functions $P(x, y)$ and $Q(x, y)$ are homogeneous in x and y. By substituting $y = vx$, a homogeneous equation can be reduced to the form in which the variables are separable.

Example. Solve $(x^2 + y^2)dx - 2xy\,dy = 0$.

This is of the form $P(x, y)dx + Q(x, y)dy = 0$, where P and Q are homogeneous functions of the second degree. Making the substitution $y = vx$, the equation becomes $(1 + v^2)dx - 2v(x\,dv + v\,dx) = 0$.

Separating variables $\qquad \dfrac{dx}{x} - \dfrac{2v}{1 - v^2} \, dv = 0$

Integrating, $\log_e x(1 - v^2) = \log_e c$, replacing $v = \dfrac{y}{x}$, $\log\left(1 - \dfrac{y^2}{x^2}\right) x = \log_e c$, and taking exponentials, $x^2 - y^2 = cx$, where c is an arbitrary constant.

The Linear Differential Equation. The differential equation

$$\frac{dy}{dx} + P(x)y = Q(x) \qquad (10)$$

in which y and $\dfrac{dy}{dx}$ appear only in the first degree, and P and Q are functions of x, is called a *linear equation of the first order.* This has the general solution

$$y = e^{-\int P(x)dx}\left[\int Q(x)e^{\int P(x)dx} \, dx + c\right] \qquad (11)$$

where c is an arbitrary constant. For the homogeneous form

$$\frac{dy}{dx} + P(x)\,y = 0 \quad \left(\text{homogeneous with respect to } y \text{ and } \frac{dy}{dx}\right) \qquad (12)$$

the general solution is $\qquad\qquad y = c_1 e^{-\int P(x)dx} \qquad (13)$
where c_1 is an arbitrary constant.

Example. An important equation in the theory of electricity is $L\dfrac{di}{dt} + Ri = E$, where i is the current, L the coefficient of self-induction (a constant), R the resistance (a constant), and E the electromotive force where E may be a constant (including zero) or a function of the time. In the latter case where $E = E(t)$

$$i = e^{-(R/L)t}\left[\int \frac{E}{L} e^{(R/L)t} \, dt + c\right]$$

If $E = E_0 \sin \omega t$, then $i = e^{-(R/L)t} E_0\left[\int e^{(R/L)t} \sin \omega t\,dt + c\right]$

If E is constant and if $i = 0$ at $t = 0$, then $i = \dfrac{E}{R}(1 - e^{-(R/L)t})$. Note that, in this case, the method of separating variables can also be used.

The Bernoulli Equation. The equation

$$\frac{dy}{dx} + P(x)y = Q(x)y^n \qquad (14)$$

in which n is a constant other than 1. By making the substitution $z = y^{1-n}$, a linear equation is obtained and the general solution is

$$y = e^{-\int P(x)dx}\left[(1-n)\int e^{(1-n)\int P(x)dx}Q(x)dx + c\right]^{\frac{1}{1-n}} \tag{15}$$

Example. Solve the equation $\dfrac{dy}{dx} - xy = xy^2$.

Substitute $z = y^{-1}$ and obtain $\dfrac{dz}{dx} + xz = -x$. The general integral is

$$z = ce^{-x^2/2} - 1 \quad \text{or} \quad y = \frac{1}{ce^{-x^2/2} - 1}.$$

Exact Differential Equation. The equation

$$P(x, y)dx + Q(x, y)dy = 0 \tag{16}$$

is called an *exact differential equation* if its left side is a complete differential

$$du = Pdx + Qdy \tag{17}$$

that is, if $\dfrac{\partial P}{\partial y} = \dfrac{\partial Q}{\partial x}$.

Then,

$$\int Pdx + \int\left[Q - \frac{\partial \int Pdx}{\partial y}\right]dy = c \tag{18}$$

is an integral or solution.

Example. Solve $(x^2 - 4xy - y^2)dx + (y^2 - 2xy - 2x^2)dy = 0$.

This is an exact equation because $\dfrac{\partial P}{\partial y} = -4x - 2y = \dfrac{\partial Q}{\partial x}$.

$$\int(x^2 - 4xy - y^2)dx = \frac{x^3}{3} - 2x^2y - xy^2$$

$$\int[(y^2 - 2xy - 2x^2) - (-2x^2 - 2xy)]dy = \frac{y^3}{3}$$

The general solution is

$$\frac{x^3}{3} - 2x^2y - xy^2 + \frac{y^3}{3} = c$$

Integrating Factor. If the differential equation $P(x, y)dx + Q(x, y)dy = 0$ is not a complete differential, look for a factor $v(x, y)$ such that $du = v(Pdx + Qdy)$ is a complete differential. Such an *integrating factor* satisfies the equation

$$Q\frac{\partial v}{\partial x} - P\frac{\partial v}{\partial y} + \left(\frac{\partial Q}{\partial x} - \frac{\partial P}{\partial y}\right)v = 0 \tag{19}$$

Example. The equation $(xy^2 - y^3)dx + (1 - xy^2)dy = 0$ when multiplied by $v = \dfrac{1}{y^2}$ becomes $(x - y)dx + \left(\dfrac{1}{y^2} - x\right)dy = 0$, of which the left side $du = (x - y)dx + \left(\dfrac{1}{y^2} - x\right)dy$ is a complete differential since $\dfrac{\partial P}{\partial y} = \dfrac{\partial Q}{\partial x}$ or $\dfrac{\partial}{\partial y}(x - y) = \dfrac{\partial}{\partial x}\left(\dfrac{1}{y^2} - x\right) = -1$. The integration gives $u = \dfrac{x^2}{2} - xy - \dfrac{1}{y}$. The general integral is $u = c$ or $x^2y - 2xy^2 - 2cy - 2 = 0$.

Riccati's Equation. $\dfrac{dy}{dx} + P(x)y^2 + Q(x)y + R(x) = 0 \tag{20}$

is called *Riccati's equation*. If a particular integral y_1 is known, place $y = y_1 + \dfrac{1}{z}$ and obtain a linear equation for z.

47. SECOND ORDER EQUATIONS

The differential equation $\quad F\left(x, y, \dfrac{dy}{dx}, \dfrac{d^2y}{dx^2}\right) = 0 \tag{21}$

is of the *second order*. If some of these variables are missing it is possible to obtain a solution easily.

Case 1. With y and $\dfrac{dy}{dx}$ missing. $\quad \dfrac{d^2y}{dx^2} = f(x) \tag{22}$

This has the solution

$$y = \int dx \int f(x)dx + cx + c_1, \text{ or } y = x \int f(x)dx - \int x f(x)dx + cx + c_1 \qquad (23)$$

where c and c_1 are arbitrary constants.

Case 2. With x and $\dfrac{dy}{dx}$ missing. $\qquad \dfrac{d^2 y}{dx^2} = f(y)$ $\qquad\qquad (24)$

Multiply both sides by $2\dfrac{dy}{dx}$ and obtain

$$x = \int \frac{dy}{\sqrt{c + 2\int f(y)dy}} + c_1 \qquad (25)$$

as a solution, where c and c_1 are arbitrary constants.

Case 3. With x and y missing. $\qquad \dfrac{d^2 y}{dx^2} = f\!\left(\dfrac{dy}{dx}\right)$ $\qquad\qquad (26)$

Place $\qquad\qquad \dfrac{dy}{dx} = p, \quad \dfrac{d^2 y}{dx^2} = \dfrac{dp}{dx}.$ $\qquad\qquad (27)$

Then $\qquad x = \int \dfrac{dp}{f(p)} + c \text{ and } y = \int \dfrac{p\,dp}{f(p)} + c_1$ $\qquad (28)$

where p is obtained by elimination.

Example. Consider the differential equation of the catenary $a\dfrac{d^2 y}{dx^2} = \sqrt{1 + \left(\dfrac{dy}{dx}\right)^2}$.

Let $p = \dfrac{dy}{dx}$, then $a\dfrac{dp}{dx} = \sqrt{1 + p^2}$. By separating variables $\dfrac{dp}{\sqrt{1 + p^2}} = \dfrac{dx}{a}$ which has the

solution $\sinh^{-1} p = \dfrac{x + c}{a}$, or $p = \dfrac{dy}{dx} = \sinh \dfrac{x + c}{a}$. Integrating this latter, $y = a \cosh \dfrac{x + c}{a} + c_1$.

Case 4. With y missing. $\qquad \dfrac{d^2 y}{dx^2} = f\!\left(\dfrac{dy}{dx}, x\right)$ $\qquad\qquad (29)$

Place $\dfrac{dy}{dx} = p$ and obtain the differential equation of the first order $\dfrac{dp}{dx} = f(p, x)$ which may possibly be solved for p. If so, then

$$y = \int p(x)\,dx + c \qquad (30)$$

Case 5. With x missing. $\qquad \dfrac{d^2 y}{dx^2} = f\!\left(\dfrac{dy}{dx}, y\right)$ $\qquad\qquad (31)$

Place $\dfrac{dy}{dx} = p$ and obtain the first order equation $p\dfrac{dp}{dy} = f(p, y)$ which may possibly be solved for p. If so, then

$$x = \int \frac{dy}{p(y)} + c \qquad (32)$$

48. LINEAR DIFFERENTIAL EQUATIONS

(1) General Theorem. The differential equation

$$\frac{d^n y}{dx^n} + P_1(x)\frac{d^{n-1} y}{dx^{n-1}} + \ldots + P_{n-1}(x)\frac{dy}{dx} + P_n(x)y = F(x) \qquad (33)$$

is called the general nth order linear differential equation. If $F(x) = 0$, the equation is called *homogeneous*; otherwise it is called *complete*. If $\phi(x)$ is a solution of the complete equation and $y_1, y_2, \ldots, y_n$ are linearly independent solutions of the accompanying homogeneous equation (that is, there is no relation of the form $a_1 y_1 + a_2 y_2 + \ldots + a_n y_n = 0$ with $a_1, a_2, \ldots, a_n$ not all zero), then the general solution of (33) is

$$y = c_1 y_1 + c_2 y_2 + \ldots + c_n y_n + \phi(x) \qquad (34)$$

The part $\phi(x)$ is called the *particular integral*, and the part $c_1 y_1 + \ldots + c_n y_n$ is called *the complementary function.*

(2) Homogeneous Differential Equation with Constant Coefficients.

$$\frac{d^n y}{dx^n} + a_1 \frac{d^{n-1} y}{dx^{n-1}} + \ldots + a_{n-1} \frac{dy}{dx} + a_n y = 0 \qquad (35)$$

is a linear homogeneous equation of the nth order with constant coefficients.

$$y_k = c e^{r_k x} \qquad (36)$$

is a solution of this equation, if r_k is a root of the following algebraic equation of the nth degree:

$$r^n + a_1 r^{n-1} + \ldots + a_{n-1} r + a_n = 0 \qquad (37)$$

If all the n roots $r_1, r_2, \ldots, r_n$ of (37) are different from each other, then

$$y = c_1 e^{r_1 x} + c_2 e^{r_2 x} + \ldots + c_n e^{r_n x} \qquad (38)$$

is a general integral of (35). If some of the roots are equal, for instance $r_1 = r_2 = \ldots = r_k$ while $r_{k+1}, \ldots, r_n$ are different from each other and from r_1, then

$$y = (c_1 + c_2 x + \ldots + c_k x^{k-1}) e^{r_1 x} + c_{k+1} e^{r_{k+1} x} + \ldots + c_n e^{r_n x} \qquad (39)$$

is the *general integral*. If $r_1 = p + iq$, $r_2 = p - iq$ are *conjugate imaginary roots* of (37), $[i = \sqrt{-1}]$, then

$$c_1 e^{r_1 x} + c_2 e^{r_2 x} = C_1 e^{px} \cos qx + C_2 e^{px} \sin qx \qquad (40)$$

Example. $\dfrac{d^2 y}{dx^2} + 13 \dfrac{dy}{dx} + 40y = 0$ has the solution $y = c_1 e^{-5x} + c_2 e^{-8x}$.

$\dfrac{d^2 y}{dx^2} + 6 \dfrac{dy}{dx} + 34 y = 0$ has the solution $y = (c_1 \cos 5x + c_2 \sin 5x) e^{-3x}$.

(3) The Complete Differential Equation with Constant Coefficients.

$$\frac{d^n y}{dx^n} + a_1 \frac{d^{n-1} y}{dx^{n-1}} + \ldots + a_{n-1} \frac{dy}{dx} + a_n y = F(x) \qquad (41)$$

The complementary function is found as above in paragraph (2). To find the particular integral, proceed as follows. Denote

$$\frac{dy}{dx} \text{ by } D, \frac{d^2 y}{dx^2} \text{ by } D^2 \ldots \frac{d^n y}{dx^n} \text{ by } D^n \text{ (Called the method of operators).} \qquad (42)$$

Write (41) as

$$(D^n + a_1 D^{n-1} + \ldots a_{n-1} D + a_n) y = F(x) \qquad (43)$$

Denote (43) by $P(D)y = F(x)$ where $P(D)$ is a polynomial in D. Then there are the following rules, in which A_i, A, B are undetermined coefficients, to be determined by substituting y_p in (41) and equating coefficients of like terms:

(a) If $F(x) = x^n + a_1 x^{n-1} + \ldots + a_{n-1} x + a_n$, assume the particular integral $y_p = x^n + A_1 x^{n-1} + \ldots + A_{n-1} x + A_n$.
If D^m is a factor of $P(D)$, assume $y_p = (x^n + A_1 x^{n-1} + \ldots + A_{n-1} x + A_n) x^m$.
(b) If $F(x) = b \sin ax$ or $b \cos ax$, assume $y_p = A \sin ax + B \cos ax$.
If $(D^2 + a^2)^m$ is a factor of $P(D)$, assume $y_p = (A \sin ax + B \cos ax) x^m$.
(c) If $F(x) = c e^{ax}$, assume $y_p = A e^{ax}$. If $(D - a)^m$ is a factor of $P(D)$, assume $y_p = x^m A e^{ax}$.
(d) If $F(x) = g(x) e^{ax}$, place $y_p = e^{ax} w$ in (41), divide out e^{ax}, and solve the equation for w as a function of x.
(e) If $F(x)$ is the sum of a number of functions, take y_p as the sum of the particular integrals corresponding to each of the functions.

Example. $\dfrac{d^2 y}{dx^2} + 4y = x^2 + \cos x$ can be written as $(D^2 + 4)y = x^2 + \cos x$.

Consider $(D^2 + 4)y = 0$ or $(D + i2)(D - i2)y = 0 [i = \sqrt{-1}]$, and by the method of paragraph (2), the complementary function is $y = c_1 \cos 2x + c_2 \sin 2x$.
For a particular integral take $y_p = ax^2 + bx + c + f \sin x + g \cos x$ [by (a), (b), (e)].
Then $\dfrac{d^2 y_p}{dx^2} = 2a - f \sin x - g \cos x$, and substituting in the original equation

$\dfrac{d^2 y_p}{dx^2} + 4y_p = 2a - f \sin x - g \cos x + 4ax^2 + 4bx + 4c + 4f \sin x + 4g \cos x = x^2 + \cos x$.

Equating coefficients, $a = 1/4$, $b = 0$, $c = -1/8$, $f = 0$, $g = 1/3$ and the general solution is $y = c_1 \cos 2x + c_2 \sin 2x + \dfrac{x^2}{4} - 1/8 + 1/3 \cos x$.

(4) Euler's Homogeneous Equation.

$$x^n \frac{d^n y}{dx^n} + ax^{n-1} \frac{d^{n-1} y}{dx^{n-1}} + \ldots + a_{n-1} x \frac{dy}{dx} + a_n y = 0 \qquad (44)$$

is called *Euler's homogeneous equation*. Place $x = e^t$, and since

$$\frac{dt}{dx} = \frac{1}{x}, \frac{dy}{dx} = \frac{dy}{dt} \frac{dt}{dx} = \frac{1}{x} \frac{dy}{dt}, \frac{d^2 y}{dt^2} = \frac{1}{x^2} \left(\frac{d^2 y}{dt^2} - \frac{dy}{dt} \right), \qquad (45)$$

(44) is then replaced by a linear homogeneous differential equation with constant coefficients.

Depression of Order. If a particular integral of a linear differential equation is known, the order of the equation can be lowered. Consider the homogeneous equation

$$\frac{d^n y}{dx^n} + P_1(x) \frac{d^{n-1} y}{dx^{n-1}} + \ldots + P_{n-1}(x) \frac{dy}{dx} + P_n(x) = 0 \qquad (46)$$

If y_1 is a particular integral of (46), substitute $y = y_1 z$. The coefficient of z will be found to vanish, and then by placing $\frac{dz}{dx} = u$, the equation is reduced to the $(n-1)$st order.

Example. Given $\frac{d^2 y}{dx^2} + p(x) \frac{dy}{dx} + q(x)y = 0$ and y_1, a particular integral of this equation.

Let $y = y_1 z$, then $\frac{dy}{dx} = y_1 \frac{dz}{dx} + z \frac{dy_1}{dx}, \frac{d^2 y}{dx^2} = y_1 \frac{d^2 z}{dx^2} + 2 \frac{dy_1}{dx} \frac{dz}{dx} + z \frac{d^2 y_1}{dx^2}$.

Substituting in the original equation

$$y_1 \frac{d^2 z}{dx^2} + 2 \frac{dy_1}{dx} \frac{dz}{dx} + z \frac{d^2 y_1}{dx^2} + p \left[y_1 \frac{dz}{dx} + z \frac{dy_1}{dx} \right] + q y_1 z = 0$$

and since the coefficient of z is zero, this reduces to

$$y_1 \frac{d^2 z}{dx^2} + \left(2 \frac{dy_1}{dx} + p y_1 \right) \frac{dz}{dx} = 0. \quad \text{Writing } \frac{dz}{dx} = u, \frac{du}{u} + \left(2 \frac{dy_1}{dx} + p y_1 \right) \frac{dx}{y_1} = 0$$

By integrating, $\qquad \log_e u + \int p \, dx + \log_e y_1^2 = \log_e c$ or $u = \frac{c}{y_1^2} e^{-\int p \, dx}$.

Another integration gives z and then y; the equation admits the solution

$$y = y_1 \int \frac{c}{y_1^2} e^{-\int p \, dx} dx + c_1.$$

Simultaneous Linear Differential Equations with Constant Coefficients. If there are two (or in general n) linear equations with constant coefficients in two (or in general n) dependent variables and one independent variable t, the symbolic or algebraic method of solution may be used. Let the equations be

$$(D^n + a_1 D^{n-1} + \ldots + a_n)x + (D^m + b_1 D^{m-1} + \ldots + b_m)y = R(t)$$
$$(D^p + c_1 D^{p-1} + \ldots + c_p)x + (D^q + d_1 D^{q-1} + \ldots + d_q)y = S(t) \qquad (47)$$

where D denotes $\frac{d}{dt}$. The equations may be written as

$$P_1(D)x + Q_1(D)y = R, \, P_2(D)x + Q_2(D)y = S \qquad (48)$$

Considering these as algebraic equations, eliminate either x or y by the method of determinants and solve the equation obtained by known methods.

Example. Solve the simultaneous equations.

$$(1) \, \frac{dx}{dt} + \frac{dy}{dt} + 2x + y = 0, \quad (2) \, \frac{dy}{dt} + 5x + 3y = 0$$

By using the symbol D these equations can be written

$$(D + 2)x + (D + 1)y = 0, \quad 5x + (D + 3)y = 0$$

Eliminating x, $(D^2 + 1)y = 0$, and from paragraph (2) this has the solution $y = c_1 \cos t + c_2 \sin t$. Substituting this in (2), $x = -\frac{3c_1 + c_2}{5} \cos t + \frac{c_1 - 3c_2}{5} \sin t$.

49. PARTIAL DIFFERENTIAL EQUATIONS

First Order

Definition. If $x_1, x_2, \ldots, x_n$ are n independent variables, $z = z(x_1, x_2, \ldots, x_n)$ the dependent variable, and if

$$\frac{\partial z}{\partial x_1} = p_1, \ldots, \frac{\partial z}{\partial x_n} = p_n \qquad (49)$$

then $\qquad F(x_1, x_2, \ldots, x_n, z, p_1, p_2, \ldots, p_n) = 0 \qquad (50)$

is a partial differential equation of the first order. An equation

$$f(x_1, x_2, \ldots, x_n, z, c_1, \ldots, c_n) = 0 \qquad (51)$$

with n arbitrary constants is called a complete solution of (50) if the elimination of the constants by partial differentiation gives the differential equation (51). Thus, given the partial differential equation

$$F = z^2 \left[\left(\frac{\partial z}{\partial x} \right)^2 + \left(\frac{\partial z}{\partial y} \right)^2 + 1 \right] - c^2 = 0 \tag{52}$$

Let

$$f = (x - h)^2 + (y - k)^2 + z^2 - c^2 = 0 \tag{53}$$

be a solution, since by differentiating it with respect to x and y

$$(x - h) + z \frac{\partial z}{\partial x} = 0 \tag{54}$$

$$(y - k) + z \frac{\partial z}{\partial y} = 0 \tag{55}$$

Substituting the values of $x - h$, $y - k$ from the last two equations into f, expression F is obtained.

A singular solution is given through the elimination of $c_1, \ldots, c_n$ from the equations $f = 0$, $\frac{\partial f}{\partial c_1} = 0, \ldots, \frac{\partial f}{\partial c_n} = 0$. This differs from the particular integral in that it is not contained in the complete integral, that is, is not obtained from the complete integral by giving particular values to the constants.

Suppose that the equation $F\left(x, y, z, \frac{\partial z}{\partial x}, \frac{\partial z}{\partial y} \right) = 0$ has the complete solution $f(x, y, z, a, b) = 0$ where one of the constants $b = \phi(a)$; then $f[x, y, z, a, \phi(a)] = 0$. The general integral is found by elimination of a between $f[x, y, z, a, \phi(a)] = 0$ and $\frac{d\phi}{da} = 0$. In every equation, the general integral and the singular integral, as well as the complete integral are to be found. The complete integral is to be found first, and from it the other two are to be derived.

Linear Differential Equations.

$$P(x, y, z)p + Q(x, y, z)q = R(x, y, z) \tag{56}$$

is a partial linear differential equation. From the simultaneous ordinary equations $\frac{dx}{P} = \frac{dy}{Q} = \frac{dz}{R}$, the two independent functional solutions $u(x, y, z) = c_1$, $v(x, y, z) = c_2$ are obtained. Then $\Phi(u, v) = 0$, where Φ is an arbitrary function, is the general solution of $Pp + Qq = R$.

Examples. Given $xp + yq = q$. Consider $\frac{dx}{x} = \frac{dy}{y} = \frac{dz}{z}$, which has the solution $\log_e c_1 x = \log_e c_2 y = \log_e c_3 z$ or $u = \frac{y}{x} = c_4$, $v = \frac{z}{x} = c_5$. Then $\Phi(u, v) = \Phi\left(\frac{y}{x}, \frac{z}{x} \right) = 0$.

Given $(ny - mz)p + (lz - nx)q = mx - ly$.

Form $\frac{dx}{ny - mz} = \frac{dy}{lz - nx} = \frac{dz}{mx - ly}$. By using the multipliers l, m, n, the equal fraction $\frac{ldx + mdy + ndz}{0}$ is obtained. Therefore $ldx + mdy + ndz = 0$, which has the solution $lx + my + nz = c_1$. In a similar manner $xdx + ydy + zdz = 0$, or $x^2 + y^2 + z^2 = c_2$. Hence the solution $\Phi(x^2 + y^2 + z^2, lx + my + nz) = 0$.

General Method of Solution. Given $F(x, y, z, p, q) = 0$, the partial differential equation to be solved. Since z depends on x and y, it follows that $dz = pdx + qdy$. Now if another relation can be found between x, y, z, p, q such as $f(x, y, z, p, q) = 0$, then p and q can be eliminated. The integral of the ordinary differential equation thus formed involving x, y, z will satisfy the given equation, $F(x, y, z, p, q) = 0$. The unknown function f must satisfy the following linear partial differential equation:

$$\frac{\partial F}{\partial p} \frac{\partial f}{\partial x} + \frac{\partial F}{\partial q} \frac{\partial f}{\partial y} + \left(p \frac{\partial F}{\partial p} + q \frac{\partial F}{\partial q} \right) \frac{\partial f}{\partial z} - \left(\frac{\partial F}{\partial x} + p \frac{\partial F}{\partial z} \right) \frac{\partial f}{\partial p} - \left(\frac{\partial F}{\partial y} + q \frac{\partial F}{\partial z} \right) \frac{\partial f}{\partial q} = 0 \tag{57}$$

which is satisfied by any of the solutions of the system

$$\frac{dx}{\frac{\partial F}{\partial p}} = \frac{dy}{\frac{\partial F}{\partial q}} = \frac{dz}{p\frac{\partial F}{\partial p} + q\frac{\partial F}{\partial q}} = \frac{-dp}{\frac{\partial F}{\partial x} + \frac{p\partial F}{\partial z}} = \frac{-dq}{\frac{\partial F}{\partial y} + \frac{q\partial F}{\partial z}} \tag{58}$$

Examples. Solve $p(q^2 + 1) + (b - z)q = 0$. Here the equations above reduce to

$$\frac{dp}{pq} = \frac{dq}{q^2} = \frac{dz}{3pq^2 + p + (b - z)q} = \frac{dx}{q^2 + 1} = \frac{dy}{-z + b + 2pq}.$$

The third fraction, by virtue of the given equation, reduces to $\dfrac{dz}{2pq^2}$. From the first two fractions, by integration, $q = ap$, where a is an arbitrary constant. This and the original equation determine the values of p and q, namely, $p = \dfrac{\sqrt{a(z-b)-1}}{a}$, $q = \sqrt{a(z-b)-1}$. Substitution of these values in $dz = pdx + qdy$ gives $dz = \left(\dfrac{dx}{a} + dy\right)\sqrt{a(z-b)-1}$. In this equation the variables are separable; this on integration gives $2\sqrt{a(z-b)-1} = x + ay + b$. There is no singular solution. In order to find the general integral, substitute for b some function of a and eliminate a from the complete solution. In the above work, had another pair of ratios been chosen, say $\dfrac{dq}{q^2} = \dfrac{dx}{q^2+1}$, another complete integral would have been obtained, namely,

$$(z-b)\left\{\frac{x+a}{2} - \sqrt{\left(\frac{x+a}{2}\right)^2 + 1}\right\} + y + B = 0.$$

Second Order

Definitions. A linear partial differential equation of the second order with two independent variables is of the form

$$L = Ar + 2Bs + Ct + Dp + Eq + Fz = f(x,y) \tag{59}$$

where $r = \dfrac{\partial^2 z}{\partial x^2}$, $s = \dfrac{\partial^2 z}{\partial x \partial y}$, $t = \dfrac{\partial^2 z}{\partial y^2}$, $p = \dfrac{\partial z}{\partial x}$, $q = \dfrac{\partial z}{\partial y}$

The coefficients $A, \ldots, F$ are real continuous functions of the real variables x and y. Let $\xi = \xi(x,y)$, $\eta = \eta(x,y)$ be two solutions of the following homogeneous partial differential equation of the first order:

$$Ap^2 + 2Bpq + Cq^2 = 0 \tag{60}$$

If $B^2 - AC = 0$, the homogeneous form of (59), $L = 0$, is called the *parabolic* type, and has the normal form

$$\frac{\partial^2 z}{\partial \xi^2} + a\frac{\partial z}{\partial \xi} + b\frac{\partial z}{\partial \eta} + cz = 0 \tag{61}$$

where a, b, c are functions of ξ and η. A familiar example is the equation of heat flow, $\dfrac{\partial u}{\partial t} = a^2 \dfrac{\partial^2 u}{\partial t^2}$ where $u = u(x,t)$ is the temperature, t is the time, a^2 is constant. If $B^2 - AC > 0$ in (60), the homogeneous form of (59) is the *hyperbolic* type which has the normal form

$$\frac{\partial^2 z}{\partial \xi \partial \eta} + a\frac{\partial z}{\partial \xi} + b\frac{\partial z}{\partial \eta} + cz = 0. \tag{62}$$

A familiar example is that of the vibrating string $\dfrac{\partial^2 z}{\partial t^2} = a^2 \dfrac{\partial^2 z}{\partial x^2}$, where z is the transverse displacement of a point on the string, with abscissa x at time t and a^2 is constant. If $B^2 - AC < 0$, the equation is of the *elliptic* type which has the normal form

$$\frac{\partial^2 z}{\partial \xi^2} + \frac{\partial^2 z}{\partial z^2} + a\frac{\partial z}{\partial \xi} + b\frac{\partial z}{\partial \eta} + cz = 0. \tag{63}$$

A familiar example is Laplace's equation $\dfrac{\partial^2 z}{\partial \xi^2} + \dfrac{\partial^2 z}{\partial \eta^2} = 0$, usually written $\nabla^2 z = 0$. The two solutions of (60) are real in the hyperbolic case and conjugate imaginary in the elliptic case. That is, in the latter case, $\xi = \frac{1}{2}(\alpha + i\beta)$, $\eta = \frac{1}{2}(\alpha - i\beta)$, where α and β are real, and $\dfrac{\partial^2 z}{\partial \xi \partial \eta} = \dfrac{1}{4}\left(\dfrac{\partial^2 z}{\partial \alpha^2} + \dfrac{\partial^2 z}{\partial \beta^2}\right)$.

As in ordinary linear equations, the complete solution consists of the complementary function and the particular integral. Also if $z = z_1$, $z = z_2, \ldots, z = z_n$ are solutions of the homogeneous equation (59), $L = 0$, then $z = c_1 z_1 + c_2 z_2 + \ldots + c_n z_n$ is again a solution.

Equations Linear in the Second Derivatives. The general type of second order equation linear in the second derivatives may be written in the form

$$Ar + Bs + Ct = V \tag{64}$$

where A, B, C, V are functions of x, y, z, p, q. From the equations

$$A\,dy^2 - B\,dx\,dy + C\,dx^2 = 0 \tag{65}$$

$$A\,dp\,dy + C\,dq\,dx - V\,dx\,dy = 0 \tag{66}$$

$$p\,dx + q\,dy = dz \tag{67}$$

it may be possible to derive either one or two relations between x, y, z, p, q called intermediary integrals and from these to deduce the general solution of (64). To obtain an intermediary integral, resolve (65), supposing the left member not a perfect square, into the two equations $dy - n_1\,dx = 0$, $dy - n_2\,dx = 0$. From the first of these and from (66), combined, if necessary, with (67), obtain the two integrals $u_1(x, y, z, p, q) = a$, $v_1(x, y, z, p, q) = b$; then $u_1 = f_1(v_1)$, where f_1 is an arbitrary function, is now an intermediary integral. In the same way, from $dy - n_2\,dx = 0$, obtain another pair of integrals $u_2 = a_1$, $v_2 = b_1$; then $u_2 = f_2(v_2)$ is an intermediary integral. For the final integral, if $n_1 = n_2$, the intermediary integral may be integrated. If $n_1 \neq n_2$, solve the two intermediary integrals for p and q, substitute in $p\,dx + q\,dy = dz$, and integrate for the complete solution.

Example. Solve
$$r^2 - a^2 t = 0 \qquad (64a)$$
The auxiliary equations are
$$dy - a\,dx = 0, \quad dy + a\,dx = 0, \text{ and } dp\,dy - a^2\,dx\,dq = 0 \qquad (66a)$$
Hence $y + ax = c_1$, $y - ax = c_2$. Combining $y + ax = c_1$ with (66a), $dp + a\,dq = 0$ is obtained, whereupon $p + aq = c_3 = f_1(y + ax)$. Combining $y - ax = c_1$ with (66a), $dp - a\,dq = 0$ is obtained, whereupon $p - aq = c_4 = f_2(y - ax)$.

Solving for p and q, $p = 1/2\,[f_1(y + ax) + f_2(y - ax)]$, $q = \dfrac{1}{2a}\,[f_1(y + ax) - f_2(y - ax)]$. Substituting these in $p\,dx + q\,dy = dz$, $dz = \dfrac{1}{2a}\,[f_1(y + a)(dy + a\,dx) - f_2(y - ax)(dy - a\,dx)]$, which is an exact differential. Integration gives $z = \phi(y + ax) + \psi(y - ax)$. The equation $r^2 - a^2 t = 0$ is called the equation of the vibrating string and may be solved by the method of homogeneous equation with constant coefficients.

The Homogeneous Equation with Constant Coefficients. An equation such as
$$\frac{\partial^2 z}{\partial x^2} + A_1\,\frac{\partial^2 z}{\partial x \partial y} + A_2\,\frac{\partial^2 z}{\partial y^2} = 0 \qquad (68)$$
where A_1 and A_2 are constants, is an equation of this type. This equation is equivalent to
$$\left(\frac{\partial}{\partial x} - m_1\,\frac{\partial}{\partial y}\right)\left(\frac{\partial}{\partial x} - m_2\,\frac{\partial}{\partial y}\right)z = 0 \qquad (69)$$
where m_1 and m_2 are roots of the auxiliary equation $X^2 + A_1 X + A_2 = 0$. The general solution of (69) is
$$z = f_1(y + m_1 x) + f_2(y + m_2 x) \qquad (70)$$

Example. Solve: $8\,\dfrac{\partial^2 z}{\partial x^2} + 2\,\dfrac{\partial^2 z}{\partial x \partial y} - 15\,\dfrac{\partial^2 z}{\partial y^2} = 0$.

The auxiliary equation is $8\,X^2 + 2\,X - 15 = (2\,X + 3)(4\,X - 5) = 0$. Hence $m_1 = -3/2$, $m_2 = 5/4$. The general solution is $z = f_1(2y - 3x) + f_2(4y + 5x)$.

If the auxiliary equation has multiple factors, the general solution is $z = f_1(y + m_1 x) + x f_2(y + m_1 x)$.

Example. Solve: $\dfrac{\partial^2 z}{\partial x^2} + 6\,\dfrac{\partial^2 z}{\partial x \partial y} + 9\,\dfrac{\partial^2 z}{\partial y^2} = 0$.

The auxiliary equation is $X^2 + 6\,X + 9 = (X + 3)(X + 3) = 0$. The general solution is $z = f_1(y - 3x) + x f_2(y - 3x)$.

If the coefficients in equation (68) are real, the imaginary roots of the auxiliary equation occur in conjugate pairs. Then the general solution will have the form
$$z = f(y + \alpha x + i\beta x) + g(y + \alpha x - i\beta x)[i = \sqrt{-1}].$$

Example. Solve: $\dfrac{\partial^2 z}{\partial x^2} - 2\,\dfrac{\partial^2 z}{\partial x \partial y} + 2\,\dfrac{\partial^2 z}{\partial y^2} = 0$.

The auxiliary equation is $X^2 - 2X + 2 = 0$ and $m = 1 \pm i$. The general solution is $z = f(y + x + ix) + g(y + x - ix)$, which can be written as $z = f_1(y + x + ix) + f_1(y + x - ix) + i[g_1(y + x + ix) - g_1(y + x - ix)]$, where f_1 and g_1 are any real functions. If, in particular, $f_1 = \cos u$ and $g_1 = e^u$, it can be shown that $z = 2\cos(x + y)\cosh x - 2e^{x+y}\sin x$.

Method of Particular Solutions. The solution of a partial differential equation which arises from a physical problem cannot contain any constants or functions which may be given arbitrary values. Sometimes, it is possible to find particular solutions of the partial differential equation which satisfy the boundary conditions, and by combining these particular solutions to give the solution of the physical problem. In this connection, it is sometimes possible to separate the variables. To illustrate this method, consider Laplace's equation:
$$\nabla^2 u = \frac{\partial^2 u}{\partial x^2} + \frac{\partial^2 u}{\partial y^2} = 0 \qquad (71)$$
Let
$$u = X(x) \cdot Y(y) \qquad (72)$$

where X is a function of x only, and Y a function of y only. By substitution and dividing by $X \cdot Y$, (71) becomes

$$\frac{1}{X}\frac{d^2 X}{dx^2} = -\frac{1}{Y}\frac{d^2 Y}{dy^2} \qquad (73)$$

Notice that the left side does not contain y, the right side does not contain x. Since the two sides are equal, they must equal a constant, denoted by $-k^2$. Thus

$$\frac{1}{X}\frac{d^2 X}{dx^2} = -k^2, \quad \frac{1}{Y}\frac{d^2 Y}{dy^2} = k^2 \qquad (73a)$$

the solutions of which are respectively

$$X = c_1 \cos k\,x + c_2 \sin kx, \quad Y = c_3\, e^{ky} + c_4\, e^{-ky} \qquad (74)$$

(see Ordinary Homogeneous Differential Equation with Constant Coefficients, second order). Hence, from (72),

$$\begin{aligned}
u &= (c_1 \cos kx + c_2 \sin kx)(c_3\, e^{ky} + c_4\, e^{-ky}) \\
&= e^{ky}(A \cos kx + B \sin kx) + e^{-ky}(D \cos kx + E \sin kx)
\end{aligned} \qquad (75)$$

where A, B, D, E are arbitrary constants. Since (71) is linear, the sum of any number of solutions is again a solution. An infinite number of solutions may be taken provided the series converges in such a way that it may be differentiated term by term. Then, if this condition is fulfilled,

$$u = \sum_{n=0}^{\infty} [e^{ky}(A_n \cos kx + B_n \sin kx) + e^{-ky}(D_n \cos kx + E_n \sin kx)] \qquad (76)$$

is a solution of (71). By development in a Fourier series, the constants can be determined so as to satisfy the given boundary conditions.

The equation of Laplace plays an important rôle in physics. Functions which satisfy it are called *harmonic*. (71) in polar coordinates becomes,

$$\frac{\partial^2 u}{\partial r^2} + \frac{1}{r^2}\frac{\partial^2 u}{\partial \theta^2} + \frac{1}{r}\frac{\partial u}{\partial r} = 0 \qquad (77)$$

In three variables, Laplace's equation in cartesian coordinates is

$$\frac{\partial^2 u}{\partial x^2} + \frac{\partial^2 u}{\partial y^2} + \frac{\partial^2 u}{\partial z^2} = 0 \qquad (78)$$

In cylindrical coordinates,

$$\frac{\partial^2 u}{\partial r^2} + \frac{1}{r}\frac{\partial u}{\partial r} + \frac{1}{r^2}\frac{\partial^2 u}{\partial \theta^2} + \frac{\partial^2 u}{\partial z^2} = 0 \qquad (79)$$

In spherical coordinates,

$$r^2\frac{\partial^2 u}{\partial r^2} + 2r\frac{\partial u}{\partial r} + \frac{\partial^2 u}{\partial \phi^2} + \cot \phi\,\frac{\partial u}{\partial \phi} + \csc^2 \phi\,\frac{\partial^2 u}{\partial \theta^2} = 0 \qquad (80)$$

SOLUTION OF LINEAR CONSTANT-COEFFICIENT INTEGRO-DIFFERENTIAL EQUATIONS BY THE LAPLACIAN TRANSFORMATION (HEAVISIDE OPERATIONAL CALCULUS)

By J. L. Barnes

50. METHOD OF TRANSFORMATION

The method for solving equations mentioned in the heading of this section is essentially the same as the Heaviside operational calculus, and is based on the Laplacian (and in special cases, Fourier) transformation.

The chief advantage of this method over others is that it provides a simpler way for solving linear constant-coefficient differential equations as well as integral and integro-differential equations of a particular (convolution) type. One of the reasons for this simplicity is that the method is straightforward.

The following treatment will be restricted to a statement of the more important properties and steps of procedure with an illustration of their use. For the purpose of simplifying this presentation the conditions under which the steps may be validly applied will be omitted. Hence the correctness of a final result obtained by the procedure should be checked in each case by showing that it satisfies the given equation and conditions.

1. Direct Laplacian transformation. Let t denote a real variable, s a complex variable (see p. 2–112), $f(t)$ a real function of t which equals zero for $t < 0$, $F(s)$ a function of s, and e the base of the natural logarithms. If

$$\int_0^\infty e^{-st} f(t) \, dt = F(s) \tag{1}$$

then $F(s)$ is called the *direct Laplacian transform* of $f(t)$, and in simpler notation

$$\mathcal{L}[f(t)] = F(s) \tag{2}$$

2. Inverse Laplacian transformation. Under certain conditions the direct transformation can be inverted, giving

$$\frac{1}{2\pi i} \int_{c-i\infty}^{c+i\infty} e^{ts} F(s) \, ds = f(t) \tag{3}$$

in which c is a real constant chosen so that the path of integration lies to the right of all the singularities of $F(s)$. If this relation holds then $f(t)$ is called the *inverse Laplacian transform* of $F(s)$. In simpler notation the transformation is written

$$\mathcal{L}^{-1}[F(s)] = f(t) \tag{4}$$

3. Transformation of nth derivative. If $\mathcal{L}[f(t)] = F(s)$, then

$$\mathcal{L}\left[\frac{d^n f(t)}{d t^n}\right] = s^n F(s) - \sum_{k=0}^{n-1} f^{(k)}(0) \cdot s^{n-1-k} \tag{5}$$

where $f^{(2)}(0)$ means $\dfrac{d^2 f(t)}{d t^2}$ evaluated at $t = 0$, and $f^{(0)}(0)$ means $f(0)$, and $n = 1, 2, 3, \ldots$.

4. Transformation of nth integral. If $\mathcal{L}[f(t)] = F(s)$, then

$$\mathcal{L}\left[\int \int \cdots \int f(t) \, dt\right] = s^{-n} F(s) + \sum_{k=-1}^{-n} f^{(k)}(0) \cdot s^{-n-1-k} \tag{6}$$

where $f^{(-2)}(0)$ means $\int \int f(t) \, dt$ evaluated at $t = 0$, and $n = 1, 2, 3, \ldots$.

5. Inverse transformation of product. If

$$\mathcal{L}^{-1}[F_1(s)] = f_1(t), \quad \mathcal{L}^{-1}[F_2(s)] = f_2(t) \tag{7}$$

then

$$\mathcal{L}^{-1}[F_1(s) \cdot F_2(s)] = \int_0^t f_1(t - \lambda) \cdot f_2(\lambda) \, d\lambda \tag{8}$$

6. Linear transformations $\mathcal{L}$ and $\mathcal{L}^{-1}$. Let k_1, k_2 denote real constants. Then

$$\mathcal{L}[k_1 f_1(t) + k_2 f_2(t)] = k_1 \mathcal{L}[f_1(t)] + k_2 \mathcal{L}[f_2(t)] \tag{9}$$

and

$$\mathcal{L}^{-1}[k_1 F_1(s) + k_2 F_2(s)] = k_1 \mathcal{L}^{-1}[F_1(s)] + k_2 \mathcal{L}^{-1}[F_2(s)] \tag{10}$$

51. PROCEDURE

To illustrate the application of the rules of procedure the following simple initial-value problem will be solved.

$$k_1 \frac{dy(t)}{dt} + k_2 y(t) + k_3 \int y(t) \, dt = u(t)$$

$$y(0) \neq 0, \; y^{(-1)}(0) \neq 0$$

where $u(t) = 0$ for $t < 0$, and 1 for $0 < t$, and k_1, k_2, k_3 are real constants. Assume that $y(t)$ has a Laplacian transform $Y(s)$, that is, $\mathcal{L}[y(t)] = Y(s)$.

Step A. Find the Laplacian transform of the equation to be solved and express it in terms of the transform of the unknown function.

Thus,

$$\mathcal{L}\left[k_1 \frac{dy(t)}{dt} + k_2 y(t) + k_3 \int y(t) \, dt\right] = \mathcal{L}[u(t)]$$

By **6** this becomes

$$k_1 \mathcal{L}\left[\frac{dy(t)}{dt}\right] + k_2 \mathcal{L}[y(t)] + k_3 \mathcal{L}\left[\int y(t) \, dt\right] = \mathcal{L}[u(t)]$$

By **3** and **4** and the given initial conditions of the problem the equation becomes

$$k_1[s\, Y(s) - y(0)] + k_2\, Y(s) + k_3[s^{-1}\, Y(s) + y^{(-1)}(0) \cdot s^{-1}] = \mathcal{L}[u(t)].$$

Step B. Solve the resulting equation for the transform of the unknown function.

Thus,
$$Y(s) = \frac{\mathcal{L}[u(t)] + k_1\, y(0) - y^{(-1)}(0) \cdot s^{-1}}{k_1\, s + k_2 + k_3\, s^{-1}}$$

Step C. Evaluate the direct transform of the given function (right member) in the original equation.

Note. One way to carry out step **C** is to find the transform from a table of transforms. An extensive table of direct and inverse Fourier transforms which in most cases can be interpreted directly as Laplacian transforms has been compiled by G. A. Campbell and R. M. Foster (Bell Telephone System Monograph B–584). In the present example $\mathcal{L}[u(t)] = \dfrac{1}{s}$, so

$$Y(s) = \frac{k_1\, y(0) \cdot s - y^{(-1)}(0) + 1}{k_1\, s^2 + k_2\, s + k_3}.$$

Step D. Obtain the solution of the problem by evaluating the inverse Laplacian transform of the function obtained by the preceding steps.

Note. One way to carry out step **D** is to find the inverse transform from a table such as that mentioned above. To employ the table, the denominator of the fraction should be factored.

$$y(t) = \mathcal{L}^{-1}[Y(s)] = \mathcal{L}^{-1}\left[\frac{k_1\, y(0) \cdot s - y^{(-1)}(0) + 1}{k_1\, s^2 + k_2\, s + k_3}\right] =$$
$$= \mathcal{L}^{-1}\left[\frac{k_1\, y(0) \cdot s - y^{(-1)}(0) + 1}{k_1\,(s + K_1)(s + K_2)}\right]$$

in which
$$K_1 \equiv \frac{k_2}{2k_1} - \frac{1}{2k_1}\,(k_2{}^2 - 4\,k_1\,k_3)^{1/2},$$

$$K_2 \equiv \frac{k_2}{2k_1} + \frac{1}{2k_1}\,(k_2{}^2 - 4\,k_1\,k_3)^{1/2}$$

To find the result it is necessary to distinguish between two cases.

Case 1: If $K_1 \neq K_2$,
$$y(t) = \{[k_1\, y(0)\, K_1 + y^{(-1)}(0) - 1]\, e^{-K_1 t} -$$
$$- [k_1\, y(0)\, K_2 + y^{(-1)}(0) - 1]\, e^{-K_2 t}\}/[k_1\,(K_1 - K_2)]$$

for $0 < t$, and $= 0$ for $t < 0$.

Case 2: If $K_1 = K_2 = K$, then $K = \dfrac{k_2}{2k_1}$, and

$$y(t) = \mathcal{L}^{-1}\left[\frac{k_1\, y(0) \cdot s - y^{(-1)}(0) + 1}{k_1\,(s + K)^2}\right]$$

From the table,
$$y(t) = \{k_1\, y(0)\, e^{-Kt} - [y^{(-1)}(0) - 1 + k_1\, y(0)\, K]\, te^{-Kt}\}/k_1,$$

for $0 < t$, and $= 0$ for $t < 0$.

To save space it will not be shown here that the solutions obtained satisfy the original equation and initial conditions.

The use of rule **C** can be avoided by using rules **E**, **F**, and **G** in place of rules **C** and **D** in the following way.

Step E. Factor the transform of the unknown function obtained by rule **B**, and evaluate the inverse Laplacian transform of each factor.

Note. The inverse transform of a rational fraction can be found only if the degree of the numerator is one or more less than the degree of the denominator.

Thus,
$$Y(s) = \frac{k_1\, y(0) \cdot s - y^{(-1)}(0)}{k_1\, s^2 + k_2\, s + k_3} + \frac{s\,\mathcal{L}[u(t)]}{k_1\, s^2 + k_2\, s + k_3}.$$

Let $y_1(t) \equiv \mathcal{L}^{-1}\left[\dfrac{k_1\, y(0) \cdot s - y^{(-1)}(0)}{k_1(s + K_1)(s + K_2)}\right] = \{[k_1\, y(0)\, K_1 + y^{(-1)}(0)]\, e^{-K_1 t} -$

$$- [k_1\, y(0)\, K_2 + y^{(-1)}(0)]e^{-K_2 t}\}/[k_1\,(K_1 - K_2)], \text{ for}$$

$0 < t$, and $= 0$ for $t < 0$. Also

$$\mathcal{L}^{-1}\left[\frac{s}{k_1(s + K_1)(s + K_2)}\right] = (K_1\, e^{-K_1 t} - K_2\, e^{-K_2 t})/[k_1(K_1 - K_2)]$$

for $0 < t$, and $= 0$ for $t < 0$. Finally, $\mathcal{L}^{-1}\{\mathcal{L}[u(t)]\} = u(t)$.

Step F. Use **5** to find the inverse transform of the product. Thus, by **6** and step **F**,

$$y(t) = y_1(t) + [k_1(K_1 - K_2)]^{-1} \int_0^t [K_1 e^{-k_1(t-\lambda)} - K_2 e^{-K_2(t-\lambda)}] u(\lambda) \, d\lambda.$$

Step G. Evaluate the (convolution) integral arising from step **F**. Thus,

$$y(t) = y_1(t) + [k_1(K_1 - K_2)]^{-1} (e^{-K_2 t} - e^{-K_1 t}), \text{ for } 0 < t, \text{ and } = 0 \text{ for } t < 0.$$

It may be easily seen that for the particular problem treated above it is much simpler to use steps C and D than steps E, F, and G. However, for a more complicated right member of the original equation it could happen that step G would be easier to carry out than step C, in which case the second method (A, B, E, F, G) should be used rather than the first (A, B, C, D).

One physical representation of the initial-value problem which we have used for illustration is the problem of finding the current response of a series electrical circuit containing constant lumped inductance, resistance, and capacitance to an applied electromotive force $u(t)$, with an initial current in the inductance and an initial charge on the condenser.

The particular advantages of this transform method are not brought out well by the simple problem used for illustration of the procedure, but appear more clearly when systems of higher order ordinary integro-differential equations or partial differential equations are treated. The complete method (of which only a part has been given above) is not restricted in its field of application to linear equations with constant coefficients, but the solution of this type of equation is most simplified.

Books and papers on the subject should be consulted for alternative methods of evaluating the direct and inverse transforms and for further properties and applications of the Laplacian transformation.

FUNCTIONS OF COMPLEX VARIABLES
By M. J. Fish
52. COMPLEX NUMBERS

Complex Numbers. A complex number or vector is the combination of two ordinary real numbers a, b in the ordered pair $(a, b) = a + ib$, where $i^2 = -1$. Real and imaginary numbers are special cases of complex numbers obtained by placing $(a, 0) = a$, $(0, b) = ib$.

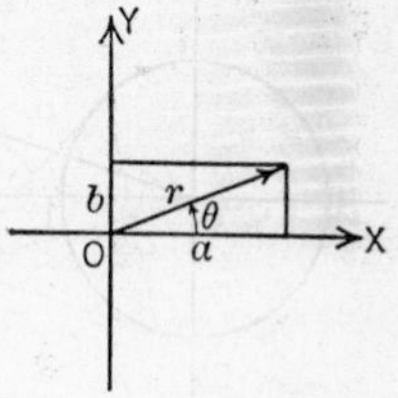

1. If $a + ib = 0$, then $a = 0$, $b = 0$.
2. If $a + ib = c + id$, then $a = c$, $b = d$.
3. $a + ib$ and $a - ib$ are conjugate complex numbers.
4. $(a + ib)(a - ib) = a^2 + b^2$.
5. $\dfrac{a + ib}{c + id} = \dfrac{(a + ib)(c - id)}{(c + id)(c - id)} = \dfrac{ac + bd}{c^2 + d^2} + i\dfrac{bc - ad}{c^2 + d^2}$.
6. $a + ib = r(\cos \theta + i \sin \theta) = e^{i\theta}$.
$a - ib = r(\cos \theta - i \sin \theta) = e^{-i\theta}$,

FIG. 1

where $r = +\sqrt{a^2 + b^2}$, $\sin \theta = \dfrac{b}{r}$, $\cos \theta = \dfrac{a}{r}$, r is called the *absolute value* (the *modulus*), and θ, the *argument*.

7. $(\cos \theta \pm i \sin \theta)^n = e^{\pm in\theta} = \cos n\theta \pm i \sin n\theta$ (n arbitrary).

8. $\sqrt[n]{a + ib} = |\sqrt[n]{r}| \left(\cos \dfrac{\theta + 2k\pi}{n} + i \sin \dfrac{\theta + 2k\pi}{n} \right) = |\sqrt[n]{r}| e^{i(\theta + 2k\pi)/n}$

where k is an integer; for $k = 0, 1, 2 \ldots, n - 1$, all the different values of the root are obtained.

Addition of Two Complex Numbers.

$$(a + ib) + (c + id) = (a + c) + i(b + d) \tag{1}$$

(See addition of vectors.)

Multiplication of Two Complex Numbers. To multiply z_1 and z_2, multiply their moduli and add their arguments. This can best be accomplished by use of the exponential form;

$$z_1 = r_1 e^{i\theta_1}, \ z_2 = r_2 e^{i\theta_2}, \ z_1 z_2 = r_1 r_2 e^{i(\theta_1 + \theta_2)} \tag{2}$$

To divide $\dfrac{z_1}{z_2}$, divide the moduli and subtract their arguments;

$$\frac{z_1}{z_2} = \frac{r_1}{r_2} e^{i(\theta_1 - \theta_2)} \tag{3}$$

53. COMPLEX VARIABLES

Analytic Functions of Complex Variables. A function $w = f(z)$, $z = x + iy$, which has at each point of a region in the z plane a derivative

$$\lim_{h \to 0} \frac{f(z + h) - f(z)}{h} = f'(z) \tag{4}$$

where $f'(z)$ has the same value independent of the manner of approach of $z + h$ to z, is called *analytic* in this region and may be developed in a convergent power series. By separation of $w = u(x,y) + i\, v(x,y)$ into its real and imaginary parts and allowing $z + h$ to approach z first along the real axis, then along the imaginary axis,

$$f'(z) = \frac{\partial u}{\partial x} + i\frac{\partial v}{\partial x} = -i\frac{\partial u}{\partial y} + \frac{\partial v}{\partial y} \tag{5}$$

Thus the Cauchy-Riemann differential equations are obtained:

$$\frac{\partial u}{\partial x} = \frac{\partial v}{\partial y}; \; \frac{\partial u}{\partial y} = -\frac{\partial v}{\partial x} \tag{6}$$

If these four partial derivatives exist and are continuous at all points of the region, the Cauchy-Riemann equations are necessary and sufficient conditions for a function to be analytic in the region. The Cauchy-Riemann equations satisfy Laplace's equation:

$$\frac{\partial^2 \phi}{\partial x^2} + \frac{\partial^2 \phi}{\partial y^2} = 0, \text{ for } \phi = u \text{ and } v \tag{7}$$

Examples of analytic functions are: z^2, $\dfrac{1}{z}$, e^x, $\sin x$ .... The function $w = x - iy$ has a different limit for the differential quotient by an approach along the real axis from that along the imaginary axis and is therefore not analytic. This can be found from the non-existence of the Cauchy-Riemann equations.

Conformal Mapping. Consider the equation $w = f(z)$. To every point in the z plane corresponds a point in the w plane, and there is a mapping of the corresponding

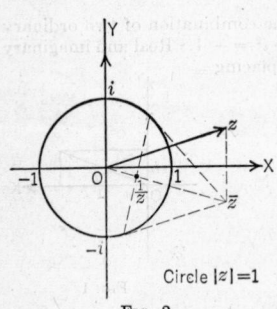

Circle $|z| = 1$

Fig. 2

points. If $w = f(z)$ is an analytic function, then at the points where $f'(z) \neq 0$, two curves in the w plane cut each other at the same angle as two corresponding curves in the z plane. In addition, each line element in the z plane has the same ratio of length to each corresponding line element in the w plane. This ratio of length is $f'(z) = \dfrac{dw}{dz}$. Such a mapping is called *conformal*. Examples. (1) $w = z + c$, where c is complex, represents a displacement of the z plane parallel to and with the magnitude of the vector c.

(2) $w = az + b$ ($a \neq 0$; $a \neq 1$), a and b complex, represents a parallel displacement of amount b, a rotation equal to the argument of a, and a stretching or contraction in the ratio $1/a$. The point $z = \dfrac{b}{1 - a}$ remains fixed.

(3) $w = 1/z$ is the inversion transformation. The point $z = 0$ transforms into $w = \infty$. The inside of the unit circle, $|z| = 1$ (Fig. 2) becomes, in the w plane, the outside of the unit circle $|w| = 1$, with the circle taken in the opposite direction. Circles and straight lines in the z plane which go through the point $z = 0$ become straight lines in the w plane. In particular, circles in the z plane which are tangent at $z = 0$ become parallel lines in the w plane.

VECTOR ANALYSIS
By M. J. Fish

54. SUM AND PRODUCT OF VECTORS

A **Vector** is a directed segment of a straight line. Quantities in physics which have magnitude and direction, such as force, velocity, acceleration, can be represented by means of vectors. A *scalar* is a quantity which has magnitude but no direction. For example, mass, density, temperature are scalar quantities

Two vectors A and B are equal if they have the same length and direction. A vector may be displaced parallel to itself in space, provided it retains the same length and direction. A vector having the same length but direction opposite to that of A is the negative of the latter and is written $-A$. If A is a vector of length a, then $|A| = a$. The vector parallel to A but with length equal to the reciprocal of the length of A is written $A^{-1} = 1/A$. The unit vector $\dfrac{A}{|A|}$ ($A \neq 0$) is a vector having the direction of A and length 1.

The Sum of two vectors A and B is $A + B = B + A$ (Fig. 1). Similarly, the sum of three or more vectors can be found by using $A + B$ as one side and continuing as above.

The sum of A and $-B$ is $A - B$ (Fig. 1), the difference of two vectors. If p is a scalar and A a vector, then $pA = Ap$ represents a vector p times as long as A with the same direction as A if p is positive and opposite if p is negative. If p, q are scalars, then

$$(p + q) A = pA + qA; \quad p(A + B) = pA + pB \tag{1}$$

In operations with vectors, the following algebraic laws are valid:

$$A + B = B + A, \text{ commutative.} \tag{2}$$

$$A + (B + C) = (A + B) + C, \text{ associative.} \tag{3}$$

$$p(A + B) = pA + pB, \text{ distributive.} \tag{4}$$

$$|A + B| \leqq |A| + |B|$$

where the equality sign holds only for A parallel to B.

Rectangular Coordinates. Fig. 2 shows a right-handed system of coordinates; that is, a right-handed rotation of 90° about OZ carries OX into OY. Let i, j, k be unit vectors

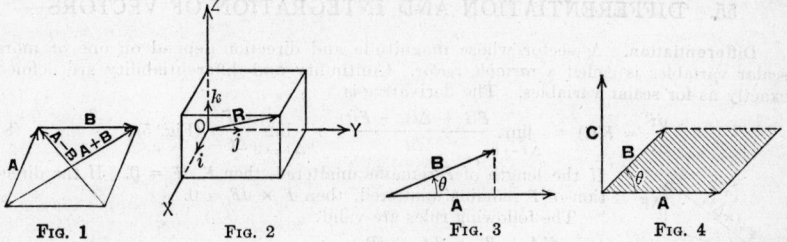

| FIG. 1 | FIG. 2 | FIG. 3 | FIG. 4 |

with the directions OX, OY, OZ, respectively. The point $P(x, y, z)$ is the terminus of a vector $OP = R$ such that

$$R = ix + jy + kz \tag{5}$$

where the three vectors on the right are called the components of R. Given two vectors $A = ia + jb + kc$ and $A_1 = ia_1 + jb_1 + kc_1$, then

$$A + A_1 = i(a + a_1) + j(b + b_1) + k(c + c_1) \tag{6}$$

Scalar Product. The scalar product of two vectors is sometimes called the inner product or the dot product. It is

$$A \cdot B = |A| \; |B| \; \cos \theta \quad \text{(Fig. 3)} \tag{7}$$

The following algebraic rules are valid:

$A \cdot B = B \cdot A$

$A \cdot (B + C) = A \cdot B + A \cdot C$

If $A \cdot B = 0$, then either $A = 0$, $B = 0$, or A is perpendicular to B.

$A \cdot A = A^2 = |A|^2$

$i \cdot i = j \cdot j = k \cdot k = 1$

$i \cdot j = j \cdot k = k \cdot i = 0$

If $A = ia_1 + ja_2 + ka_3$ and $B = ib_1 + jb_2 + kb_3$, then $A \cdot B = a_1 b_1 + a_2 b_2 + a_3 b_3$.

Vector Product. The vector product of two vectors is sometimes called the outer product or the cross-product. It is $A \times B = C$, where C is perpendicular to the plane of A and B with the magnitude $|C| = |A| \; |B| \sin \theta$ (the area of the parallelogram made by A and B, Fig. 4) and so directed that a right-hand rotation of less than 180° carries A into B. The following algebraic rules are valid:

$A \times B = -B \times A$

$A \times (B + C) = A \times B + A \times C$

$(B + C) \times A = B \times A + C \times A$

If $A \times B = 0$, then either $A = 0$, $B = 0$, or A is parallel to B.

$$i \times i = j \times j = k \times k = 0$$
$$i \times j = k = - j \times i$$
$$j \times k = i = - k \times j$$
$$k \times i = j = - i \times k$$

If $A = ia_1 + ja_2 + ka_3$ and $B = ib_1 + jb_2 + kb_3$, then $A \times B = \begin{vmatrix} i & j & k \\ a_1 & a_2 & a_3 \\ b_1 & b_2 & b_3 \end{vmatrix}$.

If $A = ia_1 + ja_2 + ka_3$
$$B = ib_1 + jb_2 + kb_3$$
$$C = ic_1 + jc_2 + kc_3$$

then the triple scalar product

$$A \cdot (B \times C) = (A \times B) \cdot C = B \cdot (C \times A) = (A\, B\, C) = \begin{vmatrix} a_1 & a_2 & a_3 \\ b_1 & b_2 & b_3 \\ c_1 & c_2 & c_3 \end{vmatrix}$$

and is equal to the volume of a parallelepiped whose three determining edges are A, B, C. The product

$$(A \times B) \times C = (A \cdot C)B - (B \cdot C)A = - C \times (A \times B)$$
$$(A \times B) \cdot (C \times D) = (A \cdot C)(B \cdot D) - (A \cdot D)(B \cdot C)$$

55. DIFFERENTIATION AND INTEGRATION OF VECTORS

Differentiation. A vector whose magnitude and direction depend on one or more scalar variables is called a *variable vector*. Continuity and differentiability are defined exactly as for scalar variables. The derivative is

$$\frac{dF}{dt} = F'(t) = \lim_{\Delta t \to 0} \frac{F(t + \Delta t) - F(t)}{\Delta t} = \lim_{\Delta t \to 0} \frac{\Delta F}{\Delta t} \quad \text{(Fig. 5)} \tag{8}$$

If the length of F remains unaltered, then $F \cdot dF = 0$. If the direction of F remains unaltered, then $F \times dF = 0$.

The following rules are valid:

$$d(A + B) = dA + dB$$
$$d(A \cdot B) = A \cdot dB + B \cdot dA$$
$$d(A \times B) = dA \times B + A \times dB = A \times dB - B \times dA$$
$$d(A \cdot B \cdot C) = A \cdot B \cdot dC + B \cdot C \cdot dA + C \cdot A \cdot dB$$

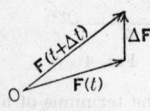

Fig. 5

The Differential Operators.

Let
$$\nabla = \text{"} del \text{"} = i \frac{\partial}{\partial x} + j \frac{\partial}{\partial y} + k \frac{\partial}{\partial z} \tag{9}$$

If V is a scalar function,

then
$$\nabla V = grad\, V = i \frac{\partial V}{\partial x} + j \frac{\partial V}{\partial y} + k \frac{\partial V}{\partial z} \tag{10}$$

If A is a vector with components A_x, A_y, A_z,

then
$$\nabla \cdot A = div\, A = \frac{\partial A_x}{\partial x} + \frac{\partial A_y}{\partial y} + \frac{\partial A_z}{\partial z} \tag{11}$$

$$\nabla \times A = curl\, A = rot\, A = \begin{vmatrix} i & j & k \\ \frac{\partial}{\partial x} & \frac{\partial}{\partial y} & \frac{\partial}{\partial z} \\ A_x & A_y & A_z \end{vmatrix} \tag{12}$$

$$\nabla^2 = Laplacian = \frac{\partial^2}{\partial x^2} + \frac{\partial^2}{\partial y^2} + \frac{\partial^2}{\partial z^2} \tag{13}$$

Formulas for Differentiation. Let U and V be scalar functions and A and B be vector functions of x, y, z. Then:

$$\nabla(U + V) = \nabla U + \nabla V; \quad \nabla \cdot (A + B) = \nabla \cdot A + \nabla \cdot B; \quad \nabla \times (A + B) = \nabla \times A + \nabla \times B$$

$$\nabla(UV) = V \nabla U + U \nabla V; \quad \nabla \cdot (UA) = U \nabla \cdot A + A \cdot \nabla U; \quad \nabla \times (UA) = \nabla U \times A + U \nabla \times A$$

$$\nabla \cdot (A \times B) = B \cdot \nabla \times A - A \cdot \nabla \times B$$

$$\nabla(A \cdot B) = A \cdot \nabla B + B \cdot \nabla A + A \times (\nabla \times B) + B \times (\nabla \times A)$$

$$\nabla \times (A \times B) = B \cdot \nabla A - A \cdot \nabla B + A(\nabla \cdot B) - B(\nabla \cdot A)$$

$$\nabla \times (\nabla \times A) = \nabla(\nabla \cdot A) - \nabla^2 A$$
$$\nabla \cdot (\nabla \times A) = 0$$
$$\nabla \times (\nabla U) = 0$$

If $R = ix + jy + kz$ (Fig. 2), then

$$\nabla \cdot R = 3; \quad \nabla \times R = 0; \quad A \cdot \nabla R = A; \quad \nabla \cdot \frac{1}{|R|} = -\frac{R}{|R|^3}; \quad \nabla^2 \frac{1}{|R|} = 0.$$

Integration. The line integral of a vector F along a curve AB denotes the integral of the tangential component of the vector along the curve; thus

$$\int_A^B F \cdot dR = \int_A^B |F_c| \, ds \quad \text{(Fig. 6)} \tag{14}$$

where $dR = idx + jdy + kdz$.

If $F = \nabla U$ is the gradient of a single-valued continuous function $U(x,y,z)$ the line integral of F depends only on the end points. Conversely, if $F(x, y, z)$ is continuous and $\int_C F \cdot dR = 0$ for any closed path C in a three-dimensional region, there is a function $U(x, y, z)$ such that $F = \nabla U$.

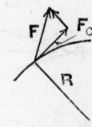

FIG. 6

56. THEOREMS AND FORMULAS

Let n be the vector of unit length perpendicular to a surface at a point P and extending on the positive side (the outward normal); dS, the element of surface, and dv, the element of volume.

The Divergence (Gauss) Theorem.   Consider any closed surface S, lying in a vector field F, then

$$\iint_S F \cdot n \, dS = \iiint_v \nabla \cdot F \, dv \tag{15}$$

where $\nabla \cdot F$ is continuous and by a vector field is meant that to every point of the region there is a corresponding value of the vector.

Stokes' Theorem.

$$\iint_S \nabla \times F \cdot n \, dS = \int_C F \cdot dR \tag{16}$$

where C is the curve bounding S.

Green's Theorem.

$$\iint_S n \cdot U \nabla V \, dS = \iiint_v U \nabla^2 V \, dv + \iiint_v (\nabla U \cdot \nabla V) \, dv \tag{17}$$

$$\iint_S n \cdot (U \nabla V - V \nabla U) \, dS = \iiint_v (U \nabla^2 V - V \nabla^2 U) \, dv \tag{18}$$

Cylindrical Coordinates.

$$x = r \cos \theta, \ y = r \sin \theta, \ z = z$$

The element of volume $dv = rdrd\theta dz$. The unit vectors u_r, u_θ, u_z are perpendicular to each other.

$$\text{Grad } V = \nabla V = \frac{\partial V}{\partial r} u_r + \frac{1}{r} \frac{\partial V}{\partial \theta} u_\theta + \frac{\partial V}{\partial z} u_z \tag{19}$$

$$\text{Div } F = \nabla \cdot F = \frac{1}{r} \frac{\partial}{\partial r}(rF_r) + \frac{1}{r} \frac{\partial}{\partial \theta}(F_\theta) + \frac{\partial}{\partial z}(F_z) \tag{20}$$

$$\text{Curl } F = \nabla \times F = \begin{vmatrix} \dfrac{u_r}{r} & u_\theta & \dfrac{u_z}{r} \\ \dfrac{\partial}{\partial r} & \dfrac{\partial}{\partial \theta} & \dfrac{\partial}{\partial z} \\ F_r & rF_\theta & F_z \end{vmatrix} \tag{21}$$

$$\nabla^2 V = \frac{1}{r} \frac{\partial V}{\partial r} + \frac{\partial^2 V}{\partial r^2} + \frac{1}{r^2} \frac{\partial^2 V}{\partial \theta^2} + \frac{\partial^2 V}{\partial z^2} \tag{22}$$

Spherical Coordinates.

$$x = r \cos \theta \sin \phi, \ y = r \sin \theta \sin \phi, \ z = r \cos \phi$$

The unit vectors u_r, u_ϕ, u_θ are perpendicular to each other.

$$\text{Grad } V = \nabla V = \frac{\partial V}{\partial r} u_r + \frac{1}{r \sin \phi} \frac{\partial V}{\partial \theta} u_\theta + \frac{1}{r} \frac{\partial V}{\partial \phi} u_\phi \tag{23}$$

$$\text{Div } F = \nabla \cdot F = \frac{1}{r^2} \frac{\partial}{\partial r} (r^2 F_r) + \frac{1}{r \sin \phi} \frac{\partial F_\theta}{\partial \theta} + \frac{1}{r \sin \phi} \frac{\partial}{\partial \phi} (\sin \phi \, F_\phi) \tag{24}$$

$$\text{Curl } F = \nabla \times F = \begin{vmatrix} \dfrac{u_r}{r^2 \sin \phi} & \dfrac{u_\phi}{r \sin \phi} & \dfrac{u_\theta}{r} \\[2mm] \dfrac{\partial}{\partial r} & \dfrac{\partial}{\partial \phi} & \dfrac{\partial}{\partial \theta} \\[2mm] F_r & rF_\phi & r \sin \phi \, F_\theta \end{vmatrix} \tag{25}$$

$$\nabla^2 V = \frac{1}{r^2} \frac{\partial}{\partial r} \left(r^2 \frac{\partial V}{\partial r} \right) + \frac{1}{r^2 \sin^2 \phi} \frac{\partial^2 V}{\partial \theta^2} + \frac{1}{r^2 \sin \phi} \frac{\partial}{\partial \phi} \left(\sin \phi \frac{\partial V}{\partial \phi} \right) \tag{26}$$

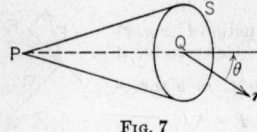

FIG. 7

Solid Angle. The lines joining the point P to points of a surface S generate a solid angle. If a is the area intercepted by these lines on a sphere of center P with radius r, then

$$\omega = \frac{a}{r^2} \tag{27}$$

is the measure of the solid angle. If S is a surface such that it does not pass through P, $\cos \theta$ is nowhere zero, and n is everywhere continuous on the surface, then

$$\omega = \int_s \frac{R \cdot n \, da}{r^3} \tag{28}$$

where $R = PQ$. If S forms the complete boundary of a three-dimensional region, the total solid angle subtended by S at P is zero if P lies outside the region, and 4π if P lies inside the region.

ALIGNMENT CHARTS—NOMOGRAMS

By J. G. Brainerd

57. DEFINITION

An **Alignment Chart** is a group of curves so placed, and with scales so arranged, that there exists a simple method of determining points on the curves which correspond to a set of simultaneous values of the variables in a given equation for which the chart has been constructed. The term *nomogram* is frequently used in place of *alignment chart*.

Use. The most extensive use of alignment charts is for the purpose of eliminating computations which (1) involve equations containing three or four variables, and (2) must be made frequently enough to warrant construction of a chart.

Example. For a very simple example involving only two variables, consider $T = 5(t - 32)/9$ which changes fahrenheit degrees (t) to centigrade degrees (T). It is possible to plot T as ordinate against t as abscissa on rectangular coordinate paper, thereby obtaining a straight line from which the value of T for any given value of t within the range of the graph can be obtained. An alignment chart of the type shown in Fig. 1

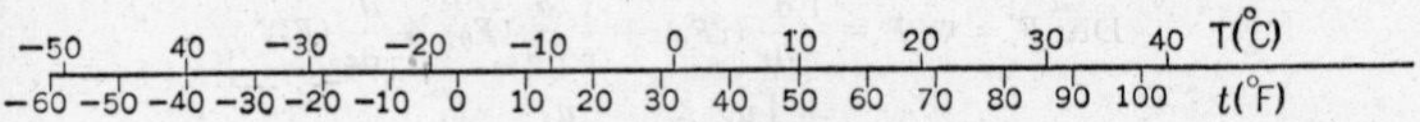

| −50 | 40 | −30 | −20 | −10 | 0 | 10 | 20 | 30 | 40 | T(°C) |

−60 −50 −40 −30 −20 −10   0   10 20 30 40 50 60 70 80 90 100 t(°F)

$$T = \tfrac{5}{9}(t-32) \quad \text{or} \quad t = \tfrac{9}{5}T + 32$$

FIG. 1

can be used to give the same information. Corresponding values of t and T are marked along a single line. This alignment chart has the advantages that it is easier to use, that it is more compact, and that interpolation is usually more accurate on it than on the graph in rectangular coordinates.

An alignment chart giving the logarithms to five places of all five-figure numbers may be printed in eight pages whereas the corresponding tables require much more space. It is, however, more difficult to construct. Charts of this type represent equations of the form

$$y = f(x) \tag{1}$$

where $f(x)$ is a function of the independent variable x, and y is the dependent variable.

58. FUNCTIONS OF THREE VARIABLES

If a problem is governed by an equation of the form $F(x, y, z) = 0$ where $F(x, y, z)$ is any function of the three variables x, y, and z (at least one of which is a dependent variable) then it *may* be possible to construct an alignment chart of the equation. Whether or not the chart *can* be constructed depends on the form of the equation. Below are listed some important forms for which it is possible to construct a chart.

Type I. $\qquad\qquad\qquad f_1(x) = f_2(y) + f_3(z)$ $\qquad\qquad\qquad$ (2)

where f_1, f_2, and f_3 are any functions of x, y, and z, respectively; for example, $2x + 3 = 5y^2 + 9 \log z$ is an equation of *Type I*. The alignment chart consists of three parallel straight lines constructed as follows:

Let $f_2(y')$ and $f_2(y'')$ be the largest and smallest values respectively of $f_2(y)$ which it is desired to have on the chart. Choose a *scale factor* m_y so that $m_y[f_2(y') - f_2(y'')]$ is equal to or less than the length which the scale can have on the paper. Plot along a straight line $Y = m_y f_2(y)$ from $f_2(y'')$ to $f_2(y')$, placing the corresponding values of y beside several points in order to have a scale.

At an arbitrary distance d from the Y scale, erect a parallel (Z) scale and repeat the above process, using an appropriate scale factor m_z for the Z scale. It is not necessary to have any point on the Z scale opposite any particular point on the Y scale.

At a distance $m_y d/(m_y + m_z)$ from the Y scale draw a line parallel to Y and Z and use this for the X scale. Let y_0 and z_0 be any two values of y and z, respectively; join the point on the Y scale corresponding to y_0 with that on the Z scale corresponding to z_0 by a straight line and mark the point x_0 where this straight line crosses the X scale. Compute from the original equation $f_1(x) = f_2(y) + f_3(z)$ the value of x ($= x_0$) when $y = y_0$ and $z = z_0$. Then using a scale factor $m_x = m_y m_z/(m_y + m_z)$, plot $X = m_x f_1(x)$ in such a way that, when $x = x_0$, the point obtained from $X = m_x f_1(x)$ will coincide with the point obtained previously for x_0. The alignment chart is now constructed. *Any straight line will cut the scales Y, X, and Z at points corresponding to values of y, x, and z which will satisfy the basic equation $f_1(x) = f_2(y) + f_3(z)$.*

Example. To plot an alignment chart on $8\frac{1}{2}$ by 11 in. paper for Ohm's law which for a simple electric circuit is $e = ri$. r is to vary between 10 and 100 ohms and i between 1 and 3 amp. Taking the logarithm of each side of the equation, there is obtained

$$\log e = \log r + \log i$$

which is an equation of Type I, with e, r, and i taking the places of x, y, and z respectively. Log e corresponds to $f_1(x)$, log r to $f_2(y)$, and log i to $f_3(z)$. When $r = 100$, log $r = 2$, which corresponds to $f_2(y')$; when $r = 10$, log $r = 1$ which corresponds to $f_2(y'')$. Taking 10 in. as the length of the scale, $m_r(2 - 1) = 10$, or $m_r = 10$, where m_r is the scale factor denoted by m_y in the general discussion. Plotting $m_r \log r$ or $10 \log r$ from $r = 10$ to $r = 100$, the R scale of Fig. 2 is obtained.

Likewise m_i, corresponding to m_z in the general discussion, is found from $m_i (\log 3 - \log 1) = 10$, or $m_i = 20.96$. Construct the I scale 6 in. from the R scale, that is, plot 20.96 log i from $i = 1$ to $i = 3$ along a line parallel to the R scale at a perpendicular distance $d = 6$ in. away from the latter.

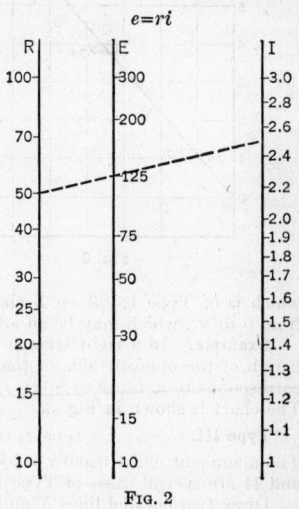

Now erect a third scale (E), between and parallel to R and I, at a distance $m_r d/(m_r + m_i) = 60/30.96 = 1.94$ in. from R. Take any values of r and i, say $r = 50$ ohms and $i = 2.5$ amp, and join by a straight line the point corresponding to $r = 50$ on the R scale with the point corresponding to $i = 2.5$ on the I scale. The point where this line crosses the E scale corresponds to $e = 50 \times 2.5 = 125$ volts. Mark it. From this point on the E scale, plot upwards m_e log e from $e = 125$ to $e =$ higher values, and from the same point plot downwards $m_e \log e$ from $e = 125$ to $e =$ lower values. The value of m_e is $m_e = m_r m_i/(m_r + m_i) = 209.6/30.96 = 6.77$.

FIG. 2

The alignment chart is now completed. By joining by a straight line (preferably scratched on the bottom of a piece of celluloid or other transparent material to facilitate interpolation) any point on one scale with any point on either other scale, the line passes through a point on the third scale such that the three points correspond to values of e, r, and i satisfying $e = ri$.

The equation $pv = RT$, where R is a constant and p, v, and T are variables, is frequently met in thermodynamics. Let T, p, and v correspond to x, y, and z, respectively, and take the logarithm of both sides. Then $\log R + \log T = \log p + \log v$, whence, with $\log R + \log T$ corresponding to $f_1(x)$, $\log p$ to $f_2(y)$ and $\log v$ to $f_3(z)$, the procedure in the above example may be followed almost identically to obtain the alignment chart.

Type II. $$f_1(x) = \frac{f_2(y)}{f_3(z)} \tag{3}$$

where $f_1(x)$ is any function of x, $f_2(y)$ any function of y, and $f_3(z)$ any function of z. The alignment chart is called a Z chart, on account of its shape. Draw two parallel lines Y and Z at a convenient distance from each other and choose scale factors m_y and m_z as before, except that the minimum values of $f_2(y)$ and $f_3(z)$ should be taken zero. Plot $m_y f_2(y)$ along Y. Plot $m_z f_3(z)$ *in the opposite direction* along Z. That is, if $m_y f_2(y)$ is plotted from bottom to top of Y (zero value at bottom), then $m_z f_3(z)$ should be plotted from top to bottom (zero value at top). Join the point corresponding to $f_2(y) = 0$ with the point corresponding to $f_3(z) = 0$ by a straight line X. This line will be of length k. Plot $k\, m_y f_1(x)/[m_z + m_y f_1(x)]$ along X, taking *as origin* the point corresponding to $f_2(y) = 0$, which is one end of the X scale. The alignment chart is now drawn; any straight line passing through the scales cuts them at points whose corresponding values of x, y, and z satisfy the original equation.

It should be noted that (1) Type II includes equations of the form $f_1(x) = f_2(y)\, F_3(z)$, where $F_3(z)$ is a function of z only, since these can be thrown into the form previously given by replacing $F_3(z)$ by $1/f_3(z)$; (2) any equation of Type II can be made an equation of Type I by taking the logarithm of both sides, for then $\log f_1(x) = \log f_2(y) - \log f_3(z)$

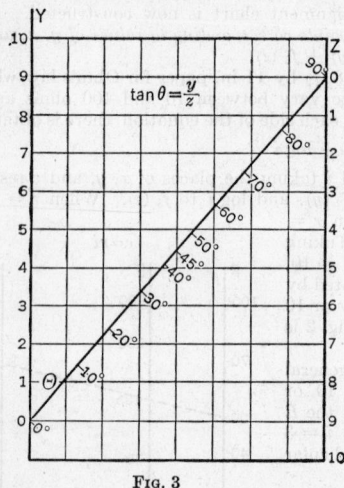

FIG. 3

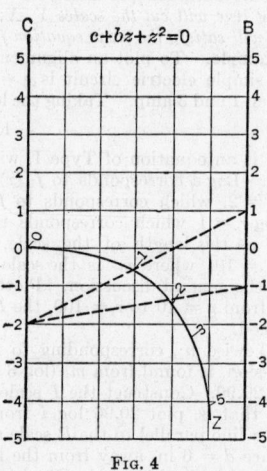

FIG. 4

which is of Type I; (3) on Z charts the X scale will always contain all values of $f_1(x)$ from 0 to ∞, which may be an advantage.

Example. In a right triangle $\tan\theta = y/z$ where θ is an angle (not 90°), y is the length of the opposite side of the triangle, and z that of the side adjacent to θ. Here θ corresponds to x, $\tan\theta$ to $f_1(x)$, $f_2(y)$ is y, and $f_3(z)$ is z. Scales Y and Z will be uniform. The chart is shown in Fig. 3.

Type III. $$f_1(x)\, f_4(z) + f_2(y)\, f_5(z) + f_3(z) = 0 \tag{4}$$

The alignment chart usually consists of two straight lines and a curved scale. (Types I and II are special cases of Type III, in which the curved scale becomes straight.)

Draw two parallel lines X and Y, as far apart as is convenient. Plot $m_x f_1(x)$ along X and $m_y f_2(y)$ along Y, choosing suitable scale factors m_x and m_y as before, and placing the respective origins opposite each other. (See Fig. 4.) Now draw two straight lines, one perpendicular to X and Y and passing through both origins, the other parallel to

X and Y and halfway between them. These are temporary construction axes which may be called U and V, respectively. Plot in the usual manner, with reference to these rectangular axes, the curve whose coordinates are

$$u = -k\frac{m_y f_4(z) - m_x f_5(z)}{m_y f_4(z) + m_x f_5(z)} \quad (5a) \quad \text{and} \quad v = \frac{-m_x m_y f_3(z)}{m_y f_4(z) + m_x f_5(z)} \quad (5b)$$

where k is the distance from either X or Y to V. Mark points with the corresponding values of z. The curve thus obtained and the X and Y scales form the desired alignment chart. A straight line passing through points on any two of the scales will intersect the third scale at such a point that the corresponding values of x, y, and z satisfy the given equation. The equations for u and v show that the ratio m_x/m_y is important in determining the shape of the curved Z scale. It is frequently desirable to try different convenient values of m_x/m_y, sketching the curve roughly each time, to obtain a Z scale of good shape so far as accuracy and ease of reading are concerned.

Example. To draw an alignment chart on $8\frac{1}{2}$ by 11 in. paper for the equation $c + bz + z^2 = 0$ which will give the real roots of this quadratic equation for b between -5 and $+5$, c between the same limits. Comparing this with the typical equation of Type III, c, b, z correspond to x, y, z, respectively, c to $f_1(x)$, b to $f_2(y)$, z^2 to $f_3(z)$, 1 to $f_4(z)$, z to $f_5(z)$. Taking 10 in. as a desirable length for the B and C scales, $m_b = 10/[5 - (-5)] = 1$ and $m_c = 1$ likewise. Then, taking $k = 3$ in.,

$$u = -3\left[\frac{1-z}{1+z}\right] \quad (6a) \quad \text{and} \quad v = \frac{-z^2}{1+z} \quad (6b)$$

Plotting the curve given by these coordinates on the construction axes U, V, Fig. 4 is obtained. Only positive values of z are shown on the Z scale; for negative roots of $c + bz + z^2 = 0$, reverse the sign of the positive roots of $c - bz + z^2 = 0$.

Type III (a).

$$\frac{f_4(z)}{F_1(x)} + \frac{f_5(z)}{F_2(y)} + f_3(z) = 0 \quad (7)$$

which is the same as the original Type III equation except that $F_1(x)$ has been written for $1/f_1(x)$ and $F_2(y)$ for $1/f_2(y)$. The alignment chart may be composed of two *intersecting* straight lines and a curved scale.

Draw an X scale horizontal and a Y scale vertical, and take the intersection as origin. Choose scale factors m_x and m_y, and call $1/m_x$ one unit along X and $1/m_y$ one unit along Y. Plot the curve whose coordinates are

$$x = -f_4(z)/f_3(z) \quad (8a) \quad \text{and} \quad y = -f_5(z)/f_3(z) \quad (8b)$$

marking points with corresponding values of z. This curve is the Z scale. Now plot $m_x F_1(x)$ along X and $m_y F_2(y)$ along Y, obtaining the X and Y scales. The alignment chart is complete; a straight line crossing the scales will cut them at points corresponding to values of x, y, and z satisfying the basic equations.

Example. Take the previous example $c + bz + z^2 = 0$ and assume that an alignment chart is desired for large values of c and b. Write the equation in the form

$$\frac{1}{x} + \frac{z}{y} + z^2 = 0$$

where $x = 1/c$, $y = 1/b$,

$x = F_1(x)$, $y = F_2(y)$, $1 = f_4(z)$, $z = f_5(z)$, $z^2 = f_3(z)$

The chart is shown in Fig. 5.

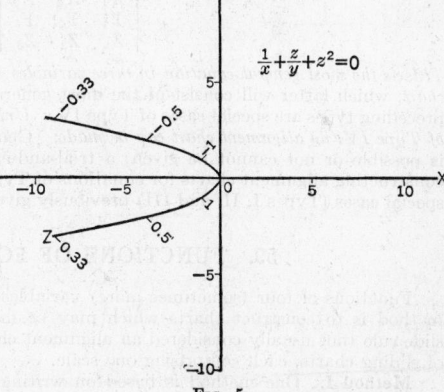

FIG. 5

It is seen from this example that a chart of this type has a complementary relation to that of Fig. 4. Large values of b and c will not fall conveniently on the latter but will on the former (since small x and y correspond to large c and b). The choice of form for a chart will thus depend on ranges of the variables and accuracy desired.

Type III (b).

$$f_2(y) + f_1(x) F_1(z) = F_2(z) \quad (9)$$

which can be obtained from the original Type III equation by dividing by $f_5(z)$ and writing $F_1(z)$ for $f_4(z)/f_5(z)$ and $F_2(z)$ for $-f_3(z)/f_5(z)$. In this form the equation is conveniently arranged for the construction of an alignment chart consisting of a straight scale, a scale on the arc of a circle, and a curved scale.

Plot in rectangular axes the curve the abscissa of any point of which is $F_1(z)$ and the ordinate $F_2(z)$. The unit for abscissas need not be the same as the unit for ordinates (i.e., scale factors should be chosen so that the curve fits on the paper for the range of z to be considered) but the same units must be used throughout the construction of the chart. The curve thus found is the Z scale, and values of z should be marked beside the points to which they correspond to give the scale.

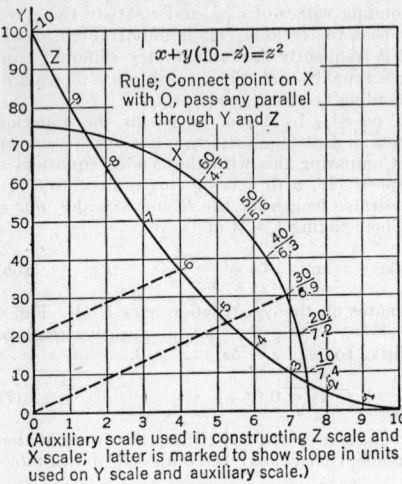

Rule; Connect point on X with O, pass any parallel through Y and Z

$x + y(10 - z) = z^2$

(Auxiliary scale used in constructing Z scale and X scale; latter is marked to show slope in units used on Y scale and auxiliary scale.)

FIG. 6

Take the vertical axis as the Y scale and plot $m_y f_2(y)$ along it, m_y being the scale factor for ordinates. Now with the origin as center draw an arc of a circle, cutting the horizontal axis at some point from which a scale is to be laid off along this arc in the counter-clockwise direction, such that the slope of the line from any point on the scale to the origin is $f_1(x)$. The scale thus formed is the X scale. This alignment chart differs from those previously considered in that two straight lines are needed to determine a set of points such that the corresponding values of x, y, and z satisfy the original equation. Draw one line from a point on the X scale to the origin. Then any *parallel* line will cut the Y and Z scales in points which, taken with the original X point, satisfy the basic equation.

Example. $y + x(10 - z) = z^2$. Here $y = f_2(y)$, $x = f_1(x)$, $10 - z = F_1(z)$, $z^2 = F_2(z)$. The chart is shown in Fig. 6.

Type IV. $X_1 Y_2 Z_3 + X_2 Y_3 Z_1 + X_3 Y_1 Z_2 - X_1 Y_3 Z_2 - X_2 Y_1 Z_3 - X_3 Y_2 Z_1 = 0$ where X_1, X_2, and X_3 are functions of x only, Y_1, Y_2, Y_3 of y only, etc. The equation may be written in determinant (q.v.) form:

$$\begin{vmatrix} X_1 & X_2 & X_3 \\ Y_1 & Y_2 & Y_3 \\ Z_1 & Z_2 & Z_3 \end{vmatrix} = 0 \tag{10}$$

This is the most general equation in three variables which can be represented by an alignment chart, which latter will consist of the most general case of three curved scales. All the preceding types are special cases of Type IV. *Unless an equation can be reduced to the form of Type IV, no alignment chart can be made.* General rules for determining whether this is possible or not cannot be given; a trial-and-error method must be used. Rules for constructing alignment charts for equations of Type IV which do not reduce to one of the special cases (Types I, II, and III) previously given will be found in texts on nomograms.

59. FUNCTIONS OF FOUR VARIABLES

Functions of four (sometimes more) variables can be handled in several ways. One method is to construct charts which may be moved with respect to one another. A slide rule (not usually considered an alignment chart) is a special and simple illustration of sliding charts, each comprising one scale.

Method I. One method is based on writing a given equation $F(x, y, z, t) = 0$ in the form of two equations by introducing a new variable u: $F_1(x, y, u) = 0$ and $F_2(z, t, u) = 0$. The latter two equations are simply simultaneous equations from which u may be eliminated to get $F(x, y, z, t) = 0$, the original equation, but they must be so chosen that the U scale can be made common to their charts.

Example. $f_1(x) = f_2(y) + f_3(z) + f_4(t)$ where $f_1(x)$ is any function of x, etc. Construct a chart for the equation $f_3(z) + f_4(t) = u$ by the rules for equations in three variables of Type I. Now construct a chart for

$f_1(x) = f_2(y) + u$ by the same rules, making the U scale common to the two three-variable charts. No graduations are necessary on the U scale in this case.

To use the chart, draw a straight line through points corresponding to z on the Z scale and t on the T scale and note where this line crosses the U scale. Through the latter point and a point corresponding to y on the Y scale, pass a line which will cut the X scale at a point corresponding to the value of x which satisfies the basic equation.

Example.
$$\frac{x}{y} = \frac{a + z}{a + t}$$

where a is a fixed constant. Each side of the equation may be set equal to u. Then a Z chart can be constructed for $x/y = u$ and another for $(a + z)/(a + t) = u$, with the U scale common. (See Type II of functions of three variables.) A straight line passing through points on the X scale corresponding to x and on the Y to y determines a point on U. Through the latter and a point on the Z scale corresponding to z a straight line may be passed which will cut the T scale at a point corresponding to a value of t which satisfies the equation.

Method II. Another method of constructing a chart for a function of four variables is to write the equation (if possible) in the form given for Type IV of functions of three variables with Z_1, Z_2, and Z_3 replaced by H_1, H_2, and H_3 where each H is some function of z and t (but not of x and y). If this can be done, then for a given value of t, a Z scale can be constructed, for another value of t, a different Z scale, etc.

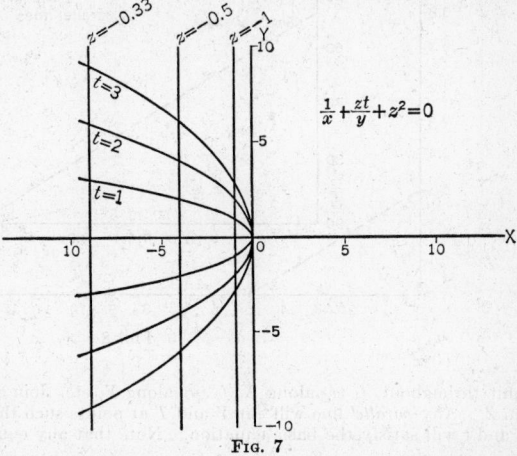

$$\frac{1}{x} + \frac{zt}{y} + z^2 = 0$$

Fig. 7.

Likewise for fixed values of z, various T scales can be drawn. Thus a family of Z and T scales is obtained so that, given a value of t, the proper Z scale can be chosen, and used with the X and Y scales in the same manner as in the case of a three-variable chart.

Example.
$$\frac{1}{x} + \frac{zt}{y} + z^x = 0$$

When $t = 1$ this becomes the equation charted in Fig. 5 as an example of Type III (a) of a function of three variables. When $t = 2, 3, 4, \ldots$, the same X and Y scales may be used, but a different Z scale is obtained for each value of t. Points on the Z scales representing the same value of z may be connected by curves, giving a family of curves. The chart is shown in Fig. 7.

Method III (Proportional Charts). If an equation is of the form
$$\frac{f_1(x)}{f_2(y)} = \frac{f_3(z)}{f_4(t)} \tag{11}$$

then it is in the form of a simple proportion ($a/b = c/d$).

Construct two sets of perpendicular axes, X and Y and Z and T (the two sets may coincide) such that Z is parallel to X and Y to T. Plot $f_1(x)$ along X, using any convenient unit, and $f_3(z)$ along Z, using the same unit. Plot $f_2(y)$ along Y (a different unit may be used) and $f_4(t)$ along T using the same unit as used along Y. Connect any point on X with any point on Y. Any *parallel* line will cut Z and T at points corresponding to values of z and t which with the values of x and y given by the first line will satisfy the basic equation.

Example.
$$\frac{x}{y} = \frac{3 + z^2}{\cos \theta}$$

Here $x = f_1(x)$, $y = f_2(y)$, $3 + z^2 = f_3(z)$ and θ, $\cos \theta$ correspond to $t, f_4(t)$, respectively. The chart is shown in Fig. 8.

Another form of proportional chart can be used when the basic equation can be thrown into the form

$$f_1(x) - f_2(y) = f_3(z) - f_4(t) \qquad (12)$$

Construct two pairs of axes, X and Y, Z and T, all parallel. Make the distance between X and Y the same as that between Z and T (which may be zero). Plot, using the same

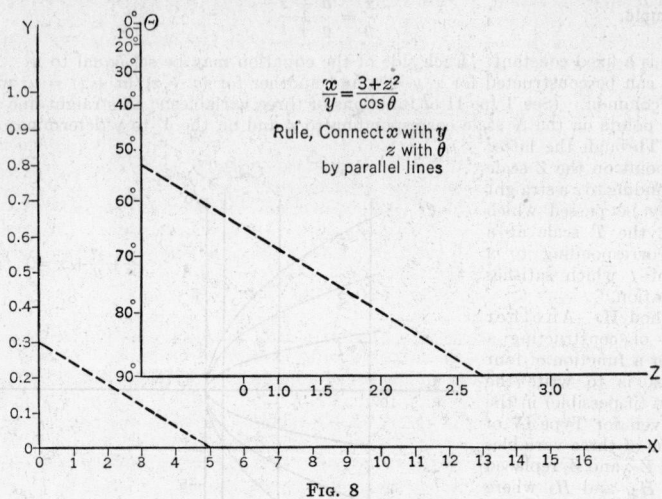

$$\frac{x}{y} = \frac{3 + z^2}{\cos\theta}$$

Rule, Connect x with y
z with θ
by parallel lines

Fig. 8

unit throughout, $f_1(x)$ along X, $f_2(y)$ along Y, etc. Join any point on X with any point on Z. Any *parallel* line will cut Y and T at points such that the corresponding values of z and t will satisfy the basic equation. Note that any equation of the form first consid-

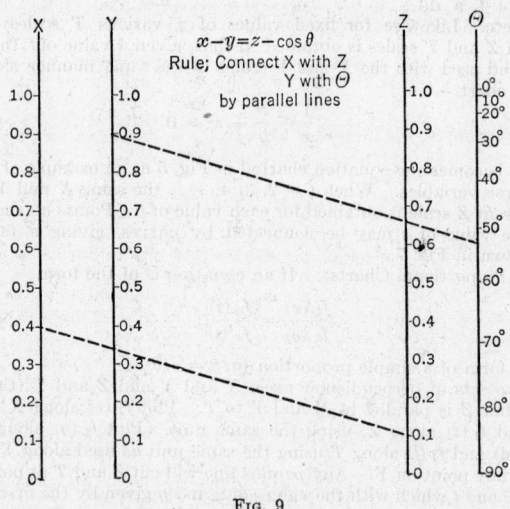

$$x - y = z - \cos\theta$$

Rule; Connect X with Z
Y with Θ
by parallel lines

Fig. 9

ered under Method III may be thrown into the form here considered by taking the logarithm of both sides.

   Example. $\qquad x - y = z - \cos\theta$
The chart is shown in Fig. 9.

PRECISION OF MEASUREMENTS

By J. L. Barnes and Churchill Eisenhart

To increase the reliability of the result of a direct physical measurement the measuring operation is applied to the same quantity more than once. It is important to know how to combine the results of such repeated observations to find the *best estimate* of the *true* value of the quantity measured. Likewise the *risk* incurred in accepting the estimate should be determined since the amount allowable will vary with the purpose for which the estimate is to be used.

60. OBSERVATIONS AND ERRORS

The Error of an Observation is the observed value of the quantity minus the true value, e.g., $e_i \equiv m_i - m$, $i = 1, 2, \ldots n$, where the m_i's are the observed values, the e_i's the errors, and m the true value which is unknown.

Errors are classified as accidental and systematic. *Accidental errors* are those which in a large number of measurements are as often negative as positive. They affect the arithmetic mean but little. All other errors are classed as *systematic*. Systematic errors due to the same cause affect the mean in the same sense, and do not tend to balance each other, but rather give a definite bias to the mean.

It is necessary to eliminate all systematic errors if accurate results are to be secured. In a search for systematic errors each possible source should be varied separately. When systematic errors have been removed there always remains a residual or accidental variability which may be reduced by refinement of apparatus and increased skill in manipulation but which cannot be completely eliminated.

Best Estimate and Measured Value. All systematic errors having been eliminated, it is possible to consider the individual repeated measurements of a quantity with a view to securing the "best estimate of the true value" of the quantity and assessing the degree of reproducibility which has been obtained. The final result will then be expressed in the form $E \pm L$, where E is the best estimate of the true value and L represents the characteristic limit of variation associated with a certain risk. In this connection, it seems appropriate to remark that the entire result, $E \pm L$, is the measured value of the quantity, and not merely E.

The Arithmetic Mean. If a large number of measurements have been made to determine directly the unknown magnitude, m, of a certain quantity, all measurements having been made *with equal skill and care*, the *best estimate* of m is the arithmetic mean, $\overline{m}$, of all the measurements.

$$\overline{m} = \frac{1}{n} \sum_{i=1}^{n} m_i \tag{1}$$

Standard Deviation, in the theory of least squares, is defined as the *root-mean-square* of the deviations e_i of a set of observations from the true value. In the equation

$$\sigma = \left(\frac{1}{n} \sum_{i=1}^{n} e_i^2 \right)^{1/2} \tag{2}$$

σ may be considered, in the language of mechanics, as the radius of gyration of a set of n equal particles, with respect to a given centroid axis.

Since neither the true value, m, nor the errors of observation, $e_i = m_i - m$, are known, the deviations from the mean, $x_i \equiv m_i - \overline{m}$, $i = 1, 2, \ldots, n$, shall henceforth be referred to as errors. Likewise, for the value of σ, the following will be used:

$$\sigma = (n-1)^{-1/2} \left[\sum_{i=1}^{n} (m_i - \overline{m})^2 \right]^{1/2} = (n-1)^{-1/2} \left(\sum_{i=1}^{n} e_i^2 \right)^{1/2} \tag{3}$$

in which n is replaced by $n-1$ since one degree of freedom is lost by using $\overline{m}$ instead of m, $\overline{m}$ being related to the m_i's.

61. THE PROBABLE ERROR

Relative Frequency of Errors. The most prominent frequency function of practical statistics is the *Gauss-Laplace* law of frequency of errors,

$$y = \frac{1}{\sigma \sqrt{2\pi}} e^{-x^2/2\sigma^2} \tag{4}$$

The curve with this equation (Fig. 1) is known in statistics as the *normal probability curve.*
It is also frequently written:

$$y = \frac{1}{\sqrt{\pi}} h \, e^{-h^2 x^2} \tag{5}$$

where $2h^2 \sigma^2 = 1$, or $h = 1/(\sqrt{2}\sigma)$, and y represents the proportionate number of errors
of value x. Thus the area under the curve is unity. The dotted curve (Fig. 1) is also an error distribution curve with a greater value of h. It will be observed that the greater the value of h the more closely are the errors clustered about the maximum ordinate, which is at $x = 0$. Hence h may be considered as a *precision index* and is a measure of the concentration of observations about their mean. Also, h is in inverse relation to σ.

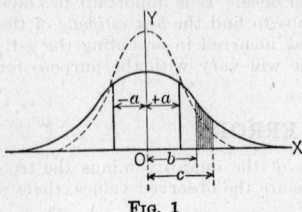

FIG. 1

Probability. The proportionate number of errors whose values lie between $x = -a$ and $x = a$ (Fig. 1) is

$$P = \frac{h}{\sqrt{\pi}} \int_{-a}^{+a} e^{-h^2 x^2} \, dx = \frac{2}{\sqrt{\pi}} \int_{0}^{ha} e^{-h^2 x^2} \, d(hx) \tag{6}$$

where P is the probability of an observational error, x, having a value between $-a$ and a. In a similar manner the shaded area in Fig. 1 represents the relative frequency or probability of errors between b and c.

Values of P corresponding to values of ha given in Table I are published by James Burgess in the *Transactions of the Royal Society*, Edinburgh, **39**, 257, 1900, and in the Smithsonian Tables.

Table I.   Values of $P = \dfrac{2}{\sqrt{\pi}} \displaystyle\int_{0}^{ha} e^{-h^2 x^2} \, d(hx)$

ha*	0	1	2	3	4	5	6	7	8	9
0.0		.01128	.02256	.03384	.04511	.05637	.06762	.07886	.09008	.10128
.1	.11246	.12362	.13476	.14587	.15695	.16800	.17901	.18999	.20094	.21184
.2	.22270	.23352	.24430	.25502	.26570	.27633	.28690	.29742	.30788	.31828
.3	.32863	.33891	.34913	.35928	.36936	.37938	.38933	.39921	.40901	.41874
.4	.42839	.43797	.44747	.45689	.46623	.47548	.48466	.49375	.50275	.51167
.5	.52050	.52924	.53790	.54646	.55494	.56332	.57162	.57982	.58792	.59594
.6	.60386	.61168	.61941	.62705	.63459	.64203	.64938	.65663	.66378	.67084
.7	.67780	.68467	.69143	.69810	.70468	.71116	.71754	.72382	.73001	.73610
.8	.74210	.74800	.75381	.75952	.76514	.77067	.77610	.78144	.78669	.79184
.9	.79691	.80188	.80677	.81156	.81627	.82089	.82542	.82987	.83423	.83851
1.0	.84270	.84681	.85084	.85478	.85865	.86244	.86614	.86977	.87333	.87680
1.1	.88021	.88353	.88679	.88997	.89308	.89612	.89910	.90200	.90484	.90761
1.2	.91031	.91296	.91553	.91805	.92051	.92290	.92524	.92751	.92973	.93190
1.3	.93401	.93606	.93807	.94002	.94191	.94376	.94556	.94731	.94902	.95067
1.4	.95229	.95385	.95538	.95686	.95830	.95970	.96105	.96237	.96365	.96490
1.5	.96611	.96728	.96841	.96952	.97059	.97162	.97263	.97360	.97455	.97546
1.6	.97635	.97721	.97804	.97884	.97962	.98038	.98110	.98181	.98249	.98315
1.7	.98379	.98441	.98500	.98558	.98613	.98667	.98719	.98769	.98817	.98864
1.8	.98909	.98952	.98994	.99035	.99074	.99111	.99147	.99182	.99216	.99248
1.9	.99279	.99309	.99338	.99366	.99392	.99418	.99443	.99466	.99489	.99511
2.0	.99532	.99552	.99572	.99591	.99609	.99626	.99642	.99658	.99673	.99688
2.1	.99702	.99715	.99728	.99741	.99753	.99764	.99775	.99785	.99795	.99805
2.2	.99814	.99822	.99831	.99839	.99846	.99854	.99861	.99867	.99874	.99880
2.3	.99886	.99891	.99897	.99902	.99906	.99911	.99915	.99920	.99924	.99928
2.4	.99931	.99935	.99938	.99941	.99944	.99947	.99950	.99952	.99955	.99957
2.5	.99959	.99961	.99963	.99965	.99967	.99969	.99971	.99972	.99974	.99975
2.6	.99976	.99978	.99979	.99980	.99981	.99982	.99983	.99984	.99985	.99986
2.7	.99987	.99987	.99988	.99989	.99989	.99990	.99991	.99991	.99992	.99992
2.8	.99992	.99993	.99993	.99994	.99994	.99994	.99995	.99995	.99995	.99996
2.9	.99996	.99996	.99996	.99997	.99997	.99997	.99997	.99997	.99997	.99998
3.0	.99998	.99999	.99999	1.00000						

$$* \, ha = 0.47694 \frac{a}{r} = \frac{1}{\sqrt{2}} \frac{a}{\sigma}$$

Probable Error, r. In the publication of results of measurements it has been customary in the United States to express these results in the form $E \pm r$, where r is the *probable error of a single observation* and is defined as *the number which the actual error may with equal probability be greater or less than.* Thus from (6),

$$\frac{2}{\sqrt{\pi}} \int_0^{hr} e^{-h^2 x^2}\, d(hx) = 0.50 \tag{7}$$

Table II.   Values of Functions of n and $(n-1)$

Factors for Computing Actual and Approximate Values of r and $r\overline{m}$

n	$\dfrac{0.6745}{\sqrt{n-1}}$	$\dfrac{0.6745}{\sqrt{n(n-1)}}$	$\dfrac{0.8453}{\sqrt{n(n-1)}}$	$\dfrac{0.8453}{n\sqrt{n-1}}$	n	$\dfrac{0.6745}{\sqrt{n-1}}$	$\dfrac{0.6745}{\sqrt{n(n-1)}}$	$\dfrac{0.8453}{\sqrt{n(n-1)}}$	$\dfrac{0.8453}{n\sqrt{n-1}}$
1					51	0.0954	0.0134	0.0167	0.0023
2	0.6745	0.4769	0.5978	0.4227	52	.0944	.0131	.0164	.0023
3	.4769	.2754	.3451	.1993	53	.0935	.0128	.0161	.0022
4	.3894	.1947	.2440	.1220	54	.0926	.0126	.0158	.0022
5	.3372	.1508	.1890	.0845	55	.0918	.0124	.0155	.0021
6	.3016	.1231	.1543	.0630	56	.0909	.0122	.0152	.0020
7	.2754	.1041	.1304	.0493	57	.0901	.0119	.0150	.0020
8	.2549	.0901	.1130	.0399	58	.0893	.0117	.0147	.0019
9	.2385	.0795	.0996	.0332	59	.0886	.0115	.0145	.0019
10	0.2248	0.0711	0.0891	0.0282	60	0.0878	0.0113	0.0142	0.0018
11	.2133	.0643	.0806	.0243	61	.0871	.0111	.0140	.0018
12	.2034	.0587	.0736	.0212	62	.0864	.0110	.0137	.0017
13	.1947	.0540	.0677	.0188	63	.0857	.0108	.0135	.0017
14	.1871	.0500	.0627	.0167	64	.0850	.0106	.0133	.0017
15	.1803	.0465	.0583	.0151	65	.0843	.0105	.0131	.0016
16	.1742	.0435	.0546	.0136	66	.0837	.0103	.0129	.0016
17	.1686	.0409	.0513	.0124	67	.0830	.0101	.0127	.0016
18	.1636	.0386	.0483	.0114	68	.0824	.0100	.0125	.0015
19	.1590	.0365	.0457	.0105	69	.0818	.0098	.0123	.0015
20	0.1547	0.0346	0.0434	0.0097	70	0.0812	0.0097	0.0122	0.0015
21	.1508	.0329	.0412	.0090	71	.0806	.0096	.0120	.0014
22	.1472	.0314	.0393	.0084	72	.0800	.0094	.0118	.0014
23	.1438	.0300	.0376	.0078	73	.0795	.0093	.0117	.0014
24	.1406	.0287	.0360	.0073	74	.0789	.0092	.0115	.0013
25	.1377	.0275	.0345	.0069	75	.0784	.0091	.0113	.0013
26	.1349	.0265	.0332	.0065	76	.0779	.0089	.0112	.0013
27	.1323	.0255	.0319	.0061	77	.0774	.0088	.0111	.0013
28	.1298	.0245	.0307	.0058	78	.0769	.0087	.0109	.0012
29	.1275	.0237	.0297	.0055	79	.0764	.0086	.0108	.0012
30	0.1252	0.0229	0.0287	0.0052	80	0.0759	0.0085	0.0106	0.0012
31	.1231	.0221	.0277	.0050	81	.0754	.0084	.0105	.0012
32	.1211	.0214	.0268	.0047	82	.0749	.0083	.0104	.0011
33	.1192	.0208	.0260	.0045	83	.0745	.0082	.0102	.0011
34	.1174	.0201	.0252	.0043	84	.0740	.0081	.0101	.0011
35	.1157	.0196	.0245	.0041	85	.0736	.0080	.0100	.0011
36	.1140	.0190	.0238	.0040	86	.0732	.0079	.0099	.0011
37	.1124	.0185	.0232	.0038	87	.0727	.0078	.0098	.0010
38	.1109	.0180	.0225	.0037	88	.0723	.0077	.0097	.0010
39	.1094	.0175	.0220	.0035	89	.0719	.0076	.0096	.0010
40	0.1080	0.0171	0.0214	0.0034	90	0.0715	0.0075	0.0094	0.0010
41	.1066	.0167	.0209	.0033	91	.0711	.0075	.0093	.0010
42	.1053	.0163	.0204	.0031	92	.0707	.0074	.0092	.0010
43	.1041	.0159	.0199	.0030	93	.0703	.0073	.0091	.0009
44	.1029	.0155	.0194	.0029	94	.0699	.0072	.0090	.0009
45	.1017	.0152	.0190	.0028	95	.0696	.0071	.0089	.0009
46	.1005	.0148	.0186	.0027	96	.0692	.0071	.0089	.0009
47	.0994	.0145	.0182	.0027	97	.0688	.0070	.0088	.0009
48	.0984	.0142	.0178	.0026	98	.0685	.0069	.0087	.0009
49	.0974	.0139	.0174	.0025	99	.0681	.0068	.0086	.0009
50	0.0954	0.0136	0.0171	0.0024	100	0.0678	0.0068	0.0085	0.0009

and $$hr = 0.47694 \qquad (8)$$

or $$r = 0.4769 \times \sqrt{2}\,\sigma = 0.6745\,\sigma \qquad (9)$$

In a similar manner it may be observed that 5 per cent of the errors, x, are greater than 2σ, and less than 1 per cent are greater than 3σ. Thus it is possible to evaluate the risk involved in accepting the mean of a number of observations.

From the preceding discussion it follows that

$$r = 0.6745\sigma = 0.6745\,(n-1)^{-\frac{1}{2}}\left(\sum_{i=1}^{n} x_i{}^2\right)^{\frac{1}{2}} \qquad (10)$$

This is the standard formula for r and should be used for results which are to be published. For rapid comparisons, however, the following approximate formula due to Peters is useful:

$$r \approx 0.8453\,[n(n-1)]^{-\frac{1}{2}}\sum_{i=1}^{n} |x_i| \qquad (11)$$

The **Standard Deviation of the Arithmetic Mean**, $\sigma_{\overline{m}}$, as calculated from data, is related to the standard deviation, σ, by the formula

$$\sigma_{\overline{m}} = n^{-\frac{1}{2}}\sigma = [n(n-1)]^{-\frac{1}{2}}\left(\sum_{i=1}^{n} x_i{}^2\right)^{\frac{1}{2}} \qquad (12)$$

From this formula and Tables I and II the limits corresponding to given risks can be determined as indicated above. It is evident that the stability of the mean increases with n, i.e., the effect of the erratic behavior of single cases decreases with increase of n.

The **Probable Error of the Arithmetic Mean** as calculated from data, $r_{\overline{m}}$, is then given by

$$r_{\overline{m}} = 0.6745\,[n(n-1)]^{-\frac{1}{2}}\left(\sum_{i=1}^{n} x_i{}^2\right)^{\frac{1}{2}} \qquad (13)$$

and Peters' formula for the approximate value is:

$$r_{\overline{m}} \approx 0.8453\,[n^2(n-1)]^{-\frac{1}{2}}\sum_{i=1}^{n} |x_i|.$$

62. APPLICATIONS

Example. The following are ten measurements, m_i, of the length of a base line. Below are given the values of the residuals, x_i, and their squares. m_i: 455.35, 455.35, 455.20, 455.05, 455.75, 455.40, 455.10, 455.30, 455.50, 455.30

Arithmetic mean, $\overline{m} = 455.330$.

x_i: 0.02, 0.02, $-$ 0.13, $-$ 0.28, 0.42, 0.07, $-$ 0.23, $-$ 0.03, $-$ 0.17, $-$ 0.03.

$x_i{}^2$: 0.0004, 0.0004, 0.0169, 0.0784, 0.0049, 0.0529, 0.0009, 0.0289, 0.0009.

Hence: $\sum_{i=1}^{10} x_i{}^2 = 0.3610$, and $\sum_{i=1}^{10} |x_i| = 1.40$.

So by the standard formulas, $r = 0.6745\,(9)^{-\frac{1}{2}}(0.3610)^{\frac{1}{2}} = 0.13$, $r_{\overline{m}} = (10)^{-\frac{1}{2}}r = 0.042$. By the approximate formulas, $r \approx 0.8453\,(90)^{-\frac{1}{2}}(1.40) = 0.12$, $r_{\overline{m}} \approx 0.039$.

For the best estimate of the base line, the result is 455.330 with probable error $\pm$ 0.042 (using result given by standard formula), usually written 455.330 $\pm$ 0.042. Note that five of the residuals are numerically less than the probable error of a single observation. In fact, in any considerable number of observations it should be the case that half of the residuals are less than the probable error.

It can be shown that the standard deviation, σ, of a *rounded number* (p. 2–05) due to rounding is $\sigma = 0.2887\,w$, where w is a unit in the last place retained. Consequently, the probable error of a rounded number due to rounding is:

$$r = 0.6745 \times 0.2887\,w = 0.1947\,w.$$

Weighted Observations. Sometimes, notwithstanding the care with which observations are taken, there are reasons for believing that certain observations are better than others. In such cases the observations are given different weights, that is, are counted different numbers of times, the weights or numbers expressing their relative practical worth. If there are n weighted observations, m_i, with weights, p_i, these being made directly on the same quantity, then the best estimate of the true value of the quantity is the *weighted arithmetic mean*, $\overline{m}$.

$$\text{Weighted mean, } \overline{m} \equiv \sum_{i=1}^{n} p_i\,m_i \Big/ \sum_{i=1}^{n} p_i$$

For the set of weighted observations we have

$$r = 0.6745\,(n-1)^{-\frac{1}{2}}\left(\sum_{i=1}^{n} p_i\,x_i{}^2\right)^{\frac{1}{2}}$$

as the probable error of an observation of unit weight, and

$$r\overline{m} = 0.6745\left[(n-1)\sum_{i=1}^{n} p_i\right]^{-\frac{1}{2}}\left(\sum_{i=1}^{n} p_i\,x_i{}^2\right)^{\frac{1}{2}}$$

as the probable error of the arithmetic mean of weighted items, in which

$$x_i \equiv m_i - \sum_{i=1}^{n} p_i\,m_i \Big/ \sum_{i=1}^{n} p_i.$$

Example. Let six observations on the same quantity be made, with weights, p_i, the sum of these weights being 21 (see tabulation below). The sum of the weighted observations, $\sum_{i=1}^{6} p_i\,m_i$, is 3741.36. The best estimate of the value of the observed quantity is $\overline{m} = 3741.36/21 = 178.16$. Subtracting this from each m_i gives the residuals x_i. The sum of the weighted squares of the residuals, $\sum_{i=1}^{6} p_i x_i{}^2$, is 62.95. Then the preceding formulas give the probable error of an observation of weight unity as $r = 2.39$ and the probable error of the weighted mean as $r\overline{m} = 0.52$. The final result then is 178.16 ± 0.52.

p_i:	5	4	1	4	3	4
m_i:	178.26	176.30	181.06	177.95	176.20	180.85
$p_i\,m_i$:	891.30	705.20	181.06	711.80	528.60	723.40
x_i:	.10	1.86	2.90	.21	1.96	2.69
$x_i{}^2$:	.010	3.460	8.410	.441	3.842	7.236
$p_i\,x_i{}^2$:	.05	13.84	8.41	.18	11.53	28.94

Probable Error in a Result Calculated from the Means of Several Observed Quantities. Let Z be a sum or difference of m (means of) observed *independent* quantities. Then if r_j, $j = 1, 2, \ldots, m$, be the probable errors in these means, the probable error in Z is equal to $\left(\sum_{j=1}^{m} r_j{}^2\right)^{\frac{1}{2}}$:

Let $Z = Az$, where z is (the mean of) an observed quantity, and A, a known number. Let r be the probable error in z. Then the probable error in Z is Ar.

Let Z be any differentiable function of the (means of) *independently* observed quantities, z_j, whose probable errors are r_j. Then the probable error in Z is equal to

$$\left[\sum_{j=1}^{m}\left(\frac{\partial Z}{\partial z_j}\right)^2 r_j{}^2\right]^{\frac{1}{2}},$$

e.g., if Z be the product of (the means of) two independently observed quantities, z_1, z_2, whose probable errors are r_1, r_2, respectively, then the probable error in Z is equal to

$$(z_1{}^2\,r_2{}^2 + z_2{}^2\,r_1{}^2)^{\frac{1}{2}}$$

A Note on the Interpretation of Standard Deviation, Probable Error, etc. The theory underlying the foregoing development depends upon the following assumptions: (1) A large number of observations have been made. (2) The observations have been made with equal care and skill so that: (2.1) there are approximately an equal number of readings above and below the mean (except in the case of weighted items), and (2.2) the individual deviations from the mean are small in most cases, and (2.3) the number of deviations diminishes rapidly as their size increases.

The extent to which the observed data satisfy the above assumptions is a measure of the extent to which we are justified in using the Gauss error curve, which is consistent with the statement that $\overline{m}$ is the best estimate of the true value m, and which leads to the factor 0.6745 used in computing probable error. Recent work has shown that, even if we were not justified in assuming the Gaussian distribution of errors, the arithmetic mean still remains the best estimate we have for m. Therefore, there is little difficulty in this regard, especially since "errors" appear to follow the Gaussian distribution as closely as any other we know. Our difficulties enter in connection with the factor 0.6745 and the accuracy of the σ, as estimated from the data.

If the number of observations is small the estimate of the standard deviation of the possible infinity of observations (of which those at hand are a sample) is itself subject to considerable error. For example, for $n = 3$ the standard error of the standard deviation is as large as the standard deviation itself, and hence the probable error calculated from $r = 0.6745\sigma$ would not be very reliable. The following table * will illustrate this. The second and third columns give the probability that the probable error of a single observation should be out 20 and 50 per cent, respectively.

n	20 per cent	50 per cent	n	20 per cent	50 per cent
5	0.64	0.24	30	0.12	0.00014
10	.40	.034	40	.076	8×10^{-6}
15	.29	.008	50	.047	6×10^{-7}
20	.21	.0002	100	.0050	

From this table it is clear that with 10 observations the odds are only 3 to 2 that the calculated probable error is within 20 per cent of the correct value, and about 30 to 1 that it is within 50 per cent of the correct value. Of course, the probable error of the mean will be correspondingly out.

The probable error of a single observation is sometimes *defined* very simply by

$$r \equiv 0.6745 \, (n-1)^{-\frac{1}{2}} \left(\sum_{i=1}^{n} x_i^2 \right)^{\frac{1}{2}}$$

and the probable error of the mean is then

$$r_{\overline{m}} = 0.6745 \, [n(n-1)]^{-\frac{1}{2}} \left(\sum_{i=1}^{n} x_i^2 \right)^{\frac{1}{2}}$$

which does not impose any condition with regard to the distribution. In this sense it is a measure of the way the values cluster about the mean value, and is in no way superior to the h defined earlier, and is inferior to just giving σ itself, since the even wager which brings in 0.6745 is no longer important. This use of the probable error as a *precision index* seems to be customary in the United States, and, indeed, it is as useful as any other index (except σ, from which it differs by merely a numerical multiplier) in connection with results from only a few observations, from results calculated from weighted items, etc. But it must be remembered that in this connection it cannot be used to draw inferences about what might happen if the measurements were repeated a large number of times.

For those who are interested in drawing such inferences, it seems fitting to remark that the use of Table I is quite legitimate for $100 < n$, and that for $30 < n < 100$ the tables may be used provided σ is multiplied by $(n-3)^{-\frac{1}{2}}$. For $n < 30$, a rough estimate can be obtained from the fact that the percentage of cases lying outside the range, mean $\pm \lambda\sigma$, is $< 100 \lambda^{-2}$ for $1 < \lambda$. A striking property of this inequality due to Tchebycheff is that it is independent of the nature of the distribution assumed.

* "The Combination of Observations," David Brunt, Cambridge University Press (1917)

SECTION 3

PHYSICAL UNITS AND STANDARDS

BY
ERNST WEBER

SECTION 3

PHYSICAL UNITS AND STANDARDS

DIMENSION SYSTEMS

1. PHYSICAL QUANTITIES AND THEIR RELATIONS

Mathematics is concerned with relations between numerical quantities, either constant or varying in a specified manner over a specified range of values. The numerical values are unique, absolute, and the same all over the world, being the expression of a fundamental perception of the mind. Any *mathematical equation* defines the values of one numerical quantity, known as the dependent, in terms of constants and one or more other numerical quantities, known as the independent variables, as for example

$$z = y^2 + 3x + 4, \quad y = c \cdot \int_0^x \frac{x^2}{\cos x} \, dx \tag{1}$$

Physics, comprising the knowledge of inanimate nature and her laws, is concerned fundamentally with the measuring of the various quantities founded or created by definition, as for example, *length, mass, electric charge.* In order to specify a *physical quantity* it is not sufficient to state merely a number. The value of a physical quantity can be determined only by comparison of the sample with a known amount of the same quantity, which process is *measuring.* The reference amount is called a unit, and the result of any measurement must be a statement of " how many times the sample was found to contain the reference amount." Thus a physical quantity Q naturally appears to be the product of a numerical value N and a unit U,

$$Q = N \cdot U \tag{2}$$

as for example: The length of a particular rod is 3.5 ft, or the rod is $3\,1/2$ times the length of 1 ft. Obviously, the reproduction of a unit must be possible at any time in order to facilitate correct measurements. This is being done by means of the " standards," which are simply a set of fundamental unit quantities kept under normalized conditions in order to preserve their values as accurately as facilities permit.

Any physical relation must be the result of a more or less obvious measurement, so that equations in physics are not merely numerical relations, but express dependences between physical quantities. Mathematics does not know "standards"; physics cannot be without "standards." The fact that physics often uses the methods of mathematics must not lead to the identification of the two sciences; it is merely an overlapping in the border regions.

Relations between Units. A unit is a particular amount of the physical quantity to be measured, defined in terms of a standard.* The choice of a unit depends on convenience, facility of reproduction, and easy subdivision so as to obtain smaller units if desired. The value of a physical quantity Q must be independent of the units used, so that for two different units of the same type

$$Q = N_1 \cdot U_1 = N_2 \cdot U_2 \tag{3}$$

The size of the unit and the numerical value of the quantity are inversely related: the larger the unit the smaller the number of units.

A unit relation is an equation between two different units of the same type

$$U_1 = N_{12} \cdot U_2 \tag{4}$$

and serves to convert from one unit U_1 to a different one U_2. The conversion is achieved by replacing U_1, taken as a factor, by its equivalent according to equation 4 so that

$$Q = N_1 \cdot U_1 = N_1 \cdot (N_{12} \cdot U_2) = (N_1 \cdot N_{12}) \cdot U_2 \tag{5}$$

As example, express the length 3.5 ft in centimeters. The unit relation is 1 ft = 30.3 cm,

---

* S. W. Stratton, Electric Units and Standards, Circular of the Bureau of Standards, No. 60, 1920.

and therefore $l = 3.5$ ft $= 3.5 \times (30.3$ cm$) = 106.25$ cm. No error is possible if this rule is followed properly.

Physical Equations. Relations between physical quantities are usually given in the form of equations. It is always possible, by the proper use of unit relations (see previous paragraph), to express each side in the same units. Since units are to be considered as factors, they may be canceled and a numerical identity must result. This fact always can be used to check the proper numerical relations and the consistency of the units used.

There are two fundamental types of physical equations:

The Mathematical Definition of a physical quantity determines a new quantity uniquely in terms of known quantities. An example is Newton's definition of mass by $f = m \cdot a$, where f is the force and a the acceleration of a moving body. If f and a are measured, m can be computed as a physical quantity with numerical value $\dfrac{N(f)}{N(a)}$ and unit $\dfrac{U(f)}{U(a)} = U(m)$. A definition should be in agreement with all the other known relations in a particular field of science; it can only be of restricted value if it contradicts other relations (see later the "absolute" electric systems).

The Statement of Proportionality defines one physical quantity as linearly depending on a combination of other, known quantities. It is always the result of an experimental investigation. An example is Newton's law of the gravitational force $f = k \dfrac{m_1 \, m_2}{r^2}$, where m_1 and m_2 are the two masses, r their center distance, and k the proportionality factor. In the case of a proportionality it is permissible to choose arbitrary units for all measurable physical quantities involved and to use the equation as a definition of the proportionality constant which, in general, will be a physical constant with numerical value and unit. In the example the value of k would be

$$\frac{N(f) \cdot N(r^2)}{N(m_1) \cdot N(m_2)} \times \frac{U(f) \cdot U(r^2)}{U(m_1) \cdot U(m_2)} = N(k) \cdot U(k).$$

Most of the fundamental laws of physics are statements of proportionalities, leading to universal physical constants, as for instance the gravitational constant k, the Planck constant h, the gas constant R, the absolute permeability of free space Π_0, and the absolute dielectric constant of free space Δ_0. It may be observed that each branch of physics is represented by at least one fundamental proportionality constant.*

Derived Physical Quantities are, in general, the result of mathematical definitions. The units of derived quantities are expressed from the combinations of the units used in the definition. All proportionality constants logically have to be considered as derived physical quantities.

Fundamental Physical Quantities. The physical quantities, arbitrarily chosen to define new quantities or derived quantities, are called fundamental physical quantities. Their number may vary according to needs and convenience. There is no possibility to designate any physical quantity as absolutely fundamental, or *a priori* fundamental. Quantities which appear to be fundamental in some one special field may be derived quantities in some other field.

2. DIMENSIONS AND DIMENSION SYSTEMS

Definition of Dimension. To choose a unit for a physical quantity one has an infinity of possibilities. The numerous units of length which were in use about 100 years ago present a good practical illustration. Yet all these units have in common the quality of being a distinct length and not, for example, a volume. It is convenient to state this fact by representing with the notation $[L]$ any unit of length whatsoever. The measurement of a physical quantity Q, therefore, leads to the statement

$$Q = N \cdot [Q] \tag{6}$$

where N is a numeric denoting the number of general units $[Q]$ which constitute the total quantity Q. According to Fourier,† who first introduced this concept into the literature, $[Q]$ is called the "dimension" of the quantity Q. Be it clearly understood that dimension is simply the expression of a general unit and therefore a characteristic peculiarity of physical quantities, not occurring in mathematics. Each new physical quantity gives

---

* In the second report of the British Association for the Advancement of Science, Committee on Standards (1873), J. Clerk Maxwell makes a statement in connection with the form of Coulomb's law for magnetic poles, p. 63, about the "absurdity" of a proportionality factor, which arouses very pointed remarks by O. Heaviside, in his Electromagnetic Theory, Vol. 1, p. 118, 1893.

† J. B. J. Fourier, Théorie analytique de la chaleur, Paris, 1822.

rise to a new "dimension" as for instance time $[T]$, force $[F]$, mass $[M]$, and so on. There are as many dimensions, or general units, as there are kinds of physical quantities.

Derived Dimensions. Many physical quantities have been introduced by mathematical definition. Velocity, for example, is defined as $v = \dfrac{ds}{dt}$, where s is the length of the path measured from a definite origin and t is the time. A possible expression for the dimension of velocity would be $[V]$. It is customary and convenient, however, to make use of the mathematical definition which is but the rule for the measurement of velocity, and to express the dimension in terms of the more familiar dimensions of length and time as a derived dimension $[V] = [L]/[T] = [L]\,[T]^{-1}$. (Read: velocity is of $(+1)$ dimension in length and (-1) dimension in time.) The use of mathematical definitions, leading to derived dimensions of a composite nature, reduces the number of symbols. Thus the measurement of volume, if scientifically conducted, gives $[Vol] = [L]^3$, or in words, "volume is of $(+3)$ dimensions in length $[L]$."

Proportionality Constants of physics have, in general, *derived dimensions*, as they are defined by the corresponding physical equations. To assign a special dimension to a proportionality constant would mean to give it preference over a physical quantity and evidently would be illogical. This seemingly obvious fact has recently been recognized internationally, when the International Electrotechnical Commission (I.E.C.), after decades of discussion, at its meeting in 1930 at Oslo adopted the viewpoint that absolute magnetic permeability is a physical quantity with dimension and not a pure numeric.* For the absolute dielectric constant this view had been expressed much earlier, and for other proportionality constants this problem never had arisen.

Fundamental Dimensions. The more familiar dimensions used to express derived dimensions are referred to as fundamental dimensions. It is advantageous to use as few of these fundamental dimensions as possible, not because the physical relations become simpler or clearer, but merely as a matter of economy in symbols. In fact, any dimension can be chosen to be a fundamental dimension in a particular field and a derived dimension in some other field of physics. No fundamental dimension can be made a starting point of natural philosophy.

Dimensional Equations. Since a physical equation constitutes in fact two equations, one for the units and one for the numerics, one can disregard the numerical factors entirely and write the general units or dimensions only, arriving thus at a dimensional equation. For instance, the law of gravitation would read $[F] = [k]\,[M]^2\,[L]^{-2}$, using $[F]$, $[k]$, $[M]$, $[L]$ as dimensions for force, gravitation constant, mass, and length, respectively. From this dimensional equation a derived dimension can be obtained for any quantity involved. Conversely, dimensional equations are used to check the correctness of physical relations, if all dimensions can be made to cancel. Finally, the validity of dimensional equations leads to the method of dimensional analysis. (See Arts. 15 to 18.)

A Set of Fundamental Dimensions is any group of fundamental dimensions, convenient and useful to express all the physical quantities of a particular field in terms of derived dimensions. The number of fundamental dimensions to make a set may vary according to the field of application. Whether or not a set of fundamental dimensions can be used beyond the field for which it was originally intended will depend upon its suitability as a dimension system. (See next paragraph.) In no case should it be used where it can lead to confusion.

A set of fundamental dimensions is *incomplete* when the number of fundamental dimensions composing it is less than the number required for a dimension system. Incomplete sets of fundamental dimensions should not be used outside the very restricted field for which they are useful; they necessarily would lead to confusing relations.

A Dimension System is composed of the smallest number of fundamental dimensions which will form a consistent and complete set for a field of science. Since each relation between physical quantities can be split up into one relation of numerics and another one of dimensions (as general units), it is possible to combine all known relations of dimensions. In setting up these relations, all proportionality factors must be taken as physical quantities. If there are m independent relations known, $(m + p)$ dimensions may be involved, of which m dimensions can be expressed by any p "fundamental" dimensions chosen arbitrarily.

This set of p "fundamental" dimensions is then called a dimension system. From the theory of numbers, therefore, it is known that one generally has a choice of $\dbinom{m + p}{p}$ possible dimension systems. Thus, if $p = 3$, $m = 3$, then one has $\dbinom{6}{3} = 20$ different

---

* A. E. Kennelly, *Trans. A.I.E.E.*, Vol. 50, p. 737, 1931.

possibilities. A necessary condition, however, is that *each* independent relation involve at least $(p + 1)$ dimensions. If this is not the case, then the number of possible dimension systems is less, so that $\binom{m + p}{p}$ indicates the *upper* limit.

Any dimension system chosen in the described manner is consistent, as well as correct, and never leads to ambiguity with respect to the expression of physical quantities. Complete dimension systems in mechanics must have three, in thermodynamics four,* and in electromagnetism four † fundamental dimensions. It seems, according to present knowledge, that five fundamental dimensions suffice for the entire range of physics, namely, the three fundamental dimensions of mechanics, an additional one for thermodynamics, and another additional one for electromagnetism.

All the known dimension systems use length $[L]$ and time $[T]$ as primary fundamental dimensions, adding various fundamental dimensions from the available physical quantities of the fields of physics. The choice of $[L]$ and $[T]$ reduces at once the maximum number of possible dimension systems to $\binom{m + p - 2}{p - 2}$.

Why Dimension Systems? Since the proper choice of units is the ultimate goal of any critical analysis of physical quantities the question may be asked: Why is it necessary to discuss dimension systems? The answer is that each physical quantity may be measured by an infinite variety of units but has only one dimension, within a given dimension system. The process of deciding upon the fundamental dimensions before fixing the units within the scope of the fundamental dimensions is, therefore, essentially a matter of economy and logic.

3. THE DIMENSION SYSTEMS OF MECHANICS

Three Fundamental Dimensions are necessary to form a complete mechanical dimension system. With length and time, $[L]$ and $[T]$, as a basis, only a single additional independent dimension is required. One can choose from mass $[M]$, force $[F]$, power $[P]$, energy $[E]$, gravitation constant $[k]$, and others. Only four alternatives have come into use. Table I shows the dimensional forms for the more important mechanical quantities in all four dimension systems.

Table I. Dimensions of Mechanical Quantities

Symbol (according to A.S.A.)	Quantity	Dynamical or Physical System	Gravitational or Technical System	Energetical System	Astrophysical System
l	Length	$[L]$	$[L]$	$[L]$	$[L]$
t	Time	$[T]$	$[T]$	$[T]$	$[T]$
v	Speed, velocity	$[L][T]^{-1}$	$[L][T]^{-1}$	$[L][T]^{-1}$	$[L][T]^{-1}$
m	Mass	$[M]$	$[F][L]^{-1}[T]^2$	$[E][L]^{-2}[T]^2$	$[L]^3[T]^{-2}[k]^{-1}$
f	Force	$[M][L][T]^{-2}$	$[F]$	$[E][L]^{-1}$	$[L]^4[T]^{-4}[k]^{-1}$
p	Pressure	$[M][L]^{-1}[T]^{-2}$	$[F][L]^{-2}$	$[E][L]^{-3}$	$[L]^2[T]^{-4}[k]^{-1}$
M	Momentum	$[M][L][T]^{-1}$	$[F][T]$	$[E][L]^{-1}[T]$	$[L]^4[T]^{-3}[k]^{-1}$
E	Energy	$[M][L]^2[T]^{-2}$	$[F][L]$	$[E]$	$[L]^5[T]^{-4}[k]^{-1}$
P	Power	$[M][L]^2[T]^{-3}$	$[F][L][T]^{-1}$	$[E][T]^{-1}$	$[L]^5[T]^{-5}[k]^{-1}$
T	Torque	$[M][L]^2[T]^{-2}$	$[F][L]$	$[E]$	$[L]^5[T]^{-4}[k]^{-1}$
k	Gravitation constant	$[M]^{-1}[L]^3[T]^{-2}$	$[F]^{-1}[L]^4[T]^{-4}$	$[E]^{-1}[L]^5[T]^{-4}$	$[k]$

The Dynamical or Physical Dimension System has as fundamental dimensions length, $[L]$, time $[T]$, and mass $[M]$. It is the most widely used system in physics and is often found even in engineering. The advantage is that any standard of mass can be preserved and copied with relative ease. Comparison of masses at various locations can be made with the ordinary balance; the local constant of gravity has no influence upon the result. This dimension system has often been referred to as the "absolute" system, but on account of inconsistent usage in the literature, it will generally be referred to herein as the physical dimension system.

The Gravitational or Technical Dimension System has as fundamental dimensions length $[L]$, time $[T]$, and force $[F]$. It is of wide use in all engineering branches, although

---

* For first reference to this fact, see Fourier's Théorie analytique de la chaleur, Paris, 1822.
† For first reference to this fact, see A. W. Rücker, *Proc. Phys. Soc. London*, 1888, Vol. 10, p. 37; *Phil. Mag.*, February, 1889, Vol. 27, p. 104.

often mixed with the physical dimension system. The advantage for the field of engineering is obvious, taking into account the prevalence of force, stress, and pressure computations.* All quantities related to force have particularly simple dimensional forms. The disadvantage is the dependence of the usual force measurements upon the local value of the constant of gravity.† Standards of force are expressed in terms of the weight of a standard mass and, therefore, are indirectly based upon the physical dimension system.

The Energetical Dimension System ‡ has as fundamental dimensions length $[L]$, time $[T]$, and energy $[E]$. The dimensional forms of most of the important quantities are simpler, and this system should appeal to the scientist because of its close relation to the universal quantity energy. The system is not in use in mechanics; it has, however, gained prominence in heat. (See Art. 4 below.) Its disadvantage is the fact that no substantial standard of energy can be preserved with which results of measurements can readily be compared, as is the case with mass or force.

The Astrophysical Dimension System has as fundamental dimensions length $[L]$, time $[T]$, and the gravitational constant $[k]$. Here is a system which admits a proportionality constant to the rôle of a fundamental quantity with a fundamental dimension which is not advisable. The temptation exists to assign arbitrarily not a fundamental but a definite dimension and, in fact, astrophysics uses $k = 1$, which means that the numerical value of k is chosen as unity and its dimensions as zero. The dimensions of the other quantities in this special case are obtained from the last column in Table I if the factor with $[k]$ is left off on account of $[k] = [L]^\circ [T]^\circ = 1$. This reduces the dimension system to an *incomplete set of dimensions* with very restricted use. To see this, choose in the physical system $m = 1$, as m is the proportionality constant in Newton's law $f = m \cdot a$, where a is the acceleration. Again, the dimensions for this special case would follow from the physical system by putting $[M] = 1$. For the gravitation constant this would yield $[k] = [L]^3 [T]^{-2}$, the same dimension as results for mass in the incomplete astrophysical set of 2 fundamental dimensions; obviously this would invite confusion. One should avoid, therefore, the making of arbitrary assignments for dimensions considered to be fundamental because it will lead to contradictions.

4. THE DIMENSION SYSTEMS OF HEAT

Four Fundamental Dimensions are necessary to form a complete heat dimension system.§ Obviously the simplest extension to four dimensions is to add a thermal fundamental dimension to the three fundamental dimensions of mechanics. As the additional thermal dimension that of temperature, $[\theta]$, has been chosen universally. Thus, three heat dimension systems are obtained according to the three first-named mechanical dimension systems from Table I. No extension of the astrophysical dimension system is known. In Table II are listed the dimensional forms for the more important thermal quantities in all three dimension systems.

Table II.   Dimensions of Thermal Quantities

Symbol (according to A.S.A.)	Quantity	Thermophysical System	Thermotechnical System	Energetical System
	3 fundamental mechanical dimensions	$[L]$, $[T]$, $[M]$	$[L]$, $[T]$, $[F]$	$[L]$, $[T]$, $[E]$
θ	Temperature	$[\theta]$	$[\theta]$	$[\theta]$
H	Quantity of heat	$[M][L]^2[T]^{-2}$	$[F][L]$	$[E]$
c	Thermal capacity	$[L]^2[T]^{-2}[\theta]^{-1}$	$[L]^2[T]^{-2}[\theta]^{-1}$	$[L]^2[T]^{-2}[\theta]^{-1}$
k	Thermal conductivity	$[M][L][T]^{-3}[\theta]^{-1}$	$[F][T]^{-1}[\theta]^{-1}$	$[E][L]^{-1}[T]^{-1}[\theta]^{-1}$
h	Emissivity	$[M][T]^{-3}[\theta]^{-1}$	$[F][L]^{-1}[T]^{-1}[\theta]^{-1}$	$[E][T]^{-1}[\theta]^{-1}$
s	Entropy	$[M][L]^2[T]^{-2}[\theta]^{-1}$	$[F][L][\theta]^{-1}$	$[E][\theta]^{-1}$

The **Thermophysical Dimension System** is the extension of the dynamical or physical mechanical dimension system by adding temperature $[\theta]$ as the fourth fundamental dimension. It is the most widely used system and has all the advantages of the physical dimension system of mechanics. This system is sometimes reduced to an incomplete set of "absolute dimensions" by arbitrarily assuming temperature as a pure numeric. The

* See the new advocation by F. A. Brooks, *J. Engg. Educ.*, Vol. 25, p. 240, 1934.
† Wm. L. DeBaufre, *Proc. Soc. Promotion Engg. Educ.*, Vol. 28, p. 655, 1928.
‡ W. Ostwald, *Berichte der Gesellschaft der Wissenschaften*, Leipzig, 1891, Vol. 43, p. 277.
§ J. B. J. Fourier, *Théorie analytique de la chaleur*, Paris, 1822.

dimensions in this case can be taken from Table II if $[\theta] = 1$ is introduced in the thermophysical system. The objections to such a procedure are obviously the same as in reducing the astrophysical system to less than the required number of fundamental dimensions, and the same argumentation can be used.

The **Thermotechnical Dimension System** is the extension of the gravitational or technical mechanical dimension system by adding temperature as the fourth fundamental dimension. Its use is rather restricted although it is the natural system to be used in engineering.

The **Energetical Dimension System** is the extension of the corresponding mechanical dimension system and has been proposed by W. Ostwald. It has not been used to any extent.

5. THE DIMENSION SYSTEMS OF ELECTROMAGNETISM

Four Fundamental Dimensions are necessary to form a complete dimension system for the field of electromagnetism exclusive of thermal phenomena.* Obviously the simplest extension to four dimensions is to add an electromagnetic fundamental dimension to the three fundamental dimensions of mechanics. In general, one can choose from among all electromagnetic quantities; in particular, one would probably prefer to choose the dimension of a quantity which comes nearest to the fundamental concept of electricity. Length and time, forming the fundamental background of sensual perception, and mass or force as the fundamental representative of mechanical inertia, demand a companion of equal basic character.

There are three fundamental electromagnetic experiments which involve all the basic quantities of electromagnetism. The two independent experimental laws forming the base of electrostatics on one side and electrodynamics on the other side are Coulomb's law

$$f_e = k_e \frac{Q_1 Q_2}{r^2} \tag{1}$$

and Ampère's law

$$f_m = k_m \frac{I_1 I_2}{r} \cdot l \tag{2}$$

expressing the force actions between two electric charges Q_1 and Q_2 at rest, and between two electric currents I_1 and I_2, respectively. k_e and k_m are the two proportionality factors, r is the center distance, and l the homogeneous length of the two conductors carrying current. As current is merely displacement of charge, the additional relation $I = \dfrac{dQ}{dt}$ must hold, which is the expression of a basic concept.

The third experimental law which connects the purely electric with the magnetic phenomena is Faraday's law of induction

$$V = - k_i \frac{d\phi}{dt} \tag{3}$$

where V is the induced voltage (emf), ϕ the magnetic flux linked with the conductor in which V is produced, and k_i another proportionality factor.

The variety of electromagnetic quantities leads one to expect a corresponding variety of dimension systems. In Table III are shown the dimensions of the more important electromagnetic quantities in eight different dimension systems of varying prominence and varying logical foundation.

The Natural Electrical Dimension Systems

The **Electrophysical Dimension System** † is the extension of the dynamical or physical mechanical dimension system by adding electric charge $[Q]$ as the fourth fundamental dimension. (See column 1 of Table III.)

The **Electrotechnical Dimension System** † is the extension of the gravitational or technical mechanical dimension system by adding electric charge $[Q]$ as the fourth fundamental dimension. (See column 2 of Table III.)

Both systems are the natural extensions of existing mechanical systems and use the basic concept of quantity of electricity as the additional fundamental dimension. Although the electron is recognized occasionally as a truly elemental quantity,‡ the tendency has prevailed to choose resistance as a fundamental dimension since it is thought to be more readily reproduced. Newer investigations show the resistance of a metal to be a very

---

* A. W. Rücker, *Phil. Mag.*, February, 1889, Vol. 27, p. 104. See also So-called Absolute Electrical Dimension Systems.

† E. Weber, *Trans. A.I.E.E.*, Vol. 51, p. 728, 1932; see also E. Brylinski, *Rev. gén. de l'élec.*, Vol. 30, p. 781, 1931, and D. Germani, *Rev. gén. de l'élec.*, Vol. 32, p. 39, 1932.

‡ Tolman, *Phys. Rev.*, Vol. 9, p. 237, 1917.

Table III. Dimensions of Electromagnetic Quantities

Symbol (according to A.S.A.)*	Quantity	Electrophysical System ①	Electrotechnical System ②	Definitive System ③
l	Length	$[L]$	$[L]$	$[L]$
t	Time	$[T]$	$[T]$	$[T]$
m	Mass	$[M]$	$[F][L]^{-1}[T]^2$	$[P][L]^{-2}[T]^{-3}$
f	Force	$[M][L][T]^{-2}$	$[F]$	$[P][L]^{-1}[T]$
E	Energy	$[M][L]^2[T]^{-2}$	$[F][L]$	$[P][T]$
P	Power	$[M][L]^2[T]^{-3}$	$[F][L][T]^{-1}$	$[P]$
Q	Electric charge	$[Q]$	$[Q]$	$[Q]$
ψ	Electrostatic flux	$[Q]$	$[Q]$	$[Q]$
D	Displacement	$[Q][L]^{-2}$	$[Q][L]^{-2}$	$[Q][L]^{-2}$
E	El. field intensity	$[M][Q]^{-1}[L][T]^{-2}$	$[F][Q]^{-1}$	$[P][Q]^{-1}[L]^{-1}[T]$
C	Capacitance	$[M]^{-1}[Q]^2[L]^{-2}[T]^2$	$[F]^{-1}[Q]^2[L]^{-1}$	$[P]^{-1}[Q]^2[T]^{-1}$
I	Current	$[Q][T]^{-1}$	$[Q][T]^{-1}$	$[Q][T]^{-1}$
V	Voltage	$[M][Q]^{-1}[L]^2[T]^{-2}$	$[F][Q]^{-1}[L]$	$[P][Q]^{-1}[T]$
R	Resistance	$[M][Q]^{-2}[L]^2[T]^{-1}$	$[F][Q]^{-2}[L][T]$	$[P][Q]^{-2}[T]^2$
ϕ	Magnetic flux	$[M][Q]^{-1}[L]^2[T]^{-1}$	$[F][Q]^{-1}[L][T]$	$[P][Q]^{-1}[T]^2$
B	Induction	$[M][Q]^{-1}[T]^{-1}$	$[F][Q]^{-1}[L]^{-1}[T]$	$[P][Q]^{-1}[L]^{-2}[T]^2$
H	Magnetizing force	$[Q][L]^{-1}[T]^{-1}$	$[Q][L]^{-1}[T]^{-1}$	$[Q][L]^{-1}[T]^{-1}$
L	Inductance	$[M][Q]^{-2}[L]^2$	$[F][Q]^{-2}[L][T]^2$	$[P][Q]^{-2}[T]^3$
F	Magnetomotive force	$[Q][T]^{-1}$	$[Q][T]^{-1}$	$[Q][T]^{-1}$
$\mathcal{R}$	Reluctance	$[M]^{-1}[Q]^2[L]^{-2}$	$[F]^{-1}[Q]^2[L]^{-1}[T]^{-2}$	$[P]^{-1}[Q]^2[T]^{-3}$
Δ	Absolute diel. const.	$[M]^{-1}[Q]^2[L]^{-3}[T]^2$	$[F]^{-1}[Q]^2[L]^{-2}$	$[P]^{-1}[Q]^2[L]^{-1}[T]^{-1}$
Π	Absolute permeability	$[M][Q]^{-2}[L]$	$[F][Q]^{-2}[T]^2$	$[P][Q]^{-2}[L]^{-1}[T]^3$
			The "Natural" Systems	

Symbol (according to A.S.A.)	Quantity	"Practical" System ④	Energetical System ⑤	Electrostatic System ⑥
l	Length	$[L]$	$[L]$	$[L]$
t	Time	$[T]$	$[T]$	$[T]$
m	Mass	$[I]^2[R][L]^{-2}[T]^3$	$[E][L]^{-2}[T]^2$	$[M]$
f	Force	$[I]^2[R][L]^{-1}[T]$	$[E][L]^{-1}$	$[M][L][T]^{-2}$
E	Energy	$[I]^2[R][T]$	$[E]$	$[M][L]^2[T]^{-2}$
P	Power	$[I]^2[R]$	$[E][T]^{-1}$	$[M][L]^2[T]^{-3}$
Q	Electric charge	$[I][T]$	$[E][V]^{-1}$	$[M]^{1/2}[L]^{3/2}[T]^{-1}[k_e]^{-1/2}$
ψ	Electrostatic flux	$[I][T]$	$[E][V]^{-1}$	$[M]^{1/2}[L]^{3/2}[T]^{-1}[k_e]^{-1/2}$
D	Displacement	$[I][L]^{-2}[T]$	$[E][V]^{-1}[L]^{-2}$	$[M]^{1/2}[L]^{-1/2}[T]^{-1}[k_e]^{-1/2}$
E	El. field intensity	$[I][R][L]^{-1}$	$[V][L]^{-1}$	$[M]^{1/2}[L]^{-1/2}[T]^{-1}[k_e]^{1/2}$
C	Capacitance	$[R]^{-1}[T]$	$[E][V]^{-2}$	$[L][k_e]^{-1}$
I	Current	$[I]$	$[E][V]^{-1}[T]^{-1}$	$[M]^{1/2}[L]^{3/2}[T]^{-2}[k_e]^{-1/2}$
V	Voltage	$[I][R]$	$[V]$	$[M]^{1/2}[L]^{1/2}[T]^{-1}[k_e]^{1/2}$
R	Resistance	$[R]$	$[E]^{-1}[V]^2[T]$	$[L]^{-1}[T][k_e]$
ϕ	Magnetic flux	$[I][R][T]$	$[V][T]$	$[M]^{1/2}[L]^{1/2}[k_e]^{1/2}$
B	Induction	$[I][R][L]^{-2}[T]$	$[V][L]^{-2}[T]$	$[M]^{1/2}[L]^{-3/2}[k_e]^{1/2}$
H	Magnetizing force	$[I][L]$	$[E][V]^{-1}[L]^{-1}[T]^{-1}$	$[M]^{1/2}[L]^{1/2}[T]^{-2}[k_e]^{-1/2}$
L	Inductance	$[R][T]$	$[E]^{-1}[V]^2[T]^2$	$[L]^{-1}[T]^2[k_e]$
F	Magnetomotive force	$[I]$	$[E][V]^{-1}[T]^{-1}$	$[M]^{1/2}[L]^{3/2}[T]^{-2}[k_e]^{-1/2}$
$\mathcal{R}$	Reluctance	$[R]^{-1}[T]^{-1}$	$[E][V]^{-2}[T]^{-2}$	$[L][T]^{-2}[k_e]^{-1}$
Δ	Absolute diel. const.	$[R]^{-1}[L]^{-1}[T]$	$[E][V]^{-2}[L]^{-1}$	$[k_e]^{-1}$
Π	Absolute permeability	$[R][L]^{-1}[T]$	$[E]^{-1}[V]^2[L]^{-1}[T]^2$	$[L]^{-2}[T]^2[k_e]$
			The "Practical" Systems	The "Fractional" Systems

* The symbols Δ and Π are used in order to retain the classical definitions of μ and ϵ.

Table III. Dimensions of Electromagnetic Quantities (*Continued*)

Symbol (according to A.S A.)	Quantity	Electromagnetic System ⑦	Gaussian System ⑧
l	Length	$[L]$	$[L]$
t	Time	$[T]$	$[T]$
m	Mass	$[M]$	$[M]$
f	Force	$[M][L][T]^{-2}$	$[M][L][T]^{-2}$
E	Energy	$[M][L]^2[T]^{-2}$	$[M][L]^2[T]^{-2}$
P	Power	$[M][L]^2[T]^{-3}$	$[M][L]^2[T]^{-3}$
Q	Electric charge	$[M]^{1/2}[L]^{1/2}[k_m]^{-1/2}$	$[M]^{1/2}[L]^{3/2}[T]^{-1}[k_e]^{-1/2}$
ψ	Electrostatic flux	$[M]^{1/2}[L]^{1/2}[k_m]^{-1/2}$	$[M]^{1/2}[L]^{3/2}[T]^{-1}[k_e]^{-1/2}$
D	Displacement	$[M]^{1/2}[L]^{-3/2}[k_m]^{-1/2}$	$[M]^{1/2}[L]^{-1/2}[T]^{-1}[k_e]^{-1/2}$
E	El. field intensity	$[M]^{1/2}[L]^{1/2}[T]^{-2}[k_m]^{1/2}$	$[M]^{1/2}[L]^{-1/2}[T]^{-1}[k_e]^{1/2}$
C	Capacitance	$[L]^{-1}[T]^2[k_m]^{-1}$	$[L][k_e]^{-1}$
I	Current	$[M]^{1/2}[L]^{1/2}[T]^{-1}[k_m]^{-1/2}$	$[M]^{1/2}[L]^{3/2}[T]^{-2}[k_e]^{-1/2}$
V	Voltage	$[M]^{1/2}[L]^{3/2}[T]^{-2}[k_m]^{1/2}$	$[M]^{1/2}[L]^{1/2}[T]^{-1}[k_e]^{1/2}$
R	Resistance	$[L]^{1/2}[T]^{-1}[k_m]$	$[L]^{-1}[T][k_e]$
ϕ	Magnetic flux	$[M]^{1/2}[L]^{3/2}[T]^{-1}[k_m]^{1/2}$	$[M]^{1/2}[L]^{3/2}[T]^{-1}[k_m]^{1/2}$
B	Induction	$[M]^{1/2}[L]^{-1/2}[T]^{-1}[k_m]^{1/2}$	$[M]^{1/2}[L]^{-1/2}[T]^{-1}[k_m]^{1/2}$
H	Magnetizing force	$[M]^{1/2}[L]^{-1/2}[T]^{-1}[k_m]^{-1/2}$	$[M]^{1/2}[L]^{-1/2}[T]^{-1}[k_m]^{-1/2}$
L	Inductance	$[L][k_m]$	$[L][k_m]$
F	Magnetomotive force	$[M]^{1/2}[L]^{1/2}[T]^{-1}[k_m]^{-1/2}$	$[M]^{1/2}[L]^{1/2}[T]^{-1}[k_m]^{-1/2}$
$\mathcal{R}$	Reluctance	$[L]^{-1}[k_m]^{-1}$	$[L]^{-1}[k_m]^{-1}$
Δ	Absolute diel. const.	$[L]^{-2}[T]^2[k_m]^{-1}$	$[k_e]^{-1}$
Π	Absolute permeability	$[k_m]$	$[k_m]$

The "Fractional" Systems

complicated function of the surrounding conditions and a function of the density of free electrons, which points in the direction of the above natural dimension systems as more satisfactory than systems using electrical resistance as a fundamental quantity.

The **Definitive Dimension System** * is the extension of an energetical mechanical dimension system (using length, time, and power) by adding electric charge $[Q]$ as the fourth fundamental dimension. (See column 3 of Table III.) As there are no standards available for power, this system is indirectly based upon the physical system. The choice of power as a fundamental quantity was obviously made in view of the extensive use of the watt as a unit in all fields of physics.

The Fractional Electrical Dimension Systems

The **Electrostatic Dimension System (ES-System)** is the extension of the dynamical or physical mechanical dimension system, by adding the proportionality constant $[k_e]$ as the fourth fundamental dimension. Notwithstanding the fact that a proportionality constant has been advanced to a fundamental dimension, all the magnetic quantities are dependent on some power of $k_e = \dfrac{1}{4\pi\Delta}$, which seems quite illogical. The most extensive use of this dimension system as a preferred one has been made by E. Bennett.† (See column 6 of Table III.)

The **Electromagnetic Dimension System (EM-System)** is the extension of the dynamical or physical mechanical dimension system, by adding the proportionality constant $[k_m]$ as the fourth fundamental dimension. Again a proportionality constant has been advanced to the rank of a fundamental dimension and all the electric quantities are dependent upon some power of $k_m = \dfrac{1}{2\pi} \cdot \Pi$, which seems quite illogical. (See column 7 of Table III.)

Both systems are complete dimension systems as they are based upon four fundamental dimensions. The emphasis placed upon the proportionality factor seems out of place, and the fact alone, that all the electromagnetic quantities appear as derived fractional

---

* G. A. Campbell, A definitive system of units, *Bull. National Research Council*, Nr. 93, p. 48, 1933.
† E. Bennett, A digest of the relations between the electrical units, *Bull. Univ. Wisconsin*, No. 880, 1917

dimensions, should indicate that better systems could be found. It is further to be noted that both systems belong in the same class of dynamical or physical dimension systems and, therefore, do not constitute a true alternative. Any preference as to the first or second system introduces a dissymmetry into the dimensional expressions and stresses a particular field of electromagnetism which cannot be the intention of any comprehensive dimension system.

The Symmetrical Dimension System. Taking cognizance of the fact that the two proportionality constants k_e and k_m differ in their dimensions by the factor $[L]^2 [T]^{-2}$, which happens to be the square of the dimension of a velocity, the relation

$$[k_e] = [k_m] [L]^2 [T]^{-2}$$

can be used to express either in the electrostatic system all the magnetic quantities in dimensions of $[k_m]$ rather than $[k_e]$, or in the electromagnetic system all the electric quantities in dimensions of $[k_e]$ rather than $[k_m]$. The last column in Table III shows the resulting hybrid system which exhibits a remarkable symmetry in the principal electric and magnetic quantities as far as the three mechanical dimensions are concerned; it might be referred to as the *generalized Gaussian dimension system*. Obviously, in all equations combining electric and magnetic quantities, an arbitrary factor must be introduced in order to balance the dimensions on both sides and this factor must have the characteristics of a velocity or some power of it. In fact, this velocity was found to be of the same value as the velocity of light in free space and this was taken as an indication of a very fundamental principle. (It is not conceivable, however, what rôle the velocity of light for free space should play in ordinary physical phenomena.) In this dimension system, then, the factor c, denoting the velocity of light in free space, appears repeatedly, as for example in the induction law $V = \dfrac{1}{c} \dfrac{d\phi}{dt}$, where the induced voltage (emf) is measured electrostatically and the magnetic flux is measured electromagnetically. (See column 8 of Table III.)

The So-called Absolute Electrical Dimension Systems

The original use of the word "absolute" in connection with electrical measurements goes back to the report of the Committee on Electrical Standards, British Association for the Advancement of Science, 1863, which states:

"The word "absolute" in the present sense is used as opposed to the word "relative" and by no means implies that the measurement is accurately made or that the unit implied is of perfect construction; in other words, it does not mean that the measurement or units are absolutely correct but only that the measurement instead of being a simple comparison with an arbitrary standard of the same kind as that measured is made by reference to certain fundamental units of another kind treated as postulates."

As the fundamental units, length, mass, and time, were commonly used, any measurement made in terms of these specific quantities is now customarily called an "absolute" measurement. To indicate the injudicious use of the word absolute it is prefixed with "so-called" in this section.

In connection with the use of dimensions it also became customary to call the dynamical or physical dimension system the "absolute" dimension systems. Assigning, then, arbitrarily, zero dimension to the proportionality factors occurring in the basic experimental laws of electromagnetism, the fractional electrical dimension systems (see Table III) reduce to the so-called "absolute" dimension systems. The additional arbitrary disposal of the dimension of the proportionality constant or constants thus leads within electromagnetism to an incomplete set of fundamental dimensions. According to the three fractional dimension systems three different sets of dimensions for the electromagnetic quantities suggest themselves and have been used.

The So-called Absolute Electrostatic Dimension System is the electrically incomplete set of the three fundamental dimensions of the physical mechanical dimension system derived from the fractional electrostatic dimension system by arbitrarily assuming k_e as purely numeric. The dimensions for this incomplete set are obtained from Table III, column 6, by introducing $[k_e] = 1$.

The So-called Absolute Electromagnetic Dimension System is the electrically incomplete set of the three fundamental dimensions of the physical mechanical dimension system derived from the fractional electromagnetic dimension system by arbitrarily assuming k_m as purely numeric. The dimensions for this incomplete set are obtained from Table III, column 7, by introducing $[k_m] = 1$.

The Gaussian or So-called Absolute Symmetrical Dimension System is the electrically incomplete set of the three fundamental dimensions of the physical mechanical dimension system obtained from a peculiar combination of the fractional electrostatic and electromagnetic dimension systems as shown in Table III, column 8, by specifying $[k_e] = [k_m] = 1$, i.e., defining both proportionality constants as pure numbers. The remarkable result is that all the electric quantities, including the current, are in the electrostatic dimension system, and the magnetic quantities are in the electromagnetic system. This Gaussian set of dimensions has been almost exclusively used in theoretical physics * on the basis that the symmetry in the dimensional expressions of electric and magnetic quantities facilitates the teaching of electromagnetism. There is, however, no definite agreement on the dimension of electric current, although most authors prefer the expression following from the electrostatic dimension system.

On the Use of the So-called Absolute Electrical Dimension Systems. Probably no other single question has raised so many discussions as the question of the "proper" dimensions of the electromagnetic quantities. As has been stated (See Art. 2) the chief advantages of using the concept of physical dimensions are;

1. The number of fundamental dimensions is the same as the number of fundamental units.

2. Physical equations can be checked by dimensional homogeneity.

3. New physical relations can be obtained by the use of dimensional analysis (See Art. 17).

It is obviously desirable to define fundamental and derived dimensions in such a way that the least amount of confusion arises and that easy communication of research is possible. The definition of complete dimension systems in electromagnetism requires from this point of view four fundamental dimensions as has been pointed out repeatedly in the past.† The arbitrary suppression of the dimension of a proportionality constant, as done in the case of the so-called "absolute" systems, leads to confusion in dimensional analysis,‡ and makes difficult the checking of the dimensional homogeneity of equations.

Recent discussions show a definite tendency towards accepting this fact and particularly to choose electric charge as the fourth fundamental dimension, leading to the electrophysical dimension system (see Table III, column (1)), in which all dimensional expressions become rather simple.§

The S.U.N. (Symbols, Units and Nomenclature) Commission of the International Union of Pure and Applied Physics in a letter by R. T. Glasebrook (Nov. 30, 1935) ¶ concedes, that "On a modern 'Maxwell' theory of electricity the permeability of space, . . . is assumed to be a quantity having dimensions."

Since physicists have generally reduced the problem of choosing three or four fundamental dimensions in electromagnetism to the question whether magnetising force H and magnetic flux density B have equal or different dimensions,‖ the concession that permeability is a physical quantity with dimension is equivalent to a rejection of the so-called "absolute" dimension systems in electromagnetism. The same report, however, stresses the fact that ". . . the S.U.N. Commission desires to take this opportunity of placing on record their recognition of the fact there are important electrical theories supported by a number of physicists in accordance with which . . ." the product of absolute permeability and absolute dielectric constant is a pure number. This is equivalent to accepting the use of the Gaussian system which is still preferred by many of the theoretical physicists.**

It may be emphasized, that the question of the proper number of fundamental dimensions or units is entirely divorced from the other question of the definition of electromagnetic units. It is well possible to retain the so-called "absolute" electrostatic units as values with dimensions following from any one of the complete dimension systems based upon so-called absolute measurements.

---

* For example, H. Hertz, Electric Waves, London, 1893; A. G. Webster, Theory of Electricity and Magnetism, London, 1897; H. A. Lorentz, The Theory of Electrons, New York, 1909; J. H. Jeans, Electricity and Magnetism, Cambridge, 1911; O. W. Richardson, The Electron Theory of Matter, Cambridge, 1914.

† A. W. Rücker, *Phil. Mag.*, February, 1889, Vol. 27, p. 104; S. W. Stratton, Electric Units and Standards, Circ. of the Bureau of Standards, No. 60, 1920, p. 10; J. Wallot, *E.T.Z.*, 1922, pp. 1329, 1372; L. Genillon, *Rev. Gén. de l'élec.*, Vol. 13, p. 173, 1923; and others.

‡ See for example P. W. Bridgman, Dimensional Analysis, Yale Univ. Press, 1922, p. 12.

§ E. Brylinski, *Rev. Gén. de l'élec.*, Vol. 38, p. 589, 1935, Vol. 39, p. 747, 1935, and Vol. 40, p. 99, 1936; A. Sommerfeld, *Zeits. f. techn. Physik*, Vol. 16, p. 420, 1935, and *Phys. Zeits.*, Vol. 36, p. 814, 1935; C. A. Budeanu, *Comité électrotechn. roumanie, Bull.* No. 21, 28; J. Fischer, *Zeits. f. Physik*, Vol. 100, p. 360, 1936; L. Genillon, *Rev. Gén. de l'élec.*, Vol. 41, p. 99, 1937. Also G. A. Campbell, E. Bennett, as in footnote on p. 3–09.

¶ See appendix to A. E. Kennelly, the M.K.S. System of Giorgi as adopted by the IEC in June, 1935, *J. Engg. Educ.*, Vol. 27, p. 303, 1936.

‖ See A. E. Kennelly, *J. Engg. Educ.*, Vol. 27, p. 291, 1936, and especially the bibliography appended thereto.

** L. Page, *Physics*, Vol. 2, p. 289, 1932; and in *Bull.* No. 93, of the *Nat. Research Council*, p. 39, 1933; M. Abraham, *Bull.* No. 93, of the *Nat. Research Council*, p. 8, 1933; L. Roy, *Rev. Gén. de l'élec.*, Vol. 39, p. 747, 1936.

Various "Practical" Dimension Systems

The fractional dimension systems were the first ones used and may duly be called the "classical" dimension systems as they had been proposed by the classical authors in the art. Their value in promoting first quantitative measurements of electromagnetic quantities cannot be doubted. Yet, the inconvenience in using fractional dimensions and the fact that proportionality factors were given such unwarranted prominence led to various proposals of so-called practical dimension systems. The aim of these systems is simplicity, stress upon fundamental concepts, and practicability.

The So-called Practical Dimension System has as fundamental dimensions length $[L]$, time $[T]$, current $[I]$, and resistance $[R]$, based upon the fact that convenient standards are available for the two electrical quantities. The system is used rather extensively in the engineering literature,* although not always explicitly stated. The fact that two fundamental electrical dimensions are chosen renders it difficult to combine it with the known mechanical dimension systems, and this is an objectionable feature. (See column 4 of Table III.)

The Energetical Dimension System is the extension of the mechanical dimension system with the same name by adding voltage $[V]$ as a fourth fundamental dimension. It had been proposed by W. Ostwald † but never has been used in the literature. (See column 5 of Table III.)

The disadvantage of all the "practical" systems is their departure from existing mechanical dimension systems from which, however, they cannot be entirely dissociated, since the fundamental standards of energy or power must be based upon the standard of mass in order to be internationally available.

UNIT SYSTEMS

6. UNITS AND UNIT SYSTEMS

Definition of Units. A physical quantity can be measured only by comparison with a like quantity. Defining a distinct amount of a physical quantity as "unit," i.e., as reference value, any physical quantity of the same kind can be compared with it, and its value is then stated in terms of a ratio number and the unit used. Obviously there is an infinity of possibilities for choosing a unit of a single physical quantity. *All the possible units of the same physical quantity must be related by purely numerical factors* which are used as the expressions for direct comparison. (See also Art. 1.)

Units and Dimensions. The general unit of a physical quantity is defined as its *dimension.* (See Art. 2.) There can be only one dimension for each physical quantity if the units are to be related by numerical factors only; but there are as many dimensions as there are physical quantities. Obviously, the concept of dimension systems, as outlined (see Art. 2), facilitates easy orientation and permits the use of a few fundamental dimensions to express all physical quantities in general units. Likewise, the concept of the fundamental unit permits the expression of all other units in terms of the fundamental units. However, whereas dimensional relations are essentially exponential equations, unit relations necessarily include numerical values in their equations.

Unit Systems. On the basis of a proper dimension system a unit system can be developed by choosing, for each fundamental dimension of the system, a specific unit, desirably related to a fundamental standard or standards. These units are called *fundamental units*; the respective physical quantities, fundamental quantities. Their number must be the same as the number of fundamental dimensions in the respective dimension system in order to constitute a complete unit system. All other physical quantities are then expressible in terms of the fundamental quantities and their units. Obviously there can be an infinity of unit systems for each complete dimension system; but for international understanding it is desirable to limit the usage to a few unit systems.

Systematic Units are all systematically derived units within a unit system, obtained by replacing the general units, as indicated in the derived dimension of the quantity, by the fundamental units of the system. Thus, in a m-kg-sec physical mechanical unit system, the systematic unit of power with the dimension $[M][L]^2[T]^{-3}$ will be 1 kg m² sec⁻³, which is known as 1 watt. The unit relations between systematic units are, there-

---

* Mie, G., Lehrbuch der Elektrizität und des Magnetismus, Stuttgart, 1910; Karapetoff, V., The Electric Circuit, The Magnetic Circuit, New York, 1910.
  † W. Ostwald, see footnote, p. 3–06.

fore, unitary, i.e., do not involve numerical factors. Unit systems with only systematically derived units are the ultimate goal in any branch of physics; they are difficult to obtain because the units should all be of convenient practical size.

Derived Units. All units which are not fundamental may be called derived units. Systematic units form the most prominent group of derived units, although all mixed units would come into this same category. Derived units can be the same for several unit systems if the defining fundamental units are the same. In many cases, where systematically derived units are inconvenient, mixed units will be used. In the m-kg-sec system "charge density" would have the systematic unit "coulomb per square meter," whereas more convenient is the unit "microcoulomb per square centimeter," a multiple of a mixed unit.

Units and Physical Equations. The form of physical equations depends upon the units employed for the various physical quantities. In general, the simplest forms will result when units of the same system are used exclusively. Two different types are, therefore, distinguished.

Systematic Physical Equations use only systematic units for all physical quantities involved. These equations are independent of the specific unit system applied, their form is the simplest obtainable without numerical factors, and their use should be preferred in all general texts. If a definite dimension system is chosen, it will, in conjunction with the proper number of fundamental units, form a sufficient basis for the correct interpretation of the general equations, written in systematic form.

Non-systematic or Hybrid Physical Equations use units from different unit systems or various multiples of units of the same system. These equations involve additional numerical factors (and numerical factors only, if all incomplete dimension sets are excluded). In all non-systematic equations it is imperative to state the units to be used for the various quantities in order to avoid confusion and misunderstandings. Many examples of non-systematic equations can be found in electromagnetism, where hybrid relations are very common. (See Art. 9.)

Comprehensive Unit Systems are composed of five fundamental units to cover the whole field of physics. The difficulties in designing a comprehensive unit system come from the restriction that all the systematic units should be convenient and practical or at least be made so by simple powers of 10. Many attempts have been made to reach international agreement on a single comprehensive system, but thus far none has succeeded. The advantage of such a system is obvious, since all physical equations could be used in their systematic form, introducing all the physical quantities in convenient practical values.

So-called Absolute Unit Systems. During the middle of the nineteenth century it became customary to refer to measurements in terms of the centimeter-gram-second mechanical unit system as "absolute" measurements, and the cgs system, as adopted and recommended by the British Association for the Advancement of Science in 1873, was called the "absolute" unit system. This designation is entirely unwarranted, as no system can claim "absoluteness." The attempts to reduce the fractional electrical dimension systems to the three so-called absolute mechanical dimensions, and then to use the absolute mechanical units in electrical measurements, have resulted in confusion and inconsistencies. It is inadvisable to use less than four fundamental units in electromagnetism, and for this reason, the so-called absolute unit systems will not be considered here at all. The complete unit systems resulting from the fractional dimension systems, which sometimes are called "complete absolute" systems because of their complete set of fundamental dimensions, will be called here *"theoretical" unit systems.*[*]

The Metric Unit Systems are based upon the international metric standards, namely: the meter and the kilogram, or any decimal multiples thereof. Only the metric systems enter in general into the discussion of comprehensive unit systems.

Metric Multiples and Metric Style. Prefixes used to indicate *multiples* and *submultiples* of various metric units are shown in the following table:

micro	$= 10^{-6}$	deka	$= 10^1$
milli	$= 10^{-3}$	hecto	$= 10^2$
centi	$= 10^{-2}$	kilo	$= 10^3$
deci	$= 10^{-1}$	myria	$= 10^4$
		mega	$= 10^6$

Example. One centimeter $= 10^{-2}$ meter; one kiloliter $= 10^3$ liters; one milligram $= 10^{-3}$ gram. Metric numbers are written with the decimal point (.) at the right of the figures denoting the unit; thus the expression, 15 meters 3 centimeters, is written 15.03 meters.

---

[*] G. Mie, " Elektrodynamik," Handbuch der experimental Physik, Vol. 11, 1932.

When metric numbers are expressed by figures, the part of the expression at the left of the decimal point is read as the number of the unit, and the part at the right, if any, as a number of the lowest denomination indicated, or as a decimal part of the unit; thus, 46.525 meters is read 46 meters and 525 millimeters, or 46 and 525 thousandths meters.

The English Unit Systems are based upon the English standards, namely: the yard and the pound, or any multiples thereof. See Units and Standards, p. 3–21.

7. THE METRIC UNIT SYSTEMS OF MECHANICS AND HEAT

The Distinctly Mechanical Unit Systems

There are several mechanical unit systems in use, which are shown in Table I, with their systematic units (the fundamental units are printed bold face) for the most important quantities. It is significant that only one technical and three physical systems have been developed. The variety of the unit systems is not due to variety in dimension systems, but rather to the choice of various multiples of the same unit quantity.

Table I. The Metric Unit Systems of Mechanics

Unit System Author Year Basic Dimension System	CGS France 1799 Physical (Dynamical)	Technical Technical (Gravitational)	MKS G. Giorgi 1902 Physical (Dynamical)	MTS France 1913 Physical (Dynamical)
Quantity	①	②	③	④
Length...................	cm	m	m	m
Time....................	sec	sec	sec	sec
Mass....................	g	$\frac{1}{9.81}$ kg mass	kg	ton
Force...................	dyne	kg force	joules/m	sthène = 10^8 dynes
Power...................	erg/sec	$\frac{1}{9.81}$ watt	watt	kilowatt
Energy..................	erg	kg force-m	joule	kilojoule

The **CGS (Centimeter-gram-second) System of Units** is a dynamical system of units and is based upon the centimeter, gram-mass, and second as fundamental units (column 1 of Table I). It was first proposed in 1795, and adopted in France by the French statute of Dec. 10, 1799. The standard to which the length unit refers is the prototype meter (see standards); the standard to which the gram has reference is the prototype mass of the kilogram (see standards). This system was endorsed and recommended for use by the British Association for the Advancement of Science in 1863 and since then has been most widely used internationally, in all sciences. Frequent objections to the cgs system are the fact that the actual standards are for multiples of these fundamental units and not for the units themselves; that the derived units for force and energy are inconveniently small for practical purposes; and that it does not fit with the practical electrical units to form a comprehensive unit system.

The **MKS (Meter-kilogram-second) System of Units** is a dynamical system of units and is based upon the meter, kilogram-mass, and second (column 3 of Table I). It was proposed by G. Giorgi * (1902) and adopted by the International Electrotechnical Commission at Paris, 1935. Its convenience lies in the fact that it is based upon the actual standards, as preserved in Paris, the meter and the kilogram-mass prototype. The disadvantage of large magnitudes for densities and gradients may be not serious, depending on general usage. The density of water is 10^3 kg per cu meter, and this is rather inconvenient in many practical computations.

The **MTS (Meter-ton-second) System of Units** is a dynamical system of units and is based upon the meter, metric ton (mass), and second (column 4 of Table I). It was proposed in 1913 † and legalized in France in 1919. The units are in some respects better adapted to practical use than those in the cgs system; but it is not suitable for extension into a comprehensive system or as a unit system for physics. Its main advantage is the fact that the density of water under normalized conditions becomes 1 ton per cu meter and thus has the same numerical value as in the cgs system (where it was 1 g per cu cm).

---

* G. Giorgi, *Elec. World*, Vol. 40, pp. 355, 368, 1902.
† See A. E. Kennelly, *Proc. Soc. Prom. Engg. Educ.*, Vol. 19, p. 229, 1928.

The " Technical " System of Units is a gravitational system of units and is based upon the meter, kilogram (force), and second as fundamental units (column 2 of Table I). Since the standard of force is defined as the weight of the prototype standard mass of the kilogram, the fundamental unit of force is variable. International agreement determined a standard value of the constant of gravity (see Units and Standards) which for all practical measurements is little different from the local value at the point of measurement. As the system is decidedly a technical system of units, widely used by engineers and the industry, this disadvantage is not serious at all. The advantages in practical design work and in numerical computations more than justify the use of this unit system, yielding very simple dimensional formulas and self-explanatory derived unit names.

The Thermal Unit Systems

Any mechanical unit system supplemented by temperature as a fourth fundamental unit constitutes a proper thermal unit system. Table II gives a summary of the units most frequently used and their coordination in the various thermal unit systems.

Table II.   The Thermal Units Most Commonly Used

Quantity	Caloric Unit System ①	CGS Thermal Unit System ②	MKS Thermal Unit System ③
Fundamental			
Length......................	cm	cm	m
Time........................	sec	sec	sec
Mass........................	(4.184 gram-seven)*	g	kg
Temperature.................	° C	° C	° C
Energy......................	cal	(erg)	(joule)
Derived			
Thermal conductivity..........	cal/sec ° C cm	erg/sec ° C cm	watt/° C m
Thermal capacity of body.......	cal/° C	erg/° C	joule/° C
Thermal capacity of substance...	cal/sec ° C g	erg/sec ° C g	watt/° C kg
Emissivity...................	cal/sec ° C cm²	erg/sec ° C cm²	watt/° C m²
Entropy.....................	cal/° C	erg/° C	joule/° C

The Caloric Unit System is based on the centimeter, second, calorie, and degree centigrade (column 1 of Table II). The peculiar definition of the unit of energy produces inconvenient systematic units of mass and force. For this reason a practical modification is widely used, by employing the non-systematic units of gram and dyne in computations. It is with this system that Fourier founded the theory of dimensions.† The most commonly used quantities and their units are shown in Table II.

The CGS Thermal Unit System is the extension of the cgs mechanical unit system (column 2, Table II) by the addition of the metric unit of temperature (degree centigrade). Although a dynamical or physical system, it is widely used in heat engineering on account of the erg as the unit of energy which provides a close link to the watt and the practical electrical unit systems. The most commonly used quantities and their units are shown in Table II.

The MKS Thermal Unit System is the extension of the mks mechanical unit system (column 3, Table II) by the addition of the metric unit of temperature (degree centigrade). It is widely used in general engineering on account of the convenient magnitudes of its fundamental units. The most commonly used quantities and their units are shown in Table II.

8.   THE METRIC COMPREHENSIVE UNIT SYSTEMS

The comprehensive unit systems are composed of five fundamental units in order to cover the whole field of physics. There are *eleven* comprehensive unit systems in use, each one with a different name; in addition, there is the QES system, which was used by J. C. Maxwell to explain the " practical " units in terms of the theoretical definitions. In Table III are shown all twelve unit systems with their authors, the year of proposal or first use, and the dimension system upon which the unit system was based (the fundamental units are bold-face type).

It can be seen that *nine* of the systems are *physical* unit systems; only one a technical system and two systems belong in the so-called "practical" class. Most of the variety can, therefore, be accounted for by slight changes in the choice of the multiple of the

---

* Gram-seven is the abbreviation for 10^7 gram as proposed by E. Bennet. See footnote, p. 3-09.
† J. B. J. Fourier, Théorie analytique de la chaleur, p. 152, Paris, 1822.

Table III. The Fundamental Units in the Comprehensive Unit Systems

Unit System	CGS Symmetric	CGS Electrostatic	CGS Electro-magnetic	QES	Rationalized Electro-magnetic	MKS
Author Year	C. F. Gauss 1833 W. Weber 1851	J. C. Maxwell 1863	J. C. Maxwell 1863	J. C. Maxwell 1881	O. Heaviside 1892	G. Giorgi 1902
Basic Dimension System	Symmetric	Electrostatic	Electro-magnetic	Electrostatic	Electro-magnetic	Practical
Quantity	①	②	③	④	⑤	⑥
Length	cm	cm	cm	Quadrant $= 10^9$ cm	cm	m
Time	sec	sec	sec	sec	sec	sec
Mass	g	g	g	eleventh-gram$=10^{-11}$ g	g	kg
Force	dyne	dyne	dyne	centi-dyne	dyne	joule/m
Power	erg/sec	erg/sec	erg/sec	watt	erg/sec	watt
Energy	erg	erg	erg	joule	erg	joule
Temperature	°C	°C	°C	°C	°C	°C
Electric charge	statcoulomb	statcoulomb	abcoulomb	coulomb	$\frac{1}{\sqrt{4\pi}}$abcoulomb	coulomb
Current	statampere	statampere	abampere	ampere	$\frac{1}{\sqrt{4\pi}}$ abampere	ampere
Resistance	statohm	statohm	abohm	ohm	4π abohm	ohm
Dielectric constant	statfarad/cm	statfarad/cm	abfarad/cm	statfarad/cm	$\frac{1}{4\pi}$ abfarad/cm	farad/m
Permeability	abhenry/cm	stathenry/cm	abhenry/cm	stathenry/cm	4π abhenry/cm	henry/m

Unit System	Rationalized Symmetric	Practical	CGSS	Electro-technical	Electro-physical	Definitive
Author Year	H. A. Lorentz 1909	{ V. Karapetoff / G. Mie, 1910	E. Bennett 1917	E. Weber 1932	E. Weber 1932	G. A. Campbell 1933
Basic Dimension System	Symmetric	Practical	Electrostatic	Electro-technical	Electro-physical	Definitive
Quantity	⑦	⑧	⑨	⑩	⑪	⑫
Length	cm	cm	cm	m	cm	m
Time	sec	sec	sec	sec	sec	sec
Mass	g	gram-seven$=10^7$g	gram-seven$=10^7$g	kg	g	kg
Force	dyne	joule/cm	joule/cm	joule/m	dyne	joule/m
Power	erg/sec	watt	watt	watt	erg/sec	watt
Energy	erg	joule	joule	joule	erg	joule
Temperature	°C	°C	°C	°C	°C	°C
Electric charge	$\frac{1}{\sqrt{4\pi}}$ statcoulomb	coulomb	coulomb	coulomb	abcoulomb	coulomb
Current	$\frac{1}{\sqrt{4\pi}}$ statampere	ampere	ampere	ampere	abampere	ampere
Resistance	4π statohm	ohm	ohm	ohm	abohm	ohm
Dielectric constant	$\frac{1}{4\pi}$ statfarad/cm	farad/cm	farad/cm	farad/m	abfarad/cm	farad/m
Permeability	4π abhenry/cm	henry/cm	henry/cm	henry/m	abhenry/cm	henry/m

mass unit or by the choice of the supplementary electrical unit. Unfortunately, many of the physical texts still use Maxwell's unit systems or the rationalized systems, so that the whole variety (except the QES system) actually can be found in the present-day literature.

Another grouping, according to the type of the dimension system (see Art. 5), shows six "fractional," three so-called practical, and three "natural" systems. Since all the quantities are given with their systematical units, it is easily seen that the natural systems (with charge as fundamental quantity) represent the most convenient arrays of units for practical use.

The "Theoretical" Comprehensive Unit Systems

All the "theoretical" dimension systems are characterized by the fact that they use as fundamental electrical dimension either k_e or k_m, the proportionality constants in the two fundamental experimental laws. In the "theoretical" unit systems these same factors are then assumed to have the magnitude unity, so that in combination with the three fundamental mechanical units all the electromagnetic units can be derived.

The CGS Electrostatic Unit System is the extension of the cgs mechanical system of units into a comprehensive system by adding the metric unit of temperature, degree centigrade, and defining the absolute dielectric constant (permittivity) as 1 statfarad per centimeter (see Units and Standards); see column 2, Table III. It is a dynamical unit system and was introduced by J. C. Maxwell.* It is frequently used in the field of electrostatics, especially in the form of an incomplete set of dimensions as a so-called absolute system which is obtained if the dimension of the dielectric constant is arbitrarily taken as zero, so that capacity will appear with the dimension "centimeter." In all texts employing the so-called absolute units and giving capacity in "centimeters," replace this unit by statfarad. The most commonly used quantities and their units in the complete cgs electrostatic system are listed in Table IV, first column. The unit system has many non-systematic units, and so the electromagnetic equations contain numerical factors (Art. 9).

The CGS Electromagnetic Unit System is the extension of the cgs mechanical system of units into a comprehensive system by adding the metric unit of temperature (degree centigrade) and defining the absolute magnetic permeability as 1 abhenry per centimeter (see Units and Standards); see column 3, Table III. It is a dynamical unit system and was introduced by J. C. Maxwell,* as an alternative to the cgs electrostatic unit system. It is frequently used in the treatment of magnetic fields, especially in the form of an incomplete set of dimensions as a so-called absolute system, which is obtained if the dimension of the permeability is arbitrarily taken as zero, so that inductance will appear with the dimension "centimeter." In all texts employing so-called absolute units and giving inductance in "centimeters," replace this unit by abhenry. The most commonly used quantities and their units in the complete cgs electromagnetic system are listed in Table IV, second column. The system has many non-systematic units, and so the electromagnetic equations contain numerical factors (Art. 9).

The CGS Symmetric Unit System is a combination of the cgs electrostatic and the cgs electromagnetic unit systems in such manner that all the electrostatic and electric current quantities appear in electrostatic units and all the magnetic quantities in electromagnetic units. In order to achieve this result a new factor was introduced into the fundamental electrical equations (see Art. 9), so that both the dielectric constant and the permeability could be defined arbitrarily as one statfarad per centimeter and one abhenry per centimeter, respectively. In this way symmetry in the expression was obtained. The new factor introduced was found to have the same numerical value as the velocity of light †; however, its identification with the velocity of light is not possible (see "Absolute" Dimension Systems, Art. 5). This symmetric system is frequently used in European publications, mostly in the form of an incomplete set of fundamental dimensions as the so-called absolute Gaussian system, which is obtained if the dimensions of both the absolute dielectric constant and the absolute permeability are taken as zero. Capacitance as well as inductance will then appear with the dimension "centimeter," which should be replaced properly by statfarad and abhenry, respectively. The "absolute" modification was the one used by C. F. Gauss and W. Weber in the classical investigations on measurements of electromagnetic quantities. The system has many non-systematic units, and so the electromagnetic equations contain numerical factors. (See Art. 9.)

The Rationalized CGS Electromagnetic Unit System was introduced and vigorously defended by O. Heaviside,‡ whereas *the rationalized cgs symmetric (Gaussian) unit system* was used by H. A. Lorentz.§ Both systems are identical with the unrationalized systems of the same name but use a factor 4π in Coulomb's and Ampère's laws instead of in the less logical positions where the classical theory had used them. As a result the electromagnetic field equations take on very simple forms. (See Art. 9.) All the units of the rationalized systems bear ratios of $\sqrt{4\pi}$ or multiples thereof to the cgs units of the same systems as shown in Table IV. This fact has prohibited their use in practical computations, although they are often found in modern treatises on electromagnetism, particularly in the English language. Where the rationalized systems have degenerated into so-called absolute systems the same considerations apply as in the unrationalized cgs systems.

---

* Reports of the Committee on Standard Resistance of the British Assoc. for the Advancement of Science, by F. Jenkin, London, 1873, especially appendix C, second report.
† W. Weber and R. Kohlrausch, *Pogg. Annalen*, Vol. 99, 1856.
‡ O. Heaviside, Electromagnetic Theory, London, 1893.
§ H. A. Lorentz, The Theory of Electrons, New York, 1909.

Table IV. The Electrical Units Most Commonly Used

Quantity	CGS. Electrostatic Unit System (theoretical units)	CGS. Electromagnetic Unit System (theoretical units)	Practical Unit System	Rational Unit System	Symbol
Electric charge.......	statcoul	abcoul	coul	$\frac{1}{\sqrt{4\pi}} \times$ theor.	Q
Surface charge density	statcoul/cm²	abcoul/cm²	coul/cm² coul/m²	$\frac{1}{\sqrt{4\pi}} \times$ "	η, σ
Electrostatic flux.....	statcoul	abcoul	coul	$\frac{1}{\sqrt{4\pi}} \times$ "	Ψ
Displacement........	statcoul/cm²	abcoul/cm²	coul/cm² coul/m²	$\frac{1}{\sqrt{4\pi}} \times$ "	D
Electric field strength.	statvolt/cm	abvolt/cm	volt/cm volt/m	$\sqrt{4\pi} \times$ "	E
Capacity............	statfarad	abfarad	farad	$\frac{1}{4\pi} \times$ "	C
Dielectric constant (permittivity)......	statfarad/cm	abfarad/cm	farad/cm farad/m	$1 \times$ "	Δ
Current.............	statamp	abamp	amp	$\frac{1}{\sqrt{4\pi}} \times$ "	I
Voltage.............	statvolt	abvolt	volt	$\sqrt{4\pi} \times$ "	V
Potential............	statvolt	abvolt	volt	$\sqrt{4\pi} \times$ "	V
Resistance...........	statohm	abohm	ohm	$4\pi \times$ "	R
Resistivity...........	statohm cm	abohm cm	ohm cm ohm m	$4\pi \times$ "	ρ
Conductance........	statmho	abmho	mho, siemens	$\frac{1}{4\pi} \times$ "	A
Conductivity.......	statmho/cm	abmho/cm	mho/cm mho/m	$\frac{1}{4\pi} \times$ "	γ
Magnetic flux........	statweber	maxwell	weber	$\sqrt{4\pi} \times$ "	ϕ
Magnetic flux density	statweber/cm²	gauss	weber/cm² weber/m²	$\sqrt{4\pi} \times$ "	B
Magnetizing force....	....	oersted	amp/cm amp/m	$\frac{1}{\sqrt{4\pi}} \times$ "	H
Magnetomotive force.	....	gilbert	amp-turn	$\frac{1}{\sqrt{4\pi}} \times$ "	F
Reluctance..........	....	....		$\frac{1}{4\pi} \times$ "	$\mathcal{R}$
Inductance..........	stathenry	abhenry	henry	$4\pi \times$ "	L
Permeability.........	stathenry/cm	abhenry/cm	henry/cm henry/m	$1 \times$ "	Π

NOTES: 1. For relations between the various units see conversion tables.
2. The unit names are used according to the latest decisions of the I. E. C. (International Electrotechnical Commission), at Paris, 1932.

The QES System of Units. J. C. Maxwell [*] has shown that, on the basis of the centimeter, gram, and second, a unit system can be devised in which again the absolute dielectric constant has the value 1 statfarad per centimeter but in which all the other electromagnetic quantities appear in the units of the so-called practical system. Since the cgs units and the practical units are in general related by high powers of 10 (see conversion tables), the fundamental unit of length should be 10^9 cm (or a quadrant), and that of mass should be 10^{-11} gram (eleventh-gram), whereas the second must be preserved as the unit of time. This system never has been used; it is not logical to let a proportionality factor retain unity as its magnitude and accept impractical fundamental units.

[*] J. C. Maxwell, Electricity and Magnetism, London, 1881.

The Various Practical Comprehensive Unit Systems

All the practical unit systems use the international units (for details see chapter on Units and Standards) for the electromagnetic quantities. Differences are only with respect to the designation of fundamental units which in turn bears upon the standards to be used. Table IV gives the most commonly used quantities with their practical units; distinction is made between the meter and the centimeter as fundamental units of length.

The So-called Practical Unit System is based upon the centimeter and second as fundamental mechanical units, adding the metric unit of temperature (degree centigrade) and two electrical units, the ampere and ohm. It was independently introduced into the literature by V. Karapetoff * and G. Mie.† The fact that two electrical units are considered fundamental would require primary standards for these and remove the prototype kilogram mass as a primary standard. The removal of the kilogram mass is perhaps the outstanding objection to the system. Another disadvantage is that the systematic unit of mass is rather large.

The MKS System of Units is a dynamical or physical system and is based upon the meter, kilogram (mass), second, degree centigrade, and ohm as fundamental units. (See column 6, Table III.) This system was accepted internationally in June, 1935, by the I.E.C. without, however, the originally proposed fundamental electrical quantity ohm; it is called the Giorgi-MKS system after its proponent.‡ Instead of the ohm the suggestion was made to use the value of the absolute permeability as 10^{-7} henry per meter which would render this system a strictly comprehensive unit system. A disadvantage of this system is the large value for the density of water, namely 10^3 kg per cu m; the advantage is the close relationship to the original standards of mechanical units.

The CGSS System of Units is a dynamical or physical system based upon the mechanical units centimeter, gram-seven (10^7 gram), and second, the metric unit of temperature (degree centigrade), and the definition of the absolute dielectric constant as a fundamental constant (column 9, Table III). The system had been proposed by E. Bennett § in 1917 and is essentially derived from the electrostatic unit system, replacing the unit statfarad per centimeter by farad per centimeter for the dielectric constant. It, therefore, has the same disadvantage of unsymmetry as Maxwell's unit system and in addition calls for a rather large unit for mass in order to bring in the electrical practical units. This system is not widely used.

The Natural Comprehensive Unit Systems

The unit systems based upon the electric charge as fundamental electrical dimension are here called "natural" comprehensive unit systems (see also Natural Dimension Systems) in order to emphasize the contradistinction from the "theoretical" unit systems based upon quantities of secondary importance.

The Electrophysical Unit System is the extension of the mechanical cgs system into a comprehensive unit system by adding the metric unit of temperature (degree centigrade) and the electromagnetic unit of charge as fundamental units (column 11, Table III). It is practically identical with the electromagnetic system of Maxwell except that it is based upon the definition of the electric charge and leaves the values of the dielectric constant and permeability adjustable with the progress of measurements pertaining to the velocity of light. Although seemingly a minor point, this is of practical importance with respect to standards. This system has been proposed recently ¶ as an alternative to the electrotechnical system in order to preserve the internationally adopted electromagnetic units which have been used very frequently.

The Electrotechnical Unit System is the extension of the mechanical "technical" system into a comprehensive unit system || by adding the metric unit of temperature (degree centigrade) and the coulomb as fundamental units (column 10, Table III). The change from kilogram force as unit of force to joule per meter makes this system identical with the kms system in regard to units, but leaves it as a gravitational system which is of distinct advantage in engineering. This system has been proposed recently ¶ as an alternative to the electrophysical unit system.

The " Definitive " System of Units is an energetical system based upon the meter, second, watt, degree centigrade, and coulomb as fundamental units (column 12, Table III). It combines the advantage of the mks system, the convenient relation between mechanical

---

* V. Karapetoff, The Electric Circuit, New York, 1910; The Magnetic Circuit, New York, 1911.
† G. Mie, Elektrizität und Magnetismus, Stuttgart, 1910.
‡ G. Giorgi, Elec. World, Vol. 40, pp. 355, 368, 1902.
§ E. Bennett, Bull. Univ. Wisconsin, No. 880, 1917.
¶ E. Weber, Trans. A.I.E.E., Vol. 51, p. 728, 1932.
|| As extension of the technical system, the meter must be taken as unit of length, not the centimeter as in the original proposal.

Table V.   Various Forms of Writing the Electromagnetic Relations

Name	Mathematical	Factor (relation)	CGS Electrostatic	CGS Electromagnetic	CGS Symmetric	Rational CGS-Electromagnetic	Rational CGS-Symmetric	Practical
Coulomb's law in free space	$F = k_{e0}\dfrac{Q_1 Q_2}{r^2}$	$k_{e0} = \dfrac{\alpha}{4\pi\Delta_0} =$	1 cm/statfarad	V^2 cm/abfarad	1 cm/statfarad	$\dfrac{V^2}{4\pi}$ cm/abfarad	$\dfrac{1}{4\pi}$ cm/statfarad	$\dfrac{V^2}{10^9}$ cm/farad
Ampère's law in free space	$F = k_{m0}\dfrac{I_1 I_2}{r}\cdot l$	$k_{m0} = \dfrac{\beta}{2\pi}\Pi_0 =$	$\dfrac{2}{V^2}$ stathenry/cm	2 abhenry/cm	$\dfrac{2}{V}$ abhenry/cm	$\dfrac{1}{2\pi}$ abhenry/cm	$\dfrac{1}{2\pi V}$ abhenry/cm	2×10^{-9} henry/cm
Absolute dielectric constant-permittivity	$D = \Delta\cdot E$	$\Delta = \Delta_0\cdot\epsilon$	1 statfarad/cm	$\dfrac{1}{V^2}$ abfarad/cm	1 statfarad/cm	$\dfrac{1}{V^2}$ abfarad/cm	1 statfarad/cm	$\dfrac{1}{4\pi}\dfrac{10^9}{V}$ farad/cm
Absolute magnetic permeability	$B = \Pi\cdot H$	$\Pi = \Pi_0\cdot\mu$	$\dfrac{1}{V^2}$ stathenry/cm	1 abhenry/cm	1 abhenry/cm	1 abhenry/cm	1 abhenry/cm	$4\pi\times10^{-9}$ henry/cm
Electrostatic induction	div $D = \alpha\cdot\rho$	$\alpha =$	4π	4π	4π	1	1	1
Magnetic circuit	$\oint H_s\cdot ds = \beta\cdot I$	$\beta =$	4π	4π	$\dfrac{4\pi}{V}$	1	$\dfrac{1}{V}$	1
Faraday's induction law	curl $E = -\lambda\cdot\dfrac{\partial B}{\partial t}$ $\left(\text{EMF} = -\lambda\dfrac{\partial\Phi}{\partial t}\right)$	$\lambda =$	1	1	$\dfrac{1}{V}$	1	$\dfrac{1}{V}$	1
Poynting vector	$S = s\cdot(E\times H)$	$s =$	$\dfrac{1}{4\pi}$	$\dfrac{1}{4\pi}$	$\dfrac{V}{4\pi}$	1	V	1

Other relations: Conservation of electricity $I = \dfrac{dQ}{dt}$

First Maxwell's relation   curl $H = \beta\cdot G + \dfrac{\beta}{\alpha}\dfrac{\partial D}{\partial t}$

Specific electric field energy $W_e = s\cdot\dfrac{1}{\alpha}\cdot 1/2\, ED$.

Specific magnetic field energy $W_m = s\cdot\lambda\cdot 1/2\, HB$.

Velocity of propagation in free space $c^2 = \dfrac{\alpha}{\beta\lambda}\dfrac{1}{\Delta_0\Pi_0}$.

NOTES: 1. The units employed for the electromagnetic quantities are those from Table IV for each system.

2. If units of various systems are used in one equation, the unit relations can be used for transformations, as for example:

$$\oint H\cdot\overline{ds} = 4\pi\cdot I \text{ if } H \text{ is in oersteds, and } I \text{ in abamperes.}$$
$$= \frac{4\pi}{10} I \text{ if } H \text{ is in oersteds, and } I \text{ in amperes.}$$

3. The factor V (or a multiple thereof) is a pure number, identical with the magnitude of the velocity of light in free space if expressed in centimeters per second.

and electrical practical units, with the selection of charge as a fundamental unit. It has the disadvantage of discarding mass as a primary unit and replacing it by the watt for which no convenient standard is known. This system has been proposed only recently by G. A. Campbell * and aims at a unique, internationally acceptable, practical unit system.

9. THE WRITING OF THE ELECTROMAGNETIC RELATIONS

On account of the many different unit systems in use, the electromagnetic relations appear in different forms. The situation is still further complicated by the fact that the practical and so-called absolute or cgs units are mixed, and, instead of systematic physical equations, so-called hybrid or non-systematic equations are obtained. In the various branches of engineering and physics various customary writing styles are observed which are listed in Table V. Since only complete dimension systems are considered, the factor V is a pure numeric, the value of which is identical with the value of the velocity of light in free space, expressed in centimeters per second.

Four of the systems in Table V write the electromagnetic equations in non-systematic form as indicated by the factors 4π or V in the direct relations between physical quantities. No unitary relations between the units can exist. Only two systems are truly "rationalized"; unitary relations hold between the units, and with systematic units no numerical factors appear in the fundamental equations.

Mixed Equations. If in one equation units from different unit systems are employed, this must be stated expressedly in order to avoid serious mistakes. A prominent example is the law of induction, often found in the form $V = -\dfrac{d\phi}{dt} \cdot 10^{-8}$; in this form V is expressed in volts (practical system) and ϕ in maxwells (cgs electromagnetic system). A proper way of writing this equation with mixed units is $V = -\dfrac{d\phi}{dt} \cdot 10^{-8}$ (V in volts, ϕ in maxwells).

In general, it is preferable to avoid the use of mixed equations, as it is necessary to remember with the symbols also the numerical factors.

UNITS AND STANDARDS

Dimensions of Units, see Dimension Systems, page 3–02.
Fundamental and Derived Units, see Unit Systems, page 3–12.
Conversion of Units, see Tables 27 to 60, Section 1.

10. LENGTH, MASS, AND TIME

The English Units and Standards

Units of Length. The foot (ft) is the *fundamental* unit of length in the foot-pound-second (fps) system. It equals, by definition, one-third of a *yard* (yd), which is the English legalized *standard* unit of length. The *United States yard* was defined by Act of Congress, July 28, 1866, as 3600/3937 the length of the *meter*. (See Metric System for definitions of metric length.)

In Great Britain, the *Imperial yard* is measured by a bronze bar preserved in the Standards Office, Westminster. Its length, in terms of the *international prototype meter*, is 3600/3937.0113 meter. For engineering purposes, the United States and British *yards* may be considered identical.

As subunits, the *inch* (in.) is defined as $1/12$ of one standard foot, and the *mil* as the one-thousandth part of one inch. The *nautical mile* (mi) is defined as one minute of arc on the earth's surface at the equator, whereas the United States mile (U. S. mi. statute) is exactly 5280 ft and practically identical with the British mile.

Unit of Capacity (Dry). The bushel (bu) is the *standard* unit of *dry* capacity. The *Winchester bushel* (U. S. standard) has a volume of 2150.42 cu in.

In Great Britain, the *Imperial bushel* (bu) is defined as the volume of 80 lb of pure water at 62 deg fahr, weighed against brass weights in air at the same temperature as the water and with the barometer at 30 in. Its volume is approximately 2219.36 cu in.

Unit of Capacity (Liquid). The *gallon* (gal) is the *standard* unit of *liquid* capacity. The *United States gallon* has a volume of 231 cu in.

---

* G. A. Campbell, *Bull. National Research Council*, No. 93, 1933.

In Great Britain, the *Imperial gallon* is defined as the volume of 10 lb of pure water at 62 deg fahr, weighed against brass weights in air at the same temperature as the water and with the barometer at 30 in. Its volume is approximately 277.420 cu in. The imperial gallon (liquid measure) equals exactly one-eighth of the Imperial bushel (dry measure). As subunits, there are used the quart (qt), which is ¼ of the standard gallon, and the pint (pt), which is ½ qt.

Units of Mass. The pound (avoirdupois) (lb avdp) is the *fundamental* unit of mass in the fps system.* It is also the English legalized *standard* unit of mass. The *United States pound (avoirdupois)* was defined by Act of Congress, 1866, as 1/2.2046 kg, but since 1895 there has been used, for greater accuracy, a value which agrees with that given by law as far as the latter is given; namely, 453.5924277 grams. This value is now used by the Bureau of Standards as an exact definition and is the basis of the customary United States weights (Circular 47, Bureau of Standards).

In Great Britain, the *Imperial pound (avoirdupois)* is the mass of a *platinum cylinder* preserved in the Standards Office, Westminster. Its legal equivalent is 453.59243 grams. For engineering purposes, the United States and British pounds (avoirdupois) may be considered as identical.

Subunits of mass are the grain (gr), defined as 1/7000 of the standard pound (avoirdupois) and the ounce (avoirdupois) (oz-avdp) which is 1/16 of the standard pound (avoirdupois). The grain was used as fundamental unit in the so-called foot-gram-second (fgs) system of units prior to 1873.

Weight vs. Mass. Unfortunately, the word " weight " is used in two different senses viz.: (1) by the layman (as well as loosely by the scientist) to designate a given *mass* or quantity of matter; and (2) by the scientist to designate the *pull* in standard gravitational force units which is exerted by the earth upon a piece of matter. The result of the commercial act of "weighing" a specific quantity is independent of the local gravitational pull of the earth, since both spring scales and balances are calibrated locally by comparison with standard masses.

For a method of determining whether or not a balance has equal arms and also for methods of correction of data obtained on an incorrect balance, see discussion on these subjects under the heading Accurate Weighing Procedure in this section.

Auxiliary Fundamental Units and Their Principal Derived Units are defined and discussed under the sections of this handbook pertaining to the topics to which they apply. In general, however, conversion factors are included in the tables of Section I.

For an interesting and rather complete history see British Weights and Measures, London, 1910, by Sir C. M. Watson.

The Metric (or French) Units and Standards

Units of Length. The centimeter (cm) is the *fundamental* unit of length in the cgs system. It equals, by definition, 1/100 of a *meter* (m) which is the *standard* unit of length. The *basic* meter for international comparisons is the *international prototype meter* which is the distance, at zero degrees centigrade, between two lines on a platinum-iridium bar located at the International Bureau of Weights and Measures, at Sèvres, France. This meter is the nearest to a duplicate, ever constructed, of the *original* meter which was constructed and deposited in the Archives of the French Republic in 1799. The meter is very nearly equal to one ten-millionth of the distance, measured at sea level, from the equator to either pole.

An interesting history of the development of the *international prototype meter* (as well as the *international prototype kilogram*—see Unit of Mass, below) is given by Wm. Parry, National Bureau of Standards, in Merriman's Civil Engineers' Handbook as follows:

"The use of the meter as the basis of geodetic surveys had become so general throughout Europe that a conference was called in Paris, France, in 1870, for the purpose of establishing a central bureau where the standards of the different countries could be compared. As a result of this conference an International Bureau of Weights and Measures was established near Paris in 1875, by the concurrent action of the principal nations of the world. One of the first tasks undertaken by the Bureau was the construction of exact copies of the meter and kilogram deposited in the Archives. Thirty-one standard meters of iridio-platinum and forty kilograms of the same alloy were constructed and carefully compared with the standards of the Archives and with one another. This great work was completed in 1889, and the meter and kilogram which agreed most nearly with the original standards were called international prototypes, and were deposited at

---

* The slug of mass, which is extensively used by engineers and physicists, is (in the English system) the mass to which an acceleration of one foot per second per second would be given by the application of a one-pound force. Unlike the pound of mass, it is not an absolute unit. Under standard gravity conditions, one slug of mass = 32.1739 lb of mass.

the International Bureau, where they are maintained today subject to the authority of the International Committee on Weights and Measures. The remaining meters and kilograms were distributed by lot to the different nations which contributed to the support of the Bureau. The United States secured two copies of the meter and two copies of the kilogram, which are in the custody of the Bureau of Standards at Washington. One of the meters, known as No. 27, and one kilogram, No. 20, were selected as the United States standards, while the other meter and kilogram are used as secondary standards. It was the declared intention of the International Committee that the various national prototypes should be returned to the International Bureau at regular intervals for the purpose of recomparing them with the international standards and with one another. In this way all measurements based upon metric standards throughout the world are ultimately referred to the international meter and kilogram."

Unit of Capacity. The liter (l) is the *standard* unit of capacity. It is defined as the volume of one kilogram of pure water at the temperature of maximum density (4 deg cent) under a pressure of 76 cm of mercury. For all practical purposes, the liter may be regarded as the equivalent of the cubic decimeter, although the former is actually slightly greater, in the amount of less than three parts in one hundred thousand.

Unit of Mass. The gram (g) is the *fundamental* unit of mass in the cgs system.* It equals, by definition, $1/1000$ of a *kilogram* (kg), which is the *standard* unit of mass. The *basic* kilogram for international comparisons is the *international prototype kilogram* which is a cylinder of platinum-iridium located at the International Bureau of Weights and Measures, at Sèvres, France. This mass is the nearest to a duplicate, ever constructed, of the *original* kilogram which was constructed and deposited in the Archives of the French Republic in 1799. The latter was made as nearly as possible equal to the mass of a cube of pure water at 4 deg cent, the sides of the cube being one-tenth the length of the original meter.

An interesting history of the development of the *international prototype kilogram* is given above under the discussion headed Units of Length.

Weight vs. Mass. See discussion under this same subheading of The English Units and Standards.

Auxiliary Fundamental Units and Their Principal Derived Units are defined and discussed under the sections of this handbook pertaining to the topics to which they apply. In general, however, conversion factors are included in the tables of Section I.

The Standard of Time

Unit of Time. The second (sec) is the *fundamental* unit of time. It equals, by definition, the 1/86,400 part of a mean solar day. The solar day is the interval of time between two successive transits of the sun across a meridian of the earth at the point of observation; this interval varies in length at different times during the year, but the average length of the interval for one year is constant.

Measures of Time. A *solar day* is measured by the rotation of the earth about its axis, with respect to the sun. In *astronomical computations* and in *nautical time* the day commences at noon, and in the former it is counted throughout the 24 hours. In *civil computations* the day commences at midnight, and is divided into two parts of 12 hours each.

A *solar year* is the time in which the earth makes one revolution around the sun. Its average time, called the *mean solar year*, is 365 days, 5 hours, 48 minutes, and 48 seconds, or nearly 365 $1/4$ days.

History of the Calendar. The Julian Calendar was established by Julius Caesar, 44 B.C., and by it one day was inserted in every fourth year. This was the same thing as assuming that the length of the solar year was 365 days and 6 hours, instead of the value given above, thus introducing a cumulative error of 11 minutes and 12 seconds every year. This calendar was adopted by the church in 325 A.D., at the Council of Nice. In the year 1582 the annual error of 11 minutes and 12 seconds had amounted to 10 days, which, by order of Pope Gregory XIII, was suppressed in the calendar, and the fifth of October reckoned as the fifteenth. To prevent the repetition of this error, it was decided to leave out three of the inserted days every 400 years, and to make this omission in the years which are not exactly divisible by 400. Thus, of the years 1700, 1800, 1900, and 2000, all of which are leap-years according to the Julian Calendar, only the last is a leap-year according to the Reformed or Gregorian Calendar. This Reformed Calendar was not adopted by England until 1752, when 11 days were omitted from the calendar. The two calendars are now often called the *Old Style* and the *New Style*.

* The slug of mass, which is extensively used by engineers and physicists, is (in the metric system) the mass to which an acceleration of one meter per second per second would be given by the application of a one-kilogram force. Unlike the kilogram of mass, it is not an absolute unit. Under standard gravity conditions, one slug of mass = 9.80665 kg of mass.

Accurate Weighing Procedure

To Determine Whether a Balance Has Equal Arms. After weighing an article and obtaining equilibrium, interchange the article and the weights. If equilibrium still obtains, the balance is true (assuming friction negligible); if equilibrium does not obtain, the pan which descends is suspended from the longer arm.

To Weigh Correctly on an Incorrect Balance. "Weigh" the article first on one pan and then on the other. The correct weight is the square root of the product of the apparent weights thus obtained.

11. FORCE, ENERGY, AND POWER

Dynamical and Gravitational Units. According to the use of two different dimension and unit systems, the dynamical (or physical, or "absolute") system and the gravitational (or technical) system, two different sets of units of force, energy, power, and derived quantities are defined in both the English and the metric systems. *One dynamical unit of force* produces an acceleration of unity on unit standard mass. The *gravitational unit of force* is defined as that force required to give a unit standard mass an acceleration equal to that produced by the gravitational pull of the earth. As the acceleration due to gravity, g, varies with location and altitude,* the gravitational unit of force is not constant, and, therefore, its relation to the dynamical unit of force will vary. By international agreement, the value $g_0 = 980.665$ cm per sec per sec $= 32.1739$ ft per sec per sec (British) has been chosen as the standard acceleration of gravity.

Force vs. Weight. The gravitational, or technical, system of units is extensively used in engineering, where it is the practice to measure forces by scales and balances calibrated by comparing them with the pull of the earth upon standard masses. These weighing devices, giving commercial weights, also measure force in gravitational units. Since the gravitational unit of force varies with g, measurements should be compared with the gravitational unit under standard conditions, $g = g_0$. Thus the local value of a force in number of standard gravitational units is g/g_0 times the force measured by scales calibrated locally, or $f = wg/g_0 = mg$. Owing to the manner in which weighing devices are calibrated, $m = w/g_0$ where f is in standard gravitational units.†

For engineering work the variation of g with latitude and elevation is usually negligible, so that the weight might be taken as the approximate value of the local pull of the earth. In scientific computations this slight difference has to be taken into consideration. For corrections required in accurate weighing see International Critical Tables, Vol. 1, p. 73.

These same corrections apply to all quantities, such as energy, pressure, power, and torque, involving the gravitational definition of force.

The English Units

Units of Force. The dynamical or physical unit of force is the *poundal*, defined as the force required to give a mass of one pound an acceleration of one foot per second per second.

The *pound-force* (or weight of the pound mass) is the gravitational or technical unit of force. It is, by definition, the force required to give a mass of one pound an acceleration equal to the value of standard acceleration due to gravity (see Force vs. Weight). If a force is measured by "weighing," the result in pounds weight must be multiplied by g/g_0, the ratio of local to standard acceleration of gravity, in order to obtain the absolute value in pound-force units. For engineering purposes this correction can usually be neglected.

The Unit of Pressure is defined as the unit of force acting upon a unit area. The most commonly employed unit is the *pound* (weight) *per square inch.* With respect to correction for local gravity, see Force vs. Weight, above.

Pressure is measured also by the height in inches of the column of water at 4 deg cent (39.1 deg fahr) or of the column of mercury at 32 deg fahr which it supports. (See Conversion Tables.)

Units of Work or Energy. The foot-poundal is the physical unit of work or energy and is defined as the work done by a force of one poundal in moving a body through the distance of one foot in the direction of the force.

The *foot-pound (force)* is the technical unit of work or energy and is defined as the work required to raise a mass (or weight) of one pound through a vertical distance of one foot at standard acceleration of gravity g_0. If measurements are made in places where the

---

* The variation of g with latitude ϕ and altitude H is given approximately by (ϕ in degrees, H in meters): $g = 978.039 (1 + 0.005295 \sin^2 \phi) - 0.000307 H$. See International Critical Tables, Vol. 1, p. 395.

† Wm. L. De Baufre, Mass, weight, and force, *Proc. Soc. Promotion Engg. Educ.*, 1928, p. 655.

local value of the acceleration of gravity g is different from g_0, a correction factor g/g_0 must be applied, if the exact value of work or energy is desired.   (See Force vs. Weight.)

The *British thermal unit* (Btu) is the quantity of heat required to raise the temperature of a one-pound mass of water either at 39 deg fahr (at its maximum density) or at 60 deg fahr, and standard pressure, through 1 deg fahr.   The mean British thermal unit is defined as the $1/180$ part of the heat required to raise the temperature of one pound mass of water from 32 to 212 deg fahr at standard pressure.   It is obvious that the reference temperature must be indicated with the unit used.

Units of Power.   Power is the time rate at which work is done.   Its physical unit is the *foot-poundal per second*, its technical units are the *foot-pound (force) per second*, or the *British thermal unit per second*.   The *horsepower* (hp or Hp) is defined as 33,000 ft-lb (force) per min or 550 ft-lb (force) per sec.

Units of Torque.   Torque is the effectiveness of a force to produce rotation.   It is defined as the product of the force and the perpendicular distance from its line of action to the instantaneous center of rotation.   Its physical unit is the poundal-foot, and its technical unit the pound (force)-foot.   (Note the reversal of force and length units in the designation of the units of torque as compared with the units of energy or work.)

The Metric Units

Units of Force.   The dynamical, or physical, unit of force is the *dyne,* defined as the force required to give a mass of one gram an acceleration of one centimeter per second per second.

The *kilogram force* (or weight of the kilogram mass) is the gravitational or technical unit of force.   It is, by definition, the force required to give a mass of one kilogram an acceleration equal to the value of standard acceleration due to gravity.   (See Force vs. Weight.)   If a force is measured by "weighing," the result in kilograms weight must be multiplied by g/g_0, the ratio of local to standard acceleration of gravity, in order to obtain the absolute value in kilogram-force units.   For engineering purposes this correction can usually be neglected.

In the electrotechnical system of units the systematic unit of force is defined as the *joule per meter,* based upon the fundamental definition of the joule.   (See Metric Units of Energy.)

The Unit of Pressure is defined as the unit of force acting upon a unit of area.   The physical unit is the *barye* or the pressure of one dyne upon one square centimeter.   A larger unit is the *bar* or 10^6 baryes, which has been adopted internationally.   (The use of bar for one dyne per square centimeter is discouraged.)

The *kilogram force per square meter* is the technical unit of pressure.   With respect to correction for local gravity, see Force vs. Weight, above.

Pressure is measured also by the height in centimeters of the column of water at 4 deg cent, or of the column of mercury at 0 deg cent, which it supports.   (See Conversion Tables.)

The *normal atmosphere* (*at*), or the standard atmospheric pressure, is defined as the pressure exerted by a column of 76 cm of mercury at sea level and 0 deg cent at standard acceleration of gravity g_0.   It is equal to 1.01321 bars or 1.0332 kg force per sq cm and is used extensively in the engineering literature.   Some confusion exists since the unit of 1 kg force per sq cm is occasionally called 1 practical atmosphere.

Units of Work or Energy.   The *erg* is the physical or so-called absolute unit of work or energy.   It is defined as the work done by a force of one dyne acting through the distance of one centimeter.   A larger unit is the *theoretical* (or absolute) *joule* defined as 10^7 ergs; it is a systematic unit in the practical electrical unit systems which is based upon the theoretical unit systems.   (See Electrical Units.)

The *international joule* is defined as the energy expended during one second by an electric current of one international ampere flowing through a resistance of one international ohm.   (See Electrical Units.)   The latest value of the international joule is equal to 1.00032 theoretical joules.

The *kilowatt-hour* is the practical unit of energy in electrical metering.   It is defined as a theoretical or an international unit (see definition of joule above) and is equal to 3600 $\times 10^3$ joules.

The *meter-kilogram force* (commonly referred to as the kilogram-meter) is the technical unit of work or energy.   It is defined as the work required to raise the mass (or weight) of one kilogram through a vertical distance of one meter at standard acceleration of gravity g_0.   If measurements are made in places where the local value of the acceleration of gravity g is different from g_0, a correction factor g/g_0 has to be applied, if the exact value of work or energy is desired.   (See Force vs. Weight.)

The *gram-calorie* or small calorie is the physical unit of heat energy. It is defined as the quantity of heat required to raise the temperature of one gram mass of water either from 14.5 to 15.5 deg cent or from 19.5 to 20.5 deg cent, at standard pressure. The two values are designated as 15 deg cent cal and 20 deg cent cal, respectively. The mean gram-calorie is defined as $1/100$ part of the quantity of heat required to raise the temperature of one gram mass of water from 0 to 100 deg cent at standard pressure. The same definitions apply to kilogram-calorie, or large calorie, if the kilogram mass is used as reference standard mass.

The *Ostwald calorie* is the quantity of heat required to raise the temperature of one gram mass from 0 to 100 deg cent. This unit is frequently used by electrochemists and is equal to 100 mean gram-calories.

The *international kilo-calorie* or international steam-table calorie (I T cal) is defined as the 1/860th part of the international kilowatthour. This new unit avoids any reference to the thermal properties of water and was recommended for international adoption at the first International Steam Table Conference (1929).* Its value is very nearly equal to the mean kilo-calorie, 1 I T cal = 1.00037 kilogram-calories (mean).

Units of Power. Power is the time rate at which work is done. Its physical unit is the *erg per second*.

A larger unit is the *theoretical* (or absolute) *watt*, defined as 10^7 ergs per second; it is a systematic unit in the practical electrical unit system which is based upon the theoretical unit systems (see electrical units).

The *international watt* is defined as the power expended by an electric current of one international ampere flowing through a resistance of one international ohm. (See Electrical Units.) The latest value of the international watt is equal to 1.00032 theoretical watts.

The *electrical horsepower* is defined as 746 absolute watts and is commonly used in the United States and in England in rating electrical machinery.

The *meter-kilogram force per second* (commonly referred to as the kilogram-meter per second) is the technical unit of power. The *metric horsepower* is defined as 75 kg-meters per sec and is the most common mechanical unit of power.

Units of Torque. Torque is the effectiveness of a force to produce rotation. It is defined as the product of the force and the perpendicular distance from its line of action to the instantaneous center of rotation. Its physical unit is the dyne-centimeter, and its technical unit the kilogram force meter. (Note the reversal of force and length units in the designation of the units of torque as compared with the units of energy and work.)

12. THERMAL UNITS AND STANDARDS

Temperature

Definition of Temperature. The *temperature* of a body may be defined as its thermal state considered from the standpoint of its ability to communicate heat to other bodies. When two bodies are placed in thermal communication, the one which loses heat to the other is said to be at the higher temperature.

Standard Temperatures. Certain thermal states or "temperatures" may be reproduced and recognized by the fact that definite physical phenomena occur at these temperatures. Such thermal states are called "fixed points," and they may, quite apart from any temperature scale, be specified by the physical phenomena characteristic of those temperatures. The two fundamental fixed points are the ice point and the steam point.

The *ice point* is defined as the temperature of melting ice, which is realized experimentally as the temperature at which pure finely divided ice is in equilibrium with pure, air-saturated water, under standard atmospheric pressure. The effect of increased pressure is to lower the freezing point to the extent of 0.007 deg cent per atmosphere.

The *steam point* is defined as the temperature of condensing water vapor at standard atmospheric pressure, and it is realized experimentally by the use of a hypsometer so constructed as to avoid superheat of the vapor around the thermometer, or contamination with air or other impurities. If the desired conditions have been attained, the observed temperature should be independent of the rate of heat supply to the boiler, except as this may affect the pressure within the hpysometer, and of the length of time the hypsometer has been in operation.

Definition of Temperature Scale. The purpose of establishing a temperature scale is to assign a number to every thermal state or temperature, and to provide a means for determining the temperature of any particular body.

---

* *Mechanical Engineering*, Feb., 1930, pp. 122, 139; Nov., 1935, p. 710.

A *temperature scale* may be defined by (1) selecting definite numbers for certain fixed points, (2) selecting some physical property of a definite substance which varies with temperature, and (3) selecting a mathematical law expressing temperatures on the scale in question in terms of the selected property of the thermometric substance.   For example, on the centigrade mercury-in-glass scale, the ice and steam points are numbered 0 and 100 respectively, the relative or "apparent" expansion of a volume of mercury enclosed in glass of a definite kind is the property used, and the mathematical relation used to express temperature on this scale is that equal increments of apparent volume of the mercury in this glass correspond to equal increments of temperature.   If some other substance is substituted for mercury, or if glass of a different kind is used, another scale is obtained which agrees with it at 0 and 100 but not at other temperatures.

Although, in general, a temperature scale depends on the thermometric substance as well as on the expression for the temperature in terms of some property of this substance, Lord Kelvin has shown that, if the property selected is the availability of energy, the scale so defined is wholly independent of the substance and depends only on the mathematical relation chosen.   Any scale so defined is known as a thermodynamic scale.

The Kelvin Temperature Scale.   The temperature scale finally chosen by Lord Kelvin is the one on which the temperature interval from the ice point to the steam point is 100 deg and the ratio of the values of any two temperatures is equal to the ratio of the heat taken in to the heat rejected by a reversible thermodynamic engine working with a source and refrigerator at the higher and lower temperatures respectively.   On this scale, which is also known as the absolute thermodynamic scale, the lowest attainable temperature is 0 and the ice point is found experimentally to be 273.16 deg.   The steam point therefore is 373.16 deg or 100 deg higher.

The *degree Kelvin* (deg K) or degree of absolute temperature is the absolute unit of temperature and is, for practical purposes, identical with the degree centigrade (deg cent) of the international temperature scale.

The Thermodynamic Centigrade Scale is derived by subtracting from the Kelvin scale a constant number of the proper magnitude to make the ice point 0 deg.   On this scale, therefore, the ice and steam points are 0 and 100 deg, respectively, and the so-called absolute zero is − 273.16 deg.

The International Centigrade Scale is a practical representation of the thermodynamic centigrade scale to such a degree of accuracy as is possible with present-day apparatus and methods.   It was adopted at the General Conference on Weights and Measures at Sèvres, France, in 1927 and is subject to revision and amendment as improved and more accurate methods of measurement are evolved.

The unit of temperature on the international scale is the *degree centigrade* (deg cent, or deg cent int) and is very nearly equal to $1/100$ the difference between the temperature of melting ice and the temperature of condensing water vapor under standard atmospheric pressure.   (See Metric Units for Pressure.)

The standard of the international temperature scale between − 190 and + 660 deg cent is deduced from the electrical resistance of a standard platinum resistance thermometer by means of a formula connecting the resistance R_t at any temperature t deg cent within the above range with the resistance R_0 at 0 deg cent.   The purity of the platinum of which the thermometer is made should be such that the ratio R_t/R_0 for certain fixed temperatures is within specified limits.*

The degree centigrade is most widely used in scientific publications and increasingly also in the engineering literature.   In many countries in Europe it is the common everyday temperature unit.   The subdivision into a hundred degrees of the temperature interval between the ice point and the steam point was first used by Celsius, a German, in 1742; therefore, in the European literature " ° C" is read "degree Celsius."

The Fahrenheit Temperature Scale subdivides the temperature interval between the ice point and the steam point into 180 parts, one part of which is chosen as the unit of temperature and named *degree Fahrenheit* (deg fahr).   The ice point is assigned the value 32 deg fahr, so that the steam point has a temperature of 212 deg fahr.

The Fahrenheit unit of temperature is in common everyday use in the English-speaking countries.   It was first introduced in England about 1665 by the physicist Fahrenheit; the choice of 32 deg fahr for the ice point has its explanation in the fact that Fahrenheit chose as zero the lowest temperature attainable by means of a salt-ice mixture.

The Réaumur Temperature Scale subdivides the temperature interval between the ice point and the steam point into 80 parts, one part of which is chosen as the unit of temperature and named *degree Réaumur* (deg R).   The ice point is assigned the value 0 deg R, as in the centigrade scale, so the steam point has a temperature of 80 deg R.

---

* See also U. S. Bureau of Standards, *Journal of Research*, Vol. 1, p. 636.

The Réaumur unit of temperature is in common everyday use in a number of European countries, especially in France and Russia. It was first introduced by Réaumur, a Frenchman, in 1731.

Relations between the Temperature Scales. In Table VI are shown the interrelations between the various temperature scales in form of equations. X indicates the unknown number of chosen temperature units and t the known number of given temperature units.

Table VI.   Relations between the Temperature Scales

$X° F =$	....	$9/5 (t° K - 273.16) + 32$	$9/5 (t° C) + 32$	$9/4 (t° R) + 32$
$X° K =$	$5/9 (t° F - 32) + 273.16$	....	$(t° C) + 273.16$	$5/4 (t° R) + 273.16$
$X° C =$	$5/9 (t° F - 32)$	$(t° K) - 273.16$	....	$5/4 (t° R)$
$X° R =$	$4/9 (t° F - 32)$	$4/5 (t° K - 273.16)$	$4/5 (t° C)$	....

Quantity of Heat and Some Derived Quantities

Units of Quantity of Heat. Quantity of heat is defined as the energy transferred from one body to another by a thermal process, i.e., by radiation or conduction. The units for the quantity of heat are the *British thermal unit* and the *calorie*, as specific thermal units; and the *erg* and *joule*, as general physical units (see units of energy, metric and English systems of units).

Thermal Capacity or Specific Heat of a Substance is the quantity of heat required to produce a unit change in temperature in a unit of mass of the substance. The common English unit is the British thermal unit per degree Fahrenheit per pound mass (Btu per deg fahr per lb); the usual metric unit is the gram-calorie per degree centigrade per gram mass (cal per deg cent per g); and the general physical unit used in the scientific literature is the erg per degree centigrade per gram mass (erg per deg cent per g). In the technical literature thermal capacity of a substance is often expressed in watt-seconds (or joules) per degree centigrade per kilogram mass (watt-sec per deg cent per kg) on account of the easy comparison with other technical units.

The Calorimetric or Water Equivalent is the quantity of heat required to produce a unit change in temperature of a body or system. It is numerically equivalent to the mass of water (in units as involved in the definition of the unit of quantity of heat used) which could be raised a unit temperature by the same total quantity of heat. The thermal capacity is expressed in British thermal units per degree Fahrenheit (Btu per deg fahr), calories per degree centigrade (cal per deg cent), or watt-seconds per degree centigrade (watt-sec per deg cent).

Thermal Conductivity is the time rate of heat transfer through unit area across unit thickness per unit difference in temperature between the end surfaces. It is measured in British thermal units per second per degree Fahrenheit per inch thickness per square inch cross-section (Btu per sec per deg fahr per in. per sq in.), in calories per second per degree centigrade per centimeter thickness per square centimeter cross-section (cal per sec per deg cent per sq cm per cm), or in watts per degree centigrade per meter thickness per square meter cross-section (watts per deg cent per sq m per m).

Emissivity or emissive power is the time rate of heat emitted by unit area for unit difference in temperature between the surface in question and the surroundings. It is measured in British thermal units per second per degree Fahrenheit per square inch (Btu per sec per deg fahr per sq in.), in calories per second per degree centigrade per square centimeter (cal per sec per deg cent per sq cm, or in watts per degree centigrade per square meter (watts per deg cent per sq m).

The Joule Equivalent

The Joule Equivalent is defined as the number of foot-pounds of energy per Btu. In Table VII are given the numerical values for the various energy units used in the English and metric systems.[*]

Table VII.—Relations between Energy Units [†]

	Joules (theoretical)	Foot-pounds (force)	Foot-poundals	Meter-kilogram (force)	Kilowatt-hour (international)
1 British thermal unit (Btu) (mean).. =	1055.18	778.26	25,040	107.599	2.93019×10^{-4}
1 gram-calorie (cal) (mean)........ =	4.1873	3.0884	99.366	0.42699	1.16279×10^{-6}
1 International kilo-calorie (I T-cal) =	4187.3	3088.4	99,366	426.99	1.16279×10^{-3}
1 Ostwald calorie... =	418.73	308.84	9936.6	42.699	1.16279×10^{-4}

[*] For a rather complete historical account see R. Glazebrook, Dictionary of Applied Physics, Vol. I, p. 477.

[†] According to the latest computations, see *Mechanical Engineering*, Vol. 57, p. 713 (1935).

13. THE THEORETICAL OR "ABSOLUTE" ELECTRICAL UNITS

The Definitions of the Theoretical Units are based upon the fundamental units of the physical (dynamical) unit system of mechanics, which is very frequently referred to as the "absolute" unit system, and has led to the electrical units being called "absolute" units. This designation is not warranted, as "absolute" implies the meaning of "ultimate." (See discussion on "absolute" electrical unit systems, p. 3–13.) According to a previous proposal,* "absolute" shall be replaced here by "theoretical," a designation which calls the attention to the fact that mere arbitrary definitions, not standards, are the basis of the units. The realization of the "absolute" units has been attempted many times in the past by so-called "absolute" measurements. An interesting account of the history and a description of the various classical methods can be found in Glazebrook's Handbook for Applied Physics, Vol. II, "Electricity," pp. 211 and on, 1922.

The Theoretical Electrostatic Units

The Theoretical Electrostatic Units are based upon the cgs system of mechanical units and are therefore frequently referred to as the *cgs electrostatic units*. No specific unit names are available. In order to avoid the cumbersome writing, for example, one "theoretical electrostatic unit of charge," it had been proposed to use the theoretical "practical" unit names and prefix them with either stat † or E.S.,‡ as for example, statcoulomb, or E.S. coulomb. The first alternative will be used here.

The Absolute Dielectric Constant (Permittivity) of free space is the fundamental quantity in the theoretical electrostatic system of units. Its numerical value is assumed as unity, and it is identical with one centimeter per statfarad if use is made of prefixing the corresponding unit of the "practical" series. As the dielectric constant is a derived quantity in the "practical" unit systems it takes a derived unit name in the electrostatic system although, in fact, it is entitled to a fundamental unit name.

The Theoretical Electrostatic Unit of Charge or the statcoulomb is defined as the quantity of electricity which, when concentrated at a point and placed at one centimeter distance from an equal quantity of electricity similarly concentrated, will experience a mechanical force of one dyne in free space. An alternative definition, based upon the concept of field lines, gives the theoretical electrostatic unit of charge as a positive charge from which in free space exactly 4π electrical field lines emerge. Both these definitions use the numerical value unity for the proportionality constant K_{e0} in Coulomb's law. (See Table V.) The quantity of electricity appears in this system as a derived quantity.

The Theoretical Electrostatic Unit of Displacement Flux (Dielectric Flux) is the "line of displacement flux" or $\frac{1}{4\pi}$ of the theoretical electrostatic unit of charge. This definition provides the basis for graphical field mapping in so far as it gives a definite rule for the selection of displacement lines to represent the character of the field.

The Theoretical Electrostatic Unit of Displacement, or Dielectric Flux Density, is chosen as one displacement line per square centimeter area perpendicular to the direction of the displacement lines. It can be given also as $\frac{1}{4\pi}$ statcoulomb per square centimeter (according to Gauss's law). In isotropic media the displacement has the same direction as the potential gradient, and the surfaces perpendicular to the field lines become the equipotential surfaces; the theoretical electrostatic unit of displacement can then be defined as one displacement line per square centimeter of equipotential surface.

The Theoretical Electrostatic Unit of Electrostatic Potential or the Statvolt is defined as existing at a point in an electrostatic field, if the work done to bring the theoretical electrostatic unit of charge, or the statcoulomb, from infinity to this point equals one erg. This customary definition implies, however, that the potential vanishes at infinite distances and has, therefore, only restricted validity. As it is fundamentally impossible to give absolute values of potential the use of potential difference and its unit (see below) should be preferred.

The Theoretical Electrostatic Unit of Electrical Potential Difference or Voltage, or the Statvolt, is defined as existing between two points in space if the work done to bring the theoretical electrostatic unit of charge, or the statcoulomb, from the one of these points to the other equals one erg. Potential difference is counted positive in the direction in which a negative quantity of electricity would be moved by the electrostatic field.

---

* G. Mie in Handbuch der Experimental Physik, Vol. 11, "Elektrodynamik," p. 430, Berlin, 1932.
† Proposed by A. E. Kennelly at the International Electrical Congress in St. Louis, 1904, *Trans.*, Vol. 1, p. 180, and used by C. Hering, Conversion Tables, J. Wiley and Sons, 1904.
‡ Proposed by A. E. Caswell, *Science*, Vol. 42, p. 695, 1915, and used by E. Bennett. A digest of the relations between the electrical units, *Bull. Univ. Wisconsin*, No. 880, 1917.

The **Theoretical Electrostatic Unit of Capacitance of the Statfarad** is defined as the capacitance which maintains an electrical potential difference of one statvolt between two conductors charged with equal and opposite electrical quantities of one statcoulomb. In some texts the statfarad is called one "centimeter," which is confusing. (See CGS Electrostatic Unit System.)

The **Theoretical Electrostatic Unit of Electric Potential Gradient, or Field Strength** (field intensity), is defined to exist at a point in an electric field, if the mechanical force exerted upon the theoretical electrostatic unit of charge concentrated at this point is equal to one dyne. It is expressed as one statvolt per centimeter.

The **Theoretical Electrostatic Unit of Current or the Statampere** is defined as the time rate of transfer of the theoretical electrostatic unit of charge and is identical with the statcoulomb per second.

The **Theoretical Electrostatic Unit of Electrical Resistance or the Statohm** is defined as the resistance of a conductor in which a current of one statampere is produced if a potential difference of one statvolt is applied at its ends.

The **Theoretical Electrostatic Unit of Electromotive Force (emf)** is defined as equivalent to the theoretical electrostatic unit of potential difference if it produces a current of one statampere in a conductor of one statohm resistance. It is identical with the statvolt but, according to its concept, requires an independent definition.

The **Theoretical Electrostatic Unit of Magnetizing Force** is defined as the magnetizing force at the center of a circle of 4π cm diameter in which a current of one statampere is flowing. This unit is equal to 4π statamperes per centimeter but has no name as the factor 4π excludes the possibility of using the prefixed " practical " unit name.

The **Theoretical Electrostatic Unit of Magnetic Flux or the Statweber** is defined as the magnetic flux whose time rate of change through a linear conductor loop (linear conductor is used to designate a conductor of infinitely small cross-section) produces in this loop an electromotive force (emf) of one statvolt.

The **Theoretical Electrostatic Unit of Magnetic Flux Density, or Induction,** is defined as the electrostatic unit of magnetic flux per square centimeter area, or the statweber per square centimeter.

The absolute magnetic permeability of free space is defined as the ratio of magnetic induction to the magnetizing force. Its unit is the stathenry per centimeter, as a derived unit; its value is given in Table V.

The **Theoretical Electrostatic Unit of Inductance or the Stathenry** is defined as connected with a conductor loop carrying a steady current of one statampere which produces a magnetic flux of one statweber. A more general definition, applicable to varying fields with non-linear relation between magnetic flux and current, gives the stathenry as connected with a conductor loop in which a time rate of change in the current of one statcoulomb produces a time rate of change in the magnetic flux of one statweber per second.

The Theoretical Electromagnetic Units

The **Theoretical Electromagnetic Units** are based upon the cgs system of mechanical units and are, therefore, frequently referred to as the cgs electromagnetic units. Only a few specific unit names are available. In order to avoid cumbersome writing, for example, one "theoretical electromagnetic unit of charge," it had been proposed to use the theoretical "practical" unit names and prefix them with either ab- [*] or E.M.,[†] as for example abcoulomb, or E.M. coulomb. The first alternative will be used here.

The theoretical electromagnetic units are based essentially upon the assumption of a fictitious magnetic quantity similar to the electric quantity or charge. It must be borne in mind that the phenomenon of magnetism is fundamentally a bipole phenomenon; a separation of positive or negative magnetic quantity has not been possible. Several of the following definitions, therefore, have to be taken cautiously. They are given because of their widespread use in theoretical physics and their continued appearance even in elementary textbooks.

The **Absolute Magnetic Permeability** of free space is the fundamental quantity in the theoretical electromagnetic system of units. Its numerical value is assumed as unity, and it is identical with one abhenry per centimeter if use is made of prefixing the corresponding unit of the "practical" series. As the permeability is a derived quantity in the practical unit systems it takes a derived unit name in the electromagnetic system, although, in fact, it is entitled to a fundamental unit name.

The **Theoretical Electromagnetic Unit of Magnetic Quantity** is defined as the magnetic quantity which, when concentrated at a point and placed at one centimeter distance from an equal magnetic quantity similarly concentrated, will experience a mechanical force of one dyne in free space. An alternative definition, based upon the concept of field lines, gives the theoretical electromagnetic unit of magnetic quantity as a positive magnetic quantity from which, in free space, exactly 4π magnetic field lines emerge. Both these definitions use the numerical value, unity, for the proportionality constant in Coulomb's law for magnetic poles. The unit of magnetic quantity thus defined is identical with 4π maxwells.

The **Theoretical Electromagnetic Unit of Magnetic Moment** is defined as the magnetic moment possessed by a magnet formed by two theoretical electromagnetic units of magnetic quantity of opposite sign, concentrated at two points one centimeter apart. The unit is expressed as 4π maxwell-centimeters.

The **Theoretical Electromagnetic Unit of Magnetic Flux** is the "field line," or $\frac{1}{4\pi}$ times the theoretical electromagnetic unit of magnetic quantity, and is called one maxwell. This definition provides the basis for graphical field mapping since it gives a definite rule for the selection of field lines to represent the character of the magnetic field.

The **Theoretical Electromagnetic Unit of Magnetic Flux Density, or Induction,** is chosen as one magnetic field line per square centimeter area perpendicular to the direction of the field lines. It can also be given as one maxwell per square centimeter and is called one gauss.

The **Theoretical Electromagnetic Unit of Magnetizing Force** (**Magnetic Intensity**) is defined as the magnetizing force which exerts a mechanical force of one dyne upon the theoretical electromagnetic unit of magnetic quantity concentrated at the point. The name of this unit is oersted.

The **Theoretical Electromagnetic Unit of Current, or the Abampere,** is defined as the current which flows in a circle of one centimeter diameter and produces at the center of this circle a magnetizing force of one oersted.

The **Theoretical Electromagnetic Unit of Inductance, or the Abhenry,** is defined as connected with a conductor loop in which a time rate of change of one maxwell per second in the magnetic flux produces a time rate of change in the current of one abcoulomb per second. In some texts the abhenry is called "centimeter," which is confusing. (See CGS Electromagnetic Unit System.)

The **Theoretical Electromagnetic Unit of Magnetomotive Force** (**mmf**) is defined as the magnetic driving force produced by a conductor loop carrying a steady current of $\frac{1}{4\pi}$ abamperes; it has the name one gilbert. The concept of magnetomotive force as the driving force in a "magnetic circuit" permits an alternative definition of the gilbert as the magnetomotive force which produces a uniform magnetizing force of one oersted over a length of one centimeter in the magnetic circuit. Obviously, one gilbert equals one oersted-centimeter.

The **Theoretical Electromagnetic Unit of Magnetostatic Potential** is defined as that existing at a point in a magnetic field, if the work done to bring the theoretical electromagnetic unit of magnetic quantity from infinity to this point equals one erg. (This customary definition implies, however, that the potential vanishes at infinite distances, and the definition has, therefore, only restricted validity.) The unit, thus defined, is identical with one gilbert. The difference in magnetostatic potential between any two points is usually called magnetomotive force (mmf).

The **Theoretical Electromagnetic Unit of Reluctance** is defined as the reluctance of a magnetic circuit in which a magnetomotive force of one gilbert produces a magnetic flux of one maxwell.

The **Theoretical Electromagnetic Unit of Electric Charge, or the Abcoulomb,** is defined as the quantity of electricity which passes through any section of an electric circuit in one second if the current is one abampere.

The **Theoretical Electromagnetic Unit of Displacement Flux** (**Dielectric Flux**) is the "line of displacement flux" or $\frac{1}{4\pi}$ of the theoretical electromagnetic unit of electric charge. This definition provides the basis for graphical field mapping in so far as it gives a definite rule for the selection of displacement lines to represent the character of the field.

The **Theoretical Electromagnetic Unit of Displacement, or Dielectric Flux Density,** is chosen as one displacement line per square centimeter area perpendicular to the direction of the displacement lines. It can also be given as $\frac{1}{4\pi}$ abcoulombs per square centimeter (according to Gauss's law). In isotropic media the theoretical electromagnetic unit of displacement can be defined as one displacement line per square centimeter of equipotential surface. (See Theoretical Electrostatic Unit of Displacement.)

The Theoretical Electromagnetic Unit of Electrical Potential Difference or Voltage, or the abvolt, is defined as the potential existing between two points in space if the work done in bringing the theoretical electromagnetic unit of charge, or the abcoulomb, from one of these points to the other equals one erg. Potential difference is counted positive in the direction in which a negative quantity of electricity would be moved by the electrostatic field.

The Theoretical Electromagnetic Unit of Capacitance, or the Abfarad, is defined as the capacitance which maintains an electrical potential difference of one abvolt between two conductors charged with equal and opposite electrical quantities of one abcoulomb.

The Theoretical Electromagnetic Unit of Potential Gradient, or Field Strength (field intensity), is defined to exist at a point in an electric field if the mechanical force exerted upon the theoretical electromagnetic unit of charge concentrated at this point is equal to one dyne. It is expressed as one abvolt per centimeter.

The Theoretical Electromagnetic Unit of Resistance, or the Abohm, is defined as the resistance of a conductor in which a current of one abampere is produced if a potential difference of one abvolt is applied at its ends.

The Theoretical Electromagnetic Unit of Electromotive Force (emf) is defined as the electromotive force acting in an electric circuit in which a current of one abampere is flowing and electrical energy is converted into other kinds of energy at the rate of one erg per second. This unit is identical with the abvolt.

The Absolute Dielectric Constant of Free Space is defined as the ratio of displacement to the electric field intensity. Its unit is the abfarad per centimeter, a derived unit; its value is given in Table V.

The Theoretical Electrodynamic Units

The Theoretical Electrodynamic Units are based upon the cgs system of mechanical units and are therefore frequently referred to as *the cgs electrodynamic units*. In contradistinction to the theoretical electromagnetic units, these units are derived from a significant experimental law, Ampère's experiment on the mechanical force between two parallel currents. (See Table V.) The units as proposed by Ampère and used by W. Weber differ from the electromagnetic units by factors of 2 and multiples thereof. They can be made to coincide with the theoretical electromagnetic units by proper definition of the fundamental unit of current. Some of the important definitions will be given for this latter case only.

For the *absolute magnetic permeability* of free space see Theoretical Electromagnetic Units.

The Theoretical Electrodynamic Unit of Current, or the Abampere, is defined as the current flowing in a circuit consisting of two infinitely long parallel wires one centimeter apart when the electrodynamic force of repulsion between the two wires is *two* dynes per centimeter length in free space. If the more natural choice of *one* dyne per centimeter length is made, the original proposal of Ampère is obtained and the unit of current becomes $1/2$ abampere.

The Theoretical Electrodynamic Unit of Magnetic Induction is defined as the magnetic induction inducing an electromotive force of one abvolt in a conductor of one-centimeter length and moving with a velocity of one centimeter per second, if the conductor, its velocity, and the magnetic induction are mutually perpendicular. The unit thus defined is called one gauss.

The Theoretical Electrodynamic Unit of Magnetic Flux, or the Maxwell, is defined as the magnetic flux represented by a uniform magnetic induction of one gauss over an area of one square centimeter perpendicular to the direction of the magnetic induction.

The Theoretical Electrodynamic Unit of Magnetizing Force, or the Oersted, is defined as the magnetizing force at the center of a circle of 4π-centimeter diameter in which a current of one abampere is flowing.

All the Other Unit Definitions, which do not pertain to magnetic quantities, are identical with the definitions for the theoretical electromagnetic units.

The Rational Units

The factor 4π occurs frequently in the definition of important units. According to Heaviside, this can be avoided by writing the fundamental electromagnetic equations in a form different from and simpler than that used by the classical authors. The form of the equations is given in Table V, and the unit definitions, which are based upon the definitions of the theoretical electromagnetic units, lead to the " rationalized " units as shown in Table IV. On account of the convenience many authors use the rationalized forms of the equations but very seldom use the rationalized units. Usually conversion into the " practical " units is preferred for any numerical computations.

The So-called "Absolute" Practical Units

The units of the theoretical electrostatic and electromagnetic series are not particularly convenient for most purposes. The "practical" series of units uses multiples and submultiples of the theoretical electromagnetic units in such manner that no new numerical factors enter the fundamental equations and that the systematic unit of energy is the joule instead of the erg. Since these "practical" units are based upon the theoretical classical units they are, in fact, also theoretical. In order to distinguish these units from the international series (see below), the former are frequently referred to as "absolute" practical units.

The Fundamental Unit Names and their relations to the theoretical units follow, with indication of the year of their international adoption.

The ampere is 10^{-1} of the theoretical electromagnetic unit of current (1881).
The coulomb is 10^{-1} of the theoretical electromagnetic unit of charge (1881).
The volt is 10^{+8} of the theoretical electromagnetic unit of potential difference (1881).
The ohm is 10^{+9} of the theoretical electromagnetic unit of resistance (1881).
The henry is 10^{+9} of the theoretical electromagnetic unit of inductance (1893).
The farad is 10^{-9} of the theoretical electromagnetic unit of capacitance (1881).
The weber is 10^{+8} of the theoretical electromagnetic unit of magnetic flux (1933).
The joule is 10^{+7} ergs (1889).
The watt is 10^{+7} ergs per second (1889).

The definitions of these theoretical "practical" units are similar to the definitions of the theoretical electromagnetic units and are obtained from them if the prefix ab- is omitted and erg or dyne is replaced by joule or joule per centimeter, respectively.

In addition, the definitions of dielectric and magnetic quantities, which formerly involved the factor 4π, are to be replaced as follows:

The Theoretical " Practical " Unit of Magnetomotive Force (mmf) is defined as the magnetic driving force produced by a conductor loop carrying a steady current of one ampere; it has the name ampere-turn. The concept of magnetomotive force as the driving force in the "magnetic circuit" permits the alternative definition of the ampere-turn as the magnetic force which produces a uniform magnetizing force of one ampere per centimeter over a length of one centimeter in the magnetic circuit.

The Theoretical " Practical " Unit of Magnetizing Force (Magnetic Intensity) is defined as the magnetizing force at the center of a circle of one-centimeter diameter in which a current of one ampere is flowing. It is expressed as one ampere-turn per centimeter.

The Theoretical " Practical " Unit of Reluctance is defined as the reluctance of a magnetic circuit in which a magnetomotive force of one ampere-turn produces a magnetic flux of one weber.

The Theoretical " Practical " Unit of Displacement Flux (Dielectric Flux) is defined as the total displacement flux emanating from a positive theoretical " practical" unit of charge, or coulomb. It is expressed as one coulomb.

The Theoretical " Practical " Unit of Displacement (Dielectric Flux Density) is defined as one coulomb of displacement flux uniformly distributed over the area of one square centimeter perpendicular to the direction of the displacement. It is expressed as one coulomb per square centimeter.

The Unit System, Which Uses the " Practical " Units, as defined in the rationalized equations, employs the absolute dielectric constant and the absolute permeability of free space as physical quantities with numerical values which are given in Table V.

The Derived Theoretical " Practical " Units can be formed either in the cgs system or in the mks system. In general, the centimeter is preferred as it gives the more convenient values for densities, whereas the meter would be preferable from the point of view of the comprehensive Giorgi-MKS system. Both alternatives are given in Table V for the more important electrical quantities.

The Bureau Internationale des Poids et Mesures decided in 1933 to replace the "international" practical units by the "absolute" practical units. At the meeting on October 8, 1935, it decided to set as the final date for this transition the year 1940.

14. THE INTERNATIONAL ELECTRICAL UNITS AND STANDARDS

Definitions of the Internationally Adopted Units *

The **International System** of electrical and magnetic units is a system for electrical and magnetic quantities which takes as the four fundamental quantities resistance, current, length, and time.

The units of resistance and current are arbitrary values that approximately correspond to the theoretical or "absolute" ohm and the theoretical or "absolute" ampere, and the units of length and time are the centimeter and second.

The international units were defined by the International Electrical Congress at Chicago in 1893 and slightly modified by the London Electrical Conference in 1908. (The International Committee of Weights and Measures has decided to discard these units in the near future.)

The **International Ampere** is defined as the current which will deposit silver at the rate of 0.00111800 gram per second.

Experimental results show that the international ampere is nearly the same as the theoretical ampere. †

An **International Coulomb** is the quantity of electricity which passes any section of an electrical circuit in one second, when the current in the circuit is one international ampere.

One international coulomb is nearly the same as the theoretical coulomb.

The **International Ohm** is defined as the resistance at 0 deg cent of a column of mercury of uniform cross-section, having a length of 106.300 cm and a mass of 14.4521 grams.

Experimental results show that one international ohm equals 1.0005 theoretical ohms. ‡

The **International Volt** is the voltage that will produce a current of one international ampere through a resistance of one international ohm.

One international volt equals 1.0005 theoretical volts.

The **International Henry** is the inductance which produces an electromotive force of one international volt when the current is changing at the rate of one international ampere per second.

One international henry equals 1.0005 theoretical henrys.

The **International Farad** is the capacitance of a capacitor if a charge of one international coulomb produces a potential difference between the terminals of one international volt.

One international farad equals 0.9995 theoretical farad.

The **International Joule** § is the energy required to transfer one international coulomb between two points having a potential difference of one international volt.

One international joule equals 1.0005 theoretical joules.

The **International Watt** § is the power expended when one international ampere flows between two points having a potential difference of one international volt.

One international watt equals 1.0005 theoretical watts.

Definitions of Auxiliary Units

In addition to the internationally adopted units, a number of auxiliary units are in use, based upon the former and derived from them.

The **International Ampere-turn** is the magnetomotive force of a conductor loop in which a current of one international ampere is flowing.

The **International Mho** is the unit of conductance and is defined as the reciprocal value of one international ohm. It is represented by the same column of mercury which serves as standard for the international ohm.

The **Faraday** is the electrical charge carried by one gram-equivalent of dissociated substance. It is identical with 96,507 international coulombs.

The **International Kilowatt-hour** is the practical unit of energy in electrical metering. It is defined as 3600×10^3 international joules.

The **International Unit of Magnetic Flux** is the international volt-second and is defined

---

* Proposed American Standard definitions of electrical terms, A.I.E.E. No. 2, August, 1932, p. 33.

† The latest determination of the ratio, international ampere to theoretical ampere, gives the value 0.999928 ± 0.000020; H. L. Curtis and R. W. Curtis, *Bur. Standards J. Research*, 1934, Vol. 12, p. 665.

‡ The latest determination of the ratio, international ohm to theoretical ohm by the N.P.L. (National Physical Lab., England) gives the value 1.00052, F. E. Smith, *Phil. Trans. Roy. Soc. London*, Vol. 214, p. 27, 1914; by the P.T.R. (Physikalisch-Technische Reichsanstalt gives the value 1.00051, E. Grüneisen and E. Giebe, *Ann. Physik*, Vol. 63, p. 179, 1920.

§ The latest computation, 1935, of the ratio of the international to the theoretical joule and watt gives the value, 1.00032.

as the magnetic flux through a conductor loop with a resistance of one international ohm, when the reversal of direction of the magnetic flux causes the transfer of one international coulomb in the conductor loop. The international volt-second equals 1.0005 theoretical volt-seconds or webers.

Definitions of Derived Units

From the eight internationally adopted and the five auxiliary international units, other units can be derived as densities and gradients. These derivatives can be formed with either the cgs system of mechanical units or the mks system and correspondingly lead to different numerical relations.

Derived Units in the CGS System. In the engineering as well as in the scientific literature the centimeter is much the preferred length unit because it gives convenient values for the derived quantities. To form a comprehensive unitary system, however, the systematic unit of mass should then be one gram-seven (10^7 gram mass), which has been advocated and partially used. (See CGS System of Units, p. 3–14.) The units of the more important electrical derived quantities, using the centimeter as unit length, are shown in Table VII under practical unit system, with the values in the left sub-column.

Derived Units in the MKS System. Although advocated since 1901 and based upon the true standards of mechanical units (see MKS System of Units, p. 3–14), the mks system has not been used in connection with electrical units. It seems to be the only reasonable comprehensive unitary system of units, yet its values for densities and gradients are inconveniently large. The units of the more important electrical derived quantities, using the meter as unit length, are shown in Table IV under practical unit system, with the values in the right sub-column.

Derived Units in the English System. In the engineering literature of the English-speaking countries the foot-pound-second system is usually employed in order to form the derived units. As unit length either the inch or the mil (one-thousandth of the inch) is chosen; as unit area the square inch or the circular mil (for circular cross-sections). In most scientific publications, however, the metric system is used or the equivalent values in the metric system are given.

The Writing of the Electromagnetic Equations is not influenced by the choice of the supplementary mechanical system used for the derived units, if the *same units* are used on *both sides of the equations*, and no new numerical factors will enter. If units from different systems are used, this fact must be expressedly stated, and the equations will need numerical factors in order to balance the two sides.

Historical

Many controversies and discussions have been instigated by the almost continuous change in electrical standards. It is difficult to compare results of more recent precision measurements with earlier ones because the conditions of the standards used then might not be known accurately enough or it might not even be known which definitions of the standards were employed. A very interesting account of the history of the international electrical units is given by A. E. Kennelly in *Proc. Soc. Promotion Engg. Educ.*, Vol. 19, p. 229, 1928.* A short review of the historical development follows here.

First Empirical Standards. The " absolute " measurements of magnetic quantities by C. F. Gauss (1833), and electrical quantities by W. Weber (1840, 1851), showed the possibility of comparing electromagnetic quantities with mechanical quantities. Comparative measurements demonstrated the need for "standards" as they existed in the meter and kilogram prototypes. The earliest attempt was by Charles Wheatstone (1843), who used 1-ft lengths of copper wire, weighing 100 grains (6.48 grams). The Jacobi etalons (1850) and the Siemens unit (1860) followed. The latter is a mercury column of 1 sq mm cross-section and 1 meter length under specified conditions and has a resistance of nearly 1 ohm (1 international ohm = 1.06300 Siemens units).

First Systematic Standards. The confusion in standards brought about the appointment of a "Committee on electrical resistance" by the British Association for the Advancement of Science which worked from 1861 to 1873 and enlisted the collaboration of Lord Kelvin, J. P. Joule, J. C. Maxwell, and others. This committee † recommended the cgs system for general use in science, defined the theoretical "practical" units of volt, ohm, and farad, and issued a standard resistance, the B.A. unit (B.A.U.), which equals 0.988 theoretical ohm, although it was intended to be exactly one theoretical ohm. The lack of more accurate methods of measurement was a severe handicap. In 1872 L. Clark

---

* See also W. Jaeger, Die Entstehung der internationalen Masse der Elektrotechnik, J. Springer, Berlin, 1932; S. W. Stratton, Electric Units and Standards, Circular No. 60 of the Bureau of Standards, Washington, 1920.

† Reports published by F. Jenkins, London, 1873.

produced a standard cell which gave a fairly constant voltage of 1.43 volts, but no standardization was recommended.

The Congresses at Paris. In 1881 an international electrical congress met at Paris and adopted for international use the theoretical units ohm, volt, ampere, coulomb, and farad. It decided upon resistance as the primary standard, of the same type as the Siemens unit, but left the detail specifications to future investigations. The desired accuracy was specified in 1882 as one per mil (whereas mechanical measurements could be made with considerably higher accuracy). Up to 1884 fourteen independent measurements of the Siemens unit in terms of the theoretical ohm were made in all major countries but the accuracy of one per mil could not be attained, so a " legal " ohm was defined as 1.06 Siemens units. The legal ohm was clearly recognized as a provisional standard until more accurate methods should be available, but it was in wide use for a considerable time.

In 1887 the Physikalisch-Technische Reichsanstalt (P.T.R.) was founded in Berlin, and immediately proceeded to refine the so-called "absolute" measurements under the guidance of H. v. Helmholtz. Up to the international congress in 1889 at Paris, not enough material could be presented, and so a change of the legal ohm was not feasible. The congress adopted, however, the theoretical joule, watt, and kilowatt (instead of the horsepower), and the quadrant (as unit of inductance), for international use.

Introduction of Three International Standards. The fourth international electrical congress at Chicago, 1893, adopted finally the specific definitions of the standards for the "international" ohm and ampere, which had been prepared at a preliminary meeting at Edinburgh (1892). Unfortunately, a third independent standard was adopted, when the Clark cell of standard make was defined as producing a voltage of 1.434 "international" volts at 15 deg cent. Shortly afterwards it was discovered that the international volt as defined from one international ampere $\times$ one international ohm differed slightly from the standard defined by the Clark cell. Disagreeable confusion resulted as all measurements had to indicate which standards were used, and troublesome corrections had to be made before measurements using different standards could be compared. Of great help was the formation of the National Physical Laboratories (N.P.L.) in London, 1902, and the Bureau of Standards (B. St.) in Washington, D. C., 1904, followed by other government institutions. At the international meeting at St. Louis, no action could yet be taken, but an international commission was appointed to study a feasible final settlement.

The Final Standards. At a preliminary international conference at Berlin-Charlottenburg, in 1905, definite proposals were prepared, but additional experimental material was requested. The meeting of the international commission in London, 1908, finally adopted the definitions of the "international" units as used today, with the ohm as the first and the ampere as the second primary standard, whereas the volt was defined as a derived unit. The values remained the same as defined at the Chicago congress, but the two zeros were added to make the decision a final one without further corrections. All further measurements could have only the purpose of defining the ratio of the "international" units to the theoretical units, and these efforts have continued. In June, 1929, the International Bureau of Weights and Measures decided to act as a central institute for the intercomparison of the national standards, basing its measurements upon the theoretical units which, according to newest methods, are subject to a very much higher degree of precision than the standards that are kept at the various governmental institutions.*

DIMENSIONAL ANALYSIS

15. DIMENSIONAL HOMOGENEITY OF PHYSICAL EQUATIONS

A Physical Quantity is defined by unit and numerical value. (See Art. 1). The designation by a mathematical symbol is, therefore, not a unique determination, and proper care has to be taken in all cases where physical quantities are used in mathematical equations. The ratio of any two like physical quantities, however, represents a unique and absolute value, provided both quantities are given in the same unit. This is the basis of physical measurements and also of fixed unit relations, as, for example, 1 meter = 100 cm.

Physical Equations are relations between physical quantities which, in general, state the balance of certain conceptual quantities as forces, energies, voltage drops, currents, momenta, and so on. Obviously all the terms in a physical equation must have the same resultant dimension if the equation is to have sense. This property of physical equations

---

is called *dimensional homogeneity* and can be checked by employing the method of dimensions as used first by Fourier.* (See Arts. 1 and 2.) In physical differential equations the differentials are to be treated as having the same dimension as the finite quantities. To use dimensional relations properly, one must adhere to a complete dimension system and must not use incomplete dimension sets; this is of particular importance in dimensional analysis as shown later.† Proportionality constants, for example, will in general be physical quantities with numerical values and dimensions.

A Complete Dimension System suitable for a particular physical equation can be obtained from the equation itself in the following manner. Suppose z quantities are involved in the equation which is composed of q terms of equal resultant dimensions on account of dimensional homogeneity. Between the z dimensions there are, of course, $(q - 1)$ independent relations at the most, so that $(q - 1)$ dimensions can be expressed in general in terms of the remaining $(z - q + 1)$ dimensions. $(z - q + 1)$ constitutes thus the least number of independent or free dimensions in this particular case.

Style. It is of value and utmost convenience to use a definite *style of writing physical equations*. The simplest and most logical expression appears to be the *unitary homogeneous form*, which, of course, involves dimensional homogeneity and is based upon the assumption that one system of units and one only shall be used for all physical quantities involved. Unitary homogeneous equations are independent of the specific unit system employed and can always be reduced to purely numerical relations since all the units cancel on account of the dimensional homogeneity; consequently they avoid the necessity of furnishing a legend with each equation in order to explain the various units to be used. Very illustrative examples of equations not having unitary homogeneity are given by Table VII in Art. 12.

Functional forms (like trigonometric or exponential functions) can have only numerical arguments; sin E, where E means energy, or voltage, has no sense because it violates dimensional homogeneity. This can be seen by expanding the function into the equivalent power series

$$\sin E = \frac{E}{1!} - \frac{E^3}{3!} + \frac{E^5}{5!} - + \cdots$$

where each term has different dimensions.

Physical Similarity

Physical Similarity can be defined as existing for two systems which are described by exactly the same differential equations with exactly the same numerical constants. This at once discards the meaning of similarity as an absolute property and brings it into the same order of approximation as the differential equation describing the phenomena. In general, difficulties do not arise from the assumption of similarity as an absolute property, but rather from the application of this concept to approximately similar systems.

Practical Similarity, as wanted for extrapolation (or model) experiments, is a vague expression and of doubtful value unless the degree of approximation is stated, or the variables enumerated with respect to which similarity is desired. Practical similarity, therefore is not a matter of mathematics; it belongs to the physical concept of a phenomenon, and it is the "classifying process" of the experimenter.‡ If it is found that two systems can be described approximately by the same differential equation, the same variables and constants, then these two systems are called approximately similar, never exactly similar.

It is possible to formulate similarity conditions for two systems suspected to be physically similar. The same information can be gained from a correctly written differential equation as can be gained from proper dimensional analysis. Never, however, can information be gained about physical constants and universal constants without resorting to tricky semi-mathematics. Physical constants are defined by fundamental relations and are not amenable to any analysis.

16. CLASS PARAMETERS AND SIMILARITY CONDITIONS

A differential equation constituting a relation between an unknown physical quantity y, an independent physical variable x, and certain physical parameters Q_i of the symbolic form

$$D\left(Q_i, y, \frac{dy}{dx}, \frac{d^2 y}{dx^2}, \ldots\right) = 0 \tag{1}$$

---

* J. B. J. Fourier, Théorie analytique de la chaleur, p. 391, Paris, 1822.
† P. W. Bridgman, Dimensional Analysis, Yale Univ. Press, 1922.
‡ N. R. Campbell, *Phil. Mag.* (6), Vol. 47, p. 482, 1924.

can be treated as a mathematical differential equation. No definite style of writing the differential equation is required for the mathematical solution. If, however, unitary homogeneity of the differential equation is established, a number of deductions are possible which have profound physical significance.

To have concrete expressions, assume the differential equation to be in the form

$$a_n \frac{d^n y}{dx^n} + a_{n-1} \frac{d^{n-1} y}{dx^{n-1}} + \ldots a_1 \frac{dy}{dx} + a_0 y = F \tag{2}$$

where the coefficients a_k may depend on the parameters Q_i, the main variable y or its derivatives, and the independent variable x, in any manner whatsoever, so that nonlinear types of equations are equally well included. If the equation is logically written, unitary homogeneity must prevail. Assuming this, the following deductions can be made:

1. Numerical Parameters. The quotients of any two additive terms in the equation are pure and unique numbers, independent of the special units employed. Since the differential quotients $\frac{d^k y}{dx^k}$ all have dimensions y/x^k, we obtain

$$\frac{a_k \, y/x^k}{a_\nu \, y/x^\nu} = \text{number}, \quad \frac{a_k \, y/x^k}{F} = \text{number} \tag{3}$$

The values of all the numbers will, in general, depend upon the specific characteristic physical constants of the substance studied, the variable x, and the applied disturbance F. Some of these numbers will not contain the variable x explicitly; they are fundamental parameters and could be given proper names (like Reynold's number), if so desired. They can have "critical" values, which in turn will decide the type of solution or the validity of the special assumptions implied in the differential equation.

2. Dimensionless Products. Since the combinations of physical quantities in equation 3 are dimensionless numbers, their mutual products and quotients, and, in fact, any combination of them, will still be dimensionless. They constitute the "numerical" parameters (if they do not contain x explicitly) and the "numerical" variables (if they contain x explicitly) of the problem and must reappear in the mathematical solution. If desired, they might be called "dimensionless products" Π_ν, and the solution written in symbolical form

$$\psi(\Pi_1, \Pi_2, \Pi_3, \Pi_4, \ldots \Pi_N) = 0 \tag{4}$$

The number N of independent products is equal to $z - k$, where z is the total number of physical quantities involved (counting also the dimensional physical constants) and k the necessary number of fundamental units for the special physical field ($k = 3$ in mechanics, $k = 4$ in thermodynamics and in electromagnetism, and $k = 5$ for the general combination of all fields). In order for equation 4 to present a complete solution, the $\Pi_1 \ldots \Pi_N$ must be truly independent; they must not be mutually deducible by multiplication or division. Of course, it is possible to have ratios of like quantities and other numbers involved in the complete solution, which never can be obtained by discussion.

3. The Class Parameters. Considering any differential equation as characteristic for a "type" of problems, the numerical parameters and variables are then identical with the "typical" or class parameters and variables, which should be chosen for graphical representations of typical solutions. The N independent class variables or parameters can be selected arbitrarily, according to convenience, from among the much larger number of possible combinations. It seems advantageous, if possible, to let only one dimensionless product, for example Π_1, contain the variable y and to write explicitly

$$\Pi_1 = \phi(\Pi_2, \Pi_3, \Pi_4, \ldots \Pi_N) \tag{4a}$$

where, of course, ϕ is in general given by the mathematical solution of the differential equation. This form is particularly valuable if a direct solution of the differential equation 2 is impossible. Then, of course, ϕ will not be a known function but equation 4a will serve to bring out the class variables for experimental study.

4. The Similarity Conditions. If all the physical parameters and variables be referred to another system and medium according to

$$F = \phi F', \quad Q_i = q_i \, Q'_i, \quad x = \xi x', \quad y = \eta y' \tag{5}$$

then all the coefficients in equation 2 will become

$$a_\kappa = \alpha_\kappa \, a'_\kappa \tag{5a}$$

where α_κ is some combination of the q_i, ξ, and η quantities. Introducing these into the differential equation 2,

$$\left(\alpha_n \frac{\eta}{\xi^n}\right) a'_n \frac{d^n y'}{dx'^n} + \left(\alpha_{n-1} \frac{\eta}{\xi^{n-1}}\right) a'_{n-1} \frac{d^{n-1} y'}{dx'^{n-1}} + \ldots \left(\alpha_1 \frac{\eta}{\xi}\right) a_1' \frac{dy'}{dx'} + (\alpha_0 \, \eta) a'_0 \, y' = \phi F' \tag{6}$$

Obviously the same differential equation will hold, or the two systems will react "similarly," if

$$\left(\frac{\alpha_n}{\xi^n}\cdot\frac{\eta}{\phi}\right) = 1, \left(\frac{\alpha_{n-1}}{\xi^{n-1}}\cdot\frac{\eta}{\phi}\right) = 1, \ldots \left(\frac{\alpha_1}{\xi}\cdot\frac{\eta}{\phi}\right) = 1, \left(\alpha_0\cdot\frac{\eta}{\phi}\right) = 1 \tag{7}$$

which are the *complete similarity conditions* for two systems with respect to the phenomenon described by differential equation 2. They cannot, in any case, be the absolute similarity condition as no absolute similarity is possible.

5. Critical Values of the Class Parameters. The general form (4a) of the solution in terms of class parameters is subject to the assumptions implied in the differential equation. Only experiments can tell whether or not a differential equation is a satisfactory approximation to the proper description of a phenomenon. In general, any solution will be satisfactory for a certain range of the parameters involved. The limiting values of the class parameters, beyond which the specific approximation becomes poor, are often referred to as *critical* values, because they give a criterion for certain phenomena to occur in a certain manner described by the differential equation. It is, of course, necessary to take into account the simultaneous values of all class parameters characteristic for a phenomenon. This leads, in graphical representation, with the class parameters as coordinates, to *regions* of types of solutions according to the number of variables. All the phenomena that come into these ranges of parameters form a "group" which always can be represented by a single type of solution no matter in which field of physics the phenomena might occur. This fact forms the basis of analogies from other fields, as, for example, electromagnetic phenomena are often likened to flow phenomena of incompressible liquids, if certain conditions of stationarity are satisfied.

Example
Stationary Flow of a Viscous Fluid through a Pipe

To illustrate the above point in the analysis of a differential equation, assume as an example the equation for the stationary flow of a viscous fluid through a pipe

$$\frac{\partial v}{\partial t} = G_z - \frac{1}{\rho}\frac{\partial p}{\partial z} + \frac{\mu}{\rho}\left(\frac{\partial^2}{\partial r^2} + \frac{1}{r}\frac{\partial}{\partial r}\right)v \tag{8}$$

(See A. G. Webster, Differential Equations of Mathematical Physics, Chap. 1.) To equation 8 the equations of continuity and compressibility have to be added in order to furnish the relations between velocity, pressure, and density of the fluid; since the additional relations add nothing from the point of view of dimensions they will not be considered here. The symbols in (8) denote, respectively, with their dimensions in the technical dimension system:

G_z body force acting per unit mass, or acceleration $[FM^{-1}] = [LT^{-2}]$.
p hydrodynamic pressure $[FL^{-2}]$.
ρ density $[ML^{-3}] = [FL^{-4}\,T^2]$.
v the axial velocity $[LT^{-1}]$.
μ viscosity coefficient $[FL^{-2}\,T]$.
r radial distance involved in the differentiations $[L]$.
t time $[T]$.

The differential equation 8 shows dimensional homogeneity as can be checked by the ordinary method of mechanical dimensions and is also unitary homogeneous as it is independent of the units used. It is, therefore, proper to apply the analysis indicated above.

1. The Numerical Parameters. The four terms of equation 8 have the following resultant dimensions which must be identical:

$$\left[\frac{\partial v}{\partial t}\right] = \left[\frac{v}{T}\right], \ [G] = [G], \ \left[\frac{1}{\rho}\frac{\partial p}{\partial z}\right] = \left[\frac{p}{\rho L}\right], \ \left[\frac{\mu}{\rho}\frac{\partial^2 v}{\partial r^2}\right] = \left[\frac{\mu v}{\rho L^2}\right] \tag{9}$$

Forming the mutual quotients by dividing the first term successively by all the following ones, then the second term by the following ones, and so on, leads to the series of distinct dimensionless terms:

$$\frac{v}{TG}, \ \frac{\rho L v}{pT}, \ \frac{\rho L^2}{\mu T}, \ \frac{L\rho G}{p}, \ \frac{G\rho L^2}{\mu v}, \ \frac{pL}{\mu v} \tag{10}$$

Here the last three terms appear as numerical parameters not containing time explicitly. They probably could be used as characteristic numbers; this, however, has not become customary.

Since $\dfrac{vT}{L}$ is also dimensionless, it can be multiplied into the other dimensionless quantities. Multiplication with the first three numbers in (10) results in

$$\frac{vT}{L} \cdot \frac{v}{TG} = \frac{v^2}{LG} \qquad \text{which is Froude's number}$$

$$\frac{vT}{L} \cdot \frac{\rho L v}{pT} = \frac{\rho v^2}{p} \qquad \text{which is the reciprocal of Newton's number} \qquad (11?)$$

$$\frac{vT}{L} \cdot \frac{\rho L^2}{\mu T} = \frac{\rho L v}{\mu} \qquad \text{which is Reynolds' number}$$

These are the three most widely known numerical parameters of general hydrodynamics and have been named after their first users. In the literature they are usually derived by philosophical arguments or long-winded dimensional deductions; here they follow naturally from the condition of unitary homogeneity of the fundamental differential equation.

2. The Dimensionless Products. Only four independent dimensionless products are possible, since the number of fundamental units $k = 3$ (only mechanical quantities are involved), the number of physical quantities, however, $N = 7$. Choose as these four products the three characteristic numbers and in addition $\frac{vT}{L}$; then there results as general type of solution in terms of dimensionless products

$$\psi \left[\frac{vT}{L}, \ \frac{v^2}{LG}, \ \frac{p}{v^2 \rho}, \ \frac{v\rho L}{\mu} \right] = 0 \qquad (12)$$

That the four combinations are independent is easily seen from the fact that each contains one variable not present in any other product. Other choices could be made with the same degree of generality; however, any such set of dimensionless numbers must be derivable from the one chosen here by multiplication or division with dimensionless numbers only.

3. The Class Parameters. Since the phenomenon is properly described by the maximum number of independent dimensionless products, these can be chosen as class parameters for a whole series of problems represented by the same differential equation. The three numbers from (11) constitute the most widely used class parameters of hydrodynamics, and any solution can be expressed in terms of them. In conducting experiments they should be chosen as variables. If it is desired to express the solution in explicit form of a principal variable, the dimensional products have to be chosen so that only one contains this variable. Suppose it is desired to solve for p; then the third dimensionless product will be selected as principal class variable

$$\frac{p}{v^2 \rho} = \phi \left[\frac{vT}{L}, \ \frac{v^2}{LG}, \ \frac{v\rho L}{\mu} \right] \qquad (12a)$$

where, of course, ϕ is not known but can be obtained by experiments. It follows

$$p = (v^2 \rho) \cdot \phi \left[\frac{vT}{L}, \ \frac{v^2}{LG}, \ \frac{v\rho L}{\mu} \right] \qquad (13)$$

4. The Similarity Conditions. If equation 8 is transformed into a system with primed quantities and the proportionality factors are designated by s with a respective subscript

$$
\begin{aligned}
G &= s_G\, G' & \rho &= s_\rho \cdot \rho' & r &= s_r \cdot r' \\
p &= s_p \cdot p' & v &= s_v \cdot v' & t &= s_t \cdot t' \\
& & \mu &= s_\mu \cdot \mu'
\end{aligned}
\qquad (14)
$$

there follows

$$\left(\frac{s_v}{s_t} \right) \cdot \frac{\partial v'}{\partial t'} = (s_G) \cdot G' - \left(\frac{s_p}{s_\rho\, s_r} \right) \frac{1}{\rho'} \cdot \frac{\partial p'}{\partial z'} + \left(\frac{s_\mu\, s_v}{s_\rho\, s_r^2} \right) \cdot \frac{\mu'}{\rho'} \left(\frac{\partial^2}{\partial r'^2} + \frac{1}{r'} \cdot \frac{\partial}{\partial r'} \right) v'$$

and the three similarity conditions are

$$\left(\frac{s_v}{s_t\, s_G} \right) = 1, \quad \left(\frac{s_p}{s_\rho\, s_r\, s_G} \right) = 1, \quad \left(\frac{s_\mu\, s_v}{s_\rho\, s_r^2\, s_G} \right) = 1 \qquad (14a)$$

which must be satisfied to insure similar flow characteristics of two viscous fluids. If these conditions are satisfied, experimental results on one liquid can be utilized for another liquid without repetition of analysis or experiments.

5. For the Critical Values of the Class Parameters occurring in this example, see Art. 17, Section 6.

17. DIMENSIONAL ANALYSIS

In the literature on this subject much controversy is found relating to a proper and convincing basis of dimensional analysis. Mathematical proofs have been offered from principles of logic; however, there is no "principle" of similarity, or similitude, which would present a reasonable mathematical basis for the general dimensional analysis. Fundamentally, dimensional analysis is identical with the analysis of physical equations, and, in particular, with the analysis of physical differential equations. The information from dimensional analysis, therefore, is identical with that obtained from differential equations subject to unitary homogeneity. (See Art. 16.) The advantage of dimensional analysis is the more systematic approach in obtaining the class parameters and the similarity conditions, although it seems advisable to take a complete differential equation as the starting point in any case.

The Π Theorem

If z physical quantities Q_κ are known to be involved in a certain physical phenomenon, the mutual dependence, in unitary homogeneous form, must be expressible as a power product as has been shown on various occasions.* For example, the quantity Q_1 takes the form

$$Q_1 = Q_2{}^{\alpha_2} \cdot Q_3{}^{\alpha_3} \ldots Q_z{}^{\alpha_z} \qquad (15)$$

where the $\alpha_2, \alpha_3 \ldots \alpha_z$ are definite and unique values which can be determined by dimensional analysis. This fact is based upon the fundamental and reasonable hypothesis of uniqueness of the results of physical measurements, no matter what units are used in measuring. Thus, for example, if $Q_1 = F$ represents force as expressed by mass, length, and time, it would be found $F = MLT^{-2}$ as a unitary homogeneous relation (see Art. 15) independent of the special units employed on the right-hand side. The unit of F, of course, is fixed by the condition of unitary homogeneity; any arbitrary choice of the unit of F would result in an additional numerical conversion factor.

On account of unitary homogeneity, the combination

$$\frac{Q_1}{Q_2{}^{\alpha_2} \cdot Q_3{}^{\alpha_3} \ldots Q_z{}^{\alpha_z}} = \Pi \qquad (15a)$$

is a numerical quantity and can be designated as a "dimensionless product." The number of possible independent dimensionless products is obviously $(z - k)$, if k is the number of independent fundamental units in the particular field. This result is the same as in the analysis of differential equations.

The most general form of a logical mathematical description of the phenomena studied must be some functional relation between the $(z - k)$ independent dimensionless product

$$\Psi \, (\Pi_1, \Pi_2, \ldots \Pi_{z-k}) = 0 \qquad (16)$$

This, of course, is but the typical solution of a differential equation in terms of class variables and class parameters, but now the functional form Ψ is not known and can be found only by experiment. The forms (15) and (16) are frequently referred to as the "Π theorem," and it is the object of dimensional analysis to find practical ways of obtaining the form (16) with greatest economy and least chance of erroneous reasoning.

The Method of Lord Rayleigh. Usually it is desired to learn the dependence of one physical quantity upon a number of other physical quantities which are supposed to enter into the problem or experiment. If the total number of quantities is z (including the physical constants), and the principal quantity chosen be Q_1, then (15) expresses the general physical relation for Q_1 according to the Π theorem. In general, the dimensions of the z quantities are not independent, but can be represented in terms of k fundamental dimensions, if the respective complete dimension system is composed of k fundamental dimensions. These can be chosen either from among the $Q_1 \ldots Q_z$ themselves, or from any one of the more common dimension systems suitable for the particular field of physics. (See Arts. 3, 4, 5.) It is essential to use a complete dimension system in order to avoid ambiguity with respect to the dimensions of the physical constants. If the dimensional expressions are introduced into (15), and if then the exponents on both sides are equated there result exactly k conditions for the $(z - 1)$ exponents $\alpha_2 \ldots \alpha_z$, permitting the expression of any k exponents in terms of the remaining $(z - 1 - k)$ indeterminate or "free" exponents.† The final expression gives then the desired physical quantity in terms of indeterminate powers of dimensionless products, but in an explicit form, which is the principal advantage of this method.

---

* J. L. Riabouschinsky, L'Aerophile, 1911; E. Buckingham, *Phys. Rev.*, Vol. 4, p. 345, 1914; F. London, *Phys. Zeits.*, Vol. 23, p. 262, 1922.

† Lord Rayleigh. *Nature*, Vol. 95, p. 66, 1915.

Example. To illustrate the method of Lord Rayleigh, assume the same example as treated in Art. 16. The differential equation gives all the parameters and variables that enter into the problem so that the list of physical quantities involved is (see the example in Art. 16):

$$v, \ t, \ G, \ \rho, \ p, \ \mu, \ l$$

Suppose it is desired to find the dependence of v on the other quantities; then the form corresponding to (15) is

$$v = t^{\alpha_1} \cdot G^{\alpha_2} \cdot \rho^{\alpha_3} \cdot p^{\alpha_4} \cdot \mu^{\alpha_5} \cdot l^{\alpha_6} \tag{17}$$

In the technical dimension system of mechanics there are three fundamental dimensions L, T, F. (See Art. 3.) It is convenient, in general, to write the dimensions of the various physical quantities in the form of a table.

Physical Quantities		t	G	ρ	p	μ	l	v
L	Exponents of Fundamental Dimensions	0	$+1$	-4	-2	-2	$+1$	$+1$
T		$+1$	-2	$+2$	0	$+1$	0	-1
F		0	0	$+1$	$+1$	$+1$	0	0

Introducing the dimensions from this table into equation 17 and equating the dimensional exponents for L, T, and F gives the three linear simultaneous equations

$$\left. \begin{array}{r} +\ \alpha_2 - 4\alpha_3 - 2\alpha_4 - 2\alpha_5 + \alpha_6 = +1 \\ +\ \alpha_1 - 2\alpha_2 + 2\alpha_3 \qquad\quad + \alpha_5 \quad = -1 \\ +\ \alpha_3 + \alpha_4 + \alpha_5 \quad = \ \ 0 \end{array} \right\} \tag{18}$$

Since there are six unknowns, three of the exponents will remain indeterminate. Suppose α_1, α_3, and α_6 are chosen for some reason to be left indeterminate; then from (18)

$$\left. \begin{array}{l} \alpha_2 = +1 + 2\alpha_3 - \alpha_6 \\ \alpha_4 = -1 - 3\alpha_3 + 2\alpha_6 + \alpha_1 \\ \alpha_5 = +1 + 2\alpha_3 - 2\alpha_6 - \alpha_1 \end{array} \right\} \tag{18a}$$

so that the velocity can be written, properly collecting terms with the same exponents,

$$v = \frac{\mu G}{p} \cdot \left[\frac{Tp}{\mu} \right]^{\alpha_1} \cdot \left[\frac{G^2 \rho \mu^2}{p^3} \right]^{\alpha_3} \cdot \left[\frac{Lp^2}{G\mu^2} \right]^{\alpha_6} \tag{19}$$

The advantage of having v explicitly given is obvious. Each one of the three independent dimensionless products is a combination of some of the dimensionless products in (10), as can be shown easily. Instead of using the indeterminate exponents α_1, α_3, α_6, any arbitrary function of the dimensionless products would be a more general expression.

$$v = \frac{\mu G}{p} \cdot \psi \left[\frac{Tp}{\mu}, \ \frac{G^2 \rho \mu^2}{p^3}, \ \frac{Lp^2}{G\mu^2} \right] \tag{20}$$

In the same way the dependence of p on the other quantities involved could be computed, and the result would be similar to (13); the special form would depend upon the particular choice of the $(z - 1 - k)$ free exponents, but could always be transformed into the form (13) by multiplying the dimensionless products by dimensionless numbers from (10).

The Method of E. Buckingham.* Suppose that the total number of physical quantities involved in a problem is z (including the physical constants), and the number of independent fundamental dimensions, necessary for the particular field of physics to which the problem belongs, is k; then k of the z quantities, which are dimensionally independent, are arbitrarily chosen as principal quantities. If Q_1 to Q_k are these principal quantities and Q_{k+1} to Q_z the secondary quantities, $(z - k)$ independent dimensionless products can be formed by multiplying indeterminate powers of the principal quantities successively with one of the secondary quantities and equating the total dimensions to zero, as, for example,

$$[\Pi_1] = [Q_1^{\alpha_1} \cdot Q_2^{\alpha_2} \ldots Q_k^{\alpha_k} \cdot Q_{k+1}] = 1 \tag{21}$$

If now the dimensions of Q_{k+1} in terms of the dimensions of the principal quantities are introduced, k linear relations for the exponents $\alpha_1 \ldots \alpha_k$ result so that all the exponents can be determined. In this way $(z - k)$ independent dimensionless products are obtained directly; their special form depends entirely upon the choice of the principal quan-

---

* E. Buckingham, *Phys. Rev.*, Vol. 4, p. 345, 1914; *Phil. Mag.* (6), Vol. 42, p. 696, 1921.

tities. The advantage of this method lies in the simple form of the equations which determine the exponents of the principal quantities; it is also possible to solve explicitly for any single quantity, if it is not a principal quantity.

Example. To illustrate the method by E. Buckingham, and to be able to compare it with the other methods, assume the same example as before, with the physical quantities

$$v, \ t, \ G, \ \rho, \ p, \ \mu, \ l$$

In choosing the three principal quantities it must be kept in mind that they will appear in all dimensionless products as factors. Suppose l, ρ. and v be chosen here; using the technical mechanical dimension system, the dimensions of all the quantities are again given in the table on page 3–42. Grouping the dimensional expressions for the dimensionless product $[l^{\alpha_1} \rho^{\alpha_3} v^{\alpha_3} \cdot t] = 1$ in a table

	l^{α_1}	ρ^{α_2}	v^{α_3}	t
$[L]$	$+ \alpha_1$	$- 4\alpha_2$	$+ \alpha_3$	0
$[T]$	0	$+ 2\alpha_2$	$- \alpha_3$	$+ 1$
$[F]$	0	$+ \alpha_2$	0	0

gives immediately the resulting equations

$$\left. \begin{array}{l} + \ \alpha_1 - 4\alpha_2 + \alpha_3 + 0 = 0 \\ + \ 2\alpha_2 - \alpha_3 + 1 = 0 \\ + \ \alpha_2 \qquad + 0 = 0 \end{array} \right\}$$

from which $\qquad \alpha_2 = 0, \quad \alpha_3 = + 1, \quad \alpha_1 = - 1$

so that the product becomes $\dfrac{vT}{l}$. Similar tables with t replaced successively by G, p, and μ, give the other three dimensionless products as $\dfrac{lG}{v^2}$ (the reciprocal of Froude's number), $\dfrac{p}{\rho v^2}$ (Newton's number), and $\dfrac{\mu}{l\rho v}$ (the reciprocal of Reynolds' number). The general solution, therefore, is a functional relation of the four dimensionless products

$$\psi \left[\frac{vT}{l}, \ \frac{lG}{v^2}, \ \frac{p}{\rho v^2}, \ \frac{\mu}{l\rho v} \right] = 0 \tag{22}$$

which is identical with the solution obtained in (12) from the analysis of the differential equation.

Note on the Application of Dimensional Analysis

It has been customary to surround dimensional analysis with an air of intuitive invention. The comparison of differential equation analysis and dimensional analysis has shown that both are based upon the condition of unitary homogeneity of physical equations. It is obvious, therefore, that dimensional analysis must lead to the same result as the analysis of differential equations, if it is properly used. The chief advantage of dimensional analysis is the fact that it deals with the class variables and parameters and thus reduces the number of variable quantities from z to $(z - k)$, if z is the number of physical quantities and k the number of fundamental dimensions. It can serve as a guide for experiments and gives the conditions of similarity without necessitating a complete solution of the problem. As a basis for model experiments it is extremely valuable. (See Art. 18.)

In applying dimensional analysis, care has to be taken to include all physical quantities which might be involved in the problem. It seems best to start from an approximate differential equation as the expression of "balance" of forces, or energies, or what not, and to include all dimensional physical constants. If any system of $z - k$ independent dimensional products has been found, other systems can be obtained by combination of two or more numerical parameters into new dimensionless products. It is not possible to replace differential equation analysis by dimensional analysis, since the latter never will give the complete form of the solution of a problem.

Dimensional analysis, as well as differential equations, have certain ranges of validity; if experiments do not check the results of an analysis, it might serve as an indication that the problem is incompletely stated and more physical quantities should be included. Neither differential equations nor dimensional analysis can ever lead to new physical constants; these are defined by the fundamental hypotheses.

18. THEORY OF MODELS

The possibility of similarity between various systems of even wholly unrelated fields suggests the exploration of phenomena by means of "models" of either enlarged or reduced scale, or by means of analogies from a different field. Just as similarity cannot be an absolute quality, but is defined as the approximate state of two systems (see Art. 16), so can a model be only an approximate reproduction of the original scale phenomenon; the approximation can, of course, be quite close over certain ranges of the main variables. It is essential, in the use of models, to state definitely the properties to be modeled and to restrict conclusions to the quantities included in the similarity considerations.

The Scale Factors. If the same differential equation is assumed to hold for two different problems of the same field, then similarity exists between the phenomena described by the differential equation. Any one term in the differential equation for *case 1* may be of the form

$$(Q_a{}^{n_1} \cdot Q_b{}^{n_2} \cdot Q_c{}^{n_3} \ldots) \frac{d^\nu y}{dx^\nu}$$

where the factor in parentheses is the coefficient of the νth differential. For *case 2* this term will become

$$(\overline{Q}_a{}^{n_1} \cdot \overline{Q}_b{}^{n_2} \cdot \overline{Q}_c{}^{n_3} \ldots) \frac{d^\nu \overline{y}}{d\overline{x}^\nu}$$

and the new physical quantities (physical constants or variables) may be related to the former ones by the expressions

$$\left. \begin{array}{c} \overline{Q}_a = s_a Q_a, \quad \overline{Q}_b = s_b Q_b, \quad \overline{Q}_c = s_c Q_b \ldots \\ \overline{y} = s_y \cdot y, \quad \overline{x} = s_x \cdot x. \end{array} \right\} \tag{23}$$

Suppose now that case 2 shall be used as a model for case 1. Each physical quantity in the model must then take a definite ratio to the same quantity in the original, and the proportionality factors (23) can be considered as *scale factors*, specifying the relations between the model and the original. Obviously, there are as many scale factors as there are physical quantities. It is not possible to choose all the scale factors arbitrarily.

Model Rules. In order to be permitted to use case 2 as a model of case 1, the conditions of similarity must be satisfied. As shown in Art. 16, the similarity conditions require, using (23) above,

$$(s_a{}^{n_1} \cdot s_b{}^{n_2} \cdot s_c{}^{n_3} \ldots) \frac{s_y}{s_x{}^\nu} = k, \tag{24}$$

k is the same constant for all the terms, so that the numerical values in the differential equations for both cases are identical.

If there are q terms in the differential equation, there will be q conditions of the type (24) or $(q - 1)$ mutual relations between the scale factors. These are called *the model rules*, as they specify size, shape, and physical properties of the model (as applied forces, densities, viscosities, and so on). The model rules depend entirely on the differential equation chosen to represent the phenomenon.

Fundamental and Dependent Scale Factors. The scale factors which can be chosen arbitrarily are called *fundamental scale factors*. The number of fundamental scale factors is identical with the number of fundamental dimensions necessary for a complete dimension system in the particular field of physics to which the problem belongs. This can be seen from the general differential equation; if z physical quantities are involved, and q terms make up the differential equation, then $(z - q + 1)$ fundamental dimensions are required. (See Art. 15.) But there are also z scale factors, which have to satisfy, according to (24), $(q - 1)$ relations, so that $(z - q + 1)$ fundamental scale factors remain which can be chosen arbitrarily. All the other scale factors follow by means of the model rules, they are dependent, and cannot be chosen freely.

Model Rules from Dimensional Analysis. Dimensional analysis leads to a description of a physical phenomenon in terms of dimensionless products which are identical with, or can be easily transformed into, the class parameters of the analysis of differential equations. (See Art. 17.) Similarity in terms of dimensional analysis exists only if the dimensionless products have the same numerical values for both the model and the original. If any one of the dimensionless products Π_ν for *case 1* is given by

$$\Pi_\nu = (Q_1{}^{\alpha_1} \cdot Q_2{}^{\alpha_2} \ldots Q_k{}^{\alpha_k}) \cdot Q_{k+\nu}$$

and for *case 2* by

$$\overline{\Pi}_\nu = (\overline{Q}_1{}^{\alpha_1} \cdot \overline{Q}_2{}^{\alpha_2} \ldots \overline{Q}_k{}^{\alpha_k}) \cdot \overline{Q}_{k+\nu}$$

and if there are the scale relations

$$\overline{Q}_1 = s_1 Q_1, \quad \overline{Q}_2 = s_2 Q_2 \ldots \quad \overline{Q}_{k+\nu} = s_{k+\nu} Q_{k+\nu}$$

then $\Pi_\nu = \overline{\Pi}_\nu$ only if $(s_1{}^{\alpha_1} s_2{}^{\alpha_2} \ldots s_k{}^{\alpha_k}) \cdot s_{k+\nu} = 1$ (25)

Since there are $(z - k)$ independent dimensionless products, the z scale factors will be related by $z - k$ relations of the type (25), so that the number of free or fundamental scale factors is k, the same as the number of fundamental dimensions. The relations (25) are called the model rules and are identical with the relations (24). They can be *conveniently obtained* by replacing in the dimensionless products all the physical quantities by their respective scale factors and equating to unity the expressions thus obtained.

Example. In order to illustrate the application of the theory of models, it will be chosen to represent the flow of water through a large pipe by the flow of mercury through a model pipe of one-tenth the diameter of the original. Using dimensional analysis, the problem is the same as treated above in Art. 17. As a problem of hydrodynamics, $k = 3$ fundamental dimensions, and, therefore, $k = 3$ fundamental scale factors are necessary. The ratio of the linear dimensions is given by $s_l = 0.1$; the ratio of the densities is $s_\rho = 13.6$, and the ratio of the viscosities can be assumed approximately as $s_\mu = 1.5$. The four dimensionless products are given by equation 22, so that the scale factors have to satisfy the conditions

$$\frac{s_v s_t}{s_l} = 1, \quad \frac{s_l s_G}{s_v{}^2} = 1, \quad \frac{s_p}{s_\rho s_v{}^2} = 1, \quad \frac{s_\mu}{s_l s_\rho s_v} = 1$$

from which the four dependent scale factors follow as

$$s_v = 1.103, \quad s_G = 12.16, \quad s_p = 16.54, \quad s_t = 0.0908$$

which means that the velocity of the mercury flow must be 1.103 of that of water, and the time scale approximately 0.0908 of that of water, and the force, per unit of mass, acting upon the mercury must be made 12.16 times that for water.

SECTION 4

THEORETICAL MECHANICS

BY

JANVIER M. RICE *

---

* Section 4 was prepared from material in previous handbooks published by John Wiley and Sons.

The editor and author wish particularly to acknowledge the contributions of Professors C. H. Burnside and E. R. Maurer. Much of their original work in Merriman's Civil Engineers' Handbook and Peele's Mining Engineers' Handbook was used in the preparation of this Section

THEORETICAL MECHANICS

1. DEFINITIONS

Mechanics is that branch of *science* which treats of forces and motion.

Statics is that branch of *mechanics* which deals with the equilibrium of forces on bodies *at rest* (or moving at a uniform velocity in a straight line).

Kinematics is that branch of *mechanics* which deals with the motion of bodies without consideration of the character of the bodies or of the influence of forces upon their motion. It considers only concepts of *geometry* and *time*.

Kinetics (or Dynamics) is that branch of *mechanics* which deals with the effect of unbalanced external forces in *modifying the motion* of bodies.

Mass and Weight, in the *gravitational system of units* employed by English engineers, are related by the formula $W = Mg$, where $W =$ weight, $M =$ mass, and $g =$ acceleration due to gravity. For a thorough discussion of these terms, see Section 3, Physical Units and Standards.

Force is that which changes or tends to change the state of rest or motion of a body.

Inertia is that property of a body by virtue of which it tends to continue in the state of rest or motion in which it may be placed, until acted on by some force.

Reaction is that *equal and opposite force* exerted by a body in opposing another force acting upon it.

Newton's Laws of Motion. *First Law.* If a body is at rest, it will remain at rest, or if in motion, it will move uniformly in a straight line, until acted on by some force.

Second Law. If a body is acted on by several forces, it will obey each as though the others did not exist, and this whether the body is at rest or in motion. Change of the motion of a body is proportional to the force and to the time during which the force acts, and is in the same direction as the force.

Third Law. If a force acts to change the state of a body with respect to rest or motion, the body will offer a resistance equal and directly opposed to the force. Or, to every action there is opposed an equal and opposite reaction.

Special Terms such as **hydrostatics, aerodynamics,** etc., are used to denote the theory of statics as applied to *liquid bodies,* the theory of dynamics as applied to *gaseous bodies,* etc. **Mechanics of materials** considers, in addition to *external forces,* the *internal forces* or *stresses* between molecules of a body. Subjects of these types are covered in other sections of this handbook. The present section on *mechanics* is confined, in general, to the discussion of motion of, and *external forces* applied to, *rigid bodies.*

STATICS

2. GRAPHICAL REPRESENTATION AND CLASSIFICATION OF FORCES

Graphical Representation of Force

A Force is completely specified by its *magnitude, direction,* and *point of application.* The word **sense** as applied to a force refers to one of the two directions along the line of action of the force. The effect of any force applied to a rigid body at rest is the same, no matter where in its own line of action the force is applied. This is known as the principle of the **transmissibility of force.** A force may be represented graphically in magnitude and direction by a straight line drawn parallel to its line of action, the length being proportional to the magnitude of the force; its sense is indicated by an arrowhead placed on the line. The English engineers' unit of force is the pound, or the earth's pull on a mass of 1 lb. A drawing which indicates the lines of action of the various forces acting on a machine or structure

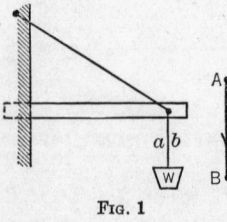

Fig. 1

is called a **space diagram**; one in which vectors are drawn to represent the magnitudes and directions of the forces is a **vector diagram**. A force is indicated on a space diagram by two lower-case letters placed on opposite sides of the line of action of the force; the vector, representing its magnitude and direction, by the same capital letters placed at the ends. Thus, in Fig. 1, AB represents the magnitude and direction of the force W, and ab its action line. The vector being read as AB indicates a downward sense; read as BA, an upward sense.

Classification of Systems of Forces

A **System of Forces** consists of any number of forces taken collectively.

Classification of Systems of Forces is made according to the arrangement of their action lines. If the action lines lie in the same plane the system is **coplanar**, otherwise **noncoplanar**. If they pass through the same point the system is **concurrent**, otherwise **nonconcurrent**. If two or more forces have the same action line they are **collinear**. A system of two equal forces, parallel, opposite in sense, and having different action lines is a **couple**. Two or more forces equivalent to a single force are **components** of the single force. **Resolution** is the operation of replacing a single force by a system of components. The single force is the **resultant** of its components. In general, the resultant of a system of forces is the simplest equivalent system. This may be a *single force*, a *single couple*, or a *noncoplanar force and couple* (or *two skewed forces*). When the resultant is a single force the **equilibrant** is a force equal in magnitude, having the same line of action but opposite sense. **Composition** is the operation of replacing a system of forces by its resultant.

3. COMPOSITION AND RESOLUTION OF CONCURRENT FORCES

Composition of Two Concurrent Forces *

Parallelogram Law. If magnitudes, lines of action, and senses of two concurrent forces acting on a rigid body are represented by OA and OB (Fig. 2), the magnitude, line of action, and sense of their resultant are represented by the diagonal OC of the parallelogram $OABC$. The points of application of the forces may be anywhere on the body in the lines OA, OB, and OC, or their extensions. The arrowheads on the lines OA, OB, and OC all point toward or all away from the point of concurrence O.

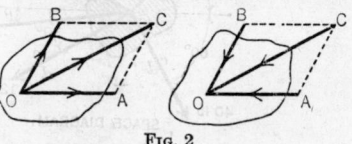

FIG. 2

Triangle Law. This law follows directly from the parallelogram law. If in the triangle ABC (Fig. 3a) AB and BC represent two concurrent forces in magnitude, direction, and sense, AC will represent their resultant in magnitude, direction, and sense; its action line will be ac through the point of concurrency, parallel to AC. It should be noted that the arrowheads on the sides AB and BC are **confluent** (point the same way around) but the arrowhead on AC is not confluent with the others. Also, the point of concurrency need not necessarily be located in or on the body but may be outside it.

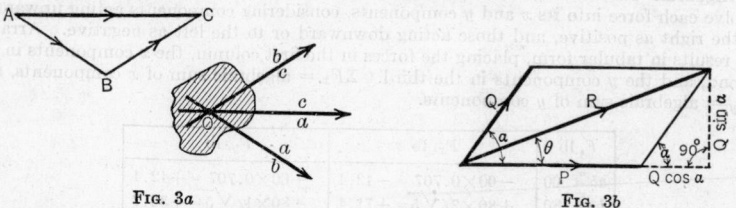

FIG. 3a

FIG. 3b

The resultant may be found **algebraically** thus: In Fig. 3b, let α be the angle between the action lines of forces P and Q, and θ the angle between R and P. Then, $R^2 = P^2 + Q^2 + 2PQ \cos \alpha$, and $\tan \theta = \dfrac{Q \sin \alpha}{P + Q \cos \alpha}$. If $\alpha = 90°$, $R^2 = P^2 + Q^2$, and $\tan \theta = Q/P$.

---

* It is evident that a pair of concurrent forces and their resultant are necessarily *coplanar*.

Resolution into Two Concurrent Forces *

A Force May Be Resolved into an infinite number of pairs of components by constructing different triangles as in Fig. 4a. The action lines of the components must be concurrent at a point on the action line of the force. A common problem is to resolve a force into *rectangular components* (often called resolved parts). In Fig. 4b, AB and BC are a set of rectangular components of the force P. Expressed *algebraically*, $AB = P$ $\cos \alpha$ and $BC = P \sin \alpha$. For rectangular components, the resolved part of a force along

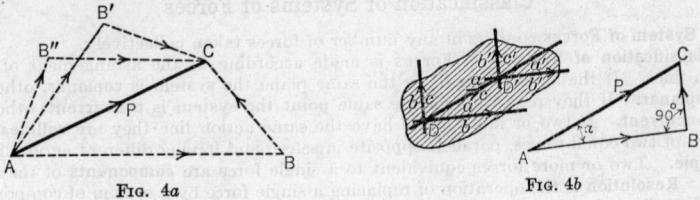

FIG. 4a   FIG. 4b

any line equals the magnitude of the force times the cosine of the angle between the lines of action of the force and its component. Action lines of the components are concurrent on the space diagram at some point on ac, as at D or D'.

Composition of More than Two Coplanar Concurrent Forces †

Graphic Method. In Fig. 5, consider body G acted on by the four forces shown. Construct a **force polygon** as follows: Plot AB parallel to ab, and scale it to represent 60

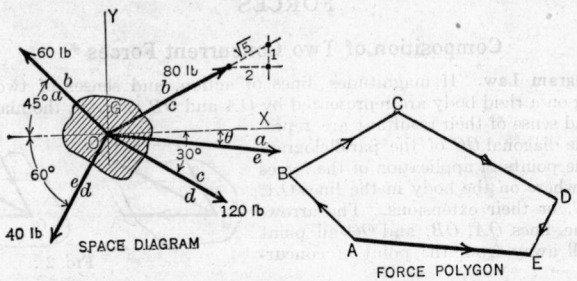

SPACE DIAGRAM   FORCE POLYGON

FIG. 5

lb.; from B plot BC parallel to bc, and scale it to represent 80 lb.; in like manner plot CD and DE, so that the arrows lead *confluently* from A to E. The resultant of the system is AE in magnitude and sense and equals 114 lb. Its action line is ae. The resultant will be the same regardless of the order in which the forces are plotted. Note particularly that the resultant is not confluent with the component forces.

Algebraic Method. Choose rectangular axes OX and OY. Referring to Fig. 5, resolve each force into its x and y components, considering components acting upward or to the right as positive, and those acting downward or to the left as negative. Arrange the results in tabular form, placing the forces in the first column, the x components in the second, and the y components in the third. ΣF_x = algebraic sum of x components, and ΣF_y = algebraic sum of y components.

F, lb	F_x, lb	F_y, lb
$ab = 60$	$-60 \times 0.707 = -42.4$	$+60 \times 0.707 = +42.4$
$bc = 80$	$+80 \times 2/\sqrt{5} = +71.4$	$+80 \times 1/\sqrt{5} = +35.7$
$cd = 120$	$+120 \times 0.866 = +104$	$-120 \times 0.5 = -60$
$de = 40$	$-40 \times 0.5 = -20$	$-40 \times 0.866 = -34.6$
	$\Sigma F_x = +113$	$\Sigma F_y = -16.5$

* It is evident that a pair of concurrent forces and their resultant are necessarily *coplanar*.
† The composition of two concurrent forces is simply a special case of this more general treatment.

Then $R = \sqrt{\Sigma F_x^2 + \Sigma F_y^2} = \sqrt{13{,}041}$
= 114 lb. Sense is downward and to the
right (Fig. 6).   Tan $\theta = \dfrac{\Sigma F_y}{\Sigma F_x} = -\,0.146;$
$\theta = -\,8°\,20'.$

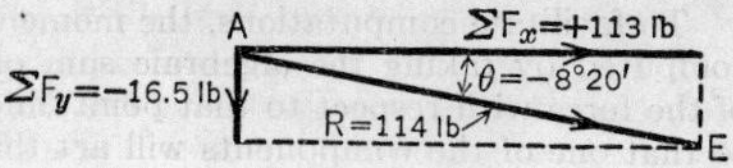

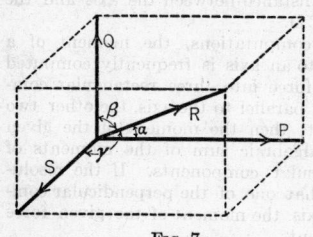

FIG. 6

Resolution into More than Two Coplanar Concurrent Forces

This type of problem has relatively little practical value. The resolution can be accomplished, however, by employing the force polygon to reverse the process of composition in a manner similar to that employed in the important special case discussed above of resolution into two concurrent forces. An infinite number of force systems is possible for any given number of the component concurrent forces.

Composition of Three Rectangular Noncoplanar Concurrent Forces

Parallelepipedon Law.* Consider the three rectangular forces, P, Q, and S (Fig. 7). On these forces construct to scale a parallelepiped. The resultant of the system is represented in magnitude and direction by the diagonal; its value is $R = \sqrt{P^2 + Q^2 + S^2}$. Its direction cosines with respect to the axes are: $\cos\alpha = P/R$, $\cos\beta = Q/R$, and $\cos\gamma = S/R$.

FIG. 7

Resolution into Three Rectangular Noncoplanar Concurrent Forces

A force F can be resolved into a set of three rectangular noncoplanar concurrent forces by *reversing* the process of composition described in the preceding paragraph. Thus, referring to Fig. 7:

$$P = R\cos\alpha; \quad Q = R\cos\beta; \quad S = R\cos\gamma$$

Composition of Any Number of Concurrent Forces †

This is the most general case of composition of concurrent forces and therefore is applicable also, of course, to the simpler cases previously discussed.

Let the forces be specified with respect to three rectangular axes passing through the point of concurrency: (a) Resolve each force into components along the X, Y, and Z axes; (b) find the algebraic sums of the x, y, and z components, and indicate them by ΣF_x, ΣF_y, and ΣF_z; (c) find the resultant of these three partial resultants by the parallelepipedon law; its value is $R = \sqrt{\Sigma F_x^2 + \Sigma F_y^2 + \Sigma F_z^2}$; its direction angles are $\alpha = \cos^{-1}\dfrac{\Sigma F_x}{R}$; $\beta = \cos^{-1}\dfrac{\Sigma F_y}{R}$; $\gamma = \cos^{-1}\dfrac{\Sigma F_z}{R}.$

Nature of Resultant of Concurrent Forces

The **Resultant** of any system of *concurrent forces* which are not in equilibrium is a *single force*.

4.   MOMENTS AND COUPLES

Moment (or Torque) of a Force about a Point

Moment or **Torque** of a force about a point is the product of the force magnitude and the distance from the point to its action line. This perpendicular distance is called the *arm* of the force, and the point is the *origin or center of moments*. The product is the measure of the rotational tendency of the force. The name of the unit of moment is a combination of the names of force and distance units, as foot-pound, inch-ton, etc. (Some writers use lb-ft as a unit of moment of a force to distinguish from ft-lb as the unit of work or energy, similar distinction being made for the other units.)

---

* The *parallelepipedon law* applies also if the three forces are not rectangular. In such cases, however, it is not practicable to obtain *directly* the value of the resultant either graphically or algebraically. A better method of solution for problems of this nature is given in the second succeeding paragraph.

† As a matter of academic interest, although of little practical value, the resultant of any number of noncoplanar concurrent forces may be represented graphically by extending the principles of the *plane* force polygon to apply to a *space* or *skew* force polygon.

To facilitate computations, the moment of a force with respect to a point is frequently computed by taking the algebraic sum of the moments of two rectangular components of the force with respect to that point; and it will often be convenient to resolve the force so that one of the components will act through the origin of moments, thus making that component have no moment.

Moment (or Torque) of a Force about a Line (or Axis)

At any point on its action line, resolve the force into two rectangular components, one being parallel to the axis. The product of the perpendicular component and the perpen-

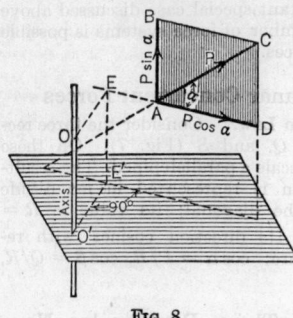

FIG. 8

dicular distance to its line of action from the axis is the *moment* of the given force about the axis. Thus (Fig. 8), $P \sin \alpha$ is the component parallel to the axis, and it has no turning effect. All the moment or turning effect is caused by the perpendicular component, and its value is $P \cos \alpha \times OE$, OE being the perpendicular distance between the axis and the parallel plane $ABCD$.

To facilitate computations, the moment of a force with respect to an axis is frequently computed by resolving the force into three rectangular components, one being parallel to the axis, the other two perpendicular to it; then the moment of the given force equals the algebraic sum of the moments of the two perpendicular components. If the resolution is made so that one of the perpendicular components cuts the axis, the moment of the given force equals the moment of the other perpendicular component.

Principle of Moments

For a Point. The moment of the resultant of any coplanar forces (not necessarily concurrent) about a point in their plane equals the algebraic sum of the moments of those forces about the point. Thus (Fig. 9), R is the resultant of P and Q, and $R \times r = P \times p - Q \times q$. Moments tending to produce counterclockwise rotation of a body are usually considered positive, and clockwise negative.

Thus, in Fig. 9, the moment of force Q about $O = -Qq$.

It is evident that the moment of a force passing through the origin of moments is zero.

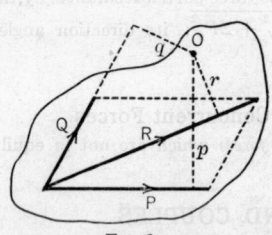

FIG. 9

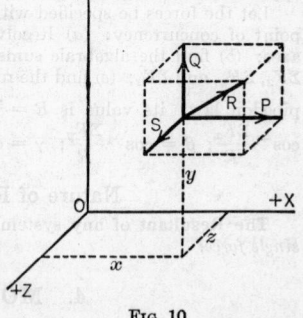

FIG. 10

For an Axis. The moment of the resultant of any forces (not necessarily either coplanar or concurrent) about a line equals the algebraic sum of the moments of those forces about the line. Thus (Fig. 10), R is the resultant of the three rectangular forces P, Q, and S. Moment of R about axis $X = S \times y - Q \times z$. P contributes nothing to the moment sum, as it is parallel to the axis of moments. Usually in such a case, counterclockwise moment is called positive and clockwise negative, the observer looking toward the origin O, from the positive ends of the axes. Thus, Q has positive moment about axis Z, but negative moment about axis X.

It is evident that the moment of a force parallel to or intersecting the axis of moments is zero.

Couples

Nature of Couples. Two equal and parallel forces of opposite sense are called a *couple*. The tendency of a couple is to produce rotation only. Since a couple has no single resultant, no single force can balance it. To prevent the rotation of a body acted upon by a couple, the application of two other forces is required, forming a second couple.

The *arm* of a couple is the perpendicular distance between the lines of action of the forces. The *moment* of a couple is constant and independent of the origin of moments; it is equal to one of the forces times the arm of the couple. Its sense is positive or negative according as rotational tendency is counterclockwise or clockwise. Couples of equal moments, in the same or parallel planes, are *equivalent* and may be replaced one by the other. Further, the *center of rotation* for a couple may be anywhere in its plane. Hence, a couple may be turned about in its own plane or moved to a parallel plane or replaced by another couple (having an arm of any given length but the same moment) without altering its effect on a rigid body.

Resultant of Couples. The resultant of any number of coplanar couples or of couples in parallel planes is a couple. Its moment and sense equal the algebraic sum of the moments of the component couples.

A couple may be represented by a **vector.** The length of the vector to scale represents the magnitude of the moment; it is drawn perpendicular to the plane of the couple from *any origin*, and an arrow is placed on it to represent the way in which the couple would cause a right-hand screw to advance. The resultant of any number of couples (in oblique or parallel planes) is a couple. The composition is effected by simply adding the vectors representing the couples in a manner analogous to the method of " Composition of Any Number of Concurrent Forces " as previously described in this section. The resultant vector defines the resultant couple.

Composition of Single Force and Couple. A *single force and couple in the same plane (or parallel planes)* may be composed into *another single force* equal and parallel to the

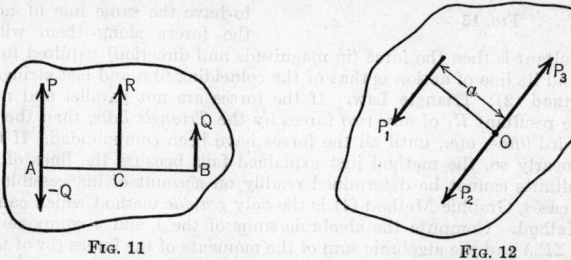

FIG. 11   FIG. 12

original force, at a distance from it equal to the moment of the couple divided by the magnitude of the force and so situated that the moment of the resultant about the point of application of the original force is of the same sign as the moment of the couple. The couple may be brought into the position shown in Fig. 11. The resultant of P, $-Q$, and Q is $R(=P)$ acting in a line through point C so that $(P - Q) \times AC = Q \times BC$. From this it follows that

$$AC = \frac{Q(AC + BC)}{P} = \frac{\text{moment of couple}}{P}$$

Resolution into Single Force through Chosen Point and Couple. A *single force* may be resolved into *another single force acting through a chosen point and a couple* (the new force being equal and parallel to the original force). In Fig. 12, P_1 is the given force and O the chosen point. Through O apply a pair of forces, opposite in sense, equal and parallel to P_1. As P_2 and P_3 balance, no change is produced in the motion of the body due to the addition. P_1 and P_3 constitute a couple of moment $= P \times a$, which is the same as moment of P_1 about O; and P_2 is a force just like P_1, but acting through the chosen point O.

5.   COMPOSITION OF NONCONCURRENT FORCES

Composition of Coplanar Nonparallel Nonconcurrent Forces

Graphic Method (1): String (or Funicular) Polygon. This method involves the resolu-tion of each force into two components in a certain way and the subsequent composition of the components to determine the resultant. Thus, to find the resultant of the three forces ab, bc, and cd acting on the body in Fig. 13, draw a force polygon, as $ABCD$, for the given forces; resolve AB into AO and OB; BC into BO and OC, etc., O having been taken anywhere: all components except the first and last occur in pairs and the forces of each pair are equal and opposite, thus OB and BO, OC and CO, etc.; choose the action lines of these components so that those of any one pair shall be collinear; thus, insert the components of AB at pleasure as at oa and ob, the components of BC so that the component BO shall act in ob, and hence the component OC in oc, etc.; thus the pairs of components consisting of equal, collinear, and opposite forces each balance, leaving only the first and last components AO and OD acting in ao and od; and their resultant (which is also the resultant of the given forces) is AD (magnitude and direction) ad (action line). The point O (Fig. 13) is called the **pole**, lines OA, OB, OC, etc., are **rays**; oa, ob, oc, etc., are **strings**, and all the strings constitute the **string (or funicular) polygon** for the forces. This polygon is also called " link," and " equilibrium polygon," the last being especially appropriate when the given forces are in equilibrium. The object in its construction is to locate one point on the action line of the resultant (or the length of arm to be used with the first and last rays of the force polygon if the resultant is a couple; see example in a later paragraph). The part of the drawing which represents the body and the lines of action of the forces is the *space diagram*; that representing force magnitudes, the *force polygon*. If the force polygon closes, the resultant is in general a couple, the forces of

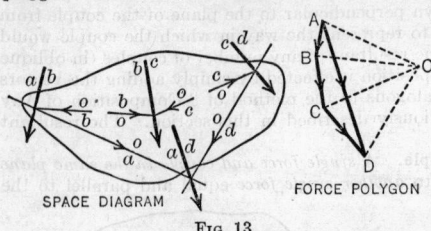

SPACE DIAGRAM   FORCE POLYGON

Fig. 13

the couple acting in the first and last strings of the string polygon, the magnitude of the forces being represented by the corresponding ray. If in addition to the force polygon closing, the first and last strings coincide, the string polygon is closed and the resultant vanishes. If the force polygon does not close, the first and last strings of the string polygon may still happen to have the same line of action but the forces along them will not be equal. The resultant is then the force (in magnitude and direction) required to close the force polygon, and its line of action is that of the coinciding first and last strings.

Graphic Method (2): Triangle Law. If the forces are not parallel and not nearly parallel, find the resultant R_1 of any two forces by the *Triangle Law*, then the resultant R_2 of R_1 and a third force, etc., until all the forces have been compounded. If the forces are parallel or nearly so, the method just explained fails because the lines of action of the several resultants cannot be determined readily on account of inaccessible intersections. In such cases, Graphic Method (1) is the only *graphic* method which can be used.

Algebraic Method. Compute the algebraic sums of the x and y components of the forces (ΣF_x and ΣF_y) and the algebraic sum of the moments of the forces (or of their components if more convenient, the result being the same), with respect to any origin O in their plane (ΣM). Then the resultant $R = \sqrt{(\Sigma F_x)^2 + (\Sigma F_y)^2}$, its angle with the x axis $= \tan^{-1}(\Sigma F_y)/(\Sigma F_x)$, and its arm with respect to O is $a = (\Sigma M)/R$. The general direction of R is apparent from the directions of its components ΣF_x and ΣF_y; a must be measured in such a direction from O that the sign of the moment of R will be the same as that of ΣM. If $\Sigma F_x = \Sigma F_y = 0$, the resultant is in general a couple whose moment $= \Sigma M$. If $\Sigma M = 0$ also, the resultant vanishes.

Composition of Coplanar Parallel Forces *

Graphic Method. If the forces are parallel or nearly so, *Graphic Method* (1) as described under the preceding heading for use with nonparallel forces may be used. *Graphic Method* (2) is not practical.

Using Graphic Method (1), if the force polygon does not close, the resultant is a single force. If it closes, the resultant is in general a couple. As an illustration of the latter, consider the four parallel forces in Fig. 14. The force polygon begins at A and ends at E, the same point; hence the resultant is not a single force (this is called a closed force polygon). Construct the funicular polygon as before. The first and last strings, ao and oe, being parallel, do not intersect.† The forces acting in those lines, AO and OE, being equal and opposite in sense, form a couple. Hence the resultant of the system is a couple whose moment is $AO(=OE) \times MN$. The *sense*, by inspection of the space diagram, is *clockwise*.

---

* Parallel forces are by nature *nonconcurrent*.
† It must be clearly understood that the fact that the forces are parallel and the fact that the first and last strings are parallel in the particular system illustrated in Fig. 14 have no bearing on each other. The first and last strings may or may not be parallel (or coincident) when the forces *either* are or are not parallel depending simply upon whether or not the resultant force vanishes (or happens to coincide in line of action with *both* of the strings).

If in addition to the force polygon closing, the first and last strings coincide, the string polygon is closed and the resultant vanishes.

Algebraic Method. This is a special case of that described under a preceding heading for use with nonparallel forces. The resultant $R = \Sigma F$. Its arm $a = (\Sigma M)/R$ and must be measured in such a direction from the origin of moments that the sign of the moment of R will be the same as that of ΣM.

If $\Sigma F = 0$, the resultant is in general a couple. If $\Sigma M = 0$ also, the resultant vanishes.

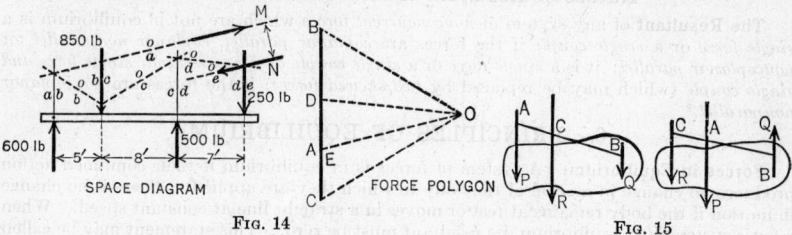

FIG. 14   FIG. 15

Simple Cases. When only two parallel forces are involved, their resultant (if a force) may be located more quickly by application of the following simple theorem based on Fig. 15. If P and Q act in the same direction, R cuts any line AB internally, and if P and Q are opposite, then externally on the side of the larger force; and in each case the segments of AB are inversely proportional to P and Q; that is, $AC/BC = Q/P$.

Composition of Noncoplanar Parallel Forces *

Graphic Methods are not advantageous in general for use in determining resultants of noncoplanar nonconcurrent force systems. Therefore only the algebraic method will be discussed.

Algebraic Method. Give to the forces F acting in the same direction one sign and to the others the opposite sign; then the resultant $R = \Sigma F$, the sense of R being indicated by the sign of ΣF. Next compute the sums of the moments of the forces with respect to two rectangular axes (x and y, say) perpendicular to the forces; call these sums ΣM_x and ΣM_y, and the arms of R with respect to those axes respectively a_x and a_y; then $a_x = (\Sigma M_x)/R$ and $a_y = (\Sigma M_y)/R$. The signs in these ratios may be disregarded; a_x and a_y have such positions that the moments of R with respect to the x and y axes have the same signs as those of ΣM_x and ΣM_y, respectively. If $\Sigma F = 0$, the resultant in general is a couple which can be determined by finding the resultant of all the forces but one; this resultant and the omitted force constitute the resultant couple. If $\Sigma M_x = \Sigma M_y = 0$ also, the resultant vanishes.

Composition of Noncoplanar Nonparallel Nonconcurrent Forces

Graphic Methods are not advantageous in general for use in determining resultants of noncoplanar nonconcurrent force systems. Therefore only the algebraic method will be discussed.

Algebraic Method. In general, the resultant is not a single force, but in such cases the system can be reduced to a force R acting through any point of the body selected and a couple C, noncoplanar with it; and if desired, R and C can in general be compounded into two noncoplanar forces. To determine R and C: select a set of coordinate axes (x, y, and z) in the body, the origin O being at the selected point referred to; determine the algebraic sums of the x, y, and z components of the given forces (ΣF_x, ΣF_y, and ΣF_z) and the algebraic sums of the moments of the forces with respect to the x, y, and z axes (ΣM_x, ΣM_y, and ΣM_z); ΣF_x, ΣF_y, and ΣF_z are the x, y, and z components of R, and ΣM_x, ΣM_y, and ΣM_z are the moments of the components of C perpendicular to the x, y, and z axes, respectively. They may be represented by vectors parallel to the axes.

$R^2 = (\Sigma F_x)^2 + (\Sigma F_y)^2 + (\Sigma F_z)^2$, and $C^2 = (\Sigma M_x)^2 + (\Sigma M_y)^2 + (\Sigma M_z)^2$; if α_1, α_2, and α_3 denote the angles between R and the x, y, and z axes, and θ_1, θ_2, and θ_3 the angles between the vector representing C and the x, y, and z axes respectively, then

$$\cos\alpha_1 = (\Sigma F_x)/R \qquad \cos\alpha_2 = (\Sigma F_y)/R \qquad \cos\alpha_3 = (\Sigma F_z)/R$$
$$\cos\theta_1 = (\Sigma M_x)/C \qquad \cos\theta_2 = (\Sigma M_y)/C \qquad \cos\theta_3 = (\Sigma M_z)/C$$

The resultant force R and the resultant couple C can be compounded into two forces as follows: take the plane of the couple so that one of the forces of the couple intersects

* Parallel forces are by nature *nonconcurrent*.

R; find the resultant of this force and R; this resultant and the other force of C are the two forces sought. In general the final two forces are skewed.

If the plane of C is parallel to R, C and R may be compounded into a single force by the method described in a previous paragraph headed " Composition of Single Force and Couple." If $C = 0$, the resultant is in general a single force; if $R = 0$, the resultant is in general a couple; if $C = R = 0$, the resultant vanishes.

Nature of Resultant of Nonconcurrent Forces

The Resultant of any system of *nonconcurrent forces* which are not in equilibrium is a *single force* or a *single couple* if the forces are *coplanar parallel, coplanar nonparallel,* or *noncoplanar parallel*; it is a *single force* or a *single couple* or a *noncoplanar single force and single couple* (which may be replaced by *two skewed forces*) if the forces are *noncoplanar nonparallel*.*

6. PRINCIPLES OF EQUILIBRIUM

Forces in Equilibrium. A system of forces is in equilibrium if their combined action produces no change in motion of the body to which they are applied. There is no change in motion if the body remains at rest or moves in a straight line at constant speed. When a force system is in equilibrium, its resultant must be zero. This statement may be called the *general condition of equilibrium*. It implies both zero force and zero couple.

Table I. Conditions of Equilibrium

Necessary and sufficient independent conditions of equilibrium for the various force systems

	System	Algebraical		Graphical	
		No.	Conditions	No.	Conditions
Coplanar	Collinear	1	$\Sigma F = 0$	1	Force polygon closes.
	Concurrent at point O	2	$\Sigma F_x = 0$, $\Sigma F_y = 0$; or, $\Sigma F_x = 0$, $\Sigma M_a = 0$, if x direction is not perpendicular to aO; or, $\Sigma M_a = 0$, $\Sigma M_b = 0$, if aOb is not a straight line.	1	Force polygon closes.
	Parallel	2	$\Sigma F = 0$; or, $\Sigma M_a = 0$, $\Sigma M_b = 0$, if line ab is not parallel to forces.	2	Force and funicular polygons close. (Latter item means that first and last strings coincide.)
	Nonparallel nonconcurrent	3	$\Sigma F_x = 0$, $\Sigma F_y = 0$, $\Sigma M = 0$; or, $\Sigma F_x = 0$, $\Sigma M_a = 0$, $\Sigma M_b = 0$, if x direction is not perpendicular to ab; or, $\Sigma M_a = 0$, $\Sigma M_b = 0$, $\Sigma M_c = 0$, if abc is not a straight line.	2	Force and funicular polygons close. (Latter item means that first and last strings coincide.)
Noncoplanar	Concurrent at point O	3	$\Sigma F_x = 0$, $\Sigma F_y = 0$, $\Sigma F_z = 0$. Combinations of moment and resolution equations can be arranged, but are not common.	2	Force polygon closes. It is warped; hence plan and elevation must show closed. Not commonly used.
	Parallel	3	$\Sigma F_z = 0$, $\Sigma M_x = 0$, $\Sigma M_y = 0$, forces parallel to z axis. Other combinations possible but not common.		Not used.
	Nonparallel nonconcurrent	6	$\Sigma F_x = 0$, $\Sigma F_y = 0$, $\Sigma F_z = 0$, $\Sigma M_x = 0$, $\Sigma M_y = 0$, $\Sigma M_z = 0$. ΣM about every axis $= 0$, and it is often convenient to employ more than three moment equations, instead of using so many resolution equations.		The projection of the system on any plane is in equilibrium, and algebraical or graphical conditions can be used to solve such projected systems.

An oblique system of x, y, z axes may be used for reference provided no two axes are at an angle of 180° with each other. Rectangular axes are preferable generally.

* It is evident that *any force system whatever,* whether *concurrent* or *nonconcurrent,* even though it includes "sub-systems" coming under all of the various classifications discussed, can be composed into a resultant which is a *single force* or a *single couple* or a *noncoplanar single force and single couple* (or *two skewed forces*).

Body in Equilibrium. A rigid body is in equilibrium if it remains at rest or moves in a straight line at constant speed; i.e., if its state of motion does not change. This condition obtains if all the external forces acting upon it (including those due to pull of gravity, friction, etc.) form a system in equilibrium.

Conditions of Equilibrium

In a problem in *statics* a body is known to be in equilibrium; hence the system composed of all the external forces acting upon it must be in equilibrium. In such a case, tests are not needed to ascertain if equilibrium exists, but they are used to set up relations involving unknown forces, distances, or angles, and the unknown elements are then computed provided their number does not exceed the number of independent equations which may be set up by means of the equilibrium conditions. When the number of unknown elements exceeds the number of independent equations, the problem is said to be statically indeterminate.

Special Conditions. If three forces are in equilibrium they must be coplanar. and concurrent or parallel; if concurrent, each force is proportional to the sine of the angle between the other two; if parallel, each force is proportional to the distance between the other two. If a force system is in equilibrium, the resultant of any part must balance the resultant of the other part. It follows that if four coplanar nonconcurrent nonparallel forces are in equilibrium, the resultant of any two is concurrent with the other two.

Stability of Equilibrium. When a body (or collection of bodies) is in equilibrium and the state is such that if when displaced slightly in any way the body returns of itself to its original position, the equilibrium is *stable*; if when displaced slightly the body moves further from its original position, the equilibrium is *unstable*; and if when displaced slightly it remains in that displaced position, the equilibrium is *neutral* or *indifferent*. The body or collection is also said to be stable, unstable, or neutral (or indifferent) under these respective conditions. When the body is stable or unstable, the system of forces is changed by the slight displacement and is no longer in equilibrium; hence the further displacement. Only when the stability is neutral is the equilibrium of the force system undisturbed by a slight displacement of the body.

7. EQUILIBRIUM PROBLEMS

General Principles

(a) It frequently happens that the external force system acting on a body as a whole cannot be solved directly owing to the presence of more unknown elements (forces, distances, and angles) than there are conditions of equilibrium. In such cases, endeavor to separate the original body into simpler parts which will permit solutions. making use of the unknowns thus determined in solving the force systems acting on other sections until the complete solution, if obtainable, has been found.

(b) To facilitate computations, it is desirable if resolution equations are used, to resolve perpendicular to one of the unknown forces; if a moment origin is used, to select it on the action line of an unknown force; if moment axes are used, to select them so as to intersect some of the unknown forces.

(c) Assume senses for unknown forces. A plus answer then indicates the sense to have been correctly assumed; a minus answer, incorrect assumption.

(d) When force polygons are used, letter action lines of wholly known forces first and those of the remainder last. Draw the force polygon to the end of the last known vector. Vectors required to close it (remembering that the senses must read confluently from the starting point back to the same point) determine unknown magnitudes and senses and/or lines of action.

Typical Problems

I. System of Coplanar Concurrent Forces in Equilibrium *with all forces known except two whose action lines only are known.* The magnitudes and senses of these two forces are to be determined.*

Example. Two smooth cylinders rest upon a 30° plane and against a vertical wall as shown in Fig. 16. Determine all forces acting on each cylinder. (a) The forces involved are 100 lb, 200 lb, P, Q, R, and S, the last four being normal to the surfaces of contact (smooth surfaces). (b) Consider the two cylinders as a single free body. The external force system is 100 lb, 200 lb, P, R, and S (Q₁ and Q₂ are internal). The system is nonconcurrent, so does not come under typical problem I. Consider the large cylinder as a free body. The external force system is 100 lb, Q, R, and S. While

* This is a common problem in the determination of the stresses of a roof or bridge truss.

this system is concurrent, it cannot be solved because there are more than two unknown quantities. Next consider the small cylinder as a free body. The force system is 200 lb, P, and Q, and this is typical problem I.

Algebraic Solution. Choose X and Y directions parallel and perpendicular to the plane. $\Sigma F_x = 0 = Q_1 \dfrac{\sqrt{60}}{8} - 200 \sin 30°$. Hence $Q_1 = \dfrac{800}{\sqrt{60}} = 103.3$ lb. $\Sigma F_y = 0 = P - 200 \cos 30°$ $- 103.3 \times 2/8$. Hence $P = 199$ lb. Consider the large cylinder as a free body. $Q_1 = Q_2 = 103.3$ lb. Use the same X and Y directions. $\Sigma F_x = 0 = S \cos 30° - 103.3 \times \dfrac{\sqrt{60}}{8} - 100 \sin 30°$.

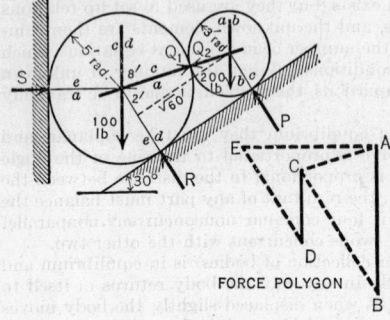

Hence, $S = 173.2$ lb. $\Sigma F_y = 0 = R - 100 \cos 30° - 173.2 \sin 30° + 103.3 \times 2/8$. Hence $R = 147.4$ lb.

Graphic Solution. Discussions (a) and (b) are same as above. The free body is the small cylinder. The force system is ab, bc, and ca, and the polygon is the triangle ABC (Fig. 16). $BC = 199$ lb, $CA = 103.3$ lb. Next, consider the large cylinder as a free body. The force system is ac, cd, de, and ea. Plot the known forces AC and CD. From D draw DE parallel to de, and from A, AE parallel to ae; these lines intersect at E. $DE = 147.4$ lb, and $EA = 173.2$ lb are the magnitudes and senses of the two unknowns.

FORCE POLYGON

Fig. 16

If the system is concurrent and all the forces are known except one, the two unknown elements will be one angle and one magnitude and sense. Both may be determined by writing the equilibrium equations, or by drawing the force polygon.

II. System of Coplanar Parallel Forces in Equilibrium *with all forces known except two whose action lines only are known.* The magnitudes and senses of these two forces are to be determined.

Example. A beam is loaded as shown in Fig. 17 and supported at the points P and Q. Determine the reactions of the supports. Consider the beam as a free body. The external force system consists of the forces 1000 lb, 5000 lb, 2400 lb, P, and Q. This is a coplanar parallel system and is typical problem II.

Algebraic Solution. Assume senses for the reactions.

$$\Sigma M_p = 0 = -4 \times 1000 - 10 \times 5000 - 14 \times 2400 + 16Q$$

Hence $Q = 5475$ lb; correct sense was assumed.

$$\Sigma M_q = 0 = 2 \times 2400 + 6 \times 5000 + 12 \times 1000 - 16P$$

Hence $P = 2925$ lb; correct sense assumed. As a check, apply a third equilibrium condition, $\Sigma F = 0$.

$$\Sigma F = 0 = -2925 + 1000 + 5000 + 2400 - 5475$$

Graphic Solution of the same problem involves the construction of a closed force polygon and a closed funicular polygon. On a line of indefinite length parallel to the forces, often called the *load line*, construct the force polygon by drawing vectors AB, BC, CD to represent 1000 lb, 5000 lb, 2400 lb. Let DE represent Q and EA represent P. The problem is to locate point E. This is done with the aid of the funicular polygon. Draw the rays OA, OB, OC, and OD. Construct the funicular polygon by drawing first the string between the last-lettered unknown force P (i.e, EA) and the first known force AB, and continuing it to the intersection of the last known string with the first-lettered unknown force. The closing line is

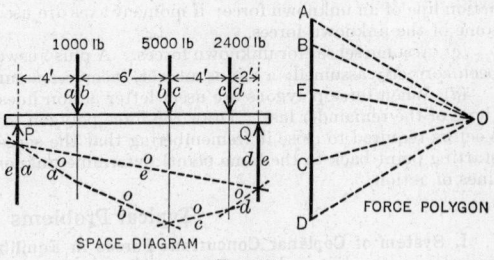

Fig. 17

oe. Draw the ray OE parallel to oe. The unknown reactions are DE and EA.

For problems of this type, the algebraic solution is preferable to the graphic.

(NOTE: This principle cannot be applied to beams having more than two points of support. Such problems require special treatment.)

III. System of Coplanar Nonparallel Nonconcurrent Forces in Equilibrium *with all forces known except two, of which the action line of one and a point in the action line of the*

other are known. The magnitude and sense of the one and the magnitude, sense, and angular direction of the other are to be determined.*

Example. A roof truss is loaded as in Fig. 18. The left end of the truss rests on a smooth horizontal support. The right end is secured to a wall by means of a pin. Determine the reactions. The external forces acting on the truss are the given loads, the left reaction P (vertical, on account of the smooth support), and the right reaction Q (inclined, through point M). The unknown quantities are the reactions P and Q. This is typical problem III.

Algebraic Solution. Assume P upward.

$\Sigma M_M = 0 = 20{,}000 \times 18 + 25{,}000 \times 24 \cos 30° - 36P$; hence, $P = 24{,}430$ lb; correct sense assumed.

Assume Q upward to the left at angle θ with horizontal.

$\Sigma F_x = 0 = 25{,}000 \sin 30° - Q \cos \theta$; $\Sigma F_y = 0 = -25{,}000 \cos 30° - 20{,}000 + 24{,}430 + Q \sin \theta$.

Solving simultaneously, $Q = 21{,}300$ lb, and $\theta = 54°$. Sense and direction were correctly assumed, hence Q acts upward to the left at 54° to the horizontal. As a check, apply condition $\Sigma M_P = 0$. $\Sigma M_P = 0 = -25{,}000 \times 12 \cos 30° - 20{,}000 \times 18 + 21{,}300 \times 36 \sin 54°$.

Graphic Solution. ab and bc are the action lines of the given loads, cd of the reaction P and da of the reaction Q. Draw the vectors AB and BC, and a line through C, parallel to cd. Choose a pole and draw the rays. Construct the funicular polygon, drawing oa through M, and draw closing string od from K to M. Draw OD through O parallel to od to intersect CD at D. Draw DA. Vectors CD and DA represent the two unknown forces, $P = 24{,}430$ lb and $Q = 21{,}300$ lb. The action line of Q is da, making angle with horizontal $= 54°$.

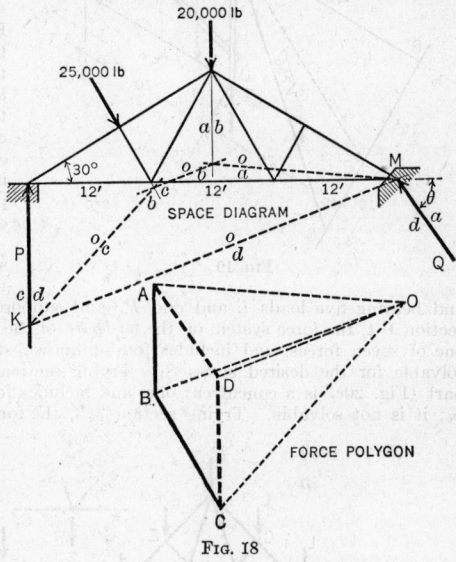

Special Case. A case coming under the above classification which requires a variation in treatment when employing the graphic method is one in which the action lines of all three forces are known but their magnitudes and senses are unknown. The procedure is in general similar to methods employed before except that, in the graphic solution, two of the unknown forces which are concurrent must be replaced by their unknown resultant acting through their point of concurrency along an unknown action line. After the magnitude and sense of this resultant have been determined (by the method employed in the above example), it is resolved into its two components along the action lines of the two unknown forces which it had replaced. These components represent the magnitudes and senses of this pair of forces.

FIG. 18

IV. System of Noncoplanar Nonparallel Nonconcurrent Forces in Equilibrium *with one force completely known and action lines (or a point in the action line) of the others known.* All unknown force magnitudes, action lines and senses are to be determined.

Example. The crane (Fig. 19) is supported by a socket at the foot of the post at D; is kept from overturning by the backstays AB and AC; and carries a load of 600 lb (E, A, F, G, D, are in the vertical XY plane). Determine the axial components of the reaction on the post at D and the tensions in the backstays. The external forces acting on the crane are the load, the reaction at D, and the tensions in the backstays at A. This is typical problem IV. Moment equations are the most convenient to apply for this solution.

$$\Sigma M_{BC} = 0 = 600 \times 40 - 20\,D_y; \quad D_y = 1200 \text{ lb}$$

$$\Sigma M_{ZA} = 0 = 600 \times 20 - 16\,D_x; \quad D_x = 750 \text{ lb}$$

$$\Sigma M_{XA} = 0 = 600 \times 4 - 16\,D_z; \quad D_z = 150 \text{ lb}$$

$$\Sigma M_{XC} = 0 = AB \times \frac{16}{\sqrt{881}} \times 25 - 1200 \times 10 + 600 \times 6; \quad AB = 622 \text{ lb}$$

$$\Sigma M_{XB} = 0 = AC \times \frac{16}{\sqrt{756}} \times 25 + 600 \times 19 - 1200 \times 15; \quad AC = 452 \text{ lb}$$

---

* This is a common problem in the determination of the reactions on a roof truss sustaining wind pressures, the truss being fixed at one end and resting on rollers at the other.

The senses of all forces are as shown in Fig. 19.

The magnitude, action line, and sense of the resultant force on the post at D can be readily determined (if desired) by the Parallelepipedon Law.

Truss Analysis

A Truss is a framework * for carrying loads, each *member* of which is subjected only to tension or compression loads. The members are usually pin-jointed with loads applied only at the joints.

The Stress in a Member at any section is the force which either of its two parts exerts internally on the other part as a result of the external forces acting on the member. Longi-

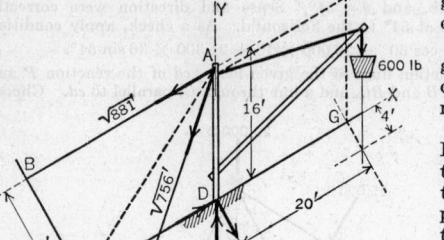

tudinal stresses, like external longitudinal forces, may be either tensile or compressive.

FIG. 19

The Analysis of a Truss under a given loading condition refers to the determination of the stresses in its members due to the loads.

Analysis by Method of Sections. First, determine the reactions on the truss due to the loads; second, imagine the truss separated into two distinct parts (that is, pass a section through the truss) so that the member under consideration is one of the members cut and so that the system of forces, including stresses, acting on either part of the truss is solvable for the desired stress; third, solve the system.

To Pass the Section, suppose the stress in HI (Fig. 20a) is required, the truss being supported at its ends and bearing five loads L and one P, and suppose the reactions determined. Trying section 1–1, the force system on the left part of the truss (Fig. 20b) is a nonconcurrent one of seven forces, and includes four unknown stresses, S_1, S_2, S_3, and S_4; it is not solvable for the desired stress S_1. Trying section 2–2, the force system on the lower part (Fig. 20c) is a concurrent one, and includes four unknown stresses, S_1, S_2, S_5, and S_6; it is not solvable. Trying section 3–3, the force system on the left part (Fig. 20d)

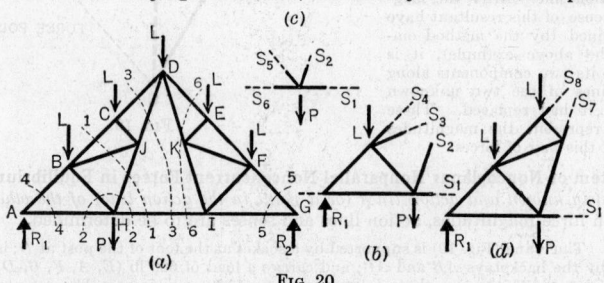

FIG. 20

is nonconcurrent with three unknown stresses, S_1, S_7, and S_8; it is solvable. In some instances different sections may be used, each leading to a solution.

S_1 having been determined, the force system of Fig. 20b becomes solvable, and then, with S_2 also determined, the force system of Fig. 20c may be solved.

Algebraic Solution. Following the general method of procedure outlined above, determine the various stresses by employing algebraic conditions of equilibrium in manners similar to those illustrated heretofore under " Equilibrium Problems."

Graphic Solution. Following the general method of procedure outlined above, determine the various stresses by employing graphic conditions of equilibrium.

In Making the Imaginary Separations of the Truss, care should be taken to cut not more than three members in which the stresses are unknown. It is advantageous to make

---

* *Redundant frames* (i.e., ones having more members than necessary to preserve their shapes under the loading conditions) are not considered in this section, since the stresses in them cannot be determined by elementary static methods.

the separation so that not more than two such members are cut. If this is done, a single force polygon will determine the two unknowns, whereas if three are cut, a force polygon and an equilibrium polygon, or the equivalent, are necessary for determining the three unknowns.

Analysis by Method of Joint Resolution.* Consider the pin at each joint as a body acted upon by forces in equilibrium.

Algebraic Solution. Determine the various stresses by employing algebraic conditions of equilibrium in manners similar to those illustrated heretofore under " Equilibrium Problems."

Graphic Solution. For each joint, draw the force polygon. In doing so, it will be advantageous to represent the forces in the order in which they occur about the joint. A force polygon so drawn will be called a polygon for the joint; and for brevity, if the order taken is clockwise, the polygon will be called a clockwise polygon, and if counter-clockwise, it will be called a counterclockwise polygon. If the polygons for all the joints of a truss are drawn separately, the stress in each member will have been represented twice. It is possible to combine the polygons so that it will be not be necessary to represent the stress in any member more than once, thus reducing the number of lines to be drawn. Such a combination of force polygons is called a *stress diagram.* Each triangular space in the truss diagram is marked by a small letter; also the space between consecutive action lines of the loads and reactions. Then the two letters on opposite sides of any line serve to designate that line, and the same large letters are used to designate the magnitude of the corresponding force.

To construct a stress diagram for a truss under given loads:

(1) Determine the reactions. (2) Letter the truss diagram as directed. (3) Construct a force polygon for all the external forces applied to the truss (loads and reactions), representing them in the order in which their application points occur about the truss, clockwise or counterclockwise. (4) On the sides of that polygon construct the polygons for all the joints. They must be clockwise or counterclockwise according as the polygon for the loads and reactions was drawn clockwise or counterclockwise. (The first polygon drawn must be for a joint at which only two members are fastened; the joints at the supports are usually such. Next, that joint is considered, and its polygon is drawn, at which not more than two stresses are unknown.)

Example. Fig. 21 represents a roof truss sustaining loads of 600, 1000, 1200, and 1800 lb; the right reaction is 2100 lb, and the left 2500 lb. *ABCDEFA* is a polygon for the loads and reactions, these being represented in the order in which their points of application occur about the truss. The polygon for joint 1 is *FABGF*; the force *BG* acts toward the joint, hence *bg* is under compression, and *GF* acts away from the joint, hence *gf* is in tension. The polygon for joint 2 is *CDEHC*; the force *EH* acts away from the joint, hence *eh* is in tension; and *HC* acts toward the joint, hence *hc* is in compression. The polygon for joint 3 is *HEFGH*; the force *GH* acts away from the joint and hence *gh* is in tension. If the work has been done correctly, *GH* is parallel to *gh*. (In Fig. 21a all the polygons are clockwise, and in Fig. 21b, counterclockwise.)

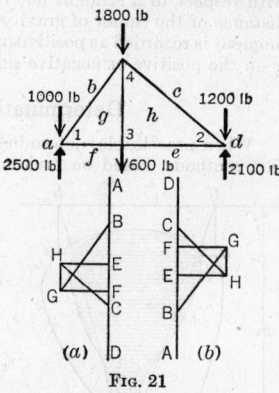

FIG. 21

8. CENTER OF GRAVITY

Definitions

The Centroid of a system of parallel forces having fixed application points is the point through which their resultant will always pass regardless of how the forces may be turned, provided they remain parallel.

The Center of Gravity of a Body † *or system of bodies* is the *centroid of the forces of gravitation* ‡ acting upon all the particles thereof. Referring the application points of such a force system to a set of coordinate axes, the coordinates of the centroid, or center of gravity (c.g.), are:

$$\bar{x} = (\Sigma F_i \cdot x_i)/\Sigma F_i = \frac{\int x dF}{F}; \quad \bar{y} = (\Sigma F_i \cdot y_i)/\Sigma F_i = \frac{\int y dF}{F}; \quad \bar{z} = (\Sigma F_i \cdot z_i)/\Sigma F_i = \frac{\int z dF}{F}$$

---

* This method is not usually so convenient for determining algebraically the stress in a single specified member.

† Sometimes called *center of mass* or *center of inertia.*

‡ For practical purposes, the forces of gravitation may be considered as parallel.

in which F_i represents the force on (or weight of) one particle and x_i, y_i, z_i are the coordinates of its application point. If a group of bodies is involved, the coordinates of the center of gravity of the group are:

$$\bar{x} = (\Sigma W_i \cdot \bar{x}_i)/\Sigma W_i; \quad \bar{y} = (\Sigma W_i \cdot \bar{y}_i)/\Sigma W_i; \quad \bar{z} = (\Sigma W_i \cdot \bar{z}_i)/\Sigma W_i$$

in which W_i represents the weight of one body and $\bar{x}_i$, $\bar{y}_i$, $\bar{z}_i$ are the coordinates of its center of gravity.* A body (or system of bodies), if supported at its center of gravity, will remain at rest in any position.

The Center of Gravity of Part of a Body may be located by the rule that its moment, with respect to any plane, equals the moment of the whole minus, algebraically, the moment of the remainder.

The Center of Gravity of a Line, Surface, or Volume is that point which would be the center of gravity if the line were replaced by a homogeneous rod of infinitesimal diameter, the surface by a homogeneous plate of infinitesimal thickness, or the volume by a homogeneous body.

Symmetry. Two points are symmetrical with respect to a third point if the line joining the two is bisected by the third. Two points are symmetrical with respect to a line or a plane if the line joining them is perpendicular to the given line or plane and is bisected by it. A body, line, surface, or volume is symmetrical with respect to a point, a line, or a plane if all the points of the body, line, surface, or volume can be paired so that each pair is symmetrical with respect to the point, line, or plane. If a homogeneous body, or a line, surface, or volume is symmetrical with respect to a point, line, or plane, its center of gravity is at the point, in the line or in the plane.

The Static Moment of a body (having weight), a line (having length), a surface (having area), or a solid † (having volume) with respect to any plane is the product of the weight, length, area, and volume and the distance of the center of gravity of the body, line, surface, or solid from the plane. The static moment of a plane line or plane surface with respect to a straight line in the plane is the product of the length or area and the distance of the center of gravity of the line or surface from the reference line. A static moment is regarded as positive or negative according as the corresponding center of gravity is on the positive or negative side of the reference plane or line.

Determination of Center of Gravity Location

When practicable, determination of center of gravity location by algebraic or integration methods, based on dividing the sum of the moments by the sum of the forces, is generally the simplest process. For some bodies of non-homogeneous nature or of very irregular shape, one of the following methods of procedure may be necessary or at least preferable:

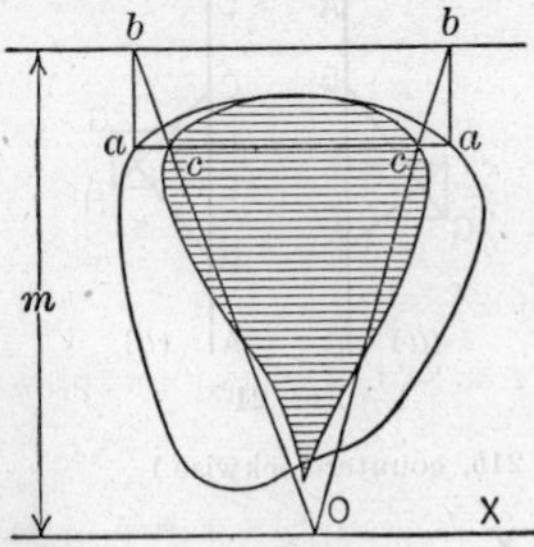

FIG. 22

Graphic Method. For application to *plane* figures.‡ Referring to Fig. 22, take a point O and a line bb on opposite sides of the figure at any convenient distance m apart; project any width of the figure parallel to bb as aa on bb, connect the projections bb with O and note the intersections cc; determine other points cc and draw a smooth curve through them as shown; measure the area A' within the curve cc; then $A'm$ is the static moment of the given figure with respect to OX; if A is the area of the given figure and y the distance of its center of gravity from OX, $y = A'm/A$. In a similar way the distance of the center of gravity from a line perpendicular to OX can be determined and its exact position thus definitely located.

Suspension Method. For application to *plane* figures.§ Suspend the body (or a model representing it) from a point near its edge and mark on it the direction of a plumb-line hung from that point. Repeat this operation, using a second suspension point. The center of gravity is at (or behind) the intersection of the two markings.

Weighing Method. Generally applied where location of c.g. in one plane only is required. Determine weight W of the body and then support it on a knife-edge (Fig. 23) and on a point support

---

* As F (in the gravitational system of units) equals W, these symbols may be used interchangeably in the two sets of formulas. Also, any one of the expressions may be read as "the sum of the moments divided by the sum of the forces (or weights)."

† The word "solid" where used herein denotes "that which has volume." Care should be taken to distinguish this from a "body," which has "mass" (as well as "volume"). Some writers use the word "solid" to denote at various times either volume or mass, which is sometimes confusing. In this section, the word "volume" is frequently used even in preference to "solid" to avoid the possibility of confusion with "mass."

‡ Including areas or flat homogeneous bodies of uniform thickness.

§ Including areas or flat bodies of uniform homogeneous thickness.

resting upon a platform scale. Weigh reaction R of the point support and measure horizontal distance a between the point and the knife-edge. Then the horizontal distance from the knife-edge to the center of gravity is $\bar{x} = Ra/W$.

Balancing Method. For general application. Balance the body (or a model representing it) on a straight-edge, marking on the body the vertical plane containing the edge. Repeat for two more balancing positions of the body. The center of gravity is at the point common to the three planes thus determined.

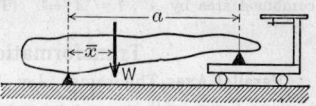

FIG. 23

9. MOMENT OF INERTIA

Plane Surfaces—Definitions

The Moment of Inertia of a Plane Surface (or figure) with respect to (or about) a line (or axis) is the sum of the products obtained by multiplying the area of each element of the surface by the square of its distance from the line.* Letting I_x denote moment of inertia about an X axis:

$$I_x = \int y^2 dA$$

in which A is the total area and y is the perpendicular distance of any element of area dA from the axis. The moment of inertia of a surface is obviously the sum of the moments of inertia of its parts. The moment of inertia of a plane surface is **rectangular** if the axis used is *in* the plane of the area; it is **polar** if the axis is *perpendicular* to the plane of the area.

The Radius of Gyration of a Plane Surface with respect to a line is the length whose square multiplied by the area of the surface equals the moment of inertia of the surface with respect to the line. Letting k denote radius of gyration:

$$I = k^2 A \quad \text{or} \quad k = \sqrt{I/A}$$

in which I is the moment of inertia and A the area.

The Product of Inertia of a Plane Surface with respect to a pair of coordinate axes in the plane is the algebraic sum of the products obtained by multiplying the area of each element of the surface by its coordinates.* Letting U_{xy} denote product of inertia with respect to X and Y axes:

$$U_{xy} = \int xy dA$$

in which A is the total area and x and y are the coordinates of any element of area dA.

The Principal Axes of Inertia of a Plane Surface at a Particular Point in the plane are the two axes about which the moments of inertia are greater and less than for any other axis, through the point in the plane.† The corresponding moments of inertia are called the **principal moments of inertia** of the surface at the point. The principal axes are always at right angles to each other. The product of inertia with respect to them is zero.

The Customary Engineer's Unit for both moment and product of inertia of a surface is biquadratic inches (in.⁴).

Determination of Moment of Inertia of Plane Surfaces

When practicable, determination of moment of inertia with respect to an axis by algebraic or integration methods is generally the simplest process. For some surfaces of very irregular shape, the following graphic method of procedure may be necessary or at least preferable:

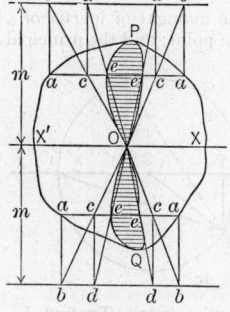

FIG. 24

Graphic Method. Let $aaaa$ (Fig. 24) be the outline and XX' the axis with respect to which the moment of inertia is desired; at any convenient distance m from XX' draw two parallels (but if XX' does not cut the figure, only one parallel, the one on the opposite side of the figure from XX'); draw any line as aa parallel to XX' and project the points aa on the nearer parallel; join the projections bb to any point O in XX', and note the intersections cc on aa; project cc on the same parallel; join the projections dd with O, and note the

---

* Moment of inertia is always positive and never zero. Product of inertia may be positive, zero, or negative, depending upon the distribution of the area with respect to the axes. If a surface has an axis of symmetry, its product of inertia with respect to that axis and one perpendicular thereto is zero.

† In certain special cases, as for axes through the point in the center of a circular area, the moment of inertia is the same for any axis and therefore there is no principal axis through that point.

intersections *ee* on *aa*. In a similar manner determine points like *ee* for other widths like *aa*, and connect all points *e* as shown. Then measure the area of the loops *OPO* and *OQO*; denoting this combined area by A'', $I = A''m^2$. (There will be only one loop if only one parallel *bb* is used.)

Transformation Formulas—Plane Surfaces

Parallel Axes Theorems. Let $I =$ *moment of inertia* (either rectangular or polar) of a plane figure with respect to any line or axis, $\bar{I} =$ that with respect to a parallel axis passing through the center of gravity of the figure, $d =$ distance between the axes, k and $\bar{k} =$ the radii of gyration with respect to the same axes respectively, and $A =$ area of the figure; then

$$I = \bar{I} + Ad^2 \quad \text{and} \quad k^2 = \bar{k}^2 + d^2$$

These show that with respect to all parallel axes the moment of inertia and the radius of gyration are least for the one passing through the center of gravity of the figure.

Similarly, let $U =$ *product of inertia* of a plane figure with respect to a pair of coordinate axes in the plane, and $\bar{U} =$ that with respect to a parallel pair whose origin is at the center of gravity; $\bar{x}$, $\bar{y}$ the coordinates of the center of gravity referred to the first pair, and A the area of the figure; then $U = \bar{U} + A\bar{x}\bar{y}$.

Relation of Rectangular and Polar Moments of Inertia. Let I_x, I_y, and $J_z =$ the moments of inertia of a plane figure with respect to x, y, and z axes respectively, the axes being *at right angles* to each other and the x and y axes in the plane; and let k_x, k_y, and $k_z =$ the corresponding radii of gyration; then $J_z = I_x + I_y$, $k_z^2 = k_x^2 + k_y^2$.

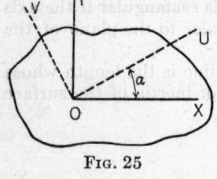

Rotated Axes Theorem. Let XOY and UOV (Fig. 25) be two sets of rectangular coordinate axes with a common origin and in a given plane figure. $I_x, I_y, I_u, I_v =$ moments of inertia of the figure with respect to x, y, u, and v axes respectively; U_{xy} and $U_{uv} =$ its products of inertia with respect to the sets of axes respectively; $\alpha =$ angle through which x axis must be rotated to bring it into u axis, regarded as positive or negative

Fig. 25

according as the turning is counterclockwise or clockwise. Then $I_u + I_v = I_x + I_y$, and

$$I_u = I_x \cos^2\alpha + I_y \sin^2\alpha - U_{xy}\sin 2\alpha$$
$$U_{uv} = 1/2(I_x - I_y)\sin 2\alpha + U_{xy}\cos 2\alpha$$

If OU and OV are *principal axes* (see definition above), $U_{uv} = 0$ and therefore $\tan 2\alpha = 2U_{xy}/(I_y - I_x)$. Hence, the principal axes of a figure at a point can be readily found if the moments of inertia and the product of inertia of the figure with respect to two rectangular axes through the point and in the plane are known.* The *principal moments of inertia* are then I_u from the formula above and I_v from the same formula after replacing α by $\left(\alpha + \dfrac{\pi}{2}\right)$. As a check, $I_u + I_v = I_x + I_y$.

Graphic Transformations—Plane Surfaces

The Inertia Circle is a device for determining *graphically* the moment of inertia of a plane figure with respect to any line of the plane through a given point; and the principal axes and principal moments of inertia for the same point. To construct the circle, it is necessary to know the moments of inertia and the product of inertia with respect to two rectangular axes through the point, in the plane figure. Suppose I_x, I_y, and U_{xy} given for the shaded area in Fig. 26. To convenient scale, plot OX' and OY' to represent I_x and I_y, and $Y'A$ to represent U_{xy} (downward if negative and upward if positive). Center C is mid-way between X' and Y'. With CA as radius, describe the inertia circle. To find I_u.

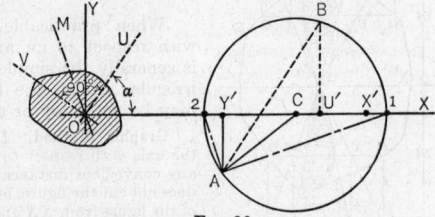

Fig. 26

draw chord AB parallel to axis OU; draw perpendicular BU'. OU' (to scale) $= I_u$, and BU' (to scale) $= U_{uv}$. OM, parallel to $A2$, is axis of least I; and a parallel to $A1$, through O, is axis of greatest I. $O2$ (to scale) is the value of least $I = I_2$; and $O1$, value of greatest $I = I_1$. *Least radius of gyration* for an axis through point $O = \sqrt{I_2/\text{area}}$.

---

* If U_{xy} and $(I_y - I_x)$ are both zero, there is no principal axis through the point.

Bodies—Definitions

The Moment of Inertia of a Body with respect to (or about) a line (or axis) is the sum of the products obtained by multiplying the mass of each elementary part by the square of its distance from the line.† Letting I_x denote moment of inertia about an X axis:

$$I_x = \int y^2 \, dm$$

in which m is the total mass and y is the perpendicular distance of any element of mass dm from the axis.* The moment of inertia of a body is obviously the sum of the moments of inertia of its parts.

The Center of Gyration of a Body with respect to a line is a point at such a distance from the line that, if the entire mass of the body were concentrated there, its moment of inertia would be the same as that of the body.

The Radius of Gyration of a Body with respect to a line is the distance from the center of gyration to the line. Letting k denote radius of gyration:

$$I = k^2 \, m \quad \text{or} \quad k = \sqrt{I/m}$$

in which I is the moment of inertia and m the mass.

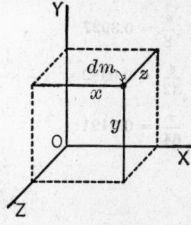

The Product of Inertia of a Body with respect to a pair of coordinate planes is the algebraic sum of the products obtained by multiplying the mass of each element of the body by its coordinates with reference to those planes.† Thus with respect to YOZ and ZOX (Fig. 27), ZOX and XOY, and XOY and YOZ planes, the products of inertia are respectively:

$$U_{xy} = \int xy\,dm; \quad U_{yz} = \int yz\,dm; \quad U_{zx} = \int zx\,dm$$

Fig. 27

The Principal Axes of Inertia of a Body at a Particular Point. The values of moments of inertia of a body for all axes through a given point are in general unequal; for one axis the moment of inertia is greater and for another it is less than for any other axis through the point. These two axes are at right angles, and they together with one at right angles to their plane and passing through the point are **principal axes of inertia of the body at the point**; the corresponding moments of inertia are the **principal moments of inertia of the body at the point.** If the point is the center of gravity of the body, the axes and moments are called *central principal axes* and *central principal moments of inertia.* For a set of principal axes, the three products of inertia, with respect to the **principal planes** determined by them, are zero.

The Customary Engineer's Unit for both moment and product of inertia is slug-ft.^{2}

Transformation Formulas—Bodies

Parallel Axes Theorems. Let I = moment of inertia of a body with respect to any line or axis, $\bar{I}$ = that with respect to a parallel axis passing through the center of gravity of the body, d = distance between the axes, k and $\bar{k}$ = the radii of gyration with respect to the same axes respectively, and m = mass of the body; then

$$I = \bar{I} + md^2 \quad \text{and} \quad k^2 = \bar{k}^2 + d^2$$

Rotated Axes Theorems. Let I_x, I_y, and I_z denote the moments of inertia of a body with respect to rectangular axes x, y, and z respectively; U_{xy}, U_{yz}, and U_{zx} its products of inertia with respect to yz and zx planes, zx and xy planes, and xy and yz planes respectively; I the moment of inertia of the body with respect to a line through the origin of coordinates having direction-angles α, β, and γ; then

$$I = I_x \cos^2 \alpha + I_y \cos^2 \beta + I_z \cos^2 \gamma - 2U_{yz} \cos \beta \cos \gamma - 2U_{zx} \cos \gamma \cos \alpha - 2U_{xy} \cos \alpha \cos \beta$$

If $U_{xy} = U_{yz} = 0$, the y axis is a principal axis at the origin.
If $U_{yz} = U_{zx} = 0$, the z axis is a principal axis at the origin.
If $U_{zx} = U_{xy} = 0$, the x axis is a principal axis at the origin.

If a homogeneous body has a plane of symmetry, any perpendicular to the plane is a principal axis of the body at the point where the line pierces the plane. If it has two planes of symmetry at right angles to each other, their intersection is a principal axis at any point of the intersection, the other two being in the planes of symmetry. If it has three planes of symmetry, their lines of intersection are the central principal axes of the body.

---

* Strictly speaking, this is the moment of inertia of the *mass* of a body. If m be replaced by w = weight, the result is the moment of inertia of the *weight* of a body.

† Moment of inertia is always positive and never zero. Product of inertia may be positive, zero, or negative, depending upon the distribution of the mass with respect to the coordinate planes. If a body has a plane of symmetry, its product of inertia with respect to that plane and one perpendicular thereto is zero.

Properties of Various Lines, Surfaces, Volumes, and Bodies

Symbols: I_i = Rectangular Moment of Inertia; k_i = Corresponding Radius of Gyration; J_O = Polar Moment of Inertia about axis through O perpendicular to plane; k_O = Corresponding Radius of Gyration; m = mass = W/g where W = weight and g = acceleration due to gravity. Moments of Inertia of bodies are given in terms of mass. For their values in terms of weight, replace m by W in the formulas.

Decimal Equivalents (*for reference*):

$\pi = 3.1416$	$\dfrac{\pi}{128} = 0.0245$	$\sqrt{10} = 3.162$	$\dfrac{1}{\sqrt{6}} = 0.408$
$\dfrac{\pi}{2} = 1.5708$		$\sqrt{12} = 3.464$	
	$\dfrac{1}{\pi} = 0.318$	$\sqrt{18} = 4.242$	$\dfrac{1}{\sqrt{8}} = 0.354$
$\dfrac{\pi}{4} = 0.7854$	$\sqrt{2} = 1.414$	$\dfrac{1}{\sqrt{2}} = 0.707$	$\dfrac{1}{\sqrt{10}} = 0.316$
$\dfrac{\pi}{8} = 0.3927$	$\sqrt{3} = 1.732$		
	$\sqrt{5} = 2.236$	$\dfrac{1}{\sqrt{3}} = 0.577$	$\dfrac{1}{\sqrt{12}} = 0.289$
$\dfrac{\pi}{32} = 0.0982$	$\sqrt{6} = 2.449$		
$\dfrac{\pi}{64} = 0.0491$	$\sqrt{8} = 2.828$	$\dfrac{1}{\sqrt{5}} = 0.447$	$\dfrac{1}{\sqrt{18}} = 0.238$

Table II.
Lines

Figure	Centroid Location
1. Any Plane Curve	C.G. is at point having coordinates $\bar{x}, \bar{y}$, where $$\bar{x} = \frac{\int x\,ds}{\text{Length}} \text{ where } ds = \sqrt{1 + \left(\frac{dy}{dx}\right)^2}\,dx$$ $$\bar{y} = \frac{\int y\,ds}{\text{Length}} \text{ where } ds = \sqrt{1 + \left(\frac{dx}{dy}\right)^2}\,dy$$
2. Circular Arc	C.G. is on axis of symmetry at $$\bar{x} = \frac{r \sin \alpha}{\alpha} = \frac{rc}{s}. \text{ If } \alpha \text{ is small, distance from C.G. to chord} =$$ approx. $\dfrac{2h}{3}$. (Error is small even for $\alpha = 45°$) *For semi-circle:* $\bar{x} = \dfrac{2r}{\pi}$ *For quadrant:* $\bar{x} = \dfrac{2r\sqrt{2}}{\pi}$, and distance from radius drawn to either end of arc $= \dfrac{2r}{\pi}$.

Plane Surfaces

Figure	Centroid Location; Moments of Inertia; Radii of Gyration
3. Any Plane Surface	C.G. is at point having coordinates $\bar{x}, \bar{y}$, where $$\bar{x} = \frac{\int\int x\,dx\,dy}{\text{Area}} = \frac{\int\int \rho^2 \cos\theta\,d\rho\,d\theta}{\text{Area}};$$ $$\bar{y} = \frac{\int\int y\,dx\,dy}{\text{Area}} = \frac{\int\int \rho^2 \sin\theta\,d\rho\,d\theta}{\text{Area}}$$ $$I_x = \int\int y^2\,dx\,dy; \quad I_y = \int\int x^2\,dx\,dy; \quad J_O = \int\int \rho^3\,d\rho\,d\theta = I_x + I_y$$ $$k_x = \sqrt{\frac{I_x}{\text{Area}}}; \quad k_y = \sqrt{\frac{I_y}{\text{Area}}}; \quad k_O = \sqrt{\frac{J_O}{\text{Area}}} = \sqrt{\frac{I_x + I_y}{\text{Area}}}$$

Table II (*Continued*)

Plane Surfaces (*Continued*)

Figure	Centroid Location; Moments of Inertia; Radii of Gyration

4. Triangle

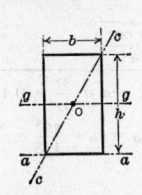

C.G. is at O = intersection of medians.

Perpendicular distance from $a-a = \dfrac{h}{3}$.

$$I_g = \frac{bh^3}{36}; \quad I_a = \frac{bh^3}{12}; \quad I_c = \frac{bh^3}{4}$$

$$k_g = \frac{h}{3\sqrt{2}}; \quad k_a = \frac{h}{\sqrt{6}}; \quad k_c = \frac{h}{\sqrt{2}}$$

5. Solid Rectangle (or Square)

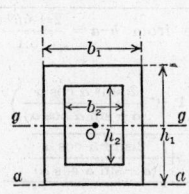

C.G. is at O = intersection of diagonals.

For Rectangle:

$$I_g = \frac{bh^3}{12}; \quad I_a = \frac{bh^3}{3}; \quad I_c = \frac{b^3h^3}{6(b^2+h^2)}; \quad J_o = \frac{bh(b^2+h^2)}{12}$$

$$k_g = \frac{h}{2\sqrt{3}}; \quad k_a = \frac{h}{\sqrt{3}}; \quad k_c = \frac{bh}{\sqrt{6(b^2+h^2)}}; \quad k_o = \sqrt{\frac{b^2+h^2}{12}}$$

For Square (letting $b = h = s$):

$$I_g = \frac{s^4}{12}; \quad I_a = \frac{s^4}{3}; \quad I_c = \frac{s^4}{12}; \quad J_o = \frac{s^4}{6}$$

$$k_g = \frac{s}{2\sqrt{3}}; \quad k_a = \frac{s}{\sqrt{3}}; \quad k_c = \frac{s}{2\sqrt{3}}; \quad k_o = \frac{s}{\sqrt{6}}$$

6. Hollow Rectangle (or Square)

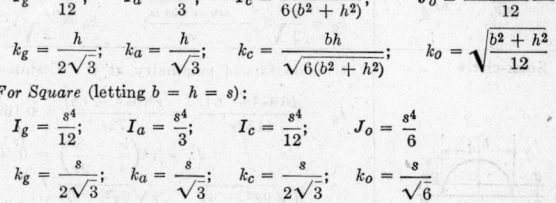

C.G. is at O = intersection of diagonals.

For Hollow Rectangle:

$$I_g = \frac{b_1 h_1^3 - b_2 h_2^3}{12}; \quad I_a = \frac{b_1 h_1^3}{3} - \frac{b_2 h_2(3h_1^2 + h_2^2)}{12}$$

$$k_g = \sqrt{\frac{b_1 h_1^3 - b_2 h_2^3}{12(b_1 h_1 - b_2 h_2)}}; \quad J_o = \frac{b_1 h_1(b_1^2 + h_1^2) - b_2 h_2(b_2^2 + h_2^2)}{12}$$

For Hollow Square (letting $b_1 = h_1 = s_1$ and $b_2 = h_2 = s_2$):

$$I_g = \frac{s_1^4 - s_2^4}{12}; \quad I_a = \frac{s_1^4}{3} - \frac{s_2^2(3s_1^2 + s_2^2)}{12}$$

$$k_g = \sqrt{\frac{s_1^2 + s_2^2}{12}}; \quad J_o = \frac{s_1^4 - s_2^4}{6}$$

(Note: For a diagonal $c-c$, $I_c = I_g$ and $k_c = k_g$)

7. Trapezoid

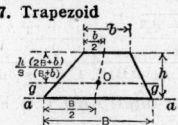

C.G. is at O, located as shown.

$$I_g = \frac{h^3(B^2 + 4Bb + b^2)}{36(B+b)}; \quad I_a = \frac{h^3(B + 3b)}{12}$$

$$k_g = \frac{h\sqrt{2(B^2 + 4Bb + b^2)}}{6(B+b)}; \quad k_a = \frac{h}{\sqrt{6}}\sqrt{\frac{B+3b}{B+b}}$$

8. Quadrilateral

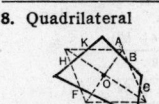

C.G. is at O, located as follows:

Divide the sides into thirds and construct the parallelogram with sides passing through the third-points as shown. The intersection of the diagonals of this parallelogram is the desired centroid.

9. Regular Polygon

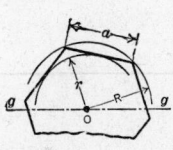

C.G. is at O = geometrical center.

Let $g-g$ be any axis through O and in plane of polygon. Then

$$I_g = \frac{\text{Area} \cdot (6R^2 - a^2)}{24} = \frac{\text{Area} \cdot (12r^2 + a^2)}{48};$$

$$J_o = \frac{\text{Area} \cdot (6R^2 - a^2)}{12} = \frac{\text{Area} \cdot (12r^2 + a^2)}{24}$$

$$k_g = \sqrt{\frac{6R^2 - a^2}{24}} = \sqrt{\frac{12r^2 + a^2}{48}};$$

$$k_o = \sqrt{\frac{6R^2 - a^2}{12}} = \sqrt{\frac{12r^2 + a^2}{24}}$$

Table II (*Continued*)

Plane Surfaces (*Continued*)

Figure	Centroid Location; Moments of Inertia; Radii of Gyration
10. Circle	C.G. is at O = geometrical center. $$I_g = \frac{\pi r^4}{4} = \frac{\pi d^4}{64}; \quad J_o = \frac{\pi r^4}{2} = \frac{\pi d^4}{32}$$ $$k_g = \frac{r}{2} = \frac{d}{4}; \quad k_o = \frac{r}{\sqrt{2}} = \frac{d}{\sqrt{8}}$$
11. Circular Sector	C.G. is on axis of symmetry at O. Distance from a–$a = \frac{2r \sin \alpha}{3\alpha}$ $= \frac{2rc}{3s}$. A = area = $r^2 \alpha$ $$I_g = \frac{Ar^2}{4}\left(1 - \frac{\sin \alpha \cos \alpha}{\alpha}\right); \quad I_a = \frac{Ar^2}{4}\left(1 + \frac{\sin \alpha \cos \alpha}{\alpha}\right)$$ $$k_g = \frac{r}{2}\sqrt{1 - \frac{\sin \alpha \cos \alpha}{\alpha}}; \quad k_a = \frac{r}{2}\sqrt{1 + \frac{\sin \alpha \cos \alpha}{\alpha}}$$
12. Semi-circle	C.G. is on axis of symmetry at O. Distance from a–$a = \frac{4r}{3\pi} = 0.424r$ $$I_g = \frac{d^4(9\pi^2 - 64)}{1152\pi} = \frac{r^4(9\pi^2 - 64)}{72\pi} = 0.1098r^4; \quad I_a = I_b = \frac{\pi d^4}{128} = \frac{\pi r^4}{8};$$ $$J_o = r^4\left(\frac{\pi}{4} - \frac{8}{9\pi}\right) = 0.5025r^4$$ $$k_g = \frac{d\sqrt{9\pi^2 - 64}}{12\pi} = \frac{r\sqrt{9\pi^2 - 64}}{6\pi} = 0.264r; \quad k_a = k_b = \frac{d}{4} = \frac{r}{2};$$ $$k_o = r\sqrt{\frac{1}{2} - \frac{16}{9\pi^2}} = 0.566r$$
13. Circular Segment	C.G. is on axis of symmetry at O. Distance from a–$a = \frac{2r^3 \sin^3 \alpha}{3A}$ $= \frac{c^3}{12A}$ where A = area = $\frac{r^2(2\alpha - \sin 2\alpha)}{2}$. $$I_g = \frac{Ar^2}{4}\left(1 - \frac{2\sin^3 \alpha \cos \alpha}{3(\alpha - \sin \alpha \cos \alpha)}\right); \quad I_a = \frac{Ar^2}{4}\left(1 + \frac{2\sin^3 \alpha \cos \alpha}{(\alpha - \sin \alpha \cos \alpha)}\right)$$ $$k_g = \frac{r}{2}\sqrt{1 - \frac{2\sin^3 \alpha \cos \alpha}{3(\alpha - \sin \alpha \cos \alpha)}}; \quad k_a = \frac{r}{2}\sqrt{1 + \frac{2\sin^3 \alpha \cos \alpha}{(\alpha - \sin \alpha \cos \alpha)}}$$
14. Annulus	C.G. is at O = geometrical center. $$I_g = \frac{\pi(d_1^4 - d_2^4)}{64} = \frac{\pi(r_1^4 - r_2^4)}{4}; \quad J_o = \frac{\pi(d_1^4 - d_2^4)}{32} = \frac{\pi(r_1^4 - r_2^4)}{2}$$ $$k_g = \frac{\sqrt{d_1^2 + d_2^2}}{4} = \frac{\sqrt{r_1^2 + r_2^2}}{2}; \quad k_o = \sqrt{\frac{d_1^2 + d_2^2}{8}} = \sqrt{\frac{r_1^2 + r_2^2}{2}}$$
15. Ellipse	C.G. is at O = geometrical center. *For semi-ellipse ABB′, C.G. is on* OA *at distance to right of* c–$c = \frac{4a}{3\pi}$. *For quarter-ellipse ABO, C.G. is at distance to right of* c–$c = \frac{4a}{3\pi}$ *and at distance above* g–$g = \frac{4b}{3\pi}$. A = area = πab $$I_g = \frac{\pi ab^3}{4} = \frac{Ab^2}{4}; \quad I_c = \frac{\pi a^3 b}{4} = \frac{Aa^2}{4}; \quad J_o = \frac{A(a^2 + b^2)}{4}$$ $$k_g = \frac{b}{2}; \quad k_c = \frac{a}{2}; \quad k_o = \frac{\sqrt{a^2 + b^2}}{2}$$
16. Parabolic Segment	C.G. is on axis of symmetry at O. Distance from c–$c = \frac{3a}{5}$. $$I_g = \frac{4ab^3}{15}; \quad I_c = \frac{4a^3 b}{7}$$ $$k_g = \frac{b}{\sqrt{5}} = 0.447b; \quad k_c = a\sqrt{\frac{3}{7}} = 0.654a$$
17. Structural Shapes	See Section 1, Tables 64 to 70.

Table II (*Continued*)
Homogeneous Bodies
(Including Nonplanar Surfaces)
("Body" is to be understood unless "Surface" is indicated.)

Figure	*Centroid Location; Moments of Inertia; Radii of Gyration*
18. Any Surface or Body of Revolution 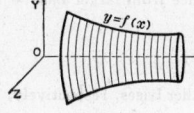	Let axis of revolution be X axis. Then generating curve is $y = f(x)$. C.G. is at point having coordinates $\bar{x}, \bar{y}, \bar{z}$. *For Surface:* $$\bar{x} = \frac{\int 2\pi xy\,ds}{\int 2\pi y\,ds} = \frac{\int xy\sqrt{1 + \left(\frac{dy}{dx}\right)^2}\,dx}{\int y\sqrt{1 + \left(\frac{dy}{dx}\right)^2}\,dx};\quad \bar{y} = 0;\quad \bar{z} = 0$$ *For Body* $\left(\text{letting } \delta = \text{density} = \frac{m}{\text{volume}}\right):$ $$\bar{x} = \frac{\int \pi xy^2\,dx}{\int \pi y^2\,dx};\quad \bar{y} = 0;\quad \bar{z} = 0.$$ $$I_x = \frac{\pi\delta}{2}\int y^4\,dx;\quad I_y = I_z = \pi\delta\int\left(\frac{y^4}{4} + x^2y^2\right)dx$$ $$k_x = \sqrt{\frac{I_x}{m}};\quad k_y = k_z = \sqrt{\frac{I_y}{m}} = \sqrt{\frac{I_z}{m}}$$ *For Thin Shell* having mass: C.G. coordinates are same as for surface. $$I_x = 2\pi\delta\int y^3\,ds = 2\pi\delta\int y^3\sqrt{1 + \left(\frac{dy}{dx}\right)^2}\,dx$$ $$k_x = \sqrt{\frac{I_x}{m}}$$
19. Thin Straight Rod 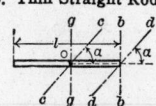	C.G. is at O = geometrical center. $$I_g = \frac{ml^2}{12};\quad I_b = \frac{ml^2}{3};\quad I_c = \frac{ml^2\sin^2\alpha}{12};\quad I_d = \frac{ml^2\sin^2\alpha}{3}$$ $$k_g = \frac{l}{\sqrt{12}};\quad k_b = \frac{l}{\sqrt{3}};\quad k_c = \frac{l\sin\alpha}{\sqrt{12}};\quad k_d = \frac{l\sin\alpha}{\sqrt{3}}$$
20. Thin Rod Bent into Circular Arc 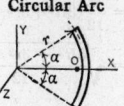	C.G. is on axis of symmetry at $\bar{x} = \frac{r\sin\alpha}{\alpha}$. $$I_x = \frac{mr^2}{2}\left(1 - \frac{\sin\alpha\cos\alpha}{\alpha}\right);\quad I_y = \frac{mr^2}{2}\left(1 + \frac{\sin\alpha\cos\alpha}{\alpha}\right);\quad I_z = mr^2$$ $$k_x = r\sqrt{\frac{1}{2} - \frac{\sin\alpha\cos\alpha}{2\alpha}};\quad k_y = r\sqrt{\frac{1}{2} + \frac{\sin\alpha\cos\alpha}{2\alpha}}\quad k_z = r$$
21. Rectangular Parallelepiped (or Cube) 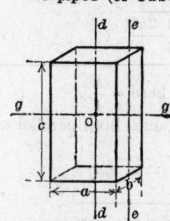	C.G. is at O = geometrical center. *For Parallelepiped:* $$I_g = \frac{m(b^2 + c^2)}{12};\quad I_d = \frac{m(a^2 + b^2)}{12};\quad I_e = \frac{m(4a^2 + b^2)}{12}$$ $$k_g = \sqrt{\frac{b^2 + c^2}{12}};\quad k_d = \sqrt{\frac{a^2 + b^2}{12}};\quad k_e = \sqrt{\frac{4a^2 + b^2}{12}}$$ *For Cube* (letting $a = b = c = s$): $$I_g = I_d = \frac{ms^2}{6};\quad I_e = \frac{5ms^2}{12}$$ $$k_g = k_d = \frac{s}{\sqrt{6}};\quad k_e = s\sqrt{\frac{5}{12}}$$
22. Right Rectangular Pyramid 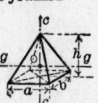	C.G. is on axis of symmetry at O. Distance from base = $\frac{h}{4}$. Drawing g-g axis through O parallel to side a: $$I_g = \frac{m}{20}\left(b^2 + \frac{3h^2}{4}\right);\qquad I_c = \frac{m}{20}(a^2 + b^2)$$ $$k_g = \sqrt{\frac{4b^2 + 3h^2}{80}};\qquad k_c = \sqrt{\frac{a^2 + b^2}{20}}$$

Table II (*Continued*)
Homogeneous Bodies (*Continued*)

Figure	*Centroid Location; Moments of Inertia; Radii of Gyration*
23. Pyramid (or Frustum of Pyramid) 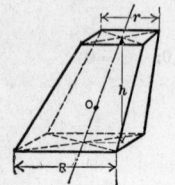	*For Surface of Any Pyramid:* C.G. of surface (base excluded) is on line joining apex with centroid of perimeter of base, at a distance two-thirds its length from the apex. *For Body of Any Pyramid:* C.G. of body is on line joining apex with centroid of base, at a distance three-fourths its length from the apex. *For Surface of Frustum of Pyramid having Regular Bases:* Letting R and r be the lengths of sides of the larger and smaller bases respectively, and h the altitude: C.G. of surface (bases excluded) is at distance from larger base $= \dfrac{h(R+2r)}{3(R+r)}$. *For Body of Frustum of Any Pyramid:* Letting A and a be the areas of the larger and smaller bases, respectively, and h the altitude: C.G. of body is at distance from larger base $= \dfrac{h(A + 2\sqrt{Aa} + 3a)}{4(A + \sqrt{Aa} + a)}$.
24. Right Elliptical Cylinder (or Circular Cylinder) 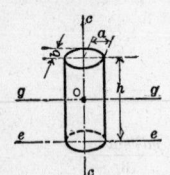	C.G. is at O = geometrical center. *For Right Elliptical Cylinder:* $I_g = \dfrac{m}{12}(3b^2 + h^2); \quad I_c = \dfrac{m}{4}(a^2 + b^2); \quad I_e = \dfrac{m}{12}(3r^2 + 4h^2)$ $k_g = \sqrt{\dfrac{3b^2 + h^2}{12}}; \quad k_c = \dfrac{\sqrt{a^2 + b^2}}{2}; \quad k_e = \sqrt{\dfrac{3r^2 + 4h^2}{12}}$ *For Right Circular Cylinder* (letting $a = b = r$): $I_g = \dfrac{m}{12}(3r^2 + h^2); \quad I_c = \dfrac{mr^2}{2}$ $k_g = \sqrt{\dfrac{3r^2 + h^2}{12}}; \quad k_c = \dfrac{r}{\sqrt{2}}$
25. Hollow Right Circular Cylinder 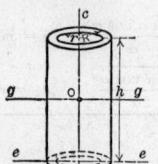	C.G. is at O = geometrical center. $I_g = \dfrac{m}{12}(3R^2 + 3r^2 + h^2); \quad I_c = \dfrac{m}{2}(R^2 + r^2); \quad I_e = \dfrac{m}{12}(3R^2 + 3r^2 + 4h^2)$ $k_g = \sqrt{\dfrac{3R^2 + 3r^2 + h^2}{12}}; \quad k_c = \sqrt{\dfrac{R^2 + r^2}{2}}; \quad k_e = \sqrt{\dfrac{3R^2 + 3r^2 + 4h^2}{12}}$ *For Thin Shell* (radius R): $I_g = \dfrac{m}{12}(6R^2 + h^2); \quad I_c = mR^2; \quad I_e = \dfrac{m}{6}(3R^2 + 2h^2)$ $k_g = \sqrt{\dfrac{6R^2 + h^2}{12}}; \quad k_c = R; \quad k_e = \sqrt{\dfrac{3R^2 + 2h^2}{6}}$
26. Right Circular Cone 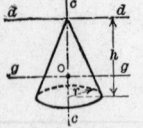	C.G. is on axis of symmetry at O. Distance from base $= \dfrac{h}{4}$. Drawing g–g axis through O and d–d axis through apex, both parallel to base: $I_g = \dfrac{3m}{20}\left(r^2 + \dfrac{h^2}{4}\right); \quad I_c = \dfrac{3mr^2}{10}; \quad I_d = \dfrac{3m}{20}(r^2 + 4h^2)$ $k_g = \sqrt{\dfrac{3}{80}(4r^2 + h^2)}; \quad k_c = \dfrac{3r}{\sqrt{30}}; \quad k_d = \sqrt{\dfrac{3}{20}(r^2 + 4h^2)}$
27. Frustum of Right Circular Cone 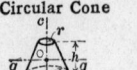	C.G. is on axis of symmetry at O. Distance from base $= \dfrac{h(R^2 + 2Rr + 3r^2)}{4(R^2 + Rr + r^2)}$. $I_c = \dfrac{3m(R^5 - r^5)}{10(R^3 - r^3)}; \quad k_c = \sqrt{\dfrac{3(R^5 - r^5)}{10(R^3 - r^3)}}$

Table II (*Continued*)

Homogeneous Bodies (*Continued*)

Figure	*Centroid Location; Moments of Inertia; Radii of Gyration*
28. Cone (or Frustum of Cone) 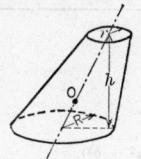	*For Surface of Any Cone:* C.G. of surface (base excluded) is on line joining apex with centroid of perimeter of base, at a distance two-thirds its length from the apex. *For Body of Any Cone:* C.G. of body is on line joining apex with centroid of base, at a distance three-fourths its length from the apex. *For Surface of Frustum of a Circular Cone:* Letting R and r be the radii of the larger and smaller bases, respectively, and h the altitude: C.G. of surface (bases excluded) is at distance from larger base $= \dfrac{h(R + 2r)}{3(R + r)}$. *For Body of Frustum of a Circular Cone:* Letting R and r be the radii of the larger and smaller bases, respectively, and h the altitude: C.G. of body is at distance from larger base $= \dfrac{h(R^2 + 2Rr + 3r^2)}{4(R^2 + Rr + r^2)}$
29. Thin Circular Lamina 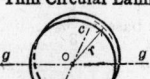	C.G. is at O = geometrical center. $I_g = \dfrac{mr^2}{4}$; $I_c = \dfrac{mr^2}{2}$ (where c–c axis is perpendicular to the plane). $k_g = \dfrac{r}{2}$; $k_c = \dfrac{r}{\sqrt{2}}$
30. Sphere 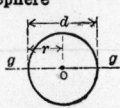	C.G. is at O = geometrical center. $I_g = \dfrac{2mr^2}{5}$ $k_g = \dfrac{2r}{\sqrt{10}}$
31. Hollow Sphere 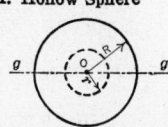	C.G. is at O = geometrical center. $I_g = \dfrac{2m}{5}\left(\dfrac{R^5 - r^5}{R^3 - r^3}\right)$; $k_g = \sqrt{\dfrac{2}{5}\left(\dfrac{R^5 - r^5}{R^3 - r^3}\right)}$ *For Thin Shell* (radius R): $I_g = \dfrac{2mR^2}{3}$; $k_g = \dfrac{2R}{\sqrt{6}}$
32. Spherical Sector 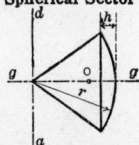	C.G. is on axis of symmetry at O. Distance from center of sphere = $\dfrac{3(2r - h)}{8}$. $I_g = \dfrac{m}{5}(3rh - h^2)$ $k_g = \sqrt{\dfrac{3rh - h^2}{5}}$
33. Hemisphere 	*For Surface:* C.G. is on axis of symmetry at distance from center of sphere = $\dfrac{r}{2}$. *For Body:* C.G. is on axis of symmetry at distance from center of sphere = $\dfrac{3r}{8}$. $I_g = \dfrac{2mr^2}{5}$; $k_g = \dfrac{2r}{\sqrt{10}}$
34. Spherical Segment 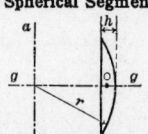	C.G. is on axis of symmetry at distance from center of sphere = $\dfrac{3(2r - h)^2}{4(3r - h)}$. $I_g = m\left(r^2 - \dfrac{3rh}{4} + \dfrac{3h^2}{20}\right)\dfrac{2h}{(3r - h)}$ $k_g = \sqrt{\left(r^2 - \dfrac{3rh}{4} + \dfrac{3h^2}{20}\right)\dfrac{2h}{3r - h}}$

Table II (*Continued*)

Homogeneous Bodies (*Continued*)

Figure	Centroid Location; Moments of Inertia; Radii of Gyration
35. Torus 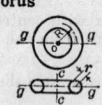	C.G. is at O = geometrical center. $$I_g = \frac{m(4R^2 + 5r^2)}{8}; \quad I_c = \frac{m(4R^2 + 3r^2)}{4}$$ $$k_g = \sqrt{\frac{4R^2 + 5r^2}{8}}; \quad k_c = \frac{\sqrt{4R^2 + 3r^2}}{2}$$
36. Ellipsoid 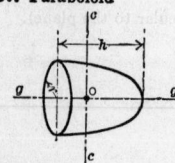	C.G. is at O = geometrical center. C.G. of *one octant* is at point having coordinates: $$\bar{x} = \frac{3a}{8}; \quad \bar{y} = \frac{3b}{8}; \quad \bar{z} = \frac{3c}{8}$$ *For Complete Ellipsoid:* $$I_x = \frac{m}{5}(b^2 + c^2); \quad I_y = \frac{m}{5}(a^2 + c^2); \quad I_z = \frac{m}{5}(a^2 + b^2)$$ $$k_x = \sqrt{\frac{b^2 + c^2}{5}}; \quad k_y = \sqrt{\frac{a^2 + c^2}{5}}; \quad k_z = \sqrt{\frac{a^2 + b^2}{5}}$$
37. Paraboloid	C.G. is on axis of symmetry at O. Distance from base = $\dfrac{h}{3}$. $$I_g = \frac{mr^2}{3}; \quad I_c = \frac{m}{18}(3r^2 + h^2)$$ $$k_g = \frac{r}{\sqrt{3}}; \quad k_c = \sqrt{\frac{3r^2 + h^2}{18}}$$

KINEMATICS

10. MOTIONS OF A PARTICLE

Motion of a Particle with respect to other particles or objects is its state of continual changing of position with respect to them.

Rectilinear Motion is motion along a straight path.

Curvilinear Motion is motion along a curved path which may be either planar or skewed.

Displacement of a Particle is its change of position and is a vector quantity. If A is the position of a particle at a time t_1, and B its position at a later time t_2, its displacement in the time interval $t_2 - t_1 = \Delta t$ is the vector AB, no matter whether the path is straight or curved.

Velocity of a Particle is its time rate of displacement (i.e., rate of change of position) and is a vector quantity. **Speed** is the magnitude of velocity without reference to direction or sense.

Acceleration of a Particle is its time rate of change of velocity and is a vector quantity.

11. RECTILINEAR MOTION

Velocity. Let s = distance measured along the path of a particle, s_1 = distance from origin at time t_1, s_2 = distance at a later time t_2, $\Delta s = s_2 - s_1 = displacement$ * in time interval $\Delta t = t_2 - t_1$. Then $average\ velocity = \Delta s/\Delta t$. If the position changes at a uniform rate (which implies no change in sense), actual velocity at any time = $\Delta s/\Delta t$.

For every case, $instantaneous\ velocity = v = \dfrac{ds}{dt} = \lim\limits_{\Delta t \to 0}\left(\dfrac{\Delta s}{\Delta t}\right)$. *Unit of Velocity* is any distance unit divided by any time unit. *Units* commonly used are feet per second and miles per hour.

Acceleration. Let v_1 = velocity of particle at time t_1, v_2 = velocity at a later time t_2, $\Delta v = v_2 - v_1$ = change in velocity in time interval $\Delta t = t_2 - t_1$. Then $average\ acceleration = \Delta v/\Delta t$. If the velocity changes at a uniform rate, the actual acceleration at any time = $\Delta v/\Delta t$. For every case, $instantaneous\ acceleration$ equals

$$a = \frac{dv}{dt} = \frac{d^2s}{dt^2} = \lim\limits_{\Delta t \to 0}\left(\frac{\Delta v}{\Delta t}\right)$$

Unit of acceleration is any velocity unit divided by any time unit. A unit commonly used is feet per second per second (i.e., ft per sec²).

Formulas for Determination of a, v, s, t. If s is given algebraically in terms of t, then v and a may be determined in terms of t by differentiation as indicated above. If a is given algebraically in terms of t, then v and s may be determined in terms of t by integration. Other relations not involving t may be determined by similar methods. The common formulas are:

$$v = \frac{ds}{dt}; \qquad a = \frac{dv}{dt} = \frac{d^2s}{dt^2}; \qquad \frac{a}{v} = \frac{dv}{ds}$$

$$s_2 - s_1 = \int_{t_1}^{t_2} v\,dt; \quad v_2 - v_1 = \int_{t_1}^{t_2} a\,dt; \quad t_2 - t_1 = \int_{s_1}^{s_2}\frac{ds}{v} = \int_{v_1}^{v_2}\frac{dv}{a}; \quad v_2{}^2 - v_1{}^2 = 2\int_{s_1}^{s_2} a\,ds$$

For Uniform Acceleration, a = constant; $v = at + v_o$; $s = 1/2 at^2 + v_o t + s_o$; $v^2 = 2a(s - s_o) + v_o{}^2$; v_o being initial velocity and s_o initial distance.

If algebraic relations between a, v, s, and t are not given but a number of pairs of corresponding values of two of the variables are known, curves may be plotted for the approximate determination of other corresponding pairs of values and of other unknowns, within the range of the data. Such curves are discussed later under "Motion Graphs."

Examples of Rectilinear Motion

Falling Body.† If a body *falls from rest* in a vacuum, $v_o = 0$, $s_o = 0$, and $a = g = 32.2$ ft per sec² (approx.). Hence $v = gt = \sqrt{2gs}$; $s = 1/2 gt^2$. If a body is *projected upward*

---

* The difference in distances along the path equals the displacement *only* when the path is a straight line. (See definition of displacement.)

† Rotation disregarded and body considered as a particle.

at an initial velocity v_o, $a = - g$ and the formulas become $v = - gt + v_o = \sqrt{-2gs + v_o{}^2}$; $s = - 1/2 gt^2 + v_ot$. Total ascent (to highest position) $= \dfrac{v_o{}^2}{2g}$, and time required $= \dfrac{v_o}{g}$.

Crank and Connecting-rod Mechanism. The problem is to find expressions for the velocity and acceleration of any point in the crosshead, as A in Fig. 1. Such a point describes rectilinear motion. Let $c = r/l$, $n = $ revolutions per second (assumed constant), $\omega = $ radians of angle described by crank per second, and $s = $ distance of A from its extreme left position, all distances expressed in feet. Then,

$$s = (l + r) - l(1 - c^2 \sin^2 \theta)^{1/2} - r \cos \theta$$

$$v = r\omega \left(\sin \theta + \frac{c \sin 2\theta}{2(1 - c^2 \sin^2 \theta)^{1/2}} \right); \quad a = r\omega^2 \left(\cos \theta + \frac{c \cos 2\theta + c^3 \sin^4 \theta}{(1 - c^2 \sin^2 \theta)^{3/2}} \right)$$

The above formulas are exact; close approximations are:

$$s = r(1 - \cos \theta) + 1/4 cr(1 - \cos 2\theta); \quad v = r\omega(\sin \theta + 1/2 c \sin 2\theta)$$

$$a = r\omega^2(\cos \theta + c \cos 2\theta)$$

Motion Graphs

Space-time, velocity-time, acceleration-time, velocity-space, acceleration-space curves for a particle are graphs showing the relations between magnitudes of s and t, v and t, a and

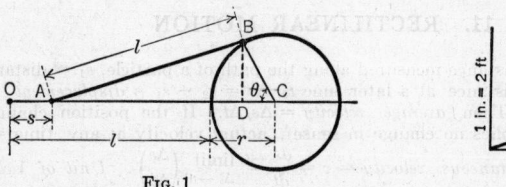

FIG. 1   FIG. 2

t, v and s, a and s, respectively. Figs. 2–6 illustrate such graphs but do not correspond to the same motion.

Space-time Diagram. In Fig. 2, the *slope* of the curve at any point represents the magnitude of the velocity. If AB and BC are measured by the s and t scales of the drawing respectively, the slope equals the velocity magnitude; thus if $AB = 0.2$ in. and $BC = 0.4$ in., $v = 0.4/4 = 0.1$ ft per sec.

Velocity-time Diagram. In Fig. 3, the *slope* of the curve at any point represents the magnitude of the acceleration.* If AB and BC are measured by the v and t scales respec-

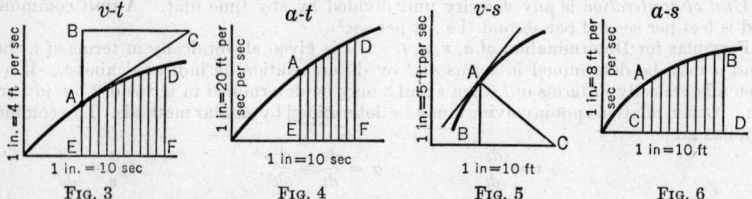

FIG. 3   FIG. 4   FIG. 5   FIG. 6

tively, the slope equals the acceleration magnitude; * thus if $AB = 0.3$ in. and $BC = 0.5$ in., $a = 1.2/5 = 0.24$ ft per sec per sec. The *area* included between any two ordinates (as AE and DF), the curve, and the t axis, represents the displacement † of the moving point in the time EF. If area is below the time axis, it is considered minus. If the area is computed by multiplying its average ordinate measured by the velocity scale (this being the average velocity) by EF measured by the time scale, the product equals the displacement; thus if the average ordinate is 0.35 in., and EF is 0.4 in., the displacement $= 1.4 \times 4 = 5.6$ ft.

Acceleration-time Diagram. In Fig. 4, the *slope* represents the rate at which the acceleration is changing.‡ The *area* (plus above and minus below time axis) included between any two ordinates (as AE and DF), the curve, and the t axis, represents the velocity change in the time EF.‡ Thus if the average ordinate is 0.3 in. and EF is 0.2 in., the velocity change $= 6 \times 2 = 12$ ft per sec.

---

* For curvilinear motion, this is tangential acceleration only.
† For curvilinear motion, this is distance along the path (not displacement).
‡ For rectilinear motion only.

Velocity-space Diagram. In Fig. 5, the subnormal represents the acceleration.* If the length of the subnormal is multiplied by the square of the velocity scale number and the product is divided by the space scale number, the result will equal the acceleration;* thus suppose that the subnormal $BC = 1/3$ in., then $a = (1/3 \times 25)/10 = 0.83$ ft per sec per sec.

Acceleration-space Diagram. In Fig. 6, the area (plus above and minus below space axis) included between two ordinates (as AC and BD), the curve, and the s axis, represents the change in the velocity square. If the area is computed by multiplying the mean ordinate measured by the acceleration scale by CD measured by the space scale, the product times two equals the change in the velocity square; thus if the average ordinate = 0.3 in., and $CD = 0.4$ in., the change = $2.4 \times 4 \times 2 = 19.2$.

Simple Harmonic Motion

Simple Harmonic Motion and Its Motion Graphs have wide application in physics and engineering. If a point P moves in a circular path of radius r at uniform speed, its projection on any diameter has *simple harmonic motion.* The radius r is called the *amplitude.* The *period* is the time required for the projection to go from one end of the diameter to the other and back. The *frequency* is the number of periods per unit time, which makes it the reciprocal of the period. Angle XOP (Fig. 7) (considered as less than 2π radians) is the *phase angle. The displacement* at any time is the distance of the point having simple harmonic motion from the center of its path or range.

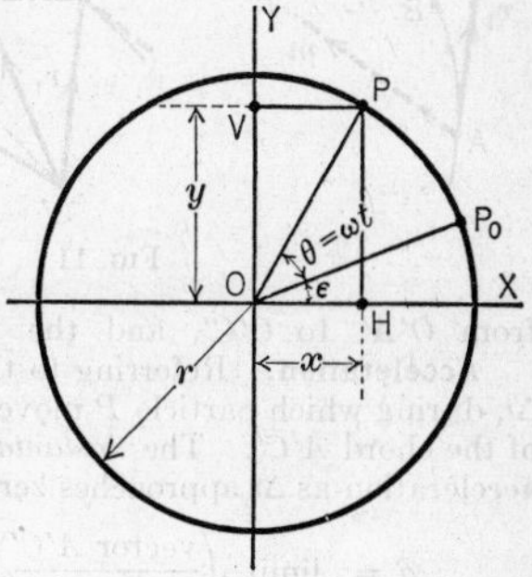

When $t = 0$, let P be at P_0. ϵ is called the *lead angle (lag, if negative).* For simple harmonic motion (*SHM*) of V in the vertical diameter, $y = r \sin(\theta + \epsilon) = r \sin(\omega t + \epsilon)$, in which $\omega = \dfrac{d\theta}{dt} =$ radians per unit time (i.e., 2π times the frequency).

$$v_y = r\omega \cos(\omega t + \epsilon) = \omega x$$
$$a_y = -r\omega^2 \sin(\omega t + \epsilon) = -\omega^2 y$$

For *SHM* of H in horizontal diameter:

$$x = r \cos(\theta + \epsilon) = r \cos(\omega t + \epsilon);^3 \quad v_x = -r\omega \sin(\omega t + \epsilon) = -\omega y$$
$$a_x = -r\omega^2 \cos(\omega t + \epsilon) = -\omega^2 x$$

If the time is reckoned from the instant when V is in its mid-position, and moving upward, $\epsilon = 0$. The three curves (Fig. 10) OA, $O'B$, and OC are the space-time, velocity-

Fig. 7

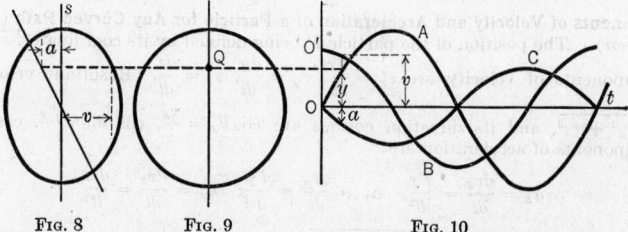

Fig. 8   Fig. 9   Fig. 10

time, and acceleration-time curves, respectively, for one complete period of a simple harmonic motion; $\epsilon = 0$; Ot represents the period; the values of y, v, and a marked are for position Q, shown. In Fig. 8 the curve is the velocity-space curve, and the inclined line the acceleration-space curve. They show how v and a vary with the displacement of the moving point; thus for the position Q, v and a have values as marked.

From the above equations and curves, it will be noted that simple harmonic motion may be defined also as any rectilinear motion in which the acceleration is always directed toward a fixed point in the path and is proportional to the distance between that point and the moving point. †

---

* For curvilinear motion, this is tangential acceleration only.
† A common example of simple harmonic motion is the motion of a weight suspended from an elastic spring.

12. CURVILINEAR MOTION

Velocity. If s is distance measured along the curved path of a particle, then the magnitude of velocity (speed) at any instant $= \dfrac{ds}{dt}$; the linear direction of the velocity is tangent to the path at the instantaneous position of the particle; and the sense of the velocity corresponds to the direction of motion of the particle at the instant.

The velocity vector changes in magnitude and direction. In Fig. 11, let A, B, C represent positions of particle P in its curved path; s, distance along the path; and v_1, v_2,

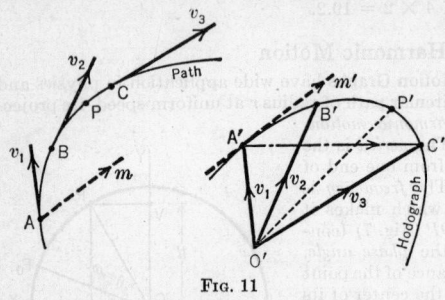

FIG. 11

v_3, velocity vectors at A, B, C. Plot velocity vectors $O'A'$, $O'B'$, $O'C'$, etc., from any origin O' to represent the velocities at A, B, C, etc. The curve $A'B'C'$, drawn through the ends of the vectors, is called a *hodograph* for the motion. For every position of P in its path there is a corresponding position P' in the hodograph; and P' describes distance s' on the hodograph while P describes distance s on the path. Vector $O'P'$ represents the velocity of P. In time Δt, P moves from A to C, its velocity changes from $O'A'$ to $O'C'$, and the velocity change is $A'C'$.

Acceleration. Referring to the hodograph (Fig. 11), *average acceleration* for interval Δt, during which particle P moves from A to C, is vector $A'C'/\Delta t$, and it has the direction of the chord $A'C'$. The *instantaneous acceleration* of P at $A = a = $ limit of the average acceleration as Δt approaches zero.

$$a = \lim_{\Delta t \to 0} \left(\frac{\text{vector } A'C'}{\Delta t} \right) = \lim_{\Delta t \to 0} = \left(\frac{\text{arc } A'B'C'}{\Delta t} \right) = \frac{ds'}{dt} = \text{speed of } P'$$

on hodograph. The direction of a is along the tangent $A'm'$, and as P' is moving clockwise, the sense is as indicated by arrow at m'. Hence acceleration at A is Am, parallel to $A'M'$ and $= \dfrac{ds'}{dt}$. Its tangential component is $\dfrac{ds}{dt}$, and its normal component is $\dfrac{v^2}{\rho}$, ρ being the radius of curvature at A. *Unit of acceleration* is any velocity unit divided by any time unit.

Components of Velocity and Acceleration

Components of Velocity and Acceleration of a Particle for Any Curved Path (*not necessarily planar*). The position of the particle P being defined by its coordinates, x, y, z, the axial components of velocity are $v_x = \dfrac{dx}{dt}$, $v_y = \dfrac{dy}{dt}$, $v_z = \dfrac{dz}{dt}$. Resultant velocity $v = \sqrt{v_x^2 + v_y^2 + v_z^2}$, and its direction cosines are $\cos \theta_x = \dfrac{v_x}{v}$, $\cos \theta_y = \dfrac{v_y}{v}$, $\cos \theta_z = \dfrac{v_z}{v}$. Axial components of acceleration are:

$$a_x = \frac{dv_x}{dt} = \frac{d^2x}{dt^2}; \quad a_y = \frac{dv_y}{dt} = \frac{d^2y}{dt^2}; \quad a_z = \frac{dv_z}{dt} = \frac{d^2z}{dt^2}$$

Resultant acceleration $a = \sqrt{a_x^2 + a_y^2 + a_z^2}$; and its direction cosines are:

$$\cos \phi_x = \frac{a_x}{a}; \quad \cos \phi_y = \frac{a_y}{a}; \quad \cos \phi_z = \frac{a_z}{a}$$

The tangential and normal components of acceleration are $a_t = \dfrac{dv}{dt} = \dfrac{d^2s}{dt^2}$, and $a_n = \dfrac{v^2}{\rho}$.

ρ being the radius of curvature. Resultant acceleration is

$$a = \sqrt{a_t^2 + a_n^2} = \sqrt{a_x^2 + a_y^2 + a_z^2}$$

If the path is a plane curve, $v_z = 0$ and $a_z = 0$.

The above discussion shows that velocities and accelerations (like forces) may be composed or resolved according to the parallelogram and parallelepipedon laws.

Motion of a Projectile

Projectile* Describing Plane Curvilinear Motion. In the following formulas air resistance is neglected; v_o = velocity of projection; θ = angle of projection (Fig. 12); x and y = coordinates of the projectile at any time t after projection; v = velocity; v_x and v_y = x and y components respectively of v; r = range on the horizontal plane through O; θ_1 = value of θ for maximum r; h = greatest height attained; and T = time of flight. The path of the projectile, or the trajectory, is a parabola as represented, and a set of parametric equations for it are:

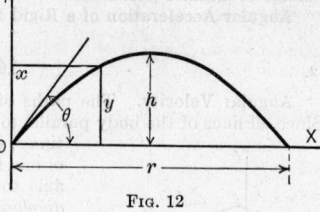

Fig. 12

$$x = v_o \cos \theta \cdot t, \quad y = v_o \sin \theta \cdot t - 1/2\, g t^2$$

from which
$$y = x \tan \theta - g x^2 / 2 v_o{}^2 \cos {}^2\theta$$

Also:

$$v_x = v_o \cos \theta; \quad v_y = v_o \sin \theta - gt; \quad v = \sqrt{v_o{}^2 - 2gy}; \quad h = \sin^2 \theta \cdot v_o{}^2 / 2g;$$

$$r = \sin 2\theta \cdot v_o{}^2 / g; \quad \theta_1 = 45°; \quad T = \frac{2 v_o \sin \theta}{g}$$

If the direction of projection is horizontal, $\theta = 0$; the equation of the path is $y = - g x^2 / 2 v_o{}^2$; and $x = v_o t$, and $y = - 1/2\, g t^2$.

The fact that the horizontal component of velocity is constant indicates that the hodograph of the motion of a projectile is a straight vertical line.

Motion Graphs

Motion Graphs similar to those previously discussed for rectilinear motion may be constructed for curvilinear motion of a particle. Great care must be exercised, however, in interpreting the significance of slopes, areas, and subnormals when acceleration or distance is involved. In this connection, reference should be made to the footnotes referred to in the previous discussion.

In general, accelerations obtained are tangential components only, while "displacements" must be replaced by "distances along the curve." Thus, in the velocity-time graph (Art. 11, Fig. 3), the slope of the curve represents the magnitude of the *tangential component* of the acceleration,† while the area under the curve represents the *distance along* the curve.

13. MOTIONS OF A BODY

Translation of a Rigid Body is a motion such that each straight line in it remains fixed in direction. The *paths* of all particles of the body are exactly alike, straight or curved (not necessarily plane curves); the *displacements* of all particles during a given time are the same; the *velocities* of all particles at any instant are the same; and their *accelerations* at any instant are the same. For these reasons, it is customary to use the expressions "velocity of the body" and "acceleration of the body." The motion is described by the same formulas as those previously derived for rectilinear and curvilinear motions of a particle.

Rotation of a Rigid Body is a motion such that one line of the body, or of its extension, remains fixed. The fixed line is the *axis*. The plane through the mass center perpendicular to the axis is the *plane of rotation*.

Plane Motion of a Rigid Body is a motion such that each particle of the body moves in a plane at a constant distance from a fixed plane through the mass center (called the *plane of motion*), while each line of the body parallel to the plane of motion turns through the same angle in the same time interval.

Three-dimensional Motion of a Rigid Body is a term covering all types of motion in three-dimensional space, including pure translation along a skewed curve as a special case. Even in the most general case, any three-dimensional motion of a rigid body may be regarded as consisting of two components: one, a translation equal to that of the mass center, and the other a rotation about some axis through the mass center.

---

* Rotation disregarded and body considered as a particle.

† However, if a velocity-time graph were made for motion along the hodograph of the original motion, the slope of the curve would represent the magnitude of the *total* acceleration of the original particle along the original path.

Angular Displacement of a Rigid Body is the change of angular position of any line in the plane of motion.

Angular Velocity of a Rigid Body is its time rate of angular displacement (i.e., rate of change of angular position).

Angular Acceleration of a Rigid Body is its time rate of change of angular velocity.

14. ROTATION

Angular Velocity. The paths of all particles are circles with centers on the axis. Since all lines of the body parallel to the plane of rotation sweep out equal angles in equal

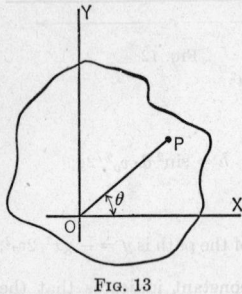

FIG. 13

times, it is customary to describe rotation by the behavior of one radial line. In Fig. 13, let θ be the angle from the x axis to the radial line OP. $\Delta\theta = \theta_2 - \theta_1$ is the *angular displacement* of the body in the time $\Delta t = t_2 - t_1$, and is expressed in any angular unit. *Average angular velocity* = $\dfrac{\theta_2 - \theta_1}{t_2 - t_1} = \dfrac{\Delta\theta}{\Delta t}$. If the angle changes at a uniform rate, actual velocity at any time = $\Delta\theta/\Delta t$. For every case, the *instantaneous angular velocity* = $\omega = \lim\limits_{\Delta t \to 0}\left(\dfrac{\Delta\theta}{\Delta t}\right) = \dfrac{d\theta}{dt}$. The sign depends on the numerator of the fraction, or the way in which θ is changing. The *unit of angular velocity* is any angular displacement unit divided by any time unit, such as radians per sec, rev per min, etc.

Angular Acceleration. *Average angular acceleration* = $\dfrac{\omega_2 - \omega_1}{t_2 - t_1} = \dfrac{\Delta\omega}{\Delta t}$. If the angular velocity changes at a uniform rate, actual angular acceleration at any time = $\Delta\omega/\Delta t$. For every case, the *instantaneous angular acceleration* = $\alpha = \lim\limits_{\Delta t \to 0}\left(\dfrac{\Delta\omega}{\Delta t}\right) = \dfrac{d\omega}{dt} = \dfrac{d^2\theta}{dt^2}$. The sign of α depends on the numerator of the fraction, or on the way in which ω is changing. The *unit of angular acceleration* is any angular velocity unit divided by any time unit, as radians per sec per sec (i.e., radians per sec²), etc.

Formulas for Determination of α, ω, θ, t. The formulas are exactly analogous to those previously derived for rectilinear motion, a, v, and s being replaced by α, ω and θ, respectively. The formulas are:

$$\omega = \frac{d\theta}{dt}; \qquad \alpha = \frac{d\omega}{dt} = \frac{d^2\theta}{dt^2}; \qquad \frac{\alpha}{\omega} = \frac{d\omega}{d\theta}$$

$$\theta_2 - \theta_1 = \int_{t_1}^{t_2}\omega dt; \;\; \omega_2 - \omega_1 = \int_{t_1}^{t_2}\alpha dt; \;\; t_2 - t_1 = \int_{\theta_1}^{\theta_2}\frac{d\theta}{w} = \int_{\omega_1}^{\omega_2}\frac{dw}{\alpha}; \;\; \omega_2^2 - \omega_1^2 = 2\int_{\theta_1}^{\theta_2}\alpha d\theta$$

Relations between Rectilinear and Angular Velocities and Accelerations. Let ω and α, respectively, be instantaneous angular velocity and acceleration of a rotating body, and v and a the corresponding instantaneous rectilinear velocity and acceleration of a point P of the body located at distance r from the axis of rotation. Then:

$$v = r\omega; \quad a_t = r\alpha; \quad a_n = r\omega^2; \quad a = r\sqrt{\alpha^2 + \omega^4}$$

Sense of v must agree with sense of ω, and sense of a_t with sense of α. Sense of a_n is always toward axis.

Motion Graphs

Motion Graphs analogous to those previously discussed for rectilinear motion may be constructed to show the relations between angular displacement, velocity and acceleration, and time. θ, ω, and α correspond to s, v, and a, respectively.

15. PLANE MOTION

Any displacement resulting from plane motion may be accomplished by a translation of the body which will bring any one line of it, which is perpendicular to the plane of motion, into final position, followed by a rotation of the body about that line into final position. The necessary amount of translation depends on the line of the body selected as axis of the rotation; the amount of the rotation does not. **The state of motion** of a body at any instant may be regarded as consisting of two components, a translational motion and a rotational motion. Thus a plane motion may be traced by giving the history of the movement of one point of the body (called a base point) in its own curved path, and a description of the rotation of the body about the selected base point.* The point selected as base should be one for which the motion is readily specified. For a wheel rolling along a straight path, the center would be selected as a base point.

Velocity of Any Point P of the body, at any instant, with respect to a fixed point O, is the vector sum of the velocity of base point A, with respect to O, and of the velocity of P with respect to A due to rotation about A. Thus (Fig. 14) O is the fixed point, A the moving base point, and P any other point of the body at distance r from A; v_1 is velocity of A with respect to O, and $v_2 = r\omega$ is velocity of P with respect to A. Resultant velocity of P with respect to $O = v$; or $v_{P \text{ to } O} = v_{P \text{ to } A} + v_{A \text{ to } O}$.

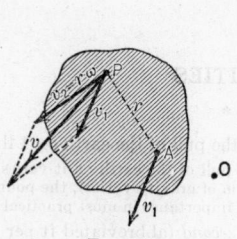

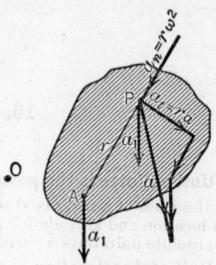

FIG. 14   FIG. 15

Acceleration of Any Point P, with respect to a fixed point O, at any instant, has two components; one is that of the base point A with respect to O, and the other that of P with respect to base A. Acceleration of P with respect to A is rotational, and is conveniently replaced by its tangential and normal components, $a_t = r\alpha$ and $a_n = r\omega^2$. Then resultant acceleration of P, with respect to O, is the vector sum of $r\alpha$, $r\omega^2$, and acceleration of A with respect to O. Thus (Fig. 15) a_1 is acceleration of A to O; and acceleration P to A is resultant of a_t and a_n. Acceleration of P to O is a = vector sum of a_1, a_t, and a_n.

Instantaneous Axis. For a body having plane motion, there is always one point in it (or in its extension), at each instant, for which the velocity with respect to A (Fig. 14) is equal and opposite to velocity of A with respect to O; that is, its velocity is zero at the instant. This point Q is called the *instantaneous (or instant) center* of rotation, and a line through Q, perpendicular to the plane of motion, is called the *instantaneous axis*. Since Q is at rest for the instant, the resultant velocities of all points at the instant are purely rotational about the instant axis. The instant center is the intersection of two lines drawn from any two points, C and D, in the plane of the motion, perpendicular to their velocities. If the velocity of the point C is known, ω for the body is determined by dividing v_C by the distance of C from Q, or by r_C. The velocity of any other point E is $\omega \times r_E$, perpendicular to the radius r_E.

The position of Q in the body (or in its extension) is continually changing; its locus is a line (usually curved) fixed in the body and moving with it, called the *body centrode*. The locus of the positions of Q in the fixed plane of motion is a line (usually curved) called the *space centrode*. The plane motion may be considered as produced by the rolling, without slipping, of the space centrode upon the body centrode.

Example: Rolling Wheel Describing Plane Motion. A wheel of 6-ft radius rolls along a straight horizontal path, and at a certain instant the point P, 2 ft from center of wheel, is in the position shown in Fig. 16a. At this instant $\omega = 16.75$ radians per sec and $\alpha = 5.6$ radians per sec². Deter-

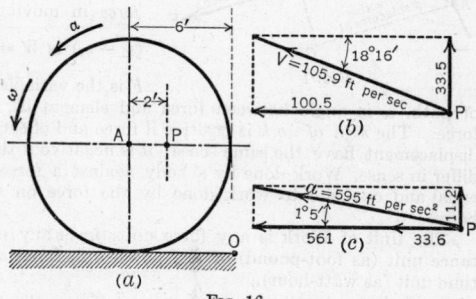

FIG. 16

---

* To simplify matters, "points" are referred to throughout this and the following discussion but "lines" through the points perpendicular to the plane of motion should be understood. Thus, in Figs. 14–15, the parallel lines through P, A, and O, perpendicular to the plane of motion, move relative to each other.

mine the velocity and acceleration of point P with respect to fixed point O at the specified instant.
Solution: Select center A as base point. From relations between v and a of any point of a rotating body, and ω and α of the body:

$v_{A \text{ to } O} = r\omega = 6 \times 16.75 = 100.5$ ft per sec, horizontally toward left.
$v_{P \text{ to } A} = r\omega = 2 \times 16.75 = 33.5$ ft per sec, vertically upward.
Therefore, $v_{P \text{ to } O} = 105.9$ ft per sec, upward to left, at $18°\ 16'$ to horizontal (Fig. 16b).
$a_{A \text{ to } O} = r\alpha = 6 \times 5.6 = 33.6$ ft per sec^2, horizontally toward left.
$a_{tP \text{ to } A} = r\alpha = 2 \times 5.6 = 11.2$ ft per sec^2, vertically upward.
$a_{nP \text{ to } A} = rw^2 = 2 \times (16.75)^2 = 561$ ft per sec^2, horizontally toward left.
Therefore, $a_{P \text{ to } O} = 595$ ft per sec^2, upward to left, at $1°\ 5'$ to horizontal (Fig. 16c).

KINETICS

16. BASIC QUANTITIES

System of Units *

The Unit of Force is the *pound* of force and equals the pull of the earth on 1 lb of mass.

Since the mass of a body is absolutely constant but the pull of the earth on it varies with geographical location and altitude (i.e., varies as the acceleration of gravity varies), the pound of force is not an absolute unit, but its variation is too slight to be of importance in most practical problems.

The Unit of Acceleration is the *foot per second per second* (abbreviated ft per sec^2).

The Unit of Mass is the *slug* and equals the mass to which an acceleration of 1 ft per sec^2 would be given by the application of a 1-lb force. Unlike the pound of mass, it is not an absolute unit. Under standard conditions, 1 slug of mass = 32.1739 lb of mass (approx.).

The Relation between Force, Mass, and Acceleration of a particle, using the above system of units, is expressed by the formula $F = ma$ $\left(\text{or } F = \dfrac{W}{g} a\right)$, where F = force in pounds, m = mass in slugs (= weight W in pounds divided by acceleration of gravity in feet per second per second), and a = acceleration in the direction of the force in feet per second per second.†

17. DERIVED QUANTITIES AND RELATIONS

Work, Power, and Energy

Work of a Force, if constant, is the product of the force and the effective displacement of its application point. *Effective displacement* of application point is the component of

FIG. 1

the displacement parallel to the force. The body exerting the force is also said to do work. In Fig. 1, the work of force F as application point describes path $AB = F \times AC$. Since $F \cdot (AB \cos \alpha) = (F \cos \alpha) \cdot AB$, the work is also equal to displacement of application point times component of force parallel to the displacement. *Work of a variable force* in moving a body through distance $\Delta S = (s_2 - s_1)$ is $W = \displaystyle\int_{s_1}^{s_2} F \cos \alpha\, ds = \int_{s_1}^{s_2} F_t ds$, in which

F is the variable force, ds is the elementary length of path, α is angle between force and element ds, and F_t is tangential component of force. The *sign of work* is positive if force and effective displacement have the same sense; it is negative if they differ in sense. Work done by a body against a force is equal and opposite to work done by the force on the body.

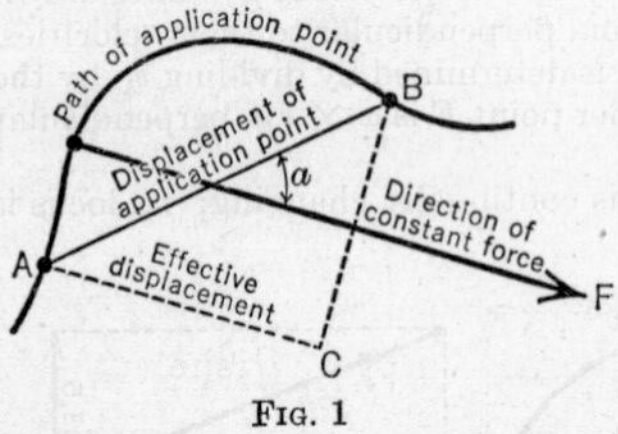

The Unit of Work is any force unit times any distance unit (as foot-pound) or any power unit times any time unit (as watt-hour).

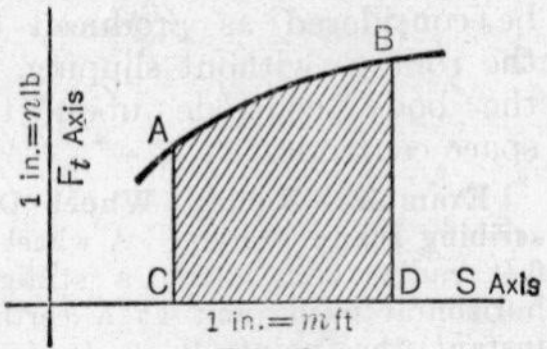

FIG. 2

Work Diagram (Fig. 2). Plot values of F_t as ordinates; corresponding values of s as abscissas; draw curve AB through ends of ordinates. Area $ABDC$ times mn equals work, in foot-pounds, done by F_t over distance $s_2 - s_1$.

---

* The units herein defined are those of the English gravitational system. For a complete discussion of English and metric gravitational and absolute units, see Sec. III.
† With any system of units, $F = Kma$, where K is a constant. In this system $K = 1$.

Work of Gravity on a body in any motion equals product of weight and change in height of the mass center. *Work of a central force F* (one always directed toward a fixed point), in any displacement of its application point, is $\int_{r_1}^{r_2} F\,dr$, in which r_2 and r_1 are the distances of the application point from the center at the beginning and end of the displacement.

Work of a Torque T on a rotating body for an angular displacement of $\theta = (\theta_2 - \theta_1)$ radians is $W = \int_{\theta_1}^{\theta_2} T\,d\theta$. If T is constant, $W = T(\theta_2 - \theta_1)$.

Mechanical Efficiency of a machine is the ratio of useful output to total input of work. Let W_u = useful work performed, W_f = useless work required to overcome friction or air or any other type of resistance, W_a = work applied to the machine. Then $W_a = Wu + W_f$, and Mechanical Efficiency $= \dfrac{W_u}{W_a}$.

Power of a Force is its time rate of doing work. The body exerting the force is also said to have power. Let P = power and W = work. Then instantaneous $P = \dfrac{dW}{dt} = F_t\dfrac{ds}{dt} = F_t v$, where v is instantaneous velocity of application point of force F.

The Unit of Power is any work unit divided by any time unit (as foot-pound per second). One horsepower = 550 ft-lb per sec = 33,000 ft-lb per min = 0.7457 kilowatt.

Power of a Torque at any instant is $P = \dfrac{dW}{dt} = T\dfrac{d\theta}{dt} = T\omega$ where ω is instantaneous angular velocity of the body.

Energy * of a *body* (or system of bodies) is the amount of work it can do, by virtue of its motion or position, against forces applied to it, while changing to a standard state.

Potential energy (PE) of a body is that possessed by virtue of its configuration. Thus, a body of weight W, located at a height above the earth's surface such that its mass center can descend h feet, has a potential energy $PE = Wh$.

Kinetic energy (KE) of a body is that possessed by virtue of its velocity, and the standard state is zero velocity. KE of a *body in translation* $= 1/2\,mv^2$. KE of a *rotating body* $= 1/2\,I\omega^2 = 1/2\,mk^2\omega^2$, I, k, and ω being moment of inertia, radius of gyration, and angular velocity, respectively, about axis of rotation. KE of a body having plane motion $= 1/2\,I\omega^2 = 1/2\,mk^2\omega^2 = 1/2\,m\bar{v}^2 + 1/2\,\bar{I}\omega^2$, in which I and k are referred to instantaneous axis, $\bar{v}$ = velocity of mass center, and $\bar{I}$ = moment of inertia about axis through mass center perpendicular to plane of motion. *Unit of energy* is same as unit of work. For KE in foot-pounds, use m in slugs, v in feet per second, ω in radians per second, and k in feet.

Principle of Conservation of Energy. If a body or system of bodies is isolated so that it neither receives nor gives out energy, its total store of energy, all forms included, remains constant; there may be a transfer of energy from one part of the system to another, but the total gain or loss in one part is exactly equivalent to the loss or gain in the remainder. This is the *principle of conservation of energy.*

Principle of Work and Kinetic Energy. Total work of the applied forces acting on any body, or on any system of connected bodies, equals the change in the kinetic energy of the body, or bodies. (This assumes no work converted into non-mechanical types of energy.) Work done $= \Delta KE$. ΔKE in translation $= 1/2\,m(v_2^2 - v_1^2)$, v_1 and v_2 being initial and final velocities. ΔKE in rotation $= 1/2\,I(\omega_2^2 - \omega_1^2) = 1/2\,mk^2(\omega_2^2 - \omega_1^2)$, ω_1 and ω_2 being initial and final angular velocities. In plane motion, change in KE is

$$\Delta KE = 1/2\,I(\omega_2^2 - \omega_1^2) = 1/2\,mk^2(\omega_2^2 - \omega_1^2) = 1/2\,m(\bar{v}_2^2 - \bar{v}_1^2) + 1/2\,\bar{I}(\omega_2^2 - \omega_1^2)$$

$$= 1/2\,m(\bar{v}_2^2 - \bar{v}_1^2) + 1/2\,m\bar{k}^2(\omega_2^2 - \omega_1^2)$$

in which I and k are referred to instantaneous axis, $\bar{I}$ and $\bar{k}$ to a parallel axis through mass center, and $\bar{v}$ is velocity of mass center.

Example. Water falling from a height of 120 ft at the rate of 1000 cu ft per min drives a turbine directly connected to an electric generator at 120 rpm. If the total resisting torque due to friction is 250 lb-ft, and the water leaves the turbine blades with a velocity of 15 ft per sec, find the power developed by the generator.

This is a problem in the conversion of potential energy to work which in turn is converted to useful kinetic energy, wasted kinetic energy, and wasted thermal energy, the total energy of the system of course remaining constant. Assume that 1 cu ft of water weighs 62.5 lb and $g = 32$ ft per sec.[2] In 1 min:

$$\Delta PE = Wh = 1000 \times 62.5 \times 120 = 7{,}500{,}000 \text{ ft-lb}$$

$$\text{Wasted } \Delta KE = 1/2\,mv^2 = \frac{1000 \times 62.5 \times \overline{15}^2}{2 \times 32} = 219{,}700 \text{ ft-lb}$$

---

* Mechanical energy (which includes potential and kinetic energy) is referred to in this definition. There are other forms of energy such as thermal, chemical, and electrical.

Wasted Friction (Thermal) $\Delta TE = T\theta = 250 \times 2\pi \times 120 = 188{,}500$ ft-lb

Therefore Useful $\Delta KE = \Delta PE -$ Wasted $\Delta KE -$ Wasted ΔTE

$$= 7{,}500{,}000 - 219{,}700 - 188{,}500 = 7{,}091{,}800 \text{ ft-lb}$$

$$P = 7{,}091{,}800/33{,}000 = 215 \text{ hp or } 215 \times 0.7457 = 160 \text{ kw}$$

Impulse, Momentum, and Impact

Linear Impulse of a constant force F for time $t = F \times t$. If the force varies in magnitude and direction, the impulse is computed from axial components of impulse; and the axial components of impulse are found by taking the time integrals of axial components of the force. The three axial component impulses are $\int_{t_1}^{t_2} F_x \, dt,\ \int_{t_1}^{t_2} F_y \, dt,\ \int_{t_1}^{t_2} F_z \, dt$; the resultant of these is the impulse of the force F. Impulse is a *vector quantity*; hence the impulse of the force equals the square root of the sum of the squares of the components. The direction cosines of the resultant vector are determined in the usual manner. *Unit of impulse* is any unit force times any unit time, as pound (force) seconds.

Angular Impulse of a force about a line for a time interval dt is the product of the moment of the force about the line and the time dt. If T represents the moment or torque of the force, the angular impulse for the time interval $(t_2 - t_1)$ is $\int_{t_1}^{t_2} T dt$. *Unit of angular impulse* is unit torque times unit time, as pound (force) feet seconds.

Sign of Impulse. Impulse of a force tending to increase velocity of the body to which the force is applied is positive; that which tends to decrease velocity is negative.

Linear Momentum of a *particle* is the product of its mass and velocity. It is a vector quantity and has the *sense* and *direction* of the velocity. *Unit of momentum* is the same as unit of impulse. Linear momentum of a *body* is the resultant, or vector sum, of the momentums of its particles. In any motion the linear momentum of a body is $m\bar{v}$, m being mass of the body and $\bar{v}$ the velocity of its mass center.

Angular Momentum of a *particle* about an axis is the moment of its momentum about that axis. In Fig. 3, let $mv =$ momentum of particle P. Resolve the momentum into

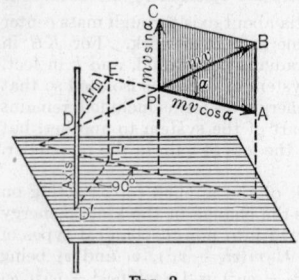

components parallel and perpendicular to the axis. DE is perpendicular distance from axis to line AP. The angular momentum of $P = mv \cos \alpha \times DE$. The angular momentum of a *body* about an axis is the algebraic sum of the angular momentums of its particles. The angular momentum of a rotating body about the axis of rotation is $I\omega = mk^2\omega$, I and k being moment of inertia and radius of gyration respectively about the axis of rotation, and ω the angular velocity. *Unit of angular momentum* is same as unit of angular impulse.

Principle of Conservation of Linear and Angular Momentum. When no external forces are acting upon a body or system of bodies, the component linear momentum along any line and the angular momentum about any line remain constant; this is the *principle of conservation of linear and angular momentum.* (This assumes no conversion of work into non-mechanical energy.)

Fig. 3

Principle of Impulse and Momentum. For *linear momentum,* the impulse of the resultant force acting for an infinitesimal time upon a body is equal to the change in linear momentum of its mass center during that time parallel to the direction of the force. Referred to coordinate axes, the change in the component of linear momentum parallel to any axis x for any length of time $t_2 - t_1$ equals the algebraic sum of the components of the impulses of the applied forces parallel to the axis in the same time, or, more briefly,

$\Delta(m\bar{v}_x) = \sum \int_{t_1}^{t_2} F_x dt$. Similarly, the change in the *angular momentum* about any axis y in the time $t_2 - t_1$ equals the algebraic sum of the angular impulses of the applied forces about the axis in the same time, or, more briefly, $\Delta(I_y\omega) = \sum \int_{t_1}^{t_2} T_y dt$.

Example. A jet of water strikes a concave vessel with a velocity of 80 ft per sec and leaves it with a velocity which has the same magnitude but makes an angle of 120° with the original direction. If the diameter of the jet is 1 in., find the force necessary to hold the vessel in position.

The sustaining force F must bisect the acute angle between the lines representing the original and final velocities. Let the line of action of F (Fig. 4) be taken as the X axis. There is no change in the Y component of momentum. The impulse of the force in the X direction in t seconds = $F \times t$ pound-seconds. The weight of water deflected in t seconds is $W = 80\pi \times 62.5t/576$ pounds. The component of original momentum in the X direction = $-80W \cos 30°/g$ pound-seconds. The component of final momentum in the X direction = $80W \cos 30°/g$ pound-seconds. The change in momentum in the X direction = $160W \cos 30°/g =$ $5W \cos 30°$ pound-seconds. The fundamental relation gives $F \times t = 5 \times 80\pi \times 62.5 \times \cos 30° \times t/576$, whence $F =$ 118 lb. Observe that the sustaining force F does no mechanical work and that the water suffers no loss of kinetic energy.

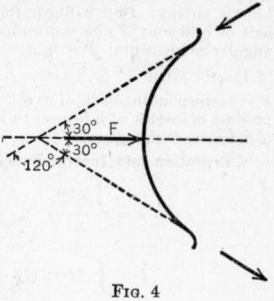

FIG. 4

Impact occurs when two bodies collide. It is *direct* when the motion is perpendicular to the striking surfaces; otherwise it is *oblique*. It is *central* if the forces which the bodies exert on each other are directed along the line joining the mass centers; otherwise it is *eccentric*. In any collision, the forces which the two bodies exert on each other are equal and opposite at each instant; hence the total impulses of these forces during the collision are equal and opposite, and according to the principle of impulse and momentum the changes in the momentums of the bodies produced by the collision must be equal and opposite; or, otherwise stated, the total momentum of the two bodies is unchanged by the collision. Or, for *direct central impact*:

$$m_1v_1 + m_2v_2 = m_1V_1 + m_2V_2$$

wherein m_1 and m_2 = the masses of the bodies, v_1 and v_2 their velocities before, and V_1 and V_2 their velocities after, the collision; but in numerical substitution, velocities in one direction are given the same sign and those in the other direction the opposite sign.

Experiments on direct central impact of spherical bodies have shown that the relative velocities of spheres after impact are always less than before the impact and that these relative velocities are opposite in direction. The ratio of the relative velocities after impact to that before impact is called *coefficient of restitution*; it seems to depend only on the material of the impinging spheres. For glass the coefficient is $15/16$, for steel and cork $5/9$, ivory $8/9$, wood about $1/2$, clay and putty 0. If e = the coefficient, then

$$(V_1 - V_2) = - e(v_1 - v_2)$$

This equation and the preceding one solved simultaneously show that

$$V_1 = v_1 - \frac{(1 + e)m_2}{m_1 + m_2}(v_1 - v_2); \quad V_2 = v_2 - \frac{(1 + e)m_1}{m_1 + m_2}(v_2 - v_1)$$

During impact there is, in general, loss of kinetic energy; * the loss is

$$1/2(v_1 - v_2)^2(1 - e^2)m_1m_2/(m_1 + m_2).$$

FIG. 5

Bodies for which $e = 0$ are said to be *inelastic*; and those for which e is nearly 1 are said to be nearly perfectly *elastic*. When a sphere is dropped on a horizontal surface of a large body from a height h, if H = the height of rebound, then $H = e^2h$. This equation furnishes a means of computing e.

Example. Ballistic Pendulum. This is a device for determining the velocity of a bullet. The bullet is imbedded in soft material, such as clay, for which $e = 0$. Referring to Fig. 5, let m_1 = mass of bullet, m_2 = mass of pendulum, k = radius of gyration about axis of suspension O, v_1 = velocity of bullet (to be determined), $v_2 = r\omega$ = velocity of bullet after impact, ω = angular velocity of pendulum after impact, and assume pendulum stationary before impact. Then angular momentum of system before impact = m_1v_1r, and angular momentum of system just after impact = $m_1r^2\omega + m_2k^2\omega$. Since total momentum of system remains constant, $m_1v_1r = m_1r^2\omega + m_2k^2\omega$. If mass center of pendulum rises to height h, $k^2\omega^2 = 2gh$. Combining last two equations to eliminate ω and solving for v_1, $v_1 = (m_1r^2 + m_2k^2)\sqrt{2gh}/m_1rk$. The quantities on the right-hand side of this equation are easily determined experimentally.

18. KINEMATIC AND KINETIC FORMULAS

Symbols. s = distance along path of motion; x, y, z = coordinates of any point; $\bar{x}, \bar{y}, \bar{z}$ = coordinates of mass center; t = time; a = resultant linear acceleration of any point; $\bar{a}$ = resultant

* As energy can be neither created nor destroyed, the total energy remains constant. The "lost" kinetic energy is simply converted into other forms, as into work done in distorting the bodies, thermal (heat) energy, etc.

linear acceleration of mass center; $a_{x,y,z}$ = components of resultant acceleration along x, y, z axes; a_t = resultant tangential acceleration of any point; a_n = resultant normal acceleration of any point; v, $\bar{v}$, $v_{x,y,z}$ = linear velocities having corresponding significances; θ = angular displacement; α = angular acceleration; ω = angular velocity; n = revolutions per unit time; r = radius (of curvature); g = acceleration of gravity = 32.2 ft per sec² (approx.); m = weight/g = mass; F = resultant force; $F_{x,y,z}$ = components of resultant force along x, y, z axes; F_t = resultant tangential force; F_n = resultant normal force; W = work; Eff = efficiency; P = power; KE = kinetic energy; Imp = linear impulse; Mom = linear momentum; T = resultant torque about axis of rotation; $T_{x,y,z}$ = torques about x, y, z axes; $Ang\ Imp$ = angular impulse; $Ang\ Mom$ = angular momentum; I = moment of inertia (for mass) about axis of rotation; $I_{x,y,z}$ = moments of inertia about x, y, z axes; $\bar{I}$ = moment of inertia about axis through mass center; $k, k_{x,y,z}$, $\bar{k}$ = corresponding radii of gyration; d = distance between axes; U = product of inertia; U_{xy} = product of inertia with respect to YOZ and ZOX planes; (U_{yz}, U_{zx} have corresponding significances); Δ indicates " change in."

Gravitation and Inertia Functions. Mass center has coordinates:

$$\bar{x} = \frac{\int x\,dm}{m}; \qquad \bar{y} = \frac{\int y\,dm}{m}; \qquad \bar{z} = \frac{\int z\,dm}{m}.$$

$$\bar{I} = \int r^2 dm; \ \bar{k} = \sqrt{\bar{I}/m}; \ I = \bar{I} + md^2; \ k = \sqrt{I/m}; \ k^2 = \bar{k}^2 + d^2;$$

$$U_{xy} = \int xy\,dm; \qquad U_{yz} = \int yz\,dm; \qquad U_{zx} = \int zx\,dm.$$

Translation—(Rectilinear Motion) *

$$v = \frac{ds}{dt}; \qquad\qquad a = \frac{dv}{dt} = \frac{d^2s}{dt^2}; \qquad\qquad \frac{a}{v} = \frac{dv}{ds};$$

$$\Delta s = \int_{t_1}^{t_2} v\,dt; \qquad \Delta v = \int_{t_1}^{t_2} a\,dt; \quad \Delta t = \int_{s_1}^{s_2}\frac{ds}{v} = \int_{v_1}^{v_2}\frac{dv}{a}; \quad \Delta v^2 = 2\int_{s_1}^{s_2} a\,ds;$$

$$F = m\bar{a}; \qquad\qquad \Delta W = \int_{s_1}^{s_2} F\,ds; \quad KE = \tfrac{1}{2}m\bar{v}^2; \qquad \Delta W = \Delta KE;$$

$$P = \frac{dW}{dt} = Fv; \qquad \Delta Imp = \int_{t_1}^{t_2} F\,dt; \ Mom = m\bar{v}; \qquad \Delta Imp = \Delta Mom.$$

Translation—(Curvilinear Motion) *

$$v = \frac{ds}{dt}; \qquad v_x = \frac{dx}{dt}; \ v_y = \frac{dy}{dt}; \ v_z = \frac{dz}{dt}; \qquad v = \sqrt{v_x{}^2 + v_y{}^2 + v_z{}^2};$$

Directional cosines of v are: $\cos\theta_x = \dfrac{v_x}{v}$; $\cos\theta_y = \dfrac{v_y}{v}$; $\cos\theta_z = \dfrac{v_z}{v}$.

$$a_x = \frac{dv_x}{dt} = \frac{d^2x}{dt^2}; \quad a_y = \frac{dv_y}{dt} = \frac{d^2y}{dt^2}; \quad a_z = \frac{dv_z}{dt} = \frac{d^2z}{dt^2}; \quad a = \sqrt{a_x{}^2 + a_y{}^2 + a_z{}^2};$$

Directional cosines of a are: $\cos\phi_x = \dfrac{a_x}{a}$; $\cos\phi_y = \dfrac{a_y}{a}$; $\cos\phi_z = \dfrac{a_z}{a}$;

$$a_t = \frac{dv}{dt} = \frac{d^2s}{dt^2}; \qquad a_n = \frac{v^2}{r}; \qquad a = \sqrt{a_t{}^2 + a_n{}^2}; \qquad \frac{a_t}{v} = \frac{dv}{ds};$$

$$\Delta s = \int_{t_1}^{t_2} v\,dt; \qquad \Delta v = \int_{t_1}^{t_2} a_t\,dt; \quad \Delta t = \int_{s_1}^{s_2}\frac{ds}{v} = \int_{v_1}^{v_2}\frac{dv}{a_t}; \quad \Delta v^2 = 2\int_{s_1}^{s_2} a_t\,ds;$$

$$F = m\bar{a}; \qquad F_x = m\bar{a}_x; \qquad F_y = m\bar{a}_y; \quad F_z = m\bar{a}_z; \quad F = \sqrt{F_x{}^2 + F_y{}^2 + F_z{}^2};$$

$$F_t = m\bar{a}_t; \qquad F_n = m\bar{a}_n; \qquad\qquad\qquad F = \sqrt{F_t{}^2 + F_n{}^2};$$

$$\Delta W = \int_{s_1}^{s_2} F_t\,ds; \qquad KE = \tfrac{1}{2}m\bar{v}^2; \qquad \Delta W = \Delta KE; \qquad P = \frac{dW}{dt} = F_t v;$$

$$\Delta Imp_x = \int_{t_1}^{t_2} F_x\,dt; \quad \Delta Imp_y = \int_{t_1}^{t_2} F_y\,dt; \quad \Delta Imp_z = \int_{t_1}^{t_2} F_z\,dt;$$

$$Imp = \sqrt{\overline{Imp_x}{}^2 + \overline{Imp_y}{}^2 + \overline{Imp_z}{}^2};$$

---

* For a rigid body in translation, accelerations and velocities of all particles are equal. However, $\bar{a}$ and $\bar{v}$ are indicated in certain of the kinetic translation formulas to make them applicable also to non-rigid bodies.

$Mom_x = m\bar{v}_x;$ $\qquad$ $Mom_y = m\bar{v}_y;$ $\qquad$ $Mom_z = m\bar{v}_z;$

$$Mom = \sqrt{Mom_x{}^2 + Mom_y{}^2 + Mom_z{}^2};$$

$\Delta Imp_x = \Delta Mom_x;$ $\quad$ $\Delta Imp_y = \Delta Mom_y;$ $\quad$ $\Delta Imp_z = \Delta Mom_z;$ $\quad$ $\Delta Imp = \Delta Mom;$

Directional Cosines of $\Delta Imp = \Delta Mom$ are: $\cos \psi_x = \dfrac{\Delta \bar{v}_x}{\Delta \bar{v}};$ $\cos \psi = \dfrac{\Delta \bar{v}_y}{\Delta \bar{v}};$ $\cos \psi_z = \dfrac{\Delta \bar{v}_z}{\Delta \bar{v}}.$

For kinetic formulas applying to a translated *body* for rotation about an axis not fixed in the body or its extension, use formulas applying to " Rotation of a *Particle* " about its axis, considering entire mass of body as concentrated at the mass center.

Rotation †

$\omega = \dfrac{d\theta}{dt};$ $\qquad\qquad$ $\alpha = \dfrac{d\omega}{dt} = \dfrac{d^2\theta}{dt^2};$ $\qquad\qquad$ $\dfrac{\alpha}{\omega} = \dfrac{d\omega}{d\theta};$

$\Delta\theta = \displaystyle\int_{t_1}^{t_2} \omega dt;$ $\qquad$ $\Delta\omega = \displaystyle\int_{t_1}^{t_2} \alpha dt;$ $\quad$ $\Delta t = \displaystyle\int_{\theta_1}^{\theta_2} \dfrac{d\theta}{\omega} = \int_{\omega_1}^{\omega_2} \dfrac{d\omega}{\alpha};$ $\quad$ $\Delta\omega^2 = 2\displaystyle\int_{\theta_1}^{\theta_2} \alpha d\theta.$

For a "Particle" ($\bar{I}$ **infinitesimal compared with I**) :

$s = r\theta;$ $\qquad\qquad$ $v = r\omega;$ $\qquad$ $a_t = r\alpha;$ $\qquad$ $a_n = r\omega^2;$ $\quad$ $a = r\sqrt{\alpha^2 + \omega^4};$

$T = F_t r = mr^2\alpha;$ $\qquad$ $F_t = mr\alpha;$ $\qquad$ $F_n = mr\omega^2;$ $F = mr\sqrt{\alpha^2 + \omega^4};$

$\Delta W = \displaystyle\int_{\theta_1}^{\theta_2} Td\theta;$ $\qquad$ $KE = 1/2\, mr^2\omega^2;$ $\qquad$ $\Delta W = \Delta KE;$ $\qquad$ $P = \dfrac{dW}{dt} = T\omega;$

$\Delta Ang\ Imp = \displaystyle\int_{t_1}^{t_2} Tdt;$ $\qquad$ $Ang\ Mom = mr^2\omega;$ $\quad$ $\Delta Ang\ Imp = \Delta Ang\ Mom.$

For a Body :

$T = I\alpha = mk^2\alpha;$ $\qquad$ $\Delta W = \displaystyle\int_{\theta_1}^{\theta_2} Td\theta;$ $\qquad$ $\Delta W = \Delta KE;$ $\quad$ $P = \dfrac{dW}{dt} = T\omega;$

$$KE = 1/2\, I\omega^2 = 1/2\, mk^2\omega^2;$$

$\Delta Ang\ Imp = \displaystyle\int_{t_1}^{t_2} Tdt;$ $\qquad$ $Ang\ Mom = I\omega = mk^2\omega;$ $\quad$ $\Delta Ang\ Imp = \Delta Ang\ Mom.$

Constrained Rotation *

Plane of rotation fixed above and parallel to horizontal XZ plane; vertical Y axis of rotation not passing through mass center (except as special case).

All previous rotation formulas apply if T is replaced by T_y. Additional formulas are:

For a Particle ($\bar{I}$ **infinitesimal compared with I**) :

$F_x = m\bar{z}\alpha - m\bar{x}\omega^2;$ $\quad$ $F_y = 0;$ $\quad$ $F_z = -m\bar{x}\alpha - m\bar{z}\omega^2;$ $\qquad$ $F = \sqrt{F_x{}^2 + F_y{}^2 + F_z{}^2};$

$T_x = F_z\bar{y} = -m\bar{x}\bar{y}\alpha - m\bar{y}\bar{z}\omega^2;$ $\quad$ $T_y = \quad F_x\bar{z} = m\bar{z}^2\alpha - m\bar{x}\bar{z}\omega^2 = mr^2\alpha$

$\qquad\qquad\qquad\qquad\qquad\qquad\qquad = -F_z\bar{x} = m\bar{x}^2\alpha + m\bar{x}\bar{z}\omega^2 = mr^2\alpha;$

$T_z = -F_x\bar{y} = -m\bar{y}\bar{z}\alpha + m\bar{x}\bar{y}\omega^2;$ $\quad$ ($\theta,\ \omega,\ \alpha$ positive for counterclockwise rotation facing origin from plus point on axis).

For a Body :

$T_x = -U_{xy}\alpha - U_{yz}\omega^2;$ $T_y = I_y\alpha;$ $T_z = -U_{yz}\alpha + U_{xy}\omega^2$ (Sign convention as above).

Center of Percussion and Center of Oscillation of a pendulum are located at distance from center of suspension $= k^2/\bar{z}$, where $\bar{z}$ is distance from center of suspension to mass center.

Plane and Three-Dimensional Motions

For Translation of Mass Center :

Consider entire mass as concentrated at mass center. Refer motion to set of fixed axes located outside the body. To determine acceleration of mass center, apply formulas for translation.

---

* In obtaining total forces and torques, effect of weight of body (this effect depending on position of plane of rotation) must not be neglected.

† Formulas are for rigid bodies.

For Rotation about Mass Center:

Consider mass center as fixed and resultant of forces as a couple. Refer motion to set of central principal axes. To determine components of angular acceleration about these axes, use formulas:

$$T_x = I_x\alpha_x + (I_z - I_y)\omega_y\omega_z; \quad T_y = I_y\alpha_y + (I_x - I_z)\omega_z\omega_x; \quad T_z = I_z\alpha_z + (I_y - I_x)\omega_x\omega_y$$

For Complete Resultant Motion:

Combine motion of translation of mass center with motion of rotation about mass center.

Work and kinetic energy changes also are equal to the respective sums of the corresponding changes under the above component motions.

19.   TRANSLATION

Kinetic Formulas for motion of translation follow directly from the kinematic formulas applying to such motion and the previous discussion on kinetic quantities and their relations. The formulas are summarized in Art. 18 (p. 4–38) under the heading "Translation." For the solution of a specific problem, careful choice of formulas will often facilitate the computations. As there is no rotation, the resultant force acts through the mass center and there is no couple.

Example. Motion of Parallel Rod of a Locomotive. The problem is to find the forces acting upon the parallel rod when it is in any position with respect to the wheels. Assume velocity of locomotive constant at 60 miles per hour on a level track; driver diameter 5.5 ft; crank length 1 ft; and weight of rod 275 lb. The forces acting on the rod are its weight and the pressures of the crank pins at its ends; the latter are represented (Fig. 6) by their horizontal and vertical components.

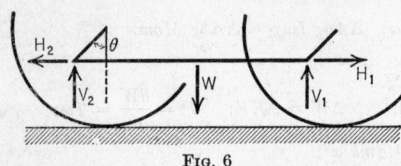

Since the resultant of all these forces acts through the mass center, $V_1 = V_2$; also $2V_1 - 275 = (W/g)a_y = 8.55a_y$ and $H_1 - H_2 = (W/g)a_x = 8.55a_x$. To determine a_x and a_y: The velocity of the center of either crank pin relative to the locomotive is $(88 \times 1)/2.75 = 32$ ft per sec (60 mi per hr = 88 ft per sec), and the relative motion of the pin being circular at constant velocity, the relative acceleration is toward the center of the crank-pin circle at all times and equals $32^2/1 =$

Fig. 6

1024 ft per sec per sec. This is also the absolute acceleration of the crank pin, since the locomotive is assumed to have no acceleration. But the rod has the same acceleration as the crank pin; hence $a_x = 1024 \sin\theta$, and $a_y = 1024 \cos\theta$. Thus $V = 1/2 (8755 \cos\theta + 275)$, and $H_1 - H_2 = 8755 \sin\theta$. In the lowest position of the rod, $\theta = 0$, $a_x = 0$, $a_y = 1024$, $H_1 = H_2$, $V = 1/2 (8755 + 275) = 4515$. In a mid-position when $\theta = 90°$, $a_x = 1024$, $a_y = 0$, $H_1 - H_2 = 8755$, and $V = 1/2 (275) = 137.5$. In the highest position, $\theta = 180°$, $a_x = 0$, $a_y = -1024$, $H_1 = H_2$, and $V = 1/2 (275 - 8755) = -4240$, the negative sign meaning that V acts downward on the rod.

20.   ROTATION

Kinetic Formulas for motion of rotation follow directly from the kinematic formulas applying to such motion and the previous discussion on kinetic quantities and their relations. The formulas are summarized in Art. 18 (p. 4–39) under the heading "Rotation." For the solution of a specific problem, careful choice of formulas will often facilitate the computations. As there is no translation, the resultant force is zero but there is a couple.

Example. A Punch is required to exert a force of 100,000 lb through a distance of $1/4$ in., and the work is to be supplied by a flywheel of radius of gyration = 1.5 ft making 120 rpm. Find the weight of the wheel, if the speed is not to be reduced below 100 rpm.

$\omega_1 = 120$ rpm $= 4\pi$ rad per sec, $\omega_2 = 100$ rpm $= (10/3)\pi$ rad per sec. Work done by punch $= 100,000/48$ lb = reduction in KE of flywheel.

Change in $KE = 1/2\, mk^2\Delta\omega^2 = W \times 2.25\ (\omega_1{}^2 - \omega_2{}^2)/64 = W \times 2.25\ (\omega_1 - \omega_2)(\omega_1 + \omega_2)/64$.

Hence $\dfrac{W \times 2.25}{64} (2\pi/3)(22\pi/3) = \dfrac{100,000}{48}$, whence $W = 1230$ lb = minimum weight of flywheel.

Constrained Rotation

Constrained Rotation refers to rotation of a body about a fixed axis which does not pass through its mass center. Such an axis, since it constrains the motion,* must be held by forces (exerted by bearings) to keep it from shifting position. These bearing reactions depend upon the weight of the body, the manner in which the mass of body is

---

* In certain cases, the "phsical path" itself constrains the rotation, as the action of the track on a train rounding a curve.

distributed about the axis, the applied forces, the angular velocity ω, and the angular acceleration α. Generally, the resultant of the applied forces for such a body is not a single force, but a single force at a selected origin and a couple. Selecting the origin on the axis of rotation, the axial components of the single force and axial components of the couple are given by the following six equations.*

$$\Sigma F_x = m\bar{z}\alpha - m\bar{x}\omega^2 \qquad \Sigma T_x = -\alpha \int xy\,dm - \omega^2 \int yz\,dm = -U_{xy}\alpha - U_{yz}\omega^2$$

$$\Sigma F_y = 0 \qquad \Sigma T_y = I_y\alpha$$

$$\Sigma F_z = -m\bar{x}\alpha - m\bar{z}\omega^2 \qquad \Sigma T_z = -\alpha \int yz\,dm + \omega^2 \int xy\,dm = -U_{yz}\alpha + U_{xy}\omega^2$$

In these equations, the axis of rotation is fundamentally the y axis; $\bar{x}$, $\bar{y}$, and $\bar{z}$ are the instantaneous coordinates of the mass center; ΣF_x, ΣF_y, ΣF_z are the sums of components of all applied forces in the axial directions; ΣT_x, ΣT_y, ΣT_z are the sums of moments of all applied forces about the axes; and the convention of signs for moments of forces, and senses of θ, ω, and α are that counterclockwise rotation, facing the origin from any plus point on an axis, is positive.

The equations are simultaneous at each instant. They are used more often to determine the forces exerted by the bearings on the axle, than to determine the resultant.

Special Cases (Fig. 7). Choose the x axis through an instantaneous location of the mass center and let XZ be a plane of symmetry of a homogeneous body. The resultant is a single force in the plane of symmetry having the Z component $-m\bar{x}\alpha$ and the X component $-m\bar{x}\omega^2$ acting at point C. $\overline{OC} = k_y^2/\bar{x}$, k_y being radius of gyration about y axis. If $\bar{x} = 0$, the resultant becomes a couple in the XZ plane, of moment $= \Sigma T_y = I_y\alpha$. If $\alpha = 0$ and $\bar{x} \neq 0$, the resultant $= -m\bar{x}\omega^2$, in the sense CO. If $\alpha = 0$ and $\bar{x} = 0$, the resultant vanishes.

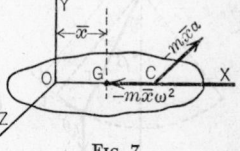

FIG. 7

Centrifugal Force. Let any particle of mass m move in a circular path of radius r about a fixed y axis. The resultant of all forces acting on the particle has a normal component $= mr\omega^2$, and a tangential component $= mr\alpha$. The component $mr\alpha$ increases or decreases the speed of the particle; the component $mr\omega^2$ continually changes the direction of the linear velocity. The resultant of such forces for all the particles of the body is equivalent to the resultant specified by the general equations above. If ω is constant and $\alpha = 0$, the resultant force acting on the particle to make it rotate in its circular path is $mr\omega^2$ toward the axis, and is called *centripetal force*. *Centrifugal force* for the particle is equal and opposite to centripetal force, and is exerted by the particle upon its neighboring particles, or upon the axis of rotation. *Centrifugal resultant* for a body is the resultant of the centrifugal forces of all its particles. Generally, this resultant is not a single force; it may be computed from the general equations by making $\alpha = 0$ and reversing senses of resultant force and couple.

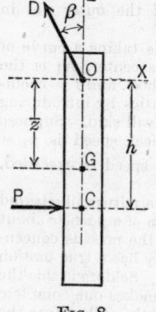

FIG. 8

Center of Percussion. A prismatic bar (Fig. 8) is suspended on a horizontal y axis at O. G is the mass center. If a force P, parallel to x axis, is applied to the body, the axle reaction OD will generally be inclined to the z axis at some angle $\pm\beta$, the angle depending on the distance h of P from the axis of rotation. If $h = k_y^2/\bar{z}$, in which k_y is radius of gyration about y axis, P will cause no x component of axle reaction; that is, β will be zero, and the point C, where the action line of P intersects OG, is the *center of percussion*. In impact-testing machines, heavy pendulums are used to deliver blows, and proper design requires the striking point to coincide with the center of percussion in order to avoid shock to the axle and detrimental vibration of the pendulum itself.

Examples of Constrained Rotation

A Simple Pendulum consists of a small heavy bob on a light string (Fig. 9).† The forces acting on it are the weight, W, and tension, T. The resultant force along the tangent $= -W\sin\theta$; the resultant force along the normal $= T - W\cos\theta$. The force equations are $Wa_t/g = -W\sin\theta$, $Wa_n/g = T - W\cos\theta$. Since $a_n = l\omega^2$, tension $T = W\left(\cos\theta + \dfrac{l\omega^2}{g}\right)$.

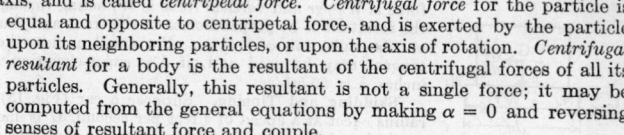

---

* In obtaining total forces and torques, effect of weight of body must not be neglected.
† Radius of gyration of bob about axis through its mass center parallel to axis of rotation is considered negligible compared with radius of its path.

To determine the motion: $a_t/g = l\alpha/g = -\sin\theta$.

The solution of this equation leads to elliptic functions. An approximate solution for small oscillations can be obtained by putting $\sin\theta = \theta$. (Difference between θ and $\sin\theta$ is less than 1 per cent if θ is less than 14°.) The differential equation becomes $\omega\,d\omega/d\theta = -g\theta/l$. If the pendulum is at the end of its swing when $t = 0$, then $\theta = \beta$, $\omega = 0$. Integrating, $\omega^2 = g(\beta^2 - \theta^2)/l$;

$\omega = \dfrac{d\theta}{dt} = \pm\sqrt{\dfrac{g}{l}(\beta^2 - \theta^2)}$. Integrating, $\theta = \beta\cos\sqrt{\dfrac{g}{l}}\,t$. Period of oscillation $= 2\pi\sqrt{\dfrac{l}{g}}$.

A **Conical Pendulum** * consists of a small heavy bob suspended from a fixed point by a light string so that it can be made to rotate about the vertical axis through the fixed point (Fig. 10). If the bob rotates with constant angular velocity, ω, the quantities ϕ, r, h are constants. Since there is no vertical acceleration, $T\cos\phi = W$. The force acting inward on the bob is $T\sin\phi$. Hence the force equation gives $T\sin\phi = Wa_n/g = Wv^2/gr$, and $\tan\phi = v^2/gr = r\omega^2/g$. Also

$h = g/\omega^2$; $T = Wl\omega^2/g$; period of one revolution $= \dfrac{2\pi}{\omega} = 2\pi\sqrt{\dfrac{h}{g}}$.

A **Compound (or Physical) Pendulum** is any rigid body suspended from a horizontal axis about which it may rotate under the action of its own weight. The forces acting on the body are its weight, acting downward at G (Fig. 11), and the reaction of the axis at O. Let $\bar{r}$ = distance OG;

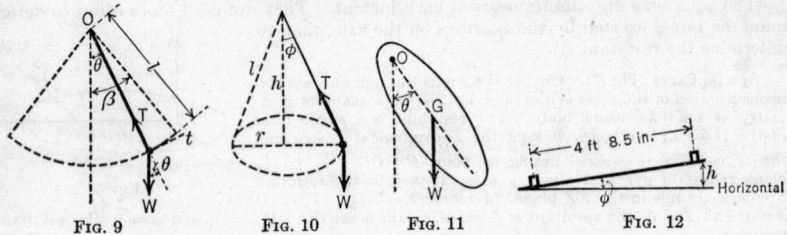

| FIG. 9 | FIG. 10 | FIG. 11 | FIG. 12 |

k = radius of gyration about O. The torque equation gives $Wk^2\alpha/g = -W\bar{r}\sin\theta$, whence $\alpha = -\dfrac{\bar{r}g}{}\sin\theta/k^2$. This is the equation of a simple pendulum (see above) of length $l = k^2/\bar{r}$ called the length of the equivalent simple pendulum. The motion of a compound pendulum is the same as the motion of the equivalent simple pendulum. The point on the compound pendulum located at the distance $k^2/\bar{r}$ from the axis of rotation is called the *center of oscillation*. It coincides with the center of percussion (see above).

Super-Elevation of Outer Rail of a Railroad Track is determined as follows (Fig. 12): Let r = radius of curvature in feet and v = speed in feet per second of car. Then horizontal centrifugal force is Wv^2/gr and vertical force is W, acting through mass center.† For the resultant to be perpendicular to the track and thus impose no side load on the rails, $\tan\phi = v^2/gr$. For small angles, the sine instead of the tangent may be used and, if h = super-elevation of the outer rail in inches, $h = 56.5v^2/gr$.

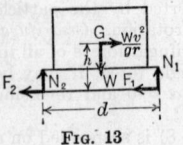

FIG. 13

Skidding and Tipping. Suppose a car (Fig. 13) is taking a curve of radius r feet at a speed of v feet per second, G is mass center, N_1 is the vertical and F_1 the horizontal pressure on the outer wheel, and f = coefficient of friction.† The problem becomes one of statics by introducing $Wv^2/gr = F_1 + F_2 = F = fW$. If $f < v^2/gr$, the car will skid. Suppose $f > v^2/gr$; then $N_1 = W(1/2 + v^2h/dgr)$, $N_2 = W(1/2 - v^2h/dgr)$. The critical speed is $v_1 = \sqrt{dgr/2h}$, when the total weight is borne on the outer wheel. If this critical speed is exceeded, the car will tip over.

Note on Use of Rotation Formulas. In practice, nearly all problems of the nature illustrated by the car problems above are solved by the use of formulas applying to rotation of a *particle* about an axis. It should be realized, however, that the assumption thus made that the mass is concentrated at the mass center is not strictly correct except in the event that the body has a true motion of translation (as exemplified by the motion of the parallel rod of a locomotive). Seldom is this the case in practice as usually every line of the body lying in the plane of motion makes one complete revolution for each revolution of the body about the center of rotation of its path. Therefore the formulas applying to rotation of a *body* are the only ones giving absolutely correct results.

For example, in the problem above on the motion of a simple pendulum, considering the path as that of the mass center, the actual torque $T = Wk^2\alpha/g$, where k is radius of gyration of bob about horizontal axis of rotation through O. Let $\bar{k}$ = radius of gyration of bob about horizontal axis through mass center parallel to axis through O. Then $k^2 = l^2 + \bar{k}^2$, and actual torque $T = W(l^2 + \bar{k}^2)\alpha/g$. But the approximate assumption made in the problem that $F_t = Wl\alpha/g$ gives $T = Wl^2\alpha/g$, which is too small by the amount $W\bar{k}^2\alpha/g$. However, when $\bar{k}$ is very small compared with l, the results obtained are sufficiently near accurate.

---

* The principle of the conical pendulum is employed in the Watt governor for steam engines.

† Radius of gyration of the car about axis through its mass center parallel to axis of rotation is considered negligible compared with radius of its path.

21. PLANE MOTION

Kinetic Formulas for plane motion are a combination of those for motions of translation and rotation. The procedure for solution of a problem is summarized in Art. 18 (p. 4–39) under the heading " Plane and Three-Dimensional Motions." The general formula given there for determination of angular accelerations reduces to $T_x = I_x \alpha = mk_x^2 \alpha$, the x axis being perpendicular to the plane of motion and passing through the mass center. The theory forming the basis for the assumptions regarding mass concentration and arrangement of forces is explained below under the general case of "Three-Dimensional Motion."

Example: Wheel on Inclined Plane. In Fig. 14, $\tan \beta = 3/4$, the wheel weighs 100 lb, diameter = 4 ft, radius of gyration = 1.6 ft. (a) Find the acceleration of the center, if the wheel rolls without slipping. (b) Find the least coefficient of friction to prevent slipping. (c) If the coefficient of friction = 0.1, find the acceleration of the center and the number of turns made while the center moves 20 ft.

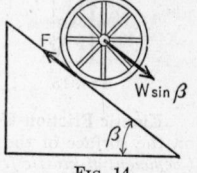

FIG. 14

(a) The forces acting to move the wheel are $W \sin \beta = 60$ lb and friction, F. The equation of motion of the center is $100a/32 = 60 - F$. The force acting to turn the wheel is F. The torque equation is $100 \times 1.6 \times 1.6\alpha/32 = 2F$. Since the wheel does not slip, $a = 2\alpha$. Elimination of F and α gives $a = 11.7$ ft per sec².

(b) Friction = min. coeff. of friction $\times$ normal pressure, or $F = fW \cos \beta = $ minimum $f \times 80$. From the equation above, $F = 23.4$ lb, whence minimum $f = 0.29$.

(c) The relation between a and α is not known when the wheel slips. $F = 80 \times 0.1 = 8$ lb. The equation of motion of the center is $100a/32 = 60 - 8 = 52$, whence $a = 16.6$ ft per sec². Distance moved by center, $x = 8.3t^2$. Time to move 20 ft is given by $t^2 = 20/8.3$. Torque equation is $100 \times 1.6 \times 1.6\alpha/32 = 2 \times 8$, whence $\alpha = 2$ rad per sec². The angle turned through, $\theta = t^2 = 20/8.3 = 2.41$ rad = 0.38 revolution.

22. THREE-DIMENSIONAL MOTION

Kinetic Formulas for three-dimensional motion are a combination of those for motions of translation and rotation. The procedure for solution of a problem is summarized in Art. 18 (p. 4–39) under the heading " Plane and Three-Dimensional Motions."

Any motion of a body may be regarded as consisting of two components: one, a translation equal to that of the mass center, and the other a rotation about some axis through the mass center. These motions may be said to be produced independently by the forces acting on the body; thus (a) the acceleration of the mass center is the same as if the whole mass were concentrated there and acted upon by forces equal in magnitude to, and the same in direction as, the actual external forces; and (b) the angular acceleration is the same as if the mass center were fixed and the actual external forces applied. The reasonableness of this will be seen from the following: imagine each force acting on the body replaced by a force acting at the mass center G and a couple (see p. 4–07); the resultant of all the forces acting at G is a single force R, and the resultant of all the couples is a single couple C; R cannot turn the body but gives it a motion of translation only, and C cannot move G but merely turns the body about some line through G. In general, C does not cause turning about a line perpendicular to the plane of C, only so if the plane of C is perpendicular to one of the principal central axes of the body. To determine the acceleration of the mass center, take fixed x, y, and z axes outside the body and resolve all external forces F_1, F_2, etc., into x, y, and z components; then

$$\Sigma F_x = m\bar{a}_x \qquad \Sigma F_y = m\bar{a}_y \qquad \Sigma F_z = m\bar{a}_z$$

m denoting the mass of the body. To determine the angular acceleration of the body, take moments of all the forces F_1, F_2, etc., about the three central principal axes; calling the sums of the moments about these axes ΣT_1, ΣT_2, and ΣT_3, the components of the angular acceleration α_1, α_2, and α_3, and the components of the angular velocity ω_1, ω_2, and ω_3, then

$$\Sigma T_1 = I_1 \alpha_1 + (I_3 - I_2)\omega_2 \omega_3; \quad \Sigma T_2 = I_2 \alpha_2 + (I_1 - I_3)\omega_3 \omega_1; \quad \Sigma T_3 = I_3 \alpha_3 + (I_2 - I_1)\omega_1 \omega_2$$

wherein I_1, I_2, and I_3 denote the three central principal moments of inertia of the body. In any motion of a body, the kinetic energy may be computed in two parts: (1) the kinetic energy of the whole body moving with a velocity equal to that of the mass center, and (2) the sum of the kinetic energies of the constituent particles of the body due to their velocities relative to an axis through the mass center.

23. FRICTION

Static and Kinetic Friction

A Smooth Surface is one which offers no resistance to the sliding of a body upon it. **A rough surface** does offer resistance to such motion. **The total reaction** (R) (Fig. 15) of the surface of one body upon another body is its resultant force. *Friction* (F) is that component of the total reaction which is tangent to the surface. *Normal reaction* (N) is that component which is normal to the surface.

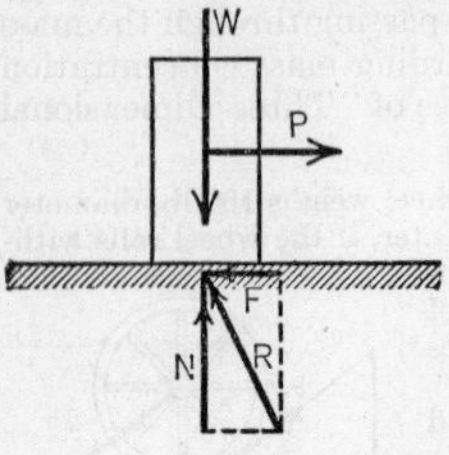

Static Friction (F) is that friction which opposes motion when there is no slipping. Its value varies as the need for it to prevent motion is developed. *Limiting friction* (F') is the value of static friction when slipping impends. *Coefficient of static friction* (f) is the ratio F'/N. *Angle of static friction* (ϕ) is defined by tan $\phi = F'/N = f$. *Angle of repose* is that angle which the surface of one body makes with the horizontal when slipping of another body upon it impends. It applies to the particular rubbing surfaces in contact. It equals the angle of static friction.

Fig. 15

Kinetic Friction (F_k) is that friction which opposes motion when one body is slipping on the surface of the other. Its value is usually less than that of the limiting friction. *Coefficient of kinetic friction* (f_k) is the ratio F_k/N. *Angle of kinetic friction* (ϕ_k) is defined by tan $\phi_k = F_k/N = f_k$.

Laws of Friction for Dry Surfaces:

1. Friction between two given bodies is directly proportional to the pressure; the coefficient of friction is constant for all pressures.

2. The coefficient and amount of friction for given pressures are independent of the area of contact.

3. The coefficient of friction is independent of the relative velocity, although static friction is greater than kinetic friction.

The preceding laws are only approximately true. The coefficient of friction is slightly greater for small pressures upon large areas than for great pressures upon small areas. The coefficient of friction decreases as the speed increases.*

Laws of Friction for Lubricated Surfaces:

The friction does not follow the laws for dry surfaces, but depends on the viscosity and thickness of the lubricant and the form of the surfaces in contact. The laws given by Goodman are:

1. The coefficient of friction of well-lubricated surfaces is from $1/16$ to $1/10$ that of dry or poorly lubricated surfaces.

2. The coefficient of friction for moderate pressures and speeds varies approximately inversely as the normal pressure; frictional resistance varies as the area of contact, normal pressure remaining the same.

3. For low speeds the coefficient of friction is abnormally high, but as the speed of the rubbing surfaces increases from about 10 to 100 ft per min, the coefficient of friction diminishes and again rises when that speed is exceeded, varying approximately as the square root of the speed.

4. The coefficient of friction varies approximately inversely as the temperature.

Coefficients of Static and Kinetic Friction are affected by the above laws of friction and also by the characters of the surfaces, the kinds of material, and the nature of any lubricant used. Rough averages for a number of materials and conditions are given in Table I, p. 4–45.†

Rolling Friction

Rolling Friction is that friction developed when one body rolls over the surface of another, and depends on the hardness of the surfaces in contact and the radius of the rolling surface. The theory is based on the idea that surfaces are slightly deformed at the place of contact and that the effect of rolling friction is the same as if the surfaces were not deformed and the rolling body passed constantly over a small obstruction. Let P (Fig. 16) be the horizontal force required to overcome the small obstruction B. Then $hP = aW$, and, since h is nearly equal to r, $P = aW/r$ (approximately). *Coefficient of rolling friction* is a, and, as an analogy with definitions of static and kinetic friction coefficients, might be defined as the ratio T_r/N, where T_r = torque resisting rolling motion and N is the normal force (in this case,

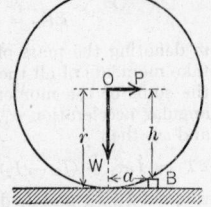

Fig. 16

---

* Recent experiments have proved also that time of contact of the surfaces affects the coefficient of static friction.
† Hudson's Manual, p. 102.

the weight of the body). The coefficient is a linear distance and is usually given in inches.

Coefficients of Rolling Friction. The following are some reported values of coefficients of rolling friction:

Lignum vitae roller on oak track...................... 0.019 in.
Elm roller on oak track............................... 0.032 in.
Cast-iron wheel (20-in. diam.) on cast-iron rail........... 0.018–0.019 in.
Railroad wheels (39.4-in. diam.) .... 0.020–0.022 in.
Iron or steel wheels on wood track..................... 0.06–0.10 in.

Table I.   Coefficients of Static and Kinetic Friction

Materials	Con-dition	Sliding Friction		Static Friction	
		ϕ	f	ϕ	f
Cast iron on cast iron or bronze......	Wet	$17\,1/4°$	0.31	....	......
Cast iron on cast iron or bronze......	Greased	$41/2°– 5\,3/4°$	0.08–0.10	$9°$	0.16
Cast iron on oak (fibers parallel).....	Dry	$16\,3/4°–26\,1/2°$	0.30–0.50	....	......
Cast iron on oak (fibers parallel).....	Wet	$12\,1/2°$	0.22	$33°$	0.65
Cast iron on oak (fibers parallel).....	Greased	$10\,3/4°$	0.19		
Earth on earth......................			......	$14°–45°$	0.25–1.0
Earth on earth (clay)...............	Damp	....	......	$45°$	1.0
Earth on earth (clay)...............	Wet	....	......	$17\,1/4°$	0.31
Hemp-rope on rough wood...........	Dry	$26\,1/2°$	0.50	$26\,1/2°–38\,3/4°$	0.50–0.80
Hemp-rope on polished wood.........	Dry	....	......	$18\,1/4°$	0.33
Leather on oak.....................	Dry	$16\,3/4°–26\,1/2°$	0.30–0.50	$26\,1/2°–31°$	0.50–0.60
Leather on cast iron................	Dry	$29\,1/4°$	0.56	$16\,3/4°–26\,1/2°$	0.30–0.50
Oak on oak (fibers parallel).........	Dry	$25\,3/4°$	0.48	$31\,3/4°$	0.62
Oak on oak (fibers crossed).........	Dry	$18\,3/4°$	0.34	$28\,1/4°$	0.54
Oak on oak (fibers crossed).........	Wet	$14°$	0.25	$35\,1/4°$	0.71
Oak on oak (fibers perpendicular)....	Dry	$10\,3/4°$	0.19	$23\,1/4°$	0.43
Steel on ice.......................	Dry	....	0.01	$1\,1/2°$	0.027
Steel on steel......................	Dry	Vel. 10 ft per sec — 0.09 Vel. 100 ft per sec — 0.03		$8\,1/2°$	0.15
Stone Masonry on concrete..........	Dry	....	......	$37\,1/4°$	0.76
Stone masonry on undisturbed ground	Dry	....	......	$33°$	0.65
Stone masonry on undisturbed ground	Wet	....	......	$16\,3/4°$	0.30
Wrought iron on wrought iron.......	Dry	$23\,3/4°$	0.44	....	......
Wrought iron on wrought iron.......	Greased	$41/2°–5\,3/4°$	0.08–0.10	$6\,1/2°$	0.11
Wrought iron on cast iron or bronze..	Dry	$10\,1/4°$	0.18	$10\,3/4°$	0.19
Wrought iron on cast iron or bronze..	Greased	....	......	$4°–4\,1/2°$	0.07–0.08

Axle Friction

Axle Friction is that friction which opposes the turning of an axle in its bearing. Its value depends on (a) the method of lubrication, (b) the lubricant, (c) its temperature, (d) the velocity of rubbing, and (e) the intensity of pressure on the bearing.

If a cylindrical axle fits loosely in a cylindrical bearing, the bearing surface will be a narrow strip or element. If the axle turns in the direction of the arrow (Fig. 17), it will rise in the bearing to some position as shown. F is friction, N normal pressure, and $R = \sqrt{F^2 + N^2} =$ resultant pressure of bearing on axle. *Coefficient of friction* (f) is the ratio F/N. *Angle of friction* (ϕ) is defined by $\tan \phi = F/N = f$. Since N and R are practically equal, we may put $N = R$, giving $F = fR$. Then the torque exerted by the bearing during each revolution of the shaft $= rfR$ pound-inches where $r =$ radius of shaft in inches. The power necessary to overcome friction when the axle makes n revolutions per second is $P = \pi nrfR/6$ foot-pounds per second.

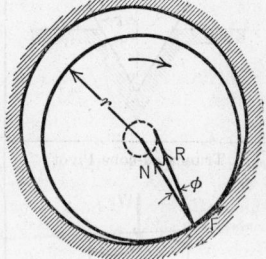

Fig. 17

Pivot Friction

Pivot Friction is that friction which opposes the turning of the end of a vertical, or inclined, shaft in its bearing. Some examples of pivot friction, with friction torque and power formulas applying, are shown in the following table:

Table II. Pivot Friction *

f = coefficient of friction. W = load in pounds.
T = torque of friction about the axis of the shaft.
r = radius in inches. n = revolutions per second.

Type of Pivot	Torque T in Pound-inches	Power P Lost by Friction in Foot-pounds per Second
Shafts and Journals (180° bearing)	$T = fWr$	$P = \dfrac{2\pi n}{12} fWr.$
Flat Pivot 	$T = {}^2/_3 fWr.$	$P = \dfrac{4\pi n}{3 \times 12} fWr$
Collar-bearing 	$T = {}^2/_3 fW \dfrac{R^3 - r^3}{R^2 - r^2}$	$P = \dfrac{4\pi n}{3 \times 12} fW \dfrac{R^3 - r^3}{R^2 - r^2}$
Conical Pivot 	$T = {}^2/_3 fW \dfrac{r}{\sin \alpha}$	$P = \dfrac{4\pi n \, fWr}{3 \times 12 \sin \alpha}$
Truncated-cone Pivot 	$T = {}^2/_3 fW \dfrac{R^3 - r^3}{(R^2 - r^2) \sin \alpha}$	$P = \dfrac{4\pi n \, fW(R^3 - r^3)}{3 \times 12 (R^2 - r^2) \sin \alpha}$

* Hudson's Manual, p. 105.

Belt or Coil Friction

Belt or Coil Friction is that friction which opposes the slipping of a belt, rope, brake band, or similar article coiled about a pulley, sheave, post, capstan, or similar device. When power is being transmitted, say by a belt driving a pulley, the tension T_1 on the driving side of the belt is greater than the tension T_2 on the driven side. Neglecting the effect of centrifugal force, which is small at low speeds, the tensions are related by the formula $T_1/T_2 = e^{f\alpha}$ where $e = 2.718 +$ (i.e., base of natural logarithms), f = coefficient of friction between belt and pulley, and α = angle of contact between belt and pulley (Fig. 18). Values of T_1/T_2 for various values of f and α are shown in the table below.

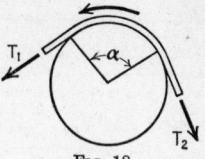

Fig. 18

Table III. Maximum Ratio T_1/T_2 (Slipping Impending)

α Radians 2π	Values of f (Coefficient of Friction)								
	0.10	0.15	0.20	0.25	0.30	0.35	0.40	0.45	0.50
0.1	1.06	1.1	1.13	1.17	1.21	1.25	1.29	1.33	1.37
0.2	1.13	1.21	1.29	1.37	1.46	1.55	1.65	1.76	1.87
0.3	1.21	1.32	1.45	1.60	1.76	1.93	2.13	2.34	2.57
0.4	1.29	1.46	1.65	1.87	2.12	2.41	2.73	3.10	3.51
0.425	1.31	1.49	1.70	1.95	2.23	2.55	2.91	3.33	3.80
0.45	1.33	1.53	1.76	2.03	2.34	2.69	3.10	3.57	4.11
0.475	1.35	1.56	1.82	2.11	2.45	2.84	3.30	3.83	4.45
0.5	1.37	1.60	1.87	2.19	2.57	3.00	3.51	4.11	4.81
0.525	1.39	1.64	1.93	2.28	2.69	3.17	3.74	4.41	5.20
0.55	1.41	1.68	2.00	2.37	2.82	3.35	3.98	4.74	5.63
0.6	1.46	1.76	2.13	2.57	3.10	3.74	4.52	5.45	6.59
0.7	1.52	1.93	2.41	3.00	3.74	4.66	5.81	7.24	9.02
0.8	1.65	2.13	2.73	3.51	4.52	5.81	7.47	9.60	12.35
0.9	1.76	2.34	3.10	4.11	5.45	7.24	9.60	12.74	16.90
1.0	1.87	2.57	3.51	4.81	6.59	9.02	12.35	16.90	23.14
1.5	2.57	4.11	6.59	10.55	16.90	27.08	43.38	69.49	111.32
2.0	3.51	6.59	12.35	23.14	43.38	81.31	152.40	285.68	535.49
2.5	4.81	10.55	23.14	50.75	111.32	244.15	535.49	1,174.5	2,575.9
3.0	6.59	16.90	43.38	111.32	285.68	733.14	1,881.5	4,828.5	12,391.
3.5	9.02	27.08	81.31	244.15	733.14	2199.9	6,610.7	19,851.	59,608.
4.0	12.35	43.38	152.40	535.49	1881.5	6610.7	23,227.	81,610.	286,744.

Power transmitted is given by $P = (T_1 - T_2)\, v$, where P is power in foot-pounds per second and v is velocity in feet per second.

Coefficients of Belt or Coil Friction. The following mean values of friction coefficients are given in Hudson's Manual, p. 106;

Table IV

Leather on wood (somewhat oily)	0.47
Leather on cast iron (somewhat oily)	0.28
Leather on cast iron (moist)	0.38
Hemp-rope on iron drum	0.25
Hemp-rope on wooden drum	0.40
Hemp-rope on polished wood	0.33
Hemp-rope on rough wood	0.50

BIBLIOGRAPHY ON THEORETICAL MECHANICS

1. BOYD, J. E., Mechanics, A Textbook for Engineers, New York, McGraw-Hill, second edition, 1930.
2. BROWN, F. L., Engineering Mechanics, New York, John Wiley & Sons, 1931.
3. ERIKSON, H. A., Elements of Mechanics, New York, McGraw-Hill, second edition, 1932.
4. JEANS, J. H., Theoretical Mechanics, New York, Ginn & Co., 1907.
5. LINDSAY, R. B., Physical Mechanics, New York, D. Van Nostrand Co., 1933.
6. MAURER, E. R., and ROARK, R. J., Theoretical Mechanics, New York, John Wiley & Sons, fifth edition, 1925.
7. MILLER, J. A., and LILLY, S. B., Analytic Mechanics, New York, Heath, 1915.
8. PLANCK, M., General Mechanics, Macmillan, 1934.
9. POORMAN, A. P., Applied Mechanics, New York, McGraw-Hill, third edition, 1930.
10. SEELY, F. B., and ENSIGN, N. E., Analytical Mechanics for Engineers, New York, John Wiley & Sons, second edition, 1933.

Belt or Coil Friction

Belt or Coil Friction is that friction which opposes the slipping of a belt, rope, brake band, or similar device coiled about a pulley, sheave, drum, capstan, or similar device. When power is being transmitted, say by a belt driving a pulley, the belt on one side is more taut than the belt on the other side.

Fig. 16

Table III. M-Ratios Ratio T_1/T_2 (Slipping Impending)

(content illegible)

SECTION 5

MECHANICS OF MATERIALS

SIMPLE STRESSES, BEAMS, COLUMNS, SHAFTS, CYLINDERS, PLATES, ROLLERS, RIVETED JOINTS AND TESTING OF MATERIALS

BY

JASPER O. DRAFFIN *

REINFORCED CONCRETE

BY

THEODORE CRANE

* The author and editor gratefully acknowledge the use of material previously prepared by Mr. Edward R. Kent and published in Kent's Mechanical Engineers' Handbook, Tenth Edition. Appreciation also is expressed to Mr. Robert Thurston Kent for his assistance and cooperation in the revision of old and the preparation of new material.

MECHANICS OF MATERIALS

SIMPLE STRESSES

By Jasper O. Draffin

1. TENSION, COMPRESSION, SHEAR

Stress or Total Stress is the resultant internal force that resists change in the size or shape of a body acted on by external forces. A change in size or shape begins when the load is applied and stops when the internal resisting stress holds the external forces in equilibrium. If the external forces acting on the body increase to the extent that the maximum stress that can be developed is unable to balance the external forces, the change in form will increase rapidly and the body will break or rupture. Stresses are measured in the same units as the forces which produce them, i.e., pounds, tons, etc.

Unit Stress or intensity of stress is defined as the stress per unit of area. Its value at any point of a section is the stress on an elementary part of the area, including the point, divided by the elementary area, and generally varies from point to point of the section. When the stress (P) is uniformly distributed over an area (A), the unit stress (s) at any point of the area is the stress on the area divided by the whole area; i.e., $s = P/A$. Unit stresses are expressed in pounds per square inch, tons per square foot, kilograms per square centimeter, and the like.

Both total stress and unit stress are often referred to simply as "stress." Confusion will be avoided if the units used are stated.

Tensile Stress or Tension is the internal force that resists the action of external forces tending to increase the length of a body. Tension is developed in a bar when the external forces act on it in the directions away from its ends. See Fig. 1. The tendency is

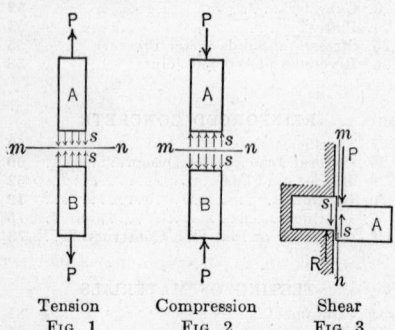

Tension	Compression	Shear
Fig. 1	Fig. 2	Fig. 3

to separate the bar into two parts, A and B. To maintain equilibrium each part is acted on at section mn by tensile stresses, s, whose resultant is equal and opposite in direction to the resultant of the external forces acting at the end of the part considered. If the forces acting on one end of the bar total 1000 lb then the stress on the section mn equals 1000 lb.

Compressive Stress or Compression is the internal force that resists the action of external forces tending to decrease the length of a body. Compression is developed in a bar when external forces act on it in the directions toward its ends. In Fig. 2, the tendency of the external forces is to shorten the bar by pushing any two parts, as A and B, closer together. As long as equilibrium is maintained, the resultant of the compressive stresses acting on either part at section mn is equal and opposite in direction to the resultant of the external forces acting at the end of the part considered.

Shearing Stress or Shear is the internal force acting along a plane between adjacent parts of a body when two equal forces parallel to the plane considered act on each part in opposite directions. The shear resists the tendency of one part to slide over the other part. In Fig. 3, the projecting part of the cantilever beam, A, is acted on by external vertical forces due to the weight of A and any loads that it carries. The resultant of these forces, P, is equal, parallel to, and opposite in general direction to the upward pressure or reaction, R, which acts on the part of the beam embedded in the wall. There exists, therefore, a tendency of the parts to assume the relative positions shown in Fig. 3. An internal force acting along the cross-section mn resists the tendency of A to slide vertically downward. This internal force is the shear acting on the cross-section. As long as equilibrium is maintained, if P equals 1000 lb, R also equals 1000 lb, and the shear acting on the section equals 1000 lb.

Simple Stress. Tension, compression, and shear are considered singly and in combination in engineering practice. When it is necessary to consider only one of these singly, the case is known as one of simple stress.

Normal Stress. A normal stress on a section is one that acts in a direction perpendicular to the section considered.

Axial Stress. Axial tension or compression exists in a straight homogeneous bar when the resultant of the applied loads coincides with the axis of the bar. The stress then is distributed uniformly over any section normal to the axis of the bar.

Axial tension is encountered in a vertical bar supported only at its upper end; the tension caused by the weight of the bar and any load carried at its lower end is uniformly distributed over the cross-section of the bar. If the resultant of the applied load does not coincide with the axis of the bar, the stress is not uniform over the cross-section of the bar. For a bar held in an inclined position, even though subjected to axial force applied at its ends, the weight of the bar itself is an external force acting on it at an angle to its axis. Therefore, this is not simple axial tension, and the stress is not uniform over a cross-section of the bar.

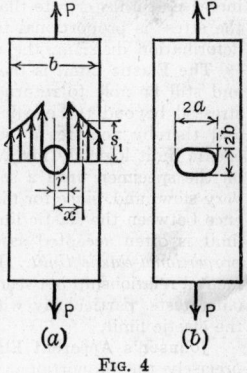

FIG. 4

Axial compression exists in a pier or prism of length not exceeding 6 to 8 times the least side or diameter, when the resultant of the load supported acts through the centers of gravity of the end sections. When the length is greater than 6 or 8 times the least side or diameter, the pier is regarded as a column in which some bending has taken place. Then the resultant of the load, though acting through the centers of gravity of the end sections, does not coincide with the axis of the column; the stresses therefore are not uniformly distributed over a cross-section and the case is not one of simple axial compression.

Effect of Notches and Holes in Members under Simple Stress. In the formula $s = P/A$, it is assumed that the stress is uniformly distributed over the cross-section of the member. But this is not true if there is any discontinuity in the cross-section, as an increase or decrease in area. In Fig. 4(a), a plate of width b, having a small hole of radius r, is subjected to an axial pull, P. The unit stress s_1, at any distance x from the center line, is given by the formula (Timoshenko and Lessells, Applied Elasticity, p. 9),

$$s_1 = \frac{s}{2}\left(2 + \frac{r^2}{x^2} + 3\frac{r^4}{x^4}\right) \tag{1}$$

where s is the unit stress, based on the load P and the area, using the full width b. Where the radius r does not exceed $b/12$, the stress $s_1 = 3s$.

For an elliptical hole of major axis $2a$ and minor axis $2b$, Fig. 4(b), the maximum unit stress is $s_1 = s(1 + 2a/b)$. Notches of small radius on opposite sides of a tension specimen produce stresses approximately twice as great as the average stress; an example of this is the common briquette used in testing cement, in which the maximum tensile unit stress at the sides is 1.75 times the average stress (Coker, *Proc.* Inter. Soc. Test. Mat., 1913).

2. DEFORMATION UNDER STRESS

Deformation is the amount of the change in the shape of a body caused by the application of external forces. When the external forces cause tension the deformation is the amount that the body is increased in length; when they cause compression, it is the amount that the body is decreased in length; when they cause shear, it is the amount that one part of the body slips over the adjacent part. The deformations accompanying tension, compression, and shear are known, respectively, as elongation, shortening, and detrusion. Deformations are measured by the same units of length used in measuring the linear dimensions of the body.

Unit Deformation, or deformation per unit of length, is determined by dividing the total amount of deformation by the original length of the body before the load causing the deformation was applied. If a steel bar 8 in. long is stretched until it becomes 8.16 in. long the total deformation, in this case elongation, is 0.16 in.; the unit deformation, ϵ, is $0.16 \div 8 = 0.02$ in. per in. of original length.

The ultimate unit deformation is the unit deformation measured after the body has ruptured; it is usually expressed as a percentage of original length. Thus, if two marks on a bar of hard steel are 2 in. apart before a test and 2.30 in. apart after rupture, the ultimate unit deformation, ϵ, is the difference between these distances divided by the original distance between the two marks: or $\epsilon = 0.30 \div 2.0 = 0.15$ in. per in. $= 15$ per cent.

Hooke's Law. It has been found by experiment that a body acted on by external forces will deform in proportion to the stress developed as long as the unit stress does not exceed a certain value, which varies for the different materials. This value is the *proportional limit*.

Stress and Strain. The word strain has been frequently used for the internal force in a body, or stress. It is present practice, however, to use the word strain as a synonym for deformation only. Thus the expression "stress and strain" is equivalent to the expression "stress and deformation." Owing to the conflicting meanings of the word strain it has been suggested that it be avoided, the word deformation being used in its place. Physicists usually define strain as the deformation per unit length.

The Proportional Limit is that unit stress at which the unit deformation begins to increase at a faster rate than does the unit stress, or it is the highest unit stress at which the stress is proportional to the deformation. It is determined by noting, on a stress-deformation diagram, the unit stress at which the curve departs from a straight line.

The Elastic Limit is the maximum unit stress to which a material may be subjected and still be able to return to its original form upon the removal of the stress. When stressed beyond the elastic limit a body will return to its original form only partially and thereby acquires a permanent deformation or "set." The determination of the elastic limit logically involves the application and release of a series of increasing loads on the specimen until a set is observed after the release of a load. This procedure is very slow; and, since for many metals experience does not indicate any significant difference between the elastic limit so determined and the proportional limit, the proportional limit is often accepted as equivalent to the elastic limit, and is frequently called the *proportional-elastic limit*. It should be remembered, however, that there is no fundamental relationship between the elastic limit and the proportional limit. In many of the older tests, particularly with timber, the proportional limit was incorrectly reported as the elastic limit.

Johnson's Apparent Elastic Limit. For some materials it is difficult to determine precisely the proportional limit since the point of departure of the stress-deformation curve from a straight line is not well defined. In view of this, J. B. Johnson proposed what he called the "apparent elastic limit" as the point on the stress-deformation diagram at which the rate of deformation is 50 per cent greater than at the origin. It is found by drawing a line, OA, Fig. 5, having a slope with respect to the vertical axis 50 per cent greater than the straight-line part of the curve; the unit stress at which this line is tangent to the curve, point B on the line $O'A'$, Fig. 5, is the apparent elastic limit.

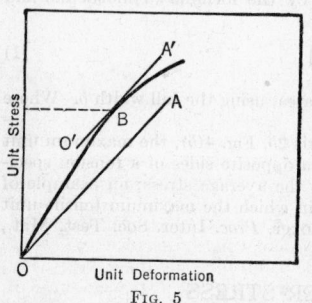

Unit Deformation

Fig. 5

The Yield Point of a material is the unit stress at which the deformation first increases markedly without any increase in the applied load. The yield point is always above the proportional limit and true elastic limit. Ductile metals have a well-defined yield point which is practically the same value as the proportional limit. For this reason, and because of the method of commercial testing, the yield point of ductile metals is sometimes reported as the elastic limit, or as the *commercial elastic limit*. The A.S.T.M. Standards, 1933, E8–33, specify that the term, yield point, shall not be used in connection with material whose stress-deformation curve in the region of yield is a smooth curve of gradual curvature.

Yield Strength is defined as the unit stress at which a material exhibits a specified limiting permanent set. It is a measure of the useful limit of materials, particularly of those whose stress-deformation curve in the region of yield is a smooth curve of gradual curvature. For methods of determining yield strength, see p. 5–87.

The Ultimate Strength, tensile or compressive strength, of a material is the highest unit stress it can sustain before rupturing.

The Point of Rupture, or breaking strength, is the unit stress at which the material tested breaks or ruptures. It is observed in tests on steel to be slightly less than the ultimate strength or maximum stress sustained before rupture because of the large reduction in area before rupture.

Stress-deformation Diagram. The relation between the unit stress and unit deformation for any material tested is shown conveniently by a stress-deformation diagram, in which ordinates to a curve represent unit stresses and abscissas the resulting unit deformations for all values of unit stress to the point of rupture. In a typical tension test on a bar of medium steel, the curve, Fig. 6, is a straight line up to a unit stress of about 35,000 lb per sq in., showing a constant ratio of unit stress to unit deformation. The proportional limit, point a, is the unit stress at which the curve deviates from the initial straight line.

At a unit stress slightly higher than the proportional limit, point b, the curve becomes approximately horizontal, showing a rapid increase in deformation without any further increase in the stress; this unit stress is the yield point. For unit stresses beyond the yield point, the curve shows that the rate of deformation increases rapidly. The end of the curve, beyond point c, marks the point of rupture which is shown to be a little lower than the maximum unit stress (ultimate strength) sustained during the test.

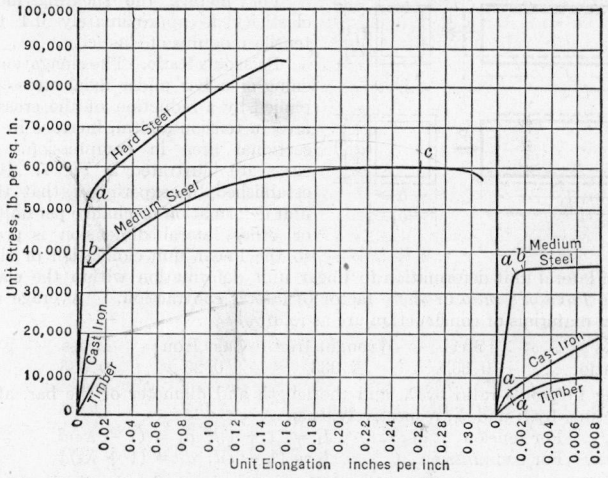

FIG. 6. Stress-Deformation Diagram

The form of the curve obtained from a test will vary according to the material tested, and will be different for compression than for tension. For some materials, like cast iron, concrete, and frequently, timber, no part of the curve is a straight line.

Modulus of Elasticity in tension or compression is the constant which expresses the ratio of unit stress to unit deformation for all values of unit stress not exceeding the proportional limit of a material. The terms *coefficient of elasticity* and *Young's modulus* are sometimes used to express this ratio.

The deformation caused by any unit stress not exceeding the proportional limit may be computed if the modulus of elasticity is known. Consider a bar of length l and cross-sectional area A acted on by an axial load P which produces a total deformation e. The unit stress is P/A, and the unit deformation is e/l. Let E represent the modulus of elasticity, s the unit stress, and ϵ the unit deformation, then

$$E = \frac{\text{Unit stress}}{\text{Unit deformation}} = \frac{s}{\epsilon} = \frac{P/A}{e/l} = \frac{Pl}{Ae} \qquad (2)$$

or

$$e = \frac{Pl}{AE} = s\frac{l}{E} \qquad (3)$$

Since l and e are linear dimensions, ϵ is an abstract number, and E is expressed in the same units as s, such as pounds per square inch, tons per square foot, or kilograms per square centimeter.

This formula can be used only for unit stresses not greater than the proportional limit because for higher unit stresses the ratio s/ϵ is not constant. The modulus of elasticity, E, is a measure of the stiffness of a body or its ability to resist deformation within the proportional limit of the material. The greater the modulus of elasticity the less will be the deformation for any unit stress not exceeding the proportional limit.

For any given material, the modulus of elasticity is often the same in tension or compression. Average values for steel, and wrought iron are respectively 30,000,000 lb per sq in. and 25,000,000 lb per sq in. Values for other materials are given in Table 23 Section 1, and Sections 11 and 12. Axial stresses are always implied when the unqualified term "modulus of elasticity" is used.

Modulus of Elasticity in Shear. The expression for the modulus of elasticity in shear is similar to that for tension or compression; but in shear the deformation is in a direction lying in the plane of shear of the body. The modulus of elasticity in shear is sometimes called the *modulus of rigidity.*

Let E_s be the shearing modulus of elasticity, s_s the unit shearing stress, e_s the total lateral deformation or detrusion due to the shear, and ϵ_s the unit detrusion, then

$$E_s = \frac{\text{Unit shearing stress}}{\text{Unit detrusion}} = \frac{s_s}{\epsilon_s} = \frac{P/A}{e_s/l} = \frac{Pl}{e_s A} \qquad (4)$$

or

$$e_s = \frac{Pl}{AE_s} = \frac{s_s l}{E_s} \qquad (5)$$

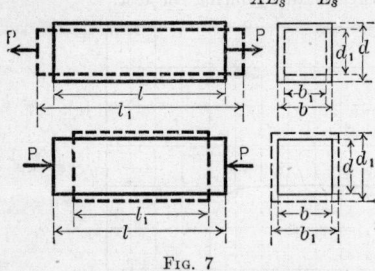

FIG. 7

For metals, the shearing modulus of elasticity is approximately 0.4 times the tensile modulus of elasticity.

Poisson's Ratio. The elongation or shortening of a bar under axial stress is accompanied by a reduction of the cross-sectional area in tension and an increase in the cross-sectional area in compression. The two cases are illustrated in Fig. 7. It has been established by experiment that the lateral unit deformation or change per unit diameter or other lateral dimension is proportional to the linear unit elongation or shortening. The ratio of lateral unit deformation to linear unit deformation within the elastic limit is known as *Poisson's ratio* or the " factor of lateral contraction." Average values for the common materials of construction are as follows:

Material	Steel	Wrought Iron	Cast Iron	Brass	Concrete
Poisson's ratio	0.333	0.333	0.25	0.333	0.10

Denoting Poisson's ratio by λ, and the length and diameter of the bar, after stress has been acting, by l_1 and d_1, respectively, then

For tension . . . . $l_1 = (1 + \epsilon)l; \quad d_1 = (1 - \lambda\epsilon)d$ (6)

For compression . . . . $l_1 = (1 - \epsilon)l; \quad d_1 = (1 + \lambda\epsilon)d$ (7)

in which l and d are the original length and diameter and ϵ the longitudinal unit elongation or shortening as the case may be.

3. PHYSICAL PROPERTIES OF MATERIALS OBSERVED IN TESTS

Elasticity. A material is elastic when it is able to deform and return to its original shape upon the removal of the load. Regardless of the amount of deformation, the ability to recover its original form is the criterion of elasticity. Steel is elastic within its elastic limit; but for higher unit stresses, causing greater deformations, much of its elasticity is lost, as the material only partially returns to its original form when the stress is removed.

Ductility and Malleability are often used synonymously to indicate the ability of a material to undergo large permanent deformations without rupture. Ductility is commonly thought of as the property which enables a material to be drawn into a wire, whereas malleability is the property which permits it to be beaten or rolled into thin sheets. Ductility is frequently more specifically defined as the ability to undergo large permanent deformations in tension, and malleability, the ability to undergo large permanent deformations in compression.

Plasticity. A material is plastic if the smallest load produces a permanent deformation. A perfectly plastic material is non-elastic and has no ultimate strength in the ordinary meaning of the term. Lead is an example of a plastic material, for a prism tested in compression will deform permanently under a small load and will continue to deform as the load is increased until it flattens out into a thin sheet. Wrought iron and soft steel become plastic when stressed beyond the elastic limit in compression, their behavior resembling that of lead; when stressed beyond the elastic limit in tension they are partly elastic and partly plastic, the degree of plasticity increasing as the ultimate strength is approached.

Brittleness. A material which can be only slightly deformed without rupture is termed brittle. Brittleness is relative, no material being perfectly brittle, that is, capable of no deformation before rupture. Many materials are brittle to a greater or less degree, glass being one of the most brittle of materials. Brittle materials have relatively short stress-deformation curves, since they are capable of only small deformations before rupture. Of the common structural materials, cast iron, brick, and stone are to be considered brittle in comparison with steel.

Brittleness and Plasticity are opposite terms. Materials which have a high degree of plasticity have no brittleness, and they rupture with considerable reduction of area. The reduction of area at rupture may be considered the measure of the plasticity or brittleness of a material, a large reduction of area indicating a high degree of plasticity and little or no reduction of area indicating a high degree of brittleness.

Toughness is the ability to withstand high unit stress together with great unit deformation, without complete fracture. The area under the curve of the stress-deformation diagram, area $OAGH$, or OJK, Fig. 8, is a measure of the toughness of the material. The distinction between ductility and toughness is that ductility deals only with the ability to deform, whereas toughness considers both the ability to deform and the stress developed during deformation.

Stiffness is the ability to resist deformation under stress. The modulus of elasticity is the criterion of the stiffness of a material.

Hardness is the ability to resist very small indentations, abrasion, and plastic deformation. There is no single measure of hardness, as it is not a single property but is a combination of several properties.

Creep or Flow of Metals. This is a phase of plastic or inelastic action. Some solids, as asphalt or paraffin, flow appreciably at room temperatures under extremely small

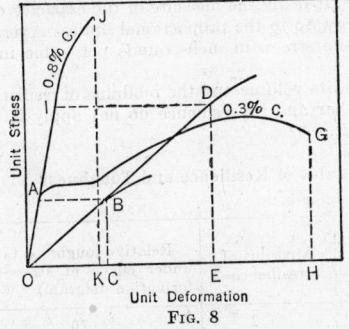

Fig. 8

Fig. 9

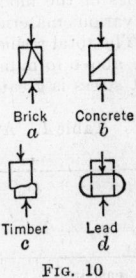

Fig. 10

stresses; while zinc, lead, and tin show signs of creep at room temperature under moderate stresses. At sufficiently high temperatures, practically all known metals creep under stresses which vary with the temperature, the higher the temperature the lower the stress at which creep takes place. This deformation due to creep continues to increase indefinitely and becomes of extreme importance in members subjected to high temperatures, as parts in turbines, boilers, superheaters, etc. Considerable work has been done on this phase of the strength of materials since about 1919, and many data have been accumulated, but the field has only begun to be explored.

Creep Limit is the maximum unit stress under which the unit distortion will not exceed a specified value during a given period of time at a specified temperature. A value which has been much used in tests and which has been suggested as a standard for comparing materials is the maximum unit stress at which the creep does not exceed 1 per cent in 100,000 hours.

Types of Fracture. The materials of engineering have varying degrees of elasticity, ductility, plasticity, and brittleness, which properties are partly indicated by the method in which a test specimen breaks. A bar of brittle material, as cast iron, will rupture in a tension test, as shown in Fig. 9a, in a clean, sharp fracture with very little reduction of cross-sectional area and very little elongation; in a ductile material such as structural steel, the reduction of area and elongation are greater, as shown in Fig. 9b. In compression, a prism of brittle material will break by shearing along oblique planes and the greater the brittleness of the material the more nearly these planes will parallel the direction of the applied force. Figs. 10a, 10b, and 10c, arranged in order of brittleness, illustrate the type of fracture in prisms of brick, concrete, and timber. Fig. 10d represents the deformation of a prism of plastic material, as lead, which flattens out under load without failure.

4. WORK AND RESILIENCE

External Work. If an axial load on a bar is increased gradually from zero to its final value, P pounds, causing an internal stress not greater than the proportional limit, the mean force acting is $1/2 P$ and the distance through which it acts is the deformation, e, inches. Let W be the external work performed on the bar, inch-pounds; then $W = 1/2 Pe$. If s = the unit stress, pounds per square inch, caused by P, A = the sectional area in square inches, l = the length in inches, and E = the modulus of elasticity in pounds per square inch, then $P = As$, and for all values of s within the proportional limit, $e = sl/E$. Substituting these values in the above expression, the work required to produce deformation in terms of s, A, and l within the proportional limit may be expressed as follows:

$$W = 1/2 As \left(\frac{sl}{E}\right) = 1/2 \left(\frac{s^2}{E}\right) Al \tag{8}$$

The factor $1/2 s^2/E$ is the work required per unit volume, the volume being Al; it is represented on the stress-deformation diagram by the area of the triangle formed by the stress-deformation curve, the ordinate representing the unit stress considered, and the axis of deformations, area ODE or OBC, Fig. 8, p. 5–07.

Resilience is a term denoting stress energy which may be recovered from a deformed body when the load causing the stress is removed. Within the proportional limit, the resilience is equal to the external work performed in deforming the bar; therefore the resilience is equal to $1/2(s^2/E) \times Al$. When s is equal to the proportional limit the factor $1/2 s^2/E$ is known as the *modulus of resilience*, it being the measure of the capacity of a unit volume of the material to store stress energy up to the proportional limit. Average values of the modulus of resilience under tensile stress, in inch-pounds per cubic inch, for various materials are given in Table I.

The total resilience of a bar is the product of its volume and the modulus of resilience. The above formulas for work performed on a bar and its resilience do not apply if the unit stress is greater than the proportional limit.

Table I.   Average Values of Tensile Modulus of Resilience and Toughness
(Inch-pounds per cubic inch)

Material	Modulus of resilience	Relative toughness (area under curve of stress-deformation diagram)
Gray cast iron	1.2	70
Malleable cast iron	17.4	3800
Wrought iron	11.6	11000
Low-carbon steel	15.0	15700
Medium-carbon steel	34.0	16300
High-carbon steel	94.0	5000
Ni-Cr steel, hot-rolled	94.0	44000
Vanadium steel, 0.98% C, 0.2% V, heat-treated	260.0	22000
Duralumin, 17 ST	45.0	10000
Rolled bronze	57.0	15500
Rolled brass	40.0	10000
Oak	2.3*	13*

* Bending.

Work Required for Rupture. Since beyond the proportional limit the deformations are not proportional to the stresses, $1/2 P$ does not express the mean value of the force acting. The formula $W = 1/2(s^2/E)Al$ therefore does not express the work required for deformations after the proportional limit of the material has been passed, and cannot express the work required for rupture. The work per unit volume required to produce deformations beyond the proportional limit or for rupture may, however, be determined from the stress-deformation diagram, as it is measured by the area included between the axis of abscissas, and the stress-deformation curve up to the deformation in question, as $OAGH$ or OJK, Fig. 8, p. 5–07. This area, however, does not represent the resilience, since part of the work done on the bar is present in the form of heat and cannot be recovered. The total work required for rupture, area $OAGH$, is taken as a measure of the toughness of the material. See p. 5–07.

5. COMBINED ELEMENTARY STRESSES

Shear Due to an Axial Stress. When an axial load acts on a bar it causes normal stress on the cross-sections and both normal and shearing stress on sections inclined to the axis. Thus in Fig. 11 the axial load P may be resolved into components P_1 and P_2 acting parallel and normal to any inclined plane as mn. P_1 causes shear and P_2 causes normal stress on the oblique section. When the section mn makes an angle of 0° or 90° with the axis, the shearing stress will be zero. When the section mn makes an angle of 45° with the axis of the bar, the unit shearing stress due to axial load (tensile or compressive) is at a maximum and is

$$s_{s\text{max}} = \frac{1}{2}\frac{P}{A}$$

where A is the cross-sectional area of the bar.

Shear Due to Normal Stresses at Right Angles. When two forces act on a body in directions at right angles to each other, causing unit stresses s_1 and s_2 (tensile stress considered positive and compressive stress negative) on planes normal to the direction of the applied forces, the maximum unit shearing stress is $s_{s\text{max}} = 1/2(s_1 - s_2)$ and acts along each of the two planes that make an angle of 45° with the planes normal to the direction of the applied forces.

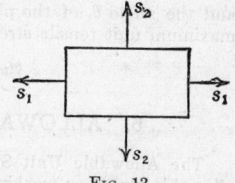

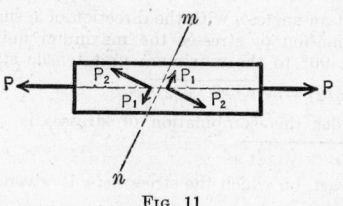

FIG. 11   FIG. 12

Tensile or Compressive Stress Due to Shear. In a body subjected to shear (e.g., a bar in torsion), a particle of unit dimensions shown enlarged in Fig. 12 has acting upon it the couple $s_s d$, and balancing it, the couple $s_s'd$. For equilibrium the two couples must be equal, hence $s_s = s_s'$. These stresses will result in a maximum tensile force normal to the plane through AC and perpendicular to the paper, $P_t = \sqrt{2s_s^2}$, and a maximum unit tensile stress normal to this plane, $s_t = \dfrac{\sqrt{2s_s^2}}{\sqrt{2}} = s_s$. Similarly, normal to the plane through BD and perpendicular to the paper, there is a maximum unit compressive stress $s_c = s_s$. These stresses are particularly important in brittle materials which, when subjected to torsion, usually fail in tension with a helical fracture.

Combined Axial Stresses. Assuming tensile stresses to be positive and compressive stresses negative, the normal stress on a section due to several applied axial loads is equal to the algebraic sum of the normal stresses caused by each load. Thus if a bar is subjected to applied axial loads P_1, P_2, P_3, and P_4 causing unit stresses on the cross-section of the bar equal to $-20,000$, $+12,500$, -6000, and $+8000$ lb per sq in., respectively, the normal axial unit stress is -5500 lb per sq in., the negative sign indicating that the combined stress is compressive.

Deformation Due to Normal Stresses at Right Angles. Let s_1 and s_2 be the unit tensile stresses in each of the two directions on the element of plate in Fig. 13, the direction of each stress being normal to the plane on which it acts. The stress s_1 will produce a unit elongation $\epsilon_1 = s_1/E$ in the direction of s_1, and at the same time, a unit lateral contraction of $\lambda\epsilon_1$ in the direction of s_2 where λ represents Poisson's ratio.

FIG. 13

Similarly the unit stress s_2 will produce a unit elongation of $\epsilon_2 = s_2/E$ in the direction of s_2 and a lateral contraction of $\lambda\epsilon_2$ in the direction of s_1. The resultant unit elongation in the direction of s_1 will then be $\epsilon_1 - \lambda\epsilon_2$, and in the direction of s_2 it will be $\epsilon_2 - \lambda\epsilon_1$. If the stress s_2 were compression and the stress s_1 tension, the resultant elongation in the direction of s_1 would be $\epsilon_1 + \lambda\epsilon_2$, and the resultant contraction in the direction of s_2 would be $\epsilon_2 + \lambda\epsilon_1$.

The effect then of two normal stresses acting at right angles to each other on a plate is to reduce the resultant deformation if both stresses are alike, and to increase the resultant deformation if the stresses are unlike. By experiment, $s = \epsilon E$, and for a uniaxial stress this accords with the definition that $s = P/A$; but if the resultant unit deformation due to biaxial loading is multiplied by E, the modulus of elasticity, the resulting unit stress in the direction of either applied load will not be the same as that obtained by $s = P/A$. Thus the question is involved whether the liability of the member to fail is measured by the stress based on the external loads or by the deformation of the material. There is a lack of complete agreement as to which criterion should be used, but if both stresses are tension or compression, it is on the side of safety to neglect the effect of the lateral stresses and to use the stress based on the external loads, or $s = P/A$. If the lateral stresses are of opposite sign from the longitudinal stresses, and increase the longitudinal deformation, the effect of the increased deformation may need to be considered. See Seely, Resistance of Materials, 2nd Ed. (John Wiley & Sons, New York), pp. 234–239.

Combined Tension or Compression and Shear. If a particle is subjected to tensile or compressive as well as shearing stresses there will be a plane in the particle normal to which the unit tensile or compressive stress will be a maximum, and two planes, each at an angle of 45° to the one on which the maximum unit tensile or compressive stresses occur, on which the unit shearing stress will be a maximum. In Fig. 14, the particle is subjected to a unit shearing stress of s_s and a unit tensile stress of s_t. Then (Seely's Resistance of Materials or Boyd's Strength of Materials),

$$s_{t\max} = (s_t/2) + \sqrt{s_s^2 + (s_t/2)^2}, \tag{9a}$$

and the plane m–n to which it is normal is at an angle θ_t with the direction of s_t such that $\tan 2\theta_t = -2s_s/s_t$. With the same combination of stresses the maximum unit compressive or minimum unit tensile stress, at 90° to the maximum unit tensile stress, is

$$s_{t\min} = s_{c\max} = (s_t/2) - \sqrt{s_s^2 + (s_t/2)^2} \tag{9b}$$

The maximum unit shearing stress under this combination of stresses is

$$s_{s\max} = \sqrt{s_s^2 + (s_t/2)^2}, \tag{9c}$$

and the angle θ_s of the planes p–q, 90° apart, on which the stress acts, is given by $\tan 2\theta_s = s_t/(2s_s)$.

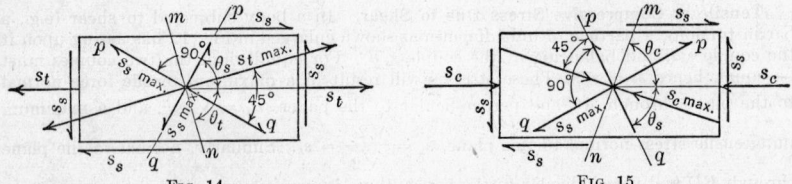

FIG. 14   FIG. 15

Where the stresses are shear and compression, Fig. 15, the maximum unit compressive stress is

$$s_{c\max} = (s_c/2) + \sqrt{s_s^2 + (s_c/2)^2} \tag{10a}$$

and the angle θ_c of the plane to which it is normal is given by $\tan 2\theta_c = 2s_s/s_c$. The maximum unit shearing stress is

$$s_{s\max} = \sqrt{s_s^2 + (s_c/2)^2}, \tag{10b}$$

and the angle θ_s of the plane on which it acts is given by $\tan 2\theta_s = -s_c/(2s_s)$. The maximum unit tensile stress for this combination of stresses is,

$$s_{t\max} = s_{c\min} = (s_c/2) - \sqrt{s_s^2 + (s_c/2)^2}. \tag{10c}$$

6. ALLOWABLE STRESS AND FACTOR OF SAFETY

The Allowable Unit Stress or the **allowable working unit stress**, commonly called **allowable stress** or **working stress**, is the maximum unit stress to which it is considered a member may safely be subjected when in service. The term allowable stress is preferable to working stress since the latter is sometimes used to indicate the actual stress in a material when in service. The allowable unit stresses for different materials ˙or various conditions of service are specified by different authorities on the basis of test or experience. In general, for ductile materials, the allowable stress is considerably less than the yield point.

The Factor of Safety is the ratio of the ultimate strength of the material to the allowable stress. The term was originated for determining the allowable stress. The ultimate strength of a given material divided by an arbitrary factor of safety, dependent upon material and the use to which it is to be put, gives the allowable stress. In present design practice, it is customary to use allowable stress as specified by recognized authorities or building codes rather than this arbitrary factor of safety. One reason for this decreasing importance of the factor of safety is that it is misleading in that it implies a greater degree of safety than actually exists in a material. For example, a factor of safety of 4 does not mean that a member can carry a load four times as great as that for which it was designed. It should also be clearly understood that, even though each part of a machine is designed with the same factor of safety, the machine as a whole does not have that factor of safety. When one part is stressed beyond the proportional limit, or particularly the yield point, the load or stress distribution may be completely changed throughout the entire machine or structure, and its ability to function may thus be changed though no part has ruptured.

Though no definite rules can be given, if a factor of safety is to be used the following circumstances should be taken into account in its selection:

1. When the ultimate strength of the material is known within narrow limits as for structural steel for which tests of samples have been made, when the load is entirely a steady one of a known amount and there is no reason to fear the deterioration of the metal by corrosion, the lowest factor that should be adopted is 3.

2. When the circumstances of 1 are modified by a portion of the load being variable, as in floors of warehouses, the factor should be not less than 4.

3. When the whole load, or nearly the whole, is apt to be alternately put on and taken off, as in suspension rods of floors of bridges, the factor should be 5 or 6.

4. When the stresses are reversed in direction from tension to compression, as in some bridge diagonals and parts of machines, the factor should be not less than 6.

5. When the piece is subjected to repeated shocks, the factor should be not less than 10.

6. When the piece is subjected to deterioration from corrosion the section should be sufficiently increased to allow for a definite amount of corrosion before the piece will be so far weakened by it as to require removal.

7. When the strength of the material or the amount of the load or both are uncertain, the factor should be increased by an allowance sufficient to cover the amount of the uncertainty.

8. When the strains are of a complex character and of uncertain amount, such as those in the crankshaft of a reversing engine, a very high factor is necessary, possibly even as high as 40.

9. If the property loss caused by failure of the part may be large or if loss of life may result, as in a derrick hoisting materials over a crowded street, the factor should be large.

In Table II are the average values of the factors of safety for different conditions as given by Merriman (Mechanics of Materials).

The factors given by different authorities for some materials show a remarkable difference: for example, Rankine specified a factor of safety of 4 for masonry under dead load whereas Unwin specified a factor of 20. This may possibly be explained as follows: If the actual crushing strength of a pier of masonry is known from direct experiment, then a factor of safety of 4 is sufficient for a pier of the same size and quality under a steady load; but if the crushing strength is merely assumed from figures given by authorities which may be an average of a wide range, then a factor of safety of 20 may be none too great. Here the factor of safety is really a "factor of ignorance."

Table II. Average Values of Factor of Safety

Material	Steady stress	Variable stress	Shocks	Material	Steady stress	Variable stress	Shocks
Cast iron.........	6	10	20	Hard steel.......	5	8	15
Wrought iron.....	4	6	10	Timber..........	8	10	15
Structural steel....	4	6	10	Brick and stone...	15	25	40

7. REPEATED STRESS

Parts Subjected to Repeated Stress. Where parts of a structure or machine are subjected to varying or repeated loads, the ordinary methods of computing stresses and of determining the strength of materials under static load conditions are not satisfactory. In general, in excess of one-half to ten million repetitions of loading are necessary before the parts come under this classification. Such parts are crankshafts, shafts carrying rotating parts, as in motors and generators, turbine blades, valve parts, piston rods in steam engines, floor beams in elevated railroads, etc.

Character of Failure. Under repeated loadings, failures take place suddenly and without warning. Formerly, it was supposed that vibration caused a change in the structure of the metals, making the fibrous material crystalline and brittle. Thus the term *fatigue of metals* came to be applied to this phenomenon. It is now well known that all metals are crystalline, and the mechanism of "fatigue" failure under repeated stress appears to be that very tiny particles of metal are stressed beyond the elastic limit. As the stress is repeated, a tiny crack, sometimes called a fatigue crack, is formed and progresses until failure occurs. This action is referred to as a *progressive failure*. Therefore, where the load is repeated, anything which causes a concentration of stress is a source of weakness.

Determination of Endurance Limit. The highest unit stress, s, at which a material can be subjected to a very large number of repetitions of loading, N, and still show no evidence of failure is called the *endurance limit*. This is usually found for any given metal by constructing an s–N diagram for that particular metal from data obtained by tests. A piece of metal is so loaded as to produce a given stress. This load is then repeated

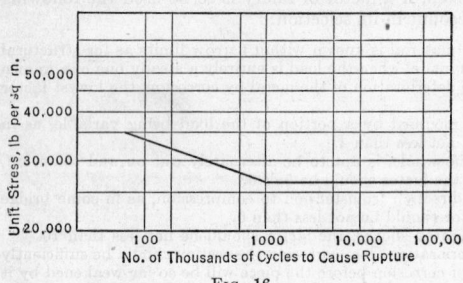

No. of Thousands of Cycles to Cause Rupture

Fig. 16

until failure occurs. Other specimens are then tested at different values of the unit stress, until finally enough points have been obtained to plot a curve. This curve will incline steeply at the higher stresses and gradually flatten out at the lower stresses until it approaches a horizontal line. The unit stress at which the curve becomes horizontal is called the endurance limit. Such a curve plotted to logarithmic scales is shown in Fig. 16. The ordinate of the horizontal portion is the endurance limit. The most common test is that of reversed bending by the rotating beam method, since this specimen is the most easily made and the testing machines are the cheapest. But tests are also made in direct tension, direct shear, direct compression, reversed torsion, and on various combinations of these.

Values of Endurance Limit. Moore and Kommers, and Moore and Jasper (*Bull. Eng. Exp. Sta.*, Univ. of Ill., Nos. 124 and 136, 1921, 1923) reach a number of conclusions concerning wrought ferrous metals. A summary of the more important of these follows:

1. It is considered as well established that for wrought ferrous metals there is an endurance limit stress below which they will withstand an indefinite number of repetitions of stress.

2. In reversed bending, there is a fairly definite relation between the endurance limit and the ultimate tensile strength and the Brinell hardness number. The endurance limit is about 50 per cent of the ultimate tensile strength, with values ranging between 40 per cent and 60 per cent. The endurance limit is between 200 and 250 times the Brinell hardness number.

3. There is no relation between the endurance limit and impact test results nor repeated-impact test results.

4. The endurance limit in reversed torsion (shear) varies from 48 to 60 per cent of the endurance limit in reversed bending.

5. The endurance limit in reversed axial stress (tension to compression) varies from 56 to 70 per cent of the endurance limit under reversed bending with nearly all the values 60 per cent or above. The reason for this low value is that practically all axial loads are slightly eccentric and cause bending. Irwin (*Proc. A.S.T.M.*, vol. xxv, Pt. II, p. 53, 1925), with a specially designed machine, found the reversed axial stress to be practically the same as that in reversed bending.

A report of Research Committee on Fatigue of Metals (*Proc. A.S.T.M.*, vol. xxx, Pt. I, p. 259, 1930) gives a concise statement of the state of knowledge at that date, which corroborates the above conclusions with the following changes or additions:

1. There is no general relationship between the yield point or the proportional limit and the endurance limit.

2. For cast ferrous metals the endurance limit is about 40 per cent of the tensile strength.

3. For non-ferrous metals there is no definite relationship between the endurance limit and the tensile strength, the values varying between 18 and 50 per cent.

4. For cast ferrous metals the endurance limit is about 26 per cent of the modulus of rupture.

5. For wrought ferrous metals the endurance limit is about 250 times the Brinell number for numbers under 400. For Brinell numbers exceeding 400, the relationship does not hold. For cast ferrous metals and for non-ferrous metals sufficient data are not available to permit judging the degree of correlation.

Table III gives the endurance limit and other properties of a number of ferrous metals. Table IV gives similar information for non-ferrous metals. The values of the endurance limit for heat-treated steels vary according to the treatment, ranging from 29,300 to 68,000 lb per sq in. for a 0.49 per cent carbon steel, from 50,000 to 108,000 lb per sq in. for a 1.20 per cent carbon steel, and from 54,000 to 120,000 lb per sq in. for a 3.50 per cent nickel steel. Table V summarizes the endurance ratios (ratio of ultimate tensile strength to endurance limit) for different types of stress. Moore and Kommers in Fatigue of Metals (McGraw-Hill, New York, 1927), p. 147, state that the ratio of the endurance limit in reversed torsion to the endurance limit in reversed bending averages as follows: Plain carbon steels, 0.55; alloy steels, 0.58; non-ferrous metals, 0.52.

Table III. Properties of Ferrous Metals Tested under Repeated Stress
(*Bull*. Eng. Exp. Sta., Univ. of Ill., Nos. 124, 136, 142, 152, 156, 164, 165)

	Yield point, Tension, lb per sq in.	Ultimate strength, Tension, lb per sq in.	Endurance limit Reversed bending, lb per sq in.	Yield point, Shear, lb per sq in.	Endurance limit Reversed torsion, lb per sq in.	Yield point, Compression, lb per sq in.	Brinell hardness number
STEEL							
0.18% C hot-rolled.........	40,300	61,500	28,000	....	....	....	....
0.37% C normalized........	34,900	71,900	33,000	22,500	16,000	38,100	132
0.37% C sorbitic............	87,300	102,600	57,000	60,200	32,500	84,500	209
0.52% C normalized........	47,600	98,000	42,000	34,600	22,000	51,000	193
0.52% C sorbitic...........	84,300	111,400	55,000	52,200	31,500	87,400	227
0.93% C pearlitic...........	33,400	84,100	30,500	22,500	16,300	29,700	162
0.93% C sorbitic...........	67,600	115,000	56,000	42,000	29,000	72,700	227
1.20% C normalized........	60,700	116,900	50,000	39,700	24,500	57,900	224
1.20% C sorbitic...........	130,100	179,900	92,000	80,600	48,000	111,500	369
Cyclops metal..............	62,000	115,900	55,000	....	37,000	....	239
Stainless steel..............	36,300	112,200	48,000	....	26,000	....	208
Cold-drawn screw stock......	55,200	86,800	41,000	....	....	....	....
Mn-steel, 0.94% Mn, 0.34% C, 0.037% Ni...............	42,100	83,400	37,000	....	....	....	154
Mn-steel, 0.94% Mn, 0.34% C, 0.037% Ni, sorbitic.........	63,750	97,500	48,000	....	....	....	198
0.35% C, 1.17% Mn, cast....	39,000	80,800	32,000	....	....	....	179
0.25% C, 0.68% Mn, cast....	26,700	67,200	27,000	....	....	....	119
CAST AND WROUGHT IRON							
0.02% C, Armco............	19,000	42,400	26,000	13,600	12,700	20,600	69
Wrought iron, longitudinal section......................	24,000	46,900	23,000	....	....	....	105
Cast-iron pipe, 1/2 in. thick...	....	26,200	12,000	....	....	96,000	162
Cast iron, 1 in. thick........	....	31,600	10,500	....	....	111,000	148
Cast iron, 3 1/2 in. thick......	....	25,300	9,000	....	....	85,000	132

Effects of Scratches and Defects on Endurance Limit of Rolled or Forged Ferrous Metals. The beginning of rupture under repeated stress is supposed to be at a point of discontinuity in the material. The same principle applies to a discontinuity on the outer surface where, in bending or torsion, the stress is greatest. The presence of scratches, sharp corners, or grooves reduces the endurance limit an appreciable amount. Moore and Kommers (*Bull. Eng. Exp. Sta.*, Univ. of Ill., No. 124) obtained the following reductions in the endurance limit, using steel of 0.02 per cent C and 0.49 per cent C, with results the same for each steel. The experiments were performed on bars of 0.40-in. diameter and turned down to 0.275-in. diameter at the bottom of the notch.

Type of defect	Percentage reduction in endurance limit based on a standard specimen	Type of defect	Percentage reduction in endurance limit based on a standard specimen
Groove, 9.85-in. radius..	0	Notch, 1/2-in. wide, square shoulders.....	51
Groove, 1-in. radius.....	0	Notch, 90° V.........	60
Groove, 1/4-in. radius...	8		

Table IV. Properties of Non-ferrous Metals and Alloys under Repeated Stress

Material	Proportional limit, Tension, lb per sq in.	Ultimate tensile strength, lb per sq in.	Endurance limit, Reversed bending, lb per sq in.	Endurance limit, Reversed torsion, lb per sq in.	Brinell hardness number 3000 Kg	Authority
Aluminum						
Rolled............................	11,275	22,600	10,500	....	45*	1
Duralumin						
As received (rolled, heated to 930° F, quenched in boiling water)............	25,030	50,960	14,000	....	100*	2
Tempered, as received bars heated to 925° F, 30 min, quenched in boiling water 2 hr..............................	18,550	51,170	12,000	....	100*	2
Annealed, as received bars heated to 700° F, 20 min, cooled in furnace..........	6,800	25,250	10,860	....	50*	2
Magnesium						
Extruded............................	1,224	32,490	7,800	....	41*	1
+4% Al, extruded as 3/4-in. round rods from 2 15/16-in. ingots at 350–400° F...	8,125	35,160	12,000		52	6
+4% Al, +0.25% Mn, extruded as above	13,500	39,010	15,000		58	6
+6.5% Al, extruded as above..........	12,000	41,330	13,000		61	6
+6.5% Al, +0.25% Mn, extruded as above..............................	15,250	44,380	15,000		65	6
+10% Cu, extruded as above..........	14,250	39,030	11,000		60	6
Electron metal						
rolled, Mg +4% Zn..................	6,260	36,500	17,000	....	64*	2
Nickel						
Cold-rolled, annealed at 550° F, 60 min, cooled in furnace....................	69,000	165,500	40,000	18,500	......	3
Hot-rolled, annealed at 1400° F, 60 min, cooled in furnace....................	25,100	76,200	31,500	....	......	3
Hot-rolled to 5/8 in. round and drawn to 9/16 in. at 2000° F, drawn to 1/2 in. round at 1600° F, annealed at 1600° F and cooled in furnace................	11,300	69,900	28,000	....	90	4
Monel metal						
As received, treatment unknown........	50,700	89,600	32,000	....	163	4
Hot-rolled to 1 1/8 in. round............	49,600	89,800	32,000	....	169	4
Constantan						
Hot-rolled, tested as received............	....	70,500	34,500	14,500	......	3
German silver						
11% Ni, 60% Cu, 29% Zn, cold-drawn, tested as received....................	12,500	58,700	17,000	....	......	3
18% Ni, 65% Cu, 17% Zn, cold-drawn, tested as received....................	20,300	62,400	22,000	....	......	3
Copper						
Cold-drawn, annealed bar cold-drawn to 1/2 in. round and left hard............	38,400	56,200	10,000	....	104	4
Annealed, extruded to 1 in. round and at 1380° F, cold-drawn to 7/8 in. and annealed at 1290° F 30 min, cold-drawn to 3/4 in. and annealed at 1290° F, 30 min................................	3,200	32,400	10,000	....	47	4
Brass						
60–40, cold drawn, annealed bar cold-drawn to 1/2 in. round and left hard...	43,200	96,700	26,000	....	179	4
60–40, annealed, extruded to 1 in. round at 1290° F, and annealed at 1020° F 30 min, drawn to 3/4 in. and annealed at 1020° F............................	15,600	54,200	22,000	....	72	4
Naval, 61–38, rolled, tested as received...	33,400	68,200	21,000	....	13.5*	1
70–30, cold-rolled........		73,200	17,500			5
70–30, cold-rolled, annealed 400° F 90 min, cooled in furnace................	26,000	73,000	20,000			5
70–30, cold-rolled, annealed 1200° F 60 min, cooled in furnace..............	....	45,000	15,000			5
81–19, cold drawn, tested as received....	21,000	76,500	23,000			5
81–19, cold-drawn, annealed 450° F 60 min, cooled in furnace..............	27,700	80,500	26,000	....		5

Table IV—*Continued*

Material	Proportional limit, Tension, lb per sq in.	Ultimate tensile strength, lb per sq in.	Endurance limit, Reversed bending, lb per sq in.	Endurance limit, Reversed torsion, lb per sq in.	Brinell hardness number 3000 Kg	Authority
Brass—*cont.*						
81–19, cold-drawn, annealed 1000° F 60 min, cooled in furnace	7,500	44,000	17,500	....		5
Muntz metal						
Hot-rolled, quenched in iced brine and drawn at 840° F	20,000	65,600	18,000	....		3
Bronze						
95–5, cold-rolled, tested as received	23,000	55,800	22,500	....		5
95–5, cold-rolled, annealed 1200° F 60 min, cooled in furnace	11,500	48,100	22,500	....		5
89–11, cold-rolled, tested as received	38,000	82,800	27,000	....		5
89–11, cold-rolled, annealed at 1100° F 60 min, cooled in furnace	24,500	67,600	27,000	....		5
Mn-Bronze						
Hot-rolled, annealed 1200° F 60 min, cooled in furnace	....	67,000	16,500	....		3
57% Cu, 41% Zn, cast	13,000	70,000	15,000	....	93*	2
Al-Bronze						
90% Cu, 10% Al, extruded to 1 9/32 in. diam., drawn to 1 1/4 in. diam., quenched in water from 1650° F annealed 1150° F 30 min, cooled in furnace	16,890	77,530	34,000	....	128	6
90% Cu, 10% Al, cast	5,080	59,320	22,000	....	96	6
90% Cu, 10% Al, cast, quenched from 1650° F, annealed 1200° F 30 min, cooled in furnace	24,890	77,750	26,000	....	142	6

Authorities: (1) R. R. Moore, *Proc. A.S.T.M.*, vol. xxv, Pt. II, 1925; (2) R. R. Moore, *Proc. A.S.T.M.*, vol. xxiii, Pt. II, 1923; (3) D. J. McAdam, *Trans. A.S.S.T.*, vol. vii, 1925; (4) H. F. Moore and T. M. Jasper, *Bull.* No. 152, *Eng. Exp. Sta.*, Univ. of Ill., 1925; (5) D. J. McAdam. *Trans. A.S.S.T.*, vol. viii, 1925; (6) R. R. Moore, *Proc. A.S.T.M.*, vol. xxiv, Pt. II, 1924.

* 500 kg.

Table V. Endurance Ratios for Ferrous Metals under Different Stress Conditions

Character of Stress	Endurance Ratio,* Per Cent		
	Wrought metals	Cast steel	Cast iron, gray
Reversed bending	40–55	42	33–46
Reversed torsion	21–37	......	......
Axial tension, zero to a maximum	......	......	49
Axial compression, zero to a maximum	......	......	59
Axial tension to axial compression	24–40†	......	......

* The ratio of the ultimate tensile strength to the endurance limit.
† With precise loading devices this value has been found to be practically the same as in reversed bending, but such refinement in loading cannot be obtained in practice.

The surface finish has an appreciable effect on the endurance limit. The standard finish used in the experiments of Moore and Kommers was obtained by polishing a smooth turned specimen with No. 0 and 00 emery cloth. Unpolished smooth turned specimens had an endurance limit 8 to 12 per cent lower than those that were polished; a rough turned finish gave a slightly lower value than the smooth turned finish. For cast-iron specimens having a 60° groove with a bottom radius of 5/64 in., the reduction in the endurance limit was only 8 per cent. Clearly, the effect of scratches, grooves, and external discontinuities is not so great in cast iron as in steel, probably because they are a relatively small addition to the large internal discontinuities of the material.

According to the theory of elasticity, a small hole, of diameter less than 1/6 the diameter of the specimen, should cause a stress at the edge of the hole three times the stress based on a uniform stress distribution, and therefore should reduce the endurance limit to

33 per cent of that which would be obtained on a solid specimen. Tests on rotating beams of various steels with a small hole drilled through a diameter gave endurance limits from 50 to 65 per cent of those for the solid beams, showing that these theoretically high stresses do not produce corresponding failures. This is probably due to readjustments in the ductile metal.

Effect of Range of Stress. The endurance limit as determined by a rotating beam is the endurance limit for a complete reversal of stress from tension to compression, and vice versa. The endurance limit is less for a complete reversal than it is for those stress combinations where the stress goes only from a maximum to zero, or from a maximum to a minimum which is above zero. Howell (*Bull. Eng. Exp. Sta.*, Univ. of Ill., No. 136) proposed the empirical relation $s = s_1(r + 3)/2$, where s = endurance limit for the range of stress r; s_1 = endurance limit for completely reversed stress of the same character as s, *i.e.*, direct stress, bending, torsion, etc.; r = ratio of the minimum stress to the maximum stress for a cycle of stress; for instance, if the stress varies from 6000 lb per sq in. compression to 10,000 lb per sq in. tension, the ratio r would be $-6000/+10,000 = -0.60$. Using the above notation, a formula was suggested by Moore, Kommers and Jasper (*Proc. A.S.T.M.*, vol. xxii, Pt. II, 1922) where $s = 3s_1/(2 - r)$. This gives values for forged or rolled iron and steel which accord fairly well with tests, being on the safe side. For a complete digest of data, see Report of Research Committee on Fatigue of Metals, *Proc. A.S.T.M.*, vol. xxx, Pt. I, p. 259, 1930.

Effect of Corrosion. If a part is subjected to repeated loads and at the same time to corrosive agencies the endurance limit may be greatly reduced from its normal value as determined in air. McAdam at the U. S. Naval Eng. Exp. Sta., Annapolis (*Proc.*, *A.S.T.M.*, vol. xxvi, Pt. II, p. 224, 1926, the first of many papers), has experimented on various steels with a number of corrosive agents. He found that the endurance limit may be reduced to one-third its normal value. Even so mild an agent as a stream of fresh water may reduce the endurance limit one-half, and salt water or water containing other salts in solution is very destructive. Practically all steels are affected, the corrosion-resistant ones less so than ordinary steels. Steam at 220 lb per sq in., and 700° F, without appreciable amounts of oxygen or liquid water did not greatly affect chromium-iron or nickel-steels, but when these steels were tested in air under a jet of steam their strengths were reduced (Fuller, *Tech. Pub.* No. 294, *A.I.M. & M.E.*, and *Metal Progress*, July, 1931, p. 79).

In *corrosion-fatigue*, the stress need not be high enough to have started fatigue cracks without corrosion. The protective film of oxide breaks down under alternating stress and allows the formation of corrosion pits which progress more rapidly under stress than without it. The pits cause a high concentration of stress at the bottom, and this cycle of the pit increasing the stress and the stress increasing the depth of the pit continues; when the stress has been raised beyond the endurance limit, a fatigue crack starts. Since fatigue action is not a function of time but of the number of reversals of stress, whereas corrosion is a function of time, it has not yet (1935) been possible to obtain "corrosion-fatigue" values which can be used directly in design.

The most effective method of protection is to keep the parts subjected to repeated loads from contact with corrosive agents as much as possible. Where this is not possible, a protective coating of some elastic material, such as varnish, cement, or enamel, will aid. Certain substances called inhibitors, such as sodium chromate, introduced into the corrosive stream or applied in some other way, have been found to help in restoring the protective film on the metal.

8. ENERGY LOADS

Classification of Loads. A static load is one that increases gradually from zero to its full intensity; its effect on a bar has been considered in preceding paragraphs. A suddenly applied load is one that just touches a bar before it is released and then acts at its full intensity from the beginning to the end of the deformation. A moving load is one that is moving when it is brought to bear on the bar; the effect of such a load, which is denoted by the word impact, is much greater than that of a static or a suddenly applied load. Suddenly applied and moving loads are often termed *dynamic loads* or *energy loads*.

Relation between Stored Energy and Size of Member. The external work (see p. 5-08) performed in deforming a bar within the proportional limit is $1/2s^2Al/E$, where s is the unit stress, A is the cross-sectional area of the bar, l is its length, E is the modulus of elasticity. This is also the energy stored in the bar. Since the energy absorbed varies directly as the square of the unit stress, it follows that large amounts of energy will be absorbed by those portions where the stress is high. It is important that where high stresses occur they should be present over as great a length of the member as possible.

If one part of a rod must have a small diameter it is advisable to have as great a length of the rod as possible with the same small diameter, as otherwise there will be a high concentration of energy in a small portion of the member and failure may result. See Seely, Resistance of Materials, 2nd Ed., p. 271.

Effect of Sudden Loads. If a sudden load P be applied to a bar, it will cause deformation ϵl, and the work done by the load will be $P\epsilon l$. Since the external work equals the internal work, $P\epsilon l = s^2 Al/2E$, and since $\epsilon = s/E$, $P = sA/2$, or $s = 2P/A$. The unit stress, and also the unit deformation, is double that under an equal load applied gradually.

However, the bar does not maintain equilibrium at the point of maximum stress and deformation, but, after a series of oscillations in which the surplus energy is dissipated in heat, it comes to rest finally with a deformation and stress due to the equal static load.

Stress Due to Live Loads. In structural design two loads are considered, the dead load or weight of the structure and the live load or superimposed loads to be carried. The stresses due to the dead load and to the live loads respectively are computed separately, regarding each as a static load. It is obvious that the stress due to the live load may be greatly increased, depending on the suddenness with which the load is applied. It has been shown above that the stress due to a suddenly applied load is double the stress caused by a static load. The term *coefficient of impact* is used extensively in structural engineering to denote the number by which the computed static stress is multiplied to obtain the value of the increased stress assumed to be caused by the suddenness of application of the live load. If s = static unit stress computed from the live load, and i = coefficient of impact, then the increase of unit stress due to sudden loading is is, and the total unit stress due to the live load is $s + is$. The value of i has been determined by empirical methods and varies according to different conditions. In the building codes of most cities, specified floor loads for buildings include the impact allowance, and no increase is needed for live loads except for special cases of vibration or other unusual conditions. For railroad bridges, the value of i depends upon the proportion of the length of the bridge which is loaded. The Report of the Building Code Committee of the U. S. Bureau of Standards, Minimum Live Loads Allowable for Use in Design of Buildings, 1925, records results of experiments by A. H. Fuller, Iowa State College. A gymnasium balcony carried by steel beams, with one end resting on a masonry wall and the other supported by rods attached to a roof truss, was loaded with a crowd of men and gave the following results:

Action of Crowd	Percentage Increase of Live Load Static Stress Due to Dynamic Effect	
	Suspender rod	Floor beams
Teetering on toes in various ways....................	30 to 165 Average 65	35 to 155 Average 80
Rising suddenly from a sitting position in chairs.......	50 to 55	35 to 45
Cheering and giving college yells....................	10 to 55 Average 35	15 to 50 Average 35

Unpublished tests by L. J. Larson on the concrete stadium at the University of Illinois during football games gave no measurable impact effect when crowds rose during exciting plays. As it is improbable that an ordinary crowd in a public building will act in perfect unison, a coefficient of impact $i = 0.5$ should be sufficient, and $i = 0.8$ is ample, for ordinary light structures. No increase in the static stress is needed when the mass of the structure, as in monolithic concrete, is great. For machinery and for unusual conditions, such as elevator machinery and its supports, each structure should be considered by itself and the coefficient assumed accordingly.

It should be noted that the meaning of the word impact used above differs somewhat from its strict theoretical meaning and as it is used in the next paragraph. The use of the terms impact and coefficient of impact in connection with live load stresses is, however, very general.

Axial Impact on Bars. If a load P is dropped from a height h on to the end of a vertical bar of cross-sectional area A, rigidly secured at the bottom end, there is produced in the bar a unit stress which increases from 0 up to s' with a corresponding total deformation increasing from 0 up to e_1. The work done on the bar is $P(h + e_1)$ which, provided no energy is expended as heat or in giving velocity to the bar, is equal to the energy $1/2 s' A e_1$ stored in the bar; i.e., $P(h + e_1) = 1/2 s' A e_1$. If e is the deformation produced by a static load P, then, within the proportional limit, $\dfrac{e_1}{e} = \dfrac{s'}{P/A}$, which combined with the previous equation gives

$$s' = s + s \sqrt{1 + \frac{2h}{e}} \quad \text{and} \quad e_1 = e + e \sqrt{1 + \frac{2h}{e}} \tag{11}$$

A wrought-iron bar 1 in. square and 5 ft long under a static load of 5000 lb will be shortened about 0.012 in., assuming that no lateral flexure occurs; but, if a weight of 5000 lb drops on its end from a small height of 0.048 in., a stress of 20,000 lb will be produced.

The formulas above give values of stress and deformation due to impact that are somewhat large, because part of the energy of the applied force is not effective in producing stress but is expended in overcoming the inertia of the bar and in producing local stresses. For light bars, they give approximately correct results.

If the bar is held horizontally and is struck at one end by a weight P moving at a velocity V producing a deformation e_1, then, as above, $1/2 s' A\ e_1 = Ph$, where h is the height through which P would have to fall to acquire the velocity V, and is given by $h = V^2/2g$, in which g is the acceleration due to gravity, usually taken as 32.16 ft per sec per sec. Combining with $\dfrac{e_1}{e} = \dfrac{s'}{P/A}$, there result

$$s' = s \sqrt{\frac{2h}{e}} \quad \text{and} \quad e_1 = e \sqrt{\frac{2h}{e}} \tag{12}$$

Impact on Beams. If a weight P falls upon a horizontal beam from a height h, producing a maximum deflection y_1 and a maximum unit stress s' in the extreme fiber, the value of s' and y_1 is given by

$$s' = s + s\sqrt{1 + 2h/y} \quad \text{and} \quad y_1 = y + y\sqrt{1 + 2h/y} \tag{13}$$

where s is the extreme fiber unit stress and y is the deflection due to P, considered as a static load. The value of s may be obtained from the flexure formula (p. 5–21); that of y from the proper formula for deflection under a static load.

If a weight P moving horizontally with a velocity V strikes a beam, the ends of which are secured against horizontal movement, the maximum fiber unit stress and the maximum lateral deflection are given by

$$s' = s \sqrt{\frac{2h}{y}} \quad \text{and} \quad y_1 = y \sqrt{\frac{2h}{y}} \tag{14}$$

where s and y are as given above and h is height through which P would have to fall to acquire the velocity V.

These formulas, like those for axial impact on bars, give results larger than those observed in tests, particularly if the weight of the beam is great. For further discussion of this subject, see Seely's Resistance of Materials, 2nd Ed., Chapter 11.

Rupture from Impact. Since the stresses caused by moving loads increase with the velocity of the load, it is obvious that rupture may be caused by impact provided the load has the requisite velocity. The above formulas, however, do not apply, since they are valid only for stresses within the proportional limit. There being no rational formulas for rupture due to impact, the only information available has been obtained through experiment. The relation between the work required for rupture from impact and the work required under static loads has been determined by Hatt. From nearly 200 experiments he determined that the work required for rupture from impact was about 30 per cent greater than that required by static loads. From available test data it does not seem that the ultimate elongation under impact (dynamic) loads is widely different from that under static loads. For the results of a large number of impact tests on cast iron, see Proc. A.S.T.M., vol. xxxiii, Pt. 1, p. 87 ff., 1933.

BEAMS

By Jasper O. Draffin

9. THEORY OF FLEXURE

Types of Beams. A beam is a bar or structural member subjected to transverse loads that tend to bend it. Usually beams are horizontal bars designed to carry vertical loads, but any structural member acts as a beam if bending is induced by external transverse forces.

A Simple Beam (Fig. 1*a*) is a horizontal member that rests on two supports at the ends of the beam. All parts between the supports have free movement in a vertical plane under the influence of vertical loads.

A Fixed Beam, Constrained Beam, or Restrained Beam (Fig. 1*b*) is one that is rigidly fixed at both ends or rigidly fixed at one end and simply supported at the other.

A Continuous Beam (Fig. 1*c*) is a member resting on more than two supports.

A Cantilever Beam (Fig. 1*d*) is a member with one end projecting beyond the point of support, free to move in a vertical plane under the influence of vertical loads placed between the free end and the support.

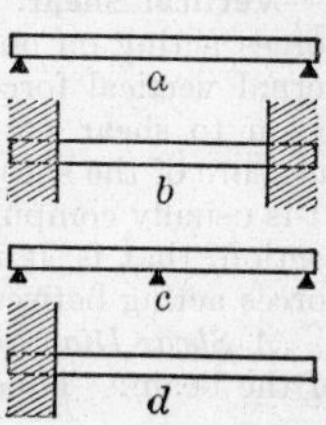

Phenomena of Flexure. When a simple beam bends under its own weight, the fibers on the upper or concave side are shortened, and the stress acting on them is compression; the fibers on the under or convex side are lengthened and the stress acting on them is tension. In addition to the longitudinal stresses acting on the fibers, shear exists along each cross-section, the intensity of the shear being greatest along the sections at the two supports and zero at the middle section.

Fig. 1

When a cantilever beam bends under its own weight the fibers on the upper or convex side are lengthened under tensile stresses; the fibers on the under or concave side are shortened under compressive stresses; the shear is greatest along the section at the support and zero at the free end.

The Neutral Surface is that horizontal section between the concave and convex surfaces of a loaded beam, where there is no change in the length of the fibers and no tensile or compressive stresses acting upon them.

The Neutral Axis is the trace of the neutral surface on any cross-section of a beam (Fig. 2).

The Elastic Curve of a beam is the curve formed by the intersection of the neutral surface with the side of the beam, it being assumed that the longitudinal stresses on the fibers are within the elastic limit.

Reactions at Supports. The reactions or upward pressures at the points of support are computed by applying the following conditions necessary for equilibrium of a system of vertical forces in the same plane: (1) The algebraic sum of all vertical forces must equal zero; *i.e.*, the sum of the reactions equals the sum of the downward loads. (2) The algebraic sum of the moments of all the vertical forces must equal zero.

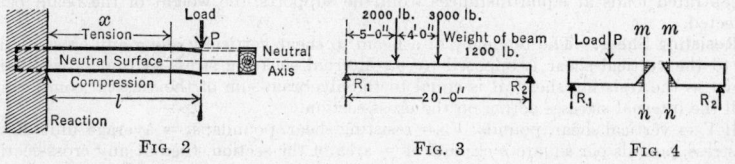

FIG. 2   FIG. 3   FIG. 4

From the first condition it is evident that in the case of a cantilever beam, where there is but one support, the reaction is equal to the sum of all vertical forces acting downward, comprising the weight of the beam and any loads that come upon it. Where there are two supports and the load is uniformly distributed, as is usually the case of the weight of the beam itself, or if equal concentrated loads are placed at equal distances from the center of the beam, each support carries one-half of the total load and the reactions are equal. If a beam supported at two points is not uniformly loaded each reaction must be computed separately by applying the second condition for equilibrium. Thus in Fig. 3 let R_1 and R_2 be the two reactions of a simple beam 20 ft long weighing 1200 lb, which carries concentrated loads of 2000 lb and 3000 lb at distances of 5 ft and 9 ft, respectively, from the left support. Taking a center of moments for convenience at the left support, and regarding the weight of the beam as a concentrated load applied at its center of gravity

$$+ 2000 \times 5 + 3000 \times 9 + 1200 \times 10 - R_2 \times 20 = 0. \quad R_2 = 2450 \text{ lb}$$

Taking a center of moments at the right support

$$R_1 \times 20 - 2000 \times 15 - 3000 \times 11 - 1200 \times 10 = 0. \quad R_1 = 3750 \text{ lb}$$

$R_1 + R_2 = 6200$ lb which is equal to the sum of all the loads acting downward.

Conditions of Equilibrium. Imagine a vertical plane cutting the beam, Fig. 4, into two parts at any section mn. The external forces acting on either part, comprising the loads and the reaction, are held in equilibrium by the tensile, compressive and shearing stresses acting on the fibers of the cross-section. From the conditions necessary for static equilibrium of a system of forces in one plane the following fundamental laws are deduced for the stresses at any cross-section:

(1) Sum of horizontal tensile stresses = sum of horizontal compressive stresses.
(2) Resisting shear = vertical shear. (3) Resisting moment = bending moment.

Vertical Shear. At any cross-section of a beam the resultant of the external vertical forces acting on one side of the section is equal and opposite to the resultant of the external vertical forces acting on the other side of the section. These forces tend to cause the beam to shear vertically along the section. The value of either resultant, which is a measure of the shearing tendency, is known as the vertical shear at the section considered. It is usually computed by finding the algebraic sum of the vertical forces to the left of the section, that is, it is equal to the left reaction minus the sum of the vertical downward forces acting between the left support and the section.

A Shear Diagram is a graphic representation of the vertical shear at all cross-sections of the beam. Thus in Fig. 5 the ordinates to the line AOB represent to scale the inten-

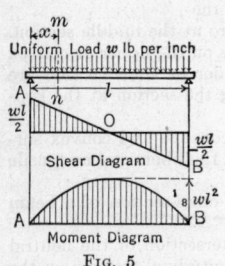

FIG. 5

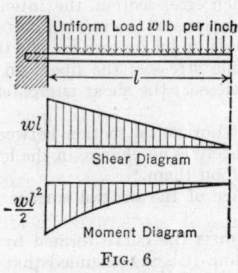

FIG. 6

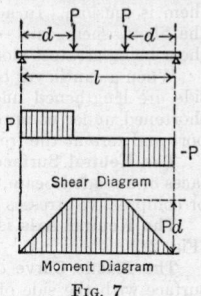

FIG. 7

sity of the vertical shear at the corresponding sections of the simple beam. In this case the vertical shear is greatest at the supports where it is equal to the reactions, and it is zero at the center of the span. In the cantilever beam, Fig. 6, the vertical shear is greatest at the point of support where it is equal to the reaction, and it is zero at the free end. Fig. 7 shows graphically the vertical shear on all sections of a simple beam carrying two concentrated loads at equal distances from the supports, the weight of the beam being neglected.

Resisting Shear. The tendency of a beam to shear vertically along any cross-section due to the vertical shear is opposed by an internal shearing stress at that cross-section known as the resisting shear; it is equal to the algebraic sum of the vertical components of all the internal stresses acting on the cross-section.

If V = vertical shear, pounds; V_r = resisting shear, pounds; s_s = average unit shearing stress, pounds per square inch; and A = area of the section, then at any cross-section

$$V_r = V = s_s A; \quad s_s = \frac{V}{A} \tag{1}$$

The resisting shear is not uniformly distributed over the cross-section, but the intensity varies from zero at the extreme fiber to its maximum value at the neutral axis.

At any point in any cross-section the vertical unit shearing stress, pounds per square inch, is

$$s_s = \frac{V A' c'}{I t} \tag{2}$$

where V = total vertical shear, pounds, for the section considered; A' = area, square inches, of cross-section between a horizontal plane through the point where the shear is being found and the extreme fiber on the same side of the neutral axis; c' = distance, inches, from the neutral axis to the center of gravity of the area A'; I = moment of inertia of the section, inches^4; t = width of section at plane of shear, inches. For a solid rectangular beam, the maximum value of the unit shearing stress is

$$s_s = \frac{3V}{2A} \tag{3}$$

where A = total area, square inches, of cross-section of the beam; for a solid circular beam, the maximum unit shearing stress is

$$s_s = \frac{4V}{3A} \tag{4}$$

Horizontal Shear. If at any point within a body subject to stress, there exists a unit shearing stress along one plane, there must also be an equal unit shearing stress along a perpendicular plane through that point. For proof of this see Laurson and Cox: Properties and Mechanics of Materials (John Wiley & Sons, New York), p. 134. In a beam, at any cross-section where there is a vertical shearing force there must be resultant unit shearing stresses acting on the vertical faces of particles which lie at that section. On a horizontal surface of such a particle, there is a unit shearing stress equal to the unit shearing stress on a vertical surface of the particle. Equation 2 therefore also gives the horizontal unit shearing stress at any point on the cross-section of a beam.

Bending Moment. The bending moment, or moment, at any cross-section of a beam is the algebraic sum of the moments of the external forces acting on either side of the section. It is considered positive when it causes the beam to bend convex downward, hence causing compression in upper fibers and tension in lower fibers of beam. When the bending moment is determined from the forces that lie to the left of the section, it is positive if it acts in a clockwise direction; if determined from forces on the right side, it is positive if it acts in a counter-clockwise direction. If the moments of upward forces are given positive signs, and the moments of downard forces negative signs, the bending moment will always have the correct sign, whether determined from the right or left side. The bending moment should be determined for the side for which the calculation will be simplest.

In Fig. 5 let M be the bending moment, pound-inches, at a section mn of a simple beam at a distance x, inches, from the left support, w = weight of the beam per 1 in. of length, and l = length of the beam, inches. Then the reactions are $1/2wl$ and $M = 1/2wl.x - 1/2x.wx$. For the sections at the supports $x = 0$ or l and $M = 0$. For the section at the center of the span $x = 1/2l$ and $M = 1/8wl^2 = 1/8Wl$, where W is the total weight.

A Moment Diagram (Figs. 5, 6, and 7) shows the bending moment at all cross-sections of a beam. Ordinates to the curve represent to scale the moments at the corresponding cross-sections. The curve for a simple beam uniformly loaded is a parabola showing $M = 0$ at the supports and $M = 1/8wl^2 = 1/8Wl$ at the center, M being in pound-inches.

The Dangerous Section is the cross-section of a beam where the bending moment is greatest. In a cantilever beam the dangerous section is at the point of support, regardless of the disposition of the loads. In a simple beam it is that section where the vertical shear changes from positive to negative, and may be located graphically by constructing a shear diagram, or numerically by taking the left reaction and subtracting the loads in order from the left until a point is reached where the sum of the loads subtracted equals the reaction. For a simple beam uniformly loaded, the dangerous section is at the center of the span.

Resisting Moment. The tendency to rotate about a point in any cross-section of a beam is due to the bending moment at that section; this tendency is resisted by the resisting moment which is the algebraic sum of the moments of all the horizontal stresses with reference to the same point.

Formula for Flexure. If M = bending moment, M_r = resisting moment of the horizontal fiber stresses, s = unit stress (tensile or compressive) on any fiber, usually that most remote from the neutral surface, and c = distance of that fiber from the neutral surface, then

$$M = M_r = \frac{sI}{c}; \quad s = \frac{Mc}{I} \tag{5}$$

where I is the moment of inertia of the cross-section with respect to its neutral axis. If s is in pounds per square inch, then M must be in pound-inches, I in inches^4, and c in inches. (For proof of the relation $M = sI/c$, see Seely's Resistance of Materials.) Formula 5 is the basis of the design and investigation of beams. It is true only when the maximum horizontal fiber stress s does not exceed the proportional limit of the material.

The **Moment of Inertia** is the sum of the products of each elementary area of the cross-section multiplied by the square of the distance of that area from the assumed axis of rotation, or

$$I = \Sigma r^2 \, \Delta A = \int r^2 \, dA \tag{6}$$

in which Σ is the sign of summation, $\Delta A =$ an elementary area of the section, and $r =$ distance of ΔA from the axis. It is evident that the moment of inertia is greatest in those sections (such as I-beams) having much of the area concentrated at a distance from the axis. Unless otherwise stated the neutral axis is the axis of rotation considered. I is usually expressed in inches^4.

Modulus of Rupture. To determine the ultimate strength of a material in bending, a beam is loaded to rupture and the maximum load which it carries is noted. The flexure formula, $s = Mc/I$, is true only for stresses within the proportional limit of the material. Therefore, the value, s, of the rupture strength obtained from the breaking load by this equation is incorrect. However, the equation is used and the nominal value so found is called the *modulus of rupture*, which is a measure of the ultimate load-carrying capacity of the beam. If the strengths in tension and compression are different, the modulus of rupture is intermediate between the two. It is to be noted that the modulus of rupture does not express the actual stress in the extreme fiber of a beam, but is a quantity useful only as a basis of comparison.

The **Section Modulus** is the factor I/c in the flexure formula. It is a measure of the capacity of a section to resist any bending moment to which it may be subjected. The section modulus is expressed in inches^3. For values of I and I/c for simple shapes used as beam sections, see Table I. Properties of standard structural shapes are given in Tables 64 to 70, Section 1, and properties for other geometric sections in Table II, p. 4-20.

Table I.   Properties of Sections of Beams *

Section of beam	Moment of inertia, I, inches^4	Section modulus, I/c, inches^3	Radius of gyration, k, inches
	$bd^3/12$	$bd^2/6$	$d/\sqrt{12} = 0.289d$
	$\dfrac{b_1d_1{}^3 - b_2d_2{}^3}{12}$	$\dfrac{b_1d_1{}^3 - b_2d_2{}^3}{6d_1}$	$\sqrt{\dfrac{b_1d_1{}^3 - b_2d_2{}^3}{12(b_1d_1 - b_2d_2)}}$
	$\pi d^4/64$	$\pi d^3/32$	$d/4$
	$\pi(d_1{}^4 - d_2{}^4)/64$	$\pi(d_1{}^4 - d_2{}^4)/32d_1$	$\sqrt{d_1{}^2 + d_2{}^2}/4$
	$bd^3/36$	$bd^2/24$ (min.)	$d/\sqrt{18} = 0.236d$

* See also Table II, p. 4-20.

Elastic Deflection of Beams. When a beam bends under load, all points of the elastic curve except those over the supports are deflected from their original positions. The radius of curvature ρ of the elastic curve at any section is expressed as

$$\rho = \frac{EI}{M} \tag{7}$$

where E = the modulus of elasticity of the material, pounds per square inch; I = moment of inertia, inches^4, of the cross-section with reference to its neutral axis; and M = bending moment, pound-inches, at the section considered. Where there is no bending moment ρ is infinity and the curve is a straight line; where M is greatest ρ is smallest and the curvature, therefore, is greatest.

If the elastic curve be referred to a system of coordinate axes in which x represents horizontal distances, y vertical distances, and l distances along the curve, the value of ρ by the aid of the calculus is found to be $d^3l/dx.d^2y$. Substituting this value in the expression $\rho = EI/M$ and assuming that dx and dl are practically equal there results the following differential equation of the elastic curve which applies to all beams when the elastic limit of the material is not exceeded:

$$EI \frac{d^2y}{dx^2} = M \tag{8}$$

Equation 8 is used to determine the deflection of any point of the elastic curve by regarding the point of support as the origin of the coordinate axis and taking y as the vertical deflection at any point on the curve and x as the horizontal distance from the support to the point considered. The values of E, I, and M are substituted and the expression is integrated twice, giving proper values to the constants of integration, and the deflection y is determined for any point. See Table III.

Example. The cantilever beam shown in Fig. 2 has a length = l, inches, and carries a load P, pounds, at the free end. It is required to find the deflection of the elastic curve at a point distant x, inches, from the support, the weight of the beam being neglected.

The moment $M = -P(l - x)$; substituting in (8), the equation for the elastic curve becomes $EI(d^2y/dx^2) = -Pl + Px$. Integrating and determining the constant of integration by the condition that $dy/dx = 0$ when $x = 0$, there results $EI(dy/dx) = -Plx + 1/2Px^2$. Integrating a second time and determining the constant by the condition that $x = 0$ when $y = 0$, there results $EIy = -1/2Plx^2 + 1/6Px^3$, which is the equation of the elastic curve. When $x = l$ the value of y, or the deflection in inches at the free end, is found to be $-Pl^3/3EI$.

Deflection Due to Shear. The deflection of a beam as computed by the ordinary formulas is that due to flexural stresses only. In short beams the deflection due to vertical shear is sometimes appreciable and may need to be considered. Because of the non-uniform distribution of the shear over the cross-section of the beam, computing the deflection due to shear by exact methods is difficult. It may be approximated by $y_s = M/AE_s$, where y_s = deflection, inches, due to shear; M = bending moment, pound-inches, at the section where the deflection is calculated; E_s = modulus of elasticity in shear, pounds per square inch; A = area of cross-section of beam, square inches (see Seely's Resistance of Materials, 2nd Ed., p. 136). Swain says (Strength of Materials, McGraw-Hill Book Co., p. 223) that for a rectangular section the ratio of deflection due to shear, to deflection due to bending, will be less than 5 per cent, so long as the depth of the beam is less than 1/8 of the length.

10. BEAMS OF UNIFORM CROSS-SECTION

Design Procedure. In designing a beam the procedure is: (1) Compute the reactions. (2) Determine the position of the dangerous section and the bending moment at that section. (3) Divide the maximum bending moment (expressed in pound-inches) by the allowable unit stress (expressed in pounds per square inch) to obtain the minimum value of the section modulus. (4) Select a beam section with a section modulus equal to or slightly greater than the section modulus required.

Web Shear. A beam designed in the above manner is safe against rupture of the extreme fibers due to bending in a vertical plane, and usually the cross-section will have sufficient area to sustain the shearing stresses with safety. For short beams carrying heavy loads, however, the vertical shear at the supports is large, and it may be necessary to increase the area of the section to keep the unit shearing stress within the limit allowed. For steel beams, the average unit shearing stress is computed by $s_s = V/A$, where V = total vertical shear, pounds; and A = area of web, square inches. For allowable average unit shearing stresses in cross-section of web of girders and rolled steel beams, as specified by different authorities, see Table II. For timber beams, see Horizontal Shear in Timber Beams, p. 5–25.

Miscellaneous Considerations. Other considerations which will influence the choice of section under certain conditions of loading are: (1) The maximum vertical deflection that may be permitted in beams coming in contact with plaster. (2) The danger of failure by sidewise bending in long beams unbraced against lateral deflection. (3) The danger of failure by the buckling of the web of steel beams of short span carrying heavy loads. (4) The danger of failure by horizontal shear, particularly in wooden beams.

Table II. Allowable Unit Stresses for Structural Steel as Specified by Different Authorities

All stresses in pounds per square inch. l = length of member; b = width of flange; k = radius of gyration; d = depth of web plate; t = thickness of web plate; all dimensions in inches.

Character of Stress	Report of U. S. Bureau of Standards		A.I.S.C. 1934, New York City	A.R.E.A
	Acceptable Steel *	Standard Steel		
Axial tension	16,000	18,000	18,000	16,000
Direct compression	12,500	14,000	18,000	12,500
Compression in columns	$16,000 - 60l/k$ Max. 12,500	$18,000 - 70l/k$ Max. 14,000	$\dfrac{18,000}{1 + l^2/(18,000k^2)}$ Max. 15,000	$15,000 - 50l/k$ Max. 12,500
Fiber stress in flexure in tension or in compression where l/b is 15 or less	16,000	18,000	18,000	16,000
Compressive fiber stress in flexure for l/b greater than 15 and not exceeding 40	$19,600 - 240l/b$	$22,000 - 270l/b$	$\dfrac{20,000}{1 + l^2/(2000b^2)}$	$16,000 - 150l/b$
Fiber stress on pins	24,000	27,000	27,000	24,000
Bearing on plane faced or rolled surfaces	24,000	27,000	....	24,000
Shear in gross section of web of girders or rolled beams where d/t does not exceed value indicated as Q.	$Q = 43$ 10,700	$Q = 43$ 12,000	$Q = 60$ 12,000	10,000
Shear where d/t exceeds the value indicated as Q	$Q = 43$ $13,300 - 62d/t$	$Q = 43$ $15,000 - 70d/t$	$Q = 60$ † $\dfrac{18,000}{1 + d^2/(7200t^2)}$	....
Shear in power-driven rivets or turned bolts	12,000	13,500	13,500	12,000
Shear in hand-driven rivets or rough bolts	9,000	10,000	10,000	9,000
Bearing on power-driven rivets, pins, or turned bolts in reamed holes, single shear	24,000	24,000	24,000	24,000
Bearing on power-driven rivets, pins, or turned bolts in reamed holes, double shear	30,000	30,000	30,000	24,000
Bearing on hand-driven rivets or unfinished bolts, single shear	16,000	16,000	16,000	18,000
Bearing on hand-driven rivets or unfinished bolts, double shear	20,000	20,000	20,000	18,000

* Steel acceptable to the building official but the origin and physical characteristics of which are not determined.

† New York specifies no values beyond $Q = 60$.

Vertical Deflection. When a beam is to be used to support or come in contact with materials like plaster, which may be broken by excessive deflection of the beam, it is usual in practice to select such a beam that the maximum deflection will not be greater than $1/360$ of the span.

It may be shown that for a simple beam, supported at the ends, with a total uniformly distributed load W, pounds, the deflection, inches, is

$$y = 30 \frac{sL^2}{Ed} \tag{9}$$

where s = allowable fiber unit stress, pounds per square inch; L = span of beam, feet; E = modulus of elasticity, pounds per square inch; d = depth of beam, inches.

If the deflection of a steel beam is to be less than $1/360$ of the span, it may be shown from equation 9 that, for a maximum allowable fiber stress of 18,000 lb per sq in., the limit of span in feet is approximately 1.8 times the depth of the beam in inches.

For the deflection due to the impact of a moving load falling on a beam, see p. 18.

Lateral Deflection. When a beam carries vertical loads, the tensile stresses in the fibers tend to hold the tension flange of the beam in line, but the compressive stresses tend to cause lateral bending of the compression flange. To obtain security against failure of long beams by excessive lateral deflection, sidewise bracing of the compresson flange should be used or the allowable unit stress for the compression fibers should be reduced. The specifications for steel structures of the American Bridge Company provide that "the lateral unsupported length of beams and girders shall not exceed 40 times the width of the compression flange. When the unsupported length l, inches, exceeds 10 times the width b, inches, of the compression flange, the stress per square inch shall not exceed $(19,000 - 300\ l/b)$." The values specified by other authorities are given in Table II. See Examples in Beam Design, p. 5-30.

Buckling of the Web. When a short-span steel beam, carrying heavy concentrated loads, has sufficient web thickness safely to resist shearing stresses, there is still a possibility that the beam is overloaded when the web is considered as a long slender column. The probability of this type of failure is not great if the web thickness is a relatively large percentage of the depth of beam, but it is great if the web is thin and the depth of the beam relatively large. Failure of the web by buckling may be guarded against by increasing its thickness, or by riveting stiffening angles to it. The A.I.S.C. specifications require stiffeners to be placed on the webs of rolled beams and plate girders at the ends, at point of concentrated loads, and at other points where h, the clear distance between flanges, inches, is more than $85t\sqrt{18,000(A/V)} - 1$, where t = thickness of web, inches; A = gross area of web, square inches; and V = total vertical shear at the section. Where stiffeners are required, the distance between them shall not be more than $85\,t\sqrt{18,000(A/V)} - 1$ inches or more than 6 ft.

Also, the web over a support may crush, if the end bearing is too short; with a thick web, crushing at the junction of the web and flange may occur, but with a thin web and deep beam the web probably will buckle because of column action before it will crush. Security against this excessive stress in the web may be provided by stiffening angles riveted to the web and bearing against the flanges over the support. Such stiffening angles should be placed either directly over the support or at a distance from the support equal to the depth of the beam. If stiffening angles are not used, the allowable reaction recommended by the A.I.S.C. (A.I.S.C.: Steel Construction, 1934) is given by $R = s_b t(a + d/4)$, where $s_b = 18,000/[1 + (d^2/6000t^2)]$, with a maximum of 15,000 lb per sq in.; R = allowable end reaction, pounds; s_b = allowable web crippling unit stress, pound per sq in.; t = web thickness, inches; a = length of bearing, inches; d = depth of beam, inches.

When the loading reaction exceeds the value of R, the web must be stiffened or additional length of bearing provided. In no case may the loading reaction exceed the maximum web shear V. Lack of proper lateral support for the top flange of the beam at the reaction point so decreases the crippling strength of the web as to render such practice inadmissible. For tests on web buckling, see *Bull.* Nos. 68, 86, and 241, *Eng. Exp. Sta.*, Univ. of Ill.

Horizontal Shear in Timber Beams. (See Horizontal Shear, p. 5-21.) In beams of a homogeneous material which can withstand equally well shearing stresses in any direction, the vertical and horizontal shearing stresses are equally important. In timber, however, the shearing strength along the grain is much less than that perpendicular to the grain, and hence the beams may fail owing to horizontal shear. Short wooden beams should be checked for horizontal shear in order that the allowable unit shearing stress along the grain shall not be exceeded. See Example 4, p. 5-30.

Restrained Beams. A beam is considered to be restrained if one or both ends are not free to rotate. This condition exists if a beam is built into a masonry wall at one or both ends, if it is riveted or otherwise fastened to a column, or if the ends projecting beyond the supports carry loads which tend to prevent the tilting of the ends which would naturally occur as the beam deflects. The shears and moments given in Table III for fixed end conditions are seldom if ever attained, since the restraining elements themselves deform and reduce the magnitude of the restraint. This reduction of restraint decreases the negative moment at the support and increases the positive moment in the central portion of the span. The amount of restraint which exists is a matter which must be judged for each case in the light of the construction used, the rigidity of the connections, and the relative sizes of the connecting members.

Table III. Bending Moment, Vertical Shear, and Deflection of Beams of Uniform Cross-section under Various Conditions of Loading

P = concentrated loads, lb.
R_1, R_2 = reactions, lb.
w = uniform load per unit of length, lb per in.
W = total uniform load on beam, lb.
l = length of beam, in.
x = distance from support to any section, in.
E = modulus of elasticity, lb per sq in.

I = moment of inertia, in.^{4}
V_x = vertical shear at any section, lb.
V = maximum vertical shear, lb.
M_x = bending moment at any section, lb-in.
M = maximum bending moment, lb-in.
y = maximum deflection, in.

SIMPLE BEAM—UNIFORM LOAD

$$R_1 = R_2 = \frac{wl}{2}$$

$$V_x = \frac{wl}{2} - wx$$

$$V = \pm \frac{wl}{2} \left(\text{when } \begin{cases} x = 0 \\ x = l \end{cases}\right)$$

$$M_x = \frac{wlx}{2} - \frac{wx^2}{2}$$

$$M = \frac{wl^2}{8} \left(\text{when } x = \frac{l}{2}\right)$$

$$y = \frac{5Wl^3}{384EI} \text{ (at center of span)}$$

SIMPLE BEAM—CONCENTRATED LOAD AT ANY POINT

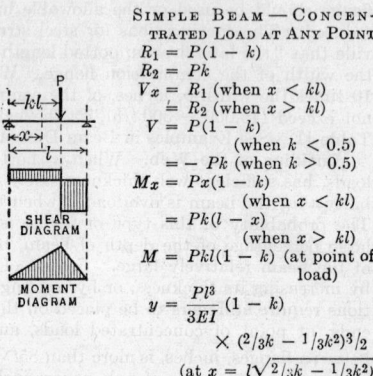

$$R_1 = P(1 - k)$$
$$R_2 = Pk$$
$$V_x = R_1 \text{ (when } x < kl)$$
$$= R_2 \text{ (when } x > kl)$$
$$V = P(1 - k)$$
$$\text{(when } k < 0.5)$$
$$= -Pk \text{ (when } k > 0.5)$$
$$M_x = Px(1 - k)$$
$$\text{(when } x < kl)$$
$$= Pk(l - x)$$
$$\text{(when } x > kl)$$
$$M = Pkl(1 - k) \text{ (at point of load)}$$
$$y = \frac{Pl^3}{3EI} (1 - k)$$
$$\times (2/3k - 1/3k^2)^3/2$$
$$(\text{at } x = l\sqrt{2/3k - 1/3k^2})$$

SIMPLE BEAM—CONCENTRATED LOAD AT CENTER

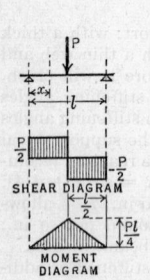

$$R_1 = R_2 = \frac{P}{2}$$

$$V_x = V = \pm \frac{P}{2}$$

$$M_x = \frac{Px}{2}$$

$$M = \frac{Pl}{4} \left(\text{when } x = \frac{l}{2}\right)$$

$$y = \frac{Pl^3}{48EI}$$

$$\text{(at center of span)}$$

SIMPLE BEAM—TWO EQUAL CONCENTRATED LOADS AT EQUAL DISTANCES FROM SUPPORTS

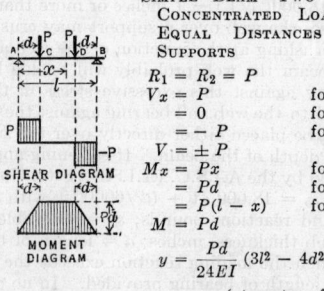

$$R_1 = R_2 = P$$
$$V_x = P \qquad \text{for AC}$$
$$= 0 \qquad \text{for CD}$$
$$= -P \qquad \text{for DB}$$
$$V = \pm P$$
$$M_x = Px \qquad \text{for AC}$$
$$= Pd \qquad \text{for CD}$$
$$= P(l - x) \quad \text{for DB}$$
$$M = Pd$$

$$y = \frac{Pd}{24EI} (3l^2 - 4d^2)$$

$$\text{(at center of span)}$$

SIMPLE BEAM—LOAD INCREASING UNIFORMLY FROM SUPPORTS TO CENTER OF SPAN

$$R_1 = R_2 = \frac{W}{2}$$

$$V_x = W \left(\frac{1}{2} - \frac{2x^2}{l^2}\right)$$

$$\left(\text{when } x < \frac{l}{2}\right)$$

$$V = \pm \frac{W}{2} \text{ (at supports)}$$

$$M_x = Wx \left(\frac{1}{2} - \frac{2x^2}{3l^2}\right)$$

$$M = \frac{Wl}{6} \text{ (at center of span)}$$

$$y = \frac{Wl^3}{60EI} \text{ (at center of span)}$$

CANTILEVER BEAM—LOAD CONCENTRATED AT FREE END

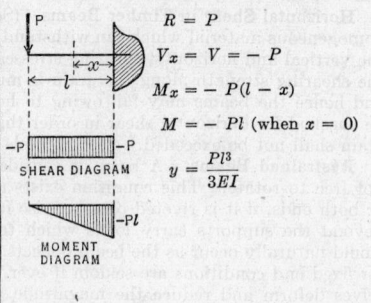

$$R = P$$

$$V_x = V = -P$$

$$M_x = -P(l - x)$$

$$M = -Pl \text{ (when } x = 0)$$

$$y = \frac{Pl^3}{3EI}$$

Table III—*Continued*

SIMPLE BEAM — LOAD INCREASING UNIFORMLY FROM CENTER TO SUPPORTS

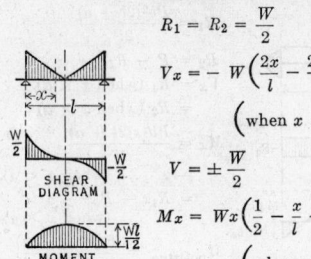

$$R_1 = R_2 = \frac{W}{2}$$

$$V_x = -W\left(\frac{2x}{l} - \frac{2x^2}{l^2} - \frac{1}{2}\right)$$

$$\left(\text{when } x < \frac{l}{2}\right)$$

$$V = \pm \frac{W}{2}$$

$$M_x = Wx\left(\frac{1}{2} - \frac{x}{l} + \frac{2}{3}\frac{x^2}{l^2}\right)$$

$$\left(\text{when } x < \frac{l}{2}\right)$$

$$M = \frac{Wl}{12} \quad \text{(at center of span)}$$

$$y = \frac{3}{320}\frac{Wl^3}{EI} \quad \text{(at center of span)}$$

CANTILEVER BEAM—UNIFORM LOAD

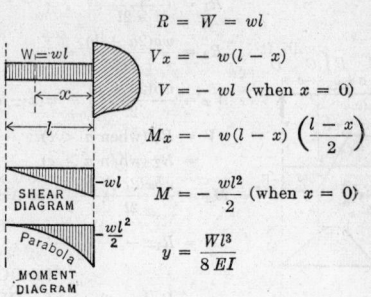

$$R = W = wl$$

$$V_x = -w(l - x)$$

$$V = -wl \quad \text{(when } x = 0)$$

$$M_x = -w(l - x)\left(\frac{l - x}{2}\right)$$

$$M = -\frac{wl^2}{2} \quad \text{(when } x = 0)$$

$$y = \frac{Wl^3}{8\,EI}$$

SIMPLE BEAM — LOAD INCREASING UNIFORMLY FROM ONE SUPPORT TO THE OTHER

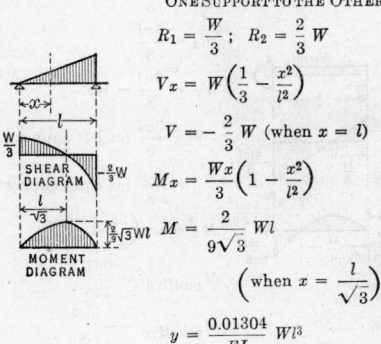

$$R_1 = \frac{W}{3} \; ; \;\; R_2 = \frac{2}{3}W$$

$$V_x = W\left(\frac{1}{3} - \frac{x^2}{l^2}\right)$$

$$V = -\frac{2}{3}W \quad \text{(when } x = l)$$

$$M_x = \frac{Wx}{3}\left(1 - \frac{x^2}{l^2}\right)$$

$$M = \frac{2}{9\sqrt{3}}Wl$$

$$\left(\text{when } x = \frac{l}{\sqrt{3}}\right)$$

$$y = \frac{0.01304}{EI}Wl^3$$

CANTILEVER BEAM—LOAD INCREASING UNIFORMLY FROM FREE END TO SUPPORT

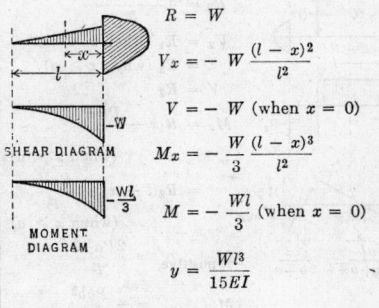

$$R = W$$

$$V_x = -W\frac{(l - x)^2}{l^2}$$

$$V = -W \quad \text{(when } x = 0)$$

$$M_x = -\frac{W}{3}\frac{(l - x)^3}{l^2}$$

$$M = -\frac{Wl}{3} \quad \text{(when } x = 0)$$

$$y = \frac{Wl^3}{15EI}$$

FIXED BEAM — CONCENTRATED LOAD AT CENTER OF SPAN

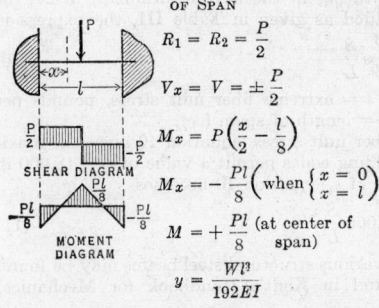

$$R_1 = R_2 = \frac{P}{2}$$

$$V_x = V = \pm \frac{P}{2}$$

$$M_x = P\left(\frac{x}{2} - \frac{l}{8}\right)$$

$$M_x = -\frac{Pl}{8} \quad \left(\text{when } \begin{cases} x = 0 \\ x = l \end{cases}\right)$$

$$M = +\frac{Pl}{8} \quad \text{(at center of span)}$$

$$y = \frac{Wl^3}{192EI}$$

FIXED BEAM—UNIFORM LOAD

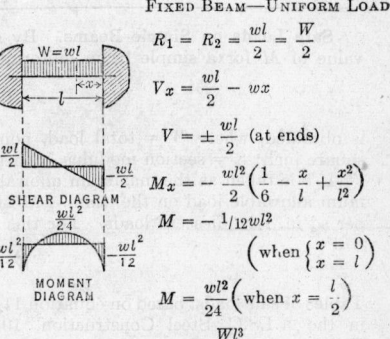

$$R_1 = R_2 = \frac{wl}{2} = \frac{W}{2}$$

$$V_x = \frac{wl}{2} - wx$$

$$V = \pm \frac{wl}{2} \quad \text{(at ends)}$$

$$M_x = -\frac{wl^2}{2}\left(\frac{1}{6} - \frac{x}{l} + \frac{x^2}{l^2}\right)$$

$$M = -1/12\,wl^2$$

$$\left(\text{when } \begin{cases} x = 0 \\ x = l \end{cases}\right)$$

$$M = \frac{wl^2}{24}\left(\text{when } x = \frac{l}{2}\right)$$

$$y = \frac{Wl^3}{384EI}$$

Table III.—*Concluded*

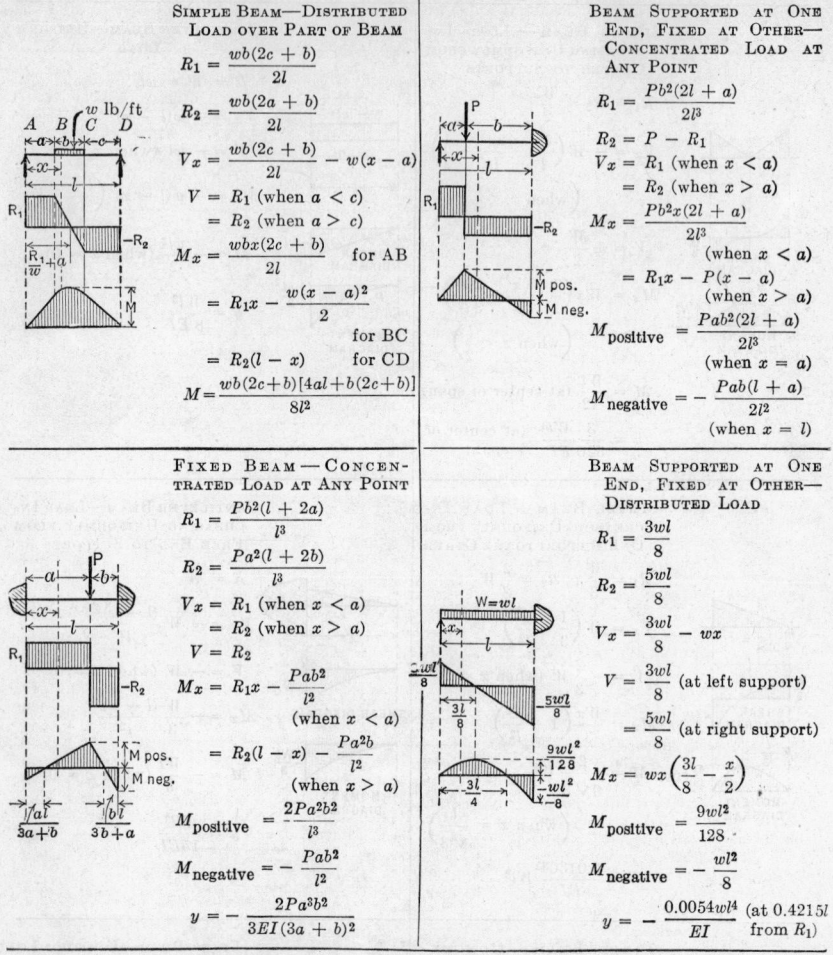

SIMPLE BEAM—DISTRIBUTED LOAD OVER PART OF BEAM

$$R_1 = \frac{wb(2c + b)}{2l}$$

$$R_2 = \frac{wb(2a + b)}{2l}$$

$$V_x = \frac{wb(2c + b)}{2l} - w(x - a)$$

$$V = R_1 \text{ (when } a < c)$$

$$= R_2 \text{ (when } a > c)$$

$$M_x = \frac{wbx(2c + b)}{2l} \quad \text{for AB}$$

$$= R_1 x - \frac{w(x - a)^2}{2}$$

for BC

$$= R_2(l - x) \quad \text{for CD}$$

$$M = \frac{wb(2c+b)[4al+b(2c+b)]}{8l^2}$$

BEAM SUPPORTED AT ONE END, FIXED AT OTHER—CONCENTRATED LOAD AT ANY POINT

$$R_1 = \frac{Pb^2(2l + a)}{2l^3}$$

$$R_2 = P - R_1$$

$$V_x = R_1 \text{ (when } x < a)$$

$$= R_2 \text{ (when } x > a)$$

$$M_x = \frac{Pb^2x(2l + a)}{2l^3}$$

(when $x < a$)

$$= R_1 x - P(x - a)$$

(when $x > a$)

$$M_{positive} = \frac{Pab^2(2l + a)}{2l^3}$$

(when $x = a$)

$$M_{negative} = -\frac{Pab(l + a)}{2l^2}$$

(when $x = l$)

FIXED BEAM—CONCENTRATED LOAD AT ANY POINT

$$R_1 = \frac{Pb^2(l + 2a)}{l^3}$$

$$R_2 = \frac{Pa^2(l + 2b)}{l^3}$$

$$V_x = R_1 \text{ (when } x < a)$$

$$= R_2 \text{ (when } x > a)$$

$$V = R_2$$

$$M_x = R_1 x - \frac{Pab^2}{l^2}$$

(when $x < a$)

$$= R_2(l - x) - \frac{Pa^2b}{l^2}$$

(when $x > a$)

$$M_{positive} = \frac{2Pa^2b^2}{l^3}$$

$$M_{negative} = -\frac{Pab^2}{l^2}$$

$$y = -\frac{2Pa^3b^2}{3EI(3a + b)^2}$$

BEAM SUPPORTED AT ONE END, FIXED AT OTHER—DISTRIBUTED LOAD

$$R_1 = \frac{3wl}{8}$$

$$R_2 = \frac{5wl}{8}$$

$$V_x = \frac{3wl}{8} - wx$$

$$V = \frac{3wl}{8} \text{ (at left support)}$$

$$= \frac{5wl}{8} \text{ (at right support)}$$

$$M_x = wx\left(\frac{3l}{8} - \frac{x}{2}\right)$$

$$M_{positive} = \frac{9wl^2}{128}$$

$$M_{negative} = -\frac{wl^2}{8}$$

$$y = -\frac{0.0054wl^4}{EI} \quad \begin{array}{l} \text{(at } 0.4215l \\ \text{from } R_1) \end{array}$$

Safe Loads on Simple Beams. By substituting in the flexure formula, p. 5–21, the value of M for a simple beam uniformly loaded as given in Table III, the expression

$$W = \frac{2}{3} s \frac{S}{L} \tag{10}$$

is obtained, where W = total load, pounds; s = extreme fiber unit stress, pounds per square inch; S = section modulus, inches³; L = length of span, feet.

If s is taken as the maximum allowable fiber unit stress, equation 10 gives the maximum allowable load on the beam. Most building codes permit a value of s = 18,000 lb per sq in. for quiescent loads. For this value of s, equation 10 becomes

$$W = 12,000 \frac{S}{L} \tag{11}$$

Tables of safe loads, based on equation 11, for various structural steel beams may be found in the A.I.S.C. Steel Construction, 1934, and in Kent's Handbook for Mechanical Engineers.

If the load is concentrated at the center of the span, the safe load is one-half the value given by equation 11. If the load is neither uniformly distributed nor concentrated at

Table IV. Allowable Unit Stresses for Timber in Bending *

Recommended by the Forest Products Laboratory, Forest Service, U. S. Dept. of Agriculture.† All values are in pounds per square inch.

Species	Continuously Dry — All Thicknesses		Occasionally Wet but Quickly Dried — 4 in. and Thinner		5 in. and Thicker		More or Less Continuously Damp or Wet — 4 in. and Thinner		5 in. and Thicker	
	Select	Common	Select	Common	Select	Common	Select	Common	Select	Common
Ash, black.............	1000	800	800	680	900	720	710	600	800	640
" commercial white...	1400	1120	1070	910	1200	960	890	760	1000	800
Aspen and large tooth aspen	800	640	580	490	650	520	440	370	500	400
Basswood.............	800	640	580	490	650	520	440	370	500	400
Beech.................	1500	1200	1150	980	1300	1040	890	760	1000	800
Birch, paper...........	900	720	670	570	750	600	530	450	600	480
" yellow and sweet..	1500	1200	1150	980	1300	1040	890	760	1000	800
Cedar, Alaska..........	1100	880	890	760	1000	800	800	680	900	720
" western red......	900	720	710	600	800	640	670	570	750	600
" northern and southern white..	750	600	580	490	650	520	530	450	600	480
" Port Orford......	1100	880	890	760	1000	800	800	680	900	720
Chestnut..............	950	760	760	650	850	680	620	530	700	560
Cottonwood, eastern and black................	800	640	580	490	650	520	530	450	600	480
Cypress, southern......	1300	1040	980	830	1100	880	800	680	900	720
Douglas fir (western Wash. and Ore.) ‡.........	1600	1200	1233	983	1387	1040	948	756	1067	800
Douglas fir (dense) ‡:....	1750	1400	1349	1147	1517	1213	1037	882	1167	933
" (Rocky Mt.)	1100	880	800	680	900	720	620	530	700	560
Elm, rock..............	1500	1200	1150	980	1300	1040	890	760	1000	800
" slippery and American	1100	880	800	680	900	720	710	600	800	640
Fir, balsam............	900	720	670	570	750	600	530	450	600	480
" commercial white....	1100	880	800	680	900	720	710	600	800	640
Gum, red, black, and tupelo	1100	880	800	680	900	720	710	600	800	640
Hemlock, eastern.......	1100	880	800	680	900	720	710	600	800	640
" western.......	1300	1040	980	830	1100	880	800	680	900	720
Hickory (true and pecan)	1900	1520	1330	1130	1500	1200	1070	910	1200	960
Larch, western.........	1200	960	980	830	1100	880	800	680	900	720
Maple, sugar and black...	1500	1200	1150	980	1300	1040	890	760	1000	800
" red and silver....	1000	800	800	680	900	720	620	530	700	560
Oak, commercial red and white...............	1400	1120	1070	910	1200	960	890	760	1000	800
Pine, southern yellow ‡...	......	1200	......	983	......	1040	......	756	......	800
" southern yellow (dense) ‡........	1750	1400	1349	1147	1517	1213	1037	882	1167	933
" northern and western white, western yellow, sugar.	900	720	710	600	800	640	670	570	750	600
" Norway..........	1100	880	890	760	1000	800	710	600	800	640
Poplar, yellow.........	1000	800	800	680	900	720	710	600	800	640
Redwood..............	1200	960	890	760	1000	800	710	600	800	640
Spruce, red, white and Sitka	1100	880	800	680	900	720	710	600	800	640
" Engelmann......	750	600	580	490	650	520	440	370	500	400
Sycamore..............	1100	880	800	680	900	720	710	600	800	640
Tamarack (eastern)......	1200	960	980	830	1100	880	800	680	900	720

* Stress in tension. The working stresses recommended for fiber stress in bending may be safely used for tension parallel to grain.

† American lumber standards. Basic provisions for American lumber standards grades are published by the U. S. Dept. of Commerce, Simplified Practice Recommendation No. 16, Lumber, revised July 1, 1926; specifications for grades conforming to American lumber standards are published in the 1933 Standards A.S.T.M., and in *Amer. Ry. Eng. Assoc. Bull.*, vol. xxx, No. 314, Feb. 1929.

‡ Exact figures given. In order to preserve the exact numerical relations among working stresses for grades involving rate of growth and density requirements, the values for Douglas fir (western Wash. and Ore.) and for southern yellow pine have not been rounded off, as have the values for the other species.

the center of the span, the beam must, in general, be designed as in the problems below. For some special conditions of loading, however, it is possible to find an equivalent uniformly distributed load (see A.I.S.C. Steel Construction, 1934, pp. 298 et seq.), in which case tables of safe loads may be used. The equations above are for beams laterally supported and are for flexure only. The other factors which influence the strength of the beam (see p. 5–23 et seq.) must still be considered.

Use of Tables in Design. Table III gives formulas for the maximum moment, vertical shear, and deflection under usual conditions of loading. Elements of various sections are given in Table I, p. 5–22. Elements of standard steel sections are given in Section 1.

Table IV gives the allowable unit stresses for timber in bending; in Table V are the allowable unit stresses for timber in compression and shear.

Examples in Beam Design: (1) **Concentrated Loads.** Find the beam section required to carry loads W_1, W_2, W_3, applied at points of a 15-ft span simple beam as follows: W_1 (assumed weight of beam) 40 lb per ft = 600 lb; W_2 = 10,000 lb at 5 ft from left support; W_3 = 8000 lb at 9 ft from left support. Computing the reactions

$$(R_1 \times 15) - (600 \times 7.5) - (10,000 \times 10) - (8000 \times 6) = 0$$
$$R_1 = 10,166 \text{ lb.}$$
$$- (R_2 \times 15) + (600 \times 7.5) + (10,000 \times 5) + (8000 \times 9) = 0$$
$$R_2 = 8433 \text{ lb.}$$

The dangerous section is directly under W_2, as at this point the vertical shear passes from positive to negative. The moment at this point is

$$M = (10,166 \times 5) - (5 \times 40 \times 2.5) = 50,330 \text{ lb-ft} = 603,960 \text{ lb-in.}$$

For an allowable unit stress of 18,000 lb per sq in., $I/c = 603,960/18,000 = 33.56$ in.$^3 = I/c$.

In Table 65, Section 1, a section modulus larger than the above is found in a 12-in., 31.8-lb American Standard beam which is, therefore, selected. If this section is used it will be necessary to support the compression flange by bracing to prevent lateral deflection, as the span length is 36 times the width of the flange. If bracing cannot be used a smaller allowable unit stress and, therefore, a larger section will be required. This larger section may be found as follows: Assume that a 12-in., 40.8-lb American Standard beam, which has a flange width $b = 5.25$ in., may be used. The allowable unit stress by the A.I.S.C. specifications (see Table II) is

$$s = \frac{20,000}{1 + \dfrac{l^2}{2000b^2}} = \frac{20,000}{1 + \dfrac{180^2}{2000 \times 5.25^2}} = 12,600 \text{ lb per sq in.}$$

$I/c = 603,960/12,600 = 47.9$ in.^{3} Thus a 12-in., 40.8-lb beam which has an I/c of 44.8 in.^{3} is too small; a 12-in., 50-lb, $I/c = 50.3$ in.^{3}, or a 15-in., 42.9-lb, $I/c = 58.9$ in.^{3} beam will be satisfactory.

2. Uniform Load. Select a beam section required to support a superimposed load of 27,000 lb. uniformly distributed over a simple beam with a span of 15 ft, assuming the beam to be braced against lateral deflection.

The beam to be used might be determined directly from a table of safe loads (see Safe Loads, p. 5–28). Such tables are given in Kent's Handbook for Mechanical Engineers. A solution can also be obtained by finding the maximum bending moment as follows:

For a uniformly distributed load, the dangerous section is at the center of the beam. The bending moment at this point (see Table III) is

$$M = \frac{Wl}{8} = \frac{27,000 \times 15 \times 12}{8} = 607,500 \text{ lb-in.}$$

For an allowable unit stress of 18,000 lb per sq in.,

$$s = \frac{607,500}{18,000} = 33.75 \text{ in.}^3$$

Referring to Table 65, Section 1, the section modulus of a 12-in., 31.8-lb American Standard beam is 36.0 in.^{3} The maximum safe load for this beam is

$$W = \frac{2sS}{3L} = \frac{2 \times 18,000 \times 36}{3 \times 15} = 28,800 \text{ lb}$$

The weight of this beam is $31.8 \times 15 = 477$ lb, making the actual total load 27,477 lb, which is less than the safe load for the beam selected, and hence this beam is satisfactory.

3. Wooden Beams. Design a southern pine girder of common structural grade to carry a load of 9600 lb, uniformly distributed over a 16-ft span simple beam in the interior of a building.

$$M = Wl/8 = 9600 \times 16 \times 12/8 = 230,400 \text{ lb-in.}$$

For an allowable unit stress of 1200 lb per sq in. (see Table IV) $I/c = 230,400/1200 = 192$ in.^{3} Referring to Table I, p. 5–22, the section modulus of a rectangular section is $bd^2/6$. Assume $b = 8$ in.; then $8d^2/6 = 192$, from which $d = \sqrt{144} = 12.0$ in. A girder 8 by 12 in. is tentatively selected.

4. Check the horizontal shear in the 8 by 12 wooden girder designed in example 3 above.

Maximum shearing stress (horizontal and vertical) is at the neutral surface over the supports. Using formula 3 for horizontal shear in a solid rectangular beam, p. 5–21,

$$V = 9600/2 = 4800, \quad A = 8 \times 12$$
$$s_s = \frac{3V}{2A} = \frac{3 \times 4800}{2 \times 96} = 75 \text{ lb per sq in.}$$

According to Table V, the safe horizontal unit shearing stress for common grade southern yellow pine is 88 lb per sq in. Since the actual horizontal unit shearing stress is less than this, the beam will be satisfactory.

Table V. Allowable Unit Stresses for Timber in Compression and Shear

Recommended by the Forest Products Laboratory, U. S. Dept. of Agriculture.*

All values are in pounds per square inch.

| Species | Compression ⊥ to Grain, Select and Common Grades | | | Horizontal Shear ‖ | | Compression ‖ to Grain (Short Columns with Ratio of Length to Least Dimension of 10 or Less) | | | | | | Average Modulus of Elasticity ‡ |
| | Continuously Dry | Occasionally Wet but Quickly Dried | More or Less Continuously Damp or Wet | Not Varied with Conditions of Exposure | | Continuously Dry | | Occasionally Wet, but Quickly Dried | | More or Less Continuously Damp or Wet | | Not Varied with Conditions of Exposure or Grade |
				Select	Common	Select	Common	Select	Common	Select	Common	
Ash, black	300	200	150	90	72	650	520	550	440	500	400	1,100,000
" commercial white	500	375	300	125	100	1100	880	1000	800	900	720	1,500,000
Aspen and largetooth aspen	150	125	100	80	64	700	560	550	440	450	360	900,000
Basswood	150	125	100	80	64	700	560	550	440	450	360	900,000
Beech	500	375	300	125	100	1200	960	1100	880	900	720	1,600,000
Birch, paper	200	150	100	80	64	650	520	550	440	450	360	1,000,000
" yellow and sweet	500	375	300	125	100	1200	960	1100	880	900	720	1,600,000
Cedar, Alaska	250	200	150	90	72	800	640	750	600	650	520	1,200,000
" western red	200	150	125	80	64	700	560	700	560	650	520	1,000,000
" northern and southern white	175	140	100	70	56	550	440	500	400	450	360	800,000
" Port Orford	250	200	150	90	72	900	720	825	660	750	600	1,200,000
Chestnut	300	200	150	90	72	800	640	700	560	600	480	1,000,000
Cottonwood, eastern and black	150	125	100	80	64	700	560	550	440	450	360	900,000
Cypress, southern	350	250	225	100	80	1100	880	1000	800	800	640	1,200,000
Douglas fir (western Wash. and Ore.) †	§ 347	§ 240	§ 213	90	72	1173	880	1067	800	907	680	1,600,000
Douglas fir (dense) †	379	262	233	105	84	1283	1027	1167	933	992	793	1,600,000
" " (Rocky Mt.)	275	225	200	85	68	800	640	800	640	700	560	1,200,000
Elm, rock	500	375	300	125	100	1200	960	1100	880	900	720	1,300,000
" slippery and Amer.	250	175	125	100	80	800	640	750	600	650	520	1,200,000
Fir, balsam	150	125	100	70	56	700	560	600	480	500	400	1,000,000
" commercial white	300	225	200	70	56	700	560	700	560	600	480	1,100,000
Gum, red, black, and tupelo	300	200	150	100	80	800	640	750	600	650	520	1,200,000
Hemlock, eastern	300	225	200	70	56	700	560	700	560	600	480	1,100,000
" western	300	225	200	75	60	900	720	900	720	800	640	1,400,000
Hickory (true and pecan)	600	400	350	140	112	1500	1200	1200	960	1000	800	1,800,000
Larch, western	325	225	200	100	80	1100	880	1000	800	800	640	1,300,000
Maple, sugar and black	500	375	300	125	100	1200	960	1100	880	900	720	1,600,000
" red and silver	350	250	200	100	80	800	640	700	560	600	480	1,100,000
Oak, commercial red and white	500	375	300	125	100	1000	800	900	720	800	640	1,500,000
Pine, southern yellow †	§	§	§	....	88	.....	880	.....	800	....	680	1,600,000
" southern yellow (dense) †	379	262	233	128	103	1283	1027	1167	933	992	793	1,600,000
" northern and western white, western yellow, sugar	250	150	125	85	68	750	600	750	600	650	520	1,000,000
" Norway	300	175	150	85	68	800	640	800	640	700	560	1,200,000
Poplar, yellow	250	150	125	80	64	800	640	700	560	600	480	1,100,000
Redwood	250	150	125	70	56	1000	800	900	720	750	600	1,200,000
Spruce, red, white and Sitka	250	150	125	85	68	800	640	750	600	650	520	1,200,000
" Engelmann	175	140	100	70	56	600	480	550	440	450	360	800,000
Sycamore	300	200	150	80	64	800	640	750	600	650	520	1,200,000
Tamarack (eastern)	300	225	200	95	76	1000	800	900	720	800	640	1,300,000

* See footnote (†), Table IV.

† See footnote (‡), Table IV.

‡ The values for modulus of elasticity are average for species, and not safe working stresses. They may be used as given for computing average deflection of beams. To prevent sag in beams, values one-half those given should be used. For safe loads for long columns, values one-third those given should be used.

§ Values given are for the Select grade. Working stresses in compression, perpendicular to the grain, for common grades of Douglas fir (western Wash. and Ore.) and southern yellow pine are 325, 225, and 200, respectively, for continuously dry, occasionally wet but quickly dried, and more or less continuously damp or wet conditions.

‖ Joint details. The shearing stresses for joint details may be taken for any grades as 50% greater than the horizontal shear values for the Select grade.

11. BEAMS OF UNIFORM STRENGTH

A **beam of uniform strength** is one in which the dimensions are such that the maximum fiber stress s is the same throughout the length of the beam. The form of the beam is determined by finding the areas of various cross-sections from the flexure formula $M = sI/c$, keeping s constant and making I/c vary with M. For a rectangular section of width b and depth d, the section modulus $I/c = \frac{1}{6}bd^2$ and, therefore, $M = \frac{1}{6}sbd^2$. By making bd^2 vary with M. the dimensions of the various sections are obtained. Table VI gives the dimensions b and d, at any section, the maximum fiber unit stress s, and the maximum deflection y, of some rectangular beams of uniform strength. In this table, the bending moment has been assumed to be the controlling factor. On account of the vertical shear near the ends of the beams, the area of the sections must

Table VI. Rectangular Beams of Uniform Strength *

s = maximum fiber unit stress, pounds per square inch; E = modulus of elasticity; w = uniform load, pounds per inch; d = depth of beam, inches; b = width of beam, inches; y = maximum deflection, inches. All other dimensions in inches.

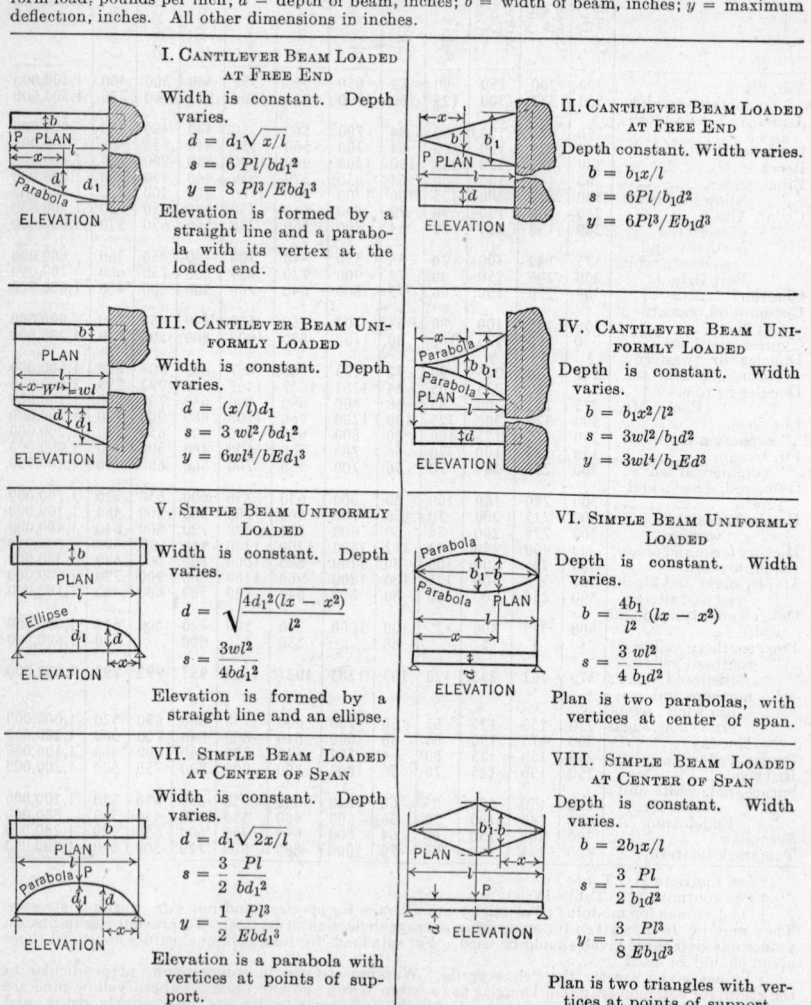

I. CANTILEVER BEAM LOADED AT FREE END

Width is constant. Depth varies.

$d = d_1\sqrt{x/l}$

$s = 6\,Pl/bd_1^2$

$y = 8\,Pl^3/Ebd_1^3$

Elevation is formed by a straight line and a parabola with its vertex at the loaded end.

II. CANTILEVER BEAM LOADED AT FREE END

Depth constant. Width varies.

$b = b_1x/l$

$s = 6Pl/b_1d^2$

$y = 6Pl^3/Eb_1d^3$

III. CANTILEVER BEAM UNIFORMLY LOADED

Width is constant. Depth varies.

$d = (x/l)d_1$

$s = 3\,wl^2/bd_1^2$

$y = 6wl^4/bEd_1^3$

IV. CANTILEVER BEAM UNIFORMLY LOADED

Depth is constant. Width varies.

$b = b_1x^2/l^2$

$s = 3wl^2/b_1d^2$

$y = 3wl^4/b_1Ed^3$

V. SIMPLE BEAM UNIFORMLY LOADED

Width is constant. Depth varies.

$d = \sqrt{\dfrac{4d_1^2(lx - x^2)}{l^2}}$

$s = \dfrac{3wl^2}{4bd_1^2}$

Elevation is formed by a straight line and an ellipse.

VI. SIMPLE BEAM UNIFORMLY LOADED

Depth is constant. Width varies.

$b = \dfrac{4b_1}{l^2}(lx - x^2)$

$s = \dfrac{3}{4}\dfrac{wl^2}{b_1d^2}$

Plan is two parabolas, with vertices at center of span.

VII. SIMPLE BEAM LOADED AT CENTER OF SPAN

Width is constant. Depth varies.

$d = d_1\sqrt{2x/l}$

$s = \dfrac{3}{2}\dfrac{Pl}{bd_1^2}$

$y = \dfrac{1}{2}\dfrac{Pl^3}{Ebd_1^3}$

Elevation is a parabola with vertices at points of support.

VIII. SIMPLE BEAM LOADED AT CENTER OF SPAN

Depth constant. Width varies.

$b = 2b_1x/l$

$s = \dfrac{3}{2}\dfrac{Pl}{b_1d^2}$

$y = \dfrac{3}{8}\dfrac{Pl^3}{Eb_1d^3}$

Plan is two triangles with vertices at points of support.

* The sections of the beams near the ends must be increased over the amounts shown to resist the vertical shear expressed by the formula $s = 3/2\,V/A$.

be increased over that given by an amount necessary to keep the unit shearing stress within the allowable unit shearing stress. The discussion of beams of uniform strength, though of considerable theoretical interest, is of little practical value since the cost of fabrication will offset any economy in the use of the material. A plate girder in a bridge or a building is an approximation in practice to a steel beam of uniform strength.

12. CURVED BEAMS

The derivation of the flexure formula, $s = Mc/I$, assumes that the beam is initially straight; therefore, any deviation from this condition introduces an error in the value of the stress. If the curvature is slight the error involved is not large, but in beams with a large amount of curvature, as hooks, chain links, frames of punch presses, etc., the error involved in the use of the ordinary flexure formula is considerable. The effect of the curvature is to increase the stress in the inside and to decrease it on the outside fibers of the beam and to shift the position of the neutral axis from the centroidal axis toward the concave or inner side.

The correct value for the fiber unit stress may be found by introducing a correction factor in the flexure formula, viz., $s = KMc/I$; the factor K depends on the shape of the beam and on the ratio R/c, where R = distance, inches, from the centroidal axis of the section to the center of curvature of the central axis of the unstressed beam; and c = distance, inches, of centroidal axis from the extreme fiber on the inner or concave side. Seely's Advanced Mechanics of Materials contains an analysis of curved beams and also Table VII which gives values of K for a number of shapes and ratios of R/c. For slightly different shapes or proportions K may be found by interpolation with a fair degree of approximation.

13. CONTINUOUS BEAMS

As in simple beams, the expressions $M = sI/c$ and $s_s = V/A$ govern the design and investigation of beams resting on more than two supports. In the case of continuous beams, however, the reactions cannot be obtained in the manner described for simple beams. Instead, the bending moments at the various sections must be determined, and from these values the vertical shears at the sections and the reactions at the supports may be derived.

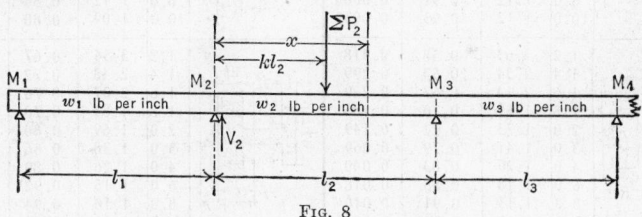

Fig. 8

Consider the second span of length l_2, in., of the continuous beam in Fig. 8. The vertical shear V_x at any section distant x, in., from the left support of the span is equal to the algebraic sum of all the vertical forces on one side of the section. Thus, if V_2 = the vertical shear at a section to the right of, but infinitely close to, the left support, $w_2 x$ = the uniform load and ΣP_2 = the sum of the concentrated loads along the distance x, applied at a distance kl_2 from the left support, k being a fraction less than unity, then

$$V_x = V_2 - w_2 x - \Sigma P_2 \qquad (12)$$

At any section distant x from the left support the bending moment is equal to the algebraic sum of the moments of all forces on one side of the section. If M_2 is the moment, lb-in., at the support to the left,

$$M_x = M_2 + V_2 x - (w_2 x^2/2) - \Sigma P_2(x - kl_2) \qquad (13)$$

Assume that $x = l_2$. Then M_x becomes the moment M_3 at the next support to the right, and the expression may be written

$$V_2 l_2 = M_3 - M_2 + (w_2 l_2^2/2) + \Sigma P_2(l_2 - kl_2) \qquad (14)$$

From the expressions 12, 13, and 14 it is evident that the bending moment M_x and the shear V_x at any section between two consecutive supports may be determined if the bending moments M_2 and M_3 at those supports are known.

Table VII. Values of Constant K for Curved Beams

Section	$\frac{R}{c}$	Values of K Inside Fiber	Values of K Outside Fiber	$\frac{Y_0}{R}$ *	Section	$\frac{R}{c}$	Values of K Inside Fiber	Values of K Outside Fiber	$\frac{Y_0}{R}$ *
	1.2	3.41	0.54	0.224		1.2	2.89	0.57	0.305
	1.4	2.40	0.60	0.151		1.4	2.13	0.63	0.204
	1.6	1.96	0.65	0.108		1.6	1.79	0.67	0.149
	1.8	1.75	0.68	0.084		1.8	1.63	0.70	0.112
	2.0	1.62	0.71	0.069		2.0	1.52	0.73	0.090
	3.0	1.33	0.79	0.030		3.0	1.30	0.81	0.041
	4.0	1.23	0.84	0.016		4.0	1.20	0.85	0.021
	6.0	1.14	0.89	0.0070		6.0	1.12	0.90	0.0093
	8.0	1.10	0.91	0.0039		8.0	1.09	0.92	0.0052
	10.0	1.08	0.93	0.0025		10.0	1.07	0.94	0.0033
	1.2	3.01	0.54	0.336		1.2	3.09	0.56	0.336
	1.4	2.18	0.60	0.229		1.4	2.25	0.62	0.229
	1.6	1.87	0.65	0.168		1.6	1.91	0.66	0.168
	1.8	1.69	0.68	0.128		1.8	1.73	0.70	0.128
	2.0	1.58	0.71	0.102		2.0	1.61	0.73	0.102
	3.0	1.33	0.80	0.046		3.0	1.37	0.81	0.046
	4.0	1.23	0.84	0.024		4.0	1.26	0.86	0.024
	6.0	1.13	0.88	0.011		6.0	1.17	0.91	0.011
	8.0	1.10	0.91	0.0060		8.0	1.13	0.94	0.0060
	10.0	1.08	0.93	0.0039		10.0	1.11	0.95	0.0039
	1.2	3.14	0.52	0.352		1.2	3.26	0.44	0.361
	1.4	2.29	0.54	0.243		1.4	2.39	0.50	0.251
	1.6	1.93	0.62	0.179		1.6	1.99	0.54	0.186
	1.8	1.74	0.65	0.138		1.8	1.78	0.57	0.144
	2.0	1.61	0.68	0.110		2.0	1.66	0.60	0.116
	3.0	1.34	0.76	0.050		3.0	1.37	0.70	0.052
	4.0	1.24	0.82	0.028		4.0	1.27	0.75	0.029
	6.0	1.15	0.87	0.012		6.0	1.16	0.82	0.013
	8.0	1.12	0.91	0.0060		8.0	1.12	0.86	0.0060
	10.0	1.12	0.93	0.0039		10.0	1.09	0.88	0.0039
	1.2	3.63	0.58	0.418		1.2	3.55	0.67	0.409
	1.4	2.54	0.63	0.299		1.4	2.48	0.72	0.292
	1.6	2.14	0.67	0.229		1.6	2.07	0.76	0.224
	1.8	1.89	0.70	0.183		1.8	1.83	0.78	0.178
	2.0	1.73	0.72	0.149		2.0	1.69	0.80	0.144
	3.0	1.41	0.79	0.069		3.0	1.38	0.86	0.067
	4.0	1.29	0.83	0.040		4.0	1.26	0.89	0.038
	6.0	1.18	0.88	0.018		6.0	1.15	0.92	0.018
	8.0	1.13	0.91	0.010		8.0	1.10	0.94	0.010
	10.0	1.10	0.92	0.0065		10.0	1.08	0.95	0.0065
	1.2	2.52	0.67	0.408		1.2	2.37	0.73	0.453
	1.4	1.90	0.71	0.285		1.4	1.79	0.77	0.319
	1.6	1.63	0.75	0.208		1.6	1.56	0.79	0.236
	1.8	1.50	0.77	0.160		1.8	1.44	0.81	0.183
	2.0	1.41	0.79	0.127		2.0	1.36	0.83	0.147
	3.0	1.23	0.86	0.058		3.0	1.19	0.88	0.067
	4.0	1.16	0.89	0.030		4.0	1.13	0.91	0.036
	6.0	1.10	0.92	0.013		6.0	1.08	0.94	0.016
	8.0	1.07	0.94	0.0076		8.0	1.06	0.95	0.0089
	10.0	1.05	0.95	0.0048		10.0	1.05	0.96	0.0057
	1.2	3.28	0.58	0.269		1.2	2.63	0.68	0.399
	1.4	2.31	0.64	0.182		1.4	1.97	0.73	0.280
	1.6	1.89	0.68	0.134		1.6	1.66	0.76	0.205
	1.8	1.70	0.71	0.104		1.8	1.51	0.78	0.159
	2.0	1.57	0.73	0.083		2.0	1.43	0.80	0.127
	3.0	1.31	0.81	0.038		3.0	1.23	0.86	0.058
	4.0	1.21	0.85	0.020		4.0	1.15	0.89	0.031
	6.0	1.13	0.90	0.0087		6.0	1.09	0.92	0.014
	8.0	1.10	0.92	0.0049		8.0	1.07	0.94	0.0076
	10.0	1.07	0.93	0.0031		10.0	1.06	0.95	0.0048

* Y_0 is distance from centroidal axis to neutral axis, where beam is subjected to pure bending.

To determine the bending moments at the supports an expression known as the *theorem of three moments* is used. This gives the relation between the moments at any three consecutive supports of a beam. For beams with the supports on the same level and uniformly loaded over each span the expression is:

$$M_1 l_1 + 2M_2(l_1 + l_2) + M_3 l_2 = -\,1/_4 w_1 l_1{}^3 - 1/_4 w_2 l_2{}^3 \tag{15}$$

in which M_1, M_2 and M_3 are the moments at three consecutive supports, l_1 the length between the first and second support, l_2 the length between the second and third support, w_1 the uniform load per lineal unit over the first span and w_2 the uniform load per lineal unit over the second span. When both spans are of equal length and when the load on each span is the same, $l_1 = l_2$, $w_1 = w_2$, and the above expression reduces to

$$M_1 + 4M_2 + M_3 = -\,1/2 w l^2 \tag{16}$$

which applies to most cases in practice.

Formulas 15 and 16 are used as follows: For any continuous beam of n spans there are $(n + 1)$ supports. Assuming the ends of the beam to be simply supported without any overhang, the moments at the end supports are zero and there are, therefore, $(n - 1)$ moments at the other supports to be determined. This may be done by writing $(n - 1)$ equations of the form of 15 or 16 for each support. These equations will contain $(n - 1)$ unknown moments and their solution will give values of M_1, M_2, M_3, etc., expressed as coefficients of wl^2. The shear V_1 at any support may be determined by substituting values of M_1 and M_2 in formula 14 and the bending moment at any point in any span

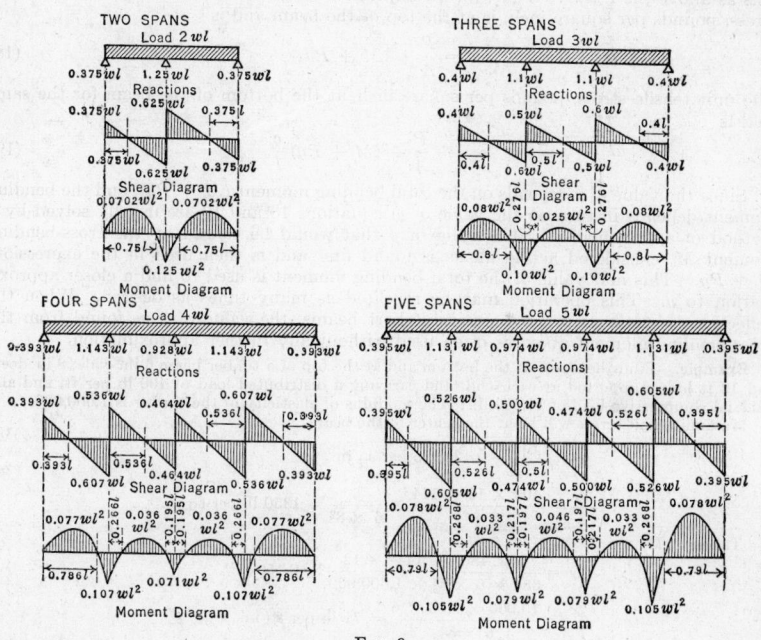

Fig. 9

may be obtained by formula 13. The shear at any point in any span may be determined from formula 12.

Fig. 9 gives values and diagrams for the reactions, shears, and moments at all sections of continuous beams uniformly loaded up to five spans. Note that the reaction at any support is equal to the sum of the shears to the right and to the left of that support.

14. AXIALLY END-LOADED BEAMS

(Condensed from Seely, Resistance of Materials, 2nd Ed., Chapter VII)

Deflection of Beam Negligible. When a beam is subjected to an axial end load as well as to a transverse bending load, the resultant unit stress developed at any point in the beam is the algebraic sum of the unit stresses produced by each of the loads acting independently of each other. If the beam of cross-sectional area A, square inches, is considered so short that its deflection under load may be neglected, the unit stress produced at any cross-section of the beam by an axial load P, pounds, is P/A. The maximum unit stress (tensile or compressive), pounds per square inch, due to the transverse or bending load is given by $s = M/(I/c)$ where M, pound-inches, is the maximum bending moment due to this load; I, inches[4], is the moment of inertia of the cross-section with respect to the neutral axis; c, inches, is the distance from the neutral axis to the extreme fiber. If the axial load is compressive, the maximum unit stress is compressive, occurring at the top of the beam, and is

$$s = \frac{P}{A} + \frac{Mc}{I} \tag{17}$$

The unit stress on the bottom fiber may be either tensile or compressive according as Mc/I is larger or smaller than P/A. If the longitudinal load P were a tensile load, the maximum unit stress would occur on the bottom fiber and would be a tensile stress.

Deflection of Beam Not Negligible. If the deflection of the beam is not negligible, the load P above cannot be considered to be an axial load with respect to any cross-sections except the end sections. The longitudinal load then has a moment arm equal to the deflection, and the stress due to this moment should be added algebraically to that caused by the other moments or loads. The stress due to deflection, y, inches (all other symbols as above), is Pyc/I. Thus, for a compressive longitudinal load, the maximum unit stress, pounds per square inch, is at the top of the beam and is

$$s = \frac{P}{A} + (M + Py)\frac{c}{I} \tag{18}$$

The unit tensile stress, pounds per square inch, at the bottom of the beam for the same load is

$$s = -\frac{P}{A} + (M + Py)\frac{c}{I} \tag{19}$$

Since the value of y depends on the total bending moment $(M + Py)$, and the bending moment depends in turn on the value of y, equations 18 and 19 are usually solved by a method of approximation. The value of y that would be caused by the cross-bending moment M, considered acting alone, is found first and is then used in the expression, $M + Py$. This new value of the total bending moment is used to find a closer approximation to y. This operation may be repeated as many times as desired. When the deflection is small, as in comparatively short beams, the value of y as found from the cross-bending moment above is often used without any further approximation.

Example. Find the stress at the bottom and at the top of a timber beam 6 in. wide, 8 in. deep, and 12 ft long, supported at each end, and carrying a distributed load of 400 lb per ft, and also an axial compressive load of 10,000 lb. The modulus of elasticity of the timber is 1,600,000. Maximum unit stress will be at the center of the beam.

$$\frac{P}{A} = \frac{10,000}{48} = 208 \text{ lb per sq in.}$$

$$\frac{Mc}{I} = \frac{400 \times 12 \times 144}{8} \times \frac{6}{6 \times 8^2} = 1350 \text{ lb per sq in.}$$

See Tables I, III, pp. 5–22, 5–26, 5–28.

$$y = \frac{5 \times 4800 \times 144^3 \times 12}{384 \times 6 \times 8^3 \times 1,600,000} = 0.456 \text{ in.}$$

$$\frac{Pyc}{I} = \frac{10,000 \times .456 \times 6}{6 \times 8^2} = 71 \text{ lb per sq in.}$$

Total unit compressive stress (top) = 208 + 1350 + 71 = 1629 lb per sq in.
Total unit tensile stress (bottom) = − 208 + 1350 + 71 = 1213 lb per sq in.

Here the stress due to deflection is small, as it usually will be in short deep beams.

COLUMNS

By Jasper O. Draffin

15. DEFINITIONS

A **Column** or **Strut** is a bar or structural member under axial compression, which has an unbraced length greater than about 8 or 10 times the least dimension of its cross-section. On account of its length, it is impossible to hold a column in a straight line under a load; a slight sidewise bending always occurs, causing flexural stresses in addition to the compressive stresses induced directly by the load. The lateral deflection will be in a direction perpendicular to that axis of the cross-section about which the moment of inertia is the least. Thus in Fig. 1A the column will bend in a direction perpendicular to aa; in Fig. 1B it will bend perpendicular to aa or bb and in Fig. 1C it is apt to bend in any direction.

The Radius of Gyration of a section with respect to an axis is equal to the square root of the quotient of the moment of inertia with respect to that axis divided by the area of the section, that is

$$k = \sqrt{\frac{I}{A}} \; ; \; \frac{I}{A} = k^2 \tag{1}$$

where I is the moment of inertia and A the sectional area. Unless otherwise mentioned, an axis through the center of gravity of the section is the axis considered. As in beams, the moment of inertia is an important factor in the ability of the column to resist bending, but for purposes of computation it is more convenient to use the radius of gyration.

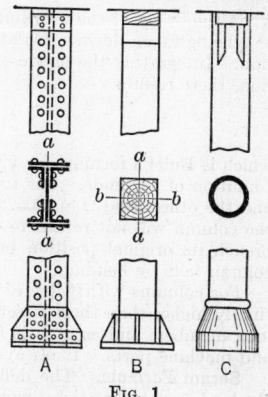

Fig. 1

The Length of a Column is the distance between points unsupported against lateral deflection.

Slenderness Ratio is the length l divided by the least radius of gyration k, both in inches. For steel, a *short column* is one in which l/k is less than about 20 or 30, and its failure under load is due mainly to direct compression; in a *medium length column*, l/k = about 30 to 175, and it will fail by a combination of direct compression and bending; in a *long column*, l/k is greater than about 175–200, and it will fail mainly by bending. For timber columns these ratios are about 0–30, 30–90, and above 90 respectively. The load which will cause a column to fail decreases as l/k increases. The above ratios apply to round-end columns. If the ends are fixed (see paragraph below), the effective slenderness ratio is one-half that for round-end columns, as the distance between the points of inflection is one-half the total length of the column. For flat ends it is intermediate between the two.

Condition of Ends. As in beams, the conditions of the points of support have an important influence on the ability of the column to resist bending. The various conditions which may exist at the ends of columns are usually divided into four classes. Columns with round ends are such that at the bearing at either end there is perfect freedom of motion, as there would be with a ball-and-socket joint at each end. Columns with hinged ends are such as have perfect freedom of motion at the ends in one plane, as in compression members in bridge trusses where the loads are transmitted through end pins. Columns with flat ends have the bearing surface normal to the axis of the column and of sufficient area to give at least partial fixity to the ends of the columns against lateral deflection. Columns with fixed ends have the ends rigidly secured so that under any load the tangent to the elastic curve at the ends will be parallel to the axis in its original position.

Experiments prove that columns with fixed ends are stronger than columns with either flat, hinged, or round ends, and that columns with round ends are weaker than any of the other types. Columns with hinged ends are equivalent to those with round ends in the plane in which they have free movement; columns with flat ends have a value intermediate between those with fixed ends and those with round ends. It often happens that columns have one end fixed and one end hinged, or various other combinations. Their relative values may be taken as intermediate between those represented by the condition at either end. The extent to which the strength is increased by fixing the ends depends upon the length of the column, fixed ends having a greater effect on long columns than on short ones.

16. COLUMN FORMULAS

There is no exact theoretical formula which gives the strength of a column of any length under an axial load. Formulas involving the use of empirical coefficients have been deduced, however, and they give results which are consistent with the results of tests of full-sized members.

Euler's Formula. In 1757 Euler published his formula, which is based on the assumption that the failure of a column is due solely to the stresses induced by sidewise bending. This assumption is not true for very short columns, which fail mainly by direct compression, nor is it true for columns of medium length such as are usually needed in practice. The failure in such cases is by a combination of direct compression and bending. For columns having a ratio of slenderness greater than 200, Euler's formula is approximately correct and agrees closely with the results of tests.

Let P = axial load, pounds; l = length of column, inches; I = least moment of inertia, inches⁴; k = least radius of gyration, inches; E = modulus of elasticity, pounds per square inch; and y = lateral deflection, inches, at any point along the column, that is caused by the load P. If a column has round ends, so that the bending is not restrained, the equation of its elastic curve is

$$EI \frac{dy^2}{dx^2} = - Py, \tag{2}$$

when the origin of the coordinate axes is at the top of the column, the positive direction of x being taken downwards and the positive direction of y in the direction of the deflection. Integrating the above expression twice and determining the constants of integration, there results

$$P = \Omega \pi^2 \frac{EI}{l^2} \tag{3}$$

which is Euler's formula for long columns. The factor Ω is a constant depending on the condition of the ends. For round ends $\Omega = 1$; for fixed ends $\Omega = 4$; for one end round and the other fixed $\Omega = 2.05$. P is the load at which, if a slight deflection is produced, the column will not return to its original position; if P is decreased the column will approach its original position but if P is increased the deflection will increase until the column fails by bending.

For columns with value of l/k less than about 150, Euler's formula gives results distinctly higher than those observed in tests. Euler's formula is now little used except for long members and as a basis for the analysis of the stresses in some types of structural and machine parts. It always gives an *ultimate* and never an allowable load.

Secant Formula. The deflection of the column is used in the Euler formula, but if the load were truly axial it would be impossible to compute the deflection. If the column is assumed to have an initial eccentricity of load of e inches (see Seely, Resistance of Materials, 2nd Ed., p. 212, for suggested values of e), the equation for the deflection y becomes

$$y_{\text{max}} = e \left(\sec \frac{l}{2} \sqrt{\frac{P}{EI}} - 1 \right) \tag{4}$$

and the maximum unit compressive stress becomes

$$s = \frac{P}{A} \left(1 + \frac{ec}{k^2} \sec \frac{l}{2} \sqrt{\frac{P}{EI}} \right) \tag{5}$$

where l = length of column, inches; P = total load, pounds; A = area, square inches; I = moment of inertia, inches⁴; k = radius of gyration, inches; c = distance from the neutral axis to the most compressed fiber, inches; E = modulus of elasticity, pounds per square inch; I and k are both taken with respect to the axis about which bending takes place. Because the formula contains the secant of the angle $(l/2\sqrt{P/EI})$ it is sometimes called the *secant formula*. It has been suggested by the committee on Steel-Column Research (*Trans., A.S.C.E.*, 1933) that the best rational column formula can be constructed on the secant type, though of course it must contain experimental constants.

The secant formula can be used also for columns that are eccentrically loaded if e is taken as the actual eccentricity plus the assumed initial eccentricity.

Rankine's Formula is a modification of an earlier formula by Gordon, and is sometimes called "Gordon's Formula." It applies to columns of slenderness ratios of 20 to 200, which are usually required in practice. Rankine's formula is based on the assumption that the maximum unit stress s, pounds per square inch, occurs in the fiber most remote from the axis on the concave side of the deflected column, and is equal to the sum of the direct unit compressive stress and the unit compressive stress due to bending alone; that is, $s = (P/A) + s_1$ in which P is the load, pounds; A the sectional area, square inches; and s_1 the unit compressive stress due to bending, pounds per square inch. The value of s_1 in this equation may be expressed in terms of P by using the flexure formula, since the action is analogous to that of beams. Let l = the length of the column, inches; I = the least moment of inertia, inches⁴; k = corresponding radius of gyration, inches; c = distance from axis to the remotest fiber on the concave side, inches; and y = lateral deflection of column, inches. Substituting in the flexure formula, $s_1 = Mc/I$, and by replacing M by its value Py and I by its value Ak^2, $s_1 = Pyc/(Ak^2)$. Hence the maximum unit compressive stress on the remotest fiber on the concave side is equal to $P/A + Pyc/(Ak^2)$. By analogy with the theory of beams the deflection y varies as l^2/c, so that by introducing an experimental coefficient ϕ, the expression for maximum unit stress may be written

$$s = \frac{P}{A} + \phi\left(\frac{Pl^2}{Ak^2}\right) = \frac{P}{A}\left[1 + \phi\left(\frac{l}{k}\right)^2\right] \tag{6}$$

which is Rankine's formula for the investigation of columns. Variations in the value of ϕ have been determined by many experiments on columns of different materials and different conditions of ends. The values in Table I are given in Merriman and have been used extensively in practice in the past. But present practice (1935) tends toward the use of the same constant for all end conditions, as tests show that for columns of the proportions in common use, variations in the material are more important than variations in end conditions.

Table I.   Value of Coefficient ϕ in Rankine's Formula

Material	Both Ends Fixed	Fixed and Round	Both Ends Round
Timber......................	1/3000	1.95/3000	4/3000
Cast iron....................	1/5000	1.95/5000	4/5000
Wrought iron................	1/36,000	1.95/36,000	4/36,000
Steel........................	1/25,000	1.95/25,000	4/25,000

The value to be taken for s in Rankine's formula is the ultimate compressive stress of the material for rupture, and the allowable compressive unit stress for design. Rankine's formula may be used in the investigation of an existing column by comparing the computed value of s with the proportional limit and with the ultimate strength of the material, thus determining the factor of safety. Similarly, the safe load P for an existing column may be computed by assuming an allowable unit stress s.

Ritter's Rational Constant. This is a theoretical value of ϕ such that it connects the curve for the Rankine formula with the curve for the Euler formula. Boyd's Strength of Materials gives its value as $\phi = s_u/(\pi^2 E)$, where s_u = ultimate compressive strength of material, pounds per square inch, and E = modulus of elasticity, pounds per square inch.

Straight-line Formula. The plotted results of actual tests on columns show that the relation between ultimate load and l/k is fairly well represented by a straight line, for columns which fail by flexure of the whole column and not by local collapse. For a value of $l/k = 0$, the average unit stress on the section, P/A, is equal to the ultimate in compression for brittle materials and to the yield point in compression for ductile materials. From the point thus determined the straight line representing the average results of tests is drawn tangent to the curve of Euler's formula for the material. The equation of the straight line is

$$\frac{P}{A} = s - C\frac{l}{k} \tag{7}$$

in which s is the unit stress at the ultimate in compression for a brittle material or at the yield point in compression for a ductile material, and C is a constant determined by experiment.

Table II gives average values of s and C for structural steel, cast iron, and wood. The loads given by the straight-line formula using the constants in this table are *ultimate loads*.

For purposes of design the straight-line formula is usually put in a form which gives allowable loads directly. Both the constant s and the constant C are divided by a factor of safety.

The straight-line formula is not suitable for investigating a column, that is, for determining the values of s due to given loads, because the term Cl/k is not a function of P/A. It may be used to find the safe load for a given column under a given unit stress, or to design a column for a given load and unit stress. From 1900 to 1930 the straight-line formula probably was used for designing more steel in America than the Rankine formula, but since 1930 the tendency has been towards the use of the Rankine type of formula. See Table V, p. 5–42.

Table II.   Ultimate Strength Constants for the Straight-line Column Formula—
$$P/A = s - Cl/k$$

Material	s lb per sq in.	C			Limit of l/k		
		Round	Fixed	One end round One end fixed	Round	Fixed	One end round One end fixed
Structural steel......	35,000	150	75	100	160	320	240
Cast iron...........	34,000*	175	88	116	90	160	115
Wood..............	5,000*	40	20	30	75	150	112

* This is less than the ultimate in compression for small specimens of cast iron or wood, but from tests of full-size columns it seems to be the value to be used for full-size castings or timbers which may contain defects.

17. WOODEN COLUMNS

Wooden Column Formulas. One of the principal formulas is that formerly used by the A.R.E.A., $P/A = s_1(1 - l/60d)$, where P/A = allowable unit load, pounds per square inch; s_1 = allowable unit stress in direct compression on short blocks, pounds per square inch; l = length, inches; d = least dimension, inches. This formula is being replaced rapidly by formulas recommended by the A.S.T.M. and A.R.E.A. Committees of these societies, working with the U. S. Forest Products Laboratory, classified timber columns into three groups, as follows (A.S.T.M. Standards, 1933, D245–33):

1. Short Columns. The ratio of unsupported length to least dimension does not exceed 10. For these columns, the allowable unit stress should not be greater than the values given in Table V, p. 5–31, under compression parallel to the grain.

2. Intermediate-Length Columns. For columns the ratio of whose unsupported length to least dimension is greater than 10, the following formula, of the fourth power parabolic type, shall be used to determine the allowable unit stress until this allowable unit stress is equal to $2/3$ the allowable unit stress for short columns.

$$\frac{P}{A} = s_1\left[1 - \frac{1}{3}\left(\frac{l}{Kd}\right)^4\right] \tag{8}$$

where P = total load, pounds; A = area, square inches; s_1 = allowable unit compressive stress parallel to grain, pounds per square inch; see Table V, p. 5–31; l = unsupported length, inches; d = least dimension, inches. $K = l/d$ at the point of tangency of the parabolic and Euler curves, at which $P/A = (2/3)s_1$. The value of K for any species and grade is $(\pi/2)\sqrt{\dfrac{E}{6s_1}}$, where E = modulus of elasticity, pounds per square inch.

3. Long Columns. For columns in which P/A as computed by the formula above is less than $2/3\ s_1$, the following formula of the Euler type, which includes a factor of safety of 3, shall be used:

$$\frac{P}{A} = \frac{\pi^2}{36}\frac{E}{\left(\frac{l}{d}\right)^2} \tag{9}$$

Timber columns should be limited to a ratio of l/d equal to 50. No higher loads are allowed for square-ended columns. The strength of round columns may be considered the same as that of square columns of the same cross-sectional area.

Use of Timber Column Formulas. The values of E (modulus of elasticity) and s_1 (compression parallel to grain) to be used in the above formulas are given in Table V, p. 5–31. Table III gives the computed values of K for some common types of timbers. These may be substituted directly in the above formula for intermediate-length columns or may be used in conjunction with Table IV, which gives the strength of columns of intermediate length, expressed as a percentage of strength (s_1) of short columns. In the tables, the term " continuously dry " refers to interior construction where there is no excessive dampness or humidity; " occasionally wet but quickly dry " refers to bridges, trestles, bleachers and grandstands; " usually wet " refers to timber in contact with the earth or exposed to waves or tide-water.

18. STEEL COLUMNS

Types. Two general types of steel columns are in use: (1) rolled shapes; (2) built-up sections. The rolled shapes have had wide use since the introduction of wide-flanged

Table III. Values of K for Columns of Intermediate Length
A.S.T.M. Standards, 1933, D245-33

Species	Continuously dry		Occasionally wet		Usually wet	
	Select	Common	Select	Common	Select	Common
Cedar, western red...................	24.2	27.1	24.2	27.1	25.1	28.1
" , Port Orford..................	23.4	26.2	24.6	27.4	25.6	28.7
Douglas fir, coast region..............	23.7	27.3	24.9	28.6	27.0	31.1
" ", dense...................	22.6	25.3	23.8	26.5	25.8	28.8
" ", Rocky Mountain region...	24.8	27.8	24.8	27.8	26.5	29.7
Hemlock, west coast.................	25.3	28.3	25.3	28.3	26.8	30.0
Larch, western......................	22.0	24.6	23.1	25.8	25.8	28.8
Oak, red and white..................	24.8	27.8	26.1	29.3	27.7	31.1
Pine, southern......................	....	27.3	....	28.6	....	31.1
" , dense..........................	22.6	25.3	23.8	26.5	25.8	28.8
Redwood............................	22.2	24.8	23.4	26.1	25.6	28.6
Spruce, red, white, Sitka............	24.8	27.8	25.6	28.7	27.5	30.8

Table IV. Strength of Columns of Intermediate Length, Expressed as a Percentage of Strength of Short Columns
A.S.T.M. Standards, 1933, D245-33

Values for the expression $\left[1 - \frac{1}{3}\left(\frac{l}{Kd}\right)^4 \right]$ in the formula: $\frac{P}{A} = s_1\left[1 - \frac{1}{3}\left(\frac{l}{Kd}\right)^4 \right]$

K	Ratio of Length to Least Dimension in Rectangular Timbers, l/d																			
	12	13	14	15	16	17	18	19	20	21	22	23	24	25	26	27	28	29	30	31
22	97	96	95	93	91	88	85	81	77	72	67	...	...	...	...	...	...	...	...	...
23	98	97	95	94	92	90	87	84	81	77	72	67	...	...	...	...	...	...	...	...
24	98	97	96	95	93	92	89	87	84	80	76	72	67	...	...	...	...	...	...	...
25	98	98	97	96	94	93	91	89	86	83	80	76	72	67	...	...	...	...	...	...
26	99	98	97	96	95	93	92	91	89	86	83	80	76	72	67	...	...	...	...	...
27	99	98	98	97	96	95	93	92	90	88	85	82	79	74	71	67	...	...	...	...
28	99	98	98	97	96	95	94	93	91	89	87	85	82	79	75	71	67	...	...	...
29	99	99	98	98	97	96	95	94	92	91	89	87	84	82	79	75	71	67	...	...
30	99	99	98	98	97	97	96	95	94	92	90	88	86	84	81	78	75	71	67	...
31	99	99	99	98	98	97	96	95	94	93	92	90	88	86	84	81	78	75	71	67

NOTE: This table can also be used for columns not rectangular, the l/d being equivalent to $0.289l/k$, where k is the least radius of gyration of the section.

sections, especially since they may be obtained with large cross-sectional area. They are easily fabricated, accessible for painting, neat in appearance where they are not covered, and convenient in making connections. A disadvantage is the probability that thick sections are of lower-strength material than thin sections owing to the difficulty of adequately rolling the thick material. For the effect of thickness of material on yield point, see *Trans. A.S.C.E.*, vol. xcviii, p. 1377, 1933.

Guiding Principles in Design. The design of steel columns is always a cut-and-try method, as no law governs the relation between area and radius of gyration of the section. A column of given area is selected, and the amount of load that it will carry is computed by the proper formula. If the allowable load so computed is less than that to be carried, a larger column is selected and the load for it computed, the process being repeated until a proper section is found.

A few general principles should guide in proportioning columns. The radius of gyration should be approximately the same in the two directions at right angles to each other; the slenderness ratio of the separate parts of the column should not be greater than that of the column as a whole; the different parts should be adequately connected in order that the column may function as a single unit; the material should be distributed as far as possible from the center line in order to increase the radius of gyration.

Steel Column Formulas. Table V gives the more commonly used formulas. Table VI gives the maximum values for the slenderness ratio for steel columns as specified by various authorities.

Example. It is required to design a rolled-section steel column 24 ft long, to carry a load of 270,000 lb, using the formula of the Chicago Building Code, $P/A = 16,000 - 70l/k$.

For the first estimate, an area of about 27 sq in. will be used. From Table 64, Section 1, a 12×12-in. wide-flange section weighing 92 lb per ft, area of 27.06 sq in., a least radius of gyration of 3.08 in. will be selected.

$P = 27.06 \{16,000 - (70 \times 24 \times 12/3.08)\} = 255,900$ lb.

This is too small. The next larger size, 99 lb per ft, has an area of 29.09 sq in., a radius of gyration of 3.09 in.

$P = 29.09 \{16,000 - (70 \times 24 \times 12/3.09)\} = 275,700$ lb, which is satisfactory.

Table V. Steel Column Formulas

Organization Recommending or Using Formula	Formula,* Allowable Load, lb per sq in.
New York City Building Code, 1930 Pacific Coast Building Officials Conference Massachusetts Building Officials Conference Philadelphia Building Code, 1929 Wisconsin Building Code American Institute of Steel Construction, 1934	$\dfrac{P}{A} = \dfrac{18,000}{1 + \dfrac{l^2}{18,000k^2}}$ Maximum 15,000 except Mass. B.O.C., which is 13,500
American Bridge Company	$l/k = 0$–60; $P/A = 13,000$ $l/k = 60$–120; $P/A = 19,000 - 100l/k$ $l/k = 120$–200; $P/A = 13,000 - 50l/k$
American Railway Engineering Association	$l/k = 0$–50; $P/A = 12,500$ $l/k = 50$–150; $P/A = 15,000 - 50l/k$ $l/k =$ above 150; $P/A = 6.4E/(l/k)^2$
Recommended Building Code for Working Stresses in Building Materials, U. S. Bureau of Standards, 1926	Standard Steel † $P/A = 18,000 - 70l/k$ Maximum 14,000 Acceptable Steel † $P/A = 16,000 - 60l/k$
Chicago Building Code	$P/A = 16,000 - 70l/k$ Maximum 14,000
United States Bureau of Public Roads	Live Load: $\dfrac{P}{A} = \dfrac{16,000}{1 + \dfrac{l^2}{13,500k^2}}$ Dead Load: $\dfrac{P}{A} = \dfrac{24,000}{1 + \dfrac{l^2}{13,500k^2}}$ Maximum is that for $l/k = 40$

* In the formulas given, P = total load on column, pounds; A = cross-sectional area, square inches; l = length of column, inches; k = least radius of gyration, inches; E = modulus of elasticity, pounds per square inch.

† Standard steel is steel which satisfies the A.S.T.M. specifications for Structural Steel for Buildings, A.S.T.M. Standards, 1934, A 9–34. Acceptable steel is steel which is acceptable to the building officials but whose origin and properties have not been definitely determined.

Table VI. Maximum Values of Slenderness Ratio (l/k) for Steel Columns

Organization or Authority Recommending or Specifying	Main Members	Secondary Members
American Railway Engineering Association, Railroad bridges...	100	120
New York City Building Code.................................	120	120
United States Bureau of Public Roads.......................	120	140
Chicago Building Code......................................	120	150
American Institute of Steel Construction...................		
American Bridge Company...................................		
Philadelphia Building Code.................................	120	200
Wisconsin Building Code....................................		
Pacific Coast Building Officials Conference................		
United States Bureau of Standards.........................	160	160
Massachusetts Building Officials Conference................	160	200

Bureau of Standards Tests of Steel Columns. The collapse of the Quebec Bridge in 1907, due to the failure of a column in the lower chord, brought about a review of ex-

Table VII. Data on Built-up Steel Columns Tested at U. S. Bureau of Standards

All columns tested with flat ends. Each tabulated value is the average of three tests. (See *Trans. A.S.C.E.*, vol. lxxxiii, pp. 1583–1688, 1919–1920.)

Type of Column	Area, sq in.	Slenderness Ratio, l/k	Useful Limit for Column, lb per sq in.	Ultimate Strength, lb per sq in.
Four 5×3×⁵/₁₆ in. angles	11.14	20	......	36,400
One 6×⁵/₁₆ in. plate	11.84	20	......	38,200
	11.14	50	28,800	32,700
	11.14	85	27,800	31,200
	11.21	120	26,600	28,300
	11.74	155	25,200	26,200
Four 5×3×⁵/₈ in. angles	22.10	20	......	44,400
One 6×⁵/₈ in. plate	22.31	20	......	43,600
	22.22	50	24,700	29,200
	22.03	85	25,300	28,100
	22.12	120	23,300	25,400
	22.34	155	21,900	22,700
Four 5×3×¹³/₁₆ in. angles One 6×⁷/₈ in. plate	28.44	85	26,200	27,700
Two 6-in., 10.5-lb channels	10.09	50	27,500	33,200
Two 8×¹/₄ in. plates	9.95	85	28,700	32,600
	10.06	120	27,000	29,300
	10.42	155	25,700	26,500
Two 6-in., 15.5-lb channels	17.03	50	26,800	32,300
Two 8×¹/₂ in. plates	17.07	85	26,700	30,600
	17.05	120	26,300	28,100
	16.81	155	24,000	24,900
Two 5-in., 6.5-lb channels	8.74	50	28,300	34,100
Two 9¹/₂×¹/₄ in. plates	8.67	85	28,000	32,400
	8.74	120	28,000	30,300
Two 5-in., 11.5-lb channels	16.43	50	25,300	29,500
Two 9¹/₂×¹/₂-in. plates	16.39	85	25,700	28,000
	16.46	120	25,700	26,900
Two 8-in., 11.25-lb channels	11.69	50	32,000	36,900
One 8-in., 18-lb I-beam	11.68	85	31,000	34,000
	11.68	120	30,000	31,900
	11.86	155	22,300	23,600
Two 8-in., 18.75-lb channels	16.88	50	22,500	29,100
One 8-in., 20.5-lb I-beam	16.92	85	23,300	26,600
	17.00	120	21,700	23,900
	16.58	155	23,300	23,300
One 8-in., 32-lb Bethlehem	9.64	50	34,700	38,000
H-beam	9.29	85	32,800	34,300
	8.64	120	31,100	32,000
One 8-in., 62-lb Bethlehem	17.85	50	24,200	31,600
H-beam	17.85	85	30,600	32,300
	17.82	120	29,300	30,000
One 8-in., 91-lb Bethlehem	27.39	50	19,700	25,200
H-beam	27.33	85	20,200	23,500
	27.54	120	19,200	21,300
Two 11×⁵/₁₆ in. plates	13.74	50	24,200	31,600
One 10-in., 25-lb I-beam	13.64	85	24,800	29,100
	13.71	120	24,500	27,200
Two 11×⁵/₈ in. plates	23.62	50	21,800	32,100
One 10-in. 35-lb I-beam	23.71	85	23,300	26,800
	23.74	120	22,500	24,800

Table VII—*Continued*

Type of Column	Area, sq in.	Slenderness Ratio, l/k	Useful Limit for Column, lb per sq in.	Ultimate Strength, lb per sq in.
Four $2 \times 2 \times 1/4$ in. angles	10.81	50	26,800	35,800
Two $9 \times 1/4$ in. plates	10.77	85	26,900	32,100
Two $5^1/4 \times 1/4$ in. plates	10.75	120	26,500	28,400
Four $2 \times 2 \times 7/16$-in. angles	18.53	50	26,000	31,800
Two $9 \times 7/16$-in. plates	18.67	85	24,500	28,300
Two $5^1/4 \times 1/4$-in. plates	18.70	120	24,000	26,300
Four 5-in. 10.1-lb. bulb angles	13.32	50	30,600	33,400
One $6 \times 5/16$-in. plate	13.37	85	29,400	31,600
	13.34	120	26,600	28,100
Four $4 \times 1/4$-in. Z-bars	11.01	50	31,300	35,700
One $7 \times 1/4$-in. plate	11.08	85	31,000	32,800
	11.11	120	28,200	29,700
Four $4 \times 5/8$-in. Z-bars	25.82	50	29,000	32,900
One $7 \times 5/8$-in. plate	25.50	85	29,700	31,400*
	25.68	120	25,500	27,300
One 6-in., 23.8-lb Carnegie	7.00	50	......	31,000
H-beam	7.00	85	......	30,400
	7.00	120	......	27,200
One 8-in., 34-lb Carnegie	10.00	50	......	33,500
H-beam	10.00	85	......	31,700
	10.00	120	......	29,200

* Average of two tests.

isting knowledge of steel columns. In 1913 the A.S.C.E., the A.R.E.A., and the U. S. Bureau of Standards cooperated in a test of columns. These columns were made to represent high-grade practice and covered a wide range of sections, both rolled shapes and built-up sections (*Trans. Am. Soc. C. E.*, vol. lxxxiii, 1919–1920).

The tests, summarized in Table VII showed that, for columns of the proportions commonly used, the effect of the variation in the steel, kinks, initial stresses, and similar defects in the column was more important than the effect of length. It also showed that the thin metal gave definitely higher strength, per unit area, than the thicker metal of the same type of section.

19. ECCENTRIC AND TRANSVERSE LOADS ON COMPRESSION MEMBERS

Eccentric Loads on Short Compression Members. Where a direct push acting on a member does not pass through the centroid but at a distance e, inches, from it, both direct and bending stresses are produced. For short compression members in which column action may be neglected, the direct unit stress is P/A, where P = total load, pounds, and A = area of cross-section, square inches. The bending unit stress is Mc/I where $M = Pe$ is the bending moment, pound-inches; c is the distance, inches, from the centroid to the fiber in which the stress is desired; I = moment of inertia, inches^4. The total unit stress at any point in the section is $s = P/A + Pec/I$, or $s = P/A(1 + ec/k^2)$, since $I = Ak^2$, where k = radius of gyration, inches.

Eccentric Loads on Columns. Various column formulas must be modified when the loads are not balanced, that is, when the resultant of the loads is not in line with the axis of the column. Let P be the load, pounds, applied at a distance e, inches, from the axis; the bending moment M is Pe. The maximum unit stress s, pounds per square inch, due to this bending moment alone, is $s = Mc/I = Pec/Ak^2$, where c = distance, inches, from the axis to the most remote fiber on the concave side; A = sectional area, square inches; k = radius of gyration in the direction of the bending, inches. This unit stress must be added to the unit stress induced if the resultant load were applied in line along the axis of the column. The modified formulas, expressed in allowable load per unit of area, are:

Modified Rankine's formula for eccentric loads (see p. 5-39):

$$\frac{P}{A} = \frac{s}{1 + \phi \left(\frac{l}{k}\right)^2 + \frac{ec}{k^2}} \tag{10}$$

Modified straight-line formula for eccentric loads (see p. 5-39):

$$\frac{P}{A} = \frac{s - \frac{Cl}{k}}{1 + \frac{ec}{k^2}} \tag{11}$$

The secant formula, see p. 5-38, can also be used for columns that are eccentrically loaded if the e in this formula is taken as the actual eccentricity plus the assumed initial eccentricity.

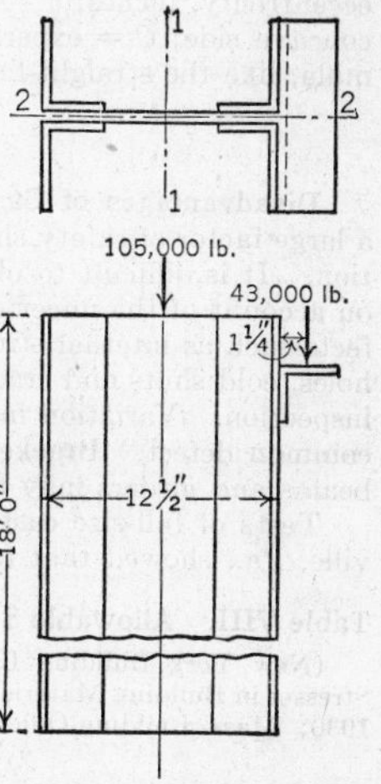

Example. Design a steel column 18 ft long to carry an axial load of 105,000 lb and an additional load of 43,000 lb which comes from a crane runway, and which is $1\,1/4$ in. beyond the outside edge of the column.

The formula used will be the A.I.S.C. formula, $P/A = 18,000/\{1 + (l^2/18,000k^2)\}$, and the shape selected will be a plate and four angles, as shown in Fig. 2.

Using 10,000 lb per sq in. as a preliminary estimate for the first selection, one plate $12 \times 5/16$ in. and four angles $5 \times 3\,1/2 \times 3/8$ in. will have an area of 15.95 sq in. The safe load for this column will now be found. The moment of inertia I_{1-1} is 412 in.^{4}, the radius of gyration k_{1-1} is 5.08 in., and the radius of gyration k_{2-2} is 2.08 in.

Considering the safe load with respect to axis 2-2 about which neither load is eccentric,

$$P = \frac{15.95 \times 18,000}{1 + \frac{(18 \times 12)^2}{18,000 \times (2.08)^2}} = 179,400 \text{ lb}$$

Consider now the safe load about axis 1-1, with respect to which the load of 105,000 lb is axial, and the load of 43,000 lb has an eccentricity of $7\,1/2$ in. The load of 43,000 lb will produce a stress due to its eccentricity, and this stress will reduce by that amount the unit load that the column can carry. The safe load will therefore be

$$P = 15.95 \left(\frac{18,000}{1 + \frac{(18 \times 12)^2}{18,000 \times (5.08)^2}} - \frac{43,000 \times 7.5 \times 6.25}{412} \right) = 183,000 \text{ lb}$$

The area exceeds that needed by about 3 sq in.; the next smaller size is one plate $12 \times 5/16$ in. and four angles $5 \times 3\,1/2 \times 5/16$ in. The area is 13.99 sq in., moment of inertia, $I_{1-1} = 356$ in.^{4} $k_{1-1} = 5.04$ in., and $k_{2-2} = 2.03$ in. With respect to the axis 2-2

$$P = \frac{13.99 \times 18,000}{1 + \frac{(18 \times 12)^2}{18,000 \times (2.03)^2}} = 154,600 \text{ lb}$$

With respect to axis 1-1,

$$P = 13.99 \left(\frac{18,000}{1 + \frac{(18 \times 12)^2}{18,000 \times (5.04)^2}} - \frac{43,000 \times 7.5 \times 6.25}{356} \right) = 149,300 \text{ lb}$$

As the load to be carried is 148,000 lb this column is satisfactory.

Column Subjected to Transverse or Cross-bending Loads. (See Seely, Resistance of Materials, 1st Ed., p. 247.) A compression member that is subjected to cross-bending loads may be considered to be (1) a beam subjected to end thrust as discussed on p. 5-35 or (2) a column subjected to cross-bending loads, depending on the relative magnitude of the end thrust and cross-bending loads, and on the dimensions of the member. The various column formulas may be modified so as to include the effect of cross-bending loads. In this form they are:

Modified Rankine's Formula for transverse loads:

$$s = \frac{P}{A}\left(1 + \phi\frac{l^2}{k^2}\right) + \frac{Pyc}{Ak^2} + \frac{Mc}{Ak^2} \tag{12}$$

105,000 lb.

43,000 lb.

FIG. 2

Modified straight-line formula for transverse loads:

$$\frac{P}{A} = \left(s - \frac{Cl}{k}\right) - \frac{Pyc}{Ak^2} - \frac{Mc}{Ak^2} \tag{13}$$

Modified secant formula for transverse loads:

$$s = \frac{P}{A}\left(1 + (e + y)\frac{c}{k^2}\right) \sec\left(\frac{l}{2k}\right)\sqrt{\frac{P}{AE}} + \frac{Mc}{Ak^2} \tag{14}$$

In these formulas, s is the maximum unit stress on the concave side, pounds per square inch; P = the axial end load, pounds; A = cross-sectional area, square inches; M = moment due to cross-bending load, pound-inches; y = deflection due to cross-bending load, inches; k = radius of gyration, inches; l = length of column, inches; e = assumed initial eccentricity, inches; c = distance, inches, from the axis to the most remote fiber on the concave side; C = experimental constant (see p. 5-40). The modified straight-line formula, like the straight-line formula, cannot be used to solve for s (see p. 5-45).

20.　CAST-IRON COLUMNS

Disadvantages of Cast-iron Columns. Tests made on cast-iron columns show that a large factor of safety should be used when the material is employed in column construction. It is difficult to obtain a practical formula for the strength of a cast-iron column on account of the uncertainty of the quality of the casting, and the danger of hidden defects such as internal stresses due to unequal cooling of the casting, cinder or dirt, blowholes, cold shuts and cracks on the inner surface, which cannot be discovered by external inspection. Variation in the thickness of the wall due to shifting of the core is another common defect. Brackets which are usually cast on the face of the column to support beams and girders may fail by shearing unless most skillfully designed.

Tests of full-size cast-iron columns made at the Watertown Arsenal and at Phoenixville, Pa.. showed that for short columns the strength in compression is much less than

Table VIII.　Allowable Safe Loads on Round Cast-Iron Columns, in Thousands of Pounds

(New York Building Law, 1929; Recommended Building Code Requirements for Working Stresses in Building Materials, U. S. Bur. of Stds., 1926; Pacific Coast Building Officials Conference, 1930; Mass. Building Officials Conference, 1929)

Weights given do not include details

Outside Diam., In.	Thickness, In.	Area, Sq In.	Weight per Foot, Lb	Least Radius of Gyration, In.	Effective Length of Column, Ft									
					8	10	12	14	16	18	20	22	24	26
6	1/2	8.64	27.0	1.95	61	56	....	....	....	....	....	....	....	....
	5/8	10.55	33.0	1.91	74	68	....	....	....	....	....	....	....	....
	3/4	12.37	38.7	1.88	86	80	....	....	....	....	....	....	....	....
	7/8	14.09	44.0	1.84	97	90	....	....	....	....	....	....	....	....
8	3/4	17.08	53.4	2.58	128	122	116	109	....	....	....	....	....	....
	7/8	19.59	61.2	2.54	147	139	132	124	....	....	....	....	....	....
	1	21.99	68.7	2.50	164	156	147	139	....	....	....	....	....	....
	1 1/8	24.30	75.9	2.46	181	171	162	152	....	....	....	....	....	....
10	1	28.28	88.4	3.20	221	212	204	195	187	178	....	....	....	....
	1 1/8	31.37	98.0	3.16	244	235	225	216	206	197	....	....	....	....
	1 1/4	34.36	107.4	3.13	267	257	246	235	225	214	....	....	....	....
	1 3/8	37.26	116.4	3.09	289	277	266	254	243	231	....	....	....	....
12	1 1/4	42.22	131.9	3.83	338	327	316	306	295	285	274	264	....	....
	1 3/8	45.90	143.4	3.79	367	355	343	332	320	308	297	285	....	....
	1 1/2	49.48	154.6	3.75	395	382	369	357	344	331	319	306	....	....
	1 5/8	52.97	165.5	3.71	422	408	394	381	367	353	340	326	....	....
14	1 1/2	58.91	184.1	4.45	479	467	454	441	429	416	403	390	378	....
	1 5/8	63.18	197.4	4.41	514	500	486	472	459	445	431	417	404	....
	1 3/4	67.35	210.5	4.38	547	532	518	503	488	473	459	444	429	....
	1 7/8	71.42	223.2	4.34	580	564	548	532	516	501	485	469	453	....
16	1 3/4	78.34	244.8	5.08	646	631	616	601	587	572	557	542	527	513
	1 7/8	83.20	260.0	5.04	685	670	654	638	622	606	590	574	559	543
	2	87.97	274.9	5.00	724	707	690	673	657	640	623	606	589	572
	2 1/8	92.63	289.5	4.96	762	744	726	708	690	672	654	636	619	601

the strength of small test specimens of cast iron. For short columns, failure of test columns takes place by shearing on an inclined plane; for long columns, failure takes place by rupture on the convex side. Failure of cast-iron columns is always a sudden, shattering failure.

Advantages of Cast-iron Columns. For buildings of moderate height cast-iron columns are sometimes used instead of wooden columns to save space, and instead of steel columns to save expense. The fact that they are cheap and can be obtained more quickly than steel built-up columns will prevent them from being superseded entirely. Moreover they can be cast in almost any desired shape with lugs and brackets attached for supporting beams or girders.

Design of Cast-iron Columns. Cast-iron columns are usually in the form of a hollow cylinder, as this is the most economical and reliable type to use. Hollow rectangular sections are permitted by some building codes and are convenient to use in outer walls where it is necessary to bond into the masonry. They are less reliable than the hollow round type and should be used only when it is impossible to use anything else.

The design will usually be governed by building laws, and the following limitations which are usually specified, should be adhered to: Minimum thickness of wall, $1/2$ to $3/4$ in.; minimum diameter of column, 6 in.; maximum length, 20 × diameter or 70 × least radius of gyration. When it becomes necessary to use a wall thickness greater than 2 in. or a diameter over 18 in. it will be cheaper and more satisfactory to abandon cast iron and substitute a steel column. Within the above limitations the ratio of length to radius of gyration should be made as small as possible; that is, if a choice may be made of two columns of equal sectional area but of different diameter and, therefore, different wall thicknesses, the one with the larger diameter will be the stronger.

The safe load on a cast-iron column as given by the building law of the City of New York is $P/A = 9000 - 40\,(l/k)$, where P = the safe load, pounds; A = area of section, square inches; l = length, inches; k = least radius of gyration. Tables VIII and IX give the safe loads for cast-iron columns according to this formula.

Table IX. Allowable Safe Loads on Square Cast-iron Columns, in Thousands of Pounds

(New York Building Law, 1929; Recommended Building Code Requirements for Working Stresses in Building Materials, U. S. Bur. of Stds., 1926; Pacific Coast Building Officials Conference, 1930; Mass. Building Officials Conference, 1929)

Weights given do not include details

Outside Width, In.	Thickness, In.	Area, Sq In.	Weight per Foot, Lb	Least Radius of Gyration, In.	Effective Length of Column, Ft									
					8	10	12	14	16	18	20	22	24	26
6	$1/2$	11.00	34.4	2.26	80	76	71	....	....	....	....	....	....	....
	$5/8$	13.44	42.0	2.21	98	92	86	....	....	....	....	....	....	....
	$3/4$	15.75	49.2	2.17	114	107	100	....	....	....	....	....	....	....
	$7/8$	17.94	56.1	2.12	129	121	113	....	....	....	....	....	....	....
8	$3/4$	21.75	68.0	2.98	168	161	154	147	140	....	....	....	....	....
	$7/8$	24.94	77.9	2.93	192	184	175	167	159	....	....	....	....	....
	1	28.00	87.5	2.89	215	205	196	187	178	....	....	....	....	....
	$1\,1/8$	30.94	96.7	2.84	237	226	216	205	195	....	....	....	....	....
10	1	36.00	112.5	3.70	287	277	268	259	249	240	231	....	....	....
	$1\,1/8$	39.94	124.8	3.65	317	307	296	286	275	265	254	....	....	....
	$1\,1/4$	43.75	136.7	3.61	347	336	324	312	301	289	277	....	....	....
	$1\,3/8$	47.44	148.3	3.57	376	363	350	338	325	312	299	....	....	....
12	$1\,1/4$	53.78	168.1	4.42	437	426	414	402	391	379	367	356	344	....
	$1\,3/8$	58.44	182.6	4.37	475	462	449	436	423	410	398	385	372	....
	$1\,1/2$	63.00	196.9	4.33	511	497	483	469	455	441	427	413	399	....
	$1\,5/8$	67.44	210.8	4.29	547	532	516	501	486	471	456	441	426	....
14	$1\,1/2$	75.00	234.4	5.14	619	605	591	577	563	549	535	521	507	493
	$1\,5/8$	80.44	251.4	5.10	663	648	633	618	603	588	572	557	542	527
	$1\,3/4$	85.75	267.9	5.05	707	690	674	658	641	625	609	593	576	560
	$1\,7/8$	90.94	284.2	5.01	749	731	714	696	679	662	644	627	609	592
16	$1\,3/4$	99.75	311.7	5.86	832	816	800	783	767	751	734	718	702	685
	$1\,7/8$	105.94	331.1	5.82	884	866	849	831	814	796	779	761	744	726
	2	112.00	350.0	5.77	934	915	896	878	859	840	822	803	785	766
	$2\,1/8$	117.94	368.6	5.73	982	963	943	923	903	883	864	844	824	804

SHAFTS

By Jasper O. Draffin

21. DEFINITIONS

Torsional Stress. A bar is under torsional stress when it is held fast at one end and a force acts at the other end to twist the bar. In a round bar, Fig. 1, with a constant force acting, the straight line a–b becomes the helix ad, and a radial line in the cross-section, ob, moves to the position od. The angle bad remains constant while the angle bod increases with the length of the bar. Each cross-section of the bar tends to shear off the one adjacent to it, and in any cross-section the shearing stress at any point is normal to a radial line drawn through the point. Within the shearing proportional limit a radial line of the cross-section remains straight after the twisting force has been applied, and the unit shearing stress at any point is proportional to its distance from the axis.

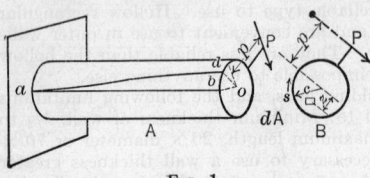

FIG. 1

The Twisting Moment, T, is equal to the product of the resultant, P, of the twisting forces, and its distance from the axis, p.

The Resisting Moment, T_r, in torsion, is equal to the sum of the moments of the unit shearing stresses acting along a cross-section with respect to the axis of the bar. If dA is an elementary area of the section at a distance of z units from the axis of a circular shaft (Fig. 1B), and c is the distance from the axis to the outside of the cross-section where the unit shearing stress is s, then the total shearing force acting on dA is $(sz/c)dA$, its moment with respect to the axis is $(sz^2/c)dA$, and the sum of all the moments of the unit shearing stresses on the cross-section is $\int (sz^2/c)\, dA$. In this expression the factor $\int z^2 dA$ is the polar moment of inertia of the section with respect to the axis. Denoting this by J, the resisting moment may be written sJ/c.

The Polar Moment of Inertia of a surface about an axis through its center of gravity and perpendicular to the surface is the sum of the products obtained by multiplying each elementary area by the square of its distance from the center of gravity of its surface; it is equal to the sum of the moments of inertia taken with respect to two axes in the plane of the surface at right angles to each other passing through the center of gravity. It is represented by J, inches⁴. For the cross-section of a round shaft,

$$J = (1/_{32})(\pi d^4), \quad \text{or} \quad 1/_2\pi\, r^4 \tag{1}$$

for a hollow shaft

$$J = (1/_{32})\,[\pi(d^4 - d_1{}^4)] \tag{2}$$

where d is the outside and d_1 the inside diameter, in inches, or

$$J = 1/_2\,[\pi(r^4 - r_1{}^4)] \tag{3}$$

where r is the outside and r_1 the inside radius, in inches.

The Polar Radius of Gyration, k_p, is also sometimes used in formulas; it is defined as the radius of a circumference along which the entire area of a surface might be concentrated and have the same polar moment of inertia as the distributed area. For a solid circular section,

$$k^2{}_p = (1/_8)d^2 \tag{4}$$

for a hollow circular section,

$$k^2{}_p = (1/_8)(d^2 + d_1{}^2) \tag{5}$$

22. DETERMINATION OF TORSIONAL STRESSES

The Torsion Formula for Round Shafts. The conditions of equilibrium require that the twisting moment, T, be opposed by an equal resisting moment, T_r, so that for the values of the maximum unit shearing stress, s_s, within the proportional limit, the torsion formula for round shafts becomes

$$T_r = T = \frac{s_s\, J}{c} \tag{6}$$

If s_s is in pounds per square inch, then T_r and T must be in pound-inches, J is in inches⁴ and c in inches. For solid round shafts having a diameter, d, inches.

$$J = \frac{1}{32}\pi d^4 \quad \text{and} \quad c = \frac{1}{2}d \tag{7}$$

and

$$T = \frac{1}{16}\pi d^3 s_s \quad \text{or} \quad s_s = \frac{16T}{\pi d^3} \tag{8}$$

For hollow round shafts

$$J = \frac{\pi(d^4 - d_1{}^4)}{32}, \quad c = \frac{1}{2}d \tag{9}$$

and the formula becomes

$$T = \frac{s_s\pi(d^4 - d_1{}^4)}{16d} \quad \text{or} \quad s_s = \frac{16Td}{\pi(d^4 - d_1{}^4)} \tag{10}$$

It should be remembered that the torsion formula applies only to solid circular shafts or hollow circular shafts and then only when the load is applied in a plane perpendicular to the axis of the shaft and when the shearing proportional limit of the material is not exceeded.

Shearing Stress in Terms of Horsepower. If the shaft is to be used for the transmission of power, the value of T, pound-inches, in the above formulas becomes $63,030\,H/n$, where H is the horsepower to be transmitted and n = r.p.m. The maximum unit shearing stress, pounds per square inch, then, is:

$$\text{For solid round shafts:} \quad s_s = \frac{321,000\,H}{nd^3} \tag{11}$$

$$\text{For hollow round shafts:} \quad s_s = \frac{321,000\,Hd}{n(d^4 - d_1{}^4)} \tag{12}$$

If s_s is taken as the allowable unit shearing stress, the diameter, d, inches, necessary to transmit a given horsepower at a given shaft speed can then be determined. It should be remembered, however, that these formulas give the stress due to torsion only, and allowance must be made for any other loads such as the weight of the shaft and pulleys, and tension in belts.

Angle of Twist. When the unit shearing stress s_s does not exceed the proportional limit the angle bod (Fig. 1) for a solid round shaft may be computed from the formula:

$$\theta = \frac{Tl}{E_s J} \tag{13}$$

where θ = angle, expressed in radians; l = length of shaft, inches; E_s = shearing modulus of elasticity of the material, pounds per square inch; T = twisting moment, pound-inches. Values of E_s for different materials are: steel, 12,000,000; wrought iron, 10,000,000; and cast iron, 6,000,000.

When the angle of twist on a section begins to increase in a greater ratio than the twisting moment, it may be assumed that the shearing stress on the outside of the section has reached the proportional limit. The shearing stress at this point may be determined by substituting the twisting moment at this instant in the torsion formula.

Torsion of Non-circular Cross-sections. The analysis of shearing stress distribution along non-circular cross-sections of bars under torsion is complex. By drawing two lines at right angles through the center of gravity of a section before twisting, and observing the angular distortion after twisting, it has been found from many experiments that in non-circular sections the shearing unit stresses are not proportional to their distances from the axis. Thus in a rectangular bar there is no shearing stress at the corners of the sections and the stress at the middle of the wide side is greater than at the middle of the narrow side. In an elliptical bar the shearing stress is greater along the flat side than at the round side.

It has been found by tests (Bach, *Elastizität u. Festigkeit*; and Young, *Bull. 4, School of Eng. Research,* Univ. of Toronto) as well as by mathematical analysis that the torsional resistance of a section made up of a number of rectangular parts is approximately equal to the sum of the resistances of the separate parts. It is on this basis that nearly all the formulas for non-circular sections have been developed. For example, the torsional resistance of an I-beam is approximately equal to the sum of the torsional resistances of the web and the outstanding flanges. In an I-beam in torsion the maximum shearing stress will occur at the middle of the side of the web, except where the flanges are thicker than the web, and then the maximum stress will be at the midpoint of the width of the flange. Re-entrant angles, as those in I-beams and channels, are always a source of weakness in members subjected to torsion. Table I gives approximate values of the maximum unit shearing stress s_s and the angle of twist θ induced by twisting bars

Table I. Approximate Formulas for Maximum Shearing Stress and Angle of Twist in Members Subjected to Torsion

(From Seely's Advanced Mechanics of Materials)

s_s = shearing unit stress, pounds per square inch; T = twisting moment, pound-inches; θ = angle of twist, radians, in length, l, inches; J = polar moment of inertia, inches^4; E_s = shearing modulus of elasticity, pounds per square inch; A = area of cross-section, square inches; y = distance of most remote edge from center of bar, inches. Tests of brittle metal are those made by Bach, *Elastizität u. Festigkeit*, 1924, except for those marked *, which are by Kommers, *Amer. Mach.*, vol. xl, p. 941, 1914.

Shape	Maximum Unit Stress		Angle of Twist
	Mathematical Analysis	Tests of Brittle Material	
	$s_s = \dfrac{16T}{\pi d^3}$		$\theta = \dfrac{Tl}{E_s J}$
	$s_s = \dfrac{16Td}{\pi(d^4 - d_1^4)}$		$\theta = \dfrac{32Tl}{\pi(d^4 - d_1^4)E_s}$
	$s_s = \dfrac{3T}{2\pi rt^2}$		$\theta = \dfrac{3Tl}{2\pi rt^3 E_s}$
	$s_s = \dfrac{2T}{\pi ab^2}$		$\theta = \dfrac{T(a^2 + b^2)l}{\pi a^3 b^3 E_s}$
	$s_s = \dfrac{T}{2\pi a_1 b_1{}^2 k(1 + k)}$ $k = \dfrac{a - a_1}{a_1} = \dfrac{b - b_1}{b_1}$		$\theta = \dfrac{T(a^2 + b^2)l}{4\pi a_1{}^3 b_1{}^3 kE_s}$
	$s_s = \dfrac{20T}{b^3}$		$\theta = \dfrac{46.2Tl}{b^4 E_s}$
	$s_s = \dfrac{1.09T}{b^3}$		$\theta = \dfrac{0.967Tl}{b^4 E_s}$
	$s_s = \dfrac{(3a + 1.8b)T}{a^2 b^2}$	$s_s = \dfrac{9T}{2ab^2}$	$\theta = \dfrac{4\pi^2 TlJ}{A^4 E_s}$ Error is small where $a > 2b$
	$s_s = \dfrac{T}{2t(a - t)(b - t_1)}$	$s_s = \dfrac{9bT}{2(b^3 a - b_1{}^3 a_1)}$	$\theta = \dfrac{Tl(at + bt_1 - t^2 - t_1{}^2)}{2u_1(a - t)^2(b - t_1)^2 E_s}$

Table I—*Continued*

Shape	Maximum Unit Stress		Angle of Twist
	Mathematical Analysis	Tests of Brittle Material	
	$s_s = \dfrac{4.8T}{b^3}$		$\theta = \dfrac{7.11Tl}{b^4E_s}$
		$s_s = \dfrac{9T}{2t^2(a + 2b_1)}$ $s_s = \dfrac{9T}{2t^2a}$ *	$\theta = \dfrac{36.2TlJ}{A^4E_s}$ *
		$s_s = \dfrac{9T}{2t^2(a + 2b_1)}$	
		$s_s = \dfrac{9T}{2t^2(a + b - t)}$	
		$s_s = \dfrac{9T}{2t^2(a + b - t)}$	
Any compact section without re-entrant angles.	$s_s = \dfrac{4\pi^2 JT}{A^4 y}$		$\theta = \dfrac{kJTl}{A^4E_s}$ $k = 4\pi^2$ for ellipse. $\;\;= 40$ to 42 for rectangles.

of various cross-sections, it being assumed that s_s is not greater than the proportional limit and that the modulus of elasticity, E_s, remains a constant.

Ultimate Strength in Torsion. In a torsion failure, the outer fibers of a section are the first to shear and the rupture extends toward the axis as the twisting is continued. The torsion formula for round shafts has no theoretical basis after the shearing stresses on the outer fibers exceed the proportional limit, as then the stresses along the section are no longer proportional to their distances from the axis. It is convenient, however, to compare the torsional strength of various materials by using the formula to compute values of s_s at which rupture takes place. These computed values of the maximum stress sustained before rupture are somewhat higher for iron and steel than the ultimate strength of the materials in direct shear. Computed values of the ultimate strength in torsion are found by experiment to be as follows: cast iron, 30,000 lb per sq in.; wrought iron, 55,000 lb per sq in.; medium steel, 65,000 lb per sq in.; timber, 2000 lb per sq in. These computed values of twisting strength may be used in the torsion formula to determine the probable twisting moment that will cause rupture of a given round bar or to determine the size of a bar that will be ruptured by a given twisting moment. In design, large factors of safety should be taken, especially when the stress is reversed as in reversing engines and when the torsional stress is combined with other stresses as in shafting.

Effect of Keyway in Shaft. The sharp re-entrant angles in keyways produce high local stresses at these points. Based on studies made by hydrodynamical and soap-film methods, the local stress in the corner has been determined as equal to the stress in a similar shaft without a keyway, multiplied by a constant, K, which depends on the radius of the corner. The constants are approximately:

Radius of corner, in	0.1	0.2	0.3	0.4	0.5	0.6	0.7
K	5.4	3.4	2.7	2.3	2.1	2.0	1.9

Under steady loading these high stresses are probably not very important, as a ductile material allows an adjustment to take place, but if the shaft is subjected to repeated loads a crack may start at the corner.

Experiments by Moore (*Bull.* 42, Eng. Exp. Sta., Univ. of Ill., 1909) on shafts from 1 1/4 to 2 1/4 in. in diameter showed that keyways reduced the elastic strength and the stiffness but did not reduce the ultimate strength. If E' = ratio of strength at the proportional limit of a shaft with a keyway to strength at the proportional limit of a shaft without a keyway, N = ratio of the angle of twist of a shaft with a keyway to that of a shaft without a keyway, w = width of keyway divided by diameter of shaft, and h = depth of keyway divided by diameter of shaft, the ratios obtained were: $E' = 1.0 - 0.2w - 1.1h$; $N = 1.0 + 0.4w + 0.7h$, for ranges of w from 0.25 to 0.50, and of h from 0.125 to 0.1875.

CYLINDERS, PLATES, ROLLERS AND RIVETED JOINTS

By Jasper O. Draffin

23. CYLINDERS

Thin Cylinders under Internal Pressure. A cylinder is regarded as thin when the thickness of the wall is small compared with the diameter. It is assumed that in such cases the tensile stress across a longitudinal section is uniformly distributed over the thickness of the wall. If p = internal pressure, pounds per square inch; l = length of cylinder, inches; t = thickness of wall, inches; d = diameter of cylinder, inches; and s = tensile stress, pounds per square inch:

$$pdl = 2\ stl \quad \text{or} \quad s = \frac{pd}{2t} \tag{1}$$

For tensile stress across a transverse section

$$\frac{p\pi d^2}{4} = st\pi d \quad \text{or} \quad s = \frac{pd}{4t} \tag{2}$$

Formula 2 applies also to the stresses in the walls of a thin hollow sphere, hemisphere, or dome. This analysis does not apply where holes are cut in the cylinder for rivets or for other purposes. Where holes are cut, the tensile stresses must be found by the method used in riveted joints. (See Art. 26.)

Thin Cylinders under External Pressure. It is difficult to derive a rational formula for the stresses in a thin cylinder under external pressure since failure occurs partly by collapse and this is greatly influenced by any slight ellipticity. Tests made by Professor R. T. Stewart (*Trans. A.S.M.E.*, vol. xxvii, p. 730) on lap-welded steel tubes showed that the length was not important provided it was not over 6 times the diameter. For ratios of t/d less than 0.023

$$p = 1000 \left[1 - \sqrt{1 - 1600 \left(\frac{t^2}{d^2} \right)} \right] \tag{3}$$

where p = collapsing pressure, pounds per square inch; t = thickness of wall, inches; and d = diameter of tube, inches. For ratios of t/d greater than 0.023

$$p = 86{,}670 \left(\frac{t}{d} \right) - 1386 \tag{4}$$

Professor A. P. Carmen made tests (*Bull.* 5, *Eng. Exp. Sta.*, Univ. of Ill., 1906) and found, with ratios of t/d less than 0.025, for cold-drawn seamless steel tubes,

$$p = 50{,}200{,}000 \left(\frac{t}{d} \right)^3 \tag{5}$$

and for seamless brass tubes $\quad p = 25{,}150{,}000 \left(\frac{t}{d} \right)^3 \tag{6}$

For an extended discussion see Strength of Thin Cylindrical Shells under External Pressure by Saunders and Windenburg, and The Collapsing Strength of Steel Tubes by Jasper and Sullivan (*Trans. A.S.M.E.*, Applied Mechanics, September–December, 1931, pp. 207–245).

Thick Cylinders. Timoshenko and Lessells (Applied Elasticity) and Swain (Strength of Materials) give the following formulas for the stresses in thick hollow cylinders under internal and external pressure. Under internal pressure only, the maximum tensile stress s_t in a tangential direction on the inner surface is

$$s_t = p \frac{(a^2 + b^2)}{(b^2 - a^2)} \tag{7}$$

where p = internal pressure, pounds per square inch; a = inside radius and b = outside radius, inches; under internal pressure the maximum compressive stress in a radial direction is on the inside and equals p, pounds per square inch.

When the cylinder is subjected to an external pressure p the maximum compressive unit stress will be at the inner surface and is

$$s_c = \frac{2\,pb^2}{b^2 - a^2} \tag{8}$$

In *shrinkage fits* a hollow cylinder or collar is forced over a cylinder or shaft having an outer diameter slightly greater than the inside diameter of the outer cylinder. This will cause compressive stresses in the inner cylinder and tensile stresses in the outer cylinder. This method is sometimes used in the manufacture of guns. Timoshenko and Lessells (Applied Elasticity) give the equation for the pressure p, pounds per square inch, between the two cylinders as

$$p = \frac{E\delta}{b} \frac{(b^2 - a^2)(c^2 - b^2)}{2b^2(c^2 - a^2)} \tag{9}$$

where E = modulus of elasticity, a = inner radius of inner cylinder, b = outer radius of inner cylinder, c = outer radius of outer cylinder, δ = amount by which the outer radius of the inner cylinder exceeds the inner radius of the outer cylinder. With the pressures known, external pressure on the inner cylinder and internal pressure on the outer cylinder, the stresses can be computed by means of equations 7 and 8.

A comparison of the various theories of failure of thick cylinders is given in Seely's Advanced Mechanics of Materials from which the following is abstracted:

For brittle materials, as cast iron, the *maximum stress theory* is recommended. For internal pressure only it gives

$$t = r_1 \left[\sqrt{\frac{s_w + p}{s_w - p}} - 1 \right] \tag{10}$$

For external pressure only it gives

$$t = r_1 \left[\sqrt{\frac{s_w}{2p + s_w}} - 1 \right] \tag{11}$$

For ductile materials the maximum strain theory is recommended. It is used by the United States Government for the design of guns. For internal pressure only it gives

$$t = r_1 \left[\sqrt{\frac{E\epsilon_w + (1 - m)p}{E\epsilon_w - (1 + m)p}} - 1 \right] \tag{12}$$

and for external pressure only

$$t = r_1 \left[\sqrt{\frac{E\epsilon_w}{E\epsilon_w - 2p}} - 1 \right] \tag{13}$$

where t = thickness, inches; s_w = allowable working unit stress, pounds per square inch; p = pressure, internal or external, pounds per square inch; r_1 is the inner radius of cylinder, inches; E = modulus of elasticity; m = Poisson's ratio; ϵ_w = allowable working unit deformation of the material.

24. PLATES

Circular Flat Plates. Table I gives equations for deflection and stresses in circular plates based mainly on the theoretical analyses developed by Grashof. (See Morley's Strength of Materials; Seely's Advanced Mechanics of Materials; Timoshenko and Lessells' Applied Elasticity.) Experience shows that the strength of flat plates is greater than is indicated by these equations.

Elliptical Flat Plates. An approximate formula for the maximum stress s in elliptical plates, simply supported at the edge, having a major axis $2a$, a minor axis $2b$, a thickness t, and carrying a distributed load of w pounds per square inch, is

$$s = \frac{(3a - 2b)}{a} \frac{wb^2}{t^2} \tag{14}$$

Table I. Maximum Stresses and Deflection for Circular Flat Plates

m = Poisson's ratio; P = concentrated load, pounds; w = distributed load, pounds per square inch; r = radius of plate, inches; t = thickness of plate, inches; E = modulus of elasticity.

Type of Load and Support	Maximum Stress at Edge	Maximum Stress at Center	Maximum Deflection at Center, $m = 1/3$
Uniform load, edge simply supported		$\dfrac{3}{8}\dfrac{wr^2}{t^2}(3 + m)$	$\dfrac{2}{3}\dfrac{wr^4}{Et^3}$
Uniform load, edge fixed	Radial direction $\dfrac{3}{4}\dfrac{wr^2}{t^2}$ Tangential direction $\dfrac{3}{4}\dfrac{wmr^2}{t^2}$	$\dfrac{3}{8}\dfrac{wr^2}{t^2}(1 + m)$	$\dfrac{1}{6}\dfrac{wr^4}{Et^3}$
Concentrated load at center, edge supported		Infinite	$\dfrac{5}{3}\dfrac{Pr^2}{\pi Et^3}$
Concentrated load at center, edge fixed	Radial direction $\dfrac{3P}{2\pi t^2}$ Tangential direction $\dfrac{3}{2}\dfrac{Pm}{\pi t^2}$	Infinite	$\dfrac{2}{3}\dfrac{Pr^2}{\pi Et^3}$
Uniform load, supported on central area of radius r_0		$\dfrac{3}{2}\dfrac{wr^2}{t^2}\left[(1+m)\log_e\dfrac{r}{r_0}\right.$ $\left. + \dfrac{1}{4}(1-m)\left(1 - \dfrac{r_0^2}{r^2}\right)\right]$	$\dfrac{3}{16}(1-m)(7+3m)\dfrac{wr^4}{Et^3}$
Load on central area of radius r_0, edge simply supported		$\dfrac{3(1+m)P}{2\pi t^2}\left[\dfrac{1}{m+1}\right.$ $+ \log_e\dfrac{r}{r_0} - \left(\dfrac{1-m}{1+m}\right)\dfrac{r_0^2}{4r^2}\right]$	$\dfrac{5}{3}\dfrac{Pr^2}{\pi Et^3}$
Load on central area of radius r_0, edge fixed		$\dfrac{3(1+m)P}{2\pi t^2}\left(\log_e\dfrac{r}{r_0} + \dfrac{r_0^2}{4r^2}\right)$ r must be $> 1.7\,r_0$	$\dfrac{2}{3}\dfrac{Pr^2}{\pi Et^3}$

Square Flat Plates. Where the load is w pounds per square inch and the plate is supported on the four edges, each b inches long, the maximum moment and maximum stress will be along a diagonal. The moment M per unit length of diagonal will be $wb^2/24$, and the unit stress will be

$$s = \frac{wb^2}{4t^2} \tag{15}$$

where t = thickness, inches.

With edges fixed and load distributed the maximum stress at the center of each of the edges is, approximately, $s = 0.20\,wb^2/t^2$. Nichols found in experiments with steel plates a value of

$$s = 0.141\frac{wb^2}{t^2} \tag{16}$$

and Bach found

$$s = 0.19\frac{wb^2}{t^2} \tag{17}$$

Rectangular Flat Plates. For a distributed load w pounds per square inch, with supports along the four sides, and assuming a uniform distribution of moment along a diagonal, Seely gives (Advanced Mechanics of Materials, p. 141) the stress as

$$s = \frac{a^2\,b^2\,w}{2t^2\,(a^2 + b^2)} \tag{18}$$

in which a is the length of the long side and b the length of the short side.

For rectangular plates fixed along the four sides, for ductile materials, Bach found experimentally that the coefficient K in the moment equation $M = Kwb^2$ was such that the moment along the fixed edge and along the center was about the same, and that the values of K (see Seely, Advanced Mechanics of Materials, p. 144) for different ratios of the length of the sides a and b were about as follows:

$$b/a = 0 \qquad 0.2 \qquad 0.4 \qquad 0.6 \qquad 0.8 \qquad 1.0$$
$$K = 0.63 \qquad 0.62 \qquad 0.56 \qquad 0.48 \qquad 0.40 \qquad 0.32$$

Timoshenko and Lessells (Applied Elasticity) give an analysis which shows that the maximum moment at the center of the plate in strips of unit width through the center of the plate, parallel to the long and short sides respectively, when the sides are simply supported, and the load is w pounds per square inch uniformly distributed over the plate, is given by the equations

$$M_{1\,max} = K_1\,wb^2 \tag{19a}$$

and

$$M_{2\,max} = K_2\,wb^2 \tag{19b}$$

the approximate deflection y is given by

$$y_{max} = \frac{Dwb^4}{Et^3} \tag{20}$$

where t = thickness, inches; E = modulus of elasticity; K_1, K_2, and D are constants given in Table II.

Table II.   Values of Constants D, K_1 and K_2 for Rectangular Plates with Supported Edges and Uniformly Distributed Loads

a = long side, b = short side, Poisson's ratio = 0.3.

a/b	D	K_1	K_2	a/b	D	K_1	K_2
1.0	0.0443	0.0479	0.0479	1.8	0.1017	0.0948	0.0479
1.1	.0530	.0553	.0494	1.9	.1064	.0985	.0471
1.2	.0616	.0626	.0501	2.0	.1106	.1017	.0464
1.3	.0697	.0693	.0504	3.0	.1336	.1189	.0404
1.4	.0770	.0753	.0506	4.0	.1400	.1235	.0384
1.5	.0843	.0812	.0500	5.0	.1416	.1246	.0375
1.6	.0906	.0862	.0493	∞	.1422	.1250	.0375
1.7	.0964	.0908	.0486				

For rectangular plates with the edges fixed, the maximum deflection is given by the same equation as for the plates with supported edges, but with the constant D given in Table III.   The maximum bending moment in a strip of unit width is at the middle of the longer fixed side and is equal to $M_{max} = Kwb^2$, K is given in Table III, and a and b are the lengths of the long and short sides respectively.

Professor Westergaard in a study of reinforced-concrete slabs supported on columns has computed the moments in medium-thick rectangular and elliptical plates (*Proc. A.C.I.*, 1921). These are plates in which there is neither an appre-

Table III.   Values of Constants D and K for Rectangular Plates with Fixed Edges and a Uniformly Distributed Load

Poisson's ratio = 0.3

a/b	1.00	1.25	1.50	1.75	2.00	∞
D	0.0138	0.0199	0.0240	0.0264	0.0277	0.0284
K	0.0513	0.0665	0.0757	0.0817	0.0829	0.0833

ciable absorption of energy by the vertical shearing stresses nor by the stretching of the middle plane of the plate.   By means of a number of simplifying assumptions the values for the moments as given in Table IV were found.

25.   STRESSES IN SOLIDS UNDER PRESSURE

Cylindrical and Spherical Rollers.   Approximate equations for areas of contact and pressures have been worked out for a number of cases (Timoshenko and Lessells' Applied Elasticity).   These are given in Table V.

Hertz Equations.   A general mathematical solution of the problem of the stresses produced by the pressure of one solid upon another, of which cylindrical and spherical rollers are a special case, was made by H. Hertz (English translation in Miscellaneous Papers by H. Hertz).   The Hertz equations are very complex and deal only with surface stresses.   Thomas and Hoersch (*Bull.* 212, *Eng. Exp. Sta.*, University of Illinois, 1930), as a part of an investigation of railroad rails and the development of transverse fissures in them, extended the Hertz equations to a study of the shearing stresses within the

Table IV. Formulas for Bending Moments in Rectangular Flat Slabs

Values are per unit width. Poisson's ratio = 0, a = longer side, b = shorter side, $\alpha = b/a$.

		Moments in Span b		Moments in Span a	
		At center of edge	At center of slab	At center of edge	At center of slab
Rectangular Slabs	Four edges simply supported	0	$\dfrac{1/8\,wb^2}{1+2\alpha^3}$	0	$\dfrac{wb^2}{48}(1+\alpha^2)$
	Span b fixed; span a simply supported	$\dfrac{1/12\,wb^2}{1+0.2\,\alpha^4}$	$\dfrac{1/24\,wb^2}{1+0.4\,\alpha^4}$	0	$\dfrac{wb^2}{80}(1+0.3\,\alpha^2)$
	Span a fixed; span b simply supported	0	$\dfrac{1/8\,wb^2}{1+0.8\,\alpha^2+6\alpha^4}$	$\dfrac{1/8\,wb^2}{1+0.8\,\alpha^4}$	$0.015\,wb^2\left(\dfrac{1+3\alpha^2}{1+\alpha^4}\right)$
	All edges fixed	$\dfrac{1/12\,wb^2}{1+\alpha^4}$	$\dfrac{1/8\,wb^2}{3+4\alpha^4}$	$1/24\,wb^2$	$0.009\,wb^2(1+2\alpha^2-\alpha^4)$
	Elliptical slab with fixed edges; diameters a and b; $b/a = \alpha$	$\dfrac{1/12\,wb^2}{1+2/3\,\alpha^2+\alpha^4}$	$\dfrac{1/24\,wb^2}{1+2/3\,\alpha^2+\alpha^4}$	$\dfrac{1/12\,wb^2\,\alpha^2}{1+2/3\,\alpha^2+\alpha^4}$	$\dfrac{1/24\,wb^2\,\alpha^2}{1+2/3\,\alpha^2+\alpha^4}$

solid. They developed methods, too long to be given here, of computing the magnitude and location of the maximum shearing stresses produced in solids under pressure, such as in railroad rails under a wheel load. They have obtained experimental verification of the correctness of their equations by a " strain-etch " method, but point out that the mathematical equations derived do not hold except for thick material and where the ratio of the length of contact to the width of contact is large.

In a cylinder of radius R, inches, under a load P', pounds per inch of length, on a plane, assuming Poisson's ratio as $1/4$ the maximum shearing unit stress $s_s = 677\sqrt{P'/R}$, the width of contact equals $0.000564\sqrt{P'R}$, the depth to the point of maximum shear is $0.000222\sqrt{P'R}$, and the maximum intensity of pressure is $2256\sqrt{P'/R}$. In the case of crossed cylinders, the empirical equation is

$$s_s = \frac{11,750\,P^{1/3}}{\left(\dfrac{R_1}{R_2}\right)^{0.271} R_2^{2/3}} \tag{21}$$

where R_1 = radius of larger cylinder; R_2 = radius of smaller cylinder; P = total pressure, pounds, between the two solids; the ratio R_1/R_2 is only true within the limits of 1 and 8. Table VI gives a number of values computed by the methods of Thomas and Hoersch.

Stribeck made extensive experiments on ball bearings in 1898–1900, and his reports are translated in *Trans. A.S.M.E.*, vol. xxix, p. 421.

Where rollers are moving, as at the end of a truss or girder or with a rolling lift bridge, under relatively high pressures, the plate on which the roller rests is the critical part. The metal of the plate tends to flow longitudinally under the backward and forward motion. Wilson (*Bull.* 191, *Eng. Exp. Sta.*, University of Illinois, 1929) reports on experiments with rollers of the size used in rolling lift bridges, between 116 in. and 476 in. radius, and concludes that the bearing capacity of a plate depends upon its thickness, the tensile strength of the material, and the diameter of the roller. He proposes the formula

$$P = (12,000 + 80\,D)\left(\frac{p - 13,000}{23,000}\right)$$

where P = safe working load, pounds per inch width of plate; D = diameter of the roller, inches; p = yielding point strength of the material in tension, pound per square inch. The thickness of the plate, inches, should not be less than $(1.0 - 0.004\,D)$ with D not less than 120 in. Steel bridges usually have one end on rollers to allow for expansion, and the usual allowable load for expansion rollers is $P = 600\,D$; P = load, pounds per lineal inch of roller, and D = diameter of the roller, inches.

Table V.   Areas of Contact and Pressures with Two Surfaces in Contact

Poisson's ratio = 0.3; P = load, pounds; P_1 = load per inch of length, pounds; E = modulus of elasticity.

Character of Surfaces	Maximum Pressure, s, at Center of Contact, lb per sq in.	Radius, r, or Width, b, of Contact Area, in.
Two spheres	$s = 0.616 \sqrt[3]{PE^2 \left(\dfrac{d_1 + d_2}{d_1 d_2}\right)^2}$	$r = 0.881 \sqrt[3]{\dfrac{P}{E}\left(\dfrac{d_1 d_2}{d_1 + d_2}\right)}$
Sphere and plane	$s = 0.616 \sqrt[3]{\dfrac{PE^2}{d^2}}$	$r = 0.881 \sqrt[3]{\dfrac{Pd}{E}}$
Sphere and hollow sphere	$s = 0.616 \sqrt[3]{PE^2 \left(\dfrac{d_2 - d_1}{d_1 d_2}\right)^2}$	$r = 0.881 \sqrt[3]{\dfrac{P}{E}\left(\dfrac{d_1 d_2}{d_2 - d_1}\right)}$
Cylinder and plane	$s = 0.591 \sqrt{\dfrac{P_1 E}{d}}$	$b = 2.15 \sqrt{\dfrac{P_1 d}{E}}$
Two cylinders	$s = 0.591 \sqrt{P_1 E \left(\dfrac{d_1 + d_2}{d_1 d_2}\right)}$	$b = 2.15 \sqrt{\dfrac{P_1}{E}\left(\dfrac{d_1 d_2}{d_1 + d_2}\right)}$

Table VI.   Shearing Stresses in Solids under Pressure

Case	Radius, R_1, in.	Length of Cylinder, in.	Radius, R_2, in.	Load, lb	Area in Contact, sq in.*	Maximum Shearing Stress, lb. per sq in.	Depth below Surface of Point of Maximum Shearing Stress, in.
Crossed cylinders...	16.5	....	14	25,000	0.215	56,500	0.121
Crossed cylinders...	40	....	14	60,000	0.502	59,800	0.179
Cylinder on plane...	16.5	2	Plane	25,000	0.512	18,600	0.100
Cylinder on plane...	40	2	Plane	60,000	1.236	18,600	0.243
Cylinder on plane...	30		Plane	39,800 lb per in. length	....	24,700	....
Soleplates Galveston Causeway Bascule Bridge..........	309	....	Plane	112,400 lb per in. length	Width 3.45 in.	12,900	1.355

* Computed by approximate equation.

26. RIVETED AND WELDED JOINTS

Riveted Joints exist where two or more parts of a structure or machine are connected by rivets. Two types of riveted joints are usually recognized, those in structures or machines, Fig. 1a, and those in internal pressure vessels, Fig. 1b. They are further classified as *butt* joints, Fig. 1c, and *lap* joints, Fig. 1d. The short plates connecting the main plates in Fig. 1c are known as *butt* or *cover* plates and sometimes as *butt straps*. Depending upon the number of rows of rivets, joints are known as single, double, and triple riveted. Fig. 1d is a triple-riveted joint.

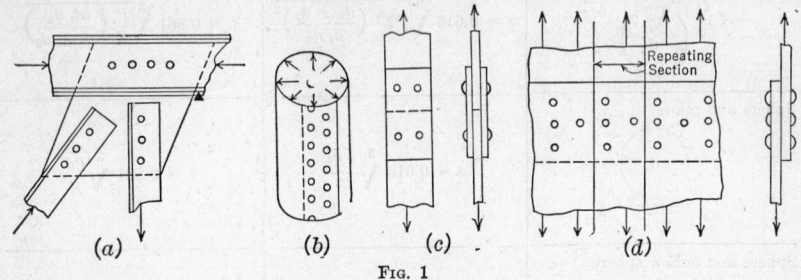

(a)   (b)   (c)   (d)

Fig. 1

Stresses in Riveted Joints are of three kinds: (1) tensile stresses in the plates or members connected, (2) shearing stresses in the rivets connecting the plates, and (3) bearing stresses in the rivets and in the plates at the surface of contact with the rivets. In computing stresses it is assumed that the rivets are far enough from the end of the plate that the rivets will not tear through the plate and that all stresses are uniformly distributed over the area under consideration. Then the unit stresses, pounds per square inch, will be equal to the load, P, pounds, divided by the area, A, in square inches, or $s = P/A$.

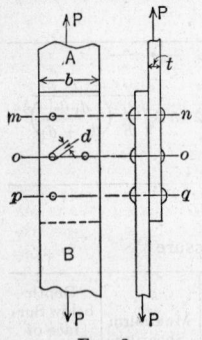

Fig. 2

First select a typical portion of the joint and then determine the load on the part selected and the area of each element which is under stress. For structural joints the entire joint is used, while for internal pressure vessels a strip called a *repeating* section is used. Fig. 2 shows such a repeating section, enlarged from Fig. 1d. The plate A will tend to tear apart at the section $m–n$ and the plate B at section $p–q$, since the entire load must be carried across these reduced sections. The area of each plate is the same and the load is the same and therefore the tensile unit stress in each plate is $s_t = P/A_t$, in which $A_t = (b - d)t$, or $s_{t_{m-n}} = P/(b - d)t$. All the rivets being of the same size, each carries one-quarter of the load and therefore the total load carried across the section $o–o$ will be $3P/4$ while the area $A_{t_{o-o}} = (b - 2d)t$, or $s_{t_{o-o}} = 3P/4(b - 2d)t$. The shearing unit stress in the rivets is $s_s = P/A_s$, where A_s is the area of the four rivets or $4\pi d^2/4$, or $s_s = P/\pi d^2$. The bearing unit stress in the plate, or rivet, is $s_b = P/A_b$, where $A_b =$ the bearing area for four rivets, each of which is dt or a total of $4\,dt$, or $s_b = P/4\,dt$.

Allowable working stresses vary considerably, those given below representing two specifications widely used. The values are in pounds per square inch.

Table VII. Allowable Working Stresses

Kind of Stress	Am. Soc. Mech. Eng., Boiler Code	Am. Inst. Steel Cons., Structural, 1934
Tensile stress, net section....................................	11,000	18,000
Shearing stress, power-driven rivets..........................	8,800	13,500
" " hand-driven rivets...........................	....	10,000
Bearing stress, power-driven rivets...........................	19,000	24,000 *
" " hand-driven rivets............................	....	16,000 *

* Where rivets are in double shear these stresses may be increased 25 per cent.

Welded Joints have come into extensive use since the World War and are now (1936) used in many places in buildings, bridges, tanks, and machinery to replace or supplement riveted joints. Welding is defined as " a localized consolidation of metals by means of heat," and there are a number of methods of welding and a considerable variety of types of joints, of which a few are shown in Fig. 3. Stresses in welded joints are computed for shear and tension or compression. In *vee* joints the stress is computed for tension, or compression, by $s_t = P/A_t$, where A_t is the area of the weld, considered equal to the area of the thinnest plate connected. Stress in *fillet* joints is computed for shear, $s_s = P/A_s$, where A_s is equal to the length of all the welds times the thickness at the throat, the throat being measured as indicated in Fig. 4.

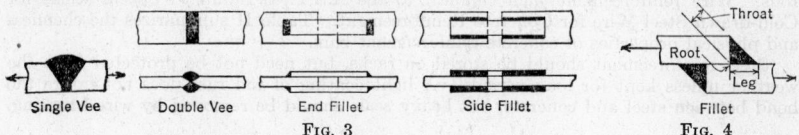

Single Vee	Double Vee	End Fillet	Side Fillet	Fillet

Fig. 3   Fig. 4

The American Welding Society's Code for Fusion Welding and Gas Cutting in Building Construction, Edition 1930, recommends the following working unit stresses, all in pounds per square inch of throat weld: Shear, 11,300; tension, 13,000; compression, 15,000. Specifications on workmanship and on the qualifications of welders are rigid. Detailed information on workmanship, specifications and tests are given in the Report of Structural Steel Welding Committee of the American Bureau of Welding, 1931, and in Practical Design of Welded Steel Structures, *J. Am. Welding Soc.*, Aug., 1933, and also in the A.S.M.E. Boiler Code.

REINFORCED CONCRETE
By Theodore Crane

General Uses

Reinforced Concrete is concrete in which metal is embedded in such a manner that the two materials act together in resisting forces; the principal function of the concrete is to resist compressive stresses, and that of the reinforcement to resist tensile stresses.

The value of combining iron and concrete, to resist respectively tensile and compressive stresses in structural members, was first discovered in France about 1865. Since that time it has become one of the most widely used structural materials for bridges, roads, retaining walls, dams, tanks, and many other types of engineering structures, as well as for buildings. It is almost universally used for multi-story industrial buildings and garages.

The choice between a structural steel or a reinforced concrete skeleton depends on comparative cost, unless the architectural design requires the use of one of these materials. H-section steel cores, extending through four or five lower stories, can be successfully used when column sizes become excessive. For industrial loads, girderless floor systems are the most satisfactory. They provide better manufacturing facilities and a higher fire-resistance than so-called "mill-construction," or beam-and-slab design. For lighter types of occupancy as commercial and residential work, ribbed floor systems are more suitable.

27. SPECIFICATIONS

Concrete. See Non-metallic Materials, Section 12.

Reinforcement. Expanded metal, triangular mesh, or wire fabric is often employed in slabs of moderate span, and in walls and partitions. The great bulk of reinforcement used, however, is in the form of bars, either plain or deformed, the deformations aiding the bond between the steel and concrete (see Fig. 1). Table I gives the areas, weights, and perimeters of standard round and square steel reinforcement.

The so-called "intermediate grade" of billet steel (see A.S.T.M. Specifications) can be generally used for all purposes where reinforcement is required. Rail steel, rerolled to rods and bars (see A.S.T.M. Specifications for Rail-steel Concrete Reinforcement Bars), is a satisfactory reinforcement in designs which do not require bending of the

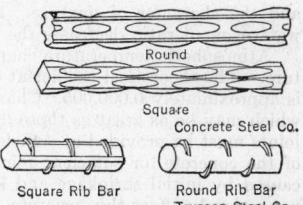

Round

Square
Concrete Steel Co.

Square Rib Bar   Round Rib Bar
Truscon Steel Co.

Fig. 1. Typical Types of
Deformed Bars

Table I. Areas, Weights, and Perimeters of Round Rods and Square Bars

Size, in.	Round Rods							Square Bars			
	1/4	3/8	1/2	5/8	3/4	7/8	1	1/2	1	1 1/8	1 1/4
Area, sq in................	0.049	0.11	0.19	0.30	0.44	0.60	0.78	0.25	1.00	1.26	1.56
Weight per ft, lb..........	0.167	0.376	0.668	1.04	1.50	2.04	2.67	0.85	3.40	4.30	5.31
Perimeter, in..............	0.78	1.18	1.57	1.96	2.35	2.75	3.14	2.00	4.00	4.50	5.00

rods. Wire reinforcement shall conform to the A.S.T.M. Standard Specifications for Cold-drawn Steel Wire for Concrete Reinforcement. Table II summarizes the chemical and physical properties of concrete reinforcement bars.

Steel reinforcement should be stored on racks, but need not be protected from the weather unless kept for long periods. A light coating of red rust does not injure the bond between steel and concrete, but heavy scale should be removed by wire brushing.

28. GENERAL PRINCIPLES OF DESIGN

Design. The design of concrete slabs, beams, and girders involves computation of the sectional area of steel required for strength in tension, and of concrete required for strength in compression. Diagonal tension, a function of the shear, is resisted by the concrete alone or with the aid of web reinforcement. Columns or struts supporting concentric loads are designed with a reinforced-concrete section in which each material is assumed to carry a portion of the compression. With comparatively heavy loads, spirals are used to increase the ultimate strength, or structural steel cores may be used to reduce the diameter of the column.

Placing of Reinforcement. All metal reinforcement should be accurately placed, supported at the proper height by concrete or metal chairs, and so secured as to prevent displacement during pouring of concrete.   Reinforcement should be cold bent, as indicated on the drawings or steel lists, around a pin whose diameter is four or more times the least dimension of the rod or bar. It should be free from coatings that might destroy or reduce the bond, as heavy rust, scale, paint, grease, etc. Heating of reinforcement for bending should not be permitted. Sufficient lap should be provided at splices to transfer the stress between bars by bond and shear. Column rods should be lapped at least 24 diameters for deformed steel or 30 diameters for plain steel. Splices should not be made at points of maximum stress.

Insulation of Reinforcement. To protect the steel from corrosion and fire, minimum thickness of concrete should be provided around the reinforcement as follows: floor slabs and walls, 1 in. (some building ordinances require 1 1/2 in. for walls); beams, girders and columns, 1 1/2 in. (most building ordinances require 2 in. for girders and columns); footings or other principal structural members where concrete is deposited directly against the ground, 3 in. (most building ordinances require 4 in.); it is also desirable to provide 2 in. protection for all members exposed to the weather, as spandrel beams and exterior columns.

Contraction Joints. Volumetric changes normally occur when concrete hardens. When concrete is cured in dry air, shrinkage commences immediately after placement, due principally to loss of water by evaporation or absorption. The preliminary shrinkage, occurring while the concrete is plastic, is fairly rapid, particularly in thin members exposed to hot sun and wind. The secondary shrinkage, occurring after the member has assumed definite form, is much slower, and is influenced by atmospheric conditions and the character of mixture. Rich concrete shrinks more than lean; decreasing the water-cement ratio decreases the shrinkage.

Atmospheric temperature changes cause changes in volume during the life of a structure. The theoretical coefficient of expansion for concrete through normal temperatures is approximately 0.000,005. Changes in atmospheric moisture cause volumetric changes which may be as great as those due to temperature changes. To meet these conditions, joints must be provided at sufficiently frequent intervals to avoid exceeding the strength of the concrete, or sufficient reinforcement must be used so to distribute deformations caused by initial shrinkage and by temperature and moisture variations that they will not seriously affect the structure.

For buildings not over 300 ft long, the reinforcement required for the principal stresses usually is sufficient to distribute secondary stresses due to shrinkage or expansion. Longer structures should be separated by transverse joints so that free movement of the adjacent parts is possible. In beam-and-slab construction this can be done by erecting two

Table II.   Chemical and Physical Properties for Concrete Reinforcement Bars
(A.S.T.M.   Designation: A16–33.)

Properties Considered	Billet-steel Bars		
	Grade, Plain Bars		
	Structural Steel	Intermediate	Hard
Phosphorus, max:			
Bessemer...............................	0.10	0.10	0.10
Open-hearth, basic.........................	0.05	0.05	0.05
acid..................................	0.08	0.08	0.08
Tensile strength, lb per sq in.	55–70,000	70–90,000	80,000 min
Yield point, min, lb per sq in................	33,000	40,000	50,000
Elongation (8 in.), min, per cent.............	1,400,000†	1,300,000†	1,200,000†
	Ten. str.	Ten. str. (16% min)	Ten. str.
Cold bend without fracture:			
Bars < $3/4$ in. diameter or thick bend, deg....	180	180	180
* d/t = ...	1	2	3
Bars > $3/4$ in. diameter or thick bend, deg....	180	90	90
* d/t = ...	1	2	3

Properties Considered	Billet-steel Bars		
	Grade, Deformed Bars		
	Structural Steel	Intermediate	Hard
Phosphorus, max:			
Bessemer...............................	0.10	0.10	0.10
Open-hearth, basic.........................	0.05	0.05	0.05
acid..................................	0.08	0.08	0.08
Tensile strength, lb per sq in	55–70,000	70–90,000	80,000 min.
Yield point, min, lb per sq in................	33,000	40,000	50,000
Elongation (8 in.), min, per cent.............	1,250,000†	1,125,000†	1,000,000†
	Ten. str.	Ten. str. (14% min)	Ten. str.
Cold bend without fracture:			
Bars < $3/4$ in. diameter or thick bend, deg....	180	180	180
* d/t = ...	1	3	4
Bars > $3/4$ in. diameter or thick bend, deg....	180	90	90
* d/t = ...	2	3	4

Properties Considered	Rail-steel Bars		
	Cold Twisted	Plain	Deformed Hot-Twisted
Phosphorus, max:			
Bessemer...............................	0.10	....	....
Open-hearth, basic.........................	0.05	....	....
acid..................................	0.08	....	....
Tensile strength, lb per sq in................	Recorded only	80,000	80,000
Yield point, min, lb per sq in................	55,000	50,000	50,000
Elongation (8 in.), min, per cent.............	5	1,200,000†	1,000,000†
		Ten. str.	Ten. str.
Cold bend without fracture:			
Bars < $3/4$ in. diameter or thick bend, deg....	180	180	180
* d/t = ...	2	3	4
Bars > $3/4$ in. diameter or thick bend, deg....	180	90	90
* d/t = ...	3	3	4

* d = diameter of pin about which specimen is bent; t = thickness or diameter of specimen.
† For bars over $3/4$ in. in thickness or diameter, a deduction of 0.25 per cent from the percentages of elongation specified shall be made for each $1/32$ in. of the thickness or diameter above $3/4$ in.
   For bars under $7/16$ in. in thickness or diameter, a deduction of 0.5 per cent from the percentages of elongation specified shall be made for each decrease of $1/32$ in. of the thickness or diameter below $7/16$ in.

sets of columns supporting parallel floor beams on either side of the joint: a common footing may be used. In girderless construction, contraction joints are placed along the centers of bays, the two sections of which are designed as cantilevers. The break between sections should be complete, and exposed joints should be filled with an elastic joint filler.

Although most damages caused by temperature and moisture changes are traceable to contraction, expansion joints occasionally are necessary where sections of concrete are poured within rigid confines, particularly around the edges of concrete roof fills adjacent to parapet and penthouse walls. Comparatively thin members, particularly in exposed positions, should be lightly reinforced with 3/8-in. round rods or wire fabric, to distribute deformations due to volumetric change and to prevent cracking. The amount of such reinforcement, of structural grade steel, may be taken as 0.3 per cent of the sectional area of the concrete.

Building Ordinances. Table III gives the allowable unit stresses applying to the design of reinforced concrete as now required by representative city ordinances and the Joint Standard Building Code. Unfortunately, there is wide variation in the requirements of different localities, and the engineer should obtain a copy of ordinances controlling his work. Outside of any local jurisdiction, the Joint Standard Building Code, published by the American Concrete Institute, is recommended as an excellent standard. Present practice (1935) is to design reinforced-concrete members on the basis of the allowable stresses in the materials, rather than on the ultimate stresses. Although most municipalities still assume fixed values for concrete mixed in certain specified proportions, it is preferable, when preliminary tests can be made, to compute allowable stresses as percentages of the ultimate compressive strength actually developed at the age of 28 days. The engineering societies have recommended this practice, which is illustrated by data taken from the Joint Code, and also by the requirements of the city of Philadelphia which permit this method to be used when proper control is exercised.

Table III. Allowable Unit Stresses in Reinforced Concrete under Static Loads
(From various codes)

Classification of Stresses	Allowable Stresses, lb per sq in.			
	1928, San Francisco*	1930, Boston†	1928, Chicago†	Joint Standard Building Code‡
Extreme fiber stress in concrete in compression in general..	715	715	700	800
Adjacent to supports of continuous beams...............	825	825	700	900
Concentric compression in concrete....................	495	495	400	500
Shearing stress in concrete when no steel is provided to resist diagonal tension................................	....	44	40	40§
Vertical shearing stress when diagonal tension requirements are satisfied..	132	132	135	120§
Bond stress:				
Between concrete and plain bars......................	88	88	70	80
Between concrete and deformed bars..................	110	110	100	100
Maximum tensile stress in steel reinforcement...........	18,000	18,000	18,000	18,000
Maximum tensile stress in cold-drawn steel wire.........	20,000	22,500	18,000	20,000

* Values based on a 28-day compressive strength of 2200 lb per sq in., corresponding to a mixture of 1 part cement to 6 parts combined aggregate, where the coarse aggregate is of granite or traprock. The proportions are by volume of cement to the combined aggregates, measured separately. For example, a 1 : 2 : 4 mixture might also be referred to as a 1 : 6 mixture.
† Values based on a 28-day compressive strength of 2200 lb per sq in.
‡ Values based on a 28-day compressive strength of 2000 lb. per sq in.
§ Values of 60 and 180 respectively may be used when special anchorage of longitudinal steel is provided.

29. BEAMS AND SLABS

Fundamental Assumptions. A plane cross-section of a beam, before bending, remains a plane section after bending; the modulus of elasticity of the concrete in compression remains constant within the assumed working stresses; the distribution of compressive stress in a beam is rectilinear; perfect adhesion exists between concrete and steel; in calculating the moment of resistance of reinforced-concrete beams and slabs, the tensile resistance of the concrete is negligible; the initial stress in the steel caused by contraction or expansion of the concrete is negligible, except in column design; the ratio of the modulus of elasticity of steel to concrete is expressed by the formula (notation given below):

$$n = \frac{E_s}{1000 f_c'} = \frac{30,000}{f_c'} \tag{1}$$

Flexure Formulas for Rectangular Beams and Solid Concrete Slabs. (See Fig. 2.)
The following notation is used: d = effective depth of beam, distance from extreme fibers in compression to center of gravity of tensile reinforcement, inches; b = width of beam or section of slab, inches; k = ratio of distance of neutral axis of cross-section from extreme fibers in compression to effective depth of beam; kd = distance of neutral axis from extreme fibers in compression, inches; j = ratio of distance between the center of compression of concrete and center of tension of steel to effective depth of beam, or ratio of arm of resisting couple to d; jd = distance between center of compression in

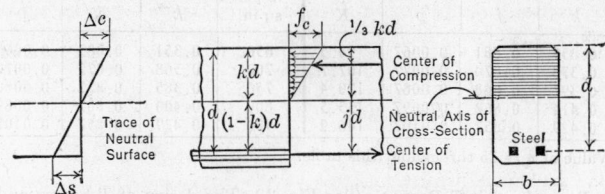

Fig. 2. Diagrams of Deformations and Stresses

concrete and center of tension in steel, or arm of resisting couple, inches; f_c = compressive unit stress in extreme fibers of concrete, pounds per square inch; f_c' = ultimate crushing unit strength of concrete at age 28 days, pounds per square inch; f_s = tensile unit stress in steel, pounds per square inch; A_s = area of cross-section of main tensile reinforcement, square inches; E_s = modulus of elasticity of steel, pounds per square inch; E_c = modulus of elasticity of concrete, pounds per square inch; n = modulus of elasticity of steel divided by modulus of elasticity of concrete, i.e., $n = E_s/E_c$; M = bending moment, inch-pound; p = percentage of reinforcement, or $\frac{A_s}{bd}$; $K = \frac{1}{2} f_c jk$.

Steel ratio, for balanced reinforcement,

$$p = \frac{1}{2 \dfrac{f_s}{f_c} \left(\dfrac{f_s}{n f_c} + 1 \right)} \tag{2}$$

Ratio of distance of neutral axis of cross-section from extreme fibers in compression to effective depth of beam,

$$k = \sqrt{2pn + (pn)^2} - pn \tag{3}$$

Ratio of arm of resisting couple to concrete depth,

$$j = 1 - \frac{k}{3} \tag{4}$$

Concrete depth as controlled by bending moment,

$$d = \sqrt{\frac{M}{\frac{1}{2} f_c jkb}} = \sqrt{\frac{M}{Kb}} \tag{5}$$

Steel area as controlled by bending moment,

$$A_s = pbd \tag{6a}$$

$$A_s = \frac{M}{f_s jd} \tag{6b}$$

Formula 5 determines the depth of a slab or beam to resist a given bending moment without exceeding a specified unit stress in the concrete. If formula 5 is used, 6a or 6b may be used to determine the steel area. Formula 6a is for general use; formula 6b determines the sectional area of the reinforcement as a percentage of the concrete section, bd. In Table IV are given values of k, j, p, and K, for $n = 15$, as computed by the above formulas. If the value of p is computed from formula 2 or taken from Table IV, the result will be to supply the exact amount of steel necessary to "balance" the concrete. This procedure is satisfactory for slabs and rectangular beams, or for other members for which the concrete section has been determined by moment considerations. It is inappropriate for the design of T-beams or others where the entire concrete section is not required by moment.

Fiber stresses,
$$f_s = \frac{M}{A_s jd} = \frac{M}{pjbd^2} \tag{7}$$

$$f_c = \frac{2M}{jkbd^2} = \frac{2pf_s}{k} \tag{8}$$

Formulas 7 and 8 are for checking fiber stresses of beams already designed.

Table IV. Formula Factors for Beams and Slabs

f_c, lb per sq in.	\multicolumn{4}{c}{$f_s = 16{,}000$ lb per sq in.}	f_c, lb per sq in.	\multicolumn{4}{c}{$f_s = 18{,}000$ lb per sq in.}
	k	j	p	K		k	j	p	K
600	0.359	0.881	0.0067	94.5	650	0.351	0.883	0.0063	100.8
650	0.378	0.874	0.0077	107.7	700	0.368	0.877	0.0072	113.1
700	0.397	0.868	0.0087	120.4	750	0.385	0.872	0.0080	125.7
750	0.414	0.862	0.0097	133.5	800	0.400	0.867	0.0089	138.7
800	0.429	0.857	0.0107	146.9	900	0.429	0.857	0.0107	165.3

NOTE: Value of $n = 15$ throughout this table.

Flexure Formulas for T-Beams. (See Fig. 3.) The design of T-beams and T-girders is divided into two classifications: (1) That in which the neutral surface falls either within the flange or at the bottom of it. (2) That in which the neutral surface falls within the web.

In case 1, the design is the same as for rectangular beams, and formulas 2 to 8 apply. The width of flange, however, is used for the value of b, and the steel ratio p is based upon the total area bd.

In case 2, which is more frequent, neglecting the compression resisted by the web·

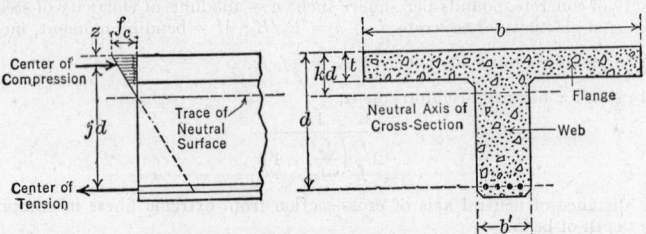

FIG. 3. Stress Diagram and Cross-section of a Reinforced-Concrete T Beam

let t = total slab thickness on either side of the web, inches; z = distance from the compression surface of the beam to the center of compression, inches; b' = width of web, inches; b = allowable width of flange, inches; $p = A_s/b'd$, that is, the steel ratio is based upon the area $b'd$. The remaining notation is the same as for rectangular beams.

Position of neutral axis,
$$kd = \frac{2ndA_s + bt^2}{2nA_s + 2bt} \tag{9}$$

Position of resultant compression,
$$z = \frac{3kd - 2t}{2kd - t} \cdot \frac{t}{3} \tag{10}$$

Arm of resisting couple, $\qquad jd = d - z \tag{11}$

Steel area as controlled by bending moment,
$$A_s = \frac{M}{f_s jd} \tag{12}$$

Fiber stresses, $\qquad f_s = \frac{M}{A_s jd} \tag{13}$

$$f_c = \frac{Mkd}{btjd(kd - t/2)} = \frac{f_s}{n} \cdot \frac{k}{1-k} \tag{14}$$

Formulas giving approximate results but erring slightly on the safe side are deduced by substituting

$$\left(d - \frac{t}{2}\right) \text{ for } jd, \text{ and } \left(\frac{1}{2}\right) \text{ for } \left(1 - \frac{t}{2kd}\right)$$

This substitution gives:

Extreme fiber stress in concrete,

$$f_c = \frac{2M}{bt\left(d - \dfrac{t}{2}\right)} \tag{15}$$

Steel area,

$$A_s = \frac{M}{f_s\left(d - \dfrac{t}{2}\right)} \tag{16}$$

Shearing Stress. Rectangular beams and slabs should be checked for shear, as a measure of the diagonal tension, and the concrete area increased if the shear is excessive. The depth of T-beams, when economically designed, is generally controlled by shearing stress. Let V = total vertical shear at the section considered, pounds; v = total unit shearing stress at the section, pounds per square inch; $j = 0.875$ (an approximation used for shear computations); b = width of beam for rectangular beams (for T-beams replace b by b' the width of web), inches; d = effective depth of beam, inches. Then,

$$v = \frac{V}{bjd} \tag{17}$$

or

$$d = \frac{V}{bvj} \tag{18}$$

Equation 17 is used to check the unit shearing stresses on rectangular beams and slabs; the size of which is normally determined by bending-moment considerations. Equation 18 is used in the direct design of T-beams, etc., the maximum allowable value being substituted for v. It should be noted that the depths of T-beams are usually determined by shear, owing to the fact that the amount of concrete provided by the floor construction is normally more than sufficient to resist the compressive stresses due to moment.

Web Reinforcement. (See Fig. 4.) Stirrups or bent rods are used for web reinforcement in beams and girders of rectangular and T-section, as it is more economical to use such reinforcement, and correspondingly higher stresses, than to increase the size of the member.

The design of web reinforcement is as follows: Let v' = allowable unit shearing stress resisted by the concrete alone, pounds per square inch; A_s = cross-sectional area of stirrups, or of inclined portion of double-bent rods, square inches (in a U-shaped or W-shaped stirrup, this is the total cross-sectional area of all legs); f_s = allowable unit tensile stress in stirrups, pounds per square inch; s = spacing of stirrups, inches; remaining notation the same as above.

Then if $v'bjd$ represents the total shearing stress carried by the concrete,

$$s = \frac{f_s jd A_s}{V - v'bjd} \tag{19}$$

If it is required that the reinforcement is to be designed to take two-thirds of the total shearing stress, as specified in some codes, the formula becomes

$$s = \frac{3}{2}\frac{f_s jd A_s}{V} \tag{20}$$

These formulas apply to vertical stirrups. Inclined stirrups or inclined bars, forming a part of the main tensile reinforcement may be designed or checked by the same formulas, by multiplying the value of the shear by the sine of the angle of inclination to the horizontal.

If L = clear span, feet, the distance from the support through which either stirrups or bent bars are required for uniformly loaded beams is given by

$$x = \frac{L}{2}\left(1 - \frac{v'}{v}\right) \tag{21}$$

Stirrups usually are placed vertically, and are either $3/8$-in. or $1/2$-in. round rods, bent to a U- or W-shape. The maximum spacing for stirrups should be limited to $3/4 \times$ depth of beam; this also is the maximum distance through which the inclined portion of a longitudinal rod, or several rods, bent at the same section, should be considered effective as web reinforcement (see Fig. 4). The diameter of the rod used for stirrups should not exceed $1/50 \times$ depth of beam. Stirrups should encircle the main longitudinal reinforcement, all free ends being anchored by hooks.

Bond. As the tensile stress in the reinforcement is transmitted from the concrete, the rods or bars must have sufficient surface area to avoid exceeding the unit bond stress per square inch. If $u =$ unit bond stress, pounds per square inch, and $\Sigma o =$ sum of perimeters, inches, of all horizontal rods under tensile stress at the section considered,

$$u = \frac{V}{(\Sigma o)jd} \quad \text{or} \quad \Sigma o = \frac{V}{ujd} \tag{22}$$

It is customary to check the bond stress after the design is completed; if the value is excessive, smaller rods should be used and the number increased, since this increases

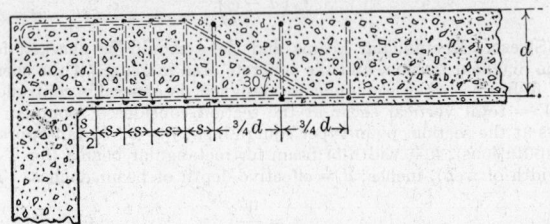

Fig. 4.   Diagram of a Web-Reinforcement in a Rectangular or T Beam

the surface area of the steel. Limiting values for bond stress are usually 80 lb per sq in. for plain rods or bars, and 100 lb per sq in. for deformed types.

Anchorage of Reinforcement. Besides the matter of bond, it is necessary to anchor the main longitudinal reinforcement at terminations where slabs, beams, or girders rest upon walls or frames, by means of hooks, into other reinforced-concrete members (see Fig. 5). Where continuous over supports, it is customary to carry half the longitudinal reinforcement of each beam to the $1/4$ or $1/5$ point of the adjacent span. This practice provides adequate anchorage; the remaining steel is usually stopped at the center line of the support.

An embedment of 50 diameters of a rod, or side of a square bar, is required to develop an allowable unit stress of 16,000 lb per sq in. in the steel, and an embedment of 56 diameters to develop a unit stress of 18,000 lb per sq in. ($u = 80$ lb per sq in.). Embedments

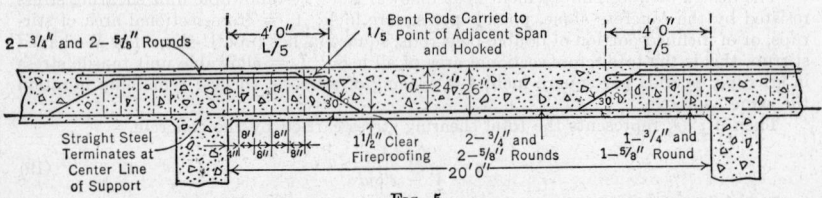

Fig. 5

of 40 diameters and 45 diameters correspond, respectively, to a strength of 16,000 and 18,000 lb per sq in. for deformed steel ($u = 100$ lb per sq in.).

Bending Moments and External Shears. Bending moments and vertical shears for continuous and restrained beams as well as for those of single spans simply supported are given on pp. 5–26 to 5–28 and p. 5–20. These values also apply to reinforced-concrete members subjected to flexure, but for continuous spans they are modified to conform to the conditions of partial restraint existing in concrete frames. Also to provide for possible variable live loads, the values of the positive bending moments used in concrete design usually are taken larger than the theoretical values.

As the function of the reinforcement is to resist the tensile stresses, the typical arrangement for beams other than cantilever is to place the rods near the bottom face throughout the central portion of the span. For beams simply supported, about two-thirds of the main tensile reinforcement consists of straight rods or bars, the other one-third being bent up at the $1/5$ point of the clear span and anchored into the supports to resist any negative moment resulting from the monolithic construction.

For continuous or restrained beams, it is usual to raise one-half the main tensile reinforcement at the points of inflection, assumed to be the $1/5$ points of the clear span, and, in the former case, to carry the reinforcement to the $1/4$ point of the adjoining span. This provides approximately equal areas near the bottom of the beam at mid-span and near the top of the beam over supports, which corresponds to the general design practice of using approximately equal coefficients for both positive and negative moments in the design of continuous members. Raising a portion of the main longitudinal reinforcement also helps to resist diagonal tension and usually permits the omission of one or two stirrups at each end of the beam.

The following equations for determining maximum bending moment are recommended by the Joint Standard Building Code for freely supported or slightly restrained continuous beams, or slabs of approximately equal spans, under uniform load.

(1) Beams and slabs of one span: positive moment near center,

$$M = \frac{Wl}{8} \tag{23}$$

(2) Beams and slabs continuous for two spans only: positive moment near center of each span,

$$M = \frac{Wl}{10} \tag{24}$$

negative moment over interior support,

$$M = \frac{Wl}{8} \tag{25}$$

(3) Beams and slabs continuous for more than two spans: positive moment near center and negative moment at support of interior spans,

$$M = \frac{Wl}{12} \tag{26}$$

positive moment near centers of end spans and negative moment at first interior support,

$$M = \frac{Wl}{10} \tag{27}$$

(4) Negative moment at end supports for Cases 1, 2, and 3,

$$M = \text{not less than } \frac{Wl}{24} \tag{28}$$

In these equations M = bending moment, pound-inches; W = total load on the beam or slab, pounds, including its own weight; l = length, inches, taken as the center-to-center span for beams simply supported, and as the clear span for continuous or restrained beams. The equations apply only to beams or slabs under uniform load and, in continuous members, to those of approximately equal spans. If the spans are substantially unequal, or subjected to other than uniformly distributed loads, the actual bending moments and shears should be computed by the methods given in the section on Beams, pp. 5–19 to 5–36. The computation of moments for continuous girders and other members subjected to concentrated loads may be simplified by determining the moments as if the members were simply supported, and then multiplying by a reducing factor corresponding to the condition of end restraint, *i.e.*, $4/5$ for semi-continuity and $2/3$ for full continuity. The design of continuous members should always provide steel over support at least equal to the amount required in mid-span to resist the negative moment.

The external vertical shear is computed as a measure of the diagonal tension, which, in reinforced-concrete members subject to flexure, is a combination of horizontal and vertical shear. For both simply supported and continuous members, shears are computed as described in the section on Beams, pp. 5–19 to 5–36. For members symmetrically loaded, the maximum shear, occurring at the face of the support, equals $1/2$ load, except as influenced by the conditions of end restraint.

Rectangular Beams.

Example. Required to design a rectangular beam, 20-ft clear span, fully continuous at supports, for a uniformly distributed load of 1500 lb per ft, including weight of beam.

Specification data: $f_c = 650$; $f_s = 18,000$; $n = 15$; v' limited to 40; maximum allowable vertical shearing stress (v) with web reinforcement = 120.

By formula 26, $M = Wl/12 = (30,000 \times 20 \times 12)/12 = 600,000$ lb-in.

By formula 5, $d = \sqrt{M/Kb} = \sqrt{600,000/(100.8 \times 10)} = 24.39$ in., = 24 in. (approximately), where breadth b is assumed as 10 in.; k from Table IV.

By formula 6, $A_s = pbd = 0.0063 \times 10 \times 24 = 1.51$ sq in.

Accept a total depth of 26 in. and a width of 10 in., with two $5/8$-in. rounds and two $3/4$-in. rounds

The value of b should be chosen as small as practicable, unless headroom is limited, deep, narrow beams being more economical. Sufficient width should be provided to give a clear space of at least 1 in. between rods and the required fireproofing on the sides. The overall depth of a beam or girder should not be more than $3b$.

Testing the shear by formula 17, $v = V/bjd = (1500 \times 10)/(10 \times 0.875 \times 24) = 71.5$ lb per sq in. As this is more than v', the value allowed for plain concrete, and less than the limit for v, 120 lb, the design is acceptable, provided web reinforcement is used. The web reinforcement is computed as follows:

By formula 20, $s = (3/2)(f_s j d A_s/V) = (3/2) \{(18,000 \times 0.875 \times 24 \times 0.22)/15,000\} = 8.3$ in., where $A_s = $ cross-sectional area of the two legs of a U-shaped stirrup, made of $3/8$-in. round rod.

By formula 21, $x = (L/2)\{1 - (v'/v)\} = (20/2)\{1 - (40/72)\} = 4$ ft 6 in.

The first stirrup is placed 4 in. $(1/2 s)$ from the face of the support. Four more stirrups, 8 in. apart, provide web reinforcement out to the section where the bent rods are effective. Beyond this section, as shown by equation 21, none is needed.

Testing the bond stress at face of support by formula 22, $u = V/[\Sigma o j d] = 15,000/[\{(2 \times 1.96) + (2 \times 2.36)\} \times 0.875 \times 24] = 82.6$ lb per sq in. This value is satisfactory for plain rods. The arrangement of reinforcement is shown in Fig. 5.

Table V gives the safe loads on rectangular beams of various dimensions and reinforcements, designed according to the above principles.

Table V. Rectangular Beams—Simple Spans

Dimensions and Weight			Reinforcement				Span of Beam, ft							
			Straight		Double Bend		10	12	14	16	18	20	22	24
h	b	Weight of Beam	No.	Size	No.	Size								
In.	In.	Lb per lin ft					Total safe load in thousands of pounds, uniformly distributed, including weight of beam							
12	6	72	1	1/2 ○	1	1/2 ○	4.0	3.4	2.9	2.5	......	......		
	8	96	2	1/2 ○	1	3/8 ○	5.0	4.5	3.8	3.4	3.0	2.7		
	10	120	2	1/2 ○	2	1/2 ○	6.7	5.6	4.8	4.2	3.7	3.4		
16	8	128	2	1/2 □	1	1/2 □	10.5	8.8	7.5	6.6	5.9	5.3		
	10	160	2	5/8 ○	2	1/2 ○	13.2	11.0	9.4	8.2	7.3	6.6		
	12	192	2	1/2 □	2	1/2 □	15.8	13.2	11.3	9.9	8.8	7.9		
20	8	160	2	5/8 ○	1	3/4 ○	17.5	14.6	12.5	10.9	9.7	8.7		
	10	200	2	3/4 ○	2	1/2 ○	21.8	18.2	15.6	13.6	12.1	10.9		
	12	240	2	3/4 ○	2	5/8 ○	26.2	21.8	18.7	16.4	14.5	13.1		
24	8	192	2	3/4 ○	1	5/8 ○	26.0	21.7	18.6	16.3	14.5	13.0	11.8	10.8
	10	240	2	3/4 ○	2	5/8 ○	32.6	27.2	23.3	20.4	18.1	16.3	14.8	13.6
	12	288	3	3/4 ○	2	3/4 ○	39.0	32.5	27.9	24.4	21.7	19.5	17.7	16.2
28	10	280	2	7/8 ○	2	5/8 ○	......	37.9	32.5	28.4	25.3	23.8	20.7	18.9
	12	336	3	3/4 ○	2	5/8 ○	......	45.5	39.0	34.1	30.3	27.3	24.8	22.7
	16	448	4	3/4 ○	2	3/4 ○	......	60.5	51.8	45.4	40.4	36.4	33.0	30.3

Bending moment
$M = WL/8$
Unit stresses
$f_s = 18,000$
$f_c = 650$

Loads to left of upper zigzag line develop shears greater than 40 lb per sq in. Loads to left of lower zigzag line develop shears greater than 60 lb per sq in. Loads in italic figures produce bond stresses greater than 100 lb per sq in. For semi-continuous spans ($M = WL/10$), multiply tabular load by 1.25. For fully continuous spans ($M = WL/12$), multiply tabular load by 1.50. When using this table for continuous or semi-continuous spans, the shear and bond stresses should be investigated.

Slabs. The design of solid concrete slabs is substantially the same as that of rectangular beams. If the panels are square or nearly so, it is necessary to determine the load to be distributed in each direction. If the longer dimension is greater than $1 \frac{1}{2} \times$ shorter dimension, as it usually is, the slab is designed to carry all the load on the shorter span, and so-called " shrinkage " steel, comprising $3/8$-in. rounds spaced 1 ft 6 in. centers, is considered adequate in the longer direction.

The total load on a strip of slab 1 ft wide, spanning between supports, is obtained by multiplying the unit load per square foot by the span. This strip is then treated as a rectangular beam of breadth $b = 12$ in.

Example. Required: to design a slab, 7-ft span, fully continuous at supports, to carry a superimposed load of 125 lb per sq ft. Specification data: Same as in the example of a rectangular beam.

Assuming a slab thickness of 4 in., weighing 48 lb per sq ft, total load per square foot = 125 + 48 = 173 lb per sq ft.

On a strip of slab 1 ft wide, total load = 173 × 7 = 1211 lb.

By formula 26, $M = Wl/12 = (1211 \times 7 \times 12)/12$ = 8477 lb-in.

By formula 5, $d = \sqrt{M/Kb} = \sqrt{8477/(100.8 \times 12)}$ = 2.65 in.

By formula 6, $A_s = pbd = 0.0053 \times 12 \times 2.65$ = 0.20 sq in.

Accept a total depth of 4 in. (approximately 1 in. below the reinforcement) with 3/8-in. rounds, 7 in. on centers.

Rods should not be spaced at a distance greater than 2 1/2 × total depth of slab; the use of very small rods at close spacings is uneconomical.

Testing the shear by formula 17, $v = V/(bjd) = 605/(12 \times 0.875 \times 2.65)$ = 21.7 lb per sq in. As this is less than the limiting value, v', the design is accepted.

Testing the bond stress at face of support, by formula 22, $u = V/(\Sigma ojd) = 605/\{(1.71 \times 1.18) \times 0.875 \times 2.65\}$ = 129 lb per sq in., where 1.71 = number of rods per foot of width, and 1.18 = perimeter of each rod. The value is rather high but may be accepted for deformed rods, provided the reinforcement is anchored at terminations and lapped over supports. Fig. 6 shows the arrangement of reinforcement.

Table VI gives the safe loads on solid concrete slabs of various dimensions and reinforcements, designed according to the above principles.

Table VI. Solid Concrete Slabs—Simple Spans

Thickness of Slab	Weight of Slab per sq ft	Reinforcement		Span of Slab, ft														
		Size	Spacing	4	5	6	7	8	9	10	11	12	13	14	15	16	17	18
In.	Lb	In.	In.	Safe Loads, lb per sq ft, including weight of slab														
3 1/2	42	3/8 O	7	332	212	148	108	83	...	...	...	...	...	...				
4	48	3/8 O	6	453	290	201	148	113	90	...	...	...	...	...				
4 1/2	54	1/2 O	6	600	384	268	196	151	120	96	...	...	...	...				
5	60	1/2 □	10	...	506	352	258	198	156	126	105	88	...					
5 1/2	66	1/2 O	7		633	440	322	247	195	158	131	110	93					
6	72	1/2 O	6			547	402	308	243	197	163	136	117	100	...	...	...	...
6 1/2	78	1/2 □	7			647	475	364	287	233	192	162	137	119	104	...	...	...
7	84	1/2 □	7			795	585	448	354	286	236	199	169	146	127	112	...	...
7 1/2	90	1/2 □	6				687	526	416	337	278	234	197	172	150	132	...	...
8	96	5/8 O	7				765	585	462	374	310	260	222	191	166	146	129	...
8 1/2	102	3/4 O	9					667	526	426	352	296	252	217	189	166	148	132
9	103	3/4 O	8 1/2					760	602	486	402	338	288	265	216	190	168	151

Bending moment
$M = WL/8$

Unit stresses
$f_s = 18,000$
$f_c = 650$

For loads shown, unit shearing stresses are less than 40 lb per sq in. Loads to left of zigzag line produce bond stresses greater than 100 lb per sq in. For semi-continuous spans ($M = WL/10$), multiply tabular load by 1.25. For fully continuous spans ($M = WL/12$), multiply tabular load by 1.50. When using the table for continuous or semi-continuous spans, the shear and bond stresses should be investigated.

T-Beams. When designing a floor system comprising slabs, beams, and girders, the slabs are first considered. These are designed as in the previous example, and the load carried by a T-beam, for which the floor slab acts as a flange, is found by multiplying the unit load per square foot of floor by the area which the beam supports, and adding to the product any other incidental loads and the weight of the stem of the beam.

The loads carried by T-girders, usually a combination of concentrated loads due to beam reactions, and the uniformly distributed weight of the girder itself, are used to compute the bending moment, which is then employed in exactly the same way as with uniformly distributed loads.

For purposes of design in computing the sectional-area of concrete available to resist compressive stresses, the width of slab which may be considered as acting as the flange of a T-beam should not exceed $1/4$ of the span-length of the beam. See Fig. 7.

The overhanging width on either side of the web should not exceed $8 \times$ slab thickness nor $1/2 \times$ clear distance to next beam. In angle beams, the overhanging width of flange should be limited to $1/12 \times$ span or $1/2 \times$ clear distance to next beam. It is always necessary to pour the floor slab forming the flange of the beam monolithically with the

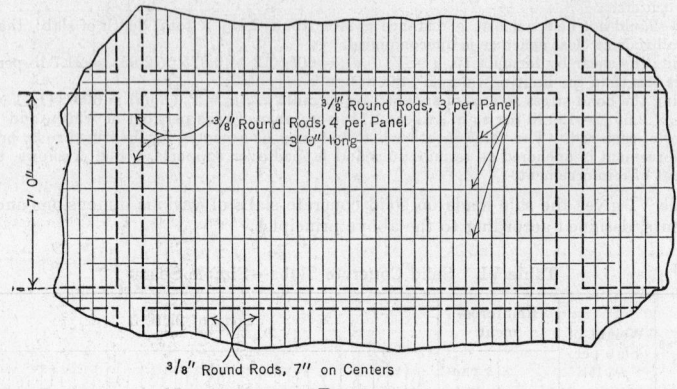

3/8″ Round Rods, 7″ on Centers

Fig. 6

web, and there must be steel in the form of stirrups or bent rods to bond the flange to the web.

The critical section for compression in T-beams and T-girders, continuous over supports, is at the face of the support. As the negative moment acts on the rectangular section of the web, the stress in the concrete at these sections is always higher than through mid-span. However, as only a short section of the beam is in compression at this point,

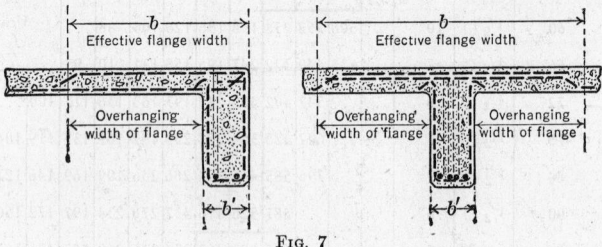

Fig. 7

good practice permits an increase of 15 per cent in the compressive stress. The straight bars in the bottom of the beam also act as compressive reinforcement, provided they are extended a sufficient distance beyond the face of the support to develop their stress in bond.

Example. Required to design a T-beam, 20-ft clear span, with ends semi-continuous, to carry a uniformly distributed load of 2000 lb per ft including the weight of the beam. Slab thickness = 4 in.; specification data, same as in the example of a rectangular beam.

Determining the depth by shear by formula 18, $d = V/(b'vj) = 20{,}000/(10 \times 120 \times 0.875) = 19$ in., where the width of the beam is assumed as 10 in., and j is taken as 0.875.

The moment by formula 27 $= M = Wl/10 = (40{,}000 \times 20 \times 12)/10 = 960{,}000$ lb-in.

By formula 16, $A_s = M/[f_s\{d - (t/2)\}] = 960{,}000/[18{,}000\{19 - (4/2)\}j = 3.14$ sq in.

Accept a total depth of 21 in., with four 1-in. rounds. The width of 10 in. will allow 1 in. between each rod and a protection of $1\,1/2$ in. on each side. Raise two rods over support as shown in Fig. 8.

By formula 20, $s = (3/2)(f_s j d A_s/V) = (3/2)\{(18{,}000 \times 0.875 \times 19 \times 0.44)/20{,}000\} = 9.87$ in., where $A_s =$ cross-sectional area of steel in the four legs of a W-shaped stirrup (3/8-in. round rod).

By formula 21, $x = (L/2)\{1 - (v'/v)\} = 10\{1 - (40/120)\} = 6$ ft 8 in., where v has its limiting value, as the beam was designed on that basis. The first stirrup is placed 4 in. $(1/2s)$ from the face of the support. Four more stirrups, 8 in. apart, provide web reinforcement out to the section where the bent rods are effective. Fifteen inches beyond this section, as shown by Fig. 8, three stirrups are placed 12 in. apart.

Testing for bond stress at face of support by formula 22, $u = V/\Sigma ojd = 20{,}000/\{(4 \times 3.14) \times 0.875 \times 19\} = 96$ lb per sq in. This value is satisfactory for deformed rods. The arrangement of reinforcement is shown in Fig. 8.

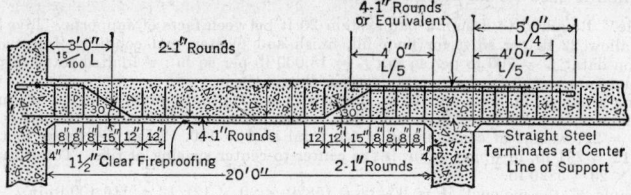

Fig. 8

Table VII gives the safe loads on T-beams of various dimensions and reinforcements designed according to the above principles.

Table VII. T-Beams—Continuous over Supports

Dimensions and Weight			Reinforcement				Span of Beam, ft									
			Straight		Double Bend		10	12	14	16	18	20	22	24	26	28
h	b'	Weight of Section $b'h$	No.	Size	No.	Size										
In.	In.	Lb per lin ft					Total safe load in thousands of pounds, uniformly distributed, including weight of beam									
12	6	72	1	5/8 ○	1	5/8 ○	8.6	7.2	6.2	5.4						
	8	96	1	3/4 ○	1	3/4 ○	12.7	10.6	9.1	7.9						
	10	120	2	5/8 ○	2	5/8 ○	17.3	14.4	12.3	10.8						
16	8	128	1	1 ○	2	3/4 ○	.....	29.8	25.6	22.4	19.9	17.9				
	10	160	2	3/4 ○	2	3/4 ○	.....	31.7	27.2	23.8	21.1	19.0				
	12	192	{1 1}	7/8 ○ 3/4 ○	1	7/8 ○ 3/4 ○	.....	37.5	32.2	28.2	25.0	22.5				
20	8	160	1	1 □	1	1 □	....	.....		36.1	32.0	28.8	26.2	24.0		
	10	200	2	7/8 ○	2	7/8 ○	....	.....		43.2	38.4	34.6	31.4	28.8		
	12	240	{1 1}	1 ○ 7/8 ○	1 1	1 ○ 7/8 ○	....	.....		49.7	44.2	39.8	36.2	33.1		
24	10	240	{1 1}	1 ○ 7/8 ○	1	1 ○ 7/8 ○	....	.....	.....	55.2	49.7	45.2	41.4	38.2	35.5	
	12	288	2	1 ○	2	1 ○	....	.....	.....	62.1	56.0	50.8	46.6	43.0	40.0	
	14	336	2	1 □	2	1 □	....	.....	.....	80.0	72.0	65.4	60.0	55.3	51.4	

Bending moment $M = WL/12$
Unit stresses $f_s = 18{,}000$
$f_c = 650$

Loads to the left of zigzag line produce shearing stresses greater than 120 lb per sq in. on the area $b'jd$. For stirrups see p. 5-65. Loads in italic figures produce bond stresses greater than 100 lb per sq in. For anchorage see p. 5-66. For semi-continuous spans ($M = WL/10$), multiply tabular load by 0.83. For simply supported spans ($M = WL/8$), multiply tabular load by 0.67. When using this table for semi-continuous and simple spans, the bond stresses should be investigated.

Ribbed Floor Construction. For floors of apartment houses, hotels, institutional buildings, and others for light occupancy (superimposed loads 30 to 100 lb per sq ft), the ribbed constructions are particularly suitable. These comprise a series of concrete ribs, 4 or 5 in. wide, separated by terra-cotta blocks, gypsum or concrete units, metal or wood pans. Rib spacing varies from 16 to 30 in., depending on the width of block or void. A continuous slab, from 2 to 3 in. thick, forms the structural surface of the floor. Plaster is applied directly to the soffits of the blocks used as fillers; under the pans, metal lath is used as a plaster base. All these designs may be used with structural-steel or reinforced-concrete frame. Bridging joists should be used on long or very heavily loaded spans.

As the structural units in such systems are actually small T-beams (the fillers, except in terra-cotta and concrete, acting merely as voids) the design is substantially the same as for T-beams. The following example applies to the metal-pan system (see Fig. 9); the same method is used for all ribbed designs.

Example. Required to design a pan system 20 ft between faces of supports. Live load 60 lb per sq ft; allow 22 lb per sq ft for floor fill, finish and plaster, end condition fully continuous. Specification data: $f_c = 700$ lb per sq in.; $f_s = 18,000$ lb per sq in.; v' limited to 40 lb per sq in.; $n = 15$; minimum thickness of concrete over metal $= 2\frac{1}{2}$ in.

Choosing a pan 20 in. wide and 10 in. deep, with a $2\frac{1}{2}$ in. topping, from the manufacturer's catalog, the weight per square foot $= 58$ lb. Loads per square foot are: live load $= 60$; floor finish, etc. $= 22$; weight of construction $= 58$; total load $= 140$. Load per linear foot of rib $= 140 \times 25/12 = 291$ lb, in which 25 in. is the center-to-center spacing of ribs. Total load on each rib $= 291 \times 20 = 5820$ lb.

By formula 26, the moment $M = Wl/12 = (5820 \times 20 \times 12)/12 = 116,400$ lb-in.

By formula 16, $A_s = M/[f_s \{d - (t/2)\}] = 116,400/[18,000 \times 10] = 0.647$ sq in., where $d = (10 + 2\frac{1}{2}) - 1.25 = 11.25$ in.; $t/2 = 2.5/2 = 1.25$ in.

Accept two $\frac{5}{8}$-in. rounds in each rib ($A_s = 0.62$ sq in.).

The stress in the concrete is then checked. By formula 14 and Table IV,

$$f_c = \frac{Mkd}{bt\{kd - (t/2)\}jd} = \frac{116,400 \times 0.368 \times 11.25}{(25 \times 2.5)\{(0.368 \times 11.25) - 1.25\}(0.877 \times 11.25)} = 270 \text{ lb per sq in.}$$

Accept a 10-in. pan with $2\frac{1}{2}$-in. topping.

The maximum shear in the ribs at face of support is checked by formula 17, $v = V/b'jd = 2910/(5 \times 0.875 \times 11.25) = 59$ lb per sq in., where $b' =$ average width of the concrete rib for metal tile, equal to 5 in. In this computation, also, the conventional value of 0.875 is used for j instead of the value 0.877 given by Table IV.

Since v is more than the limiting value, v', tapered pans (see Fig. 9) should be used adjacent to supports to provide additional concrete to resist the compressive stress, due to negative moment, as well as the shearing stress.

Testing for bond stress at face of support, by formula 22, $u = V/\Sigma ojd = 2910/\{(2 \times 2.35) \times 0.875 \times 11.25\} = 63$ lb per sq in., where j is taken as 0.875. Deformed rods are unnecessary.

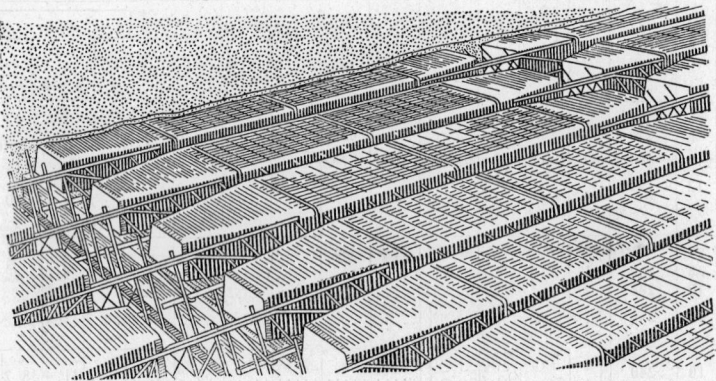

FIG. 9. Ribbed Floor Construction, Tapered Type Pan Used at Supports.

One $\frac{5}{8}$-in. rod is raised at the $\frac{1}{5}$ point of the clear span and carried over the support to the $\frac{1}{4}$ point of the adjoining span to provide a sectional area of steel over supports equal to that at mid-span.

30. COLUMNS

The principal types of reinforced-concrete columns are the tied or hooped, spiraled, and cored, the last being actually a steel column. The main columns of a building should never be less than 12-in. in diameter or in least width; good practice requires a minimum 16-in. diameter for round columns supporting girderless floor construction, and a minimum 14-in. thickness for exterior columns of industrial buildings. The diameter or least width should not be less than $\frac{1}{15}$ the average center-to-center span of the supported bay nor longer than $11 \times$ least lateral dimension of the column, unless the normal load is reduced. Dowels are used between footings and superimposed columns. Splices in vertical reinforcement should be made by lapping the rods a length of at least 24 bar diameters.

Tied Columns (see Fig. 10) are economical for comparatively light loads, as those carried in the upper stories of buildings. The ratio p of the cross-section of area of the vertical reinforcement to effective concrete area, usually taken as the gross sectional area, should not be less than 0.5 per cent nor should more than 2 per cent be considered in the computations. At least 4 rods, $5/8$-in. diameter, should be placed between 2 and 3 in. from the face of the column, enclosed by $1/4$-in. diameter ties spaced not over 12 in. apart. As both maximum and minimum percentages of steel are controlled by building ordinances, it is usually desirable to increase the column size or to use a richer mixture rather than to add vertical steel to carry load. It is extremely important, however, to have sufficient vertical reinforcement to resist bending, particularly for unsymmetrical loads.

Spiraled Columns (see Fig. 10) are usual for the interiors of buildings designed for heavy loads. Although a minimum amount of vertical reinforcement is required to resist bending stresses, the greatest economy is obtained by using rich mixtures and as large a percentage of spiral as the code or specification will permit. The vertical reinforcement should comprise at least 6 bars of $1/2$-in. minimum diameter, with cross-sectional area not less than 1 per cent nor more than 6 per cent of the core. The spiral is expressed as a percentage of the volume of the enclosed concrete and varies from $1/2$ to 2 per cent (see equation 32 below). The ratio of the per cent of spiral reinforcement to the per cent of vertical reinforcement should not be less than $1/4$. The spiral reinforcement should consist of evenly spaced, continuous spirals held firmly in place by at least three vertical spacer bars. The spacing of the spirals should not be greater than $1/6$ the diameter of the core nor over 3 in.

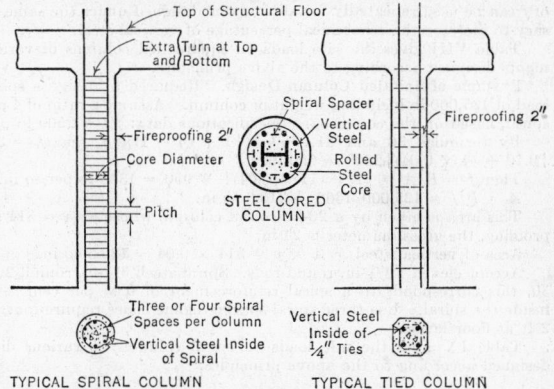

TYPICAL SPIRAL COLUMN   TYPICAL TIED COLUMN

Fig. 10

Cored Columns (see Fig. 10) are built of steel wide-flange sections enclosed by a minimum of 4 in. of concrete, reinforced with at least 0.5 per cent of vertical reinforcement and 0.5 per cent of spiral. The structural-steel core is then designed on a basis of axial compression, using a stress of 15,000 to 18,000 lb per sq in., according to the code or specification. No allowance is made for the concrete casing. The ratio of the unsupported height to the least radius of gyration of the structural-steel section should not exceed 120.

The Effective Area of a Column is that area which is considered as capable of carrying load. With tied columns, some city ordinances and many designers permit the gross cross-sectional area to be used, as in the following example; but the effective area of spiraled columns is always considered as the section enclosed within the spiral, the outer casing, usually 2 in. thick, being disregarded.

Formulas for Columns. The following formulas apply to the design of tied and spiraled columns. Let A = effective cross-sectional area of column, square inches; p = ratio of area of vertical steel to effective sectional area of concrete; P = total safe axial load, pounds, on column whose length $\geqq 11 \times$ least cross-sectional dimension; n = ratio of modulus of elasticity of steel to modulus of elasticity of concrete; f'_c = ultimate crushing unit strength of concrete at age 28 days, pounds per square inch; f_c = average unit compressive stress, in concrete, pounds per square inch; f = average unit compressive stress, P/A, in the column, pounds per square inch; D = core diameter in spiral columns, inches; a = cross-sectional area of spiral reinforcement steel; s = spacing of spiral reinforcement, i.e., pitch, inches.

For tied columns, the total safe load,

$$P = 0.225 f'_c A \{1 + (n - 1)p\} \tag{29}$$

For spiraled columns, the total safe load,

$$P = f_c A \{1 + (n - 1)p\} \tag{30}$$

where
$$f_c = 300 + (0.10 + 4p)f'_c \qquad (31)$$

The percentage of spiral reinforcement $= \dfrac{4a}{Ds} \times 100 \qquad (32)$

Example of Tied Column Design. Required: to design a round column to carry an axial load of 150,000 lb, including weight of column. For economy, use the minimum amount of vertical reinforcement, i.e., $p = 0.5$ per cent of the effective area, which is taken as the gross cross-section of the column. Specification data: $f'_c = 2000$ lb per sq in.; $n = 15$.

By formula 29, $P = 0.225 f'_c A\{1 + (n - 1)p\}$
Then $f = P/A = 0.225 f'_c \{1 + (n - 1)p\}$
Substituting the specification data for this example, $f = 450\{1 + (14 \times 0.005) = 482$ lb per sq in., and $A = P/f = 150,000/482 = 311$ sq in., which area is given by a 20-in. round column, whose area is 314 sq in.

Area of vertical steel $= A \times p = 314 \times 0.005 = 1.57$ sq in.

Accept six $5/8$-in. round rods, with $1/4$-in. round ties spaced 12 in. on centers. The steel rods are placed 2 in. inside the surface. Splices at floor levels are lapped 18 in. Note that the value of f can be used repeatedly for all columns designed under the same specification unless it is necessary to increase the economical percentage of vertical steel.

Table VIII gives the safe loads on square tied columns of various dimensions and reinforcements designed according to the above principles.

Example of Spiraled Column Design. Required to design a spiraled column to carry an axial load of 425,000 lb including weight of column. Assume a ratio of 4 per cent vertical and 1 per cent spiral, based on the core area. Specifications data: $f'_c = 2500$ lb per sq in.; $n = 12$.

By formulas 30 and 31, $P = A\{1 + (n - 1)p\}f_c$, and $f_c = 300 + (0.10 + 4p)f'_c = 300 + \{0.10 + (4 \times 0.04)\}2500 = 950$ lb.

Then $f = P/A = \{1 + (11 \times 0.04)\} \times 950 = 1368$ lb per sq in.

$A = P/f = 425,000/1368 = 310.6$ sq in.

This area is given by a 20-in. round column, whose area $= 314$ sq in. Allowing 2 in. for fireproofing, the gross diameter is 24 in.

Area of vertical steel $= A \times p = 314 \times 0.04 = 12.56$ sq in.

Accept eleven $1 1/4$-in. round rods. Spiral steel, $3/8$-in. round, $2 1/4$-in. pitch. (From equation 30, this corresponds to a spiral reinforcement of 0.98 per cent.) The vertical rods are placed inside the spiral. Use three spiral spacers (some codes require four). The vertical steel is lapped 2 ft at floor levels.

Table IX gives the safe loads on spiral columns of various dimensions and reinforcements, designed according to the above principles.

Table VIII. Square Tied Columns

Ties $= 1/4$-in. rounds, spaced 12 in. on centers. Safe axial loads in thousands of pounds, based on the Joint Standard Building Code, 1928

Column Size, in.	Core Size, in.	Vertical Reinforcement		$f'_c = 2000$ $n = 15$ Loads on Gross Area	Column Size, in.	Core Size, in.	Vertical Reinforcement		$f'_c = 2000$ $n = 15$ Loads on Gross Area
		No.	Size, in.				No.	Size, in.	
12	8	4	1/2 ○	70	20	16	8	1/2 □	193
			5/8 ○	72				3/4 ○	202
			3/4 ○	76				7/8 ○	210
			7/8 ○	80				1 □	230
14	10	4	5/8 ○	95	22	18	8	5/8 ○	233
			3/4 ○	99				1 ○	257
			7/8 ○	103				1 1/8 □	279
			1 ○	108					
			1 □	113	24	20	12	1/2 ○	278
								7/8 ○	304
16	12	4	3/4 ○	126				1 □	332
			7/8 ○	130					
			1 ○	135	26	22	12	5/8 ○	327
			1 □	140				7/8 ○	349
			1 1/8 □	148				1 ○	380
18	14	8	1/2 □	158	28	24	12	3/4 ○	386
			3/4 ○	168				1 ○	410
			7/8 ○	176				1 1/8 □	447
			1 ○	185					
					30	26	12	3/4 ○	439
								1 ○	464
								1 1/8 □	490

Table IX.   Spiral Columns

Safe axial load in thousand of pounds, based on the Joint Standard Building Code, 1928

Column Diameter, In.	Core Diameter, In.	Round Spiral Wire Size, In.	Pitch, In.	Vertical Reinforcement No.	Size, in.	$f'_c=2500$ $n=12$ Loads on Core Area	Column Diameter, In.	Core Diameter, In.	Round Spiral Wire Size, In.	Pitch, In.	Vertical Reinforcement No.	Size, in.	$f'_c=2500$ $n=12$ Loads on Core Area
16	12	1/4	1 1/2	6	1/2 O	82	28	24	7/16	2 3/4	16	1 □	568
		1/4	1 1/2	6	5/8 O	95			7/16	2 1/2	14	1 1/8 □	607
		1/4	1 1/2	6	3/4 O	111	30	26	7/16	2 3/8	15	1 1/8 □	670
		1/4	2	6	7/8 O	132			7/16	2 1/4	17	1 1/8 □	726
		1/4	1 5/8	6	1 O	159							
18	14	1/4	1 3/4	6	3/4 O	132	32	28	7/16	2 3/8	17	1 1/8 □	765
		1/4	2 1/4	6	7/8 O	152			7/16	2 1/8	19	1 1/8 □	825
		1/4	2 1/4	6	1 O	176	34	30	1/2	2 3/4	21	1 1/8 □	922
		5/16	2 1/8	6	1 □	208			1/2	2 1/2	22	1 1/8 □	983
20	16	1/4	2 3/8	8	7/8 O	201	36	32	1/2	2 5/8	23	1 1/8 □	1020
		5/16	2 1/2	8	1 O	232			1/2	2 3/8	25	1 1/8 □	1090
		3/8	2 5/8	8	1 □	272							
22	18	1/4	2 1/8	9	7/8 O	238	38	34	1/2	2 3/8	27	1 1/8 □	1180
		5/16	2 1/8	10	1 O	292			1/2	2 1/4	29	1 1/8 □	1250
		3/8	2 1/4	10	1 □	343	40	36	1/2	2 1/4	24	1 1/4 □	1310
24	20	5/16	3	10	7/8 O	281			1/2	2 1/8	26	1 1/4 □	1390
		3/8	2 7/8	12	1 O	344	42	38	1/2	2 1/8	27	1 1/4 □	1470
		3/8	2 1/8	12	1 □	415			1/2	2	29	1 1/4 □	1550
26	22	5/16	2 3/4	10	1 O	353							
		7/16	3	13	1 O	466							
		7/16	2 5/8	12	1 1/8 □	518							

31.   FOOTINGS

The Function of a Footing is to distribute concentrated loads from walls or columns over a sufficiently large area to bring the pressure within the safe bearing capacity of the soil or rock.   Plain concrete footings may be used beneath walls or columns carrying small loads, but reinforced designs are more economical for heavy construction.

Types of Reinforced-concrete Column Footings (see Fig. 11) are: the isolated column footing; the combined or continuous footing, carrying two or more columns and constructed as an inverted beam; the cantilever footing, in which the eccentricity of an exterior footing is resisted by a strap connected with an adjacent interior footing.   All types may be used either with or without piles, and the continuous footing may be developed as a mat to cover the entire foundation area.   Footings for independent columns are designed in both stepped (Fig. 11a) and pyramidal (Fig. 12c) forms.   The use of a pedestal between the footing slab and the base of the superimposed column is of value in reducing the unit compression on the top surface of the footing.

The load used in determining the soil bearing area of a footing is the load used in the design of the column in the story immediately above the footing, plus any live load or dead load in that story, plus the estimated weight of the footing itself.   Footing areas should be proportioned for dead load alone or, in industrial buildings, for the dead load plus a fraction of the live load.

The design load, used to determine the thickness and reinforcement of a footing slab, is the load defined above, less the weight of the footing.   Individual column footings must be centered beneath the column which they support.   If more than one column rests on the same footing, the center of gravity of the foundation area must coincide with the center of gravity of the loads.

Reinforced-concrete footings are designed by the same formulas as concrete beams and slabs.   The footing must be sufficiently strong to resist the stresses produced by bending moment and diagonal tension, and most building ordinances contain a requirement for "punching shear."   A two-way reinforcement, of plain or deformed rods, is used in the slab and dowels to connect the footing slab to the basement column. Pedestals may be used to obtain a uniform height from which to start the first tier of columns.

Isolated footings, preferably square in plan, are generally used unless the proximity of a property line or other obstruction makes a concentric design impossible. Under such conditions, the combined footing, or the continuous wall footing, are both preferable to the cantilever type which is highly indeterminate except when used over piles.

The design of an isolated column footing involves determining the area of the footing slab, the design load, the depth as controlled by punching shear, where this is specified by code, and the steel area as controlled by moment. The diagonal tension, compression in the concrete, and bond stress in the steel are then checked. The requirements of diag-

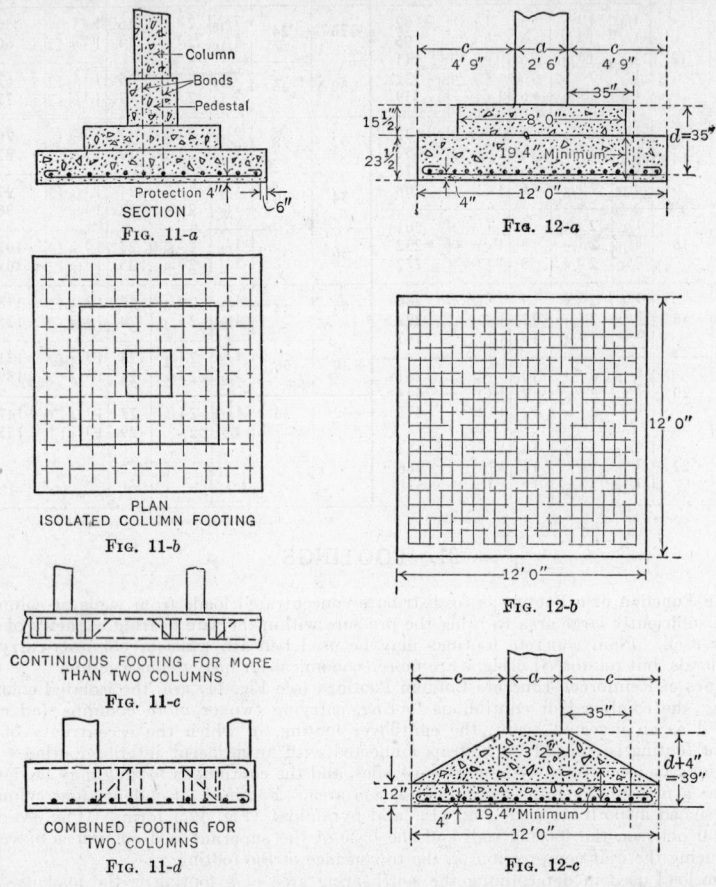

onal tension may demand increasing the thickness of the footing slab near its edge, but the concrete stresses are seldom critical if the other considerations are met, and high bond stresses may be avoided by using comparatively small rods and hooking the ends.

Example. Required to design an isolated footing for a column of 30 in. square, sustaining a load of 525,000 lb, including the weight of the column. Soil pressure, 2 tons per sq ft. Specification data: $f_c = 650$ lb per sq in.; $f_s = 16,000$ lb per sq in.; v limited to 40 lb per sq in.; punching shear limited to 120 lb per sq in.; $n = 15$; u limited to 100 lb per sq in.

Estimating the weight of the footing at 50,000 lb, area of footing slab = 575,000/4000 = 144 sq ft.

Choosing a square footing, 12 × 12 ft, w = 525,000/144 = 3646 lb per sq ft. Depth as controlled by punching shear.

$$d = \frac{(\text{Area of footing} - \text{Area of column}) \times w}{(\text{Perimeter of column}) \times (\text{Allowable punching shear})} = \frac{(144 - 6.25) \times 3646}{4 \times 30 \times 120} = 34.9 \text{ in.}$$

Accept a total depth of 39 in.

If a = width of side of column or pedestal, and c = projection of footing slab, both in feet (see Fig. 12),

$$M = 6w(a + 1.2c)c^2 = 6 \times 3646 \{2.5 + (1.20 \times 4.75)\} \times 22.56 = 4,047,000 \text{ lb-in.}$$

By formula 6b, $A_s = M/(f_s jd) = 4,047,000/(16,000 \times 0.875 \times 35) = 8.26$ sq in. Accept nineteen $3/4$-in. rounds.

Thickness d' of footing slab, as controlled by diagonal tension at distance d from face of column or pedestal (d and d' are both in inches),

$$d' = \frac{(\text{Area outside distance } d)\,w}{jv\,(\text{Perimeter at distance } d)} = \frac{[144 - \{2.5 + (35/6)\}^2] \times 3646}{0.875 \times 40 \times \{2.5 + 35/6\} \times 4 \times 12} = 19.4 \text{ in.}$$

By formula 8, minimum width of footing at top, in feet $= b = \dfrac{2M}{jkf_c a^2 \times 12}$

$$M/(1.99 \times f_c \times d^2) = 4,047,000/(1.99 \times 650 \times 1225) = 2.55 \text{ ft.}$$

By formula 22, $u = V/[\Sigma o]jd = \dfrac{(144 - 6.25) \times (3646/4)}{(19 \times 2.35) \times 0.875 \times 35} = 96$ lb per sq in., which is accept-

able for deformed rods. Fig. 12a shows the footing arranged in a stepped form; Fig. 12c shows the same footing arranged in a pyramidal form.

Table X. Square Column Footings

All reinforcement hooked

p = Projection of pedestal beyond face of column

$t_{min} = 2 \times p$; $h_{max} = 3 \times a$;

$f_s = 18,000$

$f_c = 800$

$v = 60$

L	Soil Value lb per sq ft	Column loads, thousands of pounds	Type of footing	Minimum Dimensions				Deformed Bars each way	
				a	t	t'	b	No.	Size, in.
5' 0''	4000	90	A	1' 3''	1' 1''	....	....	9	$1/2$ ○
	5000	120	A	1 3	1 2	....	....	11	$1/2$ ○
	6000	150	A	1 3	1 3	....	....	12	$1/2$ ○
6' 0''	4000	135	A	1 6	1 3	....	....	14	$1/2$ ○
	5000	175	A	1 6	1 4	....	....	16	$1/2$ ○
	6000	210	A	1 6	1 5	....	....	17	$1/2$ ○
7' 0''	4000	180	A	1 9	1 5	....	....	14	$1/2$ □
	5000	235	A	1 9	1 6	....	....	16	$1/2$ □
	6000	280	A	1 9	1 8	....	....	18	$1/2$ □
8' 0''	4000	240	B	2 0	1 9	10	2 5	13	$5/8$ ○
	5000	315	B	2 0	2 0	10	2 5	15	$5/8$ ○
	6000	375	B	2 0	2 3	10	2 5	16	$5/8$ ○
9' 0''	4000	310	B	2 3	2 0	10	2 9	16	$5/8$ ○
	5000	380	B	2 3	2 3	10	2 9	19	$5/8$ ○
	6000	470	B	2 3	2 6	11	2 9	20	$5/8$ ○
10' 0''	4000	330	B	2 6	2 3	10	3 0	14	$3/4$ ○
	5000	470	B	2 6	2 6	11	3 0	16	$3/4$ ○
	6000	575	B	2 6	2 8	11	3 0	17	$3/4$ ○
11' 0''	4000	450	B	2 9	2 5	11	3 4	16	$3/4$ ○
	5000	575	B	2 9	2 8	11	3 4	18	$3/4$ ○
	6000	690	B	2 9	2 11	12	3 4	20	$3/4$ ○
12' 0''	4000	540	B	3 0	2 7	11	3 8	14	$7/8$ ○
	5000	675	B	3 0	2 11	12	3 8	16	$7/8$ ○
	6000	820	B	3 0	3 2	13	3 8	18	$7/8$ ○
13' 0''	4000	630	B	3 3	2 10	12	3 11	17	$7/8$ ○
	5000	800	B	3 3	3 1	13	3 11	19	$7/8$ ○
	6000	950	B	3 3	3 4	13	3 11	20	$7/8$ ○

It should be noted that this example follows the procedure of most building ordinances in considering " punching shear," which usually determines the depth. Table X follows the Joint Code and gives a somewhat different design which represents advanced practice and can be advantageously applied outside of any particular jurisdiction.

32. GIRDERLESS OR FLAT SLAB CONSTRUCTION

For building three or more bays wide, where column locations give approximately square bays of equal or nearly equal size, girderless or flat slab construction is the most satisfactory for heavy loads, as are required for industrial occupancy. The advantages are a saving in story height, due to the elimination of beams and girders, better lighting facilities, and structural economy. The flared column heads are characteristic of this system, which may be designed either with or without drops over the columns. If depressed panels, usually referred to as drops, are used over the interior columns, half drops are required at the exterior columns. Beams are used to frame around stairwells and elevators, and as lintels connecting exterior columns.

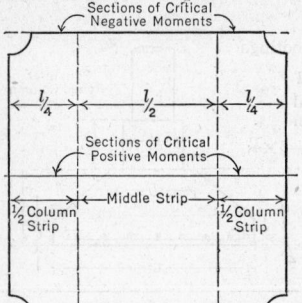

Fig. 13

For purposes of establishing the bending moments and the resisting moments of a square panel, the panel is divided into middle and column strips as shown in Fig. 13. In this figure the division is indicated in only one direction, but a similar division is also made at right angles to the strips shown.

The diameter of the column capital is usually taken as $0.225 \times$ average center-to-center span of bay. The minimum width of drop is taken as 0.33 or $0.35 \times$ length of span in that direction; except for heavy loads the shearing stresses around the perimeter of the drop are not excessive, and this requirement normally determines the dimensions of the drop. The offset, or difference in thickness between the slab and drop, varies from 2 to 4 in. It is usually controlled by the sectional area required over the column capital to resist the negative moment on the column strip. In computing this depth it is usual to allow an increase of 15 per cent in the value of the extreme fiber stress f_c, as with beams.

The bending moments used in designing the various sections are derived from empirical data and form a part of the code requirements in all city ordinances. Those used in the example are from the Joint Standard Building Code; they apply to fully continuous interior bays. The moments are generally increased by 20 or 25 per cent along the center lines of exterior bays and over the first interior supports. At the wall, or spandrel, the negative moment in the column strip is taken as 80 or 90 per cent and in the middle strip as 50 or 62.5 per cent of the corresponding moments for a normal interior panel. Half bands, containing 50 per cent of the steel required for a column strip, are placed parallel to the outer edge of exterior panels. The spacing of rods is limited to $1\frac{1}{2} \times$ slab thickness, and the ratio of steel to concrete area in any strip should not be less than 0.0025.

There are two widely used systems of reinforcement, the two-way and the four-way. In the former, bands of steel rods are designed to span from column to column, and a two-way reinforcement is placed in the central rectangular portion of the panel between the bands and running parallel to them. In the four-way system, two diagonal bands supplement the direct bands, and additional reinforcement is added in the form of short rods placed over the lines of support, perpendicular to the steel of the rectangular bands.

Practically every large city has its own individual code governing the design of girderless floors, and when working under any particular jurisdiction, the designer must apply the regulation in his locality. The following example is based upon common practice and corresponds to the average requirements of principal cities. It will be noted that the thickness of the slab, size, and depth of drop are each controlled by several criteria. Where it is possible to satisfy the design requirements in more than one way, the most economical method is shown.

Example. Required: to design an interior bay sustaining a superimposed load of 150 lb per sq ft. Drops and a two-way reinforcement will be used. Dimensions center-to-center columns, 20×20 ft. Specification data: $f_c = 650$; $f_s = 18,000$; allowable unit shearing stress (v_1) around perimeter of drop = 60 lb per sq in.; allowable unit shearing stress (v_2) around perimeter of column capital = 120 lb per sq in.

Slab thickness not less than

(1) $t = 6$ in. (a minimum often specified).

(2) $t = L/32 = 20/32 = 0.625$ ft $= 7\,1/2$ in., where t = total thickness of slab, inches; L = center-to-center span between columns on long side of panel, feet.

(3) $t = 0.02L\sqrt{w} + 1 = 0.02 \times 20\sqrt{244} + 1 = 7.25$ in., where w = the superimposed load, 150 lb per sq ft, plus the estimated weight of the slab, 90 lb per sq ft, plus estimated weight of drop, 4 lb per sq ft, distributed over the entire slab.

Accept a slab thickness of $7\,1/2$ in.

Width of drop (b) not less than $0.35L = 0.35 \times 20 = 7$ ft.

Vertical shear around perimeter of drop, $V = w(L^2 - b^2) = 244\{(20)^2 - 7^2\} = 85,644$ lb, where L^2 = area of bay, b^2 = area of drop. By formula 17, $v = V/(bjd) = 85,644/(4 \times 84 \times 0.875 \times 6) = 48$ lb per sq in., where (4×84) = the perimeter of drop, and 6 = effective depth of slab. As 60 lb per sq in. is permitted, accept a square drop, with side of 7 ft 0 in.

Diameter of column capital $c = 0.225L = 0.225 \times 20 = 4$ ft 6 in. $= 54$ in.

Total thickness of slab and drop not less than, by formula 4,

$$d = \sqrt{M/Kb} = \sqrt{767,200/(125.7 \times 84)} = 8.53,$$

where M = bending moment, pound-inches, at column head section as computed below by the equation $M = WL/30.5$. Value of K from Table IV. Assume a total thickness of 10 in., effective depth $8\,1/2$ in.

Vertical shear around perimeter of column capital,

$$V = w(L^2 - (1/4)\pi c^2) = 244\{(20)^2 - 0.7854 \times (4.5)^2\} = 93,700 \text{ lb.}$$

$$v = V/(bjd) = 93,700/(54\pi \times 0.875 \times 8.5) = 74 \text{ lb per sq in.}$$

Since 120 lb per sq in. is permitted, a total thickness of 10 in. is acceptable. This gives an offset at the drop of $2\,1/2$ in.

Steel areas as controlled by moments:

$$W = \text{total load on bay} = (20 \times 20 \times 240) + (7 \times 7 \times 30) = 97,500 \text{ lb}$$

Column strip,

$$- M = Wl/30.5 = 97,500 \times 20 \times 12/30.5 = 767,200 \text{ lb-in.}$$

$$+ M = Wl/77 = 97,500 \times 20 \times 12/77 = 303,900 \text{ lb-in.}$$

Middle strip,

$$- M = + M = Wl/102.5 = 97,500 \times 20 \times 12/102.5 = 228,300 \text{ lb-in.}$$

in which l = length, inches, between column centers in the direction in which the strip extends. The bending moment factors used in this example are from the Joint Standard Code.

Column strip:

Negative reinforcement,

$$A_s = \frac{M}{f_s jd} = \frac{767,200}{18,000 \times 0.872 \times 8.5} = 5.73 \text{ sq in.}$$

Positive reinforcement,

$$A_s = \frac{M}{f_s jd} = \frac{303,900}{18,000 \times 0.883 \times 6} = 3.19 \text{ sq in.}$$

Middle strip, both positive and negative reinforcement,

$$A_s = \frac{M}{f_s jd} = \frac{228,300}{18,000 \times 0.883 \times 6} = 2.39 \text{ sq in.}$$

For the column strip, accept 11 5/8-in. rounds each way, which satisfies the requirement of the positive moment. Raise 7 of these rods from each bay along the line of inflection, $0.3(L - c) = 0.3(20 - 4.5) = 4.65$ ft, from center of span, which gives a steel area of 4.20 sq in. The additional area = 1.53 sq in., necessary for the negative reinforcement, is furnished by 5 5/8-in. rounds placed over columns and extending 1 ft beyond lines of inflection. The 4 remaining rods in the bottom of the slab are extended into the drop panel a distance of 1 ft. For the middle strip, accept 12 1/2-in. rounds each way, which satisfies the requirement of the positive moment within 5 per cent. Raise 6 of these rods from each bay along the line of inflection, $0.3l$ from center of span, which gives a steel area equal to that at mid-span. The 6 remaining rods, in the bottom of the slab, are extended 20 diameters each side of the lines of inflection. The bent rods of both strips, in both directions, are extended entirely across the bay and to 1 ft beyond the lines of inflection of adjacent bays.

Table XI gives the dimensions and reinforcement for girderless floor construction of the square-panel, two-way reinforcement type, based on the New York City code.

Table XI. Dimensions and Reinforcement for Girderless Floor Construction, Square Panels, Two-Way System

Fiber stresses. $f_s = 16{,}000$, $f_c = 650$, $v_1 = 60$, and $v_2 = 120$ lb per sq in. All reinforcing steel, round bars. Based on New York City Code.

Side of square bay	Diameter circular capital	Side of square drop panel	Slab thickness, in.	Depth of drop, in.	Steel in column strip No.	Size	Steel in middle strip No.	Size
Superimposed Load, 100 lb per sq ft								
16' 0''	4' 0''	5' 4''	6	2	8 / 1	1/2''×26' 0'' / 1/2''×11' 9''	10	3/8''×18' 0''
17' 0''	4' 0''	5' 8''	6 1/2	2 1/4	9 / 1	1/2''×27' 9'' / 1/2''×12' 3''	10	3/8''×19' 0''
18' 0''	4' 6''	6' 0''	7	2 1/2	10 / 1	1/2''×29' 3'' / 1/2''×13' 0''	6	1/2''×20' 3''
19' 0''	4' 6''	6' 4''	7 1/4	2 1/2	11 / 1	1/2''×31' 0'' / 1/2''×13' 9''	8	1/2''×21' 3''
20' 0''	4' 6''	6' 8''	7 1/2	2 1/2	8 / 1	5/8''×32' 6'' / 5/8''×14' 3''	9	1/2''×22' 3''
21' 0''	5' 0''	7' 0''	8	2 3/4	9 / 1	5/8''×34' 0'' / 5/8''×15' 0''	10	1/2''×23' 3''
22' 0''	5' 0''	7' 4''	8 1/4	2 3/4	10 / 1	5/8''×35' 9'' / 5/8''×15' 9''	10	1/2''×24' 3''
23' 0''	5' 6''	7' 8''	8 3/4	3	11 / 1	5/8''×37' 3'' / 5/8''×16' 3''	11	1/2''×25' 6''
24' 0''	5' 6''	8' 0''	9 1/4	3 1/4	12 / 2	5/8''×39' 0'' / 5/8''×17' 0''	13	1/2''×26' 6''
25' 0''	6' 0''	8' 4''	9 1/2	3 1/4	10	3/4''×40' 6''	9	5/8''×27' 6''
Superimposed Load, 150 lb per sq ft								
16' 0''	4' 0''	5' 4''	6	2	10 / 1	1/2''×26' 0'' / 1/2''×11' 9''	7	1/2''×18' 0''
17' 0''	4' 0''	5' 8''	6 1/2	2 1/4	7 / 1	5/8''×27' 9'' / 5/8''×12' 3''	8	1/2''×19' 0''
18' 0''	4' 6''	6' 0''	7	2 1/2	8 / 1	5/8''×29' 3'' / 5/8''×13' 0''	9	1/2''×20' 3''
19' 0''	4' 6''	6' 4''	7 1/4	2 1/2	9 / 1	5/8''×31' 0'' / 5/8''×13' 9''	10	1/2''×21' 3''
20' 0''	4' 6''	6' 8''	7 1/2	2 1/2	10 / 1	5/8''×32' 6'' / 5/8''×14' 3''	11	1/2''×22' 3''
21' 0''	5' 0''	7' 0''	8	2 3/4	11 / 1	5/8''×34' 0'' / 5/8''×15' 0''	8	5/8''×23' 3''
22' 0''	5' 0''	7' 4''	8 1/4	2 3/4	9 / 1	3/4''×35' 9'' / 3/4''×15' 9''	9	5/8''×24' 3''
23' 0''	5' 6''	7' 8''	8 3/4	3	10 / 1	3/4''×37' 3'' / 3/4''×16' 3''	10	5/8''×25' 6''
24' 0''	5' 6''	8' 0''	9 1/4	3 1/4	11 / 1	3/4''×39' 0'' / 3/4''×17' 0''	10	5/8''×26' 6''
25' 0''	6' 0''	8' 4''	9 1/2	3 1/4	12 / 1	3/4''×40' 6'' / 3/4''×17' 9''	12	5/8''×27' 6''
Superimposed Load, 200 lb per sq ft								
16' 0''	4' 0''	5' 4''	6 1/2	2 1/2	7 / 1	5/8''×26' 0'' / 5/8''×11' 9''	8	1/2''×18' 0''
17' 0''	4' 0''	5' 8''	6 3/4	2 1/2	8 / 1	5/8''×27' 9'' / 5/8''×12' 3''	9	1/2''×19' 0''
18' 0''	4' 6''	6' 0''	7 1/4	2 1/2	9 / 1	5/8''×29' 3'' / 5/8''×13' 0''	10	1/2''×20' 3''
19' 0''	4' 6''	6' 4''	7 1/2	2 3/4	11 / 1	5/8''×31' 0'' / 5/8''×13' 9''	7	5/8''×21' 3''
20' 0''	4' 6''	6' 8''	8	3	8 / 1	3/4''×32' 6'' / 3/4''×14' 3''	8	5/8''×22' 3''
21' 0''	5' 0''	7' 0''	8 1/4	3 1/4	9 / 1	3/4''×34' 0'' / 3/4''×15' 0''	9	5/8''×23' 3''
22' 0''	5' 0''	7' 4''	8 3/4	3 1/4	10 / 1	3/4''×35' 9'' / 3/4''×15' 9''	10	5/8''×24' 3''
23' 0''	5' 6''	7' 8''	9 1/4	3 1/2	11 / 1	3/4''×37' 3'' / 3/4''×16' 3''	11	5/8''×25' 6''
24' 0''	5' 6''	8' 0''	9 3/4	3 1/2	12 / 1	3/4''×39' 0'' / 3/4''×17' 0''	12	5/8''×26' 6''
25' 0''	6' 0''	8' 4''	10	3 3/4	13 / 2	3/4''×40' 6'' / 3/4''×17' 9''	13	5/8''×27' 6''

TESTING OF MATERIALS

By Jasper O. Draffin

33. EQUIPMENT

Testing Machines. Machines for testing material are of varying construction and capacity, for testing specimens in tension, in compression, in torsion, and for other specific purposes. In machines for testing bars in tension or compression, the ends of the test piece are fastened in the two heads of the machine. One of the heads is moved by screws, driven by a train of gears, causing a gradually increasing stress in the test piece. Some machines are built so that the head is moved by hydraulic pressure, but the screw construction is more common in the United States, although the use of hydraulic pressure machines is increasing rapidly (1935). Usually the mechanism for applying the load to the specimen is independent of the weighing apparatus. With this arrangement the accuracy of the weighing is not affected by the deformation of the specimen which takes place as the load is applied.

The Compound Lever Machine derives its name from the weighing mechanism. The load may be applied by revolving screws or by hydraulic pressure.

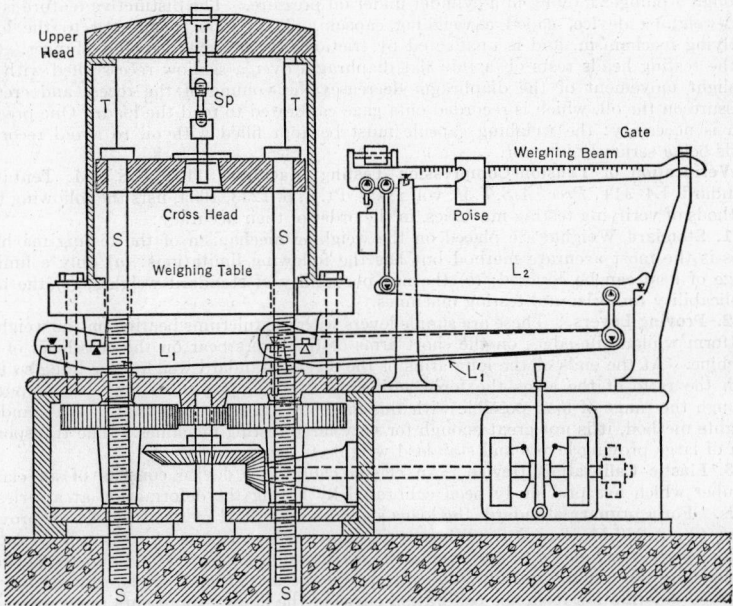

FIG. 1. Screw-power, Compound-lever Testing Machine

The Screw-power Compound-lever Testing Machine (Riehlé or Olsen Machines) is the type in most common use in the United States, and it is shown in diagram in Fig. 1. Power is supplied by a belt drive or by a direct-connected motor, and the power is transmitted through a series of gears to vertical screws which operate the crosshead of the machine. The force applied by the belt is multiplied many times by the gearing and the screws. This multiplied force is applied to the test specimen by the crosshead. If the specimen is a tension specimen it is placed between the crosshead and the upper head of the testing machine, if it is a compression specimen or a cross-bending specimen it is placed between the crosshead and the weighing table. In any event as the crosshead moves downward the specimen transmits downward pressure to the weighing table. The weighing table is supported on compound levers, $L_1 L'_1$, Fig. 1, which are fitted with knife-edge bearings, and these compound levers transmit the force, reduced, to a simple lever, L_2, Fig. 1, which, in turn, transmits the force, still further reduced, to the weighing beam.

As load is applied the beam is kept in balance by moving the poise, the position of which indicates the load on the specimen, when the beam is in balance.

The Direct-acting Hydraulic Machine has a head moved by hydraulic pressure, the intensity of which is read on a pressure gage. The load on the test piece is determined by multiplying the pressure reading by a constant which depends on the area of the cylinder. Owing to variations in the plunger friction, these machines are not adapted for accurate testing of small specimens, but are used to advantage in tests requiring big loads to rupture the specimen, and where slight variations in accuracy are permitted.

The Amsler Machine is a machine of the hydraulic type built in Schaffhausen, Switzerland, which has a considerable use in the United States. A plunger moving in a cylinder near the top of the machine raises and lowers a rigid framework with respect to a fixed tension head at the bottom and a fixed compression head at the top of the machine. Oil is pumped into the cylinder to move a plunger so carefully ground to fit the cylinder that no packing is necessary. The error due to friction is no larger than the error due to friction in knife-edge lever weighing devices. The pressure is measured by the load on a small piston which moves a pendulum so that the position of the pendulum bob indicates the force. This is a self-indicating weighing device, which eliminates much of the personal equation of balancing a weighing beam. The Amsler testing machine can be handled by a single observer, even when measurements of deformation are made, and is very rapid in its operation.

The Emery-Tatnall Machine is a hydraulic machine in which the load is applied through a plunger moving in a cylinder under oil pressure. The distinctive feature is the load-weighing device, called a weighing capsule. This is not connected to the load-applying mechanism, and is unaffected by friction between cylinder and plunger. One of the testing heads rests on a thin flat diaphragm over a shallow recess filled with oil. A slight movement of the diaphragm decreases the volume of the recess and creates pressure on the oil, which is recorded on a gage calibrated to read the load. One precaution is necessary: the weighing capsule must be kept filled with oil to avoid recorded loads being seriously in error.

Verification of Tension-Compression Testing Machines. The A.S.T.M. Tentative Standard, E4–34T, *Proc. A.S.T.M.* vol. xxxiv, Pt. 1, p. 1233, 1934, lists the following four methods of verifying testing machines, in the order of their accuracy:

1. Standard Weights are placed on the weighing mechanism of the testing machine. This is the most accurate method but has the following limitations: (*a*) only a limited range of load can be covered; (*b*) the non-portability of standard weights; (*c*) the non-applicability to horizontal testing machines.

2. Proving Levers. These are simple levers with the fulcrums bearing on the weighing platform while knife-edges on the short arms of the levers bear on the crosshead of the machine. At the ends of the long arms of the levers, standard weights are hung so that from the ratio of the arms the force acting on the weighing table may be computed. Though the range of load possible with this method is greater than that of the standard weights method, it is not great enough for very large testing machines. The transportation of large proving levers and standard weights is inconvenient.

3. Elastic Calibration Device. An elastic calibration device consists of an elastic member which has previously been calibrated by noting the deformation at a series of loads. For a primary standard, the loads should be obtained by dead weights or proving levers (see A.S.T.M., *loc. cit.*). When verifying a testing machine, load is applied to the device by the machine to be tested and the deformation noted. The difference between the load reading on the machine under test and the actual load, as determined for the observed deformation from the calibration curve of the device, represents the error in the machine being verified.

4. Comparison Method. In this method, a series of test specimens (" companion specimens ") cut from the same piece of metal are necessary. Half of the specimens are tested in a machine which has been verified by one of the other methods above, and the other half in the machine under test. The difference in load reading for the same deformation, between the two machines, is the error in the machine being tested. This method should be used only when none of the other methods above may be applied.

Accuracy and Sensitivity of Testing Machines are two distinct characteristics. A machine is accurate if the readings of the machine agree closely with the actual loads applied by the machine. A testing machine is sensitive if a small change of load is indicated by a distinct movement of the beam or other weighing mechanism. A testing machine may be very sensitive, and yet very inaccurate.

For Flexure Tests the regular tension-compression testing machines are used by arranging the specimen so that the end supports bear on the weighing table, as shown in Fig. 7, p. 5–86.

Torsion Testing Machines. In Professor Thurston's machine, invented in 1872, the specimen is held horizontally with its ends secured in two spindles. One of these spindles is rotated by power. The other spindle is connected to a pendulum carrying a heavy weight which resists the turning force as it deviates from its vertical position, thus producing a torque whose magnitude is shown by a gage or dial.

Power torsion machines are built so that the two ends of the specimen are held in rotating chucks. The power is applied at any desired speed by gearing connected to one of the chucks. The chuck at the other end is prevented from rotating by a system of levers connected to a scale beam which is balanced by a poise. The position of the poise indicates the twisting moment in pound-inches.

For Impact Tests the essential parts of the testing machine are: a moving weight which strikes the specimen with sufficient kinetic energy to cause fracture, an anvil or block on which the specimen is supported and a device for measuring the kinetic energy of the moving weight after it has broken the specimen.

In the Drop-weight Machines the impact is obtained by a hammer of known weight falling from a predetermined height on the specimen. In the Fremont machine the loss of kinetic energy in the hammer due to impact is obtained by having the weight, after breaking the specimen, strike a platen placed on calibrated springs, and measuring the downward movement of the platen against the resistance of the springs. Another method is used in the Hatt-Turner machine in which a brass stylus is attached to the falling hammer; during impact the stylus is forced by a spring against a sheet of metallized paper mounted on a drum which rotates about its vertical axis, thus causing a curve to be plotted. The speed of the drum is determined from a second curve plotted on the metallized paper by a stylus fastened to one prong of a tuning-fork. From the two curves the changes in velocity of the hammer as well as the stress-deformation relations may be calculated.

The Charpy Impact Testing Machine is used for tests of small specimens of metal under impact. The specimen rests against the vertical face of an anvil where it is held in a horizontal position and is in flexure over a short span. The impact is furnished by a pendulum which is let fall from a predetermined height, striking the specimen at the bottom of its swing. The pendulum is of known weight, and is so hung that its center of percussion is at the point of impact against the specimen. After breaking the specimen the pendulum continues its swing, and an indicating apparatus shows the maximum height to which it rises. The energy supplied by the pendulum is the product of its weight and its height of fall; the energy left after the fracture of the specimen is the product of its weight and the height of rise; the difference is the energy required to break the specimen. Specimens for the Charpy machine are notched at the middle of their length to insure a sharp plane of fracture. The uniformity of size of specimen and of size and shape of notch is very important.

The Izod Machine acts on a principle similar to that of the Charpy machine. The Izod specimen is a short notched cantilever beam held vertically and struck by a swinging pendulum, at a definite distance above the notch. The energy required for fracture is measured in a manner similar to that used with the Charpy machine.

Repeated Stress Testing Machine. The following types of machines are available for producing reversed bending: the Upton-Lewis for flat specimens; the short-specimen rotating beam; the long-specimen rotating beam; and the cantilever rotating beam. Only the long-specimen machine (sometimes known as the Sondricker or Farmer type) is here described. It consists of two supporting rings or collars, rotating in a cage of ball bearings, for supporting the specimen which is 0.40 in. in diameter and 13 in. long. The specimen is rotated by a motor; the number of revolutions is recorded by a counter attached to one end of the specimen. Suspended weights load the beam at two points and act through ball bearings to produce a uniform bending moment over the central portion of the specimen. The number of cycles of completely reversed stress equals the number of revolutions. The speeds commonly used are from 1000 to 2000 rpm.

Extensometers are used for measuring the small elastic deformations within the elastic limit, and for detecting the stress at which the elastic limit is exceeded. An extensometer consists essentially of two clamps which are fastened to the test specimen, and one or more micrometer devices by means of which a very small change of distance between the clamps can be measured. For all accurate measurement of elastic deformation of tension or compression specimens the extensometer should be attached so as to measure deformation along two or three symmetrically spaced axial lines on the specimen. Types of micrometer devices used in extensometers are: the screw micrometer, in which a very small axial motion of a screw is accompanied by a large circumferential motion of a dial attached to the screw; clockwork dial gages; multiplying levers; microscopes; and the " optical lever " in which a very small angular motion of a mirror changes the direction of a reflected ray of light. Extensometers for general use usually measure deformations to the nearest ten-thousandth of an inch.

34. STANDARD TEST SPECIMENS

Specimens for Tension Tests of Wrought Metals. (Abstracted from A.S.T.M. Standards E8–33, A7–34, A9–34 and A10–34.)   The specimen shown in Fig. 2 is recommended

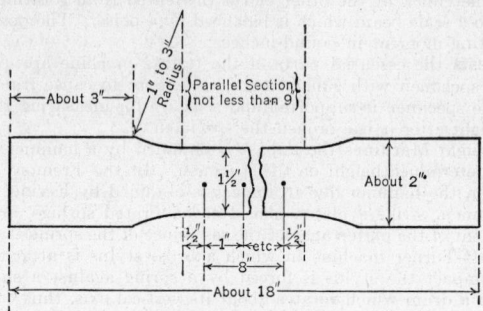

Fig. 2.   Standard 8-in. Gage Length Test Specimen

for plate, shape, and flat material having a thickness of $1/4$ in. or over.   The thickness of the specimen shall be that of the material tested.

If the material to be tested is over $1 1/2$ in. in thickness or diameter, except steel pins or rollers, it may be machined to a thickness or diameter of at least $3/4$ in. for a length of

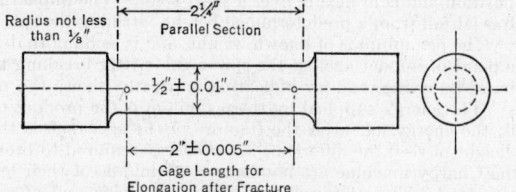

Fig. 3.   Standard 2-in. Gage Length Tension Test Specimen

at least 9 in., or it may conform to the dimension shown in Fig. 3.   Specimens for pins and rollers should conform to the dimensions of Fig. 3.

The specimen shown in Fig. 3 is recommended for general use in testing metals. The gage length, parallel section and fillets should be as shown, but the ends may be of any shape to fit the holders of the testing machine in such a way that the load is axial.

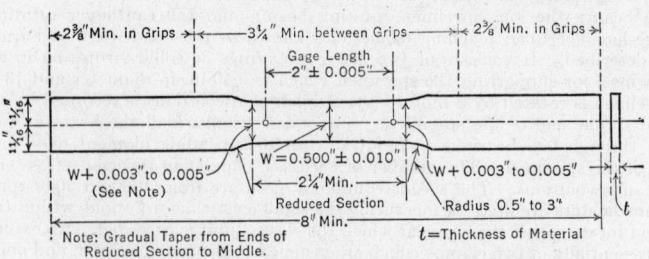

Fig. 4.   Standard Tension Test Specimen for Sheet Metals

A slight taper of the " parallel section " not to exceed a maximum of 1 per cent of the diameter within the gage length, similar to that shown in Fig. 4 for sheet materials, is desirable for all tension test specimens.

Steel specimens should be prepared for testing from the material in its rolled or forged condition except that annealed materials should be annealed as for use.

For tension tests of wrought ferrous and non-ferrous metal in the form of plate, sheet, flat wire, strip, band and hoop, without respect to width (provided the width is not less than that shown in Fig. 4), length, grade or method of manufacture, and having a thickness of from 0.01 to 0.250 in., the specimen shown in Fig. 4 is recommended.

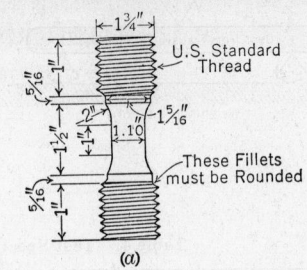

Tension test specimens of wire and rod are frequently of the full size as fabricated. It is suggested that the upper limit of size for wire be considered as 1/2 in. in diameter. For the measurement of elongation of wire or rod 1/2 in. in diameter or less which is tested in the full size, a gage length of 10 in. is frequently used.

Specimens for Tension Test of Cast Iron. Tension test bars for cast iron are classified according to the controlling thickness of the casting as: test bar *A*, thickness 0.75 in., maximum; test bar *B*, thickness 0.75 to 1.25 in.; test bar *C*, thickness 1.25 to 2.00 in. (*Proc. A.S.T.M.*, vol. xxxii, Pt. I, p. 625, 1932). It is optional to use parts of the transverse test bar for the tension test. Dimensions of the finished specimens for test bar *B* are shown in Figs. 5*a* and 5*b*.

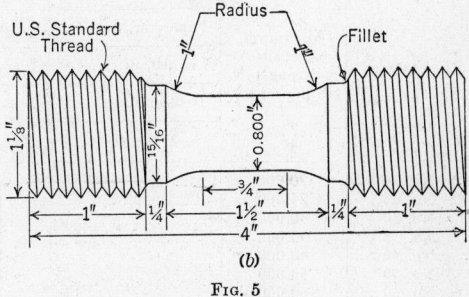

Fig. 5

Specimens for Compression Tests of Metals.   (Abstracted from *A.S.T.M. Tentative Standards*, 1934, E9–34T.)   The following three classes of compression test specimens are recommended: (1) short specimens (Fig. 6*a*), used for tests of such metals as bearing metals, which in service are used in the form of a thin plate or shell to carry load perpendicular to the surface; (2) medium-length specimens (Fig. 6*b*), used for determining the general compressive strength properties of metallic materials; (3) long specimens (Fig. 6*c*), best adapted for determining the modulus of elasticity in compression of metallic materials. In reporting the results of a compression test, it is important that the dimensions of the test specimens be given.

The suggested dimensions for the compression specimens shown in Fig. 6 are as follows.

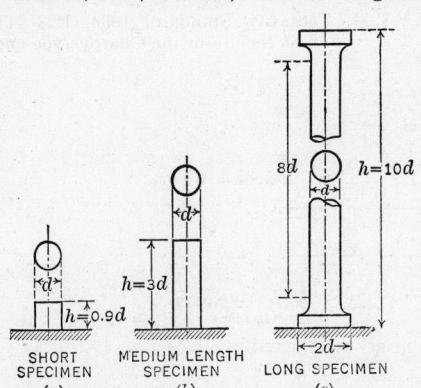

Fig. 6.   Test Specimens for Compression Tests

	Diameter, d	Height h
Short specimens...............................	1 1/8 in.* ± 0.01 in.	1 in.
Medium-length specimens......................	$\left\{\begin{array}{l} 0.798 \text{ in.} \pm 0.01 \text{ in.} \\ 1 \text{ in.} \pm 0.01 \text{ in.} \\ 1 1/8 \text{ in.} \pm 0.01 \text{ in.} \end{array}\right.$	2 3/8 in. 3 in. 3 3/8 in.
Long specimens...............................	1 1/4 in. ± 0.01 in.	12 1/2 in.

* Area of cross-section is approximately 1 sq in.

Specimens for Flexure Tests of Cast Iron. Until 1932 gray iron castings were classified as light, medium, and heavy according to thickness, and acceptance was based

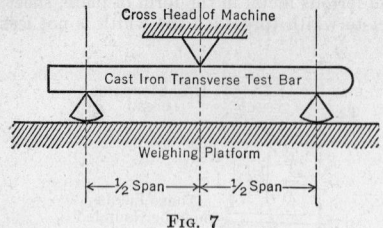

FIG. 7

on flexure or transverse tests. This specification has been revised, and A.S.T.M. Standard, A48–36 specifies acceptance on tension tests. Transverse tests are optional and are made with the machine shown in Fig. 7 on straight, cylindrical specimens having the dimensions and tested with the spans listed in Table I. The first three numbers refer to ordinary gray iron and the last four numbers to high-strength iron.

Table I. Test Specimens for Transverse Tests

Class	Minimum Tensile Strength, lb per sq in.	Test Bar *	A	B	C
		Diameter, in......	0.875	1.20	2.00
		Length, in........	15	21	27
		Test span, in......	12	18	24
			Minimum Load at Center, lb		
No. 20	20,000	....	900	1700	4,500
No. 25	25,000	....	1050	1900	5,500
No. 30	30,000	....	1200	2100	6,500
No. 35	35,000	....	1300	2300	7,500
No. 40	40,000	....	1400	2500	9,000
No. 50	50,000	....	1700	2800	11,000
No. 60	60,000	....	2000	3100	13,000

* See Specimens for " Tension Test of Cast Iron," p. 5–85.

Specimens for Impact Tests. The A.S.T.M. Tentative Standard, 1934, E23–34T recommends the test specimens shown in Fig. 8a and 8b for use in the Charpy type and Izod type impact machines respectively.

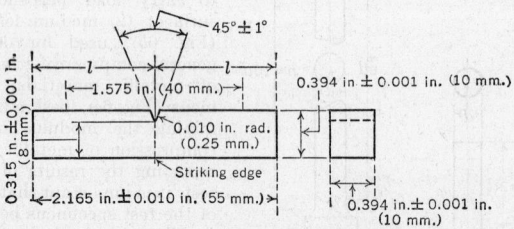

(a) SIMPLE BEAM (CHARPY TYPE) SPECIMEN

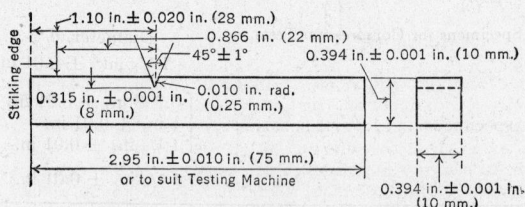

(b) CANTILEVER BEAM (IZOD TYPE) SPECIMEN

FIG. 8. Impact Test Specimens

3. Speed of Testing. Regard must be had to the time occupied in making tests of certain materials. A.S.T.M. Standard, E8–33, points out that the values of the yield point and ultimate strength may be increased by operating the testing machine at too high speed, and it recommends that the speed of the head of the testing machine shall be such that the load can be accurately weighed. In determining yield strength, the crosshead speed for the 2-in. gage length shall not exceed 0.125 in. per min.

In testing soft alloys, copper, tin, zinc, and the like, which flow under constant stress, their highest apparent strength is obtained by testing them rapidly. In recording tests of such materials the length of time occupied in the test should be stated.

4. Increment of Load. The following method has been suggested by the A.S.T.M. (loc. cit.) for choosing increments in a tension test. An increment of load, about $1/10$ of the estimated load corresponding to the knee of the stress-deformation diagram, is applied and the corresponding change of reading, Δ, of the extensometer noted. For the remainder of the test, the increments of load are made such that the extensometer readings change by approximately Δ.

After the yield point is passed, as indicated by the drop of the beam, the stress should be uniformly increased, keeping the scale beam balanced and stopping only to make occasional observations and to remove the extensometer to prevent its injury when the specimen breaks.

36. MISCELLANEOUS TESTS

Hardness Tests

Brinell's Method. J. A. Brinell, a Swedish engineer, in 1900 published information about a method for determining the relative hardness of steel, which has come into extensive use. A hardened-steel ball, 10-mm diameter (0.3937 in.), is forced with a pressure of 3000 kg, or 500 kg for soft metals, into a flat surface on the sample to be tested and allowed to remain for at least 10 sec (iron and steel), or for at least 30 sec (other metals), to make a slight spherical impression, whose diameter is measured with a microscope. The hardness is defined as the quotient of the pressure divided by the area of the surface of the impression, which is assumed to be spherical. From the measurement, the *hardness number* is calculated by the equation

$$B = \frac{P}{\pi \frac{D}{2}(D - \sqrt{D^2 - d^2})} \tag{1}$$

where P = load = 3000 kg; D = diameter of ball = 10 mm; d = diameter or width of impression, millimeters; B = Brinell hardness number. Table II gives the hardness numbers corresponding to the different values of d. A complete table of these numbers is given in A.S.T.M. Standards, 1933, E10–27, pp. 943–944.

There is a well-defined approximate relationship between the Brinell numbers and the ultimate strength of steel. Abbot (*Proc. A.S.T.M.* vol. xv, Pt. II, 1915), as a result of a large number of tests of different kinds of steel, proposed the equation $s_u = 0.70B - 26$, where s_u = ultimate strength in thousands of pounds per square inch; B = Brinell hardness number. For many steels, however, the strength is as well represented by the relation $s_u = 0.50B$.

In the Rockwell Test a steel ball $1/16$ in. in diameter (the Rockwell " B " test) or a conical diamond point (the Rockwell " C " test) is pressed against the surface of the specimen with a small but definite initial load. Then a load of 100 kg (" B " test) or 150 kg (" C " test) is applied by means of a weight acting at the end of a compound lever. This weight is removed, leaving the small initial load still on the penetrating point, and the depth of impression is measured by means of a micrometer dial gage attached to the indenting point. This gage is graduated to read directly an arbitrary system of hardness numbers corresponding (inversely) to the depth of impression. The Rockwell " B " numbers are different from the Rockwell " C " numbers. One advantage of the Rockwell over the Brinell is that a smaller indentation is produced. The ultimate tensile strength of steel, s_u, is given in thousands of pounds per square inch by the equation $s_u = 3750/(130 - R_B)$, R_B being the number ("B" test) read from the dial of the instrument.

The Vickers Pyramid Hardness-testing Machine is a British instrument in which the principle employed is the same as that in the Brinell and Rockwell machines. The operation differs in that the penetrator is a diamond in the form of a pyramid. By means of a microscope attachment, measurements are made of the distance across the diagonal of the indentation. One of the advantages of this machine is that it is suitable for any degree of hardness.

The Scleroscope is an instrument invented by A. F. Shore for determining the hardness of metals. It consists chiefly of a vertical glass tube in which slides freely a small cylinder of very hard steel, pointed on the lower end, called the hammer. This hammer is allowed to fall about 10 in. onto the sample to be tested. The distance it rebounds is taken as a measure of the hardness of the sample. A scale on the tube is divided into 140 equal parts, and the hardness is expressed as the number on the scale to which the hammer rebounds. Measured in this way the hardness of different substances is as follows: glass, 130; porcelain, 120; hardest steel, 110; tool steel, 1 per cent carbon, may be as low as 31; mild steel, 0.5 C, 26 to 30; gray iron castings, 39; wrought iron, 18; babbitt metal, 4 to 10; soft brass, 12; zinc, 8; copper, 6; lead, 2 (*Cass. Mag.*, Sept., 1908). The relationship between the scleroscope number and the ultimate tensile strength, s_u, is given by Abbott (*loc. cit.*) by the equation $s_u = 4.0S - 15$, where s_u is in thousands of pounds per square inch and S is the scleroscope number.

Moh's Scale of Hardness is commonly used in testing the hardness of rocks and minerals. Hardness is recorded in terms of the following scale: 1, talc; 2, gypsum; 3, calc spar; 4, fluor spar; 5, apatite; 6, feldspar; 7, quartz; 8, topaz; 9, sapphire; 10, diamond. A convenient test for the softer minerals is: Scratched by finger-nail, up to hardness of 2.5; by copper coin, up to hardness of 3; by knife-blade, up to hardness of 5.5.

Some smooth surface of the mineral to be tested is selected, on which a point of the standard is pressed and moved back and forth several times 1/8 in. or less. If the mineral is scratched it is softer than the standard. Two minerals of equal hardness will scratch each other. Pulverulent or splintery minerals are "broken down" by the test and

Table II. Conversion Table for Approximate Hardness Numbers Obtained by Different Methods

(Compiled mainly from manufacturers' tables)

Brinell, 3000-kg load, 10 mm ball		Rockwell Number		Shore Scleroscope Number	Vicker's Pyramid Number
Diameter of Indentation, d mm	Hardness Number	C Scale, 150 kg load, 120° diamond cone	B Scale, 100 kg load, 1/16-in. ball		
2.40	653	62	......	86	783
2.60	555	55	......	75	622
2.80	477	49	......	66	513
3.00	415	44	......	58	439
3.10	388	41	......	54	404
3.20	363	39	......	51	374
3.30	341	37	......	48	352
3.40	321	35	......	45	329
3.50	302	32	......	42	303
3.60	285	30	......	40	285
3.70	269	27	......	37	269
3.80	255	25	......	35	255
3.90	241	23	99	33	241
4.00	229	20	98	32	229
4.10	217	......	96	30	217
4.20	207	......	95	29	207
4.30	197	......	93	28	197
4.40	187	......	91	27	187
4.50	179	......	89	25	179
4.60	170	......	87	24	170
4.70	163	......	85	23	163
4.80	156	......	82	23	156
4.90	149	......	80	22	149
5.00	143	......	78	21	143
5.10	137	......	75	20	137
5.20	131	......	73	19	131
5.30	126	......	70	18	126
5.40	121	......	68	17	121
5.50	116	......	65	16	116
5.60	111	......	62	......	111
5.70	107	......	60	......	107
5.80	103	......	57	......	103
5.90	99.2	......	55	......	99.2
6.00	95.5	......	52	......	95.5
6.10	92.0	......	49	......	92.0
6.20	88.7	......	47	......	88.7
6.30	85.5	......	44	......	85.5
6.40	82.5	......	42	......	82.5

yield an " apparent " hardness often much lower than the true hardness. Rough surfaces also yield doubtful results.

Relationship between the Different Hardness Numbers. A rational relation exists between the Brinell and Rockwell numbers, and also between these numbers and the Vicker's pyramid numbers; an empirical relation exists also between the foregoing numbers and those of the Shore scleroscope. Petrenko (Tech. Paper 334, U. S. Bur. Standards) gives the following equations:

$$B = 25,000/(100-R_C) \text{ for } R_C \text{ greater than } 40$$

$$B = 1,420,000/(100-R_C)^2 \text{ for } R_C \text{ from } -20 \text{ to } 40$$

$$B = 7300/(130 - R_B) \text{ for } R_B \text{ from } 35 \text{ to } 100$$

where B = Brinell number obtained with a 10-mm ball and 3000-kg load; R_C = Rockwell number on the C scale, using a 150-kg load and a 120° diamond penetrator; R_B = Rockwell number on the B scale with a 100-kg load and a $1/16$-in. ball.

Abbott (*Proc. A.S.T.M.*, vol. xv, Pt. II, 1915) derives from tests the empirical relation $B = 5.5S - 28$, B being the Brinell number and S the scleroscope number. Table II gives these various hardness numbers in terms of one another. The values were obtained from the manufacturers of the instruments and from published experimental data. The scleroscope numbers, as tabulated, vary slightly from those given by the Sub-Committee on Hardness Conversion of the A.S.S.T. in its 1930 handbook; the committee gives a scleroscope value of 81 for a Brinell number of 627 as compared with 84 in Table II (by interpolation), whereas the committee scleroscope number is 30 for a Brinell number of 197 as compared with 28 in Table II. Both lists are the same for scleroscope number 54 which equals Brinell number 387.

Ductility Tests

Ductility as Determined from Tension Test. The usual measures of ductility are the percentage of elongation and the percentage of contraction of area of a specimen in a tension test. Since the percentage elongation varies widely over the length of a tension specimen, the gage length over which the deformation is measured should be specified. A tension test for determining ductility is not suitable for many metals, for example, a thin metal specimen which in tension usually fails without any appreciable elongation.

Bending Test for Determining Ductility. The following is the A.S.T.M. Standards, 1934, A9–34, specification for bend tests on structural steel:

Bend test specimens shall stand being bent cold through 180° without cracking on the outside of the bent portion, around a pin, the diameter of which shall have the following relation to the thickness of the specimen:

Thickness of Material	Ratio:	$\dfrac{\text{Pin Diameter}}{\text{Thickness of Specimen}}$
Up to $3/4$ in., inclusive		1
Over $3/4$ to 1 in., inclusive		$1 1/2$
Over 1 to $1 1/2$ in., inclusive		2
Over $1 1/2$ to 2 in., inclusive		$2 1/2$
Over 2 in.		3

Cupping Tests for Determining Ductility. For determining the relative ductility of thin sheet metal, the so-called cupping test is often used. There are various machines on the market for performing this test. In these, a spherical-ended plunger or ball is forced into the test specimen, which is held over a suitable die. For some machines, the maximum depth of the cup, inches, which can be formed, for others, the load required to produce the cup, just as visible " necking down " occurs, is taken as a measure of the ductility.

Short-time Tests for Endurance Limit

Short-time Tests for Endurance Limit. Since the determination of the endurance limit for any given steel or metal takes considerable time, attempts have been made to devise short-time tests which will give at least some indication of the probable endurance limit. No method has been found which is entirely satisfactory or which has been generally accepted. Two methods have shown some promise of success: (1) the rise-in-temperature method; (2) the electrical resistance method.

Rise-in-Temperature Method. (Moore and Kommers, *Bull.* 124, *Eng. Exp. Sta.*, Univ. of Ill., 1921.) A standard rotating beam specimen is held at one end and, by an eccentric movement of the other end, a bending stress is produced in a manner similar to that obtained when the beam is rotated. A thermocouple is attached to the specimen at the section of greatest stress and connected to a galvanometer. The specimen is run at 1000 rpm for 30 sec at stresses which increase by stages; a reading of the galvanometer is taken for each value of the stress. The stress at which there is a sudden increase in the reading of the galvanometer is taken as the endurance limit. For ferrous metals the results varied from 14 per cent below those found by the standard long-time method to 18 per cent above, but in the main they were within 5 or 6 per cent of the standard values. The test does not give consistent results with non-ferrous metals.

Electrical Resistance Method. This is sometimes known as the Ikeda method, after the Japanese who developed it. (See Moore and Konzo, *Bull.* 205, *Eng. Exp. Sta.*, Univ. of Ill., 1930.) It consists in determining the electrical resistance corresponding to various stresses and noting a sudden change in the resistance. The stress where the change occurs is taken as the endurance limit. The method gives results comparable with those obtained by the rise-in-temperature method and gives consistent results with non-ferrous metals. It requires delicate instruments and careful manipulation.

Creep Tests

Creep Limit Tests. The following description of the apparatus for and the method of making creep tests is abstracted from F. H. Norton's The Creep of Steel at High Temperatures, McGraw-Hill, New York, 1929. Specimens 0.505 in. in diameter with a 4-in. gage length are placed in an electric furnace. The load is applied by weights and a lever having a ratio of 10 to 1. The furnace, which holds 5 or 6 specimens at one time, is a hollow cylinder wrapped with asbestos paper and a heating coil which maintains a constant temperature through a regulating device. The extension of each specimen is measured by means of a dial connected to the lever arm which applies the load. To prevent oxidation of the specimen, a stream of nitrogen is introduced at the bottom of the apparatus.

The specimens are loaded nearly to the estimated creep limit for a given temperature, and this load is maintained for 400 hr, the elongation being measured twice a day. The load is then increased 10 per cent and maintained for 400 hr, the elongation again being measured twice a day, and this rate of increase in load is continued until the creep becomes large. Thus for each stress (at a given temperature) there will be a series of time-percentage elongation readings. A graph is plotted for each stress, with time as abscissa and percentage elongation as ordinate. This is usually a straight line. The slopes of these time-percentage elongation lines are next plotted against stress on logarithmic paper. There will be one line for each temperature and, since the points fall on a straight line, the stress corresponding to any given rate of creep for any given temperature may be read directly from the graph. Rapid progress is being made (1935) in the development and revision of standard methods of making short-time and long-time (creep) temperature tests. See A.S.T.M. Tentative Standard E22.

X-ray Inspection

X-ray Examination of Castings. When x-rays are passed through castings or forgings which contain defects, the x-rays pass through the defects more readily than through the sound metal and thus outline the defects on a photographic plate.

The x-ray examination of castings or forgings has two functions: (1) development of manufacturing technique; (2) inspection of the finished product. In Recommended Practice for Radiographic Testing of Metal Castings, A.S.T.M. Standards, E15–29, 1933, adopted 1929, the following defects are enumerated as being capable of detection by x-ray methods: gas cavities, slag inclusions, sand inclusions, pipe cavities, porosity, cracks, metal segregation. Since there are no standards governing the number, extent and character of defects, no specific requirement can be laid down, but if the defects are known to be present the user can judge of their probable effect and act accordingly.

Equipment. Equipment needed for x-ray examination consists of an x-ray tube, transformers, photographic apparatus, and a lead-lined operating chamber. The part to be examined is placed between the x-ray tube and the photographic film and an exposure made for the proper length of time. Since x-rays are very dangerous it is imperative that the operator be properly protected from them by lead-lined boxes or chambers. The operation is one requiring expensive apparatus and skilled technique, but it is very satisfactory for castings if a positive knowledge of their soundness is essential. For metal not over $3\frac{1}{2}$ in. thick, a 200-kv 8-milliampere Coolidge x-ray tube will be satisfactory. For detailed information see George L. Clark's Applied X-Rays. McGraw-Hill

Book Co., *Metals and Alloys*; St. John and Isenburger's Industrial Radiography, John Wiley & Sons, New York, 1934.

Special Tests

Proof Tests. A proof test is one in which a part of a machine or the machine as a whole is subjected to a load which equals or exceeds the allowable load but which does not test the part to destruction; for example, the hydrostatic test of cast-iron pipe at the foundry, where the pipe is subjected to a water pressure of about twice the normal working pressure.

Determination of Physical Properties from Magnetic Permeability. Tests of magnetic permeability of steel and iron seem to give some indication of the hardness, strength, and uniformity. They possess the great advantage that the test does not destroy the sample tested, and hence may be made on the actual parts to be used. Magnetic tests as an indication of hardness or strength are not standardized yet, but hold promise of future usefulness.

The variation of magnetic qualities in a bar or disk of metal has been used as a means of locating small invisible flaws. (See article by J. A. Capp, *Proc. A.S.T.M.*, vol. xxvii, Pt. II, p. 268, 1927.) This principle has been utilized in the construction of a special device, known as the transverse fissure detector car, for locating transverse fissures in railroad rails.

Special Tests of Materials, Structures, and Machines are often made. Table III gives some such tests.

Tests of Strength of Wood have not been standardized to an extent which allows their inclusion in specifications for timber, but compression tests, flexure tests, shearing tests, and impact tests are frequently made. Compression tests are made both along the grain and across the grain. Compression specimens are usually rectangular blocks, and

Table III. Special Tests of Materials, Structures, and Machines

Structural part, machine part, structure, machine or material tested	Test	Measurements
Floor panel of building.	Proof test with dead load, not to destruction.	Deflections, tensile and compressive deformations in beams and columns.
Bridge.............	Proof test with dead load or with moving load.	Deflections, tensile and compressive deformations in various members.
Riveted joints........	Tests of samples to destruction.....	Ultimate load, slip of rivets.
Rivets, metal plates....	Shearing test of samples to destruction using special shearing tools.	Ultimate load, results depend on hardness of shearing tools used.
Bolts..............	Tests of samples to destruction in tension or torsion.	Ultimate load.
Boilers.............	Tests with hydrostatic pressure. Proof tests with pressures somewhat above working pressures.	Observation of leaks, cracks, or permanent distortion of parts.
Car couplers and coupler yokes	Proof tests, tests of samples to destruction under tension and impact tension.	Ultimate load, distortion under proof load.
Wire rope...........	Tests of samples to destruction in tension.	Ultimate load, observation of manner of fracture.
Brake beams for railway cars.	Tests of samples to destruction in flexure.	Ultimate load, deflections.
Chain..............	Proof tests of entire chain in tension, tests to destruction of sample sections.	Set after removal of proof load, ultimate strength.
Large pipe..........	Hydrostatic pressure proof test.	Observation of leaks, cracks, or other evidence of failure.
Gear teeth..........	Scleroscope or Rockwell test for uniform hardness.	Hardness for various teeth.
Engraver's plates......	Brinell, Rockwell, or scleroscope tests for uniform hardness of samples.	Hardness at various points.
Strain insulators for electric transmission lines.	Proof load in tension, tension test of samples to destruction.	Evidences of failure under proof load, ultimate strength.
Eyebars.............	Tension test of sample eyebars to destruction.	Yield point, ultimate load, stretch.
Columns............	Compression tests of models or samples to destruction.	Yield point, ultimate load, deflection, axial compression.

should be tested with spherical-seated bearing blocks. Wood has a rather poorly defined proportional limit in compression. In compression along the grain there is a well-defined ultimate strength. Shearing tests along the grain are made by the use of shearing blocks placed in the testing machine, or for larger specimens by testing short, deep beams. The shearing strength of wood along the grain is of great importance. Flexure tests both of small selected specimens and of large beams are common. In flexure tests the failure may be by longitudinal shear along the neutral axis, by compression along the upper side of the beam, or by tension along the lower side. Impact flexure tests show the shock-resisting qualities of wood. Hardness tests are made by using a steel ball 0.444 in. in diameter, and noting the load which causes the ball to penetrate to one-half its diameter.

The Turner-Hatt impact testing machine is in common use in the United States for impact testing of wood. This machine consists of an anvil on which the specimen is placed, and of a weight which can be dropped from various heights. Attached to the weight is a pencil which draws a record on a rotating drum. From this record the deflections of the specimen can be measured, as the weight is dropped from successively increasing heights until rupture occurs, or until the deflections increase abnormally, showing that the proportional limit has been passed. Another method of making an impact test consists in dropping the weight from such a height that the specimen is fractured by one blow. The pencil attached to the weight traces a curve on the rotating drum whose steepness is a measure of the velocity of the falling weight. Measuring the velocity of the weight before and after fracture of the specimen the energy absorbed in fracturing the specimen can be determined. For detailed description of tests of timber, see the *A.S.T.M. Standards* D143–27 and D198–27.

BIBLIOGRAPHY ON MECHANICS OF MATERIALS

1. AMERICAN INSTITUTE OF STEEL CONSTRUCTION, Steel Construction, New York, 1934.
2. AMERICAN SOCIETY FOR TESTING MATERIALS, A.S.T.M. Standards, Philadelphia.
3. BOYD, J. E., Strength of Materials, New York, McGraw-Hill, fourth edition, 1935.
4. CRANE, T., and NOLAN, T., Concrete Building Construction, New York, John Wiley & Sons, 1927.
5. CROSS, H., and MORGAN, N. D., Continuous Frames of Reinforced Concrete, New York, John Wiley & Sons, 1932.
6. DRAFFIN, J. O., Strength of Materials, New York, John Wiley & Sons, 1928.
7. FOWLER, C. E., Engineering and Building Foundations, Vol. I., New York, John Wiley & Sons, fourth edition, 1920.
8. HOOL, G. A., and KINNE, W. S., Structural Engineers' Handbook Series, New York, McGraw-Hill.
9. HOOL, G. A., and KINNE, W. S., Reinforced Concrete and Masonry Structures, New York, McGraw-Hill, 1924.
10. HOOL, G. A., and KINNE, W. S., Foundations, Abutments, and Footings, New York, McGraw-Hill, 1923.
11. JUDGE, A. W., Engineering Materials, Vol. 3, New York, Pitman, 1932.
12. KETCHUM, M. S., Structural Engineers' Handbook, New York, McGraw-Hill, 1924.
13. KIDDER, F. E., and PARKER, H., Architects' and Builders' Handbook, New York, John Wiley & Sons, eighteenth edition, 1931.
14. LAURSON, P. G., and COX, W. J., Properties and Mechanics of Materials, New York, John Wiley & Sons, 1931.
15. MAURER, E. R., and WITHEY, M. O., Strength of Materials, New York, John Wiley & Sons, second edition, 1935.
16. MERRIMAN, T., and WIGGIN, T. H., American Civil Engineers' Handbook, New York, John Wiley & Sons, fifth edition, 1930.
17. MERRIMAN, M. and T., Strength of Materials, New York, John Wiley & Sons, seventh edition, 1928.
18. POORMAN, A. P., Strength of Materials, New York, McGraw-Hill, second edition, 1929.
19. SEELY, F. B., Advanced Mechanics of Materials, New York, John Wiley & Sons, 1932.
20. SEELY, F. B., Resistance of Materials, New York, John Wiley & Sons, second edition, 1935.
21. SUTHERLAND, H., and CLIFFORD, W. W., Introduction to Reinforced Concrete Design, New York, John Wiley & Sons, 1932.
22. TAYLOR, F. W., THOMPSON, S. E., and SMULSKI, E., Concrete, Plain and Reinforced, New York, John Wiley & Sons, fourth edition: Vol. I, 1931; Vol. II, 1928.
23. TIMOSHENKO, S., Strength of Materials, New York, D. Van Nostrand Co., 2 vols., 1930.
24. TIMOSHENKO, S., and MACCULLOUGH, G. H., Elements of Strength of Materials, New York, D. Van Nostrand Co., 1935.
25. TURNEAURE, F. E., and MAURER, E. R., Principles of Reinforced Concrete Construction, New York, John Wiley & Sons, fourth edition, 1935.
26. WILLIAMS, C. C., Design of Masonry Structures and Foundations, New York, McGraw-Hill, 1922.

SECTION 6

MECHANICS OF FLUIDS

BY

P. E. HEMKE

MECHANICS OF FLUIDS

PROPERTIES OF FLUIDS, DIVISIONS OF FLUID MECHANICS

1. INTRODUCTION, DEFINITIONS

Continuous Media. In the study of mechanics of fluids the fluids are usually regarded as *continuous media* and not as an *aggregation of discrete particles*. This conception is in conflict with the molecular theory, but it is sufficiently accurate for most engineering purposes and permits progress to be made, whereas to regard fluids as made up of separate particles presents insuperable difficulties in general.

This means then that volume elements are restricted to those whose dimensions are large in comparison with the mean free paths of the molecules contained within the volume element. In small time-intervals the average number of molecules contained in the element is then sensibly constant. That this conception of a fluid enables the investigator to make a fairly detailed and accurate exploration of a given space filled with fluid is illustrated by the fact that for air at normal temperatures a cube of side 0.001 mm contains 2.7×10^7 molecules.

Exceptions occur in the study of (a) *diffusion*, where there is a measurable interchange of molecular matter; (b) *heat conduction*, where there is an interchange of molecular kinetic energy; and (c) *internal friction*, where there is interchange of momentum between adjacent layers of the fluid.

In order to call attention to those properties of fluids which differentiate them from solids, the terms *bulk modulus* and *rigidity modulus* will be used.

The Bulk Modulus.

$$k = S_n/(\Delta v/v) \tag{1}$$

where S_n = normal force on each unit of area of a small cubical element.

v = original volume of the element.

Δv = change in volume of the element due to stress S_n.

The Rigidity Modulus.

$$N = S_s/\theta \tag{2}$$

where S_s = tangential or shearing force on each unit of area of opposite sides of a small cubical element.

θ = shearing deformation due to the stress S_s.

Fluids and Solids. Fluids have bulk moduli but no rigidity moduli; a solid has both. A fluid therefore cannot permanently resist a tangential or shear stress. The fluid yields to such stresses, different fluids yielding at different rates.

This illustrates that it is very difficult to define sharply the line of demarcation between solids and fluids. For instance, a steel ball placed on the surface of a bucket of pitch will eventually sink to the bottom. The shearing stresses caused by the relatively greater weight of the steel ball cannot be permanently resisted by the pitch. In this sense the pitch acts like a fluid. On the other hand, a tuning fork made of pitch acts like a steel tuning fork when it is struck. In this sense pitch behaves like a solid.

2. PROPERTIES OF FLUIDS

Density

Mass Density, defined as the mass per unit volume, is most frequently used. Symbol: ρ.

Weight Density, defined as the weight per unit volume, is also used. Symbol: w.

Then
$$\rho = w/g \tag{3}$$

where g is the acceleration due to gravity. If the symbol [ ] denotes dimensional equality, then $[\rho] = \left[\dfrac{M}{L^3}\right]$, M and L denoting the fundamental quantities mass and length respectively. In engineering units, mass density, ρ, is then found in slugs per cubic foot.

Specific Density in relation to water at 4.0° C is often used to specify density of certain fluids.

Density varies widely for different fluids. For a given fluid, density varies chiefly with temperature and pressure. Densities of a number of fluids are given at the end of this section.

Compressibility

Definition. Since this property of a fluid depends upon its bulk modulus, compressibility is defined in terms of the bulk modulus, k. The equation $k = S_n/(\Delta v/v)$ shows that, when the normal stress, S_n, is large for small values of Δv, the fluid is relatively more difficult to compress than it is when large values of Δv correspond to moderate values of S_n. For an incompressible fluid, $k = \infty$.

Compressibility, symbol β, is defined as the reciprocal of the bulk modulus, k. Hence this compressibility number is zero for an incompressible fluid.

For Certain Fluids, compressibility is given as the contraction in unit volume, $\Delta v/v$, per atmosphere because very large values of the normal force S_n are required to obtain measurable values of $\Delta v/v$. For other fluids such as air, hydrogen, etc., pressure changes very much with temperature, and very frequently compressibility is written:

$$\beta = \text{compressibility} = \frac{1}{v}\frac{(\partial v)}{(\partial p)} \quad T = \text{constant} \tag{4}$$

where
p = pressure in the fluid.
T = absolute temperature.

β is also written:

$$\beta = \frac{1(v_1 - v_2)}{v_1(p_2 - p_1)} \quad T = \text{constant} \tag{5}$$

Compressibilities of a number of fluids are given at the end of this section.

Viscosity

Theory. Suppose that a fluid is in motion over a plane surface, S (Fig. 1). Consider two surfaces in the fluid at distances y and $y + dy$ from this surface, S. Let u and $u + du$ be the velocities in these two surfaces in an X direction. It will be assumed that u and $u + du$ depend only on y. Observations show that:

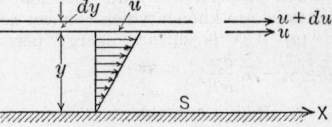

FIG. 1. Fluid Motion Near a Surface

(a) The fluid in contact with S is at rest relative to S.

(b) u is a linear function of y in that part of the fluid where its viscous properties are important.

(c) Tangential stresses exist in the fluid when it is in motion. These tangential stresses retard the more rapidly moving layers of fluid and accelerate the less rapidly moving layers. The tangential stress, S_t, follows Newton's law, i.e.,

$$S_t \propto du/dy \tag{6}$$

It varies for different fluids or for the same fluid under different conditions.

Consequently,

$$S_t = \mu du/dy \tag{7}$$

where μ is a constant for a fluid under fixed conditions, i.e., temperature, pressure, etc., of the latter. $[\mu] = \left[\dfrac{M}{LT}\right]$. In engineering units it will be given in slugs per foot second.

The quantity is sometimes called a *coefficient of viscosity*; since it is not a dimensionless number the term is not so apt. Coefficients are usually dimensionless numbers or quantities.

Maxwell Defined Viscosity as: " The tangential force on unit area of either of two horizontal planes of indefinite extent at unit distance apart, one of which is fixed, while the other moves with unit velocity, the space between being filled with the viscous fluid."

Various Units of Viscosity are in use. A *poise* is the value of μ in cgs units, i.e., in grams per centimeter second. The *Saybolt* viscosity of a fluid is the number of seconds of time required for 60 cc of the fluid to flow through a given opening in a standard instrument.

In fluid mechanics the ratio μ/ρ occurs frequently. The symbol used is $[\nu] = \left[\dfrac{L^2}{T}\right]$, that is, in engineering units it is feet^2 per second.

Viscosity of Gases usually varies chiefly with temperature and very little with pressure. Viscosity of liquids varies with temperature and pressure. Viscosity tables for a number of fluids are given in Art. 6, p. 6–08.

For Solids the tangential or shear stress is

$$S_t = G\theta \tag{8}$$

where G = shear modulus or rigidity modulus.

      θ = shear strain.

For Fluids $S_t = \mu \dfrac{d\theta}{dt}$ (9)

The equation for solids holds within the elastic limits. Beyond that limit a solid acts somewhat like a fluid, for

$$S_t = f\left(\frac{d\theta}{dt}\right) \tag{10}$$

Surface Tension

Surface Tension occurs when there is a " free surface " in the fluid as in water or at interfaces between two fluids, for example, oil and water. Observations show that across any line element drawn in the surface of the fluid there is a tension $\gamma\, ds$, the tension being normal to the element ds and in the tangent plane to the surface at ds. The quantity γ is called the surface tension of the fluid. $[\gamma] = \left[\dfrac{M}{T^2}\right]$; that is, it is a force per unit length.

For fluids which have comparatively simple molecular structures,

$$\gamma = \gamma_o\,(1{-}bt)^n \tag{11}$$

The parameters n and b vary for different fluids. Average values are $n \approx 1.2$ and $b \approx 0.005$, when $t = °C$. Values of surface tension for a number of fluids are given at the end of this section.

Relations between Properties of Fluids

The properties of fluids mentioned above are not independent of one another. Some relations are known which connect certain of the properties of fluids.

(a) If λ is surface energy per unit area, we know from thermodynamics that

$$\lambda = \gamma - T\frac{\partial \gamma}{\partial T}.$$

(b) If $\beta = 1/k$ then $\gamma\,\beta^{4/3}$ = constant (Richard & Matthews; *Zeit. phys. Chem.*, 61, 49 (1908)), holds for certain fluids.

(c) If M is the molecular weight of the fluid, T_c the critical temperature (absolute), δ and A are constants then $\gamma\,\dfrac{(M)^{2/3}}{(\rho)} = A(T_c - T - \delta)$ (Eötvos).

$\delta \approx 6$ and $A \approx 2.12$ for unassociated liquids; symbol $\approx$ denotes approximate equality.

(d) $\gamma\,\dfrac{(M)^{2/3}}{(\rho)}$ = constant for unassociated liquids, over wide ranges of temperature (Bernett and Mitchell; *Zeit. phys. Chem.*, 84, 475 (1913)).

3. KINDS OF FLUIDS

Ideal Fluids are fluids in which no tangential stresses exist irrespective of whether the fluid is in motion or not.

In spite of the fact that no such fluids actually exist many important advances have been made by considering fluids to be ideal. So-called classical hydrodynamics is largely concerned with ideal fluids.

Liquids are fluids which are practically incompressible. They have definite free surfaces. Density, viscosity, and surface tension are important properties of liquids. Water, alcohol, oil, acetone, etc., are examples of liquids. An ideal liquid is incompressible and inviscid.

Gases are fluids which have no free surfaces. They fill completely any containing vessel. Density and viscosity of gases are generally smaller than for liquids. The compressibility numbers are larger for gases than for liquids; i.e., comparatively small pressures produce large volume changes. •For many cases of fluid motion a gas may be considered incompressible.

When gases must be regarded as compressible the temperature affects the pressure and volume very much. It is necessary therefore to know the relation between pressure, volume, and temperature.

A **Perfect Gas** or ideal gas follows Charles' Law, and the relation between pressure, volume, and temperature is,

$$pv = R'T \tag{12}$$

where
    p = pressure.
    v = volume.
    T = absolute temperature.
    R' = constant depending on the weight and nature of the gas used.
The equation is also written

$$pv = wRT \tag{13}$$

where
    w = weight density of the gas.
    R = a constant depending only on the nature of the gas.

Since ideal gases do not exist, this equation is not exactly correct for real gases.

Many equations have been proposed to represent the pressure, volume, and temperature relation. Books on thermodynamics should be consulted for discussions on such equations.

4. DIVISION OF FLUID MECHANICS

Fluid Statics is concerned with fluids at rest or in equilibrium. There is no motion in any part of the fluid provided it is regarded as a continuous medium.

Hydrostatics, aerostatics, referring to water and air respectively as fluids, are terms in common use.

Pressure and buoyancy are examples of statical fluid forces.

Fluid Dynamics is concerned with forces arising from the motion of fluids.

Separate subdivisions of fluid dynamics are:

(a) Hydrodynamics referring to water as the fluid in motion.

(b) Aerodynamics referring to air as the fluid in motion.

(c) Gas dynamics referring to gases and vapors as the fluids in motion.

Hydraulics is a term which refers to engineering applications of fluid mechanics, both fluid statics and fluid dynamics. Most generally water is the fluid considered in hydraulics.

5. DENSITY OF VARIOUS LIQUIDS AND GASES

All numerical values were taken from the International Critical Tables with the exception of the standard atmosphere relations used in aeronautical work, which were taken from Technical Report 218 (1925), National Advisory Committee for Aeronautics.

Symbols:

$d_{t_1}{}^{t}$ = weight in grams per millimeter = specific gravity in terms of water at 4° C; t refers to the temperature, in degrees Centigrade, at which the weight was determined.

w^t = weight in pounds per cubic foot at temperature t.

ρ^t = mass in slugs per cubic foot at temperature t.

Conversion Factors:

1 gram per millileter   = 0.999973 gram per cubic centimeter.
1 pound per cubic foot = 0.016018 gram per cubic centimeter.
1 slug per cubic foot   = 0.5154 gram per cubic centimeter.

Table I.   Density of Water from 0° C to 100° C

$t°$ C	$d_4{}^t$	$\rho = w/g =$ mass density *	$t°$ C	$d_4{}^t$	$\rho = w/g =$ mass density *
0	0.99987	1.940	40	0.99224	1.926
4	1.00000	1.941	50	0.98807	1.918
5	0.99999	1.941	60	0.98324	1.908
10	0.99973	1.940	70	0.97781	1.898
15	0.99913	1.939	80	0.97183	1.886
20	0.99823	1.937	90	0.96534	1.873
25	0.99707	1.935	100	0.95838	1.860
30	0.99567	1.932			

* ρ is the mass density (slugs per cubic foot); w = weight of water at 4° C (pounds per cubic foot).

Table II. Density of Various Liquids at Ordinary Temperatures

Liquid	Temp. $t°$ C	$d_4{}^t$ (gm/ml)	w^t (lb/ft³)	ρ^t (slugs/ft³)
Acetone......................	15°	0.796	49.7	1.543
	25°	0.784	48.8	1.515
Benzene......................	20°	0.879	54.8	1.700
Carbon tetrachloride..........	0°	1.633	101.9	3.160
	20°	1.594	99.4	3.085
Ether........................	0°	0.736	45.9	1.426
	20°	0.714	44.5	1.381
Mercury......................	0°	13.545	845.9	26.29
	20°	13.546	845.9	26.29
Oils, mineral				
Fresno, Cal..................	20°	0.842	52.4	1.630
Lima, Ohio..................	20°	0.851	53.0	1.650
Adams Canyon, Cal..........	20°	0.921	57.4	1.780
Pipeline, Pa.................	20°	0.862	53.7	1.670
White Oak, W. Va...........	20°	0.873	54.4	1.680

Table III. Density of Vegetable and Marine Animal Oils

Oil (vegetable)	$d_{15.5°}{}^{15.5°\,C}$ (gm/ml)	$w^{15.5°\,C}$ (lb/ft³)	$\rho^{15.5°\,C}$ (slugs/ft³)	Oil (marine animal)	$d_{15.5°}{}^{15.5°\,C}$ (gm/ml)	$w^{15.5°\,C}$ (lb/ft³)	$\rho^{15.5°\,C}$ (slugs/ft³)
Cottonseed..	0.924	57.6	1.790	Menhaden..	0.932	58.1	1.805
Linseed (raw)	0.934	58.2	1.810	Salmon.....	0.927	57.8	1.797
Soya bean...	0.924	57.6	1.790	Shark......	0.910	56.8	1.760
Sunflower...	0.924	57.6	1.790	Whale......	0.924	57.6	1.790
Walnut.....	0.926	57.8	1.795				

Table IV. Density of Ethyl and Methyl Alcohol at Various Temperatures

This shows how density varies with temperature for these two liquids. The equations are empirical, and the liquids are assumed to be chemically pure.

Methyl alcohol: (a) $d_4{}^t = 0.80999 - 9.253 \times 10^{-4}t - 4.1 \times 10^{-7}t^2$
Range: $t = 0°$ C to $t = 60°$ C

(b) $d_4{}^t = 0.81015 - 1.0041 \times 10^{-3}t - 1.802 \times 10^{-6}t^2$
Range: $t = -94.5°$ C to $t = 0°$ C

Ethyl alcohol: (a) $d_4{}^t = 0.80625 - 8.461 \times 10^{-4}t + 1.60 \times 10^{-6}t^2 - 8.5 \times 10^{-9}t^3$
Range: $t = 0°$ C to $t = 80°$ C

(b) $d_4{}^t = 0.80625 - 8.45 \times 10^{-4}t + 2.9 \times 10^{-7}t^2$
Range: Below $t = 0°$ C

No lower temperature specified (Timmermans).

Table V. Density of Air (Aeronautics)

Standard density = $\rho_0 = 2.378 \times 10^{-3}$ slug per cu ft at $t = 15°$ C, $p_0 = 760$ mm Hg, dry air
Variation of density with pressure and temperature:

$$\rho/\rho_0 = 0.3789 \frac{p \text{ mm Hg}}{(t° \text{ C} + 273° \text{ C})}$$

$$= 9.624 \frac{p \text{ in. Hg}}{(t° \text{ C} + 273° \text{ C})}$$

$$= 17.32 \frac{p \text{ in. Hg}}{(t° \text{ F} + 459.4°)}$$

Variation of density with altitude:

$$\rho/\rho_0 = \left[1 - \frac{3.566 \times 10^{-3}}{(t° \text{ F} + 459.4° \text{ F})} h\right]^{4.256} ; \ h = \text{altitude in feet}$$

Table VI. Density of Various Gases

Density given at 0° C and 760 mm Hg. Symbol for density = ds

Gas	$ds \times 10^3$ (gm/ml)	w (lb/ft³)	ρ (slugs/ft³)
Acetylene.............................	1.173	0.0732	0.00227
Ammonia.............................	0.7710	.0481	.00150
Carbon dioxide........................	1.977	.1234	.00383
Carbon monoxide......................	1.250	.0780	.00242
Helium...............................	0.1785	.0112	.000346
Hydrogen.............................	0.08988	.00561	.0000174
Hydrogen chloride.....................	1.639	.1023	.00318
Krypton..............................	3.708	.231	.00719
Neon.................................	0.9002	.0563	.00175
Nitrogen (atmospheric)................	1.257	.0785	.00244
Oxygen...............................	1.429	.0892	.00277

NOTE: For ordinary calculations the gas law $pv = wRT$ may be used. For accurate work the International Critical Tables should be consulted for (pv) relations.

6. VISCOSITY OF VARIOUS LIQUIDS AND GASES

All numerical values were taken from the International Critical Tables.

Table VII. Viscosity of Water between 0° and 100°; Atmospheric Pressure

$t°$ C	$\mu \times 10^5$ (slugs/ft sec)	$\nu = \mu/\rho \times 10^5$ (ft²/sec)	$t°$ C	$\mu \times 10^5$ (slugs/ft sec)	$\nu = \mu/\rho \times 10^5$ (ft²/sec)
0	3.75	1.94	60	0.981	0.514
10	2.74	1.41	70	0.851	0.449
20	2.09	1.08	80	0.746	0.395
30	1.67	0.854	90	0.660	0.353
40	1.36	0.702	100	0.593	0.319
50	1.15	0.605			

Table VIII. Viscosity of Various Liquids; Atmospheric Pressure

Liquid	Temp. $t°$ C	$\mu \times 10^5$ slugs/ft sec	$\nu = \mu/\rho \times 10^5$ (ft²/sec)	Liquid	Temp. $t°$ C	$\mu \times 10^5$ slugs/ft sec	$\nu = \mu/\rho \times 10^5$ (ft²/sec)
Acetone.....	15	7.07	4.58	Castor oil.....	5	7860	4170
	25	6.42	4.21		10	5050	2690
Benzene.....	20	1.35	0.794		15	3160	1690
Carbon tetra-					20	2060	1110
chloride...	0	2.82	0.893		30	942	511
	20	1.89	0.613	Cottonseed oil.	15.5	171–208	96.0–117
Mercury....	0	3.51	0.134	Linseed oil....	15.5	115	63.5
	20	3.24	0.123	Olive oil......	15.5	199–211	112–119
Ethyl alcohol	0	3.74	2.39	Rape oil......	15.5	226–246	128–139
	10	3.66	2.36	Gasolines.....	Room temp.	.627–1.25	
	20	3.60	2.35	Kerosene.....	Room temp.	4.18	
	30	3.48	2.29	Light lubri-			
Methyl				cating oils...	Room temp.	5.23–314	
alcohol ...	0	1.69	1.07	Medium lubri-			
	10	1.44	0.926	cating oils...	Room temp.	314–732	
	20	1.24	0.807	Heavy lubri-			
	30	1.08	0.710	cating oils...	Room temp.	732–4180	

Table IX. Viscosity of Various Oils under Pressure

Values of $\mu\rho/\mu_0$ at $t = 40°$ C

* p kg/cm²	Rape Oil	Sperm Oil	p kg/cm²	Castor Oil	p kg/cm²	Rape Oil	Sperm Oil	p kg/cm²	Castor Oil
0	1.00	1.00	0	1.00	788	3.91	....	1164	5.26
158	1.13	1.23	24	1.03	866	....	3.14	....	....
315	1.44	1.54	228	1.37	945	3.50	....	....	....
473	1.88	1.94	551	2.30	1103	4.21	4.02	....	....
630	2.35	2.39	865	3.63					

* Note: p is above atmospheric pressure, $0 \approx 1$ atmosphere.

Table X. Viscosity of Gases—Sensibly Independent of Pressure

$$\mu = \mu_0 \left(\frac{T_0 + C}{T + C}\right)\left(\frac{T}{T_0}\right)^{\frac{3}{2}}; \ \mu \text{ in poises, } T \text{ in deg K. } C \text{ is called Sutherland's constant.}$$

Gas	Value of C	μ_0 at t° $\times 10^6$	t° C	Gas	Value of C	μ_0 at t° $\times 10^6$	t° C
Air..............	120	170.9	0	Hydrogen (average).	77.5	84.2	0
Ammonia.........	370	91.8	0	Krypton...........	188	232.7	0
Carbon dioxide....	240	137.0	0	Neon..............	56	297.3	0
Carbon monoxide..	118	166.0	0	Nitrogen...........	111	176.5	23°
Helium...........	70	187.3	0	Oxygen............	127	203.9	23°

Viscosity of Oils is often given in time of efflux through certain types of viscometers.

Kinematic Viscosity $\nu = \dfrac{\mu}{\rho}$ may be obtained from the time of efflux through various types of commercial viscometers by means of the equations:

Saybolt Universal: $\quad \dfrac{\mu}{\rho} = 2.20 \times 10^{-3}\, t - \dfrac{1.80}{t}$

Redwood: $\quad \dfrac{\mu}{\rho} = 2.60 \times 10^{-3}\, t - \dfrac{1.715}{t}$

Engler: $\quad \dfrac{\mu}{\rho} = 1.47 \times 10^{-3}\, t - \dfrac{3.74}{t}$

Redwood Admiralty: $\dfrac{\mu}{\rho} = 2.70 \times 10^{-3}\, t - \dfrac{20}{t}$

where
μ = absolute viscosity in poises
ρ = density in grams per cu cm
t = time of efflux in seconds
At room temperature.

To reduce to units of ft² per sec multiply the above by 1.076×10^{-3}.

7. SURFACE TENSION; CAPILLARY RISE

All numerical values were taken from the International Critical Tables. Surface tension γ is given in dynes per centimeter or pounds per foot. Capillary rise is given by

$$a^2 = hr = \frac{2\gamma}{(w_L - w_G)g}$$

where
h = height of capillary rise.
r = internal radius of capillary tube.
γ = surface tension.
w_L = weight density of liquid.
w_G = weight density of gas or vapor above liquid.

This formula holds strictly for cases where the angle of contact between liquid and glass is 0° and the meniscus may be considered hemispherical in shape. The angle of contact is 0° for many liquids. Examples: Water, ethyl alcohol, benzene, carbon tetrachloride, chloroform, acetic acid, aqueous solutions of various salts, glycerol, ethyl ether, turpentine, olive oil, and hydrogen peroxide.

Conversion Factor: γ (dyne/per centimeter) $\times 6.86 \times 10^{-5} = \gamma$ (poundals per foot).

Table XI. Surface Tension of Water at Various Temperatures

Air above water at ordinary pressure

t° C	γ (dyn/cm)	$a^2 = h\,r$ (cm²)	t° C	γ (dyn/cm)	$a^2 = h\,r$ (cm²)
−5	76.42 ± .20	0.1562	20	72.75 ± .05	0.1488
0	75.64 ± .10	.1545	25	71.97 ± .05	.1473
10	74.22 ± .05	.1516	30	71.18 ± .05	.1459
15	73.49 ± .05	.1501	50	67.91 ± .05	.1403

Table XII. Surface Tension of Ethyl and Methyl Alcohol

Ethyl Alcohol

$t°$ C	γ (dyn/cm) (air)	γ (dyn/cm) (vapor)	a^2 (air) (cm²)
0	24.05 ± .20	....	.....
10	23.14 ± .10	23.61 ± 0.30	.....
20	22.27 ± .10	22.75 ± 0.30	0.0576
30	21.43 ± .10	21.89 ± 0.30	.....
50	19.80 ± .20	20.14 ± 0.30	.....
70	18.22 ± .20	18.34 ± 0.30	.....
100	....	15.47 ± 0.20	.....

Methyl Alcohol

$t°$ C	γ (dyn/cm) (air)	a^2 (cm²) (air)
0	24.49 ± 0.20	.....
20	22.61 ± 0.10	0.0583
30	21.75 ± 0.10	.....
50	20.14 ± 0.20	.....
70	18.51 ± 0.20	.....
100	15.67 ± 0.20	.....

Table XIII. Surface Tension of Mercury

Space above Mercury	$t°$ C	γ (dyn/cm)	a^2 (cm²) (air)
Vacuum....................	0	475.0 (average)	0.0713 (average)
Vacuum....................	60	467.1 (average)	.0709 (average)
Air.......................	15	487.0	.0732
Hydrogen..................	20	466.0	.0702
Oxygen....................	15	487.0	.0732

Surface tension for mercury in contact with various gases is subject to variation with time. It generally decreases.

Table XIV. Surface Tension of Various Liquids at Ordinary Temperatures

Air above liquid

Liquid	$t°$ C	γ (dyn/cm)	Liquid	$t°$ C	γ (dyn/cm)
Acetone................	20	23.7	Distillates, petroleum....	20	19–29
Benzene................	20	28.9	Naphthas...............	20	19–23
Carbon tetrachloride.....	20	26.7	Kerosenes...............	20	23–32
Chloroform............	20	27.1	Gas oils................	20	28–29
Crude oils, light........	20	24–26	Lubricating oils.........	30	36–37.5
Crude oils, heavy........	20	35–38			

8. COMPRESSIBILITY OF LIQUIDS AND GASES

Numerical values in Tables XV to XIX taken from International Critical Tables.

Table XV. Compressibility of Water at Various Temperatures

Compressibility is expressed in terms of the modulus,

$$\beta = - \frac{v_1 (p_2 - p_1)}{(v_2 - v_1)}, \text{ where } p \text{ is in atmospheres}$$

$p_2 - p_1$ / $t°$ C	− 10°	0°	20°	$p_2 - p_1$ / $t°$ C	− 10°	0°	20°
500– 0	2.18×10^4	2.16×10^4	2.36×10^4	4000–3500	....	4.29×10^4	4.34×10^4
1000– 500	2.36×10^4	2.41×10^4	2.65×10^4	4500–4000	....	4.79×10^4	4.76×10^4
1500–1000	2.63×10^4	2.66×10^4	2.95×10^4	5000–4500	....	5.20×10^4	5.03×10^4
2000–1500	2.67×10^4	2.88×10^4	3.28×10^4	5500–5000	....	5.79×10^4	5.29×10^4
2500–2000	3.30×10^4	3.22×10^4	3.61×10^4	6000–5500	....	6.24×10^4	5.65×10^4
3000–2500	3.75×10^4	3.60×10^4	3.89×10^4	6500–6000	....	6.79×10^4	5.83×10^4
3500–3000	....	4.00×10^4	4.16×10^4				

Table XVI. Compressibility of Various Liquids in Terms of β at 20° C

Fluid	$(p_2 - p_1)$ (Atmospheres)	β	Fluid	$(p_2 - p_1)$ (Atmospheres)	β
Methyl alcohol.....	500– 1	12.0×10^3	Ethyl alcohol......	2000–1500	24.6×10^3
	1000– 500	15.5×10^3		2500–2000	28.3×10^3
	1500–1000	20.0×10^3	Carbon tetrachlo-		
	2000–1500	24.1×10^3	ride...........	97.7– .987	11.1×10^3
	2500–2000	28.6×10^3		197.4– 98.7	11.4×10^3
Ethyl alcohol......	500– 1	11.9×10^3		296.1–197.4	12.2×10^3
	1000– 500	16.1×10^3		394.8–296.1	13.5×10^3
	1500–1000	20.4×10^3		493.5–394.8	14.5×10^3

Table XVII. Kerosene and Lubricating Oils

Available data may be expressed by the equation:

$$\beta = (a + bp - cp^2 + dp^3) \times 10^6, \text{ where } \beta = \frac{v_0 p}{v_0 - v_p} \text{ is the mean coefficient between 0 and } p.$$

Kind of Oil	$t°$ C	$10^3 a$	$10^5 b$	$10^{12} c$	$10^{15} d$	Range, atmospheres
Kerosene...........,	20	13.05	4.206	135.9	3.687	0–12,000
Paraffin oil.........,	34	12.00	4.631	280.6	24.3	0– 4300
"Mobil A".........	40	17.4	4.30	0.0	0.0	0– 1400
"Bayonne"........	40	17.1	4.30	0.0	0.0	0– 1500

Table XVIII. Compressibility of Air

p in atmospheres, $v = 1.000$ at 0° C and one atmosphere

p (atmospheres)	p v		
	0° C	15.7° C	99.4° C
100	0.973	1.0389	1.403
150	0.984	1.0555	1.431
200	1.010	1.0855	1.467
250	1.049	1.126	1.511
300	1.0975	1.174	1.559
500	1.404	1.474	1.844
1000	1.992	2.060	2.415

Table XIX. Compressibility of Certain Gases at Various Temperatures

p in atmospheres, $v = 1.00$ at 0° C and one atmosphere

HYDROGEN

p (atmospheres)	p v		
	0° C	15.4° C	47.3° C
500	1.357	....	....
1000	1.726	1.778	1.893
1500	2.070	2.127	2.240
2000	2.389	2.445	2.561
2500	2.695	2.753	2.870

HELIUM

Range: 0 to 105 atmospheres

$t°$ C	$p v$
−50°	$pv = 0.81655 + 5.32 \times 10^{-4} p + 9.4 \times 10^{-8} p^2$
0°	$pv = 0.99945 + 5.29 \times 10^{-4} p$
50°	$pv = 1.18245 + 5.24 \times 10^{-4} p$

OXYGEN

Range: 0 to 100 atmospheres

$t°$ C	$p v$
0°	$pv = 1.001 - 9.94 \times 10^{-4} p + 2.19 \times 10^{-6} p^2$
20°	$pv = 1.07425 - 7.52 \times 10^{-4} p + 1.50 \times 10^{-6} p^2$
100°	$pv = 1.3674 - 1.60 \times 10^{-4} p + 1.37 \times 10^{-6} p^2$

The average compressibility modulus in an interval may be calculated from

$$\beta = -\frac{p_2 - p_1}{\dfrac{K_2 p_1}{K_1 p_2} - 1}$$

for a constant temperature.

FLUID STATICS

9. FLUID PRESSURE

It is a fact of common experience that, if a solid body be surrounded by a fluid, the surface areas of the solid body experience forces due to the presence of the fluid. If the fluid is in equilibrium the surface force on the solid body is perpendicular to the surface on which it acts and its direction is always from fluid to body. Since no tangential stresses exist in a fluid at rest there can be no component other than the normal component. This surface force per unit of area is called pressure. In engineering units it is most frequently convenient to express pressure in pounds per square foot.

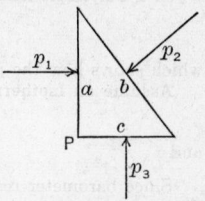

FIG. 1.   Fluid Pressures on a Triangular Prism

Consider a triangular prism (Fig. 1) whose end faces are triangles of sides a, b, and c; the length of the prism may be unity. To be in equilibrium the vector sum of the forces, $p_1 a$, $p_2 b$, $p_3 c$, due to the pressures on the faces of the prism, is zero and $p_1 = p_2 = p_3$. This does not depend on the size of the prism and if the prism shrinks in size so that b remains parallel to its original direction, the values of p_1, p_2, and p_3 remain equal. Therefore, *in a fluid in equilibrium the pressure at a point* P *is independent of the orientation of the surface element on which it acts.*

This statement is true for viscous as well as inviscid fluids, provided they are in equilibrium.

10. RELATION BETWEEN PRESSURE AND BODY FORCES

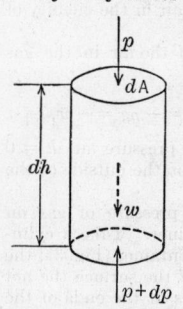

FIG. 2.   Static Fluid Forces on an Element of Fluid

By body forces are meant forces like gravitational forces. Consider a small fluid cylinder (Fig. 2) of weight density w immersed in a fluid having the same weight density. Let the height of the cylinder be dh and its cross-sectional area dA. If the axis is vertical then we have for equilibrium, if p and $p + dp$ are the pressures on the top and bottom faces,

$$w = \rho dh dA \cdot g = (p + dp - p)dA = dp dA \quad \text{or} \quad \frac{dp}{dh} = \rho g \quad (1)$$

11. APPLICATIONS OF EQUATION $\dfrac{dp}{dh} = \rho g$

Aerostatics

Temperature and Pressure, Variation with Altitude. This equation is used in aerostatics. Choose h positive when directed from the earth's surface upward. Then since pressure in the atmosphere diminishes as h increases,

$$-\frac{dp}{dh} = \rho g$$

Then
$$h - h_1 = \frac{1}{g} \int_p^{p_1} \frac{dp}{\rho} \quad (2)$$

where p corresponds to height h and p_1 to height h_1. Strictly g is not constant as h changes.

Actually $g \approx g_0 \left(\dfrac{1}{1 + \dfrac{h}{R_0}} \right)^2$ where g_0 = acceleration of gravity and R_0 = radius of the

earth. Since $\dfrac{h}{R_0}$ is usually small, $g \approx g_0 \left(1 - \dfrac{2h}{R_0} \right)$, then more accurately,

$$h - h_1 + \frac{h_1{}^2 - h^2}{R_0} = \frac{1}{g_0} \int_p^{p_1} \frac{dp}{\rho} \quad (3)$$

This introduces small errors and (2) is generally used. Using the ideal gas law $pv' = RT$, where $v' = \dfrac{v}{w} = \dfrac{1}{w}$ = specific volume in cubic feet per pound.

Hence $\dfrac{1}{\rho} = vg$ and we have,

$$h - h_i = R \int_p^{p_1} T \frac{dp}{p} \tag{4}$$

If the "polytropic law" $Pv^n = $ constant holds, then from (2) and the gas law,

$$h - h_1 = \frac{n}{n - 1} R\,(T_1 - T) \tag{5}$$

In a Polytropic Atmosphere the temperature is a linear function of the height. Also,

$$p = p_1 \left(1 - \frac{(n - 1)}{nRT_1}\,(h - h_1) \right)^{n/(n-1)} \tag{6}$$

which shows how the pressure varies with altitude.

Assume an Isothermal Atmosphere, then

$$T = T_0 = \text{constant}$$

and

$$h - h_1 = RT_0 \log_e \frac{p_1}{p} \tag{7}$$

Since barometer reading, b, is proportional to pressure,

$$h - h_1 = RT_0 \log_e \frac{b_1}{b} \tag{8}$$

Atmospheric Regions. Actually the atmosphere is separated into two regions. The lower part called the *troposphere* is about 35,000 feet high at our latitude. In the troposphere $n \approx 1.2$, which corresponds to a semihumid adiabatic atmosphere. Above the troposphere is the *stratosphere*, where the temperature is practically constant at $-67°$ F and $n = 1$.

Lift of Gas-filled Aircraft. Let $w_A = $ average weight density of the air in the vicinity of the balloon or aircraft.

$w_{c_1} = $ weight density of the air in the gas containers.

From the equation $\dfrac{dp}{dh} = -\rho g = -w$,

$p_A = p_o - w_A h$, $p_o = $ pressure at $h = 0$ and $P_A = $ pressure of air on the outside of the gas container.

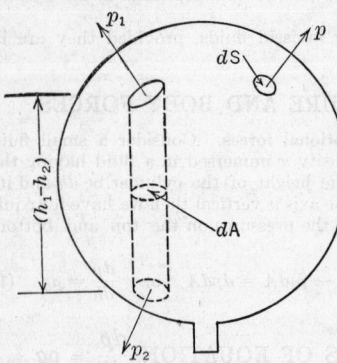

FIG. 3. Fluid Forces on a Gas Filled Container

$p_G = p_o - w_g h$, $p_G = $ pressure of gas on the inside of the gas container. Take a cylindrical element of the gas container (Fig. 3); the axis is vertical and its cross-sectional area is dA. At any point of the surface the net pressure $p = p_G - p_A = (w_A - w_G)h$. If p_1 and p_2 are net pressures at the ends of the cylindrical element, the lift,

$$\begin{aligned}
L &= \int\!\!\int_s (p_1 - p_2)dA \\
&= (w_A - w_G) \int\!\!\int\!\!\int_v (h_1 - h_2)dA \\
&= (w_A - w_G)V = (W_A - W_G)
\end{aligned} \tag{9}$$

$v = $ volume of the gas container; W_A and W_G are the weights of air displaced and the weight of the gas.

If the gas container is filled with non-homogeneous gas,

$$p = p_A h - \int_o^h w_G\,dh$$

Then $L = \displaystyle\int\!\!\int_s p\,ds = w_A v - \int\!\!\int\!\!\int_v w_G\,dv = W_A - W_G$ as before.

Effect of Temperature on Lift.

Using the gas law, $p = wRT$,

$$L = pv \left(\frac{1}{R_A T_A} - \frac{1}{R_G T_G} \right),\quad p = w_A R_A T_A = w_G R_G T_G$$

$$L = w_A v \left(1 - \frac{R_A T_A}{R_G T_G} \right) = W_A \left(1 - \frac{R_A T_A}{R_G T_G} \right) \tag{10}$$

Hydrostatics

Hydraulics. If the fluid is water, then p and w are constant

and
$$h - h_1 = \frac{1}{w}(p - p_1)$$

or
$$p = p_1 + w(h - h_1)$$

h is here regarded as positive when directed downward. There is no loss in generality in choosing $h_1 = 0$, so $p_1 =$ atmospheric pressure and

$$p = p_1 + wh \tag{11}$$

Suppose an irregular plane area A (Fig. 4) is submerged vertically in a liquid of weight density w. The total pressure on an element dA, parallel to the free surface, is

$$p = \int\int_A (p - p_1)\, dA = w \int\int_A h\, dA = w\bar{h}A \tag{12}$$

$h =$ distance of element dA from free surface.
$\bar{h} =$ distance of centroid of A from free surface.

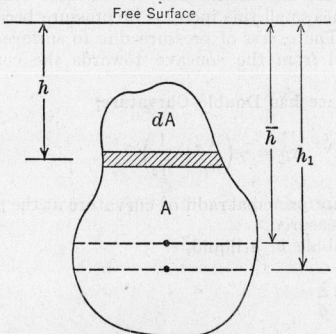

FIG. 4. Fluid Pressure on a Vertically Submerged Surface

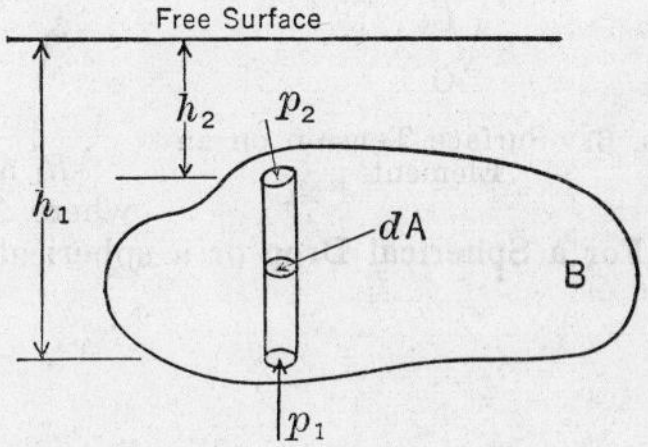

FIG. 5. Buoyant Forces on an Immersed Body

To find where the pressure acts,

$$ph_1 = \int\int_A (p - p_1)\, h\, dA = w \int\int_A h^2 dA = wI.$$

$h_1 =$ distance of center of pressure below free surface.
$I =$ moment of inertia of A about an axis in the free surface and plane of A.
$I = A\bar{h}^2 + \bar{I}$, $\bar{I} =$ moment of inertia of A about an axis through the centroid of A parallel to the axis in the free surface.

Then, $p\bar{h} + pa = wA\bar{h}^2 + w\bar{I} = p\bar{h} + w\bar{I}$

where
$$a = \frac{\bar{I}}{A\bar{h}}, \quad h_1 = \bar{h} + \frac{\bar{I}}{A\bar{h}} \tag{13}$$

Archimedes' Law. Consider a solid body, B (Fig. 5), submerged in a liquid. Divide the body into small cylindrical elements of cross-section dA and having their axis vertical. Let the ends of the cylinders be at distances h_1 and h_2 from the free surface of the liquid. The lift, L, experienced by the body, is

$$L = \int\int_A (p_1 - p_2)\, dA = \int\int\int_B w(h_1 - h_2)\, dA = wv \tag{14}$$

$r =$ volume of the body.
$w =$ weight density of the fluid.

This is *Archimedes' Law*: A body completely immersed in a fluid experiences a lift equal in magnitude to the weight of fluid displaced. This lift acts at the center of gravity of the displaced liquid.

Stability of a Completely Immersed Body:

(a) Stable if center of gravity of body is vertically below the center of gravity of displaced fluid.

(b) Unstable if the two centers of gravity are reversed as to position.

(c) Neutral if the two centers of gravity coincide as to position.

12. SURFACE TENSION AND PRESSURE

Theory.   Consider a curved free surface of a liquid (Fig. 6).   Suppose that the surface is a cylinder whose generators are perpendicular to the plane of the paper and that the height is unity.   The forces acting on a small element $AB \times 1 = ds \times 1$ are shown. Resolving normal to the surface, and letting θ become small, $\gamma\theta = \Delta pds$.   If R is radius of curvature at A,

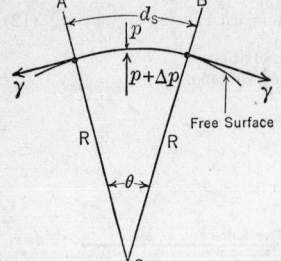

$$\Delta p = \frac{\gamma}{R} \qquad (15)$$

Δp = pressure increment due to surface tension. When R becomes small this increase in pressure becomes appreciable.   The excess of pressure due to surface tension is directed from the concave towards the convex side.

If the Surface has Double Curvature,

$$\Delta p = \gamma \left(\frac{1}{R_1} + \frac{1}{R_2} \right) \qquad (16)$$

Fig. 6.   Surface Tension on an Element

R_1 and R_2 are principal radii of curvature at the point where Δp is measured.

For a Spherical Drop or a spherical air bubble in a liquid,

$$\Delta p = \frac{\gamma}{d} \qquad (17)$$

d = diameter of the drop or bubble.

For a Spherical Soap Bubble, which has two surfaces,

$$\Delta p = \frac{2\gamma}{d} \qquad (18)$$

Rise in a Capillary Tube and Surface Tension. Observation shows that liquids meet solids at definite angles of contact.   Water, for instance, meets glass at a zero angle of contact. Inside a capillary tube (Fig. 7), the surface is sharply curved and the pressure increment due to the surface tension will cause the surface in the tube to rise to a height, h.   The pressure due to the head h must balance the pressure increment due to surface tension and the pressure at P is then atmospheric.

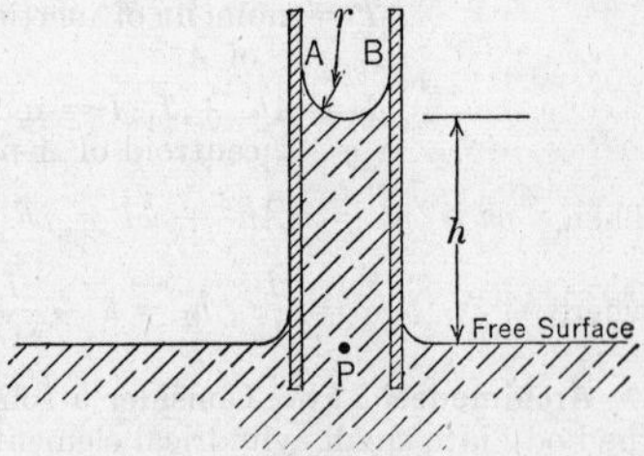

Then $\dfrac{2\gamma}{r} = wh$ (19) if it is assumed that the surface AB is hemispherical.

$$w = w_L - w_G$$

Fig. 7.   Rise in Capillary Tube Due to Surface Tension.

where w_L = weight density of the liquid and w_G = weight density of the gas above the liquid.

FLUID DYNAMICS

13. LAWS OF FLUID MOTION

Mathematical Statement. The general differential equations of fluid motion are known as the Navier-Stokes Equations.

$$\frac{\partial u}{\partial t} + u\,\frac{\partial u}{\partial x} + v\,\frac{\partial u}{\partial y} + w\,\frac{\partial u}{\partial z} = X - \frac{1}{\rho}\frac{\partial p}{\partial x} + \frac{\mu}{\rho}\left(\frac{\partial^2 u}{\partial x^2} + \frac{\partial^2 u}{\partial y^2} + \frac{\partial^2 u}{\partial z^2}\right)$$

$$\frac{\partial v}{\partial t} + u\,\frac{\partial v}{\partial x} + v\,\frac{\partial v}{\partial y} + w\,\frac{\partial v}{\partial z} = Y - \frac{1}{\rho}\frac{\partial p}{\partial y} + \frac{\mu}{\rho}\left(\frac{\partial^2 v}{\partial x^2} + \frac{\partial^2 v}{\partial y^2} + \frac{\partial^2 v}{\partial z^2}\right)$$

$$\frac{\partial w}{\partial t} + u\,\frac{\partial w}{\partial x} + v\,\frac{\partial w}{\partial y} + w\,\frac{\partial w}{\partial z} = Z - \frac{1}{\rho}\frac{\partial p}{\partial z} + \frac{\mu}{\rho}\left(\frac{\partial^2 w}{\partial x^2} + \frac{\partial^2 w}{\partial y^2} + \frac{\partial^2 w}{\partial z^2}\right)$$

u, v, w, are velocity components in x, y, and z directions of Cartesian coordinates, and X, Y, and Z are body forces per unit of volume in direction of coordinate axes, t is time, p is pressure per unit of area, ρ is mass density, and μ is the coefficient of viscosity.

No General Solutions of these equations have been found. There is therefore no general theoretical treatment of fluid motion. Special solutions are known for certain kinds of motion. Some of these will be indicated in the following sections.

Similarity Laws, Dimensional Analysis

In view of the difficulty of solving the general differential equations of fluid motion other methods are employed. One of the most helpful methods is that of applying dimensional analysis to obtain criteria for dynamically similar motions of fluids.

Dynamical Similarity. If the flows of two fluids around geometrically similar bodies are also geometrically similar then the two flows are dynamically similar if the corresponding fluid forces on the two bodies are proportional at any instant.

Inertia and Viscous Forces. In many important cases inertia and viscous forces are the only ones to be taken into account.

$$\frac{\text{Inertia force}}{\text{Viscous force}} = \frac{\rho VL}{\mu} = \frac{VL}{\nu} \tag{2}$$

L is a typical dimension of the body, V is velocity of the flow, ρ, μ and ν have been defined.

This number is called *Reynolds' number*, $\left[\dfrac{\rho VL}{\mu}\right] = [M^0 L^0 T^0]$; i.e., it is a dimensionless number. This means that its value is the same no matter what system of consistent units is used. When $\dfrac{\rho_1 V_1 L_1}{\mu_1} = \dfrac{\rho_2 V_2 L_2}{\mu_2}$ in two flows they are dynamically similar.

When Reynolds' number is large, inertia forces predominate in comparison with viscous forces. When it is small the reverse is true. Most problems in aerodynamics are concerned primarily with viscous and inertia forces.

Inertia and Gravity Forces Predominate.

$$\frac{\text{Inertia force}}{\text{Gravity force}} = \frac{V^2}{Lg} \tag{3}$$

L is a typical dimension, g is the acceleration of gravity, and V is the velocity of the flow.

$$\left[\frac{V^2}{Lg}\right] = [M^0 L^0 T^0]$$

it is also dimensionless and has the same value in any consistent set of units. This number is called *Froude's number*. When $\dfrac{V_1{}^2}{L_1 g} = \dfrac{V_2{}^2}{L_2 g}$ the motions are dynamically similar. This criterion of similarity occurs for motions of partly submerged bodies like surface ships and seaplanes.

Inertia Force and Compressibility Predominate.

$$\frac{\text{Inertia force}}{\text{Pressure force}} = \left(\frac{V}{V_c}\right)^2$$

V_c is the velocity of sound in the fluid at a given temperature, V is the velocity of the flow. $\left[\dfrac{V}{V_c}\right] = [M^0 L^0 T^0]$; it is dimensionless and has the same value in any consistent set of units. This number is called *Mach's number*.

This criterion of similarity is of importance in fluid motion where the velocity is comparable with the speed of sound in the given fluid.

Surface Tension and Inertia Predominate.

$$\frac{\text{Surface tension force}}{\text{Inertia force}} = \frac{\gamma}{\rho V^2 L} \tag{4}$$

where γ = surface tension in units of force per unit of length. $\dfrac{\gamma}{\rho V^2 L^2}$ is also dimensionless and has the same value in any consistent set of units. It is called *Weber's number*. This criterion is of importance in motions where the surface tension effects become appreciable.

It is not possible in general, in a practical sense, to satisfy the condition of similarity in flows where three or more of the types of forces mentioned occur. For example, we find that it is impossible to satisfy Reynolds' law and Froude's law simultaneously unless we use different fluids. The two fluids must be so chosen that

$$\frac{\nu_1}{\nu_2} = \left(\frac{V_1}{V_2}\right)^3 = \left(\frac{L_1}{L_2}\right)^{3/2}$$

Practically two fluids of sufficiently different ν and other suitable characteristics do not exist.

Dimensional Analysis. This method is mathematical but fairly simple. It is assumed that the fluid force is dependent on certain variables or quantities and the expression for the fluid force can then be found in terms of these assumed quantities by expressing each quantity in terms of certain fundamental quantities such as: mass, M; length, L; time, T. The expression for force obtained contains unknown functional combinations of one or more dimensionless combinations of the quantities upon which the force has been assumed to depend.

Example: Suppose the fluid force, F, depends on the mass (inertia), viscosity, velocity of flow, and upon the size of the body on which F acts. Since a comparison of geometrically similar bodies is to be made, a single quantity will determine the size.

Hence: $F = \phi(\rho,\ V,\ \mu,\ D) = \Sigma\rho^a V^b \mu^c D^e$

where F = fluid force.

           ρ = mass density of fluid.

           V = velocity of flow.

           μ = coefficient of viscosity.

           D = typical dimension of the body on which F acts.

           ϕ = function symbol.

Now $[F] = \left[\dfrac{ML}{T^2}\right]$; $[\rho] = \left[\dfrac{M}{L^3}\right]$; $[V] = \left[\dfrac{L}{T}\right]$; $[\mu] = \left[\dfrac{M}{LT}\right]$; $[D] = [L]$.

Then $[F] = \left[\Sigma \left(\dfrac{M}{L^3}\right)^a \left(\dfrac{L}{T}\right)^b \left(\dfrac{M}{LT}\right)^c L^e\right] = \left[\dfrac{ML}{T^2}\right]$

Each term of the summation must have the same dimensions in the fundamental quantities M, L, and T.

This leads to the equations:

$$a + c = 1$$
$$-3a + b - c + e = 1$$
$$b + c = 2$$

We can solve for three of the quantities in terms of the fourth. The choice is immaterial. For instance,

Hence $a = 1 - c;\ b = 2 - c;\ e = 2 - c$

          $F = \Sigma \rho^{(1-c)} V^{(2-c)} \mu^c D^{(2-c)}$

          $= \rho\ V^2 D^2 \Sigma \left(\dfrac{\rho V D}{\mu}\right)^{-c}$

          $= \rho\ V^2 D^2\ \psi \left(\dfrac{\rho V D}{\mu}\right)$

Then $\dfrac{F}{\rho V^2 D^2} = C_F = \psi \left(\dfrac{\rho V D}{\mu}\right)$

where C_F is a dimensionless number called the force coefficient. This coefficient varies for geometrically similar bodies tested at different speeds and in different fluids, but it varies according to a fixed law expressed by the function symbol.   That is, if many separate measurements of F were made by varying body size (but not shape), fluid, and fluid velocity a single curve $C_F \propto \rho \dfrac{VD}{\mu}$ would be found like the one shown in Fig. 1.

The form of this curve or the form of the ψ function cannot be determined by analysis except in special cases.   Experiments must be made to determine the curve.   If the choice of the variables upon which F depends has been correctly made the experimentally determined points fall on a single curve.   If the results do not fall on a single curve there has been an important omission in the choice of quantities upon which F was assumed to depend.   Once a single curve is obtained, however, the result may be used with confidence.   In this case the force would represent the fluid force on a body completely immersed in the fluid, and within fairly wide ranges C_F, the force coefficient, would apply to various fluids, speeds, and body size.   Shapes would always have to remain geometrically similar.

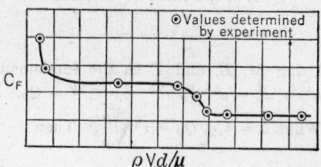

FIG. 1.   Typical Variation of Force Coefficient C_F

If the equations had been solved in the form:

$$a = b - 1; \quad c = 2 - b; \quad e = b$$

the expression for F would have been

$$F = \frac{\mu^2}{\rho}\, \psi'\!\left(\frac{\rho V D}{\mu}\right) \quad \text{and} \quad C_F = \psi'\!\left(\frac{\rho V D}{\mu}\right) = \frac{F}{\dfrac{\mu^2}{\rho}}$$

A different curve obtained by plotting C'_F against $\dfrac{\rho V D}{\mu}$ would now be obtained.

Since forces are to be proportional for dynamically similar motions the criterion obtained from the expression for F becomes

$$\frac{\rho_1 V_1 D_1}{\mu_1} = \frac{\rho_2 V_2 D_2}{\mu_2}$$

for flows around geometrically similar bodies.

Example: Suppose that the force F depends in addition to the quantities of the previous example upon the acceleration of gravity g; $[g] = \left[\dfrac{L}{T^2}\right]$

Then

$$F = \Sigma \rho^a V^b \mu^c D^e g^f$$
$$a = 1 - c; \quad b = 2 - c - 2f; \quad e = 2 - c + f$$

and

$$F = \rho V^2 D^2 f\!\left(\frac{\rho V D}{\mu},\; \frac{V^2}{Dg}\right)$$

The criteria for similarity of two flows about geometrically similar bodies are:

$$\frac{\rho_1 V_1 D_1}{\mu_1} = \frac{\rho_2 V_2 D_2}{\mu_2} \quad \text{and} \quad \frac{V_1^2}{D_1 g_1} = \frac{V_2^2}{D_2 g_2}$$

$C_F = \dfrac{F}{\rho V^2 D^2} = f\!\left(\dfrac{\rho V D}{\mu},\; \dfrac{V^2}{Dg}\right)$ would now be plotted as a surface with $\dfrac{\rho V D}{\mu}$, $\dfrac{V^2}{Dg}$, and C_F plotted along three axes.

Scale Effect.   If the expression for force is $F = C_F \rho V^2 D^2$ we may compute the force, F, from model tests by using

$$F = \frac{C_F}{C_{F_m}} F_m \left(\frac{\rho}{\rho_m}\right)\left(\frac{V}{V_m}\right)^2\left(\frac{D}{D_m}\right)^2$$

The subscript m refers to values obtained in the model tests.   If there is no scale effect the motions are dynamically similar and $C_F = C_{F_m}$.

General Rule for Determining Dynamical Similarity by Dimensional Analysis.   Let Q = quantity to be studied. Q may be a force, volume, or mass discharged in a given time, etc.   Let $q_1, q_2 \ldots q_n$ be the variables upon which Q is assumed to depend.

Rule: Form an expression in $q_1, q_2 \ldots q_n$ which has the dimensions of Q in $M, L,$ and T (or any other convenient set of fundamental quantities).   Divide Q by this expression to form the quantity coefficient, C_Q.   Next form all the *dimensionless combinations* of some or all of the quantities $q_1, q_2, \ldots q_n$ which can be made.   There are always $(n - m)$ of these dimensionless combinations, m denotes the number of fundamental quantities, i.e., if $M, L,$ and T are used $m = 3$.   Call these dimensionless combinations: $K_1, K_2 \ldots K_{n-m}$.

Then

$$C_Q = \phi(K_1, K_2 \ldots K_{n-m}) \tag{5}$$

where ϕ is a functional symbol and the nature of the function must be determined by experiment.   For dynamically similar motions $K'_1 = K''_1, \; K'_2 = K''_2, \ldots K'_{n-m} =$

K''_{n-m}, the primes representing values of the K's for flows around geometrically similar bodies.

Example: Let us find the expression for the volume of flow per second, Q, through a thin orifice of radius r, the pressure causing the flow being p. Let the fluid be viscous and incompressible. The variables on which Q depends are: p, ρ, r, and μ.

(a) a, b, c, d must be determined so that

$$[\rho^a p^b r^c \mu^d] = \left[\frac{L^3}{T}\right]$$

Using M, L, and T as the fundamental quantities $a = b - 1$, $c = 2b - 2$, $d = 1 - 2b$, then $\rho^a p^b r^c \mu^d = \rho^{b-1} p^b r^{2b-2} \mu^{1-2b} = Q_0$. For any value of b this expression has the dimension of Q. When $b = 1/2$, $Q_0 = r^2 \sqrt{\dfrac{p}{\rho}}$. Then

$$C_Q = \frac{Q}{r^2 \sqrt{\dfrac{p}{\rho}}}$$

(b) Since $n = 4$ and $m = 3$ there is one dimensionless combination, K of the quantities ρ, p, r, and μ. This is readily found as $\dfrac{r\sqrt{\rho p}}{\mu}$. Hence

$$C_Q = \frac{Q}{r^2 \sqrt{\dfrac{p}{\rho}}} = \psi \left(\frac{r\sqrt{\rho p}}{\mu}\right)$$

The criterion of similarity for flows through thin orifices made in the same manner (i.e., geometrically similar orifices) is $\dfrac{r\sqrt{\rho p}}{\mu} = $ constant.

14. DYNAMICS OF IDEAL FLUIDS

Although Ideal, i.e., Non-viscous, Incompressible Fluids do not exist in nature, many motions of real fluids resemble ideal fluid motions, wholly or partially, so closely that much may be learned by studying ideal fluid flows. This has been found to hold more and more in recent times when considerably more attention has been devoted to surface and shape refinements than formerly. It has been true especially in aeronautics.

This part of the subject has been known as classical hydrodynamics. Much material exists on this phase of the subject. Only a few of the more important parts will be mentioned.

Two-dimensional Flow of Ideal Fluids

This is usually restricted to steady flow, i.e., a flow in which the stream lines or particle paths do not change with time. Two-dimensional flow or motion is in a system of parallel planes the velocity having the same magnitude and direction at all points of a perpendicular to the set of planes.

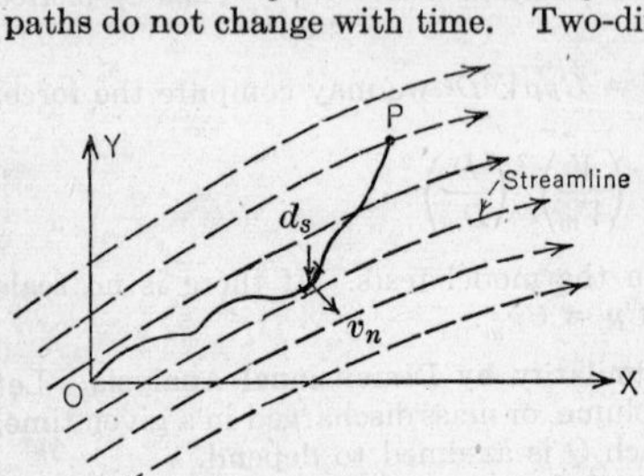

Take a set of rectangular axes (Fig. 2), OX, OY, and draw a line (continuous) from O to a point P. Consider a lamina one unit thick perpendicular to this plane as the region in which the flow is studied. The line OP is then the trace of a cylindrical surface whose generators are perpendicular to the XY plane. The volume of flow per unit time, called the flux, across the surface OP is $\int_0^P v_n ds$, where $v_n = $ flow velocity component perpendicular to OP

FIG. 2. Steady Flow of Ideal Fluid in Two Dimensions

at any point in the element ds of OP. In treatises on theoretical dynamics of fluid mechanics the following is proved.

(a) $\psi = \displaystyle\int_0^P v_n ds$ depends only on the *location* of P and not on the *shape* of the surface OP.

(b) $\psi = $ constant along a stream line. ψ is therefore called the *stream function*. The shape of stream lines for flows of ideal fluids may then be found mathematically.

(c) $u = \dfrac{\partial \psi}{\partial y}$, $v = -\dfrac{\partial \psi}{\partial x}$, where u, v are x, y components of the velocity vector.

Magnitude of velocity vector $= |q| = \sqrt{u^2 + v^2} = \sqrt{\left(\dfrac{\partial \psi}{\partial y}\right)^2 + \left(\dfrac{\partial \psi}{\partial x}\right)^2}$

Slope of velocity vector $= \dfrac{v}{u} = -\dfrac{\partial \psi / \partial x}{\partial \psi / \partial y}$

Points at which $q = 0$ are called stagnation points of the flow.

(d) $\phi = \displaystyle\int_0^P v_s ds$ is called the *velocity potential* of the flow where v_s is the flow velocity component parallel to OP at any point on the element ds.

(e) $u = \dfrac{\partial \phi}{\partial x}$, $v = \dfrac{\partial \phi}{\partial y}$, $|q| = \sqrt{\left(\dfrac{\partial \phi}{\partial x}\right)^2 + \left(\dfrac{\partial \phi}{\partial x}\right)^2}$, $\dfrac{v}{u} = \dfrac{\partial \phi / \partial y}{\partial \phi / \partial x}$

Circulation $= \displaystyle\oint v_s ds$ (Fig. 3)

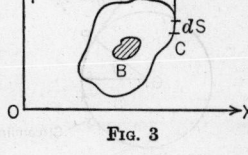

Circulation around a circuit enclosing fluid only is zero.
Circulation around a body B (once completely around the body) has a constant value Γ. Circulation around a small element is $2\omega \, dA$, where dA is area of element and ω is its angular velocity.

(f) **Equation of Continuity:**

$$\frac{\partial u}{\partial x} + \frac{\partial y}{\partial v} = 0$$

FIG. 3

(g) **Bernoulli's Equation:**

$p + {}^1/_2 \rho q^2 + \rho V = $ constant along a stream line.
$p = $ fluid pressure at any point along the stream line.
$q = $ fluid velocity at any point along the stream line.
$\rho = $ mass density of fluid.
$V = $ potential energy of unit mass of fluid at point along the stream line where pressure and velocity are p and q respectively.

Each term in the Bernoulli equation is a pressure. p is usually called the static pressure.
${}^1/_2 \rho q^2$ is the dynamic or velocity pressure.
ρV is the "difference of level" pressure.
The equation is frequently written

$$\frac{p}{\rho g} + \frac{q^2}{2g} + Z = \text{constant}$$

Each term is now a "head"; $\dfrac{p}{\rho g}$ is the static pressure head, $\dfrac{q^2}{2g}$ is the velocity head, and Z is the "difference of level" head.

(h) $\mathfrak{Z} = \dfrac{\partial v}{\partial x} - \dfrac{\partial u}{\partial y} = \dfrac{\partial^2 \psi}{\partial x^2} + \dfrac{\partial^2 \psi}{\partial y^2} = $ twice the average angular velocity of the fluid at a point in the flow. When $\mathfrak{Z} = 0$ the flow is irrotational.

(i) If ψ_1 and ψ_2 are stream functions of irrotational flows, then $\psi = \psi_1 + \psi_2$ is also an irrotational flow. This is called the *principle of superposition of flows*. It may be stated in analogous fashion using the velocity potential.

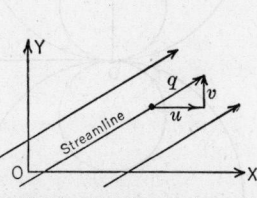

FIG. 4. Rectilinear Flow

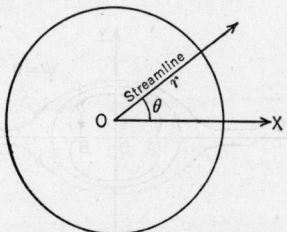

FIG. 5. Source (Sink) Flow

(j) Fundamental Flows Whose Stream Functions and Velocity Potentials Are Known:

Stream Function	*Velocity Potential*

Rectilinear Flow (Fig. 4)

$$\psi = -\,Vx + Uy \qquad\qquad \phi = Ux + Vy$$

Source and Sink Flow (Fig. 5)

$$\psi = +\,\frac{m}{2\pi}\,\theta \text{ (source)} \qquad\qquad \phi = \frac{m}{2\pi}\,\log r$$

$$\psi = -\,\frac{m}{2\pi}\,\theta \text{ (sink)} \qquad\qquad \phi = -\,\frac{m}{2\pi}\,\log r$$

m is the volume of flow from the source O in unit time.   It is called the strength of the source.

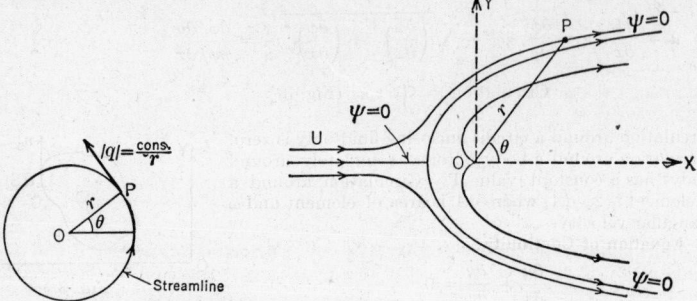

FIG. 6.   Vortex or Circulating Flow   FIG. 7.   Source in a Uniform Stream

Stream Function	*Velocity Potential*

Vortex or Circulating Flow (Fig. 6)

$$\psi = -\,\frac{\Gamma}{2\pi}\,\log r \qquad\qquad \phi = \frac{\Gamma}{2\pi}\,\theta$$

This flow is the only flow of an ideal fluid, whose stream lines are concentric circles, which is consistent with Bernoulli's law and the Newtonian laws of dynamics.

(k) Most Frequently Used Flows Obtained by Superposition of Fundamental Flows:

Source in a Uniform (Rectilinear) Flow (Fig. 7)

Stream Function: $\qquad\qquad \psi = +\,Uy + \dfrac{m\theta}{2\pi}$

$$\psi = +\,U r \sin \theta + \frac{m\theta}{2\pi}$$

The flow is separated by the $\psi = 0$ stream line as though $\psi = 0$ were a physical barrier. m is the source strength.
U is the velocity of uniform stream (parallel to X axis).

Source and Sink in a Uniform Stream (Fig. 8)

Stream Function: $\qquad \psi = -\,Uy + \dfrac{m}{2\pi}\tan^{-1}\left(\dfrac{2ys}{x^2 + y^2 - s^2}\right)$

U is the velocity of the uniform stream (parallel to X axis).
m is the strength of the source and sink. Source located at B and sink at A.
$AB = 2s$ Doublet Flow (Fig. 9)

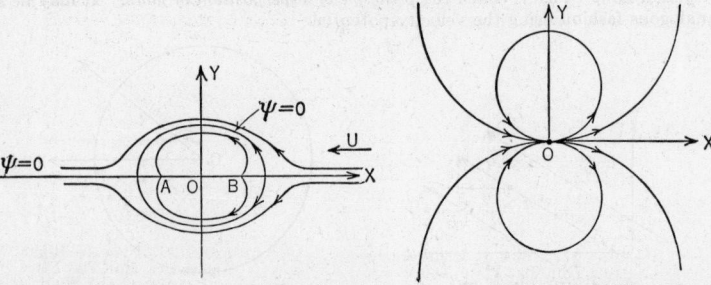

FIG. 8.   Source and Sink in a Uniform Stream   FIG. 9.   Doublet

Stream Function:
$$\psi = \frac{ms}{\pi}\left(\frac{y}{x^2+y^2}\right) = \frac{K}{\pi}\left(\frac{y}{x^2+y^2}\right)$$

A doublet is formed by letting a source and sink approach juxtaposition so that *ms* remains constant in value. K = strength of doublet.

Two-dimensional Flow around a Circular Cylinder (Fig. 10)

Stream Function:
$$\psi = -Uy + \frac{K}{\pi}\left(\frac{y}{x^2+y^2}\right)$$

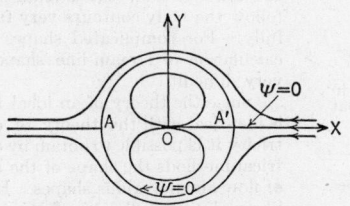

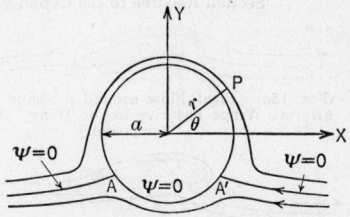

Fig. 10. Flow around a Circular Cylinder

Fig. 11. Flow around a Circular Cylinder with Circulating Flow

Flow is obtained by superposing the flow due to a doublet of strength K and a uniform rectilinear flow of velocity U parallel to the X axis. $\psi = 0$ stream line consists of X axis and a circle of radius $a = \sqrt{\frac{K}{\pi U}}$ with center at the origin, O. The stream lines outside this circle determine the flow patterns of an ideal flow around a circular cylinder. A and A' are stagnation points of the flow.

Two-dimensional Flow around a Cylinder with Circulation (Fig. 11)

Stream Function:
$$\psi = -U\left(r - \frac{a^2}{r}\right)\sin\theta - \frac{\Gamma}{2\pi}\log r$$

U is the velocity of uniform flow parallel to X axis. This is the flow velocity at points where the flow is unaffected by the presence of the cylinder.

a is the radius of the cylinder.

Γ is the strength of the circulating flow.

A and A' are stagnation points of the flow; their positions depend on the ratio $\dfrac{\Gamma}{aU}$

(1) Flows Obtained by Using Complex Numbers. If $Z = x + iy$, $i = \sqrt{-1}$ is a vector representing points in a plane, and ϕ and ψ are real and imaginary parts of a complex function $w = \phi + i\psi$, then this function with certain mathematical restrictions represents a possible irrotational flow of an ideal fluid. ϕ and ψ are the velocity potential and stream function respectively of this flow. The "velocity vector" $q' = \dfrac{dw}{dz} = u - iv$; from this the actual velocity vector q may be easily derived. By using the method of conformal transformation, shapes of various kinds and the flow patterns about such shapes may be distorted so that flows about a large number of shapes have been found.

Examples: Flow at right angles to a thin flat plate relative to the flat plate. (Fig. 12). Flow at right angles to a thin flat plate relative to the fluid (Fig. 13).

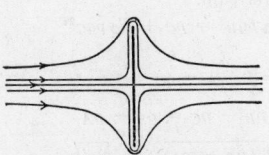

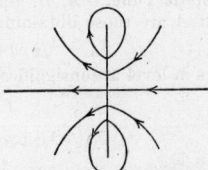

Fig. 12. Flow at Right Angles to a Thin Flat Plate Relative to the Flat Plate

Fig. 13. Flow at Right Angles to a Thin Flat Plate Relative to the Fluid

Flow around a cylinder of arbitrary cross-section relative to the cylinder (Fig. 14).

Ideal flow around a shape used in aircraft wings relative to the wing (Fig. 15a). Without circulation.

Ideal flow around a wing shape relative to the wing, circulating flow added (Fig. 15b).

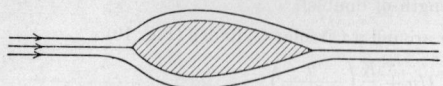

FIG. 14. Flow around a Cylinder of Arbitrary Cross Section Relative to the Cylinder

FIG. 15a. Ideal Flow around a Shape Used in Aircraft Wings Relative to the Wing. Without Circulation

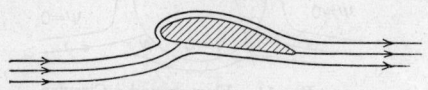

FIG. 15b. Ideal Flow around a Wing Shape Relative to the Wing. Circulating Flow Added

(m) General Form of Flow of an Ideal Fluid. From the forms of flows shown it may be seen that such flows have well-defined characteristics, the outstanding one being that, near the surface of a body in the fluid stream, the stream lines follow the body contours very faithfully. For complicated shapes the calculation of stream-line shapes is very difficult.

Since the theory of an ideal fluid is identical with the theory of electricity it is possible to obtain by electrical methods the shape of the lines of flow about various shapes. Hele-Shaw also used glycerin flowing between two parallel sheets of glass to show the form of two dimensional stream lines about variously shaped bodies. Any fluid motion of a viscous fluid at low velocities is like that of an ideal fluid in appearance.

15. APPLICATIONS OF RESULTS USING AN IDEAL FLUID

Bernoulli's Theorem

Flow through an Orifice in the Side of a Tank of Liquid. Assume that A and B (Fig. 16) are points on a stream line, A being in the surface of the liquid and B in the emerging jet.

$$p_A + \frac{1}{2}\rho q_A^2 = p_B + \frac{1}{2}\rho q_B^2 + gh\rho$$
$$p_A = p_B; \quad q_A = 0$$
$$\therefore q_b = \sqrt{2gh} \text{ (Toricelli's theorem)} \tag{6}$$

This formula is used as the fundamental formula for flows where friction is actually present.

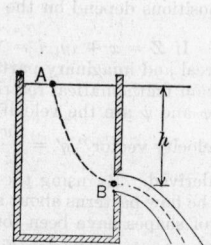

FIG. 16. Flow through an Orifice

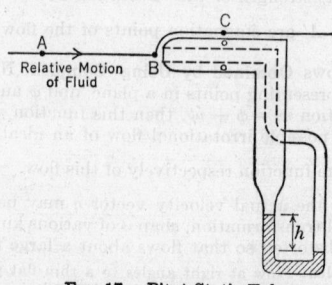

FIG. 17. Pitot-Static Tube

Pitot-Static Tube. A, B, and C (Fig. 17) are points in a stream line. Velocity and pressure at A are those obtaining in the fluid stream.

$$p_A + \frac{1}{2}\rho q_A^2 = p_B + \frac{1}{2}\rho q_B^2 = p_C + \frac{1}{2}\rho q_C^2$$

Differences in level are insignificant.

$$p_A = p_C, \quad q_B = 0, \quad q_A = q_C$$
$$\therefore \frac{1}{2}\rho q_C^2 = \frac{\rho}{2} q_A^2 = p_B - p_C = p_B - p_A \tag{7}$$
$$q_C = q_A = \sqrt{\frac{2(p_B - p_A)}{\rho}} = \sqrt{\frac{2\rho' h}{\rho}}$$

where ρ' = mass density of the manometer fluid.

With proper proportions of this instrument the formula obtained furnishes very accurate estimation of fluid velocity over wide ranges of velocities and fluids.

Flow through a Venturi Tube.   Take a stream line close to the wall of the tube (Fig. 18).

$$p_1 + \tfrac{1}{2}\,\rho q_1{}^2 = p_2 + \tfrac{1}{2}\,\rho q_2{}^2 = p_3 + \tfrac{1}{2}\,\rho q_2{}^2$$

Differences in level are insignificant.

$$p_1 - p_2 = \tfrac{1}{2}\,\rho(q_2{}^2 - q_1{}^2) = \tfrac{1}{2}\,\frac{m}{\rho}\left(\frac{1}{A_2{}^2} - \frac{1}{A_1{}^2}\right) \tag{8}$$

m is the mass of flow per unit of time; A_1 and A_2 are cross-sectional areas at (1) and (2). This formula is very reliable in actual flows for proper design.

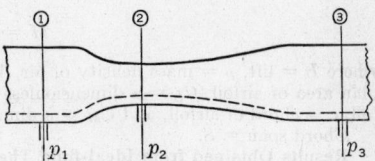

FIG. 18.   Flow through a Venturi

Lift of an Airfoil.   An airfoil is a body whose shape is such as to make it suitable for use in aircraft.   According to Lanchester, lift of airfoils arises from the superposition of a circulating flow and the ideal flow around the airfoil.   Although this circulating flow has its origin in the viscosity of the fluid, results obtained by using the ideal-flow formulas are very useful.

On stream line AB (Fig. 19),

$$p_A + \tfrac{1}{2}\,\rho q_A{}^2 = p_B + \tfrac{1}{2}\,\rho(q_B + q_{B_C})^2$$

where q_{B_C} = velocity of circulating flow at B.

Then

$$p_B = p_A + \tfrac{1}{2}\,\rho\,[q_A{}^2 - (q_B + q_{B_C})^2] \tag{9}$$

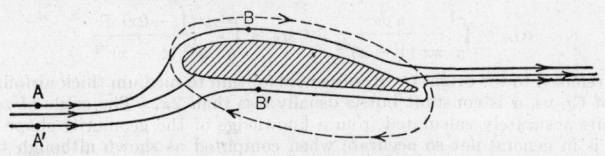

FIG. 19.   Circulation and Lift

This pressure is less than the pressure at B when $q_{B_C} = 0$, i.e., when there is no circulation.   Over the upper surface there is then a diminution in pressure with circulation present.

Similarly along $A'B'$, $p_{B'} = p_{A'} + \tfrac{1}{2}\,\rho\,[q_A{}'^2 - (q_{B'} - q_{B'_{C'}})^2] \tag{10}$

This pressure is greater than the pressure at B' when $q_{B'_{C'}} = 0$.   Over the lower surface there is then an increase in pressure with circulation present.   With such a diminution in pressure above the airfoil and increase in pressure below the airfoil there must be a lift.

When the actual calculation of pressure variation over the surface is made, using the potential functions of the flow and Bernoulli's theorem, the *Kutta-Joukowski theorem* of lift is obtained.

$$L = \rho V \Gamma \tag{11}$$

which is the lift per unit of span of the airfoil.

ρ = mass density of fluid.
V = velocity of flow.
Γ = strength of circulation of circulating flow.

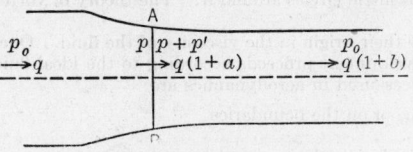

FIG. 20.   Flow through a Propeller

Velocity Increase Due to an Airplane Propeller.   If AB is the plane of the propeller disk (Fig. 20), then for flow in front of the disk,

$$p_o + \tfrac{1}{2}\,\rho q^2 = p + \tfrac{1}{2}\,\rho q^2(1 + a)^2 \tag{12a}$$

Behind the disk

$$p + p' + \tfrac{1}{2}\,\rho q^2(1 + a)^2 = p_o + \tfrac{1}{2}\,\rho q^2(1 + b)^2 \tag{12b}$$

This leads to $a = \dfrac{b}{2}$.   This shows that the gain in speed is due partly to the increase in speed ahead of the propeller and partly to the increase behind the propeller.

Applications of Ideal-fluid Theory in Aerodynamics

This part of modern fluid mechanics is replete with applications of ideal-fluid theory. The chief reason for this will appear later. It is due partly to the fact that shapes are carefully selected, that air has comparatively small viscosity, and that compressibility has no appreciable effect until very high speeds occur.

Lift and Moment of Airfoils in Two-dimensional Flow. Dimensional analysis shows that the lift and moment of an airfoil are given in the forms:

$$L = C_L \, \rho \, \frac{SV^2}{2} \tag{13a}$$

$$M = C_M \, \rho \, \frac{SV^2}{2} \tag{13b}$$

where L = lift, ρ = mass density of air, V = velocity of air relative to the airfoil, S = plan area of airfoil, C_L = a dimensionless lift coefficient, M = moment of forces on airfoil, c = chord of airfoil, and C_M = a dimensionless moment coefficient.

Chord span = S.

Results Obtained from Ideal-fluid Theory:

$$C_L = 2\pi(\alpha + \alpha_{L0}) \tag{14a}$$

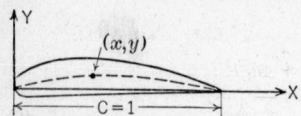

Fig. 21. Airfoil Shape

where α = angular inclination of airfoil to relative wind. This angle is called the angle of attack; α_{L0} = angle of attack for zero lift.

$C_M = C_{M0} - {}^1\!/_4 \, C_L$; C_{M0} = moment coefficient at zero lift.

If (x, y) is a point (Fig. 21) on the mean line of an airfoil, i.e., half way between upper and lower surface,

$$\alpha_{L0} = \int_0^1 \frac{y \, dx}{\pi x \, (1-x)^{3/2}} ; \quad C_{M0} = \int_0^1 \frac{y \, (1-2x) \, dx}{x^{1/2} \, (1-x)^{1/2}} \tag{14b}$$

C_{M0} is referred to the origin O. Results hold for thin to medium thick airfoils. Actually the slope of C_L vs. α is constant but is usually less than 2π. The angle of zero lift α_{L0} may be quite accurately calculated from a knowledge of the geometric shape of the airfoil. C_{M0} is in general not so accurate when computed as shown although the type of variation indicated above is usually observed in experimental work.

If the mean line of an airfoil of chord c has a form given by

$$\frac{y}{c} = h \, \frac{x}{c} \left(1 - \frac{x}{c}\right) \left(1 - \lambda \, \frac{x}{c}\right) \tag{15}$$

then

$$\alpha_{L0} = \frac{h}{4} \, (4 - 3\lambda); \quad C_{M0} = \frac{\pi h}{64} \, (7\lambda - 8) \tag{16}$$

h is a thickness parameter. This result called attention to the possibility of designing airfoils with very small center of pressure travel.

Airfoils in Three-dimensional Flow. The flow around an airfoil of finite span is best described by using vortices or vortex lines. A vortex line is a line whose direction at any point coincides with the rotation vector at that point. The motion, in planes at right angles to the vortex line, is along concentric circles around it. The theory of vortex lines is due principally to Helmholtz.

Physically vortex lines or vortices have their origin in the viscosity of the fluid. Once this origin has been accounted for, the development proceeds according to the ideal-fluid theory. The principal properties of vortices used in aerodynamics are:

(i) A vortex begins or ends on the surface or on the boundaries of the fluid.

(ii) The circulation around a circuit enclosing the vortex is constant at all points of the vortex.

(iii) Vortex lines as used in aerodynamics are usually straight lines. The velocity induced by a vortex line of this character is calculated from

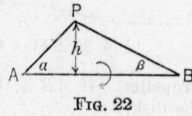

Fig. 22

$$q_P = \frac{\Gamma}{4\pi h} \, (\cos \alpha + \cos \beta) \ \ (\text{Fig. 22}) \tag{17}$$

Γ is the circulation around a circuit, it is called the strength of the vortex. q_P is at right angles to the plane PAB and in a sense depending on the direction of rotation around the core of the vortex.

The vortex system which describes most accurately three-dimensional characteristics of airfoils is shown by Fig. 23.

The airfoil or wing is replaced by a vortex segment AB, called the lifting line, which produces the necessary lift when combined with the flow due to the translation of the airfoil.

Trailing aft is a continuous sheet of vortices in the plane of the relative wind. This sheet has its origin in the pressure distribution around the airfoil and the influence of the

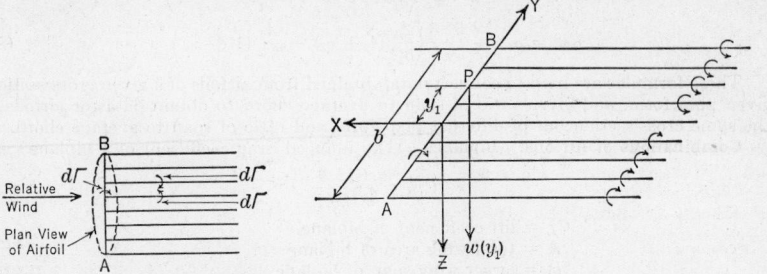

FIG. 23. Vortex System of Airfoil   FIG. 24. Induced Velocity of an Airfoil

pressure distribution on the flow. This plane sheet of vortices is actually unstable and rolls up into two twisted ribbon-like strands trailing aft approximately from points A and B. Principal effects are quite correctly represented by the continuous sheet, however, and the mathematics is much simpler.

The principal effect of the vortex system is to add a downward velocity at all points of the span AB. This downward velocity called the *induced velocity* modifies the flow as compared with the flow around an airfoil of similar cross section but of infinite span. This induced velocity is calculated from

$$w(y_1) = \frac{1}{4\pi}\int_{-b/2}^{b/2}\frac{\frac{d\Gamma}{dy}\,dy}{y_1 - y} \quad (18)$$

where $w(y_1)$ is the induced velocity at a point $P(0, y_1, 0)$ on the lifting line AB; b is the span of the airfoil (Fig. 24).

The addition of this induced velocity modifies the flow as shown (Fig. 25).

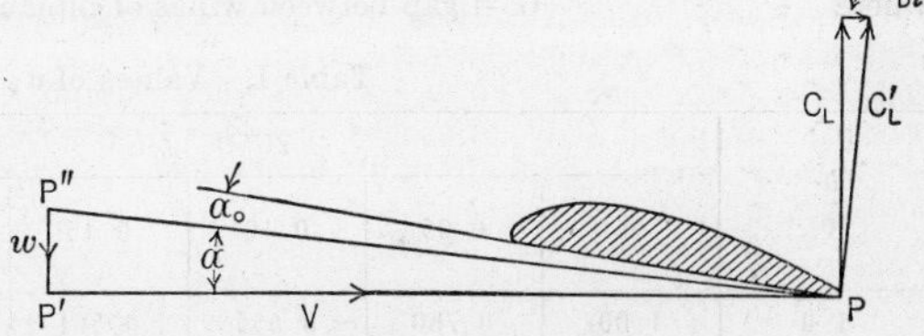

FIG. 25. Induced Drag of an Airfoil

As air approaches the airfoil of finite span the downward effect of the vortex system bends this air flow downwards so that at the wing the direction is $P''P$ as compared with $P'P$ in a two-dimensional flow around an airfoil of the same cross-section. The lift vector, varying as C_L, is tilted backwards by the angle $\frac{\omega}{V}$ radians (ω is generally small) to a new position C'_L. Since lift is measured at right angles to the relative wind V, the effect of the vortex system is represented as a component C_{Di} in what is generally considered the drag direction of the airfoil, i.e., parallel to V. The effective angle of attack is then changed from α (two-dimensional flow) to α_0 (three-dimensional flow), and $\alpha_0 = \alpha - \frac{\omega}{V}$

(radians). Also $C_{Di} = \frac{\omega}{V} C_L$. C_{Di} is called the induced drag coefficient and is given by $C_{Di} = \dfrac{Di}{\frac{\rho}{2} A V^2}$, where Di is the induced drag.

ρ and V are the same as before, and A the area of the wing.

C_{Di} and α_0 have been calculated by Glauert in the form

$$C_{Di} = \frac{C_L^2 A}{\pi b^2}(1 + \delta) \qquad (19)$$

$$\alpha_0 = \frac{C_L A}{\pi b^2}(1 + \tau) \qquad (20)$$

δ and τ depend on the variation of the circulation Γ, i.e., on the variation of load along the span. If the span loading varies as the semi-ordinates of an ellipse along the span, with the greatest ordinate at the center, δ and τ are zero. This corresponds to the ideal airfoil plan shape to produce minimum induced drag. The parameters δ and τ may be calculated for various types of airfoils.

These formulas lead to:

$$C_{D2} = C_{D1} + \frac{C_L^2}{\pi}\left(\frac{A_2}{b_2^2}(1 + \delta_2) - \frac{A_1}{b_1^2}(1 + \delta_1)\right) \tag{21}$$

$$\alpha_2{}^\circ = \alpha_1{}^\circ + \frac{57.3}{\pi}\left(\frac{A_2}{b_2^2}(1 + \tau_2) - \frac{A_1}{b_1^2}(1 + \tau_1)\right)^0 \tag{22}$$

These formulas are used to convert data obtained from airfoils of a given cross-section, given plan form, and given ratio of span to average chord to obtain data for airfoils of the same cross-section but of different plan form and ratio of span to average chord.

Combinations of Airfoils. Biplanes. The induced drag coefficient of a biplane

$$C_{Di} = \frac{C_L^2 A}{\pi (kb_1)^2} \tag{23}$$

C_L = lift coefficient of biplane.

A = total wing area of biplane.

b_1 = larger wing span of biplane.

$k = \sqrt{\dfrac{\mu^2(1 + \eta)^2}{\mu^2 + 2\sigma\mu\eta + \eta^2}}$ = Munk's span factor.

$\mu = \dfrac{b_2}{b_1}$ = ratio of spans of wings of biplane.

$\eta = \dfrac{L_2}{L_1}$ = ratio of lifts of wings of biplane.

σ = an interference factor = $f\left(\dfrac{b_1}{b_2}, \dfrac{2G}{b_1 + b_2}\right)$,

where G = gap between wings of biplane.

Table I. Values of σ

$\dfrac{b_1}{b_2}$	\multicolumn{7}{c}{$2G/(b_1 + b_2)$}						
	0	0.05	0.10	0.15	0.20	0.30	0.40
1.0	1.00	0.780	0.655	0.561	0.485	0.370	0.290
0.8	0.80	0.690	0.600	0.523	0.459	0.355	0.282
0.6	0.60	0.540	0.485	0.437	0.394	0.315	0.255

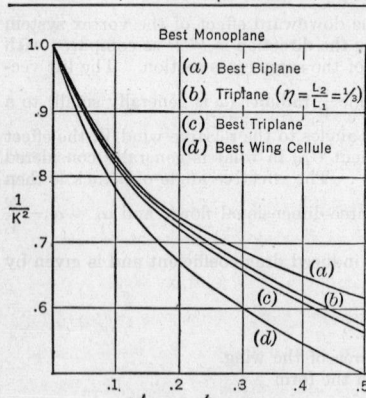

(a) Best Biplane
(b) Triplane ($\eta = \frac{L_2}{L_1} = \frac{1}{3}$)
(c) Best Triplane
(d) Best Wing Cellule

Best Monoplane

$\dfrac{1}{K^2}$

G/b_1 = gap/largest span

FIG. 26. Reciprocal of Munk Span Factor for Various Wing Arrangements

The induced drag or resistance is

$$D_i = \frac{2 L^2}{\pi \rho A V^2 (kb_1)^2} \tag{24}$$

$L = L_1 + L_2$ = total lift

The minimum drag of a biplane is

$$D_{i \min} = \frac{2L^2}{\pi \rho A V^2}\left(\frac{1 - \sigma^2}{1 - 2\sigma\mu + \mu^2}\right)$$

for a given μ and σ (25)

A biplane with equal wings ($\mu = 1$) has the least induced drag of any biplane when

$$\eta = \frac{L_2}{L_1} = 1 \text{ and}$$

$$D_{i \min} = \frac{2 L^2}{\pi \rho A V^2}\left(\frac{1 + \sigma}{2}\right) \tag{26}$$

The induced drag of multiplanes may also be calculated. The curve shown exhibits the principal properties of the induced drag of a triplane as compared with a monoplane and biplane (Fig. 26).

To be observed is that the induced drag is chiefly important at higher angles of attack.

16. DYNAMICS OF VISCOUS INCOMPRESSIBLE FLUIDS—
GENERAL DISCUSSION

This phase of the subject includes the most important parts of hydraulics and aerodynamics as well as other important phases of modern engineering.

Flow of Viscous Incompressible Fluids

It is not possible to calculate the flow lines for viscous fluids in general. When the motion is slow and the viscous effects predominate, the motion is practically identical with that of ideal fluids. For many fluids, particularly for air and gases, this resemblance is true only for exceedingly slow velocities.

It will be shown later that the effect of compressibility in flows of gases is not very large until speeds comparable with the speed of sound in the gas are reached. The study of flows of viscous, incompressible fluids covers a wide range of practical cases.

The flow appearance is materially altered when viscosity is taken into account.

The flow around a sphere shown in Fig. 27 is quite representative of such flows. This does not show detailed characteristics close to the surface. Generally speaking, the flow

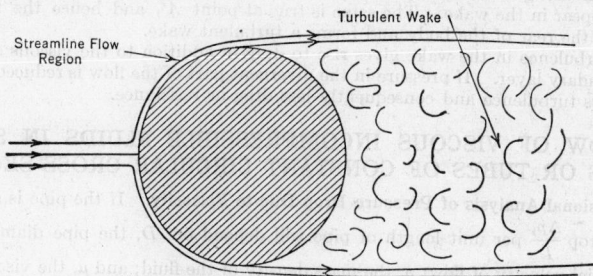

FIG. 27.   Flow of a Viscous Incompressible Fluid around a Sphere

is of the character shown. The flow in front of the sphere except in a very narrow layer close to the surface is very similar to the flow of an ideal fluid. Along a circle on the sphere surface approximately 90° from the stagnation point, the flow breaks away from the surface. On the downstream side there is a turbulent wake which is approximately a cylinder of the same diameter as the sphere. The diameter of this cylindrical turbulent wake and the conditions in the wake vary with the Reynolds' number,

$$\frac{\rho V D}{\mu} \tag{27}$$

where ρ = mass density of fluid, μ = coefficient of viscosity of the fluid, V = flow velocity, D = sphere diameter.

As body shapes approximate more nearly to such shapes which experience has shown to give very little resistance, the turbulent wake becomes very narrow and the flow is much more like an ideal flow.

Prandtl Boundary Layer Theory

According to this theory the viscous effects in a flow along a body occur principally in a very thin layer adjacent to the surface of the body. Particles of fluid adjacent to the surface of the body adhere to the surface and have no motion relative to the surface. In the immediate neighborhood of the surface the rate of change of velocity $\frac{du}{dn}$ (n being perpendicular to the surface at the point) is comparatively large, and the viscous shear forces given by $S_T = \mu \frac{du}{dn}$ may be large even if μ is comparatively small. Outside of the thin layer the rate of change of velocity is small and the viscous shear forces are insignificant. Here then the fluid flows as an ideal fluid.

The thickness of the boundary layer is in general dependent upon $\sqrt{\frac{\mu}{\rho\, VL}}$, where L is a length measured along the surface.

Breakaway of Flow

If the fluid is ideal the flow follows the contours of the body closely (Fig. 28); S is a stagnation point of the flow of the ideal fluid and SS' is a stream line of the flow. If the fluid is viscous, then the flow is like an ideal fluid outside the boundary layer. There is then a stream line CD outside the boundary layer which may be regarded as a boundary of the flow since there is no flow across a stream line. As fluid approaches A, this channel between the boundary CD and the surface of the body becomes wider, the velocity

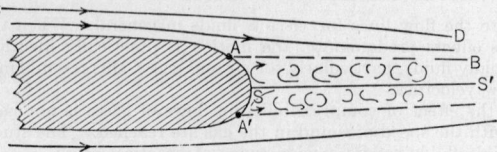

decreases and the pressure increases according to Bernoulli's theorem. If there are no viscous forces the pressure increase due to divergence of this channel is sufficient to bring the fluid to rest at S. If now there are viscous forces which retard the fluid

FIG. 28. Flow at the Rear of a Body

particles still more, the particles will come to rest at A. Then flow from S to A near the surface will take place, and the particles at rest with reference to the body will flow off downstream along AB. They are not in general in a stable configuration, and thus vortices appear in the wake. The same is true at point A', and hence the flow breaks away from the rear of the body and forms a turbulent wake.

This turbulence in the wake gives rise to drag in addition to the viscous shear forces in the boundary layer. If pressure in the divergent part of the flow is reduced by suction there is less turbulence and consequently less drag or resistance.

17. FLOW OF VISCOUS INCOMPRESSIBLE FLUIDS IN SMOOTH PIPES OR TUBES OF CONSTANT CIRCULAR CROSS-SECTION

Dimensional Analysis of Pressure Drop Due to Viscosity. If the pipe is smooth, the pressure drop $\dfrac{\Delta p_1}{L}$ per unit length of pipe will depend on: D, the pipe diameter; $\bar{u}$, the average axial velocity of flow; ρ, the mass density of the fluid; and μ, the viscosity of the fluid.

Using the method of dimensional analysis

$$\frac{\Delta p_1}{L} = \frac{\rho \bar{u}^2}{2D} f\left(\frac{\rho \bar{u} D}{\mu}\right) \tag{28}$$

The absolute pressure drop coefficient

$$C_{\Delta p_1} = \frac{\Delta p_1 / L}{\rho \bar{u}^2 / 2D} = f\left(\frac{\rho \bar{u} D}{\mu}\right) \tag{29}$$

Theory therefore indicates that the dimensionless coefficient $C_{\Delta p_1}$ is a function of the number $\dfrac{\rho \bar{u} D}{\mu}$. Experiments have verified that this is true. The form of the function f depends on the type of flow and is generally found by experiment.

The criterion for dynamical similarity of flows in two pipes is that $\dfrac{\rho_1 \bar{u}_1 D_1}{\mu_1} = \dfrac{\rho_2 \bar{u}_2 D_2}{\mu_2}$. When this is true the corresponding values of $C_{\Delta p_1}$ are alike. Not only may the velocities and pipe diameters be different but also the fluids may differ, as long as the corresponding values of $\dfrac{\rho \bar{u} D}{\mu}$ are alike then the same value of $C_{\Delta p_1}$ occurs. This has also been verified by many experiments.

Laminar Flow in Smooth Pipes—Hagen-Poiseuille Law. This flow is the simplest type of flow which occurs. The fluid moves along stream lines in the axial direction. It occurs for small values of the number $\dfrac{\rho \bar{u} D}{\mu}$. By equating the pressure drop to the viscous shear forces and assuming a steady flow, the Hagen-Poiseuille law,

$$\frac{\Delta p_1}{L} = \frac{\rho \bar{u}^2}{2D}\left(\frac{64\mu}{\rho \bar{u} D}\right) \tag{30}$$

is derived. Flows satisfying this law are called *laminar flows*. They are also called *stream-line* and *viscous* flows. For laminar flow,

$$C_{\Delta p_1} = \frac{64\mu}{\rho \bar{u} D} \tag{31}$$

Velocity Distribution in Laminar Flow in Smooth Tubes. When laminar flow is fully established the velocity is given by

$$\frac{uy}{um} = 1 - \left(\frac{2y}{D}\right)^2 \tag{32}$$

where uy = velocity at distance y from pipe axis and um = the maximum velocity in the pipe. This maximum velocity occurs along the pipe axis and is twice the average velocity $\bar{u}$.

This velocity distribution is not instantly established at the pipe entrance. If the entrance is rounded then according to Boussinesq the true laminar velocity distribution is found at a distance x_1 given by $\dfrac{x_1}{D} = 0.065 \dfrac{(\rho \bar{u} D)}{\mu}$, from the tube entrance.

For air at atmospheric pressure and room temperature moving at an average velocity of 1 ft per sec in a pipe of 2-in. diameter $x_1 \approx 11$ ft.

Total Pressure Drop for Laminar Flow in Smooth Tubes. Let

$$\Delta p = \text{total pressure drop}$$
$$\Delta p = \Delta p_1 + \Delta p_2$$

The additional term, Δp_2, which is added to the pressure loss, Δp_1, due to viscosity, arises from the gain in kinetic energy due to the change in velocity distribution.

Schiller's value seems to give the best agreement with experimental results:

$$\Delta p_2 = 2.24 \frac{\rho \bar{u}^2}{2} \tag{33}$$

The total pressure drop is then, for a length L,

$$\Delta p = \frac{\rho \bar{u}^2}{2} \frac{L}{D} \left(\frac{64\mu}{\rho \bar{u} D}\right) + 2.24 \frac{\rho \bar{u}^2}{2} \text{ for } laminar\ flow \tag{34}$$

Reynolds' Experiments. Reynolds showed that laminar flow in a circular, smooth tube changes its character gradually to a second type of flow called *turbulent flow*. He showed theoretically and by experiment that the transition from laminar flow to turbulent flow depends upon R.N. $= \dfrac{\rho \bar{u} D}{\mu}$. This dimensionless number is called *Reynolds' number*.

The exact value of R.N. at which the laminar type of flow changes to the turbulent type depends on the amount of disturbance in the fluid as it enters the tube. If R.N.$_1$ designates that value of R.N. at which turbulence or eddying first appears then it has been found by Ekman with Reynolds' original apparatus that R.N.$_1 \approx 50,000$ may be obtained by exercising extreme caution in preventing disturbance in the fluid at the pipe entrance.

It appears that for any straight, reasonably smooth pipe whose axis is horizontal R.N.$_2 \approx 2200$ is the upper limit for a flow which maintains its laminar character and for which the laminar-flow laws hold. For R.N. $\leqq 2200$ initial disturbance in the fluid at the pipe entrance die out.

Attention is called to the fact that if the pipe axis is not straight the value of R.N.$_2$ changes very materially. Gibson and Gridley found that R.N.$_2 \approx 260$ for flow of air through a brass tube 32 cm in diameter coiled around a drum 36 cm in diameter.

Application of Laminar Flow Laws. Critical velocity of several fluids flowing through smooth tubes with constant circular cross-section, axis horizontal.

Table II

Water, Temp. 20° C						
D (in.).................	1/2	1	2	3	4	6
$\bar{u}_c$ (ft per sec)...........	0.570	0.285	0.143	0.0950	0.0714	0.0475
Cfm....................	0.0465	0.0930	0.187	0.279	0.372	0.558
Gal per min.............	0.348	0.696	1.40	2.09	2.78	4.17
Castor oil, Temp. 26° C						
D (in.).................	1/2	1	2	3	4	6
$\bar{u}_c$ (ft per sec)...........	358.	179.	89.6	59.8	44.8	29.8
Cfm....................	29.3	58.5	117.0	176.0	234.0	350.0
Gal per min.............	220.	437.	875.	1315.	1750.	2620.

These tables show that for more viscous fluids laminar flows may easily occur in commercial practice.

If the tube diameter becomes small so that the tube may be termed a capillary tube then it is comparatively common to find laminar flow taking place. This is made use of in instruments known as absolute viscosimeters. The *Hagen-Poiseuille law* is successfully employed in such instruments to obtain the value of μ for liquids.

Example: To find the pressure loss due to viscosity in pumping 100 bbl per hour of an oil of specific gravity 0.90, Saybolt viscosity 300 at average temperature, through a pipe of 4-in. diameter. A barrel is to be taken as 42 U. S. gallons.

$$\frac{100 \text{ bbl}}{hr} = \frac{4200}{3600} \times \frac{231}{1728} \frac{\text{cu ft}}{\text{sec}} = 0.156 \text{ cu ft per sec} = \frac{\pi D^2 \bar{u}}{4}$$

$$\bar{u} = \frac{4}{\pi} \times \frac{0.156}{D^2} \text{ ft per sec} = 1.790 \text{ ft per sec.}$$

$$\nu = \mu/\rho = 2.20 \times 10^{-3} \times 3.00 \times 10^2 - \frac{1.80}{3.00} \times 10^{-2}$$

$$= 0.654 \text{ cm}^2 \text{ per sec} = 7.03 \times 10^{-4} \text{ ft}^2 \text{ per sec.}$$
(See Art. 6)

$$\frac{\bar{u} D}{\nu} = 848. \quad \therefore \text{ Flow is laminar.}$$

$$\frac{\Delta p_1}{L} = 0.90 \times \frac{62.4}{32.2} \times \overline{1.788}^2 \times 3 \times \frac{32}{848} = 0.633 \text{ lb per ft}^2 \text{ per ft}$$

$$\Delta p_1 = 633/144 \text{ lb per in.}^2 \text{ per 1000 ft} = 4.39 \text{ lb per in}^2 \text{ per 1000 ft of pipe.}$$

The kinetic energy term $\dfrac{\rho \bar{u}^2}{2}$ (2.24) = 0.0434 lb per in.^{2}

$\therefore$ The total pressure drop for a level pipe of constant cross-section would be $\Delta p = 4.43$ lb per in.^{2}

Transition from Laminar Flow to Turbulent Flow in Smooth Pipes. This change from laminar flow to turbulent flow does not take place suddenly but it is generally assumed in commercial practice that the laminar law holds up to values of R.N. $\approx$ 2000–2200 and that thereafter the turbulent law applies.

Turbulent Flow in Smooth Tubes of Constant Circular Cross-section. In laminar flow the interaction between adjacent fluid layers gives rise to the shearing stress, S'_T, which equals the product of rate of shear and viscosity coefficient. In turbulent flow an additional interaction occurs which, because of velocity fluctuations, is due to transfer of momentum from layer to layer of the fluid.

Velocity Distribution in Turbulent Flow of Fluids through Smooth Tubes. Just as in laminar flow, the final turbulent flow distribution is not found until a certain cross-section sufficiently far from the tube entrance is reached. It is not known what this distance is except that it seems shorter than in laminar flow and is less dependent on Reynolds' number.

Karman has recently shown theoretically that the velocity distribution is given by

$$u^* = a + b \log_{10} y^* \quad \text{(Ref. 1 Art. 17)} \tag{35}$$

where
$$u^* = u \left(\frac{\rho}{S_{T0}}\right)^{1/2}, \quad y^* = \left(\frac{S_{T0}}{\rho}\right)^{1/2} \frac{\rho y}{\mu} \tag{36}$$

S_{T0} = shearing stress at the tube wall.
y = distance from the tube wall.
u = axial velocity at distance y.

This law does not apply near the wall where $u^* = y^*$ corresponding to a laminar layer adjacent to the wall.

Nikuradse has recently shown that the law $u^* = y^*$ holds for $0 \leq y^* \leq 10$.

Then there is a transition (smooth) to $y^* \approx 100$ when the law $u^* = 5.5 + 5.75 \log_{10} y^*$ holds (Ref. 1 Art. 17).

This formula holds for large values of R.N. $= \dfrac{\rho u D}{\mu}$, whereas earlier formulas of the type $u^* = A y^{*1/B}$ and fixed values of A and B held for certain ranges of R.N. only.

The formula is not simple to apply to a given case; it is of importance, however, because it is based on sound theory. In general the velocity profile in turbulent flow is "flatter" than for laminar flow. The ratio $\dfrac{u \text{ max}}{u}$ is more nearly constant along a pipe diameter than for laminar flow.

Pressure Drop in Turbulent Flow in Smooth Tubes. The pressure drop coefficient

$$C_{\Delta p_1} = \frac{\Delta p_1}{L} \frac{2 D}{\rho \bar{u}^2} \tag{37}$$

for turbulent flow in smooth tubes of constant circular-cross section is found from the *Prandtl formula* (Ref. 2 Art. 17):

$$\frac{1}{\sqrt{C_{\Delta p_1}}} = 2 \log_{10}\left(\text{R.N.} \sqrt{C_{\Delta p_1}} \right) - 0.80 \tag{38}$$

$$\text{R.N.} = \frac{\rho \bar{u} D}{\mu} = \frac{\bar{u} D}{\nu}$$

This formula appears to be the most reliable for large values of R.N. and replaces the older formulas of Blasius and Lees.

The additional pressure loss Δp_2 arising from changes in kinetic energy due to changes in velocity distribution is $\Delta p_2 = 1.09 \left(\frac{\rho \bar{u}^2}{2} \right)$ if the pipe entrance is rounded. If the pipe entrance is sharp edged there is a further pressure drop due to the formation of a " vena contracta " downstream from the pipe entrance, and $\Delta p_2 = 1.40 \left(\frac{\rho \bar{u}^2}{2} \right)$ (Ref. 3 Art. 17).

The total pressure drop Δp for a length, L, of tube is:

$$\Delta p = C_{\Delta p_1} \left(\frac{L}{D} \right) \left(\frac{\rho \bar{u}^2}{2} \right) + 1.40 \left(\frac{\rho \bar{u}^2}{2} \right) \quad \text{Sharp-edged tube entrance} \tag{39}$$

$$\Delta p = C_{\Delta p_1} \left(\frac{L}{D} \right) \left(\frac{\rho \bar{u}^2}{2} \right) + 1.09 \left(\frac{\rho \bar{u}^2}{2} \right) \quad \text{Rounded tube entrance} \tag{40}$$

Since the formula for $C_{\Delta p_1}$ is not directly solvable for $C_{\Delta p_1}$, an approximation method must be used. For rapid work the curve shown in Fig. 29 may be used.

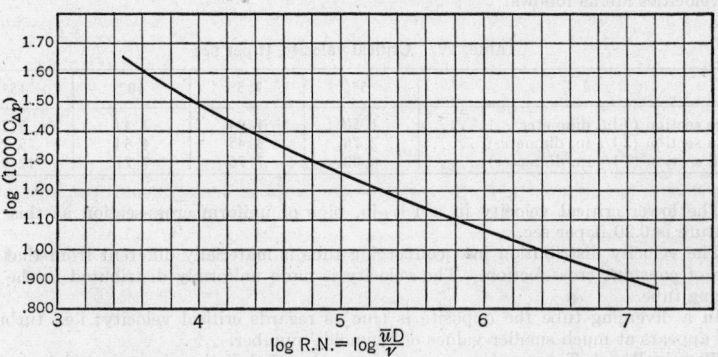

FIG. 29. Prandtl-Karman Law for Pressure Drop in Smooth Tubes. Turbulent Flow

Example: Air at 15° C is passing through a smooth circular pipe at 100 ft per sec. If $\rho = 2.40 \times 10^{-3}$ slug per cu ft and $\rho/\mu = 6000$ sec per ft², find the pressure drop in a length of 50 ft. Also for lengths of 100 ft and 1000 ft. Assume a diameter of 1/2 ft.

Solution: R. N. $= \dfrac{\rho \bar{u} D}{\mu} = 6000 \times 100 \times 1/2 = 3.00 \times 10^5$. Log R.N. = 5.4771.

Therefore the flow is turbulent.

From Fig. 29, log $(1000 \, C_{\Delta p}) = 1.160$; $C_{\Delta p_1} = 0.0144$.

$$\frac{\rho \bar{u}^2}{2} = 12 \text{ lb per ft}^2$$

Table III

For sharp-edged entrance:

$$\Delta p = 12 \, (.0288 \, L + 1.40) \text{ lbs per ft}^2$$

Length (ft)	Δp (lb per ft²)	Δp (lb per in.²)
50	34.1	0.236
100	51.3	0.356
1000	362.0	2.51

Pipes Which May Be Considered Smooth. Kemler (Ref. 4 Art. 17) has recently compiled practically all the experimental data on pipes and reduced them to the coefficient, $C_{\Delta p}$, method. The following kinds of pipes yield experimental results which follow the theoretical curves so closely that the theoretical formulas should be used:

(a) Drawn brass pipes.
(b) Glass tubes.
(c) Drawn tin pipes.
(d) Drawn lead pipes.

Any noticeable roughness of the interior surface of the pipe will cause increases in the coefficient $C_{\Delta p}$. Variations in pipe diameter also cause expansion and contraction effects if the interior surface of the pipe is smooth. For a pipe of circular cross-section

$$C_{\Delta p_1} = \frac{\pi^2 D^5 \Delta p}{8Q^2 \rho L} \tag{41}$$

where $Q =$ volume of flow in unit time. Any small variation in D therefore results in a comparatively large effect on $C_{\Delta p_1}$, the viscous coefficient.

Pipes of Non-circular Cross-section. Schiller (Ref. 5 Art. 17) has found that for smooth pipes of non-circular cross-section the criterion

$$r_m = \frac{\text{Cross-section area of pipe}}{\text{Wetted perimeter}} \tag{42}$$

usually called the mean hydraulic radius may be used instead of the Reynolds' number for finding pressure loss in the turbulent region but not in the laminar-flow region.

Pipes of Non-uniform Cross-section. No extensive experimental data exist on flow in pipes of non-uniform cross-section.

In a uniformly converging tube the critical velocity is higher than in a tube of constant cross-section area. Gibson (Ref. 6 Art. 17) shows that, for the flow of water through circular pipes having sides converging uniformly at an angle θ, temperature 14° C, critical velocities are as follows:

Table IV.   Critical velocity, ft per sec

θ	5°	7.5°	10°	15°
Large section (3-in. diameter)..........	1.50	1.94	2.44	3.25
Mean section (2 1/4-in. diameter).......	2.70	3.45	4.34	5.73
Small section (1 1/2-in. diameter).......	6.00	7.76	9.77	12.90

The lower critical velocity in a 1 1/2-in. pipe of uniform cross-section at this temperature is 0.20 ft per sec.

The velocity distribution in a converging tube is materially different from that in a tube of constant cross-section. The velocity is more uniformly distributed in the converging tube.

In a diverging tube the opposite is true as regards critical velocity; i.e., turbulent flow appears at much smaller values of Reynolds' number.

Flow in Rough Tubes. Experiments have shown that the viscous coefficient, $C_{\Delta p_1}$, for rough tubes is dependent upon other criteria than Reynolds' number alone. For circular tubes, $C_{\Delta p_1}$ depends on a "roughness number," $\frac{k}{D}$, where k is an average height of the protuberances on the interior surface compared with the diameter D. Concrete walls, rusted steel, and cast iron represent roughness of this character. Sometimes a "waviness number," $\frac{a}{b}$, modifies $C_{\Delta p_1}$. That is, the inner surface may be smooth but waves of amplitude a and wavelength b occur. Flumes made of wood and conduits made of thin metal sheet represent wavy types of roughness.

No reliable roughness criterion which represents materials commonly occurring in practice exists.

Pigott (Ref. 7 Art. 17) has recently summarized practically all the existing pipe-flow data. He assumes that

$$C_{\Delta p_1} = c \left(\frac{\nu}{\bar{u}D} \right)^n \tag{43}$$

where c is a constant and n is a roughness index varying from about 0.25 to nearly zero. Table V and the curves in Fig. 30 are used together to select the friction coefficient, $C_{\Delta p_1}$.

It is stated by Pigott that the formula $\frac{\Delta p}{L} = C_{\Delta p_1} \frac{\rho}{8} \frac{\bar{V}^2}{r_m}$ may be used with Table V given above and the curves for tubes or channels of non-circular section. $r_m =$ mean hydraulic radius.

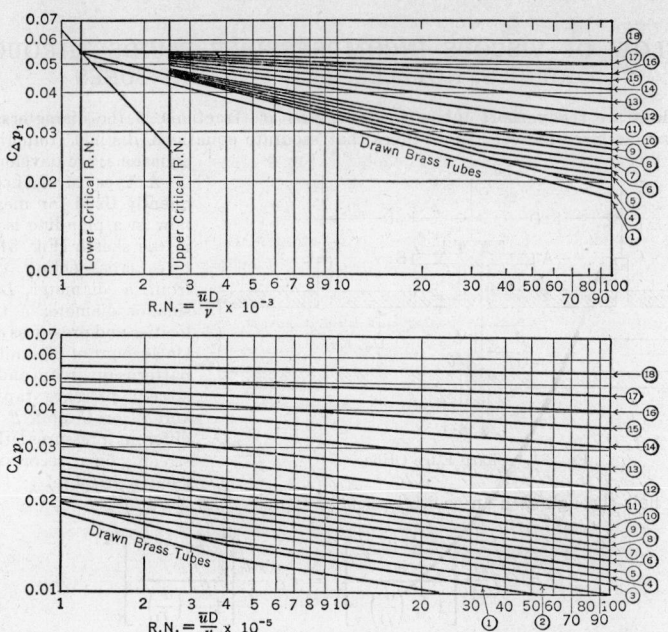

FIG. 30.   Friction Coefficient for Tubes.   (*Mechanical Engineering*, Aug. 1933, p. 501.)

Table V

Curve	1	2	3	4	5	6	7	8	9	10	11	12	13	14	15	16	17	18
A	0.35 up	....	....	....	....	....	....	....	....	....	....	....	....	0.125	....	....	....	0.0625
B	72 to 66	48 to 42	14 to 12	6 to 5	4 to 3	2	1 1/2	1 to 1 1/4	3/4	1/2	3/8	1/4	1/8	....	....	....	....	....
C	....	....	30	10 to 24	6 to 8	3 to 5	2 1/2	1 1/2 to 2	1 1/4	1	3/4	1/2	....	3/8	....	1/4	....	1/8
D	....	....	48 to 96	20 to 48	12 to 16	5 to 10	3 to 4	2 to 2 1/2	1 1/2	1 1/4	1	....	....	....	....	....	....	....
E	....	....	96	42 to 96	24 to 36	10 to 20	6 to 8	4 to 5	3	....	....	....	....	....	....	....	....	....
F	....	....	220	84 to 209	48 to 72	20 to 42	16 to 18	10 to 14	8	5	4	3	....	....	....	....	....	....

The numbers in the table designate the diameter in inches.
A = drawn tubing, brass, tin, lead, glass. *B* = Clean steel, wrought iron. *C* = Clean, galvanized. *D* = Best cast iron, cement, light riveted sheet ducts. *E* = Average cast iron, rough formed concrete. *F* = First-class brick, heavy riveted, spiral riveted. In drawn tubing, actual inside diameter is given. In pipe, nominal size of standard weight is given.

References

1. Karman, *Journal of Aeronautical Sciences*, Vol. 1, No. 1, 1934.
2. Prandtl, *Zeitschrift V.D.I.*, Vol. VII, No. 5, 1933.
3. Prandtl-Tietjens, Applied Aero and Hydrodynamics, McGraw-Hill Co., 1934.
4. Kemler, *A.S.M.E. Trans.*, Vol. 55, Hyd. 55, p. 2, 1933.
5. Schiller, Handbuch der Physik (Hopf), Vol. VII.
6. Gibson, *Proc. Roy. Soc. A*, 83–1910.
7. Pigott. *Mech. Eng.*, August, 1933.

18. FLOW OF VISCOUS INCOMPRESSIBLE FLUIDS THROUGH ORIFICES, NOZZLES, AND VENTURI TUBES

Orifices are really short tubes whose lengths are fractions of the diameters. End effects are so large for very short tubes that separate equations, distinct from the pipe equations, are developed.

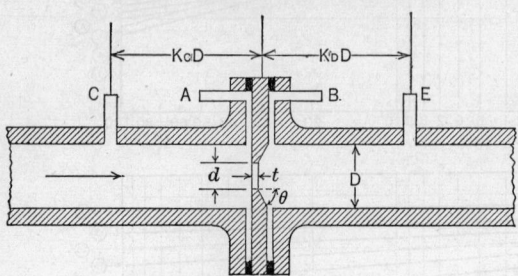

A Type of Orifice Frequently Used for measuring flow in a pipe line is shown in the sketch (Fig. 31). As the cross-section changes from a diameter D to a smaller diameter d the velocities and pressures change. On account of dissimilar flow patterns upstream and downstream, pressure taps at A and B or C and E record different pressures, the upstream taps recording the greater pressure.

Fig. 31. Sharp Edge Orifice.

The flow through such an orifice is usually expressed in the form

$$Q = C_Q \frac{\pi d^2}{4}\left[\frac{2\Delta p g}{w}\middle/ 1-\left(\frac{d}{D}\right)^4\right]^{\frac{1}{2}} = C_Q \frac{\pi d^2}{4}\left[\frac{2w_o h g}{w}\middle/ 1-\left(\frac{d}{D}\right)^4\right]^{\frac{1}{2}} \tag{44a}$$

$$= C_Q \frac{\pi d^2}{4} \frac{\bar{u}}{\left[1-\left(\frac{d}{D}\right)^4\right]^{\frac{1}{2}}} \tag{44b}$$

where Q = volume of flow in unit time.
C_Q = coefficient of volume.
Δp = pressure difference across orifice.
w = weight density of fluid flowing through the orifice.
h = head on a manometer measuring Δp.
w_o = weight density of manometer fluid.
$\bar{u}$ = average flow velocity through the orifice.

The Magnitude and Variation of C_Q depend upon the location and construction of the pressure taps, the ratios $\dfrac{d}{D}$ and $\dfrac{d}{t}$, the bevel angle θ, the workmanship of construction of the orifice and pipe surface, the location of the orifice with regard to bends, valves, etc., in the pipe line, and upon the Reynolds' number $\dfrac{\bar{u}D}{\nu}$, where ν is the kinematic viscosity of the fluid.

If two orifices in two pipes are geometrically similar and similarly located the flow coefficient depends only on Reynolds' number. A curve C_Q versus R.N. $= \dfrac{\bar{u}D}{\nu}$ obtained with a specified orifice installation will furnish information for the flow of any viscous incompressible fluid even if the calibration curve has been obtained with one certain liquid or a limited number of liquids.

A Typical Set of Curves taken from Hodgson (Ref. 1 Art. 18) obtained with an orifice of the type shown is given below (Fig. 32). The orifice had dimensions: $d = 0.8032$ cm, $t = 0.0914$ cm, $\theta = 45°$. It was mounted concentrically in pipes 0.952, 1.27, and 1.904 cm in diameter. Pressure taps were located at A and B (Fig. 31).

These curves do not show enough detail for very small values of $\sqrt{\dfrac{\bar{u}D}{\nu}}$. Hodgson states (loc. cit.) that for values

$$\sqrt{\frac{\bar{u}D}{\nu}} \le 5.00 \text{ (approx.)} \quad C_Q = k\sqrt{\frac{\bar{u}D}{\nu}} \tag{45}$$

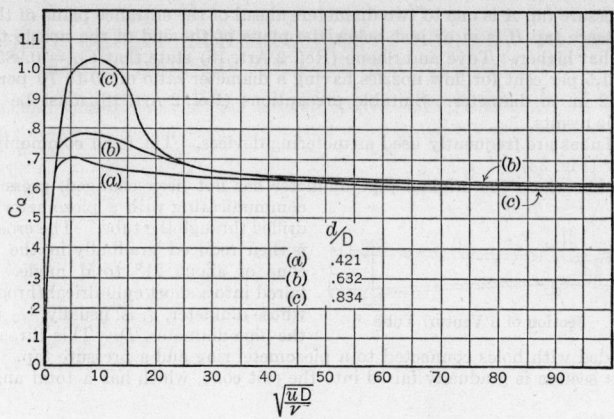

Fig. 32. C_Q vs. $\sqrt{\dfrac{\bar{u}D}{\nu}}$ for Three Orifices

Table VI

k	0.136	0.118	0.106
$\dfrac{d}{D}$	0.421	0.632	0.834

Example: Fluid whose kinematic viscosity = 0.00618 ft² per sec is pumped through a pipe line having an orifice of the type shown. The head $h = 50$ in. is read on a manometer containing a fluid of specific gravity 0.905. If the specific gravity of the fluid in the pipe is 0.900, find Q for a pipe of internal diameter 2 in. and an orifice for which $\dfrac{d}{D} = 0.421$.

Solution:

$$\bar{u}^2 = \frac{2\,w_0 g h}{w} = 2 \times \frac{0.905}{0.900} \times 32.2 \times \frac{50}{12} = 270.$$

$$\bar{u} = 16.41 \text{ ft per sec.}$$

$$\frac{\bar{u}D}{\nu} = \frac{16.41 \times 0.421 \times \dfrac{2}{12}}{0.00618} = 186.$$

$$\sqrt{\frac{\bar{u}D}{\nu}} = 13.7.$$

From the curves $C_Q \propto$ R.N. $\quad C_Q = 0.660.$

$$Q = \frac{0.660 \times \dfrac{\pi}{4} \times (.421)^2 \left(\dfrac{1}{6}\right)^2 \times 16.41}{(1 - (.421)^4)^{1/2}} = 0.0432 \text{ cfs}$$

$$= 19.4 \text{ gal per min.}$$

For more detailed information see the references at the end of this article.

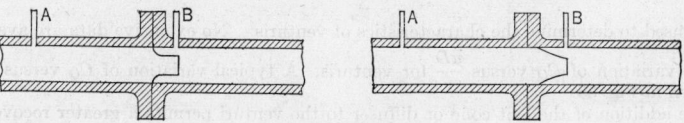

Fig. 33. Nozzles

Nozzles differ from orifices only in so far that the approach is noticeably well rounded (Fig. 33). They seem to be favored in Europe, especially in Germany, where they are called "Düsen." The coefficient defined by equation 44 is also used for nozzles. The coefficient, C_Q, is considerably higher than for orifices.

If the pressure tap A is one to two diameters ahead of the entrance plane of the nozzle and the pressure tap B is in or just below the plane of the end of the nozzle the value C_Q is somewhat higher. Tuve and Shoop (Ref. 2 Art. 18) state that $C_Q = 0.985$ is accurate within 1.5 per cent for flow nozzles having a diameter ratio of 20 to 70 per cent in pipes 2 to 12 in. in diameter. Suitable precautions (Ref. 2 Art. 18) must be taken to insure reliable results.

Venturi Tubes are frequently used as metering devices. The form commonly used is shown below (Fig. 34).

At a station where the original pipe diameter has not been changed, pressure holes communicating with a piezometer ring are drilled through the tube. The cross-section is then reduced gradually in the entrance cone of about 21° total angle. This is faired into a short cylindrical throat section whose diameter, d, is usually $1/2$ to $1/3$ of the pipe diameter, D. This throat section is also provided with holes connected to a piezometer ring and a pressure tap. The end of the throat section is gradually faired into the exit cone, which has a total angle of 5° to 7°.

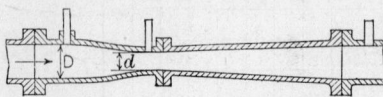

Fig. 34.   Section of a Venturi Tube

The equation

$$Q = C_Q \bar{u} \frac{\pi d^2/4}{\left[1 - \left(\dfrac{d}{D} \right)^4 \right]^{1/2}} \qquad (46)$$

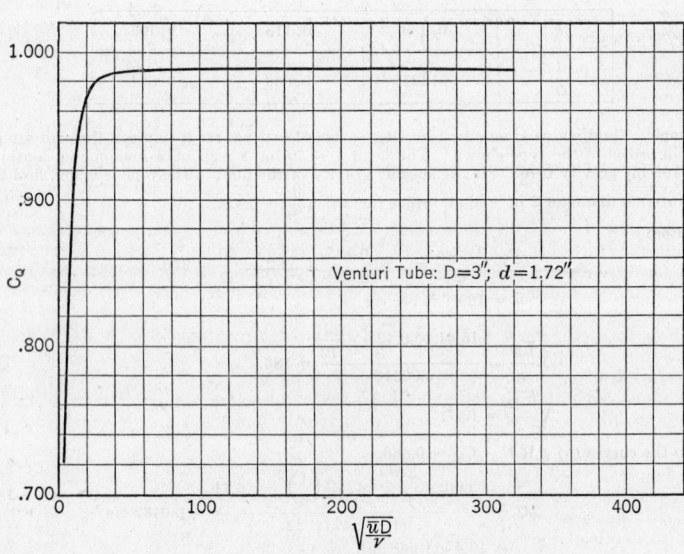

Fig. 35.   Coefficient of a Venturi Tube

is also used to determine the characteristics of venturis. No extensive data are available on the variation of C_Q versus $\dfrac{\bar{u}D}{\nu}$ for venturis. A typical variation of C_Q versus $\sqrt{\dfrac{\bar{u}D}{\nu}}$ is shown in Fig. 35.

The addition of the exit cone or diffuser to the venturi permits a greater recovery of pressure than is possible for orifices and nozzles. In normal practice this is usually from 10 to 20 per cent of the differential from entrance to throat.

References

1. Hodgson, *A.S.M.E. Trans.*, F.S.P., 51, 42, 1929.
2. Shoop and Tuve, Mechanical Engineering Practice, McGraw-Hill Co., Chapter VII.

19. FLOW OF VISCOUS INCOMPRESSIBLE FLUIDS AROUND BODIES ENTIRELY SURROUNDED BY THE FLUID

Introductory. A dimensional analysis shows that the force exerted by a moving fluid on a body is of the form

$$F = C_F \frac{\rho A V^2}{2} \tag{47}$$

where F = force.

$\quad C_F$ = a dimensionless force coefficient.

$\quad \rho$ = mass density of the fluid.

$\quad V$ = velocity of motion of the body through the fluid.

$\quad A$ = area.

The coefficient, C_F, is dependent in the general case on many dimensionless criteria. The principal criteria are: Reynolds' number, $\frac{VL}{\nu}$; Mach's number, $\frac{V}{V_c}$; Froude's number, $\frac{V^2}{Lg}$; body attitude with reference to the relative wind; body shape; relative roughness of the surface of the body, and the degree of turbulence of the moving fluid. Sometimes the surface tension forces become appreciable and must be considered.

Frequently the emphasis is placed on the component of force F along the relative velocity vector, $\overline{V}$. This component is usually called drag or resistance. For most practical cases the drag is divided into two parts: (i) friction forces tangential to the surface of the body—the resultant of these is called the *skin friction drag*; (ii) for an ideal fluid flow the normal forces on the body resolved in the direction of the relative velocity vector, $\overline{V}$, have a zero sum or resultant. Viscosity of the fluid causes a change in the flow pattern so that the pressure symmetry for the ideal fluid no longer exists. The resultant of the normal forces in the $\overline{V}$ direction is now different from zero. This additional drag is called *pressure* or *form drag*. The pressure drag is also explained by saying that it is determined by the kinetic energy of the eddies in the wake of the body.

Drag of a flat plate parallel to the relative velocity is practically all skin friction drag. If the flat plate is at right angles to the relative wind the drag is practically all pressure drag.

Tietjens (Ref. 1 Art. 19) uses the term "deformation drag" to characterize drag at very small values of Reynolds' number. The body in motion through the fluid sets up stresses which deform the fluid particles. This deformation extends to great distances from the body. For larger values of the Reynolds' number this deformation is appreciable only in the boundary layer.

Pressure drag may be measured by integration and resolution of normal forces obtained by static openings on the surface of the body. Total drag = skin friction drag + pressure drag is usually measured by means of balances.

Flow along Smooth Flat Plates. If the flat plate is in a uniform stream of fluid and the flow is parallel to the plate the drag coefficient is dependent mainly on the Reynolds' number, where R.N. $= \dfrac{uL}{\nu}$.

$\quad u$ = velocity of fluid far from the plate or it is the velocity of the plate in the quiescent fluid.

$\quad L$ = length of the plate in the direction of flow.

$\quad \nu$ = kinematic viscosity of the fluid.

For a smooth plate the variation of C_F versus R.N. resembles the variation of $C_{\Delta p}$ for a pipe.

For $1 \leq$ R.N. $\leq 5 \times 10^5$,

$$C_F = \frac{1.327}{\sqrt{\text{R.N.}}} \quad \text{(Blasius).} \tag{48}$$

For $5 \times 10^5 \leq$ R.N. $\leq 5 \times 10^6$, which is usually called the transition range, C_F changes from the Blasius law to a second type of law.

Prandtl (Ref. 2 Art. 19) has given as the law for C_F in the transition range,

$$C_F = \frac{0.074}{\sqrt[5]{\text{R.N.}}} - \frac{1700}{\text{R.N.}} \tag{49}$$

This law will not be followed closely in a given case. The transition depends on the shape of the leading edge of the plate and on the degree of turbulence of the fluid coming up to the plate.

For R.N. $> 5 \times 10^6$　　$C_F = \dfrac{0.455}{[\log_{10} (\text{R.N.})]^{2.58}}$ (Schlichting)　　　　　(50)

The value of C_F in the formulas cited is based on the entire area, A, exposed to the fluid.

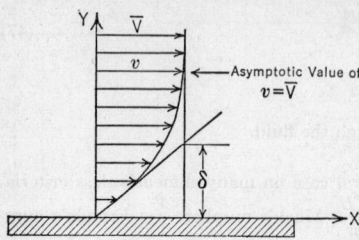

FIG. 36.　Velocity Distribution Near a Flat Plate

The gradual transition from one law to another is usually attributed to a change from laminar flow in the boundary layer to turbulent flow in the boundary layer. The velocity distribution near a flat plate is represented in Fig. 36. The velocity, V, changes approximately in a linear way with distance, Y, from the plate at very small distances from the plate. Then it gradually becomes constant, $\overline{V}$. Blasius found that if the thickness of the boundary layer, δ, is defined as the distance from the plate to the intersection of the asymptotic line $\overline{V}$ and the tangent to the velocity diagram at the origin,

$$\delta = \frac{3.40\ L}{\sqrt{\dfrac{\overline{V}L}{\nu}}}$$　　　　　(51)

where $L =$ distance from a sharp leading edge of the plate.

The flow outside this very thin layer is practically identical with an ideal fluid flow. For turbulent flow in the boundary layer an expression for δ was given by Prandtl as

$$\delta = \frac{0.37\ L}{\sqrt[5]{\dfrac{\overline{V}L}{\nu}}}$$　　　　　(52)

If the flat plate is inclined to the relative velocity vector by an angle α, then the force F is usually resolved into a component L called the lift and a component D called drag. The corresponding coefficients C_L and C_D are defined by

$$L = C_L \frac{\rho}{2} S V^2 \quad \text{and} \quad D = C_D \frac{\rho}{2} S V^2$$　　　　　(53)

where S is the plan area of the plate. Variation of C_L and C_D are like those of thin symmetrical airfoils. See Art. 20 for a discussion.

If $\alpha = 90°$ the plate has practically no lift and its drag is very nearly all pressure drag on account of the wide turbulent or eddying wake on the downstream side of the plate. The drag coefficient C_D varies with Reynolds' number and the shape of the plate. The variation with R.N. for shapes that are not unusual is not great.

Table VII

Flat plate ($\alpha = 90°$)	C_D	Reynolds' number
Square	1.04–1.263	68,000– 680,000 (Eiffel)
Circular disk	1.08–1.14	210,000–4,440,000 (Shoemaker)

The values of C_D for a large square flat plate at large values of R.N. is usually given as 1.28.

No systematic data except for specially prepared rough surface exist on the drag of rough plates.

Flow around Cylinders. The drag of cylinders is usually written

$$D = C_D\, A\, (1/2\, \rho V^2)$$　　　　　(54)

$A =$ the area of the orthogonal projection of the cylinder on a plane at right angles to the relative velocity vector.

ρ and V are as previously defined.

The drag coefficient C_D for steady flow of an incompressible fluid varies chiefly with Reynolds' number $\dfrac{\rho V d}{\mu} = \dfrac{V d}{\nu}$, where d is a typical length characterizing the size of the cross-section of the cylinder.

Lamb (Ref. 3 Art. 19) has developed a theoretical expression for C_D of the form

$$C_D = \frac{a}{\text{R.N. }(b - c \log_{10} \text{R.N.})}$$　　　　　(55)

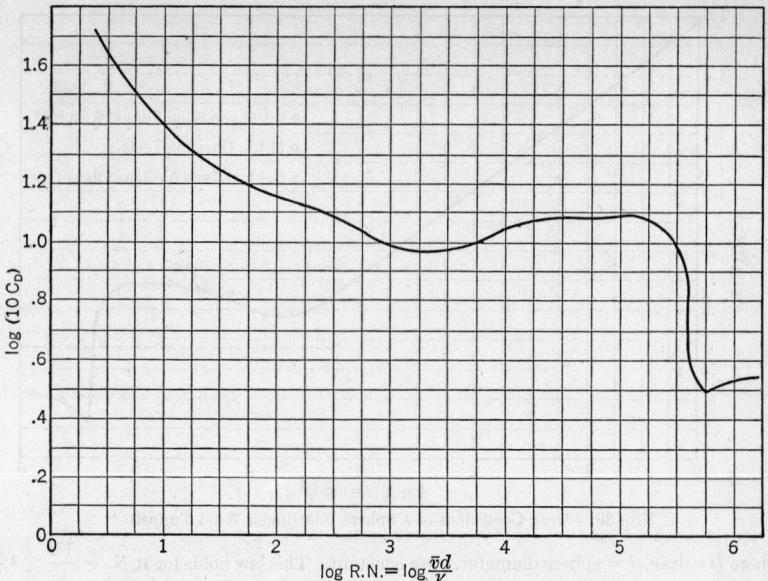

FIG. 37.   Drag of a Cylinder, d = diameter (Two Dimensional Flow)

This holds for two-dimensional flow around circular cylinders, a, b, and c being constants. Since this theoretical formula holds only for R.N. $\lesssim$ 1 it is rarely used.   For larger values of R.N. the variation of C_D versus R.N. is shown in Fig. 37.

This curve given by Prandtl (Ref. 4 Art. 19) shows a typical variation of C_D for flow around a circular cylinder whose length is infinite compared to its diameter.   The sudden drop of C_D between R.N. = 10^5 and 10^6 may vary if the cylinder is tested in a different fluid stream. For relatively greater turbulence the drop occurs for a smaller value of R.N.

As the cross-sectional area becomes more nearly " stream line " in shape the drop in C_D occurs at smaller values of R.N. Fig. 38 shows the variation of C_D with $VD \propto$ R.N. for a cylinder whose cross-section is that of a good airplane strut.   Cylinders shaped in cross-section like airfoils will be discussed in Art. 20.

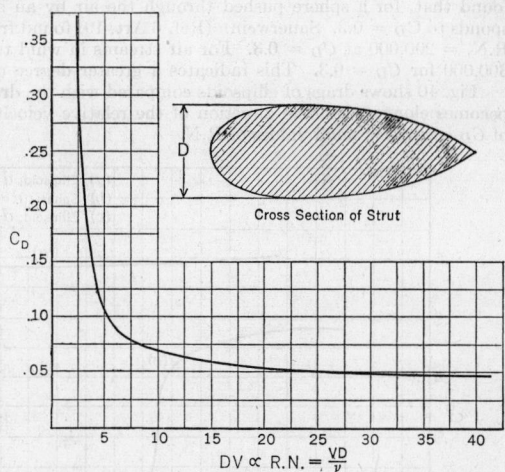

Cross Section of Strut

FIG. 38.   Drag of Streamline Strut (Diehl; Engineering Aerodynamics)

Flow around Spheres and Ellipsoids.   Spheres have relatively bad shapes and on account of a wide turbulent wake the drag of a sphere is largely pressure drag.   Stokes has derived the theoretical law

$$C_D = \frac{D}{\frac{\rho}{2}\left(\frac{\pi d^2}{4}\right)V^2} = \frac{a}{\text{R.N.}} \tag{56}$$

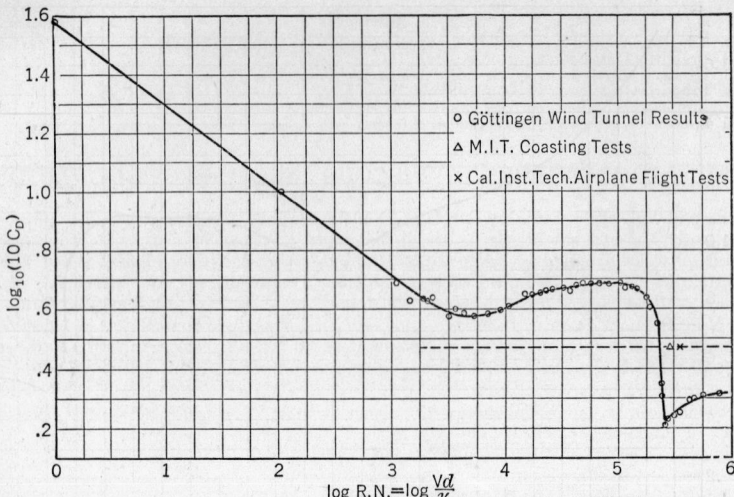

FIG. 39.   Drag Coefficient of a Sphere (Göttingen Wind Tunnel)

where D = drag, d = sphere diameter, a = a constant. This law holds for R.N. = $\dfrac{Vd}{\nu} \leqq 1/2$.

For greater values of R.N. the variation obtained in a typical experiment is shown in Fig. 39. The sharp drop just beyond R.N. = 10^5 shifts as does the drop in C_D for a circular cylinders depending on the turbulence in the fluid stream.

The value of R.N. corresponding to $C_D = 0.3$ is frequently employed in aeronautics to determine the turbulence scale of an air stream. Millikan and Klein (Ref. 5 Art. 19) found that, for a sphere pushed through the air by an airplane, R.N. $\approx$ 365,000 corresponds to $C_D = 0.3$. Sauerwein. (Ref. 6 Art. 19) found from coasting tests in still air that R.N. = 290,000 at $C_D = 0.3$. For air streams in wind tunnels R.N. is usually less than 300,000 for $C_D = 0.3$. This indicates a greater degree of turbulence in the air stream.

Fig. 40 shows drags of ellipsoids compared with the drag of a sphere. As the ellipsoid becomes elongated in the direction of the relative velocity vector the drop in the value of C_D occurs for small values of R.N.

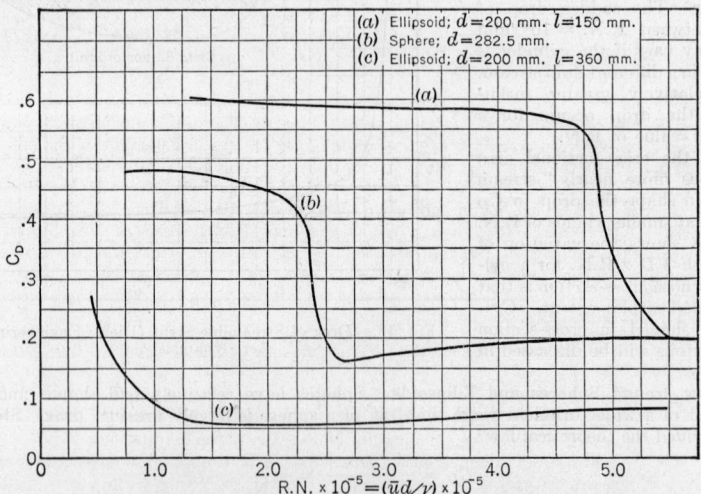

FIG. 40.   Resistances of Spheres and Ellipsoids (Göttingen Ergebnisse)

References
1. Tietjens, Applied Aero and Hydrodynamics, McGraw-Hill Co., 1934.
2. Prandtl, Goettingen Ergebnisse, Part III.
3. Lamb, Hydrodynamics (5th Ed.), Cambridge University Press.
4. Prandtl, Goettingen Ergebnisse, Part II.
5. Millikan and Klein, *Aircraft Engineering*, London, August, 1934.
6. Sauerwein, *Journal of Aeronautical Sciences*, Vol. I, July, 1934.

20. AERODYNAMICS OF VISCOUS INCOMPRESSIBLE FLUIDS

Recent Full-scale Tests on Airplane Propellers show that compressibility effects are practically non-existent at tip speeds of 600 mph. Theory indicates that the speed of sound must be attained in order that compressibility shall play an important part in determining the aerodynamic forces on bodies. Practically all our knowledge of this branch of fluid mechanics is based on the theory of a viscous incompressible fluid.

Wing Sections. Aerodynamics begins with the study of properties of wing sections, for without efficient wing sections there would be no lift. The term airfoil is in common use and refers in general to bodies whose shape makes them useful as lifting, propelling, and controlling elements of aircraft.

Efficient wing and airfoil shapes have been discovered in a relatively short time by a happy combination of theory and experiment. The cross-section of airfoils is represented by Fig. 41.

The leading edge at A is rounded so that the flow at various attitudes remains reasonably good. The thickness gradually increases to a maximum value, t, and then decreases quite gradually to almost nothing at the trailing edge B. The median or mean line is generally a flat curve like a circular or parabolic arc, although in some cases it crosses the X axis and approaches B from below the X axis. The maximum ordinate of the mean line is called the camber, m, and is located at a distance L from the lead-

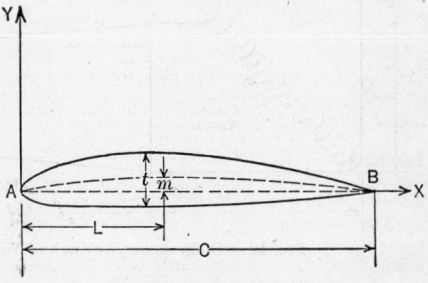

FIG. 41. Typical Airfoil Section and Section Parameters

ing edge. The length $AB = c$ is called the chord. The parameters m, L, and t are the important parameters which determine the airfoil section properties.

Table VIII. Variation of Parameters m, L, and t (average)

	m/c	L/c	t/c
Wing sections.....................	0.02 to 0.06	0.20 to 0.50	0.05 to 0.18
Propeller blade sections.............	0.02 to 0.06	0.20 to 0.50	0.06 to 0.20
Strut sections......................	0	....	0.33 average
Tail surfaces......................	0	....	Less than 0.08

Plan Forms of Airfoils vary considerably. The most common plan form now in use generally tapers from a constant value of chord over the central portion of the span to a smaller value near the wing tips which are ordinarily rounded. The thickness of the airfoil is usually tapered towards the tips to assist the plan form taper in the matter of weight saving. There are also aerodynamic advantages for taper in plan form as well as thickness. Theory and experiment agree in showing that the ratio of span to average chord, called the aspect ratio, should be large. Structural and weight considerations indicate that a small aspect ratio should be used. Values of the aspect ratio in common use vary from 6 to 8 for wings, although soaring gliders have aspect ratios in excess of 20.

Airfoil Characteristics are usually written:

$$L = \frac{C_L}{2} \rho SV^2; \quad D = \frac{C_D}{2} \rho SV^2; \quad M = \frac{C_M}{2} \rho c SV^2 \qquad (57)$$

where L = component of air force at right angles to the relative wind.

D = component of air force along the relative wind direction.

M = moment of air force (usually measured about the leading edge).

C_L, C_D and C_M are dimensionless coefficients of lift, drag, and moment respectively.

ρ = mass density of air.

S = plan area of airfoil, also called wing area.

V = relative velocity of air.

The **Aerodynamic Coefficients** C_L, C_D, and C_M for an airfoil of given shape vary chiefly with: angle of attack, α (usually measured as the angle between the chord and the relative wind direction); Reynolds' number, $\dfrac{Vc}{\nu}$; surface texture of airfoil and the degree of turbulence of the air stream.

The **Aerodynamic Characteristics of Airfoils** are usually measured in wind tunnels. Fig. 42 shows diagrammatic sketches of a modern wind tunnel. Space and power requirements usually make the initial and operating costs of large wind tunnels capable of good speed very high. In order to measure results which can safely be used to estimate

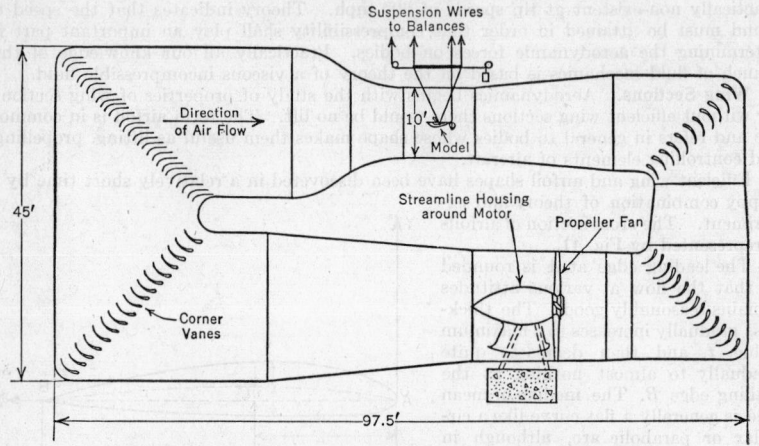

FIG. 42. Diagrammatic Sketch of Wind Tunnel (Cal. Inst. Tech.)

the performance of modern airplanes, Reynolds' numbers of the order of 2,000,000 $\left(\text{R.N.} = \dfrac{Vc}{\nu}\right)$ should be used in testing. For air at ordinary working conditions Vc must then be ≈ 330 ft per sec. An airfoil of 6 sq ft area and aspect ratio 6 should then be tested at about 200 mph wind speed. The variable density or compressed air tunnel uses air compressed to 20 atmospheres at moderate speeds and small model sizes. Since in this way ν may be reduced to approximately $1/_{20}$ of its normal value, the value of Vc may be correspondingly reduced without reducing $\dfrac{Vc}{\nu}$.

Typical airfoil characteristics measured in a wind tunnel are shown in Fig. 43 (N.A.C.A.T.R. 502).

Many experiments on airfoils verify that the variation of C_L with α predicted by theory (see Art. 13) for thin airfoils is true for the range of values of α generally used in flight. The slope, $\dfrac{dC_L}{d\alpha}$, of the C_L curve has been found to depend principally on the thickness parameter. Theory does not give any information regarding the maximum value of C_L which may be attained with a given airfoil shape. The value of C_L max. depends very much on the degree of turbulence of the airstream. Excessive values of turbulence result in optimistic predictions of C_L max.

The **Drag Coefficient** is usually written,

$$C_D = C_{Dp} + C_{Di} \tag{58}$$

where C_{Dp} is called the profile drag coefficient and C_{Di} the induced drag coefficient (see Art. 15). The profile drag coefficient must be found by experiment. It depends on t and m and also on surface smoothness. The theoretical formula derived in Art. 15 for conversion of airfoil data from one aspect ratio and plan form to another gives good results in practice. A standard aspect ratio and plan form may thus be chosen in order to investigate the properties of a particular airfoil section.

The curve C_M versus C_L in Fig. 43 shows that the linear relation between C_M and C_L

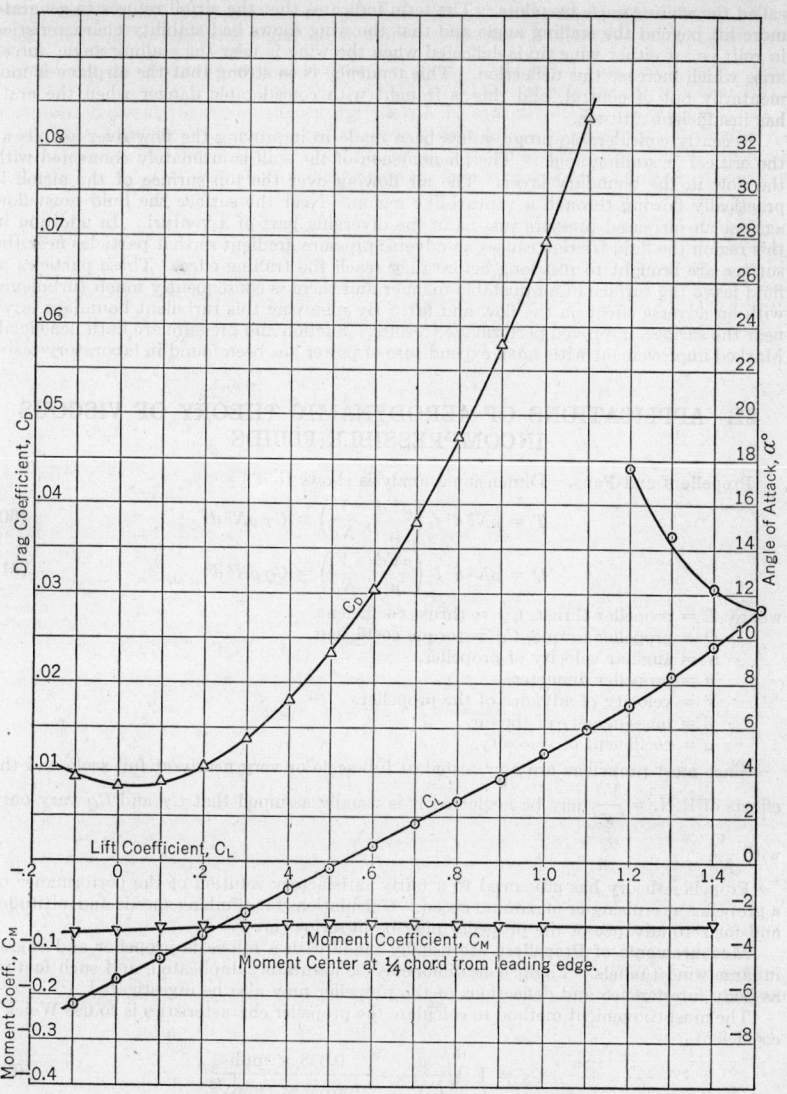

FIG. 43. Characteristics of Airfoil; Clark-Y.
Airfoil: 8' × 48'; R.N. = 6,000,000; c = chord

is realized in actual tests. C_{Mo} depends on m, L, and t. The center of pressure coefficient is

$$\frac{x_{cp}}{c} = n - \frac{C_{Mo}}{C_L} \tag{59}$$

where x_{cp} is the distance from leading edge to the center of pressure measured along the chord. Theory indicates that $n = 0.25$ for thin airfoils. Tests on airfoils indicate that n varies with thickness principally.

Critical or Stalling Angle. The most unsatisfactory part of airfoil behavior consists in the flow around the airfoil at angles near that of maximum lift. This angle is usually called the *stalling angle* by pilots.   The term indicates that the airfoil refuses to generate more lift beyond the stalling angle and that the wing shows bad stability characteristics in roll; i.e., if either wing tip is deflected when the wing is near the stalling angle, forces arise which increase this deflection.   This tendency is so strong that the airplane is momentarily out of control, and this is fraught with considerable danger when the craft has insufficient altitude.

Recently considerable progress has been made in improving the flow over airfoils at the critical or stalling angle.   The phenomenon of the stall is intimately connected with the flow in the boundary layer.   The air flowing over the top surface of the airfoil is practically flowing through a venturi-like region.   Near the surface the fluid must flow against an increased pressure just as in the diverging part of a venturi.   In addition in this region the fluid friction causes an adverse pressure gradient so that particles near the surface are brought to rest long before they reach the trailing edge.   These particles of fluid leave the surface in an unstable manner and there is consequently much turbulence with an adverse effect on the flow and lift.   By removing this turbulent boundary layer near the surface, improved performance results.   Suction and pressure are both beneficial. Marked improvement with small expenditure of power has been found in laboratory tests.

21. APPLICATIONS OF AERODYNAMIC THEORY OF VISCOUS INCOMPRESSIBLE FLUIDS

Propellers and Fans.   Dimensional analysis shows that

$$T = \rho N^2 d^4 f_1 \left(\frac{\rho V d}{\mu}, \frac{V}{Nd} \right) = C_T \rho N^2 d^4 \tag{60}$$

$$Q = \rho N^2 d^5 f_2 \left(\frac{\rho V d}{\mu}, \frac{V}{Nd} \right) = C_Q \rho N^2 d^5 \tag{61}$$

where T = propeller thrust, C_T = thrust coefficient.
   Q = propeller torque, C_Q = torque coefficient.
   N = angular velocity of propeller.
   d = propeller diameter.
   V = velocity of advance of the propeller.
   ρ = mass density of the air.
   μ = coefficient of viscosity.

Since most propellers are now tested at full scale or very nearly at full scale and the effects of R.N. $= \dfrac{Vd}{\nu}$ may be neglected it is usually assumed that C_T and C_Q vary only with $\dfrac{V}{Nd}$.

Propeller theory has advanced to a fairly satisfactory solution of the performance of a propeller at cruising or maximum speed.   Calculations for climbing speeds and altitudes and for zero advance of the propeller may be in serious error.

Measurements of Propellers are usually made with a full-scale propeller and engine in large wind tunnels.   Flight conditions may be accurately duplicated, and such factors as body interference and deflections of the propeller may also be investigated.

The most convenient method to calculate the propeller characteristics is to use Weick's coefficient

$$C_S = V \sqrt[5]{\frac{\rho}{PN^2}} = \frac{0.638 \times \text{mph}}{(\text{bhp})^{1/5} \times (\text{rpm})^{2/5}} \tag{62}$$

A typical variation of C_S versus $\dfrac{V}{Nd}$ is shown in Fig. 44.   For a desired speed and a given engine the propeller characteristics may be determined very quickly and accurately from such charts.

The Propeller Efficiency is given by

$$\eta = \frac{\text{thp}}{\text{bhp}}, \tag{63}$$

thp = thrust horsepower and bhp = brake horsepower.   The curve (line of max. η for C_S) shown in Fig. 44 is usually termed the best performance propeller since it performs best at high speed and very well at climbing speed.   Since a propeller of fixed blade angle setting for best performance does not give good performance at take-off and climb, where a smaller blade angle setting is necessary, it has become necessary to resort to variable

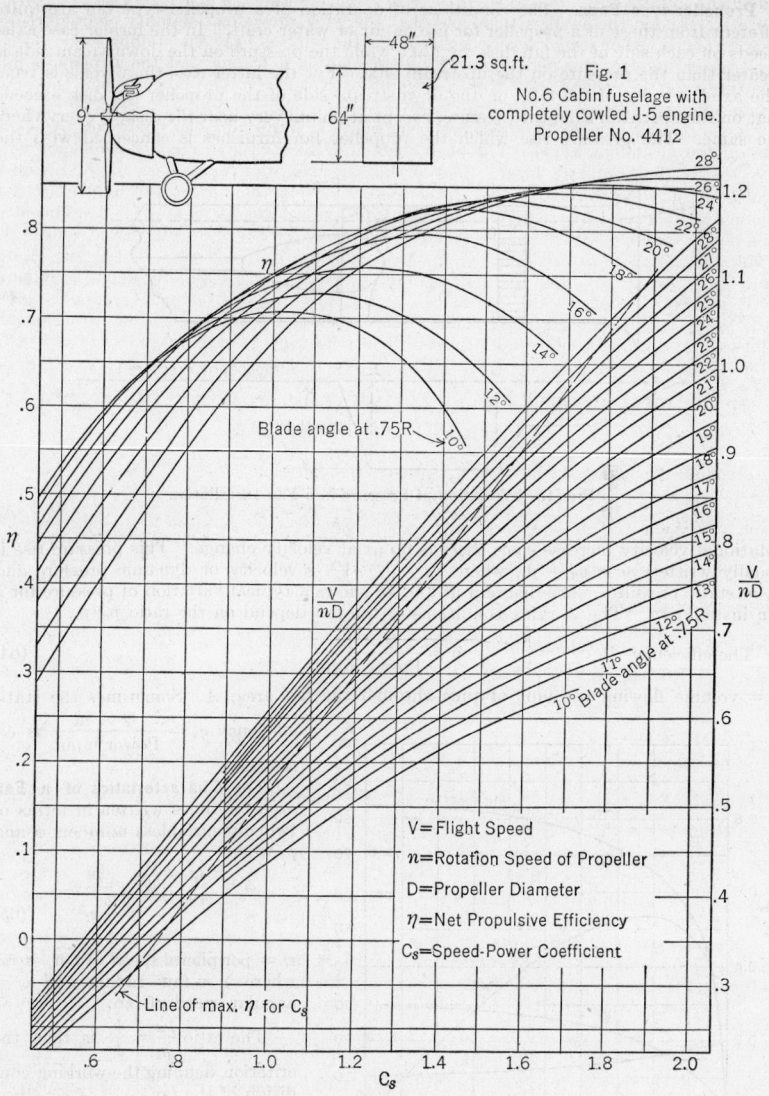

FIG. 44.   Propeller Characteristics

pitch propellers. The difference in performance of an airplane with fixed and variable pitch propellers is shown by the following table.

Table IX.   Performance of an Airplane with Fixed Pitch and Variable Pitch Propellers

Taken from N.A.C.A. Tech. Note 484

Propeller	High Speed (mph)	Maximum Rate of Climb (ft per min)	Take-off Run (ft)
Best fixed pitch............	211	1415	1445
Best variable pitch........	209	1825	669

Propeller-type Fans. The conditions of operation of a propeller-type fan are quite different from those of a propeller for use on air or water craft. In the former case axial speeds on each side of the fan disk are alike while the pressure on the downstream side is greater than the pressure on the upstream side. For the latter case the reverse is true. The axial velocity of the fluid on the downstream side of the propeller fan disk exceeds that on the upstream side; the pressure, except at points very near the disk, is everywhere the same. The pressure rise which the propeller fan furnishes is concerned with the

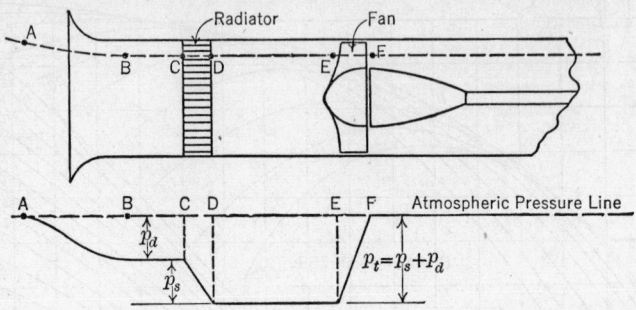

FIG. 45.   Variation of Pressure in a Fan Installation

rotational velocity increase since there is no axial velocity change. This pressure rise is usually written $p_t = p_d + p_s$, where $p_d = \frac{1}{2} \rho V^2$ = velocity or dynamic pressure and p_s = static pressure. The diagram in Fig. 45 shows a typical variation of pressure for a fan installation. The working conditions of the fan depend on the ratio p_d/p_t.

The efficiency
$$\eta = \frac{Q \times p_t}{\text{Power input}} \qquad (64)$$

Q = volume flowing per unit of time through the fan area, A. Sometimes the static efficiency $\eta_s = \dfrac{Q \times p_s}{\text{Power input}}$ is essential.

The Characteristics of a Fan are sometimes written in terms of two dimensionless numbers ϕ and ψ, where

$$\phi = \frac{Q}{A\,v_t}; \quad \psi = \frac{p_t}{\frac{\rho}{2}\,v_t^2} \qquad (65)$$

v_t = peripheral speed of fan, $= r\omega$, where r = fan radius and ω = angular speed of fan.

The ratio $\dfrac{p_d}{p_t} = \dfrac{\phi^2}{\psi}$ is then the criterion defining the working condition of the fan.

Fig. 46 shows a typical performance of a propeller fan.

Propeller fans are designed by means of the airfoil theory. Tietjens (Ref. 1 Art. 21) states that

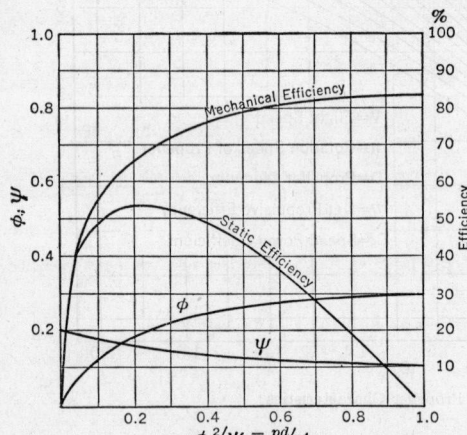

FIG. 46.   Typical Performance of a Propeller Fan
(Tietjens)

a simple method for an approximate design is given by

$$T = \frac{Q p_t}{V} = A p_t = 3.2\, n \left(\frac{\text{rpm}}{1000}\right)^2 b_2 r_2\, (r_2^2 - r_1^2) \qquad (66)$$

where T = thrust, V = axial velocity through the fan, n = number of blades, b_2 = blade width at tip, r_1 = hub radius, r_2 = tip radius. This formula depends upon a relation, $C_L V b$ = constant, where C_L = lift coefficient of an airfoil having approximately 50 per cent larger ratio of length to width than for the fan blade. This method becomes inaccurate when the ratio $\frac{p_d}{p_t} \leqq 0.3$. In such cases doubt exists about the relative efficiency of a propeller type fan as compared with other types.

Airplane Performance. The fundamental equation to determine airplane performance is

$$\frac{dh}{dt} = \left(\frac{\text{thp}_a - \text{thp}_r}{W}\right) 550 \quad \text{(Ref. 2 Art. 21)} \tag{67}$$

where h = altitude in feet.
  t = time in seconds.
  W = gross weight in pounds.
  thp_a = thrust horsepower available.
  thp_r = trust horsepower required.

This may be written $\frac{dh}{dt} = w_h - w_s$ = rising speed − sinking speed.

$$w_s = \frac{\sigma V^3}{L_p} + \frac{1}{\sigma}\frac{L_s}{V} \tag{68}$$

where σ = relative air density, $L_p = \frac{W}{f}$, f = equivalent parasite area to represent the parasite drag,

$$L_s = \frac{W}{b_e^2} \tag{69}$$

where b_e is the effective span and V = flight speed.

$$w_h = \frac{1}{L_t} T_a T_v \tag{70}$$

where $L_t = \frac{W}{\text{thp}_m}$, thp_m = thrust horsepower available at maximum speed $V = V_m$,

$$T_a = \frac{\text{thp}_a \text{ at altitude}}{\text{thp at sea level}} \tag{70a}$$

$$T_v = \frac{\text{thp}_a \text{ at speed } V}{\text{thp}_a \text{ at speed } V_m} \tag{70b}$$

A graphical solution of this equation shows that most of the important performance characteristics may be determined from a parameter

$$\Lambda = \frac{L_s L_t^{4/3}}{L_p^{1/3}} \tag{71}$$

Charts have been prepared in the reference from which it is a very simple matter to calculate landing speed, maximum velocity at any altitude, maximum rate of climb and speed at any altitude, absolute and service ceiling, and the time to climb to any altitude.

Loads on an Airplane in Flight. The load on an airplane in flight is usually expressed as $m = \frac{L}{W}$, where L is the momentary load and W the normal load which equals the gross weight. Measurements made on airplanes in flight show the following representative values of m in typical maneuvers.

Table X.   Values of m for an Airplane at Two Speeds

Maneuver	80 mph	175 mph
Sudden pull-up from a dive	3.5	9.3
Loop	3.7	5.0
Roll	4.2	5.2
Spin	3.1	2.3
Steeply banked turn	1.4	3.0

The load multiple is usually multiplied by a safety factor of 1.5 to 2 and this is then taken as a design load factor.

The sudden pull-up from a dive subjects an airplane to the most severe loads, but there are other loading conditions not quite so severe which materially change the position of the center of pressure. In others the load may be a twisting couple, for example, at high speed and in a steep dive.

Turbulence and gusts in thunder storms and over mountainous terrain cause upward or downward currents into which an airplane may run with abruptness. The load multiple for such a condition is

$$m = \frac{\dfrac{\rho}{2}\dfrac{dC_L}{d\alpha}UV}{\dfrac{W}{S}} \tag{72}$$

where ρ = mass density of the air, $\dfrac{dC_L}{d\alpha}$ = slope of the wing lift curve, U = upward or downward gust velocity, V = airplane flight speed, and $\dfrac{W}{S} = \dfrac{\text{gross weight}}{\text{wing area}}$ = wing loading. The following table shows measured values of U and the corresponding values for an airplane of wing loading $\dfrac{W}{S} = 15$ and flight speed $V = 190$ mph. Then $m = 0.215\,U$.

Table XI.   Load Multiples Due to Gusts (Ref. 3 Art. 21)

	Thunder storms	Mountainous terrain	Convection currents
Vertical velocity (ft per sec)....	44–110	10–27	7–24
m..........................	9.5–23.7	2.15–5.81	1.5–5.2

References

1. Tietjens, *Trans. A.S.M.E.*, June, 1932.
2. Oswald, National Advisory Committee for Aeronautics, Washington. *Technical Report* 408.
3. Wood, Airplane Design, Cornell University Press.

22. FLOW OF VISCOUS INCOMPRESSIBLE FLUIDS NEAR BOUNDARIES—GENERAL THEORY

The boundaries may be solid walls or surfaces of separation between two fluids. A dimensional analysis shows that the force experienced by a body in such cases is given by

$$R = \rho V^2 L^2 \phi\left(\frac{VL}{\nu}, \frac{gL}{V^2}, \frac{\gamma}{\rho g L^2}\right) \tag{73}$$
$$= C_R \rho V^2 L^2$$

where R = force exerted on the body, C_R = force coefficient.
  ρ = mass density of the fluid.
  V = relative speed of body and fluid.
  μ = coefficient of viscosity.
  g = acceleration of gravity.
  L = a typical length of the body defining its size.
  γ = surface tension of the fluid in contact with the solid boundary.

It is in general impossible in model testing to make all three numbers on which C_R depends alike. Sometimes one or two of these criteria of the motion may be disregarded. Several examples of interest will be considered.

23. RESISTANCE OF SURFACE VESSELS

Surface Ships may be broadly divided into two general types.
(a) Those which are practically supported by buoyant or hydrostatic forces.
(b) Those which are practically supported by dynamic forces.

Type (a) has been in use for a long time, and methods for predicting the characteristics for such vessels are very reliable. Froude's method is generally used. According to this method the resistance, R, is written: R = skin friction resistance + wave or eddy resistance. The former depends chiefly on Reynolds' number, $\dfrac{VL}{\nu}$, and the latter on Froude's number, $\dfrac{gL}{V^2}$. The number $\dfrac{\gamma}{\rho g L^2}$, called Weber's number, does not enter the problem unless very small models are tested.

If the subscript m designates the model, then the wave or eddy resistance, R_w, is given by

$$\frac{R_w}{R_{wm}} = \frac{\rho D}{\rho_m D_m} \tag{74}$$

where D designates displacement. This is dependent upon the fact that $\dfrac{gL}{V^2} = \dfrac{gL_m}{V_m^2}$ which defines corresponding speeds for model and full scale.

This leads to Froude's formula:

$$R = \left(R_m - C_{Rm}A_m \frac{\rho}{2} V_m^2\right)\lambda^3 + C_R A \frac{\rho}{2} V^2 \tag{75}$$

where R = resistance of full-sized ship.
   R_m = resistance of model (measured by towing the model).
   C_{Rm} = skin friction coefficient of model = f(R.N.).
   A_m = wetted surface of model.
   λ = scale ratio (full size to model).
   C_R = skin friction coefficient of full scale = f'(R.N.).
   A = wetted surface of full-sized ship.

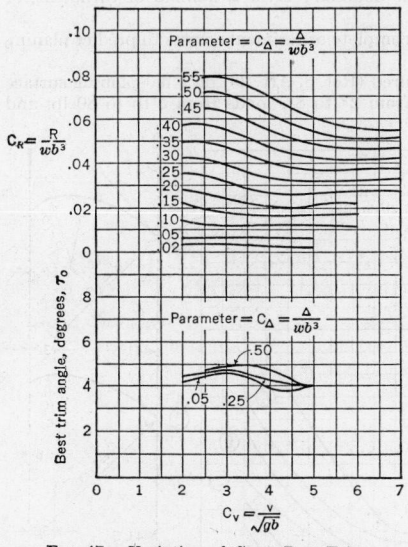

Fig. 47. Variation of C_R at Best Trim Angle and τ_0 with C_v (N.A.C.A. Tests)

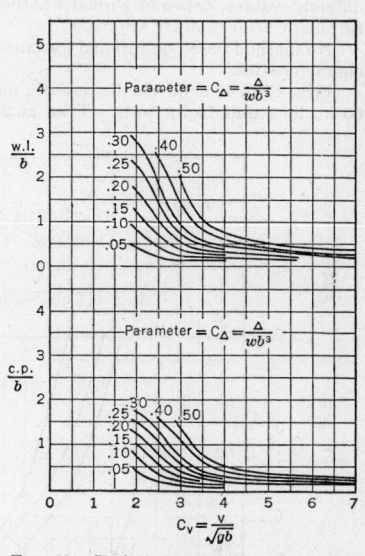

Fig. 48. Variation of w.l./b and c.p./b at Best Trim Angle with C_v

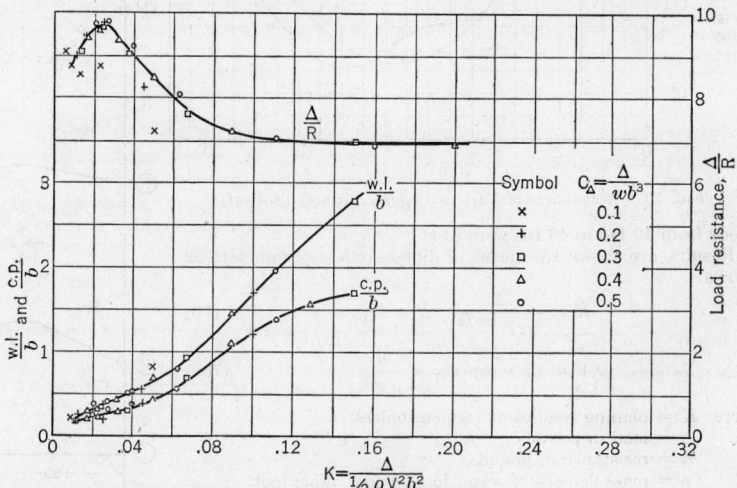

Fig. 49. Variation of Δ/R, w.l./b, and c.p./b at Best Trim Angle with Planing Coefficient, K (N.A.C.A. Tests)

Careful analyses of trial runs show that model experiments predict power within ± 2 per cent and engine revolutions within ± 1 per cent.

Type (b) Vessels in Which Dynamic Forces Predominate are usually called planing vessels or craft. Examples are fast motor boats and seaplanes. The action of the seaplanes is somewhat different in so far as the dynamic lift of the wings predominates in the later stages of the motion just preceding take-off. The Froude method cannot be employed for a planing craft for several reasons (Ref. 1, Art. 23):

(i) The wetted surface changes with the speed and with the angle of trim.

(ii) The mean speed of the water on a planing surface differs substantially from the towing speed.

(iii) At smaller scales, the friction coefficients at equal Reynolds' numbers may assume different values, depending upon whether the boundary layer is laminar or turbulent, or turbulent after laminar approach.

No method based on rational formula or complete experiments exists to predict planing characteristics.

Figs. 47 to 49 show results recently measured (Ref. 3, Art. 23) on a flat planing surface 60 in. long and 16 in. wide. Trim angles from 2° to 8°, loads from 5 lb to 80 lb, and

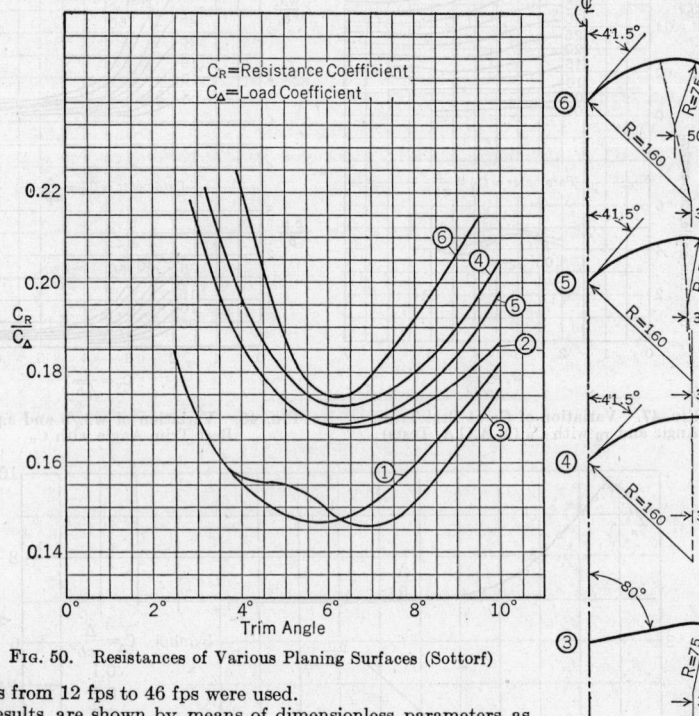

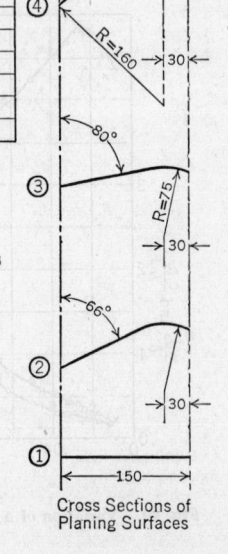

FIG. 50.   Resistances of Various Planing Surfaces (Sottorf)

Cross Sections of Planing Surfaces

speeds from 12 fps to 46 fps were used.

Results are shown by means of dimensionless parameters as follows:

$$K = \frac{\Delta}{\frac{1}{2}\rho\,V^2 b^2}\,; \quad \Delta = C_\Delta \rho\, b^3 \qquad (76)$$

$$V = C_v \sqrt{gb}\,; \quad C_R = \frac{R}{\rho\, gb^3} \qquad (76a)$$

where K = planing coefficient (dimensionless).
     Δ = load in pounds.
     R = resistance in pounds.
     ρ = mass density of water in slugs per cubic foot.
     V = planing speed in feet per second.
     b = width of planing surface in feet.

g = acceleration of gravity in feet per second per second.
C_Δ = load coefficient (dimensionless).
C_v = speed coefficient (dimensionless).
C_R = resistance coefficient (dimensionless).

Example: An aquaplane to be towed behind a motor boat weighs with the rider 200 lb. The boat makes 30 mph. How wide should the aquaplane be, at what trim should it ride, and how much pull would it exert on the tow rope?

From Fig. 49 we see that $K = 0.027$ corresponds to the best ratio of load to resistance, $\dfrac{\Delta}{R}$.

For salt water $1/2\,\rho \approx 1$; 30 mph = 44 ft per sec. Hence $K = 0.027 = \dfrac{200}{(44)^2 b^2}$; $b = 1.96$ ft, required

width. $C_v = \dfrac{V}{\sqrt{gb}} = \dfrac{44}{\sqrt{32.2 \times 1.96}} = 5.51$. From Fig. 47 we see that the best trim angle is 4°.

$\dfrac{\Delta}{R} = 9.75$ and hence the resistance on the tow line is 20.5 lb.

Some experiments have been made with planing surfaces which are not flat in a transverse plane. Sottorf (Ref. 1, Art. 23) found results as shown in Fig. 50.

Results found by Sottorf also indicate that curvature in the longitudinal plane may have favorable effects.

If the bottom of the planing surface of a planing craft ends abruptly in a step and the surface then continues for some distance aft of the step the wake behind the step will add additional resistance. Model experiments must be resorted to in such cases to obtain the resistance.

References

1. W. Sottorf, N.A.C.A. Technical Memo 739.
2. J. M. Shoemaker, N.A.C.A. Technical Note 509.

24. FLOW IN OPEN CHANNELS

Pressure Drop Coefficient. A dimensional analysis shows that the pressure drop coefficient $C_{\Delta p} = \dfrac{\Delta p}{L} \cdot \dfrac{2}{\rho} \dfrac{D'}{\bar{u}^2}$ (see Art. 17) for open channels depends upon Reynolds' number $\dfrac{\bar{u}\,D'}{\nu}$; Froude's number, $\dfrac{\bar{u}}{\sqrt{gD'}}$; and Weber's number, $\dfrac{\gamma}{\rho\,gD'^2}$. D' is a length which for open channels is usually taken as $\dfrac{A}{w.p.}$, where A = cross-sectional area of the fluid stream and $w.p.$ = wetted perimeter. It is called the mean hydraulic radius.

The Influence of Weber's Number or the surface-tension effect is usually negligible except where very small models are used. Sometimes gravity forces predominate as compared with friction forces. In such a case Froude's method may be used to determine the effect of gravity and then the friction effect may be obtained by approximate calculation or experiment. If both gravity and friction forces are important, systematic model testing must be undertaken.

Von Mises' Formula. Many formulas for obtaining the friction loss have been used in hydraulics. A recent formula by Von Mises is:

$$C_{\Delta p_1} = 0.0029 + \sqrt{\frac{k}{D'}} + \frac{3}{\sqrt{\text{R.N.}}} \tag{77}$$

where k = a roughness number, R.N. = $\dfrac{\bar{u}D'}{\nu'}$.

Values of k are given in the following table (Ref. 1, Art. 24).

Table XII

Material	$k \times 10^4$ in feet	Material	$k \times 10^4$ in feet
Glass	0.33–1.33	New cast iron	165–330
Drawn brass, lead, copper	0.33–1.65	Old cast iron	400–500
Smooth cement	12–25	Masonry (brick)	330–1000
Rough cement	33–66	Masonry (rough stone)	3300–6600
Asphalted zinc	50–100	Earth walls	16,500–33,000

Chezy's Formula. The lowest value of R.N. for which Von Mises' formula holds is R.N. ≈ 500. Other formulas are in constant use by hydraulic engineers. In the United States, Chezy's formula or modifications of it are favored. This formula is

$$Q = C_Q A \sqrt{D'} \sqrt{S} \tag{78}$$

the quantities Q, A, D' have been defined, and S = hydraulic slope = (head lost due to friction)/D'.

Values of C_Q are found in all hydraulics tables.

Reference

1. R. Von Mises, Handbuch der Experimental Physik, Vol. IV.

25. FLOW OVER NOTCHES AND WEIRS

A Common Form of Notch is a Vee-cut in the top of an end wall of a tank with the point of the Vee down. If the difference of level between the liquid surface and the point of the Vee is h, we may establish by dimensional analysis that

$$Q = g^{1/2} h^{5/2} f \left(\theta, \frac{h^{3/2} \rho g^{1/2}}{\mu} \right) = C_Q g^{1/2} h^{5/2} \tag{79}$$

In many cases viscosity effects are negligible and $C_Q = f(\theta)$. By experiment, $f(\theta) = 0.477 \tan \dfrac{\theta}{2}$. Exceptions occur if the jet runs down the vertical wall, if obstructions are placed near the notch, or the notch is too near a side wall of the channel.

Rectangular Notches or Weirs are also in common use. If the notch has a breadth b, then we find, neglecting viscosity and surface tension,

$$Q = g^{1/2} b h^{3/2} f \left(\frac{h}{b} \right) = C_Q g^{1/2} b h^{3/2} \tag{80}$$

Hydraulics tables list values of the coefficient C_Q.

26. WIND TUNNEL BOUNDARY EFFECTS

In Testing Models of Airplanes in wind tunnels the effect of the boundaries is appreciable. By means of the vortex theory it is possible to correct for this influence of the boundary. A very simple instance is a tunnel of a circular cross-section.

Prandtl found that an approximation consists in assuming constant span loading over the airfoil. The principal effect of the boundaries is due to the tip vortices at A and B. If two image vortices at A' and B' opposite in sense to A and B are added at a distance $\dfrac{2 R^2}{b}$ from the center at O, where b = airfoil span, then the system of four vortices produces a velocity field which has a zero normal velocity component at all points of a circle of radius R, center at O. It may then be demonstrated that the principal effects are given by:

$$\left. \begin{aligned} \alpha^\circ &= \alpha_T{}^\circ + \frac{\delta S C_L}{S_S} \times 57.3^\circ \\ C_D &= C_{DT} + \frac{\delta S C_L}{S_S} \end{aligned} \right\} \quad \begin{array}{l} \text{Airfoil span} \leq \\ {}^3/_4 \times \text{tunnel width} \end{array} \tag{81}$$

where $\alpha_T{}^\circ$ = an angle of attack used in the wind tunnel.

α = corrected angle of attack used in the wind tunnel.

C_{DT} = drag coefficient of the airfoil measured in the wind tunnel at $\alpha_T{}^\circ$.

C_D = corrected drag coefficient.

S = plan area or wing area.

S_S = cross-sectional area of the wind stream.

C_L = lift coefficient of airfoil measured at $\alpha_T{}^0$.

δ = a constant varying with the shape of the cross-section.

For the Circular Tunnel $\delta = +0.125$ when the boundary is solid. If the working section is open but circular in cross-section, $\delta = -0.125$. Values of δ have been determined for various types of tunnels. By leaving the working section partly open and partly closed the boundary effect may become negligible.

27. GROUND EFFECT ON AUTOMOBILES AND TRAINS

This effect has become of importance in testing the effects of shape changes on the air resistance of automobiles, trains, fast water craft, etc. Some tests have been made in wind tunnels and one under actual trial runs of an automobile. There is no conclusive experimental evidence concerning the effect of the boundary layer on the drag of a surface vehicle. If an automobile is moving in a dead calm there is no boundary layer near the surface of the ground. If a natural wind is blowing there is a boundary layer near the ground or water surface. Since the effects are more pronounced when there is a natural wind opposing the motion this condition is of interest especially in the case of a steamship steaming into a gale and also for any land craft.

Tests recently made at Case School of Applied Science using a flat plate to measure the ground effect show the following values of the air drag coefficient

$$C_D = \frac{D}{1/2 \, \rho \, A \, V^2} \tag{82}$$

where D = drag (pounds), ρ = mass density of air (slugs per cubic foot), A = projected area of model at right angles to wind stream (square feet), V = relative wind speed (feet per second). Results corrected to 15° C and 760 mm.

Table XIII

Type of model	C_D (at 0° yaw)	Reynolds' number	Length used in calculating Reynolds' number
Locomotive (Hudson J–1)................	0.632	3.57×10^6	Overall length (4 ft)
Locomotive (partially stream-lined).......	0.402	3.86×10^6	" " (4.25 ft)
Locomotive (Stream-lined)..............	0.0565	3.86×10^6	" " (4.25 ft)
Automobile (1932 model sedan)..........	0.463	0.873×10^6	" " (19 in.)
Automobile (Stream-lined).............	0.239	0.661×10^6	" " (15 in.)
Automobile (1932 sedan, run backwards)...	0.428	0.867×10^6	" " (19 in.)
Steamship (*Pres. Hoover*)................	0.392	3.0×10^6	" " (35 in.)
Steamship (Partially stream-lined)........	0.239	3.0×10^6	" " (35 in.)
Steamship (Well stream-lined)............	0.142	3.0×10^6	" " (35 in.)

Stalker (Ref. 1, Art. 27) states that if a model is tested near a flat plate from which the boundary layer has been partially removed the following results are obtained for a 0° yaw altitude:

Table XIV

Test method	Air drag
Flat plate, boundary layer partially removed......................	1.00
Flat plate, no boundary layer removed...........................	0.87
Free model, no plate...	1.11
Two identical models, one upside down, half of total drag..........	1.17

Reference

1. E. A. Stalker, *Journal of the Aeronautical Sciences*, Vol. 1, No. 3, July, 1934.

BIBLIOGRAPHY ON MECHANICS OF FLUIDS

1. AKADEMISCHE VERLAGSGESELLSCHAFT, M.B.H., Handbuch der Physik, Vol. IV, Parts 1 and 2, Leipzig, 1931.
2. BAKHMETEV, B. A., Hydraulics of Open Channels, New York, McGraw-Hill, 1932.
3. BIBLIOGRAPHY OF RECENT RESEARCH IN FLUID MECHANICS, *Journal of Applied Mechanics*, *Trans. A.S.M.E.*, March, 1935.
4. BOND, W. N., An Introduction to Fluid Motion, Edward Arnold & Co., 1925.
5. DAUGHERTY, R. L., Hydraulics, New York, McGraw-Hill, third edition, 1925.
6. DIEHL, W. S., Engineering Aerodynamics, New York, Ronald Press, 1928.
7. DRYDEN, MURNAGHAN, and BATEMAN, Hydrodynamics, Bulletin of National Research Council, No. 84, 1932.
8. DRYSDALE, C. V., Mechanical Properties of Fluids, London, Blackie & Sons, Ltd.
9. EWALD, P. P., PÖSCHL, TH., and PRANDTL, L., Physics of Solids and Fluids, London, Blackie & Sons, Ltd., 1930.
10. GLAUERT, H., Aerofoil and Air Screw Theory, Cambridge University Press, 1930.
11. INTERNATIONAL CRITICAL TABLES, New York, McGraw-Hill.
12. KING, H. W., and WISLER, C. O., Hydraulics, New York, John Wiley & Sons, third edition, 1933.
13. LAMB, HORACE, Hydrodynamics, Cambridge University Press, sixth edition, 1933.
14. MUNK, M., Fluid Dynamics for Aircraft Designers, New York, Ronald Press, 1929.

15. Pannell, J. R., Fluid Velocity and Pressure, Edward Arnold & Co., 1924.
16. Prandtl, L., Abriss der Stromungslehre, Germany, Friedr. Vieweg u. Sohn.
17. Prandtl, L. and Tietjens, O., Applied Hydro and Aero Mechanics, New York, McGraw-Hill, 1934.
18. Reid, E. G., Applied Wing Theory, New York, McGraw-Hill, 1932.
19. Reports of British Aeronautical Research Committee, H.M. Stationery Comm., London
20. Reports of National Advisory Committee for Aeronautics, Government Printing Office, Washington, D. C.
21. Russell, G. E., Text-book on Hydraulics, New York, Holt, fourth edition, 1934.
22. Schoder, E. W., and Dawson, F. M., Hydraulics, New York, McGraw-Hill, 1934.
23. Stalker, E. A., Principles of Flight, New York, Ronald Press, 1931.
24. Whitlock, T. G., Elementary Applied Aerodynamics, Oxford University Press, 1931.
25. Wood, K. D., Technical Aerodynamics, Cornell Co-op. Society, Ithaca, 1934.

SECTION 7

ENGINEERING THERMODYNAMICS

BY

MILTON C. STUART AND PAUL J. KIEFER

ENGINEERING THERMODYNAMICS

PRINCIPLES OF THERMODYNAMICS

The science of engineering thermodynamics develops means for determining the nature and amounts of the energy transformations occurring in engineering processes. Articles 1 to 7 present those principles which are common to all processes, regardless of the particular kind of working fluid used and the particular form of the machine or device in which the process is carried out.

1. ENERGY FORMS

The energies encountered in engineering thermodynamics are of several well-defined forms, named and described as follows:

(a) **Mechanical Potential Energy** is the form in which energy is stored by virtue of the relative vertical distance of a body above a horizontal reference plane.

(b) **Mechanical Kinetic Energy** is the form in which energy is stored by virtue of the relative motions existing between parts of a system.

(c) **Internal Energy** is the form in which energy is stored within a body, such as a quantity of gas, liquid, or solid, by virtue of the relative motions of, and the forces between, the molecules or atoms composing the body. It is evidenced by some properties of the body, usually temperature, but also by pressure and specific volume, and by physical phase, i.e., whether solid, liquid, or gaseous. Energy stored in substances and released in chemical reactions also comes under this classification of internal energy. In this case, the energy is ascribed to the arrangement of the atoms within the molecules. Considerable needless confusion has been introduced in many works by referring to internal energy in an ad lib. fashion as " heat." See discussion of the proper use of the term *heat* below.

The energy forms (a), (b), and (c) just described have the common characteristic that they are forms in which energy may be stored away for possible future use. The two forms (d) and (e) about to be described have quite different characteristics in that they represent the forms or means by which energy may be transferred or transformed.

(d) **Work** is a transient form of mechanical energy by means of which certain transformations of other forms of energy are brought about through the agency of a force acting through a distance. Several examples of energy transformation by means of work may be given. Work done by lifting a body stores mechanical potential energy in the system consisting of the body and the earth. Work done on a body to set it in motion stores mechanical kinetic energy in the system of which the body is one part. When a gas is compressed, work is transformed into internal energy which then exists as energy stored in the gas.

(e) **Heat,** like work, is a transient form of energy. Heat is defined as the energy in transition or transfer from one body to another by virtue of a temperature difference existing between the bodies. Conduction and radiation are the two methods through which heat transfer occurs.

Conduction is energy transfer from one body to another body at a lower temperature by tangible contact. It may be thought of as the transfer of some of the internal molecular kinetic energy of the hotter body to the more slowly moving molecules of the colder body.

Radiation is energy transmission through space from a hotter body to a colder body. In most processes involving heat flow it is impossible to distinguish the exact amounts transmitted by radiation and by conduction, but this distinction need seldom be made in practice as the category heat includes all transfer of energy due to temperature differences existing between two systems.

In identifying the various forms of energy, care must be exercised to preserve two distinctions. First there must be recognized the distinction between the group consisting of the *three stored forms of energy*, mechanical potential, mechanical kinetic, and internal energy; and the group comprising the *two transient forms*, work and heat. A second important distinction is that which exists *between internal energy and heat*. Energy stored in any molecular or atomic system such as energy in air, steam, or fuel comes under the category of internal energy. The name heat is used only to identify energy actually in transition or flow between systems at two different temperatures.

Convection is not a form of energy or energy transformation. When a body with its associated energy is moved from one position to another without state changes or energy transformations, the process is designated by the term *convection*. A typical example of convection is the movement of heated air from one part of a room to another. The internal energy has moved from one location to another, but no energy transformation has occurred. Another example of convection is the movement through a pipe of the kinetic energy or the potential energy associated with the fluid flowing in the pipe, without any energy transformations taking place.

2. UNITS OF ENERGY

Units of Energy. Any form of energy may be expressed quantitatively in any unit of energy. Fundamental units of energy are the *erg* in the metric system and the *foot-pound* in the English system. These units are derived from the standards of mass, length, and time. From the erg or foot-pound are derived numerous other energy units such as the joule, meter-kilogram, kilowatthour, horsepower-hour, etc.

From the earliest days of the science of thermodynamics there has existed an independent set of energy units, the *calorie* and the *British thermal unit* (Btu), related in no way to the standards of force or distance, but independently defined in terms of the thermal properties of water. For example, a widespread definition of the Btu is $1/180$ of the quantity of energy required (heat required) to change 1 lb of water from the ice-point to the steam-point at standard atmospheric pressure. With respect to these units there have evolved no accepted standards of definition of the units, methods of experimental procedure, or numerical results.

In order to recognize a common basis for all energy units and at the same time retain the calorie and Btu, the International Steam Table Conference, meeting in London in 1929, recommended that the international calorie be defined as $1/860$ of an International watthour. By arithmetic, using the defined relations between the English and metric systems, the Btu can be thus established, by definition, as 778.26 ft-lb.*

In honor of Dr. Joule who, in his classical experiment of raising the temperature of water by stirring it, demonstrated the conversion of mechanical potential energy into internal energy by the agency of work, the factor 778.26 is called *Joule's equivalent* and is represented by the symbol J. For all engineering purposes J may be taken as equal to 778. From the viewpoint of this treatment, J is not the "mechanical equivalent of heat," but merely a conversion factor between two energy units.

Since *power* is the time rate of expenditure of energy, we have a series of units of power which correspond to the energy units. Here, also, any power unit may be used to measure the expenditure or transition of energy by any method; either by work, or heat, or electrical energy. The watt (1 joule per sec) and the horsepower (550 ft-lb per sec) are the commonest forms of power units.

Factors for the ready conversion of the various energy and power units are found in Section 1, Tables 42 and 43. Below are given some of the definitions and conversion factors for the energy and power units most frequently encountered in engineering practice.

Conversion Factors for Energy Units.

1 Btu = 778 ft-lb (by definition) = 1055 joules = 252 calories.
1 erg = 1 dyne-cm (by definition).
1 joule = 10^7 ergs (by definition) = 0.73756 ft-lb.
1 horsepower-hour = 2545 Btu = 0.7457 kwhr.
1 kilowatthour = 860 international calories (by definition of calorie) = 1.341 hp-hr.

Conversion Factors for Power Units.

1 horsepower = 550 ft-lb per sec (by definition) = 33,000 ft-lb per min = 2545 Btu per hr = 0.7457 kw.
1 watt = 1 joule per sec (by definition).
1 kilowatt = 1000 watts (by definition) = 1.341 hp = 3413 Btu per hr.

---

* See article, The Mechanical Equivalent of Heat, Its Rise and Fall, by Eric Thorkelson, *Mechanical Engineering*, p. 347, June, 1934. Also The Passing of the Mechanical Equivalent of Heat, by E. F. Mueller, *Mechanical Engineering*, February, 1930.

3. ENERGY TRANSFORMATIONS

Processes. In a broad sense, a *process* is any event in nature in which a redistribution or transformation of energy occurs. Engineering thermodynamics considers chiefly those processes in which energy transformation occurs by means of changes in physical state of fluids.

The processes of engineering thermodynamics may be conveniently classified into well-defined groups in several ways. One classification is into the groups of reversible and irreversible processes. Another classification which is of much value is into the divisions called flow and non-flow processes.

Reversible Processes are those which meet two criteria as follows:

(*a*) The process, after completion, may be caused to occur in an exactly reverse order whereby the immediate system and any other systems associated with it may be returned from their last to their initial state.

(*b*) All the energy which was transformed during the process may be returned from its final to its original form, location, and amount.

Irreversible Processes are those which do not meet the above criteria. Among the conditions which contribute to the irreversibility of a process are the following:

(*a*) Heat flow from a higher to a lower temperature, (*b*) mixing of fluids at different temperatures, (*c*) fluid turbulence, (*d*) fluid or solid friction, (*e*) inelastic deformation.

Some examples of reversible processes are:

(*a*) A frictionless pendulum swinging in a vacuum, (*b*) a gas expanding slowly without friction or turbulence in a heat-insulated system.

Non-flow Processes are those occurring in a container or a space in such a way that the fluid does not flow in or out of the container or space during the process. An example is the expansion of steam in a cylinder during the period when the valves are closed.

Steady-flow Processes are those in which the fluid passes continuously through a region under conditions of steady flow. The conditions for the ideal steady-flow process are:

(*a*) At entrance to the region or apparatus considered, all properties which fix the state of the fluid maintain fixed values, that is, they do not vary with respect to time. Velocity of the fluid at entrance does not vary.

(*b*) Likewise, at exit from the region, fluid properties and velocity do not vary. But note that the exit properties may be and usually are quite different from the entrance properties.

(*c*) The mass flow at exit must equal the mass flow at entrance.

(*d*) At points between entrance and exit, not only may properties change in value, but they may be quite variable and unsteady. It is only at entrance and exit that conditions must be steady.

The steady-flow process or a process which closely approximates steady flow exists in most of the devices and machines employed in engineering practice. Examples are the steam engine, turbine, condenser, pump, boiler, nozzle, valve, and most heat-exchange appliances.

Other common types of processes are defined as follows:

Constant-pressure Process, in which the pressure of the fluid is constant throughout the process.

Constant-volume Process, in which the volume of the fluid is constant throughout the process.

Isothermal Process, in which the temperature of the fluid is constant throughout the process.

Adiabatic Process, in which no heat is added to or removed from the fluid during the process. (Caution: Refer to definition of heat in the previous section.)

Isentropic or Constant-entropy Process, in which the entropy is constant throughout the process.

Each of the five preceding processes may, in general, be either flow or non-flow, reversible or irreversible.

4. ENERGY EQUATIONS

Principal Symbols of Arts. 4, 5 and 6

E = internal energy, Btu per pound.

H = enthalpy, Btu per pound = $E + PV/J$.

J = Joule's equivalent, 778 ft-lb per Btu.

M = mass, pounds (numerically, the same as weight).

P = absolute pressure, pounds per square foot.

PV = flow work (displacement energy), foot-pounds per pound.

Q = energy supplied to or departing from a system or region as heat, Btu per pound.

$d'Q$ = a small quantity of heat (the inexact differential of Q).

Q_R = the unavailable energy of a process, Btu per pound.

S = entropy per pound.

T = absolute temperature, degrees fahrenheit.

T_R = absolute temperature of a receiver into which the unavailable energy of a process is rejected.

t = ordinary temperature, degrees fahrenheit.

U = velocity, feet per second.

$\dfrac{U^2}{64.34}$ = mechanical kinetic energy of a fluid stream or jet, foot-pounds per pound (64.34 = 2 × 32.17).

V = specific volume, cubic feet per pound.

W = a general symbol for work, including all the mechanical energies or effects, namely: flow work, shaft work, and mechanical kinetic and potential energies.

W_s = work supplied to or departing from a system by means of a shaft, or its equivalent, foot-pounds per pound of fluid.

Z = elevation, ft.

$(\int)$ = symbol for the integral of a function or quantity which completes a cycle.

Subscript 1 designates entrance to a system, or start of a process.

Subscript 2 designates exit from a system, or end of a process.

The First Law of Thermodynamics is the *Principle of the Conservation of Energy*. A statement of this principle most useful in this work is: In any process the net amount of energy added to a system equals the net change in energy within the system. This principle is expressed in a general energy equation as follows:

$$W + JQ = J(E_2 - E_1) \tag{1}$$

in which W stands for work and all other forms of mechanical energy; Q stands for heat, and $(E_2 - E_1)$ represents the change in internal energy within the system.

Equation 1 as written is for work and heat both entering the system. If work or heat leaves the system during the process, use minus signs for W or Q, or transpose W or Q to the right-hand side of the equation.

For mechanically reversible processes

$$W = -\int P\,dV \tag{2}$$

The minus sign is required because W is taken as positive when work is added to the system, and for this condition dV is negative.

For all reversible processes,

$$Q = E_2 - E_1 + \int P\,dV/J \tag{3}$$

and in the differential form

$$d'Q = dE + P\,dV/J \tag{4}$$

Note that equations 2, 3, and 4 apply for reversible processes only, but 1 applies for irreversible processes also.

Application of the Conservation of Energy Principle to the Steady-flow Process is made by reference to a diagrammatical sketch (Fig. 1) representing any device through which *steady flow* exists.

Energy may enter the system in the following forms and places.

(a) Mechanical potential energy (Z_1) entering with the fluid at section 1.

(b) Mechanical kinetic energy $\dfrac{U_1{}^2}{64.34}$ entering with the fluid at section 1.

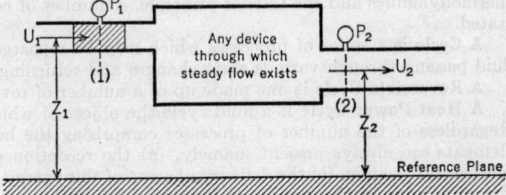

FIG. 1. Steady Flow Device

(c) Internal energy (E_1) entering with the fluid at section 1.

(d) Work required to cause flow into the system against the pressure existing at the entrance section 1 in amount equal to the product of pressure and specific volume, viz., P_1V_1 foot-pounds per pound. This energy is termed flow work or displacement energy.

(e) Heat (Q) may be supplied to the system at any point between the entrance section 1 and the exit section 2, for example, as to the water in a boiler.

(f) Shaft work (W_s) may be added to the system at any point between the entrance and exit by means of a shaft, for example, as in a compressor.

Energy may leave the system in six forms analogous to those entering: potential energy, kinetic energy, internal energy, and flow work, at the point at which the fluid leaves the system, and heat or work delivered from the system at some point between the entrance and exit. The total amount of energy within the system remains constant.

The steady flow energy equation then becomes:

$$Z_1 + \frac{U_1{}^2}{64.34} + JE_1 + P_1V_1 + W_{\text{in}} + JQ_{\text{in}} = Z_2 + \frac{U_2{}^2}{64.34} + JE_2 + P_2V_2 + W_{\text{out}} + JQ_{\text{out}}$$

Enthalpy. The combination $JE + PV$ occurs here and in other places with such frequency that there has been established a universal custom of combining them into a single term. Since E, P, and V are each properties of the fluid, the sum $E + PV/J$ is a property which is designated by the symbol H, so that, by definition, $H = E + PV/J$. Modern usage gives to this property or function the name *enthalpy* (pronounced ĕn-thăl'py, with accent on the second syllable). Other names in wide usage are heat content and total heat.

The mechanical potential energy term Z is of importance in hydraulic applications, but is usually of negligible value in thermodynamics.

The simplified energy equation for the steady-flow process is:

$$\frac{U_1{}^2}{64.34} + JH_1 + W_s + JQ = \frac{U_2{}^2}{64.34} + JH_2 \qquad (5)$$

where W_s and JQ are *net* values.

In *non-flow processes* energy may enter or leave the system as shaft work, W_s, or heat Q, and changes of energy within the system are limited to changes in internal energy, E. The non-flow energy equation is therefore similar to equation 1.

$$W_s + JQ = J(E_2 - E_1) \qquad (6)$$

For reversible non-flow processes this becomes

$$JQ = J(E_2 - E_1) + \int P dV \qquad (7)$$

5. ENTROPY AND THE AVAILABILITY OF ENERGY

The energy equations, though perfectly true, do not contain in themselves the means for evaluating them for all processes. For example, in a certain ideal (reversible) adiabatic process, the energy equation merely states that the work obtained from the process is equal to the change in the internal energy of the fluid, but no information whatever is given as to the amount of work which will be obtained or the magnitude of the change in the internal energy. The first law of thermodynamics is embodied in the energy equations. The second law of thermodynamics, as expressed in the entropy function, is required to make possible the computation of the maximum possible amount of work which may be obtained in certain ideal processes, particularly the reversible adiabatic process, and the reversible cycles upon which ideal heat engines operate.

In order to trace briefly how the entropy concept is developed from the second law of thermodynamics and the Carnot principle, a number of concepts and definitions must be stated.

A Cycle is a series of processes which may be repeated in a given order, the working fluid passing through various state changes and returning periodically to its initial state.

A Reversible Cycle is one made up of a number of reversible processes.

A Heat Power Cycle is a fluid cycle the object of which is to obtain work from heat. Regardless of the number of processes comprising the heat power cycle, three essential elements are always present, namely, (a) the reception of energy as heat from a high-temperature source, (b) the delivery of some of this energy as work, and (c) the rejection of the remainder of the energy as heat to a low-temperature receiver. The reception of energy may consist alternatively of a combustion process occurring with the working fluid, as in the internal-combustion engine.

The Cycle Efficiency is the ratio of the work delivered to the heat supplied.

Let Q = heat supplied from the source.

Q_R = heat rejected to the receiver.

W/J = work delivered by the cycle. Then for all cycles, reversible or irreversible,

$$Q = Q_R + W/J$$

(since in a cycle $\Delta E = 0$)

$$\text{Efficiency} = \frac{W/J}{Q} = \frac{Q - Q_R}{Q} = 1 - \frac{Q_R}{Q} \tag{8}$$

The Carnot Principle. In 1824 Sadi Carnot, in one of the most important contributions ever made to science, established the factors which affect the efficiency of cycles, and stated the necessary conditions for maximum efficiency. The full import of *the Carnot principle* may be given by stating it in the form of the three propositions which follow. These propositions are the embodiment of the *second law of thermodynamics*.

Proposition I. No cycle which continuously delivers work by the reception or conversion of energy at a high temperature (with rejection of any residue of energy at a lower temperature) can be more efficient than a reversible cycle operating between a source and receiver at these temperatures.

Proposition II. The efficiency of all reversible cycles working between the same temperatures is the same, irrespective of the differences in the character of the cycle or of the working fluid.

Proposition III. The efficiency of a reversible cycle depends only on the temperatures of the source and of the receiver.

Working with the third proposition of the Carnot principle, Kelvin established a thermodynamic temperature scale which made temperature a function of the amount of heat rejected and the amount of heat received in a reversible cycle. The Carnot principle states that Q_R/Q is a function of the temperature of the receiver and of the source. Kelvin made this temperature function as simple as possible by establishing the ratio of any two temperatures as being equal to the ratio of the amount of heat rejected and the amount of heat received by a reversible cycle operating between these temperatures. By computing the efficiency of a particular reversible cycle (the Carnot cycle) which used a perfect gas as the working substance, and then using the perfect gas as a thermometer, numerical values of the thermodynamic temperature scale were obtained.

The Kelvin Temperature Scale is summarized in the following relation, which may be appropriately called the *Carnot–Kelvin relation*

$$\frac{T_R}{T} = \frac{Q_R}{Q}$$

where T_R = absolute temperature of a receiver.

T = absolute temperature of a source.

Q_R = heat rejected from the reversible cycle to a receiver at a constant temperature T_R.

Q = heat added to a reversible cycle from a source at a constant temperature T.

Since the efficiency of a cycle is $1 - \dfrac{Q_R}{Q}$, the efficiency of any *reversible* cycle operating between the constant temperatures of T and T_R is

$$1 - \frac{T_R}{T} \quad \text{or} \quad \frac{T - T_R}{T} \tag{9}$$

The Carnot Cycle. Carnot further described a particular reversible cycle of much theoretical interest. Contrary to impressions sometimes received, the Carnot cycle need not be operated with a perfect gas as a working fluid. Any fluid may be used, since the Carnot principle states that the efficiency of the reversible cycle depends only on the temperatures of the source and the receiver and not on the nature of the working fluid or on any other consideration. The *Carnot cycle* is described essentially and completely by describing four processes of which it is composed, as follows:

1. A reversible isothermal expansion in which heat in the amount Q is received from a source at a constant temperature T.

2. A reversible adiabatic expansion in which the fluid passes from the source temperature T to the receiver temperature T_R.

3. A reversible isothermal compression in which heat in amount Q_R is rejected to a receiver at a constant temperature T_R.

4. A reversible adiabatic compression in which the fluid is returned from the receiver temperature T_R to the source temperature T, and its original state.

During processes 1 and 2, work is delivered to an external system. During processes 3 and 4, work must be supplied from an external system.

For this cycle, as for all cycles, the net work output $= Q - Q_R$ and the efficiency is $\dfrac{Q - Q_R}{Q}$ or $1 - \dfrac{Q_R}{Q}$. Since, from the Kelvin temperature scale, $\dfrac{Q_R}{Q} = \dfrac{T_R}{T}$, the efficiency of the Carnot cycle becomes $1 - T_R/T$. This is also the efficiency of all reversible cycles operating between temperatures of source and receiver of T and T_R respectively.

Availability of Energy. The idea of availability of energy, like the idea of reversibility, is of essential importance in thermodynamics. The availability of energy refers to the maximum amount of energy of a given process that may be transformed into work. Energy which is in the mechanical stored forms, kinetic or potential mechanical energy, may, by a reversible process, be converted wholly into mechanical work. A part of the internal energy of a gas under pressure may be converted into work. By the process of combustion, the internal chemical energy of a fuel may be first converted into heat and then a portion of this heat converted into work by means of the heat power cycle. Any quantity of energy which is already in the form of mechanical energy or which may be converted into mechanical energy or work is called available energy. In all reversible processes there is no change in the availability of the energy evolved in the process. An irreversible process always decreases the available portion of energy involved and thus increases the unavailable portion. When available energy becomes unavailable through the agency of an irreversible process, the energy is said to be degraded.

The availability of the energy for a reversible process is determined by the efficiency of a reversible cycle (any reversible cycle, the Carnot cycle, for convenience) or more simply by the mere statement of the Kelvin temperature scale. If, in a process, a quantity of heat Q is supplied to a system at a temperature T, the amount of energy Q_R which cannot under any circumstances be converted into work, and which must therefore become unavailable, depends upon the realizable receiver temperature T_R and the temperature T at which Q is added. This statement is in accordance with the fundamental relation which has been referred to as the Carnot–Kelvin relation.

$$\frac{Q_R}{Q} = \frac{T_R}{T}; \quad \text{or} \quad \frac{Q_R}{T_R} = \frac{Q}{T}; \quad \text{or} \quad Q_R = T_R \frac{Q}{T}$$

If the temperature T of the source varies from T_1 to T_2 during the addition of the heat Q the expressions above must be given in the integral form

$$\frac{Q_R}{T_R} = \int_1^2 \frac{d'Q}{T} \quad \text{or} \quad Q_R = T_R \int_1^2 \frac{d'Q}{T} \tag{10}$$

It is only for reversible processes that the above expressions are true.

Recalling that the reversible process gives the maximum amount of available energy and therefore the minimum amount of unavailable energy, it follows that for an irreversible process the amount of unavailable energy which must be discarded will be greater than the amount of unavailable energy of the reversible cycle. The important conclusion follows that, for the *irreversible* process,

$$Q_R > T_R \int \frac{d'Q}{T} \quad \text{and} \quad \frac{Q_R}{T_R} > \int \frac{d'Q}{T} \tag{10a}$$

Entropy. The above expression is known as the *inequality of Clausius*. Because of its essential utility in evaluating the availability of energy of a *reversible process* as given in equation 10, the function $\int \frac{d'Q}{T}$ was given by Clausius the name *entropy*, applicable, however, only to reversible processes.

For $d'Q$ in the above entropy expression we may substitute its value from the general energy equation for reversible process, $d'Q = dE + PdV/J$, and obtain

$$S = \int \frac{dE + PdV/J}{T}$$

This function, S, may be shown to have a very important property, namely, that its value for any given process in which a fluid passes from state 1 to state 2 is also its value for every process by which the fluid may pass from state 1 to state 2. This property is described by saying that *entropy is a point function*, meaning that the change in its value for processes depends only on the end points of the process and not at all upon the particular path taken by the process between the end points. For various reversible processes between states 1 and 2, Q may have various values, but $\int_1^2 \frac{d'Q}{T}$ and $\int_1^2 \frac{dE + PdV/J}{T}$ may have but one value. Also, it may be shown that the ratio Q_R/T_R for all processes between two states will have a single value regardless of the nature of the process and whether reversible or irreversible. For this reason entropy is sometimes defined as Q_R/T_R. An alternate definition of entropy change, true, however, only for reversible processes, is:

$$S_2 - S_1 = \int_1^2 \frac{dE + PdV/J}{T} \tag{11}$$

If the process is reversible and the path is known, the entropy change may be computed directly from equation 11. If the process is irreversible the fluid is not in a state of equilibrium at any point. The path may not be stated functionally and may not be depicted graphically. We may, however, substitute for any irreversible process any reversible process or series of reversible processes passing between the same end points. The computed entropy change for the reversible processes thus substituted is the entropy change for the original irreversible process. But *note carefully* that for the irreversible process

$$S_2 - S_1 \neq \int_1^2 \frac{d'Q}{T} \tag{12}$$

The entropy change $(S_2 - S_1)$ for any process being known, the amount of available energy Q_a for the process may be determined thus:

$$\begin{aligned} Q_R &= T_R (S_2 - S_1) \\ Q_a &= Q - Q_R \end{aligned} \tag{13}$$

In a reversible adiabatic process, $Q =$ zero, $S_2 - S_1 = \int_1^2 \frac{d'Q}{T} = 0$, $Q_R =$ zero, and there

is no change in availability. The principal use of entropy in engineering computations is to determine the final state in the reversible adiabatic for which $S_2 = S_1$.

Entropy as a Coordinate. Since entropy is a property or state function of a fluid it may be employed as a coordinate, in connection with various of the other properties, in the graphical representation of state changes. The more common diagrams in which entropy is so employed are: (a) the temperature-entropy (T, S) diagram in which absolute temperature is the ordinate and entropy per pound of fluid is the abscissa, and (b) the "Mollier" diagram (named after its inventor) in which enthalpy is the ordinate and entropy again the abscissa. The latter is of more particular convenience in connection with the portrayal of processes in which steady flow occurs.

The temperature-entropy diagram acquires a particular utility from the relationships between the properties T and S as they enter into the definition of the change of entropy of a fluid as follows:

For any process, reversible or irreversible,

$$Q_R/T_R = \Delta S, \quad \text{or} \quad Q_R = T_R \Delta S \tag{14}$$

For reversible processes, $\qquad \left. \begin{aligned} Q_R/T_R &= Q/T = \Delta S \\ Q &= T\Delta S \\ Q &= \int_a^b T dS \end{aligned} \right\} \tag{15}$

To illustrate the use of these expressions in connection with the T, S diagram let the line ab in Fig. 2 be a graphic record of the simultaneous values of the absolute temperature and the entropy of a fluid during any assumed process and state change, and let the horizontal line mn be a contour line of constant temperature at absolute temperature T_R. From equation 14 the change in the unavailable energy chargeable to the fluid as a result of the process is represented by the cross-hatched area below the line mn (the area $mnb'a'm$) since that area is the product of T_R and ΔS. Furthermore, from equation 15, if the process were one without fluid friction or other internal irreversibility and were accomplished solely by the reception of energy by the fluid (as heat), then the area between the line ab and the S axis (the area

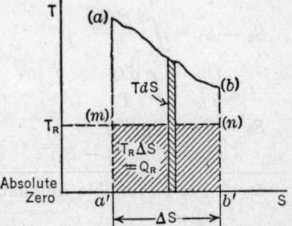

Fig. 2. T–S Relation in Process

$abb'a'a$) would represent the amount of heat received by the fluid during the process, since that area represents the summation of all infinitesimal products of T and dS between the limits of a and b, or equals $\int_a^b T dS$.

A constant temperature (isothermal) state change is represented by a straight line parallel to the S axis. Also a reversible adiabatic, being a constant entropy or isentropic process, is a straight line parallel to the T axis. For a fluid undergoing the sequence of reversible processes of the Carnot cycle the state changes are represented by the sequence of lines forming the rectangular figure $abnma$ of Fig. 3. In that figure the area $a'abb'a'$ again represents and is a measure of the "heat" energy received by the fluid during the isothermal expansion at T, the area $a'mnb'a'$ measures the unavailable energy rejected during the isothermal compression at T_R and also, since the work output of the cycle is the difference between the energy supplied and that rejected, the area *mabnm* measures the available portion of the energy supplied. The thermal efficiency of the cycle is thus the ratio $\dfrac{mabnm}{a'abb'a'}$, which equals the ratio $\dfrac{T - T_R}{T}$. The advantageous effect of increased T and of decreased T_R is thus portrayed graphically.

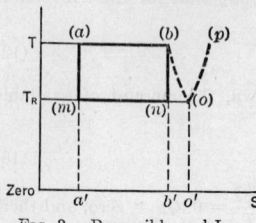

FIG. 3.   Reversible and Irreversible Cycles

For the irreversible adiabatic, due to the increase of unavailable energy (Q_R) which is inherent in any such process, the essential and invariable characteristic is an increase in the entropy of the fluid as a result of the process, this irrespective of whether the temperature may tend to decrease (as in an expansion) or to increase (as in a compression). Thus an irreversible adiabatic expansion from T to T_R starts at point b and ends at some point such as o, with increase of entropy, and a like irreversible adiabatic compression may start at o and end at some point p with an increase of entropy. The exact paths for irreversible processes cannot be shown graphically. For the expansion the increase of unavailable energy with respect to a receiver at T_R would be represented by the area $b'noo'b'$.

6. SUMMARY OF ENERGY EQUATIONS AND ENTROPY EXPRESSIONS

Table I.   Distinctions to be Made between Reversible and Irreversible Processes

For All Reversible Processes	For All Irreversible Processes *
$W + JQ = J(E_2 - E_1)$ (1)	Same as for reversible
$W = -\int P\,dV$ (2)	$W < \int P\,dV$ *
$Q = (E_2 - E_1) + \int P\,dV/J$ (3)	$Q < (E_2 - E_1) + \int P\,dV/J$
$d'Q = dE + P\,dV/J$ (4)	$d'Q < dE + P\,dV/J$ *
$dS = \dfrac{dE + P\,dV/J}{T}$ (11)	For an irreversible process, substitute any reversible process between the same end points, and compute entropy change from (11)
$dS = \dfrac{d'Q}{T}$	$dS > \dfrac{d'Q}{T}$
$S_2 - S_1 = \int_1^2 \dfrac{d'Q}{T}$ (12)	$S_2 - S_1 > \int_1^2 \dfrac{d'Q}{T}$
$\dfrac{Q_R}{T_R} = \int \dfrac{d'Q}{T}$ (10)	$\dfrac{Q_R}{T_R} > \int \dfrac{d'Q}{T}$ (10a)
$S_2 - S_1 = Q_R/T_R$ (13)	Same as for reversible
$Q_R = T_R(S_2 - S_1)$	Same as for reversible
For Reversible Adiabatic	For Irreversible Adiabatic
$Q = 0$	Same as for reversible
$\int \dfrac{d'Q}{T} = 0$	Same as for reversible
$S_2 - S_1 = 0$	$S_2 > S_1$
$Q_R = 0$	$Q_R > 0$
$\dfrac{Q_R}{T_R} = 0 = S_2 - S_1$	$\dfrac{Q_R}{T_R} = (S_2 - S_1) > 0$
$dE = -P\,dV/J$	$dE \neq P\,dV/J$ *
$W = J \int dE = -\int P\,dV$	$\int dE = W/J \neq \int P\,dV$ *

* For irreversible processes, the path cannot be definitely stated. Such expressions as $\int P\,dV$ must be considered as pertaining to a substitute reversible path between the same end points.

Table I—*Continued*

For All Reversible Cycles	For All Irreversible Cycles.
$(\oint) \, dS = 0$	Same as for reversible
$(\Sigma)Q = (\Sigma)W/J$	Same as for reversible
$(\oint) \, dE = 0$	Same as for reversible
$(\Sigma)\dfrac{Q_R}{T_R} = (\oint)\dfrac{d'Q}{T} = 0$	$(\Sigma)\dfrac{Q_R}{T_R} > (\oint)\dfrac{d'Q}{T}$
Efficiency $= \dfrac{Q - Q_R}{Q} = \dfrac{W}{JQ}$ (8)	Same as for reversible
Efficiency $1 - T_R/T$ (9) (with constant source temperature)	Eff. $< (1 - T_R/T)$

Steady-flow Energy Equation for Reversible and Irreversible Processes

$$\frac{U_1{}^2}{64.34} + JH_1 + W_s + JQ = \frac{U_2{}^2}{64.34} + JH_2 \tag{5}$$

Adiabatic Flow through Orifices, Nozzles, etc.

Reversible	Irreversible
$\dfrac{U_2{}^2 - U_1{}^2}{64.34} = J(H_1 - H_2)_{S=C}$	$\dfrac{U_2{}^2 - U_1{}^2}{64.34} = J(H_1 - H_2)_{S_2 > S_1}$
$\quad = \displaystyle\int_1^2 V\,dP$	and $\quad (H_1 - H_2) < (H_1 - H_2)_{S=C}$

Adiabatic Engines, Turbines, etc. (W_s = shaft work)

Reversible	Irreversible
$W_s = J(H_1 - H_2)_{S=C}$	$W_s = J(H_1 - H_2)_{S_2 > S_1}$
$\quad = \displaystyle\int_1^2 V\,dP$	and $\quad (H_1 - H_2) \neq (H_1 - H_2)_{S=C}$

For All Adiabatic Flow Processes

Reversible	Irreversible
$J(H_1 - H_2)_{S=C} = \displaystyle\int_1^2 V\,dP$	$J(H_1 - H_2) \neq \displaystyle\int_1^2 V\,dP$

Throttling Flow (Irreversible)

$$W_s = 0; \quad Q = 0; \quad \Delta\frac{V^2}{64.43} = 0 \qquad \begin{array}{l} P_2 < P_1 \\ H_1 = H_2 \quad \text{and} \quad S_2 > S_1 \end{array}$$

Summary of Energy Equations for Non-Flow Processes

For all non-flow processes,

$$W_s + JQ = J(E_2 - E_1) \tag{6}$$

in which $\qquad\qquad W_s$ = shaft work, or equivalent.

For all reversible non-flow processes,

$$JQ = J(E_2 - E_1) + \int P\,dV \tag{7}$$

For all reversible processes, $\quad W_s = -\displaystyle\int P\,dV$

For irreversible processes, $\quad W_s \neq \displaystyle\int P\,dV.$

For constant volume processes, $W_s = 0 \qquad Q = E_2 - E_1.$

For constant pressure reversible processes, $W_s = P(V_1 - V_2), \quad Q = (H_2 - H_1)$

For adiabatic reversible processes, $Q = 0, \quad S_2 = S_1;$

$$W_s = J(E_2 - E_1)_{S=C} = -\int P\,dV.$$

7. GENERAL THERMODYNAMIC RELATIONS

Equations expressing general relations which exist between and among the various thermodynamic properties of any substance are called general thermodynamic relations. These equations are of value in calculating various properties of fluids from experimentally determined values of other properties. They are also of use in the development and application of the general theory of thermodynamics in the fields of physics and chemistry. The general thermodynamic relations are derived by the application of certain mathematical methods to the general energy equations presented in Art. 4 and 5.

The following symbols are used in this article. No units are attached to the quantity, and the Joule's equivalent J is not used, since it is desired to leave the equations in a general form, applicable in any consistent system of units.

c_P = specific heat at constant pressure.
c_V = specific heat at constant volume.
d = "differential of."
∂ = "partial differential of."
E = internal energy per unit mass.
$H = E + PV$, or enthalpy per unit mass.
l_P = latent heat of pressure change.
l_V = latent heat of expansion.
P = pressure, force per unit area.
$\Psi = E - TS$, or "psi" function, per unit mass.
Q = energy in transition by conduction or radiation, per unit mass.
R = the gas constant (1545/mol wt, in ft-lb-°F system, and 82.9×10^6/mol wt, in cm-gram-°C system).
S = entropy per unit mass.
T = absolute temperature.
V = volume per unit mass.
W = mechanical effects, per unit mass of fluid.
$Z = E + PV - TS$, or "zeta" function, per unit mass.

Inserting in the general energy equation,

$$W + Q = E_2 - E_1 \tag{1}$$

the expression

$$W = -\int P\,dV \tag{2}$$

and the entropy expression,

$$Q = \int T\,dS \tag{15}$$

there is obtained an equation which contains only property functions, and which is the basis for the derivation of the general thermodynamic relations. This basic equation is, for reversible processes,

$$-\int P\,dV + \int T\,dS = E_2 - E_1$$

or in differential form:

$$T\,dS - P\,dV = dE \tag{16}$$

In addition to the five properties or functions T, S, P, V, and E of the foregoing equations, there are defined three additional property functions as follows:

$H = E + PV$,   enthalpy
$\Psi = E - TS$,   psi function (after Gibbs)
$Z = E + PV - TS$,   zeta function (after Gibbs)

A very great number of relations may be written connecting these eight state functions.* In this work only a few are presented that have been found to be particularly useful in connection with the engineering aspects of thermodynamics. These formulas provide significant relations between the property functions of a fluid and are relations that must be true for any fluid whatever. Relations between partial derivatives of the state functions are:

---

* Bridgman in his Condensed Collection of Thermodynamic Formulas (Harvard University Press) presents an ingenious collection of tables by which any of the general thermodynamic relations may be readily obtained. He notes that, including relations involving W and Q, 11×10^6 relations between first derivatives are possible and 9.5×10^{21} between second derivatives.

$$\left(\frac{\partial T}{\partial V}\right)_S = -\left(\frac{\partial P}{\partial S}\right)_V \quad (17)$$

$$\left(\frac{\partial E}{\partial V}\right)_S = \left(\frac{\partial \Psi}{\partial V}\right)_T = -P \quad (21)$$

$$\left(\frac{\partial T}{\partial P}\right)_S = \left(\frac{\partial V}{\partial S}\right)_P \quad (18)$$

$$\left(\frac{\partial E}{\partial S}\right)_V = \left(\frac{\partial H}{\partial S}\right)_P = T \quad (22)$$

$$\left(\frac{\partial S}{\partial V}\right)_T = \left(\frac{\partial P}{\partial T}\right)_V \quad (19)$$

$$\left(\frac{\partial H}{\partial P}\right)_S = \left(\frac{\partial Z}{\partial P}\right)_T = V \quad (23)$$

$$\left(\frac{\partial S}{\partial P}\right)_T = -\left(\frac{\partial V}{\partial T}\right)_P \quad (20)$$

$$\left(\frac{\partial \Psi}{\partial T}\right)_V = \left(\frac{\partial Z}{\partial T}\right)_P = -S \quad (24)$$

A very useful characteristic of a fluid is one which shows the energy required as heat to effect a unit change in the magnitude of the pressure, the temperature, or the specific volume of a unit mass of the fluid when one of these properties is maintained constant. Such a characteristic of the fluid is known as a *thermal capacity*. The familiar specific heat at constant pressure c_P is thus one of the several thermal capacities, being the amount of heat energy required to change the temperature of unit mass of the substance one degree while the pressure is maintained constant. Four thermal capacities are of particular practical utility. These, together with their names and conventional symbols, are:

$$\left(\frac{\partial' Q}{\partial T}\right)_P = c_P; \quad \text{specific heat at constant pressure} \quad (25)$$

$$\left(\frac{\partial' Q}{\partial T}\right)_V = c_V; \quad \text{specific heat at constant volume} \quad (26)$$

$$\left(\frac{\partial' Q}{\partial P}\right)_T = l_P; \quad \text{latent heat of pressure change} \quad (27)$$

$$\left(\frac{\partial' Q}{\partial V}\right)_T = l_V; \quad \text{latent heat of expansion} \quad (28)$$

The notation $d'Q$ and $\partial'Q$ which appears in these relations is a reminder of the important consideration that Q is not a point function. Relations among these coefficients and the other properties are as follows:

$$dS = \frac{c_P}{T} dT + \frac{l_P}{T} dP \quad (29)$$

$$dS = \frac{c_V}{T} dT + \frac{l_V}{T} dV \quad (30)$$

$$l_P = T\left(\frac{\partial S}{\partial P}\right)_T = -T\left(\frac{\partial V}{\partial T}\right)_P \quad (31)$$

$$l_V = T\left(\frac{\partial S}{\partial V}\right)_T = T\left(\frac{\partial P}{\partial T}\right)_V \quad (32)$$

$$c_P = -l_P\left(\frac{\partial P}{\partial T}\right)_S = T\left(\frac{\partial V}{\partial T}\right)_P\left(\frac{\partial P}{\partial T}\right)_S \quad (33)$$

$$c_V = -l_V\left(\frac{\partial V}{\partial T}\right)_S = -T\left(\frac{\partial P}{\partial T}\right)_V\left(\frac{\partial V}{\partial T}\right)_S \quad (34)$$

$$c_P - c_V = l_V \frac{dV}{dT} - l_P \frac{dP}{dT}$$

$$= l_V\left(\frac{\partial V}{\partial T}\right)_P \left[\text{or} = -l_P\left(\frac{\partial P}{\partial T}\right)_V\right]$$

$$= T\left(\frac{\partial P}{\partial T}\right)_V\left(\frac{\partial V}{\partial T}\right)_P \quad (35a)$$

or

$$= -T\left(\frac{\partial P}{\partial T}\right)_V^2\left(\frac{\partial V}{\partial P}\right)_T \quad (35b)$$

or

$$= -T\left(\frac{\partial V}{\partial T}\right)_P^2\left(\frac{\partial P}{\partial V}\right)_T \quad (35c)$$

$$c_P/c_V = k = -\frac{\left(\frac{\partial V}{\partial T}\right)_P \left(\frac{\partial P}{\partial T}\right)_S}{\left(\frac{\partial P}{\partial T}\right)_V \left(\frac{\partial V}{\partial T}\right)_S} = -\left(\frac{\partial V}{\partial T}\right)_P \left(\frac{\partial T}{\partial P}\right)_V \left(\frac{\partial P}{\partial V}\right)_S$$

$$= \left(\frac{\partial V}{\partial P}\right)_T \left(\frac{\partial P}{\partial V}\right)_S \tag{36}$$

$$\left(\frac{\partial c_P}{\partial P}\right)_T = -T\left(\frac{\partial^2 V}{\partial T^2}\right)_P \tag{37}$$

$$\left(\frac{\partial c_V}{\partial V}\right)_T = T\left(\frac{\partial^2 P}{\partial T^2}\right)_V \tag{38}$$

The utility of equations 31 to 38, correlating as they do the thermal capacities and the property functions P, V, T, and S, is quite varied. They afford an opportunity for cross-checking the consistency of the more difficultly and generally less accurately measurable calorimetric data on thermal capacities by use of the more accurately determinable relations among the property functions of a fluid.

Equation 32, which is in effect the historical Clapeyron's equation, has the particular utility that it enables the computation of the latent heat of vaporization of a fluid solely from data on the change of volume during vaporization and the relation between the pressure and temperature of saturated vapor. Thus, interpreting the latent heat of expansion in terms of the heat supplied during vaporization at constant temperature,

$$l_V = \frac{Q_{\text{vaporization}}}{\Delta V_{\text{vaporization}}} = \frac{H_{fg}}{V_{fg}}$$

(see Art. 16), whence, from equation 32,

$$H_{fg} = V_{fg}\, T \left(\frac{dP}{dT}\right)$$

In this expression, since the ratio dP/dT for a saturated vapor is the same for any process whether at constant volume or otherwise, it is written as the total derivative instead of the partial derivative. Physically it is the rate of change of the saturation pressure with temperature (the slope of the P–V curve) at the temperature T.

Several useful expressions which correlate the internal energy and enthalpy with the thermal capacities and the property functions follow.

$$dE = c_V\, dT + \left[T\left(\frac{\partial P}{\partial T}\right)_V - P\right]dV \tag{39}$$

$$\left(\frac{\partial E}{\partial V}\right)_T = T\left(\frac{\partial P}{\partial T}\right)_V - P \tag{40}$$

$$\left(\frac{\partial E}{\partial T}\right)_V = c_V \tag{41}$$

$$dH = c_P\, dT + \left[-T\left(\frac{\partial V}{\partial T}\right)_P + V\right]dP \tag{42}$$

$$\left(\frac{\partial H}{\partial P}\right)_T = V - T\left(\frac{\partial V}{\partial T}\right)_P \tag{43}$$

$$\left(\frac{\partial H}{\partial T}\right)_P = c_P \tag{44}$$

The Joule–Thomson Experiment. A type of physical experiment which is of much value in assisting to ascertain and check the characteristics of a fluid is the *Joule–Thomson* experiment. In this experiment the fluid is caused to flow to, throttle through, and pass from a porous plug, without energy reception or departure as heat and without appreciable velocity or velocity change in any phase of the process. The pressures and temperatures are measured on each side of the plug.

The energy equation for this pure throttling and wholly irreversible process is $H_1 = H_2$. Alternatively, its characteristic is that $dH = 0$. Introducing this consideration in equation 42, the relation for the process becomes

$$c_P\,(\partial T)_H = \left[T\left(\frac{\partial V}{\partial T}\right)_P - V\right](\partial P)_H$$

or

$$\left(\frac{\partial T}{\partial P}\right)_H = \frac{1}{c_P}\left[T\left(\frac{\partial V}{\partial T}\right)_P - V\right] \tag{45}$$

The coefficient $(\partial T/\partial P)_H$ in this expression is called the *Joule–Thomson coefficient* (μ).

It is evidently to be interpreted as the change of temperature of the fluid per unit fall of pressure under the above irreversible adiabatic throttling conditions. It may be shown that for a perfect gas, which has the state equation $PV = RT$, there would be no temperature change. With most gases, excepting hydrogen, there is a temperature drop or *cooling effect* at normal temperature levels, but a temperature *rise* at temperature levels above the so-called *inversion temperature*. For most gases the inversion temperature is high but for hydrogen it is at about −80 deg cent.

This experiment is further useful for reducing the readings of a gas thermometer to the energy or thermodynamic scale of temperature and for determining the location of the absolute thermodynamic zero of temperature.

The cooling effect which is characteristic of the actual gases is used regeneratively for the liquefaction of gases by the *Linde* process.

GASES

Symbols and Notations

A = area, square feet.
a = a coefficient in specific heat formulations.
b = a coefficient in specific heat formulations.
c_p = specific heat at constant pressure, Btu per pound.
c_v = specific heat at constant volume, Btu per pound.
E = molecular (internal) energy, Btu per pound.
f = a coefficient in specific heat formulations; also "a function of."
H = enthalpy $(E + PV/J)$, Btu per pound.
J = Joule's equivalent (=778 ft-lb per Btu).
k = ratio of c_p/c_v (a variable, but approaching constancy).
M' = mass rate of flow, pounds per second.
m = molecular weight.
n = an exponential constant (as in the property relation PV^n = a constant).
P = absolute pressure, pounds per square foot.
Q = energy transferred by heat (radiation or conduction), Btu per pound.
R = the gas constant for any given gas.
S = entropy, per pound.
T = absolute temperature, degrees Rankine (=degrees fahrenheit + 460).
U = velocity, feet per second.
V = specific volume, cubic feet per pound.
W = shaft-work, foot-pounds per pound.

8. GAS LAWS

P-V-T Relation for the Perfect Gas. The relation between the pressure, specific volume, and temperature of a perfect gas in any given condition or state is given by the *characteristic equation for gases*, which is:

$$PV = RT \qquad (1)$$

in which R is a constant for any gas, and is called the *gas constant*.

The above relation embodies Boyle's and Charles' laws.

Boyle's Law states that, when the temperature of a given mass of gas is held constant, the volume and pressure vary inversely, or PV = a constant.

Charles' Law states that, when the volume of a given mass of gas is held constant, the change in the pressure of the gas is proportional to the change in temperature, or $\frac{\Delta P}{\Delta T}$ = a constant.

Gas Constant. Actual gases at moderate pressure and also very low-pressure vapors approach this perfect gas criterion that R is a constant. However, for many practical purposes it may be sufficiently accurate to neglect this variation, and it is therefore customary to assign to the various gases values of R which correspond to some standard state. In Table I are presented, for the gases of more usual interest, the values of the gas constant as determined by physical measurement of the specific volume (V_0) at the standard atmospheric pressure (14.7 lb per sq in. abs) and 32 deg fahr. There are also tabulated the molecular weights of the fluids (m, referred to oxygen as 32), the product of the molecular weight and the gas constant ($= mR$), and the product mV_0. For a more complete table of the properties of gases see Section 1.

Table I. Characteristic Properties of Gases

Gas	V_0, at 14.7 lb and 32° F	R	m	mR	mV_0
Sulfur dioxide (SO_2).............	5.47	23.6	64.0	1512	350
Carbon dioxide (CO_2).............	8.10	34.9	44.0	1536	356
Oxygen (O_2).....................	11.2	48.3	32.0	1546	358
Atmospheric air..................	12.4	53.3	(29.0)	(1545)	(358)
Nitrogen (N_2) (atmos.)*..........	12.74	54.9	(28.1)	(1545)	(358)
Nitrogen (N_2) (chem.)............	12.8	55.1	28.0	1543	358
Carbon monoxide (CO)..........	12.8	55.1	28.0	1545	358
Ammonia (NH_3).................	20.8	89.5	17.0	1516	354
Helium (He)....................	89.7	386	4.0	1544	359
Hydrogen (H_2).................	178	767	2.0	1546	358.5

Representative value of $mR = 1545$; of $mV_0 = 358$.

* By "atmospheric nitrogen" is meant the residue of atmospheric air after abstraction of the oxygen but retaining the argon, carbon dioxide, etc., which exist in traces in the atmosphere.

It is significant that in this table the values of mR and of mV_0 are found to show relative uniformity, particularly for the permanent gases of less than three atoms per molecule. For convenience it is customary to select as representative the values of 1545 and 358 for these respective quantities, designating them as the "universal gas constant" (mR) and the "standard mol volume" (mV_0).* It follows from this approximate constancy of the product mV_0 that the specific volumes of the permanent gases at a given temperature and pressure are inversely proportional to their molecular weights, or that the densities are directly proportional.†

9. SPECIFIC HEAT OF GASES

Specific Heat. When energy is delivered to or withdrawn from a substance *as heat* (by conduction or radiation) and during the process the temperature of the substance changes, the ratio of the quantity of heat interchange per unit mass of the substance to the change in temperature is called the *specific heat, c,* of the substance for the particular process. Symbolically,

$$c = \frac{Q}{\Delta t} \qquad (2)$$

where c = specific heat of the substance for the process in question.

Q = energy interchange as heat during the process, per unit mass of substance, regarded as positive if incoming and negative if outgoing.

Δt = change of temperature of the substance, regarded as positive if increasing and negative if decreasing.

In the case of solids and liquids there is only one characteristic process which is of usual concern, namely, the heat interchange while the substance is at constant pressure. Therefore when the specific heat of such a substance is quoted it may be taken implicitly to be the specific heat *at constant pressure*. With gases, however, there is in practice an infinite variety of processes or state changes of the gas during which energy may be transferred as heat, frequently under circumstances where energy transition as work occurs simultaneously and affects correspondingly the temperature change. Thus the specific heat of a given gas may have an infinite range of values. For definiteness, however, there is commonly quoted for any particular gas its specific heat for a *constant volume* state change and that for a *constant pressure* state change, the two being designated respectively as the *specific heat at constant volume* ($_v$) and the *specific heat at constant pressure* (c_p).

Not only is the specific heat of a substance dependent upon the type of process but also, for a given process, it may vary with other conditions, such as the instantaneous temperature at which the process is operating. In that case, to determine the specific heat *at* a particular temperature we must pass to differential changes of temperature, dt, in place of Δt and write

$$c = \frac{d'Q}{dt}‡ \qquad (2a)$$

* Since a mass of m pounds of a fluid is commonly known as a "mol" the volume of m pounds is known as the "mol volume."

† This relationship is one of the bases for Avogadro's "law," which states that for all gases at a given pressure and temperature the number of molecules per unit volume is the same. If that were strictly true the densities of various gases would necessarily be proportional to their molecular weights and their specific volumes would be inversely proportional. The above relative uniformity of mV_0 is an approximate verification of the hypothesis.

‡ See p. 7–05 for meaning of symbol $d'Q$.

Transposing, $d'Q = cdt$, and for a finite rise from temperature t_1, to temperature t_2,

$$Q = \int_{t_1}^{t_2} cdt \qquad (3)$$

This expression shows the use to which information concerning the specific heat is frequently put, namely, that of computing the amount of energy transferred *as heat* during the performance of a specified process. If the specific heat varies with the temperature (as it usually does) a functional relation between c and t must be known before the expression may be integrated. A functional relation which is frequently found to be suitable is of the form,

$$c = a + bt + ft^2$$

where a, b, and f are coefficients which are determined by experiment.

Specific Heat of Actual Gases. For the perfect gas, c_v and c_p must either be constants or functions only of the temperature. Whether they are constants or variables their difference must be constant $(c_p - c_v = R/J)$.

In all the real gases these specific heats are found actually to vary rather materially with the temperature and to a slight degree with the pressure,* and also there is evidence that their difference is not exactly constant nor does it exactly equal R/J, where R is the gas constant as ascertained from specific volume data (Table II). However, a degree of accuracy which is sufficient for most practical purposes as well as a great gain in convenience is attained if these specific heats are regarded as effectively constant when the temperature range is moderate and as a function only of the temperature for greater ranges, and also if their differences may be regarded as virtually constant.

In Table II are presented, for certain gases of more usual engineering interest, expressions for the relations between the specific heat at constant volume (c_v) and the absolute temperature (T) and also corresponding values of the mean $(c_p - c_v)$ $(=R/J)$, and finally of the mean values of c_p and c_v and of the mean value of the ratio c_p/c_v $(=k)$ for the temperature range between 32 and 400 deg fahr. Unless materially greater temperature ranges are involved, these mean values may be employed as generally representative figures. In the table two values are presented for certain of the gases, those designated by the bracketed a being ones proposed by Partington and Shilling† as the result of exhaustive analyses of all available data and those designated by the bracketed b being

Table II. Specific Heats of Gases
(At Standard Atmospheric Pressure)
According to (a) Partington and Shilling, (b) Goodenough and Felbeck.

Expressions for c_v at the Absolute Temperature T (deg R)	Mean Values, 32° to 400° F			
	$c_p - c_v$ $(= R/J)$	c_v	c_p	k
Carbon dioxide (CO_2)				
(a) $0.1260 + 0.0_457\,T - 0.0_872\,T^2$	.0457	0:162	0.208	1.28
(b) $0.1037 + 0.0_3115\,T - 0.0_7284\,T^2 + 0.0_{11}247\,T^3$	.0451	0.171	0.216	1.26
Oxygen (O_2)				
(a) $0.1539 + 0.0_530\,T + 0.0_830\,T^2$	.0622	0.156	0.218	1.40
(b) $0.1545 + 0.0_8375\,T^2$	.0621	0.156	0.218	1.40
Air				
(a) $0.1699 + 0.0_533\,T + 0.0_833\,T^2$	.0687	0.173	0.241	1.40
Nitrogen, atmospheric				
(a) $0.1751 + 0.0_545\,T + 0.0_834\,T^2$	.0708	0.177	0.248	1.40
Nitrogen (chem.) and carbon monoxide				
(a) $0.1760 + 0.0_534\,T + 0.0_834\,T^2$	.0711	0.178	0.249	1.40
(b) $0.1766 + 0.0_8428\,T^2$	.0710	0.179	0.250	1.40
Hydrogen (H_2)				
(a) $2.314 + 0.0_3193\,T$	.985	2.44	3.43	1.40
(b) $1.990 + 0.0_3331\,T$	.986	2.21	3.20	1.44

(Note that, for example, $0.0_53\,T$ is the symbol for 0.000003 T or 0.3 $T \times 10^{-5}$.)

* For air at 140 deg fahr the specific heat has been shown to vary with the pressure according to the relation $c_p = 0.2414 - 0.0_42014\,P - 0.0_92478\,P^2 - 0.0_{12}3795\,P^3$. For ranges less than 1500 lb per sq in. the relation $c_p = 0.2414 - 0.0_42\,p$ is quite adequately accurate. See Ford, Compressor Theory and Practice.

† Partington and Shilling, The Specific Heat of Gases, Benn Ltd., London, 1924.

ones proposed by Goodenough and Felbeck * as the result of like analyses. The two are observed to check closely except for H_2 and CO_2. The differences in these at least reflect the difficulties in the way of accurate experimental determinations.

All of the relations are observed to be of the form

$$c = a + bT + fT^2 + \dots$$

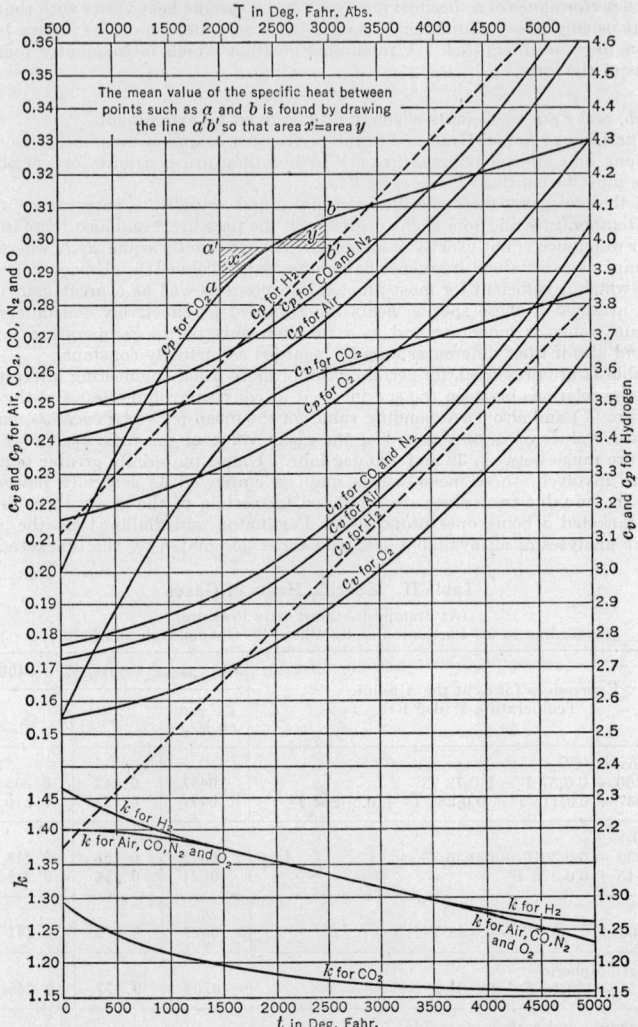

FIG. 1.   Chart of c_p, c_v, and k for Several Gases †

where a, b, and f are numerical coefficients which are established from the experimental evidence.

Fig. 1 shows the values graphically of the specific heat at constant pressure (c_p), specific heat at constant volume (c_v), and their ratio $(k = c_p/c_v)$ for air, CO_2, N_2, O_2, CO, and H_2 in the temperature range 0 deg fahr to 5000 deg fahr.

* Goodenough and Felbeck, *Univ. of Illinois Bull.* 139, 1923.
† Reproduced, by permission, from Barnard, Ellenwood, and Hirshfeld, *Heat-Power Engineering*, Part I, John Wiley & Sons.

ENERGY EQUATIONS FOR GASES

7–19

10. PROPERTY RELATIONS OF GASES

For vapors, such as steam, ammonia, etc., the relations which exist between the properties which must be known for the solution of engineering problems are given in tables of properties of the substances in question.   For gases that adequately approach perfect gas characteristics, the relations between properties are given by means of quite simple mathematical equations.   The properties and characteristic constants of gases which are of interest are P, V, T, E, H, S, c_v, c_p, k, and R.   In addition to the relations between specific heats and temperatures given on p. 7–17 the following table gives the more useful relations which exist between and among the various properties of gases.

Table III.   General Property Relations: Perfect Gas

$$\frac{PV}{T} = R, \text{ a constant for any given gas.} \tag{4}$$

$$\Delta E = \int_1^2 c_v \, dT, \text{ if } c_v \text{ is a function of } T, \text{ or}$$

$$= c_v (T_2 - T_1), \text{ if } c_v \text{ is effectively constant, or} \tag{5}$$

$$= \frac{1}{J (k-1)} (P_2 V_2 - P_1 V_1). \tag{5a}$$

$$\Delta H = \int_1^2 c_p \, dT, \text{ if } c_p \text{ is a function of } T, \text{ or}$$

$$= c_p (T_2 - T_1), \text{ if } c_p \text{ is effectively constant, or} \tag{6}$$

$$= \frac{k}{J (k-1)} (P_2 V_2 - P_1 V). \tag{6a}$$

$$\frac{c_p}{c_v} = k; \quad c_p - c_v = \frac{R}{J}; \quad c_p = \frac{Rk}{J (k-1)} \tag{7}$$

$$\Delta S = \int_1^2 c_v \frac{dT}{T} + \frac{R}{J} \log_e \frac{V_2}{V_1}, \text{ if } c_v \text{ is a function of } T, \tag{8}$$

$$= c_v \log_e \frac{T_2}{T_1} + \frac{R}{J} \log_e \frac{V_2}{V_1}, \text{ if } c_v \text{ is constant;} \tag{8a}$$

$$= \int_1^2 c_p \frac{dT}{T} - \frac{R}{J} \log_e \frac{P_2}{P_1}, \text{ if } c_p \text{ is a function of } T, \tag{8b}$$

$$= c_p \log_e \frac{T_2}{T_1} - \frac{R}{J} \log_e \frac{P_2}{P_1}, \text{ if } c_p \text{ is constant;} \tag{8c}$$

$$= c_p \log_e \frac{V_2}{V_1} + c_v \log_e \frac{P_2}{P_1}, \text{ if } c_p \text{ and } c_v \text{ are constant.} \tag{8d}$$

11. ENERGY EQUATIONS FOR GASES

All the energy equations of Art. 4 apply to processes with all fluids, therefore to processes with perfect gases.   The general method of solving processes with gases is to set up the energy equation in a form in which the energy transformation for the process is equated to a property change, such as the following.

For a non-flow reversible constant pressure process $Q = H_2 - H_1$. The property H must then be expressed in terms of some directly measurable properties such as P, V, and T, and a characteristic constant such as R or specific heat.   In the above example,

$$H_2 - H_1 = \Delta H = c_p (T_2 - T_1) \quad \text{or} \quad = \frac{k}{J (k-1)} (V_2 - V_1)P$$

if c_p is taken as constant.

Table IV below gives a summary of the special property and energy relations required for the usual processes encountered with gases.   Note that the term *mechanical effects* includes shaft work, flow work, and changes in mechanical kinetic or potential energy.

$$\text{Mechanical effects} = W_s + (P_1V_1 - P_2V_2) + \frac{U_1^2 - U_2^2}{64.34} + (Z_1 - Z_2).$$ For non-flow processes, mechanical effects consist only of shaft work.

Table IV.   Special Property and Energy Relations for State Changes of Perfect Gas

Constant (specific) volume:

$$\frac{P}{T} = \frac{R}{V} = \text{a constant during the state change} \tag{9}$$

$$\Delta E = \int_1^2 c_v \, dT = \frac{1}{J(k-1)} (P_2 - P_1)V$$

$$\Delta H = \int_1^2 c_p \, dT = \frac{k}{J(k-1)} (P_2 - P_1)V$$

$$\Delta S = \int_1^2 c_v \frac{dT}{T}, \quad \text{or} \quad = c_v \log_e \frac{P_2}{P_1} \text{ if } c_v \text{ is constant}$$

Mechanical effects, if reversible = zero; $Q = \Delta E$.

Constant pressure:

$$\frac{V}{T} = \frac{R}{P} = \text{a constant during the state change} \tag{10}$$

$$\Delta E = \int_1^2 c_v \, dT = \frac{1}{J(k-1)} (V_2 - V_1)P$$

$$\Delta H = \int_1^2 c_p \, dT = \frac{k}{J(k-1)} (V_2 - V_1)P$$

$$\Delta S = \int_1^2 c_p \frac{dT}{T}, \quad \text{or} \quad = c_p \log_e \frac{V_2}{V_1} \text{ if } c_p \text{ is constant}$$

Mechanical effects, if reversible = $P(V_1 - V_2)$; $Q = \Delta H$.

Isothermal (constant temperature):

$$PV = RT = \text{a constant during the state change} \tag{11}$$

$$\Delta E = \text{zero}; \quad \Delta H = \text{zero}; \quad \Delta S = \frac{R}{J} \log_e \frac{P_1}{P_2} \quad \text{or} \quad = \frac{R}{J} \log_e \frac{V_2}{V_1}$$

Mechanical effects, if reversible $= - RT \log_e (P_1/P_2)$ or

$$- RT \log_e (V_2/V_1) \tag{12}$$

$$Q = \frac{RT}{J} \log_e \frac{P_1}{P_2} \quad \text{or} \quad \frac{RT}{J} \log_e \frac{V_2}{V_1} \tag{13}$$

Reversible adiabatic (isentropic):

$$PV^k = \text{a constant during the change}; \quad TV^{k-1} = \text{a constant};$$

$$\frac{T}{P^{(k-1)/k}} = \text{a constant} \tag{14, 15, 16}$$

$$\Delta E = \int_1^2 c_v \, dT \quad \text{or} \quad = \frac{R}{J(k-1)} T_1 \left[\left(\frac{P_2}{P_1} \right)^{(k-1)/k} - 1 \right] \text{ if } k \text{ is constant} \tag{17}$$

$$\Delta H = \int_1^2 c_p \, dT \quad \text{or} \quad = \frac{kR}{J(k-1)} T_1 \left[\left(\frac{P_2}{P_1} \right)^{(k-1)/k} - 1 \right] \text{ if } k \text{ is constant} \tag{18}$$

$$\Delta S = \text{zero}; \quad Q = \text{zero}; \quad \text{mechanical effects} = J\Delta E.$$

Irreversible adiabatics may frequently be characterized approximately by the property relations:

$$PV^n = \text{a constant}; \quad TV^{n-1} = \text{a constant}; \quad \frac{T}{P^{(n-1)/n}} = \text{a constant} \tag{19, 20, 21}$$

$$\Delta E = \int_1^2 c_v \, dT \quad \text{or} \quad = \frac{R}{J(k-1)} T_1 \left[\left(\frac{P_2}{P_1} \right)^{(n-1)/n} - 1 \right] \tag{22}$$

$$\Delta H = \int_1^2 c_p \, dT \quad \text{or} \quad = \frac{kR}{J(k-1)} T_1 \left[\left(\frac{P_2}{P_1} \right)^{(n-1)/n} - 1 \right] \tag{23}$$

$$\Delta S = c_v \frac{n-k}{n} \log_e \frac{P_2}{P_1}, \quad \text{where} \begin{cases} n > k \text{ in a compression.} \\ n < k \text{ in an expansion.} \end{cases}$$

Mechanical effects $= J\Delta E$ but $\neq - \int_1^2 P \, dV$; $Q = \text{zero}$.

Table IV—*Continued*

Throttling process is primarily characterized by the relation:

$$H_2 = H_1 \tag{24}$$

Polytropics, which virtually are internally reversible but are not adiabatic, may frequently be characterized by the property relations:

$$PV^n = \text{a constant}; \quad TV^{n-1} = \text{a constant}; \quad \frac{T}{P^{(n-1)/n}} = \text{a constant} \tag{19, 20, 21}$$

$$\Delta E = \int_1^2 c_v \, dT = \frac{R}{J(k-1)} T_1 \left[\left(\frac{P_2}{P_1} \right)^{(n-1)/n} - 1 \right] \tag{22}$$

$$\Delta H = \int_1^2 c_p \, dT = \frac{kR}{J(k-1)} T_1 \left[\left(\frac{P_2}{P_1} \right)^{(n-1)/n} - 1 \right] \tag{23}$$

$$S = c_v \frac{n-k}{n} \log_e \frac{P_2}{P_1}, \quad \text{where} \quad \begin{cases} n < k \text{ in a compression with heat emission.} \\ n > k \text{ in an expansion with heat emission.} \end{cases}$$

$$\text{Mechanical effects} = \frac{R}{n-1} T_1 \left[\left(\frac{P_2}{P_1} \right)^{(n-1)/n} - 1 \right] \tag{25}$$

$$Q = \frac{R}{J} \frac{(n-k)}{(k-1)(n-1)} T_1 \left[\left(\frac{P_2}{P_1} \right)^{(n-1)/n} - 1 \right] \tag{26}$$

12. GRAPHICAL REPRESENTATION OF GAS STATE CHANGES

The property relations and state changes of gases may with advantage be portrayed graphically by curves drawn to coordinate axes of selected properties. The properties which are so employed with most frequency are the absolute pressure P as ordinate and specific volume V as abscissa. To these coordinates may be drawn contour lines of constant volume, constant pressure, or constant entropy (reversible adiabatic) state changes as well as any other sort of state changes. The typical forms of curves representing the commonly occuring state changes, as they would appear on P–V coordinates, are shown in Fig. 2. One evident feature of the family of curves is their increasing "steepness" with increase in the magnitude of n.

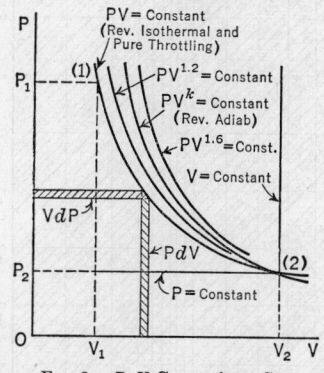

FIG. 2. *P–V Curves for a Gas*

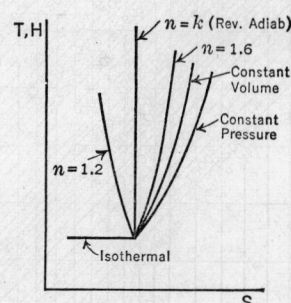

FIG. 3. *T–S or H–S Curves for a Gas*

Aside from the general utility of the P–V curves they offer the usual particular utility that $-\int_1^2 P \, dV$ is represented by the area below the state change curve and that this area is thus a graphic measure of the work in a mechanically reversible non-flow process, as well as the sum of all the *mechanical effects* in a mechanically reversible process, but *only* for a reversible one. In this connection note similarly that $\int_1^2 V \, dP$ is the area "back of" the state change curve and that, referring to the figure,

$$P_1 V_1 + \int_1^2 P \, dV - P_2 V_2 = -\int_1^2 V \, dP$$

However, for a reversible steady-flow process,

$$W + (U_1{}^2 - U_2{}^2)/64.34 + P_1 V_1 - P_2 V_2 = -\int_1^2 P dV$$

whence

$$W + (U_1{}^2 - U_2{}^2)/64.34 = -P_1 V_1 - \int_1^2 P dV + P_2 V_2 = \int_1^2 V dP$$

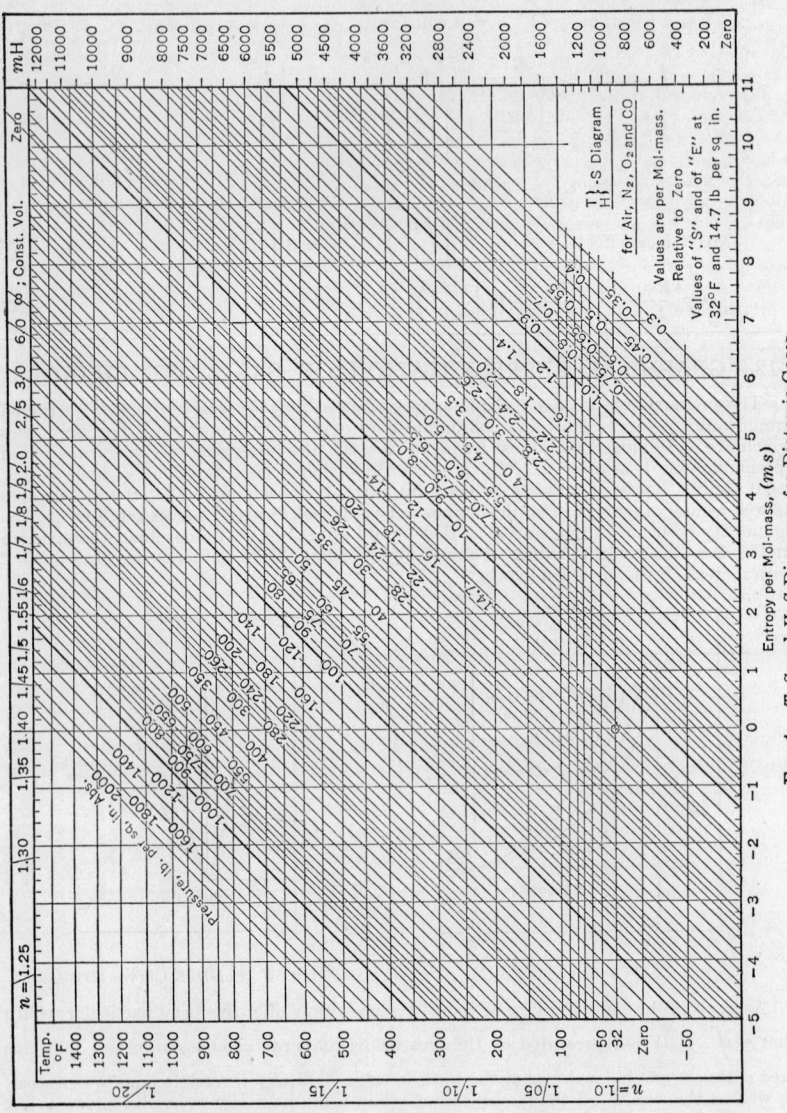

FIG. 4.   T–S and H–S Diagrams for Diatomic Gases

This is to say that for a steady-flow reversible process the summation of the shaft work and the change of kinetic energy, or either individually if the other is negligible or not germane, is measured graphically by the area "back of" the state change curve.

Curves T–S and H–S, though not commonly provided for gases, may for some purposes be used to advantage, particularly with T and H plotted jointly against S, Fig. 3.

A T, H–S diagram for air, N_2, O_2, and CO appears in Fig. 4.   For the plotting of the properties of these four diatomic gases, advantage is taken of the unique phenomenon that for all, the specific heat *per mol-mass* (per m pounds, where m is the molecular weight) is the same and therefore that their enthalpy and entropy per mol-mass are identical.* The relation for the specific heat per mol-mass, or the "molar" specific heat, of these gases, is

$$mc_v = 4.924 + 0.0_495\ T + 0.0_796\ T^2;\quad m(c_p - c_v) = 1.99\ \text{(Partington and Shilling,)}$$

$$mc_v = 4.945 + 0.0_612\ T^2;\quad m(c_p - c_v) = 1.98\ \text{(Goodenough and Felbeck,)}$$

The relation of Partington and Shilling has been used for the plotting of the curves, Fig. 4.

The values of mH and mS used in the figure are ones relative to a standard reference state at 32 deg fahr (492 deg R) and 14.7 lb per sq in. abs, at which state the entropy and the internal energy are regarded as zero.   The values of T and mH have been plotted to logarithmc scales in order to make the pressure contours virtually straight lines (departing from those only by reason of specific heat variation with temperature).   On this figure any polytropic or adiabatic state change conforming to the relation "$PV^n = $ constant" would be representable by a straight line of the proper slope.   The slope corresponding to various values of n may be found by passing a line through the reference state point, at 32 deg and 14.7 lb, and the proper one of the various indices appearing in left and upper margins.   For a state change passing through any other state, pass a line of proper slope through the desired state point.

13. FLOW OF GASES THROUGH PIPES, NOZZLES, AND ORIFICES

Flow of Gases through Pipes or Ducts

For flow through pipes or ducts, if the energy transitions as heat and velocity changes are negligible, the energy equation becomes $H_1 = H_2$ $(dH = 0)$.   A further condition is actual increase of entropy in the amount of $-\dfrac{1}{J} \displaystyle\int \dfrac{V}{T}\, dP$ (if $dH = 0$), or of $\dfrac{R}{J} \log_e \dfrac{P_1}{P_2}$ for a perfect gas.   The pressure *drop* that actually occurs in passage from (1) to (2) is thus an indicator of the entropy increase and corresponding energy degradation.

The usual practical concern in such flow is this pressure drop, and its relation to the features that influence it.   Those features are (1) the general geometrical form and relative interior roughness of the flow-channel and (2) its length if a channel of extensive character, (3) the diameter and area of a circular channel, the equivalent diameter $(= \sqrt{\text{Area}/0.7854})$ and area of an extensive non-circular channel, or any size dimension of a non-extensive channel such as a valve or elbow, (4) the mass-rate of flow of the gas through the channel, and (5) the temperature, pressure, gas constant, and absolute viscosity of the gas.

For conditions of relatively small pressure drop along an extensive channel, or of greater pressure drop if the gas temperature remains effectively constant, an expression suitably relating these factors is

$$\frac{\Delta P}{L} = \frac{f'}{64.34}\,\frac{RT}{P}\,\frac{(M'/A)^2}{D},\quad \text{or} \quad = \frac{f'}{40}\,\frac{RT}{P}\,\frac{(M')^2}{(D)^5} \tag{27}$$

where A = cross-sectional area of channel, square feet.

D = diameter of circular channel, feet, or equivalent diameter of non-circular channel $(= \sqrt{\text{area}/0.7854})$.

f' = "friction factor" (see below).

L = length of channel, feet.

M' = mass-rate of flow, pounds per second.

P = *mean* pressure in line, pounds per square foot, or pressure at any point if pressure drop is relatively small.

ΔP = pressure drop in length L, pounds per square foot.

R = gas constant, foot-pounds/(pounds $\times$ degrees Rankine).

T = mean absolute temperature of gas, degrees Rankine (=deg fahr + 460).

The value of the friction factor, f', depends on the interior form and relative surface roughness of the channel through which the flow occurs.   For a given character of channel it bears further a relatively definite relation to certain criteria that serve indirectly as indices of the general character of the flow (that is, as regards whether turbulent or stream

---

* This may be verified by reference to the expressions of Table II, multiplying the various coefficients in the expressions for air, N_2, O_2, and CO by the respective molecular weights.

lin: in character and, if turbulent, the order of turbulence). The basic one of such criteria is the ratio

$$\frac{DU}{\mu V}, \quad \text{or} \quad \frac{DUP}{\mu RT} \text{ for a gas}$$

where U = velocity, feet per second.
   V = specific volume, cubic feet per pound.
   μ = absolute viscosity of the fluid, pounds per foot-second (= absolute viscosity in poises $\times$ 0.0672).

This criterion will be recognized as the Reynolds' index (section 6, Art. 13).

For purposes of practical computation it is advantageous to recognize that $M' = AU/V = (\pi/4)D^2\,U/V$, whereby the above index may be modified to a more convenient form, $\dfrac{M'}{\mu D}\left(= \dfrac{\pi}{4} \times \text{Reynolds' index}\right)$. Further convenient criteria are combinations of f' and the above, namely, $\dfrac{\Delta P}{L}\dfrac{P}{RT}\dfrac{(M')^3}{(\mu)^5}$ and $\dfrac{\Delta P}{L}\dfrac{P}{RT}\dfrac{(D)^3}{(\mu)^2}$. $\left(\text{These are respectively } \dfrac{f'(RI)^5}{133} \text{ and } \dfrac{f'(RI)^2}{64.34}\right)$.

Table V gives reasonable values of f' as found by experiment for the flow through *circular* ducts of various relative interior-surface roughnesses at the various characters of flow indicated by the quoted values of the above criteria. For other than circular ducts equation 27 still applies, but further specific information would be required as regards the proper values of f' and of its relation to the Reynolds' index.

Table V. Turbulent Flow through Circular Channels
(Stream-line Flow Would Rarely be Encountered with Gas)

Reynolds' Index $\dfrac{DU}{\mu V}$	"A" $\dfrac{M'}{\mu D}$	"B" $\dfrac{\Delta P}{L}\dfrac{P}{RT}\dfrac{M'^3}{\mu^5}$	"C" $\dfrac{\Delta P}{L}\dfrac{P}{RT}\dfrac{D^3}{\mu^2}$	Friction Factor, f'
Criteria				
Interior Surface, Relatively Fairly Rough				
3×10^3	2.36×10^3	9.4×10^{13}	7.2×10^3	0.052
10^4	7.85×10^3	3.3×10^{16}	6.8×10^4	0.044
3×10^4	2.36×10^4	2.0×10^{18}	5.3×10^5	0.038
10^5	7.85×10^4	2.6×10^{21}	5.4×10^6	0.035
3×10^5	2.36×10^5	6.0×10^{23}	4.6×10^7	0.033
10^6 and up	7.85×10^5 and up	2.4×10^{26} and up	5.0×10^8 and up	0.032
Interior Surface, Relatively Quite Smooth				
3×10^3	2.36×10^3	9.1×10^{13}	7.0×10^3	0.050
10^4	7.85×10^3	2.6×10^{16}	5.4×10^4	0.035
3×10^4	2.36×10^4	5.3×10^{18}	4.0×10^5	0.029
10^5	7.85×10^4	1.7×10^{21}	3.6×10^6	0.023
3×10^5	2.36×10^5	3.7×10^{23}	2.8×10^7	0.020
10^6	7.85×10^5	1.3×10^{26}	2.7×10^8	0.017
3×10^6	2.36×10^6	2.7×10^{28}	2.1×10^9	0.015
10^7	7.85×10^6	1.0×10^{31}	2.0×10^{10}	0.013

Units for the items of the several criteria are as above.
In using the table to ascertain f' in equation 27:
   (a) If M', μ and D are specified, plus all except f' and one other term of equation 27, as for example ΔP, use column "A."
   (b) If P, R, T, μ, M', ΔP, and L are specified and the required diameter (D) is to be estimated, use column "B."
   (c) If P, R, T, μ, ΔP, D, and L are specified and the attainable M' is to be estimated, use column "C."
   For conditions of relatively small pressure drop through non-extensive channels and obstructions, such as pipe fittings or valves, an expression suitably relating the pressure drop and the controlling variables is

$$\Delta P = \frac{r'}{40} \frac{RT}{P} \frac{(M')^2}{(D)^4} \tag{28}$$

where all symbols and units are as in equation 27, excepting that D = any representative linear dimension of the obstructing device, such as the interior diameter of a pipe fitting; and r' = a "resistance factor" the magnitude of which depends on the geometrical form of the flow channel through the device, and also depends in principle on $M'/\mu D$ (the modified form of the Reynolds' index, Table V) but in practice is nearly constant *for a particular character of flow channel*, irrespective of the value of the criterion. For example, the value of r' for a short-radius, 90-deg circular elbow is about 1.0.

Flow through Orifices, Nozzles, etc., with Large Velocity Changes

For such flow, which is almost invariably adiabatic $(Q = 0)$, the energy equation becomes

$$\frac{U_2{}^2 - U_1{}^2}{64.34} = J(H_1 - H_2)$$

with an ideal constancy of the entropy if ideal flow, without fluid friction or turbulence, were securable. Because of friction, there is always some entropy increase. A necessary adjunct in the usual analysis of such flow is the continuity equation

$$M' = A_1 U_1/V_1 = A_2 U_2/V_2$$

The usual objective in the analyses of orifice or nozzle flow is an estimate either of the velocity U_2 at any section of area A_2, or of the mass-rate of flow M'. As it is convenient to evolve such estimates by considering ideal and thus isentropic flow, it is advantageous to combine the energy and continuity equations to give the relations

$$U_{2,\text{ ideal}} = 8.02 \sqrt{\frac{J(H_1 - H_2)_S}{1 - (A_2/A_1)^2 (V_1/V_2)_S{}^2}}$$

and

$$\frac{M'}{A_2}\text{ (ideal)} = \frac{U_{2,\text{ ideal}}}{V_{2,S}} = \frac{8.02}{V_{2,S}} \sqrt{\frac{J(H_1 - H_2)_S}{1 - (A_2/A_1)^2 (V_1/V_2)_S{}^2}},$$

where the subscript S indicates the constancy of the entropy for ideal expansion.

For the flow of gases (and of supersaturated vapors, p. 7-49), introduction of their isentropic relations (p. 7-20) enables the transpositions of the above equations to more useful ones involving the initial temperature T_1, the initial and terminal pressures, P_1 and P_2, and pertinent characteristics of the gas. The resultant equations are

$$U_{2,\text{ ideal}} = \frac{8.02 \left\{ \begin{array}{c} \sqrt{RT_1}, \text{ or} \\ \sqrt{P_1 V_1} \end{array} \right\} \sqrt{\dfrac{k}{k-1}\left[1 - \left(\dfrac{P_2}{P_1}\right)^{(k-1)/k}\right]}}{\sqrt{1 - \left(\dfrac{A_2}{A_1}\right)^2 \left(\dfrac{P_2}{P_1}\right)^{2/k}}} \qquad (29)$$

$$\frac{M'}{A_2}\text{ (ideal)} = \frac{8.02 \left\{ \begin{array}{c} P_1/\sqrt{RT_1}, \\ \text{or } \sqrt{P_1/V_1} \end{array} \right\} \sqrt{\dfrac{k}{k-1}\left[\left(\dfrac{P_2}{P_1}\right)^{2/k} - \left(\dfrac{P_2}{P_1}\right)^{(k+1)/k}\right]}}{\sqrt{1 - \left(\dfrac{A_2}{A_1}\right)^2 \left(\dfrac{P_2}{P_1}\right)^{2/k}}} \qquad (30)$$

or

$$= \frac{8.02 \left\{ \begin{array}{c} P_2/\sqrt{RT_1}, \text{ or} \\ P_2/\sqrt{P_1 V_1} \end{array} \right\} \sqrt{\dfrac{k}{k-1}\left(\dfrac{P_1}{P_2}\right)^{(k-1)/k}\left[\left(\dfrac{P_1}{P_2}\right)^{(k-1)/k} - 1\right]}}{\sqrt{1 - \left(\dfrac{A_2}{A_1}\right)^2 \left(\dfrac{P_2}{P_1}\right)^{2/k}}} \qquad (31)$$

For air at moderate temperature, with $R = 53.3$ and $k = 1.4$, these become

$$U_{2,\text{ ideal}} = \frac{109.7\sqrt{T_1}\sqrt{1 - (P_2/P_1)^{0.286}}}{\sqrt{1 - (A_2/A_1)^2 (P_2/P_1)^{1.429}}}$$

$$\frac{M'}{A_2}\text{ (ideal)} = \frac{2.055\,(P_1/\sqrt{T_1})\sqrt{(P_2/P_1)^{1.429} - (P_2/P_1)^{1.714}}}{\sqrt{1 - (A_2/A_1)^2 (P_2/P_1)^{1.429}}}$$

or

$$= \frac{2.055\,(P_2/\sqrt{T_1})\sqrt{(P_1/P_2)^{0.286}\,[(P_1/P_2)^{0.286} - 1]}}{\sqrt{1 - (A_2/A_1)^2 (P_2/P_1)^{1.429}}}$$

In these equations the denominator originated in effecting an elimination of the term U_1 from the original energy equation. Consequently its reciprocal is frequently regarded and designated as a "correction factor for the initial velocity." It may evidently be omitted when U_1 is of relatively negligible magnitude, or in general when (A_2/A_1) is less than 0.10.

Table VI. Pertinent Functions of P_2, P_1, and k

$\dfrac{P_2}{P_1}$	$\left(\dfrac{P_2}{P_1}\right)^{2/k}$			$\sqrt{\dfrac{k}{k-1}\left[1-\left(\dfrac{P_2}{P_1}\right)^{(k-1)/k}\right]}$			$\sqrt{\dfrac{k}{k-1}\left[\left(\dfrac{P_2}{P_1}\right)^{2/k}-\left(\dfrac{P_2}{P_1}\right)^{(k+1)/k}\right]}$			$\sqrt{\dfrac{k}{k-1}\left[\left(\dfrac{P_1}{P_2}\right)^{(k-1)/k}-1\right]}$		
$k=$	1.3	1.4	1.67	1.3	1.4	1.67	1.3	1.4	1.67	1.3	1.4	1.67
0.9	0.850	0.860	0.881	0.323	0.322	0.321	0.297	0.299	0.302	0.330	0.332	0.335
0.8	.709	.727	.765	0.466	0.465	0.462	.393	.396	.404	0.491	0.496	0.505
0.7	.578	.601	.652	0.585	0.582	0.577	.445	.451	.465	0.635	0.645	0.665
0.6	.456	.482	.542	0.694	0.689	0.680	.469	.479	.500	0.781	0.798	0.834
0.5	.344	.371	.435	0.800	0.793	0.778	.469	.484	.513	0.939	0.967	1.027
0.4	.244	.270	.333	0.909	0.898	0.875	.449	.467	.505	1.123	1.166	1.264
0.3	.157	.179	.236	1.026	1.009	0.978	.406	.427	.475	1.354	1.424	1.584
0.2	.084	.100	.145	1.159	1.136	1.089	.336	.360	.415	1.681	1.799	2.074
0.1	.029	.037	.063	1.337	1.299	1.227	.227	.250	.308	2.274	2.508	3.081

At P_2/P_1 = critical pressure ratio

$\dfrac{P_2}{P_1}$	1.3	1.4	1.67	1.3	1.4	1.67	1.3	1.4	1.67	1.3	1.4	1.67
0.546	0.394			0.752			0.472			(0.865)		
.528		.402			0.764			0.484			(0.917)	
.487			0.422			0.791			0.513			(1.054)

It is evident from equations 30 or 31 that, if facilities are to be provided for ideal or isentropic flow at a particular rate and with a given initial state, a definite relation exists between the transverse areas A_2 at successive sections in a flow channel and the pressure P_2 at those sections. Solution of the equations for A_2 at successive values of P_2 would further disclose that, again if facilities for isentropic flow are to be provided: the fluid stream (a) must first be convergent (that is, with decreasing area), until the pressure attains a certain proportion of the initial pressure, and (b) must thereafter diverge.

Except under rather abnormal conditions as regards U_1, at the consequent point of minimum area or the *throat* of the stream,

$$\left(\frac{P_2}{P_1}\right)_{\text{throat, ideal flow}} = \left(\frac{2}{k+1}\right)^{k/(k-1)}.$$

This particular ratio is conventionally known as the *critical pressure ratio*. By introduction of the ratio into equation 30 it develops that

$$\frac{M'}{A_{\text{throat}}} \text{ (ideal)} = 8.02 \left\{ \begin{matrix} P_1/\sqrt{RT_1} \\ \text{or } \sqrt{P_1/V_1} \end{matrix} \right\} \sqrt{\frac{k}{k+1}\left(\frac{2}{k+1}\right)^{2/(k-1)}} \qquad (32)$$

$$= 0.53\, P_1/\sqrt{T_1} \text{ for air at moderate temperature.}$$

Values of various of the functions of P_2, P_1, and k that appear in the above equations are tabulated for convenience in Table VI for values of P_2/P_1 from 0.9 to 0.1 and at values of k of 1.3, 1.4, and 1.67, these being fair average values of k at moderate temperature for, respectively, triatomic, diatomic, and monatomic gases.

For values of P_2/P_1 between 1.0 and 0.9 (that is, for values of $\Delta P/P_1$ from zero to 0.1), accurate evaluation of these functions is bothersome. Convenient equivalents that give results accurate within 0.5 per cent are tabulated herewith.

Table VII. Equivalents of Pertinent Function, for $\Delta P/P_1$ from 0.0 to 0.10

Function	Equivalent when $\Delta P/P_1$ is not greater than—	
	0.10	0.01
$(P_2/P_1)^{2/k}$	$1 - \dfrac{2}{k}\left(\dfrac{\Delta P}{P_1}\right)$	$\dfrac{P_2}{P_1}$
$\sqrt{\dfrac{k}{k-1}\left[1 - \left(\dfrac{P_2}{P_1}\right)^{(k-1)/k}\right]}$	$\sqrt{\dfrac{\Delta P}{P_1}\left[1 + \dfrac{0.5}{k}\dfrac{\Delta P}{P_1}\right]}$	$\sqrt{\dfrac{\Delta P}{P_1}}$
$\sqrt{\dfrac{k}{k-1}\left[\left(\dfrac{P_2}{P_1}\right)^{2/k} - \left(\dfrac{P_2}{P_1}\right)^{(k+1)/k}\right]}$	$\sqrt{\dfrac{\Delta P}{P_1}\left[1 - \dfrac{1.5}{k}\dfrac{\Delta P}{P_1}\right]}$	$\sqrt{\dfrac{\Delta P}{P_1}}$
$\sqrt{\dfrac{k}{k-1}\left(\dfrac{P_1}{P_2}\right)^{(k-1)/k}\left[\left(\dfrac{P_1}{P_2}\right)^{(k-1)/k} - 1\right]}$	$\sqrt{\dfrac{\Delta P}{P_2}\left[1 - \dfrac{(1.5-k)}{k}\dfrac{\Delta P}{P_2}\right]}$	$\sqrt{\dfrac{\Delta P}{P_2}}$

Nozzles. Regarding the term *nozzle* as inclusive of any simple flow channel that aims to provide ideally suitable facilities for an isentropic expansion and acceleration of a flowing gas, the foregoing relations provide all that is necessary for estimates of the velocity or the mass-rate of flow ideally securable with specified P_1 and T_1 and upon expansion to pressure P_2 at a section of area A_2. Recall that, from above thermodynamic considerations, a convergent channel is adequate for an expansion to a region that is at any pressure greater than or equal to the critical pressure ($=0.528\, P_1$ for air or other diatomic gases, see Table VI), whereas convergence to a throat and a subsequent carefully controlled divergence are required to enable an approach to isentropic expansion to a region having a pressure less than the critical.

Actual flow conditions are conventionally accounted by employing *coefficients* of *velocity* and *discharge*, also a *nozzle efficiency*, where

Coefficient of velocity $(C_U) = U_{2,\,\text{actual}}/U_{2,\,\text{ideal}}$

Coefficient of discharge $(C_D) = M'_{\text{actual}}/M'_{\text{ideal}}$

$$\text{Nozzle efficiency} = \frac{(U_2{}^2 - U_1{}^2)_{\text{actual}}}{(U_2{}^2 - U_1{}^2)_{\text{ideal}}}$$

$$= \frac{U_2{}^2\,(\text{actual})}{U_2{}^2\,(\text{ideal})} \text{ if } U_1 \text{ is negligible}$$

Thus $U_{2,\text{ actual}} = C_U \times U_{2,\text{ ideal}}; \quad M'_{,\text{ actual}} = C_D \times M'_{,\text{ ideal}}$

$$\frac{U_2{}^2}{64.34} \text{ (actual)} = \text{Eff. }_\text{nozzle} \times \frac{U_2{}^2}{64.34} \text{ (ideal) (if } U_1 \text{ is negligible)}$$

The discharge coefficient for the flow of a gas through well-formed convergent nozzles or through the convergent portion of convergent-divergent nozzles attains a value of 0.98 and over at conventional rates of flow, but so decreases at very low rates (sensible decrease beginning at a Reynolds' number of about 2×10^5) as in general to require calibration when nozzles are employed at such rates. The efficiency of advantageously formed convergent nozzles or of the convergent section of convergent-divergent nozzles attains values of 0.96 and over.

The inertia of the rapidly flowing fluid entering the divergent section of convergent-divergent nozzles does not permit so efficient an expansion in that section, reducing the efficiencies of such nozzles to 0.92 or less. Improper design or unsuitable operation, in the feature of an $\dfrac{\text{Exit area, } A_2}{\text{Throat area, } A_{th}}$ ratio greater than that suitably corresponding to the actual $\dfrac{\text{Discharge region pressure, } P_2}{\text{Throat pressure, } P_{\text{crit}}}$ ratio (that is, *over-expansion*), or the reverse condition (*under-expansion*), will act to further and materially decrease the efficiency.

Orifices. The control or the metering of gases is frequently effected (without concern as to efficient jet formation) by directing flow through circular apertures located in plates or diaphragms. These apertures, or orifices, may be simply straight-sided holes through a thin plate (or its equivalent), or a converging profile may be provided on the upstream side of an orifice in a thicker plate. The orifice plates may be located at the entrance end or the exit end of a duct or as a constrictive passage in the run of a duct or pipe, the location being in general one of convenience or expediency. Provisions are necessary for measurement of at least the supply pressure (P_1) and temperature (T_1) and the pressure differential (ΔP) across the orifice.

Several unique characteristics pertain to orifice flow. One pertains more directly to a smoothly convergent orifice, and relates to the circumstance that by reason of its convergence such an orifice provides for and effects a full and efficient expansion within its confines from the initial pressure down to any pressure that exceeds or equals the critical pressure. By the same token, however, it will do no more, with the consequences that:

(a) If the pressure in the discharge region *exceeds* (or equals) the critical pressure the gas will have expanded *to the discharge-region pressure* when it has reached the orifice throat, so that the ideal mass-rate of flow is directly computable by equations 30 or 31 (see also Table VI and/or VII), with P_2 regarded as the discharge-region pressure and A_2 as the throat-area of the orifice. Rounded orifices may advantageously be employed that provide facilities for direct measurement of P_2 at the throat.

(b) If the pressure in the discharge region *is less than* the critical pressure the gas will have expanded at the orifice throat *only to the critical pressure*, so that the ideal mass-rate of flow is to be computed either by equations 30 or 31 (see also Table VI), with A_2 regarded as the throat area and P_2 as the critical pressure, or preferably it is directly computed by equation 32. The persistence of the critical pressure at the orifice throat, irrespective of the amount by which the discharge-region pressure may be less than the critical, is well substantiated by experiment. Subsequent expansion from the critical to the discharge-region pressure occurs after passing the throat, quite as in a convergent-divergent nozzle, but now in a highly turbulent and irreversible manner because of the absence of a suitably divergent guide channel. Flow through orifices to regions at a pressure less than the critical is frequently known as *unaffected* flow, as the flow rate is not affected by the discharge-region pressure.

With a thin-plate orifice somewhat parallel conditions exist. They differ, however, in the features that:

(c) Even in the absence of a convergent channel, the fluid will itself establish and issue as a convergent stream and will consequently have expanded efficiently to any pressure exceeding or equal to the critical pressure when it has reached the stream-section of minimum area, or the *vena contracta*; but

(d) The location and area of this *vena contracta* may be quite variable. Its location may range from a distance that is downstream from the orifice by perhaps the diameter of the orifice when the pressure differential (ΔP) is small and the flow rate low, to a location virtually in the plane of the orifice at maximum flow rates, thus making uncertain the suitable location at which to measure P_2. Its area may correspondingly range from some 60 per cent of the orifice area when the flow rate is low to effectively 100 per cent of the orifice area when the flow rate is maximum and the *vena contracta* is in the orifice plane.

Actual flow rates through orifices are estimated by multiplying the ideal rate, computed in the manner and by the equations indicated above, by a suitable coefficient of discharge. This coefficient may be as high as 0.99 for rounded-entrance orifices and also for thin-plate orifices at maximum flow rates, but for the latter orifices at lower rates it may be as low as about 0.6 if in the use of the equations the actual orifice area is used as A_2, rather than the (usually not measurable) stream area at the *vena contracta*. At quite low rates of flow ($\Delta P/P_1$ not much greater than 0.01) some degree of coordination of coefficients may be secured for geometrically similar orifices, if installed in geometrically similar environs and with geometrically similar locations of the pressure taps, by correlating the coefficient with the Reynolds' index.

When metering orifices are employed in circumstances where the velocity of approach of the stream to the orifice is not inherently negligible and a correction for initial velocity is necessary, that correction may be made by routine inclusion of the denominator of equations 30 or 31, or it may alternatively be made by measuring P_1 by means of a suitably placed impact tube in the upstream, when the denominator may be taken as unity.

Diffuser and Ejector. When a fluid is supplied at a lower pressure but higher and sufficient velocity the corresponding mechanical kinetic energy of the stream may be caused to effect its delivery against a higher pressure. The process is a decelerative compression that is the reverse of the accelerative expansion occurring in a nozzle; its energy relation is identical with that of a nozzle excepting as regards a reverse significance of subscript 1 as pertaining to a supply region now of *lower pressure and higher velocity* and of subscript 2 as pertaining to a discharge region of *lower velocity and higher pressure*. The required channel form is effectively the reverse of that of a nozzle, or is alternatively that of a nozzle through which the direction of flow is reversed, with need simply for a divergent (vs. convergent) channel if the $\dfrac{\text{Lower (supply) pressure}}{\text{Higher (discharge) pressure}}$ ratio exceeds the critical ratio of the fluid, and a convergent-divergent channel otherwise. Given the pressure, temperature, and velocity of the entering stream, the relation expressing the discharge pressure against which it might be caused to deliver if deceleration were continued to a negligible velocity is:

$$\left.\begin{aligned}
P_{2,\text{ideal}} &= P_1\left[\frac{k-1}{kRT_1}\frac{U_1{}^2}{64.34}+1\right]^{k/(k-1)} \\[2mm]
\text{and}\qquad P_{2,\text{actual}} &= P_1\left[\frac{k-1}{kRT_1}\frac{U_1{}^2}{64.34}+1\right]^{n/(n-1)}
\end{aligned}\right\} \tag{33}$$

where $n =$ the effective P–V exponent of the more or less irreversible adiabatic compression process, the value of which exponent will exceed the k of the gas in a degree that corresponds to the degree of turbulence and irreversibility associated with the flow.

The principle of diffuser action is employed in the after-section of the Venturi meter, in the impact and Pitot tube (see below), in the delivery sections of centrifugal blowers, and in ejectors. In this last a lower-pressure and high-velocity jet acts to entrain mechanically a second fluid, thereby to withdraw it from some region of like pressure and then to deliver the mixture by diffuser action to a region of higher pressure, with, however, the encountering of high turbulence and rather low efficiency.

Impact and Pitot Tube. These devices employ primarily a small tube the open end of which is squarely across the path of a flowing stream and the other end of which is extended to a point outside of the stream and is closed by some suitable pressure-measuring device. The action at the stream-end of the tube is a decelerating compression of the thread of fluid as it approaches among the (extended) axis of the open tube, essentially equivalent to that action as it occurs in a diffuser. The velocity of that stream thread is directly computable by equation 29 without denominator or its equivalent (Table VII), P_1 being the *impact* pressure measured as indicated above and P_2 the *static* pressure of the region in which the fluid is flowing as measured wholly without impact effect. The Pitot tube provides facilities for both measurements by a single instrument consisting of two concentric tubes, with impact pressure imposed on the open end of the center one and the static pressure transmitted to the interior of the outer tube by small flush openings in its walls. The value of T_1 is that taken with a thermometer which likewise is exposed to impact effect.

The impact or Pitot tube determines only a point velocity, whereas the mass or volumetric rate of flow in a stream depends on an average velocity. For ascertaining an average a conventional procedure is to take an arithmetical mean of a series of velocity determinations made at a number of points so located that the velocity at each individual one is reasonably representative of the mean velocity in one of the same number of equal subdivisions of the aggregate cross-sectional area of the stream. For a circular stream or duct a schedule that reasonably accomplishes this specifies locations taken at points along one or more diameters, and along each at radial distances on each side of the center line of the stream as follows:

$$r_1 = R\sqrt{1/n}, \quad r_2 = R\sqrt{3/n}, \quad r_3 = R\sqrt{5/n}, \quad r_{n/2} = R\sqrt{(n-1)/n}$$

where R = radius of stream, and n = total number of locations to be employed in traversing a diameter, with $n/2$ locations on each side of the center line. An alternative procedure permits tube locations at any desired points along a diameter and ascertains the mean velocity by finding the mean ordinate of a curve plotted with individual velocities as ordinates and with the square of the corresponding radial distances of the tube from the center line as abscissas, the curve extending to the square of the stream or duct radius.

14. COMPRESSION OF GASES IN COMPRESSORS

A compressor is actually or in effect a steady-flow device. From the steady-flow energy equation,

$$W_{\text{in}}, \text{ft-lb per lb of fluid} = \frac{U_2{}^2 - U_1{}^2}{64.34} + Jc_p\,(T_2 - T_1) + JQ_{\text{out}}$$

or

$$= \frac{U_2{}^2 - U_1{}^2}{64.34} + \frac{k}{k-1}\,(P_2\,V_2 - P_1\,V_1) + JQ_{\text{out}}$$

where the subscripts 1 and 2 refer to conditions respectively at the intake and the discharge regions of the compressor. Under most conditions of compressor operation any energy transition by conduction or radiation (as heat) is an outward one; therefore the term Q_{out} is introduced in these relations. Work energy is always put into the cycle, so the term W_{in} is also introduced.

Isothermal Compression.   Using the characteristic equation of state of a gas, $PV = RT$, and considering the process as reversible isothermal,

$$W_{\text{in}}, \text{ reversible isothermal compression, ft-lb per lb} = \frac{U_2{}^2 - U_1{}^2}{64.34} + RT_1 \log_e \frac{P_2}{P_1}$$

or

$$= \frac{U_2{}^2 - U_1{}^2}{64.34} + P_1\,V_1 \log_e \frac{P_2}{P_1},$$

For cases where the kinetic energy term can be omitted the equations become,

$$W_{\text{in}}, \text{ reversible isothermal compression, ft-lb per lb} = P_1\,V_1 \log_e \frac{P_2}{P_1}$$

$$= RT_1 \log_e \frac{P_2}{P_1}$$

If $\dfrac{P_2 - P_1}{P_1}$ does not exceed 0.01,

$$W_{\text{in}} \text{ (ideal)} = \frac{U_2{}^2 - U_1{}^2}{64.34} + (P_2 - P_1)V_1$$

which is the usual equation for low-pressure fan performance.

The power requirement for isothermal compression is

$$\text{Hp input, reversible isothermal compression} = \frac{M'P_1\,V_1 \log_e P_2/P_1}{550} = \frac{P_1\,V'_1 \log_e P_2/P_1}{550}$$

or

$$= \frac{M'RT_1 \log_e P_2/P_1}{550}$$

When $\dfrac{P_2 - P_1}{P_1}$ does not exceed 0.01,

$$\text{Hp input} = \frac{M'[\,(P_2 - P_1)\,V_1 + (U_2{}^2 - U_1{}^2)/64.34\,]}{550}$$

In these relations,

M' = pounds of gas delivered per second.
$M'\,V_1 = V'_1$ = volume of gas, in cubic feet per second, at the state under which it exists in the region from which the compressor suction is taken.

Adiabatic Compression, Single Stage.   The work required for single-stage adiabatic compression,

$$W_{\text{in}}, \text{ reversible adiabatic compression, ft-lb per lb} = Jc_p\,T_1\,[(P_2/P_1)^{(k-1)/k} - 1]$$

or

$$= \frac{k}{k-1}\,P_1 V_1\,[(P_2/P_1)^{(k-1)/k} - 1]$$

The power required

$$\text{Hp input, reversible adiabatic compression} = \frac{M'Jc_p\,T_1[(P_2/P_1)^{(k-1)/k}-1]}{550}$$

or

$$= \frac{\dfrac{k}{k-1}\,P_1V'_1\,[(P_2/P_1)^{(k-1)/k}-1]}{550}$$

When $\dfrac{P_2-P_1}{P_1}$ does not exceed 0.10,

$$W_{\text{in}},\ \text{reversible adiabatic compression, ft-lb per lb} = RT_1\frac{P_2-P_1}{P_1}\left(1-\frac{1}{2k}\frac{P_2-P_1}{P_1}\right)$$

or

$$= V_1(P_2-P_1)\left(1-\frac{1}{2k}\frac{P_2-P_1}{P_1}\right)$$

Also,

$$\text{Hp input, reversible adiabatic compression} = \frac{M'RT_1\dfrac{P_2-P_1}{P_1}\left(1-\dfrac{1}{2k}\dfrac{P_2-P_1}{P_1}\right)}{550}$$

or

$$= \frac{V'_1(P_2-P_1)\left(1-\dfrac{1}{2k}\dfrac{P_2-P_1}{P_1}\right)}{550}$$

When $\dfrac{P_2-P_1}{P_1}$ does not exceed 0.01, the last term in the expression $\left(1-\dfrac{1}{2k}\dfrac{P_2-P_1}{P_1}\right)$ becomes negligible.

Adiabatic Compression, Multistage with Complete Recooling between Stages.

$$W_{\text{in}},\ \text{ideal two-stage isentropic compression} = 2\,Jc_p\,T_1\,[(P_2/P_1)^{(k-1)/2k}-1]$$

or

$$= \frac{2k}{k-1}\,P_1\,V_1\,[(P_2/P_1)^{(k-1)/2k}-1]$$

Where, with N stages of compression, the intermediate pressures follow the schedule:

$$P' = [(P_1)^{(N-1)}(P_2)]^{1/N}; \qquad P'' = [(P_1)^{(N-2)}(P_2)^2]^{1/N};$$
$$P''' = [(P_1)^{(N-3)}(P_2)^3]^{1/N};\ \ldots\ ;\ P^{N-1} = [(P_1)(P_2)^{(N-1)}]^{1/N}$$

the corresponding minimum work requirement for the entire compressor is

$$W_{\text{in}} = NJc_p\,T_1[(P_2/P_1)^{(k-1)/Nk}-1]$$

or

$$= \frac{Nk}{k-1}\,P_1\,V_1\,[(P_2/P_1)^{(k-1)/Nk}-1]$$

LIQUIDS AND VAPORS

Symbols

f = a subscript attached to any property of a saturated liquid.

g = a subscript attached to any property of a (dry) saturated vapor.

fg = a subscript employed to designate the change of any property between the saturated liquid and saturated vapor states, at constant pressure.

E = molecular (internal) energy, Btu per pound.

H = enthalpy $(E + PV/J)$, Btu per pound.

J = Joule's equivalent $(=778\ \text{ft-lb per Btu})$.

p = pressure, pounds per square inch (absolute).

P = pressure, pounds per square foot (absolute).

Q = energy transferred as heat (by conduction or radiation), Btu per pound.

S = entropy, per pound.

t = temperature, degrees fahrenheit.

T = temperature, degrees Rankine (fahrenheit absolute).

U = velocity, feet per second.

V = specific volume, cubic feet per pound mass.

W = shaft work, foot-pounds per pound mass.

x = quality of a vapor-liquid mixture; also a subscript to any property to characterize it as that of a vapor-liquid mixture.

15. PHYSICAL CONDITIONS

A liquid and its vapor may exist in several conditions defined as follows:

(a) **Saturated Liquid.** If heat is added to a liquid which is maintained at a certain constant pressure, the liquid will not boil until a certain temperature is reached. This temperature is called the saturation temperature corresponding to the pressure on the liquid, and the liquid which is at the saturated temperature is called saturated liquid.

(b) **Compressed Liquid** is liquid at a temperature less than the saturation temperature corresponding to the pressure, or conversely it is liquid having an imposed pressure greater than the saturation pressure corresponding to the temperature of the liquid.

(c) **Saturated Vapor** is the dry vapor at the saturation temperature corresponding to the pressure. It is the vapor at the temperature and pressure of the saturated liquid from which it is formed. The saturated state represents an equilibrium condition between a liquid and its vapor.

(d) **Wet Vapor** is a physical mixture of saturated vapor and saturated liquid; the ratio between the mass of vapor and the mass of the mixture is known as the quality of the mixture, and is represented by the symbol x.

(e) **Superheated Vapor** is the state in which vapor is not in contact with the liquid and its temperature is above the saturated temperature corresponding to the pressure, the excess of temperature being known as the degrees of superheat.

16. PROPERTIES OF LIQUIDS AND VAPORS

The properties of liquids and vapors which are of use in engineering computations are pressure, temperature, specific volume, entropy, enthalpy, and internal energy. It becomes necessary to be able to obtain the numerical values of these properties for fluids in any of the conditions described above. For gases the relations among the several properties are given by relatively simple mathematical formulations known as characteristic equations, so that tables of properties are not required. For liquids and vapors, however, the characteristic equations are found to be entirely too complex in form for direct use in practical work. As a consequence it is the custom of the engineer to depend upon the physicist for the primary experimental determinations of the functional relations and to use for practical computations tabular statements of the properties of the liquids and vapors at a great variety of states.

Among the engineering fluids for which adequately complete and reliable tables of properties are available are steam and the refrigerants ammonia (NH_3) and carbon dioxide (CO_2); less complete tables exist for a number of other vapors. These tables are usually drawn up in sections which give separately the properties of saturated liquid and vapor and of superheated vapor, these generally being arranged variously with pressure or temperature or perhaps entropy as the major argument. An abridgment of the latest American tables of the properties of steam appears on pp. 7–33 to 7–39. The symbols are those which at this writing are accepted as standard and which are used throughout this section. It will be observed that the subscripts f and g are used to denote properties at the saturated liquid state and at the saturated vapor state respectively, and that the subscript fg denotes the change of a property between the same two states. The properties given in the columns of Table I are briefly described as follows:

Columns 1 and 2 state the saturation pressure of water and steam corresponding to the temperature. The published tables always present for convenience two tabulations identical in form except that one employs even units of the pressure as the major argument and the other even degrees of temperature. The pressures are invariably absolute pressures, in pounds per square inch, and not gage pressures. The temperatures are degrees Fahrenheit.

Columns 3, 4, and 5 give, respectively, the specific volume of saturated water, the increase of specific volume during evaporation, and the specific volume of (dry) saturated steam.

Column 6 records the enthalpy (formerly called total heat or heat content) of saturated water with respect to an arbitrarily assigned zero of enthalpy for saturated water at 32 deg fahr (and 0.0887 lb per sq in.). As the PV/J item in the enthalpy function, $E + PV/J$, is only 0.00026 Btu per lb for saturated water at 32 deg fahr, it follows that the placing of a zero enthalpy at that temperature is essentially equivalent to regarding the internal energy of water at 32 deg fahr as also relatively zero.

Column 7 records the increase of enthalpy during evaporation and thus in fact the energy supply per pound (normally supplied as heat) which is required to accomplish the evaporation.

Table I. Saturated Steam: Pressure Table *

Abs. Press., lb/sq in.	Temp. °F	Specific Volume			Enthalpy			Entropy			Abs. Press., lb/sq in.
		Sat. Liquid	Evap.	Sat. Vapor	Sat. Liquid	Evap.	Sat. Vapor	Sat. Liquid	Evap.	Sat. Vapor	
p	t	V_f	V_{fg}	V_g	H_f	H_{fg}	H_g	S_f	S_{fg}	S_g	p
1/2″ Hg	58.83	0.01603	1256.9	1256.9	26.88	1058.8	1085.7	0.0533	2.0422	2.0955	1/2″ Hg
3/4″ Hg	70.44	0.01605	856.5	856.5	38.47	1052.5	1091.0	0.0754	1.9856	2.0609	3/4″ Hg
1″ Hg	79.06	0.01607	652.7	652.7	47.06	1047.8	1094.9	0.0914	1.9451	2.0365	1″ Hg
1 1/2″ Hg	91.75	0.01610	445.3	445.3	59.72	1040.8	1100.6	0.1147	1.8877	2.0024	1 1/2″ Hg
2″ Hg	101.17	0.01613	339.5	339.5	69.10	1035.7	1104.8	0.1316	1.8468	1.9784	2″ Hg
2 1/2″ Hg	108.73	0.01616	275.2	275.2	76.63	1031.5	1108.1	0.1450	1.8148	1.9598	2 1/2″ Hg
3″ Hg	115.08	0.01618	231.8	231.8	82.96	1027.9	1110.8	0.1561	1.7885	1.9446	3″ Hg
1.0	101.76	0.01614	333.8	333.9	69.69	1035.3	1105.0	0.1326	1.8442	1.9769	1.0
2.0	126.10	0.01623	173.94	173.96	93.97	1021.6	1115.6	0.1750	1.7442	1.9192	2.0
3.0	141.49	0.01630	118.84	118.86	109.33	1012.7	1122.0	0.2009	1.6847	1.8856	3.0
4.0	152.99	0.01636	90.72	90.74	120.83	1005.9	1126.8	0.2198	1.6420	1.8618	4.0
5.0	162.25	0.01641	73.59	73.61	130.10	1000.4	1130.6	0.2348	1.6088	1.8435	5.0
6.0	170.07	0.01645	62.03	62.05	137.92	995.8	1133.7	0.2473	1.5814	1.8287	6.0
7.0	176.85	0.01649	53.68	53.70	144.71	991.7	1136.4	0.2580	1.5582	1.8162	7.0
8.0	182.87	0.01652	47.38	47.39	150.75	988.1	1138.9	0.2674	1.5379	1.8053	8.0
9.0	188.28	0.01656	42.42	42.44	156.19	984.8	1141.0	0.2758	1.5200	1.7958	9.0
10.0	193.21	0.01658	38.44	38.45	161.13	981.8	1143.0	0.2834	1.5040	1.7874	10.0
11.0	197.75	0.01661	35.15	35.17	165.68	979.1	1144.8	0.2903	1.4894	1.7797	11.0
12.0	201.96	0.01664	32.40	32.42	169.91	976.5	1146.4	0.2968	1.4760	1.7727	12.0
13.0	205.88	0.01666	30.06	30.08	173.85	974.1	1147.9	0.3027	1.4636	1.7663	13.0
14.0	209.56	0.01669	28.05	28.06	177.55	971.8	1149.3	0.3082	1.4521	1.7604	14.0
14.696	212.00	0.01670	26.80	26.82	180.00	970.2	1150.2	0.3119	1.4446	1.7564	14.696
16.0	216.32	0.01673	24.75	24.76	184.35	967.4	1151.8	0.3184	1.4312	1.7496	16.0
18.0	222.40	0.01678	22.16	22.18	190.48	963.5	1154.0	0.3274	1.4127	1.7402	18.0
20.0	227.96	0.01682	20.078	20.095	196.09	959.9	1156.0	0.3356	1.3960	1.7317	20.0
22.0	233.07	0.01685	18.363	18.380	201.25	956.6	1157.8	0.3431	1.3809	1.7240	22.0
24.0	237.82	0.01689	16.924	16.941	206.05	953.4	1159.5	0.3500	1.3670	1.7170	24.0
26.0	242.25	0.01692	15.701	15.718	210.54	950.4	1161.0	0.3564	1.3542	1.7106	26.0
28.0	246.41	0.01695	14.647	14.664	214.75	947.7	1162.4	0.3624	1.3422	1.7046	28.0
30.0	250.34	0.01698	13.728	13.745	218.73	945.0	1163.7	0.3680	1.3310	1.6990	30.0
32.0	254.05	0.01701	12.923	12.940	222.50	942.5	1165.0	0.3732	1.3206	1.6938	32.0
34.0	257.58	0.01704	12.209	12.226	226.09	940.0	1166.1	0.3783	1.3107	1.6890	34.0
36.0	260.94	0.01707	11.570	11.587	229.51	937.7	1167.2	0.3830	1.3014	1.6844	36.0
38.0	264.16	0.01710	10.998	11.015	232.79	935.5	1168.3	0.3876	1.2925	1.6800	38.0
40.0	267.24	0.01712	10.480	10.497	235.93	933.3	1169.2	0.3919	1.2840	1.6759	40.0
42.0	270.21	0.01715	10.010	10.027	238.95	931.2	1170.2	0.3961	1.2759	1.6720	42.0
44.0	273.06	0.01717	9.582	9.599	241.86	929.2	1171.1	0.4000	1.2682	1.6683	44.0
46.0	275.81	0.01719	9.189	9.207	244.67	927.2	1171.9	0.4039	1.2608	1.6647	46.0
48.0	278.45	0.01722	8.829	8.846	247.37	925.4	1172.7	0.4076	1.2537	1.6613	48.0
50.0	281.01	0.01724	8.496	8.514	249.98	923.5	1173.5	0.4111	1.2469	1.6580	50.0
52.0	283.49	0.01726	8.189	8.206	252.52	921.7	1174.3	0.4145	1.2404	1.6549	52.0
54.0	285.90	0.01728	7.902	7.919	254.99	920.0	1175.0	0.4178	1.2340	1.6518	54.0
56.0	288.23	0.01730	7.636	7.653	257.38	918.3	1175.7	0.4210	1.2279	1.6489	56.0
58.0	290.50	0.01732	7.388	7.405	259.71	916.6	1176.4	0.4241	1.2220	1.6461	58.0
60.0	292.71	0.01735	7.155	7.172	261.98	915.0	1177.0	0.4271	1.2162	1.6434	60.0
62.0	294.85	0.01737	6.937	6.955	264.18	913.4	1177.6	0.4300	1.2107	1.6407	62.0
64.0	296.94	0.01739	6.732	6.749	266.33	911.9	1178.2	0.4329	1.2053	1.6382	64.0
66.0	298.98	0.01741	6.539	6.556	268.43	910.4	1178.8	0.4356	1.2001	1.6357	66.0
68.0	300.98	0.01743	6.357	6.375	270.49	908.9	1179.4	0.4384	1.1950	1.6333	68.0
70.0	302.92	0.01744	6.186	6.203	272.49	907.4	1179.9	0.4410	1.1900	1.6310	70.0
72.0	304.82	0.01746	6.024	6.041	274.45	906.0	1180.5	0.4435	1.1852	1.6287	72.0
74.0	306.68	0.01748	5.870	5.887	276.37	904.6	1181.0	0.4460	1.1805	1.6265	74.0
76.0	308.50	0.01750	5.723	5.741	278.25	903.2	1181.5	0.4485	1.1759	1.6244	76.0
78.0	310.28	0.01752	5.584	5.602	280.09	901.9	1182.0	0.4509	1.1714	1.6223	78.0
80.0	312.03	0.01754	5.452	5.470	281.90	900.5	1182.4	0.4532	1.1670	1.6202	80.0
82.0	313.74	0.01756	5.325	5.343	283.67	899.2	1182.9	0.4555	1.1627	1.6182	82.0
84.0	315.42	0.01757	5.204	5.222	285.42	897.9	1183.4	0.4578	1.1586	1.6163	84.0
86.0	317.06	0.01759	5.089	5.107	287.13	896.7	1183.8	0.4599	1.1545	1.6144	86.0
88.0	318.68	0.01761	4.979	4.997	288.80	895.4	1184.2	0.4621	1.1505	1.6126	88.0
90.0	320.27	0.01763	4.874	4.892	290.45	894.2	1184.6	0.4642	1.1465	1.6107	90.0
92.0	321.83	0.01764	4.773	4.791	292.07	893.0	1185.0	0.4663	1.1427	1.6090	92.0
94.0	323.37	0.01766	4.676	4.694	293.67	891.8	1185.4	0.4683	1.1389	1.6072	94.0
96.0	324.88	0.01768	4.584	4.602	295.25	890.6	1185.3	0.4703	1.1352	1.6055	96.0
98.0	326.37	0.01769	4.494	4.512	296.80	889.4	1186.2	0.4723	1.1316	1.6038	98.0

* Reprinted from the Abridged Edition of Steam Tables and Mollier Diagram, by Professor J. H. Keenan, 1931, by permission of the publisher, The American Society of Mechanical Engineers.

Table I. Saturated Steam: Pressure Table *—Continued

Abs. Press., lb/sq in.	Temp. °F.	Specific Volume			Enthalpy			Entropy			Abs. Press., lb/sq in.
		Sat. Liquid	Evap.	Sat. Vapor	Sat. Liquid	Evap.	Sat. Vapor	Sat. Liquid	Evap.	Sat. Vapor	
p	t	V_f	V_{fg}	V_g	H_f	H_{fg}	H_g	S_f	S_{fg}	S_g	p
100.0	327.83	0.01771	4.408	4.426	298.33	888.2	1186.6	0.4742	1.1280	1.6022	100.0
102.0	329.27	0.01773	4.326	4.344	299.83	887.1	1186.9	0.4761	1.1245	1.6006	102.0
104.0	330.68	0.01774	4.247	4.265	301.30	886.0	1187.3	0.4779	1.1211	1.5990	104.0
106.0	332.08	0.01776	4.171	4.189	302.76	884.9	1187.6	0.4798	1.1177	1.5974	106.0
108.0	333.44	0.01777	4.097	4.115	304.19	883.8	1188.0	0.4816	1.1144	1.5959	108.0
110.0	334.79	0.01779	4.026	4.044	305.61	882.7	1188.3	0.4834	1.1111	1.5944	110.0
112.0	336.12	0.01780	3.958	3.976	307.00	881.6	1188.6	0.4851	1.1079	1.5930	112.0
114.0	337.43	0.01782	3.892	3.910	308.36	880.6	1188.9	0.4868	1.1048	1.5915	114.0
116.0	338.72	0.01783	3.828	3.846	309.71	879.5	1189.2	0.4885	1.1017	1.5901	116.0
118.0	340.01	0.01785	3.766	3.784	311.05	878.5	1189.5	0.4901	1.0986	1.5887	118.0
120.0	341.26	0.01786	3.707	3.725	312.37	877.4	1189.8	0.4918	1.0956	1.5874	120.0
122.0	342.50	0.01788	3.652	3.670	313.67	876.4	1190.1	0.4934	1.0926	1.5860	122.0
124.0	343.73	0.01789	3.597	3.615	314.96	875.4	1190.4	0.4950	1.0897	1.5847	124.0
126.0	344.94	0.01791	3.542	3.560	316.23	874.4	1190.6	0.4965	1.0868	1.5834	126.0
128.0	346.14	0.01792	3.487	3.505	317.49	873.4	1190.9	0.4981	1.0840	1.5821	128.0
130.0	347.31	0.01794	3.433	3.451	318.73	872.4	1191.2	0.4996	1.0812	1.5808	130.0
132.0	348.48	0.01795	3.383	3.401	319.95	871.5	1191.4	0.5011	1.0784	1.5796	132.0
134.0	349.64	0.01796	3.335	3.353	321.17	870.5	1191.7	0.5026	1.0757	1.5783	134.0
136.0	350.78	0.01798	3.288	3.306	322.37	869.6	1191.9	0.5041	1.0730	1.5771	136.0
138.0	351.91	0.01799	3.242	3.260	323.56	868.6	1192.2	0.5056	1.0703	1.5759	138.0
140.0	353.03	0.01801	3.198	3.216	324.74	867.7	1192.4	0.5070	1.0677	1.5747	140.0
142.0	354.14	0.01802	3.155	3.173	325.91	866.7	1192.6	0.5084	1.0651	1.5735	142.0
144.0	355.22	0.01804	3.112	3.130	327.06	865.8	1192.9	0.5098	1.0625	1.5724	144.0
146.0	356.31	0.01805	3.071	3.089	328.20	864.9	1193.1	0.5112	1.0600	1.5712	146.0
148.0	357.37	0.01806	3.031	3.049	329.32	864.0	1193.3	0.5126	1.0575	1.5701	148.0
150.0	358.43	0.01808	2.992	3.010	330.44	863.1	1193.5	0.5140	1.0550	1.5690	150.0
152.0	359.47	0.01809	2.954	2.972	331.54	862.2	1193.7	0.5153	1.0526	1.5679	152.0
154.0	360.51	0.01810	2.917	2.935	332.64	861.3	1193.9	0.5166	1.0502	1.5668	154.0
156.0	361.53	0.01812	2.882	2.900	333.72	860.4	1194.1	0.5180	1.0478	1.5658	156.0
158.0	362.54	0.01813	2.846	2.864	334.80	859.5	1194.3	0.5193	1.0454	1.5647	158.0
160.0	363.55	0.01814	2.812	2.830	335.86	858.7	1194.5	0.5205	1.0431	1.5636	160.0
162.0	364.54	0.01816	2.779	2.797	336.91	857.8	1194.7	0.5218	1.0408	1.5626	162.0
164.0	365.52	0.01817	2.746	2.764	337.95	857.0	1194.9	0.5230	1.0385	1.5616	164.0
166.0	366.50	0.01818	2.715	2.733	338.99	856.1	1195.1	0.5243	1.0363	1.5606	166.0
168.0	367.46	0.01819	2.683	2.701	340.01	855.2	1195.3	0.5255	1.0340	1.5596	168.0
170.0	368.42	0.01821	2.653	2.671	341.03	854.4	1195.4	0.5268	1.0318	1.5586	170.0
172.0	369.37	0.01822	2.623	2.641	342.04	853.6	1195.6	0.5280	1.0296	1.5576	172.0
174.0	370.31	0.01823	2.594	2.612	343.04	852.7	1195.8	0.5292	1.0275	1.5566	174.0
176.0	371.24	0.01825	2.566	2.584	344.03	851.9	1196.0	0.5304	1.0253	1.5557	176.0
178.0	372.16	0.01826	2.538	2.556	345.01	851.1	1196.1	0.5315	1.0232	1.5548	178.0
180.0	373.08	0.01827	2.511	2.529	345.99	850.3	1196.3	0.5327	1.0211	1.5538	180.0
182.0	374.00	0.01828	2.484	2.502	346.97	849.5	1196.4	0.5339	1.0190	1.5529	182.0
184.0	374.90	0.01829	2.458	2.476	347.94	848.6	1196.6	0.5350	1.0169	1.5520	184.0
186.0	375.78	0.01831	2.433	2.451	348.89	847.9	1196.8	0.5362	1.0149	1.5511	186.0
188.0	376.67	0.01832	2.407	2.425	349.83	847.1	1196.9	0.5373	1.0129	1.5502	188.0
190.0	377.55	0.01833	2.383	2.401	350.77	846.3	1197.0	0.5384	1.0109	1.5493	190.0
192.0	378.42	0.01834	2.359	2.377	351.70	845.5	1197.2	0.5395	1.0089	1.5484	192.0
194.0	379.27	0.01835	2.335	2.353	352.61	844.7	1197.3	0.5406	1.0070	1.5475	194.0
196.0	380.13	0.01837	2.312	2.330	353.53	844.0	1197.5	0.5417	1.0050	1.5467	196.0
198.0	380.97	0.01838	2.289	2.307	354.43	843.2	1197.6	0.5427	1.0031	1.5458	198.0
200.0	381.82	0.01839	2.267	2.285	355.33	842.4	1197.8	0.5438	1.0012	1.5450	200.0
205.0	383.89	0.01842	2.213	2.231	357.56	840.5	1198.1	0.5465	0.9964	1.5429	205.0
210.0	385.93	0.01844	2.162	2.180	359.76	838.6	1198.4	0.5491	0.9918	1.5409	210.0
215.0	387.93	0.01847	2.113	2.131	361.91	836.8	1198.7	0.5516	0.9873	1.5389	215.0
220.0	389.89	0.01850	2.066	2.084	364.02	835.0	1199.0	0.5540	0.9829	1.5369	220.0
225.0	391.81	0.01853	0.0208	0.0393	366.10	833.2	1199.3	0.5565	0.9786	1.5350	225.0
230.0	393.70	0.01856	1.9778	1.9964	368.14	831.4	1199.6	0.5588	0.9743	1.5332	230.0
235.0	395.56	0.01859	1.9367	1.9553	370.15	829.7	1199.8	0.5612	0.9702	1.5313	235.0
240.0	397.40	0.01861	1.8970	1.9156	372.13	827.9	1200.1	0.5635	0.9661	1.5295	240.0
245.0	399.20	0.01864	1.8589	1.8775	374.09	826.2	1200.3	0.5658	0.9620	1.5278	245.0
250.0	400.97	0.01867	1.8223	1.8410	376.02	824.5	1200.5	0.5680	0.9581	1.5261	250.0
260.0	404.43	0.01872	1.7536	1.7723	379.78	821.2	1201.0	0.5723	0.9504	1.5227	260.0
270.0	407.79	0.01877	1.6895	1.7083	383.44	818.0	1201.4	0.5765	0.9430	1.5194	270.0
280.0	411.06	0.01882	1.6302	1.6490	387.02	814.7	1201.8	0.5805	0.9357	1.5163	280.0
290.0	414.24	0.01887	1.5745	1.5934	390.50	811.6	1202.1	0.5845	0.9287	1.5132	290.0

* Reprinted from the Abridged Edition of Steam Tables and Mollier Diagram, by Professor J. H. Keenan, 1931, by permission of the publisher, The American Society of Mechanical Engineers.

Table I. Saturated Steam: Pressure Table *—*Continued*

Abs. Press., lb/sq in. p	Temp. °F t	Specific Volume			Enthalpy			Entropy			Abs. Press., lb/sq in. p
		Sat. Liquid V_f	Evap. V_{fg}	Sat. Vapor V_g	Sat. Liquid H_f	Evap. H_{fg}	Sat. Vapor H_g	Sat. Liquid S_f	Evap. S_{fg}	Sat. Vapor S_g	
300.0	417.33	0.01892	1.5225	1.5414	393.90	808.5	1202.4	0.5883	0.9220	1.5102	300.0
320.0	423.29	0.01901	1.4279	1.4469	400.47	802.5	1203.0	0.5957	0.9089	1.5046	320.0
340.0	428.96	0.01910	1.3439	1.3630	406.75	796.6	1203.4	0.6027	0.8965	1.4992	340.0
360.0	434.39	0.01918	1.2689	1.2881	412.80	790.9	1203.7	0.6094	0.8846	1.4940	360.0
380.0	439.59	0.01927	1.2015	1.2208	418.61	785.3	1203.9	0.6157	0.8733	1.4891	380.0
400.0	444.58	0.0194	1.1407	1.1601	424.2	779.8	1204.1	0.6218	0.8625	1.4843	400.0
420.0	449.38	0.0194	1.0853	1.1047	429.6	774.5	1204.1	0.6277	0.8520	1.4798	420.0
440.0	454.01	0.0195	1.0345	1.0540	434.8	769.3	1204.1	0.6334	0.8420	1.4753	440.0
460.0	458.48	0.0196	0.9881	1.0077	439.9	764.1	1204.0	0.6388	0.8322	1.4711	460.0
480.0	462.80	0.0197	0.9456	0.9653	444.9	759.0	1203.9	0.6441	0.8228	1.4670	480.0
500.0	466.99	0.0198	0.9063	0.9261	449.7	754.0	1203.7	0.6493	0.8137	1.4630	500.0
520.0	471.05	0.0198	0.8701	0.8899	454.4	749.0	1203.5	0.6543	0.8048	1.4591	520.0
540.0	474.99	0.0199	0.8363	0.8562	459.0	744.1	1203.2	0.6592	0.7962	1.4554	540.0
560.0	478.82	0.0200	0.8047	0.8247	463.6	739.3	1202.9	0.6639	0.7878	1.4517	560.0
580.0	482.55	0.0201	0.7751	0.7952	468.0	734.5	1202.5	0.6686	0.7796	1.4482	580.0
600.0	486.17	0.0202	0.7475	0.7677	472.3	729.8	1202.1	0.6731	0.7716	1.4447	600.0
620.0	489.71	0.0202	0.7217	0.7419	476.6	725.1	1201.7	0.6775	0.7638	1.4413	620.0
640.0	493.16	0.0203	0.6972	0.7175	480.8	720.5	1201.2	0.6818	0.7562	1.4380	640.0
660.0	496.53	0.0204	0.6744	0.6948	484.9	715.9	1200.8	0.6861	0.7487	1.4348	660.0
680.0	499.82	0.0205	0.6527	0.6732	488.9	711.3	1200.2	0.6902	0.7414	1.4316	680.0
700.0	503.04	0.0206	0.6321	0.6527	492.9	706.8	1199.7	0.6943	0.7342	1.4285	700.0
720.0	506.19	0.0206	0.6128	0.6334	496.8	702.4	1199.2	0.6983	0.7272	1.4255	720.0
740.0	509.28	0.0207	0.5944	0.6151	500.6	697.9	1198.6	0.7022	0.7203	1.4225	740.0
760.0	512.30	0.0208	0.5769	0.5977	504.4	693.5	1198.0	0.7060	0.7136	1.4196	760.0
780.0	515.27	0.0209	0.5602	0.5811	508.2	689.2	1197.4	0.7098	0.7069	1.4167	780.0
800.0	518.18	0.0209	0.5444	0.5653	511.8	684.9	1196.7	0.7135	0.7004	1.4139	800.0
820.0	521.03	0.0210	0.5293	0.5503	515.5	680.6	1196.0	0.7171	0.6940	1.4111	820.0
840.0	523.83	0.0211	0.5149	0.5360	519.0	676.4	1195.4	0.7207	0.6877	1.4084	840.0
860.0	526.58	0.0212	0.5013	0.5225	522.6	672.1	1194.7	0.7242	0.6815	1.4057	860.0
880.0	529.29	0.0213	0.4881	0.5094	526.0	667.9	1194.0	0.7277	0.6754	1.4031	880.0
900.0	531.95	0.0213	0.4756	0.4969	529.5	663.8	1193.3	0.7311	0.6694	1.4005	900.0
920.0	534.56	0.0214	0.4635	0.4849	532.9	659.7	1192.6	0.7344	0.6635	1.3980	920.0
940.0	537.13	0.0215	0.4520	0.4735	536.2	655.6	1191.8	0.7377	0.6577	1.3954	940.0
960.0	539.66	0.0216	0.4409	0.4625	539.6	651.5	1191.1	0.7410	0.6520	1.3930	960.0
980.0	542.14	0.0217	0.4303	0.4520	542.8	647.5	1190.3	0.7442	0.6464	1.3905	980.0
1000.0	544.58	0.0217	0.4202	0.4419	546.0	643.5	1189.6	0.7473	0.6408	1.3881	1000.0
1050.0	550.53	0.0219	0.3960	0.4179	554.0	633.6	1187.6	0.7550	0.6273	1.3822	1050.0
1100.0	556.28	0.0222	0.3738	0.3960	561.7	623.9	1185.6	0.7624	0.6141	1.3765	1100.0
1150.0	561.81	0.0224	0.3540	0.3764	569.2	614.3	1183.5	0.7695	0.6014	1.3709	1150.0
1200.0	567.14	0.0226	0.3356	0.3582	576.5	604.9	1181.4	0.7764	0.5891	1.3656	1200.0
1250.0	572.30	0.0228	0.3187	0.3415	583.6	595.6	1179.2	0.7831	0.5772	1.3603	1250.0
1300.0	577.32	0.0230	0.3029	0.3259	590.6	586.3	1177.0	0.7897	0.5654	1.3552	1300.0
1350.0	582.21	0.0232	0.2884	0.3116	597.5	577.2	1174.7	0.7962	0.5540	1.3501	1350.0
1400.0	586.96	0.0235	0.2748	0.2983	604.3	568.1	1172.4	0.8024	0.5428	1.3452	1400.0
1450.0	591.58	0.0237	0.2621	0.2858	611.0	559.1	1170.0	0.8086	0.5318	1.3404	1450.0
1500.0	596.08	0.0239	0.2502	0.2741	617.5	550.2	1167.6	0.8146	0.5212	1.3357	1500.0
1600.0	604.74	0.0244	0.2284	0.2528	630.2	532.6	1162.7	0.8262	0.5003	1.3265	1600.0
1700.0	612.98	0.0249	0.2089	0.2338	642.5	515.0	1157.5	0.8373	0.4801	1.3174	1700.0
1800.0	620.86	0.0254	0.1913	0.2167	654.7	497.2	1151.8	0.8482	0.4601	1.3083	1800.0
1900.0	628.39	0.0260	0.1754	0.2014	666.8	478.9	1145.7	0.8589	0.4402	1.2990	1900.0
2000.0	635.6	0.0265	0.1610	0.1875	679.0	460.0	1139.0	0.8696	0.4200	1.2896	2000.0
2200.0	649.2	0.0277	0.1346	0.1623	703.7	420.0	1123.8	0.8912	0.3788	1.2700	2200.0
2400.0	661.9	0.0292	0.1112	0.1404	729.4	376.4	1105.8	0.9133	0.3356	1.2488	2400.0
2600.0	673.8	0.0310	0.0895	0.1205	756.7	327.8	1084.5	0.9364	0.2892	1.2257	2600.0
2800.0	684.9	0.0333	0.0688	0.1021	786.7	272.3	1058.9	0.9618	0.2379	1.1996	2800.0
3000.0	695.2	0.0367	0.0477	0.0844	823.1	202.5	1025.6	0.9922	0.1754	1.1676	3000.0
3200.0	704.9	0.0459	0.0142	0.0601	887.0	75.9	962.9	1.0461	0.0651	1.1112	3200.0
3226.0	706.1	0.0522	0	0.0522	925.0	0	925.0	1.0785	0	1.0785	3226.0

* Reprinted from the Abridged Edition of Steam Tables and Mollier Diagram, by Professor J. H. Keenan, 1931, by permission of the publisher, The American Society of Mechanical Engineers.

Table II. Superheated Steam *

Temperature—Degrees Fahrenheit

Abs. Press., lb/sq in. (Sat. Temp.)		Sat. Water	Sat. Steam	150°	200°	250°	300°	350°	400°	450°	500°	550°	600°	700°	800°	900°	1000°
1 (101.76)	V	0.02	333.9	362.7	392.5	422.3	452.1	481.9	511.7	541.6	571.3	601.1	630.9	690.6	750.2	809.8	869.4
	H	69.7	1105.0	1127.0	1149.8	1172.4	1195.0	1217.8	1240.7	1263.9	1287.2	1310.9	1334.6	1383.0	1432.6	1483.3	1535.2
	S	0.1326	1.9769	2.0144	2.0503	2.0835	2.1142	2.1433	2.1707	2.1968	2.2218	2.2458	2.2688	2.3125	2.3535	2.3922	2.4291
5 (162.25)	V	0.02	73.61		78.17	84.19	90.21	96.21	102.19	108.19	114.16	120.14	126.11	138.05	149.99	161.91	173.83
	H	130.1	1130.6		1148.2	1171.3	1194.2	1217.2	1240.2	1263.5	1286.9	1310.7	1334.4	1382.9	1432.5	1483.2	1535.1
	S	0.2348	1.8435		1.8712	1.9050	1.9361	1.9654	1.9930	2.0192	2.0443	2.0683	2.0914	2.1351	2.1761	2.2149	2.2517
10 (193.21)	V	0.02	38.45		38.88	41.92	44.98	48.00	51.01	54.02	57.02	60.02	63.01	68.99	74.96	80.92	86.89
	H	161.1	1143.0		1146.3	1169.9	1193.2	1216.4	1239.6	1262.9	1286.4	1310.1	1334.0	1382.6	1432.3	1483.1	1535.0
	S	0.2834	1.7874		1.7925	1.8271	1.8587	1.8838	1.9161	1.9430	1.9676	1.9916	2.0148	2.0586	2.0997	2.1385	2.1753
14.696 (212.00)	V	0.02	26.82			28.40	30.52	32.59	34.65	36.70	38.75	40.79	42.83	46.91	50.97	55.03	59.09
	H	180.0	1150.2			1168.6	1192.0	1215.6	1239.0	1262.4	1286.0	1309.7	1333.7	1382.4	1432.1	1482.9	1534.9
	S	0.3119	1.7564			1.7832	1.8154	1.8452	1.8731	1.8996	1.9249	1.9490	1.9722	2.0161	2.0572	2.0961	2.1330
20 (227.96)	V	0.02	20.10			20.79	22.36	23.90	25.43	26.94	28.45	29.95	31.46	34.46	37.44	40.43	43.42
	H	196.1	1156.0			1167.0	1191.1	1214.8	1238.3	1261.9	1285.5	1309.3	1333.4	1382.1	1432.0	1482.8	1534.8
	S	0.3356	1.7317			1.7474	1.7802	1.8104	1.8386	1.8652	1.8906	1.9148	1.9380	1.9819	2.0232	2.0620	2.0989
40 (267.24)	V	0.017	10.497				11.044	11.843	12.623	13.392	14.161	14.922	15.682	17.190	18.686	20.18	21.68
	H	235.9	1169.2				1186.5	1211.3	1235.6	1259.7	1283.7	1307.8	1332.0	1381.2	1431.3	1482.3	1534.4
	S	0.3919	1.6759				1.6990	1.7309	1.7599	1.7871	1.8128	1.8373	1.8607	1.9050	1.9464	1.9854	2.0224
60 (292.71)	V	0.017	7.172				7.260	7.821	8.353	8.878	9.398	9.911	10.423	11.435	12.436	13.439	14.440
	H	262.0	1177.0				1181.2	1207.7	1232.8	1257.4	1281.9	1306.2	1330.7	1380.2	1430.6	1481.8	1533.9
	S	0.4271	1.6434				1.6488	1.6827	1.7128	1.7406	1.7667	1.7915	1.8151	1.8597	1.9014	1.9406	1.9775
80 (312.03)	V	0.018	5.470					5.806	6.217	6.618	7.015	7.406	7.793	8.558	9.313	10.067	10.817
	H	281.9	1182.4					1203.8	1229.9	1255.2	1280.0	1304.7	1329.3	1379.2	1429.9	1481.3	1533.5
	S	0.4532	1.6202					1.6473	1.6785	1.7070	1.7336	1.7586	1.7824	1.8274	1.8694	1.9086	1.9456
100 (327.83)	V	0.018	4.426					4.594	4.934	5.263	5.585	5.903	6.215	6.831	7.439	8.044	8.644
	H	298.3	1186.6					1199.7	1226.9	1252.8	1278.0	1303.0	1327.9	1378.2	1429.2	1480.7	1533.1
	S	0.4742	1.6022					1.6185	1.6512	1.6805	1.7075	1.7329	1.7569	1.8023	1.8445	1.8838	1.9209
120 (341.26)	V	0.018	3.725					3.781	4.077	4.359	4.632	4.899	5.162	5.680	6.189	6.693	7.196
	H	312.4	1189.8					1195.2	1223.8	1250.4	1276.1	1301.4	1326.5	1377.2	1428.5	1480.2	1532.7
	S	0.4918	1.5874					1.5940	1.6283	1.6584	1.6859	1.7115	1.7359	1.7816	1.8240	1.8635	1.9007

Temp (sat.)															
140 (353.03)	V	6.161	5.728	5.297	4.857	4.410	4.182	3.951	3.713	3.465				0.018	3.216
	H	1532.2	1479.7	1427.8	1376.2	1325.1	1299.7	1274.1	1247.9	1220.5				324.7	1192.4
	S	1.8836	1.8462	1.8066	1.7640	1.7179	1.6933	1.6667	1.6393	1.6084				0.5070	1.5747
160 (363.55)	V	5.385	5.006	4.627	4.240	3.846	3.645	3.440	3.227	3.005				0.018	2.830
	H	1531.8	1479.1	1427.1	1375.2	1323.7	1298.0	1272.1	1245.4	1217.1				335.9	194.5
	S	1.8687	1.8313	1.7915	1.7487	1.7022	1.6774	1.6504	1.6224	1.5906				0.5205	1.5636
180 (373.08)	V	4.782	4.444	4.105	3.760	3.407	3.226	3.041	2.849	2.646				0.018	2.529
	H	1531.4	1478.5	1426.3	1374.2	1322.2	1296.3	1270.0	1242.7	1213.5				346.0	1196.3
	S	1.8555	1.8180	1.7782	1.7351	1.6882	1.6631	1.6364	1.6073	1.5742				0.5327	1.5538
200 (381.82)	V	4.299	3.995	3.688	3.376	3.056	2.892	2.722	2.547	2.358				0.018	2.285
	H	1531.0	1478.0	1425.6	1373.1	1320.8	1294.6	1267.9	1240.0	1209.8				355.3	1197.8
	S	1.8438	1.8062	1.7662	1.7228	1.6756	1.6502	1.6231	1.5934	1.5592				0.5438	1.5450
220 (389.89)	V	3.903	3.628	3.347	3.062	2.769	2.617	2.462	2.299	2.122				0.019	2.084
	H	1530.6	1477.4	1424.8	1372.1	1319.3	1292.9	1265.7	1237.3	1205.9				364.0	1199.0
	S	1.8331	1.7954	1.7553	1.7117	1.6641	1.6384	1.6109	1.5805	1.5450				0.5540	1.5369
240 (397.40)	V	3.574	3.321	3.063	2.800	2.529	2.389	2.244	2.092	1.9250				0.0186	1.9156
	H	1530.2	1476.8	1424.1	1371.0	1317.8	1291.1	1263.5	1234.4	1201.9				372.1	1200.1
	S	1.8234	1.7856	1.7453	1.7014	1.6534	1.6275	1.5996	1.5684	1.5317				0.5635	1.5295
260 (404.43)	V	3.295	3.062	2.823	2.579	2.327	2.195	2.060	1.9165					0.0187	1.7723
	H	1529.7	1476.3	1423.3	1370.0	1316.3	1289.3	1261.3	1231.5					379.8	1201.0
	S	1.8144	1.7765	1.7360	1.6919	1.6435	1.6174	1.5890	1.5571					0.5723	1.5227
280 (411.06)	V	3.056	2.839	2.617	2.389	2.153	2.030	1.9019	1.7655					0.0188	1.6490
	H	1529.3	1475.7	1422.5	1368.9	1314.8	1287.5	1259.0	1228.4					387.0	1201.8
	S	1.8060	1.7680	1.7274	1.6830	1.6343	1.6078	1.5790	1.5462					0.5805	1.5163
300 (417.33)	V	2.849	2.646	2.438	2.224	2.002	1.8863	1.7648	1.6347					0.0189	1.5414
	H	1528.9	1475.1	1421.7	1367.8	1313.3	1285.6	1256.7	1225.3					393.9	1202.4
	S	1.7983	1.7601	1.7193	1.6747	1.6256	1.5988	1.5695	1.5359					0.5883	1.5102
350 (431.71)	V	2.435	2.260	2.080	1.8945	1.7003	1.5981	1.4899	1.3712					0.0191	1.3245
	H	1527.9	1473.6	1419.8	1365.1	1309.4	1280.9	1250.7	1217.1					409.8	1203.6
	S	1.7809	1.7424	1.7012	1.6561	1.6059	1.5783	1.5477	1.5117					0.6061	1.4966
400 (444.58)	V	2.125	1.9704	1.8119	1.6472	1.4740	1.3817	1.2828	1.1726					0.0194	1.1601
	H	1526.8	1472.1	1417.7	1362.3	1305.5	1276.0	1244.3	1208.3					424.2	1204.1
	S	1.7658	1.7270	1.6854	1.6396	1.5884	1.5599	1.5276	1.4892					0.6218	1.4843

* Reprinted from the Abridged Edition of Steam Tables and Mollier Diagram, by Professor J. H. Kennan, 1931, by permission of the publisher, The American Society of Mechanical Engineers.

Table II. Superheated Steam *—Continued

Temperature—Degrees Fahrenheit

Abs. Press., lb/sq in. (Sat. Temp.)		Sat. Water	Sat. Steam	500°	550°	600°	620°	640°	660°	680°	700°	750°	800°	850°	900°	950°	1000°
450 (456.27)	V	0.0196	1.0303	1.1204	1.2127	1.2972	1.3299	1.3616	1.3932	1.4242	1.4548	1.5299	1.6032	1.6752	1.7455	1.8148	1.8834
	H	437.4	1204.1	1237.6	1271.0	1301.5	1313.2	1324.9	1336.5	1348.0	1359.4	1387.8	1415.7	1443.2	1470.6	1498.2	1525.8
	S	0.6361	1.4732	1.5091	1.5430	1.5725	1.5835	1.5942	1.6046	1.6148	1.6248	1.6487	1.6714	1.6928	1.7133	1.7331	1.7524
500 (466.99)	V	0.0198	0.9261	0.9905	1.0775	1.1558	1.1861	1.2153	1.2444	1.2727	1.3009	1.3697	1.4365	1.5018	1.5655	1.6284	1.6903
	H	449.7	1203.7	1230.5	1265.8	1297.3	1309.4	1321.1	1333.2	1344.9	1356.6	1385.3	1413.6	1441.5	1469.1	1496.9	1524.8
	S	0.6493	1.4630	1.4915	1.5274	1.5579	1.5692	1.5802	1.5908	1.6012	1.6113	1.6356	1.6586	1.6802	1.7009	1.7210	1.7404
550 (476.92)	V	0.0200	0.8402	0.8823	0.9658	1.0398	1.0679	1.0953	1.1223	1.1487	1.1746	1.2381	1.2996	1.3596	1.4181	1.4756	1.5321
	H	461.3	1203.0	1222.8	1260.3	1293.1	1305.5	1317.7	1329.8	1341.8	1353.6	1382.8	1411.5	1439.7	1467.6	1495.8	1523.8
	S	0.6616	1.4536	1.4747	1.5126	1.5443	1.5559	1.5671	1.5780	1.5886	1.5990	1.6236	1.6468	1.6687	1.6897	1.7100	1.7296
600 (486.17)	V	0.0202	0.7677	0.7922	0.8728	0.9431	0.9695	0.9954	1.0206	1.0452	1.0694	1.1285	1.1855	1.2411	1.2953	1.3483	1.4003
	H	472.3	1202.1	1214.7	1254.6	1288.7	1301.5	1314.1	1326.4	1338.6	1350.6	1380.3	1409.3	1437.8	1466.1	1494.4	1522.8
	S	0.6731	1.4447	1.4582	1.4986	1.5316	1.5436	1.5551	1.5662	1.5770	1.5874	1.6125	1.6360	1.6582	1.6794	1.6999	1.7196
700 (503.04)	V	0.0206	0.6527	......	0.7251	0.7905	0.8143	0.8376	0.8602	0.8822	0.9038	0.9559	1.0063	1.0554	1.1029	1.1484	1.1929
	H	492.9	1199.7	......	1242.4	1279.7	1293.3	1306.6	1319.4	1332.0	1344.5	1375.1	1404.9	1434.1	1463.0	1491.9	1520.8
	S	0.6943	1.4285	......	1.4720	1.5080	1.5208	1.5329	1.5444	1.5557	1.5665	1.5923	1.6165	1.6392	1.6608	1.6817	1.7018
800 (518.18)	V	0.0209	0.5653	......	0.6128	0.6750	0.6974	0.7189	0.7395	0.7596	0.7791	0.8265	0.8723	0.9157	0.9577	0.9982	1.0374
	H	511.8	1196.7	......	1228.8	1270.1	1284.6	1298.6	1312.1	1325.3	1338.2	1369.7	1400.4	1430.3	1459.9	1489.3	1518.8
	S	0.7135	1.4139	......	1.4462	1.4862	1.4998	1.5127	1.5248	1.5365	1.5477	1.5744	1.5992	1.6225	1.6446	1.6659	1.6864
900 (531.95)	V	0.0213	0.4969	......	0.5234	0.5844	0.6057	0.6258	0.6452	0.6639	0.6821	0.7257	0.7675	0.8072	0.8451	0.8815	0.9166
	H	529.5	1193.3	......	1213.6	1259.8	1275.5	1290.3	1304.5	1318.3	1331.7	1364.2	1395.8	1426.5	1456.8	1486.8	1516.8
	S	0.7311	1.4005	......	1.4208	1.4656	1.4803	1.4938	1.5067	1.5188	1.5304	1.5579	1.5835	1.6074	1.6301	1.6518	1.6727
1000 (544.58)	V	0.0217	0.4419	......	0.4495	0.5111	0.5317	0.5509	0.5692	0.5870	0.6040	0.6449	0.6837	0.7202	0.7547	0.7877	0.8199
	H	546.0	1189.6	......	1196.5	1248.7	1265.8	1281.6	1296.6	1311.0	1324.9	1358.5	1391.0	1422.6	1453.6	1484.3	1514.8
	S	0.7473	1.3881	......	1.3949	1.4455	1.4615	1.4760	1.4895	1.5022	1.5144	1.5427	1.5691	1.5936	1.6169	1.6390	1.6603
1100 (556.28)	V	0.0222	0.3960	......	......	0.4500	0.4705	0.4893	0.5071	0.5239	0.5401	0.5788	0.6152	0.6490	0.6810	0.7115	0.7408
	H	561.7	1185.6	......	......	1236.6	1255.4	1272.5	1288.3	1303.4	1317.9	1352.6	1386.1	1418.7	1450.4	1481.8	1512.8
	S	0.7624	1.3765	......	......	1.4257	1.4433	1.4590	1.4733	1.4866	1.4993	1.5285	1.5557	1.5810	1.6048	1.6274	1.6491
1200 (567.14)	V	0.0226	0.3582	......	......	0.3985	0.4189	0.4373	0.4547	0.4710	0.4865	0.5233	0.5578	0.5897	0.6195	0.6478	0.6750
	H	576.5	1181.4	......	......	1223.4	1244.2	1262.7	1279.6	1295.5	1310.6	1346.5	1381.1	1414.4	1447.2	1479.3	1510.8
	S	0.7765	1.3656	......	......	1.4058	1.4254	1.4423	1.4576	1.4716	1.4848	1.5151	1.5431	1.5692	1.5937	1.6168	1.6388

Note: In the following table each pressure (with saturation temperature in parentheses) has three property rows — V (specific volume), H (enthalpy), S (entropy). Columns "Sat. Liquid" and "Sat. Vapor" are followed by twelve superheat columns (the temperature column headings are not printed on this page).

Press. (Sat. Temp.)		Sat. Liquid	Sat. Vapor	1	2	3	4	5	6	7	8	9	10	11	12
1400 (586.96)	V	0.0235	0.2983	0.3144	0.3361	0.3548	0.3717	0.3874	0.4021	0.4365	0.4678	0.4964	0.5229	0.5476	0.5712
	H	604.3	1172.4	1192.4	1218.9	1241.3	1260.8	1278.6	1295.2	1333.8	1370.8	1406.5	1440.8	1474.3	1506.9
	S	0.8024	1.3452	1.3643	1.3891	1.4096	1.4272	1.4429	1.4574	1.4899	1.5199	1.5477	1.5736	1.5976	1.6204
1600 (604.74)	V	0.0244	0.2528		0.2706	0.2908	0.3083	0.3239	0.3384	0.3708	0.4002	0.4264	0.4503	0.4725	0.4935
	H	630.2	1162.7		1188.2	1216.2	1239.6	1260.1	1278.6	1320.3	1360.0	1398.1	1434.3	1469.3	1502.9
	S	0.8262	1.3265		1.3503	1.3760	1.3971	1.4152	1.4313	1.4666	1.4986	1.5283	1.5555	1.5808	1.6042
1800 (620.86)	V	0.0254	0.2167			0.2384	0.2574	0.2736	0.2880	0.3195	0.3472	0.3716	0.3938	0.4140	0.4330
	H	654.7	1151.8			1186.3	1215.3	1239.4	1260.6	1306.2	1348.7	1389.5	1427.8	1464.3	1498.8
	S	0.8482	1.3083			1.3399	1.3661	1.3874	1.4058	1.4444	1.4787	1.5105	1.5392	1.5656	1.5897
2000 (635.61)	V	0.0265	0.1875			0.1931	0.2145	0.2320	0.2468	0.2781	0.3047	0.3279	0.3486	0.3673	0.3847
	H	679.0	1139.0			1149.0	1186.6	1216.0	1240.7	1291.4	1337.0	1380.5	1421.1	1459.2	1494.7
	S	0.8696	1.2896			1.2988	1.3326	1.3586	1.3802	1.4230	1.4599	1.4938	1.5242	1.5518	1.5765
2200 (649.3)	V	0.0277	0.1623				0.1760	0.1960	0.2120	0.2438	0.2696	0.2919	0.3115	0.3289	0.3451
	H	703.7	1123.8				1150.9	1188.7	1218.4	1275.7	1324.8	1371.3	1414.2	1454.0	1490.4
	S	0.8912	1.2700				1.2943	1.3278	1.3536	1.4021	1.4418	1.4779	1.5102	1.5390	1.5644
2400 (661.9)	V	0.0292	0.1404					0.1637	0.1816	0.2148	0.2401	0.2618	0.2805	0.2969	0.3121
	H	729.4	1105.8					1155.5	1192.8	1259.1	1312.3	1361.6	1407.1	1448.7	1486.1
	S	0.9133	1.2488					1.2928	1.3253	1.3813	1.4224	1.4628	1.4969	1.5270	1.5531
2600 (673.8)	V	0.0310	0.1205					0.1314	0.1540	0.1896	0.2151	0.2361	0.2542	0.2699	0.2842
	H	756.7	1084.5					1110.0	1162.5	1241.0	1299.2	1351.9	1399.8	1443.2	1481.7
	S	0.9364	1.2257					1.2481	1.2938	1.3602	1.4074	1.4484	1.4842	1.5157	1.5426
2800 (684.9)	V	0.0333	0.1021						0.1275	0.1674	0.1934	0.2141	0.2315	0.2466	0.2603
	H	786.9	1058.9						1123.8	1221.3	1285.5	1341.6	1392.1	1437.6	1477.3
	S	0.9618	1.1996						1.2559	1.3384	1.3905	1.4342	1.4720	1.5049	1.5326
3000 (695.3)	V	0.0367	0.0844						0.0983	0.1476	0.1742	0.1947	0.2118	0.2265	0.2396
	H	823.1	1025.6						1066.3	1199.3	1271.1	1331.0	1384.3	1431.7	1472.9
	S	0.9922	1.1676						1.2028	1.3155	1.3737	1.4203	1.4602	1.4946	1.5233
3200 (704.9)	V	0.0459	0.0601							0.1293	0.1572	0.1777	0.1945	0.2088	0.2214
	H	887.0	962.9							1174.5	1255.9	1320.1	1376.1	1425.6	1468.4
	S	1.0461	1.1112							1.2907	1.3567	1.4067	1.4487	1.4845	1.5144
3226 (706.1)	V	0.0522	0.0522							0.1271	0.1552	0.1757	0.1924	0.2067	0.2192
	H	925.0	925.0							1171.2	1253.8	1318.7	1375.0	1424.9	1467.8
	S	1.0785	1.0785							1.2874	1.3545	1.4050	1.4472	1.4832	1.5133
3500	V									0.1042	0.1349	0.1556	0.1720	0.1860	0.1981
	H									1129.7	1231.2	1303.0	1363.3	1416.0	1461.6
	S									1.2484	1.3307	1.3866	1.4318	1.4699	1.5017

* Reprinted from the Abridged Edition of Steam Tables and Mollier Diagram, by Professor J. H. Keenan, 1931, by permission of the publisher, The American Society of Mechanical Engineers.

Column 8 is the sum of the items in columns 6 and 7. It records the enthalpy of the vapor with respect to an arbitrarily assigned zero of enthalpy for saturated water at 32 deg fahr.

Column 9 gives the entropy of saturated water with reference to a zero of entropy for water at the customary reference temperature 32 deg fahr.

Column 10 gives the change of entropy during evaporation at constant pressure and temperature.

Column 11 is the total entropy of the saturated vapor and must equal the sum of the items of columns 9 and 10.

Properties of Superheated Vapor. Steam tables also provide extensive tabular data on the properties of superheated steam. In such tabulations, because a vapor which is not contiguous with its liquid may be superheated to any temperature above the saturation temperature corresponding to the pressure, the properties are given for a wide range of temperatures or of degrees of superheat at each pressure. An abridged edition of the superheated steam section of the Keenan table appears in Table II, pp. 7–36 to 7–39.

The properties listed are seen to be the specific volume, enthalpy, and entropy. For convenience there is repeated directly below the pressure item the corresponding saturation temperature; and in columns 3 and 4 are repeated the several properties for saturated water and saturated steam at the given pressure. The remaining columns give the properties at the temperatures which are noted at the head of the column.

Properties of Compressed Liquid and Wet Vapor. The tables described have provided means for the direct determination of all the necessary properties of saturated liquid, saturated vapor, and superheated vapor. The two additional conditions of fluids for which data are frequently required are those of compressed liquid and wet vapor. It will be found that the table for the saturated condition supplies the requisite primary data for determination of the properties at these latter conditions, but some computations are necessary. The following describes the procedures to be followed.

Compressed Liquid is defined as liquid at a temperature less than the saturation temperature corresponding to the pressure under which it may be placed. An equivalent but alternative and frequently useful definition is that of a liquid under an externally imposed pressure which exceeds the saturated vapor pressure corresponding to the temperature. Simple illustrative conditions would be that of water in an open stream under atmospheric pressure but at 70 deg fahr instead of at the saturation temperature of 212 deg fahr which corresponds to the pressure, or that of boiler feedwater at 328 deg fahr but under a pump pressure of 400 lb per sq in. instead of the saturation pressure of 100 lb per sq in. which corresponds to the temperature.

As regards the specific volume, internal energy, and entropy of compressed water, those items are predominantly dependent on and influenced by the temperature but are unquestionably influenced slightly by superpressure. Therefore, for accurate work, especially at high liquid processes, it becomes necessary to have data showing the effect of superpressure in the values of these properties. However, for most ordinary work the values of V, E, and S for compressed water are regarded as the same as those of saturated water at the specified temperature (not pressure) of the compressed water.

As regards the enthalpy of compressed water the situation differs, for the reason that the enthalpy property $(E + PV/J)$ contains directly the pressure property as an inherent component and so must be definitely influenced by any material superpressure. At a given temperature, it may be estimated from saturation data with good accuracy by adding to the value of the enthalpy of saturated water (H_f), as quoted in the saturated vapor table at the specified temperature (not pressure), the excess PV/J occasioned by the superpressure. More specifically,

$$H_{\text{compressed liquid at } t \text{ and } P} = H_{f, \text{ at } t} + (P - P_f)V_f/J \tag{1}$$

In many practical instances in which P does not greatly exceed P_f the item $(P - P_f)V_f/J$ may be found to be relatively minor in magnitude and with adequate accuracy the enthalpy of the compressed liquid may be taken as that of saturated liquid at the temperature (not pressure) to which it is compressed.

Wet Vapor is a physical mixture of saturated vapor with droplets or fog of saturated but unvaporized liquid which is mechanically entrained with the vapor. The ratio of mass of vapor to the mass of the mixture of liquid and vapor is called the quality and is designated by the symbol x. For a wet vapor the temperature is the same as the saturation temperature corresponding to the pressure. The specific volume, enthalpy, and entropy may be computed as follows:

$$V_x = V_f + xV_{fg} \tag{2}$$

$$H_x = H_f + xH_{fg} \tag{3}$$

$$S_x = S_f + xS_{fg} \tag{4}$$

17. GRAPHICAL REPRESENTATION OF VAPOR PROPERTIES

One may choose as coordinates any pair of properties of a fluid and depict graphically the manner of their joint variation as the fluid progresses through any characteristic sequence of states. Of the various diagrams which might be so devised those which have been found to be most generally useful are the P–V diagram, the T–S diagram and the H–S or Mollier diagram. These are described and discussed in the following paragraphs.

P–V Diagram. In the P–V diagram, as represented for a typical fluid in Fig. 1, the absolute pressure is employed as the ordinate and the specific volume as the abscissa. In the diagram the slightly oblique and curved line on the left which is labeled the *saturated liquid line* shows the manner of variation of the specific volume of saturated liquid as the pressure (and temperature) is progressively increased. The state of a compressed liquid at any given pressure (but a temperature less than saturation) would be represented by a point to the left of the saturated liquid line, this by reason of the lesser specific volume at the lesser temperature. Consequently the general region which lies to the left of the saturated liquid line is known as the *compressed liquid region.*

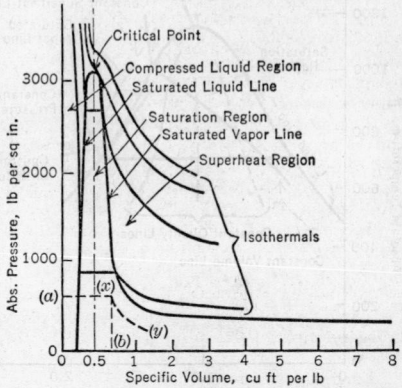

FIG. 1. P–V Diagram, Water and Water Vapor

The sloping line labeled the *saturated vapor line* similarly shows the relation between the pressure and specific volume of (dry) saturated vapor. The length of any horizontal line intercepted by the liquid and vapor lines thus represents the increase of specific volume during vaporization at constant pressure (V_{fg}). Therefore, since by the equation $V_x = V_f + x V_{fg}$, the state of a wet vapor mixture of quality x and at any given pressure would be represented by a point on that pressure line and lying at a distance $x V_{fg}$ to the right of the liquid line. The region between the two saturation lines is known as the *saturation region.*

Since the superheating of a vapor at a given pressure effects an increase of the specific volume the state of a superheated vapor would be represented by a point to the right of the saturated vapor line, whence the region to the right of that line is known as the *superheat region.*

The saturated liquid and saturated vapor lines are observed to join at a *critical pressure,* which for water is at 3226 lb per sq in., and at which pressure the saturation temperature of water is 706.1 deg fahr. The saturation temperature at the critical pressure is similarly known as the *critical temperature.* The diagram indicates that a liquid under that pressure would on warming pass imperceptibly into a dense superheated vapor state without the appearance of the characteristic phase of vaporization at constant temperature.

The *isothermal lines* which appear in the figure are contour lines of constant temperature and indicate the specific volume of a fluid at any given temperature and pressure or, alternatively, the pressure corresponding to a given state as designated by the temperature and specific volume. Since the temperature is constant during vaporization at constant pressure the isothermals become straight horizontal lines within the saturation region. In the compressed liquid region the isothermals are very nearly vertical, showing the very slight change (decrease) of volume of a liquid as it is compressed at constant temperature. In the superheat region the isothermals are approximately hyperbolic curves, approaching that curve more exactly at very low pressures or considerable superheats.

For temperatures which are above the critical a vapor may not be condensed at any finite pressure. Some writers consider the critical temperature isothermal to provide an arbitrary line of demarcation between the *gas phase* (above the line) and the *vapor phase* (below the line) of a substance.

In addition to the isothermal lines one might draw contour lines of *constant quality, constant superheat, constant internal energy, constant enthalpy,* or *constant entropy,* which lines might be useful for various particular purposes. Also any sort of state change whatsoever may be represented by a suitable curve or line on the diagram.

In connection with the P–V diagram it should be remarked that the product PV corresponding to any state of a fluid is represented by the rectangular area bounded by the coordinates, by a constant pressure line through the state point, and by a constant volume line through the point, that is, by an area such as $oaxb$ for state x. Also for any manner of state change as represented by the line xy, the $\int_x^y P\,dV$ is represented by the area between the line and the V-axis (that is, by the area *below* the line), and the $\int_x^y V\,dP$ is represented by the area between the line and the P-axis (the area *back of* the line).

T–S Diagram. In the T–S diagram (Fig. 2) *absolute* temperature is the ordinate, and entropy per pound mass (relative to liquid at 32 deg fahr) is the abscissa. The saturated liquid line, the critical point, and the saturated vapor line have the same significance as in the P–V diagram.

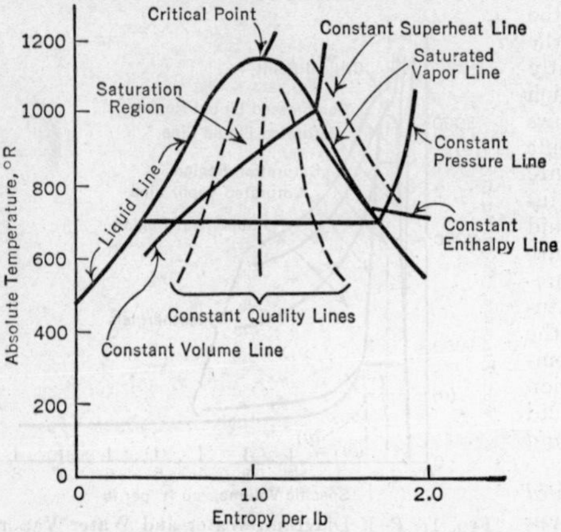

Except at quite high pressures, constant pressure contour lines nearly coincide with the saturated liquid line up to the saturation temperature corresponding to a particular pressure, from which point that pressure line proceeds across the saturation region at the saturation temperature of vaporization. The compressed liquid region is a thin band along the saturated liquid line.

At any temperature (or pressure) the horizontal intercept between the liquid and saturated vapor lines measures the increase of entropy S_{fg} during vaporization, and, since for a wet vapor mixture $S_x = S_f + x S_{fg}$, the state of a wet vapor of quality x is represented by a point on the pressure line at a distance $x S_{fg}$ to the right of the liquid line. Contour lines of constant quality will appear as in the diagram.

Typical contour lines of constant specific volume, constant enthalpy, and constant superheat also appear in the diagram.

The principal utility of the T–S diagram will be recalled to arise from the facts that for any process

$$Q_R = T_R\,\Delta S$$

and for any reversible process

$$Q = \int T\,dS$$

Thus for any state change of a fluid, as plotted on T–S coordinates, the change of the unavailable energy (Q_R) with reference to a receiver temperature T_R and chargeable to a pound mass of the fluid is represented by the area bounded by the S-axis below, by the T_R line above, and on the sides by the initial and final entropy lines. Likewise the heat energy reception or departure which accompanies a *reversible* state change is represented by the area between the state change curve and the S-axis (*below* the curve). A reversible adiabatic process is an isentropic (constant entropy) one and is represented by a straight vertical line.

H–S (" Mollier ") Diagram. The coordinates of the Mollier diagram are the enthalpy and entropy of the fluid, each per pound mass and each with reference to zero relative values of those properties for a liquid at 32 deg fahr. By reason of the intimate utility of the enthalpy property for all circumstances in which steady-flow processes occur, a portion of the diagram is invariably incorporated with the formal tables of vapor properties.

Referring to Fig. 3, the saturated liquid line, the critical point, and the saturated vapor line have the same significance as in the P–V and T–S diagrams. The compressed liquid region is practically restricted to a rather narrow band immediately above the saturated liquid line.

Constant pressure lines in this compressed liquid band approach the saturated liquid line as the excess of their pressure over the saturation pressure approaches zero. Within the saturation region the constant pressure lines are straight lines and are also constant temperature contours. The vertical distance between the intersections of a constant pressure line with the saturated liquid and saturated vapor lines measures the increase of enthalpy during vaporization, and the horizontal distance measures the entropy of vaporization.

FIG. 2. T–S Diagram, Water and Water Vapor

On entering the superheat region the constant pressure lines veer upward, and the constant temperature contours approach constant H lines with increase of superheat.

Contour lines of constant quality and of constant superheat are also drawn in Fig. 3, and other contour lines might be shown. However, the two noted are usually the ones which appear. It may be remarked that the common Mollier chart, as used for many

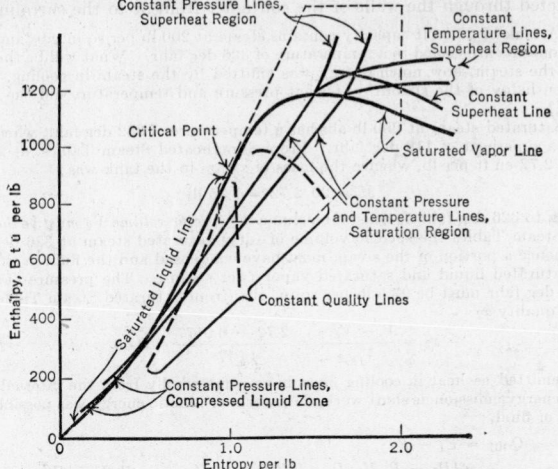

FIG. 3.   *H–S* Diagram, Water and Water Vapor

practical purposes, shows to larger scale only a small region around the saturated vapor line, such as that enclosed by dotted lines in the upper portion of Fig. 3.

18. STATE CHANGES AND PROCESSES

In the consideration of the various actual processes which are encountered in engineering thermodynamics certain classes of state changes of fluids occur with marked frequency. Several of these will be examined in detail.

For the analysis of any process it is the first requisite that the initial state of the fluid be adequately specified. For the fluids and the states which are encountered in engineering thermodynamics information concerning any two properties is, in general, sufficient for designation of the state. In practice it is commonly found that one or more of the specified properties will be those which we are best equipped to measure readily, that is, the pressure or temperature or perhaps the specific volume.

A second requisite is the specification of the character of the state change. In this connection it will be found that many of the actual processes are characterized by the actual or effective constancy of some property of the fluid during the state change. To illustrate, a state change taking place in a fluid which is retained within a closed and non-extensible vessel is one in which the specific volume remains constant or is a constant volume process; one taking place during the passage of a fluid through a device such as a boiler or superheater may closely approach constant pressure conditions and be taken as effectively such; the ideal state change taking place during the expansion of a fluid in an engine or turbine is the reversible adiabatic, which is characterized by a constant entropy of the fluid.

As a third feature it will be observed that, as the result of such constancy of one property of the fluid during a change of its state and thus a change of its other properties, this particular property is known at the cessation of the process. Therefore, to designate the final state of the fluid and thus to complete the description of the process, it will in general be necessary to specify the magnitude of one additional property at the final state. With sufficient information thus available for fixing that state, all the other properties may then be determined.

A fourth feature of most process analyses is the desirability or necessity for determining the energy transformations and transitions accompanying the processes.

The following representative processes with steam vapor will be analyzed: (a) constant volume process, (b) constant pressure process, (c) reversible adiabatic process, and (d) throttling process. Each analysis is illustrated and to a large extent developed by the use of an example.

Constant Volume Process. The simplest circumstance under which a constant volume process may take place is that in which a fluid is retained within a closed container while the state change is effected through the transition of energy to or from the system as heat conducted through the walls of the container from or to the surrounding region.

Example. A tank of 20 cu ft capacity contains steam at 200 lb per sq in. abs and 500 deg fahr. The tank and contents are cooled to a temperature of 326 deg fahr. What will be the final pressure and quality of the steam, how much energy was emitted by the steam in cooling, and what was the change of enthalpy of the steam? At what pressure and temperature did the steam become (dry) saturated?

Solution. Saturated steam at 200 lb abs has a temperature of 382 deg fahr, whence at state (1) the steam had a superheat of 118 deg fahr. From Superheated Steam Tables, at 200 lb and 500 deg fahr, $V_1 = 2.72$ cu ft per lb, whence the mass of steam in the tank was

$$M = 20/2.72 = 7.35 \text{ lb}$$

After cooling to 326 deg fahr at constant volume *the specific volume V_2 must be the same.* From the Saturated Steam Tables the specific volume of (dry) saturated steam at 326 deg fahr is 4.534 cu ft per lb, whence a portion of the steam must have condensed and the fluid in the tank become a mixture of saturated liquid and saturated vapor (wet steam). The pressure of this saturated mixture at 326 deg fahr must be 97.5 lb per sq in. abs (from Saturated Steam Tables).

To find the quality x_2

$$x_2 = \frac{V - V_{f,2}}{V_{fg,2}} = \frac{2.72 - 0.0177}{4.517} = 0.60$$

The energy emitted as heat in cooling must have come wholly from the internal energy of the steam since no energy emission as shaft work, flow work, or kinetic energy was possible. Therefore, for each pound of fluid,

$$
\begin{aligned}
Q_{out} &= E_1 - E_2 \\
&= [H_1 - P_1 V_1/J] - [(H_{f,2} + x_2 H_{fg,2}) - P_2 V_{x,2}/J] \\
&= \left[1267.9 - \frac{200 \times 2.72}{5.4} \right] \\
&\quad - \left[(296.4 + 0.60 \times 889.7) - \frac{97.5 \times 2.72}{5.4} \right] \\
&= 1167.0 - 780.1 = 386.9 \text{ Btu per lb.}
\end{aligned}
$$

Total energy emitted, as heat, $= 7.35 \times 386.9 = 2844$ Btu.

Change of enthalpy $= H_2 - H_1$

$$
\begin{aligned}
&= (H_{f,2} + x_2 H_{fg,2}) - H_1 \\
&= 829.3 - 1267.9 = -438.6 \text{ Btu per lb.}
\end{aligned}
$$

To find the pressure and temperature at which the steam became (dry) saturated it is necessary to search the Saturated Steam Tables for the state at which $V_g = 2.72$. This is found at a pressure of 166.7 lb per sq in. abs and a temperature of 366.8 deg fahr.

Note that in this non-flow, constant volume circumstance only the change of internal energy $(E_2 - E_1)$ measures or denotes an energy quantity, the change of PV becoming simply a change in that product of properties, *without an energy significance.*

Constant Pressure Process. A constant pressure process may readily be conceived to occur (a) without flow, as in a cylinder with piston, or (b) with steady flow, as in any vessel such as a steadily steaming boiler, a steadily operating condenser, etc., the state change being effected in either case by energy transition to or from the fluid, this usually as heat.

Example. A pound of water *in a cylinder (with piston)* is initially at 200 deg fahr and 235.3 lb per sq in. gage, and by energy reception as heat is transformed to steam of 98 per cent quality at the same pressure, the constancy of pressure being attained by permitting the piston to retreat as the fluid expands.

Compute the amount of energy required to effect the process and also that portion of this energy which is stored internally in the fluid.

Solution.

$$
\begin{aligned}
JQ &= J(E_2 - E_1) - W \\
&= J(E_2 - E_1) + W_{out}
\end{aligned}
$$

In this device the work output at the piston face equals $\int_1^2 P\,dV = P(V_2 - V_1)$, since the pressure P is constant. Therefore

$$
\begin{aligned}
Q_{in} &= (E_2 - E_1) + P(V_2 - V_1)/J \\
&= (E_2 + PV_2/J) - (E_1 + PV_1/J) \\
&= H_2 - H_1, \text{ for a non-flow constant-pressure process.}
\end{aligned}
$$

For the specific data of the problem:

$$H_1 = 167.9 + \frac{(250 - 11.5) \times 144 \times 0.0166}{778}$$

$$= 168.7 \text{ (exactly)} = 168.0 \text{ (approx.)}$$

$$H_2 = 376.0 + 0.98 \times 824.5 = 1184.0$$

$$Q = \Delta H = 1184.0 - 168.7 = 1015.3 \text{ Btu per lb}$$

$$E_1 = 167.9 - \frac{11.5 \times 144 \times 0.0166}{778} = 167.9$$

$$E_2 = 1184.0 - \frac{250 \times 0.98 \times 1.841}{5.4} = 1100.5$$

$$\Delta E = 1100.5 - 167.9 = 932.6 \text{ Btu per lb}$$

The difference between the energy supplied (ΔH) and that stored as molecular energy in the steam (ΔE) is transferred directly via the fluid to the piston face and is there delivered as work $[P(V_2 - V_1), = 1015.3 - 932.6 = 82.7]$.

The foregoing example has had to do with a non-flow constant pressure process. For the circumstance of steady flow at constant pressure through a device such as a boiler, since there is no shaft work,

$$Q_{\text{in}} = (H_2 - H_1) + (U_2{}^2 - U_1{}^2)/64.34\,J$$

As the change of kinetic energy in the usual device of this character would very rarely indeed exceed 1 Btu per lb and would usually be much less, this in comparison with a change of enthalpy which commonly would be some thousand Btu in magnitude, the kinetic energy term becomes effectively negligible and may be omitted. Thus for both a non-flow and a steady-flow constant pressure process the energy received by the fluid is measured by its change of enthalpy.

Reversible Adiabatic Process. Recalling that, by definition, *any process whatsoever in which no energy enters or departs from the system as heat is designated as an adiabatic process*, we may immediately write the following general energy equations for an adiabatic non-flow and an adiabatic steady-flow process:

$$W = J(E_2 - E_1), \text{ for a non-flow adiabatic process}$$

$$W + (U_1{}^2 - U_2{}^2)/64.34 = J(H_2 - H_1), \text{ for a steady-flow adiabatic process}$$

These equations are universally applicable whether the adiabatic process may be ideal and reversible or actual and thus irreversible. For the further condition of a *reversible* adiabatic process there is introduced the additional feature that the entropy remains constant during the process, or the process is isentropic. It may well be remarked that the outstanding practical utility of the entropy property lies in this very feature of its constancy during a reversible adiabatic process. To denote such constancy we employ the letter S as a subscript attached to any change of properties of a fluid during an isentropic process. Thus, rewriting the above equations but now in the special form which is applicable to the reversible adiabatic,

$$W = J(E_2 - E_1)_S, \text{ for a non-flow reversible adiabatic}$$

$$W + (U_1{}^2 - U_2{}^2)/64.34 = J(H_2 - H_1)_S, \text{ for a steady-flow reversible adiabatic}$$

For an easy and accurate determination of the fluid properties after isentropic expansion from a given initial state to a specified final pressure the H–S (Mollier) chart obviously is useful. Also the final quality after expansion to a given pressure or temperature *within the saturation region* may be computed directly by the equation

$$x_2 = \frac{S - S_{f,\,2}}{S_{fg,\,2}} = 1 - \frac{S_{g,\,2} - S}{S_{fg,\,2}} \tag{5}$$

where S is the initial and constant entropy. The final quality being known, the other properties may be computed as required.

Example. Steam at 200 lb per sq in. abs and a quality of 0.995 is delivered to an ideal steam turbine, expands adiabatically and reversibly therein to a pressure of 14.7 lb per sq in. abs, and is discharged at that pressure.

Compute the entropy, quality, and enthalpy of the steam leaving the turbine and the shaft work which would ideally be obtainable per pound of steam used, assuming negligible kinetic energies entering and leaving the turbine.

Solution.

$$S_1 = S_{g,\,1} - (1 - x_1)S_{fg,\,1} = 1.5450 - 0.005 \times 1.0012 = 1.5400.$$

$$S_2 = S_1 = 1.5400.$$

$$x_2 = \frac{1.5400 - 0.3119}{1.4446} = 0.850.$$

$$H_2 = 1150.2 - 0.15 \times 970.2 = 1004.7.$$

$$H_1 = 1197.8 - 0.005 \times 842.4 = 1193.6.$$

$$W = J(H_1 - H_2)_S = J(1193.6 - 1004.7) = 778 \times 188.9 = 147{,}000 \text{ ft-lb.}$$

Throttling Process. Technically, a pure throttling process is one in which a fluid expands adiabatically but thoroughly irreversibly through a labyrinthal or porous obstruction in a line, the arrangement being such that the velocities of the stream approaching, through, and departing from the obstruction shall be very small and their differences wholly negligible.   No shaft work is performed.

This process is approached closely in practice in the "wire-drawing" of a vapor

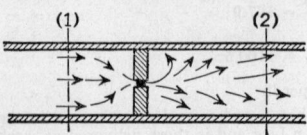

(1)   (2)

(or gas) through a constriction in a line such as a partially closed valve or small orifice.   In such devices there is unquestionably an accretion of velocity and kinetic energy directly in the constriction, but this momentary unidirectional velocity is immediately dissipated by reason of the high degree of turbulence existing in the stream directly after the constriction, whereby the kinetic energy in the stream finally departing from the region $(U_2^2/64.34)$

Fig. 4.   Throttling Process

is negligible or differs negligibly from that in the stream approaching the region $(U_1^2/64.34)$. (See Fig. 4.)

The process is also approached, but less exactly (owing to energy dissipation as heat), in the flow of a vapor through a long pipe line in which there is a distinct pressure drop due to friction.

To discern the working scheme for analyzing the throttling process, note that in fitting the general steady-flow energy equation (equation 5, Art. 4) to the conditions of the process the Q and W terms disappear and the kinetic energy terms are either negligible or effectively canceled, whence

$$H_1 = H_2$$

This equality of the initial and final enthalpy is the outstanding characteristic of the throttling process.

Example.   Steam at 250 lb abs and 99 per cent quality is throttled to a pressure of 200 lb abs. What is the state of the steam after throttling, and what is the loss of available energy, assuming that the steam were being supplied to a reversible engine operating with a 70 deg fahr exhaust?

Solution.

$$H_1 = 1192.3 = H_2.$$

To ascertain the second state, since H_g at 200 lb abs is 1197.8 the fluid must still be a slightly wet mixture.   To ascertain the quality,

$$H_2 = 1192.3 = H_{f,\,2} + x_2\,H_{fg,\,2} = 355.3 + x_2\,842.4, \ x_2 = 0.9935$$

To ascertain the increase of unavailable energy:

$$S_1(\text{at } 250 \text{ lb and } 99\%) = 1.5165; \ S_2(\text{at } 200 \text{ lb and } 99.35\%) = 1.5385$$

$$\Delta S = 0.0220; \ \Delta Q_R = T_2\,\Delta S = (70 + 460) \times 0.0220 = 11.7 \text{ Btu per lb.}$$

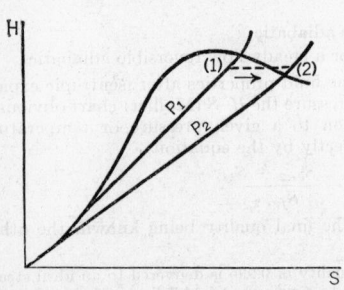

Fig. 5.   *H–S* Diagram for Throttling Process

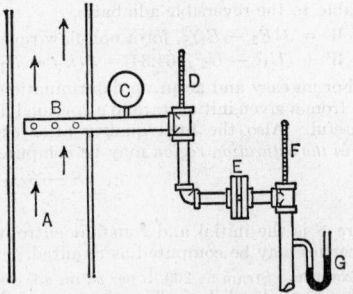

Fig. 6.   Throttling Calorimeter

The Throttling Calorimeter.   Both by reference to the above example and to a Mollier diagram (see Fig. 5) it becomes apparent that if a wet vapor passes through a throttling process the requisite equality of the initial and final enthalpies will in general produce an increase in the quality of the vapor.*   Also if the initial quality of the vapor is sufficiently high and the pressure drop sufficiently great, some degree of superheat may well exist in the exit or lower pressure vapor.   By reason of the latter circumstance and the additional facts (a) that *in the superheat region the pressure and temperature will suffice to determine*

---

* This statement must be made with some qualification.   To illustrate, inspection of the Mollier diagram of steam (Keenan tables) shows that with initial pressures in excess of about 500 lb per sq in. a throttling through a moderate pressure range may in fact act to increase the moisture content.

the state and enthalpy of the fluid and (*b*) that these P and T properties are both directly measurable ones, the throttling phenomenon may be and is regularly employed in a device which is known as the *throttling calorimeter* and is used for ascertaining the enthalpy and quality of steam which contains a limited amount of moisture.

Referring to Fig. 6, a simple arrangement of such a device is there indicated. In the figure, A is a steam line through which is passing the steam the enthalpy and quality of which are desired. Pipe B is a *sampling tube* through which it is endeavored to draw a true sample of the steam in A. Gage C or thermometer D determines the saturation pressure or temperature of the steam supply. These obviously should "check" if the steam is saturated. Between the flanges at E is located a plate with a small ($1/16$ in. to $1/8$ in. diameter) orifice through which the sample is throttled to the discharge pressure, which is usually about atmospheric. Thermometer F, and mercury manometer G, together with data on the barometric pressure, provide the requisite data on the temperature and pressure of the throttled fluid by which its state may be ascertained from the Superheated Steam Tables. Thus the enthalpy of the leaving steam and thereby that of the entering steam is determinable.

The quality of the steam sample is found by solving for x in the expression for the enthalpy of wet steam:

$$H_2 = H_1 = H_{f,1} + x_1 H_{fg,1}; \quad \text{or} \quad x_1 = (H_2 - H_{f,1})/H_{fg,1}$$

An alternative method is to enter the Mollier chart at the intersection of the P_2 and t_2 lines, pass across at constant H to P_1, and read the quality directly.

This device if properly constructed and operated will give the enthalpy and quality of the sample with good accuracy, although a slight correction for radiation may be desirable. A serious practical difficulty lies in the securing of a truly representative sample of the steam in line A. Also its use is limited to fairly dry and fairly high-pressure steam since an excess of moisture or low steam pressure will prevent the superheating, and *its whole utility depends on the possibility of fixing the state of superheated steam from knowledge of its pressure and temperature.*

19. FLOW OF VAPORS THROUGH NOZZLES AND ORIFICES

The general energy equations for a nozzle are invariably applicable whether the fluid flowing is a gas or a vapor, whence we may refer immediately to the basic energy equations. Those equations are repeated here for convenience:

$$\frac{U_x^2 - U_1^2}{64.34} = J(H_1 - H_x) \tag{6}$$

$$M' = \frac{U_1 A_1}{V_1} = \frac{U_x A_x}{V_x} \quad \text{(continuity equation)} \tag{7}$$

$$U_x = 223.7 \sqrt{\frac{H_1 - H_x}{1 - \left(\frac{A_x}{A_1}\right)^2 \left(\frac{V_1}{V_x}\right)^2}} \tag{8}$$

where the factor $\sqrt{\dfrac{1}{1 - \left(\frac{A_x}{A_1}\right)^2 \left(\frac{V_1}{V_x}\right)^2}}$ is to be considered the correction factor for initial velocity.

$$\frac{M'}{A_x} \text{ (ideal)} = 8.02 \sqrt{\frac{k}{k-1}} \frac{P_1}{\sqrt{RT_1}} \sqrt{\left(\frac{P_x}{P_1}\right)^{2/k} - \left(\frac{P_x}{P_1}\right)^{(k+1)/k}} \tag{9}$$

which does not include the correction factor for initial velocity.

In actual flow the nozzle efficiency and the coefficient of velocity are introduced, e_n and C_v, respectively:

$$e_n = \frac{(U_x^2 - U_1^2) \text{ actual}}{(U_x^2 - U_1^2) \text{ ideal}} = \frac{(H_1 - H_x) \text{ actual}}{(H_1 - H_x)S} \tag{10}$$

$$C_v = \frac{U_{x,\text{ actual}}}{U_{x,\text{ ideal}}} = \sqrt{e_n} \tag{11}$$

Quite as it was with the flow of a gas, given the state of the fluid as supplied, the problem of applying these equations in developing either the ideal or the actual nozzle form is that of ascertaining the simultaneous values of H_x and V_x as expansion proceeds to successively lower pressures. However, as may be anticipated, the detailed procedure in ascertaining these values may differ in the cases of the gas and of the vapor, particularly if the vapor is one for which tables of properties are available. Such tables being available for the vapors of major engineering importance, it is the practice (at least among engineers of the United States) to utilize them, although it will appear subsequently that in considerations of actual flow certain difficulties are encountered in that procedure.

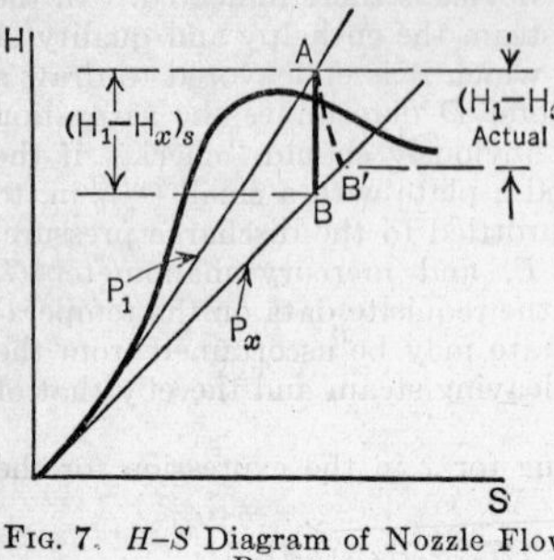

For the circumstance of the ideal expansion the values of the desired properties are easily obtained by recognizing the isentropic character of the expansion and then following the methods of the example on p. 7–45, using either the vapor tables alone or those jointly with a Mollier (H–S) chart. The appearance of an ideal state change as represented on H–S coordinates would be that of a line such as AB in Fig. 7. The essential characteristic of the line is the ideal constancy of the entropy.

The procedure in investigating the nozzle form for ideal expansion is perhaps shown to best advantage by an illustrative example.

Fig. 7. *H–S* Diagram of Nozzle Flow Process

Example. Determine the characteristic form and dimensions of a steam nozzle which shall provide for the flow and reversible expansion of 2 lb of steam per second from an initial state of 200 lb per sq in. abs and 420 deg fahr to a discharge region at a pressure of 60 lb abs. Do this by computing the areas required upon expansion to successive pressures of 160, 120, 115, 109, 85, and 60 lb. Assume the ideal case of reversible adiabatic expansion and also assume negligible entrance velocity.

Solution for P_x of 160 lb per sq in.

$$H_1 = 1222.3; \quad V_1 = 2.436; \quad S_1 = 1.5735.$$

$$S_x = S_1 = 1.5735; \quad t_x \text{ (from Superheat Table)} = 376.4 \text{ deg fahr.}$$

$$H_x = 1202.7; \quad \Delta H = 19.6; \quad U_x = 223.7 \sqrt{19.6} = 990 \text{ ft per sec.}$$

$$V_x = 2.894; \quad M'/A_x = 990/2.894 = 342; \quad A_x = 0.00585 \text{ sq ft.}$$

Solution for P_x of 120 lb per sq in.

$$S_x = S_1 = 1.5735; \quad x_x = 1 - \frac{1.5874 - 1.5735}{1.0956} = 1 - 0.0127 = 0.987.$$

$$H_x = 1189.8 - 0.0127 \times 877.4 = 1178.7; \quad \Delta H = 43.6; \quad U_x = 1480.$$

$$V_x = 3.725 - 0.0127 \times 3.707 = 3.678.$$

$$M'/A_x = 1480/3.678 = 401.5; \quad A_x = 0.00498.$$

The major results at these and the other specified pressures are tabulated below.

Tabular Results

p_x (lb per sq in.)	t, or x	H_x	ΔH	U_x	V_x	M'/A_x	A_x (sq ft)
200	420	1222.3	......	......	2.436	......	......
160	376	1202.7	19.6	990	2.894	342	0.00585
120	0.987	1178.7	43.6	1480	3.678	402	0.00498
115	0.984	1175.3	47.0	1530	3.817	402	0.00498
109	0.981	1171.1	51.2	1600	4.001	400	0.00500
85	0.964	1151.1	71.2	1890	4.978	379	0.00528
60	0.943	1124.4	97.9	2210	6.7605	327	0.00612

Scrutiny of the above tabular results indicates that:

(a) For a given initial state a particular enthalpy, specific volume, and area (per unit mass-rate of flow) are again associated with each successive pressure.

(b) The critical pressure phenomenon is again evidenced by the minimum area, or throat, which occurs in the above example upon expansion to about 57 per cent (115/200) of the supply pressure.

(c) For expansion to any pressure equal to or less than the critical a convergent passage is proper.

(d) A subsequent divergent passage is required in order to provide properly for a controlled and directed expansion to a pressure which is less than the critical.

(e) For expansion to a discharge region pressure which is greater than the critical the required exit area for a given mass-rate of flow will depend on both the supply state and the discharge region pressure or, conversely, the mass-rate of flow at given supply and discharge region pressures will be proportional to the exit area.

(f) On the contrary, for expansion to a discharge region which is at a pressure equal to or less than the critical the invariable existence of the critical pressure at the throat and a fixed value of the critical ratio will act to cause the required throat area for a given mass-rate of flow to depend only on the state of the fluid supply or, conversely, the mass-rate of flow obtained with a given supply state depends only on the throat area and is independent of the discharge region pressure (although the proper final exit area for suitable accommodation of the entire expansion must depend also on the discharge region pressure).

One feature in which vapor flow and gas flow will differ slightly is that the critical ratio for a vapor does not appear to be strictly a constant. Thus, in the example, in which the steam supply was moderately superheated, the critical ratio appears to have the value of about 0.57. By similar investigation it would be found that the critical ratio for steam would apparently range from about 0.55 for highly superheated steam supply to about 0.58 for saturated steam supply. However, this variation does not require much concern, owing to the very slight change of the cross-sectional area of the nozzle at pressures between about 55 and 60 per cent of the supply pressure.

An important characteristic of this ideal expansion, which is clearly indicated in the above tabulation and was evident in Fig. 7, is the progressive condensation of a portion of the vapor with progressive expansion. Quoting specific figures, the reversible adiabatic expansion of the initially superheated supply would require the actual condensation of about 2 per cent of the vapor prior to reaching the throat and about 6 per cent prior to reaching the 60 lb exit pressure, and the example above would indicate that 13 per cent should condense if the expansion were continued to atmospheric pressure. In making these quality computations it was inherently assumed that a stable thermal equilibrium was maintained between the liquid and the vapor as the expansion proceeded, whence the expansion would be designated as being of the equilibrium type. A further consideration will be given to the possibility of an actual expansion of this type.

Actual Expansion of a Vapor. Any actual expansion through a nozzle is necessarily irreversible by reason of the unescapable friction and turbulence accompanying the high-velocity flow. The influence of such irreversibility and the general manner of accounting for it in air-nozzle design has been considered above. It will similarly be considered for steam-nozzle design in the following paragraphs, but first it needs to be noted that without question additional causes for irreversibility exist in the case of vapor flow, or more particularly in the case of a vapor which is supplied in a saturated or only slightly superheated state. This additional irreversibility is occasioned by a temporary unstable condition which has been found to exist in rapidly expanding vapor. The condition is that known as supersaturation and is characterized by a retarding or deferring of the partial condensation which we have seen would accompany the equilibrium type of expansion. Experiments indicate that complete supersaturation and action like a superheated vapor persist until a pressure is reached which is about one-half of that at which condensation would normally begin. This is approximately equivalent to stating that for initially dry and saturated steam complete supersaturation persists down to and somewhat beyond the critical pressure. Assuming superheated and supersaturated steam with frictionless adiabatic expansion having the basic property relation

$$PV^{1.3} = \text{a constant} \tag{12}$$

the following relations are derived:

$$\frac{M'}{A_x} \text{ (ideal)} = 16.7 \sqrt{\frac{P_1}{V_1}\left[\left(\frac{P_x}{P_1}\right)^{1.54} - \left(\frac{P_x}{P_1}\right)^{1.77}\right]} \tag{9a}$$

or, if $(P_1 - P_x)/P_1$ does not exceed about 0.33,

$$\frac{M'}{A_x} \text{ (ideal)} = 8.02 \frac{1}{\sqrt{P_1 V_1}} \sqrt{P_x(P_1 - P_x) - 0.15(P_1 - P_x)^2} \tag{9b}$$

or, if $(P_1 - P_x)/P_1$ does not exceed about 0.1,

$$\frac{M'}{A_x} \text{ (ideal)} = 8.02 \sqrt{\frac{P_x(P_1 - P_x)}{P_1 V_1}} \tag{9c}$$

or, if $(P_1 - P_x)/P_1$ does not exceed about 0.01,

$$\frac{M'}{A_x} \text{ (ideal)} = 8.02 \sqrt{\frac{P_1 - P_x}{V_1}} \tag{9d}$$

Also for the special consideration of a value of P_x equal to the critical pressure, in which circumstance the flow rate per unit area is recalled to be the maximum,

$$\frac{M'}{A_{\text{throat}}} \text{ (ideal)} = 3.78 \sqrt{P_1/V_1} \tag{9x}$$

The critical ratio for the flow of superheated and supersaturated steam becomes

$$\frac{P_{\text{critical}}}{P_1} = \left(\frac{2}{1.3+1}\right)^{1.3/0.3} = 0.545 \tag{13}$$

Diffuser and Ejector. The diffuser is in principle the reverse of a nozzle and is a device by which a lower pressure, high-velocity jet may deliver itself at a low velocity at and against a higher pressure. Referring to the Mollier diagram of Fig. 8, a fluid passing reversibly through a nozzle from pressure P_1 to the lower pressure P_2 would change state along the path ab, at constant entropy, decreasing enthalpy, increasing specific volume, and increasing velocity. A diffuser in which the action was wholly reversible would take the high-velocity fluid under the conditions existing at the nozzle outlet, b, and return it along state path ba to its original state and to a region of the higher original pressure P_1. All the state changes which occurred in the ideal nozzle would occur in the ideal diffuser in the reverse order.

The contour of the channel required by the diffuser is determined from exactly the same considerations which determine the contour of a nozzle, namely, consideration of the steady-flow energy equation and the continuity of flow principle. Parallel features of the two devices would be that, just as expansion in a nozzle to a lower pressure which exceeds about one-half of the higher calls for a converging section only, so a compression in a diffuser from a lower pressure in excess of one-half of the higher would require only a diverging section. Similarly, if the stream velocity to the diffuser were sufficient to enable discharge to a region the pressure of which exceeded twice that of the lower-pressure supply

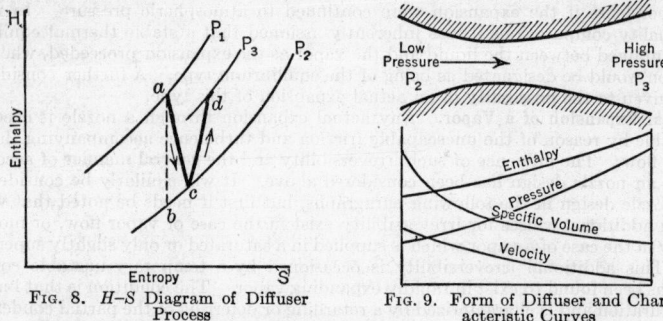

FIG. 8. H-S Diagram of Diffuser Process

FIG. 9. Form of Diffuser and Characteristic Curves

region, the diffuser channel would be initially convergent and then divergent from a throat. The general form of a diffuser for operation under the latter condition is shown in Fig. 9. Below the diffuser are depicted the decreasing velocity and specific volume and the increasing pressure and enthalpy as the fluid flows from the lower-pressure to the higher-pressure region.

In Fig. 8 there is also shown the character of the *actual* processes in a serial arrangement of nozzle and diffuser. The line ac represents the actual expansion in the nozzle from pressure P_1 to pressure P_2, and the line cd represents the recompression in the diffuser. The paths are both of increasing entropy and so, if in general the recompression may be one to a final enthalpy H_3 equal to the original enthalpy H_1, the final pressure P_3 must be less than the original pressure P_1 by an amount which depends on the degree of irreversibility of the two processes.

For the compression of a gas in a diffuser, if the stream were carried to a negligible exit velocity U_3, the pressure to and against which it might be delivered would depend on the pressure, temperature, and velocity of the supply stream. Thus, by a development of the energy equation,

$$\frac{U_2^2}{64.34} = \frac{k}{k-1} R T_2 \left[\left(\frac{P_3}{P_2}\right)^{(n-1)/n} - 1\right]$$

or

$$P_{3,\,\text{max}} = P_2 \left[\frac{k-1}{kRT_2}\frac{U_2^2}{64.34} + 1\right]^{n/(n-1)} \tag{14}$$

in which $P_{3,\,\text{max}}$ = maximum discharge pressure against which the stream could be delivered from diffuser after deceleration to a negligible velocity.

P_2 = pressure of the region of the supply stream.

U_2 = velocity of the supply stream, feet per second.

T_2 = supply region temperature, degrees Rankine.

$k = c_p/c_v = 1.40$ for air.

n = the effective P–V exponent of the more or less irreversible adiabatic compression process, the value of which exponent would equal k for ideal reversible compression, would exceed k for irreversible compression, and would be an index of the character of the diffuser performance.

Common applications of the diffuser are found in the downstream section of the Venturi meter and in centrifugal pumps and compressors. In the latter, high-velocity streams are created at the periphery of a rotating element and stationary diffusers are employed to utilize the kinetic energy of the streams for delivery to discharge regions of higher pressure.

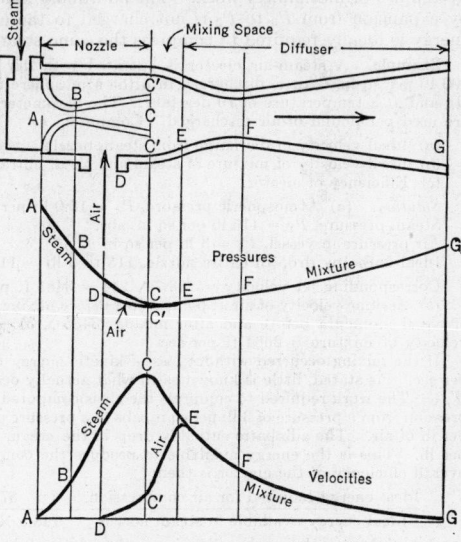

The diffuser forms an essential component of the *ejector*, which is a device in which the kinetic energy of one fluid is used to pump another fluid from a region of lower to one of higher pressure. In the steam air ejector, Fig. 10, a high-velocity jet of steam is produced by the steam nozzle AC. Air drawn into the ejector from a region of low pressure D mixes with the jet, and the mixture is compressed in the diffuser EG and discharged into a region of higher pressure beyond G. The changes in pressure, velocity, enthalpy, and entropy occurring throughout the ejector are shown graphically in Fig. 10. The steam is sup-

FIG. 10. Ejector and Characteristics

plied to the nozzle at a pressure P_1 considerably higher than the pressure P_3 at which the air is to be discharged. Along AC occurs the increase of velocity in the nozzle. Along DC' is a slight increase in velocity as the air is drawn into the ejector. Between C and some indefinite point E the steam and air mix at nearly constant pressure and with an increase in air velocity and decrease of steam velocity. This mixing is considered to occur by a wholly irreversible process described as inelastic impact, but with conservation of momentum of the streams of fluid. From E to G the mixture is compressed with decreasing velocity and increasing entropy and enthalpy. The diffuser requires a minimum section at F if the absolute pressure at E is less than about half the pressure at G. Because of lack of knowledge of just what occurs during the mixing process and also of the efficiency of the compression process in the diffuser, no satisfactorily exact analysis of the complete ejector has been made. Design is largely by empirical methods.

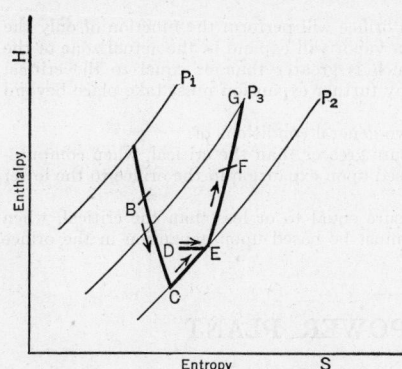

FIG. 11. H–S Diagram for Ejector Process

However, it is not difficult to compute the efficiency of an ejector from performance data.

Let
M'_s = mass of steam used in unit time.
M'_a = mass of air handled in unit time.
$M'_s (H_1 - H_3)_S$ = adiabatic decrease in enthalpy of steam from nozzle supply pressure P_1 to air discharge (not suction) pressure P_3.
$M'_a W_a$ = adiabatic work of compression of air from air suction pressure P_2 to air discharge pressure P_3.

Then efficiency of ejector = work required to compress air adiabatically, divided by available energy supplied by steam above discharge pressure, or

$$\text{Ejector eff.} = \frac{M'_a\, W_a}{JM'_s (H_1 - H_3)_S} \tag{15}$$

The efficiency computed in this manner corresponds to the efficiency which should be used if the air were compressed in a steam-driven piston or centrifugal air pump directly by the use of mechanical work.   The additional kinetic energy obtained in the steam jet by expansion from P_3 to P_2 is not charged to the ejector, since exactly that amount of energy is ideally required to compress the same steam back from P_2 to P_3 in the diffuser.

Example.   A steam-air ejector is operated with dry saturated steam at a gage pressure of 100 lb per sq in.   Air is discharged into the atmosphere from a vessel under a vacuum of 24.4 in Hg and at a temperature of 70 deg fahr.   The barometer is 30.5 in. Hg.   Three pounds of steam are used per pound of air discharged.   Compute:

(*a*) Ideal velocity of discharge from steam nozzle.
(*b*) Ideal velocity of mixture of steam and air at entrance to diffuser.
(*c*) Efficiency of ejector.

Solution.   (*a*) Atmospheric pressure, $P_3 = 15.0$ lb per sq in. abs.
Steam pressure, $P_1 = 115$ lb per sq in. abs.
Air pressure in vessel, $P_2 = 3$ lb per sq in. abs.
Ideal enthalpy drop in entire nozzle, 115 to 3 lb $= 1189 - 945 = 244$ B.t.u.
Corresponding jet velocity $= 223.7 \sqrt{244} = 3485$ ft per sec.

(*b*) Assume velocity of air at point *c*, just before mixing, to be 200 ft per sec.   Applying principle of equal momenta before and after mixing $(3485 \times 3) + 200 =$ velocity of mixture $\times 4$.   Ideal velocity of mixture $= 2664$ ft per sec.

If the mixing occurred without loss of kinetic energy the velocity of mixture would be 3030 ft per sec.   As stated, little is known as to what actually occurs at this point.

(*c*) The work required to compress the air is computed on the basis of reversible adiabatic compression from a pressure of 3 lb per sq in. abs to a pressure of 15 lb per sq in., which gives 57,000 ft-lb per lb of air.   The adiabatic enthalpy drop in the steam nozzle from 115 lb to 15 lb is 148.8 Btu per lb.   This is the energy available to produce the compression of the *air* in the diffuser.   The overall efficiency of the ejector is then:

$$\frac{\text{Ideal energy required for air compression}}{\text{Ideal energy available in steam nozzle}} = \frac{57,000}{148.8 \times 778 \times 3} = 0.164 = 16.4 \text{ per cent}$$

In steam condenser applications, the air withdrawn from the condenser is saturated with water vapor at the temperature of the air-vapor mixture.   In computing the work of compression it is this mixture which must be considered.   For high vacuum in condensers it becomes necessary to use two or three stages of ejectors in series, condensing the steam between stages to reduce the amount of steam which otherwise would need to be compressed in the diffusers.

Flow of a Vapor through an Orifice.   An orifice will perform the function of only the convergent portion of a nozzle.   Therefore, a vapor will expand in the actual zone of the orifice to any discharge region pressure which is greater than or equal to the critical pressure, but not to any lower pressure.   Any further expansion must take place beyond the orifice.

It follows that we again encounter the two general conditions of:

(*a*) Flow with the discharge region pressure greater than the critical, when computation of the ideal rate of discharge may be based upon expansion in the orifice to the lower pressure, and

(*b*) Flow with the discharge region pressure equal to or less than the critical, when computation of the ideal rate of discharge must be based upon expansion in the orifice only to the critical pressure.

THE STEAM POWER PLANT

20.   THE RANKINE CYCLE

Symbols

e = efficiency.
f = a subscript designating the saturated liquid state.
g = a subscript designating the dry saturated vapor state.
H = enthalpy, Btu per pound of fluid.
J = Joule's equivalent, 778 (ft-lb per Btu).
M = proportional mass of vapor passing to a particular heater in a regenerative cycle.

P = pressure (absolute), pound per square foot.
p = absolute pressure, pounds per square inch.
Q = energy transferred as heat, Btu per pound of fluid.
S = entropy per pound mass, and also a subscript designating constancy of entropy, during a process.
T = absolute temperature, degrees Rankine (=degrees fahrenheit absolute).
t = temperature, degrees fahrenheit.
U = linear velocity, feet per second.
V = specific volume, cubic feet per pound.
W = energy in transition as shaft work, foot-pounds per pound of fluid.

Two general methods are at present available for the production of power from the energy stored in the fuels. These are the internal-combustion engine and the type of composite device familiarly exemplified by the *steam power plant*. The thermodynamic principles which underlie the steam power plant cycles are presented here.

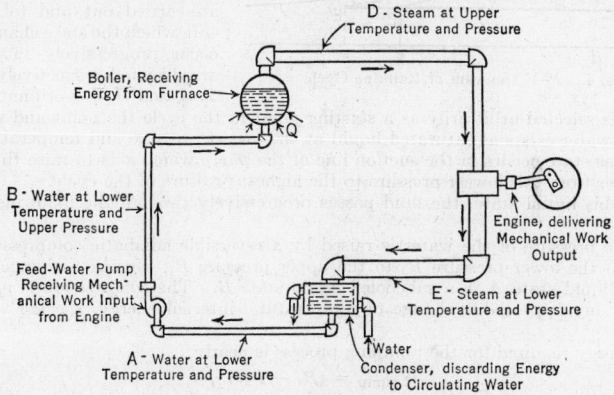

FIG. 1.   Elementary (Rankine Cycle) Steam Power Plant

The Carnot Cycle is the classical example of a wholly reversible temperature-engine cycle in which energy that is being supplied at an elevated temperature is reduced to a lower temperature, in which process the maximum possible portion of that energy is converted into work. Also this cycle, notwithstanding its impracticability and unattainability, is in certain features the prototype of the various steam power plant cycles

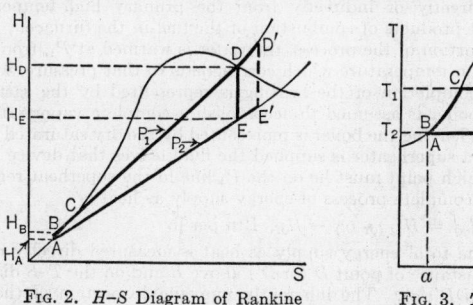

FIG. 2.   H–S Diagram of Rankine Cycle

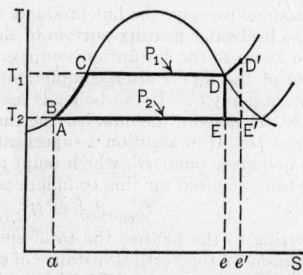

FIG. 3.   T–S Diagram of Rankine Cycle

and in all cases it acts as an invaluable guide in the selection and development of those cycles. The Carnot cycle is described on p. 7–07.

The Rankine Cycle, of the actual steam plant cycles, is of concern not only because of its simplicity, practicability, and historical importance but also because the other, more complex cycles may in a sense be regarded as refinements of the Rankine. The ideal Rankine cycle consists in general of (a) the warming, constant temperature vaporization and, perhaps, further superheating of the working fluid of the cycle at a constant upper pressure, this through the addition of energy from the source whereby the fluid is brought from the lower to the upper temperature limit of the cycle; (b) the isentropic expansion of the fluid to the lower temperature and pressure limits of the cycle; (c) the complete condensation of the fluid by the emission of energy at the lower temperature and pressure, this energy departure constituting the rejection of the unavailable energy to the receiver; and (d) the return of the condensed fluid to the upper pressure by reversible adiabatic compression, whereupon the fluid cycle may be repeated. These processes take place

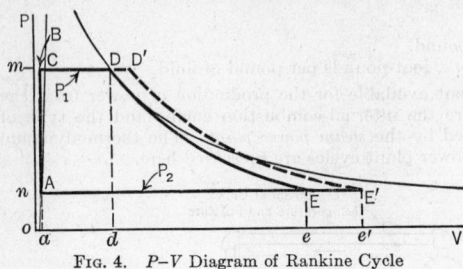

FIG. 4. P–V Diagram of Rankine Cycle

successively in the boiler and superheater, the engine, the condenser, and the feed pump.

To facilitate the description and analysis of the cycle, reference will be made to Fig. 1, which is a diagrammatic representation of the arrangement of the essential pieces of apparatus in which the processes are carried out, and to Figs. 2, 3, 4, in which the state changes which occur progressively in the cycle are depicted respectively on H–S, T–S, and P–V coordinates.

There is selected arbitrarily as a starting point in the cycle the point and state A at which the water exists as saturated liquid at the lowest pressure and temperature of the cycle. This state occurs in the suction line of the *pump* which acts to raise the pressure of the water from this lowest pressure to the highest pressure of the cycle.

From this initial state, the fluid passes progressively through the following series of processes:

(1) The pressure of the water is raised by a reversible adiabatic compression in the *pump* from the lower pressure P_2 to the upper pressure P_1, causing a change from the saturated liquid state A to a subcooled liquid state B. The compression is not accompanied by any appreciable change of temperature, internal energy, specific volume, or entropy.

The energy required for the pumping process is nearly:

$$W_{\text{pump}} = (P_1 - P_2)V_{f,\,2}$$

where $V_{f,\,2}$ = specific volume of saturated liquid of temperature T_2. In Fig. 4 the product $(P_1 - P_2)V_{f,\,2}$ is represented by the area $mBAnm$, which area thus represents the pump work.

(2) The second distinctive process of the Rankine cycle is the warming, vaporizing, and perhaps superheating of the fluid, all occurring under a virtually constant pressure. The energy supply for accomplishing these several phases of the cycle is provided by heat conduction through the heating surfaces of the boiler and the superheater (if the latter is supplied) and is furnished directly or indirectly from the primary high-temperature energy source, namely, the hot products of combustion of the fuel in the furnace.

In the feedwater heating portion of the process, the water is warmed at P_1, from temperature T_2 up to the saturation temperature which corresponds to that pressure, whence the state of the liquid after completion of the heating is represented by the saturated liquid state point C. If the boiler is assumed to accomplish a complete vaporization of the water, the state of the fluid leaving the boiler is represented by the dry saturated vapor state point D. If in addition a superheater is supplied the fluid leaves that device at the superheated state point D', which point must lie on the P_1 line in the superheat region.

The heat required for this complete process of energy supply as heat is

$$Q_{\text{supplied}} = H_{D\,(\text{or }D')} - H_B, \text{ Btu per lb}$$

Referring to the figures, the total energy supply as heat is measured directly on the H–S diagram by the vertical distance of point D (or D') above B and on the T–S diagram by the area $aBCDea$ (or $aBCDD'e'a$). The inherently unavailable portion of the heat energy supply is represented by the area $aAEea$ (or $aAE'e'a$) on the T–S diagram.

(3) The next state change in the ideal Rankine cycle is the reversible adiabatic expansion of the fluid from the upper temperature and pressure to the lower. To accomplish this the fluid is delivered to the *engine* at constant pressure and expands therein, after which it departs from the engine at a constant lower pressure. The term engine is here used in a generic sense to designate the main prime mover of the plant, whether that be actually a reciprocating engine or turbine engine. It is in this composite delivery, expansion, and rejection process which takes place in the engine that the available portion of the previously supplied heat energy is transformed to shaft work.

Because the property characteristic of a reversible adiabatic state change is the constancy of the entropy, the expansion through the ideal engine is represented on the H–S and T–S diagram by the vertical isentropic line DE (or $D'E'$). The line DE in the P–V diagram portrays the typical appearance of this reversible adiabatic state change on those coordinates.

The work delivered by the engine is

$$W_{engine} = J(H_D - H_E)[or\ J(H_{D'} - H_{E'})]\ \text{ft-lb per lb}$$
$$= J(H_1 - H_2)_S$$

where the subscript S indicates constant entropy.

The work output of the ideal engine is measured on the H–S diagram by the vertical distance of point D above E. The method of computing the enthalpy at E, given the entropy and pressure, has been given on p. 7–40.

The engine work is represented on the P–V diagram by the area back of the expansion line, or

$$W_{engine,\ ideal} = \text{area}\ mDEnm,\ \text{or} = + \int_1^2 VdP$$

It is to be emphasized that this expression for the engine work applies to any ideal engine, whether of the reciprocating or turbine type.

(4) The closing process of the cycle is a condensation of the exhaust steam from the engine, by which the fluid is returned at constant pressure from the state E to the initial saturated liquid state A and during which there occurs the discarding of the inescapably unavailable residue of the previously supplied heat energy. In the ideal cycle and in many practical installations this process is accomplished during passage through a *condenser* in which the energy departure and the condensation are effected by energy transfer as heat conducted from the steam through the condenser structure to circulating water. The same state change and energy rejection may be accomplished, however, in various other practical manners, as by condensation in the atmosphere, in a heating system, or in any other process in which the low temperature energy of the exhaust steam may be employed to advantage.

The heat rejected in the condensation process is

$$Q_{condenser} = H_E - H_A\ (\text{or}\ H_{E'} - H_A),\ \text{Btu per lb}$$

On the H–S diagram the vertical distance between state points E and A measures the energy rejected in the condensation.

On the T–S diagram this energy discard as heat $= T_2\ (S_A - S_E)$ is represented by the area $aAEea$ (or $aAE'e'a$). Therefore, as the area $aBCDea$ measured the amount of energy supplied from the source as heat, the difference between these two areas, or the area $ABCDEA$, measures the net amount of work obtainable from the operation of the cycle, that is, the net amount after debiting the engine output with the portion of its work which must be employed to drive the pump.

The cycle is thus completed.

21. MEASURES OF EFFICIENCY AND PERFORMANCE

The Thermal Efficiency of a Heat Engine Cycle, or of a heat engine alone, is defined as the ratio between the amount of work output and the amount of heat energy which must be supplied in order to accomplish that output, or

$$\text{Thermal efficiency}\ (e_t) = \frac{\text{Work output from system}}{\text{Heat supplied to system}}$$

The thermal efficiency of the Rankine cycle $= \dfrac{(H_1 - H_2) - (P_1 - P_2)V_{f,\ 2}/J}{(H_1 - H_{f,\ 2}) - (P_1 - P_2)V_{f,\ 2}/J}$. This is a very nearly exact value. An approximation is

$$\frac{(H_1 - H_2)_S}{H_1 - H_{f,\ 2}}$$

where
$\quad H_1 =$ enthalpy of the steam as supplied at P_1.
$(H_1 - H_2)_S =$ decrease of enthalpy by isentropic expansion to P_2.
$\quad H_{f,\ 2} =$ enthalpy of saturated water at P_2.
$\quad V_{f,\ 2} =$ specific volume of saturated water at P_2.

The error arising from use of the approximation is usually regarded as negligible except when the modern higher boiler pressures (500 lb per sq in. and up) are employed.

In order to measure the effectiveness with which a cycle might ideally utilize the temperature range encountered in the cycle and thus to designate the degree to which the ideal cycle efficiency approaches the Carnot efficiency for that temperature range there is employed a figure of merit which is known as the *type efficiency* of the cycle. This is defined as the ratio between the ideal thermal efficiency of a cycle and the thermal efficiency of a Carnot cycle operating between the extremes of temperature found in the cycle under consideration, or

$$\text{Type efficiency} = \frac{\text{Ideal thermal efficiency of cycle}}{(T_1 - T_2)/T_1}$$

No actual engine can attain a performance equal to that of an ideal engine operating on the same cycle, because of the numerous irreversible actions which will inescapably occur in any real process. Heat will be radiated or otherwise dissipated from higher to lower temperature levels without full realization of its available energy; and mechanical irreversibility will occur owing to fluid friction, throttling and turbulence, and to the friction of moving parts of the engine mechanism, etc. The result must be less actual work output per pound of fluid than that ideally obtainable in the ideal cycle upon which the engine operation is based.

In order to evaluate the relative effectiveness of an actual engine and the degree to which it approaches ideal performance there is employed a measure of performance which is known as the *engine efficiency* * and which is defined as the ratio between the output actually obtained per pound of steam supplied to the engine and the output ideally obtainable upon isentropic expansion of that steam, or

$$\text{Engine efficiency} = \frac{\text{Actual output per pound of steam supplied to engine}}{\text{Work ideally obtainable by isentropic expansion}}$$

$$= \frac{\text{Actual efficiency}}{\text{Ideal efficiency}}$$

The actual output of an engine is necessarily determined by test. Such a test requires a determination of the actual power output of the engine and the mass of steam supplied per unit time.

The power delivered to the piston face of a reciprocating engine may be measured by the engine indicator, the shaft horsepower output of any engine may likewise be measured by a suitable dynamometer, or for a direct-connected engine-generator set the electrical power output may be determined by proper electrical instruments. The mass-rate of steam supply may be determined by condensing and weighing the steam or by various types of steam flow-meters or calibrated orifices. The state of the steam is determined by its absolute pressure and its quality (ascertained by means of a calorimeter) or its temperature, if superheated. The various pressures are found by gages or manometers.

By reason of the variety of manners and positions which may be selected in designating the output of an engine a like variety of engine efficiencies may be assigned to a given machine. Each output mentioned above is successively less than the preceding one by reason of the progressive energy dissipation through mechanical and electrical losses. It is obvious that due attention must be given to this condition in quoting values of engine efficiency or in interpreting quoted values.

If adequate test data are available on the actual steam requirements and the power output of an engine, these data may be combined with the factors 2545 (Btu per horsepower-hour) or 3413 (Btu per kilowatthour), and the numerator of the efficiency equation may thereby be evaluated. Thus

Actual output per pound of steam supplied, Btu,

$$= \frac{\text{Power output, hp (or kw)} \times 2545 \text{ (or 3413)}}{\text{Steam supplied, pounds per hour}}$$

The denominator of the efficiency equation, that is, the output ideally obtainable per pound of steam supplied, may be computed for an engine according to the conditions of the particular type of cycle upon which the system operates. For the Rankine cycle the work ideally obtainable per pound of steam is $(H_1 - H_2)_S$. This is called the *adiabatic enthalpy drop*.

The ratio between the steam supplied per hour and the power output is known as the *steam rate* of an engine and is commonly expressed in terms of the pounds of steam supplied per horsepower-hour (or kilowatthour) or

$$\text{Actual steam rate} = \frac{\text{Pounds of steam supplied per hour}}{\text{Output in hp (or kw)}}$$

---

* Unfortunately various terms have been used to designate this efficiency: "efficiency ratio," "relative efficiency," "Rankine efficiency," and "turbine efficiency." *Engine efficiency* is the term employed in the Power Test Codes of the American Society of Mechanical Engineers.

The engine efficiency may be expressed concretely in the form:

$$\text{Engine efficiency} = \frac{2545/\text{Actual steam rate, lb per hp-hr}}{\text{Output ideally obtainable, Btu per lb}}$$

$$= \frac{3413/\text{Actual steam rate, lb per kwhr}}{\text{Output ideally obtainable, Btu per lb}}$$

The Actual Thermal Efficiency is a figure which in its basic significance is quite parallel to the ideal thermal efficiency of a cycle or an engine, which is broadly defined as the fraction $\dfrac{\text{Work output from system}}{\text{Heat supplied to system}}$. However, in evaluating this actual efficiency for an operating engine or engine-generator unit or for a complete operating plant the useful output may in practice be variously regarded as the indicated power output of a reciprocating engine, or as the shaft power output of any engine, or as the electrical power output of an engine-generator unit, or as the net electrical output at the bus-bars of a complete plant. Also in ascribing a value to the energy supply, that quantity may be taken variously as the energy supplied as heat (at the boiler), that supplied as chemical energy in the fuel, etc. It is thus apparent that a considerable variety of interpretations may be applied to the term without need for confusion if due care is employed in making the interpretation. In any individual case, and irrespective of its particular interpretation, the thermal efficiency may invariably be regarded as a ratio between the useful output delivered and the energy supplied for the procuring of that output, or

$$\text{Actual thermal efficiency} = \frac{\text{Useful output from system}}{\text{Energy supplied to system}}$$

In utilization of actual test data, it is commonly more convenient to express it in terms of a specific output or supply, that is, an output (or supply) per unit time, per unit mass of steam supplied to an engine or per unit mass of fuel supplied to a plant. For example, the specific output per pound of steam to an engine is expressed by the relation

$$\text{Actual output, Btu per lb of steam to engine} = \frac{2545 \; (\text{or } 3413)}{\text{Actual steam rate, lb per hp-hr (or kwhr)}}$$

A parallel relation for the complete plant, in terms of the fuel rate, is

$$\text{Actual output, Btu per lb of fuel to plant} = \frac{2545 \; (\text{or } 3413)}{\text{Actual fuel rate, lb per hp-hr (or kwhr)}}$$

Either of these relations may be employed directly as the numerator of the efficiency fraction of the above equation.

Several distinctive practices are followed in interpreting the denominator of the efficiency fraction in the various circumstances in which efficiency is to be determined. For the simple Rankine cycle it is the established practice to regard the energy supply which is assignable to each pound of steam and is chargeable against the engine as the enthalpy difference between that of saturated liquid at the temperature of the engine exhaust and that of the steam as supplied to the engine. It is to be observed that for this case no concern is given to the actual temperature at which the condensate may be leaving the condenser; this is in order to avoid penalizing the engine for any subcooling of the condensate which may occur by reason of unfavorable characteristics of the condenser. For the engine of the Rankine cycle, the efficiency thus becomes

$$\text{Actual thermal eff. of engine} = \frac{2545 \; (\text{or } 3413)/\text{Steam rate}}{H_1 - H_{f,\,2}}$$

For the entire power plant it is the established practice to regard the chemical energy released by a complete combustion of the fuel as the energy supply. That energy when evaluated per pound of fuel is known as the calorific value or heating value of the fuel. It is determined by calorimetric measurement made upon representative samples of the fuel. Introducing this quantity in the efficiency fraction,

$$\text{Actual thermal eff., complete plant} = \frac{2545 \; (\text{or } 3413)/\text{Fuel rate}}{\text{Heating value of fuel, Btu per lb}}$$

The *heat rate of an engine or of a plant* is defined as the amount of energy actually to be supplied per horsepower-hour (or per kilowatthour) of useful output. This may readily be expressed in terms of the steam rate, or the fuel rate, and the energy supply per pound of steam or of fuel, or

Actual heat rate, Btu per hp-hr (or kwhr)

$$= \text{Steam rate of engine} \times \text{Energy supplied per lb of steam}$$

or

$$= \text{Fuel rate of plant} \times \text{Heating value, Btu per lb of fuel}$$

Example 1. A Rankine cycle type of steam plant is operating with a boiler pressure of 300 lb per sq in. abs and a 20 lb per sq in. abs back pressure. There is no superheater, and the steam delivered by the boiler has a 99 per cent quality. Compute the properties of the steam or water at each significant point of the ideal cycle, the ideal feed pump work (in foot-pounds and in Btu per pound of steam), the requisite heat supply, and the ideal minimum energy discard per pound of steam.

How many pounds of steam would be required in the ideal Rankine plant per net horsepower-hour output? Compute the Rankine cycle thermal efficiency and the type efficiency.

Solution.

Water leaving condenser: $P_A = P_2 = 20 \times 144$; $V_A = V_{f,2} = 0.0168$; $t = 228.0$ deg fahr; $H_A = H_{f,2} = 196.1$; $S_A = S_{f,2} = 0.3356$.

Water leaving pumps: $P_B = P_1 = 300 \times 144$; $V_B = V_{f,2} = 0.0168$; $t = 228.0$ deg fahr; $H_B = 196.1 + 144 \times (300 - 20) \times 0.0168/778 = 197.0$; $S_B = S_A = 0.3356$.

Steam leaving boiler: $P_D = 300 \times 144$; $V_D = 0.99 \times 1.541 = 1.526$; $t = 417.3$ deg fahr; $H_D = 393.9 + 0.99 \times 808.5 = 1194.2$; $S_D = 0.5883 + 0.99 \times 0.9220 = 1.5010$.

Steam leaving engine: $P_E = 20 \times 144$; $t = 228.0$ deg fahr; $S_E = S_D = 1.5010$; $x_E = (1.5010 - 0.3356)/1.3960 = 0.835$; $H_E = 196.1 + 0.835 \times 959.9 = 997.6$; $V_E = 0.832 \times 20.10 = 16.73$.

Pump work $= 144(300 - 20) \times 0.0168 = 680$ ft-lb $= 0.87$ Btu per lb.

Engine work $= 778(997.6 - 1194.2) = -153,000$ ft-lb $= -196.6$ Btu per lb.

Net work output $= -153,000 + 680 = -152,300$ ft-lb $= -195.7$ Btu per lb.

Energy supplied as heat $= 1194.2 - 197.0 = 997.2$ Btu per lb.

Energy discard $= 196.1 - 997.6 = -801.5$ Btu per lb.

Steam ideally required per horsepower-hour of plant output $= (33,000 \times 60)/152,300 = 13.00$ lb (or $= 2545/195.7$), $=$ the ideal "steam rate" of cycle.

Rankine cycle efficiency $= 195.7 \div 997.2 = 0.196$ or 19.6 per cent.

Carnot cycle thermal efficiency $= (417.3 - 228.0) \div (417.3 + 460) = 0.216$ or 21.6 per cent.

Type efficiency $= 0.196 \div 0.216 = 0.907$ or 90.7 per cent.

Example 2. The engine of the cycle of Example 1 develops 300 hp and uses 6000 lb of steam per hour. Compute actual thermal efficiency, heat rate, and engine efficiency.

Solution.

Steam rate $= 6000 \div 300 = 20$ lb per hp-hr.

Actual thermal efficiency $= 2545 \div (20 \times 997.2) = 0.128$ or 12.8 per cent.

Heat rate $= 20 \times 997.2 = 19,944$ Btu per hp-hr.

Engine efficiency $= (2545/20) \div 195.7 = 0.653$ or 65.3 per cent, also
$= 0.128 \div 0.196 = 0.653$ or 65.3 per cent.

22. THE ENERGY ("HEAT") BALANCE

In the thermodynamic design of a steam power plant and in the analysis of its actual operation attention is very commonly given to what is known as the "*heat*" *balance* of the plant. By this is meant, more exactly, a comprehensive energy analysis and energy accounting for the purpose of ascertaining the ultimate destination of all portions of the original energy supply in the fuel and also for the more important purpose of correcting in so far as may be practicable any wastage of available energy.

Two viewpoints are available in the development of such an energy analysis. On the simpler but less valuable basis concern is given only to the distribution of the energy with regard to its physical location and destination, ascribing losses only as energy may obviously be dissipated by radiation to the atmosphere from hot pipes or surfaces, in the hot stack-gases from the furnace, by conduction to the circulating water, or by mechanical friction in the moving parts of machines. Because the development of such an accounting is dependent only on the conservation of energy principle it may be designated as a *first law energy balance*.

The evolution of a first law balance must proceed from specific information concerning the type, arrangement, and interconnections of all steam-using equipment which is installed in the plant and from concrete data or estimates concerning operating conditions and operating efficiencies obtaining in the numerous individual units which comprise the plant. From such information a detailed bookkeeping account may be developed which shall record specifically the amount and character of all energy entering or departing from each device and shall permit a summarization portraying the direction, magnitude, and destination of all component parts of the energy stream en route through the plant.

Such a summarization of the energy account may, as usual, be presented to advantage graphically. Either one of two general types of procedure is commonly employed in the graphic representation. One is illustrated in Fig. 5, in which are depicted diagrammatically the primary components of a simple steam power plant, the interconnecting pipes joining the several devices, the direction of flow between them, the amount of fluid flowing per hour, and pertinent properties of the fluid en route. In the figure there are intentionally presented a plant character and performance which are *not* representative of better modern practice, in order that certain unfortunate features of the plant may the better be recognized. It is observed that the plant is so devised that the various *auxiliary* engines exhaust at about atmospheric pressure and that the exhaust steam from those engines is condensed as far as possible in a heater in which some degree of feedwater heating is thus accomplished.

The second method of presentation of the first law balance appears in Fig. 6. In that figure the character of the interconnections between parts or the fluid properties at

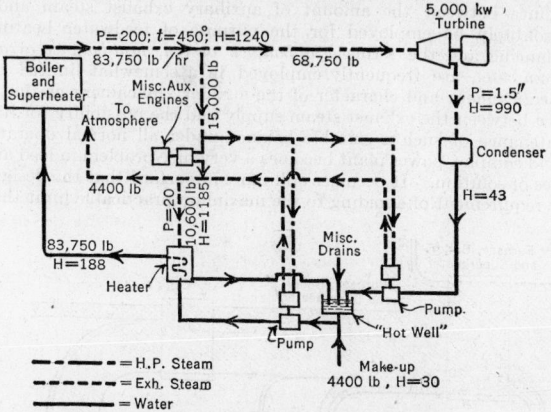

Fig. 5. Diagram for First Law Energy Balance

specific points are not emphasized but instead there is shown graphically the relative magnitude of the energy quantities at each significant stage in the energy stream. The energy magnitudes are in general expressed in terms of the total enthalpies of the mass of fluid passing a given section in a unit time. The enthalpies are those with respect to a

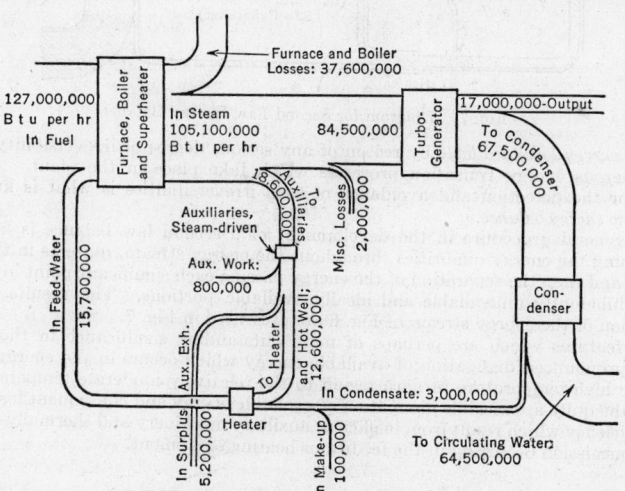

Fig. 6. Diagram for First Law Energy Balance

relative zero of enthalpy for water at 32 deg fahr, and in that feature the diagram may be to an extent misleading as the fluid does not and practically could not attain that temperature at any point in the cycle. This procedure is followed because it is the conventional and more convenient one. The figure portrays with maximum clarity the general directions of the energy stream through the plant, the manner of distribution of the energy en route, and the unfortunately small proportion of the initial energy from the fuel which actually is made available as work output.

It is to be observed that in Fig. 5 the combined steam exhaust from the various auxiliary engines is shown to be in excess of that which can practicably be condensed in the feedwater heater, whereby there exists a surplus of auxiliary exhaust which must be rejected to the atmosphere. This condition would obviously be an inefficient one. To avoid its existence, as well as to avoid the opposite circumstance of an exhaust steam supply which is insufficient for adequate feedwater heating, is one frequent objective of the development of an energy balance in the design of a plant. Also, in recognition of the necessity of assuring a proper balance between the amount of auxiliary exhaust steam and the amount which can profitably be employed for the purpose of feedwater heating, the notion of energy balancing and the terms *heat-balance design, heat-balance arrangement, heat-balance diagram,* etc., are frequently employed in a somewhat limited sense referring only to the arrangement and character of the auxiliary machinery as that influences the proper balance between the exhaust steam supply and the possibility for its utilization.

The maintenance of such a suitable balance under all normal operating conditions in the large and complex power plant becomes a very nice problem indeed and one offering many varieties of solution. It becomes still more important that the designer adequately recognize the requirement of avoiding to the maximum practicable limit the *dissipation of*

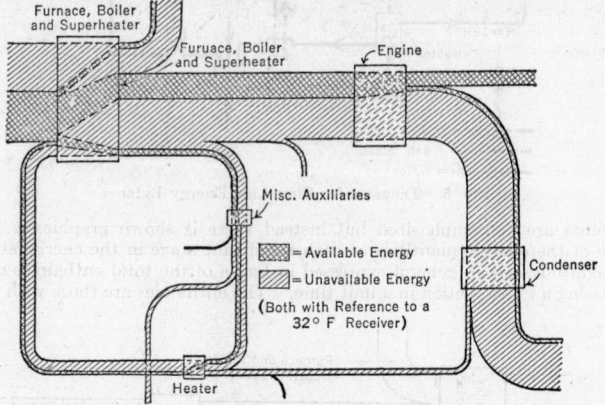

Furnace, Boiler and Superheater

Furnace, Boiler and Superheater

Engine

Misc. Auxiliaries

◫ = Available Energy

▨ = Unavailable Energy

(Both with Reference to a 32° F Receiver)

Condenser

Heater

FIG. 7.   Diagram for Second Law Energy Balance

available energy to unavailable by reason of any serious degree of irreversibility in any of the numerous energy transition processes which take place in the plant. A valuable device for the detection and avoidance of such irreversibilities is what is known as a *second law energy balance.*

The general procedure in the development of a second law balance is first that of determining the energy quantities throughout the energy stream, quite as in the first law balance, and then the separation of the energy passing each significant point in the stream into its inherently unavailable and ideally available portions. The results of such a subdivision of the energy stream of Fig. 6 are presented in Fig. 7.

The features which are perhaps of more outstanding significance in the figure are (a) the pronounced dissipation of available energy which occurs in the energy transition from the high-temperature furnace region to the relatively moderate-temperature steam and (b) the quite appreciable dissipation of available energy and consequent loss of overall plant efficiency which result from inefficient auxiliary machinery and thermally irreversible heat transmission occurring in the feedwater heating equipment.

23.   MODERN VAPOR CYCLES *

From consideration of the Carnot cycle and its efficiency fraction, $(T_1 - T_2)/T_1$, it is evident that the efficiency of a temperature-engine cycle may be increased by increase of the temperature at which the fluid receives its energy from the source, or by decrease of the temperature to which the fluid expands reversibly in the engine and at which therefore it discards the unavailable residue of energy to the receiver. In a vapor cycle such as the

* For a more complete discussion of this subject see Heat Power Engineering, Barnard, Ellenwood and Hirshfeld. Part I, Chap. XVIII, John Wiley & Sons, 1926.

Rankine the temperature of energy rejection is established primarily and practically by that of the atmosphere or of the natural supplies of water in the streams, lakes, or seas. The attainment of suitable cyclic efficiency requires that the fluid shall expand as closely as practicable to this temperature. With water as the working fluid, this requires that a very low pressure (high vacuum) be maintained in the condenser. In order to gain efficiency by increase of the temperature of energy reception in the Rankine vapor cycle the temperature of vaporization may be raised by increase of vapor pressure or the average temperature of energy reception may be raised moderately by superheating after vaporization is completed.

For a like temperature range in each, the Rankine cycle may not attain the thermal efficiency of a wholly reversible cycle such as the Carnot. For a cycle operating without superheat this is in one sense due to the lower average temperature of the liquid during warming from the condensing to the vaporizing temperature. From an alternative and perhaps more fundamental viewpoint the reduced efficiency is due to thermal irreversibility associated with the liquid-warming phase of the cycle. This irreversibility may be reduced by the use of *stage* or *regenerative* feed-heating, and the cyclic efficiency may thereby be sensibly bettered. The improvement of efficiency resulting from superheating may be doubly realized by the expedient of *resuperheating* the vapor after partial expansion through the engine. The benefits of high vaporization temperatures may be obtained without the disadvantage of high attendant pressures by the use of a fluid of lower vapor pressure than water. All these expedients are employed in modern power plant practice.

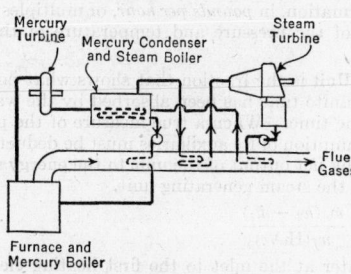

FIG. 8. Binary-fluid (Mercury-water)
Cycle

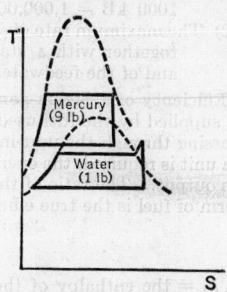

FIG. 9. *T–S* Diagram for
Mercury-water Cycle

The Regenerative Feed-heating Cycle employs a method of progressive liquid warming in a series of heaters which are activated by steam extracted from the engine after more or less complete expansion therein. Thermal irreversibility is thus reduced by accomplishing the first portion of the warming with lower-temperature steam the available energy of which has been well realized in the engine, by similarly accomplishing the next step in the warming of the liquid by medium-temperature steam, and so on. This particular method of efficiency betterment by reduction of thermal irreversibility in the feed-heating is simply illustrative of the gains invariably to be secured by the reduction of any irreversible features. The cycle is best analyzed in detail by writing and solving the energy equation for each successive heater in order from the highest-pressure heater down. Thereby the relative amount of steam to be extracted for each heater may be computed, whereupon the available energy output obtainable in each successive portion of the engine may be determined.

The Reheating Cycle may effect an ideal efficiency betterment only if the resuperheating of the partially expanded steam is accomplished by energy supplied directly from the primary source (the hot furnace gases) and if the resuperheating serves to raise the average temperature of energy reception by the fluid from that source. The analysis of the cycle is quite like that of the Rankine cycle except in the necessity for recognizing the two-stage character of the expansion in the engine and for properly accounting the additional energy supplied to the fluid in the resuperheater. The cycle lends itself well to the addition of regenerative feed-heating.

Binary-Fluid Cycles are employed for the purpose of permitting high average temperatures of energy reception from the source without the handicap of difficultly high fluid pressures in the higher-temperature portion of the cycle. This is accomplished by employing in that portion of the cycle a fluid which has favorable vapor pressure-temperature characteristics. Such advantageous pressure-temperature characteristics may be utilized by employing a fluid of relatively lower vapor pressure in a higher-temperature section of the composite cycle and a fluid of higher vapor pressure in a lower-temperature section. A compound cycle of this character which employs the two fluids mercury and water is in successful use at this writing. The general scheme of arrangement of the apparatus of this binary-fluid cycle is shown in Fig. 8. Observe that the energy rejected from the condensing mercury forms the energy source for the vaporizing water. In Fig. 9 there is shown a T-S chart for 9 lb of mercury and for 1 lb of water. These are about the requisite proportions between the rates of mercury and water circulation in the cycle, because the relative latent heats are such that the heat delivered in condensing 1 lb of mercury after expansion through the mercury turbine is about one-ninth of the heat required to evaporate 1 lb of water.

24. THE STEAM GENERATING UNIT *

Steam Generating Unit is the modern name used to describe the combined equipment required in the steam power cycle for the addition of heat to the working fluid, water. This consists not only of a furnace and boiler but, in the more modern plants, may include some or all of other heat-absorbing energy elements such as a superheater, economizer, air preheater, steam reheater, and air- or water-cooled furnace walls.

The Steam-Generating Capacity of the unit may be expressed either in terms of

(1) The maximum rate of heat absorption by the unit, expressed either in *kilo Btu* (kB) *per hour*, or in *mega Btu* (mB) *per hour* (kB = 1000 Btu, mB = 1000 kB = 1,000,000 Btu), or

(2) The maximum rate of steam formation, in *pounds per hour*, or multiples thereof, together with a statement of the pressure and temperature of the steam and of the feedwater.

The Efficiency of a Steam-generating Unit is the fraction that shows what portion of the heat supplied by the fuel used in a definite time has been absorbed by the water and steam passing through the unit in the same time. When a true measure of the performance of a unit is required, the energy consumption of its auxiliaries must be deducted from the gross output. The ratio of the resulting net output of the unit to the energy supplied in the form of fuel is the true efficiency of the steam generating unit.

$$\text{Eff.} = \frac{w_n(h_2 - h_1)}{w_f(\text{H.V.})}$$

in which h_1 = the enthalpy of the feedwater at the inlet to the first heating element of the unit (e.g., to the economizer when installed, otherwise to the boiler itself), in Btu per pound.

h_2 = the enthalpy of the steam at the outlet from the superheater (or from the boiler if no superheater is installed), in Btu per pound.

H.V. = the heating value of the fuel, *as fired*, in Btu per pound.

w_f = weight of fuel fired, in pounds per hour.

w_n = net weight of steam delivered by the superheater, in pounds per hour.

= gross weight − auxiliary steam.

The Energy Used by the Auxiliaries may be consumed by steam jets, steam engines, turbines, or electric motors needed to operate the various pieces of equipment which comprise the generating unit. The electric energy consumed should be converted into its steam equivalent. The total steam equivalent of all auxiliaries should then be deducted from the total weight of steam produced in order to determine the net energy output of the generating unit. The weight of auxiliary steam equivalent to the electrical energy consumption of the auxiliaries, in pounds per hour, is

$$w_s = (F_n)(1 - E_a)\left(\begin{array}{c}\text{Rate of}\\\text{firing,}\\\text{tons}\\\text{per}\\\text{hour}\end{array}\right)\left(\begin{array}{c}\text{Auxiliary}\\\text{energy of the}\\\text{steam-generating}\\\text{unit, kilowatthours}\\\text{per ton of fuel}\end{array}\right)\left(\begin{array}{c}\text{Actual}\\\text{evaporation,}\\\text{pounds of}\\\text{steam per}\\\text{pound of fuel}\end{array}\right)$$

or

$$w_s = (F_n)(1 - E_a)\left(\begin{array}{c}\text{Auxiliary power of}\\\text{the steam-generating}\\\text{unit, in kilowatts}\end{array}\right)\left(\begin{array}{c}\text{Actual}\\\text{evaporation,}\\\text{pounds of}\\\text{steam per}\\\text{pound of fuel}\end{array}\right),$$

in which F_n = net fuel rate of the station, in pounds of fuel fired per kilowatthours sent out from the station.

E_a = fraction of the main generator gross output required to operate all the station auxiliaries, as determined by test.

* This section is reprinted in a modified form, by permission, from Barnard, Ellenwood, and Hirshfeld, Heat-Power Engineering, Part II, John Wiley & Sons.

The Losses of Energy that Occur in a Steam-generating Unit and thereby affect its efficiency are the following:

(1) *Loss from the incomplete combustion of the fuel* as evidenced by the presence of:
    (*a*) combustible in the refuse collected in the ash pit;
    (*b*) combustible, such as solid carbon, carbon monoxide, hydrogen, and hydrocarbons, in the exit gas.

(2) *Loss to the stack not caused by incomplete combustion but due to:*
    (*a*) the dry exit gases leaving the last heating surface at a higher temperature than that of the atmosphere;
    (*b*) the water vapor, which accompanies the dry gas, leaving the last heating surface at a higher temperature than that of the air and fuel from which it came.

(3) *Loss by heat transfer from the entire unit to the surrounding air.*

The magnitudes of these losses are variables which depend upon the type and quality of fuel used, size and type of equipment, load on the unit, and the manner in which the plant is operated.

The Boiler Energy Balance

A study of the magnitudes of the losses is of importance to the operating engineer. It serves as a basis for comparison of the performance of different steam-generating units. Any tabulation prepared with the object of evaluating the various energy items of a plant constitutes an energy balance. Such a tabulation applied to a steam-generating unit is usually called a boiler energy balance. The items generally found in such a statement are:

1. Energy absorbed by steam in the boiler.
2. Energy carried away by the dry flue gas.
3. Energy loss due to unburned combustible in refuse.
4. Energy loss due to incomplete combustion of C to CO instead of to CO_2.
5. Energy carried away by surface moisture in the fuel.
6. Energy carried away by moisture resulting from combustion of hydrogen.
7. Energy carried away by moisture in the air used for combustion.
8. Radiation and unaccounted-for losses.

Convenient methods for determining each of these items will be outlined briefly in the succeeding paragraphs.

1. Energy Absorbed by Steam in Boiler.

$$Q = (H_2 - H_1)W \tag{1}$$

where H_2 = enthalpy of steam at exit, Btu per pound.
    H_1 = enthalpy of water at entrance, Btu per pound.
    Q = heat absorbed by steam, Btu per pound of fuel.
    W = pounds of steam per pound of fuel as fired.

2. Energy Carried away by Dry Flue Gas. The weight of dry flue gas per pound of fuel may be found in the following manner: The gases found in the analysis of a sample of the dry products of combustion of a fuel are CO_2, CO, O_2 and N_2. These constituents are determined as volumetric percentages, or the analysis gives the volume of each constituent per 100 volumes of mixture.

Therefore since a molecular weight in pounds of any gas occupies approximately 358 cu ft at 32 deg fahr and atmospheric pressure, the relative weight of the percentage volume of each gas in the mixture will be its percentage volume multiplied by *molecular weight in pounds*.

If the carbon balance is used as a basis of calculation, it is assumed that all the carbon appearing in the flue gas in the form of CO_2 and CO has come from the carbon in the fuel *that was burned.*

Hence

$$\frac{\text{Lb of dry flue gas}}{\text{Lb } (CO_2 \text{ and } CO)} = \frac{{}^{44}/_{358}\,CO_2 + {}^{28}/_{358}\,CO + {}^{32}/_{358}\,O_2 + {}^{28}/_{358}\,N_2}{{}^{44}/_{358}\,CO_2 + {}^{28}/_{358}\,CO}$$

$$= \frac{44\,CO_2 + 28\,CO + 32\,O_2 + 28\,N_2}{44\,CO_2 + 28\,CO}$$

But CO_2 is, by weight, ${}^{12}/_{44}$ carbon and ${}^{32}/_{44}$ oxygen, and CO is, by weight, ${}^{12}/_{28}$ carbon and ${}^{16}/_{28}$ oxygen; therefore

$$\frac{\text{Lb dry flue gas}}{\text{Lb carbon in fuel}} = \frac{44\,CO_2 + 28\,CO + 32\,O_2 + 28\,N_2}{{}^{12}/_{44} \times 44\,CO_2 + {}^{12}/_{28} \times 28\,CO}$$

$$= \frac{44\,CO_2 + 28\,CO + 32\,O_2 + 28\,N_2}{12\,(CO_2 + CO)}$$

Since a pound of fuel does not contain a pound of carbon, and since, in any event, all the combustible is seldom burned, the above expression can be multiplied by the percentage of carbon in the fuel *actually burned*, C_g (equal to C in fuel − C in refuse), to get the weight of flue gas per pound of fuel. Thus

$$W_{fg} = \frac{\text{Lb dry flue gas}}{\text{Lb coal}} = C_g \times \frac{44\ CO_2 + 28\ CO + 32\ O_2 + 28\ N_2}{12\ (CO_2 + CO)} \tag{2}$$

Sulfur dioxide has been purposely omitted from the above expression since the quantity of this gas present in a sample of dry flue gas is generally quite small, and also since its presence can not be detected with the ordinary apparatus available for flue-gas analysis. The weight and volume of SO_2 can be computed easily if desired from the elementary combustion equation $S + O_2 = SO_2$.

Assuming specific heat and pressure each to be essentially constant, the energy carried away by the dry flue gas is

$$h_2 = W_{fg} \times C_p \times (t_c - t_1) \tag{3}$$

where t_c = gas temperature, at boiler outlet, degrees fahrenheit.

t_1 = air temperature at entrance to furnace, degrees fahrenheit.

C_p = mean specific heat of dry flue gas between t_1 and t_c, Btu per pound per degree fahrenheit.

C_p = 0.240–0.250 average value.

3. Energy Loss Due to Unburned Combustible in Refuse. The unburned combustible in the refuse consists of small amounts of unburned or incompletely burned fuel, and may be assumed to be essentially carbon. The energy loss involved is

$$h_3 = C_r \times 14,600 \tag{4}$$

where C_r = weight of combustible in refuse per pound of fuel.

14,600 = approximate heating value of this combustible per pound.

4. Energy Loss Due to Incomplete Combustion of C to CO. When insufficient air is supplied for combustion or when air and fuel are not intimately and thoroughly mixed, part of the carbon may burn to CO instead of CO_2. A pound of C burning to CO_2 releases 14,540 Btu per lb of carbon, whereas when a pound of carbon is burned to CO, only 4480 Btu are released per pound of carbon. The loss here, then, is $14,540 - 4480 = 10,160$ Btu per lb C burning to CO.

The weight of C burning to CO can be determined from the flue-gas analysis by a method similar to that employed in paragraph 2.

$$\frac{\text{Weight of carbon monoxide}}{\text{Weight of carbon monoxide and dioxide}} = \frac{{}^{28}/_{358}\ CO}{{}^{44}/_{358}\ CO_2 + {}^{28}/_{358} \times CO}$$
$$= \frac{28\ CO}{44\ CO_2 + 28\ CO}$$

where CO and CO_2 are percentages of carbon monoxide and carbon dioxide by volume.

Since all the carbon in the flue gas (present as CO_2 and CO) must have come from that carbon in the fuel *that was actually burned*, and since, by weight, carbon monoxide is ${}^{12}/_{28}$ carbon, and carbon dioxide is ${}^{12}/_{44}$ carbon, then the weight of carbon, W_c, present in the CO content of the flue gases is

$$\frac{{}^{12}/_{28} \times 28\ CO}{{}^{12}/_{44}\ CO_2 + {}^{12}/_{28}\ CO} \times C_g = \frac{CO}{CO_2 + CO} \times C_g$$

where C_g, CO_2, and CO are as in paragraph 2.

The energy loss resulting from the CO is

$$h_4 = W_c \times 10,160 = 10,160 \times \frac{CO}{CO_2 + CO} \times C_g \tag{5}$$

5. Energy Carried away by Surface Moisture in Fuel. Most of the surface moisture in a fuel probably evaporates between temperatures of 70 and 120 deg fahr. To accomplish this, energy must be supplied by the fuel in sufficient amount (a) to raise the moisture to the vaporization temperature, (b) to evaporate it at this temperature, and (c) to raise its temperature to that of the flue gas at exit from the boiler. Steam tables would be required for a scientific calculation of this item. In lieu of this rather elaborate method the following simplification can be used:

$$h_5 = W_{mf} \times (1090 - t + 0.46\ t_c) \tag{6}$$

where W_{mf} = pounds of surface water per pound of fuel.

t = temperature of fuel, degrees fahrenheit.

t_c = temperature of gases at boiler outlet, degrees fahrenheit.

6. Energy Carried away by Moisture Resulting from Combustion of H_2. At precisely what temperature the formation of water vapor takes place is unknown. It is generally assumed, however, that it occurs at the outset of combustion. Whence, the parenthetical quantity in the preceding equation can be used to determine the loss per pound of moisture, or since 9 lb of moisture result from the combination of 1 lb of H_2

$$h_6 = 9H(1090 - t + 0.46\, t_c) \tag{7}$$

where H = percentage of H_2 in fuel by weight; other symbols as in equation (6).

7. Energy Carried away by Moisture in Air. The moisture in the air used for combustion has already been raised in temperature to the vaporization point and has been completely vaporized. Hence the only energy absorbed by it within the furnace is that required to raise the temperature of this vapor to that of the flue gases at boiler outlet, or

$$h_7 = W_{ma}\, 0.46(t_c - t_1) \tag{8}$$

where t_c = flue gas temperature at boiler outlet, degrees fahrenheit.

t_1 = air temperature at entrance to furnace.

W_{ma} = weight of moisture in air per pound of fuel.

8. Radiation and Unaccounted-for Losses. It is generally assumed that the preceding seven items constitute the principal manners in which the heating value of the fuel is distributed. Hence all other items are included under the head of radiation and unaccounted-for, or

$$h_8 = \text{H.H.V. of fuel} - \text{items } 1\text{--}7 \text{ inclusive} \tag{9}$$

Example. The following typical problem will illustrate the determination of the various items of the boiler heat balance.

Given: Coal analysis, as fired, C, 65%; O, 8%; H, 5%; N,1 %; ash, 13%; H_2O, 8%; heating value, 11,850 Btu per lb. Pounds of steam per pound of coal = 8.5.

Flue gas analysis (by volume) CO_2, 12.8%; CO, 0.6%; O_2, 5.4%; N_2, 81.2%.

Air and fuel enter furnace at 70 deg fahr; gas temperature at boiler outlet = 470 deg fahr; temperature of steam in boiler = 400 deg fahr; combustible in refuse = 20%; moisture in air = 0.5% of weight of dry air. Boiler pressure = 210 lb per sq in. abs. Feed water temperature = 180 deg. fahr.

Solution. Since Refuse = Ash + Carbon, Weight of refuse = $\dfrac{0.13}{0.80} \times 0.20 = 0.0325$ lb per lb coal, as fired.

Hence, carbon burned = $C_g = 0.65 - 0.0325 = 0.6175$ lb per lb coal, as fired.

Weight of dry flue gas, by equation (2) = 11.62 lb per lb coal, as fired.

Weight of dry air supplied = $DFG + H_2O + SO_2 + Ash - 1 = 11.2$ lb per lb coal as fired.

"DFG" signifies dry flue gas.

Boiler Energy Balance

Eq.	Energy Item	Calculation	Btu	%
1	Absorbed by boiler............	$(1207.9 - 147.87)8.5$	9,000	76.00
2	Absorbed by DFG............	$11.62 \times 0.24 \times (470 - 70)$	1,118	9.41
3	Loss due C in refuse..........	$0.0325 \times 14,600$	475	4.00
4	Loss due CO.................	$0.6175 \times 10,160 \times 0.6(12.8 + 0.6)$	280	2.36
5	Absorbed by H_2O in fuel.......	$0.08(1090 + 0.46 \times 470 - 70)$	99	0.83
6	Absorbed by H_2O from H_2.....	$9 \times 0.05(1090 + 0.46 \times 470 - 70)$	556	4.70
7	Absorbed by H_2O in air.......	$0.005 \times 11.2 \times 0.46(470 - 70)$	103	0.86
8	Radiation, etc................	By difference	219	1.84
		Total......	11,850	100.00

Overall boiler efficiency = $9000 \div 11,850 = 0.76 = 76$ per cent.

Interpretation of Boiler Balance. The energy balance as calculated gives the distribution of the *actual* energy quantities. Some of the losses can be reduced or eliminated entirely; others are always present and are *inherent* losses. An energy balance setting forth the inherent losses will enable the reader to tell at a glance where improvement may be made, and where no further gain will be possible. For instance, air supplied for combustion may be reduced, thus decreasing the excess air, and hence energy carried away by dry flue gas; but the air cannot be reduced below the theoretical requirements. Similarly, by suitable baffling and maintenance of optimum flue-gas velocity and rate of fuel firing, the temperature of the flue gas may be reduced, but it can never be reduced below the temperature of the steam leaving the boiler (without an economizer). The following tabulations will further clarify the point. All items are per pound of fuel as fired.

Distribution of Inherent Losses

Eq.	Name	Calculation	Btu	%
2	Absorbed by DFG	$9.26* \times 0.24 \times (400 - 70)$	733.4	6.19
3	Loss due C in refuse	....	0.0	0.00
4	Loss due CO	....	0.0	0.00
5	Absorbed by H_2O in fuel	$0.08(1090 - 70 + 0.46 \times 400)$	96.3	0.81
6	Absorbed by H_2O from H_2	$9 \times 0.05(1090 - 70 + 0.46 \times 400)$	541.8	4.57
7	Absorbed by H_2O in air	$0.005 \times 8.92* \times 0.46(400 - 70)$	67.7	0.57
8	Radiation, etc.	....	0.0	0.00
1	Absorbed by ideal boiler	By difference	10,410.8	87.86
		Total	11,850.0	100.00

* Theoretical, for perfect combustion.

Comparison of Actual and Inherent Losses

Item	Actual %	Inherent %
Absorbed by boiler	76.00	87.86
Absorbed by dry flue gas	9.41	6.19
Loss due C in refuse	4.00	0.00
Loss due CO	2.36	0.00
Absorbed by H_2O in fuel	0.83	0.81
Absorbed by H_2O from H_2	4.70	4.57
Absorbed by H_2O in air	0.86	0.57
Radiation, etc.	1.84	0.00
Total	100.00	100.00

25. STEAM ENGINES AND TURBINES

The engine of the steam cycle treated in Arts. 20–23 may be either of two general types, the reciprocating engine, commonly referred to as the *steam engine,* or the turbine engine, commonly referred to as the *steam turbine.* Given the same initial conditions of the steam and the same exhaust conditions the ideal thermal efficiencies of the steam engine and the turbine are exactly the same. The use of one or the other for a specific purpose is determined by practical or economic considerations. The measures of efficiency and performance developed in Art. 21 are applicable to both the steam engine and the steam turbine.

A **Simple Steam Engine** is one in which the expansion of steam is completed in one cylinder.

A **Compound Steam Engine** is one in which the steam progressively expands in two or more cylinders. The term *compound,* without qualification, refers to the two-cylinder arrangement. A *triple-expansion* engine means that the expansion is completed in three stages or cylinders, and a *quadruple-expansion* engine means that the expansion is completed in four stages or cylinders. Compound engines may have the cylinders arranged in various ways such as: tandem-compound, cylinders placed one behind the other in line; angle-compound, cylinder axes placed at right angles to one another; cross-compound, cylinders arranged side by side; and vertical triple expansion, three cylinders placed with axes vertical.

An engine may operate *non-condensing,* i.e., exhausting to the atmosphere, or *condensing,* i.e., exhausting into a condenser in which a vacuum is maintained.

A **Single-acting Engine** is one in which steam is admitted only to one side of the piston. A *double-acting* engine is one in which steam is admitted alternately to each side of the piston.

Valves. A *slide valve* is a valve which controls the inlet and exhaust of steam by sliding across the ports. A *poppet valve* is a disk, fitting a port, which is raised or lowered for the control of inlet and exhaust. A *Corliss valve* has a cylindrical surface which oscillates through a small angle to open or close the port. Each event is separately controlled. The main feature of this valve is the quick closure of the steam port, obtained by a trip-gear on the inlet valve. The more recent high-speed Corliss engine has positive control of the valves at all times.

The exhaust valve of the *uniflow engine* is the piston itself, which functions with respect to the exhaust ports located at the middle of the cylinder. The inlet valves, located at the ends of the cylinder, may be of any type.

Steam Engine Speed is governed in two ways: by throttling the steam supply, or by varying the cut-off.

Indicator Diagram. An indicator diagram is a diagram (see Fig. 8), showing the steam pressure in the engine cylinder at each point of the stroke. Such a diagram may be actually obtained by means of a steam-engine indicator, which is an instrument which causes a pencil to record on paper the pressure in the cylinder at every point of the stroke. The diagram drawn by the pencil shows whether the valves are properly adjusted, and it is also used in figuring the power developed in the cylinder, and the approximate steam consumption. A diagram of a non-condensing engine in which the steam is cut off at about one-quarter of the stroke is shown in Fig. 10.

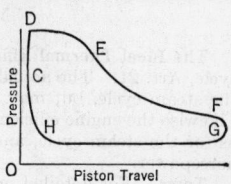

FIG. 10. Indicator Diagram of a Simple Steam Engine

The lines and points have the following significance.

Point of Admission, C, is the point at which the steam valve opens.

Admission Line, CD, shows the rise of pressure due to the admission of steam to the cylinder by opening the steam valve.

Steam Line, DE, is drawn when the steam valve is open and steam is being admitted to the cylinder.

Point of Cut-off, E, is the point where the admission of steam is stopped by the closing of the valve. It is often difficult to determine the exact point at which the cut-off takes place. It is usually located where the outline of the diagram changes its curvature from convex to concave.

Expansion Curve, EF, shows the fall in pressure as the steam in the cylinder expands doing work.

Point of Release, F, shows when the exhaust valve opens.

Exhaust Line, FG, represents the change in pressure that takes place when the exhaust valve opens.

Back-pressure Line, GH, shows the pressure against which the piston acts during its return stroke.

Point of Exhaust Closure, H, is the point where the exhaust valve closes. It cannot be located definitely, as the change in pressure is at first due to the gradual closing of the valve.

Compression Curve, HC, shows the rise in pressure due to the compression of the steam remaining in the cylinder after the exhaust valve has closed.

Initial Pressure is the pressure acting on the piston at the beginning of the stroke.

Terminal Pressure is the pressure above the line of perfect vacuum that would exist at the end of the stroke if the steam had not been released earlier. It is found by continuing the expansion curve to the end of the diagram.

The Indicated Mean Effective Pressure, found by dividing the diagram area by its length and multiplying the quotient by the pressure scale of the diagram, is in a broader sense that equivalent pressure which, if acting unopposed upon the piston face during the power stroke of a cycle, would produce the net amount of work output actually delivered per cycle.

Indicated Work per Cycle, ft-lb, = Imep $\times A \times L$

$$= P_m \times A \times L$$

where P_m = abbreviation for the mean effective pressure, pounds per square foot.

A = piston area, upon which the pressure acts, square feet.

$P_m A$ = mean effective force acting on piston face, pounds.

L = length of piston stroke, feet.

The indicated horsepower is

$$\text{Ihp} = \frac{P_m A L N}{33,000}$$

where N = the number of power strokes per minute (2 per revolution for simple double-acting engine).

The Brake Horsepower of an engine is calculated by the use of

$$\text{Bhp} = \frac{2 \pi r w n}{33,000}$$

where r = radius of brake arm, feet.

w = force acting at end of brake arm, pounds.

n = number of revolutions per minute.

The Brake Mean Effective Pressure, Bmep, useful for comparison purposes, is found by dividing the Bhp by the term $\dfrac{LAN}{33,000}$.

The mechanical efficiency of the engine may be stated,

$$\text{Mechanical efficiency} = \frac{\text{Bmep}}{\text{Imep}} = \frac{\text{Bhp}}{\text{Ihp}}$$

The Ideal Thermal Efficiency of the steam engine is the same as that for the Rankine cycle, Art. 21. The actual thermal efficiency of the steam engine is the same as that for the steam cycle, but may be based on either indicated horsepower or brake horsepower. Likewise the engine efficiency, heat rate, and steam rates of the steam engine are the same as for the steam cycle, and each may be based on either indicated horsepower or brake horsepower.

Tests. For detailed methods of tests of steam engines, as well as of all other power machinery, reference should be made to the Power Test Codes published by the American Society of Mechanical Engineers, New York.

The following summary represents briefly the generally accepted ideas regarding the cylinder action and the losses in the reciprocating steam engine.

A. The losses of available energy in the steam engine are due to the following causes arranged in the approximate order of magnitude of loss:

1. Initial or surface condensation.
2. Incomplete expansion and early release.
3. Throttling of steam flowing through partly open valves.
4. Leakage of steam past piston and closed valves.
5. Friction of moving parts.
6. Heat loss by radiation and conduction.
7. Compression and early admission.

B. Initial or surface condensation is increased by the following conditions:

1. Early cut-off and large ratio of expansion.
2. Large pressure and temperature range in a single cylinder.
3. Small cylinder diameters, because the exposed surface is large in comparison with the volume.
4. Steam supply saturated or wet.
5. Long valve passages and the use of the same passage for admission and exhaust steam.

C. Conditions favorable to reduction of initial condensation are:

1. Late cut-off and small expansion ratio (but this increases loss due to incomplete expansion in simple engines).
2. Superheat.
3. Separate valves for admission and exhaust, and short valve passages.
4. High compression.
5. Compounding.
6. Uniflow principle.

Types of Turbines

In the Turbine Engine, or steam turbine the energy conversion to work is accomplished by means of the conversion of the available portion of the internal energy of the steam into mechanical kinetic energy of a jet in stationary or moving nozzles, and then the conversion of this mechanical kinetic energy of the jet into work on a shaft by allowing the jet to change its direction of motion while passing over moving vanes or blades.

In the Impulse Turbine the steam pressure drop and consequent development of kinetic energy take place solely in the stationary nozzles, and the work is obtained by the conversion of this kinetic energy into work on moving blades. In the *reaction* turbine only a part (about half) of the kinetic energy conversion occurs in the stationary nozzle, the remainder of the kinetic energy conversion being accomplished by a pressure drop in the steam as it passes through the moving blades. The efficiencies and other performance of the steam turbine are the same as for the reciprocating engine except that for the turbine the items of indicated horsepower and mechanical efficiency are missing.

De Laval Turbine. The characteristic features of the *De Laval turbine* are the diverging nozzles which expand the steam to the back pressure in a single stage, and a single steel disk, mounted on a slender flexible shaft, carrying the blades on its periphery.

The Rateau Turbine consists of a number of De Laval elements in series. The steam expands in several pressure stages until completely expanded to the back pressure.

The Parsons Turbine is a reaction turbine in which there are a large number of rows of blades mounted on a rotor or revolving drum. Between each of these rows of blades is a row of stationary blades attached to the casing. The steam expands to a lower pressure in both sets of blades. A set of stationary blades and the following set of moving blades constitute what is known as a *stage*.

Several combinations of these different types are in use. A summary of the principal features of construction and the operating characteristics of several widely used types of turbines is given in Table I.

Table I *

Classification	Type	Characteristics	
		Physical	Operating
Impulse	De Laval	One nozzle or set of nozzles. Single disk with one row of blades. One passage of steam across blades.	High steam velocities. High wheel velocities. Large pressure drop in nozzle.
	Simple Curtis	One nozzle or set of nozzles. Single disk with two or more rows of blades. Intermediate reversing blades. One passage of steam across each blade row.	Moderate wheel speed. Large pressure drop in nozzle. Same pressure throughout stage.
	Re-entry (a) Axial flow (b) Tangential type	One nozzle or set of nozzles. Single row of blades or buckets. Reversing chambers to redirect steam on blades one or more times.	Usually moderate wheel speed. High wheel speeds in geared sets. Large pressure drop in nozzle.
	Rateau	Series of De Laval wheels with intermediate diaphragms carrying orifices. Usually, large number of stages.	Small pressure drop per stage. Most efficient ratio of wheel speed to steam speed can be secured.
	Multistage Curtis	Series of simple Curtis wheels separated by diaphragms carrying orifices. Usually relatively few stages.	Relatively large pressure drop per stage.
Reaction	Axial flow, Parsons	Series of alternate rows of converging fixed and moving blades. Moving blades mounted usually on several drums. Steam flows axially.	Small pressure drop per row. Large number of rows. Long spindles. Most efficient ratio of wheel speed to steam speed possible.
	Radial flow, Ljungstrom	Series of radial rings of converging reaction blades. Alternate rings revolve in opposite directions.	High ratio of blade speed to steam speed. Elaborate steam packing devices.
Combination Types	Curtis-Rateau	One Curtis stage followed by several simple-impulse stages.	Only moderate temperatures and pressures in casing due to large pressure drop in first nozzle.
	Curtis-Parsons	One Curtis stage followed by a series of Parsons stages. Usually disk and drum construction.	Temperatures in casing low, since steam is expanded in nozzle.

* Based on Kent.

26. STEAM CONDENSERS AND OTHER HEAT TRANSFER APPARATUS

Steam Condensers are either of the *jet* type, in which the condensate mixes with the cooling water and from which both are discharged together, or of the *surface* type, in which the two fluids are kept separate by thin metallic walls and are handled independently.

The Weight of Water necessary to condense a given weight of steam may be found for any type of condenser from the equation that expresses the energy balance for the condenser. Neglecting the effect of the presence of air, changes in velocity, and heat lost to the atmosphere,

$$w_s(H_s - H_c) = w_w(H_2 - H_1)$$

where w_s and w_w = the respective weights, in pounds, of steam and condensing water flowing through the condenser in a unit of time, usually the hour.

H_1 and H_2 = the respective enthalpies of the condensing water entering and leaving the condenser, in Btu per pound.

H_s = the enthalpy of the steam entering the condenser, in Btu per pound.

H_c = the enthalpy of the condensate leaving the condenser, in Btu per pound.

Then, the weight of condensing water per unit weight of steam becomes

$$\frac{w_w}{w_s} = \frac{H_s - H_c}{H_2 - H_1}$$

or, very closely,

$$\frac{w_w}{w_s} = \frac{H_s - (t_c - 32)}{t_2 - t_1} = \frac{H_s - (t_c - 32)}{t_s - (t_1 + \theta_b)}$$

where t_1 and t_2 = the respective temperatures of the condensing water entering and leaving the condenser, in degrees fahrenheit.

t_c = the temperature of the condensate leaving the condenser, in degrees fahrenheit.

t_s = the temperature of the exhaust steam (assuming no superheat), in degrees fahrenheit.

$\theta_b = t_s - t_2$ = terminal temperature difference.

With jet condensers, $t_c = t_2 = t_{\text{mix.}} = t_s - \theta_b$.

Therefore,

$$\frac{w_w}{w_s} = \frac{H_s - t_{\text{mix.}} + 32}{t_{\text{mix.}} - t_1}$$

$$= \frac{H_s - t_s + \theta_b + 32}{t_s - (t_1 + \theta_b)}$$

Most problems of heat transmission in surface condensers can be solved by the use of the following:

$$w_s(H_s - H_c) = \frac{AU(t_2 - t_1)}{\log_e \left(\dfrac{t_s - t_1}{t_s - t_2}\right)} = w_w\, c_w(t_2 - t_1)$$

where A = the amount of condenser heating surface, in square feet.

c_w = the specific heat of the condensing water.

U = the thermal transmittance, in Btu per hour per degree fahrenheit per square foot of condenser heating surface.

e = Napierian base of logarithms = 2.71828.

The mean temperature difference

$$\frac{t_2 - t_1}{\log_e \left(\dfrac{t_s - t_1}{t_s - t_2}\right)}$$

is commonly called the *logarithmic mean temperature difference*.

Assuming c_w as unity, permissible for fresh water where extreme accuracy is not essential,

$$\log_e \left(\frac{t_s - t_1}{t_s - t_2}\right) = \frac{U}{(w_w/A)}$$

in which (w_w/A) is the number of pounds of circulating water used per hour per square foot of condensing surface.

$$t_s = t_1 + (t_2 - t_1) + \theta_b = t_1 + \frac{H_s - H_c}{(w_w/A)} + \theta_b$$

$$= t_1 + \frac{H_s - H_c}{(w_w/w_s)}\left[\frac{\theta_b}{t_2 - t_1} + 1\right]$$

$$= \frac{t_1 + (t_2 - t_1)}{1 - (e)^{-U/(w_w/A)}}$$

These equations are useful in showing how the steam temperature, and the corresponding absolute pressure, are influenced by the variations in each of the individual factors and ratios appearing in the right-hand members.

Feedwater heaters are either of the *open* type, in which the two fluids mix and from which both are discharged together, or of the *closed* type, in which the two fluids are kept separate and are handled separately.

Neglecting heat loss through the shell

$$w_s(H_a - H_b) = w_f(H_2 - H_1)$$

in which w_s and w_f = the quantities of steam and feedwater flowing through the heater, respectively.

H_a and H_b = the respective enthalpies of the hot fluid entering and leaving the heater, in Btu per pound.

H_1 and H_2 = the respective enthalpies of the feedwater entering and leaving the heater, in Btu per pound.

Since the condensate formed in the open-type heater mixes with the feedwater, H_b and H_2 are equal in this type of heater. For moderate feedwater temperatures c_p of water is near unity; the term $(t_2 - t_1)$ may be substituted for the term $(H_2 - H_1)$, where t_2 and t_1 are the respective temperatures of the feedwater leaving and entering the heater. The problems of heat transmission in the closed feedwater heater are treated the same as those of the surface condenser.

An economizer is an apparatus by which some of the heat from gases leaving the boiler is recovered and used principally to heat feedwater. For heat transmission in economizers,

$$\text{Mean temperature difference} = \frac{\theta_a - \theta_b}{\log_e \dfrac{\theta_a}{\theta_b}}$$

where θ_a = the initial temperature difference of the two fluids, degrees fahrenheit.

θ_b = the final temperature difference of the two fluids, degrees fahrenheit.

And

$$w_g\, c_g(t_a - t_b) = \frac{A U(\theta_a - \theta_b)}{\log_e \dfrac{\theta_a}{\theta_b}} = w_f\, c_f(t_2 - t_1)$$

where w_g = weight, in pounds, of flue gas through the economizer per unit time.

w_f = weight, in pounds, of feedwater through the economizer per unit time.

c_g and c_f = the respective specific heats of the flue gas and feedwater.

Air preheaters, used also to recover some of the heat from gases leaving the boiler, may be of two general types, recuperative and regenerative. For the recuperative type in which the heat is transferred from the flue gases to the air through thin metallic walls the principles of heat transmission are the same as for the economizer. In the regenerative type the heat-transmitting surfaces are exposed alternately to the heat-surrendering gases and to the heat-absorbing air.

THE INTERNAL-COMBUSTION ENGINE

27. GENERAL CHARACTERISTICS

The Internal-combustion Engine constitutes one of the two general types of devices for realizing as shaft work some portion of the available energy associated with the high-temperature products of the combustion of a fuel, the other device being represented by the composite arrangement of furnace, steam boiler, and steam engine or turbine treated in Arts. 20–26. It will be recalled that in the latter arrangement the stored chemical energy of the fuel is released by a process of combustion carried out in a furnace at high temperature levels but at constant atmospheric pressure, that the energy so released is then in part delivered by conduction to moderate-temperature steam which is formed in the boiler under high pressure, and that this steam acts as a carrier through the medium of which energy is delivered to the engine, in which there is finally accomplished a partial transformation of the energy to shaft work and from which the unavailable residue of energy is discarded at about atmospheric temperature. In distinction to this serial procedure in the steam plant the internal-combustion engine effects a more direct utilization of the chemical energy released by the combustion by so confining the burning fuel mixture that a *high pressure is produced (or maintained) in the hot combustion products themselves,* whereby through a suitable mechanism these products may act directly upon a piston to motivate a shaft against whatever resisting force may be imposed by the external load.

The Characteristic Conditions for which the internal-combustion engine must be designed may be summarized as follows:

(A) A major portion of the material which must be introduced into the engine cylinder is the atmospheric air which supplies the oxygen necessary for the combustion. The induction of air from the atmosphere to the engine cylinder may be accomplished in various ways. A very common method is to employ one complete piston stroke for this purpose. An engine which does so is said to operate upon a *four-stroke* cycle. That cycle is described in the following. The alternative or *two-stroke* cycle is considered briefly later.

In a continuous graphic record of (a) the pressure existing within the space enclosed by the cylinder and piston at any point of the piston travel and (b) the total volume of that space at the same piston position, such as is furnished by the engine *indicator*, this induction or *suction* stroke would be represented by a line such as the line *ab* in Fig. 1. During this entry of the fluid through the *intake* valve the pressure within the cylinder will be less than that at the entrance to the induction system by the amount of the pressure drop necessary to accelerate the fluid and to overcome fluid friction in the intake passages.

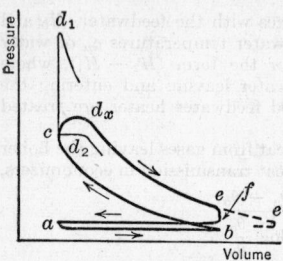

FIG. 1. Indicator Diagram of Internal Combustion Engines

(B) For both practical and theoretical reasons it is necessary that prior to the combustion of the fuel the fuel mixture or at least the air portion of this mixture shall have been brought to a pressure and temperature materially above those of the atmosphere. This is accomplished by a compression which is caused to take place by a return or *compression* stroke of the piston with all valves closed. For this stroke the simultaneous fluid pressures and volumes would be represented by points on the line *bc*.

(C) For motivation of the engine it is necessary that during the next or *power* stroke of the piston the average fluid pressure shall be materially greater than that during the other strokes. This pressure increase is effected by a pronounced temperature increase of the fluid during and resulting from combustion while confined within the cylinder. This combustion is initiated at or about a point in the piston travel which would be represented by point *c* in the figure.

The rate of combustion (and thus the rates of energy release and of temperature and pressure rise as a result of combustion) is a characteristic which is in effect the major basis for classification of modern engine types. Suitable control of the conditions under which the combustion occurs might permit or cause it to be so rapid and explosive in character as to take place at virtually constant volume and produce a more or less " vertical " rise of temperature and pressure, such as indicated by the line cd_1 in Fig. 1. Alternatively the combustion might be caused to proceed with such lesser rapidity that it would continue through a portion of the power stroke, with the production of a somewhat lesser temperature and pressure rise than would occur under the first conditions. Lines cd_x or cd_2 would be representative of the latter condition.

The exact rate of energy release under this second schedule might be caused to be virtually anything from the one producing almost constant volume combustion to one so relatively slow as simply to maintain a constant temperature and thus to permit a gradual pressure drop following the initiation of the combustion. The line cd_x may be taken as a general one representing any sort of combustion conditions which might obtain. However, the prototype of one of the standard cycles which are employed in present-day internal-combustion engine practice, that is, the *Diesel cycle*, is one in which it is assumed that the pressure shall be maintained constant during and by the combustion, producing a combustion line as represented by cd_2 in the figure. The constant volume combustion of line cd_1 is a basic characteristic of the *Otto cycle*.

To permit the constant volume combustion of the Otto cycle it is necessary that at point *c* in the cycle the engine cylinder shall contain the fuel and air in intimate mixture and thus in effective condition for ignition (by electric spark) and *explosive* combustion. This condition is obtainable by (1) the use of either gaseous fuels or relatively volatile liquid fuels and (2) the atomization and intimate mixing of the fuel with the air in some portion of the cycle prior to the completion of the compression. This mixing is ordinarily done outside of the engine cylinder in a mixing valve or *carburetor* and during the induction of the air on stroke *ab*. It is to be noted, however, that this very presence of a combustible mixture in the cylinder during the compression stroke imposes certain definite limits on the extent of the compression which may be employed in the Otto cycle, because of the temperature rise produced by the compression and the resultant tendency toward spontaneous pre-ignition of the mixture, and also by reason of the tendency of numerous fuels toward an abnormally rapid combustion and the production of abnormally and seriously high combustion temperature and pressure if compression is carried beyond certain limits. This latter phenomenon is known as *detonation.*

The progressive, constant pressure combustion of the conventional *Diesel cycle* is securable (1) by withholding the fuel from the engine cylinder until about the completion of the compression stroke, which implies that only air shall have entered during the suction stroke, and (2) by a subsequent progressive injection of an atomized jet of the (liquid) fuel into the cylinder during the combustion period *at a properly controlled rate.* Except in various smaller engines operating on a so-called *semi-Diesel* cycle, the ignition of the fuel is accomplished by compression of the air to so high a pressure P_c that at the end of compression it shall have attained a temperature high enough to induce spontaneous ignition upon the fuel injection. Even under this condition, however, to accomplish suitable ignition and combustion requires that the fuel must be injected in a very finely atomized state.

(D) Returning to a consideration of the events of the cycle—except as there is some incompleteness of combustion at point *d* by reason of chemical equilibrium and thus a persistence of combustion, or *after-burning,* beyond that point, the *remainder* of the power or *expansion stroke* provides solely for an expansion of the high-temperature products of combustion. This continues until the end of the stroke is reached, at or somewhat before which point the exhaust valve is opened. Line *de* is representative of this expansion phase. It will be observed that an expansion to the same total volume as that at the beginning of compression (V_b) predicates a release of the combustion products at a pressure which is materially higher than the intake or atmospheric pressure, and also their rejection or exhaust at a temperature very considerably above atmospheric temperature. The available energy loss associated with this temperature and pressure excess might be reduced by arranging for a continuation of the expansion to some greater volume such as the volume $V_{e'}$ of the figure. Such cycles have been and are frequently proposed but have not been developed commercially.

(E) Directly upon opening of the exhaust valve there occurs a rapid drop of pressure within the cylinder due to the escape of a portion of the combustion products through the exhaust passages, and upon the following or *exhaust* stroke in a four-stroke cycle the remainder of the products are ejected by the returning piston, except as a portion is left in the *clearance space* between the piston and the head end of the cylinder. These two exhaust processes are represented by lines *ef* and *fa* in Fig. 1. During the exhaust stroke the pressure within the cylinder would exceed that of the exterior by the amount necessary to accelerate the fluid and to overcome fluid friction in the exhaust system. The particular mass of products which remains in the clearance space at the end of any given exhaust stroke is replaced by an equivalent mass at the end of the next cycle; this clearance residue may therefore be regarded as continuously entrapped within the cylinder.

The performance of a complete cycle has thus been described. Observe that for its accomplishment four strokes of the piston have been required, and therefore, as noted above, the cycle would properly be designated as a *four-stroke* cycle. An engine operating on this four-stroke schedule would be described as a *four-cycle* engine whether it might conform to the Otto cycle or the Diesel cycle or any modification of either as regards the degree of compression or the character of combustion.

In lieu of the four-stroke schedule it is possible and wholly practicable to accomplish the introduction of the air or the mixture into the cylinder, its compression, the combustion and expansion, and a sufficient clearing of the combustion products from the cylinder, in two piston strokes. A cycle so carried out is designated, as remarked above, as a *two-stroke* cycle, and an engine operating on the cycle is a *two-cycle* engine. The arrangements by which the cycle is accomplished differ in detail in various engines, but the general procedure is in effect (a) to cause the exhaust valves (or ports) to open rather early in the *expansion* stroke, thus facilitating as far as possible the escape of the combustion products without the provision of a separate exhaust stroke, and (b) to force the air (or the mixture) into the cylinder and jointly to sweep out the residual combustion

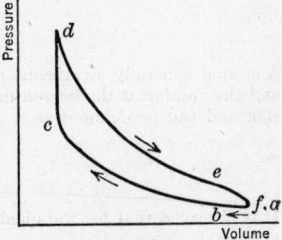

FIG. 2. Indicator Diagram of a 2-cycle Engine

products by the use of a low-pressure *scavenger* blower which is caused to discharge to the cylinder during the early portion of the compression stroke, thus eliminating a separate intake stroke. The general appearance of the pressure-volume diagram of a two-stroke cycle is shown in Fig. 2, in which equivalent phases in the two- and the four-stroke cycles are denoted by the same letters as were used in Fig. 1.

The idealized conditions of operation of an internal-combustion engine may be taken to involve the following general features:

(a) Zero resistance and thus zero pressure drop through the intake system, whereby the cylinder pressure during admission might be that of the atmosphere, P_a.

(b) A reversible adiabatic compression of the air or mixture, the adiabatic feature being in distinction to the actual condition of energy transfer as heat between the fluid and the water-cooled or air-cooled cylinder of the real engine.

(c) A reversible adiabatic combustion phase, which again is in distinction to the actual condition of energy escape as heat from the burning mixture to the cylinder during combustion.

(d) A reversible adiabatic expansion of the combustion products, with, however, the possibility of some persistence of combustion during and after expansion if conditions of chemical equilibrium were encountered during combustion.

(e) An instantaneous pressure drop upon opening of the exhaust valve *at the end* of the expansion stroke, and zero resistance and thus zero pressure drop through the exhaust system, whereby the cylinder pressure during exhaust might be that of the atmosphere, P_a.

28. THE OTTO CYCLE

A pressure-volume diagram for an Otto cycle conforming to the above-mentioned ideal features would be like that of Fig. 2. The extent of the compression and expansion employed is a feature which affects the final products' temperature and thus the efficiency of the cycle. The outstanding influence of these features may be indicated approximately by quite artificial and unreal analyses which are known as the *air standard* analyses. In these analyses it is presumed (1) that air alone is caused to pass through the typical state changes of the cycles, (2) that the temperature and pressure rises which in the actual cycles are produced by the chemical energy release during combustion shall in this hypothetical cycle be produced by a like supply of energy to the air as heat from some external source, (3) that the energy discarded by the cycle equals the energy emission during a constant-volume cooling of the air from the temperature T_e to the original temperature T_1, and (4) that the specific heat of the air may be regarded as constant and as that of air at normal atmospheric temperature.

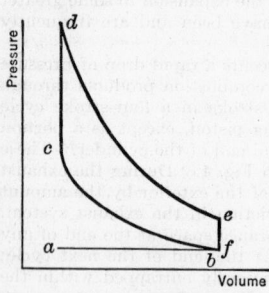

FIG. 3. Indicator Diagram of Otto Cycle (Air Standard)

A significant item associated with the *internal-combustion engine* cycle is the ratio between (1) the total volume in the cylinder at the end of intake and beginning of compression and (2) the clearance or residual volume in the cylinder when the piston is at the end of the compression stroke. This ratio is known as the *ratio of compression* and will be denoted as r_c. Referring to Fig. 3, which is representative of the events in the ideal Otto cycle,

$$\text{Compression ratio, } r_c, = \frac{V_b}{V_c}$$

A second generally significant ratio is that between the volume at the end of expansion and the volume at the beginning of expansion. This ratio is known as the *ratio of expansion* and will be denoted as r_e. Referring again to Fig. 3,

$$\text{Expansion ratio, } r_e, = \frac{V_e}{V_d}$$

It is observed that for the ideal Otto cycle the expansion ratio and the compression ratio are equal.

An air standard analysis of the Otto cycle indicates that its thermal efficiency depends only upon the compression ratio of the cycle and increases with increase in compression ratio in accordance with the relation

$$\text{Thermal efficiency, air standard Otto cycle} = 1 - \frac{1}{(r_c)^{0.4}} \qquad (1)$$

Although more exact estimates of ideal performance as well as actual engine tests show that efficiency is likewise influenced by the proportions of the fuel-air mixture, with improved efficiency at mixtures with some excess of air, the evidence of the air standard analysis is well corroborated with respect to the effect of the compression ratio.

The evidence offered by equation (1) that, for the air standard Otto cycle, the thermal efficiency is determined solely by the compression or expansion ratio, is indicated graphically by the curve A of air standard thermal efficiency vs. compression ratio in Fig. 4. In the figure there are also represented, in curves B, C, and D, the results of computations made by Goodenough and Baker* for the ideal (indicated) thermal efficiency of an Otto cycle employing real mixtures of gasoline and air. In their computations careful attention was given to the effect of specific heat variation and of chemical equilibrium during combustion, employing the then (1926) best available data. Curve E shows the actual thermal efficiencies (based on indicated horsepower) attained on test of a very high-grade, single-cylinder Otto engine in which the compression

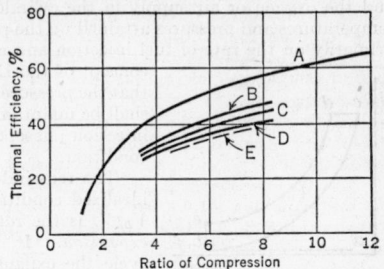

FIG. 4. Thermal Efficiencies of Otto Cycles

ratio could be varied at will, the results being those reported by Ricardo † when using a non-detonating fuel and a fuel mixture containing air 15 per cent in excess of the amount theoretically required for complete combustion of the fuel.

The results of the ideal efficiency computations (curves B, C, and D) and the actual efficiency results (curve E) distinctly corroborate the evidence offered by the air standard cycle computations in so far as those predict the material influence of compression and expansion ratio on efficiency. In addition the ideal efficiency curves indicate a material influence of the character of the fuel mixture on the ideal efficiency. Test results on actual engines operating with mixture strengths which are readily explosive further corroborate the evidence of the ideal curves, to wit, that decrease of the mixture strength acts to increase efficiency quite distinctly.

Progress in the use of distinctly weak mixtures is handicapped by the difficulty in ignition and rapid burning of the mixture and by the material reduction in the power capacity of a given size engine with reduction in mixture strength, maximum power being secured both in the ideal cycle and in the actual engine with mixtures in which the air supply is some 5 to 10 per cent less than the theoretical requirement. Progress in the direction of the higher compression ratio is handicapped by the detonation tendency of many fuels but similarly is facilitated by the development and utilization of fuels which are less detonative in character (such as gasoline-benzol blends, gasoline treated with various catalysts, alcohol, etc.). The tendency of the efficiency curves toward a gradual flattening with increase of compression ratio and a very pronounced increase of the peak pressure of the cycle without commensurate increase of the engine power will undoubtedly act to limit the ratio for which it is economically worth while to strive. With ordinary gasolines, values of the ratio in excess of about 6 cannot be used to advantage owing to detonation.

The departure of actual engine efficiency from the ideal is attributed to a number of factors, such as (1) a failure to burn portions of the fuel which are in intimate contact with the cylinder walls, (2) untimely burning of portions of the fuel during the compression stroke, this occasioned by localized contacts with hot portions of the cylinder or exhaust valve, and (3) energy conduction through the cylinder walls as heat during the combustion and expansion. The efficiency of multiple-cylinder engines is frequently decreased very materially by a poor distribution of a properly proportioned fuel mixture, that is, by the delivery of over-weak mixture to certain cylinders and over-rich mixture to others. The efficiency of two-cycle Otto engines is commonly rather less than that of a four-cycle engine by reason of a direct wastage of fuel mixture through the exhaust during the dual exhaust-induction phase of that cycle.

---

* Goodenough and Baker, A Thermodynamic Analysis of Internal Combustion Engine Cycles, Univ. of Illinois Engineering Experiment Station Bull. 160, 1927.
† See Ricardo, Engines of High Output, Macdonald and Evans, London, 1926.

29. THE DIESEL CYCLE

The distinctive characteristics of the *Diesel cycle* are the induction and compression of air only to a temperature well above the ignition temperature of the fuel, whereby upon injection of an atomized fuel oil jet at the end of the compression stroke ignition will automatically occur and combustion will continue so long as fuel injection is continued and the oxygen or air supply in the cylinder does not become depleted. The resulting temperatures and pressures attained by the products during the fuel admission will depend primarily on the rate of fuel injection and combustion. In the *conventional* present-day concept of the Diesel cycle the rate is presumed to be such that the pressure which was reached at the end of compression shall be maintained during the piston travel to the end of the injection phase. Line *cd* of Fig. 5 is representative of such a condition.

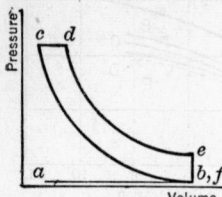

The remainder of the cycle of the figure conforms to the idealized conditions noted for the Otto cycle. In the figure, V_b/V_c is the *ratio of compression*, and V_e/V_d is the *ratio of expansion*. It is obvious that in the conventional Diesel cycle the expansion ratio is less than the compression ratio.

FIG. 5. Indicator Diagram of Diesel Cycle (Air Standard)

For any given compression ratio the duration of the energy supply phase, *cd*, would be increased and the expansion ratio would be correspondingly decreased with increase in the *amount* of energy supplied to the engine per cycle. Interpreted in association with the actual engine, the amount of energy supplied per cycle is measured by the amount of fuel supplied per cycle and thus by the rate and duration of the fuel injection. Note in this connection that the ideal limiting amount of fuel which might properly be injected per cycle is established by the amount of oxygen and thus of air which had been inducted into the engine cylinder on the intake stroke of the cycle. Decreased fuel injection per cycle implies increased expansion ratio and increased air excess.

For the Conventional Diesel Cycle with constant pressure combustion the air standard analysis indicates that the cycle efficiency is influenced jointly by the compression ratio and the expansion ratio in accordance with the relation

$$\text{Thermal efficiency, air standard Diesel cycle} = 1 - \frac{1}{(r_c)^{0.4}} \frac{(r_c/r_e)^{1.4} - 1}{1.4(r_c/r_e - 1)} \qquad (2)$$

For a given compression ratio the Diesel efficiency is less than that of the Otto and departs progressively from the Otto with decreasing values of the expansion ratio r_e. This last fact is due directly to the increase of the temperature T_e (at the end of the expansion and the beginning of the energy rejection phases of the cycle) with decrease of the expansion ratio. This temperature increase is in turn due jointly to the increasing temperature T_d resulting from greater energy supply to the fluid during the longer injection phase and the concurrently lesser opportunity for temperature drop during the expansion phase. In spite of this apparent handicap the actual Diesel engine is in general able to attain thermal efficiencies higher than those obtained by the Otto, owing to the compensating advantage that the detonating character of the fuel used with the Otto engine and the very high maximum pressures encountered in that cycle limit its practicable compression ratio to about 5 or 6, whereas the Diesel engine may and commonly does employ compression ratios of 12 or over.

In the Diesel engine a very thorough atomization of the fuel oil jet is necessary as well as a jet momentum sufficient to cause the fuel particles to penetrate the mass of highly compressed air, and also there needs be a considerable turbulence in that air, all in order that the fuel and oxygen molecules may quickly become intimately associated and rapid combustion may thereby be facilitated. It has been the usual practice to assist the atomization of the fuel and the mixing by introducing with the fuel jet a jet of very highly compressed air which was furnished by an accessory compressor. With more recent advances in the art, fuel nozzles are being developed which provide adequate pulverization and dissemination of the fuel without the aid of the air jet. The two methods of introducing the fuel are known respectively as *air injection* and *airless injection* or, as the latter is frequently although rather inaptly termed, *solid injection*.

For Methods of Testing and Reporting the Performance of internal-combustion engines, reference should be made to the Test Code for Internal Combustion Engines published by the American Society of Mechanical Engineers, 29 W. 39 St., New York City.

It may be stated that the items brake horsepower, indicated horsepower, mechanical efficiency, brake mean effective pressure, indicated mean effective pressure, etc., have the same significance and are determined in quite the same manner as described for the steam engine, Art. 25.

For the single-acting four-cycle engine Ihp $= \dfrac{PALN}{2 \times 33,000}$ per cylinder, and for the two-cycle single-acting engine the Ihp per cylinder is $\dfrac{PALN}{33,000}$.

In American practice the thermal efficiency of the internal-combustion engine is based upon the higher heating value of the fuel.

REFRIGERATION

Symbols and Abbreviations

C.P. = coefficient of performance.
c_p = specific heat at constant pressure.
H = enthalpy, Btu per pound of fluid.
J = Joule's equivalent (778 ft-lb per Btu).
k = specific heat ratio, c_p/c_v.
P = pressure, pounds per square foot, absolute.
P_1 = pressure of refrigerant in condenser or cooler.
P_2 = pressure of refrigerant in evaporator or refrigerator.
Q = energy transferred as heat, Btu per pound of fluid.
S = entropy per pound mass of fluid.
T = temperature, degrees Rankine (degrees fahrenheit absolute).
V = specific volume, cubic feet per pound.

The refrigerating machine is the practical example of the reversed heat engine, in that it acts to abstract energy as heat from a region of lower temperature and to deliver heat to a region of high temperature and does this by the supplying of energy to the machine usually as shaft work but also possibly as heat from some still higher temperature level.

The objective of the heat engine is the transformation to work of a maximum portion of the energy which is supplied from a high-temperature source, but a necessary accompaniment of the engine is the rejection of an unavailable residue of energy to that universal energy receiver, the atmosphere. The heat engine thus operates through a temperature range which extends from atmospheric temperature upward. In distinction, the refrigerating machine has for its practical objective only the securing and maintenance of a temperature which is below that of the atmosphere, but again the energy which it discards must go to the same general energy receiver, the atmosphere. Consequently the refrigerating machine operates through a temperature range which extends downward from the temperature of the atmosphere.

30. THE CARNOT REFRIGERATION CYCLE

The Reversed Carnot Cycle may be described as one abstracting energy from a lower-temperature region and returning it to a region of higher temperature by means of the work supplied. Examining this reversed Carnot cycle by the aid of the T–S diagram of Fig. 1 it is seen that, by operating the cycle in the direction indicated, heat Q_2 may be abstracted from a region at the lower temperature T_2 in the amount $T_2(S_b - S_a)$, and heat Q_1 may be delivered to a region at the higher temperature T_1 in the amount $T_1(S_c - S_d)$ or $T_1(S_b - S_a)$. For the operation of this complete cycle work will be required in the amount $Q_1 - Q_2$, or alternatively, $W/J = Q_1 - Q_2 = (T_1 - T_2)(S_b - S_a)$.

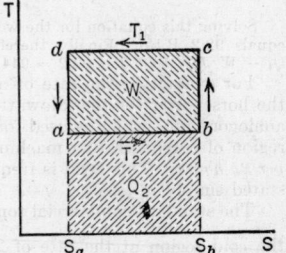

FIG. 1. Carnot Refrigeration Cycle

31. PERFORMANCE AND CAPACITY

As a natural objective in refrigeration is the removal of energy from the lower temperature region with a minimum expenditure of work, a suitable index of the performance of a refrigeration machine is the ratio between the amount of heat removed, or the refrigerating effect, and the work required. This ratio is called the *coefficient of performance* of the machine, or

$$\text{Coefficient of performance (C.P.)} = \frac{\text{Heat removed } (Q_2)}{\text{Work required } (W/J)}$$

For the reversed Carnot cycle the coefficient thus becomes

$$\text{C.P.} = \frac{Q_2}{W/J} = \frac{T_2(S_b - S_a)}{(T_1 - T_2)(S_b - S_a)} = \frac{T_2}{T_1 - T_2}$$

This Carnot or reversible cycle coefficient is the maximum coefficient of performance conceivably obtainable with any refrigerating machine operating in any manner with any fluid between a given (constant) lower temperature T_2 and a given (constant) upper temperature T_1.

The Carnot refrigeration cycle may ideally be realized with any vapor. It is instructive to see how a fluid such as water might be used. Referring to the T–S diagram of a vapor, as presented in Fig. 2, and starting with the substance at state d in a saturated liquid state at the upper temperature (and pressure) of the cycle, let the liquid be expanded adiabatically and reversibly in a cylinder to state a. As it expands, the temperature drops, part of the liquid vaporizes, and some work output is obtained. Between states a and b additional liquid is caused to vaporize at the constant lower temperature and pressure of the cycle by the absorption of energy as heat from the cold region. Here the refrigeration is accomplished. After the partial vaporization to some suitable state b, work energy is supplied and the vapor and liquid mixture is compressed isentropically to a state c which in the figure is the saturated vapor state at the upper pressure and temperature.

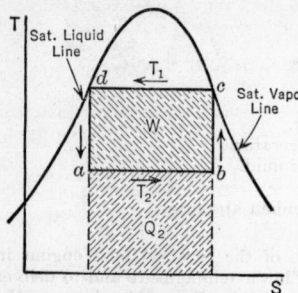

Fig. 2. Carnot Refrigeration Cycle with a Vapor

The vapor is now condensed at the constant upper temperature and pressure to the original state at d, condensation being effected by heat energy rejection in an amount equal to that absorbed from the lower-temperature region plus the *net* work of the cycle. The net work is that required for the compression less that regained by the expansion.

Example. A Carnot refrigeration cycle is operated between the temperatures of 50 and 100 deg. fahr. What vapor pressures would be required if the fluid were steam, and what would be the coefficient of performance? What refrigeration would be accomplished per pound of steam?

Solution. From the saturated steam tables the necessary pressure would be 0.178 and 0.95 lb per sq in abs, respectively. The coefficient of performance would equal $(50 + 460)/(100 - 50)$ or 10.2. The heat rejected per pound of steam to the upper temperature region at 100 deg. fahr would be the enthalpy or "latent heat" of evaporation at that temperature or, from the steam tables, 1036.3 B.t.u. per lb. From the definition of coefficient of performance and the necessary energy relations of the cycle,

$$10.2 = \frac{\text{Refrigeration}}{\text{Work}} = \frac{1036.3 - \text{Work per lb}}{\text{Work per lb}}$$

Solving this equation for the work term, the net work required per pound of steam circulating equals 92.2 B.t.u. Finally therefore the refrigeration accomplished per pound of steam = $Q_1 - W/J = 1036.3 - 92.2 = 944.1$ Btu.

For evaluating the rate of available energy delivery from an engine or power plant the horsepower (or the kilowatt) is employed as the conventional unit of capacity. The analogous unit which is used for expressing the rate of heat energy intake from the cold region of a refrigerating machine, or its *refrigerating capacity*, is the *tons of refrigeration per 24 hours*. This term is frequently abbreviated, and the rate of refrigerating effect is stated simply in *tons*.

The standard commercial ton is arbitrarily defined as a removal of energy as heat from the cold region at the rate of 288,000 Btu per 24 hours or $\left(\dfrac{288,000}{24 \times 60}\right) = 200$ Btu per minute. The unit originates from the fact that the "latent heat of fusion" of ice is approximately 144 Btu per lb or $(144 \times 2000 =)$ 288,000 Btu per short ton, whence a refrigerating machine which is operating at a capacity of one ton is absorbing energy at a rate equal to that which would exist if one ton of ice were melting in the refrigerated region each 24 hours.

An index of refrigerating-machine performance which is employed in practice rather more than the coefficient of performance is a derived one which is associated with the ton unit of capacity, namely, *horsepower required per ton* of refrigeration per 24 hours. The relation between the performance so expressed and the coefficient of performance is readily obtained by recalling that

$$\text{Refrigerating effect, Btu per minute} = \text{tons (per 24 hours)} \times 200$$

and
$$\text{Work required, Btu per minute} = \text{Hp} \times \frac{2545}{60} = \text{Hp} \times 42.4$$

whence
$$\text{Coefficient of performance} = \frac{\text{Tons} \times 200}{\text{Hp} \times 42.4} = \frac{4.71}{\text{Hp per ton}}$$

It is practically advantageous to modify the reversed Carnot cycle, or Carnot refrigeration cycle, in some particulars and to carry out the resulting fluid cycles in a succession of apparatus through which the fluid is caused to flow progressively and in each of which one phase of the cycle is accomplished. These practical adaptations fall in general into three classifications:

(*a*) *Vapor cycles*, in which the transfer of the vapor from the lower temperature and pressure of the cycle to the upper is accomplished through the agency of work supply to a *compressor*.

(*b*) *Gas (air) cycles*, in which the transfer of the fluid from the lower temperature and pressure to the upper is likewise effected by a *compressor*.

(*c*) *Vapor cycles* in which the transfer of the vapor from the lower pressure and temperature to the upper is accomplished in an *absorption system*, primarily through the agency of heat supplied at a still higher temperature.

These several practical cycles are considered in some detail in the following articles.

32. THE VAPOR COMPRESSION SYSTEM

The practical vapor compression system of refrigeration differs in principle from the Carnot cycle in two features. The one is the segregation of the several phases of the cycle into various devices to and through which the vapor is caused to flow progressively. The other is that, owing to the failure to develop as yet a practicable engine or turbine in which to accomplish the expansion of the condensed liquid from the upper temperature and pressure of the cycle to the lower, this expansion is in practice done in an irreversible throttling process which takes place in an *expansion valve*.

The resulting cycle as it would appear with these modifications, but still idealized in some respects, is represented in the *T–S* and *H–S* diagrams of Figs. 3 and 4, respectively. A diagrammatic representation of the arrangement of the apparatus appears in Fig. 5.

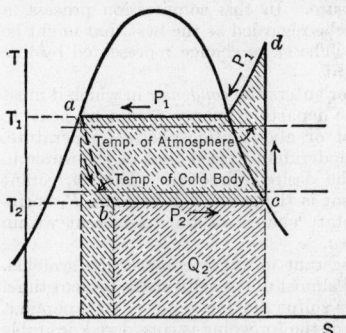

Fig. 3. Vapor Compression Cycle, *T–S* Diagram

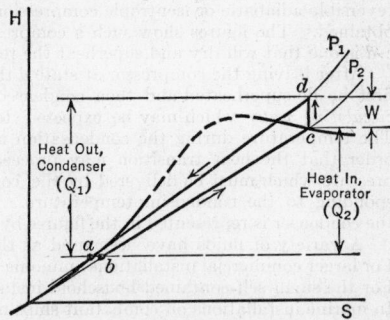

Fig. 4. Vapor Compression Cycle, *H–S* Diagram

Starting at point *a* in each figure the fluid, which is called the *refrigerant*, leaves a storage tank in which it exists as a liquid at about atmospheric temperature and at its corresponding saturation pressure P_1. Between *a* and *b* the fluid is permitted to escape under control through the expansion valve to the low-pressure region of the cycle. Owing to the throttling character of the process the enthalpy of the fluid at state *b* must equal that at state *a*, with the result that a sensible portion of the liquid must vaporize, but owing to the lower pressure of the vapor its temperature must have fallen. Specifically it must have dropped to the saturation temperature corresponding to the lower pressure.

After leaving the expansion valve the low-temperature and low-quality vapor mixture enters the *evaporator.* Here the provision is made for the absorption of energy as heat by the fluid from the region or substance which it is desired to refrigerate. The pipe coils which constitute the evaporator may be placed directly in the region that is to be cooled, in which event the system would be said to be one with *direct expansion,* or they may be placed in and act to cool some liquid with low freezing point, such as calcium chloride brine, which is circulated to the region that is to be cooled and which thus acts simply as a convective energy carrier.

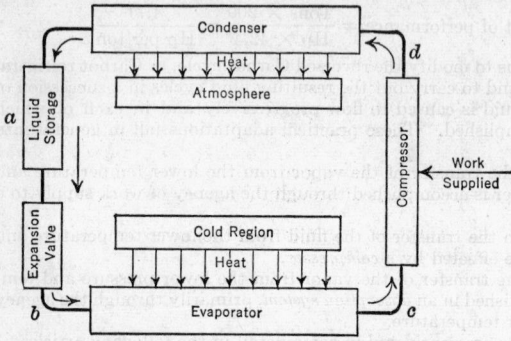

FIG. 5. Elements of Vapor-Compression Refrigeration Cycle

The latter system would be known as one with *indirect expansion.* In either event the reception of energy by the refrigerant will act to cause it to evaporate. The amount of energy received by each pound of the refrigerant and thus the degree of completeness of its evaporation will depend on the rapidity of its circulation, on the temperature difference between the fluid in the evaporator and its environs, and on other operating conditions. In the figures the fluid is shown as leaving the evaporator at state

c, which is the saturated vapor state. It may in fact leave as a wet vapor mixture or even moderately superheated. In connection with the process of evaporation in the evaporator it is to be observed that the temperature therein must be *below* the temperature of the cold region in order that heat transition may occur in the desired direction. The pressure maintained therein must be the saturation pressure corresponding to the temperature, which pressure we shall designate as P_2.

From the evaporator the refrigerant passes to the *compressor.* The function of the compressor is twofold. The one function is that of withdrawing the fluid from the evaporator at a rate sufficient to maintain the necessary reduced pressure and temperature in the evaporator. The other is that of compressing and delivering the fluid at a temperature which is adequately *above* that of the atmosphere or of the region or substance to which the fluid must next discard its " load " of energy. The increase of temperature of the vapor must be accompanied by increase of pressure. In this compression process, a reversible adiabatic or isentropic compression must be regarded as the best that might be obtained. The figures show such a compression. The state change represented by line c–d is one that will dry and superheat the refrigerant.

After leaving the compressor at state d the vapor enters the *condenser* in which it must first be de-superheated and then condensed. The departing energy passes as heat to *circulating water* which may be expected to be at or about atmospheric temperature. The temperature during the condensation must moderately exceed that of the water in order that the heat transition may proceed in the desired direction. The refrigerant pressure which must be delivered by the compressor is the saturation pressure P_1 corresponding to the condensing temperature. The state change of the refrigerant within the condenser is represented in the figures by line d–a.

A variety of fluids have been used as the refrigerant in vapor compression systems. For larger commercial installations ammonia is used almost universally at the present time. For the small self-contained household installations sulfur dioxide vapor is very popular. In marine installations on combatant ships neither of the foregoing is considered desirable on account of their active toxicity, and carbon dioxide is preferred. Various hydrocarbons such as ethyl chloride and propane are also used. Ammonia offers the advantages of moderate condenser pressures and moderate specific volume at the evaporator pressure. Sulfur dioxide offers the further advantage of even more moderate pressures but requires considerably more compressor displacement on account of fairly high specific volumes at the evaporator pressure. Carbon dioxide has the disadvantage of requiring very high pressures in both the condenser and the evaporator.*

Probably the most effective means of improving the performance of a refrigerating

---

* For a complete description of the various refrigerants, a discussion of their adaptability under various conditions, and tables and charts of their thermodynamic properties see Macintire, Handbook of Mechanical Refrigeration, John Wiley & Sons, 1928.

process, but at the same time one that is too frequently overlooked, is that of providing adequate, well-designed and well-maintained heat-transfer surfaces in the evaporator and in the condenser and an ample amount of cool circulating water to the condenser. The effect is to reduce as far as practicable the total temperature range, $T_1 - T_2$, through which the refrigerant must pass by enabling its lower temperature T_2 to be a minimum amount below the requisite cold region temperature and its upper temperature T_1 to be a minimum amount above the circulating water supply temperature.

The energy relations for the several phases of the cycle, both for actual operation and for the ideal cycle, are (regarding all kinetic energy terms as negligible), per pound of vapor circulated,

for the expansion valve, $\qquad H_a = H_b$

for the evaporator, $\qquad H_b + Q_{\text{in},\,b-c} = H_c,$ or

$$Q_{\text{in},\,b-c} = H_c - H_b = H_c - H_a$$

for the compressor,

$$JH_c + W_{\text{in},\,c-d} = JH_d + JQ_{\text{out},\,c-d}, \text{ or}$$
$$W_{\text{in},\,c-d} = J(H_d - H_c) + JQ_{\text{out},\,c-d}\,*$$
$$= J(H_d - H_c)_S \text{ for isentropic compression}$$

for the condenser, $\qquad H_d = H_a + Q_{\text{out},\,d-a},$ or

$$Q_{\text{out},\,d-a} = H_d - H_a$$

for the complete cycle,

$$W_{\text{in}} = J[(Q_{\text{out},d-a} - Q_{\text{in},\,b-c}) + Q_{\text{out},\,c-d}] = J(H_d - H_c + Q_{\text{out},\,c-d})*$$

Coefficient of performance

$$= \frac{H_c - H_a}{H_d - H_c + Q_{\text{out},\,c-d}}$$
$$= \frac{H_c - H_a}{(H_d - H_c)_S}, \text{ for isentropic compression}$$

In these relations, the several subscripts are to be interpreted as referring to locations with respect to the various apparatus of the plant rather than to particular states indicated by the letters on the foregoing H-S or T-S diagrams.

Example. For an indirect-expansion ice-making installation operating with ammonia assume that the brine leaves the cooler (evaporator) at 14 deg fahr and that to obtain this temperature the necessary vapor temperature in the evaporator is 5 deg fahr. Also assume that the cooling water is supplied at 70 and leaves at 80 deg fahr, enabling the ammonia to condense at 86 deg fahr.

Assuming dry saturated vapor at the compressor suction, isentropic compression, and no sub-cooling of the liquid from the condenser, ascertain the pressures in the evaporator and the condenser, the temperature after compression, and the ideal coefficient of performance and horsepower per ton of refrigeration. Compare with the Carnot cycle performance between the vapor temperatures in the evaporator and condenser and with a Carnot cycle performance between the lowest brine temperature and the cooling water supply temperature. Indicate the reasons for the lower performance of the vapor cycle as compared with the Carnot between the same temperature limits.

Solution. From tables of the properties of ammonia (Bureau of Standards):

Evaporator (suction) pressure = saturated pressure corresponding to 5 deg fahr = 34.3 lb per sq in. abs (= 19.6 lb gage).

Condenser (discharge) pressure = saturated pressure at 86 deg fahr = 169.2 lb per sq in. abs (= 154.5 lb gage).

For saturated vapor at 5 deg fahr, $H = 613.3$ ($= H_c$), and $S = 1.3253$ ($= S_c$).

After compression at a constant entropy of 1.3253 to 169.2 lb abs, t (from charts) = 210 deg fahr and $H = 713$ ($= H_d$).

For saturated liquid at 86 deg fahr, $H = 138.9$ ($= H_a$ and H_b).

Coefficient of performance $= \dfrac{613.3 - 138.9}{713 - 613.3} = \dfrac{474.4}{99.7} = 4.76.$

Horsepower per ton of refrigerating effect per 24 hours $= \dfrac{4.71}{4.76} = 0.99.$

Carnot performance between (460 + 5 =) 465 deg R and (460 + 86 =) 546 deg R

$$= \frac{465}{546 - 465} = 5.74.$$

Carnot performance between (460 + 14 =) 474 deg R and (460 − 70 =) 530 deg R

$$\frac{474}{530 - 474} = 8.47.$$

---

* As with any compressor, energy departure as heat *which might act to reduce the enthalpy increase* acts to reduce instead of increase the work requirement. In distinction, any heat emission occasioned by mechanical friction in moving parts obviously acts to increase the work.

The ammonia cycle coefficient is lower than the Carnot (4.76 vs. 5.74) because of (a) the irreversible throttling in the expansion valve and (b) the higher temperature at which the heat is rejected during the de-superheating of the ammonia vapor leaving the compressor.

Charts Having Absolute Pressure Plotted against Enthalpy are found most useful to show the refrigeration process. Fig. 6 shows such a chart for the refrigerant freon, upon which is drawn a characteristic cycle diagram. The throttling process is represented by

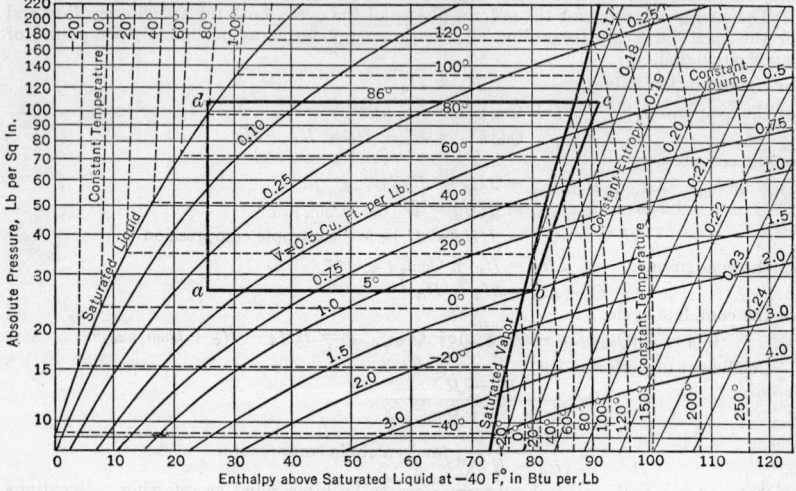

FIG. 6. *P–H* Diagram for Freon *

the line *da*; the absorption of energy as heat in the evaporator is represented by the line *ab*; the adiabatic compression process is represented by the line *bc*; and the discarding of energy as heat to the atmosphere is represented by the line *cd*.

Table I shows the physical properties of the refrigerants in most common use.

Table I. Some Properties of Refrigerants

Refrigerant	Symbol	Molecular Weight	Boiling Point at 1 Atmos., °F	Critical Temperature, °F	Critical Pressure, lb/sq in. abs	Freezing Point, °F	Liquid Density at Boiling Point, lb/cu ft	Gas Density,* lb/cu ft	Ratio of Specific Heats, $k=c_p/c_v$
Dichloromethane	CH_2Cl_2	84.906	105.0	421.0	670±	−142.0	186.9	0.225	1.14
Hexane	C_6H_{14}	86.112	155.9	454.6	435	−137.7	38.29	0.205	1.0
Pentane	C_5H_{12}	72.906	97.1	387.0	470	−203.4	38.09	0.185	1.0
Ethyl chloride	C_2H_5Cl	64.497	54.5	369.0	764	−217.7	56.50	0.177	1.13
Butane ‡	C_4H_{10}	58.080	30.9	307.8	510	−211.0	37.51	0.1549	1.11
Sulfur dioxide	SO_2	64.064	14.0	315.0	1127	− 97.6	91.15	0.1694	1.26
Isobutane	C_4H_{10}	58.080	+ 10.0	272.7	522	−229.0	37.20	0.1543	1.11
Methyl chloride	CH_3Cl	50.481	− 11.4	289.6	954	−153.2	62.30	0.1336	1.20
Dichlorodifluoromethane §	CCl_2F_2	120.916	− 22±	....	....	−247±	....	0.338±‡	1.12
Ammonia	NH_3	17.032	− 28.0	270.3	1636	−107.9	42.56	0.0446	1.32
Propane	C_3H_8	44.064	− 44.0	204.1	647	−309.8	36.35	0.1158	1.15
Propylene	C_3H_6	42.048	− 53.7	196.1	645	−301.4	38.12	0.1087	
Carbon dioxide	CO_2	44.00	−109.3†	88.0	1058	− 69.9	....	0.1144	1.30
Ethane	C_2H_6	30.048	−127.5	90.1	694	−277.6	34.13	0.0782	1.22
Ethylene	C_2H_4	28.032	−154.7	− 48.9	717	−272.9	35.49	0.0729	
Methane	CH_4	16.032	−258.9	−115.7	657	−297	19.20	0.0415	1.32

*At 30 in. Hg and 70 deg. fahr.   †Solid.   ‡At 32 deg. fahr.   §Also called "F-12" and "freon."

33. THE AIR COMPRESSION SYSTEM

The apparatus required for an air compression system is in principle the equivalent of that required for a vapor system, *except that* for obtaining the low air temperature

* Redrawn, by permission, from Barnard, Ellenwood, and Hirshfeld, Heat-Power Engineering, Part III, John Wiley & Sons.

it is necessary that the compressed air shall do work in its expansion, instead of being permitted simply to throttle through an expansion valve. An air engine is therefore employed for effecting the pressure and temperature drop which must occur as the air passes to the cooling coils.

The arrangement of the elemental components of an air compression system of refrigeration is shown diagrammatically in Fig. 7 and the ideal state changes of the cycle are represented in the T, H–S, and P–V diagrams of Figs. 8 and 9, respectively.

Referring to the several locations and state points indicated on the figures, state a represents air at slightly above atmospheric temperature but under a pressure considerably above atmospheric. The air at this state enters the *expander cylinder* or engine through which it would ideally expand isentropically to a state b, at which state the pressure commonly would

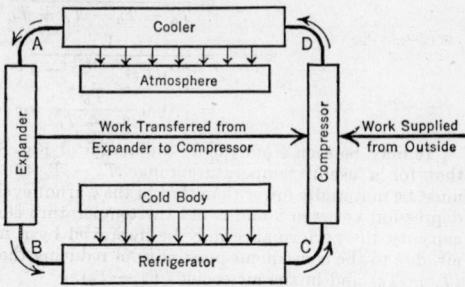

FIG. 7. Elements of Air-compression Refrigeration Cycle

still exceed considerably the atmospheric pressure but the temperature would be 50 deg fahr or more below the temperature of the region which it is desired to refrigerate. The work output from the expander engine is available for and would actually be used for assisting in driving the compressor of the system.

Between states b and c the air passes at ideally constant pressure through the refrigerating coils and there absorbs energy by heat transition from the cold region, departing from the refrigerating coils at a temperature still moderately below that of the cold region.

After leaving the coils at state c the air enters the compressor cylinder and is compressed to its original pressure at a but to a temperature considerably above that of the

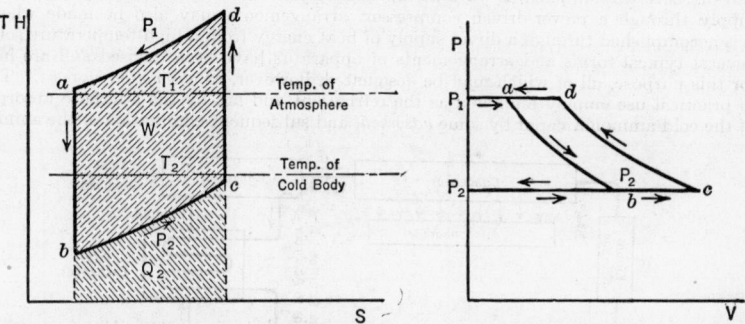

FIG. 8. *T–S* Diagram for Air-compression Cycle

FIG. 9. *P–V* Diagram for Air Compression Cycle

atmosphere. An isentropic state change, $c - d$, is represented in the figures, but as usual heat emission from the air during its compression would act to reduce the work required for the compression. The work necessary for driving the compressor comes partly from an external source and partly from the expander engine.

Upon leaving the compressor at state d the hot air passes at ideally constant pressure through a cooler where it emits energy as heat to the circulating water and is thus recooled to the original state a.

Presuming the ideal conditions of constant pressure cooling and warming and isentropic expansion and compression the energy relations for the various phases of the cycle are; for the expander cylinder, per pound of air,

$$W_{\text{out}} = Jc_p(T_a - T_b)$$
$$= Jc_p \, T_b[(P_1/P_2)^{(k-1)/k} - 1]$$

for the refrigerating coils, $\qquad Q_{\text{in}} = c_p(T_c - T_b)$

for the compressor, $\qquad W_{\text{in}} = Jc_p(T_d - T_c)$
$$= Jc_p \, T_c[(P_1/P_2)^{(k-1)/k} - 1]$$

for the air cooler, $Q_{\text{out}} = c_p(T_d - T_a)$
for the complete cycle,

$$W_{\text{in, net}} = Jc_p(T_c - T_b)[(P_1/P_2)^{(k-1)/k} - 1]$$

Coefficient of performance

$$= \frac{T_c - T_b}{T_d - T_a - T_c + T_b}, \quad \text{or}$$

$$= \frac{1}{(P_1/P_2)^{(k-1)/k} - 1}, \quad \text{or}$$

$$= \text{either } \frac{T_b}{T_a - T_b} \quad \text{or} \quad \frac{T_c}{T_d - T_c}$$

It may be seen from the T–S diagram of Fig. 8 or from the last expressions above that for a useful temperature range $T_a - T_c$ the air cycle coefficient of performance must be materially lower than that of the Carnot cycle, owing to the necessary temperature depression between b and c and the temperature elevation between d and a. At a given capacity the performance may be improved by a more rapid mass-rate of circulation of air, due to the consequent possibility of reducing the temperature range in the refrigerator $(T_c - T_b)$ and in the air cooler $(T_d - T_a)$.

The air compression system once held sway in marine installations, as the *dense air* system, but now it is practically abandoned partly because of its relatively poorer coefficient of performance and partly because of operating difficulties arising from the freezing of any moisture in the air and the consequent stoppage of the expander valves, etc.

34. THE ABSORPTION SYSTEM REFRIGERATION THROUGH THE SUPPLYING OF ENERGY AS HEAT

In the refrigerating systems hitherto considered the energy required for passing the refrigerant from the lower temperature and pressure of the cycle to the upper temperature and pressure was supplied as work at the compressor. Instead of effecting this by work supply through a power-driven compressor, arrangements may also be made whereby it is accomplished through a direct supply of heat energy from a high-temperature source. Several typical forms and arrangements of apparatus have been devised and are in use for this purpose, all of which may be designated, however, as *absorption systems*. Those in practical use employ ammonia as the refrigerant and act by the alternate absorption of the cold ammonia vapor by some *adsorbent* and subsequent elimination of the ammonia

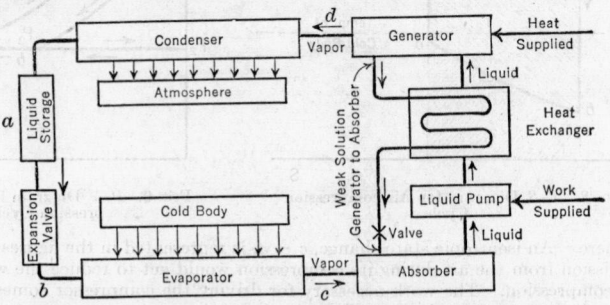

FIG. 10. Elements of Vapor-absorption Refrigeration Plant

at a higher temperature by the application of heat energy. The system in most common use employs water as the ammonia adsorbent.

The elements of an ammonia absorption system are shown diagrammatically in Fig. 10. The usual condenser, expansion valve, and evaporator are evident. Through these occurs the customary progressive flow of the refrigerant. The distinctive items of the system are the *absorber, liquid pump, heat exchanger,* and *generator*. These jointly replace the conventional compressor of the compression system, and through them there is a closed circuit of an ammonia-water solution. The general actions in this circuit are as follows.

The cold vapor leaving the evaporator passes to the absorber and is there avidly absorbed by a weak solution of water and ammonia known as the *weak aqua*. This absorption process has the characteristic of emitting energy, whence it is necessary that cooling water be circulated through coils in the absorber in order to maintain the temperature of the liquid sufficiently low and thus permit the building up of an adequate ammonia concentration. The weak aqua in the absorber thus becomes eventually a *strong aqua* and is then delivered by the liquid pump through the heat interchanger to the generator. In the generator heat energy is supplied, usually by a low-pressure steam coil, and the temperature of the strong aqua is thereby raised sufficiently that the ammonia which had been taken up in the absorber is eliminated from the strong aqua and is thus delivered as ammonia vapor to the condenser. The resulting weak aqua then completes the aqua circuit by returning through the heat exchanger to the absorber. The action in the exchanger is the mutual one of warming the strong aqua which is en route from the absorber to the generator by the cooling of the weak aqua which is returning from the generator to the absorber.

In certain smaller absorption systems the liquid pump, which is observed to be the only moving part required in the system, is dispensed with by employing the same element alternately as the absorber and as the generator, with a consequent intermittent action of the system. Also there is an ingenious system in use in household units in which the pump is dispensed with by introducing hydrogen gas in the evaporator and absorber, with the result that the system is under virtually the same *total* pressure throughout. Circulation is brought about by differences in the densities of the liquids in various parts of the system. The total pressure in the evaporator is the sum of the partial pressures of the hydrogen gas and the ammonia vapor, but the temperature is established only by the partial pressure of the saturated ammonia vapor.

Various other adaptations of the absorption system employ other absorbents, such as anhydrous ammonium nitrate and silica gel.

The energy relations for the condenser, expansion valve, and evaporator of an absorption system are in principle the same as those for a compression system, but in practical application they may become more complicated because there may be a carry-over of some of the adsorbent (such as water vapor in the aqua system) from the generator to and through the condenser and evaporator. For the absorber, pump, exchanger, and generator, together with the various accessory apparatus which are found in the actual plant, the energy relations become still more involved by reason of the semi-chemical character of the processes of vapor absorption by and elimination from the adsorbent.

It will have been observed that the elemental requisites for refrigeration are simply a supply of a liquid refrigerant under some pressure, an expansion valve, and the coils in which the expanded refrigerant may evaporate at the lower pressure and temperature. If an unlimited supply of the liquid refrigerant were available and if its saturation pressure at the desired refrigeration temperature should perchance be above the pressure of the atmosphere, then continued refrigeration might be secured simply by letting the refrigerant escape. It would thus appear that the greater portion of the equipment which is employed for effecting a practical, economical, and continuously operating refrigeration system is required only in order that the refrigerant may be recovered and be reliquefied at atmospheric temperature.

GAS AND VAPOR MIXTURES, HUMIDITY, AND AIR CONDITIONING

Symbols and Abbreviations

a = subscript designating the air constituent of a mixture.

f = subscript designating the saturated liquid state.

g = subscript designating the (dry) saturated vapor state.

fg = subscript designating the change of a property during change of a fluid from the saturated liquid to the saturated vapor state.

l = subscript designating a liquid constituent of a mixture.

m = subscript designating a mixture.

P = subscript designating constancy of pressure.

V = subscript designating constancy of specific volume.

v = subscript designating a vapor constituent of a mixture.

w = subscript designating the water (vapor, liquid, or both) constituent in a mixture.

x, y, z = subscripts designating the several constituents x, y, and z of a (gas) mixture.

ϕ = relative humidity.

c = specific heat, of a constituent or a mixture.

E = molecular energy, Btu per pound of a constituent or of a mixture.
H = enthalpy, Btu per pound of a constituent or of a mixture.
k = ratio of specific heats (c_p/c_v).
m = molecular weight of a constituent (or of mixture).
M = mass of a constituent (or of mixture).
P = partial pressure of a constituent (or total pressure of mixture).
Q = energy transferred by radiation or conduction (as heat).
R = gas constant of a constituent (or of a mixture).
S = entropy per pound of a constituent (or of mixture).
t = temperature, degrees fahrenheit.
T = temperature, degrees Rankine (degrees fahrenheit absolute).
$V_{x,\,y,\,\text{or}\,z}$ = volume (not specific volume) of a constituent x, y, or z in a mixture if the constituent is segregated and put under the temperature and total pressure of the mixture, as in volumetric analysis.
V_g = specific volume of (dry) saturated vapor.
x = quality (saturated-vapor fraction) of a mixture of saturated liquid and vapor.

Various of the fluids which are encountered in engineering processes are mixtures either of gases or of a gas and vapor. Thus dry air is itself a mixture primarily of oxygen and nitrogen, and atmospheric air is a further mixture of dry air with superheated water vapor or with saturated vapor and perhaps some unvaporized liquid, as in clouds or during fog and rainfall. Several of the simpler of such types of mixtures are presented in the following.

35. GAS MIXTURES

The Actual Gas Mixture consists of a haphazard aggregation of molecules of each constituent, the molecules of any single constituent being distributed uniformly throughout the entire space and also acting or moving quite as if they occupied the space alone. As a consequence the total pressure exerted by the mixture against the walls of its container by reason of the molecular bombardment of those walls may be distributed between several *partial* pressures, each of which is individually attributable to the molecules of a corresponding individual constituent and each of which would be the pressure exerted by that constituent if it alone should fill the space or volume occupied by the mixture (V_m) at the common temperature (T_m) of it and of all the components of the mixture. The values of the partial pressures of the gases in a mixture are:

$$P_x = M_x R_x \frac{T_m}{V_m} = 1545 \frac{M_x}{m_x} \frac{T_m}{V_m}$$

$$P_y = M_y R_y \frac{T_m}{V_m} = 1545 \frac{M_y}{m_y} \frac{T_m}{V_m}$$

$$P_z = M_z R_z \frac{T_m}{V_m} = 1545 \frac{M_z}{m_z} \frac{T_m}{V_m}$$

where P_x, P_y, and P_z = the partial pressures attributable individually to constituents x, y, and z.
M_x, M_y, and M_z = the relative masses of those constituents.
R_x, R_y, and R_z = their individual gas constants.
m_x, m_y, and m_z = their molecular weights.
T_m = the mixture temperature.
V_m = the volume occupied by the mixture.

The Relation between the Partial Pressure of any one constituent (as x) and that of any other (as y) is

$$\frac{P_x}{P_y} = \frac{M_x}{M_y}\frac{R_x}{R_y} = \frac{M_x/m_x}{M_y/m_y} \tag{1}$$

Also,

$$\frac{P_x}{P_m} = \frac{P_x}{P_x + P_y + P_z} = \frac{M_x R_x}{M_x R_x + M_y R_y + M_z R_z}$$

$$= \frac{(M_x/M_m)R_x}{(M_x/M_m)R_x + (M_y/M_m)R_y + (M_z/M_m)R_z}$$

$$= \frac{\dfrac{M_x/M_m}{m_x}}{\dfrac{M_x/M_m}{m_x} + \dfrac{M_y/M_m}{m_y} + \dfrac{M_z/M_m}{m_z}}$$

where M_m = mass of mixture, $M_x + M_y + M_z$.

P_m = total pressure, $P_x + P_y + P_z$.

The several ratios M_x/M_m, M_y/M_m, and M_z/M_m in the last relation evidently represent the mass proportions of each constituent with respect to the mass of the whole, as would be determined by or would determine the gravimetric analysis of the mixture. It frequently happens that, as in the practical analysis of furnace gases or of an internal-combustion engine exhaust, the several constituents of a gas mixture are in effect segregated progressively and their relative volumes are determined *when maintained under the original temperature but brought (individually) to the original total pressure of the mixture.* An expression of the proportional composition of a mixture in terms of the ratios of the individual volume of the constituent, when so segregated and at the temperature and total pressure of the mixture, to the actual mixture volume is known as its *volumetric* analysis.

The Volume of Each Component under such temperature and pressure conditions is

$$V_x = M_x R_x \frac{T_m}{P_m} = 1545 \frac{M_x}{m_x} \frac{T_m}{P_m}, \text{ etc.,}$$

and the ratio between those volumes for any pair of the constituents is

$$\frac{V_x}{V_y} = \frac{M_x R_x}{M_y R_y} = \frac{M_x/m_x}{M_y/m_y} \left(\text{and } = \frac{P_x}{P_y}, \text{ by eq. 1}\right) \qquad (2)$$

Also relations are readily obtainable by which to convert from gravimetric to volumetric analyses, and *vice versa.* Thus

$$\frac{V_x}{V_m} = \frac{V_x}{V_x + V_y + V_z} = \frac{M_x/m_x}{M_x/m_x + M_y/m_y + M_z/m_z}$$

$$= \frac{\dfrac{M_x/M_m}{m_x}}{\dfrac{M_x/M_m}{m_x} + \dfrac{M_y/M_m}{m_y} + \dfrac{M_z/M_m}{m_z}} \qquad (3)$$

and

$$\frac{M_x}{M_m} = \frac{M_x}{M_x + M_y + M_z} = \frac{V_x m_x}{V_x m_x + V_y m_y + V_z m_z}$$

$$= \frac{(V_x/V_m)m_x}{(V_x/V_m)m_x + (V_y/V_m)m_y + (V_z/V_m)m_z} \qquad (3a)$$

Relations are thus available by which to ascertain the partial pressure of any constituent of a gas mixture and by which to convert from gravimetric to volumetric analysis, or the reverse. It remains to be observed that any given mixture has its own effective or equivalent gas constant, molecular weight, and specific heats, which may be used in analyses of mixture processes quite as for any single gas.

R_m, **the Equivalent Gas Constant for the Mixture,** is obtained from

$$R_m = (M_x/M_m)R_x + (M_y/M_m)R_y + (M_z/M_m)R_z \qquad (4)$$

Since, for the gases, $mR = 1545$, an equivalent molecular weight may be computed for a mixture by the relation

$$m_m = \frac{1545}{R_m} \qquad (4a)$$

c_m, **an Equivalent Specific Heat for the Mixture,** is obtained from

$$c_m = \frac{M_x}{M_m} c_x + \frac{M_y}{M_m} c_y + \frac{M_z}{M_m} c_z \qquad (5)$$

With the foregoing relations at hand it is in general possible to proceed with analyses of engineering processes with a gas mixture quite as though the mixture were a single gas, *so long as the mass proportions of the mixture do not change* during the process. In this connection it will be recalled that the practice of regarding a gas mixture as effectively equivalent to a single gas is exemplified by the treatment of the properties and energy relations of air as though it were a single gas.

36. GAS AND VAPOR MIXTURES

There are Several Distinctive Conditions of Gas-vapor Mixtures which are of general concern and which are classifiable as:

(a) Mixtures of gas and (low-pressure) superheated vapor, as exemplified by the air and superheated water vapor which constitutes normal atmospheric air.

(b) Mixtures of gas and (low-pressure) saturated vapor, as exemplified by the atmosphere at the incipiency of fog or rainfall.

(c) Mixtures of gas, saturated vapor, and saturated liquid, as exemplified by the atmosphere during fog or rainfall.

Considering these in order:

(a) The low-pressure vapors, when even véry moderately superheated, and in fact even when saturated if at a sufficiently low vapor pressure, are found to conform closely to the gas characteristics. As a consequence, engineering computations involving gas-superheated vapor mixtures are commonly made as for gas mixtures, employing the foregoing gas mixture and gas relations. However, with respect to a given mixture, before one may proceed with confidence upon that basis it is necessary first to verify the fact of, or to ascertain the degree of, superheat of the vaporous constituent. To do so it is necessary to possess data concerning the temperature and total pressure of the mixture and the mass proportion of the vapor. It is further necessary to recall that the vapor pressure (or temperature) of a *saturated* vapor is established solely and unchangeably by its temperature (or pressure), as is also the density or any other property of the saturated vapor. The following example will illustrate the principles involved perhaps better than a collection of formulas, since recourse must be had to the steam tables in any case.

Example 1. A parcel of atmospheric air at a (total) pressure of 14.7 lb per sq in. (abs) and a temperature of 70 deg fahr is found (by hygrometric determination) to contain 0.009 lb of water vapor per lb of air (not mixture). Is the vapor superheated and, if so, by how many degrees? What is the partial pressure of the air? Compute the density of each constituent, the density of the mixture, the mass of vapor per pound of mixture, and the density of moisture-free air at the above temperature and pressure. What is the equivalent gas constant and molecular weight of the mixture? Compute the enthalpy per pound of mixture, relative to air and water at 32 deg fahr.

Solution. By equation (1) et seq.:

$$P_v, \text{ if superheated} = 14.7 \ \dfrac{\dfrac{0.009/1.009}{18}}{\dfrac{0.009/1.009}{18} + \dfrac{1.0/1.009}{29}} = 0.210 \text{ lb per sq in.}$$

Temperature of saturated vapor at 0.21 lb per sq in. = 54.4 deg fahr (from steam tables). Vapor is therefore superheated by (70 − 54.4 =) 15.6 deg fahr.
$P_{air} = 14.7 − 0.21 = 14.49$ lb per sq in.

$$\text{Density, vapor} = \frac{0.21 \times 144}{86 \times (70 + 460)} = 0.00066 \ (86 = R \text{ for superheated vapor}).$$

$$\text{Density, air} = \frac{14.49 \times 144}{53.3 \times (70 + 460)} = 0.07393.$$

$$\text{Density, mixture} = 0.07459 \text{ lb per cu ft.}$$

$$\text{Vapor per pound of mixture} = \frac{0.00066}{0.07459} \left(\text{or} \ \frac{0.009}{1.009} \right) = 0.00892 \text{ lb.}$$

$$\text{Density, moisture-free air} = \frac{14.7 \times 144}{53.3(70 + 460)} = 0.07493 \text{ lb per cu ft.}$$

$R_m = 0.00892 \times 86 + 0.99108 \times 53.3 = 53.6$; $m_m = 1545/53.6 = 28.8$
H_{air} per pound of mixture = $0.99108 \times 0.241 \times (70 − 32) = 9.07$ Btu.
H_{vapor} per pound of mixture = $(M_v/M_m)H_{g,\,70°}$ (since for low-pressure vapor H depends solely on temperature) = $0.00892 \times 1090.8 = 9.73$ Btu.
$H_{mixture, per lb} = 9.07 + 9.73 = 18.80$ Btu.

(b) In the consideration of mixtures consisting of a gas and a saturated vapor, or so-called *saturated* mixtures, the items of outstanding significance are that, although the strictly gaseous constituents continue to conform to the typical gas characteristics, the *saturated* vapor constituent now acts independently, that is, in conformity with the typical vapor characteristics. The application of these considerations, as well as certain additional features and properties of a saturated mixture, are developed in the following examples.

Example 2. An air-water vapor mixture at 14.7 lb per sq in. total pressure is known to be saturated (i.e., the vapor constituent is saturated vapor) at 70 deg fahr. Ascertain the partial pressures and densities of the vapor and air constituents and the density of the mixture. Compute the mass of vapor per pound of air and per pound of mixture, and the relative enthalpy per pound of mixture.

Solution.

P, saturated vapor at 70 deg fahr. by steam tables, = 0.363 lb per sq in.
P of air = 14.7 − 0.363 = 14.337 lb per sq in.

$$\text{Density of vapor} = 1/869, \text{ by tables, or} = \frac{0.363 \times 144}{86 \times (460 + 70)} = 0.00115$$

$$\text{Density of air} = \frac{14.337 \times 144}{53.3 \times (460 + 70)} = 0.07301$$

$$\text{Density of mixture} = 0.07416$$

Vapor per pound of air = 0.00115/0.07301, or (eq 1) $\dfrac{0.363}{14.337} \times \dfrac{18}{29} = 0.0157$.

Vapor per pound of mixture = 0.00115/0.07416, or 0.0157/1.0157 = 0.0155.
$R_m = 0.0155 \times 86 + 0.9845 \times 53.3 = 53.8$.
$H_{vapor, per \, lb \, of \, mix.} = 0.0155 \times 1090.8$ = 16.91 Btu
$H_{air, per \, lb \, of \, mix.} = (1.000 - 0.0155) \times 0.241 \times (70 - 32)$ = 9.02 Btu

$H_{mixture, per \, lb}$ = 25.93 Btu

Example 3. Referring to the mixture of example 1 (0.009 lb of vapor per lb of air, not mixture), ascertain the temperature at which the mixture would become saturated upon cooling at constant (total) pressure, and compute the amount of energy removal as heat necessary to have effected the specified cooling, Btu per pound of mixture.

Solution. As the low-pressure vapor conforms to gas characteristics down to saturation, and as the same mass proportions between the vapor and air will persist so long as the cooling is not sufficient to have produced any condensation of the vapor, the vapor pressure at saturation is the same as in example 1 or 0.210 lb per sq in. The temperature at which the vapor (and mixture) will become saturated is therefore its saturation temperature corresponding to that pressure, or 54.4 deg fahr.

$H_{air, per \, lb \, of \, mix.} = 0.99108 \times 0.241 \times (54.4 - 32)$ = 5.35 Btu
$H_{vapor, per \, lb \, of \, mix.} = 0.00892 \times 1083.7$ = 9.67 Btu

$H_{mixture, per \, lb}$ = 15.02 Btu

Energy abstracted for constant pressure cooling = $\Delta H = 18.80 - 15.02 = 3.78$ Btu per lb of mixture.

R is the same as in example 1.

In connection with the last example it is to be noted that the temperature at which a (unsaturated) mixture becomes saturated upon cooling at constant pressure is known as the *dew point* of the original mixture.

(c) Mixtures of a gas, saturated vapor, and saturated liquid may be encountered when a saturated mixture is cooled or compressed, or when a volatile liquid is introduced into a space containing a gas but in a greater amount than can exist in the space as saturated vapor at the existing temperature. Again the gas constituent conforms to the gas characteristics, but the properties of the saturated liquid and vapor are independently interrelated in accordance with the saturation characteristics of the vapor. The following example illustrated one phase of these considerations.

Example 4. The mixture of examples 1 and 3 is further cooled at a total pressure of 14.7 lb per sq in. to a temperature of 40 deg fahr. Ascertain the partial pressures and densities of the remaining vapor and of the air; the masses of saturated vapor and of the fog or rain which must have condensed out, pound per pound of air and per pound of mixture; the quality of the vapor-fog mixture; the enthalpy of the mixture; and the heat-energy removal necessary to have cooled from the dew point to 40 deg fahr.

Solution.

P, saturated vapor at 40 deg fahr, by steam tables, = 0.1217 per sq in.
P of air = 14.7 − 0.1217 = 14.578 lb per sq in.
Density of vapor (by tables) = 1/2445 = 0.00041.

Density of air = $\dfrac{14.578 \times 144}{53.34 \times (460 + 40)} = 0.07878$.

Vapor per pound of air = 0.00041/0.07878 = 0.0052 lb.
Fog per pound of air = 0.009 − 0.0052 = 0.0038 lb.
Fog per pound of mixture = 0.0038/1.009 = 0.00376 lb.
Vapor per pound of mixture = 0.0052/1.009 = 0.00515 lb.
Quality of vapor-fog component = 0.0052/0.009 = 0.577 = 57.7%.

$H_{vapor, per \, lb \, of \, mix.} = (0.0052/1.009) \times 1077.1$ = 5.55 Btu
$H_{fog, per \, lb \, of \, mix.} = (0.0038/1.009) \times 8.05$ = 0.03 Btu
$H_{air, per \, lb \, of \, mix.} = (1.0/1.009) \times 0.241 \times (40 - 32)$ = 1.91 Btu

H, per pound of mixture.......................... = 7.49 Btu
Energy abstracted, = $\Delta H = 15.02 - 7.49 = 7.53$ Btu per lb of mixture.

37. HUMIDITY AND HYGROMETRY

In many circumstances, as in scientific ventilation and air conditioning, it becomes most essential that air of closely prescribed temperature and moisture content shall be provided. This moisture content may be designated in several ways, but the index commonly employed by the engineer is that of the *relative humidity* of the mixture. This is defined as the *ratio between the density of the actual (superheated) vapor in the mixture and the density of saturated vapor at the temperature of the mixture.* As for both circumstances the density of the (low-pressure) vapor is satisfactorily computable by the gas relation, density $= P/RT$, it follows that the relative humidity is also expressed by the ratio between the actual partial pressure of the vapor in the mixture and its saturation pressure corresponding to the mixture temperature. Thus, denoting relative humidity by the symbol ϕ

$$\phi = \frac{\text{Actual vapor density}}{\text{Density, sat. vapor at mixture temperature}}$$

or
$$= \frac{\text{Actual vapor pressure}}{\text{Sat. pressure at mixture temperature}}$$

To illustrate, the mixture of example 1 would be said to have a relative humidity of $(0.00066/0.00115$ or $0.210/0.363 =) 0.575$, or 57.5 per cent. In the same parlance, the saturated mixture of example 2 would be said to have a relative humidity of 100 per cent. Likewise, in accordance with example 3, the mixture of example 1 would attain a 100 per cent relative humidity upon cooling to its dew point (at 54.4 deg fahr). Its humidity might alternatively have been brought to 100 per cent if supplied with $(0.0155 - 0.00892)$ 0.0066 lb of moisture (per pound of mixture) while maintained at 70 deg fahr and atmospheric pressure.

Devices Which Determine the Humidity of gas-vapor mixtures are known as *hygrometers* or *psychrometers.* The type which is most used by the engineer consists simply of two thermometers, with the bulb of one *dry* and the bulb of the other covered by a wick which is kept *wet* with the same liquid as exists in the vapor phase in the mixture (as the water in atmospheric air). An active current of the mixture under test is caused to pass across the wet bulb, effecting a continuous vaporization from the bulb and consequent cooling and temperature depression, due to the energy absorption required for producing the vaporization.

The immediate environs of the wet bulb are thus a region to which there pass steadily the air and superheated vapor in the air mixture under test, where the water which passes up the wick is evaporated, and from which there departs a mixture of air and *saturated* vapor. By writing the steady-flow energy equation for this region it is possible to develop an expression for direct evaluation of the mass of the vapor per pound of air (not mixture) in the air mixture as supplied. From these data the relative humidity is readily computable by the methods of example 1 and the above.

In developing the equation the following symbols are employed:

t_d = dry bulb (actual mixture) temperature, degrees fahrenheit.

t_w = temperature registered by wet bulb, degrees fahrenheit.

$M_{v,1}$ = mass of (superheated) vapor per pound of air (not mixture) in the approaching mixture at t_d.

$M_{v,2}$ = mass of (saturated) vapor per pound of air (not mixture) in the *mixture* leaving the immediate surface of the wet-bulb wick, at t_w.

$M_{v,2} - M_{v,1}$ = mass of liquid passing up wick, at t_w and vaporizing, pound per pound of air (not mixture).

$H_{f,1}$ = enthalpy of saturated liquid at t_d, Btu per pound.

$H_{g,1}$ = enthalpy of (superheated) vapor in the approaching mixtures at t_d, Btu per pound. At the very low vapor pressures encountered this effectively equals the enthalpy of saturated vapor (H_g) *at the same temperature,* t_d. (See example 1.)

$H_{fg,1}$ = enthalpy of vaporization at t_d.

$H_{f,2}$ = enthalpy of liquid passing up wick to wet bulb, at t_w, Btu per pound.

$H_{g,2}$ = enthalpy of saturated vapor leaving wet bulb, at t_w.

$H_{fg,2}$ = enthalpy of vaporization at t_w.

$H_{a,1}$ = enthalpy of air (not mixture) approaching at t_d Btu per pound.

$H_{a,2}$ = enthalpy of air (not mixture) leaving at t_w Btu per pound.

c_p = specific heat of air at constant pressure = 0.241.

Q_r = energy to wet bulb as heat by radiation, etc., from its warmer environs, Btu per pound of air (not mixture).

Writing the steady-flow energy equation for the wet bulb by equating the sum of the energies coming to the bulb via the water which passes up the wick, via the approaching mixture and by radiation, to the sum of the energies leaving via the departing air and saturated vapor, all energies being in Btu per pound of air (not mixture),

$$(M_{v,2} - M_{v,1}) \times H_{f,2}] + [1.0 \times H_{a,1} + M_{v,1} \times H_{g,1}] + Q_r = [1.0 \times H_{a,2} + M_{v,2} \times H_{g,2}]$$

or, collecting terms in $M_{v,1}$,

$$M_{v,1}(H_{g,1} - H_{f,2}) = M_{v,2}(H_{g,2} - H_{f,2}) - (H_{a,1} - H_{a,2}) - Q_r$$

But $\quad H_{g,\,1} - H_{f,\,2} = H_{f,\,1} + H_{fg,\,1} - H_{f,\,2} = H_{f,g\,1} + (t_d - t_w)$

$\quad\quad\quad H_{g,\,2} - H_{f,\,2} = H_{fg,\,2}$

and $\quad H_{a,\,1} - H_{a,\,2} = c_p(t_d - t_w) = 0.241(t_d - t_w)$

whence,
$$M_{v,\,1} = \frac{M_{v,\,2}\,H_{fg,\,2} - 0.241(t_d - t_w) - Q_r}{H_{fg,\,1} + (t_d - t_w)} \qquad (6)$$

In this relation the value of $M_{v,\,2}$ is directly computable from equation 1 (Art. 35), that is, $M_{v,\,2} =$ (for air and water vapor) $18\,P_{v,\,2}/29\,(P_{\text{mix}} - P_{v,\,2})$, where $P_{v,\,2}$ is the saturation pressure of the vapor at t_w. (See also example 2.)

Measurement of Q_r is quite impracticable in actual use of the wet and dry bulb hydrometer, but tests indicate that with a conventional wick-covered mercury thermometer the radiation correction may be compensated with reasonable accuracy if the observed wet-bulb temperature be reduced by about 0.016 (1.6 per cent) of the observed wet-bulb depression $(t_d - t_w)$.

The application of equation 6 is shown by the following example, which contains data such as would be secured in the use of a wet and dry bulb hydrometer with the mixture of example 1.

Example 5. Observed psychrometric data taken with a wet and dry bulb hydrometer in air at a barometric pressure of 14.7 lb per sq in. were

$$t_d = 70 \text{ deg fahr;} \quad t_w = 60.65 \text{ deg fahr}$$

Compute the mass of vapor per pound of air (not mixture) and the relative humidity of the mixture as supplied.

Solution.

Corrected wet-bulb temperature $= 60.65 - 0.016(70 - 60.65) = 60.50$ deg fahr.

Saturated vapor pressure at 60.50 deg fahr $= 0.2608$ lb per sq in.

$M_{v,\,2} = 18 \times 0.2608/29 \times (14.7 - 0.2608) = 0.01121.$

$H_{fg,\,1}$ (at 70 deg fahr) $= 1052.7;\ H_{fg,\,2}$ (at 60.50 deg fahr) $= 1057.9.$

$$M_{v,\,1} = \frac{0.01121 \times 1057.9 - (0.241 \times 9.50)}{1052.7 + 9.50} = \frac{9.58}{1062.2} = 0.0090.$$

$\dfrac{P_{v,\,1}}{14.7 - P_{v,\,1}} = $ (by equation 1) $\dfrac{0.009/18}{1/29} = \dfrac{1}{69};\ P_{v,\,1} = 14.7/70 = 0.210.$

Relative humidity $= 0.210/0.363 = 57.8$ per cent.

Psychrometric Charts for Air-water Vapor Mixtures at or about a total pressure of 14.7 lb per sq in., as well as tables giving the mass of saturated vapor per pound of air at various temperatures but at the standard atmospheric pressure, are provided in the various mechanical engineering handbooks and give in graphical and tabular form the results of computations such as the foregoing. Their utility is in general limited, however, to the above total pressure. A psychrometric chart in common use is that devised by H. W. Carrier and shown on p. 7-92 as Fig. 1.

The Ferrel Psychrometric Formula,* with empirical constants that hold for temperatures between -40 and 140 deg fahr, is:

$$\frac{p' - p}{t_d - t_w} = 0.000367\ p_m\left(\frac{t_w + 1539}{1571}\right)$$

where $p =$ the actual partial pressure of the water vapor in the mixture, in inches of mercury absolute.

$\quad p' =$ the saturation pressure at the wet-bulb temperature, in inches of mercury absolute.

$\quad t_d =$ the dry-bulb temperature, in degrees fahrenheit.

$\quad t_w =$ the wet-bulb temperature, in degrees fahrenheit.

$\quad p_m =$ the total pressure of the mixture (commonly the barometric pressure), in inches of mercury absolute.

This relation is the wet-bulb energy equation with certain constants supplied. With the dry-bulb and wet-bulb temperatures and the total mixture pressure experimentally determined, the actual partial pressure of the water vapor in the mixture may be found from this formula.

The saturation pressure of water vapor for temperatures at 32 deg fahr and above may be found from steam tables or charts. For convenience, Table I is included, in which the *saturation pressures of water vapor in contact with ice* at temperatures from -20

---

*U. S. Dept. of Agriculture, Weather Bureau Bull. 235.

to 31 deg fahr are given. The values in this table are from the Weather Bureau Bulletin 235.

With the partial pressure, p, of the water vapor in the mixture known, the *dew point* can then be found, since the dew point of the mixture is the saturation temperature

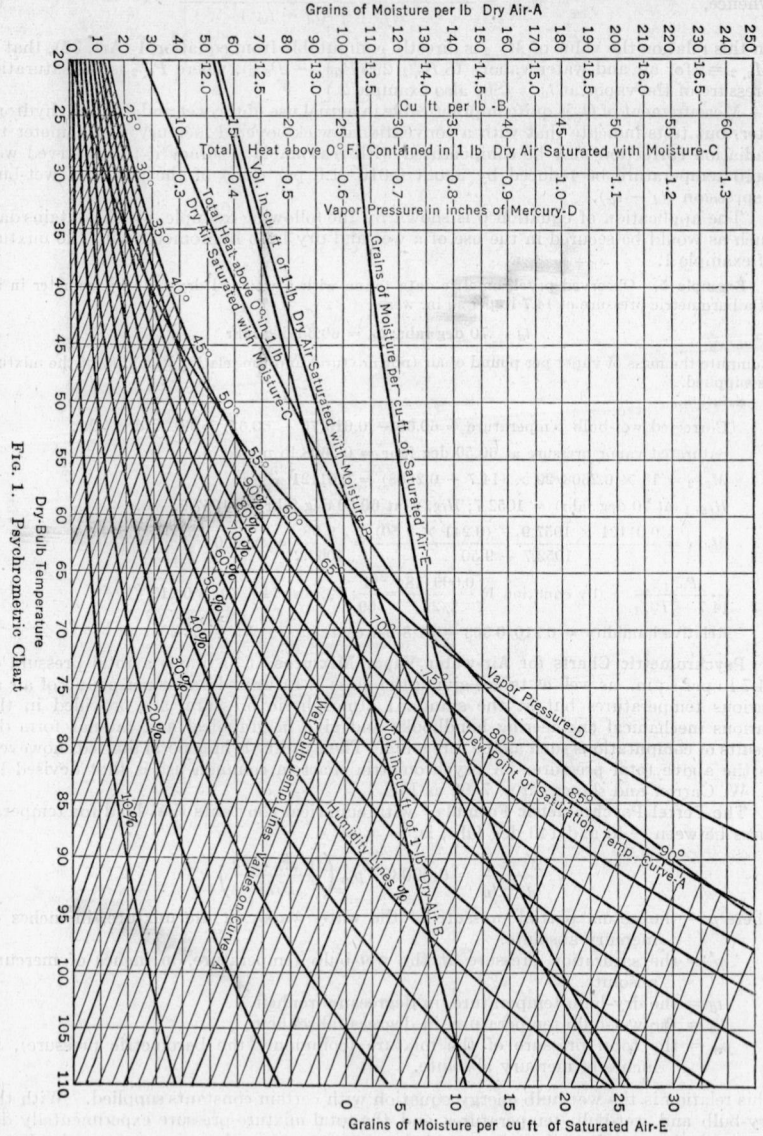

Fig. 1. Psychrometric Chart

corresponding to this vapor pressure. If the mixture were cooled at constant pressure, the dew point would be that temperature at which condensation of the water vapor would start. The dew point is shown as t_3 in Fig. 2. The relationship between dry-bulb temperature, wet-bulb temperature, and dew point is also shown in the same figure for the mixture in which the water vapor is superheated.

Table I. Pressures of Saturated Water Vapor in Contact with Ice

t Deg. Fahr	p In. Hg	t Deg Fahr	p In. Hg	t Deg Fahr	p In. Hg	t Deg Fahr	p In. Hg
−20	0.0126	−7	0.0260	6	0.0515	19	0.0979
−19	0.0133	−6	0.0275	7	0.0542	20	0.103
−18	0.0141	−5	0.0291	8	0.0570	21	0.108
−17	0.0150	−4	0.0307	9	0.0600	22	0.113
−16	0.0159	−3	0.0325	10	0.0631	23	0.118
−15	0.0168	−2	0.0344	11	0.0665	24	0.124
−14	0.0178	−1	0.0363	12	0.0699	25	0.130
−13	0.0188	0	0.0383	13	0.0735	26	0.136
−12	0.0199	+1	0.0403	14	0.0772	27	0.143
−11	0.0210	2	0.0423	15	0.0810	28	0.150
−10	0.0222	3	0.0444	16	0.0850	29	0.157
− 9	0.0234	4	0.0467	17	0.0891	30	0.164
− 8	0.0247	5	0.0491	18	0.0933	31	0.172

The density of the atmosphere * is given by the equation:

$$d_m = \frac{B - 0.38\, p_v}{0.754\, T_d} \qquad (7)$$

In this equation, the vapor pressure, p_v, may be computed with adequate accuracy by the following modification of Apjohn's equation:

$$p_v = 0.49\, p_w - \frac{B}{30} \frac{(t_d - t_w)}{90} \qquad (8)$$

where d_m = density of atmosphere, a mixture of air and water vapor, pounds per cubic foot.

B = barometric pressure, inches of mercury at 32 deg fahr.

p_v = actual vapor pressure, inches of mercury at 32 deg fahr.

p_w = pressure of saturated water vapor at the wet bulb temperature, in pounds per square inch (as found from steam tables).

t_d (T_d) = dry-bulb temperature, degrees fahrenheit (absolute).

t_w = wet-bulb temperature, degrees fahrenheit.

The density is to be computed to only three significant digits (e.g., 0.0764).

The vapor pressure needs to be computed to only two significant digits (e.g., 0.63 in. of mercury).

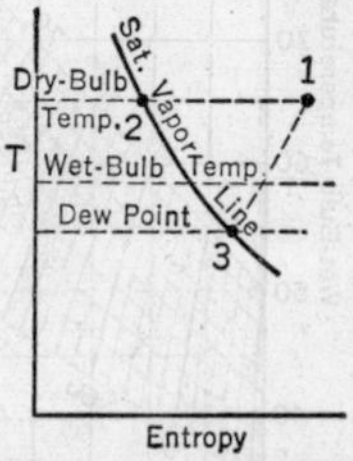

FIG. 2. T–S Diagram Illustrating Dew Point

Temperatures must be measured to the nearest single degree fahrenheit; barometric pressure to 0.01 in. of mercury.

Computation of density to four significant digits demands measurements of temperature to closer than 0.1 deg fahr.

The items of greatest fundamental interest in connection with hygrometry are (a) partial pressure of the vapor in the atmosphere, (b) relative humidity, and (c) dew point. Summarizing, these may be determined as follows: (a) The *partial pressure* of the vapor in the atmosphere may be found from (1) the theoretical formula (equations 1 and 6) as illustrated in example 5; (2) Ferrel's equation by solving for p; (3) steam tables, if dry-bulb temperature and humidity are known, by use of $p = \phi p_g$, where p is the partial pressure of the vapor, ϕ is the relative humidity, and p_g is the saturation pressure at the dry-bulb temperature; (4) Carrier or similar psychrometric charts by direct reading with dry-bulb and wet-bulb temperatures known; (5) equation 8. (b) *Relative humidity* may be found from (1) the theoretical formula as illustrated in example 5; (2) Ferrel's equation, in which $\phi = p$/saturation pressure at dry-bulb temperature; (3) Carrier or similar psychrometric charts by direct reading, with dry-bulb and wet-bulb temperatures known; (4) tables giving values of humidity for various dry-bulb and wet-bulb temperatures. (c) The *dew point* may be found from (1) Carrier or similar psychrometric chart by direct reading with dry-bulb and wet-bulb temperatures known; (2) steam tables, the temperature of saturation at the partial pressure of the vapor; (3) dew-point instrument, which measures dew-point temperature directly.

* Based upon considerations discussed in three articles by Professor C. H. Berry of Harvard University, published in *Combustion*, vol. 6, August, 1934, p. 15; September, 1934, p. 24; October, 1934, p. 21.

38. AIR CONDITIONING

Air Conditioning consists chiefly of the simultaneous control of temperature, humidity, motion, and purity of air to meet the requirements of human comfort. Some of the principal factors that affect human comfort and welfare as influenced by air environment are the (1) dry-bulb temperature, (2) humidity, (3) motion, (4) distribution, (5) dust content, (6) bacteria content, and (7) odors. Other factors which may influence comfort, but the effects of which are not so well established at the present time, are (8) light, (9) ozone content, (10) ionic content, and (11) pressure.

Human Occupancy of a confined space produces at least six important alterations in the properties of the air: (1) the oxygen content is decreased slightly; (2) the carbon dioxide content is increased slightly; (3) products of decomposition, usually accompanied by odors, are given off; (4) the air temperature is raised; (5) the humidity is increased by evaporation of moisture from the skin and lungs; and (6) the number of positive and negative ions in a unit volume of the air is decreased.

Effective Temperature may be defined as an arbitrary index of the degree of warmth or cold felt by the human body in response to temperature, humidity, and air movement. The numerical value of the effective temperature index for any given air condition is fixed by the temperature of saturated air which, at a velocity or turbulence of 15 to 25 ft per min, induces a sensation of warmth or cold like that of the given condition. Fig. 3 shows the effective temperature-humidity relation at various values of humidity and dry-bulb temperature when the air movement is between 15 and 25 ft per min. The intersection of the dry-bulb and the wet-bulb temperature lines will give the relative humidity and also the effective temperature. This figure shows the comfort zone as established by experiment, upon which are shown the average comfort lines for winter and summer. The fact that the summer average is greater than the winter average is probably due partly to adaptation to seasonal weather and partly to differences in clothing worn in the two seasons.

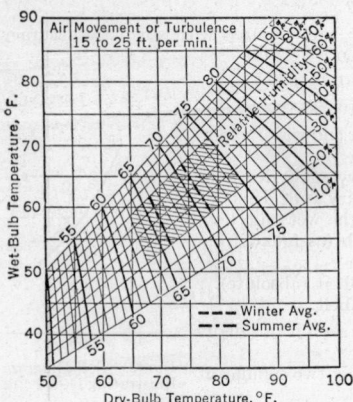

Fig. 3. Effective Temperature and Comfort Zones

It is now recognized that the importance of air motion in air conditioning ranks second only to temperature. In an occupied space, air having all the other essential qualities but lacking motion feels stagnant, stuffy, and depressing, because the vitiated air next to the body is not replaced by air possessing satisfactory qualities. The air in an occupied space should be in constant motion sufficient to give uniformity in temperature and humidity without objectionable draft.

Air Purity is a vital problem principally in manufacturing establishments, crowded rooms, or tenement buildings. The air should be free from all toxic, unhealthful, or disagreeable gases and fumes and relatively free from odors and dust.

In an occupied space, at least 10 cu ft of fresh air per minute per person should be provided from an outside source to remove body heat, body odors, and products of respiration. In rooms where the occupants smoke, an additional 6 to 7 cu ft of fresh air per minute per person should be provided. This volume of air change is inadequate to provide proper air motion. It is customary to provide the minimum quantity of fresh air required for the removal of heat and odors and to recirculate the additional volume required for proper air motion.

Control of Relative Humidity is very important if comfortable conditions are to be maintained. Cold, outside air in winter usually will have a very low relative humidity after it has been heated. Such air should be humidified. On the other hand, air in the summer months may have a too great relative humidity. The standard established by the American Society of Heating and Ventilating Engineers states: The relative humidity shall be not less than 30 per cent, nor more than 60 per cent, in any case. The effective temperature shall range between 64 and 69 deg when heating or humidification is required and between 69 and 73 deg when cooling or dehumidification is required.

Air-conditioning Equipment has evolved from the air washer which has been used in large buildings for many years. In the air washer, air is forced through a chamber containing a water spray and then over baffle plates which eliminate free moisture and wet particles of solid matter. Although the air washer was initially used for the removal of dust from the air, its principal use in air conditioning is to change the water-vapor content of the air. Under typical winter conditions, merely heating the air will result in a water-vapor content too low to satisfy comfort requirements. Under usual summer conditions, mere cooling to the desired final temperature will result in too high a water-vapor content. The most satisfactory method which has been devised for effecting a desired water-vapor content at a desired dry-bulb temperature, and one which is used in the large majority of cases, is that which is known as the dew-point method. In the dew-point method of temperature and humidity control, air is brought to a saturated condition at the temperature at which it contains the desired quantity of moisture. This temperature is the dew point of the desired final condition of the air. The air may then be merely heated from this dew point to bring it to the desired dry-bulb temperature and relative humidity. The required dew-point condition can be reached only by the removal or addition of water.

The moisture content may be reduced by sufficiently cooling the air to cause condensation of excess vapor or by physical-chemical means.

An increase in moisture content may be accomplished by a combination of heating and addition of water. This heating and water addition may be done simultaneously or separately, providing that the mixture be brought to a saturated condition at the desired dew-point temperature. Heating and humidification may be accomplished simultaneously by means of a warm water spray. In another process, the air is first preheated, without the addition of moisture, until its wet-bulb temperature is equal to the dew point of the desired final air. Then, without the addition or removal of heat, the air is *saturated* in a water spray. This will bring it to the required, saturated, dew-point condition. Finally, by heating from this dew-point temperature, the air-vapor mixture will be brought to the desired final condition of dry-bulb temperature and relative humidity. Example 6 illustrates the process just described.

Example 6. The outside air has a dry-bulb temperature of 40 deg and a relative humidity of 65 per cent. It is desired to condition the air to dry-bulb temperature of 74 deg and relative humidity of 45 per cent, which will give an effective temperature of about 69 deg.

The air is (1) heated before it enters the washer until the wet-bulb temperature is equal to the dew point of the final air, then (2) saturated in the spray to the temperature equal to the dew point of the final condition, then (3) heated to the dry-bulb temperature required. This brings it to the final desired relative humidity.

A tabulation of the air condition in the various stages will illustrate the process.

Table II

	Initial Air Condition	After Heater	After Spray	Final Air Condition
Dry-bulb temperature, degrees fahrenheit.......	40.0	72.0	51.3	74.0
Relative humidity...........................	0.65	0.205	1.00	0.45
Wet-bulb temperature, degrees fahrenheit.......	35.6	51.3	51.3	60.5
Dew point, degrees fahrenheit.................	29.6	29.6	51.3	51.3
Vapor pressure, pounds per square inch.........	0.0791	0.0791	0.1869	0.1869

The preheat temperature and the temperature of the water spray need not be definitely as described as long as the air from the spray is saturated and at the temperature of 51.3 deg. If the water is warmer than 51.3 deg, not so much preheating is required. Example 7 illustrates the dehumidification of air under summer conditions.

Example 7. The outside air has a dry-bulb temperature of 95 deg and a relative humidity of 65 per cent. It is desired that the final condition of example 6 be attained.

Table III

	Initial Condition	After Cooler	Final Condition
Dry-bulb temperature, degrees fahrenheit.......	95.0	51.3	74.0
Relative humidity...........................	0.65	1.00	0.45
Wet-bulb temperature, degrees fahrenheit.......	84.0	51.3	60.5
Dew point, degrees fahrenheit.................	81.4	51.3	51.3
Vapor pressure, pounds per square inch.........	0.5297	0.1869	0.1869

In this case the cooler must decrease the temperature of the saturated mixture to the desired dew point of 51.3 deg.

BIBLIOGRAPHY

1. ALLEN, J. R., and BURSLEY, J. A. Heat Engines, New York, McGraw-Hill, fourth edition, 1931.
2. AMERICAN SOCIETY OF HEATING AND VENTILATING ENGINEERS' GUIDE.
3. AMERICAN SOCIETY OF MECHANICAL ENGINEERS, POWER TEST CODES.
4. AMERICAN SOCIETY OF REFRIGERATING ENGINEERS' DATA BOOK.
5. BADGER, W. L. Heat Transfer and Evaporation, Chemical Catalog Co., 1926.
6. BARNARD, W. N., ELLENWOOD, F. O., and HIRSHFELD, C. F. Elements of Heat Power Engineering, New York, John Wiley & Sons, third edition, 1933.
7. BEHAR, M. F. Manual of Instrumentation, Instruments Publishing, 1932.
8. BIRTWISTLE, G. Principles of Thermodynamics, New York, Macmillan, 1925.
9. BUTTERFIELD, T. E., JENNINGS, B. H., and LUCE, A. W. Steam and Gas Engineering, New York, D. Van Nostrand, second edition, 1933.
10. CHURCH, E. F., JR. Steam Turbines, New York, McGraw-Hill, 1928.
11. CRAIG, D. P., and ANDERSON, H. J. Steam Power and Internal Combustion Engines, New York, McGraw-Hill, 1931.
12. DIEDRICHS, H., and ANDRAE, W. C. Experimental Mechanical Engineering, New York, John Wiley & Sons.
13. ELLIOT, B. G., and CONSOLIVER, E. L. The Gasoline Automobile, New York, McGraw-Hill, fourth edition, 1932.
14. EWING, J. A. Thermodynamics for Engineers, New York, Macmillan, 1920.
15. FISHENDEN, M., and SAUNDERS, H. M. Calculation of Heat Transmission, London, Stationery Office, 1932.
16. FRASER, E. S., and JONES, R. B. Motor Vehicles and Their Engines, New York, D. Van Nostrand, fourth edition (revised), 1930.
17. GEBHARDT, G. F. Steam Power Plant Engineering, New York, John Wiley & Sons.
18. GREENE, A. M., JR. Elements of Heating and Ventilation, New York, John Wiley & Sons, 1913.
19. HARDING, L. A. Steam Power Plant Engineering, New York, John Wiley & Sons.
20. HARDING, L. A., and WILLARD, A. C. Heating, Ventilating and Air Conditioning, New York, John Wiley & Sons.
21. HASLAM, R. T., and RUSSELL, R. P. Fuels and Their Combustion, New York, McGraw-Hill, 1926.
22. HOFFMAN, J. D. Handbook for Heating and Ventilating Engineers, New York, McGraw-Hill, second edition, 1926.
23. KEENAN, J. H. Steam Tables and Mollier Diagram, The American Society of Mechanical Engineers.
24. KENT, R. T. Mechanical Engineers' Handbook, New York, John Wiley & Sons.
25. KIEFER, P. J., and STUART, M. C. Principles of Engineering Thermodynamics, New York, John Wiley & Sons, 1930.
26. MACINTIRE, H. J. Handbook of Mechanical Refrigeration, New York, John Wiley & Sons, 1928.
27. MacNAUGHTON, E. Elementary Steam Power Engineering, New York, John Wiley & Sons, second edition, 1933.
28. MALEEV, V. L. Internal-Combustion Engines—Theory and Design, New York, McGraw-Hill, 1933.
29. McADAMS, W. H. Heat Transmission, New York, McGraw-Hill, 1933.
30. MORRISON, L. H. American Diesel Engines, New York, McGraw-Hill.
31. MORSE, F. T. Power Plant Engineering and Design, New York, D. Van Nostrand.
32. MOYER, J. A. Power Plant Testing, New York, McGraw-Hill, third edition.
33. MOYER, J. A., and FITTZ, R. V. Air Conditioning, New York, McGraw-Hill, 1935.
34. POLSON, J. A. Internal Combustion Engines, New York, John Wiley & Sons, 1931.
35. PYE, D. R. Internal Combustion Engines, Vols. I and II. Oxford, England, Clarendon Press, 1931.
36. ROYDS, R. Heat Transmission in Boilers, Condensers and Evaporators, New York, Van Nostrand, 1921.
37. SCHACK, A., GOLDSCHMIDT, H., and PARTRIDGE, E. P. Industrial Heat Transfer, New York, John Wiley & Sons, 1933.
38. SEVERNS, W. H., and DEGLER, H. E. Steam, Air, and Gas Power, New York, John Wiley & Sons, second edition, 1933.
39. SHOOP, C. F., and TUVE, G. L. Mechanical Engineering Laboratory Practice, New York, McGraw-Hill.
40. STREETER, R. L., and LICHTY, L. C. Internal Combustion Engines, New York, McGraw-Hill, fourth edition, 1933.
41. TRINKS, W. Industrial Furnaces, New York, John Wiley & Sons, Vol. I, third edition, 1934. Vol. II, 1935.

SECTION 8

ELECTRICITY AND MAGNETISM

BY

CHARLES WEYL AND IRVEN TRAVIS

ELECTRICITY AND MAGNETISM

Scope

In this section are presented the principles of electricity and magnetism together with formulas basic to the solution of electric and magnetic circuits.

1. SYSTEMS OF UNITS

Three Systems of Units are in use, in terms of which electric and magnetic quantities are expressed. These systems are known as the cgs electrostatic system, the cgs electromagnetic system, and the practical system (see Section 3). The various units in the practical system have been given short names which are in common use, e.g., ampere, volt, coulomb, etc. For the sake of brevity the corresponding units of the electrostatic system will be designated by these same names with the prefix " stat," and the corresponding units in the cgs electromagnetic system will be designated by these same names with the prefix " ab," the latter prefix arising from the term " absolute " sometimes applied to this system.

The use of the electrostatic and electromagnetic systems of units arises from the manner in which certain of the fundamental quantitative relations, or " laws," were originally formulated. The practical system is related to the electromagnetic system by even multiples of ten times the units in the latter, e.g., 1 volt $= 10^8$ abvolts, 1 ampere $= 10^{-1}$ abampere, 1 ohm $= 10^9$ abohms.

Quantitative Relations between electric quantities given here are independent of the system of units employed provided all the quantities involved are expressed in the same system of units. For some of the magnetic quantities, certain additional practical units have been introduced which are not related to the cgs electromagnetic units by multiples of 10; consequently, to avoid confusion it is best to reduce all quantities to electromagnetic units before applying any of the formulas given.

Standard symbols for quantities are given in Section 1, Table 4. When vector relations are involved the symbol is in bold face type.

ELECTRON THEORY

2. ELECTRICITY AND MATTER

Electrical Entities. Contemporary physics identifies electricity with matter. For example, an atom of the element hydrogen is thought of as consisting of a single nuclear quantity or charge of electricity called a *proton* about which rotates a second charge of electricity called a *negative electron*. These two charges are equal in magnitude and opposite in sign. Each represents what is believed to be the smallest quantity of electricity which can exist discretely. They are in effect atoms of electricity. Almost the entire mass of the atom resides in the proton. The electron * has a mass of approximately $1/1800$ of the mass of the proton. The orbital electron may revolve in elliptical or circular paths. The radii and eccentricities of the possible paths of the electron in the hydrogen atom can be computed. While hydrogen is the simplest of the elements, all elements are believed to consist of nuclei made up of tightly packed protons and electrons, surrounded by rotating orbital electrons. The intra-atomic spaces between the nucleus and the orbital electrons are believed to be enormous relative to the size of the electron or proton. Every atom containing an equal number of electrons and protons is said to be a neutral atom.

Although the proton and the negative electron are the most common of the electrical entities, and their properties have been most thoroughly studied, two others which have been observed are important. The *positive electron* or *positron* consists of a positive

---

* The term electron used alone means negative electron. When positive electron is meant the word positive will always be used.

charge, equal in magnitude to the charge carried by the negative electron, associated with a mass equal to the mass of the electron. The positive electron has no place in the atom model described above. The *neutron* is an entity having a mass approximately equal to that of the proton but having no electric charge. It is not known whether or not a neutron consist of an intimately bound proton and electron. The accuracy with which its mass has been determined is not great enough to disprove or to strengthen this hypothesis.

A fifth entity, intimately associated with the four already mentioned but somewhat different in concept, is the *photon*. A photon is a quantum of electromagnetic radiation (q.v.) having a definite frequency and a definite energy content. It was supposed, on the basis of the Bohr-Sommerfeld theory, which gave rise to the atom model described above, that a photon (light, x-rays, etc.) was radiated or absorbed when and only when an electron jumped from one orbit to another. This is now believed to be untrue.

The study of electricity has to do with the properties of these entities, in particular the proton and negative electron.

Mass, Energy, and Frequency Relations. Modern quantum physics identifies mass with energy. Thus the law of conservation of energy has been revised to require that the total mass plus energy of the universe be conserved. Quantum physics also to a certain degree identifies electric particles with electromagnetic waves. Under some circumstances entities which have properties normally ascribed only to particles, exhibit characteristics normally observed only in waves. In such cases the energy of the particle and the frequency of the wave are proportional.

The above principles are stated in the following experimental laws:

(a) Whenever energy is transformed into mass or mass is transformed into energy

$$E = mc^2 \tag{1}$$

in which E is the energy transformed, m is the mass transformed, and c is the velocity of light in vacuo. ($c = 3 \times 10^{10}$ cm per sec approximately.)

(b) A photon of electromagnetic radiation always has associated with it an energy proportional to its frequency.

$$E = h\nu \tag{2}$$

in which E is the energy of the photon, ν is its frequency, and h is a constant factor known as Planck's constant. ($h = 6.55 \times 10^{-27}$ erg-second.)

In nuclear disintegration, in emission of particles or waves by bombardment, and in transmutation of elements the above principles find application. For example, if a photon of radiation strikes a nucleus it may cause the emission of a positron and an electron. In this case

$$\frac{h\nu}{c^2} = \text{Mass of positron} + \text{Mass of electron}$$

$$+ \frac{1}{c^2} \text{(Energy of positron + Energy of electron)} \tag{3}$$

3. PROPERTIES OF ELECTRICAL ENTITIES

The Negative Electron. The results of experiment justify the following assumptions regarding the electron:

(a) No charge of electricity can be produced which is not an integral multiple of the charge carried by a simple electron. The value of this charge is

$$e = 4.774 \times 10^{-10} \text{ cgs electrostatic unit} \tag{4}$$

(b) The mass of an electron may be defined as the force required to give it unit acceleration.* Experiments indicate that the mass of an electron, as thus defined, is

$$m = 8.999 \times 10^{-28} \text{ gram} \tag{5}$$

The " effective " mass of the electron increases with increase in velocity (see equation 8).

Unless otherwise stated, wherever the expression " mass of an electron " is used in this article, it is to be understood that this effective mass is meant.

(c) An electron having a charge e and moving with velocity v produces the same magnetic field as an elementary length ds of a conduction current of strength i, where $ev = ids$ (see Art. 11).

(d) Every neutral atom of matter contains at least one electron which is held in position by forces analogous to elastic forces, that is, an electron may oscillate within the atom, or may be displaced by an impressed electrostatic field. The electrons are always of the same nature irrespective of the substance in which they exist.

---

* That is, $f = ma$, where f is the force, a is the acceleration, and $m = \dfrac{f}{a}$ is the mass, computed at low electron velocities (less than one-tenth the velocity of light).

(*e*) An electron may be forced from the atom by the influence (mutual repulsion) of a "free" electron moving at a high velocity in its immediate vicinity. This action is usually spoken of as a bombardment, or collision, although it is not necessary to assume that the free electron hits the atom.

(*f*) When a neutral atom loses an electron, this atom manifests the properties of a positively charged body and is called a positive ion.

(*g*) When a neutral atom gains an electron, this atom manifests the properties of a negatively charged body and is called a negative ion.

(*h*) In every substance there exists, in addition to the electrons within the atoms, a certain number of "free" electrons, i.e., electrons which can move freely in the interatomic spaces; these free electrons may also pass from one substance to another. Under certain conditions, e.g., in a gas at ordinary pressures, a free electron may attach to itself one or more atoms or molecules.

The Positive Particles. Experiment also justifies the following assumptions regarding the positively charged particles:

(*a*) The smallest positive charge that it has been found possible to produce is numerically equal to that of an electron, viz., 4.774×10^{-10} cgs electrostatic unit.

(*b*) This smallest possible positive charge when associated with a particle having a mass of the same order of magnitude as that of a hydrogen atom is called a proton.

(*c*) This smallest possible positive charge when associated with a particle having a mass of the same order of magnitude as that of the negative electron is called a positive electron.

(*d*) Other positively charged particles may consist of atoms from which one or more electrons have been expelled. Their masses therefore depend upon the number of protons in the nuclei of the atoms. A "free" positively charged particle may also attach to itself one or more neutral atoms or molecules.

(*e*) The term "ion" is usually reserved to designate any charged body having a mass of the order of magnitude of that of a molecule or atom. In this sense a positive or negative electron is not an ion, but the proton is an ion. If, however, the electron becomes attached to an atom or molecule, then this combination forms an ion. In the discharge of electricity through gases at low pressure, the negative electron, although it is not attached to an atom or molecule, is sometimes called an ion.

The Photon. Experiment justifies the following assumptions regarding the photon:

(*a*) The photon is a discrete quantity or *quantum* of electromagnetic radiation (see p. 8–03).

(*b*) The photon is electrically neutral, not being attracted or repelled by electric charges.

(*c*) Photons are capable of producing ionization. A photon may be absorbed by an atom, an electron being emitted in the process. It is thought that occasionally a photon may vanish and give rise to a pair of oppositely charged electrons. When this happens the charge of the universe remains unchanged and the energy of the photon is converted into the mass of the two electrons.

(*d*) Deflection of photons by magnetic fields has not been observed.

(*e*) The energy and frequency of a photon always satisfy the relation $E = h\nu$.

The Neutron. Experiment justifies the following assumptions regarding the neutron:

(*a*) The neutron is electrically neutral, not being deflected from its path by electric charges or magnetic fields.

(*b*) The mass of the neutron is nearly (or perhaps exactly) the same as that of the proton. The best measured value is 1.0051 ± 0.005.

(*c*) Transmutation can be effected by neutrons. For example, a neutron plus a nitrogen nucleus yields a boron nucleus plus a helium nucleus.

(*d*) Neutrons are capable of producing ionization through the intermediary of recoiling nuclei.

Determination of the Constants. A few fundamental principles properly combined yield a powerful set of working tools for the investigation of the properties and the constants of the entities described above. These principles are:

(*a*) If a charged particle falls through a difference of potential, it acquires a kinetic energy equal to the loss of potential energy.

$$ \tfrac{1}{2}\, mv^2 = eV \qquad (6) $$

(*b*) If a charged particle is acted upon simultaneously by electric and magnetic fields which are mutually perpendicular, its path is a circle, the radius of curvature of which is

$$ \rho = \frac{mv}{He} \qquad (7) $$

(c) Supersaturated water vapor condenses quickly on charged particles formed in the presence of the supersaturated vapor.

(d) Matter inserted in the path of a moving particle may absorb energy and thus reduce the velocity of the particle. When a photon encounters a barrier of matter it also may lose energy; this changes the frequency of the photon but does not change its velocity.

The cloud chamber of C. T. R. Wilson, which makes use of principle (c) above, enables the observer to photograph the paths of particles or waves through a gas. The character of the paths under various conditions allows the calculation of many of the fundamental constants to be made.

Mass of the Electron. Experiment shows that the mass as defined by $m = f/a$ (see footnote, p. 8-03) varies with the velocity of the electron, changing appreciably as the velocity of the electron becomes greater than about one-tenth that of light. The formula which represents the experimental facts is

$$m = \frac{m_0}{\sqrt{1 - \left(\dfrac{v}{c}\right)^2}} \qquad (8)$$

where m_0 (= 8.999×10^{-28} gram) is the " rest " or minimum mass of the electron, v is the velocity of the electron, and c is the velocity of light (3×10^{10} cm per sec). There are two theories as to the constitution of the mass m.

1. The earlier theory assumes that the mass is made up of two parts: one a purely mechanical or Newtonian mass invariant with velocity; and a second part, electromagnetic in origin, which is associated with the charge of the electron and which represents the energy of the magnetic field caused by the moving electron. This second part is a function of the velocity of the electron.

2. A second theory dispenses entirely with the concept of mechanical mass and attributes the inertial properties of the electron wholly to the energy associated with the electron.

Relativity, on theoretical grounds, requires that the mass of the electron ($m = f/a$) should change as indicated in equation 8.

4. EMISSION PHENOMENA

Thermionic Emission of Electrons. When a metal is heated to a high temperature in a high vacuum it gives off electrons freely. The amount of the electron emission is subject to the temperature of the metal or cathode and to the electric field at its surface, as due, for example, to a neighboring anode.

The theory assumes that in accordance with the kinetic theory of matter the electrons within the metal are in a constant state of motion, and that of those nearest the surface a certain proportion escape, a few at high, the greater number at lower, velocities in accordance with Maxwell's distribution law. When an electron leaves the surface the metal becomes positively charged, thus putting a retarding force on the electron and tending to make it return. The distance traversed by the electron is greater the greater its initial velocity, and in the presence of a neighboring neutral charged surface it may not return at all. The higher the temperature of the heated metal or cathode the greater the velocities of the electron leaving it, and the greater the volume of electron discharge.

An electron can escape from a metal when, and only when, its kinetic energy is greater than the work which must be done in escaping; that is, when

$$\tfrac{1}{2} mv^2 = w_0 \qquad (9)$$

where m is the mass of the electron, v is the component of its velocity normal to the emitting surface, and w_0 is the electron affinity or internal work of electron evaporation of the emitting substance.

With a given cathode temperature there is a maximum electron current beyond which an increase in anode voltage is ineffective. Under these conditions all the electrons emitted from the cathode are drawn to the anode. This condition is known as *voltage saturation.*

This electron current follows the law

$$i = Ne = AT^\lambda \epsilon^{-(w_0/KT)} \qquad (10)$$

where i is the saturation current per square centimeter of emitting surface, N is the number of electrons emitted per second per square centimeter, e is the charge per electron, A a constant of the material, T the absolute temperature in degrees Centigrade, λ a number not much different from unity, ϵ the base of the Napierian system of logarithms, and K the Boltzmann constant. As far as the individual electron is concerned, this is a statistical law. The value of the current given in equation 10 is independent of the potential of the anode.

With a given anode voltage there is a maximum electron current beyond which an increase in cathode temperature is ineffective. This is due to the condition known as *space charge*. When the cathode is first heated, electrons are emitted with varying velocities. If the anode voltage is zero the first few of these electrons experience no external force, except a slight attraction toward the cathode. These first few electrons ultimately land on the anode or on the walls of the container. The succeeding electrons experience a repulsion due to the electrons, previously emitted but still near the cathode, in the space between the anode and cathode; and if the energies of the newly emitted electrons are small, their motion will be retarded or even reversed. There is thus built up an electric field of force tending to decelerate an electron emerging from the cathode and to make it return to the cathode. If there is no removal of electrons from the space surrounding the cathode this electric field increases in strength until a condition of equilibrium is reached, that is, until as many electrons are entering the cathode as are leaving it. The charge due to the presence of these electrons constitutes the space charge. From the above it is evident that for a given anode voltage an increase in cathode temperature beyond a certain value will serve only to increase the space charge without increasing the current to the anode. This condition is known as *temperature saturation*.

Electron Tubes. A glass bulb, either evacuated or gas filled, and containing two or more electrodes is called an *electron tube*. Electrons (and positive ions) are produced in such tubes by the thermionic emission, photoelectric emission (q.v.), or by bombardment, and are caused to move by the action of an electric field. This electron flow is made to serve various purposes depending upon its magnitude, velocity, and method of control. The various tubes are classified according to number of electrodes, purpose, or particular electronic characteristic utilized.

The two-electrode tube (hot cathode and cold anode in highly evacuated bulb) conducts in only one direction and is an excellent rectifying device for small alternating currents. If a third electrode in mesh or grid form be placed between the cathode and anode, relatively very small potentials on the grid will cause wide variations in the potential gradient at the cathode surface and hence large changes in the number of electrons reaching the anode. Three-electrode tubes are used as amplifying devices, as modulators, demodulators, oscillators, electrostatic voltmeters, relays, etc. Their principal applications are in the field of communication such as telephone, radio, phonograph, talking motion pictures, and transmission of pictures by wire and television, but their applications in other fields are innumerable. Tubes having two and even three control electrodes in addition to the cathode and anode are being extensively employed.

Other important types of electron tube are the x-ray tube, the cathode-ray tube, the gaseous rectifier tube, and the photoelectric cell.

Cathode Rays and Canal Rays. At the occurrence of an electric discharge in an electron tube and at a certain value of the pressure of the gas contained in the tube, it is noticed that a greenish phosphorescence occurs on the walls of the tube. By placing solid bodies in the tube it appears that the phosphorescence is due to something proceeding in straight lines perpendicularly from the surface of the cathode. The name *cathode rays* has been given to this agent which produces the phosphorescence. These rays are deflected by both electric and magnetic fields and communicate a negative electric charge to an insulated conductor. They consist of a stream of rapidly moving electrons. The amount of the deflection of the rays, under the action of magnetic and electrostatic fields, can be calculated or observed.

Cathode-ray tubes with hot cathodes (incandescent filament) have been constructed in which potential differences of a million or more volts are impressed between anode and cathode. A window of extremely thin aluminum foil permits a substantial proportion of the electron stream to emerge into the open air. The behavior of chemical substances and of living tissue under the bombardment of these rays is being studied. Cathode-ray tubes are used as oscillographs and as receiving tubes for television.

If the cathode of a tube producing cathode rays is perforated, faint luminous streaks are seen to proceed through these perforations in a direction opposite to that of the cathode rays. The name *kanalstrahlen* or *canal rays* has been given to this phenomenon. These rays are also deflected by both electric and magnetic fields but to a lesser extent and in relatively the opposite direction from the deflection of cathode rays, and they communicate a positive charge to an insulated conductor.

In terms of the electron theory these rays are positively charged ions. Calculations from actual measurements, making this assumption, show that the charge carried by each of these ions is numerically equal but opposite to that of an electron, and that the mass of each ion is never less than the mass of a hydrogen atom, but may be greater, depending upon the nature of the gas and the pressure in the tube. That is, the cathode particle is an electron traveling in one direction, and the canal-ray particle is what is left of the atom which has lost an electron, traveling in the opposite direction.

Electromagnetic Waves. Under certain conditions, disturbances which are propagated through space arise in the electric and magnetic fields associated with the points in space. Such disturbances are described mathematically by the equations

$$H = F_1(x - vt) \tag{11}$$

$$E = F_2(x - vt) \tag{11a}$$

in which E and H are the electric and magnetic fields (q.v.), x is the distance from some datum to the point in question along the direction of propagation, v is the velocity of propagation, and t is the time. These disturbances are called *electromagnetic waves.*

The physical concept of an electromagnetic wave is aided if one visualizes a medium (this medium is called the ether) in which the wave exists as a transverse vibration. Many of the experimentally observed properties of electromagnetic waves can be explained on the basis of the assumption of an ether through which the waves are propagated. An electromagnetic wave which is a simple harmonic vibration is termed a monochromatic wave. A monochromatic wave has a definite *frequency* which is the reciprocal of the number of periods per second. The character of a given wave is dependent upon its frequency. The various classes of waves extend over a considerable band of frequencies. In order of increasing frequency these classes are:

(a) Long radio waves.
(b) Radio broadcast waves.
(c) Short radio waves.
(d) Ultra-short radio waves.
(e) A band not yet completely investigated.
(f) Heat waves.
(g) Infra-red rays.
(h) Visible light.
(i) Ultra-violet rays.
(j) X-rays.
(k) Gamma rays from radioactive substances.
(l) Cosmic rays.

The mechanism of producing the radiations in groups (a) to (d) from about 10^4 to about 3×10^{10} cycles per second is that of accelerating electrons in electric circuits. The mechanism of producing the radiations in groups (f) to (l) from about 10^{13} to more than 10^{22} cycles per second is that associated with the increase of temperature of a substance, the sudden stopping of high-velocity electrons, or the forced or spontaneous disruption of atoms or atomic nuclei. It is with these extremely high-frequency radiations that the quantum theory is associated.

Photoelectric Effect. Experiment shows that when light of sufficient energy falls upon a substance electrons are liberated from the surface. The number of electrons released per unit time is directly proportional to the intensity of the incident light. The maximum energy of electrons released is independent of the intensity of the incident light but directly proportional to the frequency of the light. The energy equation representing this effect is

$$h\nu = \tfrac{1}{2} mv^2 + P \tag{12}$$

in which h is Planck's constant, ν is the frequency of the incident radiation, $\tfrac{1}{2} mv^2$ is the kinetic energy of the liberated electron, and P is the energy required to free the electron from the parent body. P is called the *work function* of the given surface. If equation 12 is written

$$\tfrac{1}{2} mv^2 = h(\nu - \nu_0) \tag{13}$$

then ν_0 is the threshold frequency of the substance.

The work function for the alkali metals is lower than that for other substances. Special films having extremely low work functions have been produced by the use of potassium, rubidium, and other elements. It is possible to construct photoelectric surfaces having selective frequency characteristics such that color sensitivity is produced.

Photoelectric cells consisting of a photoelectric surface and an anode in an evacuated glass tube are used commercially for automatic control, product testing, television, etc.

X-rays. When cathode rays strike a target of metal, x-rays are radiated from the metal surface. The wave-length spectra of such x-rays depend primarily on the velocity of the impinging electrons and the material of the target. In general, the higher the voltage between anode and cathode, and the denser the metal of the target, the shorter will be the wave-length of the x-radiation.

The x-ray output of a tube operating at constant potential difference between anode and cathode consists of a continuous spectrum superposed with a number of characteristic lines.

The cathode stream has been shown to consist of electrons traveling at high velocities. Thomson and Stokes have shown, by means of the electromagnetic theory of Maxwell, that the deceleration of these electrons at the anode may produce a pulse of electromagnetic radiation. They have shown further that the radiated energy traversing a unit area at a point P, distant from the region of deceleration of one of the electrons, is for electron velocities small compared to the velocity of light

$$S_p = \frac{ae^2\beta}{4\,\pi r^2 c^2} \sin^2 \theta \tag{14}$$

in which a is the electron deceleration.

    e is the charge of the electron.

    β is ratio of velocity of electron before deceleration to velocity of light in vacuo.

    r is distance from P (at which energy flux is S_p) to the source of radiation.

    c is velocity of light in vacuo.

    θ is angle measured from line of travel of electron before deceleration to line joining source of radiation to the point P.

A further development of this electromagnetic pulse theory, by expressing the pulse as a Fourier integral, predicts the spectrum of the radiation to be of the form:

$$I_\lambda d\lambda = K \sin^2 \left(\frac{\pi l}{\lambda}\right) d\lambda \tag{15}$$

in which I_λ is the x-ray intensity between the wave-lengths λ and $(\lambda + d\lambda)$.

    l is the pulse thickness, i.e., the product of its velocity c and the time for deceleration of the electron producing the pulse.

    K is a constant.

This expression indicates a continuous radiation with all frequencies from zero to infinity. Duane found that the continuous x-ray spectrum was limited by a maximum frequency ν_{max} in such a way that

$$h\nu_{max} = eV \tag{16}$$

in which e is the electronic charge and V is the maximum x-ray tube voltage—which agrees with the quantum theory. The electromagnetic theory offers no suggestion concerning the cause of the characteristic line spectra mentioned above.

X-rays are of immense value in diagnosis and therapeutics in medicine, in the examination and inspection of engineering materials for structure and flaws, and in the study of the constitution of matter. The molecules of matter act as diffraction gratings of an x-ray. The resulting interference patterns yield important evidence with regard to the arrangement and spacing of the atoms composing the substance.

Absorption, Scattering, Reflection, and Refraction. The following principles observed in the study of x-rays apply with slight modifications to the other electromagnetic radiations.

When monochromatic x-rays traverse matter, the intensity (I) of the beam after traversing a distance x in a given material is associated with the initial intensity (I_0) by:

$$I_x = I_0 \epsilon^{-\mu x} \tag{17}$$

where ϵ is the base of the natural system of logarithms and μ is the linear absorption coefficient, defined by the relation above shown.

Other absorption coefficients defined for convenience are:

The mass absorption coefficient $\mu_m = \dfrac{\mu}{\rho}$ where ρ is the density of the absorbing material.

The atomic absorption coefficient $\mu_a = \dfrac{\mu}{n}$ where n is the number of atoms per cubic centimeter of the volume occupied by the absorbing material.

If the heterogeneous radiation from an x-ray tube traverses matter the absorption coefficient varies with the thickness of the absorbing material. Its value is found to depend chiefly upon the x-ray tube voltage and upon the atomic number of the absorbing material, assumed to be an element.

Two effects are noted when x-rays traverse matter. Electrons are ejected from the absorbing material at high velocities (see photoelectric effect). The radiation is scattered, reducing the intensity along the lines of incidence of the primary beam. Thus μ may be conveniently divided into two parts, τ and σ. The coefficient τ represents the transformation of the energy of the original beam of x-rays into high-speed electrons; σ is the coefficient describing the scattered radiation. Experiment shows that not all the scattered radiation has the same wave-length as the primary beam. The number of photoelectrons ejected by x-rays, at such speeds that the energy of the photoelectron is nearly equal to the energy $h\nu$ of an incident photon, has been shown to be equal, within the limits of experimental error, to the number of photons (" truly absorbed ") represented by accurate measurements of τ.

Measurement of x-ray wave-lengths can be made by taking advantage of the regularity of atomic structure in crystals. W. L. and W. H. Bragg showed that x-rays of wave-length λ incident upon the face of a crystal at a glancing angle θ would, if the crystal planes were separated by a distance d, be reinforced upon reflection, if:

$$n\lambda = 2 d \sin \theta \quad (n = \text{integer}) \tag{18}$$

This is known as Bragg's law.

By calculations based on an assumed crystal structure, experimental data of density, Avogadro's number and the molecular weight, the value of d may be obtained for some more simply constructed crystals. Then Bragg's law may be used to measure wave-lengths of an x-ray beam.

Ionization of Gases. Under ordinary circumstances at atmospheric pressure, gases are very poor conductors of electricity. By irradiation with x-rays or radioactive substances, by brush discharge, corona, or contact with hot flame, and by other known means, it is possible to make a gas a comparatively good conductor. The process is known as *ionization*. It appears that agents such as those mentioned have the power of breaking down a portion of the gas molecules into free electrons and positively charged particles.

According to the quantum theory, radiation is absorbed by an atom in discrete amounts. The absorption of these quanta makes an electron jump from its then orbit to one of greater radius. If sufficient energy is absorbed the electron leaves the atom altogether and becomes, at least temporarily, a free electron. This leaves the remainder of the atom positively charged. This positively charged particle is known as a positive ion. The electrons and positive ions thus released respond to the force exerted by an electric field and in moving give rise to an electric current. The gas thus becomes conducting. In the absence of such an electric field the electrons and positive ions tend to recombine, and when the radiation producing ionization is removed, this recombination eventually renders the gas non-conducting. At sufficiently high gas pressures the free electrons and positive ions tend to attract neutral molecules to which they attach themselves. At low pressures, however, the mean free paths of the molecules are so great that the charged particle rarely comes within attracting distance of the molecule.

It is assumed that all substances contain at all times some free ions. In a gas under the action of an electric field these ions may attain sufficient velocity to detach electrons from neutral molecules by " collision." The electric field in this instance becomes an ionizing agent. As the ionization increases the gas becomes more and more conducting until the rate of recombination of ions balances the rate of ionization.

Theory of Corona. When the voltage between two conductors becomes sufficiently great, the electric field, which is greatest at the surface, ionizes the air at the surfaces of the conductor. The increase in the conductivity of the air or other gas surrounding the conductor is equivalent to an increase in the effective diameter of the conductor to the value at which the decreasing electric field is balanced by the dielectric strength of the air. The phenomenon is known as *corona*. When the corona is formed, there is visible a faint violet light near the conductor. If the voltage is raised, a *brush discharge* occurs in which bluish streaks like the bristles of a brush are visible near the surface of the conductor. If the voltage is still further increased, a disruptive spark discharge takes place between conductors.

In transmission lines, corona is accompanied by power losses, frequently of serious proportions. It can be controlled by the use of larger-diameter conductors and by operating with voltages low enough to prevent its formation.

DIRECT-CURRENT CIRCUITS

5. ELECTRIC CHARGE, CURRENT, AND ELECTROMOTIVE FORCE

Electric Charge and Electric Current. The unit of electric charge (or quantity of electricity) is called a *coulomb* in the practical system of units. In terms of the charge carried by an electron it requires 6.28×10^{18} electrons to equal a coulomb. An electric charge in motion constitutes an electric current. The rate at which a quantity of electricity flows past a given point in a circuit determines the value of the current. In the practical system of units, the unit of current is called an *ampere* and is the flow of one coulomb per second. (See Section 3 for relationship between practical and other units and for international standards for practical units.)

Electromotive Force. The agent which tends to produce or to maintain an electric current in a circuit is called an *electromotive force* (often abbreviated emf). The names in common use are *difference of potential* and *voltage*, the latter being derived from the practical unit of electromotive force, the *volt* (see Section 3). Electromotive force is not a force in the mechanical sense. Quantitatively it is the electrical energy developed per unit charge

$$E = W/Q \qquad (1)$$

where E is the electromotive force in volts, Q is the charge in coulombs, and W is energy or work in joules. (One joule = 1 watt-second = 10^7 ergs.) The energy W is that required to move the charge Q between two points the difference of potential of which is E. For a more fundamental definition of emf see Section 3.

Sources of Emf. The primary sources of emf are:

1. *Electromagnetic Induction* (see p. 8–27, Art. 12).

2. *Contact of Two Dissimilar Bodies.* Under this head, apart from primary cells and storage batteries, may be included the following sources of emf:

(a) *Volta effect* (contact emf). When two dissimilar substances are brought in contact an emf is developed between them. This is explained by the electron theory on the basis of the fact that certain substances have less tendency to give up electrons than other substances. Zinc releases electrons more easily than copper; therefore, if zinc is brought into contact with copper, some of the electrons leave the zinc and enter the copper making the copper negative and the zinc positive. The emf's thus produced are usually very small. According to the electron theory frictional electricity is due to the same cause. However, where the conductivities of the substances are low, friction is required to bring the surfaces into sufficiently intimate contact for the transference of electrons.

(b) *Thermoelectric effects.* If a closed circuit is made of two different metals and the two junctions are held at the same temperature, no current will flow because although emf's are developed at both junctions (see Volta effect, above) they are equal and opposite. If, however, one junction is held at a higher temperature than the other a current will flow as long as the difference of temperature is maintained. This is known as the *Seebeck effect*. According to the electron theory the relative release of electrons is a function of the temperature of the metal. Such junctions are used in thermometry and also for current measurements. The *Peltier effect* is the inverse of the Seebeck effect. If a current is sent through the junction of two dissimilar metals, heat is absorbed by the junction when the current flows in one direction and is emitted by the junction when the current is reversed. The sign of the Peltier effect is connected with the direction of the thermoelectric current which would be produced at a given junction. A current which cools a junction (Peltier effect) flows in the same direction as the thermoelectric current when that junction is heated, and conversely. The *Thomson effect* is apparently an extension of the Peltier effect. In certain metals heat is carried in the direction of the current flow when the current flows from hot to cold regions. When the current flows from cold to hot regions, the hotter parts are cooled. In other metals these effects are reversed.

(c) *Pyroelectric effect.* When certain crystals such as quartz and tourmaline are heated an emf is developed between faces. If the crystal be broken into fragments or even ground to powder, each particle will exhibit this same electrical effect.

(d) *Piezoelectric effect.* When certain crystals such as quartz and rochelle salt are subjected to mechanical pressure, electric charges proportional to the pressure appear on certain parts of the crystal. If a crystal of rochelle salt (cut so that two of its faces are perpendicular to its optical axis) is compressed between two electrically connected metal plates applied to the two opposite crystal faces, and a metal band is placed around the middle of the crystal between the end plates, an emf of considerable magnitude will be developed between the band and end plates, upon small changes of pressure between end plates. Compression produces a positive charge on one plate and a negative charge on the other plate. Tension causes the charges to reverse. The pressure due to sound waves may under proper conditions produce emf's of several volts. The piezoelectric effect is reversible. A variable emf applied between the plates and band will cause the crystal to expand and contract mechanically in synchronism with the varying applied emf. This effect has been experimentally applied in loud-speaking telephone receivers. Certain crystals, notably quartz, vibrate at natural periods, dependent upon the thickness of the crystal and its elastic constants, if an emf is applied which has the same frequency as the natural frequency of the crystal. The energy supplied by the electrical oscillator may cause very violent vibrations of the crystal. The constancy of frequency of properly constructed quartz vibrators is so great that they are universally employed to control master oscillators for radio. The natural frequency of vibrations of such crystals lies between about ten thousand and several hundred thousand vibrations per second.

Direction of an Emf. The direction of the emf in any portion of a circuit is taken as the direction in which a positive charge would be forced around a circuit containing only this one source of emf. A closed circuit may contain several sources of emf; in this case the resultant emf acting around the circuit is the algebraic sum of all these emf's, those acting around the circuit in one direction being taken as positive and those acting around the circuit in the opposite direction being taken as negative. Those which act in the opposite direction to the resultant emf are called " back " or " counter " emf's.

A convenient symbol for a source of constant emf is shown in Fig. 1; the long light line represents the positive terminal and the short heavy line the negative terminal. Fig. 2 shows two emf's acting around a circuit in the same direction, and Fig. 3 shows two acting around the circuit in opposite directions. In the first instance the resultant emf is $E_1 + E_2$ and the two emf's are said to be " in series aiding," whereas in the second the resultant emf acting in the right-handed direction around the circuit is $E_1 - E_2$ and the two emf's are said to be " in series opposing." When E_2 is less than E_1 then E_2 is a back or counter emf.

Difference of Electric Potential. Consider a portion of a path A between any two points 1 and 2 in an electric circuit (Fig. 3). The total work done on a unit charge, by the emf's external to this portion of the path when a unit charge moves from 1 to 2, is called the " drop of electric potential " from 1 to 2. The term " difference " of electric potential is also commonly used to designate this quantity; the term " drop " is preferable since it signifies the direction of the difference. Electric potential drop is of the same nature as emf and is expressed in the same units. It is frequently abbreviated " p.d."

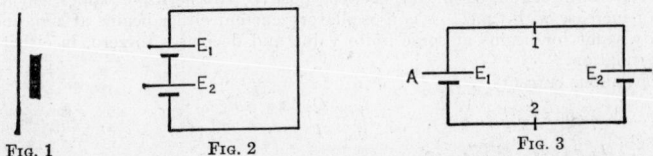

FIG. 1   FIG. 2   FIG. 3

Potential drop may be due either (1) to a back emf, analogous to the back pressure of a pump, or (2) to an opposing force analogous to that due to the resistance of a pipe to the flow of water. The symbol for potential drop is V when it is desired to distinguish it from electromotive force.

Positive and Negative Terminals. That terminal of a device which is at the higher potential is called the positive terminal, the other being called the negative terminal. The drop of potential is always from the positive to the negative terminal, irrespective of the direction of flow of electricity through the device.

Conductors and Insulators. (See also p. 8–62, Conduction of Electricity in Solids and Fluids.) All substances may for practical purposes be divided into two classes: conductors, and insulators or dielectrics. With conductors a continuously applied emf is accompanied by a continuous flow of electric current. With dielectrics upon first applying an emf there is a transient flow of current until the back emf produced by the establishment of a positive charge at one terminal and a negative charge at the other terminal exactly balances the applied emf, after which current ceases to flow. Strictly speaking, every substance conducts electricity to some extent; that is, a constantly applied emf is always accompanied by a constant flow of current. In those substances which are classed as dielectrics this constant flow is negligibly small. A perfect dielectric may be defined as a substance through which it is impossible to maintain a continuous flow of electricity; no such conductor exists, but very poor conductors are approximately such. The electron theory of conduction assumes that any substance contains, in addition to the electrons and protons which form its atoms and molecules, a certain number of free electrons which like the molecules are in violent agitation. These free electrons or ultimate particles of negative electricity tend to drift towards the point of highest potential when an emf is applied to the substance. This drift constitutes the electric current. According to the theory, good conductors have great numbers of these free electrons, and poor conductors and dielectrics have comparatively very few. In dielectrics the momentary flow of electricity is believed to be due to the displacement of *bound electrons* in the atoms without their actual removal from the atom to which they are bound. The greater the applied emf the greater the displacement of the electron within the atom until a point is reached at which the electron is torn from the atom and the dielectric " breaks down," becoming a partial conductor. This breakdown tends to destroy the solid dielectrics.

Metals are the best conductors and are almost universally employed for electric circuits. For the properties of metals as conductors see Section 11. Carbon and most moist substances are fair conductors; dry non-metallic bodies such as air and other gases (at normal pressure), porcelain, glass, rubber, and dry paper are very good insulators.

A wire covered with an insulating substance or supported on insulating substances is said to be " insulated," even though its ends are connected to a source of emf. For the properties of insulating materials see Section 12.

If decomposition takes place when a current of electricity is passed through liquids which are chemical compounds, the liquid is called an *electrolyte*. Certain solid chemical compounds and fused salts behave as electrolytes. For a discussion of electrolysis and electrolytes see Section 10.

Continuous, Direct, Pulsating, Alternating, and Transient Current. A *continuous* electric current is defined as a current which does not vary with time. A *direct* current is a current which is always in the same direction but may vary or pulsate in value. The term *direct current* is ordinarily used to designate either a continuous current or a current which varies or pulsates only by an inappreciable amount, such as the current from a battery or direct-current generator (q.v.). A *pulsating* current is a direct current which pulsates by an appreciable amount, such as the current from a rectifier (q.v.). An *alternating* current is a current which reverses in direction, being first positive and then negative, but alternates between constant maximum positive and negative values (see p. 8–45, Arts. 19 and 20). A *transient* current (see p. 8–57, Art. 24) is a current which flows when a circuit is closed, opened or altered, that is, before a steady state of direct or alternating current has been reached or when such a state is in any way altered. Transients may be "oscillatory" or "non-oscillatory." An oscillatory current is a current which reverses in direction, oscillating between positive and negative values which either decrease or increase with time. A non-oscillatory current either begins at zero and rises to a steady value, or begins at some finite value and decreases to zero, in either event without oscillation.

For continuous currents

$$I = \frac{Q}{T} \tag{2}$$

where I is the current in amperes, Q is the charge of electricity passing a given cross-section of the circuit, and T is the time in seconds. When the flow of current is not continuous its value at any instant is given by

$$i = \frac{dq}{dt} \tag{3}$$

where i is the *instantaneous* value of the current in amperes and $\frac{dq}{dt}$ is the instantaneous rate of flow of charge through a given cross-section of circuit in coulombs per second.

6. OHM'S LAW, RESISTANCE AND CONDUCTANCE

Ohm's Law. If a steady difference of potential V (in volts) is impressed across a conductor which (a) is held at constant temperature and in which (b) there is no internal emf,

$$V = rI \tag{4}$$

where I is the steady current in amperes which will flow through the conductor and r is the factor of proportionality called the *resistance* of the conductor. The drop in potential V is therefore equivalent to the drop in potential rI, this latter being called the *resistance drop*. Equation 4 may also be written

$$I = gV \tag{5}$$

where I and V are the same as before and g is termed the *conductance* of the conductor. Obviously *under the conditions stated*

$$g = \frac{1}{r} \tag{6}$$

The practical unit of resistance is the *ohm*, and the practical unit of conductance is the *mho*. For standards and conversion factors see Section III and tables in Section I.

Equations 4 and 5 are forms of what is called Ohm's law. If there is one or more counter emf's between the terminals across which V is impressed the relationship is given by

$$V = rI + E \tag{7}$$

where V, r, and I are the same as in equation 4 and E is the algebraic sum of *counter emf's* within the circuit. In this computation all counter emf's have positive signs while all emf's in the direction of the current receive negative signs; hence such an emf is a negative counter emf. Equation 7 is sometimes referred to as the *modified* Ohm's law.

Terminal and Impressed Voltage. The application of this equation is shown by considering a simple circuit containing a generator and a motor or other receiving device,

Fig. 4. Let I be the current in this circuit, r_g the internal resistance of the generator, r_m the internal resistance of the motor, r_l the total resistance of the "line" or connecting wires, E_g the emf developed by the generator, E_m the back emf developed by the motor, V_g the terminal voltage of the generator, and V_m the terminal voltage of the motor. Through the generator the current flows from the $-$ to the $+$ terminal, the emf is from the $-$ to the $+$ terminal, and the drop of potential is from the $+$ to the $-$ terminal. Hence

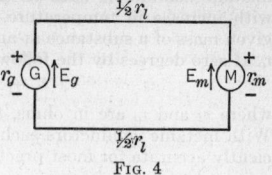

Fig. 4

$$V_g = E_g - r_g I \tag{7a}$$

i.e., the terminal voltage is less than the generator emf by an amount equal to the resistance drop in the armature circuit. Through the motor the current flows from the $+$ to the $-$ terminal, the emf is from the $-$ to the $+$ terminal, and the drop of potential is from the $+$ to the $-$ terminal. Hence

$$V_m = E_m + r_m I \tag{7b}$$

i.e., the terminal voltage is greater than the back emf of the motor by an amount equal to the resistance drop through the motor.

The terminal voltage of the motor is less than that of the generator by an amount equal to the resistance drop in the line, i.e.,

$$V_m = V_g - r_l I \tag{7c}$$

The expression *impressed* emf is also used to designate the rise of potential from the negative to the positive terminal of any receiving device, for example, a motor, bank of lamps, etc., regardless of whether or not the device contains a source of emf.

Resistance and Conductance. It should be carefully noted that the definitions of resistance and conductance expressed by equations 4 and 5 hold only when there is no emf in the portion of the circuit under consideration; this condition is realized only when the current remains constant in value (i.e., a continuous current) and the conductor is of uniform material and at constant temperature throughout. Also, the definition is meaningless unless the same current flows through each cross-section of the conductor and the drop of potential is the same between all points in the two end surfaces; i.e., the end surfaces must be equipotential surfaces. For cylindrical conductors whose ends are equipotential surfaces and for any homogeneous conductor or wire of constant cross-section in which the diameter of cross-section is small in comparison with the length of the conductor, and through which the current is continuous and uniformly distributed

$$r = \rho \frac{l}{A} \quad \text{and} \quad g = \gamma \frac{A}{l} \tag{8}$$

where r is the resistance in ohms, l is the length of the conductor in centimeters, A is the cross-sectional area in square centimeters, and ρ is called the *resistivity* in ohms per centimeter cube or, more briefly, ohm centimeters. Similarly g is the conductance in mhos and γ is the *conductivity* in mhos per centimeter cube or mho centimeters. Note that the word "cube" used in the resistivity-conductivity units refers to a cube of unit dimensions and is *not* an exponent. The ρ may be defined as the resistance in ohms of a cube of the material under consideration having a length of 1 cm and a cross-section of 1 sq cm. Similarly γ may be defined as the conductance in mhos of a cube of the material under consideration having a length of 1 cm and a cross-section of 1 sq cm. It is evident from equations 6 and 8 that

$$\rho = \frac{1}{\gamma} \tag{9}$$

ρ and γ depend upon the material and temperature of the conductor and upon the choice of units (see next paragraph), but are independent of the shape and size of the conductor. Hence ρ is sometimes called the *specific resistance* and γ the *specific conductance* of a substance.

Equation 8 cannot be directly applied to irregularly shaped conductors, but the following equation may be applied to elementary volumes of irregular conductors and the total resistance found by processes of summation or integration:

$$r = \rho \frac{dl}{dA} \quad \text{and} \quad g = \gamma \frac{dA}{dl} \tag{10}$$

where dl is the length and dA is the cross-sectional area of an elementary cylinder or prism of the volume of the conductor.

Temperature Coefficient of Resistance. Practically all substances show a variation of resistance with change in temperature. All metals and most alloys used in electrical engineering increase in resistance with increase in temperature; the resistance of non-metallic conductors such as carbon and electrolytes, also of most dielectrics, decreases with increase in temperature. In general, the relation between the resistance r_t of a given mass of a substance at any temperature t may be expressed in terms of its resistance r_0 at zero degrees by the following power series:

$$r_t = r_0 \,(1 + at + bt^2 + ct^3 + \text{etc.}) \qquad (11)$$

where r_t and r_0 are in ohms, t is in degrees centigrade, and a, b, c, etc., are constants. With metallic conductors such as copper and aluminum the following expression is sufficiently accurate for most practical purposes:

$$r_t = r_0 \,(1 + \alpha_0 t) \qquad (12)$$

where r_t and r_0 are as above and α_0 is called the *zero degree temperature coefficient of resistance*. α_0 is the change in ohms per ohm per degree in the neighborhood of zero centigrade. For dielectrics the linear relationship expressed by equation 12 is not sufficiently accurate. When resistance increases with temperature α is positive; when resistance decreases with temperature α is negative. (For properties of resistance materials see Section 11.)

7. DIRECT-CURRENT NETWORKS

Resistances and Conductances in Series. When several conductors are connected end to end so that the same current flows through each of them (Fig. 5), they are said to be connected *in series*. Let I_{12} be the current in each conductor in the direction from 1 to 2; let r', r'', r''', etc., be the resistances of the various conductors and E_{12}', E_{12}'', E_{12}''', etc., the emf's in the circuit between 1 and 2 in the direction from 1 to 2. Then the potential drop from 1 to 2 is

$$V_{12} = r'I_{12} - E_{12}' + r''I_{12} - E_{12}'' + r'''I_{12} - E_{12}''' + \text{etc.}$$

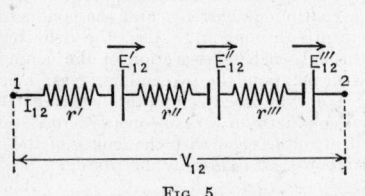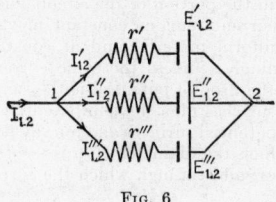

FIG. 5   FIG. 6

Therefore, the resistances between the points 1 and 2 are equivalent to a single resistance

$$r = r' + r'' + r''' + \text{etc.}, \qquad (13)$$

and the emf's between the points 1 and 2 are equivalent to a single emf:

$$E_{12} = E_{12}' + E_{12}'' + E_{12}''' + \text{etc.} \qquad (13a)$$

The equivalent conductance of several conductances g', g'', g''', etc., in series when there are no emf's in the path, is g where

$$\frac{1}{g} = \frac{1}{g'} + \frac{1}{g''} + \frac{1}{g'''} + \text{etc.} \qquad (13b)$$

Resistances and Conductances in Parallel. When several conductors are connected to two common junction points so that the same potential drop is established through each (Fig. 6), they are said to be *in parallel*. Let the currents, emf's, and resistances be as designated in the figure. Then since $\Sigma I = 0$ (Kirchhoff's Law)

$$I_{12} = I_{12}' + I_{12}'' + I_{12}''' + \text{etc.}$$

and from equation 7a

$$V_{12} = r'I_{12}' - E_{12}' = r''I_{12}'' - E_{12}'' = r'''I_{12}''' - E_{12}''' = \text{etc.}$$

from which relations the currents in the individual branches may be calculated.

When there are no emf's in the various branches, the combined resistance of the several branches from 1 to 2 is r where

$$\frac{1}{r} = \frac{1}{r'} + \frac{1}{r''} + \frac{1}{r'''} + \text{etc.} \qquad (14)$$

and the combined conductance is

$$g = g' + g'' + g''' + \text{etc.} \qquad (14a)$$

where g', g'', g''', etc., are the individual conductances.

In the special case of two conductors in parallel, and no emf in either, the combined resistance is

$$r = \frac{r_1 r_2}{r_1 + r_2} \tag{14b}$$

Series-parallel Circuits. When a circuit is made up of several conductors some of which are in series and some in parallel, it is called a *series-parallel circuit*. The total resistance or conductance of such a circuit can be calculated from the constants of the several branches by applying successively the formulas for series and for parallel circuits.

Kirchhoff's Network Laws. The relations given above for conductors in series and in parallel are special cases of two general laws, namely:

1. The algebraic sum of the currents coming to any junction in a network of conductors is always zero.

2. The algebraic sum of the potential drops around any closed loop in a network of conductors is always zero.

These two statements are known as Kirchhoff's laws. By making use of them one can always predetermine (a) the current in each branch of a network when the resistance of each branch and the emf in each branch are known, or (b) the emf in each branch when the current in each branch and the resistance of each branch are known.

It should be carefully borne in mind in applying these laws that a current leaving a point is equivalent to a negative current entering that point, and that an emf in any chosen direction is equivalent to a rise of potential in that direction. In working out any problem concerning a network of circuits it is convenient to make a diagram of the network and to place on each branch in this diagram a number or symbol to represent the value of the current (the directions of the current are arbitrarily assumed) and wherever there is an emf to place a number or symbol to represent its value and an arrow or subscripts to indicate its direction. Then at any junction point those currents represented by arrows pointing toward the point are to be considered positive and those represented by arrows pointing away from the point are to be considered negative; and for any closed mesh those currents and emf's represented by arrows pointing around the mesh in the clockwise direction are to be considered positive and those pointing around the mesh in the counter-clockwise direction are to be considered negative. With this understanding, these laws may be written

$$\Sigma I = 0 \text{ at every point} \tag{15}$$

$$\Sigma E - \Sigma rI = 0 \text{ for every closed mesh} \tag{16}$$

where I, r, and E represent the current, the resistance, and the emf respectively in each branch of the mesh, and the symbol Σ indicates the algebraic sum of the quantities following it.

These equations enable one to write down a set of simultaneous equations for the given network, but it will be found in the case of networks having more than one mesh, that at least one of the current equations may be derived directly from the other current equations, and that at least one of the potential equations may be derived from the other potential equations. That is, the number of independent equations of each form will be at least one less than the number which it is possible to write down. It should also be noted that it is frequently unnecessary to write down formally all the possible independent equations; many of the simpler problems can be solved by writing down two independent expressions for the potential drop between each pair at points and equating them.

Solution of Networks. In solving networks of conductors there are several alternative methods all of which are equivalent as far as results are concerned. Directions for solution by one method are here given. In Fig. 7 let the resistances and emf's be given. It is desired to find the currents in the five branches. There are four junction points, A, B, C, and D. Since the currents and their directions are unknown some

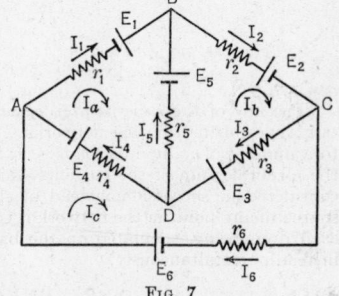

Fig. 7

assumption of direction must be made. Assume directions of currents in all branches and indicate by arrows and symbols I_1, I_2, I_3, I_4, I_5, and I_6. This is shown in the figure. Apply the first law to junctions A, B, and C as follows, remembering that a current approaching a junction is positive and a current leaving a junction is negative.

Since $\Sigma I = 0$

At junction A	$I_4 + I_6 - I_1 = 0$	(17a)
At junction B	$I_1 + I_5 - I_2 = 0$	(17b)
At junction C	$I_2 - I_3 - I_6 = 0$	(17c)

If the first law is applied to the currents at the junction D, there will result an equation derivable from equations 17. The second law is next applied to the closed loops formed by branches. The potential drops will be summed *clockwise* about the loops. The following conventions will be adopted:

1. All potential drops will be positive, and all potential rises will be negative.

2. In summing potential drops around a mesh, a given emf will be considered positive when we proceed from its positive to its negative pole, *regardless of the direction of the current through it.*

3. In summing potential drops around a mesh, a given emf will be considered negative when we proceed from its negative to its positive pole, *regardless of the direction of the current through it.*

4. In summing potential drops around a mesh, the difference of potential across a given resistance will be considered positive if the assumed direction of the current is clockwise with respect to that mesh.

5. In summing potential drops around a mesh, the difference of potential across a given resistance will be considered negative if the assumed direction of the current is counter-clockwise with respect to that mesh.

Applying the above conventions to Fig. 7 the equations representing the second law may be written

Mesh $ABDA$	$r_1 I_1 - E_1 + E_5 - r_5 I_5 + r_4 I_4 + E_4 = 0$	(18a)
Mesh $BCDB$	$r_2 I_2 + E_2 + r_3 I_3 - E_3 + r_5 I_5 - E_5 = 0$	(18b)
Mesh $ADCA$	$- E_4 - r_4 I_4 + E_3 - r_3 I_3 + r_6 I_6 - E_6 = 0$	(18c)

Any further mesh equations are derivable from equations 18. The six equations 17 and 18 permit the solution for currents in all branches. When these equations are solved a positive sign in front of a current indicates that the assumed direction of the current was correct. When a negative sign appears in front of a current, that current actually flows in a direction *opposite* to the direction assumed.

It is frequently convenient to use fictitious currents called *mesh currents* since the first law is automatically taken care of when writing the second law equations by means of mesh currents. Referring again to Fig. 7, the circular arrows represent the mesh currents. The second law equations may then be written

Mesh a	$r_1 I_a + r_5(I_a - I_b) + r_4(I_a - I_c) = E_1 - E_5 - E_4$	(19a)
Mesh b	$r_2 I_b + r_3(I_b - I_c) + r_5(I_b - I_a) = E_3 + E_5 - E_2$	(19b)
Mesh c	$r_6 I_c + r_4(I_c - I_a) + r_3(I_c - I_b) = E_6 + E_4 - E_3$	(19c)

These three equations may be solved for I_a, I_b and I_c. The branch currents can then be found from

$$\left.\begin{array}{l} I_1 = I_a \\ I_2 = I_b \\ I_3 = I_b - I_c \\ I_4 = I_a - I_c \\ I_5 = I_b - I_a \\ I_6 = I_c \end{array}\right\} \qquad (20)$$

The law of the *superposition of currents and voltages* simplifies the calculation of certain types of distributing networks. If electric energy is being supplied over a network to a number of individual loads: (1) the current at any point in the network is equal to the algebraic sum of the currents which would flow if the individual load currents were considered in succession instead of simultaneously, and (2) the voltage drop from the source to any point in the network is equal to the algebraic sum of the drops to that point, each drop being calculated on the basis of individual load currents, taken successively instead of simultaneously.

8. ENERGY AND POWER

Electric Energy and Power. From the definition of emf and potential drop it follows that the total work done by the external agents in forcing Q units of electricity from any point 1 in a circuit to any point 2 is $W = VQ$. (See equation 1.) From the definition of electric current the quantity of electricity carried from 1 to 2 when the current I is established from 1 to 2 is $Q = It$, where t is the time during which the current exists. Hence when a current I is established through any device for a time t by an impressed voltage V, the energy input to this device is

$$W = VIt \qquad (21)$$

and the power input, i.e., energy input per unit time, is

$$P = VI \qquad (22)$$

When V and I are expressed in volts and amperes respectively the power input is in watts; if t is in seconds, the energy input is in joules or watt-seconds. When V and I are in statvolts and statamperes respectively, or in abvolts and abamperes respectively, the power input is in ergs per second; if t is in seconds the energy input is in ergs.

Applying the above relations to the simple circuit shown in Art. 6, Fig. 4, containing a generator and a motor (armature circuit only is considered), the power input to the motor armature is

$$P_i = E_mI + r_mI^2 \qquad (22a)$$

the power output of the generator armature is

$$P_o = E_gI - r_gI^2 \qquad (22b)$$

and the power lost in the line is

$$P_l = r_lI^2$$

The term r_gI^2 represents the power lost in heating the armature circuit of the generator due to its resistance, and the term r_mI^2 represents the power dissipated as heat in the armature circuit of the motor. The net electric input to the generator armature is E_gI, and the gross mechanical output of the motor armature is E_mI. The gross mechanical input to the generator is greater than E_gI and the net mechanical output of the motor is less than E_mI by an amount equal to the friction and " core loss " in the respective machines.

Joule's Law. That portion of the power input to any device which is equal to the product of the resistance of the conductors forming the winding of the device and the square of the current through this winding is always converted into heat. That is, when a current I flows through a resistance r, heat is always " dissipated " in this resistance, and the rate of dissipation is

$$P_h = rI^2 \qquad (23a)$$

This experimental fact is known as " Joule's law." This law applies directly only to continuous or non-varying currents. The relation $P_h = rI^2$ is, however, used as the basis for defining the " effective " resistance of a conductor to an alternating current (q.v.).

Effective Resistance and Conductance. In Art. 6, equation 4, resistance was defined as the factor of proportionality in Ohm's law. On this basis it was shown that resistance is a variable factor dependent upon material, temperature, size, and shape of conductor and upon current distribution. Furthermore, equation 4 applies only where there is no internal emf in the circuit. The most general definition of the resistance r of a substance between any two equipotential surfaces intersecting the path of a current I is

$$r = \frac{P_h}{I^2} \qquad (23b)$$

where P_h is the power dissipated as heat between the two equipotential surfaces and I is the effective value of the total current from one surface to the other. With a varying current this dissipation of heat may occur in four different ways, viz.: (1) as heat due to the conduction current through the substance, (2) as heat due to dielectric hysteresis accompanying the displacement current through the substance (when the substance is an insulator), (3) as heat due to magnetic hysteresis accompanying the varying magnetic flux produced by the current, and (4) as heat due to eddy currents induced in neighboring conductors.

In a continuous current the last three effects do not occur, and the heat is that due to the conduction current only. The resistance offered by a substance to a continuous current is called the " true," " ohmic," " continuous-current," or " direct-current " resistance, as distinguished from the " effective " resistance offered by the substance to a varying current. The effective resistance, even when there are no losses due to dielectric or magnetic hysteresis, is in general greater than the ohmic resistance, owing to the skin effect.

Similarly, the general definition of conductance is

$$g = \frac{P_h}{V^2} \qquad (23c)$$

where P_h has the same meaning as above and V is the effective value of the potential difference between the two equipotential surfaces. When the voltage is non-varying the conductance is called the " true," " ohmic," " continuous-current," or " direct-current " conductance as distinguished from the " effective " conductance to a varying current.

It should be noted that the ohmic resistance and conductance are reciprocals of each other, but that this is not true for the effective resistance and conductance.

ELECTROKINETICS AND THE MAGNETIC CIRCUIT

9. MAGNETS AND MAGNETISM

Magnets and Magnetic Substances. A magnet may be defined as any body which possesses the property of attracting pieces of iron or steel * and which when freely suspended takes up a definite position with respect to the geographical meridian. A magnetic substance is any body which acquires this property when it is placed near a magnet or near a conductor carrying an electric current. A body which is given this property is said to be " magnetized." A magnetic needle is a magnetized needle of iron or steel; the north-seeking end of such a needle is called its north pole, and the south-seeking end its south pole. When such a needle is freely † suspended near a magnet or a conductor carrying an electric current a couple is bound to be exerted upon it which causes it to take up a definite direction. The needle is said to " point " in the direction of a line drawn through it from its south to its north pole.

See Section 11 for the magnetic properties of substances used in electrical engineering.

Magnetic Effects. The following classification due to S. R. Williams covers the various types of phenomena associated with magnetism.

1. Magneto-magnetics is covered by the paragraph immediately following in this section.

2. Magneto-mechanics includes mechanical strains due to magnetic stresses and magnetic strains due to mechanical stresses.

3. Magneto-acoustics covers the production of sound by magnetization and the influence of mechanical vibrations on magnetism.

4. Magneto-electrics involves the relationship between magnetic and electric circuits, the principal phenomena of which are covered in following paragraphs.

5. Magneto-thermics covers the influence of heat on magnetism, and vice versa.

6. Magneto-optics covers the influence of magnetism on light, and vice versa.

7. Cosmical magnetism.

Magnetic Field of Force. Any region in which a magnetic substance (e.g., a piece of soft iron), when placed therein, becomes magnetized is said to be a *magnetic field*. A magnetic field exists in and around every magnetized substance and around every electric current. The direction of the magnetic field at any point P is arbitrarily chosen as the direction in which a small magnetic needle point would point when placed at P without disturbing appreciably the existing conditions.

Ferromagnetism. Much of the contemporary theory of ferromagnetism is based on spectrum analysis and interpreted by the Bohr-Sommerfeld atomic model and its modifications. Specifically the elementary magnetic particle is the so-called " spinning " electron. The model of the atom used to account for the elementary magnetic effect requires that the electron spin about an axis passing through its center, as distinguished from the rotation in circular or elliptical orbits around the atomic nucleus. In this manner each orbital electron has a magnetic momentum due to its moving electrical charge and an angular momentum due to its moving mass.

Uncompensated Spins. It is assumed that all such orbital electrons spin, but that in general, at any particular energy level or shell within the atom, all electrons may be divided into two equal groups—those that spin in one direction and those that spin in the opposite direction, thus producing a *null* magnetic effect. This effect is known as compensated electron spins. In certain elements however it is consistent with the theory to believe that uncompensated electron spins occur in one or more shells. In other words, there are, for example, more electrons spinning in one direction than in the other, in a given shell. These excess or uncompensated electron spins are an important factor in the phenomena of ferromagnetism.

---

* With a force in excess of the gravitational force, which is extremely small.

† A needle is said to be freely suspended when no controlling force is exerted upon it through its suspension tending to make it take up any definite position.

Exchange. Fundamentally ferromagnetism consists of the reorientation of the magnetic moments of the uncompensated electron spins due to the magnetizing force of an externally applied magnetic field. While this accounts for the major ferromagnetic properties of the ferromagnetic elements such as iron, cobalt and nickel, it fails to account for the absence of such ferromagnetic properties in other elements also known to have uncompensated electron spins. This apparent discrepancy is removed when the so-called "exchange forces" are considered. For an element to exhibit ferromagnetic properties it is required that in addition to the existence of uncompensated electron spins, these spins must be parallel in contiguous atoms. Were this not the case the magnetic moments of individual atoms would be random in direction and hence the resultant magnetic moment of an appreciable region within the substance would be nil. It has been found that there must be a certain ratio existing between the diameter of an atom and the diameter of an electron shell that has uncompensated spins, in order to permit the alignment of magnetic moments in contiguous atoms. This ratio is necessary because the electron spins and charges influence each other, dependent upon the distance between them. This influence, which is known as the *exchange*, must have a proper value in order that the uncompensated spins can be aligned to produce ferromagnetic effects. These forces of exchange tend to keep the spins parallel in neighboring atoms while the forces of thermal agitation tend to destroy this alignment. When the temperature of the substance becomes great enough the forces of exchange are completely overcome and the substance loses its ferromagnetic properties. The temperature at which this occurs is the well-known Curie point. According to the theory, magnetic saturation depends both on the uncompensated electron spins and the exchange. Rough approximation makes the saturation point a function of the product of the number of uncompensated electron spins and the exchange.

Domain. In ferromagnetic substances the forces of exchange are sufficiently large so that the uncompensated electron spins in neighboring atoms are more stable when their magnetic moments are parallel, than under any other orientation, even when no external magnetic field is applied. However, this situation holds true only over very small regions in the given specimen of the substance. These regions, which are called "domains," have been found experimentally to have the volume equivalent to a cube approximately $1/1000$ inch on an edge. Ferromagnetic substances are completely divided into such domains, each domain being magnetized to saturation in a definite direction. Any specimen of a ferromagnetic substance is said to be unmagnetized when the directions of magnetization of the individually magnetically saturated domains are oriented at random with respect to each other. Thus, the application of an external magnetic field tends to reorient the individually magnetically saturated domains in the direction of this applied field.

Crystal Structure. X-ray analysis has shown that most materials are of crystalline structure. In the case of the ferromagnetic substances these crystals are too small to be seen individually. However, their properties have been studied by means of spectrum analysis and photomicrography. Due to this crystalline structure there is in general more than one axis of stable magnetic saturation. In the cubic crystal, characteristic of iron, there are six equally stable axes of magnetic saturation.

Magnetization Curves. On the basis of uncompensated electron spins, forces of exchange, the existence of domains and the multiple axes of equally stable magnetization, it is now possible to interpret the major ferromagnetic phenomena. When a small external field (say less than 10 oersteds) is applied to an unmagnetized specimen of a ferromagnetic substance, the saturation magnetization within each crystal changes its direction from its axis of stable magnetization to that axis of stable magnetization which is most nearly in line with the applied field. This process takes place as sudden individual reorientations within the individual crystals and the strength of the field required to produce these effects is dependent on the original deviation of these orientations from that of the applied field. These sudden jumps constitute the explanation of the well-known Barkhausen effect. The portion of the magnetization curve represented by the foregoing process is that up to but not including the knee of the curve. At the knee it is assumed that all individual crystals have directions of stable magnetization which lie nearest to the direction of the applied field. When stronger fields than this are applied (order of magnitude 10 to 100 oersteds) the domains themselves are rotated as a whole until the axes of magnetization of all crystal are coincident with direction with the applied field. Needless to say beyond this point an increased applied field produces no further increase in flux density due to the ferromagnetic phenomena.

On the basis of the foregoing theory it is possible to account for the shape of the magnetization curve and actually to calculate many of the known quantities which are used in ferromagnetic practice.

Magnetic Flux. Consider a small closed turn of wire, Fig. 1, placed in a magnetic field with its plane perpendicular to the direction of the field. Experience shows that when such a turn of wire is removed from the field in any manner whatever (the coil remaining short-circuited on itself or forming part of a closed circuit), or when the magnetic field is caused to disappear in any manner whatever, a momentary emf is set up or *induced* in this coil, which in turn causes a momentary electric current to flow through the coil. This emf exists only while the coil is moving across the field or while the field through the coil is varying.

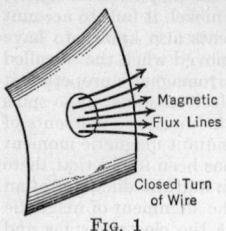

Magnetic Flux Lines

Closed Turn of Wire

FIG. 1

The time integral of the induced emf when the coil is removed entirely from the magnetic field is taken as the measure of the magnetic flux existing through the coil when in its original position. That is, calling e the emf induced in the coil at any instant by its motion through the field, and t the time during which the emf exists in the coil, then the magnetic flux ϕ through the coil when in its original position is

$$\phi = \int_0^t e \, dt \tag{1}$$

When e is in volts and t is in seconds, ϕ is in volt-seconds. When e is in abvolts and t is in seconds, the unit for ϕ is called the *maxwell* or a *line*. See Section 3. This quantity ϕ is readily measured by means of a ballistic galvanometer.

Magnetic Flux Density. Experience shows that the magnetic flux through any closed loop, such as the turn of wire described above, depends upon the area inclosed by this loop. The magnetic flux per unit area through any surface perpendicular to the direction of the field is defined as the *magnitude* of the *magnetic flux density* at this surface, and is usually represented by the symbol B. By the magnitude of the flux density at any point is meant the magnitude of the flux density at any infinitely small surface drawn perpendicular to the field at this point. The *direction* of the *magnetic flux density* at any point is the same as that in which a magnetic needle would point if placed at this point; i.e., the direction of the flux density and the direction of the magnetic field are the same. The vector having the above-defined magnitude and direction is called the flux density and is usually designated by the symbol $\boldsymbol{B}$. When the flux density has the same value B at every point of a surface of area A and is perpendicular to this surface, then the total flux through this surface is

$$\phi = BA \text{ maxwells} \tag{2}$$

The total magnetic flux across any surface S may in general be expressed mathematically by the surface integral

$$\phi = \int (B \cos \alpha) ds \text{ maxwells} \tag{3}$$

where ds represents any elementary area of this surface and $(B \cos \alpha)$ the component of the flux density perpendicular to ds. The unit of magnetic flux density in the cgs electromagnetic system is called the *gauss*; no name has been given to the corresponding practical unit.

Magnetic Flux Lines. Magnetic flux can be represented by lines drawn in the field in such a direction that their direction coincides at each point with the direction of the field at that point, and of such a number that their density at each point (number per unit area perpendicular to their direction) is equal to the magnetic flux density at that point. Such lines are called "magnetic flux lines." Experience shows that lines thus drawn in a magnetic field always form closed loops, i.e., a magnetic flux line has no ends. As a consequence of this fact the total magnetic flux coming up to any surface in a magnetic field is always equal to the total flux leaving that surface.

10. ELECTROMAGNETISM

Magnetic Fields Due to Electric Currents. Experience shows that every filament or stream line of electric current is always accompanied by a magnetic field the flux lines of which link the stream line of current. That is, the flux lines thread the loops formed by the stream lines and the stream lines thread the loops formed by the flux lines; see Fig. 2.

Right-handed Screw Law. The direction of the current flowing around any electric circuit and the direction in which the flux lines due to that current thread this circuit are related to each other in the same manner as the direction of motion of a point on the edge of the head of a right-handed screw placed at the center of the circuit and the direction of advance of the screw. Or, if one faces the electric circuit looking in

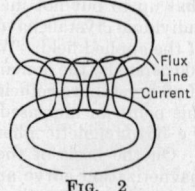

Flux Line

Current

FIG. 2

the direction of the flux lines threading it, the current producing these lines is in the clockwise direction around the circuit. The relative direction of the current and its magnetic flux may be briefly described by saying that the current is in the right-handed screw direction with respect to the flux which it produces.

Induced Emf. The measure of magnetic flux is based on the experimental fact that, whenever the magnetic field threading an electric circuit changes, an emf is induced in that circuit. When the circuit is formed by a single turn of wire this induced emf is, from the definition above, equal to the rate of change of this flux with respect to time, i.e., $e = \dfrac{d\phi}{dt}$. When the circuit is in the form of a coil each turn of which links the flux, the emf induced in each turn is equal to $\dfrac{d\phi}{dt}$, where ϕ is the flux which links that particular turn. When each turn links the same number of flux lines, then the total induced emf in a coil of N turns is

$$e = N\frac{d\phi}{dt} \text{ abvolts} \tag{4}$$

where ϕ is in maxwells.

When the change in flux is due to a motion of a circuit or part of a circuit through a magnetic field the induced emf in any conductor is also equal to the number of flux lines which cut across this conductor per unit time.

Magnetic Linkages. The condition that each turn of a coil be linked by the same flux ϕ seldom exists; some of the flux lines usually link only part of the turns. In general, the total emf is

$$e = \frac{d}{dt}(\phi_1 + \phi_2 + \ldots + \phi_n) \text{ abvolts} \tag{4a}$$

where ϕ_1, ϕ_2, etc., represent the fluxes linking the various turns. The sum $(\phi_1 + \phi_2 + \ldots + \phi_n)$ may be called the total number of *magnetic linkages* or *flux linkages*, and may be conveniently represented by the symbol λ, viz.,

$$\lambda = \phi_1 + \phi_2 + \ldots + \phi_n \text{ maxwells} \tag{4b}$$

and the total induced emf may then be written

$$e = \frac{d\lambda}{dt} \text{ abvolts} \tag{4c}$$

When all the N turns link the same flux, ϕ, then $\lambda = N\phi$.

Direction of Induced Emf. The direction of the induced emf around a circuit is found to be in the left-handed screw direction with respect to the increase of flux; viz., if one faces the circuit looking in the direction of the increase of flux, the induced emf is in the counter-clockwise direction. The current which would be set up by this emf, however, would produce a flux linking the circuit in the right-handed screw direction. Hence a change in the magnetic flux through an electric current always sets up an emf which tends to produce a current around this circuit in such a direction as to set up an opposing flux. This fact may be expressed mathematically by writing a minus sign before $\dfrac{d\phi}{dt}$ in equation 4, i.e., by putting

$$e = -N\frac{d\phi}{dt} \tag{4d}$$

The value of $\left(-N\dfrac{d\phi}{dt}\right)$ is then the emf induced in the circuit in the right-handed screw direction with respect to the increase of flux. Or stated in other words $\left(-N\dfrac{d\phi}{dt}\right)$ represents the rise of electric potential and $N\dfrac{d\phi}{dt}$ represents the drop of potential around the circuit in the right-handed screw direction with respect to the increase of flux.

11. MAGNETIZING FORCE AND THE MAGNETIC CIRCUIT

Simple Magnetic Circuit. In certain simple magnetic circuits the treatment is mathematically analogous to that of simple electric circuits. An expression similar to Ohm's law (see Art. 6) is employed. Consider a closed magnetic circuit such as a uniformly wound torus, Fig. 3.

For this circuit we may write

$$\mathcal{F} = \mathcal{R}\phi \tag{5}$$

where $\mathfrak{F}$ is called the *magnetomotive force* (abbreviated mmf) and is analogous to electro-motive force; $\mathcal{R}$ is a factor of proportionality called the *reluctance* and is analogous to resistance; and ϕ, the flux, is analogous to electric current. It must be remembered in considering this analogy that an unvarying flux is thought of as static condition, whereas electric current is defined as the motion of electric charge. Therefore, there is no true *physical* analogy. Equation 5 is sometimes called Ohm's law for magnetic circuits.

Magnetomotive Force. The mmf $\mathfrak{F}$, of equation 5, may also be expressed

$$\mathfrak{F} = 4\pi NI * \tag{6}$$

where $\mathfrak{F}$ is in *gilberts*, N is the total number of turns of the coil, and I is the current in abamperes flowing through the coil. The current-turns NI are frequently spoken of as the *ampere-turns* when I is given in amperes. Obviously $\mathfrak{F}$ is in direct proportion to the ampere-turns. In general, mmf may be expressed

$$\mathfrak{F} = 4\pi \Sigma NI \tag{6a}$$

where ΣNI represent the algebraic summation of all current-turns linking the magnetic circuit. The mmf is taken as positive when the current links the flux lines in the right-

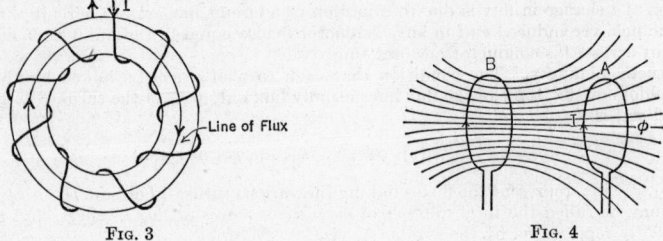

FIG. 3　　　　　　　　　　　　　　FIG. 4

handed screw direction, and negative when the current links the flux lines in the left-handed screw direction.

Work Done by a Varying Magnetic Flux. Consider a coil A (Fig. 4) of N turns of wire, and let each of these N turns be linked by a flux ϕ due to some external agent, e.g., another coil B in which an electric current is flowing. Let the flux ϕ through A due to B be increasing at any instant at the rate $\dfrac{d\phi}{dt}$ in the left-handed screw direction with respect to the current I in A at this instant. Then there is induced in A at this instant an emf in the direction of I equal to $e = N\dfrac{d\phi}{dt}$, and therefore the electric power developed in A at this instant is $ei = NI\dfrac{d\phi}{dt}$. This power is transmitted to the coil A as a result of the varying flux through it; hence the power

$$p = NI\frac{d\phi}{dt} \tag{7}$$

may be looked upon as the magnetic power input, this power being converted within the coil into electric power.

Magnetizing Force or Magnetic Field Intensity. Experience shows that the magnetic flux density produced at any point by a given mmf depends (a) upon the position of the point with respect to the source of the mmf and (b) upon the nature of the substances through which this mmf produces the magnetic flux. These facts lead to the conception of the flux density at any point in a magnetic field as being due to a "magnetizing force" H at that point, this magnetizing force H depending solely upon the mmf producing the field and the distribution of the flux lines, as distinguished from the flux density B which depends not only upon these two items but also upon the nature of the medium at the point in question.

The magnetizing force (also called the "magnetic field intensity") at successive points along any closed path in a magnetic field may be defined by the relation that its line integral around such a path is equal to the total mmf acting around this path, viz.,

$$4\pi\Sigma NI = \int (H\cos\theta)dl \tag{8}$$

* The factor 4π arises from the manner in which the conceptions of the magnetic field were originally developed.

where dl represents any elementary length of this path (see Fig. 5); ($H \cos \theta$) the value of the component of the magnetizing force at dl in the direction of dl; and ΣNI the total number of current turns linked by the path. Experience shows that such a definition leads to a simple means of expressing in a quantitative manner the interrelations of a number of experimental facts. Magnetizing force may also be expressed as the force in dynes which would act on a " unit magnetic pole."

When the path coincides in direction with the magnetizing force at each point, equation 8 may be written

$$4\pi \Sigma NI = \int H dl \tag{8a}$$

Direction of the Magnetizing Force. Experience shows that *except* for points inside a permanent magnet the magnetizing force H and the flux density B are always in the same direction. For points inside a permanent magnet the direction of the magnetic field intensity H, due solely to the magnet itself, is opposite to the direction of the flux lines, i.e., a permanent magnet produces a "demagnetizing force " on itself.

Lines of Magnetizing Force. The magnetizing force at any point in a magnetic field may be represented by lines drawn in the field in a direction such as to coincide with the direction of the magnetizing force at each point, and of such a number per unit area perpendicular to their direction that their density at each point gives the value of the magnetizing force at that point. Such lines are called *lines of magnetizing force* or *lines of magnetic field intensity*. In general the lines of magnetizing force and the magnetic flux lines coincide in direction (except within the substance of permanent magnets), but their densities are different. Only in non-magnetic substances do the flux lines and lines of magnetizing force coincide in both number and direction. The simple expression " lines of force " is frequently used to designate either the flux lines or the lines of magnetic intensity, but it is evident that such loose use of this term is likely to lead to confusion when speaking of the magnetic field within a magnetic substance.

Magnetizing force is of the nature of mmf per unit length. The cgs electromagnetic unit of magnetizing force is called a *gilbert per centimeter* or an *oersted*. When the mmf

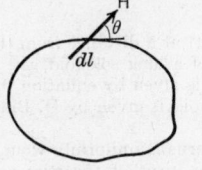

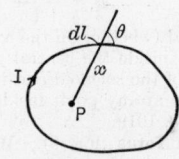

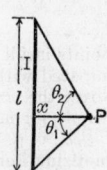

Fig. 5   Fig. 6   Fig. 7

is expressed in ampere-turns, the magnetizing force is expressed in ampere-turns per centimeter or per inch.

When the medium surrounding the stream lines of an electric current is of a uniform magnetic nature throughout, the magnetizing force at any point may be calculated from the shape and distribution of the stream lines of the current, irrespective of whether the medium be non-magnetic or highly magnetic.

Magnetizing Force at Any Point Due to an Element of a Current-stream Line (Fig. 6). Consider any closed stream line of electric current and let the surrounding medium be uniform in its magnetic properties throughout the region in which the magnetic field produced by this stream line exists. It can be shown that each elementary length dl of this stream line may be considered as contributing to the magnetizing force H at any point P in this region an amount

$$dH = \frac{(I \sin \theta)dl}{x^2} \tag{9}$$

where I is the current flowing along this stream line, x the distance from P to dl, and θ the angle between x and dl. The direction of dH is perpendicular to the plane determined by x and dl. The total magnetizing force at P is then the vector sum or vector integral of dH for all the elementary lengths into which the stream line is divided.

Magnetizing Force Due to a Straight Wire (Fig. 7). Applying equation 9 to the case of a straight wire of circular cross-section carrying a current I, the magnetizing force at any point P due to a length l of this wire is

$$H = \frac{I}{x}(\sin \theta_1 + \sin \theta_2), \tag{9a}$$

where x is the perpendicular distance from P to the wire and θ_1 and θ_2 the angles designated in Fig. 7.

If the wire is very long compared with x, this becomes

$$H = \frac{2I}{x} \qquad (9b)$$

This formula also holds approximately for any point outside a wire of any shaped cross-section, provided x is large compared with the maximum diameter of this section. For a point inside a long wire of circular cross-section of radius a the magnetizing force is also given by equation 9b when I is taken to represent that part of the current inside the circle through P concentric with the axis of the wire. When the current density is uniform over the cross-section, as is usual, the magnetizing force inside the wire is

$$H_i = \frac{2xI}{a^2} \qquad (9c)$$

Magnetizing Force on the Axis of a Circular Coil of N Turns. Let I be the current, r the mean radius of the coil, and x the distance of the point from the center of the circle; then

$$H = \frac{2\pi N I r^2}{(r^2 + x^2)^{3/2}} \qquad (9d)$$

Magnetizing Force Due to a Solenoid. A solenoid is a helical coil of wire, each turn having the same radius. Let N = total number of turns, I = current in abamperes, r = mean radius of the helix in centimeters, l = length of helix in centimeters. Then at any point on the axis of the helix (inside or outside) at a distance of x centimeters from its center, the magnetizing force in gilberts per centimeter is

$$H = \frac{2\pi N I}{l}\left[\frac{0.5l + x}{\sqrt{r^2 + (0.5l + x)^2}} + \frac{0.5l - x}{\sqrt{r^2 + (0.5l - x)^2}}\right] \qquad (9e)$$

This formula holds only when the thickness of the winding is small compared with the mean radius r. When l is large compared with r this reduces to

$$H = \frac{4\pi N I}{l} \qquad (9f)$$

For all points inside the solenoid (whether on the axis or not) at a distance from the ends large compared with r, that is, inside the central portion of a long solenoid, the field is uniform over the cross-section of the solenoid and its value is given by equation 9f. An exact formula for field intensity at any point inside a solenoid is given by O. Billieux in *Rev. gén. élec.*, 6, p. 827, Dec. 13, 1919.

Magnetizing Force Inside a Torus (Fig. 8). When a torus is uniformly wound with an insulated wire so that the turns of the wire are close together and cover the entire surface of the torus, the magnetic field is confined entirely within the space inclosed by these turns, and therefore, when the core on which the wire is wound is of uniform magnetic material throughout, both the lines of magnetizing force and the flux lines must be concentric circles, as shown in the figure. The magnetizing force will have the same value at every point on the circumference of any one of these circles, and, therefore, from equation 8a the value of H at any point P within the core is

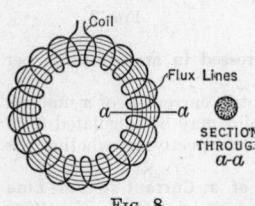

FIG. 8

$$H = \frac{4\pi N I}{l} \qquad (9g)$$

where N is the total number of turns on the core, I the current in each turn, and l the length of the circumference through P. Unless the ring has a large radius compared with the radius of the cross-section of the core, H will not be uniform over this section, since l for the various points in the cross-section will differ considerably.

It should be noted that the value of H is independent of the material of the core provided only that the core be of uniform material throughout. That is, equation 9g applies to an iron core as well as to an air or wood core, provided the iron is uniform throughout and there is no air gap across the path of the flux lines. Even a mechanically perfect contact between two pieces of iron of the same kind, however, is sufficient to make the above formula useless.

Magnetic Permeability. Permeability is defined by the following equation:

$$\mu = \frac{B}{H} \qquad (10)$$

where, in the cgs electromagnetic system, B is in gausses and H in gilberts per centimeter. The cgs electromagnetic system of units is based on the assumption of the value of unity for μ for free space. The permeability of most substances differs inappreciably from unity. Aside from iron, steel, nickel, cobalt, and synthetic magnetic alloys, all the materials used in electrical engineering have a permeability which may be considered equal to that of air. The permeability of non-magnetic substances is for all practical purposes a constant irrespective of the flux density. A physical picture of permeability may be gained from the following. A coil carrying an unvarying current produces a magnetic field in the air surrounding it. If a substance is placed, for example, inside of this coil without changing the amount or distribution of the flux inside the coil, this substance has a permeability of unity (cgs emu). If the flux inside the coil is altered in value or distribution, the permeability of the introduced substance differs from unity.

Paramagnetic, Diamagnetic, and Ferromagnetic Substances. Considering empty space truly non-magnetic all substances may be divided into three classes. *Paramagnetic* substances have a permeability relative to that of free space ($\mu_s = 1$) slightly greater than unity. For example, relative to free space the permeability of air is *greater than unity* by 3.8×10^{-7} and for aluminum by 2.3×10^{-5}. *Diamagnetic* substances have a permeability

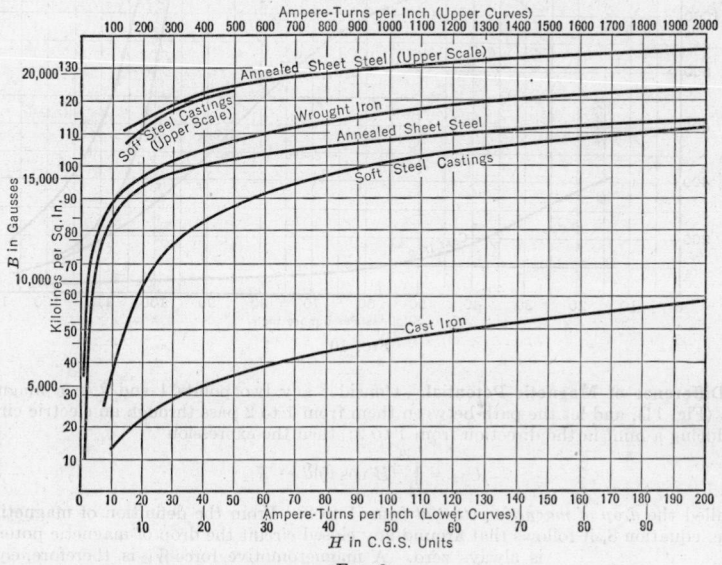

Fig. 9

relative to that of free space slightly less than unity. For example, relative to free space the permeability of hydrogen is *less than unity* by 6.3×10^{-8}, for copper 8.8×10^{-6}, and for bismuth (the most diamagnetic of all elements) 1.8×10^{-4}. *Ferromagnetic* substances including iron, steel, nickel, cobalt, and magnetic alloys have permeabilities greatly in excess of unity. Under certain conditions the permeability of steel may exceed 2000. Furthermore, the permeabilities of ferromagnetic substance vary greatly with flux density. The permeability of such substances also depends upon previous heat treatment, the exact composition of the material, and its previous magnetic history (see Section 11).

Magnetization Characteristic. It is most convenient in calculations involving ferromagnetic materials to use the magnetization characteristic of the material. This characteristic shows the relationship between the flux density B and the magnetizing force H.

A typical curve is shown in Fig. 9. From the relation $\mu = \dfrac{B}{H}$ the curve shown in Fig. 10 may be derived from Fig. 9. The shapes of the characteristics shown in Figs. 9 and 10 depend not only upon the material but also upon the exact manner of magnetization. For diamagnetic and paramagnetic substances, since the permeability is constant and equal to unity with negligible error, there is no point in plotting a magnetization characteristic since $B = H$ throughout.

North and South Poles. That portion of the surface of any magnetized body from which the flux lines pass out into the air (or any substance of lower permeability) is said to be a north magnetic pole, and that portion of the surface at which the flux lines enter the body is said to be a south magnetic pole. A *unit north pole* is a pole from which 4π flux lines emerge into the surrounding air. When a magnetic needle is placed near the surface of a magnetized body its north-seeking end points away from this surface when this surface is a north pole and toward the surface when this surface is a south pole.

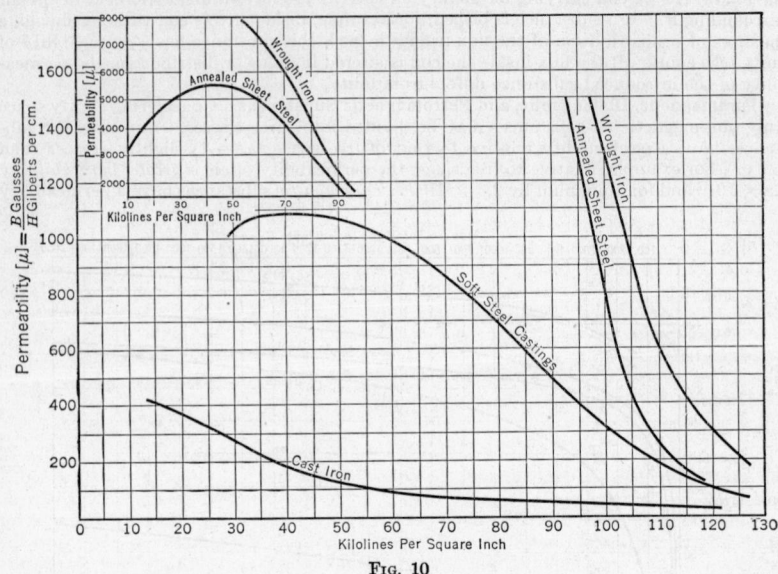

FIG. 10

Difference of Magnetic Potential. Consider any two points 1 and 2 in a magnetic field (Fig. 11), and let the path between them from 1 to 2 pass through an electric circuit producing a mmf in the direction from 1 to 2; then the expression

$$U_{12} = \int_1^2 (H \cos \theta) dl - \mathfrak{F}_{12} \tag{11}$$

is called the *drop of magnetic potential* from 1 to 2. From the definition of magnetizing force, equation 8, it follows that around any closed circuit the drop of magnetic potential is always zero. A magnetomotive force $\mathfrak{F}_{12}$ is, therefore, equivalent to a rise of magnetic potential from 1 to 2.

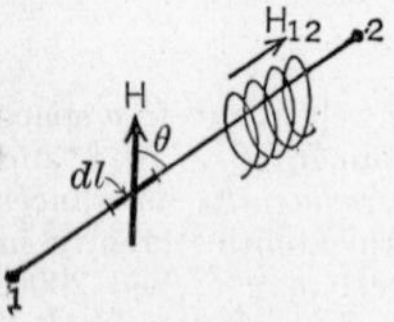

When there is no source of mmf between 1 and 2 and the path coincides with a line of magnetizing force, the drop of magnetic potential is

$$U_{12} = \int_1^2 Hdl \tag{11a}$$

FIG. 11

Magnetic potential difference is of the same nature as mmf and may, therefore, be expressed in the same units, viz., gilberts or ampere-turns.

Magnetic Equipotential Surfaces. A surface, drawn in a magnetic field in such a manner that this surface is perpendicular at each point to the magnetizing force at this point (i.e., to the line of magnetizing force through this point) is called a " magnetic equipotential surface."

Magnetic Reluctance. To establish a magnetic flux ϕ through a given portion of a substance which is not itself linked by a source of mmf, a difference of magnetic potential must always be established between the end surfaces of this substance. Let U be the magnetic potential drop established from one surface to the other; then the quotient

$$\mathcal{R} = \frac{U}{\phi} \tag{12}$$

is defined as the magnetic reluctance of the given portion of the substance. It should be noted that the above definition is meaningless except when applied to a portion of a substance of which the end surfaces are magnetic equipotential surfaces and through every cross-section of which the same flux passes.

Factors upon Which Reluctance Depends. The magnetic reluctance of a given portion of a substance included between two equipotential surfaces and bounded laterally by a surface which no flux line passes depends upon (a) the magnetic permeability of the substance, (b) the dimensions of this portion of the substance, and (c) the distribution of the flux lines over each cross-section perpendicular to them. The relations are identical with those which determine the electrical resistance of a conductor, the magnetic permeability taking the place of the electric conductivity. For example, for a straight bar of constant cross-section A and length l, through which the flux lines are straight, parallel, and uniformly distributed, the reluctance is

$$\mathcal{R} = \frac{l}{\mu A} \tag{13}$$

Note particularly that this formula for reluctance is applicable only under the special conditions just stated. Formulas for other cases are much more complex; see Douglas, J. F. H., Reluctance of Irregular Magnetic Fields, *Proc.*, A.I.E.E., 34, May, 1915.

Magnetic reluctance is not a constant quantity even for a given material and given flux distribution, unless this material is non-magnetic. For all highly magnetic materials μ depends upon the magnetizing force and therefore also upon the flux density. It should also be noted that the magnetic reluctance does not represent a " resistance " in the sense of something which causes a dissipation of energy.

Magnetic Permeance. The reciprocal of magnetic reluctance is called *magnetic permeance.* The permeance of a straight bar under the conditions specified above is

$$\mathcal{P} = \frac{\mu A}{l} \tag{13a}$$

The permeability of a substance is, therefore, equal to the permeance of a unit cube of this substance when the flux through the cube is parallel to four edges of the cube and is uniformly distributed over the section at right angles to these four edges.

Magnetic permeance is analogous to electric conductance, except that it is not a factor which affects the dissipation of energy in a substance. It does, however, enter into the expression for the energy stored in a magnetic field in the same way that the electrostatic capacity of a dielectric is a determining factor in the expression for the energy stored in the electric field (see p. 8-44, Art. 18).

Kirchhoff's Laws for the Magnetic Circuit. As already noted (equation 3) the total magnetic flux coming up to any surface in a magnetic field is always zero, provided a flux leaving a surface is considered as a negative flux coming up to that surface. This fact may be represented by the formula

$$\Sigma \phi = 0 \tag{14}$$

for every surface in the field. Similarly, from the definition of magnetic potential drop, it follows that the total magnetic potential drop around any closed circuit is zero, or that the total mmf acting around any closed circuit is equal to the sum of the reluctance drops around that circuit, which may be represented by the formula

$$\Sigma \mathcal{F} = \Sigma \mathcal{R} \phi \tag{15}$$

These two equations are identical in form with those representing Kirchhoff's laws for the electric circuit. They are, however, not so easy to use for practical calculations, for the magnetic flux is not confined to approximately geometrical lines like the currents in a network of insulated wires, but in general fills all space surrounding the coils which establish the mmf's; also, when there is iron or other magnetic material in the circuit, the permeability depends on the flux density and the previous history of the iron. (The distribution of magnetic flux in and around an iron circuit is analogous to the distribution of current in and around an uninsulated mass of copper of the same shape as the iron circuit immersed in a liquid having a conductivity about equal to that of carbon.) Only in the special case of a uniformly wound circular ring or toroid are the lines of induction confined entirely to an iron circuit; in general a certain number also exist in the air and in whatever other substances are in the vicinity of the iron circuit.

12. ELECTROMAGNETIC INDUCTION

Induction. When the current in a given electric circuit varies with time the magnetic flux accompanying this current also varies with time, and, since this flux links the current which produces it, an emf is induced in each turn of the circuit equal to the rate at which the flux through this turn is varying, and in such a direction as to oppose the change in the current. That is, an increasing electric current is always accompanied by a back emf due to the increase in the magnetic flux which accompanies this increase in current.

Again, when an electric current decreases, its accompanying flux decreases and an emf is set up in the circuit tending to oppose this decrease, i.e., tending to keep the current from decreasing. This is analogous to the effect of inertia in ordinary matter.

If the current in a given circuit is constant, but there is a variation with time of the permeances of the flux paths or of the number of turns linking a given flux path, an emf is produced in the circuit in a direction such as to tend to produce a current which would oppose the variation.

These phenomena are known as *induction*.

Coefficient of Self-induction or Inductance. In general, the coefficient L by which the rate of change of the current $\left(\dfrac{di}{dt}\right)$ in any circuit must be multiplied to give the self-induced emf e is called the *coefficient of self-induction* or simply the *inductance* of the electric circuit. In general, then, the self-induced emf in an electric circuit is

$$e = L \frac{di}{dt} \tag{16}$$

where L is the inductance of the electric circuit and $\dfrac{di}{dt}$ represents the change in the current per unit of time. Since $e = \dfrac{d\lambda}{dt}$ (see equation 4c) where λ is the number of magnetic linkages between the electric circuit and the flux established by the current i, the inductance may also be defined by the relation

$$L = \frac{\partial \lambda}{\partial i} \tag{16a}$$

That is, the inductance is equal to the increase in the number of linkages per unit increase in the current.

It should be noted that e in equation 16 is not the *total* induced emf, even of an isolated circuit, this being given by

$$e = \frac{\partial \lambda}{\partial i} \frac{di}{dt} + \frac{\partial \lambda}{\partial t} \tag{17}$$

in which the first term is the self-induced emf, and the second term is an emf induced by motion.

When the permeability of the magnetic circuit is independent of the current the inductance is also independent of the current. For example, the expression for the inductance of a coil which is not in the vicinity of any ferromagnetic substance may be written

$$L = \frac{\lambda}{i} \tag{18}$$

where λ is the total flux linkages corresponding to the current i in the coil. Since in this case λ is directly proportional to i, L is at most a function of time and is independent of the value of i. When every flux line is linked by every stream line of electric current, and the permeability of the entire magnetic circuit is independent of current,

$$L = \frac{4\pi N^2}{\mathcal{R}} \tag{18a}$$

where N is the number of turns forming the electric circuit and $\mathcal{R}$ is the reluctance of the complete magnetic circuit.

When the equation 18 holds the *total* induced emf may be written

$$e = \frac{d}{dt}(Li) \tag{19}$$

The practical unit of inductance is called the henry; for the relation between the henry and the abhenry and millihenry see Section III.

Coefficient of Mutual Induction or Inductance. In general, the coefficient M_{ab} by which the rate of change of the current $\left(\dfrac{di_b}{dt}\right)$ in a circuit B must be multiplied to give the electromotive force e induced by this current in another circuit A, is called the *coefficient of mutual induction* or simply the *mutual inductance* between A and B. See Fig. 4. In general, then, the emf induced in any circuit A by a varying current i_b in any other circuit B is

$$e_a = M_{ab} \frac{di_b}{dt} \qquad (20)$$

where M_{ab} is the mutual inductance between A and B. The first letter of the double subscript indicates the circuit in which the flux linkages are considered; the second, the circuit in which the current is considered.

It can be shown from the principle of the conservation of energy that the mutual inductance of a circuit A with respect to a second circuit B must be equal to the mutual inductance of B with respect to A, that is, $M_{ab} = M_{ba}$. Whence, the emf induced in B when the current in A increases by an amount di_a is

$$e_b = M_{ba} \frac{di_a}{dt}$$

Since $e_a = \frac{d\lambda_{ab}}{dt}$ where λ_{ab} is the number of linkages between the circuit A and the flux through A due to the current i_b, the mutual inductance may also be defined by the relation

$$M_{ab} = \frac{\partial \lambda_{ab}}{\partial i_b} \qquad (21)$$

That is, the mutual inductance between two circuits A and B is equal to the increase in the number of magnetic linkages of the circuit A per unit increase of the current in B, and vice versa. When the permeability of the magnetic circuit is independent of the current the mutual inductance is also independent of the current and equal to the linkages of A per unit current in B, and vice versa. When every flux line linking both A and B is linked by every turn in A and every turn in B, then

$$M_{ab} = \frac{4\pi N_a N_b}{\mathcal{R}_{ab}} \qquad (22)$$

where N_a and N_b are the number of turns forming the circuits A and B respectively and $\mathcal{R}_{ab}$ is the reluctance of that part of the magnetic circuit through which the flux from A to B passes when there is current in one coil only.

The units of mutual inductance are the same as those of self-inductance.

Instantaneous Potential Drop through a Coil. Consider a coil of wire which has a resistance r and an inductance L. Then when this coil contains no other source of emf than its own self-induced emf, the expression for the instantaneous potential drop through the coil is

$$v = ri + L \frac{di}{dt} \qquad (23)$$

where i is the instantaneous value of the current and $\frac{di}{dt}$ the increase in this current per unit of time.

When there is another coil near the first coil, and the two coils have resistances r_1 and r_2 and self-inductances L_1 and L_2 respectively, and a mutual inductance M, then the potential drops through them are respectively

$$\left. \begin{array}{l} v_1 = r_1 i_1 + L_1 \dfrac{di_1}{dt} + M \dfrac{di_2}{dt} \\[2mm] v_2 = r_2 i_2 + L_2 \dfrac{di_2}{dt} + M \dfrac{di_1}{dt} \end{array} \right\} \qquad (24)$$

where i_1 and i_2 are the currents in the two coils in the same direction with respect to the magnetic circuit. These differential equations are perfectly general and can be applied to the solution of any circuit containing constant r's, L's and M's regardless of the nature of the variation of any applied emf in the circuit. The solution of transient as well as steady-state conditions are obtainable from equations 24 as will be indicated later (see Art. 24 to 26).

Skin Effect. A conductor of finite cross-section may be looked upon as made up of separate filaments each carrying its portion of the total current. When the same potential gradient is established through all of the filaments of the conductor the exterior filaments are linked by fewer flux lines than the interior filaments. If the emf producing the potential gradient through the wire is an alternating one, the induced back emf in the interior filaments will be greater than in those nearer the surface. Since the potential drop is the same across all the filaments the resistance drops in the internal filaments is less than in the external ones. This can be brought about only by the current distributing itself over the cross-section of the conductor in such a manner that the current density in the interior of the wire will be less than at the surface, i.e., the current is forced toward the surface filaments or " skin " of the wire; hence the term *skin effect* is applied to this phenomenon.

The self-induced emf depends not only upon the amount of flux set up but also upon the rapidity of its variation; hence the skin effect becomes more pronounced the greater the frequency of the impressed emf. It is also greater the larger the cross-section of the conductor, the greater its conductivity, and the greater its magnetic permeability. The skin effect also depends slightly upon the temperature since the conductivity changes with temperature.

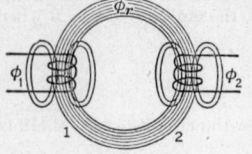

FIG. 12

Leakage Inductance. In discussing the action of a transformer which consists of two electric circuits linking the same iron core, it is necessary to deal with the resultant flux due to the currents in both electric circuits or windings; the fluxes due to the two windings separately have no meaning. Referring to Fig. 12, let ϕ_r represent that portion of the resultant flux due to the currents i_1 and i_2 in the two windings 1 and 2, and let ϕ_1 represent that part of the total flux which links 1 only and ϕ_2 that part of the total flux which links 2 only. Let λ_1 be the linkages between ϕ_1 and circuit 1, and λ_2 the linkages between ϕ_2 and circuit 2. Then

$$L_1' = \frac{\lambda_1}{i_1} \quad \text{and} \quad L_2' = \frac{\lambda_2}{i_2} \tag{25}$$

are called the *leakage inductances* of the two windings respectively; the reluctances of the paths of ϕ_1 and ϕ_2 are practically constant since the air portion of these paths forms a greater part of the reluctance in each.

Let i_1 be the current in winding 1 and i_2 the current in winding 2 linking the flux path in the opposite direction to i_1 (this is the actual relation in a transformer during most of the time), and let e_1 be the impressed emf across the terminals of the first or primary winding and e_2 the terminal emf at the terminals of the second or secondary winding when the current i_2 is flowing. Then

$$\left. \begin{aligned} e_1 &= r_1 i_1 + L_1' \frac{di_1}{dt} + N_1 \frac{d\phi_r}{dt} \\ e_2 &= N_2 \frac{d\phi_r}{dt} - r_2 i_2 - L_2' \frac{di_2}{dt} \end{aligned} \right\} \tag{26}$$

where r_1 and r_2 are the resistances of the two windings and N_1 and N_2 are the numbers of turns in the two windings respectively.

Comparing equation 26 with 24 and noting that $e_1 = v_1$ and $e_2 = -v_2$, and i_2 in 26 is taken in the opposite direction from i_2 in 24, it may be shown that

$$\left. \begin{aligned} L_1' &= L_1 - \frac{N_1}{N_2} M \\ L_2' &= L_2 - \frac{N_2}{N_1} M \end{aligned} \right\} \tag{27}$$

Whence the leakage inductance of each winding is very much less than the total self-inductance of that winding.

Energy of the Magnetic Field. Energy is required to establish a flow of electricity just as energy is required to set a column of water in motion, this " energy of motion " of electricity being analogous to the kinetic energy of a moving body. This energy of motion is most conveniently expressed in terms of the magnetic field which accompanies the flow of electricity or electric current; the mathematical expression for it may be put into various forms.

Magnetic Energy of a Single Electric Circuit, Permeability Constant. For example, consider a single electric circuit and the magnetic field which is established around this circuit when the current in it increases from zero to a value of I. When the current increases by di the linkages increase by an amount $d\lambda$ in the right-handed screw direction with respect to the current. The electric energy output of the circuit during this change is, from equation 4c, $id\lambda$, which is also equal to the magnetic energy input into the magnetic circuit which it links. Hence the total energy input into the magnetic circuit or magnetic field is

$$W = \int_0^{LI} i\, d\lambda = \int_0^I Li\, di \tag{28}$$

since by definition $d\lambda = L\,di$; see equations 4c and 16. When the permeability is constant L is also constant, whence for constant permeability

$$W = 1/_2\,LI^2 \tag{29}$$

This equation may also be written

$$W = \frac{1}{2}\lambda I = \frac{\mathfrak{F}^2}{8\pi\mathfrak{R}} = \frac{1}{8\pi}\,\mathfrak{R}\phi^2 \tag{29a}$$

where $\mathfrak{F}$ is the mmf ($=4\pi NI$ when the coil has N turns in a concentrated winding), $\mathfrak{R}$ is the reluctance of the magnetic circuit, and ϕ the total magnetic flux.

Since the impressed mmf per unit length of a magnetic flux line is equal to the magnetizing force H, and the flux per unit area perpendicular to this flux line is equal to the flux density B, the energy per unit volume of the magnetic field is

$$w = \frac{HB}{8\pi} = \frac{\mu H^2}{8\pi} = \frac{B^2}{8\pi\mu} \tag{30}$$

These various formulas should be compared with the corresponding formulas (p. 8–44) for electrostatic energy.

Magnetic Energy of Two or More Electric Circuits, Permeability Constant. It can also be readily shown that the total energy required to establish currents I_1, I_2, etc., in several electric circuits linking one or more magnetic circuits of constant reluctance is

$$W = 1/_2\,L_1I_1{}^2 + 1/_2\,L_2I_2{}^2 + 1/_2\,L_3I_3{}^2 + \cdots$$
$$+ M_{12}I_1I_2 + M_{13}I_1I_3 + M_{23}I_2I_3 + \cdots \tag{31}$$

where the L's and M's represent the self- and mutual inductances respectively. This may also be written

$$W = \frac{1}{2}\sum_{n=1}^{N}\phi_n I_n \tag{31a}$$

where the summation is an algebraic one and includes every complete turn of the electric circuit, I_n being the current in the nth turn and ϕ_n the magnetic flux linking this turn in the right-handed screw direction with respect to the current.

The energy per unit volume at any point in the magnetic field due to any number of electric circuits is represented by equation 30, where H and B are taken as the resultant magnetizing force and flux density respectively at this point.

When the permeability is not constant the energy transferred to unit volume of the magnetic field due to any number of currents is

$$w = \frac{1}{4\pi}\int_0^B H\,dB \tag{32}$$

provided the magnetizing force H and the flux density B are either in the same or directly opposite directions, as, for example, in a uniformly magnetized iron torus. To integrate this expression requires a knowledge of the relation between B and H. Note also that, owing to the phenomenon of magnetic hysteresis, part of the energy required to establish a magnetic field in iron or other magnetic substance is dissipated as heat and is not recoverable when the field disappears; therefore, only part of the energy represented by this formula is " stored " in the field in a recoverable form.

Hysteresis. When any completely demagnetized ferromagnetic substance is subjected to an increasing magnetizing force H, a curve such as Fig. 9 results. The dotted curve in Fig. 13 is also a representation of the phenomenon. Such a curve is variously termed a *rising characteristic*, a *virgin curve*, or a *neutral curve*; all these names are reserved for the special case of a magnetization curve of a *demagnetized* body.

If from any positive value of H, the magnetizing force is decreased the flux density will also decrease, but not along the same curve as the original rising characteristic. For decreasing values of H, B is greater than for the corresponding value on the rising characteristic. The magnetized body retains a part of its magnetization. It will be noticed that, when the magnetizing force is reduced to zero, there is still a positive value of B, which is dependent upon the maximum positive value of H on the rising characteristic, before H is decreased. The flux density which remains when H has been reduced to zero is called the *residual magnetism* and is in the nature of permanent or semi-permanent magnetism. If now the magnetizing force is reversed (e.g., by reversing the direction of the current through the magnetizing coil) a value of H will be found which will reduce B to zero. This value of H is called the *coercive force*. By proceeding through a cycle of values for the magnetizing force—from zero to a positive maximum, to zero, to a negative maximum, and back to zero—a loop of flux densities will be obtained. Such a loop is called a *hysteresis loop*, and each substance is capable of having an infinity of different hysteresis loops depending on the conditions of magnetization. During part of the magnetizing cycle the electric circuit is transferring energy to the magnetic circuit, and during the remainder of the cycle energy is retransferred from the magnetic to the electric circuit. When any ferromagnetic substance is present in the magnetic circuit more energy is transferred to the magnetic circuit than is retransferred to the electric circuit. The difference between these two amounts of energy is a loss and is dissipated as heat. Part of this loss is called the *hysteresis loss* and is presumably due to friction accompanying the change in orientation of the elementary magnets within the ferromagnetic substance. It may be shown that the hysteresis loss per cycle per cubic centimeter in any magnetic substance due to a complete cycle of changes of the flux density and the magnetizing force is equal to $\dfrac{1}{4\pi}$ times the area of the corresponding hysteresis loop provided this loop is determined under such conditions that there is no mechanical motion and no change in the relative distribution of the lines of force. This relation is based

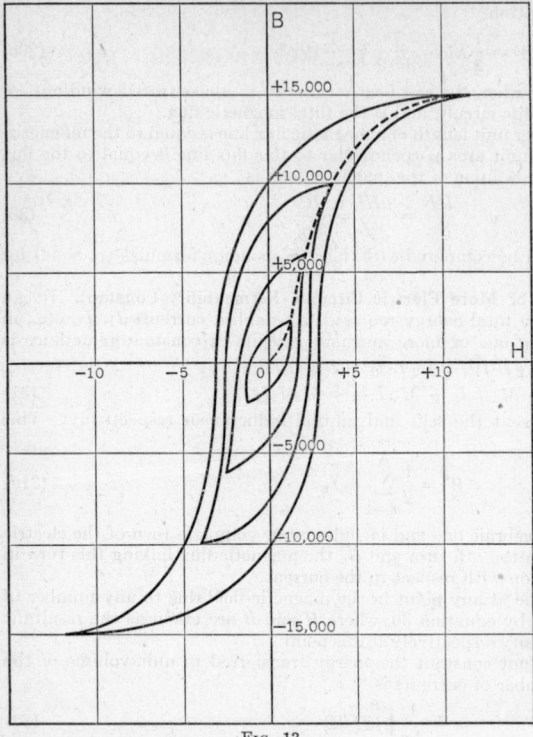

Fig. 13

on the further assumption that unit distance on one scale represents one gauss and that unit distance on the other scale represents one gilbert per centimeter. The following empirical formula is useful in determining hysteresis loss.

$$w = \eta B_m{}^{1.6} \text{ ergs per cubic centimeter per cycle} \tag{33}$$

where η is a coefficient depending upon the substance and B_m is the maximum flux density reached during a cycle.

The power loss per unit weight of magnetic material is given by

$$P_h = kfB_m{}^{1.6} \text{ watts per pound} \tag{33a}$$

where f is the frequency in cycles per second and k is a constant.

Eddy Currents. Since a varying magnetic field induces an emf in every path which links the flux, such an emf will in general cause a flow of current in the magnetic materials composing the magnetic circuit. Such currents, called *eddy-currents* or *Foucault currents*, cause rI^2 losses. Eddy currents can be distinguished from ordinary induced currents by the fact that they are due solely to the lines of force which pass *through* the space occupied by the conducting mass. Ordinary induced currents are produced by lines of force which *link* the conductor but do not pass through the space occupied by the conducting mass. It is customary wherever possible to laminate magnetic cores in order to increase the resistance of the path of induced eddy currents. The eddy current loss in metal sheets is given by

$$P_e = \frac{\pi^2}{6 \times 10^{16}\rho} (afB_m)^2 \text{ watts per cubic centimeter} \tag{34}$$

where ρ is the resistivity of the material, a is the thickness of each sheet, f is the frequency of the eddy-currents, and B_m is the maximum value of the flux density during a cycle. Equation 34 holds provided (a) that the lines of force are parallel to the planes of the laminations, (b) that the laminations are thoroughly insulated from each other, and (c) that the thickness of each lamination is small in comparison with its other dimensions. The combination of hysteresis loss and eddy current loss is called *total core loss.*

13. MECHANICAL FORCES OF ELECTROMAGNETIC ORIGIN

Mechanical Forces in the Magnetic Field. Experience shows that all bodies in which an electric current exists, and all bodies in which a magnetic flux exists, exert in general mutual mechanical forces upon one another tending to produce a relative motion of these bodies such as will increase the energy of the magnetic field. Let f be the component of the force tending to move any body in the field in a given direction and let dW be the increase in the energy of the field due to displacing the body a distance dx in this direction; then

$$f = \frac{dW}{dx} \tag{35}$$

provided this displacement does not alter the existing mmf's in the field.

Similarly calling T the component of the torque tending to turn any body in the field about a given axis, and dW the increase in the magnetic energy due to the turning of the body through an angle $d\alpha$ radians about this axis, then

$$T = \frac{dW}{d\alpha} \tag{35a}$$

provided this displacement does not alter the existing mmf's in the field.

Equations 35 and 35a also give the actual force and torque respectively during a change in position which does cause a change in the mmf's in the field, provided dW is taken to represent the net increase in the energy of the field. This force and torque may differ greatly from the steady-state force and torque.

Force Produced by a Magnetic Field on a Coil Carrying a Current. When the magnetic flux, threading an electric circuit in the right-handed screw direction with respect to the current, increases by an amount $d\phi$, the energy output of the circuit is $dw = NId\phi$, where N is the number of turns linked by this increase in flux and I is the current in each turn. This is the energy input into the magnetic field. Whence if an increase in flux $d\phi$ is produced through the coil when it moves a distance dx, the force acting on the coil in the direction of dx is

$$f = NI \frac{d\phi}{dx}; \tag{36}$$

$d\phi$ represents the increase in the flux linking the coil in the right-handed screw direction with respect to the current in it or the number of flux lines which cut the coil as the result of its motion. Similarly, when the coil is so mounted that it can move only about a fixed axis, then the value of the torque tending to turn it about this axis is

$$T = NI \frac{d\phi}{d\alpha} \tag{36a}$$

where $d\phi$ represents the increase in the flux linking the coil in the right-handed screw direction with respect to the current in it when the coil turns through an angle α (in radians).

From these relations it follows that a coil carrying an electric current, when in a magnetic field due to any other agent (current or permanent magnet), always tends to take up that position in which it will embrace the maximum possible flux linking the coil in the right-handed screw direction with respect to the current in it. This accounts for the attraction of two parallel coils when they carry currents in the same direction, and the repulsion of two such coils when they carry currents in opposite directions. This principle is useful in determining the direction of motion of the moving element in such devices as the electric motor, galvanometer, current balance, and electrodynamometer.

Torque on the Coil When Its Plane Is Parallel to the Magnetic Field. When the coil is placed with its plane parallel to the flux lines due to some other agent (e.g., a permanent magnet or another coil carrying a current), the flux linking the coil due to this agent is zero; see Fig. 14. Let the two circles represent sections of the two sides of the coil, its plane being perpendicular to the page; and let the dot in the left-hand circle indicate that the current is up through this side of the coil and the cross in the other circle that it is down through the

Fig. 14

other side. Let B be the flux density of the field constant for each point along the flux line since the flux lines are parallel; let A be the area of the coil; and let $\phi = BA$, that is, ϕ represents the total flux which would be produced through the coil by a uniform field of flux density B at right angles to it. Then the torque on the coil when its plane is parallel to the field is

$$T = N\phi I \tag{37}$$

This relation is useful in calculating the torque on the moving element of a galvanometer, ammeter, electrodynamometer, wattmeter, etc.

Average Torque on a Coil Rotating in a Magnetic Field. Consider a coil which is rotating with an angular velocity ω about a fixed axis in a magnetic field due to some other agent (e.g., an armature coil rotating in the magnetic field produced by the current in the field coils). Let the current in this coil be constant and in the same direction with respect to the coil while the coil turns from the position in which it embraces the maximum flux ϕ in the left-handed screw direction to the position (a half revolution to a 2-pole machine) when it embraces this same maximum flux ϕ in the right-handed screw direction. The total change in the flux while the coil turns through this angle, π radians in a 2-pole machine, is 2ϕ, whence the average torque turning the coil through this half revolution is

$$T = \frac{2N}{\pi} I\phi \tag{38}$$

That is, the average torque is proportional to the product of the current and the total flux per pole. When a commutator is provided to change the direction of the current every half turn, the torque is in the same direction for a complete turn.

Force on a Wire in a Magnetic Field. Consider a wire of length l forming part of a closed circuit, Fig. 15. Let B be the value of the flux density at the wire and I the current in the direction indicated, and let the lines representing the flux be perpendicular to the wire in the direction from the eye to the page. When this wire moves a distance dx to the left the flux threading the closed loop formed by the circuit is increased by an amount $d\phi = Bldx$, whence the force acting on the wire is (from equation 36):

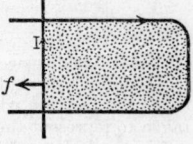

Fig. 15

$$f = BlI \tag{39}$$

Left-hand Rule. The relative directions of this force, the flux density B, and the current I may be conveniently determined by pointing the forefinger of the left hand in the direction of the flux and the middle finger in the direction of the current: then if the thumb is held perpendicular to these two fingers it will point in the direction in which the force tends to move the wire. Compare with the right-handed rule for emf.

Force between Two Current-carrying Conductors. The mutual force between any two electric circuits carrying currents i_1 and i_2, due to the magnetic field of these currents, may be readily found by combining equations 31 and 35. This gives for the component of this force in any direction the value

$$f_x = i_1 i_2 \frac{dM}{dx} \tag{40}$$

where dM is the increase in the mutual inductance between the two circuits when one circuit is displaced a distance dx with respect to the other, the distance dx being measured in the direction in which it is wished to find the component of the force. In this formula, i_1 and i_2 are both to be considered as positive when they link the mutual flux in the same direction. From this relation follows the well-known fact that two coils, or conductors, carrying currents which are in the same direction attract each other, since when one coil is moved toward the other their mutual inductance increases.

The mutual inductance of two long parallel wires when they are far apart relative to their diameters is

$$M = 2l \log_e \frac{2l}{D} \tag{41}$$

where D is their distance apart and l their length, both in centimeters. Hence, from equation 40 the force exerted by one of two parallel wires on the other is

$$f = \frac{2i_1 i_2}{D} \text{ dynes per centimeter} \tag{42}$$

and is at right angles to the wires and in the plane formed by them. This formula is also approximately true for parallel conductors of any cross-section, provided they are far apart relative to the greatest dimension of their cross-section. When this condition does not hold, e.g., in parallel bus-bars close to each other, the formula for the force is much more complex (see Dwight, H. B., Repulsion between Strap Conductors, *Elec. World*, 70. p. 522, Sept. 15, 1917).

Forces on Magnetic Bodies in a Magnetic Field. In general, the reluctance of a magnetic field to the flux set up by a given mmf depends upon the relative positions of the various magnetic bodies in the field with respect to one another and with respect to the electric circuit producing this mmf. When any magnetic body in the field is displaced the total reluctance will, in general, be changed owing chiefly to the change in the dimensions of the air portion of the circuit. From equations 29a and 35 it can be shown that the force acting on any magnetic body in the field is in the direction of the flux lines threading it and has the value

$$f = -\frac{1}{8\pi}\,\phi^2\,\frac{d\mathcal{R}}{dx} \tag{43}$$

(provided the mmf remains constant) where ϕ represents the total flux threading the body and $d\mathcal{R}$ represents the increase in the reluctance of the magnetic circuit corresponding to a displacement dx of the body in the direction of the flux lines. The minus sign in this formula indicates that the force is always in the direction in which a motion of the body would decrease the reluctance of the circuit. In deducing this expression it is assumed that the permeability of each body in the field is constant. It can also be shown that to a close approximation the same formula holds for actual magnetic bodies, for which the permeability is not a constant.

The above relation accounts for the attraction of one magnet for another when their unlike poles are nearer each other than their like poles, and the repulsion of two magnets when their like poles are nearer than their unlike poles. It also accounts for the attraction of iron or other paramagnetic substance by either pole of a magnet or by either " face " of an electric circuit, and the repulsion of a diamagnetic substance by either pole of a magnet or either face of an electric circuit.

ELECTROSTATICS AND THE DIELECTRIC CIRCUIT

14. ELECTROSTATIC FIELDS, POTENTIALS AND CURRENTS

Electric Fields of Force. In any portion of a substance in which the electricity is acted upon by a force tending to move it, there is said to be an *electric field of force*, or briefly an *electric field*. An electric field is also said to exist in any region of free space where a charge, if placed there, would have a force exerted upon it tending to move it.

Intensity of an Electric Field. The *intensity of an electric field F* at any point is defined as the force exerted on a unit positive charge at this point by the agent or agents producing the field, i.e., by the agent or agents tending to move the charge. The direction of the field intensity, or the direction of the field, is defined as the direction of the force acting on a positive charge at this point. A positive charge then moves or tends to move in the direction of the field, and a negative charge moves or tends to move in the opposite direction.

The unit of electric field intensity has not been given any special name, but since it is of the same nature as emf per unit distance, the intensity at any point may be conveniently expressed as so many volts, abvolts, or statvolts per centimeter or per inch. See Section III. Hence electric field intensity is frequently called the potential, or voltage, " gradient."

Lines of Electric Force. Lines of Electric Intensity. A line drawn in an electric field in such a manner that its direction at each point coincides with the direction of the field at that point is called a *line of electric force*. A line of force is usually a curved line, though in certain special cases it may be straight. Any number of such lines may be drawn in an electric field, but no two of these lines can intersect. The density of these lines, i.e., the number drawn through unit area perpendicular to their direction, may be chosen arbitrarily to represent the value of the field intensity at this area, and when so drawn are preferably called *lines of electric intensity*, as distinguished from flux and stream lines defined below. The term *lines of force*, however, is frequently used to designate any one of these three sets of lines, but this loose use of the term is likely at times to lead to much confusion. The term *line of electric force* will be used in this article to designate merely the direction of the field at any point; in any statement involving the density of these lines the proper one of the other terms will be employed.

Electric Equipotential Surfaces. A surface drawn in an electric field in such a manner that it is perpendicular at each point to the line of force through that point is called an *electric equipotential surface.* The electric intensity has no component along such a surface, and therefore no work is required to move a charge from one point to another over any path in such a surface.

Emf's and Differences of Potential. The work done by the field intensity F in moving unit positive charge around any closed path or circuit (Fig. 1) in an electric field is defined as the emf acting around this path. Emf is not a force in the mechanical sense but is work per unit charge. The relation between emf E and field intensity F, where F is the magnitude of the vector F, is analogous to that between work and mechanical force, viz.:

$$E = \int_0 (F \cos \theta) dl \tag{1}$$

where dl represents an elementary length of the path, $(F \cos \theta)$ the component of the field intensity along dl, and $\int_0$ represents the integral around this closed path. When the field intensity has the same value F at every point of a path and coincides in direction with the path at every point, the emf acting around the closed loop is

$$E = Fl \tag{1a}$$

where l is the total length of the path.

In Fig. 1 let the path from 1 to 2 be in the direction of the line of force from 1 to 2, let E_{12} be an emf whose source is between 1 and 2 and whose direction is from 1 to 2; then the general expression for the potential drop from 1 to 2 is

$$V_{12} = \int_1^2 Fdl - E_{12} \tag{2}$$

If the field intensity along the path from 1 to 2 is negligible, then $V_{12} = -E_{12}$; hence an emf in a given direction is equivalent to a negative drop of potential, i.e., is equivalent to an actual rise of potential. Comparing equation 2 with equation 1 it is evident that the total drop of potential around a closed circuit is always zero. This relation is conveniently expressed by the formula

$$\Sigma V = 0 \tag{3}$$

which holds for every closed path or circuit. This is one way of stating Kirchhoff's second law. See Art. 7, equation 16.

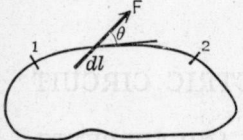

Fig. 1

Voltage Gradient. Since from equation 2 the magnitude of the field intensity F is equal in volts to the drop in voltage per unit length in the direction of F, the electric field intensity is also frequently called the voltage gradient.

Flow of Electricity. Whenever an electric field is set up in a substance by any means whatever a displacement of the electricity in that substance always takes place, the nature of the displacement depending upon the nature of the substance. The positive electricity within the substance is displaced or orientated in the direction of the field intensity and the negative electricity in the opposite direction, until an opposing force is set up which just balances the forces due to the impressed field. In metallic conduction, the flow of electrons in a direction opposite to the field constitutes the electric current. In electrolytes there is a migration of positive ions in the direction of the field, and of electrons opposite to the direction of the field. It is believed that, in good insulators, actual migration is negligible but that molecules of the substance are deformed and reorientated in such a manner as to produce a momentary motion of positive electricity in the direction of the field, and of negative electricity opposite to the direction of the field. (See Art. 27 and Art. 28.)

The displacement of the electricity within a substance cannot be measured directly, but only in terms of some effect produced thereby. Two effects which always result when electricity is displaced are: (1) a magnetic field is established around the path along which the displacement takes place (but disappears when the electricity comes to rest); and (2) heat is developed in the path of the displacement. The magnetic field produced by a displacement or flow of electricity is usually taken as the measure of the rate of flow, i.e., of the quantity of electricity displaced per unit time through a surface perpendicular to the direction of the displacement. This rate of flow is called the *intensity* of the electric current, or simply the electric current.

A flow of positive electricity in one direction is equivalent magnetically to a flow of an equal amount of negative electricity in the opposite direction; hence the total flow along the given path is the sum of the positive electricity displaced per unit time in one direction past a point in this path plus the negative electricity displaced per unit time past this point in the opposite direction. The *direction* of the electric current is taken as the direction in which the positive electricity is displaced, and it is, therefore, the same as the direction of the field intensity.

Current Due to Varying Electric Field. When the electric field in any substance is varying, the total magnetic effect produced is found to depend not only upon the rate of displacement of the electricity within the substance, but also upon the rate of change of the electric field.   In fact, a magnetic field is produced around a path in free space along which the intensity of the electric field is varying.   In dealing with varying electric fields it is found convenient to consider the variation of the field intensity as equivalent to an actual flow of electricity, and to take as the total equivalent electric current the flow of electricity which would produce the same magnetic field as that actually observed; the actual flow of electricity is in general less than this equivalent current, but the difference is negligible except in substances which are good insulators.

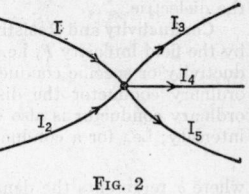

Fig. 2

Continuity of an Electric Current. When a varying electric field is considered as equivalent to an electric current, it is found that the total equivalent current coming up to any point or surface in any network of circuits, no matter how complicated, is always equal to the total current leaving that point or surface, irrespective of the nature of the substances through which the currents are constant or are varying.   For example, in Fig. 2,

$$i_1 + i_2 = i_3 + i_4 + i_5 \tag{4}$$

Or calling the currents coming up to any point positive, and the currents leaving that point negative, the algebraic sum of all the currents at any point in a network of circuits is always zero.   This fundamental principle is conveniently expressed by the formula

$$\Sigma i = 0 \tag{4a}$$

which holds at every junction point both for variable and for continuous currents. This is a generalized form of Kirchhoff's first law. See Art. 7, equation 15.

Stream Lines of Electric Current. Current Density. As a consequence of the continuity of an electric current, the total current in any substance of any size or shape may be looked upon as made up of a number of small streams of electricity flowing side by side, the strength (quantity of electricity per second) of each stream being constant throughout its length.   If the cross-section of each stream at any point is so chosen that each stream represents unit current (unit quantity per second), then the number of these streams crossing unit area of a surface perpendicular to their direction will be equal to the current per unit area of this surface, or to the current density at this surface.   Each such stream may be represented graphically by a line coinciding with its axis; such lines are called *stream lines*.   When the stream lines are drawn as described their direction at any point gives the direction of the current at this point, and the number of these lines per unit area perpendicular to their direction is equal to the current density at this point.

For an insulated wire the stream lines are parallel to the axis of the wire, except in the immediate vicinity of its ends; in a long wire this non-uniformity at the ends is negligible. All the stream lines in an ordinary wire may also, in practice, be considered as coinciding, and the wire may, therefore, be treated as a geometrical line as regards external effects. However, for a short rod or strip (such as an ammeter shunt) connected in the circuit by wires attached to its ends, the stream lines are not in general parallel but diverge from one terminal and converge toward the other.

Conduction Current and Displacement Current. Experience shows that, when an electric field is established in any substance, the total equivalent electric current set up depends (1) upon the value of the field intensity, (2) upon the rate of change of the field intensity, and (3) upon the nature of the substance in which the field is established.   The current density σ at any point at any instant may in general be expressed by the relation:

$$\sigma = \gamma F + \frac{1}{4\pi} \frac{d}{dt} (kF) \tag{5}$$

where F is the field intensity, γ and k are coefficients depending upon the chemical nature and physical condition of the substances at the point in question, and $\dfrac{d}{dt}$ means the rate of change with respect to time.   The factor 4π arises from the historical definition of the quantity k; see below.   The total current may then be considered as the sum of the two components having respectively the densities

$$\sigma_1 = \gamma F \quad \text{and} \quad \sigma_2 = \frac{1}{4\pi} \frac{d}{dt} (kF) \tag{6}$$

The first of these components (σ_1) is called the conduction current; the second $\sigma(_2)$ is commonly called the displacement current. The term displacement current, however, is something of a misnomer, for both components of the total current are probably due, in part at least, to a displacement of electricity. The conduction current is the only appreciable component in substances usually classed as conductors, and the displacement current is appreciable only in substances ordinarily classed as dielectrics. The conduction current in a dielectric is usually small, though measurable; it is frequently called the leakage current. When the electric field in a dielectric is rapidly varying, the displacement current may be many times greater than the conduction or leakage current through the dielectric.

Conductivity and Resistivity. The quotient of the density σ_1 of the conduction current by the field intensity F, i.e., the coefficient γ in the expression $\sigma_1 = \gamma F$ is called the conductivity or specific conductance of the substance at the point in question. Since in an ordinary conductor the displacement current is inappreciable, the conductivity of an ordinary conductor is also equal to the density of the total current divided by the field intensity; i.e., for a conductor

$$\sigma = \gamma F \qquad (7)$$

where σ represents the density of the total current. Experience shows that for a given conductor at constant temperature (and also at constant pressure, in a gas) this coefficient γ is a constant irrespective of the strength, distribution, or time variation of the current. The value of γ for a dielectric, however, is not in general a constant but depends upon the time variation of the field intensity.

The above relation between σ and F may also be written

$$F = \rho\sigma \qquad (7a)$$

where ρ is the reciprocal of the conductivity γ. The constant ρ is called the *resistivity* or *specific resistance* of the substance. Values of γ and ρ for various conductors and insulating materials are given in Section XI. For the units of conductivity and resistivity, see Section III.

15. DIELECTRIC FLUX

Dielectric Flux and Dielectric Flux Density. As noted above, the displacement current through a dielectric at any point depends upon the rate of change of the electric field intensity and upon the nature of the dielectric. The density of this displacement current at any point may be expressed by the relation

$$\sigma_2 = \frac{1}{4\pi} \frac{d}{dt} (kF) \qquad (8)$$

where F is the field intensity and k a coefficient depending upon the nature of the dielectric. The coefficient k in this expression is the so-called *dielectric coefficient* or *dielectric constant*.

The quantity kF, whose rate of change is equal to 4π times the density of the displacement current, is called the *dielectric flux density* and may be represented by the symbol D. Then

$$D = kF \qquad (9)$$

The direction of the dielectric flux density is arbitrarily chosen to be the same as that of the electric field intensity F. Through any surface of area A at each point of which the dielectric flux density has a constant value D and is perpendicular to that surface, there is said to exist a *dielectric flux* equal to DA. The total dielectric flux through a surface may be represented by the symbol ψ.

In general, the total dielectric flux through any surface is

$$\psi = \int D \cos \alpha \, ds \qquad (10)$$

where ds represents any elementary area of this surface, $D \cos \alpha$ the component of flux density normal to the surfaces at ds, and $\int$ the sum of all the products $D \cos \alpha \, ds$ for that surface. The total displacement current through this surface is then

$$i = \frac{1}{4\pi} \frac{d\psi}{dt} \qquad (11)$$

Lines of Dielectric Flux. The electric flux through any surface may be represented by lines drawn in the same direction as the lines of electric intensity, but of such a density that their number per unit area perpendicular to their direction at any point is equal to the dielectric flux density at this point. The number of these lines cutting any surface is then equal to the total dielectric flux through this surface. The ratio of the number of flux lines through any surface to the number of lines of electric intensity through that surface is equal to the dielectric coefficient of the substance in which the field exists.

Electric Charge and Dielectric Flux. Within any substance of uniform structure throughout, the dielectric flux lines are continuous lines; i.e., the number of these lines coming up to one side of a surface within such a substance is equal to the number of these lines leaving the other side of that surface. Experience shows that it is impossible to produce an appreciable dielectric flux in those substances ordinarily classed as conductors; hence dielectric flux lines cannot pass through a good conductor, but terminate at its surface. Every dielectric is a conductor to at least a slight extent, and on account of this fact not all the dielectric flux lines coming up through one dielectric to the surface of contact between this dielectric and another pass through the second dielectric, but some of them terminate at this surface.

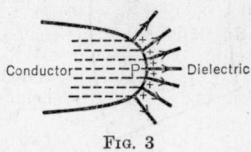

Fig. 3

Experience shows that, to establish an electric field in the dielectric around a conductor, electricity must be conducted through the conductor to the surface of contact between the conductor and the dielectric. For example, consider a good conductor in contact with a perfect dielectric (Fig. 3); a momentary conduction current must flow through the conductor along the stream lines of the conduction current, represented by the dotted lines. While the field is being established (and therefore varying), a displacement current is set up in the dielectric requiring an equal conduction current in the conductor, and consequently $\frac{1}{4\pi}$ times the rate of change of the dielectric flux (ψ) established in the dielectric must be equal to the conduction current (i) flowing up to this surface through the conductor, i.e.,

$$\frac{1}{4\pi}\frac{d\psi}{dt} = i$$

or

$$\psi = 4\pi \int i\,dt = 4\pi Q, \tag{12}$$

where Q is the quantity of electricity conducted through the conductor to this surface.

This relation is a general one, viz., the total dielectric flux from any area A in the surface of a conductor is equal to 4π times the total charge on this area. Hence every flux line originates at a positively charged conducting surface and terminates at a negatively charged conducting surface, 4π of these lines connecting each unit positive to each unit negative charge.

The quantity of electricity conducted through a conductor when a momentary current is established through it can be measured readily by means of a ballistic galvanometer, and consequently the dielectric flux (equal to $4\pi Q$) may readily be determined.

Dielectric flux may be expressed in the same units as electric charge, viz., coulombs, statcoulombs, or abcoulombs; see Section III.

Surface Density of Charge. When there is no current in a conductor there can be no electric field within it (see equation 7); and therefore the surface of a conductor in which no current is flowing is always an equipotential surface. Hence the lines of electrostatic intensity, in the surrounding dielectric, and therefore the dielectric flux lines also, must leave or enter this surface in a direction perpendicular to it. The dielectric flux density in the dielectric just outside a conducting surface in which there is no electric current is perpendicular to this surface and has the magnitude

$$D = 4\pi\sigma_c \tag{13}$$

where σ_c is the charge per unit area of the surface at this point, or the *surface density* of the charge.

Dielectric Flux Density Due to a Number of Charged Conductors. It can be shown that, when any number of charged conductors are surrounded by a uniform dielectric, the dielectric flux density at any point in the field may be expressed by considering each elementary surface having a charge q as producing at any point P at a distance r from q a flux density equal to q/r^2, in the direction of the line from q to P when q is positive and in the direction of the line from P to q when q is negative. The total flux density at P due to all the charges is then the vector summation

$$D = \sum \frac{q}{r^2} r_1 \tag{14}$$

in which r_1 is a unit vector in the direction from q to P.

16. ELECTROSTATIC CAPACITANCE, CONDENSERS, AND INDUCTION

Electrostatic Capacitance and Condensers. To establish a given dielectric flux ψ through a given dielectric a certain difference of electric potential is always required. Consider any portion of an electric field (Fig. 4) between the two equipotential surfaces S and S_1 bounded laterally by a surface tangent at each point to the flux line through that point. Let V be the drop of potential from S to S_1, and let ψ be the dielectric flux through this region. When there is no source of emf between S and S_1 the quotient

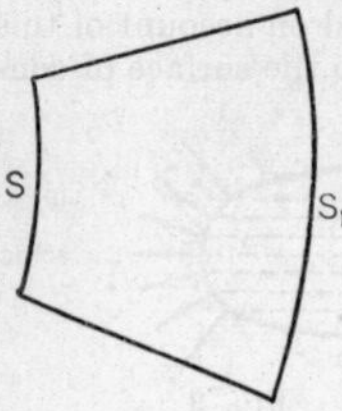

$$C = \frac{\psi}{4\pi V} \tag{15}$$

is defined as the electrostatic capacitance of this portion of the field.

When the equipotential surfaces S and S_1 are the surfaces of two conductors, the two conductors and the dielectric between

Fig. 4

them are said to form an *electric condenser*. When all the flux lines from one conductor end on the second conductor (e.g., when they are given equal and opposite charges by connecting them respectively to the two terminals of a source of emf), then the flux from one to the other is equal to $4\pi Q$ where Q is the numerical value of the total charge on either conductor. The capacitance of the condenser may then be written

$$C = \frac{Q}{V} \tag{15a}$$

When there are several charged conductors in the field, the total flux from one conductor does not in general end on another single conductor, but some of the flux lines from conductor 1 may run to 2, some to 3, etc. Let ψ_{12} be that portion of the flux from any conductor 1 which ends on any other conductor 2, and let V_{12} be the drop of potential from 1 to 2; then the capacitance between conductor 1 and conductor 2 is

$$C_{12} = \frac{\psi_{12}}{4\pi V_{12}} \tag{15b}$$

Or, calling Q_{12} that portion of the charge on 1 which is balanced by an equal and opposite charge on 2, the capacitance between 1 and 2 is

$$C_{12} = \frac{Q_{12}}{V_{12}} \tag{15c}$$

The unit of capacitance in the practical system of units is the farad, but as this is a very large unit, a unit equal to one-millionth of a farad, called the microfarad, is usually employed. The cgs electrostatic unit is called the statfarad, and the cgs electromagnetic unit the abfarad. See Section III.

Potential Coefficients, Electrostatic Induction Coefficients. Consider any number of conductors 0, 1, 2, 3, etc., either (1) at a great distance from all other conductors or (2) completely surrounded by a hollow conducting shell, the inside surface of which is to be considered as one of the conductors, say 0, of the system. The electrostatic condition of such a system of conductors is uninfluenced by any electrostatic effects produced outside the system; it may therefore be called an *electrostatically independent system*.

Any conductor of an electrostatically independent system may be chosen as a conductor of reference; let this reference conductor be designated as conductor 0. Let v_{10}, v_{20}, v_{30}, etc., represent the potential drop from 1 to 0, from 2 to 0, from 3 to 0, etc., and let q_0, q_1, q_2, q_3, etc., represent the charges on 0, 1, 2, 3, etc. Then, if the relative positions of the various conductors and insulators in the field remain unaltered and the specific inductance capacitances of the various insulating materials between the conductors are constant (not necessarily the same for each insulating material, however), the following relations hold for all values of the charges on and potential drops between conductors irrespective of how the conductors may be connected (provided the connecting wires are of small cross-section compared with the dimensions of the conductors):

$$\left.\begin{aligned}
v_{10} &= A_{11}q_1 + A_{12}q_2 + A_{13}q_3 + \text{etc.}, \\
v_{20} &= A_{12}q_1 + A_{22}q_2 + A_{23}q_3 + \text{etc.}, \\
v_{30} &= A_{13}q_1 + A_{23}q_2 + A_{33}q_3 + \text{etc.}, \\
q_0 &= -\ (q_1 + q_2 + q_3 + \text{etc.}),
\end{aligned}\right\} \tag{15d}$$

where all the A's are constants depending upon the distances apart of the conductors and the nature of the insulating medium between them. The coefficients A in these equations may be called the *potential coefficients* of the system of conductors.

The above equations may also be written:

$$\left.\begin{array}{l} q_1 = B_{11}v_{10} + B_{12}v_{20} + B_{13}v_{30} + \text{etc.,} \\ q_2 = B_{12}v_{10} + B_{22}v_{20} + B_{23}v_{30} + \text{etc.,} \\ q_3 = B_{13}v_{10} + B_{23}v_{20} + B_{33}v_{30} + \text{etc.,} \\ q_0 = -\ (q_1 + q_2 + q_3 + \text{etc.}), \end{array}\right\} \tag{15e}$$

where the B's are also constants and may be expressed directly in terms of the potential coefficients A by solving the equations for q_1, q_2, q_3, etc. The constants B are called the electrostatic induction coefficients, and like the constants A are independent of how the conductors may be charged and of how they may be interconnected. The B's may be expressed directly in terms of the normal and grounded capacitances of the various conductors.

By the *normal capacitance* between any two conductors is meant the capacitance of the condenser formed by these two conductors when all the other conductors are connected to one another and to the conductor of reference, the two conductors of course being insulated therefrom. The normal capacitance between any two conductors of a system, say 1 and 2, is then, from equation 15e

$$C_{12} = \frac{B_{11}B_{12} - B_{12}{}^2}{B_{11} + B_{22} + 2B_{12}} \tag{15f}$$

When the arrangement of the conductors is perfectly symmetrical (as in a three-conductor cable), $B_{11} = B_{22}$ and the normal capacitance between 1 and 2 is

$$C_{12} = 1/2\ (B_{11} - B_{12}) \tag{15g}$$

By the *grounded capacitance* of any conductor of a system is meant the capacitance of the condenser formed by this conductor as one plate, and all the other conductors, including the conductor of reference, connected together as the other plate. The grounded capacitance of conductor 1, say, is then, from equation 15g,

$$C_{1g} = B_{11} \tag{15h}$$

That is, the electrostatic coefficient of self-induction of any given conductor is the same as the grounded capacitance of this conductor.

Electrical Images. The distribution of charge upon conductors may often be found most simply by a method devised by Lord Kelvin. Let it be supposed that a charge $+q$ is placed in the neighborhood of an infinite conducting plane. There will be produced on the plane a charge density σ, which together with the charge $+q$ will produce a given distribution of electric field intensity throughout the region. This field intensity can be shown to be equal to the field intensity which would be produced, in the absence of the conducting plane, by the charge $+q$ and a second charge $-q$ placed at a position such that $+q$ and $-q$ are symmetrical about the plane. The charge $-q$ is called the *electrical image* of the charge $+q$, the name being suggested by the optical analogy.

The capacitance of an actual condenser formed by a wire and the earth (assuming the earth to be an infinite conducting plane parallel to the wire) is the same as the capacitance to neutral of the fictitious condenser formed by the wire and its image.

Factors upon Which Capacitance Depends. The capacitance of a given portion of a dielectric depends upon (a) the dielectric coefficient k, (b) the length of the dielectric flux lines through the dielectric, (c) the cross-section of the dielectric at right angles to the flux lines, and (d) the distribution of the flux lines over this cross-section (compare with electric conductance). In general, the capacitance of any portion of a dielectric bounded laterally by flux lines and at the ends by equipotential surfaces (Fig. 4) can be expressed by the formula

$$C = \frac{k\psi}{4\pi \int Ddl} \tag{16a}$$

where k is the dielectric coefficient, ψ the total dielectric flux through the given portion of dielectric, dl any elementary length along one of the flux lines, and D the component of the dielectric flux density in the direction of dl at this point, the integral being taken along the flux line from one end surface to the other. When the end surfaces are conductors charged with $+Q$ and $-Q$ units respectively, then

$$C = \frac{kq}{\int Ddl} \tag{16b}$$

By the application of this formula the capacitance of various practical forms of condensers may be calculated. It should be noted that the capacitance of a condenser depends upon the distribution of the dielectric flux (k being assumed constant), but not upon the absolute value of the flux; i.e., for a given dielectric and given distribution of flux the capacitance is a constant. In general, when any conductor or dielectric of a different specific inductive capacitance is placed in the electric field set up by the charged plates of a condenser, the distribution of the flux, and therefore the capacitance of the condenser, are altered.

Relation between Conductance and Capacitance. Comparing $r = \dfrac{\rho \int \sigma dl}{I}$ and equation 16a, it is apparent that, when the dielectric flux lines and the current stream lines have the same distribution in any given region, the ratio of the conductance of this region to the capacitance of this region is $4\pi\gamma/k$, where k is the dielectric coefficient and γ the conductivity of the material in this region. Hence the formulas for the capacitance and conductance of the dielectric between the plates of any shape or size of condenser differ only by a constant coefficient. That is, if C is the capacitance of any condenser, then

$$g = \frac{4\pi\gamma}{k} \cdot C \tag{17}$$

is the conductance of the dielectric between its plates.

Charge and Discharge of a Condenser. To charge a condenser a difference of electric potential must be established between its plates. This may be done, as noted above, by connecting the two plates of the condenser respectively to the two terminals of any source of emf; see Fig. 5. If the dielectric has a very high resistance and the source of emf has

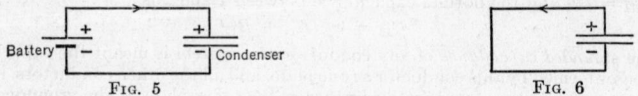

Battery   Condenser

Fig. 5   Fig. 6

a constant value E, the current set up in this circuit will continue only until a difference of potential equal to E has been established across the two plates of the condenser, or until a charge equal to CE has been transferred from the *negative* to the *positive* plate of the condenser. The establishment of the electric flux through the dielectric of the condenser may be looked upon as setting up in the dielectric itself an opposing force analogous to the opposing force set up in a spring when it is compressed. When the opposing force just balances the impressed force a steady state is attained, just as the compressing of a spring ceases when the force producing the compression is just balanced by the opposing force due to the elasticity of the spring.

When a condenser has thus been charged, the wires connecting it to the source of emf may be removed and the condenser remains charged for a length of time depending upon the resistance of the dielectric separating the plates; the higher this resistance the longer the time that the condenser remains charged. If the plates are moved apart they still retain their charges, one plate a positive charge and the other a negative charge, but the distribution of these charges on the plates will in general become altered. Experience shows that a mechanical force is required to separate the charged plates irrespective of whether or not they are connected to the source of emf.

When the two charged plates are short-circuited by a wire, as shown in Fig. 6, a momentary current is established through the wire, and the electric field between the plates and the charges disappear. The quantity of electricity discharged through the wires is equal to the quantity of charge originally on either plate. A charged condenser, therefore, acts like a source of emf, the direction of this emf around the circuit containing the condenser being in the direction through the condenser from its negative to its positive plate. A condenser when it is being charged may also be looked upon as producing a back emf, that is, an emf opposing the emf which charges it. When a condenser is considered from this point of view only the conducting portion of the circuit is to be considered in applying Kirchhoff's laws. When the condenser has an appreciable leakage its resistance must be considered to be in parallel with its emf.

Charging Current and Leakage Current. The displacement current through the dielectric of a condenser is frequently called the *charging* current. The conduction current through the dielectric is called the *leakage* current. Let C be the capacitance of the condenser, g the conductance of the dielectric, and v the voltage across the condenser; then the total current through the condenser is

$$i = gv + C\frac{dv}{dt} \tag{18}$$

where $\dfrac{dv}{dt}$ represents the rate of charge of v with time. The component gv of this current

is the leakage current, and the component $C\,\dfrac{dv}{dt}$ is the charging current.

Capacitances in Series. When several capacitances * are connected end to end so that the same dielectric flux passes through each of them, they are said to be *in series*. The total capacitance of any number of individual capacitances C_1, C_2, C_3, etc., connected in series is C where

$$\frac{1}{C} = \frac{1}{C_1} + \frac{1}{C_2} + \frac{1}{C_3} + \cdots \tag{19}$$

Capacitances in Parallel. When several capacitances are connected between the same pair of equipotential surfaces so that the same potential drop is established through each, they are said to be *in parallel*. When there are no emf's in any of the circuits between the two equipotential surfaces the total equivalent capacitance of any number of capacitances C_1, C_2, C_3, etc., connected in parallel is

$$C = C_1 + C_2 + C_3 + \cdots \tag{20}$$

Specific Inductive Capacitance and Dielectric Coefficient. From equation 16a it is evident that, when the capacitance of a given condenser is measured (1) with a dielectric A between the plates and (2) with some other dielectric B between these plates, then the ratio of the two capacitances is the same as the ratio of the dielectric coefficients of the two dielectrics. The *specific inductive capacitance* of any dielectric is defined as the ratio of the capacitance of a condenser having this substance as its dielectric to the capacitance of the same condenser when air forms the dielectric between the plates. The specific inductive capacitance is, therefore, independent of the system of units employed.

The cgs electrostatic system of units is based on the arbitrary choice of unity as the dielectric coefficient of free space; hence, in this system the specific inductive capacitance and the dielectric coefficient are numerically equal. In the cgs electromagnetic system of units the dielectric coefficient of free space is not unity but $\dfrac{1}{9 \times 10^{20}}$ (i.e., the reciprocal of the square of the velocity of light). In the practical system of units, when the centimeter is taken as the unit of length, the dielectric coefficient of free space is $\dfrac{1}{9 \times 10^{11}}$. Hence, calling K the specific inductive capacitance of any dielectric referred to free space as unity, and k its dielectric coefficient, then in the

cgs electrostatic system $\qquad\qquad k = K$

cgs electromagnetic system $\qquad\quad k = \dfrac{K}{9 \times 10^{20}}$

Practical system (cm as unit of length) $k = \dfrac{K}{9 \times 10^{11}}$

Values of the specific inductive capacitance of various insulating materials are given in Section 12.

17. DIELECTRIC LOSSES

Electric Absorption and Residual Charge. The value of the dielectric coefficient k of a given dielectric is not strictly a constant unless the dielectric is perfectly homogeneous. For such non-homogeneous substances as glass, mica, rubber, paper, and cloth, the dielectric coefficient is found to depend upon the time of electrification, i.e., upon the length of time that the voltage is applied, its value increasing with the time of electrification. This phenomenon is sometimes described as *electric absorption*, the idea being that the charge from the plates of the condenser soaks into the dielectric, for an increase in the dielectric coefficient for a given impressed voltage means a greater quantity of electricity conducted to the plates. This idea is also in accord with the experimental fact that when such a condenser is discharged by short-circuiting it with a wire, Fig. 6, the wire then being removed, a *residual* charge appears on the plates after a lapse of a few seconds.

Dielectric Hysteresis. A phenomenon closely associated with electric absorption is the fact that when the electric field in a heterogeneous dielectric is caused to vary rapidly an amount of heat is dissipated in the dielectric greatly in excess of that which can be accounted for in terms of its leakage resistance as determined by continuous-current measurements. This may be due in part to an actual increase in the resistance of the

---

* Either condensers, or dielectrics of different kinds, sizes, or shapes, in contact along equipotential surfaces.

dielectric with the speed of variation of the field, or it may be due to a phenomenon analogous to magnetic hysteresis, i.e., to a lag of the dielectric flux density behind the electric field intensity. Whatever may be the cause of this extra loss of power for rapidly varying fields, it is generally described as the loss due to "dielectric hysteresis." The heat developed is in many cases quite appreciable.

Dielectric Strength. When an electric field is established by a charge on a conductor, and the intensity of this field is increased, corona forms in the dielectric at the surface of conductors, and if this field is further increased a point is reached at which the dielectric breaks down. Under some conditions (corona) the breakdown is not permanent but results in the acquisition of a much higher conductivity by the dielectric only while the voltage gradient is maintained above the critical value, the dielectric regaining its insulating property when the field is reduced below this critical value.

18. ELECTROSTATIC ENERGY AND MECHANICAL FORCES

Electrostatic Energy. From the general relation expressed by equation 18, it is evident that when the potential difference between the plates of a condenser is increased from 0 to V the energy input is

$$W = \int_0^t gv^2 \, dt + \int_0^V Cv \, dv \tag{21}$$

The energy represented by the first term on the right-hand side of this equation is dissipated as heat in the dielectric, but the energy represented by the second term, which, when C is constant, may be written

$$W = 1/2 \, CV^2 \tag{22}$$

does not represent a dissipation of heat; this is a fact of experience. Moreover, when the condenser is discharged, by short-circuiting its plates with a wire, this same amount of energy $1/2 \, CV^2$ is transferred to the wire. Hence, the energy represented by $1/2 \, CV^2$ is said to be stored in the condenser, or preferably in the dielectric of the condenser, for the electric force F exists only in the dielectric. This stored energy is called the "electrostatic" energy. It is analogous to the energy stored in a spring when the spring is compressed or stretched. Equation 22 may also be written

$$W = \frac{1}{2} \frac{Q^2}{C} = \frac{1}{2} QV = \frac{1}{8\pi} \psi V \tag{22a}$$

The electrostatic energy per unit volume of an electric field may be written

$$w = \frac{DF}{8\pi} = \frac{kF^2}{8\pi} = \frac{D^2}{8\pi k} \tag{22b}$$

where k is the dielectric coefficient, F the magnitude of the electric field intensity or potential drop per unit distance, and D the magnitude of the dielectric flux density or flux per unit area perpendicular to the direction of the drop.

It should be noted that equations 22 to 22b are based on the assumption that k is a constant, independent of the value of F. When this condition does not hold, the energy required to establish the field is $\int_0^V Cv \, dv$, the evaluation of which depends upon the relation between C and v.

Mechanical Forces in an Electric Field. Experience shows that all bodies (conductors or insulators) in an electric field exert, in general, mutual mechanical forces upon one another tending to produce such a relative motion as will decrease the energy of the field. Let f be the component of the force tending to move any body in the field in a given direction, and let dW be the increase in the energy of the field due to displacing the body a distance dx in this direction; then

$$f = -\frac{dW}{dx} \tag{23}$$

provided this displacement does not cause a change in the existing electric charges in the field. As a consequence of this general relation it can be shown that every charged surface exerts a force of repulsion on every other surface charged with electricity of the same sign, and a force of attraction on every surface charged with electricity of the opposite sign.

In the special case of the two conductors forming a condenser the force of attraction exerted by one conductor on the other is

$$f = -\frac{V^2}{2} \frac{dC}{dx} \tag{23a}$$

where V is the p.d. across the condenser, C is the capacitance of the condenser, and dC represents the increase in the capacitance of the condenser when one conductor moves a distance dx away from the other. This relation results from the substitution of equation 22a in 23. For example, the capacitance of a parallel plate condenser is approximately

$$C = \frac{kA}{4\pi x}$$

where k is the dielectric coefficient, A the area of the smaller plate, and x the distance between the plates. Hence the force of attraction is

$$f = \frac{V^2 kA}{8\pi x^2} \tag{24}$$

ALTERNATING-CURRENT CIRCUITS

19. GENERAL DEFINITIONS

The definitions given below are applicable to currents, electromotive forces, potential differences, or any other function of time. They are the definitions recommended by the sectional committee on electrical definitions of the A.I.E.E.

Periodic Quantities

An **Oscillating Quantity** is a quantity which as a function of some independent variable (such as time) alternately increases and decreases in value, always remaining within finite limits.

A **Periodic Quantity** is an oscillating quantity the values of which recur for equal increments of the independent variable.

The **Period** of a periodic quantity is the smallest value of the increment of the independent variable which separates recurring values of the quantity.

A **Cycle** is the complete series of values of a periodic quantity which occur during a period.

The **Frequency** of a periodic quantity, in which time is the independent variable, is the reciprocal of the period.

The **Angular Velocity** of a periodic quantity is the frequency multiplied by 2π.

An **Alternating Quantity** is a periodic quantity which has alternately positive and negative values.

As **Examples** and to avoid repetition the following statements will be given in terms of electric currents.

If a given current is represented by the equation

$$i = f(t) \tag{1}$$

and if the function $f(t)$ has the property that

$$f(t) = f(t + T) \tag{2}$$

in which T is a constant, then the current is said to be periodic in time and T is the period. If time is measured in seconds then $1/T$ represents the number of periods per second and is usually denoted by f. The frequency f may also be said to be the number of cycles per second. If, as often happens, the current is expressible more simply as

$$i = f(\omega t) \tag{3}$$

in which ω is defined by

$$f(\omega t) = f(\omega t + 2\pi) \tag{4}$$

then the constant ω, being equal to 2π divided by the period or 2π times the frequency, is the angular velocity as defined above. That is

$$\omega = 2\pi f = \frac{2\pi}{T} \tag{5}$$

Maximum, Average, and Rms or Effective Values

The **Instantaneous Value** of an alternating current is the value of the current at any instant. Instantaneous values of current, potential difference, and emf will be designated by small letters throughout this article, viz., i, v, and e.

The **Maximum Value** of an alternating current is the numerical value of its maximum instantaneous value. Maximum values will be designated by capital letters with the subscript m.

The **Half-period Average Value** of a symmetrical alternating current * is the absolute value of the algebraic average of the values of the current taken throughout a half period, beginning with a zero value. If the current has more than two zeros during a cycle, that zero shall be taken which gives the largest half-period average value. The expression for the half-period average of a symmetrical alternating current i (t) having a period T is

$$I_{av} = \frac{2}{T} \int_{t_0}^{t_0 + \frac{1}{2} T} i(t) \, dt \tag{6}$$

where t_0 is chosen such that $i(t) = 0$ at t_0 and I_{av} is the largest value obtainable.

The Rms or Effective Value. The square root of the means of the squares of the instantaneous values of an alternating current over a complete period is called the *rms* or the *effective* value of the alternating current. In specifying the value of an alternating current as so many amperes, this rms value is always meant unless specifically stated otherwise. In the same manner the square root of the mean of the squares of the instantaneous values of an alternating potential difference over a complete period is called the rms value of the alternating potential difference. When the value of an alternating potential difference is specified as so many volts, this rms value is always meant unless specifically stated otherwise.

The reason for selecting this particular function of the instantaneous values of an alternating current or a potential difference as a measure of the current or the potential difference, is that the deflection of all instruments used in alternating-current measurements is a function of this rms value. Moreover, the average power dissipated as heat in a resistance, r, when an alternating current of rms value I flows through it, is rI^2.

Rms values will be designated throughout this article by capital letters without subscripts. The general expression for the rms value of an alternating current is

$$I = \sqrt{\frac{1}{T} \int_0^T i^2 \, dt} \tag{7}$$

and similarly for an alternating potential difference.

Form Factor, Crest or Peak Factor, Deformation Factor

The Form Factor of a symmetrical alternating current is the ratio of the effective value of the current to its half-period average value.

The Peak or Crest Factor of an alternating current is the ratio of the maximum value of the current to its effective value.

The Equivalent Sinusoidal Current of a given alternating current is a sinusoid having the same period and the same effective value as the given alternating current.

The Deformation Factor of an alternating current is the ratio of the maximum value of the equivalent sinusoidal current to the maximum difference between the corresponding values of the current considered and the equivalent sinusoid, when the two are superimposed in such a way as to make this difference a minimum.

Power, Power Factor, Volt-amperes, Reactive Power

Power. Let v be the value at any instant of the potential drop from any point 1 to any other point 2, and let i be the instantaneous value of the current from 1 to 2 at this same instant; then the *power input* at this instant is

$$p = vi \tag{8}$$

When v and i are both positive (i.e., in the direction from 1 to 2, say) or when they are both negative, the power input is positive; but when v is positive and i negative, or vice versa, the power input is negative, i.e., there is an actual power output.

The average value of the product vi over a complete period for both v and i (or over any whole number of periods) is the *average power* input or output, usually called simply the power input or output (input when the average of vi is positive, output when the average of vi is negative), the word average being understood. That is, the average power input is

$$p = \frac{1}{T} \int_0^T p \, dt = \frac{1}{T} \int_0^T vi \, dt \tag{9}$$

T being the time for a complete period.

Power Factor. Only in certain special cases (see below) is the average power input P equal to the product of the rms value V of the potential difference by the rms value I

---

* A symmetrical alternating quantity is one of which all values separated by a half period have the same magnitude but opposite sign. The term half-period average has no meaning for alternating currents which are not symmetrical.

of the current; it can never be greater and as a rule is less. The ratio of the average power P to the product of the rms value V of the potential difference by the rms value I of the current is called the *power factor* of the circuit between the terminals considered, i.e.,

$$\text{Power factor} = \frac{P}{VI} \tag{10}$$

When V is expressed in volts and I in amperes, then P must be in watts; when V is expressed in kilovolts and I in amperes, P must be in kilowatts.

Apparent Power. The product of the rms volts across the terminals of a circuit and the rms amperes through it is called the *volt-amperes* or *apparent power* taken by the circuit; this product divided by 1000 is called the kilovolt-ampere input. Or, when V is in volts and I in amperes

$$\text{Volt-amperes} = VI \tag{11}$$

$$\text{Kilovolt-amperes} = \frac{VI}{1000} \tag{11a}$$

Reactive power has no accepted definition when either the current or emf is non-sinusoidal. For reactive power with sinusoidal currents and emf's see below.

20. SINUSOIDAL CURRENTS AND VOLTAGES

A Simple Sinusoidal Current (simple harmonic current) is an alternating current the instantaneous values of which are equal to the product of a constant and the sine of an angle having values varying linearly with time. Thus

$$i = I_m \sin(\omega t + \theta) \tag{12}$$

where t represents time in seconds, measured from any arbitrarily chosen instant; I_m the maximum value of the current; $\omega = 2\pi f = 2\pi/T$, where f is the frequency in cycles per second and T the period as a fraction of a second; and θ a constant which depends upon the instant chosen as the zero of time.

The quantity I_m is often called the *amplitude* of the sinusoidal current.

The Phase of a periodic current for a particular value of the independent variable is the fractional part of a period through which the independent variable has advanced, measured from an arbitrary origin. For a simple sinusoidal current, the origin is usually taken as the last previous passage through zero from the negative to positive direction. The phase angle is the angle obtained by multiplying the phase by 2π if the angle is to be expressed in radians, or by 360° if the angle is to be expressed in degrees.

In general, when a sine-wave emf is impressed on a circuit the resulting current is likewise a sine function of time (transient state ignored) having the same frequency, but the emf and current do not reach their maximum values simultaneously. Let the current be represented by equation 12 and the voltage be given by

$$v = V_m \sin \omega t \tag{13}$$

where t is the time measured from the instant when $v = 0$, and is increasing in the positive direction. The voltage reaches its maximum value when $t = \frac{\pi}{2\omega}$; the current reaches its maximum value when $t = \frac{\pi}{2\omega} - \frac{\theta}{\omega}$. Hence when θ is positive the voltage or potential drop reaches its maximum value θ/ω seconds after the current reaches its maximum, or the current reaches its maximum value θ/ω seconds before the potential drop reaches its maximum; when θ is negative the current reaches its maximum value θ/ω seconds after the potential drop reaches its maximum. In the first case, the current is said to "lead" the potential drop; and in the second, the current is said to "lag" the potential drop. The angle θ is called the angular phase difference between the current and potential drop.

When the phase difference is zero the current and potential drop are said to be "in phase"; when the phase difference is $\pi/2$ radians or 90° the current and potential drop are said to be "in quadrature"; when the phase difference is π radians or 180° the current and potential drop are said to be "in opposition."

Power and Power Factor. Let the voltage drop from terminal 1 to terminal 2 through any piece of apparatus be $v = \sqrt{2}V \sin(\omega t + \theta_v)$, and the current from terminal 1 to terminal 2 be $i = \sqrt{2}I \sin(\omega t + \theta_i)$, where V and I are the rms values and $\sqrt{2}V$ and $\sqrt{2}I$ are the maximum values. Then the instantaneous power input is

$$p = vi = VI[\cos(\theta_v - \theta_i) - \cos(2\omega t + \theta_v + \theta_i)] \tag{14}$$

A study of Fig. 1 will show the physical meaning of this expression.   The average power input is

$$P = VI \cos (\theta_v - \theta_i) \tag{14a}$$

where $(\theta_v - \theta_i)$ is the angular phase difference between the current and voltage.

Putting θ for this difference in phase, viz., $\theta = \theta_v - \theta_i$, equation 14a may be written:

$$P = VI \cos \theta \tag{14b}$$

Whence the power factor of the load supplied to the apparatus is (from equation 10):

$$\cos \theta = \frac{P}{VI} \tag{14c}$$

Since with sine-wave currents and voltages the power factor is equal to the cosine of the angle which expresses the difference in phase between them, this difference in phase is frequently called the "power-factor angle."   If the wave shape is not a pure sine curve, the power factor cannot be interpreted as the cosine of the phase difference, for phase difference has no definite meaning except in reference to sine waves; see definitions above. A non-sinusoidal voltage and current may both reach their zero values at the same in-

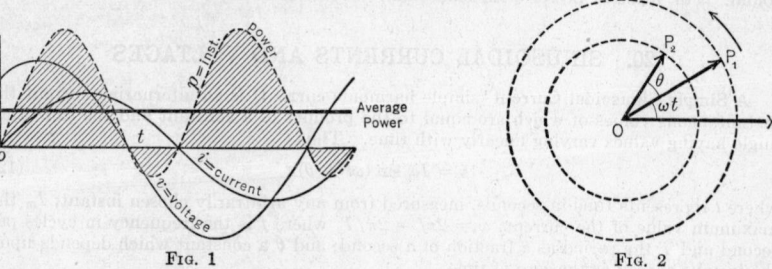

FIG. 1   FIG. 2

stant, and in a sense may be said to be "in phase," but the power factor as defined by equation 10 may be far from unity.

The Reactive Power in a circuit in which a sinusoidal current is flowing is equal to the effective emf times the effective current times the sine of the phase difference between them.   When the emf and current are in volts and amperes respectively the reactive power is in *vars*.

Vector Representation of Sinusoids.   Consider any sine function

$$i = I_m \sin \omega t$$

The value of i at any instant may be represented graphically, see Fig. 2, by the vertical projection (i.e., the vertical distance from P_1 to OX) of a point P_1 at the end of a radius $OP_1 = I_m$ which revolves * at a constant angular velocity ω about a fixed point O, the angle ωt being measured from the horizontal fixed line OX.   Similarly, any other sine function

$$v = V_m \sin (\omega t + \theta)$$

may be represented by the vertical projection of the point P_2 at the end of a radius $OP_2 = V_m$ also revolving about O with a constant angular velocity ω, the angle between OP_1 and OP_2, when the frequency of both i and v is the same, remaining fixed in value and equal to the difference in phase θ between v and i.   That is, v and i may be represented by rotating vectors (q.v.).   When v and i are of the same frequency the relative position of the two vectors remains fixed.   Similarly any number of currents and voltages of the same frequency may be represented by rotating vectors which remain fixed with respect to one another.

Instead of referring the various rotating vectors to a fixed line OX, this line of reference may also be considered as rotating with the same speed as the various vectors, or any one of the vectors may be chosen as the line of reference, for example, the vector OP_1 in Fig. 2.   The rotating vectors referred to this rotating line of reference are then fixed with respect to this line of reference, and the entire diagram may be considered as fixed, as in Fig. 3, the originally chosen fixed line of reference OX rotating in the opposite direction with an angular velocity ω.

Instead of making the vectors equal in length to the maximum values of the sine functions they may be chosen equal in length to their rms values.   This merely introduces

* Counter-clockwise rotation was adopted (1911) as standard by the International Electrotechnical Commission.

a factor $\sqrt{2}$ so that the instantaneous value of the quantity which any rotating vector is considered to represent is equal to $\sqrt{2}$ times the perpendicular distance from the end of the vector to the fixed line of reference.

Since the rms values and phase relations of sine-wave currents and voltages may be represented by vectors, sine-wave currents may be added in exactly the same manner as vectors are added, and similarly for sine-wave voltages. To add any two sine-wave currents or voltages not only their effective values but also their phase relation must be known; the resultant of two alternating voltages of rms values V_1 and V_2 is never the arithmetical sum of V_1 and V_2, except when the two voltages are exactly in phase, and similarly for alternating currents.

In Fig. 3, considering OI as equal to the rms value I of the current and OV as representing the rms value V of the voltage, the vector voltage V may be considered as made up of two components, viz.:

$$V_1 = V \cos \theta \text{ in phase with the vector } I$$

$$V_2 = V \sin \theta \text{ in quadrature with the vector } I$$

The average power corresponding to the component $V_1 = V \cos \theta$ is, from equation 14b, $V_1 I = VI \cos \theta$, and is equal to the total power corresponding to V and I. The average power corresponding to the component $V_2 = V \sin \theta$, since the angle between the current and this component of the voltage is 90°, is equal to zero. The voltage component $V_1 = V \cos \theta$ is therefore frequently called the "power" component of the voltage, and the component $V_2 = V \sin \theta$ is frequently called the "wattless" component of the voltage. These terms, however, are not recommended. It is preferable to refer to these two components as the in-phase and quadrature components respectively. The terms active and reactive components are also used.

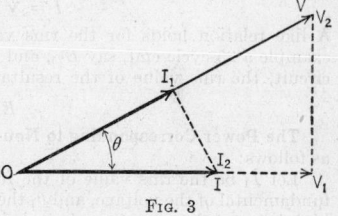

FIG. 3

Similarly, the vector current I may be considered as made up of two components, viz.:

$$I_1 = I \cos \theta \text{ in phase with } V$$

$$I_2 = I \sin \theta \text{ in quadrature with } V$$

The first component is called the in-phase component of the current and the second the quadrature component of the current.

21. NON-SINUSOIDAL PERIODIC CURRENTS AND VOLTAGES

Fourier Series, Harmonics. It can be shown that any single-valued, periodic function (which fulfills certain mathematical conditions always fulfilled by electric currents) may be represented by a sum of sinusoids of which the frequencies form an arithmetical progression. Hence any current $i(t)$ can be written

$$i(t) = A_0 + A_1 \sin 2\pi \frac{t}{T} + A_2 \sin 2\pi \frac{2t}{T} + \ldots + A_n \sin 2\pi \frac{nt}{T} + \ldots$$

$$+ B_1 \cos 2\pi \frac{t}{T} + B_2 \cos 2\pi \frac{2t}{T} + \ldots + B_n \cos 2\pi \frac{nt}{T} + \ldots \quad (15)$$

where the values of the coefficients A and B are given by the integrals:

$$A_n = \frac{2}{T}\int_0^T i(t) \sin 2\pi \frac{nt}{T} dt \quad (15a)$$

$$B_n = \frac{2}{T}\int_0^T i(t) \cos 2\pi \frac{nt}{T} dt \quad (15b)$$

The series (15) is called a *Fourier series*.

If an analytic expression for $i(t)$ is available and if the integrations (15a) and (15b) can be performed, the terms of the Fourier series (15) may be written out. In practice the function $i(t)$ will usually be obtainable only in the form of a plotted curve and the evaluation of the A's and B's must be carried out by graphical means. This process is called *harmonic analysis*. Various means of harmonic analysis have been devised, of which the Fisher-Hinnen method is perhaps the most convenient in ordinary cases. See Pender's Handbook for Electrical Engineers.

If the terms involving the same frequencies are combined, and if $\frac{2\pi}{T} = \omega$, (15) may be written

$$i(t) = I_1 \sin (\omega t - \theta_1) + I_2 \sin (2\omega t - \theta_2) + \ldots + I_n \sin (n\omega t - \theta_n) + \ldots \quad (16)$$

The term $I_1 \sin (\omega t - \theta_1)$ is called the *fundamental*, and the terms $I_n \sin (n\omega t - \theta_n)$ are called *harmonics*. The *order* of a harmonic is the ratio of the harmonic frequency to the frequency of the fundamental. Each harmonic is characterized by two constants, its amplitude I_n and the angle θ_n. It should be noted that this angle may be given in either of two ways:

$$I_n \sin (n\omega t - \theta_n) \quad (17a)$$
$$I_n \sin n (\omega t - \theta_n') \quad (17b)$$

In the first notation the angle θ_n is taken relative to the period of the harmonic, whereas in the second notation the angle θ_n' is taken relative to the period of the fundamental. It follows that

$$\theta_n = n\theta_n' \quad (18)$$

Rms Value of Non-sinusoidal Currents. The rms value of a non-sinusoidal current can be obtained directly from equation 7, Art. 19, or if the rms values I_1, I_2, I_3, etc., of the fundamental and harmonics are known the rms value of the resultant current is

$$I = \sqrt{I_1{}^2 + I_2{}^2 + I_3{}^2 + \ldots} \quad (19)$$

A like relation holds for the rms value of a non-sinusoidal voltage. Similarly, if for example a 25-cycle emf, say E_{25}, and a direct emf, say E_d, are acting in series in the same circuit, the rms value of the resultant emf of the combination is

$$E = \sqrt{E_{25}{}^2 + E_d{}^2}$$

The Power Corresponding to Non-sinusoidal Currents and Voltages may be computed as follows:

Let I_1 be the rms value of the fundamental of the current, V_1 the rms value of the fundamental of the voltage, and θ_1 the difference in phase between these two fundamentals, both being of the same frequency; let I_2, V_2, and θ_2 be the corresponding quantities for the second harmonic; let I_3, V_3, and θ_3 be the corresponding values for the third harmonic, etc. Then the average power is

$$p = V_1 I_1 \cos \theta_1 + V_2 I_2 \cos \theta_2 + V_3 I_3 \cos \theta_3 + \text{etc.} \quad (20)$$

That is, each harmonic contributes an amount to the total power equal to the power it would develop were the other harmonics not present. If, for example, the third harmonic is not present in the current wave, then this harmonic contributes nothing to the average power even though there may be a large third harmonic in the voltage wave. Again, when a 25-cycle alternating emf E_{25} and a direct emf E_d are acting in series on the same circuit the power developed is the sum of the powers which each would develop if they acted separately, but the resultant emf of the combination is not $E_{25} + E_d$, but, as noted above, $\sqrt{E_{25}{}^2 + E_d{}^2}$.

22.   CURRENT AND VOLTAGE RELATIONSHIPS

Electric Circuit Parameters. The following are restatements of principles given in foregoing articles:

(a) The flow of a current i through a resistance R is always accompanied by a drop of electric potential, or voltage drop, in the direction of this current, equal at each instant to the product of the resistance and the current.

$$v_r = Ri \quad (21)$$

(b) The flow of a current i through a self-inductance L is always accompanied by a voltage drop, in the direction of this current, equal at each instant to the product of the inductance and the rate of increase of the current.

$$v_L = L \frac{di}{dt} \quad (22)$$

(c) The flow of a current i_b through a conductor B which has, with respect to another conductor A, a mutual inductance M, is always accompanied by a voltage drop in the conductor A equal at each instant to the product of the mutual inductance and the rate of increase of the current in the conductor B.

$$v_M = M \frac{di_B}{dt} \quad (23)$$

The direction of the mutual inductive drop in the conductor A is such as to link *in the right-handed screw direction* the magnetic flux produced by the current in the conductor B.

(*d*) The flow of a (displacement) current i through a capacitance C is always accompanied by a time rate of change of voltage drop equal at each instant to the current divided by the capacitance.

$$\frac{dv_C}{dt} = \frac{i}{C} \tag{24}$$

The voltage v_C is therefore equal to the integral of i/C from the instant at which v_C was zero up to the instant under consideration

$$v_C = \int_{t_0}^{t} \frac{i}{C} \, dt \tag{24a}$$

Since the value of this integral is always zero at the lower limit, it is customary to omit the limits of integration and write simply

$$v_C = \frac{1}{C} \int i \, dt \tag{24b}$$

The quantities R, L, C, and M are called *electric circuit parameters*.

Operative Impedance. Any portion of an electric circuit which contains a resistance, an inductance, or a capacitance, or which contains two or more of these quantities, is said to offer an impedance to the flow of an electric current.

The drop of electric potential through any portion of an electric circuit due solely to its resistance, inductance, and capacitance is called the *impedance drop* in this portion of the circuit.

The impedance drop through an impedance formed by a resistance R, inductance L, and capacitance C in series, due to the flow of a current i through it, is

$$v = Ri + L\frac{di}{dt} + \frac{1}{C}\int i \, dt \tag{25}$$

The drop of potential

$$v_A = M\frac{di_B}{dt}$$

in any conductor A due to the mutual inductance between A and any other conductor B is called the *mutual impedance drop* in A due to the current i_B in B.

The group of operations represented by the three terms in the right-hand member of 25 is often represented by the single symbol **Z**.

$$\mathbf{Z} = R + L\frac{d}{dt} + \frac{l}{C}\int dt \tag{25a}$$

The operator **Z** is referred to as the *operative impedance* of the portion of the circuit under consideration.

The term *operative mutual impedance* is used when the mutual impedance drop is written $\mathbf{Z}_m i$, where

$$\mathbf{Z}_m = M\frac{d}{dt} \tag{25b}$$

It is customary in electric circuit theory to use the notation $p = \dfrac{d}{dt}$. Thus **Z** defined above is often written $\mathbf{Z}(p)$.

Emf. Electromotive force has been defined as that property of a device which tends to produce an electric current in a circuit. It is convenient in electric circuit theory to narrow this definition to include only those sources of potential difference not defined as impedance drops. Making use of this restricted definition of emf, Kirchhoff's second law is stated: " The sum of the emf's is, at any instant, equal to the sum of the impedance drops," whereas making use of the more general definition this law is stated: "The sum of the emf's is at any instant equal to the sum of the resistance drops."

Impedance Equations for a Network. Kirchhoff's second law applied to mesh 1 of Fig. 4 gives

$$Z_{12}i_{12} + Z_{13}i_{13} + Z_{14}i_{14} + Z_{15}i_{15} = e_{12} + e_{13} + e_{14} + e_{15} \tag{26}$$

where the Z's are the operative impedances of the several branches which make up this mesh, the i's are the *branch currents*, and the e's are the emf's, if any, in the respective branches of the mesh, the positive sense of each emf being taken as clockwise around the mesh.

In terms of the *mesh currents* defined in Art. 7, the equation may also be written

$$(Z_{12} + Z_{13} + Z_{14} + Z_{15})i_1 - Z_{12}i_2 - Z_{13}i_3 - Z_{14}i_4 - Z_{15}i_5 = e_{12} + e_{13} + e_{14} + e_{15} \tag{27}$$

This relation may be simplified by putting

$$Z_{11} = Z_{12} + Z_{13} + Z_{14} + Z_{15} \qquad (27a)$$

and

$$e_1 = e_{12} + e_{13} + e_{14} + e_{15}$$

Equation 27 then becomes

$$Z_{11}i_1 - Z_{12}i_2 - Z_{13}i_3 - Z_{14}i_4 - Z_{15}i_5 = e_1 \qquad (28)$$

In this equation the operator Z_{11} is the sum of the operative impedances of the several branches of mesh 1, and e_1 is the algebraic sum, in the clockwise direction, of all emf's in this mesh.

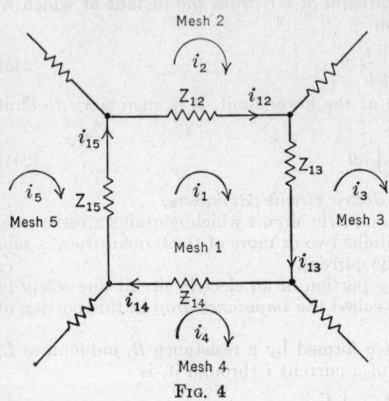

Fig. 4

If as many independent mesh equations, of the form 28, as there are mesh currents in a given network, are written down, the set of equations can be solved for the various currents. Such equations are called the *impedance equations* of the network.

Differential Equations in Terms of Quantity of Electricity. When capacitances exist in any of the meshes of the network the impedance equations contain some derivatives and some integrals. Equations of this type are more difficult to handle than true differential equations. It is often more convenient therefore to express the relation shown by equation 28 in terms of the quantity of electricity q. If we write

$$i_r = \frac{dq_r}{dt} \qquad (29)$$

then equation 28 becomes

$$Z'_{11}q_1 - Z'_{12}q_2 - Z'_{13}q_3 - Z'_{14}q_4 - Z'_{15}q_5 = e_1 \qquad (30)$$

in which

$$Z'_{rs} = \left(Z_{rs} \frac{d}{dt} \right) = \left(\frac{1}{C_{rs}} + R_{rs}\frac{d}{dt} + L_{rs}\frac{d^2}{dt^2} \right) \qquad (31)$$

Equation 30 is a true differential equation.

Superposition. *Linear differential equations* are differential equations, such as the above, having coefficients which are constants, or which are functions of the independent variable only. They have the property that the sum of the solutions is also a solution. That is, if x_1 and x_2 are two solutions of a given linear differential equation then $x_1 + x_2$ is also a solution of the given equation.

Suppose the equation to be non-homogeneous, and let the non-homogeneous term be A_1. Call the particular solution of the equation corresponding to this condition x_1. Now let the non-homogeneous term be given the value A_2, the remainder of the equation remaining the same, and let the particular solution corresponding to this condition be x_2. Then it can be shown that $x_1 + x_2$ is a solution of the equation when the non-homogeneous term is given the value $A_1 + A_2$.

The above principles jointly are called the *principle of superposition*. Electrical networks in which this principle holds are called *linear networks*.

Exponential Emf, Charge, Current, and Impedance. Derivatives and integrals of the simple exponential function bear simple relationships to the function itself. Furthermore, any arbitrary function may be expressed in terms of a sum of exponential terms. For these reasons, and especially because the simple sinusoidal function is simply expressible as a sum of exponential terms, it is customary to formulate the solution of electric circuit problems in terms of exponential currents.

It has been shown that, when the parameters of a given network (the factors R, L, M, and C) are constants, the electric charge equations for this network are a set of simultaneous, linear differential equations with constant coefficients. The complete solution of such a set of equations is a sum of terms of the form

$$q = Q\,t^g\,\epsilon^{\beta t} \qquad (32)$$

where Q, g, and β are constants, the values of which can be expressed in terms of the applied emf's, the parameters of the network, and the conditions which existed in the network at the time of application of the emf's. The solutions of the current equations of the network may therefore likewise be expressed as a sum of the terms of the form

$$i = I t^g \epsilon^{\beta t} \tag{33}$$

The general forms (32) and (33) rarely occur, and so the usual case in which $g = 0$ will be assumed here. In the exponential current

$$i = I \epsilon^{\beta t}$$

the quantities I and β are often called the *initial value* and the *periodicity* of the current respectively.

From equation 25a the impedance drop corresponding to the current

$$i = I \epsilon^{\beta t}$$

is

$$v = \mathbf{Z}i = \left(R + L\beta + \frac{1}{\beta C} \right) I \epsilon^{\beta t} \tag{34}$$

The factor in the parenthesis is a *constant* for any given value of β. That is, for a current of the form $I \epsilon^{\beta t}$ the operative impedance

$$Z = R + L \frac{d}{dt} + \frac{1}{C} \int dt \tag{35}$$

reduces to the simple algebraic quantity

$$\mathbf{Z}(\beta) = R + \beta L + \frac{1}{\beta C} \tag{35a}$$

This quantity will be referred to as the *exponential impedance*.

From the above it is evident that an exponential voltage drop is always associated with an exponential charge and current.

23. STEADY-STATE SOLUTION

Definition of a Steady State. The complete solution of a non-homogeneous linear differential equation having constant coefficients, consists of a particular function which satisfies the given equation plus the most general solution of the homogeneous equation (see Section II).

In stable * electrical systems the charges and currents represented by the solutions of the homogeneous equations decrease rapidly with time. After a brief interval following the application of emf's to such a system the currents and charges are represented by the particular solutions of the non-homogeneous equations only. When this condition has been reached the system is said to have attained a *steady state*. During the interval before this condition is reached the system is said to be in a *transient state*.

In linear electrical systems the steady-state currents and usually the charges have the same wave form (i.e., are represented by time functions of the same type) as the impressed voltages.

Sinusoidal Emf's. A sinusoidal emf given by

$$e = \sqrt{2}E \cos(\omega t + \phi) \tag{36}$$

may be written as the sum of the two exponential components

$$e' = E' \epsilon^{j\omega t} \tag{37}$$
$$e'' = E'' \epsilon^{-j\omega t} \tag{37a}$$

in which $j = \sqrt{-1}$ and in which

$$E' = \frac{1}{\sqrt{2}} E \epsilon^{j\phi} \tag{37b}$$

$$E'' = \frac{1}{\sqrt{2}} E \epsilon^{-j\phi} \tag{37c}$$

In equation 36 the constant E is the rms value of the emf, and ω is its angular velocity.

In electric circuit theory the phase differences between various quantities having the same frequency are of importance. Since these differences in phase are independent of the instant at which they are evaluated, it is customary to refer to the angle ϕ (which is the phase angle when $t = 0$) as the phase angle of the emf. The two constants E' and E'' in equations 37 are the initial values of the two exponential components of e, and $j\omega$ and $(-j\omega)$ are the periodicities of these two components. Note that the two initial values E' and E'' are conjugate complex numbers,† and that the two periodicities $j\omega$ and $(-j\omega)$ are conjugate imaginaries.

---

* For a definition of stability refer to Art. 25.

† Complex numbers will be printed in bold-face type throughout this article.

Complex Number Solution. It can be proved that during steady state an exponential current having a given periodicity exists in a stable linear network when and only when there is impressed upon the network an exponential emf having the given periodicity.

Each current which flows in a given network due to the application of a sinusoidal emf is therefore composed of two exponential components, each due to one of the exponential components of the sinusoidal emf. The superposition theorem states that these two components may be computed separately.

Let the sinusoidal emf, given by equation 36, be applied to a mesh (say mesh 1) of a network, and consider the currents flowing due to the component e', equation 37. Each of these currents will be of the form

$$i_k' = I_k' \, \epsilon^{j\omega t} \tag{38}$$

and each self-impedance drop (see 35a) will have the form

$$Z_{kk}i_k' = \left(r_k + j\omega L_k + \frac{1}{j\omega C_k}\right)I_k' \, \epsilon^{j\omega t} \tag{39}$$

Mutual impedance drops will be of a similar form. Hence any one of the impedance equations such as 28 will contain the factor $\epsilon^{j\omega t}$ in every term, and this factor can be divided out. This results in a set of equations containing as unknowns the complex numbers representing the initial values of the exponential currents and as coefficients the complex numbers obtained by putting $p = j\omega$ in the various operative impedances.

The initial value of the exponential current i_k' flowing in the kth mesh may be written

$$I_k' = A_k \, \epsilon^{j\theta_k} \tag{40}$$

The currents which flow in the network due to the other component e'' of the sinusoidal emf will be of the form

$$i_k'' = I_k'' \epsilon^{-j\omega t} \tag{41}$$

The initial values of these currents will be obtained from a set of complex number equations in which every term is the conjugate of the corresponding term in the set of equations for I_k'. The initial value of any one of these currents, say I_k'', can be shown to be the conjugate of the initial value, I_k', of the corresponding current, viz.,

$$I_k'' = A_k \, \epsilon^{-j\theta_k} \tag{42}$$

The actual steady-state sinusoidal current flowing in the kth mesh due to the application of the sinusoidal emf to the first mesh is the sum of the two exponential currents i_k' and i_k'',

$$i_k = i_k' + i_k'' = 2A_k \cos(\omega t + \theta_k) \tag{43}$$

If, in solving the mesh equations, the initial values 37b and 37c were replaced by the values $E\epsilon^{j\phi}$ and $E\epsilon^{-j\phi}$, then a new value of A_k equal to $\sqrt{2}$ times the value in equation 43 would be obtained. Let this value be called I_k, i.e.,

$$I_k = \sqrt{2} \, A_k \tag{44}$$

In terms of the quantity I_k the current i_k is

$$i_k = \sqrt{2} \, I_k \cos (\omega t + \theta_k) \tag{45}$$

From the above we have the following simple procedure for finding the steady-state currents produced in a network by a group of sinusoidal emf's of a given frequency:

(a) Write the operative impedance equations 27 and 28 described in Art. 22.

(b) Replace each emf in the network by a complex number having a modulus equal to the rms value of the given emf, and a phase angle equal to the phase angle of the given emf (when expressed in cosine form).

(c) Replace the self- and mutual operative impedances of the several meshes of the network by complex numbers obtained by putting $p = (j\omega)$, where ω is the angular velocity of the given sinusoidal electromotive forces.

(d) Replace each current in the network by an unknown complex number, and solve for these complex numbers.

(e) The rms values of the various currents are the moduli of the corresponding complex numbers, and the phase angles of the currents (when expressed in cosine form) are the phase angles of these complex numbers.

This method is known as the *complex number method* for alternating currents.

The complex numbers obtained from the operative impedances are usually referred to as *vector impedances* or often simply as *impedances*. Although the term impedance is used for both the differential operator and the complex number, the term used without qualification usually means the complex number. A still more general definition of impedance is given below. The algebra of complex numbers is treated in the section on mathematics.

Impedance, Admittance, Reactance, Susceptance. In previous paragraphs the terms operative impedance and vector impedance were defined. Although the term *impedance* is loosely used to designate either of these, the accepted definition of impedance is: The impedance of a portion of an electric circuit, to a completely specified periodic current and potential difference, is the ratio of the effective value of the potential difference between the terminals to the effective value of the current, there being no source of emf in the portion under consideration.

Impedance defined in this way is a real number which in a sinusoidal current and voltage reduces to the modulus value of the vector impedance defined above.

Admittance is defined as the reciprocal of the impedance. The *vector admittance* is the reciprocal of the complex number representing the vector impedance.

Impedance and admittance, as thus defined, both depend upon the frequency and wave shape of the current. Impedance is expressed in the same units as resistance (e.g., ohms), and admittance in the same units as conductance (e.g., mhos).

The *reactance* of a portion of a circuit for a sinusoidal current, and hence for any one of the frequencies of a periodic current, is the ratio of the quadrature component of the potential difference for a particular frequency to the value of the current for that frequency, there being no source of emf in the portion of the circuit under consideration.

The *susceptance* of a portion of a circuit for a sinusoidal potential difference, and hence for any one of the frequencies of a periodic potential difference, is the ratio of the quadrature component of the current for a particular frequency to the value of the potential difference for that frequency, there being no source of emf in the portion of the circuit under consideration.

From the definitions given above it may be shown that for sine-wave currents and voltages of a given frequency the following relations hold for any portion of a circuit:

$$\left.\begin{aligned}
\boldsymbol{Z} &= r + jx & \boldsymbol{Y} &= g - jb \\
Z &= \sqrt{r^2 + x^2} & Y &= \sqrt{g^2 + b^2} \\
Z &= \frac{1}{Y} & Y &= \frac{1}{Z} \\
r &= \frac{g}{Y^2} & g &= \frac{r}{Z^2} \\
x &= \frac{b}{Y^2} & b &= \frac{x}{Z^2}
\end{aligned}\right\} \tag{46}$$

where r = effective resistance, x = reactance (taken positive when inductive and negative when capacitive), g = effective conductance, b = susceptance (taken positive when inductive and negative when capacitive), Z = impedance, Y = admittance, $\boldsymbol{Z}$ = vector impedance, and $\boldsymbol{Y}$ = vector admittance, all for the given portion of circuit.

Vector Impedances in Simple Circuits. The vector impedances of the various circuit elements to a sinusoidal current having an angular velocity ω are:

In a resistor $\qquad\qquad \boldsymbol{Z}_r = R$

In an inductor $\qquad\qquad \boldsymbol{Z}_L = j\omega L$

In a capacitor $\qquad\qquad \boldsymbol{Z}_C = \frac{1}{j\omega C} = -j\left(\frac{1}{\omega C}\right)$

The mutual impedance in a device having mutual inductance is

$$\boldsymbol{Z}_M = j\omega M$$

The product (ωL) or (ωM) corresponding to a self-inductance L, or to a mutual inductance M, is called the *reactance* of this inductance at the angular velocity ω. Similarly the expression $-\dfrac{1}{\omega C}$ corresponding to a capacitance C is called the *reactance* of this capacitance at the angular velocity ω. Note that the reactance of a capacitance is always negative. These statements are in agreement with the previous definition of reactance.

In general, then, the vector impedance of any mesh, or the mutual vector impedance of any two meshes, may be written in the form

$$\boldsymbol{Z} = r + jx \tag{47}$$

where r is the sum of the effective resistances and x is the algebraic sum of the reactances of the several portions of the network which make up this impedance.

The vector impedance $(r + jx)$ may also be expressed in the form

$$\boldsymbol{Z} = Z \angle \theta \tag{48}$$

where $\qquad\qquad Z = \sqrt{r^2 + x^2} \tag{48a}$

is the modulus of the complex number $(r + jx)$ and

$$\theta = \tan^{-1}\left(\frac{x}{r}\right) \tag{48b}$$

is the phase angle of this complex number.

In equation 48 the symbol $\angle$ is read " at an angle of " and has the same mathematical significance as ϵ^j. Thus $Z \angle \theta$ is identical with $Z\epsilon^{j\theta}$.

When two or more vector impedances Z_1, Z_2, etc., are connected in series, so that the same current I flows through each the total impedance drop through the group is

$$V = Z_1 I + Z_2 I + \ldots \tag{49}$$
$$= (Z_1 + Z_2 + Z_3 \ldots) I$$

hence two or more vector impedances in series are equivalent to a single vector impedance equal to the sum of the several impedances.

When two or more vector impedances Z_1, Z_2, etc., are connected in parallel, so that the voltage drop is the same for each, the total current through the group is

$$I = \frac{V}{Z_1} + \frac{V}{Z_2} + \ldots$$
$$= \left(\frac{1}{Z_1} + \frac{1}{Z_2} + \ldots\right) V \tag{50}$$

It is customary to express this law in terms of the vector admittances Y_1, Y_2, ... Two or more vector admittances in parallel are equivalent to a single vector admittance equal to the sum of the several admittances.

Calculation of Power. The average power in a circuit in which the current is i and the voltage drop is v is

$$P = \frac{1}{T} \int_0^T vi \, dt$$

With a sinusoidal current and voltage

$$v = \sqrt{2}V \cos(\omega t + \theta_v) \quad \text{and} \quad i = \sqrt{2}I \cos(\omega t + \theta_i)$$

this power is equal to $P = VI \cos(\theta_v - \theta_i)$

The vector voltage and vector current in this case are

$$V = V\epsilon^{j\theta_v}$$
$$I = I\epsilon^{j\theta_i}$$

of which the product *is not* the average power. The average power is given by the *real part* of the product of the vector voltage by the *conjugate* of the vector current.

$$P = \text{real part of } (V \epsilon^{j\theta_v})(I \epsilon^{-j\theta_i}) \tag{51}$$

This may be expressed in terms of the components of the vector current and voltage as follows:

Let
$$V = V_1 + j V_2$$
$$I = I_1 + j I_2$$
then $P = V_1 I_1 + V_2 I_2 \tag{52}$

Complicated Circuits. The vector impedance equations described give the complete steady-state solution of any complicated electrical network. If there are n meshes in the network these equations are

$$\left.\begin{array}{l} Z_{11}I_1 - Z_{12}I_2 - Z_{13}I_3 \ldots - Z_{1n}I_n = E_1 \\ - Z_{12}I_1 + Z_{22}I_2 - Z_{23}I_3 \ldots - Z_{2n}I_n = E_2 \\ - Z_{13}I_1 - Z_{23}I_2 + Z_{33}I_3 \ldots - Z_{3n}I_n = E_3 \\ - Z_{1n}I_n - Z_{2n}I_2 - Z_{3n}I_3 \ldots + Z_{nn}I_n = E_n \end{array}\right\} \tag{53}$$

which can be solved either by successive substitutions or by the method of determinants. If the number of equations is small the solution by substitution usually results in less labor. If there are many meshes the method of determinants often results in a saving of time. These methods for solving algebraic equations in complex numbers are described in the section on mathematics.

Resonance. It has been pointed out that the reactance of a circuit is positive when it contains inductances only and negative when it contains capacitances only. The reactance under both conditions is a function of frequency. It is apparent therefore that the net reactance of a circuit containing both inductance and capacitance may vary through wide limits as the frequency of the current varies over a given range. If the resistance is small the current in a circuit for a given magnitude of potential difference may be excessive at a particular frequency of the applied voltage. This phenomenon is known as *resonance*. More generally, resonance exists between one coordinate of a system, which is executing oscillations, and a periodic agency, which maintains the oscillations, when a small amplitude of the periodic agency produces in the system a relatively large amplitude of oscillation.

Amplitude resonance exists when the resonance is such that any change in the period of the emf without changing its amplitude produces a decrease in the amplitude of the current.

Natural resonance exists when the period of the applied emf is the same as the natural period of oscillation of the system.

Phase resonance exists when the angular phase difference between the fundamental components of the current and the emf is 90°.

The two simplest cases of resonance, called parallel resonance and series resonance, occur when a capacitor and an inductor both having negligible resistance are connected in parallel and have impressed on them an emf having a frequency

$$f = \frac{1}{2\pi\sqrt{LC}}$$

With parallel resonance the current is zero; with series resonance the current is infinite. These are limiting values applicable when the resistances are zero.

TRANSIENTS

24. GENERAL EQUATIONS

Definition of a Transient State. The currents in an electric circuit are said to be in a transient state in the interval of time between a change in the emf or impedance conditions in the circuit and the establishment of a steady state (q.v.). During this interval, currents flow which usually decrease rapidly with time. Some transient currents persist for a comparatively long period of time.

Natural Periodicities, Characteristic Determinant. In Art. 23 it was stated that steady-state exponential currents of a given periodicity could exist in a stable linear network only when there was impressed on the network an emf having the given periodicity. This is not true of transient currents. If there are no emf's whatever applied to a network having n meshes the exponential impedance equations are

$$\left.\begin{array}{l} Z_{11}(\beta)\,I_1 - Z_{12}(\beta)I_2 - \ldots - Z_{1n}(\beta)I_n = 0 \\ - Z_{21}(\beta)\,I_1 + Z_{22}(\beta)I_2 - \ldots - Z_{2n}(\beta)I_n = 0 \\ \cdots \\ \cdots \\ - Z_{n1}(\beta)I_1 - Z_{n2}(\beta)I_2 - \ldots + Z_{nn}(\beta)I_n = 0 \end{array}\right\} \quad (1)$$

The condition that this set of homogeneous equations be consistent (i.e., that the currents are not all zero) is that the determinant formed of the coefficients be zero. The values of β which make the determinant zero are the periodicities of current which can exist in the network when no emf of a corresponding periodicity is impressed on the network.

These values of β are called the *natural periodicities* of the network. The determinant coefficient will be called the *characteristic determinant* of the network and will be written $D(\beta)$. This determinant is a polynomial in β because each of the Z's is a polynomial in β. Since each of the Z's may be of second degree, the characteristic determinant may be a polynomial of the $2n$th degree in β giving rise to $2n$ natural periodicities.

Nature of the Roots of the Characteristic Determinant. The roots of the characteristic determinant are usually real or complex; in some cases (for example, in an idealized network having no resistances) they may be pure imaginaries.

Since all the coefficients of the polynomial $D(\beta)$ are real numbers the imaginary or complex roots always occur in conjugate pairs. Thus if a given root has the value

$$\beta_k = \alpha_k + jw_k \quad (2)$$

one of the other roots will have the value

$$\beta_{k'} = \alpha_k - jw_k \quad (2a)$$

The roots may all have different values or some may be repeated. With repeated roots the form of the transient currents is different from that occurring in networks for which the characteristic determinant has no repeated roots.

The various natural periodicities will be denoted by

$$\beta_1, \beta_2, \ldots, \beta_k, \ldots, \beta_M$$

where M is the total number of different values of the roots. If a given root, say the kth, is repeated r_k times, then the factor $(\beta - \beta_k)$ occurs $r_k + 1$ times in the expression for $D(\beta)$, hence the following equation expresses the characteristic determinant as a function of the roots:

$$D(\beta) = (\beta - \beta_1)^{r_1+1} (\beta - \beta_2)^{r_2+1} \ldots (\beta - \beta_k)^{r_k+1} \ldots (\beta - \beta_M)^{r_M+1} \tag{3}$$

Form of Transient Current, No Repeated Roots. When all the roots of the characteristic determinant are different, the current in, say, the w mesh will have a component with periodicity β_1 and initial value I_{w1}, a component with periodicity β_2 and initial value I_{w2}, etc. The current in this mesh can therefore be written

$$i_w = \sum_{k=1}^{M} I_{wk} \, \epsilon^{\beta_k t} \tag{4}$$

The initial values of I_{wk} depend upon the conditions which existed in the network at $t = 0$, as explained in the last paragraphs.

If the conjugate pairs of complex or pure imaginary roots be added together, sine or cosine terms result. The current in the w mesh can then be written

$$i_w = \sum_{k=1}^{s} I_{wk} \, \epsilon^{\alpha_k t} + \sum_{k=s+1}^{M} I_{wk} \, \epsilon^{\alpha_k t} \cos(\omega_k t + \theta_k) \tag{4a}$$

in which s is the number of real roots and $M - s$ is the number of roots which are complex or pure imaginary.

Form of Transient Current, Repeated Roots. It can be shown that the component of transient current in the w mesh having the periodicity β_k, where β_k is a repeated root of the characteristic determinant, is

$$i_{wk} = I_{wk0} \, \epsilon^{\beta_k t} + I_{wk1} \, t\epsilon^{\beta_k t} + \ldots + I_{wkr_k} \, t^{r_k} \epsilon^{\beta_k t}$$

where r_k is the number of times the root is repeated. Hence in general

$$i_{wk} = \sum_{k=1}^{M} \sum_{g=0}^{r_k} I_{wkg} \, t^g \epsilon^{\beta_k t} \tag{5}$$

The initial values I_{wkg} depend upon the conditions which existed in the network at $t = 0$.

Boundary Conditions. The character of the time functions representing the transient currents were stated above, but the initial values of the exponential currents were undetermined. The number of these initial values to be determined is always equal to the degree of the characteristic determinant $D(\beta)$ multiplied by the number of mesh currents in the impedance equations. This number can never exceed $2n^2$ where n is the number of mesh currents. The set of equations 1 provides a means of reducing this number; if in each equation the term involving a given current, say I_k, be transferred to the right-hand side and the equations be considered as non-homogeneous in $(n-1)$ currents, then it is possible to find each of the $(n-1)$ currents in terms of I_k. This results in a reduction in the total number of undetermined initial values to the degree of the determinant $D(\beta)$. Hence as many additional conditions as the degree of the characteristic determinant must be specified in order to make the statement of the problem complete. *Mathematically* the additional statements required are called *boundary conditions* and may take various forms. *Physically* these additional statements represent a specification of the condition of the electrical network at the instant of occurrence of the change which initiated the transient under consideration. Practically it is convenient to specify the various charges and currents existing in the network at $t = 0$. Special circumstances arise in which the number of charges and currents in the network may exceed the degree of $D(\beta)$; a number equal to the degree of $D(\beta)$ only may then be specified, the others being determined by the impedance equations.

A particular set of boundary conditions which is of importance is that set which specifies an electrical system initially without energy. They are called the *equilibrium conditions*, and a system for which they are applicable is said to be in equilibrium.

Indicial Admittance. The current response in a mesh of an electrical network initially in equilibrium to a unit emf applied to a pair of terminals in the given mesh is called the *input indicial admittance* of the network at those terminals. The current response in another mesh of the network under the same conditions is called the *transfer indicial aamittance* from the mesh in which the emf is inserted to the mesh in which the current is considered. The indicial admittance consists of a sustained or steady-state term plus a transient term, the boundary conditions for the transient term being those of equilibrium. The indicial admittance has the important property that an expression for the total current (including both sustained and transient currents) which flows in a network due to the application of an emf of any type whatever can be found when the indicial admittance is known. This expression, known as the Duhamel integral, is

$$i_k(t) = \frac{d}{dt} \int_0^t h_{jk}(t-\lambda)\, E_j(\lambda) d\lambda \tag{6}$$

in which $i_k(t)$ = the total current in the kth mesh.

$E_j(t)$ = the emf impressed in the jth mesh.

$h_{jk}(t)$ = the transfer indicial admittance from the jth mesh to the kth mesh.

λ = a variable of integration.

Various means for obtaining the indicial admittance have been devised, some of which are:

(a) *Direct solution* of the differential equations for the network when the emf is put equal to unity and equilibrium boundary conditions are imposed. This method is extremely cumbersome in complicated cases, and indeed reduces to method (b).

(b) *Partial fraction expansion* method, so called because the method of its derivation.

$$h_{ij}(t) = \sum_{k=1}^{M} \sum_{g=0}^{r_k} \frac{B_{kg}{}^{ij}}{g!} t^g\, \epsilon^{\beta_k t} \tag{7}$$

in which the constants $B_{kg}{}^{ij}$ are the constants in the partial fraction expansion

$$\frac{A_{ij}(\beta)}{D(\beta)} = \sum_{k=1}^{M} \sum_{g=0}^{r_k} \frac{B_{kg}{}^{ij}}{(\beta-\beta_k)^{g+1}} \tag{7a}$$

where $A_{ij}(\beta)$ is the cofactor corresponding to the ij element of the determinant $D(\beta)$. In equations 7 and 7a

M = the number of different valued roots.

r_k = the number of times the kth root is repeated.

k, g = variables of summation.

(c) Solution of the *infinite integral equation*

$$\frac{1}{\beta Z(\beta)} = \int_0^\infty \epsilon^{-\beta t} h(t)\, dt \tag{8}$$

in which $Z(\beta)$ is the exponential impedance for any periodicity β.

(d) The *operational method* of obtaining a power series for $h(t)$; if $\dfrac{1}{Z(\beta)}$ admits of an asymptotic expansion of the form

$$\frac{1}{Z(\beta)} = \sum_{n=0}^{\infty} \frac{a_n}{\beta^n} \tag{9}$$

then the indicial admittance is given by

$$h(t) = \sum_{n=0}^{\infty} \frac{a_n t^n}{n!} \tag{9a}$$

in which the coefficients a_n have the same values as in equation 9.

25. CIRCUIT STABILITY

Stable and Unstable Systems. Let a given dynamical system be supposed to be moving under the action of applied forces in some known manner described by a set of differential equations. If any small disturbing influences be applied to the system it may deviate only slightly from the previous condition of motion or it may depart from it further and further. If the deviation is slight the system is said to be *dynamically stable*, otherwise the system is *dynamically unstable*. It is clear that a given motion might be stable for one type of disturbance and unstable for another type. The disturbance will be supposed to be general in nature so that the motion will be considered stable only if it is stable for all kinds of disturbances.

An electrical network in which currents flow under the action of applied emf's may be stable or unstable in the sense defined above depending upon the character of the parameters of the network.

Two over-compounded direct-current generators operating in parallel without an equalizer connection have the property that a disturbing influence which increases the emf of one machine slightly results ultimately in a considerable increase in emf and an unbalance of load which renders the system inoperative. Such a system is said to be unstable. Other examples of electrical systems which may be unstable are: electric arcs, vacuum-tube amplifiers or oscillators, alternators in parallel, discharges in gas-filled tubes, etc.

In electric power systems protective equipment, which is designed to maintain continuous operation, is always provided. When such equipment is actuated as the result of some abnormal condition, the system is electrically different before and after such device has performed its function. The differential equations are therefore changed, and a system which might have been unstable is often transformed into one in which no current or emf departs further and further from its normal value. The term stable is usually applied to a system which *with its protective equipment* will not be rendered inoperative by any small disturbance. For other special meanings ascribed to stability and not consistent with *dynamical stability* see Electric Circuits and Electric Lines in Pender's Handbook for Electrical Engineers.

Method of Small Oscillations. Let the variables in the system of differential equations describing a dynamical system be $q_1, q_2, q_3, \ldots q_n$, and let the disturbances applied to the system be such that these variables are replaced by

$$(q_1 + S_1), (q_2 + S_2), \ldots, (q_n + S_n)$$

The quantities $S_1, S_2, \ldots, S_n$ are initially small since the disturbance was assumed to be small. A quantity is said to be small when it is in absolute value less than some quantity λ which is such that its square may be neglected.

If, after the disturbance, $S_1, S_2, \ldots, S_n$ always remain small, the motion is stable, otherwise unstable. The investigation of the stability of a given motion by a study of the behavior of the S's has proved extremely fruitful. The method is known as the *method of small oscillations.*

Criteria for Stability. An inspection of the time functions representing the transient currents in an electrical system indicates that the given system will be unstable if the characteristic determinant has:

    (a) Real roots which are positive.
    (b) Complex roots having positive real parts.
    (c) Pure imaginary roots which are repeated.

Certain criteria for the existence of any of the above were deduced by Routh and later developed independently and in a somewhat different form by Hurwitz. These criteria are somewhat difficult to apply in practice and are applicable only to systems described by differential equations having constant coefficients. They are useful, however, in electrical systems which are approximately linear and are valuable in various other dynamical systems, such as the dynamical system of airplanes.

Test Functions of Routh and Hurwitz. Let the characteristic determinant be written in the form

$$D(\beta) = a_0 \beta^m + a_1 \beta^{m-1} + a_2 \beta^{m-2} + \ldots + a_{m-1} \beta + a_m$$

then the conditions that there be no complex root having a positive real part or a real root which is positive are:

1. A necessary but not sufficient condition is that all the a's have the same sign.
2. A necessary and sufficient condition is that the following test functions all are positive when the equation $D(\beta) = 0$ is put in such form that a_0 is positive.

$$T_1 = a_1 \tag{10}$$

$$T_2 = \begin{vmatrix} a_1 & a_0 \\ a_3 & a_2 \end{vmatrix} \tag{10a}$$

$$T_3 = \begin{vmatrix} a_1 & a_0 & 0 \\ a_3 & a_2 & a_1 \\ a_5 & a_4 & a_3 \end{vmatrix} \tag{10b}$$

$$T_4 = \begin{vmatrix} a_1 & a_0 & 0 & 0 \\ a_3 & a_2 & a_1 & a_0 \\ a_5 & a_4 & a_3 & a_2 \\ a_7 & a_6 & a_5 & a_4 \end{vmatrix} \tag{10c}$$

$$T_5 = \begin{vmatrix} a_1 & a_0 & 0 & 0 & 0 \\ a_3 & a_2 & a_1 & a_0 & 0 \\ a_5 & a_4 & a_3 & a_2 & a_1 \\ a_7 & a_6 & a_5 & a_4 & a_3 \\ a_9 & a_8 & a_7 & a_6 & a_5 \end{vmatrix} \tag{10d}$$

and so on, until a determinant which is identically zero is obtained. The total number of test functions required is in general equal to the degree of $D(\beta)$. A set of conditions which are often encountered in electric circuits can be shown to be sufficient but not necessary for the system to be stable. These conditions are:

(a) All resistances, inductances, and capacitances are positive.

(b) The total resistance in any mesh is greater than the sum of the mutual resistances of the given mesh with respect to the various other meshes.

(c) The total capacitance in any mesh is greater than the sum of the mutual capacitances of the given mesh with respect to the various other meshes.

(d) The product of the self-inductances in any two meshes is greater than the square of the mutual inductance between the two meshes.

26. EXAMPLES OF SIMPLE TRANSIENTS

Transient with Resistance and Inductance. The establishment of a direct current in a coil having resistance r and inductance L due to the action of a constant emf E is of practical importance. Let the current in the coil at the instant of impressing the emf be I_0. Then the current t seconds after closing the switch is

$$i = \frac{E}{r} + \left(I_0 - \frac{E}{r}\right)\epsilon^{-(r/L)t} \tag{11}$$

In equation 11 the term E/r is the sustained current and $\left(I_0 - \frac{E}{r}\right)\epsilon^{-(r/L)t}$ is the transient current. The ratio L/r is a measure of the time required for the transient current to become negligible; this ratio is often called the *time constant* of the circuit.

If the current is initially zero the conditions are those of equilibrium, and if E is put equal to unity equation 11 becomes the indicial admittance.

$$h(t) = \frac{1}{r}(1 - \epsilon^{-(r/L)t}) \tag{12}$$

The short circuit current of a coil which has resistance and inductance only and in which a current I_0 is flowing is given by equation 11 when E is put equal to zero:

$$i = I_0 \epsilon^{-(r/L)t} \tag{13}$$

Transient with Resistance and Capacitance. The charging of a condenser of capacitance C through a resistor of resistance r due to the action of a constant emf E will be considered here. It is assumed that the conductance of the condenser and the inductance of the resistor are zero. The condenser is assumed to have a charge q_0 at the instant of closing the switch. The current t seconds after the switch is closed is

$$i = \left(\frac{E}{r} - \frac{q_0}{rC}\right)\epsilon^{-(1/rC)t} \tag{14}$$

The charge on the condenser at the same instant is

$$q = CE + (q_0 - CE)\epsilon^{-(1/rC)t} \tag{15}$$

The time constant of this circuit is rC, this product being a measure of the time required for the transient current to become negligible.

If the conditions of equilibrium are imposed, i.e., $q_0 = 0$, and if E is put equal to unity, equation 14 becomes the indicial admittance.

$$h(t) = \frac{1}{r}\epsilon^{-(1/rC)t} \tag{16}$$

The discharge of a condenser, initially charged to a potential $V_0 = q_0/C$, through a resistor is given by equation 14 when E is put equal to zero. The current is

$$i = -\frac{V_0}{r}\epsilon^{-(1/rC)t} \tag{17}$$

The potential on the condenser at any instant is equal to the negative of the ri drop.

$$V = V_0\,\epsilon^{-(1/rC)t} \tag{18}$$

Transient with Resistance, Inductance and Capacitance in Series. If a single series circuit containing parameters r, L, and C is closed upon an emf E at the instant $t = 0$, and if the charge on the condenser is q_0 and the current through the circuit is I_0 at $t = 0$, the current t seconds after the switch is closed is

$$i = I_0\,\epsilon^{-\alpha t}\cos\omega t - \left[\frac{\alpha}{\omega}I_0 + \frac{\alpha^2 + \omega^2}{\omega}(q_0 - CE)\right]\epsilon^{-\alpha t}\sin\omega t \tag{19}$$

and the charge on the condenser is

$$q = CE + \frac{I_0 + \alpha(q_0 - CE)}{\omega} \epsilon^{-\alpha t} \sin \omega t + (q_0 - CE)\epsilon^{-\alpha t} \cos \omega t \qquad (19a)$$

in which

$$\alpha = \frac{r}{2L} \qquad (19b)$$

$$\omega = \sqrt{\frac{1}{LC} - \frac{r^2}{4L^2}} \qquad (19c)$$

If the conditions of equilibrium are imposed ($I_0 = 0$, $q_0 = 0$) and E is put equal to unity in equation 19 the indicial admittance is obtained

$$h(t) = \frac{1}{\omega L} \epsilon^{-\alpha t} \sin \omega t \qquad (20)$$

The term $\epsilon^{-\alpha t}$ appearing in equations 19 and 20 produces a decrease with time of the function which it multiplies; it is called the *damping factor* of the current or charge in which it appears. The constant ω is the natural angular velocity of the network. This constant can have a real or imaginary value depending upon the relative values of $\frac{1}{LC}$ and $\frac{r^2}{4L^2}$. When the resistance is extremely small α may be negligible in comparison with $\frac{1}{LC}$ and ω may be taken as $\frac{1}{\sqrt{LC}}$. This value of ω is called the undamped angular velocity of the circuit. If the resistance is increased, the amount of damping may be increased to such an extent that ω is zero. This condition is known as *critical* damping and is the borderline between oscillatory currents and non-oscillatory currents. If the resistance is increased further, over-damping results, ω becomes imaginary, and the current and charge are represented by hyperbolic functions instead of by trigonometric functions of time.

CONDUCTION OF ELECTRICITY IN SOLIDS AND FLUIDS

By Carl C. Chambers

27. CONDUCTION IN SOLIDS

The Solid State. The solid state is characterized by the possession of a structure. That is, each atom or molecule in the solid state has permanent neighbors. Most of the physical properties of solids depend markedly upon the atomic arrangement in the solid. Therefore any satisfactory discussion of these physical properties must be based upon the structure of the solid state. By far the major part of solid matter is crystalline, where, by crystalline, we mean built up out of some fundamental unit which repeats itself identically at regular intervals in three dimensions.

The crystalline form of the solid state is divided into three classes: (1) the ionic form, which includes most inorganic salts and minerals, (2) the molecular form, which includes the organic crystals and a few inorganic substances, and (3) metals.

In the ionic form of crystal structure, the crystal lattice points are occupied by the separate ions of the salt. For instance, in NaCl the Na ions are at certain points in the lattice and the Cl ions are at other points to form the rocksalt crystal. In this class are included many salts involving radicals such as $SO_4^=$, ClO_3^-, $CO_3^=$, and NO_3^-. In many of the complex minerals, such as silicates, the structure becomes very complicated, the unit cell often containing several hundred atoms.

In the molecular form of crystal structure, the atoms are held together within the molecule by direct valence bonds (homopolar), and the molecules are held together by the relatively weaker bonds (van der Waals forces, etc.) to form the crystals. The low melting point of these solids is due directly to the fact that the crystal bonds are comparatively weak.

Metals differ from this last group by being made up of metallic atoms occupying the lattice points. These atoms are packed very close together, being held together by electrostatic fields due to the charges on the atoms arising from the loss of the valence electrons, and the concentration of these electrons between the positive ions. These electrons easily move about within the crystal from atom to atom and are to be identified with the so-called *free electrons*. In general, the true metals are characterized by simple unit crystal cells. Manganese is an exception to this generalization, having in one form 58 atoms in the unit cell. So far as Mn is concerned it should be classed in crystal structure with the intermetallic compounds (alloys) since it appears as four different kinds of atoms corresponding to manganese in four different states. In general, the intermetallic compounds are more complicated than the true metals. These compounds always have fewer free electrons than there are valence electrons in the separate atoms.

The structures of the borderline metals such as Se, Te, Sb, Bi are quite different from those of the true metals. In these substances the atoms are bound to one another in much the same way that molecules are held together. One atom can be considered as replacing a missing electron in the valence energy level of each of its nearest neighbors.

There are but few non-crystalline solids. The various glasses now appear to be the only definite example of an amorphous solid. The atoms in these solids are held together in much the same way as in crystalline forms of the same material except that the bonding is so flexible that the bonding conditions can be satisfied without building up a regularly repeated structure. With respect to conduction of electricity, non-crystalline substances are best treated as liquids.

Theory of Conduction in Crystalline Solids. The general scheme which is used in describing the behavior of electrons in a crystal is that which is sometimes known as the "method of copies." Each free electron is considered to move in the same field of force without interaction with the other electrons. This omission of any mutual interaction between the electrons is partially compensated for by supposing that the field in which an electron moves is that due to the ions at the lattice points, modified by a contribution equal to the average field produced by all the other electrons. When the allowable quantum states of energy of an electron in such a field have been determined, the electrons are supposed to be assigned to the various states in a manner governed by the temperature and in such a way that the Pauli exclusion principle (no more than one electron occupying a given quantum state) is satisfied.

Because of the periodic nature of the field in a crystal, certain energy levels must be excluded, so that there are very definite and finite energy states allowable for the free electrons. According to wave mechanical theory in its simplest form, an electron moving in a certain direction with a velocity v has associated with it a set of waves moving in the same direction and having a wave length $\lambda = \dfrac{h}{mv}$, where h is Planck's constant and m is the mass of the electron. The motion of an electron in a field of force can be studied by following the motion of a system of de Broglie waves; in particular, the scattering of the waves in a field of force, analogous to the scattering of light in a non-homogeneous medium, is interpreted as the probability that the electron will travel in the direction of the various scattered waves. Thus, if the wave-length λ is such that it satisfies a Bragg relation (see x-rays) with respect to the field of force (the periodic potential due to the crystal structure), then the waves are so greatly scattered or reflected that they are really not propagated through the crystal at all. Thus an electron with a momentum $p = mv = h/\lambda$, where λ satisfies a Bragg relation in every direction, could not move about within the crystal. In general, it is found that these excluded energies form bands of finite width in the energy scale separated by bands of allowed energies.

The difference between insulators and conductors is based upon the energy levels of these bands of prohibited states and on the number of electrons available. In an insulator all the energy levels in an allowed band are filled while no electrons are in the next higher allowed band. Thus no electron can have its energy increased unless the increase is of sufficient magnitude to raise the electron energy above that of the forbidden energy band directly above the highest filled band. The application of an emf to the material cannot raise the electron energy enough to make such a jump except for very narrow bands. In a true metal, because of the small size of the unit cell, the wave length λ is very small. The forbidden bands are therefore at such high energy levels that the electrons do not fill the energy states in the lowest energy band so that all the electrons can be considered as free. In alloys which are good conductors even though the unit cell is large, the conductivity is explained on the basis that the forbidden bands are so narrow as to be essentially non-existent. The presence of these bands explains the decrease in conductivity due to impurities in metals as well as the lower conductivity of alloys. In the so-called semi-conductors (q.v.) absorbed radiation (light) or heat causes electrons to jump over the forbidden band forming free electrons. In addition, after these electrons have left the lower energy band, the remaining electrons have a certain freedom of motion.

On the basis of the theory, heat affects the conductivity by means of two processes. First, it tends to increase the energy level of the electrons which in insulators and semiconductors increases the number of electrons in the unoccupied bands. Second, it causes an oscillation of the atoms about the lattice points, causing a departure from the periodic form of the field. This perturbation of the periodic structure splits the forbidden bands and tends to introduce new forbidden bands. Both these effects tend to decrease the resistance in insulators and semi-conductors where the forbidden bands are already of major importance. In metals the first has a negligible effect while the introduction of forbidden bands due to the second causes the resistance to increase with temperature.

Quantitative calculations using this theory are very complex, but approximations applicable to metals, except at very low temperatures, have made the calculation of conduction in metals reasonable.

Conduction in Metals. Metals, as discussed above, are characterized by the fact that the free electrons can exist in practically any energy state from zero energy up to an energy well above that ever reached by the electrons. Because of the finite volume of the metal the waves representing the electrons must have certain wave lengths in order to set up standing waves in the metal (if they were not standing waves the average resultant at any point would be zero). Thus the electron energies cannot take on a continuous set of values but can exist only in those energy states satisfying this condition. The statistical distribution in energy of particles satisfying this condition as well as the Pauli exclusion principle is called the Fermi-Dirac statistics.

If the periodic variation of the field within the crystal is neglected, the resulting constant potential is such that, considering this potential as zero, the piece of metal is conceived as a region populated with electrons obeying the Fermi-Dirac statistics and surrounded by a potential wall, the barrier. This barrier prevents the electrons from escaping from the metal. The Fermi-Dirac distribution function is

$$f = \frac{2}{h^3} \frac{1}{e^{(\epsilon - W_i)/kT} + 1} \tag{1}$$

$$W_i = \frac{h^2}{2m} \left(\frac{3n}{8\pi}\right)^{2/3}$$

where e is napierian base, ϵ is the energy of the electron, k is Boltzmann's constant, h is Planck's constant, T is the absolute temperature, m is the mass of the electron, and n is the number of electrons per unit volume. When T is zero, f is either zero or $2/h^3$, depending on whether ϵ is greater or less than W_i. Thus W_i is the maximum energy level occupied by an electron when all the lower energy levels are filled. If v_m is the velocity of the electron in the maximum energy level, $1/2\, m v_m^2 = W_i$ or

$$v_m = \frac{h}{m} \left(\frac{3n}{8\pi}\right)^{1/3} \tag{2}$$

The specific heat is obtained from any distribution law by integrating to find the total energy and differentiating this energy with respect to T. On the basis of a Maxwellian gas distribution, as used by Drude in the old theory of the electron gas in metals, the specific heat was $3/2\, nk$ which for n, of such a value to give reasonable conductance, was greater than the measured total specific heat of the metal for most temperatures. But the specific heat of the atoms alone agreed with the experimental specific heat. This was the notorious difficulty with the older theory. The new theory as presented here avoids this, since the specific heat of the electron gas is given by

$$\frac{2\pi m}{3} \frac{(2\pi k)^2}{h^2} \left(\frac{3n}{8\pi}\right)^{1/3} T$$

a value which is negligible compared with the specific heat of the atoms alone for all reasonable values of T.

In order to find the conductivity of the metal, the change in the distribution function f due to the presence of an electric field must be determined. This was originally done by Lorentz for the Maxwellian distribution in connection with the Drude theory. This method has been carried over into the new theory.

The distribution function $f(v)$ is isotropic, a function of v in magnitude only. Taking the electric field in the x direction, Lorentz postulated that the new distribution function could be approximated by

$$f = f_0(v) + v_x g(v) \tag{3}$$

where $f_0(v)$ is the distribution function without an applied field and $g(v)$ is a function to be determined, depending upon the electric field, by the conditions that the total number of free electrons remain the same and that f should remain constant in time. The postulated form (3) is clearly only an approximation argued to be valid since (3) differs only slightly from $f_0(v)$.

Since the energy of the electrons is increased because of the application of the electric field, there will be a distortion of the standing wave pattern within the metal. This causes definite permitted energy changes in the electron. Since these are difficult if not impossible to calculate, the classical idea of mean free path is borrowed to avoid this difficulty. Using the above conditions $g(v)$ becomes

$$g(v) = \frac{l}{v^2} \frac{eE}{m} \frac{df_0}{dv} \tag{4}$$

where e is the charge on an electron, l is the mean free path, and E is the electric field intensity.

The current density is given by the number of electrons times their velocity in the direction of the current times the charge on an electron, or

$$J = e \int_{-\infty}^{\infty} v_x f dw = e \int_{-\infty}^{\infty} v_x^2 \, g(v) dw \tag{5}$$

where the single integral sign replaces a triple integral and $dw = dv_x \, dv_y \, dv_z$.

Substituting from (4)

$$J = \frac{le^2 E}{m} \int_{-\infty}^{\infty} \frac{v_x^2}{v^2} \frac{df_0(v)}{dv} \, dw$$

carrying out the integration

$$J = \frac{8\pi}{3} \frac{e^2 l}{h} \left(\frac{3n}{8\pi}\right)^{2/3} E$$

or the conductivity is

$$\sigma = \frac{8\pi}{3} \frac{e^2 l}{h} \left(\frac{3n}{8\pi}\right)^{2/3} \tag{6}$$

In an analogous manner the heat current (rate of flow of heat) is given by

$$W = \frac{1}{2} m \int_{-\infty}^{\infty} v_x^2 v^2 g(v) dw$$

$g(v)$ is here calculated with the condition that J the electric current is zero. This condition results in the presence of both an electric field and a rate of change of T in the direction of the field. (W_i in equation 1 is a first approximation for the calculation of $g(v)$. Here it is necessary to use the second approximation in order that W shall differ from zero.) Calculation of $g(v)$ and integration gives for the heat current

$$W = \frac{8\pi^3}{9} \frac{lk^2 T}{h} \left(\frac{3n}{8\pi}\right)^{2/3} \left(\frac{dT}{dx}\right) \tag{7}$$

The coefficient of $\frac{dT}{dx}$ is the *thermal conductivity*, usually denoted by κ.

An important ratio, the Wiedermann-Franz ratio, is the ratio of the heat conductivity to the electric conductivity

$$\frac{\kappa}{\sigma} = \frac{1}{3} \pi^2 \left(\frac{k}{e}\right)^2 T$$

$$= 7.1 \times 10^{-11} \qquad\qquad \text{at } T = 291° \text{ K } (18° \text{ C.})$$

This value agrees remarkably with the measured value for many metals.

Thermionic Emission. A piece of metal has been pictured as a region of depressed potential in space, occupied by an electron gas obeying the distribution law given by equation 1. If the value of this depression of the potential is W_a in energy units, only those electrons with a velocity component perpendicular to the barrier corresponding to a kinetic energy greater than W_a can get over the wall. If the barrier is taken in the yz plane then those electrons with a velocity such that $1/2 \, m \, v_x^2 > W_a$ can get out of the metal. Let $1/2 \, m \, v_0^2 = W_a$; then the current due to all of the electrons escaping (the saturation thermionic current) is given by

$$i = 2e \left(\frac{m}{h}\right)^3 \int_{v_x = v_0}^{\infty} \int_{-\infty}^{\infty} \int_{-\infty}^{\infty} \frac{v_x dv_y dv_z dv_x}{e^{(\epsilon - W_i)/kT} + 1}$$

Integrating, the current becomes

$$i = \frac{4\pi em}{h^3} (kT)^2 e^{-(W_a - W_i)/kT} \tag{8}$$

provided that W_a is considerably greater than W_i. Experimentally $W_a - W_i$ is the so-called work function which varies from 1 to 6 equivalent volts. If there are as many free electrons as there are atoms in the metal, W_i is about 6 volts. The experiments of Davisson and Germer indicate that W_i is such that there are twice as many electrons as there are atoms.

The constant A, when equation 8 is written

$$i = A\,T^2 e^{-(W_a - W_i)/kT} \qquad (8a)$$

is calculated on the basis of this theory to be 120.4 amperes per square centimeter per degree squared. The classical thermodynamic theory predicts half this value or 60.2.

Experimentally several metals indicate that 60.2 is right while some are very much less and some are very much more, a few even greater than 120.4. In order to explain this variation in A, Fowler and Nordheim have postulated that the metal is not only a depression of potential but that it is also surrounded on its surface by a wall. That is, W_a is greater than W_0, the value of potential outside of the metal. They have shown that even though the energy of the electron is less than W_a, there is a certain probability that it would get out of the metal, and likewise even though the energy of the electron is greater than W_a there is a probability that it would not get out of the metal. Thus in the determination of equation 8 the integration must extend over all energies and the selection must be obtained by means of a probability function $D(\epsilon)$ times the integrand.

Photoelectric Effect. Photoelectric effect is explained in a manner similar to thermionic emission except that here the emitted electrons gain the energy necessary to traverse the barrier not by heat but from the absorption of a photon of light energy. The energy of each photon of frequency ν is given by $h\nu$ (see Photons). Thus any electron within the metal which absorbed a photon of frequency ν would have an energy $\epsilon + h\nu$ where ϵ was the energy of the electron before absorbing the photon. If the component of the velocity of this electron perpendicular to the barrier corresponds to an energy greater than W_a, the electron will escape. For cold metals the maximum value of ϵ is W_i. Thus the minimum frequency which will cause an electron to escape, the *threshold frequency*, $h\nu_{min}$, is given by

$$W_a = W_i + h\nu_{min}$$

In order to calculate the current for any given light it is necessary to know how and where the light is absorbed by the electrons as well as the probability that an electron having absorbed a photon will retain that energy until it gets to the barrier. This subject is too complex to treat here.

Photoconductivity. Photoconductivity is the increase in the conductivity of a semi-conductor due to the incident light. This phenomenon is attributed to the absorption of photons by electrons in one band causing them to jump over the prohibited band into a free band in which they can freely move. Very little quantitative theory has been developed for photoconductivity. Experimentally, threshold frequencies have been determined indicating a width for the prohibited bands.

Photovoltaic Effect. The photovoltaic effect is the development of an emf due to incident light at the boundary between certain semi-conductors and metals. Although this phenomenon is probably in some manner connected with photoconductivity, no satisfactory quantitative or even qualitative theory has been presented.

Effect of Temperature on the Resistance of Metals. Equation 6 does not contain the temperature explicitly; however, both l the mean free path and n the density of the free electrons may vary with temperature. Measurements of the resistance show that it does vary with temperature. The resistance of a metal for small ranges can be written

$$r = r_0 + \alpha T$$

where r_0 and α are independent of T, although α is not truly constant over wide ranges. In general, α increases with temperature, large changes being observed in the neighborhood of melting points. Lindeck finds that $r\alpha$ is constant for metals.

Roughly the resistance decreases as the absolute temperature or a little more rapidly than the temperature. At temperatures in the neighborhood of 100° K and 200° K the curves of resistance versus temperature point toward a vanishing resistance at some temperature above absolute zero. On continuing the curves below 100° K, it is found that for most metals they flatten out and approach some small finite resistance at absolute zero. With some metals, however, the resistance curve begins to flatten out, but then at some low temperature it suddenly drops rapidly so that below this temperature the resistance is so low that a current set up in a coil would still be 2/3 of its initial value after a lapse of 4 days. This phenomenon is called *superconductivity* or *supraconductivity*. It has been found that superconductivity is destroyed by too large currents. However, if after superconductivity is so destroyed a magnetic field is set up to counteract the field due to the current in the cold wire, the wire again becomes superconducting. No accepted theory of conduction in metals fits this phenomenon.

Conductivity of Alloys. Each component of an alloy contributes to the conductivity. If the alloy is purely a mechanical mixture its conductivity is an additive property of the volume percentages of the components. Isomorphous mixtures have a conductivity always less than that calculated from the mixture law, as would be expected from the general theory of conduction in solids. The formation of a solid solution is accompanied by considerable increase in resistance which also increases with concentration. The presence of foreign substances always increases the resistance, for alloys of relatively high conductivity. The temperature coefficients of intermetallic compounds are about the same as for metals, but of solid solutions they are much less. The temperature coefficients are sometimes used to determine the constitution of alloys.

28. CONDUCTION IN FLUIDS

Conduction in Liquids. The most important liquids from the point of view of electrical conduction are salts in solution. The theory of Arrhenius is the outstanding theory of conduction in such liquids (*Trans. Farad. Soc.*, 15, 10, 1919). According to Arrhenius, salts in solution are extensively broken up into ions. In very dilute solutions the number of ion pairs, which increases with dilution, is in many cases practically equal to the number of molecules. With regard to the controlling factors in this ionization, there is no satisfactory theory. The current in such solutions is due to the actual migration of these ions. The question of the mobility of ions plays an important rôle but is too complex to treat here.

The conductivities of pure liquids are very small, so small in fact that the presence of impurities is believed by some investigators to be the explanation of what conductivity there is.

Conductivity in Gases. A normal gas is supposed to consist of molecules of the substance distributed at random throughout the gas having a density of distribution small compared with that of either the liquids or the solids. These molecules dart back and forth within the gas in a chaotic manner, colliding and rebounding from one another. The activity depends upon the temperature. The separation between these molecules except at the instant of a collision, is very great compared with the dimensions of the individual molecules. At distances as great as a few thousandths of a centimeter from one of these molecules the molecule can be considered an electrically neutral particle. An electric field in such a gas would therefore cause a negligible drift of these molecules.

If some of the molecules are broken up to form electrons and ions (ions are atoms or molecules which have lost or gained one or more electrons) an electric field would cause these particles to move through the gas. An electric field set up between two conducting electrodes, an anode and a cathode, the positive and negative electrodes respectively, causes the positive ions (ions which have lost electrons) to tend to move toward the cathode, and it causes the electrons and negative ions (ions which have gained electrons) to move toward the anode. These positive charges moving in one direction and negative charges moving in the opposite direction add to form a resultant positive current in the direction of motion of the positive charges.

These charged particles collide with the other molecules of the gas or with other charged particles. At each of these collisions one of several results may occur, depending upon the circumstances under which the collision occurs. A charged particle colliding with a molecule may rebound, continuing to be attracted as before; it may split the molecule into two separate ions; or it may knock an electron out of the molecule, resulting in a new ion and a new molecule, or in an electron, the original ion, and a molecular ion. A charged particle colliding with a charged particle of opposite sign may recombine to form a neutral particle. The probabilities for these various processes are very complicated in ordinary discharges.

Production of Electrons and Ions in Gases. A molecule is supposed to consist of the nuclei of the several atoms forming the molecule around which the atomic electrons or at least some of the atomic electrons rotate in orbits having associated with each orbit a definite energy. In order for an electron in one of these orbits to absorb energy it must move to one of the other orbits having a certain definite higher energy. Thus an electron in an atom or molecule can absorb energy only in very definite quantities called quantums of energy. The electrons in normal molecules are in very definite and particular orbits. When one or more of these electrons have jumped into orbits of higher energy levels, the molecule is said to be in an excited state. If still more energy is absorbed by these electrons they are freed entirely from the field of the molecule and become free electrons. Thus there is a definite minimum quantity of energy which will free an electron from an atom or molecule in the normal state, that is, ionize it. The minimum energy is usually called the *minimum ionizing potential* since it is usually measured in terms of the potential difference through which an electron must move in order to acquire this minimum ionizing energy.

The processes by means of which these electrons can be made to absorb this ionizing energy may be divided into six classes: (1) ionization by *electron impact*, (2) *photoioniza-tion*, (3) *cumulative ionization*, (4) ionization by *positive ion impact*, (5) ionization by *collisions of the second kind*, and (6) *thermal ionization*. There are several other processes of ionization, which are not known to occur often enough to warrant their discussion.

When electrons are emitted from the cathode in an electron tube by means of ther-mionic emission, photoelectric effect, or cold emission, they are accelerated toward the anode through the gas owing to the electric field. If before an electron collides with a molecule it moves through a potential greater than the minimum ionizing potential, there is a certain finite probability that when it does collide with a molecule that molecule will be ionized. This process of ionization is called ionization by electron impact.

If a photon of light having a frequency such that $h\nu$ is greater than the minimum ionizing potential collides with a molecule, there is a finite probability that the molecule will be ionized. For molecules of most gases the minimum ionizing potential is of such a value that only the shorter ultra-violet light and x-rays have a ν great enough to cause ionization. This process is called photo-ionization.

When an atomic electron absorbs only enough energy to raise the atom or molecule to an excited state, it could be ionized by means of another collision with a particle hav-ing less energy than the regular minimum ionizing potential. Thus it is possible for ionization to take place without even the minimum ionizing potential. This process of ionization is called cumulative ionization. Cumulative ionization does not occur as often as one would expect because an atom remains in the excited state for only a very small interval of time. The atom returns to its normal state, that is, having orbits of stable energy levels, radiating the resulting freed energy in the form of light. This is the process by which the light in a neon sign is produced.

Ionization by positive ion impact is similar to the process of ionization by electron impact, the ions being first formed by means of one of the other processes of ionization.

Ionization by collisions of the second kind is the name given to the collision, usually due to their normal Brownian motion, of two atoms or molecules one or both being in the excited state. One atom returns to the normal state, the liberated energy being used to ionize the other atom.

When the temperature of a gas reaches several thousand degrees, the Brownian motion of the molecules may become great enough so that they ionize upon collision. This form of ionization is supposed to occur in the sun and other hot stars. This process is called thermal ionization.

In any of these several ways, gases can be made conductors. In fact, it is practically impossible to have a gas in which there are no ions. In the earth's crust are many radio-active substances giving off radiation having the same characteristics as very hard x-rays. In addition to this, cosmic rays have been shown to be a major cause of residual ioniza-tion in gases.

Recombination of Ions. Ions, after having been produced in a gas, dart back and forth owing to their Brownian motion, the electric field, and their own attraction for one another of opposite charge. When two ions of opposite charge get near to each other they will tend to combine to form a neutral particle. This process of recombination goes on so fast in a gas that in order for there to be many ionized molecules, the production of ionization must go on at a correspondingly rapid rate. If the process for the production of ions is stopped, the gas soon loses all its ionization and is no longer in a conducting state.

The Effect of Pressure on the Conduction in Gases. In a gas the electrons, ions, and molecules move between collisions distances that are distributed at random from zero to a comparatively long distance. Very few go a long distance and very few go a short distance. The average distance that a particle moves without a collision is called the *mean free path*. The mean free path gives a simple quantitative measure of the distances that a particle moves between collisions. It is customary to calculate or measure the mean free path and then assume that all the particles move just that distance between collisions. On this assumption a rough estimate of the electric field intensity necessary for ionization by electron and ion impact can be made. If E is the electric field intensity in volts per centimeter, l is the mean free path in centimeters, and V is the minimum ionizing potential in volts then $E = V/l$ is the field intensity necessary to cause ioniza-tion. l is found to be practically inversely proportional to the pressure. At normal atmospheric pressure, air has a mean free path of approximately 10^{-5} cm. The values of other gases are of the same order of magnitude while V is of the order of 10 volts. Thus at pressures greater than a few millimeters of mercury the field must be large to produce ionization. At high vacuums (a small fraction of a millimeter) the free paths are so long that very little ionization takes place so that, unless electrons or ions come out of the electrodes, the gas (or vacuum) makes a good insulator.

Space-charge Effect. The velocity of drift of the ions through a gas is comparatively small. Therefore when even a small current flows the density of the charges of the ions is great enough to affect appreciably the electric field due to the electrodes. These charges in the space between the electrodes are called the *space charge*. Predictions of space charge are very complex so that the engineering of discharge tubes proceeds mostly by trial and error.

BIBLIOGRAPHY ON ELECTRICITY AND MAGNETISM

1. A.I.E.E., Report on Proposed American Standard Definitions of Electrical Terms, 1932.
2. BOHR, NIELS, *Philosophical Magazine*, 6, p. 476, 1913.
3. BOZORTH, R. M., Present Status of Ferromagnetic Theory, *Elec. Eng.*, Vol. 54, p. 1251, Nov. 1935.
4. BRAGG, W. H., Introduction to Crystal Analysis, D. Van Nostrand Co., 1928.
5. BUSH, V., Operational Circuit Analysis, New York, John Wiley & Sons, 1929.
6. CAMPBELL, N. R., Modern Electrical Theory, New York, Macmillan Co., 1922.
7. CARSON, J. R., Electric Circuit Theory and the Operational Calculus, New York, McGraw-Hill Book Co., 1927.
8. COMPTON, A. H., X-rays and Electrons, D. Van Nostrand Co., 1926.
9. COMPTON, K. T., and I. LANGMUIR, Electrical Discharges in Gases, Part I, *Rev. Mod. Phys.*, 3, 191, 1931.
10. DAHL, O. G. C., Electric Circuits, Theory and Applications, New York, McGraw-Hill Book Co., 1928.
11. DARROW, K. K., Statistical Theories of Matter, Radiation and Electricity, *Rev. Mod. Phys.*, 1, 90, 1929.
12. FARADAY, M., Experimental Researches in Electricity, 3 vols., London, 1839–1855.
13. FOWLER, R. H., Thermionic Emission Constant A, *Proc. Roy. Soc.*, A122, 36, 1929.
14. FRENKEL, J., Elementary Theory of Wave Mechanics, New York, Oxford University Press, 1932.
15. HAAS, A., Wave Mechanics and the New Quantum Theory, London, 1928.
16. HAGUE, B., Electromagnetic Problems in Electrical Engineering, London, Oxford University Press, 1929.
17. HEAVISIDE, O., Electromagnetic Theory, 5 vols., London, Benn Bros., 1925.
18. HEAVISIDE, O., Electrical Papers, 2 vols., Boston, Copley Publishers, 1925.
19. HUGHES, A. L., and L. A. DU BRIDGE, Photoelectric Phenomena, 1932.
20. JEANS, J. H., Mathematical Theory of Electricity and Magnetism, Cambridge, England, University Press, 1908.
21. KRONIG, R. DE L., Theory of Supraconductivity, Part II, *Zeits. Physik*, 80, 203, 1933.
22. LANGMUIR, I., and K. T. COMPTON, Electrical Discharges in Gases, Part I, *Rev. Mod. Phys.*, 3, 191, 1931.
23. LINFORD, L. B., Recent Developments in the Study of the External Photoelectric Effect, *Rev. Mod. Phys.*, 5, 34, 1933.
24. LORENTZ, H. A., The Theory of Electrons, Leipzig, 1909.
25. MAXWELL, J. C., A Treatise on Electricity and Magnetism, 2 vols., London, Oxford University Press, 1904.
26. MILLIKAN, R. A., The Electron, University of Chicago Press, 1924.
27. PENDER, H., Electricity and Magnetism for Engineers; Parts I and II.
28. ROENTGEN, WILHELM CONRAD, On a New Form of Radiation, *Electrician*, 36, p. 415, Jan. 24; p. 850, April 24, 1896.
29. RUSSELL, A., The Theory of Alternating Currents, Cambridge, England, University Press, 1914.
30. RUTHERFORD, E., Radioactivity.
31. SOMMERFELD, A., Atomic Structure and Spectral Lines, London, 1923.
32. STARLING, S. G., Electricity and Magnetism for Advanced Students, London, Longmans, Green & Co., 1924.
33. STEINMETZ, C. P., Transient Electric Phenomena and Oscillations, New York, McGraw-Hill Book Co., 1920.
34. TAYLOR, H. S., A Treatise on Physical Chemistry, Chapter XI by J. R. PARTINGTON.
35. THOMPSON, S. P., Elementary Lessons in Electricity and Magnetism, New York, Macmillan Co., 1915.
36. THOMSON, J. J., Elements of Electricity and Magnetism, New York, Macmillan Co., 1921.
37. THOMSON, J. J. and G. P., Conduction of Electricity through Gases, London, Macmillan & Co.
38. TOWNSEND, J. T., Ionization of Gases by Collision.
39. VAN VLECK, J. H., The Theory of Electric and Magnetic Susceptibilities, Oxford University Press, 1932.
40. VON LAUE, M., Phénomènes d'interférence des rayon de Röntgen, *Le Radium*, 10, p. 47, 1913.
41. WEBSTER, A. G., Theory of Electricity and Magnetism; London, Macmillan & Co., 1897.
42. WILSON, A. H., Theory of Electronic Semi-Conductors, Part II, *Proc. Roy. Soc.*, 42, A134, p. 277, 1931.
43. ZWORYKIN, V. K., and E. D. WILSON, Photocells and Their Application, New York, John Wiley & Sons, 1934.

Space-charge Effects. The velocity of drift of the ions through a gas is comparatively small. Therefore when even a small current flows the density of the charges of the ions is great enough to affect appreciably the electric field due to the electrodes. These charges in the space between the electrodes are called the space charge. Predictions of space-charge are very complex so that the engineering of discharge tubes proceeds mostly by trial and error.

BIBLIOGRAPHY ON ELECTRICITY AND MAGNETISM

1. A.I.E.E., Report on Proposed American Standard Definitions of Electrical Terms, 1922.
2. Abraham, Max, Theorie der Elektrizität, 5 ed., 1914.
3. Bouasse, H. M., Present Status of Electrodynamic Theory, Elec. Eng., Vol. 51, p. 1251, Nov. 1932.
4. Bragg, W. H., Introduction to Crystal Analysis, D. Van Nostrand Co., 1928.
5. Bush, V., Operational Circuit Analysis, New York, John Wiley & Sons, 1929.
6. Carson, J. R., Modern Mathematical Theory, New York, Macmillan Co., 1922.
7. Carter, G. W., Electrical Circuit Theory and the Operational Calculus, New York, McGraw-Hill Book Co., 1927.
8. Cohen, L., Alternating Currents, D. Van Nostrand Co., 1922.
9. Carson, J. R., and J. Lyashkin, Electrical Discharge in Gases, Part I, Rev. Mod. Phys., p. 191, 1930.
10. Darrow, K. K., Electric Circuits, Theory and Applications, New York, McGraw-Hill Book Co., 1929.
11. Darrow, K. K., Statistical Theories of Matter, Radiation and Electricity, Rev. Mod. Phys., p. 90, 1929.
12. Faraday, M., Experimental Researches in Electricity, 3 vols., London, 1839–1855.
13. Faraday, M., Transactions Bakerian Lecture 1, Roy. Soc., A37, No. 30, 1823.
14. Fleischl, J., Elementary Theory of Wave Mechanics, New York, Oxford University Press, 1935.
15. Haas, A., Wave Mechanics and the New Quantum Theory, London, 1928.
16. Hague, B., Electromagnetic Problems in Electrical Engineering, London, Oxford University Press, 1929.
17. Heaviside, O., Electromagnetic Theory, 3 vols., London, Benn Bros., 1925.
18. Heaviside, O., Electrical Papers, 2 vols., Boston, Copley Publishers, 1925.
19. Jeans, J. H., and J. A. Fleming, Principles of Electronics, Cambridge, England, University Press, 1908.
20. Jeans, J. H., Mathematical Theory of Electricity and Magnetism, Cambridge, England, University Press, 1908.
21. Kennard, E. H., Theory of Superconductivity, Part II, Rev. Mod. Phys., p. 205, 1932.
22. Lyashkin, L., and J. Townsend, Electrical Discharge in Gases, Part I, Rev. Mod. Phys., p. 191, 1930.
23. Langmuir, I., Recent Developments in the Study of the Emission of Electrons, Rev. Mod. Phys., p. 223, 1930.
24. Lorentz, H. A., The Theory of Electrons, Leipzig, 1909.
25. Maxwell, J. C., A Treatise on Electricity and Magnetism, 2 vols., London, Oxford University Press, 1904.
26. Millikan, R. A., The Electron, University of Chicago Press, 1924.
27. Pender, H., Electricity and Magnetism for Engineers, Parts I and II.
28. Rothmund, William Conrad, On a New Form of Radiation, Electrician, 56, p. 416, Jan. 1906.
29. Russell, A., The Theory of Alternating Currents, Cambridge, England, University Press, 1914.
30. Rutherford, E., Radioactivity.
31. Sommerfeld, A., Atomic Structure and Spectral Lines, London, 1923.
32. Starling, S. G., Electricity and Magnetism for Advanced Students, London, Longmans, Green & Co., 1924.
33. Starling, S. G., Transient Electric Phenomena and Oscillations, New York, McGraw-Hill Book Co., 1926.
34. Thornton, B. S., A Treatise on Physical Chemistry, Chapter XI by B. H. Harkins.
35. Thomson, J. J., Elementary Lessons in Electricity and Magnetism, New York, Macmillan Co., 1919.
36. Thomson, J. J., Elements of Electricity and Magnetism, New York, Macmillan Co., 1921.
37. Thomson, J. J. and G. P., Conduction of Electricity through Gases, London, Macmillan & Co.
38. Townsend, J. T., Ionization of Gases by Collision.
39. Van Vleck, J. H., The Theory of Electric and Magnetic Susceptibilities, Oxford University Press, 1932.
40. von Laue, M., Phénomènes d'interférence des rayons de Röntgen, La Radium, 10, p. 15, 1919.
41. Watson, A. G., Theory of Electricity and Magnetism, London, Macmillan & Co., 1891.
42. Wilson, H. A., Theory of Electromagnetic Conduction, Part II, Proc. Roy. Soc., 42, A134, p. 277, 1931.
43. Zworykin, V. K. and E. D. Wilson, Photocells and Their Applications, New York, John Wiley & Sons, 1934.

SECTION 9

RADIATION AND LIGHT

BY

ERNST WEBER

ACOUSTICS

BY

R. B. LINDSAY

METEOROLOGY *

BY

EDGAR W. WOOLARD, R. J. MARTIN, AND H. L. DRYDEN

* Articles 35 to 41 previously prepared by Edgar W. Woolard, meteorologist; 42 by O. S. Peters, Associate Engineer; and 43 by H. L. Dryden, Scientist, of National Bureau of Standards for the American Civil Engineers' Handbook, have been revised by Edgar W. Woolard and R. J. Martin of the U. S. Weather Bureau, and H. L. Dryden of the National Bureau of Standards.

RADIATION, LIGHT, ACOUSTICS AND METEOROLOGY

THEORY OF RADIATION

By Ernst Weber

1. FUNDAMENTALS

Radiation is the transportation of energy through space; a detectable medium of transmission has not been discovered as yet. The assumption of an all-pervading ether as the carrier of radiated energy has proved unsatisfactory; it is, however, not impossible that ether or some other medium, not yet known, does exist.

The Nature of Radiation. At one time, all radiations were believed to be electromagnetic waves of various wavelengths (see Art. 3). At present the corpuscular nature of radiation must be conceded, as many phenomena can be explained only if the energy of radiation is associated with particles, like electrons or atoms (see Art. 4). The wave and corpuscular points of view are now being adopted alternatively as required by the occasion. The common basis of both aspects, the true nature of radiation, has not been established.

Radiation travels with a velocity v which depends on the medium through which it is propagated. Since the frequency ν of radiation is dependent only on the source, it does not vary with the medium. The ratio $v/\nu = \lambda$ is called the wavelength of radiation and depends like v on the medium.

Fundamental Definitions

Total Emissive Power is the time rate of total radiant energy emitted per unit area of the radiating body. It is measured in ergs per second per square centimeter or in watts per square centimeter.

Spectral Distribution of Emissive Power. The total emissive power of a body may be composed of radiations of many wavelengths. The graph of the emissive power as a function of wavelength is called the spectral distribution of emission. This spectrum is continuous if emissive power is a smooth continuous function of wavelength, or discontinuous if emission occurs only over small ranges of wavelengths. The discontinuous spectral distribution can have the character of lines, if a sharp selective radiation at certian wavelengths is evident, or of bands if many lines are so close that the discontinuity is apparent only on a very large scale of wavelength. The total emissive power is the integral of the spectral emissive power over all wavelengths from zero to infinity, and is, of course, identical with the area under the spectral distribution curve.

Monochromatic Emissive Power is the time rate of radiant energy emitted per unit area of a radiating body, at a particular wavelength. It can be determined most conveniently from the spectral distribution of emissive power as the ordinate at this particular wavelength.

Intensity of Radiation is the amount of power transmitted through unit area perpendicular to the direction of propagation of radiation.

Density of Radiation is the total radiant energy contained in unit volume. The radiation of the sun has an energy density at the earth's surface of approximately 4.3×10^{-5} erg per cu. cm.

Absorption. Radiation of incident intensity I_0 passing through matter of thickness δ loses intensity according to the exponential law

$$I = I_0 \varepsilon^{-\mu \delta} \tag{1}$$

where μ is called the absorption coefficient and has the dimension $[\mu] = [L]^{-1}$. The extinction coefficient, or index of absorption, is defined as the numerical parameter

$$\kappa = \frac{\lambda}{2\pi} \mu \tag{2}$$

where λ is the wavelength of radiation within the absorbing medium. Since the wavelength in vacuum is $\lambda_0 = n\lambda$, where n is the index of refraction, another coefficient can be defined as

$$k = n\kappa = \frac{\lambda_0}{2\pi}\mu \qquad (2a)$$

The use of the various definitions is not standardized, and many confusing statements have resulted.

Absorptivity, A, is the ratio of absorbed energy to incident energy of radiation and is a pure numeric always less than unity. A perfectly absorbing body, $A = 1$, is usually referred to as a *black body*.

Scattering is a particular kind of absorption whereby the radiation is diffusely reflected in all directions by the interaction with the inner structure of the substance and thus reduced in intensity in the direction of propagation.

Spectral Distribution of Absorptivity. The absorptivity varies greatly with wavelength. The graph of absorptivity against wavelength gives the spectral distribution of the absorption characteristics of a particular substance, and can be continuous (gradually changing) or discontinuous (selective). In case of discontinuous spectral distribution it can have the character of lines, if a sharp selective absorption at certain wavelengths is evident, or of bands, if many lines are so close that the discontinuity is apparent only on a very large scale of wavelength.

Mass Absorption Coefficient μ_d is the absorption coefficient μ divided by the density d of the absorbing substance, $\mu_d = \mu/d$. Its unit is cm^2 per gram.

Reflection. If radiation is incident upon a surface of a substance, part of it will enter the substance, part of it will be turned back, reflected. If the surface is rough, reflection will occur in all directions, and the radiation is said to be *diffusely* reflected. If the irregularities in the surface are small compared with the wavelength, the radiation will be *regularly* reflected, i.e., the reflected radiation will propagate in a definite direction determined by the equality of the angle of reflection and the angle of incidence. The angle of reflection is the angle which the outward normal to the surface makes with the direction of propagation of the reflected radiation; the angle of incidence similarly is the angle which the inward normal to the surface makes with the direction of propagation of the incident radiation.

Reflectivity or the Coefficient of Reflection, R, is the ratio of reflected to incident energy of radiation and is a pure numeric always less than unity. A perfectly reflecting body, $R = 1$, is usually referred to as a *perfect mirror*. The reflectivity depends upon the angle of incidence (see Reflection) as well as upon the wavelength. If for a particular wavelength $R = 1$ the reflecting body is said to act like a perfect mirror at this wavelength.

Total Reflection. If radiation comes from a medium of higher refractive index and enters a medium of lower refractive index, total reflection may occur, i.e., for angles of incidence larger than a certain critical value θ_c all the radiation is reflected; the critical angle is designated as the angle of total reflection.

Lambert's Law. If radiation falls perpendicularly upon a surface which reflects diffusely, the intensity of the reflected radiation varies approximately with the cosine of the angle made with the normal to the surface; for larger angles with the normal, the approximation becomes poor.

Transmissivity, T, of a body is the ratio of the intensity of radiation leaving the body to the incident intensity of radiation; it is a numerical value, and varies greatly with the thickness of the body and wavelength. If, for any particular wavelength, $T = 0$, i.e., no radiation is transmitted, the body is said to be *totally opaque* for this wavelength; if on the other hand $T = 1$, i.e., all the radiation is transmitted without loss of intensity, the body is said to be *totally transparent* for this wavelength. Obviously, the sum of the three characteristic numerics must always be equal to unity

$$A + R + T = 1 \qquad (3)$$

Refraction. Radiation changes its direction and velocity of propagation with the medium in which it travels. The ratio of the velocity in vacuum to that in a medium is called the *refractive index*, or the *index of refraction* for that medium. It is a numeric always larger than unity and varies greatly with the wavelength.

Refractivity is defined as the difference between refractive index and unity, $n - 1$. Like the refractive index, it varies with the wavelength. *Specific refractivity* is the quotient of refractivity of a medium and its density.

Snell's Law of Refraction. If radiation in one medium is incident upon the surface of another medium at an angle α, it will proceed into this medium with an angle β between the normal to the surface and the direction of propagation. β is called the angle of refraction, and the ratio of the sines of the two angles is the relative index of refraction of the second medium against the first

$$n_{21} = \frac{\sin \alpha}{\sin \beta} = \frac{n_2}{n_1} \tag{4}$$

The *relative index of refraction* is equal to the quotient of the absolute indices of refraction of each medium.

Dispersion. The fact that the refractive index varies with wavelength is called dispersion of radiation. Polychromatic radiation (containing radiation of many wavelengths) can be separated into its monochromatic components by utilizing the fact of dispersion (see Spectroscopy). Historically, normal and anomalous dispersion are differentiated. The former covers the cases of increasing index of refraction with decreasing wavelength; the latter refers to the converse dependents.

Diffraction. The normal laws of refraction and reflection cease to be valid if the objects in the path of radiation are of a size comparable with the wavelength of the radiation. The peculiar disturbance caused by such an object is called diffraction. A regular array of diffracting objects is usually referred to as a *diffracting grating*, and is used to determine the wavelength of the incident radiation.

2. TYPES OF RADIATION

The various types of radiation that are known can be grouped either according to their characteristics or according to their origin. The more important kinds of radiation, grouped according to their most evident nature, are briefly defined below.

a. Wave Radiations

Thermal Radiation is that radiation emitted by solids or liquids, which depends only on the temperature of the substance. The spectral distribution of emissive power is continuous (see Art. 12) and changes smoothly with temperature. Thermal radiation is thought to be produced entirely by the thermal agitation of atoms or molecules.

Characteristic Line Radiation is emitted by gases and vapors if properly " excited." Excitation may occur in the flame (by thermal agitation), in electric arcs or sparks, by bombardment with electrons or atoms, and by absorption of radiation of suitable wavelength. The spectral distribution of emissive power in this case is discontinuous and either of distinct line character or in the form of bands (see Art. 10).

X-Rays. The term x-rays is applied to the secondary radiation of a substance upon which high-speed electrons are impinging. The energy distribution has the same character for all elements and consists of a continuous energy spectrum upon which is superimposed a line spectrum which in its details is characteristic of the element serving as the secondary emitter (see Art. 14). The very hardest x-rays produced in the course of natural disintegration of radioactive substances are called γ-rays and show again a characteristic line spectral distribution in energy.

Fluorescence and Phosphorescence are the secondary emission of characteristic visible radiation if a substance is excited by radiation of suitably shorter wavelength even without perceptible rise of the temperature of the emitter. In the case of fluorescence the secondary radiation ceases with the primary radiation; in the case of phosphorescence the secondary radiation persists for an appreciable time after the primary radiation has been stopped.

Cosmic Rays are the extremely penetrating type of radiation which is supposed to originate in the interstellar spaces. Their exact nature is not yet explored, and various points of view are current.

b. Corpuscular Radiations

Electron Radiation is the emission of corpuscular electrons from the atoms or molecules of substances. As primary radiation, it may be caused by thermal agitation (thermionic emission, especially in electron tubes), by very high electric fields (cold emission, corona discharge, and cathode rays), and by the natural decay of radioactive substances (as β-rays). As secondary radiation, it can be produced by ultraviolet rays and x-rays (photo-electricity), or by bombardment with high-speed ionized atoms or molecules.

Positive Radiation is the emission of corpuscular positively charged particles from atoms or molecules of substances. If these particles have a small mass approximately corresponding to that of electrons, they are called *positrons*; as secondary radiation they are produced by bombardment of heavy metals with high-energy γ-rays or high-speed α-particles. *Proton radiation* is the emission of positively charged hydrogen nuclei with a mass approximately corresponding to that of the hydrogen atom; it occurs as secondary radiation if substances are bombarded with high-speed α-rays. α-rays are positively charged particles identified as helium nuclei with approximately the mass of helium atoms; as primary radiation they may be produced by the natural decay of the heaviest elements (radioactivity), by intense electric fields in the very low-pressure discharge tube (canal rays). As secondary radiation, they are the result of artificial atomic disintegration by bombardment with high-speed protons.

Neutron Radiation is the secondary emission of corpuscular electrically neutral particles from atoms of substances if bombarded with very high-speed α-rays so as to produce artificial disintegration. The mass of the neutron corresponds approximately to that of the hydrogen atom.

3. WAVE ASPECTS OF RADIATION

Definition of Wave. The simplest type of a wave is the sinusoidal wave which is presented by any phenomenon the intensity of which varies sinusoidally with time at any point in space, as well as with distance at any particular instant of time (see Fig. 1). The mathematical formulation for a one-dimensional (or plane) wave is given by

$$a = A \sin \frac{2\pi}{\lambda} (x \pm vt) \qquad (5)$$

This form is symmetrical in x and vt so that the variation in space and time is sinusoidal. A is the amplitude or crest value of the wave, λ is called the wavelength; if $(x \pm vt) = n\lambda + \phi$, where n is any integer and ϕ any arbitrary quantity, the variable a takes on the same values, thus demonstrating its periodicity. The velocity with which the wave propagates in space is v, the upper sign denoting progression in the direction of the negative x-axis, the lower sign in the direction of the positive x-axis.

$$\nu = v/\lambda \qquad (6)$$

is the frequency of the local variation in time.

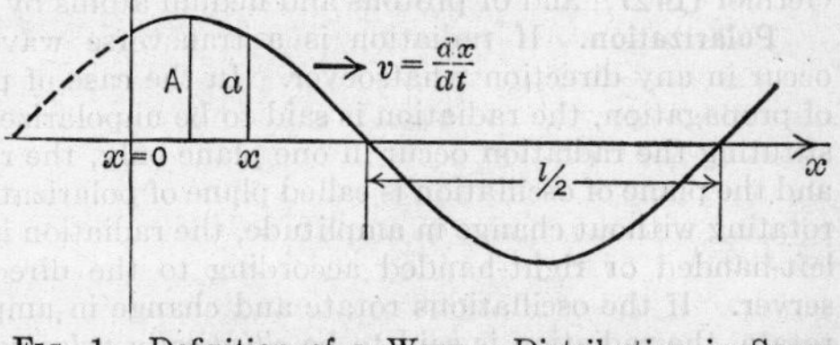

More complex, yet periodic, wave forms can be obtained by an algebraic superposition of several waves of different parameters. Instead of plane waves, cylindrical or spherical waves can arise if the origin of the waves is a linear infinitely long emitter or a point source, respectively.

Fig. 1. Definition of a Wave. Distribution in Space at a Particular Instant of Time.

Definition of Wave Packet. In dispersive media (see Dispersion, Art. 1), the velocity of propagation of radiation is a function of the frequency, and is related to the velocity in vacuum by $v = c/n$, if n is the refractive index. The superposition of a number of waves with infinitesimally different frequencies will, at a certain time t, give an absolute maximum for a point x. It can be shown that the progressing individual waves will superimpose at any other instant to give a maximum which appears to travel with a velocity

$$U = \frac{c}{\dfrac{d}{d\nu}(n\nu)},$$ which is called the group velocity of the wave train. The more individ-

ual waves are superimposed, the sharper will be the maximum, and reversely.

Longitudinal and Transverse Waves. The oscillation constituting the radiation can be either in the direction of propagation or perpendicular to it. In material substances waves of both types are possible; in vacuum only transverse waves are known. Radiation proper, which does not need any specifically known medium for its propagation, is composed of transverse waves.

The Electromagnetic Wave. The simplest case is the plane electromagnetic wave which is progressing in one direction and entirely homogeneous in all directions perpendicular to the direction of propagation. It is characterized by the electric field vector E, the magnetic field vector H, and the velocity of propagation v, which form a right-handed coordinate system (see Fig. 2). The wave is transversal, which means that both field vectors are oscillating in time perpendicularly to their direction of propagation. The velocity of propagation in any medium is given by

$$v = \frac{c}{\sqrt{\epsilon\mu}} \qquad (7)$$

where c is the velocity of electromagnetic waves in vacuum (identical with the velocity of light); ϵ and μ are the relative dielectric constant and magnetic permeability of the medium, respectively.

The superposition of various plane electromagnetic waves leads to more complex forms of electromagnetic vibrations, and the theory can easily be extended to cylindrical and spherical electromagnetic waves.

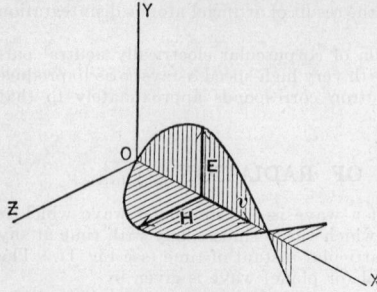

FIG. 2. The Plane Electromagnetic Wave

Characteristics of the Wave Nature of Radiation

Certain phenomena can be explained only if a wave nature of radiation is assumed.

Interference is the property by which waves of the same frequency but traveling in different directions superimpose in such a manner that they give alternate regions of stationary high and low (or zero) intensities. In the case of light, dark and light spots or bands will alternate on a screen. Interference can be produced by diffraction through narrow slits (Young, 1801), reflection from mirrors under different angles (Fresnel, 1811), diffraction from ruled gratings (Rowland, 1885), and reflection from mirrors at different distances (Michelson, 1895). The interference patterns can serve to determine the wavelength of the radiation, as was first done for light by Young in 180 . The most recent applications were the confirmation of the wave nature of electrons by Davisson and Germer (1927), and of protons and helium atoms by O. Stern (1930).

Polarization. If radiation is a transverse wave phenomenon the oscillations may occur in any direction whatsoever. In the case of perfect symmetry about the direction of propagation, the radiation is said to be unpolarized or natural. If the oscillations constituting the radiation occur in one plane only, the radiation is said to be *plane polarized*, and the plane of oscillation is called plane of polarization. If the oscillations are uniformly rotating without change in amplitude, the radiation is said to be *circularly polarized*, either left-handed or right-handed according to the direction of rotation as seen by an observer. If the oscillations rotate and change in amplitude with the same period as they rotate, the radiation is said to be *elliptically polarized*, either left-handed or right-handed according to the direction of rotation as seen by an observer. Circularly polarized radiation can be decomposed into two plane-polarized radiations at right angles to each other, of equal amplitude, and in quadrature time phases. Elliptically polarized radiation can be decomposed into two plane-polarized radiations in the direction of two conjugate diameters with proper time phases. Plane-polarized radiation can be decomposed into two oppositely rotating circularly polarized radiations. Any experiment establishing polarization of a radiation suggests transverse waves.

Velocity of Propagation in Different Media. From the laws of refraction (see Art. 1) it follows that the velocity of propagation of waves in media should decrease with increasing refracting index. This was first established experimentally by Foucault in 1850 for light radiation and therefore serves to support the wave aspect of radiation in general.

The Electromagnetic Spectrum of Radiation

Electromagnetic Theory of Light. Maxwell was the first to assume the identity of light and electromagnetic waves, and Hertz demonstrated it by showing the phenomena of reflection and interference for short electromagnetic waves. Further experiments have shown that the state of polarization is determined by the properties of the field vector H which with the direction of propagation determines the plane of polarization. If the vector H is oscillating without changing direction, the electromagnetic wave is said to be plane polarized; if it is rotating, the wave can be circularly or elliptically polarized (see Polarization, above). The photographic action of light is due to the electric field vector E. The index of refraction is identified with $n = \sqrt{\epsilon\mu}$, where, of course, ϵ and μ, the dielectric constant and the magnetic permeability, have to be chosen as variable with the wavelength in order to account for the fact of dispersion.

Bohr's Model of Atoms. To account for the origin of the characteristic line radiation (spectra), Bohr assumed a model for the atom with the mass concentrated in the center, the nucleus, composed of positive particles and a few " nuclear " electrons, so that a positive charge $Z \cdot e$ results (e is the charge of the electron). This nucleus is thought to be surrounded by electrons in orbital motion where Z is the atomic number of the element.

In the permanent state the orbits of the electrons are definite ones, determined by the matrix quantum rules of Heisenberg and Born, or the stationary solutions of Schroedinger's wave equation. By one of various processes of absorption, the orbital electrons can be thrown transiently into certain wider orbits and on returning will emit an electromagnetic wave of definite frequency ν determined by

$$h\nu = E_2 - E_1 \qquad (8)$$

where $E_2 > E_1$ are the energy values connected with the two orbits marking the ends of the journey, and h is the quantum of action of Planck. The number of frequencies for an atom is finite, as are the number of possible energy states, so that the spectral lines can be described. This principle applies not only to the visible light, but equally well to ultraviolet, x- and γ-radiation, as shown in Table I.

TABLE I. The Electromagnetic Spectrum

(From L. B. Loeb and A. S. Adams: The Development of Physical Thought, John Wiley & Sons, New York, 1933.)

Wavelength Range	Source	Name	Name of Discoverer and Means of Detection and Study
∞ to 100 cm	Movements of electricity in large systems with capacity and self-inductance	Radio waves	Predicted by Maxwell, discovered by Hertz
100 cm to 0.022 cm	Electrical oscillations of minute systems, metal filings	Very short electromagnetic waves	Nichols and Tear. Large gratings, interferometers, electrical detectors. Also Glagoliewa-Arkadiewa
0.022 cm to 7×10^{-5} cm	Oscillations or vibrations of charged atomic or molecular systems, ions in crystals or gas molecules; rotation of dipoles	Infra-red or heat waves	Rubens and Bayer. Paschen. Gratings and residual rays
7×10^{-5} cm to 4×10^{-5} cm	Loosely bound outer valence electrons	Visible light	Prisms, gratings, interferometers
4×10^{-5} cm to 1.6×10^{-5} cm	Outer electrons more tightly bound	Ultraviolet	Schumann and Lyman gratings
1.6×10^{-5} cm to 1.2×10^{-6} cm	Inner electrons of light atoms, or electrons in stripped light atoms or shells next to valence shells of heavy atoms	Extreme ultraviolet or soft x-rays	Millikan and Bowen. Vacuum spectrograph and gratings
1.2×10^{-6} cm to 1.6×10^{-8} cm	Interior electrons of elements	Very readily observed by all methods	Thibaud reflected from glass gratings at grazing incidence
1.6×10^{-8} cm to 1.25×10^{-9} cm	Innermost electrons of atoms, shorter waves apply to heaviest elements	X-rays hard and soft, K and L series	Crystal gratings. Method of Laue, Bragg and also from $Ve = 1/2\ mv^2 = h\nu$; $\nu = c\lambda$.
1.25×10^{-9} cm to 5.56×10^{-11} cm	Nuclear electrons. Latter are hardest ones from RaC	γ-rays	Robinson, deBroglie, Ellis, Meitner. From $1/2\ mv^2 = h\nu$, ν from magnetic fields
? $\times 10^{-12}$ cm to ? $\times 10^{-13}$ cm	Possibly creation of nuclei of complex atoms in space	Cosmic rays	Absorption coefficients in water and air. Kohlhörster, Hess, Millikan. Estimated from absorption. May be neutrons or particles

Debye's Model of Molecules. The valence of an atom is determined by the number of electrons in the outermost electronic layer in Bohr's model of atoms. Molecules formed with atoms of the same kind (polyatomic substances) or of different kinds (chemical compounds) incorporate their valence electrons into a stable new structure, which in general will show certain symmetries. Vibrations of the atoms within a molecule on account of absorption by thermal agitation, or rotations, give rise to radiation of relatively long wave-lengths, the thermal or infra-red radiation with a distribution of the frequencies in bands (band spectrum).

Wave Nature of Matter. The attempts to explain the interaction of matter and radiation led to the conclusion that any particle of mass m moving with a speed v can be thought to be associated with a wave the frequency of which is given by the interrelation of energy:

$$h\nu = W = \frac{mc^2}{\sqrt{1 - (v/c)^2}} \tag{9}$$

where h is the quantum of action of Planck and c the velocity of light in vacuum. The velocity of propagation of the wave is defined as

$$V = c^2/v > c$$

in order to satisfy the wavelength relation for radiation $\tag{10}$

$$\lambda\nu = V \tag{11}$$

but no physical meaning can be attached to a velocity larger than the velocity of light in vacuum. The associated wave for electrons has a wavelength similar to those of very hard x-rays, and this has been verified by interference experiments on crystals by G. P. Thomson.

Electromagnetic Spectrum of Radiation. Table I shows the completely closed range of electromagnetic radiations from longest to shortest wavelengths with the supposed sources of radiation.

4.   CORPUSCULAR ASPECTS OF RADIATION

A Corpuscle is defined as that which possesses a momentum (as a vector quantity) of amount $p = mv$ and a kinetic energy $W = 1/2\, mv^2$ according to Newtonian, or $p = \dfrac{mv}{\sqrt{1 - (v/c)^2}}$ and $W = \dfrac{mc^2}{\sqrt{1 - (v/c)^2}}$ according to relativistic mechanics. Its presence becomes obvious by collisions with other particles which can be made visible in certain cases (Wilson's cloud chamber).

The Photon. Electromagnetic radiation transports energy in amounts which are integer multiples of fundamental quanta $(h\nu)$. Einstein suggested that a quantum of radiation, $h\nu$, be considered as associated with the characteristics of a corpuscle of velocity c, the velocity of light in vacuum. From the relativistic expression of energy (equation 9) it is seen that the mass of a photon must approach zero as its velocity approaches c. The momentum of a photon is defined as $p = h\nu/c$.

The Photon Gas. There are as many distinct types of photons as there are different wavelengths in the radiation spectrum. Radiation as a corpuscular phenomenon can then be treated with statistical methods similar to the kinetic theory of gases with the fundamental difference that the distribution in frequency ν takes the place of the distribution in velocity of gas molecules; each photon is assumed to have the same velocity c in vacuum. For statistical methods radiation is called the photon gas.

Characteristics of the Corpuscular Nature of Radiation

Rectilinear Propagation of Radiation. The most striking corpuscular characteristic of radiation is its propagation along straight lines so that definite shadows are cast. This led Newton to his corpuscular theory and initiated the whole field of geometrical optics (see Art. 5).

Collision of Radiation and Electrons. If monochromatic radiation of quantum $h\nu_1$ falls upon a scattering substance, the secondary radiation from the substance is of longer wavelength than the incident radiation, $\nu_2 < \nu_1$. This can be explained only if the photon colliding with an electron, or atom, loses some of its energy (its speed c cannot change) to the electron or atom which will be accelerated and proceed in a direction determined by the law of the conservation of momentum. The experimental evidence is due to A. H. Compton, and the phenomenon is consequently named *Compton effect*.

If monochromatic radiation of quantum $h\nu$ falls upon metals, electrons will be liberated with a kinetic energy given by the Einstein relation

$$1/2\, mv^2 = h\nu - \omega_0 \tag{12}$$

where ω_0 is the amount of energy necessary to free the electron from its surroundings within the metal, and is independent of the frequency of the incident light. This *photoelectric effect* is explainable only by assuming corpuscular collision of radiation and electrons according to the laws of conservation of energy and momentum.

Penetrating Power of Radiation. Einstein's hypothesis attributes a momentum $p = h\nu/c$, proportional to frequency ν, to the photon, so that a radiation will be the more penetrating from the corpuscular point of view the shorter its wavelength is. This agrees well with experimental facts. It is customary to measure the penetrating power by the absorption coefficient (see Art. 1) in a standard material.

The Corpuscular Spectrum of Radiation. The proportionality of momentum (corpuscular aspect) and frequency (wave aspect) of the photon leads to the same scheme of identification as Table I for the electromagnetic spectrum.

BIBLIOGRAPHY ON THEORY OF RADIATION

1. An Outline of Atomic Physics. John Wiley, 1932.
2. ADAMS, E. P. The Quantum Theory. *National Research Council Bulletin*, Vol. 7, part 3, 1923.
3. BOHR, N. The Theory of Spectra and Atomic Constitution. London, Cambridge University Press, 1922.
4. BRAGG, W. The Universe of Light. New York, Macmillan & Co., 1934.
5. CONDON, E. U., MORSE, P. M. Quantum Mechanics. New York, McGraw-Hill, 1929.
6. DARROW, K. K. Introduction to Contemporary Physics. New York, D. Van Nostrand.
7. DRUDE, P. Theory of Optics. (Trans. from the German by MANN and MILLIKAN.) London, Longmans, Green.
8. LEWIS, W. C. M. Quantum Theory. (Vol. 3 of System of Physical Chemistry.) Longmans, Green, 1924.
9. RICHTMYER, F. K. Introduction to Modern Physics. New York, McGraw-Hill, 1928.
10. SOMMERFELD, A. Atombau und Spektrallinien. F. Vieweg & Söhne, 1924.
11. THOMSON, J. J. The Corpuscular Theory of Matter. London, Scribner, 1907.

GEOMETRY OF RADIATION

By Ernst Weber

Geometry of radiation deals with "rays" which are identical with the directions of propagation of the electro-magnetic waves in the wave picture and with the paths of the photons in the corpuscular picture of radiation. It is applicable only if the interaction of radiation and matter involves objects whose dimensions are large compared with the wavelengths of the radiation considered. Thus, any problem of electromagnetic radiation from antennas can be treated by the geometrical method if the objects can be considered as large compared with the wavelength. Historically the first, and still the most important, application of the geometric method lies in the field of optics, although with proper interpretation the results can be applied to any other type of radiation.

5. PRINCIPLES OF GEOMETRICAL OPTICS

The ray from the light source is called the *incident* ray. If light in air is incident upon a polished surface of a transparent medium part of it will be regularly reflected, the other part will enter the medium. Referring to Fig. 1, the point of incidence P is the point where an incident ray strikes the surface of the medium. The plane determined by the outside normal n to the surface at this point, and the incident ray, is called the plane of incidence, and the angle α which these two directions make is the angle of incidence.

Laws of Reflection and Refraction. Both the reflected and refracted rays lie in the plane of incidence, on opposite sides of the surface of the medium. The angle γ of the reflected ray with the outside normal, the angle of reflection, is equal to α, $\gamma = \alpha$; the angle β of the refracted ray with the inside normal, the angle of refraction, is determined from the law of Snell

$$\frac{\sin \alpha}{\sin \beta} = n \qquad (1)$$

where n is the relative index of refraction of the medium against air. $n > 1$ for all transparent media. For normal incidence and regular optical behavior $\alpha = \beta = \gamma = 0$, no deviation of the ray occurs. If a plane surface is totally reflecting it is called a plane mirror.

Real and Virtual Image. Referring to Fig. 2, if MN indicates the surface of a plane mirror, the rays issuing from the source P and striking the mirror at the points A and B will be reflected and reach the eye as the rays C and D. To the eye these rays will appear as coming from the point Q behind the mirror. Q is called the "image" of P and more specifically a virtual image because the rays C and D do not actually pass through Q and therefore cannot be received there on a screen and be made visible. A real image is, then, one that can be received on a screen and be made visible.

Total Reflection. If light passes from a medium of large refractive index into one of small refractive index, the relative index of refraction according to equation 1 becomes less than unity. The angle α_c for which $\sin \beta = 1$ so that $\sin \alpha_c = n$ is called the **critical**

angle because no light enters the second medium. For angles $\alpha > \alpha_c$, the light is said to be totally reflected as there is no refracted ray.

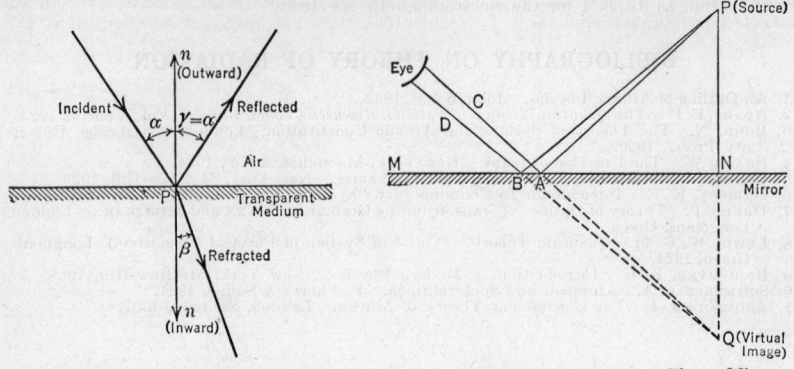

FIG. 1. Reflection and Refraction of a Ray   FIG. 2. Virtual Image from a Plane Mirror

Optical Distance of two points in a medium of refractive index n is the actual length of the path l covered by the ray between the two points multiplied by the value of the refractive index. If a ray passes through different media, the optical distance between any two points is the sum of the optical paths within each medium, $\sum_i l_i n_i = \sum_i o_i$. A surface is called *aplanatic* if for each of its points the sum of the optical paths to two fixed points has a constant value.

Fermat's Principle. Using the definition of the optical distance, the laws of refraction and reflection can be expressed, according to Fermat, in a single principle: rays of light (and for that matter, of any radiation) travel along such lines that the optical distance between any two points of the rays is a minimum.

6. SPHERICAL MIRRORS AND LENSES

Concave Spherical Mirrors (Fig. 3). A spherical mirror is concave if its center of curvature C is on the side from which the light is incident. By the general law of reflection, a point source P will form a real image at a point Q so that PCQ lie on a straight line,

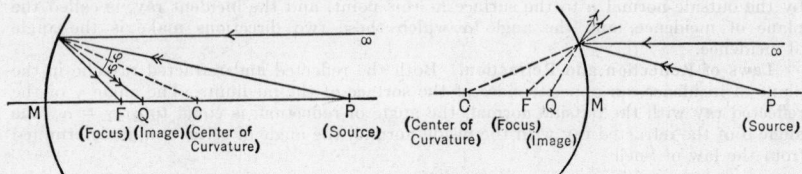

FIG. 3. Reflection from a Concave Spherical Mirror   FIG. 4. Reflection from a Convex Spherical Mirror

the optical axis, and that the angle of incidence is equal to the angle of reflection. Rays through the center C are reflected in themselves; rays parallel to the optical axis converge at a point F midway between C and M, the principal focus, or simply *focus*, of the mirror. If the distances are designated as $MF = f$, $MP = p$, and $MQ = q$, the relation exists

$$1/p + 1/q = 1/f \tag{2}$$

which holds for any position of P if p, q, and f are counted positive on the right-hand side and negative on the left-hand side of the mirror center M. For negative values of q the images become virtual.

Convex Spherical Mirrors (Fig. 4). A spherical mirror is convex if the center of curvature C is on the side opposite to that from which the light is incident. The same relations hold as for the concave mirror, except that the focal distance f has negative values in accordance with the proper interpretation of equation 2.

Images Formed by Spherical Mirrors (Figs. 5 and 6).   The position of the image Q' of any point P' near but not in the optical axis of a mirror is found most expediently by the intersection of two principal rays, the ray through the center of curvature C and the reflected ray through the focus F.   Any object PP' perpendicular to the optical axis

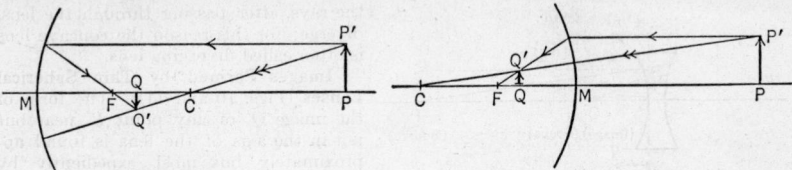

FIG. 5.   Image Formed by a Concave   FIG. 6.   Image Formed by a Convex Spherical
Spherical Mirror   Mirror

will produce an image QQ' again vertical to the axis and of definite characteristics; Table I shows all the possibilities of position and character of images formed by spherical mirrors.

Table I.   Images Formed by Spherical Mirrors

(Figs. 3 and 4)

Mirror	Position of Object (PP') P	Position of Image (QQ') Q	Character of Image
Concave	At ∞ Between ∞ and C At C Between C and F At F Between F and M At M	At F Between F and C At C Between C and ∞ At ∞ From ∞ behind M to M At M	Real Real, inverted, diminished Real, inverted, same size Real, inverted, magnified Virtual, erect, magnified erect, same size
Convex	At ∞ Between ∞ and M At M	At F Between F to M At M	Virtual Virtual, erect, diminished erect, same size

Thin Spherical Lenses.   A lens is a portion of a refracting medium which is bounded by two spherical surfaces or by one spherical and one plane surface.   The straight line through the center of curvature of the two surfaces is called the axis of the lens.   If one of the surfaces is a plane, then the axis is a straight line perpendicular to this plane and

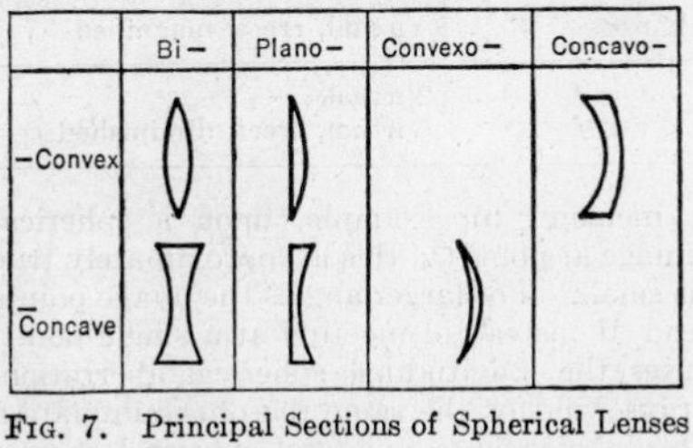

	Bi–	Plano–	Convexo–	Concavo–
–Convex				
‾Concave				

FIG. 7.   Principal Sections of Spherical Lenses

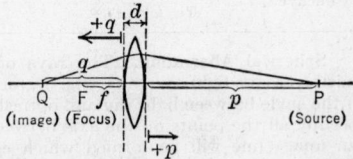

FIG. 8.   Refraction by Thin Convex Lens

going through the center of the spherical surface.   Any plane through the axis is said to be a principal section of the lens; Fig. 7 shows the principal sections of the common types of lenses.

Thin Convex Spherical Lenses (Fig. 8).   By the general laws of refraction, a ray coming from the point source P in the axis of the lens will be refracted twice as it passes through the lens and form an image at the point Q.   For thin lenses (large radii of curvature) relation 2 will hold true if the distances p and q are measured from the nearest surface of the lens and if both are taken positive when on opposite sides of the lens. f is the focal length and is defined by

$$1/f = (n - 1)(1/r_1 - 1/r_2) \qquad (3)$$

where r_1 and r_2 are the radii of curvature of the two surfaces, both taken positive if on the same side of the lens, and n is the refractive index of the lens. All rays parallel to the axis converge at a point F the principal focus, or simply focus, at a distance f from the nearest surface. Rays passing through the optical center will not be deviated. For thin lenses the optical center can be approximately identified with the two points where the axis meets the surfaces of the lens.

Thin Concave Spherical Lenses (Fig. 9). The same relations hold as for the convex lens, the only difference being that the focus is on the same side as the light source so that the rays, after passing through the lens, diverge; for this reason the concave lens is often called diverging lens.

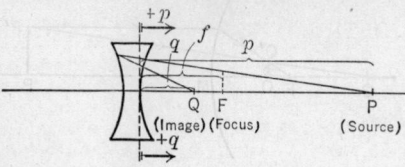

FIG. 9.   Refraction by Thin Concave Lens

Images Formed by Thin Spherical Lenses (Figs. 10 and 11). The form of the image Q' of any point P' near but not in the axis of the lens is found approximately but most expediently by the intersection of two principal rays, the ray through the optical center and the ray parallel to the axis, refracted through the focus. For the actual construction it suffices to consider the plane through the optical center and perpendicular to the axis as the refracting plane. Any object PP' perpendicular to the axis will produce an image QQ' again perpendicular to the axis and of definite characteristics; Table II shows the possible positions and characteristics of images formed by convex and concave lenses.

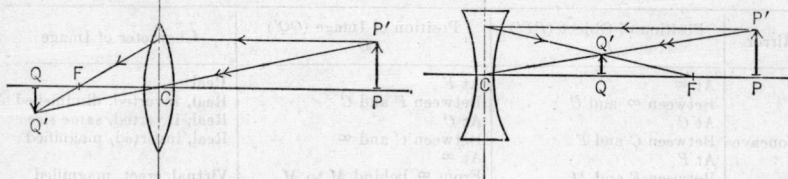

FIG. 10.   Image Formed by Thin Convex Lens   FIG. 11.   Image Formed by Thin Concave Lens

Table II.   Images Formed by Spherical Lenses
(Figs. 8 and 9)

Lens	Position of Object	Position of Image	Character of Image
Convex	$u = +\infty$	$v = f$	Real
	$\lvert 2f \rvert < u < +\infty$	$f < v < 2f$	Real, inverted, diminished
	$u = \lvert 2f \rvert$	$v = 2f$	Real, inverted, same size
	$\lvert f \rvert < u < \lvert 2f \rvert$	$2f < v < \infty$	Real, inverted, magnified
	$u = \lvert f \rvert$	$v = \infty$	
	$0 < u < \lvert f \rvert$	$-d < v < -\infty$	Virtual, erect, magnified
Concave	$u = +\infty$	$v = f$	Virtual
	$0 < u < +\infty$	$0 < v < f$	Virtual, erect, diminished

Spherical Aberration. The rays of light incident, for example, upon a spherical mirror, from a light source P (Fig. 3), form an image at point Q; this is approximately true if the angle between light ray and optical axis is small. For larger angles the image points occupy all the points on the axis between Q and M instead of meeting at a single point; an image line will be formed which constitutes the longitudinal spherical aberration. If a screen is placed at point Q the reflected rays will, for the same reason, illuminate a circular area instead of a sharp point image; this is referred to as lateral spherical aberration. The same holds for all types of spherical mirrors and lenses.

Chromatic Aberration. Since the refractive index varies with wavelength, the image produced by white light from a convex lens, for example, will be, in fact, a superposition of many monochromatic images at slightly different foci. The yellowish green image is the brightest, and the one upon which the screen will be focused, so that the other images superimpose slightly out of focus and thus blur the resultant white image. This effect is known as chromatic aberration, and can be minimized by using several lenses instead of a single one. An arrangement which tends to refocus the monochromatic images into a single sharp image is called achromatic. Chromatic aberration is produced with any type of single lens.

The Focal Length of a convex lens can most readily be determined on an optical bench. In front of a light source fine cross-wires are placed. The light, after passing through the lens, forms an image on a screen which is clearly focused. If p is the distance of the cross-wires, q that of the screen, from the center plane of the lens, then by equation 2 the focal length can be computed. With a concave lens it is necessary to use a convex lens also. From the resultant focal length F and the known focal length f of the convex lens that of the concave lens, f', can be determined by

$$1/f' = 1/F - 1/f$$

7. OPTICAL INSTRUMENTS *

Magnification, increasing visibility of detail, is secured by bringing the image of an object nearer to the eye, or by any other means of increasing the visual angle which the object subtends. Vision with the unaided normal eye is, however, most distinct at a distance of 25 to 30 cm because the accommodating mechanism of the eye is unable to focus sharply on the retina points nearer than this. A magnifying optical system produces in effect the required increase in the visual angle while forming an image (real or virtual) farther from the eye than the least distance of distinct vision. Often the arrangement is such that the eye views a virtual image at an infinite distance, so that the muscles of accommodation may be completely relaxed.

The Simple Microscope (Fig. 12). A single converging lens if placed closer to an object than the principal focal length produces an enlarged virtual image, which is seen on looking through the lens. The magnification produced is $1 + d/f$ for an eye whose least distance of distinct vision is d. A simple plano-convex lens, with the plane side toward the eye, gives good images for magnification less than eight diameters, that is, with focal lengths greater than about 3 cm. The image may be much improved, especially where the magnification is considerable, by the use of special combinations of lenses designed to reduce spherical and chromatic aberration so as to give a fairly large field of view approximately free from distortion and color.

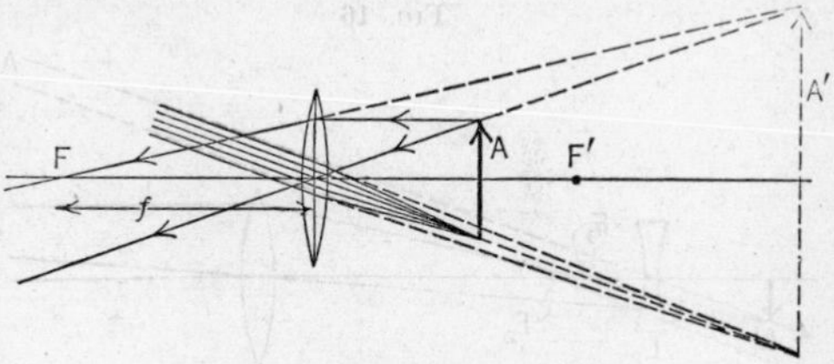

Fig. 12

The Ramsden or Positive Eyepiece. (Fig. 13) consists of two converging lenses, usually plano-convex, with their convex surfaces facing each other, of equal focal length, and separated by 2/3 the focal length of either. A virtual image of the object or real image A is formed by the field-lens L_1 at A'. The eye-lens L_2 forms an image of this at infinity. This eyepiece is fairly, but not quite, achromatic.

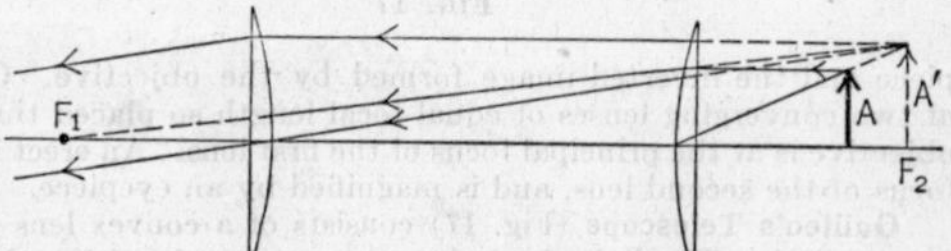

Fig. 13

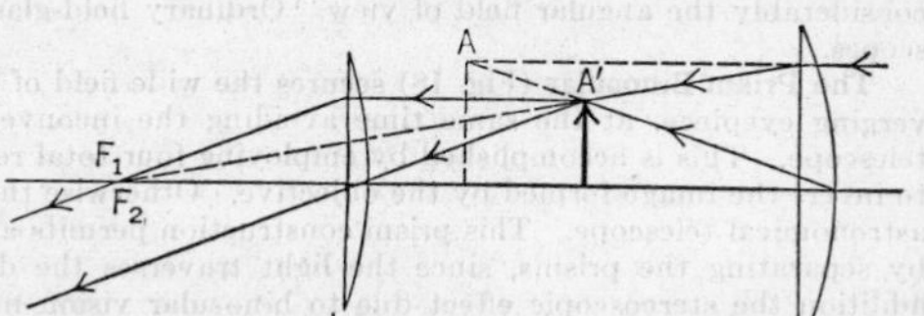

Fig. 14

Huyghens or Negative Eyepiece (Fig. 14). Two converging lenses, usually plano-convex, with the plane surfaces toward the eye, are so arranged as to divide equally between them the deviation produced on incident light parallel to and close to the axis. The field-lens L_1 has three times the focal length of the eye-lens L_2, and the two are separated by the difference in their focal lengths. Light which if unhindered would converge at A is deviated by L_1 to form an image at A', of which L_2 forms an image at infinity. This eyepiece is highly achromatic and free from disturbing spherical aberration.

For Measuring Microscopes and Telescopes in which the eyepiece is fitted with cross-hairs, the positive eyepiece is far more suitable than the negative because the image of the hairs being formed by both lenses is corrected for both chromatic and spherical aberration, and because the cross-hairs can be easily adjusted to suit different eyes by altering their distance from the eyepiece.

The Compound Microscope (Fig. 15) in its simplest form consists of two converging lenses. The objective L_1 forms within the tube a real, inverted, magnified image A' of the object A. This image is viewed through the eyepiece L_2 and further magnified. A microscope is usually fitted with

* From the American Civil Engineers' Handbook, by Merriman and Wiggin, 5th Edition.

either a Huyghens or a Ramsden eyepiece, according to the purpose for which it is to be used. The objective is also generally a combination of several lenses to overcome spherical and chromatic aberration while admitting as much light as possible. In microscopes of the highest power a drop of oil of cedar is placed between the slide and the objective; this is known as "immersion." The smallest interval that can be optically resolved is about 0.00005 mm, and the limit of resolution of the microscope is attained when the total magnification is about 1200.

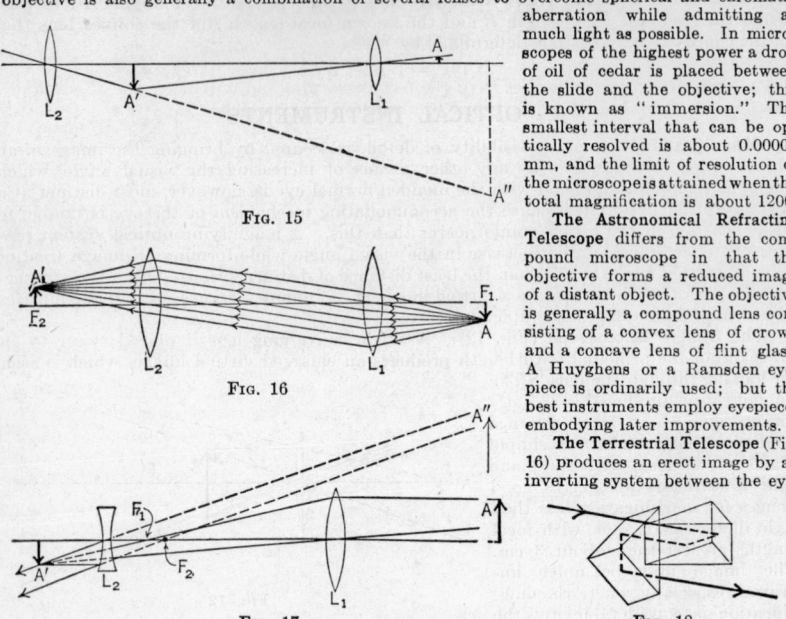

Fig. 15

Fig. 16

Fig. 17

Fig. 18

The Astronomical Refracting Telescope differs from the compound microscope in that the objective forms a reduced image of a distant object. The objective is generally a compound lens consisting of a convex lens of crown and a concave lens of flint glass. A Huyghens or a Ramsden eyepiece is ordinarily used; but the best instruments employ eyepieces embodying later improvements.

The Terrestrial Telescope (Fig. 16) produces an erect image by an inverting system between the eye-piece and the inverted image formed by the objective. One form of inverting system consists of two converging lenses of equal focal length so placed that the inverted image A formed by the objective is at the principal focus of the first lens. An erect image A' is then formed at the principal focus of the second lens, and is magnified by an eyepiece.

Galileo's Telescope (Fig. 17) consists of a convex lens L_1 for objective and a concave lens L_2 for eyepiece. The light from L_1, converging so that if unhindered it would form at A' a real, inverted image of the distant object A, is intercepted by L_2 and rendered parallel or slightly divergent as if it came from A'', which is a virtual, erect image of A. The use of the diverging eye-lens limits considerably the angular field of view. Ordinary field-glasses and opera-glasses are Galilean telescopes.

The Prism Binocular (Fig. 18) secures the wide field of view that accompanies the use of a converging eyepiece, at the same time avoiding the inconvenient length of the ordinary terrestrial telescope. This is accomplished by employing four total reflections within two right-angled prisms to invert the image formed by the objective. Otherwise the construction is the same as that of the astronomical telescope. This prism construction permits a considerable shortening of the telescope by separating the prisms, since the light traverses the distance between them three times. In addition the stereoscopic effect due to binocular vision may be greatly increased by placing the centers of the objectives much farther apart than the pupils of the eye. The increased field of view is obtained at a sacrifice of illumination.

In Reflecting Telescopes the object lens is replaced by a concave mirror with parabolic surface. The mirror is of glass and coated with a thin film of either silver or aluminum. The parabolic surface of the mirror renders it completely achromatic and, therefore, of special value in astronomic photography. The first reflecting telescope was constructed by Newton, in 1670, and is known as the Newton Reflector. The largest reflecting telescope in actual use is at the Mount Wilson Observatory in California; it is 100 inches in diameter and 43 feet in focal length. A new reflecting mirror of 200 inches in diameter has just been completed and will also be installed at the Mount Wilson Observatory.

BIBLIOGRAPHY ON GEOMETRY OF RADIATION

1. CONRADY, A. E. Applied Optics and Optical Design. Oxford University Press, England, 1929.
2. Handbuch der Physik, Vol. 28, Geometrical Optics. Berlin, J. Springer, 1927.
3. HARDY, A. C., PERRIN, F. H. The Principles of Optics. New York, McGraw-Hill.
4. HOUSTOUN, R. A. A Treatise on Light. London, Longmans, Green, 1933.
5. KÖNIG, A. Geometrische Optik. Akademische Verlags-Gesellschaft, Leipzig, 1929.
6. MARTIN, L. C. Optical Measuring Instruments. London, Blackie & Sons, Limited.
7. STEINEIL, A., VOIT, E. Applied Optics. (Trans. from the German by J. W FRENCH.) London, Blackie & Sons, Limited.

PHYSICS OF RADIATION

By Ernst Weber

For electromagnetic radiation from resonating circuits and antennas, and thermionic emission, see the volume *Electrical Communication* of this handbook series.

8. PROPAGATION OF LIGHT

The Velocity of Light* in vacuum is approximately 186,000 miles per second, and was first determined in 1675 by O. Roemer, a Danish astronomer. According to recent measurements by Michelson (1926), the velocity of light in vacuum is $2.99796 \pm 0.00004 \times 10^{10}$ cm per sec, but a slight variation is suspected to take place.

The Color of Light is determined by its spectral distribution. The range of visible light extends from about $\lambda = 380$ m$\mu = 3800$ A (extreme violet), to about $\lambda = 780$ m$\mu = 7800$ A (extreme red).

The Refractive Index of light varies considerably with wavelength, normally increasing in value with decreasing wavelength (normal dispersion). It is customary to give refractive indices for yellow light of $\lambda = 589.3$ mμ wavelength (bright radiation of sodium vapor) in order to facilitate comparison. For *gases* the refractive index is not much different from unity and varies only slightly with wavelength; Table I gives some representative values. For *liquids* the refractive index lies between 1 and 2 and shows variation with temperature as well as with wavelength. Table II gives some representative values.

Table I. Index of Refraction of Gases

(From Smithsonian Tables; reduced to 0° C and 760 mm Hg, at wavelength $\lambda = 589.3$ mμ, sodium light.)

Substance	Symbol	Index of Refraction	Substance	Symbol	Index of Refraction
Hydrogen.......	H_2	1.000 132	Carbon monoxide	CO	1.000 346
Water vapor.....	H_2O	1.000 249 to 1.000 259	Carbon dioxide..	CO_2	1.000 448 to 1.000 454
Oxygen.........	O_2	1.000 271	Sulfur dioxide...	SO_2	1.000 686
Air..............	.....	1.000 2926	Benzene........	C_6H_6	1.001 700 to 1.001 823
Nitrogen........	N_2	1.000 296 to 1.000 298			

Table II. Index of Refraction for Liquids

(At 20° C and at wavelength $\lambda = 589.3$ mμ, sodium light; various sources)

Substance	Symbol	Index of Refraction	Substance	Symbol	Index of Refraction
Water...........	H_2O	1.332 99	Benzene........	C_6H_6	1.501
Ethyl ether......	$C_2H_5OC_2H_5$	1.351	Phenol.........	C_6H_5OH	1.550
Ethyl alcohol....	C_2H_5OH	1.361	Bromine........	Br	1.654
Gylcerin.........	$C_3H_8O_3$	1.474			

Table III. Index of Refraction of Glass

(From the Handbook of Chemistry and Physics, 1933)

Variety of Glass	Wavelength in Millimicrons							
	361	434	486	589	656	768	1200	2000
Zinc crown...............	1.539	1.528	1.523	1.517	1.514	1.511	1.505	1.497
Higher dispersion crown.....	1.546	1.533	1.527	1.520	1.517	1.514	1.507	1.497
Light flint................	1.614	1.594	1.585	1.575	1.571	1.567	1.559	1.549
Heavy flint...............	1.705	1.675	1.664	1.650	1.644	1.638	1.628	1.617
Heaviest flint.............	....	1.945	1.919	1.890	1.879	1.867	1.848	1.832

Transparent Solids, if optically *isotropic*, refract regularly. The most important representative is glass, which has very marked dispersive properties in the visible range; this fact is utilized in prism spectroscopy. Table III shows the variation of the refractive index with wavelength for various standard kinds of glass in general use for optical purposes.

* The expression "light" is commonly used to designate monochromatic visible radiation (scientific usage) or total visible radiation from a light source.

Transparent Crystals, if optically anisotropic, have, in general, different propagation properties in all three space directions and therefore must be characterized by three principal refractive indices. They exhibit certain symmetries with respect to two definite crystallographic directions, called the optical axes; the crystals themselves are called *optically biaxial.*

Certain *transparent crystals* exhibit rotational symmetry with respect to a single crystallographic direction, called the optical axis; the crystals themselves are called *optically uniaxial* and must be characterized by two principal refractive indices. The most widely known representatives are quartz and Iceland spar. Very complete tables of the indices of refraction can be found in the International Critical Tables.

Metals absorb as well as reflect light; in general, they are entirely opaque, except when used in very thin films. The optical behavior of metals is characterized by refractive index n, index of absorption K, and reflectivity R. The optical indices of metals are not directly measurable; they must be computed from the observation of changes of polarization (see Art. 9) in the reflected light. In general, the metals show an apparent irregular and large variation of their optical indices with the wavelength of the incident light; this has led to a theory of resonance of the conduction electrons. Table IV gives the optical

Table IV. Optical Constants of Metals
(At a wavelength $\lambda = 589.3$ mμ; various sources)

Metal	Symbol	Index of Refraction n	Index of Absorption K	Reflectivity R	Metal	Symbol	Index of Refraction n	Index of Absorption K	Reflectivity R
Aluminum...	Al	1.44	5.32	0.83	Nickel......	Ni	1.79	1.86	0.62
Bismuth.....	Bi	1.90	1.93	0.65	Silver......	Ag	0.18	20.2	0.95
Copper......	Cu	0.64	4.08	0.73	Steel........		2.7	1.28	0.57
Gold........	Au	0.36	7.70	0.85	Tungsten...	W	3.46	0.94	0.54
Mercury.....	Hg	1.73	2.87	0.78					

Table V. Diffuse Reflecting Power
(For visible spectrum; various sources)

Material	Reflecting Power in Per cent	Material	Reflecting Power in Per cent
Cloth		Paper—*Continued*	
White linen, dull finish...........	81	Olive green	15
Red cotton (diamine fast red).....	44	Ultramarine blue...............	3.5
Blue woolen (lanacyl).............	25	Black..........................	5
Blue woolen (salacine)	15	Pigment	
Blue flannel.....................	17.5	Chromium oxide, Cr_2O_3........	27
Blue linen (navy blue)	17	Cobalt oxide, Co_2O_3..........	3
Black cotton (diamine)...........	33	Lead oxide, PbO...............	52
Black cotton (columbia)..........	29	Lead carbonate, $PbCO_3$.......	90
Black cotton (sulfur).............	2.4	Magnesium oxide, MgO.........	86
Black felt.......................	14	Red iron oxide, Fe_2O_3.........	52
Black velvet.....................	1.8	Zinc oxide, ZnO...............	82
Black woolen (salacine)	12	Stone and minerals	
Green leaf (tulip tree)..............	22	Asphalt (pavement).............	15
Lampblack (paint).................	3.2	Macadam road.................	12
Paints		Granolith (pavement)..........	17
White lead......................	75	Bluestone (sandstone)..........	18
Zinc lead.......................	69	Limestone (Indiana)............	43
Paper		Brick, light buff...............	48
White blotting..................	82	darker.....................	40
Cheap white....................	70	red........................	30
Light gray.....................	73	darker and glazed...........	23
Medium gray...................	45	Feldspar......................	39
Dark gray......................	20	Quartz (powder)...............	81
Pink...........................	60	Marble white, unpolished........	53.5
Buff...........................	60	Slate (dark clay)..............	6.7
Chocolate brown................	20		

indices for a few metals at a wavelength $\lambda = 589.3$ mμ (sodium light) as determined by Drude.* All metals show low reflectivity for ultraviolet, increasing values through the visible spectrum, and act as almost perfect mirrors for infra-red and longer wavelengths.

* P. Drude, *Wied. Annalen*, 1890, vol. 36, p. 885; vol. 39, p. 481.

Most common materials reflect diffusely. Table V gives the diffuse reflective power for the more important engineering materials. Rather complete tables of spectral reflectivity of pigments and transmissivity of dyes can be found in M. Luckiesh, The Basis of Color Technology, *Journal of the Franklin Institute*, vol. 184, p. 73, 1917; and M. Luckiesh, The Measurement of the Transmission Factor, *Journal of the Franklin Institute*, vol. 186, p. 111, 1918.

9. POLARIZATION OF LIGHT

Double Refraction and Polarization. The fact that optically uniaxial crystals propagate light selectively with respect to their optical axis can best be explained by the assumption of the polarization of light. As defined in Art. 3, a light wave is called plane polarized if the oscillations of each of the electromagnetic field vectors occur in a fixed plane. In the case of optically uniaxial crystals (in relation to which the concept of polarization was originally introduced), double refraction takes place; that is, an incident pencil of light, propagating in a direction other than the optical axis, is broken up into two pencils: the ordinary and the extraordinary "ray," both of which travel with different velocities within the crystal. The two resulting rays, on emerging, are plane polarized in two perpendicular planes. It is customary to call "ordinary ray" that ray which is plane polarized *in* the principal plane (a plane parallel to the optical axis and the incident ray); this ray is uniformly refracted in all directions and thus behaves like ordinary light. It is customary to call "extraordinary ray" that ray which is plane polarized perpendicular to the principal plane; this ray is non-uniformly refracted, the refractive index varying symmetrically about the optical axis. The extraordinary ray thus behaves differently from ordinary light. Upon leaving the crystal, the two plane-polarized waves have, on account of their different velocities within the crystal, a phase difference

$$\delta = \frac{2\,\pi d}{\lambda}\,(n_1 - n_2) \tag{1}$$

where d is the length of the path within the crystal, λ the wavelength in air, and n_1 and n_2 the refractive indices for the two rays in the directions of propagation. The resulting light from a uniaxial crystal is, therefore, in general, elliptically polarized.

Production of Plane-polarized Light. Double refraction provides a means of producing plane-polarized light from natural light by suppressing the ordinary ray, as for example, in a Nicol prism. In the case of tourmaline the high value of absorptivity for the ordinary ray naturally suppresses it so that the plane-polarized extraordinary ray remains. If light falls upon transparent substances at such an angle of incidence that reflected and refracted rays are perpendicular to each other, the reflected light will be almost completely plane polarized (Brewster's law).

Photoelasticity. Isotropic transparent substances, if subjected to strain, become doubly refracting. Plane-polarized light, in passing through the substance, is then decomposed into two rays, polarized, respectively, parallel and perpendicular to the direction of stress. On account of their different velocities of propagation they suffer a relative phase difference, so that the light leaving the medium is, in general, elliptically polarized (see Art. 3). The amount of the phase difference is proportional to the stress and the thickness of the medium, so that a stress analysis can be performed. For practical purposes, models of the structure to be investigated are cut out of xylonite,* and subjected to stresses proportional to those acting on the original.

Optical Rotation. In many substances plane-polarized light experiences a rotation of the plane of polarization proportional to the length of the path within the substance. According to Fresnel, it is thought that the plane-polarized ray decomposes into two oppositely rotating circularly polarized rays which propagate with different velocities, so that they suffer a relative phase difference; on leaving the substance, they combine into a plane-polarized ray, the plane of polarization of which appears to be rotated with respect to that of the incident light. The specific rotation is measured in angular degrees per decimeter for liquids and solutions, and in angular degrees per millimeter in solids; it is called negative if the rotation is left-handed, and positive if it is right-handed, as seen by an observer. Substances exhibiting optical rotation are called *optically active*. Applications are found in commerce and medicine in the test for sugar. Instruments used to measure the optical rotation are called saccharimeters or polarimeters. Table VI shows the values of specific rotation of a few common substances at 20° C, for sodium light. Quartz shows a very marked increase of the specific rotation with decreasing wavelength. Rather complete tables can be found in the International Critical Tables, Volume 7.

---

* Tuzi: A New Material for the Study of Photoelasticity, *Sci. Papers Ins. Phys. Chem. Res.*, Tokio, 7 (1927), p. 79.

Table VI.   Specific Optical Rotation

(At 20° C and λ = 589.3 mμ, sodium light; various sources)

Substance	Specific Rotation	Unit
Solids:		
Quartz................................	+ 21.68	Angular degrees per millimeter
Sodium bromate........................	+ 2.8	" " " "
Liquids:		
Amyl alcohol...........................	− 5.7	" " " decimeter
Nicotine...............................	−162	" " " "
Turpentine............................	− 37	" " " "
Solutions:*		
Albumine..............................	− 25 to 38	" " " "
Dextrose..............................	+ 52.25	" " " "
Lactose...............................	+ 52.4	" " " "
Levulose (fruit sugar).................	− 87.1	" " " "
Maltose...............................	+138.3	" " " "
Sucrose (cane sugar)..................	+ 66.3	" " " "

* Solvent; water (1 g in 100 g).

Magnetic Rotation.   Optically isotropic substances, when exposed to a strong magnetic field, rotate the plane of polarization of plane-polarized light.   This is called the *Faraday effect* after its discoverer (1845), and depends on the magnetic field intensity H.   It is termed positive if the rotation occurs in the direction of the current which produces the magnetic field.   The angle of rotation in angular minutes is given by

$$\theta = r.l.H \cos \alpha$$

where r is Verdet's constant (see Table VII), l (centimeters) the length of the path of light within the magnetic field of intensity H (oersteds), and α the angle which H makes with the ray of light.

Table VII.   Magneto-optic Rotation

(At 20° C and wavelength λ = 589.3 mμ, sodium light; various sources)

Substance	Verdet's Constant	Remarks
Solids:		
Flint glass (medium)................	+ 0.0420	
Quartz (⊥ to optical axis)...........	+ 0.0172	
Liquids and solutions:		
Benzene...........................	+ 0.0297	
Ethyl alcohol......................	+ 0.0107	
Ferric chloride.....................	− 0.2026	Aqueous solution, 1.4331 g per cm³
Ferrous chloride...................	+ 0.0025	" " 1.6933 "
Sodium carbonate.................	+ 0.0140	" " 1.1006 "
Water.............................	+ 0.0130	
Gases (at atmospheric pressure):		
Air...............................	+ 6.83 × 10⁻⁶	
Carbon dioxide....................	+13.00 "	
Nitrogen..........................	+ 6.92 "	
Oxygen...........................	+ 6.28 "	

Kerr Effect.   Transparent substances, when subjected to a strong electrostatic field, become doubly refracting.   Plane-polarized light, in passing through the substance, is decomposed into two rays polarized in the direction of the electric field and perpendicular to it, respectively.   On account of their different velocities of propagation, they suffer a relative phase difference, so that the light leaving the medium is in general elliptically polarized.   A high-voltage condenser with liquid dielectric (preferably nitrobenzene), employing this electro-optical effect, is called a *Kerr cell*, and is of use in some phases of television.

10.   LIGHT SPECTROSCOPY

The Visible Spectrum* is the graphic arrangement of the visible radiant energy against wavelength or frequency.   The wavelength is usually measured in millimicrons, 1 mμ $= 10^{-7}$ cm, or in angstroms, 1A $= 10^{-8}$ cm (practically).   Three different kinds of

* The term visible spectrum is also used to designate the band of colors constituting white light.

spectra are commonly distinguished: the emission spectrum, representing the spectral distribution of emissive power of a light source; the reflection spectrum, representing the spectral distribution of reflectivity of a regularly reflecting surface; and the absorption spectrum, representing the spectral distribution of the absorbing power of transparent substances. The best-known representative of the last type is the solar absorption spectrum, or the Fraunhofer lines, discovered in 1817.

Spectroscopy. The spectral distribution of radiant energy composing light can be directly observed in a spectroscope. The most common type of spectroscope, first used by Newton (1666), utilizes the dispersion of light passing through a prism of glass (see Fig. 1). Later types of spectroscopes use the diffraction of light by fine gratings (Rowland, 1882), and the interference patterns resulting from reflections by mirrors (interferometer by Michelson). A very high-power spectroscope, using an echelon grating (Michelson, 1898), has been particularly successful in finding the fine structure of spectral lines. Monochromatic radiations are located by comparison with standard radiations. Table VIII gives a few of the wavelengths useful for the calibration of spectroscopes and their respective sources. The primary standard for absolute wavelength measurements is the wavelength of the red cadmium line determined by Benoist, Fabry, and Perot (1907), as 6438.4696 angstroms, and adopted internationally.*

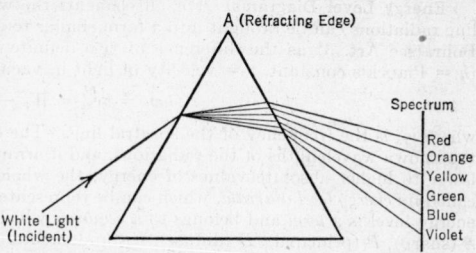

Fig. 1.　Dispersion of White Light by a Glass Prism

Table VIII.　Wavelengths for Calibration of the Spectroscope

(Selected from R. A. Houstoun, A Treatise on Light)

Source	Wavelength $m\mu$	Color	Corresponding Fraunhofer Absorption Line
Potassium nitrate on Pt wire in Bunsen flame...	$\begin{cases} 770.2 \\ 766.8 \end{cases}$	Red	
Lithium sulfate on Pt wire in Bunsen flame	670.78	Red	
Hydrogen vacuum tube (α line)...............	656.28	Red	C
Sodium bicarbonate on Pt wire in Bunsen flame..	$\begin{cases} 589.00 \\ 589.59 \end{cases}$	Orange	D_2 D_1
Mercury arc..................................	546.07	Green	
Thallium chloride on Pt wire in Bunsen flame....	535.07	Green	
Hydrogen vacuum tube (β line)..............	486.14	Greenish blue	F
Hydrogen vacuum tube (γ line)..............	434.04	Indigo	f
Cadmium spark in air.......................	396.84	Violet	H

The Performance of a Spectroscope is judged by the brightness of the spectrum, which depends in the first place on the aperture of the instrument, i.e., the ratio of diameter to focal length of the collimator lens which is the convex lens between light source and prism or grating; and by the *resolving power*, which is the ratio of any given wavelength λ to the smallest increment $d\lambda$ that can be distinctly observed, i.e., $\lambda/d\lambda$. The resolving power varies with the wavelength and spectroscope; it is largest for diffraction and echelon gratings, where it can reach 250,000.

Origin of Line Spectra. The most important part of spectroscopy is the one dealing with the line emissions or characteristic spectra of the various chemical elements. The occurrence of distinct frequencies of the emitted energy (lines) indicates a definite vibratory origin within the atom and is attributed to electronic oscillations of some rather vague kind (see Art. 3). The grouping of lines into series was first established empirically for the hydrogen spectrum, and a formula was given by Balmer (1885), later generalized by Rydberg (1890) as

$$n = N \left(\frac{1}{(m_1 + \beta_1)^2} - \frac{1}{(m + \beta)^2} \right) \qquad (2)$$

---

* The adoption of the wavelength standard as exactly 6438.4696 angstroms represents, in fact, an absolute definition of the unit angstrom which is slightly different from the practical definition $1A = 10^{-8}$ cm as derived unit. It is, therefore, generally preferred to give wavelengths in millimicrons.

where N is a universal constant, the Rydberg constant, and n are the wave numbers (number of wavelengths per centimeter) of the various lines of any one series obtained by letting m take all integer values from unity on. The constants β and β_1 are characteristic for each individual series, and m_1 is a definite integer which determines the type of a series; thus $m_1 = 1$ gives the Lyman (ultraviolet), $m_1 = 2$ the Balmer (visible), $m_1 = 3$ the Paschen, and $m_1 = 4$ the Brackett (the last two in the infra-red), series of the hydrogen atom. In general each spectral line can be either a singlet, if even with largest resolving power only a single line can be detected, or a doublet, triplet, up to octet. The whole series is then referred to as a multiplet series, its order being equal to that of the highest order line that occurs in the series.

Energy Level Diagrams. For all elements the wave numbers of their characteristic line radiations can be brought into a form similar to equation 2 which was interpreted by Bohr (see Art. 3) as the difference of two definite energy terms. If multiplied by hc (h = Planck's constant, c = velocity of light in vacuum), equation (2) becomes

$$hcn = h\nu_{rs} = W_r - W_s \qquad (3)$$

where ν_{rs} is the frequency of the spectral line. The energy terms can be computed from the known wavelengths of the radiations, and if arranged systematically, ascending from lower to higher absolute values of energy, the whole system of terms for an element is called its *energy level diagram*, which can be represented graphically. In the diagram each energy level is a *term* and belongs to a *sequence* which is designated by a capital letter as S (sharp), P (principal), D (diffuse), F (fundamental). The main terms of each sequence are differentiated by integer order numbers (the values m or m_1 in equation 2) in front of the letter symbols; a superscript indicates the multiplicity of the sequence (determined by the highest order multiple in the sequence); and a subscript designates the component of the multiple within the main term. For example, 3^4P_2 is the second component of the third main term of the principal sequence which is a quadruplet. The spectral lines, then are given by transitions like $3^4P_2 \rightarrow 2^3D_1$, the difference in the corresponding energies determining uniquely the frequency of radiation emitted according to equation (3). Empirical selection rules prohibit certain lines so that transitions are possible only between neighboring sequences, and only if the changes of the subscripts are ± 1 or 0.

Excitation of Line Spectra. Emission of the characteristic radiation occurs when electrons "fall" from higher to lower energy levels. For this to happen, atoms must first absorb energy and be "raised" to higher energy levels, which can be done either by bombardment with high-speed electrons (arcs, sparks), irradiation with x-rays, resonance radiation (incident radiation of same frequency as emitted radiation), or by collisions with atoms of the same or other elements.

Doppler Effect. A light source moving towards an observer with a relative radial velocity s appears to emit radiations of wavelength λ'

$$\lambda' = \frac{v - s}{v} \cdot \lambda$$

where v is the velocity of light and λ the absolute wavelength emitted by the source (Doppler, 1843). Spectroscopic identification of stars and planets reveals their relative velocities, s, when the spectral lines are compared with earthly sources. At very low gas pressures the thermal velocity of molecules can also produce a Doppler effect.

Zeeman Effect. Strong magnetic fields resolve the spectral lines of elements into a varying number (two to seventeen) of finer lines showing different states of polarization with, however, a typical structure for all lines. Zeeman (1896) first discovered this effect and propounded a simple theory. Quantum mechanics tries to explain it by means of a magnetic moment resulting from assumed "electron spins." A similar effect occurs when observing absorption lines in a strong magnetic field. This effect is called the *inverse* Zeeman effect, and occurs in the sunspots, indicating vast magnetic storms.

Stark Effect. Stark (1913) discovered that strong electric fields resolve spectral lines of various elements into a varying number of finer lines showing different states of polarization. The transverse effect upon different lines is different and depends either linearly or squarely on the field strength. A longitudinal effect (electric field parallel to light) has also been found. Explanations have been tried by assuming a change in the electrical potential energy of the orbital electrons.

Raman Effect. Transparent substances, if illuminated with strictly monochromatic light, can exhibit in their spectrum in addition to the strong line of the incident frequency (the only one to be expected according to the classical theory of scattering light) fainter lines of lower and higher frequencies (Raman, 1928). The presence of the new frequencies is explained by assuming that light is composed of photons which either lose energy to molecules or gain energy from excited molecules, as they pass through the substance.

11. ULTRAVIOLET RADIATION

The ultraviolet spectrum extends from approximately 380 mμ wavelength down to the softest x-rays. The longer ultraviolet rays, of vital importance for organisms, are often called *actinic rays*.

Absorption. Most optically transparent substances absorb ultraviolet radiation. Thus ordinary window glass does not transmit wavelengths shorter than approximately 350 mμ, whereas uviol glass, 1 cm thick, stops transmitting at approximately 300 mμ as do ordinary crown and flint glass. Quartz 1 mm thick is transparent for ultraviolet radiation down to a wavelength $\lambda = 170$ mμ, fluorite even to 100 mμ. One millimeter of air (at a pressure of 760 mm Hg) absorbs all wavelengths below $\lambda = 170$ mμ; the solar spectrum as measured on the surface of the earth stops at 250 mμ on account of the absorption by the air.

Refraction and Reflection. The refractive indices of the ultraviolet-transparent glasses and crystals show normal dispersion. Metals are highly absorbing and have low reflectivity in the ultraviolet region.

Spectroscopy of Ultraviolet. Since all glass absorbs ultraviolet radiation to a considerable extent, prisms and lenses for ultraviolet spectroscopy must be made of quartz or fluorite. In using quartz, correction must be made for the effects of double refraction and optical rotation. For spectrophotographic investigations of ultraviolet radiation of the shorter wavelengths, a vacuum spectrograph must be used on account of the absorption characteristics of air. Convenient sources of ultraviolet radiation are electric sparks between metals; each metal has a definite and characteristic spectral line distribution, one of which can be used as a standard for wavelength measurements. The most efficient source is the mercury-vapor arc.

The ultraviolet spectrum can be made visible by fluorescent screens or by photography.

Fluorescence. Many organic substances in solution emit characteristic monochromatic visible radiation, that is fluorescent, when illuminated by white light or ultraviolet radiation. These fluorescent substances strongly absorb radiations in the near and extreme ultraviolet region. Hence, to explain fluorescence, quantum theory assumes that this range will excite the electrons and raise them to high energy levels from which they may fall back in one or in several energy steps; in the latter case this gives rise to characteristic visible radiations. Table IX gives a few organic substances exhibiting strong fluorescence (from Handbook of Chemistry and Physics, 1933). Inorganic gases and vapors, as well as crystals, show fluorescence under certain conditions. Much valuable information can be found in R. W. Wood's Physical Optics. Practical use of fluorescence is made in luminous paints and in the analysis of paints, oils, and rubber, whereby impurities in composition can be detected by differences in fluorescent properties.

Table IX. Fluorescence of Organic Substances in Solution
(From Handbook of Chemistry and Physics)

Substance	Solvent	Wavelength (mμ)	Color
Anthracene	Alcohol	400, 430, 436	Violet
Quinine sulfate	Water	437	Violet
Esculine	Alcohol	460	Blue
Fluorescin	Water (alkaline)	542	Green
Rhodamin	Water	554	Yellow
Eosine	Alcohol or water	589	Yellow
Naphthalin, red	Alcohol	632	Orange
Resorcin, blue	Water	650	Red

Phosphorescence. A number of crystals show persistent fluorescence, even after the exciting source has been removed. Usually any prolonged luminescence of crystals is called phosphorescence; however, a substance is truely phosphorescent only if small metallic impurities cause the storage of radiation energy.

Photography. Light-sensitive emulsions of silver bromide in gelatin on glass are capable of forming pictures by chemical action. Certain very small sulfur-containing organic bodies present in the gelatin react with the incident light and upon "development" form centers for the reduction of silver bromide to metallic silver. Ordinary dry plates are light sensitive in the wavelength range of 220 to 500 mμ with a maximum of sensitiveness in the violet. Below 250 mμ the gelatin begins to absorb strongly so that special plates are necessary. By utilizing fluorescence of organic substances in the various ranges of the visible spectrum, emulsions can be formed which are sensitive up to 720 mμ (known as verichromatic or panchromatic plates or films).

12. THERMAL (INFRA-RED) RADIATION

Thermal Radiation is assumed to be produced by the agitation of the molecules or atoms of a substance and extends continuously over a wavelength range from a characteristic minimum frequency up to wavelengths in the far ultraviolet. It represents a continuous energy distribution depending only upon, and being characteristic of, the temperature of the body. The term infra-red radiation refers to that part of the spectrum which extends from approximately 780 mμ up to the very shortest electromagnetic oscillations produced in electric circuits.

Kirchhoff's Law. For any body in thermal equilibrium at a certain temperature T the ratio of monochromatic emissive power E_λ to absorptivity A_λ is the same function of wavelength, or in other words, every substance emits as much heat radiation as it receives for any wavelength and temperature. This law was deduced analytically by Kirchhoff (1860) and has been verified experimentally.

Black-body Radiation. A black body is defined as being perfectly absorbing for all wavelengths, $A_\lambda = 1$. In this case Kirchhoff's law leads to $(E_\lambda/A_\lambda)_b = E_{\lambda b}$, or the characteristic function of Kirchhoff is identical with the spectral distribution of emissive power of a black body. For practical purposes, Lummer and Pringsheim showed that the characteristics of the black body are closely approximated by a heated hollow sphere with blackened inner surface. Through a small hole in the surface of the sphere the internal state of radiation can be observed with a bolometer. The experimental curve of the spectral distribution of black-body radiation is given in Fig. 2 for several absolute temperatures.

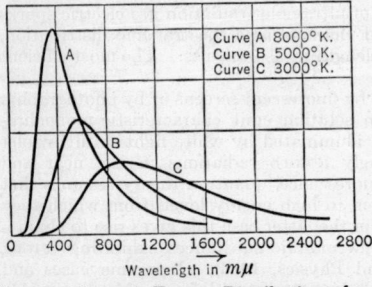

Curve A	8000° K.
Curve B	5000° K.
Curve C	3000° K.

FIG. 2. Spectral Energy Distribution of a Black Body. The Ordinates of the Curves B and C must be divided by 6 and 50, respectively, in order to obtain the proper relative values.

Wavelength in $m\mu$

Wien's Displacement Law. The wavelength of the black-body spectrum at which maximum radiation occurs for any particular temperature is connected with this temperature by the relation

$$\lambda_m T = 2900 \ \mu^0 K \qquad (4)$$

formulated by Wien. With this law, Wien also showed that, given a spectral distribution of radiation energy for one temperature T_1, the distribution curve for any other temperature T_2 can be constructed.

Spectral Distribution of Thermal Radiation. Introducing the concept of the "quantum" $h\nu$ as a definite fundamental unit of energy associated with the frequency ν, Planck (1900) formulated a theory of black-body radiation in which the various molecules are considered as oscillators having the same frequency but different and integer multiples of the energy unit. The monochromatic emissive power obtained as the statistical average over the contributions of all the molecules is then given by the exponential form

$$E_{\lambda b} = \frac{c_1}{\lambda^5} \cdot \frac{1}{e^{c_2/\lambda T} - 1} \qquad (5)$$

where c_1 and c_2 are universal constants. Equation 5 gives very accurately the experimental curves obtained by Lummer and Pringsheim. For very small values of (λT) this leads to Wien's approximate expression for the spectral emissive power

$$E_{\lambda b} \approx c_1 \lambda^{-5} e^{-c_2/\lambda T} \qquad (5a)$$

which is much simpler to use and gives good approximation even for the maxima of the spectral curves. For very large values of (λT) equation 5 leads to Rayleigh's approximate form for the spectral emissive power

$$E_{\lambda b} \approx \frac{c_1 T}{c_2 \lambda^4} \qquad (5b)$$

which, again, is simpler to use than Planck's form.

Stefan-Boltzmann Law. Stefan showed empirically that for thermal radiation the total emissive power of a body varies with the fourth power of the absolute temperature. If two bodies of different temperatures exchange heat radiation, the rate of flow of energy per unit area from the higher temperature T_1 to the lower T_2 is given by $[\sigma \cdot (T_1{}^4 - T_2{}^4)]$, where σ is the Stefan constant of radiation, $\sigma = 5.735 \times 10^{-5}$ erg per sec per sq cm per deg Kelvin to the fourth power. This law was tested experimentally by Lummer and Pringsheim over a range from 100 to 1300 deg cent, and found to hold accurately.

Optical Pyrometry. The temperature of glowing solids and vapors can be determined by using the radiation characteristics of a black body. In many cases the emitter can be considered approximately as a black body, so that Wien's displacement law, equation 4, can be applied directly if λ_m is determined; or Stefan's law can be applied if a thermocouple is used to measure the total radiation. In the visible range, a photometer calibrated in terms of known temperatures may be employed. For emitters deviating appreciably from the black-body characteristics, corrections have to be made according to the method used. The temperature of the sun was found to be 6000 deg cent; that of the carbon arc crater, between 3500 and 4000 deg cent.

Measurement of Heat Radiation. Small energies, radiated for example by glowing bodies, can best be measured by a thermocouple which by the heat absorbed in the junction generates a small thermal electromotive force indicated by a galvanometer. To increase the deflection, a *thermopile*, a series arrangement of a number of thermocouples, can be used. The *bolometer* utilizes the increase of resistance of a thin blackened wire with the absorption of the heat rays; the wire forms one arm in a Wheatstone bridge. The *radiometer* measures the torque exerted when the heat rays fall upon small mica vanes in a low-pressure tube, the torque being produced by the unequal pressures set up on the two sides of the vanes.

Transmission of Infra-red Radiation. Most kinds of glass do not transmit wavelengths longer than about 2.5 μ; quartz will transmit up to 4 μ and fluorite up to 11 μ. The best material for use in infra-red spectroscopy is rock salt and sylvin, which transmit wavelengths up to 18 μ. Metals show, in general, high reflectivity over the infra-red spectrum, and act as almost perfect mirrors.

Spectroscopy in the Infra-red. The spectral distribution of emissive power in the infra-red spectrum is best determined by bolometric or thermocouple measurements. The refracting system must use fluorite, quartz or rock salt, in order to avoid absorption of the infra-red rays. The calibration of the infra-red range is best accomplished by reference to the known absorption bands of water which extend beyond 6μ. Tungsten lamps or straight Nernst lamps serve as sources of infra-red spectra. For photographic spectroscopy specially prepared plates are required.

Residual Rays. Quartz, fluorite, and rock salt reflect certain wavelengths in the far infra-red almost perfectly. If, therefore, heat radiation is reflected several times from the surfaces of such crystals, all other radiations will be weakened considerably and almost pure monochromatic radiation remains, which is called *residual rays*.

13. PHOTOELECTRICITY

Photoelectric Effect. When a metallic surface is illuminated by light (preferably ultraviolet), x-rays, or γ-rays, electrons are emitted from the surface. Their number is strictly proportional to the intensity, their velocity is proportional to the frequency, of the incident radiation. This phenomenon was discovered first by Hertz, and later by Hallwachs, and is often referred to as *Hallwachs' effect*.

Einstein's Relation. If the photoelectric discharge is influenced by a supporting or counteracting potential, a definite negative stopping potential is found for each frequency, at which no emission occurs however strong the intensity of the incident light may be. This indicates that the frequency of the incident light is an essential factor in the liberation of the electrons. Einstein (1905) propounded a theory of light quanta in analogy to Planck's energy quanta of thermal radiation and proposed the relation

$$^1/_2 \, mv^2 = h\nu - p \tag{6}$$

for the kinetic energy and thus the velocity of an emitted electron. The kinetic energy, therefore, appears as the difference between the energy $h\nu$ of the incident light quantum, $h = 6.55 \times 10^{-27}$ erg sec (Planck's quantum of action), and the work function p, i.e., the amount of energy needed to just force an electron from the metal; obviously p determines the stopping potential. The work p can be divided into one part ω needed to detach an electron from the atom and, therefore, a function of the position of the electron within the atom; and another part p' constituting the work to liberate the electron from the metal as a whole and, therefore, in close relation to Richardson's work function for thermionic emission (see Thermonics). Equation 6 has been found true even for incident x-radiation, the electrons liberated coming then from the inner shells of the atoms; consequently ω may now assume the most prominent part.

Photoconductivity. When a semi- or non-conductor with an electrical voltage applied at its ends is exposed to light, either transverse or parallel to the direction of the electric field, its resistance is instantaneously lowered and an appreciable current will flow. The primary effect is a true photoelectric effect, following the relation of equation 6, but many superimposed secondary effects mask it. In general, photoconductivity refers to any phenomenon wherein light influences the conductivity of the substance. Selenium and zincblende are the most striking materials exhibiting photoconductive properties.

Photoionization.   Many gases and vapors when illuminated by light of short wavelength, preferably from the ultraviolet, show marked ionization phenomena as a result of the instantaneous absorption of photons. The vapors of the alkali metals being readily ionizable amplify the photoelectric effect normally present.

Photoelectric Cells.   The industrial utilization of the photoelectric and photoconductive effects has resulted in various devices called photoelectric cells. In general, these cells are evacuated or gas filled and shielded from light except for a glass or quartz window through which the incident radiation enters and falls upon a target substance; the resulting photoelectric current is then indicated by a meter. According to the application of the cell, the window material can be used to correct the light sensitiveness of the target substance either to approximate that of the human eye, or to restrict it to some definite portion of the spectrum. Such cells are used as intensity meters in illumination design, as protective or active relays in power circuits, as regulating or governing devices, and in the transmission of pictures (television) and sound. Complete information is furnished by the catalogs of the manufacturing companies.

Spectrophotometry.   Photoelectric cells are especially well adapted for comparative measurements of the spectral energy distribution of radiations, particularly in transmission and reflection spectra. Individual observation can be replaced by automatic recorders; color analyses as well as spectral line analyses are thus greatly facilitated.

14. X-RAYS

The X-ray Region in the electromagnetic spectrum extends from the shortest ultraviolet wavelengths at about 0.8 mμ down to 0.008 mμ. X-rays are essentially a secondary radiation produced when very high-speed electrons impinge upon a metallic target. They were discovered accidentally by Roentgen (1895).

Absorption of X-rays.   X-rays are absorbed by all substances to a varying degree, depending upon wavelength and absorber. Usually a specimen of aluminum is taken as the reference standard for absorption measurements, and the mass absorption index μ_d of this specimen is used as a measure of the hardness of x-rays; the smaller μ_d, the harder the x-rays. A related measure is the penetration power giving the thickness of aluminum required to reduce the intensity of x-rays to a definite fraction of the incident intensity. The mass absorption coefficient shows very marked peak values for certain wavelengths which depend on the atomic number of the element and indicate a relation to the structure of the inner, more closely bound, electrons of the $K, L,$ and M levels (see X-ray Spectroscopy).

Refraction of X-rays.   The refractive index of most substances for x-rays is very slightly less than unity and shows in general normal dispersion. The measurement of the refractive index is extremely difficult and is mainly based upon the critical angle for total reflection. In the region of the wavelengths corresponding to the characteristic line radiation of substances, x-rays show very distinct anomalous dispersion which can be used for examining the structure of matter.

Ionization by X-rays.   Quantitative measurements of x-ray intensities are in general based upon the ionization effects in air or gases. For this purpose special ionization chambers are used which give an indication of the rate of ionization produced by, and proportional to the intensity of, the x-rays.

Photographic Action of X-rays.   X-rays produce in emulsions used for photographic purposes the same effects as ultraviolet light. On account of their relatively low intensity, the time of exposure is long, but can be shortened considerably by using " intensifying " screens, usually coverings of fluorescent character. Since x-rays cast shadows, and by their penetrating power render most substances transparent in varying degrees, photographs can be made which reveal the inner structural outlines of organisms. This application of x-ray photography is especially valuable in the medical sciences as a fundamental diagnostic help.

Diffraction of X-rays.   An x-ray passing through a thin crystal plate produces on a photographic plate a bright central spot in the direction of the incident ray surrounded by a regular pattern of spots of distinctly different intensities. This pattern changes with the relative orientation of x-ray and crystal plate and obviously is caused by the diffractive interaction of the crystal structure and the x-ray photons. It is usually referred to as a *Laue pattern* and forms the basis of x-ray crystallography since its arrangement gives an indication of the internal structure of the crystals.

Bragg's Law.   In order to explain the regularity of the pattern, Bragg assumed that each plane of atoms within the crystal individually reflects the x-rays, and he arrived at the relation
$$n\lambda = 2d \sin \theta \tag{7}$$

where n is a variable integer, λ the wavelength of the incident x-rays, d the spacing between parallel atomic planes, and θ the angle between an atomic plane and the incident x-rays. The angle θ can be observed or computed from the distances between spots in the Laue pattern, so that equation 7 gives the relation between wavelength λ and grating space d of the atomic planes.

X-ray Crystallography. Bragg's law provides the means of exploring the atomic structure of crystals by observation of the Laue pattern. If the wavelength of the x-rays is known and the reflection angle θ observed, equation 7 leads to values for d. From Laue patterns with the x-rays incident in normal directions to the principal crystallographical planes, the distances of all possible atomic planes can be computed and finally the arrangement of the chemical atoms can be constructed. In locating the atomic planes the *Miller indices* are used; these constitute a triplet of numbers each designating the reciprocal of the intersects of the plane with a cartesian coordinate system. The triplet (2, 1, 0), for example, defines all planes parallel to one which intersects the x-axis at one half, the y-axis at one arbitrary unit, and is parallel to the z-axis. Table X gives for various crystals the spacings between atomic planes parallel to the plane indicated, and also the expansion coefficient which takes into account the change of the spacings with temperature. The value for rock salt (a cubic crystal) is defined for the face parallel planes as 0.281400 mμ and is used as a primary standard for crystallographic measurements.

Table X. Grating Spacings of Various Crystals

(From X-rays in Theory and Experiment, A. H. Compton and S. K. Allison)

Crystal	Parallel to to Plane	Grating Spacing in Angstroms	Linear Expansion Coefficient (perpendicular to crystal plane)
Calcite	Cleavage	3.029	1.02×10^{-5} per deg cent
Gypsum	Cleavage	7.579	3.78×10^{-5} " " "
Mica	Cleavage	9.928	1.53×10^{-6} " " "
Quartz	Prism	4.245	1.04×10^{-5} " " "
Rock salt	(1, 0, 0)	2.814	4.0×10^{-5} " " "
Sugar	(1, 0, 0)	10.57	

X-ray Analysis of Materials. The Laue pattern and its variation as the Debye-Scherrer pattern for pulverized crystals are used in industry for testing and checking of materials including the study of temperature influences, elasticity, hardening, melting points, and so on. *Radiography* refers to the industrial applications of x-ray photography and fluoroscopy for detecting flaws, inhomogeneities, yielding points in structural parts; to the investigation of materials under operating conditions; and to other uses. In art, the use of x-ray photographs permits the identification of true antiques, old paintings, and the like.

X-ray Spectroscopy. If x-rays fall upon a solid substance, a characteristic secondary radiation is observed which has for each chemical element a definite energy spectrum, although being similar in form for all elements. The spectral distribution of the secondary radiation can be investigated by utilizing Bragg's law (equation 7) if a crystal of known grating d is employed as analyzer. The intensity of the radiation can be measured either with the ionization chamber or by photography. Two types of spectra are discernible, a characteristic line spectrum and a continuous spectrum. The line spectrum is due to electrons in the inner orbits which by collision with the incident x-ray photons are raised to outer orbits and in returning emit radiation of a particular frequency. The continuous spectrum is due to the absorption by atoms of x-radiation of insufficient amounts to raise their electrons to higher orbits. There is for any hardness of incident x-rays a definite critical shortest wavelength at which the continuous spectrum abruptly ends. This wavelength limit constitutes the converse to the photoelectric effect, and the continuous spectrum is often referred to as the *inverse photoelectric effect*. From the line spectra, *energy level diagrams* can be deduced in the same way as in light spectroscopy (see Art. 10). The results of x-ray spectroscopy were instrumental in building up the nuclear models of atoms.

BIBLIOGRAPHY ON PHYSICS OF RADIATION

1. ALLEN, H. S. Photo-Electricity. London, Longmans, Green.
2. BALY. E. C. C. Spectroscopy. New York, Longmans, Green.
3. BELL, L. On the Ultra-Violet Energy in Artificial Light Sources. *Electrical World*, Vol. 59, p. 807, 1912.
4. BORN, M. Optik. Berlin, J. Springer, 1933.
5. BUCKINGHAM, J. Matter and Radiation. Oxford University Press, England, 1930.

6. BULLOCK, E. R.   Chemical Reactions of the Photographic Latent Image.   New York, D. Van Nostrand.
7. CAMPBELL, N. R., RITCHIE, D.   Photoelectric Cells.   London, Sir Isaac Pitman & Sons, 1929.
8. CLARK, G. L.   Applied X-rays.   New York, McGraw-Hill Book Co.
9. COBLENTZ, W. W., EMERSON, W. B.   Luminous Radiation from a Black Body.   Bureau of Standards, Sci. Paper 305, 1917.
10. COMPTON, A. H., ALLISON, S. K.   X-rays in Theory and Experiment.   New York, D. Van Nostrand, 1935.
11. FOOTE, P. D., MOHLER, F. L.   The Origin of Spectra.   New York, Chemical Catalog Co., 1922.
12. FOWLER, A.   Report on Series in Line Spectra.   London, Fleetway Press, 1922.
13. Handbuch der Physik.   Vols. 19, 20 and 21.   Berlin, J. Springer, 1928–29.
14. HICKS, W. M.   Treatise on the Analysis of Spectra.   Macmillan, 1922.
15. HOUSTOUN, R. A.   A Treatise on Light.   London, Longmans, Green, 1933.
16. HUGHES, A. L., DUBRIDGE, L. A.   Photo-electric Phenomena.   New York, McGraw-Hill Book Co., 1932.
17. KAYE, G. W. C.   X-rays.   London, Longmans, Green.
18. LEWIS, S. J.   Spectroscopy in Science and Industry.   London, Blackie & Sons, Limited.
19. LOWRY, T. M.   Optical Rotatory Power.   London, Longmans, Green.
20. LUCKIESH, M.   Ultra-Violet Radiation.   New York, D. Van Nostrand.
21. LYMAN, T.   The Spectroscopy of the Extreme Ultra-Violet.   London, Longmans, Green.
22. MEES, C. E. K.   Artificial Illuminants for Use in Practical Photography.   *Trans. Illum. Engg. Soc.*, Vol. 10, p. 947, 1915.
23. Molecular Spectra in Gases.   *National Research Council, Bulletin* 57, December, 1926.
24. PAULING, L., GOUDSMIT, S. A.   The Structure of Line Spectra.   New York, McGraw-Hill Book Co.
25. Photography as a Scientific Implement.   London, Blackie & Son, Limited.
26. Pyrometry.   American Institute of Mining and Metallurgical Engineers.   New York, 1920.
27. RAWLING, S. O.   Infrared Photography.   Blackie & Son, Limited, London.
28. RICHTMYER, F. K.   Introduction to Modern Physics.   New York, McGraw-Hill Book Co., 1928.
29. ST. JOHN, A., ISENBURGER, H. R.   Industrial Radiography.   New York, John Wiley & Sons.
30. SIEGBAHN, M.   Spectroscopy of X-rays.   (Trans. by G. LINDSAY.)   Oxford University Press, England, 1925.
31. TERRILL, H. M., ULREY, C. T.   X-ray Technology.   New York, D. Van Nostrand, 1930.
32. VALASEK, J.   Elements of Optics.   New York, McGraw-Hill Book Co.
33. VON HEVESY, G.   Chemical Analysis by X-rays and Its Applications.   New York, D. Van Nostrand.
34. WOOD, R. W.   Physical Optics.   Macmillan.
35. WYCKOFF, R. W. G.   Structure of Crystals.   New York, Chemical Catalog Co.
36. ZWORYKIN, V. K., WILSON, E. D.   Photo-cells and Their Applications.   New York, John Wiley & Sons, 1930.

Tables

1. Handbook of Chemistry and Physics.   Cleveland, Ohio, Chemical Rubber Publishing Co.
2. International Critical Tables.   New York, McGraw-Hill Book Co.
3. LANDHOLT-BOERNSTEIN.   Physikalische-Chemische Tabellen.   Berlin, J. Springer, 1923-1931.
4. The Smithsonian Tables, Washington, D. C.

PHYSIOLOGY OF RADIATION

By Ernst Weber

15. VISION

The Eye.   Radiation enters the eye through the cornea or outer coating, penetrates the anterior chamber (filled with aqueous humour), the lens, the posterior chamber (filled with a gelatinous, vitreous humour), and is received on the retina, a network of fine fibers which transmit in some way the sensory impressions through the optical nerve to the brain where they are transformed into perceptions.   The range of radiation leading to visual perception is from approximately 380 to 780 mμ.   The most sensitive point of the retina is called the yellow spot, and has a depression, the fovea centralis, where vision is most distinct.   To bring objects into such relative position to the eye that they will be received at the fovea centralis requires a delicate adjustment apparatus which is provided by the muscle fibers holding the eye.   Being a multirefracting medium, the eye suffers from both spherical and chromatic aberration (see Art. 5).

Fechner's Law.   The sensation of light as produced by the eye varies logarithmically with the intensity of the stimulus.   This law, found by Fechner to hold true for most sensory perceptions, is an excellent illustration of natural economy.

Spectral Visibility.   The visual sensation of the eye varies greatly with the wavelength of light, reaching a maximum at about 556 mμ (yellow).   If white light is used as a standard to be compared with the spectral monochromatic radiations, the relative intensity of white light causing the same sensation as the spectral light is called the *relative visibility*.   The spectral distribution of relative visibility is shown in Fig. 1, assuming the visibility of yellow-green light, $\lambda = 556$ mμ, as 100 per cent.   The visibility falls off very sharply from this maximum and shows that essentially only the wavelengths between 480 and 640 mμ constitute the easily visible spectrum.

Color Vision. The retina is composed of nervous fibers known as rods and cones, of which only the cones seem to be responsive to colors; the cones are, at the same time, fairly insensitive so that, at low intensities of light, colors cannot be distinguished (twilight vision). The rods are more sensitive; they contain a light-sensitive substance, the visual purple, but apparently they cannot transmit color sensation. Perception of color is not instantaneous; of all the spectral colors the blue sensations are most active, whereas the green sensations are most sluggish.

Purkinje Effect. At low intensities, before twilight vision is reached, there is a distinct shift of the maximum in the visibility curve (Fig. 1) towards a shorter wavelength; this is known as the Purkinje effect. This shift of the spectral visibility curve tends to make color

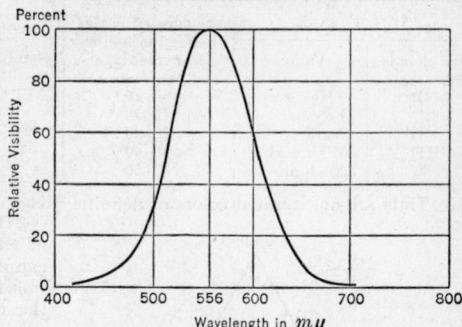

Fig. 1. Spectral Distribution of Relative Human Visibility

sensations variable quantities, and color photometry very difficult.

Theories of Color Vision. Two types of theories have been advanced to explain the facts of normal and abnormal color sensitiveness of the eye. The first type of theory is due to Young and Helmholtz, and proposes the existence of three distinct modes of response of the eye corresponding to the three fundamental color sensations: red, green, and blue. Each of these partial responses represents a definite spectral distribution, the perception of color being the superposition of the three partial responses; Fig. 2 indicates the partial

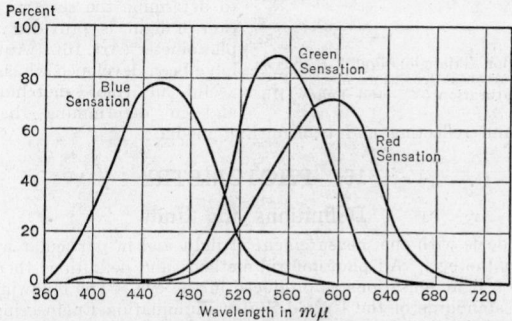

Fig. 2. Relative Excitation of the Three Primary Sensations by Monochromatic Light of Different Wave Lengths

responses for each wavelength. This theory is capable of accounting very readily for the specific types of color-blindness known as red and green color-blindness. The second type of theory initiated by Hering is based upon antagonistic colors and associates chemical building-up and breaking-down processes with the sensation of complementary colors; from this hypothesis it follows that complementary colors cannot be seen at the same point at the same time. This theory readily accounts for afterimages and contrast colors. It seems difficult to accept any one theory exclusively.

Saturation of a color is its degree of freedom from admixture with white light. Monochromatic radiation can be said to have a saturation of 100 per cent, and white light is of zero saturation.

Hue is that property of color by which the various spectral regions are characteristically distinguished. It is most easily determined by comparison with the spectral colors as blue, yellowish, and so on. Equal hues can still differ in saturation. Complementary hues produce white light when mixed. White can be said to have no hue.

Brightness of a color is closely related to its diffuse reflection factor, and can be classified accordingly. It is customary for artistic purposes to distinguish the values of colors by their relative brightnesses. Table I gives the values of colors as suggested by Luckiesh.

Table I. Scale of Color Values
(From Light and Shade and Their Application, M. Luckiesh)

Artist's Scale		Suggested Scale Reflection factors in percentage	Artist's Scale		Suggested Scale Reflection factors in percentage
Symbols	Values		Symbols	Values	
B	Black	0–10	LL	Low light	50–60
LD	Low dark	10–20	L	Light	60–70
D	Dark	20–30	HL	High light	70–80
HD	High dark	30–40	W	White	80–90
M	Medium	40–50			

Tints are unsaturated colors of definitely recognizable hue.

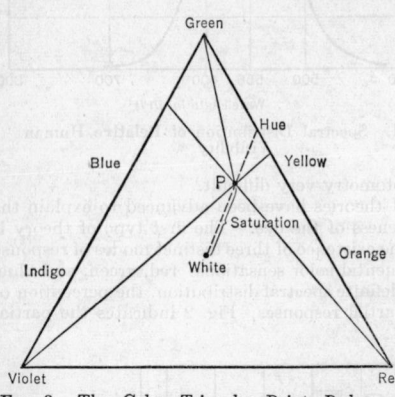

FIG. 3. The Color Triangle; Point P has a Ratio of the Fundamental Sensations $R : G : V = 9.7 : 6 : 11.5$, a Saturation 58% and Yellow Hue

The Color Triangle (Fig. 3). The laws of color mixtures and relative intensities can most readily be visualized in the so-called color triangle. Any point within the triangle indicates by its relative distance from the three fundamental colors in the apices the relative amounts of these fundamental colors. The resultant color, or hue, can be determined by drawing a line from the center (white) through the color point; where it intersects the triangle, the equivalent monochromatic wavelength can be read. The relative distance of the point on this line from the center gives the saturation in percentage.

Analysis of Colors. An objective means to determine the spectral energy distribution of light is provided by the spectral photometer (Art. 16). Automatic methods have been developed which are particularly useful in color matching and mixing, and in determining the characteristics of illuminants and reflecting and transmitting media.

16. PHOTOMETRY

Definitions and Units

Photometry deals with the measurement of light and in particular with the capacity of light to affect the eye. All photometric methods and definitions therefore must take into consideration light sensations as produced in the eye. The following definitions are based upon the standards of the United States Illuminating Engineering Society (IES).

Luminous Flux, F, is the rate of flow of radiant energy evaluated with reference to visual sensation. Although defined as a rate of flow of energy, it may be regarded for photometric purposes as an entity. The *lumen* is the unit of luminous flux and is equal to the flux emitted in a unit solid angle by a source whose average candlepower (see below) throughout the unit solid angle is 1 candle. A source having a uniform candlepower in all directions of 1 candle would emit 4π lumens.

Luminous Intensity, I, of a source of light in a given direction is the solid angular intensity of the luminous flux emitted by the source in the direction considered when the flux involved acts, as far as computations and measurements are concerned, as if it came from a point; mathematically it can be defined as $I = dF/d\omega$, where $d\omega$ is the elemental solid angle. The unit of luminous intensity is the *candle*, and the term candlepower is the luminous intensity expressed in candles. The *international candle* as accepted by France, England, and United States is defined with reference to the standard English sperm candle which under specified conditions is said to have a luminous intensity of exactly 1 international candle. The hefner is the standard used in Germany; it is defined with reference to a standard lamp of specified dimensions, burning amyl acetate or banana oil, and was invented in 1884 by Hefner-Alteneck. The value of the hefner is 0.9 international candle. The Bureau of Standards uses as a primary standard a pentane lamp of specified dimensions which gives an intensity of 10 international candles. Other standards have been proposed, but none seems reliable enough to warrant replacement of the pentane or Hefner-Alteneck lamps.

Mean Horizontal Candlepower of a source is the average intensity in a horizontal plane normal to the axis of the source. The *mean spherical candlepower* of a source is the average intensity over all directions; if the luminous flux is known, the mean spherical candlepower can be computed by dividing the flux by 4π.

Mechanical Equivalent of Light.* The luminous equivalent of radiation at maximum visibility (at $\lambda = 556$ mμ) is defined by

$$1 \text{ lumen} = 0.001496 \text{ watt}$$
$$1 \text{ watt} = 668 \text{ lumens.}$$

Illumination at a given point of a surface is the luminous flux incident on the surface at this point; mathematically it can be defined as $E = dF/dS$, where dS is the surface element receiving the flux element dF. A point source, giving a uniform luminous intensity I in a certain direction, sets up through the small surface dS perpendicular to this direction and at a distance R from the source the elemental flux $dF = I \cdot d\omega$; since the surface element is $dS = R^2 \cdot d\omega$, it follows that $E = I/R^2$ (inverse square law). The units of illumination depend on the reference area chosen and are called *lux* for 1 lumen per square meter, *foot-candle* for 1 lumen per square foot, and *phot* for 1 lumen per square centimeter. The interrelations of the various units are shown in Table II.

Table II. Interrelations between the Units of Illumination

1 Unit is equal to	Lux	Foot-candle	Phot	Milliphot
1 lux	1	0.0929	10^{-4}	10^{-1}
1 foot-candle	10.76	1	0.001076	1.076
1 phot	10^4	929	1	10^3
1 milliphot	10	0.929	10^{-3}	1

Brightness of a surface element dS is defined as the quotient of the luminous intensity produced by the surface element divided by the area as projected into the direction normal to the line from the observer to the surface element; mathematically it is defined as $b = dI(\theta)/dS \cdot \cos \theta$, where $dI(\theta)$ is the luminous intensity in the direction θ and θ the angle between the normal to dS and the line from dS to the observer. The unit of brightness is the candle per square centimeter. For perfectly diffusing surfaces the *average brightness* or flux brightness is used as a more convenient measure; it is defined as the total diffuse luminous flux emitted by one side of a surface element dS divided by dS, and its unit is the *lambert* which is equal to π candles per square centimeter. A more practical unit is the millilambert. For interrelations of the various units see Table III.

Table III. Interrelations between the Units of Brightness

1 Unit is equal to	Candle per sq cm	Lumen per sq cm per steradian	Candle per sq. in.	Lambert	Milli-lambert
1 candle per sq cm	1	1	6.4516	3.1416	3141.6
1 lumen per sq cm per steradian	1	1	6.4516	3.1416	3141.6
1 candle per sq in	0.1550	0.1550	1	0.4869	486.9
1 lambert	0.3183	0.3183	2.0538	1	1000
1 millilambert	0.3183×10^{-3}	0.3183×10^{-3}	0.0020538	0.001	1

Lambert's Laws. A perfectly diffusing surface receives an illumination or emits a luminous intensity (by reflection or true emission) which varies with the cosine of the angle between the normal to the surface and the direction of the incident or emitted (reflected) ray; for perfectly diffusing surfaces the illumination and brightness are therefore constant under all angles of observation. These cosine laws of incidence and emission are only approximately true for the practical substances so that in measurements of illumination or brightness the angle of observation always should be stated.

Instruments and Methods

Equality and Contrast Methods. Most photometric instruments compare an unknown light source with a known light source either simultaneously (comparison) or, by means of a third light source, alternatively (substitution method). To observe the equivalence of two sources either an equality method can be employed in which the two sources

---

* H. E. Ives, *Journal Optical Soc. of America*, vol. 12, p. 75, 1926.

illuminate different parts of the same surface, the adjustment being made for equal brightness, or a *contrast method* can be used in which four fields are observed, two receiving light from one source and the other two from the other source, an absorbing medium decreasing the flux received on one field in each instance, and adjustment being made for equal contrast. The special type of table upon which most photometric measurements are made is called a photometer bench.

Bunsen Photometer. A piece of white paper with a grease or wax spot in its center is held between the two sources of light being compared. The relative distances between paper and sources are adjusted until the paper presents uniform brightness. If the luminous intensities of the two light sources are I_1 (known) and I_2 (unknown), and the distance for observation from one side of the paper r_1 and r_2, from the other side of the paper r'_1 and r'_2, then the unknown intensity follows as

$$I_2 = I_1 \frac{r_2 r'_2}{r_1 r'_1} \tag{1}$$

The advantages are simplicity and cheapness; the error may, however, be as great as 5 per cent or more.

Lummer and Brodhun Photometer. The most essential part is the cube, a combination of two rectangular prisms so fitted together that the light reflected by mirrors from the two sources can be either compared for equality or adjusted for equal contrast. Calibrated filters may be used to adjust the light intensities. The accuracy is very high, about one-half of one per cent, and is considered the highest obtainable accuracy in photometric work.

Illuminometers. These are small portable photometers, usually employing some form of Lummer and Brodhun cube and having a small built-in electric lamp with either adjustable distance, or filters, or both. On a test screen the light from the known source is compared with either the light incident on a surface (illumination) or the light emitted by a surface (brightness). American designs are the Sharp-Millar and the Macbeth type, based upon the original Weber illuminometer. Care must be taken to shield properly and to avoid errors on account of deviations from the cosine laws.

Ulbricht Sphere. To measure the mean spherical candlepower, the Ulbricht sphere has come into predominant use. It consists of a large hollow sphere, coated with highly reflecting paint on its inner surface and having a window of transparent glass. The brightness of this window, shielded from the direct light of the source at the center of the sphere, is proportional to the mean spherical candlepower of the source and can be determined by an illuminometer.

Color Photometry. Methods have been devised which try to eliminate the influence of color in photometric work. The flicker photometer of Rood is perhaps the most useful means of utilizing the fact that two colored surfaces, if presented in quick alternation, appear colorless and thus permit a comparison of illumination. The most objective method is suggested by spectrophotometry, which, however, does not yield results immediately useful in photometry because the relative visibility of the human eye is not taken into account.

Colorimeters are instruments for the measurement of the hue and the saturation of colors. *Trichromatic* colorimeters mix the three fundamental sensations by means of glass filters in order to match the color to be determined; the hue and saturation can then be computed from the color triangle (see Art. 15). *Monochromatic* colorimeters first determine by comparison with the spectral colors the dominant hue of the unknown color and then mix it with white light until the proper saturation is obtained.

17. ELEMENTS OF ILLUMINATION

Artificial Light Sources

Artificial Light Sources. There are four distinct groups of light sources in common use for artificial lighting: the incandescent electric lamps, almost the exclusive illuminant in cities and wherever electricity is available under economic conditions; the illuminating gas and other flame sources where electricity is not economically available; the arc lamps mainly for special purposes; and the vapor lamps which have recently come into more prominent use for public lighting on account of their higher economy.

Luminescence and Incandescence. Radiation of energy can be produced thermally (incandescence), or by atomic or molecular excitation (luminescence). In the first case (incandescent lamps and flames) a continuous spectrum is usually produced which extends far beyond the visible range and thus seriously influences the efficiency. In the second case (arcs and vapor lamps) characteristic line radiation is produced which has sharply distinct color features; this radiation is particularly applicable for decorative and advertising lighting but has little value for ordinary illumination, except when properly corrected by mixed color radiations.

Luminosity Curves. Fig. 4 gives the spectral energy distribution curves of the common illuminants over the visible range. From the spectral distribution of radiated energy the luminosity curves for the various illuminants can be obtained if for each wavelength the relative energy is multiplied with the respective value at the same wavelength of the relative visibility curve from Fig. 1. The luminosity curve is the most important characteristic of illuminants as it shows graphically the distribution of optically useful energy. Unfortunately no single illuminant is known to give an energy radiation just within the visible range and distributed similarly to the sun's spectral energy distribution, which it is desirable to obtain since the maximum of the energy radiation of the sun almost coincides with the point of maximum visibility at $\lambda = 556$ mμ. The deviations of the energy distribution of most ordinary illuminants from the energy distribution of the sun account for their "color defects"; these can be corrected with sacrifices in economy.

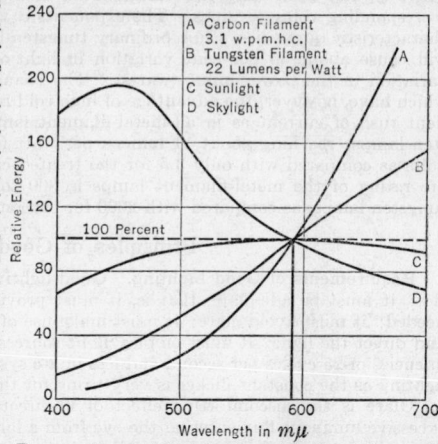

FIG. 4. Spectral Distribution of Radiant Energy in Some Common Illuminants

Luminous Efficiency. A comparison of the luminosity curve with the total radiation energy spectrum reveals the loss of radiation for optical purposes. It is customary to designate the ratio of the total luminous radiation in lumens to the total energy radiation in watts as luminous efficiency. Table IV gives a few selected values of luminous efficiency for the common illuminants and in addition those for the sun and the black body as a matter of comparison. Since the mechanical equivalent of luminous radiation (see Art. 16) is 668 lumens per watt, it is readily seen that the luminous efficiency of all the common light sources is extremely low and even for the sun not comparable with accustomed efficiency values in other fields of engineering.

Brightness of Light Sources. Table IV also gives the values of the brightnesses of various illuminants as compared with those of the sun and the black body.

Table IV. Luminous Efficiencies and Brightnesses of Light Sources

Light Source	Brightness (candles per sq cm)	Luminous Efficiency (lumens per watt)
Sun, outside of earth's atmosphere	200,000	100
at horizon	600	
Clear sky (average)	0.4	
Black body at 6500° K	294,000	90
at 4000° K	24,350	52.2
Electric arcs		
searchlight arc	50,000 to 70,000	
crater of carbon arc	16,000	
mercury-vapor arc (glass)	2.3	14
Incandescent electric lamps		
1000 watts, gas-filled tungsten	1,210	20.0
500 watts, gas-filled tungsten	1,000	18.1
100 watts, gas-filled tungsten	579	12.9
40 watts, vacuum tungsten	203	10.0
tantalum (2 watts per candle)	53.1	5.0
treated carbon (3.1 watts per candle)	70.6	3.4
untreated carbon (4 watts per candle)	54.9	2.6

Characteristics of Electric Incandescent Lamps. The characteristic curves of incandescent lamps give the variation with voltage of the light output in lumens, the efficiency in lumens per watt, the power input in watts, the current in amperes, and the resistance in ohms, taking all the values as 100 per cent at rated voltage which also is considered as

100 per cent. These characteristics can, with a reasonable degree of approximation, be brought into the exponential form

$$\frac{Q_1}{Q_2} = \left(\frac{V_1}{V_2}\right)^\alpha \tag{2}$$

where Q_1 and Q_2 are any two values of the characteristic quantities, and V_1 and V_2 the corresponding voltage values. The exponents α vary with the lamps as well as with the characteristic quantities. For ordinary tungsten lamps a 10 per cent voltage variation will cause about 35 per cent variation in light output (lumens), and about 15 per cent variation in the power input (watts). The changes are much larger for carbon lamps which have, however, the advantage of high cold resistance so that there is no initial transient rush of current as in all-metal-filament lamps. The efficiency is highest for tungsten lamps, reaching about 11 lumens per watt for the medium 60-watt lamps at 120 volts as compared with only 3.5 for the treated carbon lamp of equal size. The average life rating of the metal-filament lamps is 600 to 1000 hours, the higher values being for tungsten lamps, as compared with 2000 for carbon-filament lamps.

Principles of Good Lighting

Requirements of Good Lighting. Good lighting must have the following characteristics: it must be adequate, that is, it must provide sufficient illumination at the places needed; it must avoid glare; it must make use of lighting fixtures which properly diffuse and direct the light; it must employ light sources of suitable color and steadiness. Frequencies of 25 cycles per second and less in a-c systems are generally not suitable for good lighting as the constant flicker is very tiring for the eyes.

Glare is the discomforting effect of ill-directed light. It can be caused either by excessive luminous flux entering the eye from a large light source at a relatively small distance, by excessive brightness of a light source in the field of view as unshaded electric lamps or flames, or by excessive contrast in brightness between light source and surroundings as reflections from metals and polished surfaces or dark ceilings and walls. Glare is not only uncomfortable but also injurious to the eye if exposure is prolonged. It is especially important to avoid glare under working conditions. The best means to avoid glare is obviously to eliminate its causes by using indirect lighting, direct lighting from large distances, or properly designed diffusers, and by painting the walls and ceilings in light colors.

Diffusion of Light. Substances which transmit light but in diffused form are called translucent. Diffusely transmitted or reflected light is "softer" than regularly transmitted or reflected light and more comfortable to the eye. Good lighting employs properly diffused light as obtained either by placing diffusing materials in front of clear glass lamps or by using translucent glass bulb lamps of the frosted or white type; the reduction of the intensity of light is approximately between 5 and 15 per cent, the higher reduction being for the white glass bulb.

Directive Reflection of Light. To direct light to the places where it is needed, reflectors of either metallic or enamel type are used. It is convenient for non-commercial lighting to combine reflection and diffusion; for this purpose porcelain enameled steel or mat surfaces of white paint should be used which have a diffuse reflection factor of about 0.6 to 0.8, the higher factors for paints. Metallic coatings on the bowls of lamps are used in indirect lighting to enhance the light flux thrown on the ceiling; silver has the highest reflection factor (0.92) but deteriorates very rapidly, whereas chromium, tin, or aluminum with reflectivities of 0.65 to 0.62 are more durable and therefore to be preferred. To provide economical indirect lighting the ceiling should be of white plaster which has a diffused reflection factor of 0.90 to 0.95 when new, or 0.80 to 0.85 when old. It must be observed that all the energy not reflected by a reflector is absorbed by it and tends to raise its temperature. It is also important to know the angular distribution of the reflected light intensities in order to shape the reflectors properly; this is usually determined by measurement with photometers. Tables and figures can be found in F. E. Cady and H. B. Dates: Illuminating Engineering, John Wiley & Sons, 1928, p. 300 ff.

Reflection from Walls. It is important to consider the wall finish and its influence upon the lighting characteristics of a room. The various colors have different reflectivities, usually higher for the lighter and lower for the darker tones. Surfaces with reflectivities less than 0.50 usually appear agreeable if in mat finish. Table V gives the reflectivities of various colored surfaces (see also Table V, page 9-16, for the diffuse reflectivities of various materials).

Recommended Illuminations for Various Purposes. To have adequate illumination at the point at which the eye is directed most of the time, certain recommendations are made by the various factory codes which can be found in the publications of the American Engineering Standards Committee. It is the generally accepted recommendation to use

Table V. Reflection Factors from Colored Surfaces

(For illumination by Mazda lamps)

Reflection Factor in Per Cent	Colors of Surfaces				
80 to 75	Ivory white				
75 to 70	Ivory				
70 to 65	Bright yellow	Light gray			
65 to 60		Lichen gray	Buff	Latin green	
60 to 55		Silver gray	Tan (Ivory)		Pale azure + white
55 to 50		Medium gray	Buff stone		Shell pink
50 to 45		French gray		Light green	Pink
45 to 40		Darker gray		Bright sage	Pale azure
40 to 35			Light brown		Light blue
35 to 30					Sky blue
30 to 25			Tan		
25 to 20		Dark gray	Brown	Olive green	
20 to 15		Dark gray	Cocoanut brown	Forest green	Cardinal red

50- and 60-watt lamps in homes and in low-ceiling offices in order to insure adequate illumination for general purposes. Table VI gives a selected list of recommended values for illumination.

Table VI. Recommended Values of Illumination

(Standards set by the various codes sponsored by the American Engineering Standards Committee)

Space	Illumination (foot-candles)	
	Recommended	Minimum
Auditorium	5	3
Cars (railway)	8	5
Club rooms: lounge	5	3
reading room	12	8
Drafting rooms	25	15
Gymnasium: shower and locker rooms	6	4
swimming pool	8	5
exercising floors	12	8
Halls	3	2
Hotels: lobby	8	5
dining room	6	4
writing room	12	8
corridors, stairways	3	2
Libraries: reading room	12	8
stack room	6	4
Offices: close work	15	10
no close work	10	8
file and other rooms	6	4
Schools: auditorium	8	5
corridors	5	3
laboratories	12	8
classrooms, library, study rooms	12	8
drawing rooms	25	15
Walks	0.5	0.1
Factories: roadways, yard thoroughfares		0.02
storage spaces		0.25
where discrimination is not essential		0.5
where slight discrimination is essential		1
where moderate discrimination of detail is essential		2
where close discrimination of detail is essential		3
where discrimination of minute detail is essential*		5

* See special codes for special purposes.

13. THERAPY OF RADIATION

All radiations of the electromagnetic spectrum have been found useful for therapeutic purposes. The physical properties of the radiations are to be found under Physics of Radiation, page 9-15.

Infra-red Radiation

Physiological Action. Infra-red radiation produces heat (Art. 12) when absorbed by organic tissues, which, in general, show more or less selective absorptivity. In the visible range most of the radiation is absorbed by the skin and the superficial layers of flesh; for deep therapy, wavelengths in the range from 700 to 1500 mμ (near infra-red) prove most penetrating, the skin being apparently more transparent for these wavelengths. Beyond 2μ, the longer the wavelength the less penetrating will be the radiation. The heat produced by infra-red radiation has decided thereapeutic effects on arthritis, fractures, and internal injuries and acts stimulatingly on the muscles and tendons.

Sources of Infra-red Radiation. The natural and most efficient source for infra-red therapy is the sun. Next come the gas-filled tungsten lamps glowing at about 3000 deg K which give off very high radiation energies in the near infra-red. Carbon lamps at lower temperatures and other glowing sources and flames have characteristic radiations with band spectral energy distributions of varying widths and locations; they are in general less efficient than tungsten lamps.

Ultraviolet Radiation

Physiological Action. Ultraviolet radiation (Art. 11) is highly stimulating and seems of utmost importance for organic life; the wavelength range from 300 to 400 mμ constituting the shortest-wavelength part of the daylight spectrum and often referred to as "actinic rays" is of particular practical value. Shorter wavelengths also have decided therapeutic effects on human beings; they are, however, easily absorbed by air so that proper care has to be taken to use non-absorbing materials in the path of the rays. Wavelengths at about 280 mμ are supposed to be injurious to organisms and should be avoided in therapeutic uses. In the range from 200 to 300 mμ ultraviolet radiation is highly germicidal and is used practically for the sterilization of food and water supplies. Ultraviolet therapy is entirely superficial, is absorbed by the skin, and produces the tan or sunburn. It is important to time the exposure to ultraviolet radiation and to increase the exposure gradually from very short intervals to not more than about one-half hour depending on the strength of the source and its spectrum.

Photochemical Actions. Industrially the strongly actinic effects of ultraviolet radiation are utilized in chemical processes of bleaching, vulcanizing, and so on. The more recently found food vitamins which are essential for health and the proper performance of biological functions are influenced by ultraviolet radiation, and their production can be stimulated by short-time irradiations. In particular, vitamin D, known to possess antirachitic qualities, is produced industrially in this way.

Sources of Ultraviolet Radiation. Again the most important source is natural sunlight. Artificial sources are provided by the pure carbon arcs; the blue and white burning arcs have slightly different characteristic line radiations in the ultraviolet region. The most important source for therapeutic uses is, however, the high-pressure mercury-arc lamp which produces very strong line radiations in the near ultraviolet—the most active range; high-power mercury arc lamps use water cooling to reduce the heating effects.

X-radiation

Physiological Action. X-radiation is injurious to most organic tissues but can be utilized, if properly directed, to destroy malignant internal growths as well as to cure skin diseases. It is the most widely used weapon in non-surgical medical treatment. The penetrating power of x-rays depends on the voltage of the x-ray tubes; their destroying action, on the voltage and the time of exposure (dosage). Over-exposure causes very severe burns lasting for a disproportionately long time; great care has to be taken to avoid even slight burns.

Sources of X-rays. The Coolidge vacuum x-ray tube with an applied voltage of 10 to 100 kv is the most commonly used source of x-rays; voltages up to 220 kilovolts are used if particularly high penetration power is desired. For production and properties of x-rays see Art. 14.

Dosage of X-rays. The energy of x-rays can be determined by ionization measurements (see Art. 14). A unit of x-ray energy has been defined from ionization measurements, the *international Roentgen*, which is equal to that quantity of x-radiation which produces in a standardized ionization chamber under normal conditions (0 deg cent and 760 mm Hg) an indication of 1 electrostatic unit of charge. Dosage meters are available which give a visual indication of the ionization produced by the x-rays. With the dosemeter, when inserted in the x-ray apparatus, there is often connected an automatic switch which controls the time of exposure so as to make it independent of human action. On account of the danger of burns, x-ray treatment should never be administered except by properly trained persons.

BIBLIOGRAPHY ON PHYSIOLOGY OF RADIATION

1. BELL, L. Art of Illumination. New York, McGraw-Hill Book Co., 1912.
2. BENFORD, F. E. Visible Radiation from the Low Pressure Mercury Arc. *Soc. M.P.E.*, Vol. 30, pp. 365, 390, 1927.
3. BIGELOW, F. A. Treatise on the Sun's Radiation. New York, John Wiley & Sons, 1918.
4. CADY, F. E., DATES, H. B. Illuminating Engineering. New York, John Wiley & Sons, 1928.
5. CHILD, C. D. Electric Arcs. New York, D. Van Nostrand, 1913.
6. COBB, P. W. Some Experiments on the Speed of Vision. *Trans. Illum. Engg. Soc.*, Vol. 19, p. 150, 1924.
7. Code of Lighting School Buildings. *Trans. Ill. Engg. Soc.*, Vol. 13, p. 185, 1918; Vol. 18, p. 577, 1923.
8. DAHR, N. R. The Chemical Action of Light. London, Blackie & Sons, Limited.
9. DATES, H. B. Practical Applications of the Principles of School Lighting. *Trans. Illum. Engg. Soc.*, Vol. 17, p. 642, 1922.
10. DOBSON, G. M. B., GRIFFITH, I. O., HARRISON, D. N. Photographic Photometry. Oxford University Press, England, 1926.
11. HELMHOLTZ, H. V. Handbuch der physiologischen Optik. (English trans. by J. C. SOUTHALL.) 3 Vols. Banta.
12. HIGBIE, H. H. Lighting Calculations. New York, John Wiley & Sons, 1934.
13. HOUSTOUN, R. A. Vision and Colour Vision. London, Longmans, Green, 1932.
14. HOWELL, W. H. Textbook of Physiology. 11th edition. Philadelphia, Saunders, 1931.
15. HURST, G. M. Handbook of the Theory of Color. New York, D. Van Nostrand.
16. LAURENS, H. Physiological Effects of Radiant Energy. New York, Chemical Catalog Co., 1933.
17. LUCKIESH, M. The Lighting Art. Its Practice and Possibilities. New York, McGraw-Hill Book Co., 1917.
18. LUCKIESH, M. Light and Work. New York, D. Van Nostrand, 1924.
19. LUCKIESH, M. Lighting the Home. New York, Century, 1920.
20. LUCKIESH, M. Artificial Sunlight. New York, D. Van Nostrand, 1930.
21. LUCKIESH, M. Ultra-Violet Radiation. New York, D. Van Nostrand, 1923.
22. LUCKIESH, M., TAYLOR, A. H., SINDEN, R. H. Data Pertaining to Visual Discrimination and Desired Illumination Intensities. *Jour. Franklin Institute*, Vol. 192, p. 757, 1921.
23. MARTIN, L. C. Color Matching by Natural and Artificial Light. *Illuminating Engineering*, Vol. 13, p. 31, 1920.
24. MILLAR, P. S. Illumination Photometers and Their Use. *Trans. Illum. Engg. Soc.*, Vol. 2, p. 546, 1907.
25. MORTON, R. A. Radiation in Chemistry. New York, D. Van Nostrand, 1928.
26. ROSE, E. B., TAYLOR, A. H. The Integrating Sphere. *Trans. Illum. Engg. Soc.*, Vol. II, p. 453, 1916.
27. SCHROEDER, H. History of Incandescent Electric Lamp Manufacture. *Gen. Elec. Rev.*, Vol. 14, p. 426, 1911.
28. SOLOMON, M. Electric Lamps. New York, D. Van Nostrand, 1908.
29. SPOEHR, H. A. Photosynthesis. New York, Chemical Catalog Co., 1926.
30. STOCKS, H. B. Colour. London, Scott, Greenwood & Son, 1916.
31. WALSH, J. W. T. Photometry. London, Constable & Co., Limited, 1926.
32. Yearly Reports of Lamp Committee. *Proc. Nat. Elec. Lamp Assoc.*
33. Yearly Reports on Progress of the Illuminating Engineering Society, *Trans. Illum. Engg. Soc.*

ACOUSTICS

By R. B. Lindsay

19. NATURE OF SOUND

Sound, from the physical point of view, consists of compressional disturbances produced and propagated in solid or fluid media. This includes not only those disturbances which are ultimately (by transmission through the air) audible to the individual but also a large field of disturbances (supersonic, etc.) which are outside the range of audibility and are rendered evident to the senses in other ways, e.g., by touch, etc. The whole field is usually known by the name *acoustics*.

Consider a metal bar which is struck with a hammer. Originally all parts of the bar are at rest with respect to one another; equilibrium exists. The impact of the hammer upsets the equilibrium and squeezes a portion of the bar by producing a relative displacement. (Note that if the bar were rigid it would have to move as a whole—but no material medium is rigid.) The motion of the "squeeze" along the rod constitutes what is called a *compressional wave*. If the rod is in air some of the motion is communicated to the air in its neighborhood and a compressional wave in air results.

The study of acoustics is concerned with the production of such disturbances, their propagation, and their absorption. It must be remembered that the displacements from equilibrium involved here are usually very small. In particular in the case of harmonic or sinusoidal sound waves in air the maximum fractional change in density due to the passage of the waves having the intensity of conversational speech is of the order of 10^{-7} and the maximum corresponding change in pressure (the so-called excess pressure) is about 1 dyne per sq cm. A compressional wave of the same intensity in a metal like platinum at ordinary temperature will correspond to a maximum change in stress of about 370 dynes per sq cm but the corresponding fractional change in density is only of the order of 10^{-10}. The solid is of course much less compressible than the gas. The displacement velocities involved in such displacements are also ordinarily very small, varying from 10^{-2} cm per sec for plane waves in gases to about 10^{-5} cm per sec for similar waves in solids. This velocity, however, must not be confused with the velocity of propagation of the sound wave itself, which may be very large (see Art. 20).

General Properties of Sound Waves. For practical purposes the most important type of wave is the simple harmonic or sinusoidal. A snap-shot picture of a plane wave of this character progressing in the x direction is symbolized in Fig. 1 where a part of such a wave is shown. The ordinate measures the displacement ξ which is being propagated. The maximum ordinate, A, is called the *amplitude* of the wave. A positive maximum is said to correspond to a *crest*, a negative one to a *hollow*. The distance between two successive maxima is the *wavelength*, designated by λ.

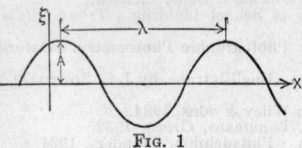

Fig. 1

The wave propagation corresponds to the motion of the whole figure to the right along the x axis with a velocity c. Mathematically such a situation can be symbolized by

$$\xi = A \sin \frac{2\pi}{\lambda}(ct - x) \tag{1}$$

It may be noted that either the sine or the cosine may be used. The number of complete wavelengths which pass a given point per second is the *frequency* of the wave, usually denoted by ν and referred to in cycles or cycles per second. The relation

$$\lambda = \frac{c}{\nu} \tag{2}$$

is fundamental in the theory of harmonic waves. Written in terms of frequency

$$\xi = A \sin (\omega t - kx) \tag{3}$$

in which $\omega = 2\pi\nu$ and $k = \omega/c = 2\pi/\lambda$. This form is often preferred because of its greater simplicity. The quantity $\frac{2\pi}{\lambda}(ct - x) = \omega t - kx$ is called the *phase* of the wave.

Types of Waves. The wave symbolized by equation (1) is called a plane wave because the displacement at a given time and value of x is the same over the whole plane through this point perpendicular to the x axis, or, as is sometimes said, all points in this plane are in the same phase. Using still another common phraseology the *wave front* of the wave is a plane. Another type of wave of great value in acoustics is the *spherical* wave in which the wave fronts are spheres. Such a wave results when a disturbance takes place at a point in a homogeneous medium and spreads in all directions from this point as center with the same velocity. Far away from the source a small portion of the wave front may be considered a plane.

Although sound waves have been considered as compressional waves in a material medium, it is quite possible for other types of elastic waves in solids to give rise to acoustic waves in air. Thus the transverse waves in strings, membranes, plates, and rods are of importance in sound. These will be mentioned later in Art. 26.

The progress of a sound wave in air can be made visible by a method due to Foley. (*Physical Review*, vol. 35, 373, 1912.) The wave sent out by a spark discharge is photographed in the light of another suitably timed spark, the excess density produced by the passage of the wave providing enough change in the refractive index of the air to register on the photographic plate. This method is valuable in the picturization of the reflection, refraction, and diffraction of sound.

20. VELOCITY OF SOUND

The general expression for the velocity of a compressional wave in a deformable medium is

$$c = \sqrt{\frac{dp}{d\rho}} \tag{4}$$

where dp is the change in *pressure* accompanying the change $d\rho$ in *density*. Since the compressions and rarefactions accompanying the propagation of sound through a gas are adiabatic, the relation between pressure p and volume V is the well-known one

pV^{γ} = constant (γ being the ratio (c_p/c_v) of specific heat at constant pressure to that at constant volume), and equation (4) becomes for a gas

$$c = \sqrt{\frac{\gamma p}{\rho}} \tag{5}$$

In the case of air, for example, for $p = 1$ atmosphere $= 1.01 \times 10^6$ dynes per sq cm and $\rho = 0.001205$ gram per cu cm at 20 deg cent and 76 cm of Hg and $\gamma = 1.403$, $c = 344$ meters per sec in good agreement with the experimental value.

The **Velocity of Sound in a Perfect Gas** is independent of the pressure. This is practically true of all real gases, although a slight increase is observed with pressure of the order of 50–100 atmospheres (see International Critical Tables, Vol. VI). The temperature dependence is obtained from equation 5 by the use of the general gas equation, which for a perfect gas is $pV = RT$, T being the absolute temperature and R the gas constant. Thus the velocity at any temperature t degrees centigrade in terms of the velocity at 0 deg cent is given by the formula

$$c_t = c_0\sqrt{1 + t/273} \tag{6}$$

For air in the neighborhood of 0 deg cent and room temperature the increase in c is about 0.61 meter per sec per degree centigrade. The velocity of sound for gases is always lowered slightly by confinement in a tube.

The **Velocity of Sound in Air** depends slightly on the presence of water vapor. Thus for saturated air at 20 deg cent and standard pressure, c is about 0.40 per cent greater than for dry air at the same temperature and pressure.

For velocity of sound in a *liquid* equation (4) takes the form

$$c = \sqrt{\frac{E}{\rho}} = \sqrt{\frac{1}{K\rho}} \tag{7}$$

where E is the bulk modulus or coefficient of volume elasticity, and in the alternative form K is the compressibility. Both E and ρ depend on the temperature and pressure, but since the equation of state of liquids is not known in general form the precise temperature and pressure dependence of c in this case can be described only by empirical formulas relating to specific substances. The velocity of sound in liquids is almost uniformly greater by a factor of several times than the velocity in gases, the one notable exception being hydrogen where c at 0 deg cent is 1270 meters per sec. In general, aqueous solutions have higher c than water.

The **Velocity of Sound in Solids** is given by the formula

$$c = \sqrt{\frac{E + 4\mu/3}{\rho}} \tag{8}$$

in which μ is the *shear* modulus or *rigidity* of the solid. For the case of compressional waves in long narrow rods equation (8) must be replaced by

$$c = \sqrt{\frac{Y}{\rho}} \tag{9}$$

Y being Young's modulus. For a large number of solids the former velocity is greater than the latter by roughly 10 per cent. It is interesting to note that the velocity of transverse waves (i.e., flexural or torsional) in a solid is given by $c = \sqrt{\mu/\rho}$, which is less than the value from equation 8 for any given solid under the same conditions. In general the velocity in metallic solids exceeds that in non-metallic solids, although glass, marble, and some varieties of wood are decided exceptions. In the latter case the velocity naturally depends considerably on the relation of the direction of the sound propagation with respect to the grain of the wood. Few data are available on the direct measurement of the velocity of sound in crystals, metallic or otherwise.

Change of Velocity with Frequency. Equation (4) would indicate that the velocity of sound is independent of the frequency. This is found to be approximately true for sound in gases. Pierce * found, however, that the velocity of sound in air at 0 deg cent varies from 332.45 m per sec at 41,009 cycles per sec to 331.64 m per sec at 1,479,900 cycles per sec. This is for entirely unconfined air. The velocity of sound in liquids is slightly dependent on the frequency but the change is small, that in water being a decrease of only 5 per cent as the frequency ranges from 40,000 cycles to 600,000 cycles. The variation with frequency of sound velocity in solids has not yet been studied thoroughly enough to state conclusive results.

---

* *Proc. Am. Acad. Arts and Sci.*, vol. 60, p. 271, 1925.

When gases and liquids are confined in tubes the decrease in velocity due to viscosity may be considerable. This is also a function of the frequency, the change here growing smaller as the frequency increases (see Art. 24).

Since a sound wave is propagated through a material medium, the sound velocity depends on the large-scale motion of the medium. Hence in the free atmosphere the velocity is considerably affected by wind currents.

Wave Length of Sound Waves. A harmonic wave with frequency 256 cycles per sec has a wavelength in air at 20 deg cent of 1.34 meters. In water at the same temperature the wavelength is 5.70 meters, and in a brass *rod*, 13.7 meters. The influence of the change in velocity with the nature of the medium is evident.

Doppler Effect. When a source of sound moves relatively to an observer, a phenomenon occurs which is known as the *Doppler effect*. Consider a stationary observer at B, Fig. 2 (i.e., stationary with respect to the air), with the sound source at A emitting waves of frequency ν moving towards him with velocity v which is assumed less than c, the velocity of sound in a stationary medium. Since the frequency of the source is ν, this is the number of waves sent out in 1 sec while the source is moving from A to C. These waves will strike the ear of the observer within $1 - v/c$ seconds. Consequently the frequency of the sound as he will observe it is not ν, but

$$\nu' = \frac{\nu}{1 - v/c} \tag{10}$$

Otherwise expressed, there is an apparent increase in the pitch. This is easily observed when a train with whistle blowing approaches one, and is even more commonly noted with approaching automobiles.

When the source recedes from the observer, fewer waves are received per second and the apparent frequency, ν'', is lower than the true frequency. Then

$$\nu'' = \frac{\nu}{1 + v/c} \tag{11}$$

The situation is similar though not identical when a moving observer approaches or recedes from a stationary source. Here the observer, so to speak, goes to meet or runs away from the waves, respectively. Analysis shows the relations between apparent and true frequencies, for approach and recession, respectively, to be:

$$\nu' = \nu(1 + v/c) \tag{12}$$

$$\nu'' = \nu(1 - v/c) \tag{13}$$

The velocity v may be larger than c, resulting in the " bow " wave, characteristic, for example, of the flight of a rifle bullet through the air.

21. REFLECTION AND REFRACTION

The concept of an acoustic wave traveling forward steadily in one direction or spreading outward from a single source is a highly idealized one. Actually all acoustic waves move in bounded media and wherever boundaries are encountered the phenomena of reflection and refraction occur resulting in more or less complicated wave patterns.

Reflection. As a simple illustration, suppose that a plane wave of sound progressing to the right meets a rigid wall parallel to the wave front. Reflection takes place, i.e., the space to the left of the wall is now occupied by a wave moving toward the left as well as the original wave moving toward the right. Symbolically the disturbance may be represented by

$$\xi = A \sin (\omega t - kx) + B \sin (\omega t + kx + \varepsilon) \tag{14}$$

where the term with the plus sign before the kx represents the reflected wave, A and B are the amplitudes of the two waves respectively, and ε is the phase change that accompanies reflection. ε can be shown to be zero when a plane wave of sound is reflected in going from an acoustically rare to an acoustically dense medium, from air to a rigid wall, for example. When the sound is reflected in going from a dense to a rare medium, e.g., water to air, the change of phase is π. It is to be understood in this result that the positive direction of particle displacement is always in the direction in which the wave is being propagated.

The Acoustic Density is measured by the product of the ordinary density and the velocity of sound in the medium. This quantity is called in technical acoustics the *specific acoustic resistance* * for a plane wave (see Arts. 23 and 33).

---

* See bibliography, page 9-54, references 8, 10, and 13.

Echo. When sound in air is reflected from a large wall or barrier the result is known as an *echo.* This will be recognized as a distinct sound if the reflecting surface is sufficiently far away from the observer so that the original sound has died down by the time the reflected wave reaches him.

Reverberation. If a multitude of echoes follow on each other at very short time intervals the result is known as *reverberation.* This is observed in large closed spaces and if the walls and other objects in the room are not sufficiently absorbing can constitute a serious impediment to hearing in halls (see Art. 32).

Reflecting Surfaces and Media. If the surface dimensions are large compared with the wavelength of the sound, the incident plane wave beam will be reflected approximately as such; but if the dimensions are small compared with the wavelength the reflected sound will be scattered in all directions. In the former case the sound that might be scattered outside the beam is nullified by the interference of the reflected waves (i.e., the cancelation of the crest of one wave by the hollow of another) from various parts of the reflector. This interference is no longer materially operative when the reflector is small. It thus turns out that plane reflectors exercise a selective action.

Sound waves can also be reflected in other types of mirrors, e.g., parabolic, in which if a point source of sound is placed at the focus the reflected sound will consist largely of plane waves with wave front normal to the axis of the mirror. Owing to the relatively large wavelength of audible sound in air the focusing of sound in such a mirror is not very precise. The situation is even worse in liquids.

Reflection occurs not only when a sound wave encounters the boundary between two media but also when sound passing down a tube meets an abrupt change in area. The fractional sound energy (see Art. 27) reflected compared with the incident energy can be readily computed * and turns out to be

$$\left(\frac{S_1 - S_2}{S_1 + S_2}\right)^2 \tag{15}$$

where S_1 and S_2 are the two areas of cross-section in question. It is usually assumed for elementary purposes (Art. 26) that when a plane wave of sound passing through a tube is incident on the open end, the reflection is complete. This of course is not entirely true since some radiation takes place.

Oblique Reflection. The discussion of reflection so far has been confined to the case where the incident sound wave front is parallel to the reflecting surface. In unconfined regions, of course, oblique incidence is more common. Reflection then follows the optical law: *the angle of reflection equals the angle of incidence.* The ratio of the sound energy per square centimeter per second reflected to that incident is *

$$\left(\frac{\rho_2/\rho_1 - \cot\theta_2/\cot\theta_1}{\rho_2/\rho_1 + \cot\theta_2/\cot\theta_1}\right)^2 \tag{16}$$

where ρ_1 and ρ_2 are the mean densities of the two media respectively at the boundary of which the reflection takes place, and θ_1 and θ_2 are the angles of incidence and refraction respectively.

Refraction. With oblique incidence there also occurs transmission into the second medium accompanied by bending of the wave front, i.e., *refraction.* The law of refraction is the same as that of Snell in optics, namely,

$$\frac{\sin\theta_1}{\sin\theta_2} = \frac{c_1}{c_2} \tag{17}$$

Very good illustrations of the refraction of sound are provided by transmission through the atmosphere in which a temperature gradient and winds exist. A wave traveling from a region of high temperature to one of low temperature has its front bent toward the normal. Actually there are usually no sharp boundaries and the bending is a more or less continuous process. The increased range of sound in still air when the temperature gradient is negative, i.e., cold air near the ground and warmer air higher up, is to a considerable extent accounted for by this refraction. Acoustic mirages have the same source. Refraction also takes place when sound passes through a region where the wind velocity is changing from place to place. This is called convective refraction, and it is well to note that the wave front is then no longer normal to the *ray* as it is in a stationary medium.

Reflection and refraction play a considerable rôle in the scattering of sound in the atmosphere, which is found in general to be greater for high frequencies than for low.

---

* See bibliography, page 9-54, reference 13.

22. DIFFRACTION

Effect of Rigid Obstacles.   When sound in passing through a medium encounters a more or less rigid obstacle in addition to reflection and refraction there results *diffraction*, i.e., the *bending* of the sound waves around the obstacle.   Here the situation is precisely analogous to the behavior of light waves in passing the edge of an obstacle.   Acoustical diffraction accounts for our ability to hear sound around a corner and at the same time for the difficulty of producing sharp acoustic shadows with ordinary audible sounds; the sound waves with their greater length are able to bend more than the very much shorter light waves.   The reception of sound by the individual auditor is largely conditioned by the diffraction caused by the human head.   A careful study has been made of this, for the effect both on speech and on hearing.   It is found,* for example, that for a point source on a rigid sphere there are two directions of maximum intensity, one directly in front of the source and the other directly behind the sphere, the latter intensity being naturally the smaller of the two.   The intensity falls to a minimum in a direction approximately at right angles to that of maximum intensity.   The angle increases with increasing frequency of sound and the magnitude of the minimum intensity decreases as the frequency increases, i.e., short-wavelength sounds do not so readily bend around the spherical obstacle.   For a given frequency the variation in intensity around the obstacle is greater near than far from the sphere.

A similar discussion can be given for a sphere having two sound receivers on the opposite ends of a diameter (e.g., the head with the two ears).   It turns out that the intensity of an outside source of sound at the sphere is greatest when the line joining the two receivers is directed toward the source and least when the line is perpendicular to the source direction.   Here again for given source distance the difference is more marked for short waves than for long and for a given wavelength more marked at short distances than long.

These results have an immediate application in respect to the human head and to sound-receiving instruments like microphones for mapping the distribution of sound intensity in a room.   The diffraction of sound due to the presence of such instruments can thus be compensated for theoretically.

Scattering.   The special phenomenon of diffraction by an obstacle of dimensions much smaller than the wavelength is known as *Rayleigh scattering*.   Here the sound is scattered in all directions and its intensity varies inversely as the fourth power of the wavelength, analogously to light scattering.   "Harmonic" echoes are due to this type of scattering. When a compound musical note is sounded near a group of obstacles like a grove of trees the intensity of the octave is raised above that of the fundamental by the scattering.

When sound emerges from an opening, diffraction produces in general a scattering in all directions.   If the frequency is very high this effect is much reduced and a more or less sharp beam of sound results.   This suggests the use of supersonic waves in signaling (see Art. 29).

Diffraction is also important in the use of baffle plates in some loud speakers.   The actual calculation of the diffracting effect of such plates is extremely complicated.

23. INTENSITY OF SOUND

Definition.   The propagation of sound waves involves the transfer of energy, and it is this idea which is expressed in the concept of acoustic intensity, which is the *average* rate of flow of energy per unit area normal to the direction of propagation.   Care must be taken to distinguish between intensity and loudness.   The former is a purely physical quantity, whereas the latter is a physico-psychological one.   We shall discuss it further below.   At the moment consider merely the intensity.   It can be shown that the intensity I of a plane or spherical wave (the two predominant types) is given most simply by the formula

$$I = \frac{1}{2}\frac{p^2_{max}}{\rho_0 c} \tag{18}$$

where p_{max} = maximum excess pressure, ρ_0 = average density, and c = velocity of the wave.   The quantity $\rho_0 c$ is the *specific acoustic resistance* of a plane wave.   For a given p_{max}, a large acoustic resistance means a small intensity, and vice versa.   This has considerable bearing on all acoustic transmission problems, e.g., sound proofing and reduction of noise (see Art. 33).

For a sound wave in air at 20 deg cent and 76 cm of Hg the intensity of ordinary conversational speech (with $p_{max} = 1$ dyne per cm^2) is approximately 1.21×10^{-9} watt per

---

* See bibliography, page 9-54, reference 13.

$cm^2 = 1.21 \times 10^{-3}$ microwatt per cm^2. Interestingly enough it develops that the ear is sensitive to sounds of intensity as low as 4×10^{-10} microwatt per cm^2. It should be noted that the frequency does not enter (18) explicitly. On the other hand, if the intensity is expressed in terms of displacement amplitude instead of pressure, the frequency ν is necessarily involved, equation (18) being replaced by

$$I = {}^1/_2\, \rho_0\, c\omega^2\, \xi^2_{max} \tag{19}$$

with ξ_{max} = maximum displacement and $\omega = 2\pi\nu$. For constant amplitude the intensity thus varies as the square of the frequency. Hence for supersonic waves of reasonable amplitude the intensity can become relatively very large; e.g., for $\nu = 500{,}000$ cycles per sec in air and $\xi_{max} = 10^{-4}$ cm, $I = 2.07 \times 10^5$ microwatts per cm^2. For acoustic instruments which record pressure changes, equation (18) is the more useful one. For others, equation (19) is employed.

The Measurement of Intensity in absolute units is now largely replaced by the logarithmic unit, the *bel*, which is of particular advantage in denoting the relative levels of intensity of several sounds. The difference in intensity of two sounds whose absolute intensities are I_1 and I_2 respectively is α bels, where

$$\alpha = \log_{10} I_2/I_1 \tag{20}$$

More commonly the *decibel* (*db*), which is one-tenth of a bel, is used. To illustrate, if one calls an average excess pressure of 1 dyne per cm^2 (strictly this is the root-mean-square value which $= 0.707\, p_{max}$) the normal level for ordinary speech, the threshold of audibility has a minimum lying about 70 db below this level, and the threshold of feeling (i.e., where hearing is painful) has a maximum lying about 70 db above this level. We may think of audible sound therefore as lying in a maximum range of some 140 db.*

24. INFLUENCE OF THE MEDIUM ON THE PROPAGATION OF SOUND

Spherical Waves. From a point source, sound spreads in a perfectly homogeneous medium in the form of a spherical wave, the mathematical expression for the displacement in a harmonic wave of this kind being

$$\xi = \frac{A}{r} \sin(\omega t - kr) \tag{21}$$

From equation (19) it is seen that the intensity of such a wave is given by the expression

$$I_s = {}^1/_2\, \rho_0\, c\omega^2\, A^2/r^2 \tag{22}$$

i.e., the intensity falls off inversely as the square of the distance from the source. This is in contrast to a plane wave (see equation 3), for which the intensity is independent of distance. The diminution of intensity of a spherical wave is a purely geometrical phenomenon—as the wave spreads in all directions, the same amount of energy at any instant flows across spheres of larger radii, whose surfaces increase as the square of the radii. In addition to this geometrical decrease in intensity with distance all material media act to dissipate acoustic energy and so decrease intensity by absorption.

Causes of Sound Absorption in Fluid Media

Viscosity acts to retard the relative motion of adjacent layers of the medium, and so adds a damping force to the elastic restoring force normally present. The effect is to produce an exponential decrease in displacement amplitude with distance; i.e., the amplitude A must be multiplied by $e^{-\alpha r}$ where e is the Naperian base $(= 2.71828\ldots)$ and $\alpha = {}^2/_3\, \mu\omega^2/\rho_0\, c^3$. μ, the coefficient of viscosity for air at 20 deg cent, is approximately 18×10^{-5} gram per cm per sec and for water at 20 deg cent is 10^{-2} gram per cm per sec. It will be observed that the damping coefficient increases with the square of the frequency. For $\omega = 1000$ in air, $\alpha = 0.24 \times 10^{-8}$; i.e., a wave in air could proceed a distance of about 4000 km without having its amplitude reduced to more than $1/e$ as far as viscosity is concerned. This is a very slight effect and hardly observable except at high frequencies. The effect is much more marked when the medium is confined as in a tube, for here the fluid tends to stick to the walls. For a tube whose diameter is large compared with

$\sqrt{8\pi^2\, \mu/\rho_0\, \omega}$ the theory † again indicates exponential damping with $\alpha = \dfrac{1}{ac}\sqrt{\dfrac{\omega\mu}{2\rho_0}}$, where a = radius of the tube. For a tube of radius 1 cm and $\omega = 1000$, $\alpha = 2.5 \times 10^{-4}$ for air at 20 deg cent. Associated with the absorption is a decrease in the velocity of sound

---

* See bibliography, page 9-54, reference 19.
† See bibliography, page 9-54, references 9 and 13.

which in the instance just cited is theoretically 0.86 per cent. Actually both the absorption and the decrease in velocity depend on the material of the confining tube and are greater in practice than the theory predicts.

For capillary tubes, i.e., where $a << \sqrt{8\pi^2 \, \mu/\rho_0 \, \omega}$, the viscous absorption is naturally very much greater, the value of α being $\dfrac{2}{a} \sqrt{\dfrac{\omega\mu}{p_0}}$, where p_0 is the average value of the fluid pressure in the tube. Here the waves are very rapidly damped out, with α having, for moderate frequencies, values in the neighborhood of 10 to 100. This accounts for the large absorption of sound in carpets and other materials with small interstices.*

The effect of viscosity is enhanced by the conduction by the vibrating gas or liquid of the heat produced during the compressions accompanying the passage of the wave. The order of magnitude here is the same as that involved in viscosity damping.

Changes in Physical Properties. In the actual propagation of sound through such media as the atmosphere and the sea the numerous changes in the physical properties of the medium due to temperature, etc., produce by reflection, refraction, and diffraction a damping of a directed beam which is much more pronounced than that due to either of the causes just mentioned.

Recently it has been found by Knudsen † that the absorption of sound in air depends on temperature and humidity in a characteristic manner. Thus the absorption coefficient per centimeter (α) for air at 20 deg cent and for a frequency of 1500 cycles per sec has a maximum value of 10^{-4} at a relative humidity of 10 per cent. For a frequency of 10,000 cycles per sec the maximum is about 6.5×10^{-4} and occurs at a relative humidity of about 18 per cent. These figures are of course much larger than those theoretically predicted on the basis of viscosity absorption. It has been established that this absorption is due almost entirely to the energy transfers between the oxygen molecules of the air. This opens up a new field for the study of sound absorption.

25. VIBRATING SYSTEMS AS SOURCES OF SOUND

Free Oscillations. Most vibrating systems do not oscillate as a whole but are the seat of more or less complicated wave patterns. For the sake of simplicity, however, it is often convenient to think of such bodies as if they moved as a whole. Thus a membrane in which the amplitude at the center is greater than that elsewhere may often conveniently be assumed to oscillate like a piston moving to and fro. The same is true of the air in the opening of a Helmholtz resonator.

The vibration of a body conceived from this point of view is governed by what may be called its "elements," viz., its *inertia* (measured by *mass*), *stiffness* (elastic restoring factor), and *dissipative resistance* (damping factor). The *stiffness* is defined analytically as the restoring force per unit displacement; the *resistance* is the damping force per unit velocity. These are the analogs of inductance, capacitance (strictly reciprocal of capacitance), and resistance, respectively, in an oscillating electric circuit. A knowledge of these elements is sufficient to describe completely the behavior of the system if disturbed from equilibrium and thereafter left to itself. Under such circumstances the system is said to be *free*.

Let m denote the mass, f the stiffness, and R the damping factor of the system. It turns out that a disturbance from equilibrium will lead to oscillations if and only if ‡

$$R^2/4m^2 < f/m \tag{23}$$

and the frequency of the oscillation is

$$\nu_f = \frac{1}{2\pi} \sqrt{\frac{f}{m} - \frac{R^2}{4m^2}} \tag{24}$$

If the damping factor is small enough so that the left side of the inequality (23) is very much smaller than the right, the free or natural frequency is approximately

$$\frac{1}{2\pi} \sqrt{\frac{f}{m}} \tag{25}$$

As an illustration consider a membrane (e.g., a telephone diaphragm) which when replaced by an equivalent piston has

$$m = 0.50 \text{ gram}, \qquad f = 2.5 \times 10^7 \text{ dynes per cm}$$

$$R = 250 \text{ dyne sec per cm}$$

Then $R^2/4m^2 = 6.25 \times 10^4 \text{ sec}^{-2}$, while $f/m = 5 \times 10^7 \text{ sec}^{-2}$, so that in equation (24)

---

* See bibliography, page 9-54, references 9 and 13.
† *J. Acous. Soc. Am.*, vol. 6, p. 199, 1935; *Science*, vol. 81, p. 578, 1935.
‡ See bibliography, page 9-54, references 7, 9, and 11.

ν_f = 1124.6 vibrations per sec whereas equation 25 gives 1125.4 vibrations per sec, the difference being negligible for most practical purposes.

Although the effect of the damping on the frequency is very small, the amplitude of the harmonic oscillation dies away exponentially; i.e., the displacement ξ may be written

$$\xi = Ae^{-(R/2m)\cdot t}\cos(2\pi\nu_f t + B) \tag{26}$$

where A = initial amplitude and B = initial phase. The amplitude decreases to A/e = 0.37 A in the time $t' = 2m/R$, which in the above illustration is $1/250$ sec. All free physical oscillations are damped, the damping arising from a variety of factors, such as internal viscosity of the vibrator, viscosity of the medium, or energy communicated to the medium by the vibrator and carried away in the form of radiation.

Forced Oscillations. More interesting and important than free oscillations are those imposed on the system by an external harmonic force, e.g., the fluctuating magnetic field in the telephone diaphragm. If the frequency of the force is $\nu = \omega/2\pi$ and its amplitude is F_0, the displacement is *

$$\xi = F_0/\omega Z \cdot \cos(\omega t - \alpha) \tag{27}$$

where $Z = \sqrt{(m\omega - f/\omega)^2 + R^2}$, and is defined as the *mechanical impedance* of the system (cf. analogy to electrical impedance). The quantity α is the phase difference between the force and displacement and equals $\tan^{-1}\dfrac{R}{m\omega - f/\omega}$. The displacement velocity is usually more important. Denoting this by $\dot{\xi}$ we have

$$\dot{\xi} = F_0/Z \cdot \cos(\omega t - \beta) \tag{28}$$

where $\beta = \tan^{-1}\dfrac{m\omega - f/\omega}{R}$ = phase difference between force and velocity ($\alpha + \beta = 90°$). It is seen that the magnitude of both ξ and $\dot{\xi}$ depends on the impedance; a large impedance, other things being equal, corresponds to a small displacement, and vice versa (cf. the alternating-current analogy: current = emf ÷ impedance).

The impedance is a minimum for $\nu = \dfrac{\omega}{2\pi} = \dfrac{1}{2\pi}\sqrt{\dfrac{f}{m}}$. This is called the *resonance frequency.* For systems with small damping it coincides effectively with the free oscillation frequency. Physically this means that a system will vibrate most vigorously if subjected to a harmonic force with frequency equal to its own natural frequency. At resonance the force contributes energy to the system at maximum average rate and the system itself dissipates energy at an equal rate: if a vibrating tuning-fork is held over the open end of an air column in resonance with the fork, the air in the tube vibrates vigorously and the note is much reinforced; at the same time the fork more rapidly uses up its original store of energy and comes to rest sooner than it otherwise would. Examples of resonance are at hand throughout acoustical phenomena, as well as in vibration phenomena in general.

The damping exercises an important influence on resonance; if the damping factor is small the response of the system at resonance is great but the tuning is sharp; that is, the response drops rapidly as the frequency of the force is altered from the resonance frequency. On the other hand, large damping leads to a smaller resonance response but a broader peak and more diffuse tuning. The same effect is well known in electrical oscillating circuits.

A good illustration of such a vibrating system as we have been considering is a Helmholtz resonator which consists of an enclosure usually but not necessarily spherical in shape communicating with the outside by means of a small orifice. The mass of the system is the mass of the air in the opening which vibrates under external influence against the air cushion provided by the air in the enclosure or resonator chamber, the latter supplying the stiffness of the system. The damping comes mainly from the radiation of sound into the surrounding medium. The resonance frequency is †

$$\nu = \frac{1}{2\pi} c \sqrt{\frac{c_0}{V}} \tag{29}$$

in which c = velocity of sound in air, V = volume of the resonator chamber, and c_0 = a quantity with dimensions of length called the conductivity of the opening. It is rather difficult to compute but is of the order of magnitude of the diameter of the orifice. Resonators have many practical uses, among them being the construction of sensitive sound detectors and instruments for the measurement of sound intensity (see Art. 34).

---

* See bibliography, page 9-54, references 7, 9, 11, and 13.
† See bibliography, page 9-54, references 7 and 13.

26. SPECIAL VIBRATING SYSTEMS

Vibration of Strings. If a string with line density (mass per unit length) ρ and stretched with tension τ is pulled aside from its equilibrium position and let go, a *transverse* wave travels along the string with velocity *

$$v = \sqrt{\frac{\tau}{\rho}} \tag{30}$$

If the string is of finite length l and is fastened at both ends so that no motion is possible there, it turns out that the string is the seat of waves in both directions which combine to form standing waves of only certain frequencies, viz.,

$$\nu = \frac{n}{2l} \sqrt{\frac{\tau}{\rho}} \tag{31}$$

where n is *any* integer. These allowed values of ν are the *characteristic* or *natural* frequencies of the stretched string. $n = 1$ corresponds to the fundamental, and $n = 2, 3, 4$ ... to the successive harmonics or overtones. By the imposition of a harmonic force the string can, of course, be forced to vibrate with any frequency, but *resonance* (Art. 25) ensues when the frequency of the force coincides with one of the set (equation 31). When a string vibrates with one of its characteristic frequencies, it is said to be in a character'stic mode of oscillation. Each mode is also characterized by the presence of certain points where no motion ever takes place: these are the so-called nodal points or *nodes* in distinction to the places of maximum disturbance or *loops*. Fig. 3 indicates the first three characteristic modes of vibration of a stretched string. The full line in each sketch represents the undisturbed position of the string; the dotted and dashed lines represent the extreme

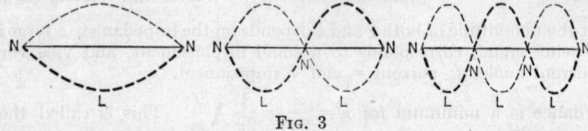

Fig. 3

positions assumed by the string. Nodes and loops are indicated by N and L respectively. Of course the ends are, strictly speaking, nodes by virtue of the fastening. Obviously the distance between successive nodes is one-half wavelength (see equation 2 in connection with equation 31).

String Instruments. The most important acoustical application of the vibration of strings occurs in musical instruments. Here strings may be vibrated by plucking (harp), by bowing (violin), or by striking with a hammer (piano). If a string is plucked at one of its possible nodes, the corresponding harmonic or harmonics wiii be absent. This is known as Young's law: thus plucking at the center removes all harmonics of even order. In any event the higher harmonics are relatively weak in the plucked string. The theory of the struck string has not been completely worked out. Much depends on the precise manner and duration of the blow. But Young's law is again true and is utilized to minimize the harmonics above the sixth. The same is true of the bowing of the violin string. No matter how a string is excited, much of the effect depends on the presence of resonating surfaces and air spaces.

The Vibrations of Air Columns (e.g., organ pipes) are mathematically quite analogous to those of strings. Here, to be sure, the characteristic frequencies depend on whether both ends of the tube are open or only one. If both ends are open the natural frequencies * are $\frac{nc}{2l}$ (c = velocity of sound in air); if only one end is open they are $\frac{(2n+1)c}{4l}$. The difference comes from the fact that the wave pattern must have a node at the closed end of the tube while it has a loop at the open end. The values cited are not quite correct, for radiation from the open end has been neglected. To take account of this the length, l, in the formula must be slightly increased.

Quality. It is the combination of harmonics in the vibration which gives the sound radiation from such a system its characteristic *quality* (see Art. 31 on the analysis of musical sounds); it is this which distinguishes sounds of essentially the same frequency or pitch produced by different systems (e.g., violin and flute).

Membranes and Diaphragms. For the practical production of sound, circular membranes and diaphragms are of the utmost importance. A membrane is supposed to be

---

* See bibliography, page 9-54, references 9 and 11.

perfectly flexible, i.e., to possess no rigidity, and many of the diaphragms used in sound generators more nearly approximate plates. The mathematical details in either instance are too difficult to give here. A circular membrane of radius a clamped around the periphery has a very complicated set of characteristic frequencies. The simplest of these correspond to vibrations symmetrical about the center and have frequencies given approximately by

$$0.77 \frac{c}{2a}, \quad 1.76 \frac{c}{2a}, \quad 2.76 \frac{c}{2a} \tag{32}$$

where c = velocity of flexural waves in the membrane = $\sqrt{\tau/\rho}$, in which τ = superficial tension or force per unit length in the membrane and ρ = mass per unit area. It will be noted that the harmonics bear no integral multiple relationship to one another, differing thus from the harmonics of the string and air column. Corresponding to the nodal points of these systems, the membrane has a set of nodal lines which in symmetrical vibrations are concentric circles. In the higher modes of vibration there also exist nodal diameters. The situation for vibrating plates is even more involved and the wave patterns more complicated, although the characteristic frequencies have been computed in special instances. As has been intimated in Art. 25, the tendency in practical work is to operate with the equivalent piston vibrator.

Energy Radiation. In practical acoustics an important feature of vibrating systems is the rate of energy radiation into the surrounding medium, and in particular the efficiency of the system as a radiator, viz., the ratio of the radiation output to the input. It can be shown that the average rate of radiation of frequency $\omega/2\pi$ from one side of a diaphragm into a semi-infinite medium of density ρ is

$$\frac{1}{4} \pi\rho \frac{\omega^2}{c} a^4 \dot{\xi}_0^2 \tag{33}$$

where a is the radius of the *equivalent piston* and $\dot{\xi}_0$ is the maximum displacement velocity. Here c is the velocity of sound in the medium. The efficiency of telephone diaphragms is rather low except at the resonance frequencies. The Fessenden oscillator * for under-water sound signaling has, however, an efficiency as high as 50 per cent at an output of 500 watts. The output of all sources is very largely conditioned by the type of acoustic coupling used: a diaphragm placed in the throat of a horn will have a larger output for the characteristic frequencies of the horn, since the resonance principle comes into play.

27. TRANSMISSION THROUGH TUBES

Many important acoustic problems involve the transmission of sound through tubes; for example, speaking tubes, horns for the production and amplification of sound as well as for its reception, stethoscopes, special types of acoustic filters, and apparatus for the measurement of acoustical intensity and impedance.

Effect of Length. If a plane sound wave produced by a diaphragm or other source is led into a cylindrical tube, the wave form will depend in the first place on the length of the tube. If the tube is short, the reflected wave from the end of the tube away from the source will combine with the direct wave to form a more or less complicated pattern; if the tube is very long the reflected wave may be largely damped out and a wave traveling effectively in one direction results.

Change in Cross-section. Consider a wave traveling in one direction and note what happens to it when the size of the tube is altered.* At A, in Fig. 4a, the wave coming

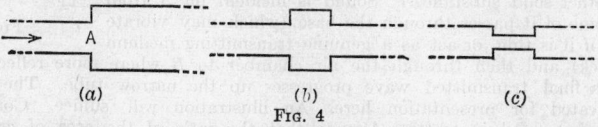

(a)   (b)   (c)

Fig. 4

from the left encounters an abrupt increase in cross-section. In Art. 21 it was noted that reflection ensues so that to the left of A there are waves in both directions. The wave that goes across A is therefore weakened in intensity and indeed by an amount which depends on the ratio of the cross-sections (formula 15). The ratio of the total energy flow (watts) in the transmitted wave to the right of the boundary to that in the incident wave may be called the power transmission ratio and will be denoted by P_r. There is no change in phase of the transmitted wave. Incidentally P_r is the same in either direction.

* See bibliography, page 9-54, reference 13.

The loss in intensity can be very much mitigated by the use of a connector joining the two tubes so as to make the change in dimensions less abrupt; the longer the connector the greater is P_r.

In Fig. 4b, again, a plane wave coming from the left meets an expansion of finite length which joins the main line. In Fig. 4c the analogous case of a constriction is illustrated. Calculation and experiment indicate that P_r in both examples is a function of the frequency, being fairly close to unity for low frequencies but becoming very small for a considerable range of high frequencies, then rising and falling again in a series of alternate peaks and hollows, as in Fig. 5. Such a structure is said to be *selective*. Change in phase of the transmitted wave is also involved. This has important application to the pinching of a sound tube in order to control intensity.

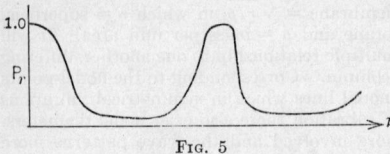

FIG. 5

Orifices or Side Openings. Another important case of transmission is that through a tube containing one or more orifices in the side. The physical effect of the openings is to cut down the transmission by producing reflection due to the inertia of the air in the orifices; each one is a boundary between the confined air in the tube and the much larger mass of unconfined air outside. Of course there is some actual radiation of sound from the openings, but contrary to what might at first be supposed this is less than the inertia effect. Viscous damping in the openings also plays an insignificant rôle unless they are very narrow. Calculation and experiment indicate that P_r is small for low frequencies and rises as the frequency increases. If more than one hole is used, as their number (they are assumed to be evenly spaced) increases, P_r for low frequency decreases until finally no sound passes through the tube up to a certain frequency: it acts as a high-frequency-pass acoustic filter (see the schematic diagram in Fig. 6a.*)

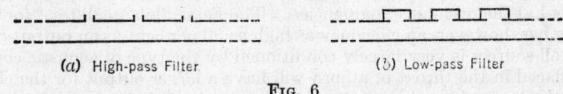

(a) High-pass Filter   (b) Low-pass Filter

FIG. 6

It is seen that all the transmission problems discussed so far in this section involve acoustic filtration to a certain extent. The same is true of a Helmholtz resonator placed over an orifice in the side of a tube. Here, as might be expected, P_r is reduced materially only in the neighborhood of the resonance frequency of the resonator. If, however, one attaches a whole series of resonators to evenly spaced openings (Fig. 6b), the resulting structure is found to act as a low-pass filter: i.e., P_r is different from zero up to a certain frequency dependent on the dimensions of the various parts; it then falls to zero and stays so for a considerable frequency interval. It then rises again and transmission and attenuation bands succeed each other in a way which can be predicted theoretically. The use of more elaborate side branch attachments permits the construction of filters having transmission bands at any desired frequency and of any desired frequency range.

The Stethoscope. Another important instrument which is essentially an acoustic filter is one form of the stethoscope (see Fig. 7) consisting of a thin air chamber with a broad base of hard rubber or other solid substance.† Sound is incident on A from the left; some of it passes through the base (which may vibrate as a whole if it is thin, or act as a genuine transmitting medium if it is thick) and then through the air chamber to B where more reflection takes place and a final transmitted wave progresses up the narrow tube. The theory is too complicated for presentation here. An illustration will suffice. Consider the stethoscope immersed in water. Assume that the ratio of the area of cross-section at A to that at $B = 225$ and that the thickness of the chamber is 0.3 mm; then at $\nu = 750$ cycles per sec $P_r = 0.13$. This contrasts with $P_r = 0.0012$ for the ordinary power transmission ratio going directly from water to air without change in tube cross-section. It must be emphasized that this type of stethoscope is highly selective. For medical purposes, small conical horns are now being used extensively (see Art. 28).

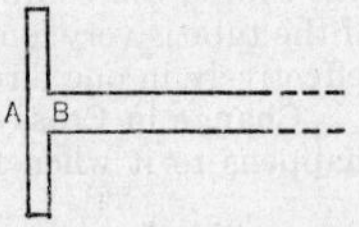

FIG. 7

---

* See bibliography, page 9-54, references 8, 10, and 13.
† See bibliography, page 9-54, reference 13.

28. HORNS

The horn occupies a significant place in the discussion of acoustic transmission.*
Strictly speaking, any tube of finite length may be a horn. However, it is usual to restrict
the term to tubes of varying cross-section.

The Principal Types are shown diagrammatically in Fig. 8, where (a) represents a
conical horn in which the area of cross-section $S = S_0 x^2$ (x denoting the coordinate distance along the horn axis
from some chosen origin and
S_0 the cross-sectional area
for unit x); (b) represents
an *exponential* horn with
$S = S_0 e^{mx}$, where m is a
parameter governing the
flare (this horn has the
property that the area S is the

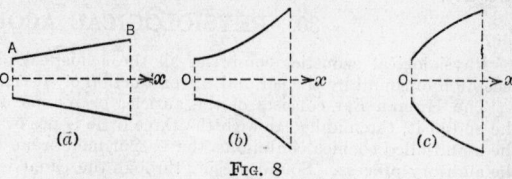

FIG. 8

geometric mean of the areas at the same distance on either side of S); (c) represents a
parabolic horn in which $S = S_0 x$. There are other types of flaring horns but their
properties are very similar to the exponential variety.

The Horn as a Receiver of Sound. If the horn were not there, little difference in the
intensity of the sound would be noted at the points A and B. However, with the horn
in place, and sound directed toward the large end, there is considerable increase in the intensity at the throat (i.e., the small end) over the intensity at B with no horn present. The
ratio of these intensities is the *intensity amplification* (I.A.) of the horn and a measure of
the horn's utility as a receiver. The mathematical theory by which this quantity is computed is complicated, and it must be made clear that the qualitative idea of the horn's
"concentrating" the sound by reflection from the walls, etc., is quite inadequate except
at high frequencies. The action of a horn like that of any air column is mainly dependent
on *resonance* characteristics. This is clearly shown in the fact that when I.A. for a conical
horn, for example, is plotted as a function of frequency, it shows a number of peaks and
hollows, the peaks corresponding to the resonance frequencies of the horn considered as a
vibrating air column.

This selectivity is most marked in the conical horn. The parabolic horn gives a much
more uniform response and is being widely used in connection with sound-motion pictures.
The exponential horn, other things being equal, gives the largest I.A. and is often used in
loud-speaker units for public-address systems.

The Horn as a Transmitter. A good receiving horn is a good transmitting horn.
Naturally the behavior always depends on the acoustical attachments. In general, however, the resistance component of the impedance (Arts. 23 and 25) of the horn at the
throat is the best criterion of the horn's action. This is greater for flaring horns than for
conical horns of similar dimensions.

The use of horns in musical instruments is well known. Recently large exponential
horns have proved valuable in the acoustic detection of aircraft.

29. SUPERSONICS

Considerable interest has been displayed during the past two decades in the use of high-
frequency, inaudible sound in under-water signaling, for supersonic waves are not so easily
diffracted as audible waves and hence can be directed more or less in a beam. Moreover,
high-frequency sound oscillators have a much higher radiation efficiency than low-
frequency ones; i.e., much more of the energy of the oscillator actually goes into radiation.
For signaling, frequencies of 50,000 to 100,000 have been employed. The effective damping increases with the frequency and hence precludes the use of much higher frequencies.

Sources. A widely used source of supersonic radiation is the *quartz* oscillator (first
used for signaling purposes by Langevin in France during the Great War). Quartz like
some other asymmetric crystals (notably Rochelle salt) when subjected to stress becomes
electrically polarized. Thus if a slab of quartz cut parallel to the optic axis is inserted between two metal plates connected to an a-c circuit, the slab will oscillate with the impressed
alternating emf, the oscillations being particularly vigorous at resonance.

Another source of supersonic waves is the *magnetostriction oscillator* developed by
Pierce.† When a rod of magnetic material is magnetized it changes its length; when
placed in an oscillating magnetic field mechanical vibrations are thus set up with the frequency of the field.

* See bibliography, page 9-54, references 8, 10, and 13.
† *Proc. Am. Acad. Arts and Sci.*, vol. 63, p. 1, 1928.

Other Uses. In addition to their use for signaling, supersonic waves have been studied for their physical, chemical, and biological effects. Wood and Loomis * have produced sound waves of frequency about 300,000 cycles and with very high intensity, in some cases reaching a radiation pressure of 3000 dynes per cm². When the vibrations are communicated to liquids stable emulsions are often formed, e.g., mercury in water. These waves have also been used in the measurement of the velocity of sound in liquids (see Art. 20).

30. PHYSIOLOGICAL ACOUSTICS

Physiological acoustics comprises all the acoustical phenomena associated with the reception of sound by the ear and the production of speech sounds.

The Human Ear consists of the auricles or pinnae, the canal with the eardrum at the end of it, the middle ear with the three little bones or ossicles, and the inner ear with the liquid-filled cochlea containing the basilar membrane which is presumably the seat of the auditory process. Sound passing through the canal is communicated to the inner ear via the drum and ossicles. The actual mechanism of audition is still a subject of much investigation, and there are several theories of hearing, the chief of which is still that of Helmholtz which assigns resonance characteristics to the fibers in the basilar membrane.†

Intensity and Loudness. As explained in Art. 23, the ear is sensitive to sounds of intensity as low as 4×10^{-10} microwatt per cm² and the threshold of feeling as well as that of audibility are both functions of frequency or pitch (the physiological interpretation of frequency). For most normal persons the frequency range of audibility runs from about 20 to 16,000 cycles per sec. A few people can hear up to 20,000. The work of Fletcher should be consulted for details. The connection between intensity and loudness is a matter of some interest: the former is a purely physical quantity (Art. 23); the latter is physiological. The general law connecting the two is a special case of the so-called Weber-Fechner psychophysical law that equal increments of sensation correspond to equal increments in the *logarithm* of the stimulus. This makes it particularly convenient to use the decibel notation (Art. 23) for loudness. Thus the difference in the loudness level of two sounds of physical intensity I_1 and $I_2(I_2 > I_1)$ respectively is

$$L = 10 \log I_2/I_1 \qquad (34)$$

in decibels. The relation is complicated by differences associated with pitch. We cannot go into the discussion of the loudness of complex tones.

Frequency. To every frequency corresponds a minimum perceptible intensity difference; e.g., for a sound or sensation level of 50 db above the audible threshold, $\Delta I/I = 0.10$. There exists a similar minimum perceptible pitch difference, which varies from 0.5 cycle per sec at 50 cycles to 9 cycles per sec at 3000 cycles per sec. For further details, the work of Knudsen should be consulted.

Beats. The presentation simultaneously to the ear of two sounds of definite frequencies ν_1 and ν_2 leads, when the two sounds are of approximately the same intensity and ν_1 and ν_2 do not differ too much, to the well-known phenomenon of beats. Even when the sounds differ widely, a "difference" tone of frequency $\nu_2 - \nu_1$ is heard, and what at first seems more remarkable, a summation tone of frequency $\nu_1 + \nu_2$ together with various linear combinations of these frequencies. The explanation has been sought in the fact that the eardrum is an asymmetrical vibrator, i.e., that the displacement for given excess pressure is not the same in the positive as in the negative direction.

Sound Direction. One of the most striking aspects of hearing is the localization of the direction of a source of sound. The listening individual tends to turn so that this direction is the perpendicular bisector of the line joining the two ears. Presumably two distinct effects are involved: the *binaural intensity* and the *binaural phase* effects respectively.‡ If the phase is the same at both ears a variation in intensity about the head will produce an angular displacement of the apparent source of sound. However, this is very uncertain and for many observers the effect fails to exist at all in frequency regions where localizability still persists. On the other hand, if the intensity is maintained constant and the phase is varied, the apparent shift about the head persists for all frequencies for which tests have been made, although observers differ considerably on the upper limit (about 1300 for most people).

The Origin of Speech is found in the currents of air which are forced by the lungs to pass through the vocal passages exciting to vibration the so-called vocal cords in the larynx and then passing through the cavities of nose and throat. The functions of tongue and lips in the formation of sounds must not be forgotten, of course. The whole mecha-

---

* *Phil. Mag.*, vol. 4, p. 417, 1927.
† See bibliography, page 9-54, references 16, 19, 27, and 41.
‡ See bibliography, page 9-54, references 13, 16, 19, and 27.

nism is too involved for description here, and reference should be made to Fletcher's very complete discussion.

The Flow of Energy in Speech varies greatly from one individual to another and in a given individual from one sound to another. Thus for a single speaker the *average* intensity involved in a certain syllable may be of the order of 100 microwatts per cm² while the *peak* intensity in the same syllable may be as high as 2000 microwatts per cm². Naturally, these figures depend on the point in front of the mouth where measurements are made, since the intensity falls off with distance. It has been found that the average intensity in normal speech is about 7 microwatts per cm² at a point 9 cm from the mouth. Among speech sounds the vowels rank highest in energy content, the semi vowels next, and consonants lowest.

The work of D. C. Miller has made it clear that the peculiar quality of vowel sounds depends on certain frequency regions regardless of the fundamental pitch used. Thus the quality of the vowel *u* (the vowel sound in "pool") depends essentially on a low-frequency component in the neighborhood of 400 cycles per sec and a high-frequency around 800 cycles per sec. Corresponding figures for long *e* (the vowel sound in "team") are 375 and 2400. Complete tables are given in Fletcher's book.

Articulation. By the use of electric and acoustic filters, certain frequency ranges can be eliminated from speech and the effect on articulation studied. By articulation is understood the percentage of intelligible syllables in a selected list. The results may be summarized as follows: (*a*) frequencies above 1550 cycles per sec are just as important for articulation as those below; specifically by using only frequencies above or only frequencies below this value an articulation of 65 per cent results; (*b*) the elimination of all frequencies below 1000 cycles per sec results in an articulation of 86 per cent; (*c*) the elimination of all above 1000 cycles per sec, an articulation of 40 per cent; (*d*) the elimination of all frequencies below 1000 yields the same articulation as the elimination of all frequencies above 3000. With music the elimination of the low frequencies renders it thin and metallic, and cutting out the high frequencies makes it fuller and, so to speak, thicker (H. Fletcher, Speech and Hearing).

31. MUSICAL SOUNDS

A Musical Sound may be defined as a single sustained sound of definite pitch or a composite of such sounds having frequencies related to each other by simple integral ratios. The frequencies used cover practically the whole audible range (Art. 30). The intensity of musical sounds is in general much greater than that involved in speech. For principal sources of musical sounds, viz., strings, organ pipes, membranes, and horns, see Art. 26.

Characteristics Which Distinguish Music from Other Sound. Musical sounds are seldom simple; they usually are composites of several sounds, viz., the fundamental or note of lowest frequency and the overtones or harmonics with frequencies which are integral multiples of the fundamental. This implies that any complex tone can be analyzed into a set of harmonic components (often called partials): *Ohm's acoustical law.* The *quality* of a complex tone depends on the number and relative strength of the various harmonics or partials and does not depend on their differences in phase. The early work on the analysis of complex sounds was due to Miller * using the phonodeik and mechanical analyzers. More detailed studies have recently been made at the Bell Telephone Laboratories, and complete acoustic spectra of many instruments have been obtained using electrical analyzers and filters.†

The Basis of Musical Scales is found in the fact that the ear recognizes as pleasing combinations of simple tones whose frequencies are in the ratio of *small* whole numbers. These are the so-called consonant intervals ‡ (a musical interval is the ratio of the two frequencies concerned), and the principal ones are: octave, 1 : 2; fifth, 2 : 3; fourth, 3 : 4; major third, 4 : 5; minor third 5 : 6; major sixth, 3 : 5, minor sixth, 5 : 8. As the numbers become larger, dissonance results; the interval 7 : 8 is recognized as dissonant. It is probable, however, that the range of accepted consonance can be increased by custom and education.

The Ideal Musical Scale would consist of a set of simple notes in approximately equal steps and including only consonant intervals. This has never been achieved exactly in practice. The two most important scales, the consonant diatonic and the equally tempered scales, are indicated in the accompanying table.

---

* See bibliography, page 9-54, reference 23.
† See bibliography, page 9-54, reference 19.
‡ See bibliography, page 9-54, reference 3.

Table I.   Musical Scales

Note	C	D	E	F	G	A	B	C'
Frequency on diatonic scale........	256	288	320	341 1/3	384	426 2/3	480	512
Interval with C.................	1	9:8	5:4	4:3	3:2	5:3	15:8	2:1
Frequency on equally tempered scale	256	287.4	322.6	341.8	383.7	430.5	483.2	512

Most of the notes on the scale form consonant intervals with each other, but the steps are decidedly unequal, so that in using it one cannot play in any key at will; i.e., the frequencies bearing the same relation to D as those in the scale bear to C are not all found in the list, and hence to play in the key of D would involve introducing extra frequencies. This complicates matters considerably, hence in the piano the equally tempered scale is used.   This has 12 intervals in the octave: the individual notes are C, C$\sharp$, D, D$\sharp$, E, F, F$\sharp$, G, G$\sharp$, A, A$\sharp$, B, C.   (Not all these are listed in the table.)   The interval between each successive pair of notes is $2^{1/12} = 1.05946$, and therefore music can be played in any key with this scale.   There are *no* exactly consonant intervals, but apparently the defects are too slight to be observed by most people.

Musical Pitch Specification has been very variable, and various standards have been used within the history of modern music.   The classical pitch of Handel and Mozart assigned a frequency of 422 cycles per sec to A whereas the modern " American concert pitch " uses 440 for the same note.   The modern " international pitch " assigns 435 cycles per sec to A.   In the equally tempered scale this gives middle C a frequency of 258.65 cycles per sec.

32. ARCHITECTURAL ACOUSTICS

The first important experiments on the acoustical properties of rooms were carried out by W. C. Sabine in Cambridge, Massachusetts, in the last decade of the nineteenth century.   He was apparently the first to realize the importance of reverberation in its relation to the amount of absorbing material present.

Sound Absorption and Reverberation.   When a sound is produced in a closed space, if the walls were perfect reflectors there would be no diminution in the intensity and if the production of sound continued the total energy would therefore increase indefinitely. Actually, however, the sound is absorbed not only by the air but also and primarily by the walls and other furnishings, so that a given amount of energy is dissipated in a certain time.   Technically the reverberation time is that which elapses after the stopping of a sustained note having one million times the minimum audible intensity and the resulting reverberant sound has dropped to the audible threshold.   The relation between this time, T, in seconds and the dimensions of the room is given approximately for moderate-sized and not too greatly absorbing halls by the formula*

$$T = 0.049 \, V/a \tag{35}$$

in which V = volume of the room in cubic feet, and a = total absorbing power of the walls and materials in the room.   This latter quantity represents the average fraction of the incident sound energy per unit area which is not thrown back into the room (i.e., average absorption coefficient) multiplied by the total surface area exposed.   It is calculated by multiplying the absorption coefficient for each particular article by its area and summing over the whole area.   Thus, denoting by α_i the absorption coefficient for a certain group of similar articles with area S_i, the total absorbing power is

$$a = \Sigma \alpha_i \, S_i = \bar{\alpha} \, S$$

where the sum is taken over all the absorbing material.   The quantity α is called the average absorption coefficient, and S is the total surface.

Sabine's experimental measurements of T for most of the auditoriums which he tested were in rather good agreement with equation (35).   In particular the precise shape of the room (barring such things as deep recesses, etc.) does not seem to affect T.   Sabine's experimental method was simply to start and stop an organ pipe and measure the time for the decaying sound to become inaudible.

Recent work on reverberation indicates that Sabine's formula (equation 35) is unsatisfactory for very large halls or rooms where the absorption is very great, i.e., where $\bar{\alpha}$ is greater than 0.5.   Eyring † has recently derived a more general formula, viz.,

$$T = -\frac{0.05 \, V}{S \log (1 - \bar{\alpha})} \tag{36}$$

* See bibliography, page 9-54, reference 33.
† *J. Acous. Soc. Am.* vol. 1, p. 217, 1930.

This agrees with Sabine's quite closely for $\bar{\alpha}$ small but departs from it considerably when $\bar{\alpha}$ is larger than 0.5. Eyring's formula checks rather well with experimental determinations for "dead" rooms. Other methods of averaging lead to still different though analogous formulas. The whole question is at present somewhat unsettled. For example, the above formula does not take into account the absorption of sound in the air of the room, which further reduces T.

It is clear that, if sufficient intensity of sound is secured, the most important single factor in the satisfactory acoustical use of a room is the reverberation time.* If it is too great, any given sound like a spoken syllable or musical note will take so long to build up and decay that speech becomes inarticulate and music blurred. A short reverberation time greatly increases articulation. Of course too short a time gives the impression of acoustic "deadness," particularly with music. In general a larger value of T can be tolerated for music than for speech; hence it is easier to set an optimum value in the latter case. Knudsen has made the most complete tests of this matter. He has found, for example, that the optimum T for rooms with volume about 300,000 cu ft (without audience) is about 2.75 sec. In general, for a given T, the articulation is greater for vowels than for consonants. The figures depend on the size of the room. For smaller halls of volume up to 40,000 cu ft to be used for both speech and music, a period of about 1 sec is indicated.

Absorption Coefficients. For a room of given size the control of T rests with the absorption. The unit commonly used is 1 sq ft of open window, which is effectively a perfect absorber. The absorption coefficient α_i for any particular material is then defined as the ratio of the absorbing power of 1 sq ft of the substance to that of 1 sq ft of open windows. The measurement of absorption has been carried out by a number of methods. The following table gives some typical values.† It is of interest to note that some substances show highly selective absorption, in particular the high absorbers.

Table II. Sound-absorption Coefficients

Material	Sound-Absorption Coefficients Frequencies 128 512 2048	Weight	Composition	Thicknesses	Stock Sizes
Acousti - Celotex, Single B, 5/8 in.	0.11 0.45 0.68	13 oz per sq ft	Cane fiber tile perforated with 441 holes per sq ft	5/8 in. 13/16 in. 1 1/4 in.	6 in. by 12 in. 12 in. by 12 in. 12 in. by 24 in.
Acoustic Flexfelt	0.27 0.56 0.68		Rock wool felted between metal netting and stucco lath	Required thickness	4 ft by 4 ft 4 ft by 8 ft
Acoustone 1/2 in.	0.48 0.59	1 1/4 lb. per sq ft	Artificial stone filaments bonded together in tile form in a large variety of shapes and colors	1/2 in. 3/4 in. 1 in.	6 in. by 6 in. 6 in. by 12 in. 12 in. by 12 in. 9 in. by 18 in. Special sizes up to 24 in. by 36 in. available
Akoustolith Plaster 1/2 in.	0.21 0.29 0.37		Light-weight plastic material	Applied 1/2 in. in thickness over usual ground coats	
Akoustolith A, Tile, 1 in.	0.14 0.48 0.83	About 4 lb per sq ft	Artificial stone	1 in. 1 1/2 in. 2 in.	3 in. by 16 in. 4 in. by 8 in. 5 in. by 10 in. 12 in. by 12 in. 8 in. by 16 in. for 1-in. thickness
Balsam wool 1 in.	0.15 0.52 0.66	320 lb per 1000 sq ft	Balsam wool mat covered one side with a Kraft paper liner, other side with fireproof cloth mesh	1 in.	Packed in rolls 34 in. wide, containing 124 sq ft

* See bibliography, page 9-54, references 22, 26, and 35.
† Selected values from Knudsen's Architectural Acoustics (John Wiley and Sons, 1932). Used by special permission. For more complete list of data, reference should be made to the original table, probably the most complete in existence.

Table II. Sound-absorption Coefficients—*Continued*

Material	Sound-Absorption Coefficients Frequencies 128 512 2048	Weight	Composition	Thicknesses	Stock Sizes
Fir-Tex, 1 in.	0.32 0.39 0.41	1.2 lb per sq ft	Made from Douglas fir. Contains about 10 per cent of bark; 0.1 per cent resin for fiber waterproofing set upon fiber by 0.1 per cent alum solution giving considerable fireproofing	1 in. 1 1/2 in.	12 in. by 12 in.
Insulite Acoustile, Type 37	0.21 0.38 0.46	750 lb. per 1000 sq ft	Wood fiber fabricated into tiles	3/4 in.	Sizes range from 6 in. by 6 in. up to 24 in. by 24 in.
Kalite No. 102, 3/4 in., on metal lath	0.37 0.40 0.53	About onehalf of ordinary plaster	Made of graded sizes of a special pumice mixed with a gypsum binder. The inherent porosity of the pumice together with the method of mixing gives a plaster with many communicatting channels. Calcined gypsum ($CaSO_4 \cdot 1/2\ H_2O$), 34.85 per cent; pumice 60.33 per cent	Can be applied in thicknesses of 1/2, 3/4, 1 in.	
Macoustic plaster, stippled to depth of 1/2 in.	0.12 0.31 0.58	2 lb. per sq ft	A fibrous plaster	Applied 1/2 in.	
Masonite	0.18 0.32 0.33	700 lb per 1000 sq	Made chiefly of longleaf pine and southern gum	7/16 in.	4 ft by 12 ft
Rockoustile 1 in.	0.18 0.57 0.72	1.5 lb per sq ft	Rock wool product	1 in.	6 in. by 12 in. 12 in. by 12 in.
Sabinite	0.34 0.49	2 to 3 lb. per sq ft	Gypsum base plaster. No stippling or special art in application required. No. 38 is a special humidity - resisting material, utilizing a hydraulic binder, for the acoustical treatment of natatoria and similar humid rooms	Applied in two coats, about 1/2 in.	
Silent-Ceal	0.29 0.68 0.75	3 lb. per sq ft	Rock wool fill; special metal furring; No. 20 gage perforated metal primary membrane; fabric secondary membrane	Determined by requirements of job	
Transite tile, 1 in.	0.19 0.81 0.72	3 lb. per sq ft	1 in. sound-absorbing block faced with perforated Transite 3/16 in. asbestos paper	1 3/16 in.	6 in. by 6 in. 12 in. by 12 in.

Sound Proofing has become a significant branch of architectural acoustics. When sound strikes a wall, part is reflected and part is absorbed in the true sense of being ultimately dissipated into heat. Another part passes through the wall in the form of compressional waves. Finally some of the incident sound energy causes the wall to vibrate as a whole, and it is indeed in this way that most of the sound energy gets across the wall into the room space on the other side. This suggests that to prevent sound transmission from air to air through walls they should be made as rigid as possible. On the other hand, rigidity facilitates wave transmission through the walls and flooring of sounds originating there, so that the problem of complete sound proofing is somewhat complicated. The use of double walls with a fairly wide air space is of considerable help, as is also the use of inner floors floating on insulating material resting in turn on the main structural floor.

33. NOISE AND ITS PREVENTION

Noise. Previously the scientific definition of noise was any sound or set of sounds having no definite pitch or pitch components. At the present time it would be perhaps fairer to consider as noise any *disturbing* sound, regular or otherwise. For some people, a large amount of radio " music " is quite definitely noise. The endeavor is now under way to study very thoroughly the effect of noise in all forms on the individual, particularly with respect to fatigue and the lowering of mental and motor efficiency. No safe generalizations are yet at hand, though it is widely believed that city noise is ultimately harmful to man (A. H. Davis, Modern Acoustics).

Noise Measurement. In order to study noise it is necessary to measure its intensity (e.g., by means of a microphone coupled with some kind of amplifier system), its wave form (by oscillographic observation), and the distribution of energy among the various component frequencies. One difficulty encountered is the fact that physical intensity must be translated into physiological loudness, i.e., one must use a noise meter which closely simulates the response of the ear.

In the use of noise meters the usual plan is to vary the intensity of a standard note until it is judged subjectively to be of the same loudness as the noise being measured. The level of the sound in decibels (db) above the audible threshold is then taken as a measure of the noise. The results in all cases depend more or less on the frequency. Thus the average street noise may run from 10 db at 8000 cycles per sec to 35 db at 1000 cycles per sec. At a particularly noisy corner of a busy city, the level may reach 50 db (Fletcher). A boiler factory in operation runs from 95 to 100 db (Davis). In a quiet residence the figure should not be above 15. These last values are averages over a considerable range of frequency. Of course there is fluctuation with time.

For the important effect of noise on speech articulation the work of Fletcher should be consulted.

In the Reduction of Noise from Machinery, which is probably the largest single source of indoor noise and much outdoor noise as well, the general principle is the prevention of the transfer of vibrational energy to surfaces large enough to communicate this energy to the air in the form of acoustical radiation. In general, the amount of sound given to the air directly by the moving parts is negligible compared with that due to the vibration of the supports and foundation. It is therefore desirable as far as possible to insert between moving parts and supports material of very different specific acoustical resistance (see Art. 23) from either. The material should also have as large a damping coefficient as possible.

For a very complete discussion of the possibility of noise prevention in large cities, reference should be made to City Noise, published by the Noise Abatement Commission, Department of Health, New York, 1930.

34. CERTAIN ACOUSTICAL INSTRUMENTS AND MEASUREMENTS

The measurements of leading importance in acoustical work are those of the intensity of sound and acoustic impedance.

The Rayleigh Disk. The classical method for measuring intensity is that employing the Rayleigh disk.* This is a small thin disk of glass about $1/2$ cm in diameter suspended by a quartz fiber so that its plane faces are vertical. When such a disk is immersed in a sound beam it tends to set itself so that its plane is normal to the direction of particle displacement. The sound wave thus exerts a torque on the supporting fiber which can be measured by the angular deflection of the disk. Theory indicates that this torque depends on the mean square of the particle velocity in the sound wave. It is therefore a measure of the intensity (Art. 23).

---

* See bibliography, page 9-54, references 8 and 13

Webster's Phonometer is another intensity-measuring instrument consisting of a tunable cylindrical resonator with a diaphragm mounted in its mouth.* This diaphragm is tuned to resonance with the sound whose intensity is to be measured by changing the tension in the wires supporting it. The diaphragm vibrates under the action of the air vibrations produced by the sound in the mouth of the resonator, and the motion of the diaphragm causes rotation of a small concave mirror from which light is reflected. The displacement amplitude of the diaphragm is proportional to the pressure amplitude of the sound at the diaphragm, and hence the intensity can be computed from equation (18).

The Hot-wire Microphone. A fine platinum wire heated to red heat and exposed to a fluctuating current of air in the neck of a resonator suffers a decrease in resistance which is proportional to the mean square particle velocity and hence to the intensity of the sound. This arrangement is called the hot-wire microphone.*

It is of interest to note the important rôle played by the resonator in the last two instruments mentioned.

Of the Electroacoustical Methods of measuring intensity only two can be mentioned: the condenser microphone and the ribbon microphone.† The former consists of a thin stretched circular diaphragm fastened about the periphery and attracted toward a metal plate by means of a static electric charge. When sound waves impinge on the diaphragm they alter the capacity of the system and hence produce a small alternating current in the circuit of which the diaphragm and plate are a part. This current is amplified and used as a measure of intensity on proper calibration. The great advantage of the instrument is its remarkably uniform sensitivity over a wide range of frequencies.

The ribbon microphone consists of a light metallic ribbon suspended in a magnetic field and exposed to air vibrations on both sides. The vibrations of the ribbon produced by an incident sound wave lead to the induction of an emf corresponding to the oscillations in the wave. This instrument has the advantage of possessing directional characteristics, a property not possessed by the condenser microphone and other pressure-operated instruments.

The Measurement of Acoustic Impedance has recently become of importance as a means of estimating the performance of acoustic apparatus such as horns (Art. 28). Reference should be made to the literature.

BIBLIOGRAPHY

British and American

General—Elementary

1. BRAGG, SIR WILLIAM. The World of Sound. London, Bell and Sons. Latest printing, 1933.
2. FLEMING, J. A. Waves and Ripples. New York, Macmillan, 4th issue, 1923.
3. STEWART, G. W. Introductory Acoustics. New York, D. Van Nostrand, 1932.
4. TYNDALL, JOHN. Lectures on Sound. New York, Appleton, 1867.
5. WATSON, F. R. Sound. New York, John Wiley, 1935.
6. WOOD, ALEXANDER. Sound Waves and Their Uses. London and Glasgow, Blackie, 1930.

General—Advanced

7. CRANDALL, J. B. Theory of Vibrating Systems and Sound. New York, D. Van Nostrand 1926.
8. DAVIS, A. H. Modern Acoustics. London, Bell and Sons, 1934.
9. LAMB, SIR HORACE. Dynamical Theory of Sound. London, Arnold, 2d ed., 1925.
10. OLSON, H. F., and MASSA, F. Applied Acoustics. Philadelphia, Blakiston, 1934.
11. RAYLEIGH, LORD. The Theory of Sound. London, Macmillan, 2 volumes, 2d ed. rev. and enl., 1929.
12. RICHARDSON, E. G. Sound: A Physical Text-book. London, Arnold, 1927.
13. STEWART, G. W., and LINDSAY, R. B. Acoustics. New York, D. Van Nostrand, 1930.
14. WOOD, A. B. A Text-book of Sound. London, Bells and Sons, 1930.

Special Subjects

15. BAGENAL, H., and WOOD, ALEXANDER. Planning for Good Acoustics. London, Methuen 1931.
16. BEATTY, R. T. Hearing in Man and Animals. London, Bell, 1932.
17. DAVIS, A. H., and KAYE, G. W. C. The Acoustics of Buildings. London, Bell, 1927.
18. DOUGLAS, D., The Science of Voice. New York, Carl Fischer, 1929.
19. FLETCHER, H. Speech and Hearing. New York, D. Van Nostrand, 1929.
20. GLOVER, C. W. Practical Acoustics for the Constructor. Cleveland, Ohio, 1934.
21. HART, M. D., and SMITH, W. W. The Principles of Sound Signalling. London, Constable, 1925.
22. KNUDSEN, V. O. Architectural Acoustics. New York, John Wiley, 1932.
23. MILLER, D. C. The Science of Musical Sounds. New York, Macmillan, 1916.
24. NATIONAL RESEARCH COUNCIL, COMMITTEE ON ACOUSTICS. Certain Problems in Acoustics. Washington, 1922.

---

* See bibliography, references 8 and 13.

† See bibliography, references 8, 10, and 13.

25. RICHARDSON, E. G. The Acoustics of Orchestral Instruments and the Organ. London, Arnold, 1929.
26. SABINE, P. E. Acoustics and Architecture. New York, McGraw-Hill, 1932.
27. WILKINSON, G., and GRAY, A. A. The Mechanism of the Cochlea. London, Macmillan, 1924.
28. DRYSDALE, C. V., and others. Mechanical Properties of Fluids. London, Blackie, 1923.
29. HUMPHREYS, W. J. Physics of the Air. Philadelphia, Lippincott, 2d ed., 1928.
30. LAMB, SIR HORACE. Hydrodynamics. Cambridge, University Press, 6th ed., 1932.
31. LOVE, A. E. H. Mathematical Theory of Elasticity. Cambridge, University Press, 3d ed., 1920.
32. McLACHLAN, N. W. Loud Speakers. Oxford, University Press, 1934.
33. SABINE, W. C. Collected Papers on Acoustics. Harvard University Press, Cambridge, Mass., 1922.
34. TIMOSHENKO, D. Vibratory Problems in Engineering. New York, D. Van Nostrand, 1928.
35. WATSON, F. R. Acoustics of Building. New York, John Wiley, 2d ed., 1930.

German

36. AIGNER, F. Unterwasserschalltechnik. Berlin, Krayn, 1922.
37. FISCHER, F., and LICHTE, H., Tonfilm. Leipzig, Hirzel, 1931.
38. Handbuch der Physik, Vol. VIII, Akustik. Berlin, Springer, 1927.
39. Handbuch der experimental Physik, Vol. XVII (2 and 3), Technische Akustik. Leipzig, Akad. Verlag., 1934.
40. Handbuch der experimental Physik, Vol. XVII (1), Ultra Akustik (all so far published). Leipzig, Akad. Verlag., 1934.
41. HELMHOLTZ, H. VON. Die Lehre von den Tonempfindungen. Braunschweig, Vieweg, 6th ed., 1913. English translation, On the Sensations of Tone as a Physiological Basis for the Theory of Music (from the 3d German ed. by A. J. ELLIS). London, Longmans, Green, 1875.
42. MÜLLER-POUILLET. Lehrbuch der Physik, vol. 1, part 3, Akustik. Braunschweig, Vieweg, 1929.
43. PETERS, I. Die mathematischen und physikalischen Grundlagen der Musik. Leipzig and Berlin, Teubner, 1924.
44. POHL, R. W. Einführung in die Mechanik und Akustik. Berlin, Springer, 1930. English translation by W. M. DEANS. London, Blackie, 1932.
45. TRENDELENBURG, F. Fortschritte der physikalischen und technischen Akustik. Leipzig, Akad. Verlag., 2d ed. with bibliography, 1934.

French

46. DAVID, P. L'électro-acoustique. Paris, Hermann, 1930.
47. FOCH, A. Acoustique. Paris, Libraire Armand Colin, 1934.
48. GALBRUN, H. Propagation d'un onde sonore dans l'atmosphère. Paris, Gauthier-Villars, 1931.

METEOROLOGY *

By Edgar W. Woolard, R. J. Martin, and H. L. Dryden

35. SIGNALS OF UNITED STATES WEATHER BUREAU

Flag Signal for cold wave warning is shown in Fig. 1.

Storm and Hurricane Warnings are given by the flags in Fig. 2.

A red flag with a black center indicates that a storm of marked violence is expected. The pennants displayed with the flags indicate the direction of the wind: red, easterly (from northeast to south); white, westerly (from southwest to north). The pennant above the flag indicates that the wind is expected to blow from the northerly quadrants; below from the southerly quadrants.

Two red flags with black centers, displayed one above the other, indicate the expected approach of a tropical hurricane, or of one of those extremely severe and dangerous storms which occasionally move across the Lakes and northern Atlantic coast.

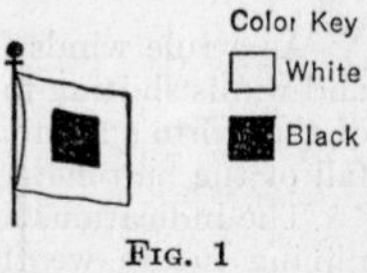

Color Key
☐ White
■ Black

FIG. 1

Wind Pressure on Flags. Tests at the U. S. Navy Yard, Washington, D. C., using the largest flags that could be handled in the wind tunnel, form the basis for an empirical formula for determining the pressure of wind on flags, for use in

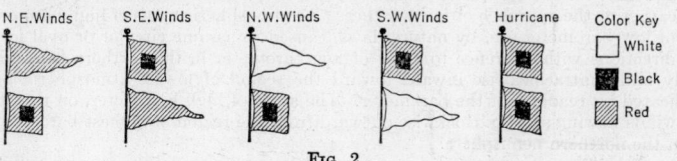

N.E.Winds   S.E.Winds   N.W.Winds   S.W.Winds   Hurricane

Color Key
☐ White
■ Black
▨ Red

FIG. 2

designing flagpoles. Two sizes of flags were used—one 3 by $5\frac{1}{2}$ ft and the other $2\frac{1}{2}$ by $4\frac{1}{4}$ ft —and velocities varying from 20 to 60 miles per hour were applied. The following formula was

---

* Articles 35 to 41 by Edgar W. Woolard and R. J. Martin of the U. S. Weather Bureau and Article 43 by H. L. Dryden of the Bureau of Standards; revised from material previously prepared for Merriman's Civil Engineers' Handbook.

found to represent the results, the constant varying but slightly with size of flags, being less for the larger flag:

$$R = 0.0003A V^{1.9}$$

in which R is the resistance in pounds, A is the area of flag in square feet, and V is the velocity of wind in miles per hour. This formula is for steady wind pressure. It was not found practicable to measure the forces produced by wind gusts.

36. LOCAL WEATHER PREDICTIONS

The wind and barometer indications for the United States are generally summarized in Table I (E. B. Garriott, U. S. Dept. Agriculture).

Table I. Wind and Barometer Indications

Wind Direction	Barometer Reduced to Sea Level	Character of Weather Indicated
SW to NW.	30.10 to 30.20 and steady.........	Fair, with slight temperature changes, for 1 to 2 days
SW to NW.	30.10 to 30.20 and rising rapidly	Fair, followed within 2 days by rain
SW to NW.	30.10 to 30.20 and falling slowly	Warmer, with rain within 24 to 36 hours
SW to NW.	30.10 to 30.20 and falling rapidly	Warmer, with rain within 18 to 24 hours
SW to NW.	30.20 and above and stationary	Continued fair, with no decided temperature change
SW to NW.	30.20 and above and falling slowly	Slowing rising temperature and fair for 2 days
S to SE....	30.10 to 30.20 and falling slowly	Rain within 24 hours
S to SE....	30.10 to 30.20 and falling rapidly	Wind increasing in force, with rain within 12 to 24 hours
SE to NE..	30.10 to 30.20 and falling slowly	Rain in 12 to 18 hours
SE to NE	30.10 to 30.20 and falling rapidly	Increasing wind, and rain within 12 hours
E to NE...	30.10 and above and falling slowly	In summer, with light winds, rain may not fall for several days. In winter, rain within 24 hours
E to NE...	30.10 and above and falling rapidly	In summer, rain probable within 12 to 24 hours. In winter, rain or snow, with increasing winds, will often set in when the barometer begins to fall and the wind sets in from the NE
SE to NE..	30.00 or below and falling slowly	Rain will continue 1 to 2 days
SE to NE..	30.00 or below and falling rapidly	Rain, with high winds, followed, within 36 hours, by clearing, and in winter by colder
S to SW....	30.00 or below and rising slowly	Clearing within a few hours, and fair for several days
S to E.....	29.80 or below and falling rapidly...	Severe storm imminent, followed, within 24 hours, by clearing, and in winter by colder
E to N.....	29.80 or below and falling rapidly...	Severe northeast gale and heavy precipitation; in winter, heavy snow, followed by a cold wave
Going to W	29.80 or below and rising rapidly	Clearing and colder

As a rule winds from the east quadrants and falling barometer indicate foul weather; and winds shifting to the west quadrants indicate clearing and fair weather. The rapidity of the storm's approach and its intensity are indicated by the rate and the amount in the fall of the barometer.

The indications afforded by the wind and the barometer are the best guides for determining future weather conditions. As low barometer readings usually attend stormy weather, and high barometer readings are generally associated with clearing or fair weather, it follows that falling barometer indicates precipitation and wind, and rising barometer fair weather or the approach of fair weather. As atmospheric areas of high barometer and areas of low barometer are, by natural laws, caused to assume circular or oval forms, the wind directions with reference to areas of low barometer in the northern hemisphere are spirally and contraclockwise inward toward the region of lowest atmospheric pressure, as indicated by readings of the barometer. The areas of high barometer, on the contrary, show winds flowing spirally clockwise outward from the region of highest barometric pressure in the northern hemisphere.

The wind directions thus produced give rise to, and are responsible for, all local weather signs. The south winds bring warmth; the north winds cold; the east winds, in the middle latitudes, indicate the approach from the westward of a low-barometer, or storm, area; and the west winds show that the storm area has passed to the eastward. The indications of the barometer generally forerun the shifts of the wind. This much is shown by local observations.

During the colder months, when the land temperatures are below the water temperatures of the ocean, precipitation will begin along the seaboards when the wind shifts and blows steadily from the water over the land without regard to the height of the barometer. In such cases the moisture in the warm ocean winds is condensed by the cold of the continental area. During the summer months, on the contrary, the onshore winds are not necessarily rain winds, for the reason that they are cooler than the land surfaces and their capacity for moisture is increased by the warmth that is communicated to them by the land surface. In such cases thunderstorms commonly occur when the ocean winds are intercepted by mountain ranges or peaks. If, however, the easterly winds of summer increase in force, with falling barometer, the approach of an area of low barometric pressure from the west is indicated and rain will follow within a day or two.

From the Mississippi and Missouri valleys to the Atlantic coast, and on the Pacific coast, rain generally begins on a falling barometer, whereas in the Rocky Mountain and Plateau districts, and on the eastern Rocky Mountain slope, precipitation seldom begins until the barometer begins to rise, after a fall.

Table II.   Temperature in the United States
Prepared by the Weather Bureau, U. S. Department of Agriculture

States	Stations	Mean Jan.	Mean July	Extremes Highest	Extremes Lowest	States	Stations	Mean Jan.	Mean July	Extremes Highest	Extremes Lowest
Ala	Birmingham	45	80	107	−10	Mont	Kalispell	20	64	101	−34
	Mobile	52	81	103	−1		Miles City	14	73	111	−49
Ariz	Flagstaff	26	64	93	−25	Neb	N. Platte	23	73	108	−35
	Phoenix	51	90	119	12		Omaha	22	77	111	−32
	Yuma	54	91	120	22	Nev	Winnemucca	29	71	108	−28
Ark	Fort Smith	40	82	108	−15	N. C	Charlotte	41	78	103	−5
	Little Rock	41	81	108	−12		Hatteras	47	78	93	8
Calif	Fresno	46	82	115	17		Wilmington	46	79	103	5
	Los Angeles	55	70	109	28	N. D	Bismarck	8	70	108	−45
	Sacramento	46	73	114	17	N. H	Concord	22	68	102	−35
	San Diego	54	67	110	25	N. J	Atlantic City	32	72	104	−9
	San Francisco	50	58	101	27		Cape May	34	73	100	−7
	Denver	30	72	105	−29	N. Mex	Santa Fe	29	69	97	−13
Col	Grand Junc	24	78	105	−21		Albany	23	73	104	−24
	Pueblo	30	74	104	−27		Binghamton	24	70	99	−28
Conn	New Haven	28	72	101	−15	N. Y	Buffalo	25	70	97	−20
D. C	Washington	33	77	106	−15		N. Y. City	31	74	102	−13
	Jacksonville	55	82	104	10		Oswego	24	70	100	−23
Fla	Key West	70	84	100	41		Cincinnati	30	75	108	−17
	Pensacola	52	81	103	7	Ohio	Columbus	29	75	104	−20
	Tampa	60	81	98	19		Toledo	26	73	103	−16
	Atlanta	43	78	103	−8	Okla	Oklahoma	36	81	108	−17
Ga	Augusta	47	81	106	3	Oreg	Portland	39	67	104	−2
	Savannah	51	82	105	8		Erie	27	71	97	−16
Idaho	Boise	30	73	121	−28	Pa	Phila	33	76	106	−11
	Cairo	35	80	106	−16		Pittsburgh	31	75	103	−20
Ill	Chicago	24	72	105	−23	R. I	Block Island	31	68	92	−6
	Springfield	26	76	108	−24	S. C	Charleston	50	81	104	7
Ind	Indianapolis	28	76	106	−25	S. D	Huron	11	72	111	−43
	Des Moines	20	75	110	−30		Yankton	17	74	108	−36
Iowa	Dubuque	19	74	106	−32		Chattanooga	41	78	104	−10
	Keokuk	25	77	110	−27	Tenn	Memphis	41	81	106	−9
Kan	Dodge City	29	78	109	−26		Nashville	39	79	106	−13
	Wichita	31	79	109	−22		Abilene	44	83	110	−6
Ky	Louisville	34	79	107	−20		Amarillo	35	77	106	−16
La	New Orleans	54	82	102	7	Tex	El Paso	45	81	113	−5
	Shreveport	47	83	110	−5		Galveston	54	83	101	8
Me	Portland	22	68	103	−21		San Antonio	52	84	107	4
Md	Baltimore	34	77	105	−7	Utah	Salt Lake City	29	76	105	−20
Mass	Boston	28	72	104	−18	Vt	Burlington	19	70	100	−29
	Detroit	24	72	105	−24	Va	Lynchburg	38	78	105	−7
Mich	Marquette	16	65	108	−27		Norfolk	41	79	105	2
	Port Huron	22	69	104	−25		Seattle	40	63	98	3
Minn	Duluth	8	64	99	−41	Wash	Spokane	28	69	108	−30
	St. Paul	13	72	104	−41		Walla Walla	33	74	113	−17
Miss	Vicksburg	48	81	104	−1	W. Va	Elkins	30	70	99	−28
	Kansas City	28	78	111	−22		Parkersburg	32	75	106	−27
Mo	St. Louis	31	79	110	−22	Wis	La Crosse	16	73	104	−43
	Springfield	34	77	106	−29		Milwaukee	21	70	104	−25
Mont	Helena	20	66	103	−42	Wyo	Cheyenne	26	67	100	−38

37. WEATHER OBSERVATIONS

Mean Temperature. When maximum and minimum readings of temperature are taken, the mean of the two may be taken as the mean temperature of the day. The mean of all the daily means in a month is the mean temperature of the month. When a recording thermometer is used the area between the curve and an axis of abscissas is to be divided by the length of that axis in order to obtain the mean temperature for the elapsed time.

Rainfall. The rain gage used by voluntary observers consists of a cylindrical receiver 8 in. in diameter which has a funnel-shaped bottom that discharges into a tube 2.53 in. in diameter. The cross-section of tube is one-tenth that of the receiver, and hence height of water in tube is ten times as great as actual rainfall. The depth in the tube is measured by a stick which is so graduated as to read the true rainfall in inches. The tube is 20 in. long so that a precipitation of 2 in. or less can be measured without emptying it.

Self-registering rain gages are used at main stations of U. S. Weather Bureau. Snowfall is caught, melted, and then measured; roughly 10 in. of snow make 1 in. of water. A rain gage at the top of a building gives a less rainfall than one on the ground.

Voluntary observers of the Weather Bureau record maximum and minimum temperature, precipitation, wind direction, general character of day, and miscellaneous phenomena such as halos, dates of frost, hail, sleet, auroras, and tornadoes. The general character of the day is recorded " clear " when the sky is 3/10 or less obscured, " partly cloudy " when from 4/10 to 7/10 is obscured, and " cloudy " when more than 7/10 is obscured.

38. RAINFALL AND EVAPORATION

Table III. Evaporation

Place	Position of Pan	Diameter of pan, ft	Annual Evaporation, in.
Salton Sea, Calif.	1500 ft inland	2	164.50
Salton Sea, Calif.	500 ft at sea	4	108.65
Salton Sea, Calif.	7500 ft at sea	4	106.45
Indio, Calif.	15 miles from Salton Sea	6	119.33
Mecca, Calif.	1/2 mile from Salton Sea	6	107.81
Brawley, Calif.	20 miles from Salton Sea	6	103.55
Mammoth, Calif.	40 miles from Salton Sea	6	125.53
North Yakima, Wash.	1/2 mile west of city	4	67.96
Hermiston, Ore.	On raft in reservoir	4	68.05
	On ground	3	97.29
Granite Reef, Ariz.	Floating in Salt River	4	97.74
	On ground	4	115.18
California, Ohio	Floating in reservoir	4	45.99
Birmingham, Ala.	Floating in reservoir	4	51.74
Dutch Flats, Neb.	A few miles from Mitchell	4	65.67
Deer Flat, Idaho	On raft near water edge	4	77.43
	On ground of embankment	3	79.00
Ady, Ore.	Floating in borrow pit	4	53.45
Fallon, Nev.	Floating in canal	4	53.65
Lake Tahoe, Calif.	2 ft above water	4	42.21
Elephant Butte, N. Mex.	Near Rio Grande River	4	86.95
Carlsbad, N. Mex.	In the city	4	107.25
	In an alfalfa field	4	94.35
Lake Avalon, N. Mex.	A few miles from Carlsbad	4	94.51

The evaporation from a pan 2 ft in diameter is about 75 per cent, that from a pan 4 ft in diameter is about 50 per cent, and that from a pan 6 ft in diameter is about 30 per cent greater than the evaporation from a large pond or lake. The above figures may be roughly corrected by using these percentages; thus, at Birmingham, Ala., the true annual evaporation is 34.50 in.

The U. S. Weather Bureau maintains at selected locations hook gage measurements of evaporation losses from cylindrical pans 10 in. deep and 4 ft in diameter, exposed on wood frames, bottom of pans 1 in. above the ground, generally on level ground, and in full sunshine. Detailed description published in *Monthly Weather Review*, December, 1916, or in Circular L, Instrument Division, Weather Bureau, No. 559. From comparisons available, it appears that losses from bodies of water of considerable area are 50 to 60 per cent as great as from pans exposed as above. The records are published in detail in the reports issued by the state section directors of the U. S. Weather Bureau, and in the Annual Reports of the Chief of the Weather Bureau.

Measurements of Evaporation are made by placing water-tight pans at the level of the ground and noting daily the variations in depth, together with the rainfall. On a water surface similar measurements may be made by floating boxes. It is found that the evaporation from large water surfaces is less than that from pans, that it is greater in dry and desert regions than in cultivated ones, that it decreases as the humidity of the air increases, and that it increases with the temperature of the air and the velocity of the wind.

In the North Atlantic states the annual evaporation from land surfaces is, on the average, about 40 per cent, and that from water surfaces is about 60 per cent of the annual rainfall. In low and level localities these percentages are decreased; for high regions and steep slopes they are increased. In some arid localities west of the Rocky Mountains nearly all the rainfall evaporates from land surfaces, and the evaporation from water surfaces may be several times as great as the rainfall.

Experiments made in 1909-10 by the U. S. Department of Agriculture gave the figures listed in Table III for the annual evaporation at twenty places in the United States, the evaporating pan being at or very near the surface of the ground or water.

Table IV. Maximum Intensity of Rainfall

Station	Inches per Hour for			Station	Inches per Hour for		
	5 min	10 min	60 min		5 min	10 min	60 min
Bismarck, N. D........	9.00	6.54	3.07	Chicago, Ill............	6.00	5.46	2.30
St. Paul, Minn.........	7.32	6.06	2.60	Galveston, Tex........	10.20	8.82	5.31
New Orleans, La........	9.24	7.20	3.66	Omaha, Neb...........	6.84	4.86	2.25
Milwaukee, Wis........	6.36	5.16	2.10	Dodge City, Iowa......	6.36	6.12	2.31
Kansas City, Mo.......	9.60	6.96	4.79	Norfolk, Va...........	7.96	6.30	2.72
Washington, D. C......	9.24	7.26	3.42	Cleveland, Ohio.......	6.60	4.74	1.88
Jacksonville, Fla.......	9.36	7.20	3.13	Atlanta, Ga...........	8.28	6.72	3.23
Detroit, Mich..........	10.32	8.40	3.09	Key West, Fla.........	7.80	6.18	4.30
New York City.........	9.00	7.56	2.48	Philadelphia, Pa.......	7.80	6.06	3.81
Boston, Mass..........	6.60	5.46	1.80	St. Louis, Mo.........	7.08	6.24	3.47
Savannah, Ga..........	8.64	6.72	3.56	Cincinnati, Ohio.......	6.60	5.76	2.08
Indianapolis, Ind.......	9.96	6.48	2.68	Denver, Colo..........	10.92	8.16	2.20
Memphis, Tenn...:....	9.36	7.62	3.25	Duluth, Minn..........	6.72	5.82	3.27

This table has been compiled from all the available records at stations of the U. S. Weather Bureau which are equipped with self-registering rain gages.

39. SPEED OF WINDS IN THE UNITED STATES

U. S. Weather Bureau records of the average speed of wind in miles per hour at selected stations, and the highest speeds ever reported for a period of 5 minutes, are given in Table V.

The Beaufort Scale is used by seamen. In Table V the corresponding velocity per hour in statute miles and in nautical miles is added.

Table V. Wind Velocities

Station	Average	Highest	Station	Average	Highest
Abilene, Texas................	10	51	Louisville, Ky.................	9	58
Albany, N. Y.................	8	59	Lynchburg, Va................	5	48
Alpena, Mich.................	10	47	Memphis, Tenn...............	9	58
Atlanta, Ga..................	10	51	Miles City, Mont.............	6	47
Bismarck, N. D..............	10	60	Montgomery, Ala.............	7	41
Boise, Idaho.................	6	43	Moorhead, Minn..............	10	56
Boston, Mass................	14	60	Nashville, Tenn..............	9	58
Buffalo, N. Y................	15	73	New Orleans, La.............	8	66
Charlotte, N. C..............	7	42	New York, N. Y..............	15	94
Chattanooga, Tenn............	8	50	North Platte, Nebr...........	9	73
Chicago, Ill.................	11	65	Omaha, Nebr................	9	51
Cincinnati, Ohio..............	8	43	Palestine, Texas..............	7	47
Cleveland, Ohio..............	13	60	Philadelphia, Pa..............	10	68
Denver, Colo.................	7	53	Pittsburgh, Pa...............	10	56
Detroit, Mich................	12	67	Portland, Me................	9	48
Dodge City, Kan.............	13	56	Red Bluff, Calif..............	7	46
Dubuque, Iowa...............	7	47	Rochester, N. Y..............	9	60
Duluth, Minn................	12	60	St. Louis, Mo................	11	62
Eastport, Me................	10	58	St. Paul, Minn...............	9	78
El Paso, Texas...............	10	58	Salt Lake City, Utah..........	8	53
Fort Smith, Ark..............	7	57	San Diego, Calif..............	7	43
Galveston, Texas.............	11	71	San Francisco, Calif..........	9	50
Havre, Mont.................	9	57	Sante Fé, N. Mex............	7	42
Helena, Mont................	8	54	Savannah, Ga................	9	68
Huron, S. D.................	11	56	Spokane, Wash...............	6	41
Jacksonville, Fla.............	9	58	Toledo, Ohio.................	11	65
Kansas City, Mo.............	11	57	Vicksburg, Miss..............	7	49
Keokuk, Iowa................	9	49	Washington, D. C.............	6	53
Knoxville, Tenn..............	7	59	Wilmington, N. C.............	9	51

Table V. Wind Velocities—*Continued*

Intensity of Force of Wind, Beaufort's Scale	Velocity	
	Statute Miles per Hour	Nautical Miles per Hour
0. Calm. Full-rigged ship, all sail set, no headway..	0 to 3	0 to 2.6
1. Light Air. Just sufficient to give steerageway....	8	6.9
2. Light Breeze. Speed of 1 or 2 knots, " full and by "	13	11.3
3. Gentle Breeze. Speed of 3 or 4 knots, " full and by "	18	15.6
4. Moderate Breeze. Speed of 5 or 6 knots, " full and by "..	23	20.0
5. Fresh Breeze. All plain sail, " full and by "......	28	24.3
6. Strong Breeze. Topgallant sails over single-reefed topsails..	34	29.5
7. Moderate Gale. Double-reefed topsails..........	40	34.7
8. Fresh Gale. Treble-reefed topsails (or reefed upper topsails and courses)...........................	48	41.6
9. Strong Gale. Close-reefed topsails and courses (or lower topsails and courses)....................	56	48.6
10. Whole Gale. Close-reefed main topsail and reefed foresail (or lower main topsail and reefed foresail)	65	56.4
11. Storm. Storm staysails........................	75	65.1
12. Hurricane. Under bare poles..................	90 and over	78.1 and over

The words " intensity " and " force," used in connection with this scale, have no direct relation to pressure, but refer to speed or velocity.

40. BAROMETRIC OBSERVATIONS

Whenever pressure is specified in terms of the height of a column of mercury, it is always tacitly understood that it is the height the column balancing the pressure would have under "standard conditions," that is, at 0 deg cent, and where g has the standard value $g_0 = 980.665$ cm per sec per sec adopted by the International Committee of Weights and Measures. In all cases where the mercury column (if of average barometric height and at ordinary atmospheric temperature) is to be read closer than 2 or 3 mm (0.1 in.) one or more of the corrections described below must be made or the accuracy of the reading will be imaginary.

Corrections. Let l be the height of the mercury column as read at t degrees centigrade with a scale correct at t_0 degrees centigrade whose coefficient of linear expansion is β. Let ϕ be the latitude and H the elevation in meters above sea level.

(1) Temperature of the Mercury. Subtract 0.000182 lt.

(2) Temperature of the Measuring Scale. Add $\beta (t - t_0)l$. For brass $\beta = 0.000019$; for glass $\beta = 0.000008$. If, as is usual, the scale is correct at 0 deg cent, the complete correction, (1) and (2), for the expansion of both the mercury and the scale may be made by subtracting from the observed reading $(0.000182 - \beta) lt$, which gives

$$0.000163 \ lt \text{ for a brass scale, and}$$
$$0.000174 \ lt \text{ for a glass scale.}$$

Under ordinary conditions the correction may amount to as much as 4 mm.

(3) Capillary Depression in a Cistern Barometer. Add to the reading of the top of the meniscus the amount given in the table below corresponding to the internal diameter of the tube and the height of the meniscus. This somewhat uncertain correction can be avoided by using a tube at least 25 mm in diameter.

Table VI. Capillary Depression of Mercury
(After Mendeléeff and Gutkowsky. Kohlrausch, 1910)

Diameter	Height of the Meniscus in Millimeters							
	0.4	0.6	0.8	1.0	1.2	1.4	1.6	1.8
mm	mm	mm	mm	mm	mm	mm	mm	mm
4	0.83	1.22	1.54	1.98	2.37	....	....	....
5	0.47	0.65	0.86	1.19	1.45	1.80	....	....
6	0.27	0.41	0.56	0.78	0.98	1.21	1.43	....
7	0.18	0.28	0.40	0.53	0.67	0.82	0.97	1.13
8	....	0.20	0.29	0.38	0.46	0.56	0.65	0.77
9	....	0.15	0.21	0.28	0.33	0.40	0.46	0.52
10	....	....	0.15	0.20	0.25	0.29	0.33	0.37
11	....	....	0.10	0.14	0.18	0.21	0.24	0.27
12	....	....	0.07	0.10	0.13	0.15	0.18	0.19
13	....	....	0.04	0.07	0.10	0.12	0.13	0.14

(4) Pressure of the Mercury Vapor. This causes a slight depression at high temperatures, but is less than 0.01 mm under 40 deg cent.

(5) Variation of weight with Latitude and Elevation. Multiply by $g/g_0 = (1 - 0.0026 \cos 2\phi - 0.000\ 000\ 2\ H)$, the local height obtained by applying the above corrections to the reading. The correction for elevation is only 0.1 mm at 700 m, but the correction for latitude may amount to as much as 2 mm.

Table VII. Mean Barometer Height b at an Elevation of H Meters above Sea Level (Kohlrausch)
Air at 10 deg cent (50 deg fahr) $b_0 = 760$ mm.

$H =$	0	100	200	300	400	500	600	700	800	900	1000 m
$b =$	760	751	742	733	724	716	707	699	690	682	674 mm
$H =$	1000	1100	1200	1300	1400	1500	1600	1700	1800	1900	2000 m
$b =$	674	666	658	650	642	635	627	620	612	605	598 mm

The international meterological formula for reducing height b of mercurial barometer at t deg cent and latitude ϕ to height b_0 at 0 deg cent and latitude 45° is

$$\log_\epsilon b_0 = \log_\epsilon b + \frac{H(1 - 3/8\ \epsilon/b)}{(18{,}429 + 67.5\ t + 0.003\ H)(1 + 0.0026 \cos 2\phi)}$$

41. HUMIDITY

There is always present in the atmosphere a greater or less quantity of invisible water vapor, mixed with the other gases. The *absolute humidity* is the mass of water vapor present per unit volume; and the gas pressure which this water vapor is exerting is called the *vapor pressure*. The ratio of the actual absolute humidity to the maximum quantity of water vapor that could be present at the existing temperature is the *relative humidity*. By means of suitable tables, the relative humidity may be computed from the difference between simultaneous readings of an ordinary thermometer and a thermometer with a wetted and amply ventilated bulb. The temperature at which the actual absolute humidity would be the maximum possible—i.e., the temperature at which the existing quantity of water vapor would produce saturation—is called the *dew point*.

Table VIII. Annual Means of Relative Humidity and Precipitation for Many Years

Stations		Annual Percentage of Relative Humidity at 8 A.M. 75th Meridian Time	Annual Amount Precipitation, in.	Stations		Annual Percentage of Relative Humidity at 8 A.M. 75th Meridian time	Annual Amount Precipitation, in.
Ala.........	Birmingham.	79	53.18	Ill........	Cairo.......	80	40.72
	Mobile......	84	61.61		Chicago.....	76	32.86
Ariz........	Flagstaff....	*	22.80		Springfield...	80	36.45
	Phoenix.....	57	7.78	Ind........	Indianapolis..	77	39.90
	Yuma.......	60	3.47		Des Moines..	80	32.04
Ark........	Fort Smith..	80	38.85	Iowa......	Dubuque....	79	32.90
	Little Rock..	80	48.38		Keokuk.....	78	32.64
Calif......	Fresno......	73	9.39	Kan......	Dodge City..	79	20.51
	Los Angeles..	77	15.23		Wichita.....	78	30.24
	Sacramento..	82	17.95	Ky........	Louisville....	76	43.26
	San Diego...	80	10.30	La........	New Orleans.	83	57.46
	San Francisco	86	22.02		Shreveport...	83	43.37
Col.......	Denver.....	64	14.05	Me........	Portland.....	75	41.94
	Grand Junc..	64	8.83	Md........	Baltimore....	72	42.56
	Pueblo......	66	11.67	Mass........	Boston......	73	40.14
Conn........	New Haven..	74	45.53	Mich......	Detroit......	79	32.05
D. C.........	Washington..	74	42.16		Marquette...	78	32.47
Fla.........	Jacksonville..	83	49.74		Port Huron..	81	28.93
	Key West....	78	38.11	Minn.....	Duluth......	83	27.94
	Pensacola....	81	57.85		St. Paul.....	80	27.24
	Tampa......	85	49.36	Miss........	Vicksburg....	82	51.93
Ga.........	Atlanta......	78	48.27	Mo......	Kansas City .	77	37.11
	Augusta.....	82	44.90		St. Louis....	76	37.44
	Savannah....	77	47.23		Springfield...	81	41.78
Idaho........	Boise.......	70	13.10	Mont........	Helena......	68	13.63

* Not Computed

Table VIII.—*Continued*

Stations		Annual Percentage of Relative Humidity at 8 A.M. 75th Meridian Time	Annual Amount Precipitation, in.	Stations		Annual Percentage of Relative Humidity at 8 A.M. 75th Meridian Time	Annual Amount Precipitation, in.
Mont.....	Kalispell......	81	15.02	R. I........Block Island..		80	41.30
	Miles City....	79	13.79	S. C........Charleston....		79	45.22
Neb......	N. Platte.....	81	18.39	S. D......	Huron........	82	20.65
	Omaha.......	78	27.77		Yankton......	80	25.30
Nev........Winnemucca..		67	8.54	Tenn.....	Chattanooga..	79	51.61
N. C......	Charlotte.....	78	46.05		Memphis.....	78	47.72
	Hatteras......	81	52.97		Nashville.....	80	47.20
	Wilmington...	81	46.93	Tex......	Abilene.......	75	25.17
N. D........Bismarck.....		81	16.34		Amarillo......	76	20.99
N. H.......Concord......		79	37.51		El Paso.......	54	9.16
N. J......	Atlantic City.	80	40.56		Galveston.....	84	44.77
	Cape May....	*	40.75		San Antonio...	82	27.18
N. Mex....Santa Fe.....		60	14.27	Utah.......Salt Lake City		60	16.13
N. Y......	Albany.......	78	34.58	Vt.........Burlington....		77	31.61
	Binghamton...	80	34.58	Va........	Lynchburg....	76	40.53
	Buffalo.......	78	36.00		Norfolk.......	79	44.09
	N. Y. City....	74	42.99	Wash.....	Seattle.......	87	34.03
	Oswego.......	79	35.21		Spokane......	77	16.62
Ohio......	Cincinnati....	77	38.55		Walla Walla...	71	17.01
	Columbus.....	79	36.34	W. Va....	Elkins.......	85	44.93
	Toledo.......	78	32.03		Parkersburg...	80	39.41
Okla.......Oklahoma City		80	31.15	Wis......	La Crosse.....	82	30.81
Oreg.......Portland......		85	41.62		Milwaukee....	78	30.08
Pa.......	Erie.........	75	36.93	Wyo.......Cheyenne.....		66	14.99
	Philadelphia...	74	40.41				
	Pittsburgh....	77	36.17				

* Not Computed

42. PROTECTION AGAINST LIGHTNING

The following discussion and rules have been abstracted from a Safety Code for Protection against Lightning which has been prepared for the American Engineering Standards Committee under the sponsorship of the National Bureau of Standards and the American Institute of Electrical Engineers. The material included here is intended to indicate the general principles to be followed. For details as to materials and methods reference should be made to the Code.

Protection of Buildings and Miscellaneous Property

Fundamental Principles of Protection. The fundamental theory of lightning protection for buildings is to provide means by which a discharge may enter or leave the earth without passing through a non-conducting part of the structure, as for example, parts which are made of wood, brick, tile, or concrete. Damage is caused by the heat and mechanical forces generated in such non-conducting portions by the discharge, whereas in metal parts the heat and mechanical forces are known to be of negligible effect if the metal has sufficient cross-sectional area. There is a strong tendency for lightning discharges on structures to travel on those metal parts which extend in the general direction of the discharge. Hence, if metal parts are provided, of proper proportions and distribution, damage can be largely prevented. However, because lightning has such a wide range of characteristics, it is difficult to provide any practicable means which will afford absolute protection under all conditions, although the degree of protection afforded by present practice is high if the installation is properly made.

The required condition that there be a metallic path for the part of the discharge which is intercepted is met most fully by a grounded metal or metal-covered structure which presents what might be thought of as an infinite number of parallel conductors from the uppermost part of the structure to earth. It is substantially met by a steel-framed structure, which, though faced with brick, terra-cotta, or other building material, usually has, or at relatively small cost can be equipped with, a sufficient number of metal terminals or receiving points on the upper portions which connect with the frame to protect it thoroughly.

For a structure which is built wholly or partly of non-conducting materials, one of the best defenses against direct hits by lightning is to surround it with a ring of grounded metallic masts or poles of sufficient height. Or, if the structure is not large, a single mast erected nearby may be sufficient. Experiments have indicated that, under certain assumed test conditions, such a vertical conductor will generally divert to itself all direct hits which might otherwise fall within a cone-shaped space of which the apex is the top of the conductor, and the base a circle of radius two to four times the height of the conductor. This agrees with theoretical deductions. Incidentally, any metallic structure, or adequately protected structure, will function in the same manner as a mast. Thus a tall steel windmill or water-tower or rodded steeple will tend to protect nearby structures of lesser height, although before relying upon such protection care should be taken to see that the structure lies well within the cone-shaped space mentioned above.

Generally, however, on account of architectural considerations, the mast type of protection is not feasible. More suitable protection is provided by the installation of lightning conductors. Here the required conditions of protection are closely approximated by placing air terminals or receiving points on the uppermost parts of the building, with interconnecting and grounding conductors attached to the building itself. By this means a relatively small amount of metal properly proportioned and distributed is made to afford a satisfactory degree of protection and at the same time, if necessary, to afford a minimum of interference with the contour of the structure. It should be stated, however, that this type of protection is to be considered only for structures in which very small induced sparks do not present an appreciable element of danger, as they do in oil tanks, cotton warehouses, and powder-storage houses. These require much more elaborate precautions to insure their safety than do the general run of buildings.

When designing and installing a system of protection of the lightning-rod type the following principles should be followed:

(a) The structure should be examined and all points or parts most likely to be struck by lightning should be noted, with the view of erecting air terminals thereon for the reception of the discharge. The object is to intercept the discharge immediately above the parts likely to be struck rather than to attempt to divert it in a direction it is not likely to take. The receiving points should be placed high enough above the structure to obviate danger of fire from the arc; the more inflammable the roof material the higher the points should be placed.

(b) Conductors should be installed with the view of offering the least possible obstruction to the passage of a stroke between air terminals and ground. The most direct path is in general the best, and there should be no sharp bends or loops for the lightning to jump across. The obstruction is practically inversely as the number of widely separated paths, so from each air terminal there should be at least two paths to ground and more if practicable. The number of paths is increased and the obstruction lessened by connecting the conductors to form a cage enclosing the building.

(c) When a stroke is about to take place to earth the surrounding surface of the ground for a radius of several miles carries an electric charge. As the discharge takes place this surface charge moves radially toward the ground end of the air path, forming an electric current in the ground. Near the point where the discharge enters the ground the current density becomes high, and if the flow takes place through the foundation wall of a building damage may result. Ground connections should therefore be distributed more or less symmetrically about the circumference of a structure rather than grouped on one side. With ground connections properly distributed the current will be collected at the outer extremities and a flow underneath the building minimized. In every case, for the foregoing reason, at least two ground connections should be made at opposite extremities of the structure. Satisfactory ground connections are made in the majority of cases by extending the rod into the earth to a distance of 6 to 10 ft. Driven rods or plates may be used as alternatives. If there is a water pipe nearby connection should be made to it.

(d) If a lightning conductor system is placed on a building within or about which are metal objects of considerable size within a few feet of the conductor, there will be a strong tendency for sparks, or sideflashes, to jump from the conductor to the metal at its nearest point. To prevent damage an interconnecting conductor should be provided at all places where sideflashes are likely to occur.

(e) Within buildings where metallic objects may be liable to a dangerous rise of potential due to a lightning flash, the metal, if not interconnected with the lightning-rod system, should under some circumstances be independently grounded.

(f) Since a lightning conductor system as a general rule is expected to remain in working condition for long periods with little attention, the mechanical construction should be strong and the materials used such as to offer high resistance to corrosion.

(g) The minimum permissible weight of copper conductor for all ordinary buildings is 187 1/2 lb per 1000 ft. The foregoing general principles are embodied in the detailed specifications mentioned at the beginning of this article, which correspond to the approval requirements of underwriters' laboratories. An approved lightning conductor, therefore, will meet the requirements of the Safety Code.

Protection of Structures Containing Inflammable Liquids and Gases from Lightning

Lightning is responsible for a majority of the tank fires of the petroleum industry. In a Report on Records of Oil Tank Fires in the United States, 1915–1925, published by the American Petroleum Institute, it was stated that lightning caused 55 per cent of the fires recorded.

1. Reduction of Damage. Certain types of structures used for the storage of inflammable liquids and gases are essentially self-protecting. Protection, of a greater or less degree, may be secured for others through the installation of various types of protective equipment, such as screens, rods, or protective towers, and by other means.

2. Fundamental Principles of Protection. Protection of structures and their contents from lightning involve the following principles.

(a) The storage of inflammable liquids and gases in all-metal structures essentially gas-tight.

(b) The use in all necessary breathing vents of efficient flame arresters.

(c) The maintenance of containers in good condition, so far as **potential hazards** from electrical discharges are concerned.

(d) The avoidance, so far as possible, of the accumulation of explosive mixtures, in and about such structures.

(e) The avoidance of spark gaps in metallic conductors or between metallic conductors at points where there may be an accumulation of explosive mixtures or an escape of inflammable vapors or gases to the air.

(f) In connection with structures not inherently self-protecting, the establishment of cones of protection through the use of grounded screens, rods, or towers, or the equivalent.

(g) The location of structures containing inflammable liquids and gases not inherently self-protecting, in positions of lesser exposure with regard to lightning. Thus elevated positions should be avoided.

43. WIND PRESSURE ON STRUCTURES

Windstorm Damage. According to the statistics of one of the large insurance companies * well over one-half of the total windstorm damage is caused by the high winds that accompany ordinary storms and thunder-storms. Much of the loss is directly attributable to the omission of anchorage of buildings to foundations, of roofs to the walls, to inadequate fastening of tiles and other roof coverings, and to similar neglect of good practice in construction details. It is not customary to design such details for definite wind loads, and aside from exceptional cases any reasonable provision gives ample strength.

Protection against very severe storms can be accomplished only by adequate engineering design of the whole structure.

Wind Velocity Measurement. When it is desired to design a structure to withstand high winds, great difficulty is experienced in determining the maximum wind velocity to which the structure will be exposed. The records of the Weather Bureau give the maximum average velocity indicated for a 5-min period, known as the *maximum*, and the velocity of the fastest mile, known as the *extreme*. At 100 miles per hour average velocity the *extreme* velocity is really the average over a period of 36 sec. The maximum gust velocities are known to be much greater. What then shall be the speed for which the design is to be made?

When the records at any one place are examined, it is found that the high velocities occur very infrequently. Therefore for such structures as telephone or power lines an attempt is made to balance the cost of replacement against the cost of insurance. In other words, it is cheaper to rebuild occasionally than to build the structure strong enough initially to withstand the maximum wind speeds. In buildings and other structures the element of human safety enters and the considerations of cost are not the only ones. Yet so far as tornadoes are concerned, it is usually felt to be impracticable to build strong enough to withstand the maximum speeds. The cost of insurance is far less than the increased construction costs.

FIG. 3

Robinson Anemometers. Prior to January 1, 1928, the official Weather Bureau instrument was a Robinson-type cup anemometer with a 4-cup driving unit (Fig. 3). The readings of this instrument were usually published without correction. Because of the large errors of that instrument at high speeds a change was made on January 1, 1928, to a 3-cup unit which had smaller errors. Beginning January 1, 1932, corrections for instrumental errors were applied to the data before publication, and no single type of instrument was considered as standard. At the present time an extensive investigation of anemometer design is in progress to develop a type of instrument having small errors.

---

* Associated Factory Mutual Fire Insurance Co., Boston, Mass. Handbook on Windstorms.

Table IX. Indicated Wind Speeds by Robinson Cup Anemometers

True Speed, miles per hour	Indicated Speed, Old 4-cup Standard	Indicated Speed, 1928 3-cup Standard	True Speed, miles per hour	Indicated Speed, Old 4-cup Standard	Indicated Speed, 1928 3-cup Standard
5	5	5	60	78	63
10	11	10	65	85	68
15	17	15	70	91	73
20	23	20	75	98	79
25	30	25	80	105	84
30	37	31	85	112	89
35	44	36	90	118	95
40	50	41	95	125	100
45	57	47	100	132	105
50	64	52	105	138	111
55	71	57	110	145	116

Note. Values above a true speed of 75 miles per hour are extrapolated, but are probably correct to the precision given, namely, 1 mile per hour.

Pitot Tubes. The standard instrument adopted by the National Bureau of Standards, National Physical Laboratory, and other scientific organizations for the measurement of air velocities is a Pitot-static tube of proper design. The instrument consists of an open tube facing into the wind and a concentric tube closed to the air stream except for several small holes drilled radially and sufficiently far from the nose that the air flows by smoothly when the tube is in line with the wind direction. A pressure gage is used to measure the difference in the pressure between the two tubes. The second tube gives the static pressure, i.e., the pressure that would be shown by a gage moving with the air. The first gives the static pressure plus the increased pressure produced by reducing the velocity to zero at the mouth of the tube. The differential pressure is $1/2\, dV^2$, where d is the density of the air and V the wind speed, and is known as the velocity pressure. Pitot-static tubes of poor design usually indicate a higher pressure because of a failure to give the true static

Table X. Wind-velocity Pressures

True Wind Speed, miles per hour	Velocity Pressure, lb per sq ft	True Wind Speed, miles per hour	Velocity Pressure, lb per sq ft	True Wind Speed, miles per hour	Velocity Pressure, lb per sq ft	True Wind Speed, miles per hour	Velocity Pressure, lb per sq ft
5	0.06	35	3.13	65	10.80	95	23.08
10	0.26	40	4.09	70	12.53	100	25.57
15	0.58	45	5.18	75	14.38	105	28.19
20	1.02	50	6.39	80	16.36	110	30.94
25	1.60	55	7.73	85	18.47	115	33.82
30	2.30	60	9.21	90	20.71	120	36.82

Note. The formula becomes $\dfrac{1}{2g}\, dV^2$ if the pressure is measured in pounds per square foot and the density in pounds per cubic foot.

pressure. Values of the velocity pressure at various wind speeds are given in Table X above for an air density of 0.07651 lb per sq ft corresponding to 15 deg cent, 760 mm Hg.

The dimensions of several standard Pitot tubes, which may be used without calibration if the supporting bracket is at least 20 diameters behind the static holes, are given in the figure.

Dines Tube Anemometer. The laboratory standard Pitot tubes are not suitable for use in field measurements of wind velocity but an instrument of this general type is in occasional use, namely, the Dines tube anemometer. In

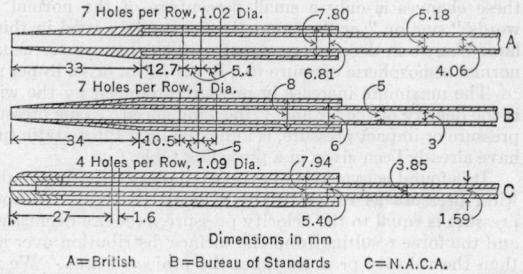

7 Holes per Row, 1.02 Dia.   7.80   5.18
A
33   12.7   5.1   6.81   4.06
7 Holes per Row, 1 Dia.   8
B
34   10.5   5   6   3
4 Holes per Row, 1.09 Dia.   7.94   3.85
C
27   1.6   5.40   1.59
Dimensions in mm

A = British   B = Bureau of Standards   C = N.A.C.A.
Fig. 4

this instrument, the impact tube is kept pointed into the wind by means of a weather vane while the static tube is vertical. Because of this arrangement of the static tube a calibration factor is necessary and it has recently been shown that the factor depends to some extent on the wind direction and on the exact constructional details of the instrument.*

The pressures developed are transmitted to a float or diaphragm whose motion is recorded by a pen on a chart. Gusts are shown in the records, and average velocities over comparatively short intervals of time can be estimated by a consideration of the inertia effects.

Electrical Anemometers. Recently several instruments giving an indication and record of wind velocity have been developed. They consist of an electric generator driven by either a 4-cup or 3-cup Robinson anemometer wheel. The voltage is indicated or recorded, the scale being graduated in terms of wind velocity. Gust velocities are indicated and can be evaluated for comparatively short time intervals by a consideration of the inertia effects.

Bridled Cup Anemometer. Still another type of instrument for field indication of wind velocity is the bridled cup anemometer, available in an instrument developed by Julien P. Friez. A multiblade turbine wheel is rotated against a spring system to a position of equilibrium such that the spring torque balances the wind torque on the wheel. The spring system is arranged to give a uniform wind velocity scale on the indicating dial.

Interpretation of Records. The only records available in sufficient quantity to be of any service to the engineer are those of the Weather Bureau for the maximum velocity over a 5-min period and the velocity of the fastest mile. The use and interpretation of these records in connection with any particular engineering project must be left to the judgment of the engineer in charge. If it is desired to build so strong that the structure will not fail under any possible circumstances, it is believed that the design should be made for a wind speed of 150 miles per hour.

It is commonly believed that the natural gusty wind imposes severe racking stresses which are greater than those imposed by a steady wind of the same speed. This is probably true only in rare instances, for most of the puzzling effects of high winds in lifting roofs, causing walls to fail outwards, etc., are readily explained by the nature of the pressure distribution in a steady wind.

Design Practice. The current practice of most structural engineers is to consider neither the shape of the structure, the nature of the exposure, nor the probable maximum wind velocity. All these variable factors are lumped together in a design wind load of usually 20 to 30 lb per sq ft. In addition, the usual factors of safety for the material are often waived, and the allowable working stresses increased 25, 50, or even 100 per cent— a procedure described by Fleming † as giving an intellectual assent to the theories of the textbook and ignoring them in actual practice. It would seem to be more logical to retain the same working stresses and to design for a properly selected wind velocity. To that end we attempt to give experimental data known to apply with sufficient accuracy for design purposes on the wind pressures on various engineering structures. From these data the wind load actually encountered at a selected wind velocity may be computed.

Method of Giving Wind Pressure Data.‡ The nature of the reaction between the wind and an obstacle to its progress is extremely complicated. Two characteristics should be emphasized. First, the reaction consists of a surface distribution of pressure, and the representation of the action by a single resultant force or by an average wind pressure is only a convenient device useful for certain purposes. Second, when there is no wind there is a distribution of pressure over the surface due to the normal atmospheric pressure of approximately 14.7 lb per sq in. The effect of the wind is a modification of this normal pressure, at some points an increase, at others a decrease, in pressure. The magnitude of these changes is only a small percentage of the normal atmospheric pressure, and the words " suction " or " vacuum " as commonly used in this connection do not imply any large change in density or pressure. The changes are usually less than 2 per cent of the normal atmospheric pressure (0.3 lb per sq in. or 42 lb per sq ft).

The maximum increase in pressure produced by the wind is equal to $1/2\, dV^2$, where d is the density of the air and V the wind speed. This pressure, usually termed the velocity pressure or impact pressure, is indicated by a Pitot-static tube of standard design. Values have already been given in a preceding table.

It is found convenient to express all observed pressure differences including the average wind pressure as ratios to the velocity pressure. Although the maximum increase in pressure is equal to the velocity pressure, pressure decreases of greater amount often occur and the force resulting from the surface distribution over a structure is frequently greater than the velocity pressure times the projected area. We may regard the ratio, or coefficient as it is sometimes called, as a shape factor. Thus if the shape factor is 1.5, we may

---

* Annual Report of the National Physical Laboratory, 1926, p. 217.
† Wind Pressure on Structures. Robin Fleming (Engineering News Co., 1915).
‡ From Sci. Paper 523, Bureau of Standards.

readily find the average pressure at any wind speed by multiplying by 1.5 the velocity pressure taken from the table.

The shape factor for a thin square flat plate normal to the wind is 1.12, and therefore the wind force on such a plate is 1.12 times the velocity pressure times the area. On an infinitely long thin rectangular plate the shape factor is 2.0. Other values are given later.

In the above examples the shape factor is very nearly independent of size or wind speed. In general, the shape factor depends to some degree on the size and speed, the variations being said to be due to scale effect. For bodies with flat surfaces and sharp edges, the scale effect is in general so small as to be negligible for the present purpose. For spheres and cylinders the variation is great, and critical regions of speed and size occur where the shape factor decreases very rapidly. In these cases it is difficult to predict the average pressure on a full-scale structure from model tests. The important practical structure of this type is the tall chimney.

It should be especially emphasized that no single value of the wind pressure is applicable to all types of structures for a given wind velocity. The variations in shape factor are sufficiently large to demand individual treatment.

Flat Plates, Signs, etc. The shape factor for a thin flat plate depends on the ratio of length to breadth. With the wind normal to the plate, the shape factor varies from 1.12 for a square or round plate to 1.33 for a rectangular plate of length-breadth ratio equal to 6. The wind force also varies with the angle of the plate to the wind. The direction of the resultant force is very nearly at right angles to the plate, and if the force is expressed as an average pressure over the area of the plate (*not* projected normal to the wind), the maximum shape coefficients observed are 1.75 for a square plate, 1.00 for a rectangular plate of length-breadth ratio equal to 3 and 1.34 for a rectangular plate of length-breadth ratio equal to 6. The detailed values for several angles to the wind are given in International Critical Tables, Vol. 1, p. 406. For approximately square signs, a shape factor of 1.75 should be used. For rectangular signs, the factor may be reduced as indicated by the above values.

Structural Shapes, Bridge Trusses. The shape factor for a very long thin flat plate is 2. In attempting to apply this value to built-up structures such as bridge trusses or radio towers difficulty is experienced owing to shielding. Experiments on built-up members have been published in *Ergebnisse der aerodynamischen Versuchsanstalt zu Göttingen*, Vol. III, 1927; and experiments are in progress at the National Physical Laboratory of Great Britain. Reference should be made to the original publication for details as to the variation of the shape factors with angle.

On simple structural steel shapes such as angles, I beams, and built-up columns, the wind pressure is referred to the product of the length of the section by the greater dimension of the cross-section. The resultant force is resolved parallel to this dimension and perpendicular to it, and two shape factors are given. We consider here only the shape factor for the component perpendicular to the greater dimension of the cross-section; i.e., the component giving the highest stress. The maximum values observed ranged from 1.6 to 2.2., usually being about 2 and occurring when the wind was normal to the face of greater area. We may therefore conclude that a safe value for isolated structural steel shapes is 2.

A number of model bridge trusses were tested. When used singly, the shape factors were from 1.4 to 1.6 referred to the projected area of the truss. When two trusses were placed one behind the other with wind normal to the plane of the truss, the shape factor for the front truss was from 1.4 to 1.6 for all positions of the rear truss, and for all models, whereas that for the rear truss varied, with the distance apart from 0.0 to 1.2, depending on the ratio of open to closed area.

Further experiments were made on one model at a given spacing (2.75 times the vertical dimension of truss) by varying the wind direction in both horizontal and vertical directions. Variation in the vertical plane is most important, the shielding effect disappearing at an angle of 15 deg.

A further experiment was made on a model consisting of two trusses spaced a distance equal to the maximum vertical dimension of the truss with floor between. In this case the shape factor referred to the area of *one* truss reached the value 1.85, and at varying angles in the vertical plane a large lifting force was found. Bridges across deep canyons or in other locations where variations of the wind direction in a vertical direction are possible may need some provision to take care of possible lifting forces.

The most recent and authoritative data on the wind pressure on open frameworks are contained in the paper Winddruck auf vollwandige Bauwerke und Gitterfachwerke, by O. Flachsbart, published in the first volume of *Mémoires de l'association internationale des ponts et charpentes*, Zurich, 1932. The shape coefficient of a single truss of a given perimeter was found to be a function of the solidity ratio, i.e., the projected area of the individual truss members divided by the total projected area within the perimeter of the framework.

The coefficient is approximately independent of the distribution of the individual members. Flachsbart proposed for design purposes a coefficient of 2.0 for solidity ratios between 0 and 0.2, 1.8 for those between 0.2 and 0.3, 1.6 for those between 0.3 and 0.9, and 2.0 for those between 0.9 and 1.0.

For two frameworks, one behind the other, at distances of the order of the width of the framework, the shape coefficient to be applied to the area of *one* truss is as follows:

Solidity Ratio	Shape Coefficient
0.1	3.6
.2	2.7
.3	2.4
.4	2.2
.5	2.0

In any large project where wind forces are an important item, wind-tunnel tests of a model will more than pay their cost.

Buildings, Skyscrapers. For tall buildings of usual proportions it appears that a shape factor in the neighborhood of 1.5 is required.* For slender towers the factor probably approaches 2.0 as for a long prism. For buildings of approximately cubical form, the factor is from 0.8 to 1.0. As is true for bridge structures, model tests are justified in important projects. Otherwise an estimate should be made from the known shape factors given in the table below:

Cube	0.8
Thin square flat plate	1.1
Prism 1 by 3	1.5
Very long prism	2.0

Frequently questions arise as to the strength of individual walls. Here the load depends on the pressure in the interior of the building which in turn depends on the number, size, and location of openings. It seems probable that in many cases the average pressure on a wall may equal twice the velocity pressure. The average pressure over small areas may reach three times the velocity pressure. It should especially be noted that the force may be in either direction depending on the pressure within the building, and the outward collapse of walls in high winds is readily explained without the necessity of assuming a very low barometric pressure.

Roofs. The force on a roof also depends on the pressure within the building, which is somewhat indeterminate. The distribution on the outer surface is such as to give ordinarily a lifting force provided the pitch of the roof does not exceed 30 deg. There seems to be no occasion for providing for a wind load acting downward on the roof under these conditions. There is every reason to provide for substantial lifting forces which are present even when the wind does not penetrate beneath the roof covering. If the interior is not subject to the full velocity pressure through broken windows or otherwise, the upward loading is of the order of 0.7 to 1 times the velocity pressure. Under special circumstances, such as in a factory-type building with windows broken on the windward side, the loading may reach twice the velocity pressure. The roof should accordingly be securely anchored to the walls and the walls in turn to the foundations.

When the pitch of the roof exceeds 30 deg, regions of increased pressure appear as shown by the experiments of T. E. Stanton (*Proc. Inst. C. E.*, London, 156, 1903–04, p. 78).

A large number of measurements of wind pressure on roofs and buildings were published in *Jahrbuch der deutschen Gesellschaft für Bauingenieurwesen*, 1927, p. 87.

Volume 97 of *Engineering News-Record* contains analyses of the effects of the Florida hurricane of 1926 which show that pressures of 55 to 65 lb per sq ft were attained. The wind velocity was independently estimated as 132 miles per hour, which would give the observed pressures on structures having a shape factor of 1.5.

Additional model experiments on an approximately cubical structure are given in Volume 100, No. 13, p. 508, by Professor Dawley of the Kansas State Agricultural College. These give shape factors from 0.7 to 0.85, depending on the presentation of the model to the wind and the presence or absence of windows and doors.

Chimneys, Standpipes, Gas-holders, Flag Poles, Transmission Lines. If the product of diameter in feet by wind speed in miles per hour is less than about 40, the shape factor for cylindrical structures may be taken from the Table XI.

The flow about cylinders in this region in a steady wind is very definitely periodic, the frequency in cycles per second being equal to about 0.3 times the ratio of the wind speed in miles per hour to the diameter in feet. Care should be taken that the natural period of vibration of the structure does not correspond to the above eddy frequency at high wind speeds. It is understood that in some cases transmission lines have been observed to

---

* Scientific Paper 523, Bureau of Standards.

vibrate (in segments) with the eddy frequency and under certain conditions cause fatigue failures.

When the product of diameter in feet by wind speed in miles per hour exceeds 40, the shape factor is found to decrease to a comparatively low value. Experiments on full-scale cylinders in a natural wind indicate a value as low as 0.3 to 0.4. The flow is no longer definitely periodic but is very irregular and often unsymmetrical. Sufficient information is not available to justify such a radical reduction in the shape factor. Until the flow about large cylinders

Table XI. Shape Factors for Cylindrical Structures

Ratio of Length to Diameter	Shape Factor	Ratio of Length to Diameter	Shape Factor
1	0.63	10	0.83
2	0.69	20	0.92
3	0.75	40	1.00
5	0.74	Infinite	1.20

is fully understood, it is recommended that the same shape factors be used as for small cylinders.

In transmission lines, the problem of shielding again appears since individual wires are near each other. It is common practice to compute the wind force not on the actual wire but on the wire assumed coated with ice $1/2$ in. in thickness. The shielding depends on the spacing of the wires, and on the wind speed. With a spacing of about 1 ft, the force on the shielded wires is about 50 per cent of that on the front unshielded wire. The factor for an unshielded wire may be taken from the table above.

If the wind blows at an angle to a single wire, the force remains nearly normal to the wire and the magnitude of the force falls off approximately as the square of the sine of the angle of the wire to the wind.

General Remarks on the Choice of Shape Coefficients. It has been assumed in the foregoing treatment that the winds of high velocity might come from any direction, and only the maximum shape coefficients are given. Under certain special conditions it may be found that high winds are likely to prevail only from certain directions. Some further study than that given here is then necessary.

In any extensive construction where wind loads are an important factor, the shape factor should be determined by wind tunnel experiments on a model.

Air Resistance of Automobiles. The observed shape coefficients found for automobiles of conventional design vary from about 0.75 to 1.35* depending on the exact shape. Special streamline automobiles and racing cars have been designed for which the shape coefficient is as low as 0.2. The area to which the shape coefficients apply is the area of projection on a plane normal to the usual direction of motion.

An average value is of doubtful service since in most cases the resistance of a particular automobile is desired for certain specified conditions of car speed, wind speed, and wind direction. This is most readily found by wind tunnel experiments on a model, since full-scale conditions are not easily controlled.

The effect of natural winds is an important one, especially as the speed of the car approaches or exceeds 100 miles per hour. Lateral forces, lifting forces, and turning moments become of appreciable magnitude. Some experiments described in Research Papers 591 and 749 of the U. S. Bureau of Standards show that a streamline model may maintain its advantage of a lower resistance to motion as compared to conventional model up to relative wind angles of 40 deg. The lateral forces are also less for the streamline model. The vertical lifting forces do not differ much for relative wind angles up to 40 deg. However, the turning moments, which tend to produce skidding, are considerably greater for the streamline model.

Air Resistance of Trains. A few papers have appeared on the determination of the air resistance of trains.† It appears from the experiments of Goss that the shape factor for an isolated car is about 0.5, applied to the area of projection normal to the usual direction of motion. For the first car in a train the factor is about 0.4, second car about 0.036, other intermediate cars about 0.04, last car 0.1.

The French experiments were carried out on a train consisting of locomotive, tender, and two cars, the dimensions of which are not given. The coefficients appear to be of the same order of magnitude as those found by Goss, except for the intermediate car. Those interested should consult the original papers for details as to the shapes of the cars.

No information is available on the effect of angle of the train to the relative wind. It seems probable that as with automobiles a comparatively small side wind will introduce a fairly large side force.

---

* *Public Roads*, vol. 6, No. 9, Nov. 1925, p. 203. *Zeitschrift für Flugtechnik und Motorluft-schiffahrt*, vol. 15, 1924, p. 22; also 13, 1922, p. 201. *Motorwagen*, vol. 26, 1923, p. 355.

† W. F. M. Goss, Atmospheric resistance to the motion of railway trains, *Proc. Western Ry. Club*, vol. 10, p. 347, 1897–98. Ch. Maurain, A. Touissant, and R. Pris, Mésure de la résistance de l'air sur le matériel des chemins de fer, *Comp. Rend.*, vol. 177, p. 308, July, 1923.

SECTION 10

CHEMISTRY

BY

JOSEPH MATTIELLO AND SIDNEY B. TUWINER

CHEMISTRY

GENERAL CHEMISTRY

1. CHEMICAL ELEMENTS

Atoms. All forms of matter may be decomposed by the proper choice of conditions of treatment to ultimate units upon which the modern science of chemistry is based. These are known as *atoms*. These ultimate units cannot then be further reduced by the conditions of temperature, pressure, electrical voltage, etc., ordinarily available.

Ninety-two kinds of such atoms, variously combined and associated, constitute the building blocks of the material universe.

Elements. A substance composed of a multitude of a single kind of atom is known as an *element*. There are thus ninety-two elements, named and classified in Table I. All the atoms of an element may be considered to be identical with respect to mass and other properties. For convenience the names of these elements have all been abbreviated to *symbols*, as H for hydrogen, O for oxygen, etc.

Table I. The Chemical Elements

In the following table, in every case the atomic number is given as well as the atomic weight. The atomic weights are those of 1934.

Name *	Symbol	Atomic Number	Atomic Weight	Nature
Actinium	Ac	89	....	....
Aluminum	Al	13	26.97	Metal
Antimony (stibium)	Sb	51	121.76	Metal
Argon	A	18	39.944	Inert gas
Arsenic	As	33	74.91	Metalloid
Barium	Ba	56	137.36	Metal
Beryllium (glucinum)	Be	4	9.02	Metal
Bismuth	Bi	83	209.00	Metal
Boron	B	5	10.82	Metalloid
Bromine	Br	35	79.916	Liquid
Cadmium	Cd	48	112.41	Metal
Calcium	Ca	20	40.08	Metal
Carbon	C	6	12.000	Metalloid
Cassiopeium (see Lutecium)	Cp	71	....	....
Celtium (see Hafnium)	Ct	72	....	....
Cerium	Ce	58	140.13	Metal
Cesium	Cs	55	132.91	Metal
Chlorine	Cl	17	35.457	Gas
Chromium	Cr	24	52.01	Metal
Cobalt	Co	27	58.94	Metal
Columbium (niobium)	Cb	41	93.3	Metal
Copper (cuprum)	Cu	29	63.57	Metal
Dysprosium	Dy	66	162.46	Metal
Erbium	Er	68	165.20	Metal
Europium	Eu	63	152.0	Metal
Fluorine	F	9	19.00	Most active gas
Gadolinium	Gd	64	157.30	Metal
Gallium	Ga	31	69.72	Metal
Germanium	Ge	32	72.60	Metal
Glucinum (same as beryllium)	Gl	4	....	....
Gold (aurum)	Au	79	197.2	Metal
Hafnium (celtium)	Hf	72	178.6	Metal
Helium	He	2	4.002	Inert gas
Holmium	Ho	67	163.5	Metal
Hydrogen	H	1	1.0078	Lightest gas
Indium	In	49	114.76	Metal
Iodine	I	53	126.92	Metalloid
Iridium	Ir	77	193.1	Metal

* Names of the more abundant elements are in bold-face type.

Table I. The Chemical Elements—Continued

Name *	Symbol	Atomic Number	Atomic Weight	Nature
Iron (ferrum)	Fe	26	55.84	Metal
Krypton	Kr	36	82.7	Inert gas
Lanthanum	La	57	138.92	Metal
Lead (plumbum)	Pb	82	207.22	Metal
Lithium	Li	3	6.940	Metal
Lutecium (cassiopeium)	Lu	71	175.0	Metal
Magnesium	Mg	12	24.32	Metal
Manganese	Mn	25	54.93	Metal
Masurium	Ma	43	....	....
Mercury (hydrargyrum)	Hg	80	200.61	Metal
Molybdenum	Mo	42	96.0	Metal
Neodymium	Nd	60	144.27	Metal
Neon	Ne	10	20.183	Inert gas
Nickel	Ni	28	58.69	Metal
Niobium (see Columbium)	Nb	41	....	....
Niton (see Radon)	Nt	86	....	....
Nitrogen	N	7	14.008	Gas
Osmium	Os	76	191.5	Metal
Oxygen	O	8	16.000	Gas
Palladium	Pd	46	106.7	Metal
Phosphorus	P	15	31.02	Metalloid
Platinum	Pt	78	195.23	Metal
Polonium	Po	84	(210)	....
Potassium (kalium)	K	19	39.096	Metal
Praseodymium	Pr	59	140.92	Metal
Protoactinium	Pa	91	....	....
Radium	Ra	88	225.97	Metal
Radon	Rn	86	222.	Emanation
Rhenium	Re	75	186.31	....
Rhodium	Rh	45	102.91	Metal
Rubidium	Rb	37	85.44	Metal
Ruthenium	Ru	44	101.7	Metal
Samarium	Sm	62	150.43	Metal
Scandium	Sc	21	45.10	Metal
Selenium	Se	34	78.96	Metalloid
Silicon	Si	14	28.06	Metalloid
Silver (argentum)	Ag	47	107.880	Metal
Sodium (natrium)	Na	11	22.997	Metal
Strontium	Sr	38	87.63	Metal
Sulfur	S	16	32.06	Metalloid
Tantalum	Ta	73	181.4	Metal
Tellurium	Te	52	127.61	Metalloid
Terbium	Tb	65	159.2	Metal
Thallium	Tl	81	204.39	Metal
Thorium	Th	90	232.12	Metal
Thulium	Tm	69	169.4	Metal
Tin (stannum)	Sn	50	118.70	Metal
Titanium	Ti	22	47.90	Metal
Tungsten (wolfram)	W	74	184.0	Metal
Uranium	U	92	238.14	Metal
Uranium–X₂ (isotope of protoactinium)	UX₂	91	(234)	....
Vanadium	V	23	50.95	Metal
Xenon	Xe	54	131.3	Inert gas
Ytterbium	Yb	70	173.04	Metal
Yttrium	Y	39	88.92	Metal
Zinc	Zn	30	65.38	Metal
Zirconium	Zr	40	91.22	Metal

* Names of the more abundant elements are in bold-face type.

Molecules. The reactions of the elements are the result of the reactions of the constituent atoms. Combinations of atoms are known as *molecules*, which are the ultimate units obtained by physical division of *compounds*. Compounds are the products of the combination of two or more elements. The symbol H may be taken to represent either the element hydrogen or a single hydrogen atom. Similarly, O may represent either the element oxygen or a single oxygen atom. The formula H_2O, which represents a molecule of water, indicates that such a molecule consists of two atoms of hydrogen and one of oxygen. Atoms and elements are thus represented by symbols; molecules and compounds, by formulas.

Most of the gaseous elements, at ordinary temperatures, are *diatomic*, i.e., their molecules consist of two atoms. Thus we have the formulas: H_2, O_2, Cl_2, Br_2, N_2, etc.

Reactions. Formulas, representing compositions, may be combined into *chemical equations* representing *reactions*. Thus $2H_2 + O_2 \rightarrow 2H_2O$. This is an abbreviated statement of the fact that two molecules of hydrogen may, under favorable conditions, react with one of oxygen to yield two molecules of water. The hydrogen and oxygen are called *reactants*; the water is called the *product*. It will be observed that the number of hydrogen and of oxygen atoms in the reactants is equal to the number in the product. The equation is then said to be *balanced*. All true equations must be balanced since matter can neither be created nor destroyed, in accordance with the *Law of Conservation of Matter*.

2. CHEMISTRY OF WATER

A Molecule of Water, corresponding to the formula H_2O, consists of two atoms of hydrogen with an atomic weight of 1.008 and one of oxygen with an atomic weight of 16. The proportion of the constituent elements by weight is therefore approximately one-ninth hydrogen and eight-ninths oxygen.

Water may be formed according to the reaction $2H_2 + O_2 \rightarrow 2H_2O$ by the spontaneous reaction of hydrogen and oxygen in a gaseous mixture. The combination occurs with explosive violence upon the application of a small spark or flame. Decomposition of water into its constituents can be accomplished only by the application of considerable energy by the passage of an electric current through the liquid. Pure hydrogen is then liberated at the cathode or negative electrode, while pure oxygen gas is liberated at the anode or positive electrode. This is the reverse reaction of that of combination, in which rôles of reactants and products are interchanged.

Decomposition. Certain very active metallic elements displace one of the two hydrogen atoms in the water molecule.

$$\left.\begin{array}{l} 2Na + 2H_2O \rightarrow 2NaOH + H_2 \\ 2K + 2H_2O \rightarrow 2KOH + H_2 \end{array}\right\} \tag{1}$$

These elements, sodium and potassium, react with water very vigorously to liberate hydrogen. The products other than hydrogen are sodium hydroxide and potassium hydroxide, respectively. These dissolve and remain in solution in the excess of water. Other metallic elements such as barium, calcium, magnesium, etc., displace hydrogen similarly from water, though less vigorously in the order given.

Other, less active, metals such as iron, displace hydrogen from water only when in the form of steam at high temperature.

$$3Fe + 4H_2O \rightarrow Fe_3O_4 + 4H_2 \tag{2}$$

In this case, an oxide, magnetic iron oxide, is formed.

Hydroxides. Oxides of some of the metallic elements combine with water with great avidity. The products are *hydroxides*.

$$\left.\begin{array}{l} Na_2O + H_2O \rightarrow 2NaOH \quad \text{(sodium hydroxide)} \\ K_2O + H_2O \rightarrow 2KOH \quad \text{(potassium hydroxide)} \\ CaO + H_2O \rightarrow Ca(OH)_2 \text{ (calcium hydroxide)} \\ BaO + H_2O \rightarrow Ba(OH)_2 \text{ (barium hydroxide)} \end{array}\right\} \tag{3}$$

Hydrates. Many salts combine with water to form hydrated compounds. Thus

$$\left.\begin{array}{l} CuSO_4 + 5H_2O \rightarrow CuSO_4 \cdot 5H_2O \\ Al_2(SO_4)_3 + 18H_2O \rightarrow Al_2(SO_4)_3 \cdot 18H_2O \\ CaCl_2 + 6H_2O \rightarrow CaCl_2 \cdot 6H_2O \end{array}\right\} \tag{4}$$

Such compounds are called *hydrates*. The special method of writing their formulas is to be noted. It indicates that the water they contain is loosely bound and may be readily removed by the application of heat. Often the number of molecules of water which a hydrate contains depends upon the temperature of its formation and the availability of the water. At sufficiently high temperatures all are reduced to the anhydrous condition.

Oxides of aluminum, iron, and the heavy metals are more stable and combine with water much less readily.

Acids. Oxides of non-metallic elements also combine readily with water. The products are *acids*.

$$\left.\begin{array}{l} N_2O_5 + H_2O \rightarrow 2HNO_3 \quad \text{(nitric acid)} \\ P_2O_5 + 3H_2O \rightarrow 2H_3PO_4 \text{ (phosphoric acid)} \\ SO_3 + H_2O \rightarrow H_2SO_4 \quad \text{(sulfuric acid)} \end{array}\right\} \tag{5}$$

3. VALENCE, IONIC DISSOCIATION, AND ATOMIC DISINTEGRATION

Atomic Forces. Modern theory recognizes that the forces which bind atoms into molecules are electrical in character, and are the forces of attraction of unlike charges.

Positive and Negative Valence. Atoms, or groups of atoms, which have a tendency to gain electrons are said to be acidic in character; atoms, or groups of atoms, which tend to lose electrons are said to be basic. The non-metals are acidic, the metals basic. The number of electrons which a non-metal may gain is called its *negative valence*; the number of electrons which a metallic atom may lose is called its *positive valence*.

Oxygen with a negative valence of two may combine with two atoms of hydrogen with a positive valence of one to form H_2O. The rule is that the sum of the positive valences in a stable inorganic substance must equal the sum of the negative valences to give molecules which are electrically neutral. Thus in potassium dichromate, $K_2Cr_2O_7$, potassium has a positive valence of one, chromium a positive valence of six, and oxygen a negative valence of two. The sum of the positive valences is $2 \times 1 + 2 \times 6 = 14$; the sum of the negative valences is $7 \times 2 = 14$. In sulfuric acid, H_2SO_4, hydrogen has a positive valence of one, sulfur a positive valence of six, and oxygen a negative valence of two. The sum of the positive valences is $2 \times 1 + 1 \times 6 = 8$, and the sum of the negative valences is $4 \times 2 = 8$. In this way a knowledge of valence may be very helpful in the writing of formulas.

Ions. Many inorganic compounds dissociate in aqueous solutions into positive elements or groups of elements and an equal number of negative elements or groups of elements. The ultimate units of these dissociation products differ from ordinary atoms or groups of atoms in that they carry units of positive or of negative electricity; they are called ions. Such solutions are capable of conducting an electric current and show a number of other electrical manifestations which will be treated in the section on Electrochemistry. The subject of ionic dissociation is very important for the reason that the properties of these solutions are equivalent to the summation of the properties of the constituent ions, which serves to simplify their treatment very considerably.

Isotopes. Modern theory assumes that atoms consist merely of configurations of positive and negative electric charges and that their properties, and thus the properties of the elements, depend upon these configurations. The simplest of these is that of the hydrogen atom, while all the heavier atoms are supposed to consist merely of multiples of this fundamental atomic unit. This is confirmed by the observation that the atomic weights of most of the elements are approximately integers. Those which appear to deviate from this rule have, in many cases, been shown to be mixtures of two or more so-called isotopes whose atomic weights are, in fact, integers. *Isotopes* are simply variations of an element, identical in every property except in those depending upon their atomic weights.

Many isotopes are known, and more are constantly being discovered and isolated. Those of greatest present interest are of the element hydrogen, which has been found to contain three. Inasmuch as the atomic weights of isotopes differ by integral values, and since the atomic weight of the simplest and most abundant isotope of hydrogen has an atomic weight of approximately one, the second isotope is twice as heavy, so that here the difference in behavior between isotopes is greatly accentuated. It is for this reason that so much interest has been devoted to this subject. The second hydrogen isotope is found in comparatively minute amounts accompanying the first; its concentration entails such a great amount of effort that it is, at present, very expensive. The third hydrogen isotope has not as yet been isolated but is known to exist on the basis of evidence obtained from the so-called mass spectroscope. Efforts to effect its concentration have already met with considerable success.

Heavy Water. The second hydrogen isotope combines with oxygen to form water having a molecular weight of 20—so-called *heavy water*—as compared with 18 for ordinary water. This " heavy water " is actually present in small concentrations in natural waters and may be concentrated by selective decomposition such as may be produced by electrolytic decomposition, a method which has been the subject of numerous refinements.

Table II. Formula for Different Waters

	Atomic Weight of Hydrogen	Formula	Atomic Weight of Water
Ordinary water	1	H_2O	18
Heavy water	2	D_2O	20

Radioactivity and Atomic Disintegration. Although the elements are ordinarily stable against decomposition, certain of the heavier ones change spontaneously. Thus the element radium changes gradually into lead accompanied by the *emission of rays* which are common to all radioactive substances. The so-called *alpha-rays* are known to be doubly charged atoms of helium, the *beta-rays* electrons, and the *gamma-rays* are radiations similar to light but of much shorter wavelength. The alpha-rays are positively charged while the beta-rays are negative, an observation which indicates that matter is fundamentally electrical in nature.

The alpha- and beta-rays consist of material particles at high velocities. Similar rays have been artificially induced by purely electrical means. By the impact of such particles on otherwise stable atoms, elements have been transmuted, a feat which was long deemed impossible.

4. ACIDS, BASES, AND SALTS

Acids

The Simplest Acids, and those which typify in many respects the properties of acids in general, are those of the halogen elements: fluorine, chlorine, bromine, and iodine in simple combination with hydrogen, represented by the formulas H_2F_2, HCl, HBr, and HI. The most common of these is HCl, known as hydrogen chloride or hydrochloric acid. This substance may be produced from its constituent elements by introducing a flame into a gaseous mixture of hydrogen and chlorine or by exposing the mixture to light.

Hydrochloric Acid is very soluble in water, in which it undergoes ionic dissociation according to the following equation:

$$HCl \rightarrow H^+ + Cl^- \tag{6}$$

the positive and negative signs indicating electric charges. This reaction goes practically to completion, for which reason hydrochloric acid is known as a strong acid.

The Acid Character of a Solution is due solely to the presence of hydrogen ions, H^+. Perhaps the most characteristic and distinguishing property of solutions of acids is the sour taste which may be regarded as the taste of hydrogen ion. Hydrosulfuric acid, or hydrogen sulfide, H_2S, is an example of a very weak acid which dissociates only very slightly, and which manifests the properties of acids very sparingly. Other acids which are even weaker, and a great number of intermediate strength, are known.

Sulfuric Acid is an example of an acid which may dissociate to furnish two hydrogen ions for each molecule.

$$H_2SO_4 \rightarrow 2H^+ + SO_4^{--} \tag{7}$$

The SO_4 group which furnishes the SO_4^{--} ion (doubly charged) is called a *radical*, and is bivalent. A *radical* is a group of atoms which is found in a series of compounds and which gives them a characteristic property common to them all. Phosphoric acid, H_3PO_4, may furnish three hydrogen ions, and contains the trivalent radical PO_4.

Bases

Sodium Hydroxide, together with other hydroxides, are called bases. They dissolve in water to yield alkalis, or alkaline solutions, ionizing as follows:

$$NaOH \rightarrow Na^+ + OH^- \tag{8}$$

The monovalent radical OH thus yields the OH^- ion which is as characteristic of alkalis as H^+ is of acids and which gives alkaline solutions a soapy feel and an alkaline, or caustic taste.

Calcium Hydroxide, $Ca(OH)_2$, is an example of a base which may furnish two hydroxyl ions per molecule. Trivalent and higher bases are generally very insoluble, and are therefore only weakly alkaline.

Neutralization

If an acid solution, containing hydrogen ions, is mixed with an alkaline solution, containing hydroxyl ions, the two react with considerable evolution of heat. For the case of sodium hydroxide and hydrochloric acid, the following series of equations indicates the reaction:

$$NaOH \rightleftarrows Na^+ + OH^-$$
$$HCl \rightleftarrows Cl^- + H^+ \tag{9}$$
$$\Updownarrow$$
$$H_2O$$

Thus the hydrogen and hydroxyl ions react to form water which is identical with the solvent. The solution thus contains only sodium, Na^+, and chloride, Cl^-, ions if the acid and base are in equivalent proportions. Upon evaporating the solution, these ions combine to form solid, crystalline sodium chloride.

$$Na^+ + Cl^- \rightarrow NaCl \quad \text{(common salt)} \tag{10}$$

If only the initial reactants and the final product are considered, omitting the ionic intermediates, we have

$$NaOH + HCl \rightarrow NaCl + H_2O \tag{11}$$

This molecular equation is the more concise, and is generally used for that reason. The ionic equations, however, indicate the true course of the reaction.

This process is called *neutralization* for the reason that the acid and basic properties truly neutralize one another unless there is an excess of one or another of the reactants, in which cases the neutralization is only partial. The acid and the base owe their properties to hydrogen and to hydroxyl ions, neither of which are present in the resulting salt typified by sodium chloride. A large number of salts are known, some of which will be discussed below.

Calcium hydroxide, $Ca(OH)_2$, each molecule of which is capable of neutralizing two of HCl, is known as a diacid base. Similarly aluminum hydroxide, $Al(OH)_3$, is a triacid base, etc. Sulfuric acid, H_2SO_4, is a dibasic acid, while phosphoric acid, H_3PO_4, is a tribasic acid.

Reversibility

Many reactions of chemistry are reversible, i.e., the products may become reactants so that the process moves backwards. Equilibrium will be attained when the forward and backward reactions progress at the same rate so that the proportions of the substances involved do not change with time. In the ionization of hydrogen sulfide to hydrogen and hydrosulfide ions.

$$H_2S \leftrightarrows H^+ + HS^- \tag{12}$$

the double arrow indicates the reversibility. The tendency to react in the forward direction will be proportional to the concentration of H_2S; the tendency to move backwards will be proportional to the concentration of H^+ and also proportional to the concentration of HS^-. Thus we have:

$$\text{Forward tendency} = K_1 (H_2S) \tag{12a}$$

$$\text{Backward tendency} = K_2 (H^+)(HS^-) \tag{12b}$$

where the parentheses indicate numerical concentration of the substances included therein in any convenient units. For convenience in calculations of this sort the unit generally employed is the mol per liter. The mol is simply the molecular weight expressed in grams. For example, a mol of hydrogen (H_2) gas would be 2 grams; a mol of oxygen (O_2) gas 32 grams. A mol of any substance contains 6.06×10^{23} molecules, so that it is a practical unit proportional to the number of molecules.

At equilibrium the forward and backward tendencies in the above equation must be equated.

$$\left. \begin{array}{l} K_1 (H_2S) = K_2 (H^+)(HS)^- \\[2mm] \dfrac{(H^+)(HS^-)}{(H_2S)} = \dfrac{K_1}{K_2} = K \end{array} \right\} \tag{13}$$

or

where K is a constant known as the *dissociation constant*. If this constant is determined experimentally we have a mathematical equation from which we may determine the concentrations of reactants or products under any given conditions. This is an example of the so-called *Law of Mass Action*.

The second stage in the ionization involves the reaction:

$$HS^- \leftrightarrows H^+ + S^- \tag{14}$$

from which the equilibrium equation 15, may be derived:

$$\frac{(H^+)(S^=)}{(HS^-)} = K' \tag{15}$$

By multiplying equation 13 by equation 15

$$\frac{(H^+)^2(S^=)}{(H_2S)} = KK' = K'' \tag{16}$$

which is the equation for the complete ionization

$$H_2S \leftrightarrows 2H^+ + S^= \tag{17}$$

Thus it is seen that the factors which affect, and the equations which represent, a chemical equilibrium are independent of other intermediate equilibria. Equation 16 indicates, among other things, that the ionization of a typical weak acid, hydrogen sulfide, is repressed by increasing (H^+) through introduction of a strong acid such as HCl.

Hydrolysis

An important application of these principles is in the *hydrolysis* of certain salt solutions. To illustrate, a solution of sodium sulfide, Na_2S, will ionize to $2Na^+ + S^{--}$. Water also dissociates very slightly into hydrogen and hydroxyl ions.

$$H_2O \leftrightarrows H^+ + OH^- \tag{18}$$

The equation which describes this dissociation quantitatively is similar in form to that of the dissociation of hydrogen sulfide.

$$\frac{(H^+)(OH^-)}{(H_2O)} = K_{H_2O} \tag{19}$$

In fairly dilute solutions the concentration of the water (H_2O) does not change appreciably in percentage with small variations in the concentrations of dissolved substances so that it is usual to assume that it is a constant. The above then becomes

$$(H^+)(OH^-) = K'_{H_2O} = 10^{-14} \text{ numerically} \tag{19a}$$

The hydrogen ions formed by the dissociation of the water may combine with the sulfide ions of the sodium sulfide to form hydrosulfide ions described above. The equation for the equilibrium which may thus be established is

$$\frac{(H^+)(S^{--})}{(HS^-)} = K'_{HS^-} = 1.2 \times 10^{-15} \tag{20}$$

Combining the two equations we have

$$\frac{(OH^-)(HS^-)}{(S^{--})} = \frac{K_{H_2O}}{K'_{HS^-}} = 8.3 \tag{21}$$

which is the dissociation equation for the reaction

$$S^{--} + H_2O \leftrightarrows HS^- + OH^- \tag{22}$$

or as a molecular equation

$$Na_2S + H_2O \leftrightarrows NaHS + NaOH$$

This reaction is the reverse of neutralization, and is called *hydrolysis*. It represents the dissociation of a salt to an acid (or acid salt) and a base. Only salts formed from a weak acid, or a weak base, or both, hydrolyze appreciably. A salt of a weak acid and a strong base hydrolyzes to an alkaline solution; a salt of a strong acid and a weak base hydrolyzes to an acid solution.

pH and Acidity

The equation for the dissociation of water

$$(H^+)(OH^-) = K_{Ion} = 10^{-14} \tag{23}$$

expresses the interdependence of hydrogen- and hydroxyl-ion concentrations in aqueous solutions. These vary over such a wide range that their logarithms rather than their absolute values are employed. Taking logarithms of both sides.

$$-\log (H^+) - \log (OH^-) = 14 \tag{24}$$

The negative logarithm of hydrogen-ion concentration, $-\log (H^+)$, is called the pH and is a measure of acidity. The lower the pH the higher is the acidity or the lower the alkalinity. If the pH is 7 the hydrogen- and hydroxyl-ion concentrations are equal and the solution is neutral. This is the case in pure water or in solutions of neutral salts which do not hydrolyze appreciably. Solutions having a pH lower than 7 are acid; those having a pH higher than 7 are alkaline. As an example, a hydrogen-ion concentration of 10^{-5} mol per liter corresponds to a pH of 5. The pH of a solution may be measured by certain organic indicators which change in color according to the acidity or alkalinity; also by means of certain electrode potential methods and others of lesser importance.

5. SOLUTIONS AND RULES FOR SOLUBILITY

Solubility and Saturation

The above treatment is valid only for weak acids. Similar equations will now be derived which are quantitatively valid only for difficultly soluble salts.

Calcium sulfate, $(CaSO_4)$, in contact with water will dissolve according to the following equation:

$$\text{Solid } CaSO_4 \leftrightarrows Ca^{++} + SO_4^{--} \tag{25}$$

The reversibility of the reaction indicates that the dissolved salt tends to precipitate back to the solid phase. At equilibrium the two tendencies will be equal and the solution will then be said to be *saturated* with respect to the salt.

Table III. Solubilities of Certain Salts in Water at 18° (Professor Alexander Smith)*

	K	Na	Li	Ag	Ba	Sr	Ca	Mg	Zn	Pb
Cl	32.95	35.86	77.79	0.0_316	37.24	51.09	73.19	55.81	203.9	1.49
	3.9	5.42	13.3	0.0_410	1.7	3.0	5.4	5.1	9.2	0.05
Br	65.86	88.76	168.7	0.0_41	103.6	96.52	143.3	103.1	478.2	0.598
	4.6	6.9	12.6	0.0_66	2.9	3.4	5.2	4.6	9.8	0.02
I	137.5	177.9	161.5	0.0_635	201.4	169.2	200.0	148.2	419.0	0.08
	6.0	8.1	8.5	0.0_71	3.8	3.9	4.8	4.1	6.9	0.0_22
F	92.56	4.44	0.27	195.4	0.16	0.012	0.0016	0.0076	0.005	0.07
	12.4	1.06	0.11	13.5	0.0_29	0.001	0.0_32	0.0_214	0.0_25	0.003
NO$_3$	30.34	83.97	71.43	213.4	8.74	66.27	121.8	74.31	117.8	51.66
	2.6	7.4	7.3	8.4	0.33	2.7	5.2	4.0	4.7	1.4
ClO$_3$	6.6	97.16	313.4	12.25	35.42	174.9	179.3	126.4	183.9	150.6
	0.52	6.4	15.3	0.6	1.1	4.6	5.3	4.7	5.3	3.16
BrO$_3$	6.38	36.67	152.5	0.59	0.8	30.0	85.17	42.86	58.43	1.3
	0.38	2.2	8.20	0.025	0.02	0.9	2.3	1.5	1.8	0.03
IO$_3$	7.62	8.33	80.43	0.004	0.05	0.25	0.25	6.87	0.83	0.002
	0.35	0.4	3.84	0.0_314	0.001	0.0_257	0.007	0.26	0.02	0.0_43
OH	142.9	116.4	12.04	0.01	3.7	0.77	0.17	0.001	0.0_35	0.01
	18.0	21.0	5.0	0.001	0.22	0.063	0.02	0.0_32	0.0_45	0.0_84
SO$_4$	11.11	16.83	35.64	0.55	0.0_323	0.011	0.20	35.43	53.12	0.0041
	0.62	1.15	2.8	0.020	0.0_410	0.0_36	0.015	2.8	3.1	0.0_313
CrO$_4$	63.1	61.21	111.6	0.0025	0.0_338	0.12	0.4	73.0	....	0.0_42
	2.7	3.30	6.5	0.0_315	0.0_415	0.006	0.03	4.3	....	0.0_65
C$_2$O$_4$	30.27	3.34	7.22	0.0035	0.0086	0.0046	0.0_356	0.03	0.0_36	0.0_315
	1.6	0.24	0.69	0.0_32	0.0_338	0.0_326	0.0_443	0.0027	0.0_44	0.0_55
CO$_3$	108.0	19.39	1.3	0.003	0.0_311	0.0011	0.0013	0.1	0.004?	0.0_31
	5.9	1.8	0.17	0.0_31	0.0_311	0.047	0.0_313	0.01	0.0_33?	0.0_33

* Previously published in Mining Engineers' Handbook, by Robert Peele.

The upper figure of each pair is the number of grams of the anhydrous salt held in solution by 100 cc of water; the lower is the molar solubility, i.e., the number of mols (molecular weight expressed as grams) contained in 1 liter of saturated solution. The numbers for small solubilities have been abbreviated; thus $0.0_64 = 0.0000004$.

Solubility Product

It may be assumed that the tendency of solid calcium sulfate to pass into solution as calcium and sulfate ions is constant since it depends only upon the character of the solid salt. The reverse tendency to precipitate solid calcium sulfate from the solution may be assumed to be proportional to the concentrations of the ions taking part in the reaction. Thus

$$CaSO_4 \rightarrow Ca^{++} + SO_4^{--} \quad \text{Forward tendency} = K_1 \text{ a constant}$$
$$Ca^{++} + SO_4^{--} \rightarrow CaSO_4 \quad \text{Backward tendency} = K_2 (Ca^{++})(SO_4^{--}) \tag{26}$$

When the solution is saturated with calcium sulfate the reaction is in a state of equilibrium, and we may equate the two, obtaining

$$K_1 = K_2 (Ca^{++})(SO_4^{--}) \tag{27}$$

or
$$(Ca^{++})(SO_4^{--}) = K_1/K_2 = K_{sol} = 2.25 \times 10^{-4}$$

where K_{sol} is called the solubility product constant.

The constancy of the product of the two ion concentrations at equilibrium would indicate, for example, that calcium sulfate would be considerably less soluble in sodium sulfate solution than in pure water since an increase in (SO_4^{--}) must be accompanied by a decrease in (Ca^{++}).

For the case of the solubility of calcium sulfate in pure water it will be noted that each molecule of salt that dissolves yields an ion of calcium and an ion of sulfate. Hence the calcium-ion concentration expressed in mols per liter (Ca^{++}) must be equal to the solubility of the salt in mols per liter. The same applies to the sulfate-ion concentration. The solubility-product constant is therefore equal to the square of the solubility in mols per liter for the simple type of salt exemplified by calcium sulfate.

Solubilities are generally expressed in grams per liter or grams per 100 grams of water. For purposes of calculations of complex solubility relations these should always be converted to molal units as will be explained in greater detail under the title Chemical Calculations. (See p. 10–10.)

Precipitation

If a solution contains ions of a salt and the product of their concentrations in mols per liter exceeds the solubility product as calculated, precipitation must occur until finally the product of the concentrations of the ions which remain equals the computed constant. It has been shown that the solubility product of calcium sulfate

$$(Ca^{++})(SO_4^{--}) = K_{sol} = 2.25 \times 10^{-4} \tag{28}$$

We now ask what will be the amount of calcium sulfate precipitated per liter of solution upon the addition of sulfuric acid sufficient to produce a concentration of 0.1 M (0.1 mol per liter).

Since the quantity of sulfuric acid is large compared with the small amount of calcium sulfate present, we may assume that the sulfate-ion concentration is 0.1 (SO_4^{--}). Substituting this value in the above equation we find that the concentration of calcium ion after precipitation is $2.25 \times 10^{-4}/0.1$, or 2.25×10^{-5} mol per liter. The amount present in a saturated solution in pure water is 1.5×10^{-2} mol per liter, as shown in Table III. The amount precipitated is therefore the difference of the two, or $0.015 - 0.0000225$, which is equal to 0.0149775, so that all but a very small quantity of the salt is precipitated by the sulfuric acid.

It sometimes happens that, owing to complex ion formation, the true ion concentrations are difficult to compute. Another difficulty may arise in the application of the principle to very soluble salts, in which case it may not be truly valid. Finally it is to be observed that in some cases a precipitate may be formed in a colloidal state so that it may not be observed, the solution remaining clear. These difficulties do not, however, destroy the usefulness of the method, which may constitute an important tool in the calculation of solubilities of salts in solutions of specified composition.

6. CHEMICAL CALCULATIONS

Percentage Composition by Weight. In Table IV the molecular weight of calcium phosphate, $Ca_3(PO_4)_2$, is given as 310.28. With the atomic weights given in Table I, the percentage composition of the compound may be calculated as follows:

Ca...................... $3 \times 40.08 \div 310.28 = $ 38.7%
P...................... $2 \times 31.02 \div 310.28 = $ 20.0%
O...................... $2 \times 4 \times 16 \div 310.28 = $ 41.3%

                                                                          100.0%

To Determine the Formula from Analysis, divide the percentage of each element by its atomic weight and determine the lowest integer ratios between the quotients. Thus, in the above example,

$$\frac{38.7}{40.08} : \frac{20.0}{31.02} : \frac{41.3}{16} = 3 : 2 : 8$$

Computations from analysis will not always work out with mathematical precision. Elements, however, always combine in simple proportions represented by whole numbers.

To Determine the Weight of a Substance Consumed or Produced in a Reaction. The unit of mass used in chemical calculations is the mol. If the data of the problem are specified in grams, the gram-mol is the proper unit. This is equal to the molecular weight in grams. Given g grams of a substance, this will be equivalent to g/M gram-mols, where M is the molecular weight.

Example. A high-grade phosphate rock containing phosphate equivalent to 85 per cent of "bone phosphate," $Ca_3(PO_4)_2$, is treated with an excess of sulfuric acid which converts 95 per cent of the phosphate to phosphoric acid. How much phosphoric acid would be produced from 100 grams of rock? The reaction (for purposes of calculation) is

$$Ca_3(PO_4)_2 + 3H_2SO_4 \rightarrow 2H_3PO_4 + 3CaSO_4$$

The balanced equation shows that one mol of calcium phosphate may be converted to two mols of phosphoric acid. One hundred grams of rock contain $100 \times 0.85 \times 0.95 = $ 80.75 grams of converted $Ca_3(PO_4)_2$.

Molecular weight of $Ca_3(PO_4)_2$ is 310.28.

$80.75/310.28 = 0.260$ mol of $Ca_3(PO_4)_2$ yielding $0.260 \times 2 = 0.52$ mol of H_3PO_4 of molecular weight 98.06, which is equivalent to $0.520 \times 98.06 = 51.0$ grams of phosphoric acid.

Thus 100 grams of rock will be converted to 51.0 grams of phosphoric acid. The units used are immaterial. Thus 100 lb of rock would yield 51 0 lb of acid, and 100 tons would yield 51.0 tons. For convenience in industrial calculations, the pound-mol or molecular weight in pounds is often used instead of the gram-mol. The principles involved are the same.

Gas Calculations. (See also Art. 16, Chemistry of Gases.) The weight of a unit volume of a perfect gas varies directly as the pressure and inversely as the absolute temperature.

$$\frac{w_1}{w_2} = \frac{P_1}{P_2} \times \frac{T_2}{T_1}$$

(29)

Table IV.   Composition, etc., of More Important Industrial Compounds*

Name	Formula	Mol wt	Sp gr	Name	Formula	Mol wt	Sp gr
Acetic acid............	$HC_2H_3O_2$	60.03	1.06	Magnesium carbonate..	$MgCO_3$	84.32	3.04
Alcohol (grain).........	$C_2H_5 \cdot OH$	46.05	0.785	" sulf (epsom salt)	$MgSO_4 \cdot 7\,H_2O$	246.50	1.68
" (wood).........	$CH_3 \cdot OH$	32.03	0.791	Manganese dioxide.....	MnO_2	86.93	5.03
Alumina...............	Al_2O_3	102.2	3.86	Mercuric chlor (corro-			
Alum, ammonium......	$Al_2(SO_4)_3 \cdot$	906.95	1.64	sive sublimate)......	$HgCl_2$	271.52	5.40
	$(NH_4)_2SO_4 \cdot$			Nitric acid...........	HNO_3	63.02	1.53
	$24\,H_2O$			Phosphoric acid.......	HPO_3	80.05	2.30
" , potassium.......	$Al_2(SO_4)_3 \cdot$	949.06	1.76	Potassium carbonate	$K_2CO_3 \cdot$	174.23	2.04
	$K_2SO_4 \cdot 24H_2O$			(potash)	$2\,H_2O$		
Ammonia..............	NH_4OH	35.03	0.88	Potassium chlorate.....	$KClO_3$	122.56	2.34
Am chlor (sal-ammoniac)	NH_4Cl	53.50	1.52	" chloride.....	KCl	74.56	1.99
Ammonium nitrate.....	NH_4NO_3	80.05	1.73	" chromate....	K_2CrO_4	194.20	2.73
" sulfate.....	$(NH_4)_2SO_4$	132.14	1.77	" cyanide.....	KCN	65.11	1.52
Arsenious oxide (white				" ferricyanide	$K_3Fe(CN)_6$	329.20	1.81
arsenic).............	As_4O_6	395.84	3.74	" ferrocyanide.	$K_4Fe(CN)_6 \cdot$	422.35	1.85
Barium carbonate......	$BaCO_3$	197.37	4.27		$3\,H_2O$		
" sulf (blanc fixe).	$BaSO_4$	233.44	4.40	" hydroxide	KOH	56.11	2.04
Boric acid.............	H_3BO_3	62.02	1.43	(caustic potash)			
Calcium acetate (acet of	$Ca(C_2H_3O_2)_2 \cdot$	176.13	......	" nitrate (salt-	KNO_3	101.11	2.10
lime)	H_2O			peter)			
Calcium carbide........	CaC_2	64.07	2.22	" permanganate	$KMnO_4$	158.03	2.70
" carbonate......	$CaCO_3$	100.07	2.85	" sulfate.....	K_2SO_4	174.27	2.66
" oxide(quicklime)	CaO	56.07	3.30	Silver nitrate (lunar			
" hydroxide	$Ca(OH)_2$	74.09	2.08	caustic)...........	$AgNO_3$	169.89	4.35
" (slaked lime)				Sodium borate (borax)..	$Na_2B_4O_7 \cdot$	382.16	1.69
" phosphate	$Ca_3(PO_4)_2$	310.28	3.18		$10\,H_2O$		
(phos of lime)				" carbonate (soda)	Na_2CO_3	106.00	2.47
" sulf (anhydrite)	$CaSO_4$	136.13	2.96	" bicarbonate....	$NaHCO_3$	84.01	2.20
Calcium sulf (gypsum)..	$CaSO_4 \cdot 2H_2O$	172.17	2.32	" chloride (salt).	$NaCl$	58.46	2.17
" (plaster paris)	$CaSO_4 \cdot 1/2H_2O$	145.14	......	" cyanide.......	$NaCN$	49.01	
Carbon tetrachloride....	CCl_4	153.84	1.58	" hydroxide	$NaOH$	40.01	2.13
" disulfide......	CS_2	76.14	1.29	(caustic soda)			
Cupric arsenite (paris	$CuHAsO_3$	187.54	......	" nitrate (Chile	$NaNO_3$	85.01	2.27
green)...............				saltpeter)			
Cupric oxide..........	CuO	79.57	6.37	" silicate (water	$Na_2Si_4O_9$	303.20	......
" sulfate (bluestone)	$CuSO_4 \cdot 5H_2O$	249.72	2.28	glass)			
Ferric oxide...........	Fe_2O_3	159.68	5.18	" sulfate	$Na_2SO_4 \cdot$	268.18	......
Ferrous oxide..........	FeO	71.84	......	(Glauber salts)	$7\,H_2O$		
" sulf (copperas)..	$FeSO_4 \cdot 7H_2O$	278.02	1.90	" sulfite........	$Na_2SO_3 \cdot 7\,H_2O$	252.18	1.59
Hydrochloric acid......	HCl	36.47	......	" thiosulfate.....	$Na_2S_2O_3 \cdot 5H_2O$	248.22	1.73
Hydrogen peroxide.....	H_2O_2	34.02	......	Sulfur dioxide.........	SO_2	64.07	......
Lead acetate (sugar of	$Pb(C_2H_3O_2)_2 \cdot$	379.20	2.50	Sulfuric acid..........	H_2SO_4	98.09	......
lead)	$3\,H_2O$			Tartaric acid..........	$H_2C_4H_4O_6$	150.05	1.75
Lead carbonate (white	$2PbCO_3 \cdot$	775.31	......	Tin chloride..........	$SnCl_4$	260.84	2.28
lead)	$Pb(OH)_2$			Vanadium oxide.......	V_2O_5	182.00	3.36
Lead monoxide (litharge)	PbO	223.10	9.37	Zinc chloride..........	$ZnCl_2$	136.29	2.91
" oxide (red lead)...	Pb_3O_4	685.30	9.10	" oxide (zinc white).	ZnO	81.37	5.78
" sulfate........	$PbSO_4$	303.17	6.23	" sulfate........	$ZnSO_4 \cdot 7\,H_2O$	287.55	1.97

* Previously published in Mining Engineers' Handbook, by Robert Peele.

Table V. Weights of Common Gases

Name	Chemical Symbol	Relative Weight Air = 1	At 760 mm Hg, 0° C; kg per cu m	At 29.92 in. Hg, 32° F; lb per cu ft
Air........................	$O + 4\,N$	1.00000	1.2932	0.08072
Oxygen.....................	O	1.1056	1.4298	0.0893
Hydrogen....................	H	0.06926	0.08957	0.005592
Nitrogen....................	N	0.97137	1.25615	0.07841
Carbon monoxide...........	CO	0.9569	1.2344	0.07706
Carbon dioxide.............	CO_2	1.52901	1.9774	0.1234
Methane....................	CH_4	0.559	0.727	0.04539
Sulfuretted hydrogen..........	H_2S	1.177	1.522	0.09501
Ammonia...................	NH_3	0.5967	0.7697	0.04805

The volume of a given weight of gas varies inversely as the pressure and directly as the absolute temperature in accordance with the law.

$$pV = nRT \tag{30}$$

where p is the pressure, V is the volume, n is the number of mols, R is the gas law constant and T is the absolute temperature.

Example. If 1000 cu ft of air at 25 deg cent and 14.7 lb per sq in. of pressure are compressed to 50 lb per sq in. and heated to 350 deg cent, what will be the volume occupied?

For use in gas calculations, the temperatures must be converted to the absolute scale by addition of 273.2. Thus 25 deg cent is equivalent to 298.2 deg abs, while 350 deg cent is equivalent to 623.2 deg abs. From equation 30,

$$V_2 = \frac{nRT_2}{nRT_1} \times \frac{p_1}{p_2} \times V_1 = \frac{623.2}{298.2} \times \frac{14.7}{50} \times 1000 = 614.4 \text{ cu ft}$$

INDUSTRIAL CHEMISTRY

It is useful, in discussing the compounds of the elements, to make a systematic classification into certain families the members of which show many similarities. The following groups of elements will be discussed (hydrogen and oxygen have already been considered):

1. The alkali metals, sodium, potassium, lithium, cesium, and rubidium.
2. The alkali earth metals, calcium, strontium, and barium.
3. Magnesium, zinc, cadmium, and mercury.
4. Copper, silver, and gold.
5. Rhodium, rhuthenium, platinum, palladium, osmium, and iridium.
6. Aluminum.
7. Iron, nickel, and cobalt.
8. Chromium and manganese.
9. Lead, tin, and titanium.
10. Nitrogen, phosphorus, arsenic, antimony, and bismuth.
11. The halogens: chlorine, bromine, iodine, and fluorine.
12. Sulfur, selenium, and tellurium.
13. Carbon, boron, and silicon.

Only those substances and reactions which are of industrial importance, or which throw a useful light on industrial processes, are treated. The formulas for the various salts are included. These formulas show the water of hydration contained in the materials as they are usually shipped and marketed. The formulas of minerals are the nominal formulas generally accepted and do not indicate small quantities of elements considered "impurities."

7. THE ALKALI METALS

Sodium

The most abundant of the alkali metals is sodium, which is found as the chloride, sulfate, nitrate, and carbonate in commercial deposits.

Sodium Chloride ($NaCl$), or common salt, is obtained as the mineral halite or as a constituent of natural brines. It is, directly or indirectly, the starting material for almost all industrial chemicals which contain sodium or chlorine.

Sodium Sulfate (Na_2SO_4) is obtained from the minerals mirabilite and glauberite, but chiefly as a by-product from the manufacture of hydrochloric acid. By heating concentrated sulfuric acid with sodium chloride a reaction takes place in two stages.

$$H_2SO_4 + NaCl \rightarrow NaHSO_4 + HCl \tag{1}$$

The sodium bisulfate thus formed then reacts with additional sodium chloride to produce more hydrochloric acid and sodium sulfate.

$$NaHSO_4 + NaCl \rightarrow Na_2SO_4 + HCl \tag{2}$$

Sodium Bisulfate ($NaHSO_4$) is an intermediate product in the formation of sulfuric acid. Commercially, the most important source is from the manufacture of nitric acid from soda niter, which is treated with sulfuric acid and heated to distil the nitric acid which is formed.

$$NaNO_3 + H_2SO_4 \rightarrow NaHSO_4 + HNO_3 \tag{3}$$

Unlike the reaction for the manufacture of hydrochloric acid, this reaction stops at the bisulfate stage so that large quantities of sodium bisulfate, called niter cake, are produced as a by-product, and may be used to manufacture hydrochloric acid from sodium chloride.

Sodium bisulfate is an example of an *acid salt* which may be formed from a polybasic acid by partial neutralization so that the metallic element replaces only a part of the available hydrogen.

Sodium Bicarbonate ($NaHCO_3$) along with sodium carbonate occurs in soil and in certain lakes. It is made industrially by the Solvay process, in which a solution of sodium chloride is saturated with ammonia and carbon dioxide gases. The ammonia and carbon dioxide form ammonium bicarbonate which ionizes.

$$\left.\begin{array}{l} NH_3 + CO_2 + H_2O \rightarrow NH_4^+ + HCO_3^- \\ NaCl \rightarrow Na^+ + Cl^- \end{array}\right\} \rightarrow NaHCO_3 + NH_4Cl \qquad (4)$$

We have thus a solution containing four ions. On cooling, sodium bicarbonate, which is the least soluble salt which might be formed, precipitates out. Ammonium chloride, NH_4Cl, may then be obtained by evaporation of the solution and sold as sal ammoniac.

Sodium Carbonate (Na_2CO_3) is obtained by heating the bicarbonate.

$$2NaHCO_3 \rightarrow Na_2CO_3 + CO_2 + H_2O \qquad (5)$$

Sodium carbonate is the salt of a strong base and a weak acid, so that its solutions are moderately strongly alkaline and it is useful wherever a cheap, moderately strong alkali is needed. Solutions of the bicarbonate are weakly alkaline.

Disodium Phosphate ($Na_2HPO_4 \cdot 12H_2O$) is manufactured in a way which will exemplify this use of sodium carbonate. A solution of phosphoric acid is partially neutralized to form an acid salt.

$$H_3PO_4 + Na_2CO_3 \rightarrow Na_2HPO_4 + CO_2 + H_2O \qquad (6)$$

Disodium Phosphate hydrolyzes to some extent in solution and is slightly alkaline. It is used extensively in the textile industry.

Trisodium Phosphate ($Na_3PO_4 \cdot 12H_2O$) is strongly alkaline and can be formed only by the action of a strong alkali, caustic soda, on a solution of disodium phosphate.

$$Na_2HPO_4 + NaOH \rightarrow Na_3PO_4 + H_2O \qquad (7)$$

Sodium Hydroxide ($NaOH$), or caustic soda, is made commercially by suspending slaked lime in a solution of sodium carbonate.

$$Na_2CO_3 + Ca(OH)_2 \rightarrow CaCO_3 + 2NaOH \qquad (8)$$

The calcium carbonate is less soluble than the lime so that the reaction goes almost to completion. The precipitate is filtered, and the solution evaporated to give solid sodium hydroxide. The electrolytic process for making caustic soda will be discussed under Electrochemistry.

Sodium Nitrate ($NaNO_3$), called soda niter or saltpeter, is found in deposits in Chile. It is used for the manufacture of nitric acid and niter.

Sodium salts, as well as the salts of the other alkali metals, are strongly ionized in solution. The metal ions of this family are colorless and very stable in aqueous solutions so that the properties of these solutions are primarily those of the non-metallic ion or ions. These metals show a valence of unity in all their compounds.

The metals themselves are of very low density and have a brilliant metallic luster when a fresh surface is cut. They form compounds with all the non-metals and react with most of the elements spontaneously as well as with many compounds. They oxidize readily in the air to form the oxides Na_2O, K_2O, etc., and must therefore be kept under mineral oils. They ignite in the atmosphere to form peroxides such as Na_2O_2. This peroxide appears to violate the rules of valence, but it is believed to have a structure Na—O—O—Na, the oxygen atoms being joined, and thus canceling two of their available valences. Compounds of this kind are not generally very stable, except organic compounds, which belong to another realm of chemistry.

Potassium

Potassium is widely distributed in nature, particularly in the form of silicates, orthoclase, muscovite (mica), and leucite, and the products of their decomposition such as the clays.

Commercial deposits are comparatively few. In certain localities such as Stassfurt, Germany, there has been a deposition from sea water together with sodium and magnesium, in the minerals carnallite, kainite, and sylvite. Limited deposits of niter are found in Chile and elsewhere. Other sources are alunite and certain brines.

Potassium Chloride (KCl) is obtained from sylvite (KCl), carnallite ($KCl \cdot MgCl_2 \cdot 6H_2O$), and kainite ($KCl \cdot MgSO_4 \cdot 3H_2O$). It is used as a source of other potassium compounds.

Potassium Nitrate (KNO_3) is manufactured from the chloride by reaction with sodium nitrate. The two salts are dissolved to saturation, and the solution cooled. Under the conditions, potassium nitrate is the least soluble combination of the four ions, and crystallizes out.

It is an important constituent of fertilizers, supplying both the potassium and the nitrate which are important plant foods. It is also used as a constituent of gunpowder.

Potassium Carbonate (KCO_3) is similar to sodium carbonate, and is made by the leaching of the ash residues of plants such as kelp.

Potassium Hydroxide (KOH) is made by a process similar to that of the manufacture of sodium carbonate. It is similar in its properties to sodium hydroxide and is seldom used because of its greater cost.

Potassium Sulfate (K_2SO_4) is obtained from the minerals kalinite ($KAl(SO_4)_2 \cdot H_2O$), and alunite $\{K[Al(OH_2)]_3(SO_4)_2 \cdot 3H_2O\}$. It is useful as a constituent of fertilizers.

Lithium, Cesium, and Rubidium

The Other Alkali Metals are found only in very limited deposits and are of minor importance.

8. THE ALKALI EARTH METALS—CALCIUM, STRONTIUM, AND BARIUM

Calcium

Calcium salts are widely distributed in nature. The most important source is limestone, which is composed chiefly of the mineral calcite.

Calcium Oxide (CaO), or quicklime, is produced by heating limestone ($CaCO_3$) in vertical kilns.

$$CaCO_3 \rightleftharpoons CaO + CO_2 \qquad (9)$$

It is a white, amorphous solid which reacts vigorously with water to form **calcium hydroxide** [$Ca(OH)_2$], or slaked lime. Thus

$$CaO + H_2O \rightarrow Ca(OH)_2 \qquad (10)$$

This reaction is used in the making of *mortar*. In the setting of mortar there is an evaporation of water and a reaction with the carbon dioxide of the air.

$$Ca(OH)_2 + CO_2 \rightarrow CaCO_3 + H_2O \qquad (11)$$

The calcium carbonate sets to a solid mass.

Calcium hydroxide is soluble in water to a very limited extent. More concentrated mixes are prepared by mechanically suspending excess lime in a saturated solution. Such a preparation is called milk of lime. This is the cheapest alkali and one that finds considerable application.

Calcium Sulfate ($CaSO_4 \cdot 2H_2O$) is widely distributed in nature as the mineral gypsum. When gypsum is heated at 150 deg cent it is converted to *plaster of paris*.

$$2CaSO_4 \cdot 2H_2O \rightleftharpoons (CaSO_4)_2 \cdot H_2O + 3H_2O \qquad (12)$$

When water is added to plaster of paris, gypsum is formed by hydration, a reversal of the above reaction, while the paste dries and expands slightly, thus filling in the details of casts as it sets to a hard mass.

Calcium Hypochlorite ($CaOCl_2$), or chloride of lime, is prepared by passing chlorine gas over slaked lime.

$$Ca(OH)_2 + Cl_2 \rightleftharpoons CaOCl_2 + H_2O \qquad (13)$$

The reaction is reversible so that chloride of lime, otherwise known as *bleaching powder*, is used as source of free chlorine, which is an active bleaching agent.

Calcium Bicarbonate [$Ca(HCO_3)_2$] is formed by treating a suspension of the highly insoluble carbonate in water with carbon dioxide. The bicarbonate is very soluble, and the above reaction explains its presence in natural waters which flow over limestone deposits.

$$CaCO_3 + CO_2 + H_2O \rightleftharpoons Ca(HCO_3)_2 \qquad (14)$$

When a solution of the bicarbonate is boiled, carbon dioxide is driven off and the above reaction is reversed.

Temporary Hardness in water is due to the presence of considerable amounts of calcium and magnesium bicarbonates. These react with soaps, which are the sodium and potassium salts of certain organic acids, to give insoluble calcium and magnesium salts which will not produce the desired suds nor have the desired cleansing properties. Temporary hardness may be removed, as has been noted, by simple boiling which precipitates the insoluble carbonates (hence temporary) or, more conveniently, by treating the water with an alkaline substance such as lime or caustic soda,

$$Ca(HCO_3)_2 + Ca(OH)_2 \rightarrow 2CaCO_3 + 2H_2O$$
$$Ca(HCO_3)_2 + 2NaOH \rightarrow CaCO_3 + Na_2CO_3 + 2H_2O \tag{15}$$

with similar reactions for the magnesium. It will be observed that, if lime is used, it should not be added in excess since soluble calcium hydroxide will produce additional hardness.

Permanent Hardness is hardness in water that cannot be removed by boiling. It is due to the presence of small amounts of calcium sulfate, which is slightly soluble, or magnesium sulfate. Permanent hardness may be removed by treatment with sodium carbonate.

$$CaSO_4 + Na_2CO_3 \rightarrow CaCO_3 + Na_2SO_4 \tag{16}$$

Magnesium sulfate reacts similarly.

Ordinarily water contains both permanent and temporary hardness, in which case sodium hydroxide may be used to produce sodium carbonate by reaction with the bicarbonates, and this in turn may precipitate the permanent hardness. An alternative would be to use a combination of lime and sodium carbonate in the proper proportions.

Water-softening compounds which are sold are, in general, to be avoided since each water requires a specific treatment which must be determined from its analysis.

Certain minerals and artificial insoluble substances called *permutits* have the property of removing calcium and magnesium ions from solution, and replacing them with harmless sodium ions. Both temporary and permanent hardness may be removed in this way. The permutit may afterwards be reactivated by treatment with sodium chloride brine which reverses the process.

Calcium Carbonate ($CaCO_3$), besides being the chief constituent of limestone, is the basic material of marble, alabaster, pearl, coral, shells of marine animals, and chalk. The last is used both as the natural and as the artificially precipitated calcium carbonate in the pigment *whiting* which finds uses in the paint and paper industries.

Strontium

Strontium is similar in its properties to calcium. It is found in the minerals strontianite ($SrCO_3$) and celestite ($SrSO_4$). The chief application of strontium is in the sugar industry, in which its salts are used to precipitate the sugar from molasses, and in medicinal preparations.

Barium

Barium is mined in considerable quantity, particularly for the pigment industry.

Barium Carbonate ($BaCO_3$) is found as the mineral witherite.

Barium Sulfate ($BaSO_4$) is found as barite which is ground to produce a cheap white pigment. Precipitated barium sulfate is much finer and therefore more useful for this purpose.

Barium Sulfide (BaS) is made by heating barite with coke (carbon).

$$BaSO_4 + 4C \rightarrow BaS + 4CO \tag{17}$$

A solution of the sulfide, together with one of zinc sulfate, precipitates a mixture of barium sulfate and zinc sulfide, called *lithopone*, a white composite pigment.

$$BaS + ZnSO_4 \rightarrow ZnS + BaSO_4 \quad \text{(lithopone)} \tag{18}$$

Barium sulfate is also used in mixtures with titanium dioxide in pigments sold as Titanox B.

The pure alkali earth metals are similar in appearance to the alkali metals, and are only slightly less reactive. They are bivalent in all their compounds and give colorless ions.

⸱9. MAGNESIUM, ZINC, CADMIUM, AND MERCURY

Magnesium

Magnesium is obtained chiefly from salt brines containing magnesium chloride. It also occurs in dolomitic rock, which contains the mineral magnesite ($MgCO_3 \cdot CaCO_3$), and in many silicate rock formations.

Magnesium metal is very active at elevated temperatures or when in a finely divided condition. In the massive state and near room temperatures, however, the metal is so stable that it forms the basis of an important series of structural alloys.

Magnesium Oxide (MgO), or magnesia, is obtained similarly to calcium oxide by calcination of the carbonate. It is used as an insulating material and in some cements.

Magnesium Sulfate ($MgSO_4 \cdot 7H_2O$), or Epsom salt, is soluble salt produced by treating the carbonate with sulfuric acid. Uses are in tanning, dyeing, and soap-making.

$$MgCO_3 + H_2SO_4 \rightarrow MgSO_4 + CO_2 + H_2O \tag{19}$$

Zinc

The important zinc minerals are sphalerite, smithsonite, willemite, zincite, franklinite, and calamine.

Zinc Sulfide (ZnS) is found as the mineral sphalerite. This ore is generally converted to the oxide by roasting.

$$2ZnS + 3O_2 \rightarrow 2ZnO + 2SO_2 \tag{20}$$

The sulfur dioxide liberated is converted to sulfuric acid, which is a by-product.

Pure zinc sulfide is white. It is made by treating a solution of zinc sulfate with hydrogen sulfide or an alkaline sulfide.

$$ZnSO_4 + H_2S \leftrightharpoons ZnS + H_2SO_4 \tag{21}$$

The reaction is reversible, so that care must be exercised to prevent the sulfuric acid (or hydrogen ion) from becoming too concentrated. The pure white sulfide is used as a pigment. With barium sulfate it is sold as lithopone, already discussed under barium sulfate.

Zinc Carbonate ($ZnCO_3$) is obtained as smithsonite or calamine. It is converted by heat to the oxide.

$$ZnCO_3 \rightarrow ZnO + CO_2 \tag{22}$$

Zinc Oxide (ZnO) is obtained as the mineral zincite or by roasting the sulfide or carbonate. When heated with powdered coal it is converted to metallic zinc vapor which is condensed to the molten metal.

$$ZnO + C \rightarrow Zn + CO \tag{23}$$

If the zinc vapor is suddenly chilled in the absence of air it is precipitated as *zinc dust*, a blue metallic powder which is used as a paint pigment. If the vapor is burned in air, a pure form of white oxide is obtained which is sold for pigmenting paints, enamels, rubber, etc.

$$2Zn + O_2 \rightarrow 2ZnO \tag{24}$$

Zinc Sulfate ($ZnSO_4 \cdot 7H_2O$) is obtained by treating sphalerite with dilute sulfuric acid.

$$ZnS + H_2SO_4 \leftrightharpoons ZnSO_4 + H_2S \tag{25}$$

The salt may then be crystallized from the solution.

Zinc Hydroxide [$Zn(OH)_2$] is precipitated as an insoluble gelatinous precipitate by treating zinc salts in solution with an alkali.

$$ZnSO_4 + 2NaOH \rightarrow Zn(OH)_2 + Na_2SO_4 \tag{26}$$

An excess of alkali redissolves the hydroxide, forming a sodium salt—sodium zincate.

Sodium Zincate (Na_2ZnO_2) is thus obtained

$$Zn(OH)_2 + 2NaOH \rightarrow Na_2ZnO_2 + 2H_2O \tag{27}$$

It will be observed that zinc hydroxide, which generally shows basic characteristics, may under alkaline conditions act as an acid. Hydroxides which have this property are called amphoteric. They include the hydroxides of zinc, aluminum, tin, titanium, and others.

Metallic zinc itself reacts with alkali to form the zincate

$$Zn + 2NaOH \rightarrow Na_2ZnO_2 + H_2 \tag{28}$$

All the metals which form amphoteric hydroxides are thus attacked by both acids and alkalis.

Cadmium

Cadmium is obtained along with zinc from most of its ores. Its compounds are very similar to those of zinc except that the hydroxide is not amphoteric. It forms the insoluble yellow sulfide (CdS) which finds application as a pigment.

Both zinc and cadmium are bivalent in all their compounds, and form colorless ions in solution.

While both zinc and cadmium metals are quite active, they form coatings of oxides when exposed to the air, which help to resist corrosion under most conditions. Iron coated with zinc is called *galvanized*. Cadmium is even more corrosion-resisting than zinc.

Mercury

The principal source of mercury is cinnabar.

Mercuric Sulfide (HgS) is found as cinnabar. It is obtained in pure form by precipitation from solutions of mercury salts treated with hydrogen sulfide or alkali sulfides. This reaction is similar to the precipitation of zinc and cadmium sulfides.

Metallic Mercury is obtained readily by roasting cinnabar.

$$HgS + O_2 \rightarrow Hg + SO_2 \tag{29}$$

The mercury is volatilized and condensed as the heavy metallic liquid, quicksilver. It dissolves all the common metals except iron, platinum, and nickel as *amalgams*.

Mercury forms two series of salts corresponding to valences of one and two. The monovalent compounds are called mercurous salts; the bivalent are called mercuric.

Mercurous Nitrate [$Hg(NO_3)\cdot 2H_2O$] and *mercuric nitrate* [$Hg(NO_3)_2$] are formed by treating metallic mercury with hot nitric acid. If an excess of mercury is present the mercurous salt is formed; in the presence of excess nitric acid, the product is mercuric nitrate. Mercurous nitrate may be formed by adding mercury to a solution of mercuric nitrate.

Mercuric Fulminate [$Hg(ONC)_2$] is obtained by the action of mercury with nitric acid and alcohol. It is used as a detonator.

Mercuric Sulfate ($HgSO_4$) is obtained by the reaction of mercury with hot sulfuric acid.

$$Hg + 2H_2SO_4 \rightarrow HgSO_4 + SO_2 + 2H_2O \tag{30}$$

Mercuric Chloride ($HgCl_2$), or corrosive sublimate, is obtained by the sublimation of mercuric sulfate with salt.

$$HgSO_4 + 2NaCl \rightarrow HgCl_2 + Na_2SO_4 \tag{31}$$

Mercurous Chloride ($HgCl$), or calomel, is produced by subliming mercuric chloride and mercury.

$$HgCl_2 + Hg \rightarrow 2HgCl \tag{32}$$

10. COPPER, SILVER, AND GOLD

Copper

Copper is found as native copper, covellite, chalcocite, bornite, chalcopyrite, enargite, tetrahedrite, cuprite, malachite, azurite, and chrysocolla. Copper is similar to mercury in that it forms two series of salts corresponding to valences of one and two. These are termed cuprous and cupric.

Cuprous Sulfide (Cu_2S) and **cupric sulfide** (CuS) are found as chalcocite and covellite respectively. They are roasted to give the oxides,

$$Cu_2S + O_2 \rightarrow Cu_2O + SO_2 \tag{33}$$

the sulfur dioxide being converted to sulfuric acid. The complex sulfides bornite (Cu_5FeS_4) and chalcopyrite ($CuFeS_2$), and the arsenious and antimonial sulfides enargite (Cu_3AsS_4) and tetrahedrite ($Cu_8Sb_2S_7$), are treated similarly.

Cuprous Oxide (Cu_2O) and **cupric oxide** (CuO) are obtained as cuprite (Cu_2O) and, along with impurities, by the roasting of the sulfide ores. By complex metallurgical operations they are converted to impure, or *blister*, copper which is refined electrolytically. (See Electrochemistry.)

Cupric Sulfate ($CuSO_4 \cdot 5H_2O$) is prepared by allowing dilute sulfuric acid to react with pure copper in the presence of air.

$$2Cu + 2H_2SO_4 + O_2 \rightarrow 2CuSO_4 + 2H_2O \tag{34}$$

It may be crystallized as commercial blue vitriol.

Cupric Hydroxide [$Cu(OH)_2$] is formed by adding an alkali to a solution of a copper salt. It is a blue, gelatinous precipitate.

$$CuSO_4 + 2NaOH \rightarrow Cu(OH)_2 + Na_2SO_4 \tag{35}$$

Cupric hydroxide is dissolved by ammonium hydroxide, giving a deep blue solution,

$$Cu(OH)_2 + 6NH_4OH \rightarrow Cu(NH_3)_6(OH)_2 + 6H_2O \tag{36}$$

The cuprammonium hydroxide is practically completely ionized. The blue color is that of cuprammonium ion. Such solutions are used to dissolve cellulose for the manufacture of a kind of artificial fiber.

The above reaction, in which a *complex ion* is formed, differs from the process of solution of the amphoteric hydroxides inasmuch as it is specific for the particular alkali, ammonium hydroxide. Sodium hydroxide, which is a stronger alkali, does not dissolve cupric hydroxide. Other metallic hydroxides, such as cuprous, zinc, iron, nickel, chromium, tin, silver, and titanium, also form complexes with ammonia. Only those of cuprous and silver, however, of the common metals are as stable as that of cuprammonium ion.

We have already described the acid salts sodium bisulfate and disodium phosphate which are formed by partial neutralization of polybasic acids. In a similar way basic salts may be formed by partial neutralization of polyacid bases. Basic carbonates of copper are found as the minerals malachite [$Cu_2(OH)_2CO_3$] and azurite [$Cu_3(OH)_2(CO_3)_2$]. These are leached with dilute sulfuric acid to form solutions of the sulfates.

$$Cu_2(OH)_2CO_3 + 2H_2SO_4 \rightarrow 2CuSO_4 + 3H_2O + CO_2 \qquad (37)$$

The copper is then recovered from the impure solution by electrowinning. (See Electrochemistry.) Copper and other metals which form gelatinous hydroxides tend to form basic salts of such great complexity and of such variety that their compositions appear to be indefinite. The hydroxides themselves, when precipitated from solutions of the sulfates, generally carry considerable sulfate in the precipitate, the amount depending on the conditions which prevail. These precipitates may therefore be considered to be complex basic salts although it is more usual to consider them as hydroxides with " contaminating " or " absorbed " acid radicals.

Cuprous ions are colorless in solution; cupric ions are colored blue.

Silver

Silver occurs as the native metal and as the minerals argentite, hessite, proustite, pyrargyrite, stephanite, and cerargyrite. It is commonly found in association with lead, zinc, copper, nickel, and gold ores and is obtained as a by-product from the smelting and refining of these metals besides being recovered from the high-silver ores.

In the smelting of lead ores, zinc is added to the molten lead and forms an immiscible liquid which floats. The silver, being more soluble in the zinc than in the lead, is extracted into the upper layer which may then be drawn off and the zinc vaporized from the dissolved silver. Silver is also obtained as a sediment in the electrolytic refining of copper and zinc and may be recovered from the " mud." (See Electrochemistry.) Native silver is soluble in mercury, with which it forms an amalgam. Certain ores are treated in this way, the mercury being afterwards removed from the silver by distillation.

Silver Sulfide (Ag_2S) is found as the mineral argentite from which the silver is usually recovered by cyaniding. (See below.) The same applies to the telluride hessite (Ag_2Te), and to the arsenious and antimonial minerals proustite (Ag_3AsS_3), pyrargyrite (Ag_3SbS_3), and stephanite (Ag_5SbS_4).

The pure sulfide, a gelatinous black precipitate, is obtained, as are the sulfides of copper, zinc, mercury, etc., by treating a solution of a silver salt with hydrogen sulfide or an alkaline sulfide.

Silver Nitrate ($AgNO_3$) is obtained by treating silver with hot, strong nitric acid.

$$3Ag + 4HNO_3 \rightarrow 3AgNO_3 + NO + 2H_2O \qquad (38)$$

The nitrate is soluble, and may be crystallized from the solution. Its chief uses are in photography and medicine.

Silver Chloride ($AgCl$), **silver bromide** ($AgBr$), and **silver iodide** (AgI) are highly insoluble salts prepared by treating solutions of silver nitrate with solutions of chlorides, bromides, or iodides. They are precipitated in highly dispersed form in gelatin for use in photographic plates, film, and paper, and for medicinal preparations. The chloride is found as the mineral cerargerite; the other two halides occur in rare deposits.

Silver chloride and silver bromide dissolve in ammonium hydroxide to give the complex ion $Ag(NH_3^+)_2^-$ similar to the cuprammonium complex. The iodide is so highly insoluble that it does not dissolve. Solutions of thiosulfates and of cyanides, however, dissolve even the iodide and the sulfide, which is not affected by ammonia, to give the complex ions $Ag(S_2O_3)_2^-$ and $Ag(CN)_2^-$. It is for this reason that sodium thiosulfate, or hypo, is used in photographic fixing baths to dissolve silver salts, while sodium cyanide solutions are used to dissolve sulfide and complex ores of silver in the process of cyaniding.

Silver is monovalent in all its compounds and forms colorless ions. It is a very unreactive metal, and its salts are decomposed to the metal when exposed to light or considerable heat.

Gold

Gold is found chiefly as the native metal but also as the complex gold and silver tellurides, sylvanite and calaverite. It is obtained as a by-product, along with silver, from copper, lead, zinc, and nickel smelters and refineries.

Gold forms two series of compounds corresponding to valences of one and three, but none of the simple salts are stable. It forms the same cyanide complex as does silver, $Au(CN)_2^-$, and is recovered from its ores by cyaniding as well as by amalgamation. The metal is even less reactive than silver. It is insoluble in the mineral acids as are the other metals, but dissolves in a mixture of nitric and hydrochloric acids, called *aqua regia*, to form the complex chlorauric ion $AuCl_4^-$.

11. RHODIUM, RUTHENIUM, PLATINUM, PALLADIUM, OSMIUM, AND IRIDIUM

These metals are extremely inert toward chemical attack. All except rhodium and iridium, however, are dissolved by aqua regia, a mixture of hydrochloric and nitric acids, forming soluble complex chlorides. Platinum in specially prepared forms is useful as a catalyst in many chemical processes, sulfuric acid manufacture by the contact process being the most important.

12. ALUMINUM

By far the most important source of aluminum is the mineral bauxite. Gibbsite and alunite are also used, while cryolite is chiefly important as a flux for bauxite in the electrochemical manufacture of the metal. Aluminum is an important constituent of clays and many rocks.

Aluminum Oxide (Al_2O_3) is found as the hard mineral corundum used as an abrasive, and in the hydrated form as bauxite.

Aluminum Sulfate [$Al_2(SO_4)_3 \cdot 18H_2O$] is manufactured by the reaction of strong sulfuric acid and bauxite.

$$Al_2O_3 + 3H_2SO_4 \rightarrow Al_2(SO_4)_3 + 3H_2O \tag{39}$$

It is used in water purification, mordanting, paper-making, and fire-proofing cloth.

Alum [$K_2SO_4 \cdot Al_2(SO_4)_3 \cdot 24H_2O$] is typical of a large group of complex salts called alums. It is readily crystallized from a solution containing potassium and aluminum sulfates. Its importance is due to the fact that, owing to its perfect crystallization, it is readily prepared in a very pure form, whereas the other aluminum salts are usually contaminated and are not completely soluble in water. It is prepared by the addition of potassium sulfate to a solution of aluminum sulfate. It is used in mordanting and for photographic fixing baths as well as in baking powders and other products.

Sodium and ammonium may replace potassium in alum, giving sodium and ammonium alum, respectively.

Aluminum Hydroxide [$Al(OH)_3$], or a basic salt, is formed as a gelatinous white precipitate when aluminum salts are treated with alkali. It is precipitated in drinking water from aluminum sulfate or alum, to coagulate the suspended matter and thus produce a clear liquid. It is amphoteric, forming aluminates which are, in the case of the alkali metals, soluble.

$$Al(OH)_3 + NaOH \leftrightarrows NaAlO_2 + 2H_2O \tag{40}$$

The aluminates of calcium and magnesium are important constituents of portland cements.

Aluminum metal itself is prepared electrolytically from bauxite. (See Electrochemistry.) It is quite reactive but forms an inert protective coating of aluminum oxide.

Aluminum is trivalent in all its compounds and forms colorless ions.

13. IRON, NICKEL, AND COBALT

Iron

Iron occurs in the minerals pyrrhotite, pyrite, marcasite, magnetite, hematite, limonite, and copiapite, besides being present in all silicate rocks.

Iron forms two series of compounds, corresponding to valences two and three, called ferrous and ferric.

Ferrous Oxide (FeO) and **ferric oxide** (Fe_2O_3) result from the rusting (oxidation) of iron. Ferric oxide is found as the mineral hematite; a combination of the two oxides occurs as magnetite ($FeO \cdot Fe_2O_3$). The oxides are heated in a blast furnace with coke to yield metallic iron (pig iron).

$$\left. \begin{array}{l} FeO_3 + 3C \rightarrow 2Fe + 3CO \\ FeO + C \rightarrow Fe + CO \end{array} \right\} \tag{41}$$

Ferrous Carbonate ($FeCO_3$) is found as the mineral siderite. Under heat it decomposes to ferrous oxide which may be treated with coke to give the metal.

$$FeCO_3 \rightarrow FeO + CO_2 \tag{42}$$

Sulfides of Iron are found as the minerals pyrrhotite ($Fe_{11}S_{12}$) (composition variable), pyrite (FeS_2), and marcasite (FeS_2). These substances are not true salts and do **not**

conform to the usual rules of valence. They are roasted to give iron oxide and sulfur dioxide which is converted to sulfuric acid.

$$2FeS_2 + 5O_2 \rightarrow 2FeO + 4SO_2 \tag{43}$$

Some ferrous sulfate is also formed inadvertently in the process.

Ferrous Sulfide (FeS) is precipitated as are the sulfides of zinc, copper, etc., by treatment of a solution of a ferrous salt with hydrogen sulfide or a soluble sulfide. In this form it is a black gelatinous substance. It is also formed by direct reaction of its elements under heat.

Ferrous Sulfate ($FeSO_4 \cdot 7H_2O$) is produced as a by-product of many industrial processes such as the pickling of steel and the manufacture of titanium oxide pigments. It is used in water treatment, being cheaper than aluminum sulfate, and as a source of electrolytic iron. Solutions of the salt oxidize slowly in the presence of air to ferric sulfate, provided excess of sulfuric acid is present. Otherwise a basic ferric sulfate is formed.

$$4FeSO_4 + O_2 + 2H_2O \rightarrow 4Fe(OH)SO_4 \tag{44}$$

Ferric Sulfate $Fe_2(SO_4)_3 \cdot 9H_2O$ is reduced to ferrous sulfate by hydrogen sulfide in solution.

$$2Fe^{+++} + H_2S \leftrightarrows 2Fe^{++} + 2H^+ + S \tag{45}$$

If the acid (or hydrogen-ion) concentration is not too high, ferrous sulfide is precipitated, and ferric sulfide can never be obtained. Ferric sulfate is similar to aluminum sulfate in forming alums such as ferric ammonium sulfate [$(NH_4)_2SO_4 \cdot Fe_2(SO_4)_3 \cdot 24H_2O$]. Both ferrous and ferric ions form stable cyanide complexes, the former giving ferrocyanide $Fe(CN)_6{}^{----}$, the latter ferricyanide $Fe(CN)_6{}^{---}$.

Potassium Ferrocyanide [$K_4Fe(CN)_6$] is made by heating scrap iron and potassium carbonate with nitrogenous organic compounds such as slaughter-house wastes. The mass is then leached with water, and the solution evaporated until the potassium ferrocyanide crystallizes out.

Potassium Ferricyanide [$K_3Fe(CN)_6$] is produced by treating a solution of potassium ferrocyanide with chlorine.

$$2K_4Fe(CN)_6 + Cl_2 \rightarrow 2K_3Fe(CN)_6 + 2KCl \tag{46}$$

Ferric Ferrocyanide [$Fe_4\{Fe(CN)_6\}_3$] and **ferrous ferricyanide** [$Fe_3\{Fe(CN)_6\}_2$] are insoluble blue salts which give colloidal, or highly dispersed, suspensions. The former is Prussian blue; the latter Turnbull's blue. Prussian blue is used as a paint pigment. Mixed with the yellow lead chromate it forms a green pigment known as chrome green.

Metallic iron is highly reactive but tends to form an oxide film which is protective under certain conditions. Its properties are markedly affected by impurities and alloying constituents.

Ferrous Hydroxide [$Fe(OH)_2$] and **ferric hydroxide** [$Fe(OH)_3$] are formed as gelatinous precipitates by treatment of solutions of iron salts with alkalis. The former is pale green, the latter brown.

Cobalt and Nickel

These metals are found as linnaeite [$(Co \cdot Ni)_3S_4$], cobaltite (CoAsS), smaltite [$(Co \cdot Ni)As_2$], millerite (NiS), pentlandite [$(Fe \cdot Ni)S$], niccolite (NiAs), and garnierite [$H_2(Ni \cdot Mg)SiO_4 \cdot H_2O$].

Both cobalt and nickel are similar to iron in forming bivalent and trivalent compounds (cobaltous and cobaltic, nickelous and nickelic). Both also form cyanide complexes.

Both metals behave similarly to metallic iron, and form even more stable protective films. They are obtained electrolytically. (See Electrochemistry.)

14. CHROMIUM AND MANGANESE

Chromium

The chief ore of chromium is chromite ($FeO \cdot Cr_2O_3$), which is very similar to magnetite ($FeO \cdot Fe_2O_3$).

Sodium Chromate ($Na_2CrO_4 \cdot 10H_2O$) is produced by the reaction of chromite with lime and sodium carbonate.

$$4(FeO \cdot Cr_2O_3) + 8Na_2CO_3 + 6O_2 \rightarrow 8Na_2CrO_4 + 4FeO + 8CO_2 \tag{47}$$

The lime keeps the mass porous and forms some calcium chromate. The mass is then leached, and the calcium chromate reacts with the excess of sodium carbonate to form the insoluble calcium carbonate and additional sodium chromate.

Sodium Dichromate ($Na_2Cr_2O_7 \cdot 2H_2O$) is formed when the solution of sodium chromate prepared as described above is acidified with sulfuric acid.

$$2Na_2CrO_4 + H_2SO_4 \rightarrow Na_2Cr_2O_7 + Na_2SO_4 + H_2O \tag{48}$$

By analogy with the salts of other polybasic acids, an acid salt $NaHCrO_4$ might be expected. Such a compound is not stable, however, and decomposes immediately to the dichromate

$$2NaHCrO_4 \rightarrow Na_2Cr_2O_7 + H_2O \qquad (49)$$

The dichromate may therefore be considered a dehydrated acid salt of chromic acid. That the dichromates are essentially acid salts may be seen from the fact that a solution of the dichromate is converted by alkali to the neutral chromate.

$$Na_2Cr_2O_7 + 2NaOH \rightarrow 2Na_2CrO_4 + H_2O \qquad (50)$$

Sodium dichromate is more readily crystallized from the solution than the chromate, and is formed for that reason.

The tendency of acid salts of chromic acid to dehydrate is further manifested by the behavior of the acid itself which is always obtained as the anhydride.

Chromic Anhydride (CrO_3), usually called chromic acid, is formed by the treatment of sodium dichromate with concentrated sulfuric acid.

$$Na_2Cr_2O_7 + H_2SO_4 \rightarrow Na_2SO_4 + 2CrO_3 + H_2O \qquad (51)$$

The anhydride separates in the form of red needles. It is used in chromium plating.

Oxidation and Reduction. Chromium differs from the other metals studied thus far in forming an acid, although it will be remembered that the hydroxides of some of the other metals are amphoteric, sharing acidic and basic qualities.

The essentially metallic, and hence base-forming, character of chromium is shown by the fact that the chromates and dichromates are not very stable but tend to pass to chromic and chromous salts. Thus sulfurous acid, formed by passing sulfur dioxide into water, converts the dichromate to chromic sulfate.

$$Na_2Cr_2O_7 + 3SO_2 + H_2SO_4 \rightarrow Cr_2(SO_4)_3 + Na_2SO_4 + H_2O \qquad (52)$$

In this reaction the valence of chromium drops from six to three, while that of the sulfur in the SO_2 passes from four to six. The diminution of positive (or increase of negative) valence of an element is called reduction, and increase of positive (or decrease of negative) valence is called oxidation. The two always occur simultaneously. A substance such as sodium dichromate which tends to oxidize another is called an oxidizing agent; sulfur dioxide which tends to reduce dichromate is called a reducing agent.

In a restricted sense, oxidation is sometimes used to imply the addition of oxygen to a substance, and reduction its removal. The more general case, however, may or may not involve oxygen either as a product or reactant.

A large number of reducing agents are available which may replace the sulfur dioxide in equation 52.

Chromic Sulfate $[Cr_2(SO_4)_3]$ is prepared industrially by the reduction of sodium dichromate in solution with reducing agents such as sulfur dioxide, starch, sugar, glucose, and others in the presence of excess sulfuric acid. Although it is quite soluble, it does not crystallize readily in pure form so that it is generally used in solution along with its oxidation products. Such solutions are used in tanning and in the mordanting of textiles.

Chromic salts in which the chromium has a valence of three are very similar to ferric salts. Chromic hydroxide is also very similar to ferric hydroxide although somewhat amphoteric, forming chromites with strong alkalis. Like aluminum and iron, chromium salts form well-crystallized alums.

Chromium Acetate $[Cr(C_2H_3O_2)_3]$ is a particularly good mordant formed by reducing sodium dichromate in the presence of acetic acid.

Chromic Oxide (Cr_2O_3) is formed by heating sodium dichromate with coke. It is used as a green pigment, known as chrome oxide green.

Chromium also forms a series of chromous salts similar to the ferrous salts, in which the chromium is bivalent. Chromium forms ammonium and cyanide complexes and highly complex basic salts, particularly with sulfate. Owing to the fact that simple chromic ions are rarely obtained, chromic salts are either green or violet, depending upon the conditions of preparation.

The metal itself is very resistant to corrosion, and is used as a thin protective or decorative coating on plate.

Manganese

Manganese is found as pyrolusite, psilomelane, manganite, rhodocrosite, and rhodonite.

Manganese Dioxide (MnO_2) is found chiefly as the mineral pyrolusite and, more sparingly, as psilomelane, a more impure form. It is important as a source of manganese for steel alloys and for the manufacture of other compounds. A very important direct use is in the manufacture of dry cells. Manganese dioxide has weak acidic properties, forming manganites with strong alkalis. It is a fairly strong oxidizing agent.

Potassium Permanganate ($KMnO_4$) is formed by treating pyrolusite with a boiling solution of potassium hydroxide and potassium chlorate.

$$2MnO_2 + KClO_3 + 2KOH \rightarrow 2KMnO_4 + KCl + H_2O \qquad (53)$$

The solution is evaporated and the residue fused. Under these conditions the reaction does not go to completion since some **potassium manganate** (K_2MnO_4) is also formed.

The fusion mass is leached and further oxidized with chlorine. Potassium permanganate crystallizes in metallic crystals which dissolve readily to give a purple solution (color of permanganate ions). Permanganate in solution is similar to dichromate in its strong oxidizing power.

Manganese forms manganous salts in which the element is bivalent, and manganic salts in which it is trivalent. These are similar to ferrous and chromous, and ferric and chromic salts. The manganous compounds are readily oxidized by the air to the more stable manganic forms.

15. LEAD, TIN, AND TITANIUM

Lead

Lead is obtained chiefly from galena, but also from anglesite, pyromorphite, and cerussite.

Lead Sulfide (PbS) is found as galena. It may also be precipitated as a black gelatinous precipitate by treating solutions of lead salts with hydrogen sulfide or soluble sulfides. Galena is roasted under carefully controlled conditions to react as follows:

$$\left. \begin{array}{l} 2PbS + 3O_2 \rightarrow 2PbO + 2SO_2 \\ PbS + 2O_2 \rightarrow PbSO_4 \\ 2PbO + PbS \rightarrow 3Pb + SO_2 \\ PbSO_4 + PbS \rightarrow 2Pb + 2SO_2 \end{array} \right\} \qquad (54)$$

Molten lead is the final product. The sulfur dioxide is converted to sulfuric acid.

Lead is highly resistant to most types of corrosion and is used for pipes, chemical equipment, etc.

Lead Oxide (PbO), or litharge, is formed by heating lead in a strong blast of air. It is used in glass-making and as a source of lead salts. The corresponding hydroxide [$Pb(OH)_2$] is amphoteric, forming plumbites.

Minium (Pb_3O_4), or red lead, is formed by heating litharge in a blast of air at 600–700 deg fahr. It is used as a red paint pigment.

Lead Dioxide (PbO_2) is formed by treating red lead with nitric acid. It is essentially acidic, forming salts known as plumbates. Minium may be regarded as lead plumbate (Pb_2PbO_4).

Lead Carbonate ($PbCO_3$) is found as cerussite. The basic salt known as white lead and corresponding approximately to the formula $Pb_3(OH)_2(CO_3)_2$ although the composition is variable, is formed by the corrosion of lead in carbon dioxide, acetic acid being added to aid in the process. White lead may also be formed by treating a solution of lead acetate with carbon dioxide, and also electrolytically. It is used as a white paint pigment.

Lead Sulfate ($PbSO_4$) is found as anglesite. It is precipitated by the mixture of solutions containing lead and sulfate. By the complete roasting of galena ore a product is sublimed which is called sublimed white lead, and which contains lead sulfate, lead oxide, and a small amount of zinc oxide.

Lead Acetate [$Pb(C_2H_3O_2)_2$] is made by treating litharge with acetic acid. It is the only common salt of lead, beside the nitrate, which is readily soluble.

Lead Nitrate [$Pb(NO_3)_2$] is formed by treating litharge with dilute nitric acid and evaporating the solution.

Lead Chromate ($PbCrO_4$), or chrome yellow, is formed as a yellow precipitate when a solution of lead nitrate or acetate is treated with one of sodium dichromate. It is used as a pigment. A mixture of chrome yellow and Prussian blue is sold as chrome green.

Lead may have valences of one, two, or four. Its ions are colorless.

Tin

Tin is obtained chiefly from the mineral cassiterite.

Stannic Oxide (SnO_2) is found as cassiterite. The ore is heated with coke to produce the metal, which is highly resistant to corrosion and is therefore used to coat tin cans. Tin forms two series of salts, corresponding to valences of two and four, called stannous and stannic, respectively.

$$SnO_2 + 2C \rightarrow Sn + 2CO \qquad (55)$$

Stannic Chloride (SnCl₄) is formed by the reaction of chlorine gas and tin. It is a rather volatile liquid which fumes strongly in moist air. It is used as a mordant.

Stannous Chloride (SnCl₂) is formed in solution by treating stannic chloride with metallic tin. It tends to pass to the stannic form and is thus an active reducing agent. It is used as a mordant.

Stannic Sulfide (SnS₂) and **stannous sulfide** (SnS) are among the most insoluble of the sulfides. They are formed by treating solutions of the tin salts with hydrogen sulfide or a soluble sulfide. Stannic sulfide is soluble in solutions of soluble alkaline sulfides. Stannous sulfide is soluble in polysulfide solutions. Complex salts are formed.

Titanium

Titanium is very abundant in nature, being obtained from deposits of ilmenite and rutile.

Titanium Dioxide (TiO₂) is found as rutile. As a white pigment material it is obtained from solutions of titanium sulfate. Such solutions hydrolyze when boiled and yield a basic sulfate which, when calcined, is converted to the oxide. The corresponding hydroxide (titanic acid) is amphoteric.

Titanium dioxide is marketed as a high-grade white pigment with extremely high covering power and whiteness. It is obtainable in mixtures with " fillers " such as barium sulfate and calcium sulfate.

Titanium Sulfate [Ti(SO₄)₂] is obtained by treating ilmenite or rutile with strong sulfuric acid at elevated temperatures. The iron in the minerals is simultaneously converted to ferrous sulfate. Normal titanium sulfate cannot be isolated by crystallization to any definite composition. Titanyl sulfate (TiOSO₄) does, however, crystallize very well and may be dissolved to form solutions of basic sulfate.

Titanium Chloride (TiCl₄) is produced by treating ilmenite ore with dry chlorine gas. It is a volatile liquid similar to stannic chloride, and it fumes in the presence of moist air. It is used as a material for the formation of smoke screens and as a mordant.

Titanium also forms titanous salts in which the element is trivalent. Titanous ion is a strong reducing agent tending strongly to pass to the titanic state. Titanic salts in solution are colorless to amber. Titanous salts are violet.

16. CHEMISTRY OF GASES

The metallic elements and their compounds, with but rare exceptions, do not exist in the gaseous state at ordinary temperatures. Among the non-metals, however, numerous substances, both elements and compounds, are gaseous.

Kinetics

The molecules in a gas are supposed to be in rapid random motion with negligible forces of attraction or repulsion among them. As a consequence a gas may occupy any size or shape of container. Compression of a gas merely results in crowding the molecules; expansion does the reverse. Temperature is measured by the mean energy of translatory motion of the molecules; pressure is the result of the incessant bombardment on the containing walls. The fundamental assumption in the chemistry of gases is that the pressure and temperature depend only upon the number of molecules in a unit of volume and upon their mean energy. They do not depend upon the chemical nature. If temperature and pressure are given certain fixed values, the number of molecules in a unit volume is the same for all gases. This is *Avogadro's hypothesis*. The unit of volume which is generally taken is 22.4 liters since that volume of hydrogen weighs 2.016 grams, that volume of oxygen weighs 32 grams, and that volume of any substance is the molecular weight in grams. For this reason 22.4 liters is called the gram-molecular volume. It contains 6.06×10^{23} molecules at standard conditions of any gaseous substance. Standard conditions are when temperature and pressure are 0 deg cent and 760 mm of mercury, respectively.

Gas Laws

One of the most important consequences of this assumption is that the volumes of gases taking part in a reaction are proportional to the number of molecules involved. Thus at constant temperature and pressure

$$2CO + O_2 \rightarrow 2CO_2$$

$$2V + 1V \rightarrow 2V \quad (V = \text{volume}) \tag{56}$$

expresses the reaction of carbon monoxide gas with oxygen. Two volumes of carbon monoxide combine with one of oxygen to yield two of carbon dioxide. This rule applies even though one or more of the reactants or products may not be gaseous. Thus

$$C + O_2 \rightarrow CO_2$$
$$12 \text{ grams} + 1V \rightarrow 1V \tag{57}$$

indicates that, in the burning of carbon, one volume of oxygen is required for every one of carbon dioxide produced.

$$2H_2 + O_2 \rightarrow 2H_2O$$
$$2V + 1V \rightarrow 2V \tag{58}$$

indicates that two volumes of hydrogen will combine with one of oxygen to form two of water.

Table I. Common Gases

(From Kohlrausch, 1910)

Gas	Specific Gravity or Density*	Molecular Mass	Specific Heat (0°–200° C) Constant Pressure	$\frac{c_p}{c_v}$ ‡	Melting Point ° C	Boiling Point ° C	Water Dissolves cu cm †		Symbol
							At 0° C	At 20° C	
Air (free of CO₂).	1.2928	28.98	0.238	1.40	....	− 193	29	19	Air
Acetylene.......	1.1759	24.02	....	1.26	− 81.5	− 83.6	1730	1030	C₂H₂
Ammonia........	0.7708	17.03	0.52	1.32	− 78	− 33.5	(12×10⁵)	(7×10⁵)	NH₃
Carbon dioxide...	1.9768	44.00	0.218	1.30	− 57	− 78.2	(1800)	(900)	CO₂
Carbon monoxide.	1.2503	28.00	0.243	1.41	− 207	− 190.0	35.4	23.2	CO
Chlorine.........	3.2197	70.92	0.121	1.32	− 102	− 33.4	(4600)	(2300)	Cl₂
Hydrogen.......	0.08985	2.016	3.41	1.41	− 259	− 252.6	21.1	18.1	H₂
Nitrogen........	1.2507	28.02	0.244	1.41	− 210.5	− 195.7	23.5	15.4	N₂
Nitrous oxide....	1.9777	44.02	0.225	1.28	− 103	− 90	1300	650	N₂O
Oxygen.........	1.4292	32.00	0.220	1.40	− 227	− 182.8	48.9	31.0	O₂

* Numbers in this column to be divided by 1000.
† These columns contain the number of cubic centimeters of gas that will be dissolved at a barometric pressure of 76 cm in 1 liter of water.
‡ This column gives the ratio of the specific heat at constant pressure to that at constant volume.

Temperature is a measure of the mean kinetic energy of translation of the molecules. Pressure is the energy of random bombardment in a unit of volume. If the volume of a fixed quantity of gas is held constant, the two must be proportional. Moreover, if the pressure is held constant a gas will expand and contract proportionally with the temperature. This is known as Charles' law. These relations may be expressed as:

$$P \alpha T \quad (V \text{ constant})$$
$$V \alpha T \quad (p \text{ constant})$$
or
$$PV = nRT \tag{59}$$

which is the perfect gas law equation, where P is the pressure, V is the volume, T is the absolute temperature (0 deg cent = 273.2 deg abs), n is the number of gram-mols, and R is a universal constant.

It will be observed that at the zero of the absolute scale of temperature a gas would have either zero volume, or zero pressure, or both. Actually all gases become liquid before this point is reached, but this temperature (− 273.2 deg cent) has a theoretical significance as the absolute zero of temperature. It will also be noted that the volume is inversely proportional to the pressure if the temperature and quantity of gas are held constant. This is known as Boyle's law.

A vapor is distinguished from a true gas in that it may be converted to a liquid by increase in pressure. The minimum pressure necessary for the conversion is known as the vapor pressure of the liquid. Such a condensation is always companied by a liberation of heat which, unless removed by cooling, will raise the temperature of both the liquid and the residual vapor. This increase will continue to raise the vapor pressure until it becomes equal to the pressure of the vapor phase. Equilibrium will then be established and no further change will occur.

If heat is abstracted *at a constant temperature* under sufficient pressure, vapor will continue to condense. Conversely, if heat is applied liquid will vaporize (evaporate).

The heat required to vaporize a gram of liquid is known as the *latent heat of vaporization*.

The temperature at which the vapor pressure of a liquid becomes equal to the pressure of the atmosphere is known as the *boiling point*. At this temperature the liquid will continue to evaporate as long as heat is applied. In general, boiling points are lowered as the pressure decreases, and vice versa.

All gases become vapors at sufficiently low temperatures. The highest temperature at which this will occur is known as the *critical temperature*, and the vapor pressure of the liquid at this temperature is known as the *critical pressure*. In the vicinity of the critical temperature and pressure, the force of attraction between the molecules of a gas becomes appreciable and the simple assumptions which led to the gas law equation are no longer valid. Semi-empirical equations are then employed to relate the temperature, pressure, and volume. The one most generally accepted is van der Waal's equation.

$$\left(P + \frac{a}{V^2}\right)(V - b) = nRT \tag{60}$$

where a and b are constants for the gas.

This relationship is used whenever a more exact relation than that expressed by the simple gas law is desired, or where the temperature is very low, or the pressure very high.

Certain gases (actually vapors) may be liquefied at atmospheric temperatures, and the liquid vaporized at a lower pressure, at a lower temperature, absorbing heat in the process. Such is the principle of refrigerating machines. To qualify as a refrigerant, a substance must of course have a critical temperature above that of the atmosphere or available cooling water and should have a vapor pressure which is not too high to be obtained with an ordinary compressor. Also the vapor pressure at the lowest temperature to be attained should not be so low as to require a high vacuum. Ammonia, carbon dioxide, sulfur dioxide, and numerous organic substances are all suited to various requirements of refrigerants, and each has its specific use.

Air

Air is a mixture of gases in the following proportions.

	Per Cent by Volume	Per Cent by Weight
Nitrogen	78.03	75.80
Oxygen	20.99	23.22
Carbon dioxide	0.03	0.05
Argon	0.94	
Neon		
Krypton		
Xenon	0.01	0.93
Helium		
Hydrogen		

Oxygen is the constituent which supports the combustion of fuels and other combustible materials. Nitrogen may be obtained by burning off the oxygen and absorbing the carbon dioxide in an alkaline solution. It will then be contaminated with small quantities of the inert gases which are not readily removable. In this form it may be used for the synthesis of ammonia by the Haber process.

Air may be liquefied by chilling to a sufficiently low temperature. The constituents may then be separated by fractional distillation. Nitrogen (boiling point −196 deg cent) comes off first, next oxygen (boiling point −182.8 deg cent), followed by argon and neon.

The inert gases are monatomic and do not combine with any of the elements. For this reason they are used where an absolutely inert gas is required. Argon is used for filling the bulbs of incandescent lamps. Neon is used in gas tubes through which an electric current is passed to effect the characteristic orange-red glow. Air also contains water vapor and dust in varying amounts.

17. NITROGEN, PHOSPHORUS, ARSENIC, ANTIMONY AND BISMUTH

These elements constitute a family varying from the purely non-metallic nitrogen to bismuth which is distinctly metallic. That the division of the two classes of elements is not a sharp one is thus indicated.

Nitrogen

Nitrogen, a gaseous element, is very abundant in the atmosphere, but its comparatively inert behavior makes it difficult to obtain in a fixed, or combined, form. Its compounds are valuable elements in fertilizers and as a source of nitric acid.

Ammonia (NH_3) is made by passing a mixture of nitrogen and hydrogen over a catalyst of metallic oxides.

$$N_2 + 3H_2 \rightarrow 2NH_3 \qquad (61)$$

The reaction goes more rapidly at higher temperatures but also becomes less complete owing to the reversibility. Hence a compromise must be struck to obtain the best results. The equilibrium may be expressed by a mass law equation similar to that for reactions in solutions.

$$\frac{(N_2)(H_2)^3}{(NH_3)^2} = K, \text{ the equilibrium constant} \qquad (62)$$

If the pressure on the mixture is increased it will be observed that the concentration of both the reactants and the product is increased. Since the numerator of the equilibrium equation varies as the fourth power of the concentration of the reactants while the denominator varies as the square of the concentration of the product, the latter must increase faster than the former to maintain the constancy of the quotient. Hence the proportion of products to reactants increases at high pressures and the reaction goes forward. Extremely high pressures are, in fact, used in the industry.

Most of the ammonia produced in this way is converted to nitric acid; a mixture of the ammonia gas and air is passed over a platinum catalyst at a red heat. The following reactions occur.

$$
\left.
\begin{aligned}
&NH_3 + 2O_2 \rightarrow H_2O + HNO_3 && \text{(nitric acid)}\\
&2NH_3 + 3O_2 \rightarrow 2H_2O + 2HNO_2 && \text{(nitrous acid)}\\
&4NH_3 + 5O_2 \rightarrow 6H_2O + 4NO && \text{(nitric oxide)}\\
&4NH_3 + 7O_2 \rightarrow 6H_2O + 4NO_2 && \text{(nitrogen tetroxide)}\\
&4NH_3 + 3O_2 \rightarrow 6H_2O + 2N_2 && \text{(nitrogen)}\\
&4NH_3 + 6NO \rightarrow 6H_2O + 5N_2 && \text{(nitrogen)}
\end{aligned}
\right\} \qquad (63)
$$

Any ammonia which is converted to nitrogen is, of course, wasted. In order to minimize this loss the temperature must be accurately controlled (750–800 deg cent). The nitrogen tetroxide, nitric oxide and nitrous acid are then further oxidized with air in the presence of water vapor.

$$
\left.
\begin{aligned}
&3NO_2 + H_2O \rightarrow 2HNO_3 + NO\\
&2HNO_2 + O_2 \rightarrow 2HNO_3\\
&2NO + O_2 \rightarrow 2NO_2
\end{aligned}
\right\} \qquad (64)
$$

Nitric acid ionizes practically completely in water, in which it is very soluble. It is a strong acid and a strong oxidizing agent. The chief uses are in the manufacture of salts used as fertilizers such as calcium nitrate and ammonium nitrate, and for the nitration of organic chemicals, particularly for dyes, explosives, lacquers, and celluloid. Nitric acid is also made from nitric oxide, produced by the direct combination of nitrogen and oxygen of the atmosphere in an electric arc. Sodium nitrate, or Chile saltpeter, mined chiefly in Chile, is also used as a source of the acid. (See p. 10–13.)

Nitrates of the metals are all very soluble in water. Nitrate ion, as well as the other simple ions containing nitrogen, such as ammonium (NH_4^+), and nitrite (NO_2^-), are colorless. Nitrogen may have valences of one, two, three, four, or five.

Phosphorus

Phosphorus, like nitrogen, is an important element of fertilizers. It is found as the mineral apatite $[(Ca_5)(Cl \cdot F)(PO_4)_3]$, the important constituent of phosphate rock. Apatite is heated with coke and sand in an electric or fuel furnace. The calcium of the mineral combines with the silica of the sand while the coke reduces the phosphate to elementary phosphorus which is volatilized and condensed as solid white phosphorus or burned in air to the solid white phosphorus pentoxide (P_2O_5).

White phosphorus is very inflammable and for that reason is used as a constituent in the manufacture of matches. A less reactive red variety is obtained by heating white phosphorus to about 250 deg cent in the absence of air.

Phosphorus Pentoxide (P_2O_5), or phosphoric anhydride, is used as a dehydrating agent. It combines with water to form phosphoric acid.

Phosphoric Acid (H_3PO_4) is a syrupy liquid which is a mildly strong acid very soluble in water. Besides being produced from phosphorus pentoxide it is also manufactured by treating phosphate rock with dilute sulfuric acid.

$$Ca_3(PO_4)_2 + 3H_2SO_4 \rightarrow 3CaSO_4 + 2H_3PO_4 \qquad (65)$$

Superphosphate [CaH$_4$(PO$_4$)$_2$] (composition variable) is an acid calcium phosphate prepared by treating phosphate rock with strong sulfuric acid.

$$Ca_3(PO_4)_2 + 2H_2SO_4 \rightarrow CaH_4(PO_4)_2 + 2CaSO_4 \qquad (66)$$

The acid salts are soluble, and may therefore be used to supply both calcium and phosphate to the soil.

The phosphates of sodium have already been discussed (p. 10-13). In general, all the normal phosphates of the metals are quite insoluble except those of the alkali metals and ammonium. The acid phosphates, on the other hand, are generally soluble. For this reason, phosphates tend to dissolve in acid solutions.

Arsenic

Arsenic is found in numerous ores of iron, nickel, lead, and zinc, and as orpiment and realgar. It is obtained chiefly as a by-product of metallurgical operations. Its uses are in dyeing, medicine, and vermin and insect poisons. Arsenic forms two series of compounds corresponding to valences of three and five. The former are called arsenious or arsenites, the latter arsenic or arsenates.

Arsenious Sulfide (As$_2$S$_3$) is found as the mineral orpiment. It is prepared in pure form, as are the heavy metal sulfides, by treating arsenious salts or arsenites with hydrogen sulfide or a soluble sulfide. It is a yellow insoluble precipitate.

Arsenic Sulfide (As$_2$S$_5$) is prepared by treating an arsenic salt or an arsenate with hydrogen sulfide or a soluble sulfide. It is yellow and insoluble. The sulfides of arsenic have the peculiar property, along with similar sulfides of antimony and tin, of dissolving in solutions of sulfides and of polysulfides to form complex sulfur compounds.

Arsenious Acid (H$_3$AsO$_3$) and **arsenic acid** (H$_3$AsO$_4$) are in reality amphoteric hydroxides which might be written As(OH)$_3$ and AsO(OH)$_3$. Here, however, the acid properties, though weak, are more pronounced than the basic so that they are ordinarily considered acids. Arsenious acid is produced when arsenious salts are treated with alkali, or arsenites with acids. The arsenates are very similar in properties to the phosphates.

Arsenious Oxide (As$_2$O$_3$), or white arsenic, is formed as a fume in the roasting of arsenic-bearing ores. It is the starting material for the preparation of other arsenic compounds. Important insecticides are **lead arsenate** [Pb$_3$(AsO$_4$)$_2$] and paris green [Cu$_3$(AsO$_3$)$_2$·Cu(C$_2$H$_3$O$_2$)$_2$].

Antimony

The chief antimony mineral is stibnite. The element is also obtained as a by-product from lead ores.

Like arsenic, antimony forms two series of compounds corresponding to valences of three and five; the metallic properties are, however, more pronounced. The element itself has a metallic luster and is used in many important alloys.

Antimony Trisulfide (Sb$_2$S$_3$) is found as the mineral stibnite. It may be formed from solutions of antimony salts in typical fashion as is also antimony pentasulfide (Sb$_2$S$_5$) from solutions of antimonic salts or antimonates. Both sulfides are soluble in solutions of sulfides or polysulfides.

Antimony Trioxide (Sb$_2$O$_3$) is formed by the combustion of antimony with limited oxygen. It has found some use as a white pigment. Antimony salts are used in medicine.

Bismuth

Bismuth is found chiefly as native metallic bismuth and as bismuthinite. The ores are smelted to obtain the metal which is used in low melting point alloys. Salts of bismuth hydrolyze extensively to basic forms.

Bismuth Subnitrate [Bi(OH)$_2$NO$_3$] is used extensively in medicine. It is formed by treating bismuth with nitric acid and hydrolyzing the nitrate with water.

Bismuth does not manifest any acidic properties as do nitrogen, arsenic, and antimony. It is purely basic and should therefore be classified as a metal.

18. THE HALOGENS—CHLORINE, BROMINE, IODINE, AND FLUORINE

Chlorine

Chlorine is found widely distributed as chlorides, the most important of which is sodium chloride, or common salt. The element is prepared as a yellow-green gas by the electrolysis of sodium chloride brine. (See Electrochemistry.) It is generally liquefied under pressure and shipped in cylinders or tank cars. Chlorine is used for a great variety of chlorination processes, as a bleach, and for the preparation of hypochlorites and chlorates.

The metallic chlorides have already been discussed. They are all quite soluble with the exception of cuprous, mercurous, silver, gold, and platinum. Lead chloride is sparingly soluble.

Hydrochloric Acid (HCl), or muriatic acid, is prepared from sodium chloride and sulfuric acid as has already been described (p. 10–12). It is the most corrosive of the common acids, and is used in the pickling of metals and for a variety of miscellaneous purposes.

Chlorine dissolves in alkaline solutions to form hypochlorites from which it may be released as required for the bleaching of fabrics, paper, and other products. Calcium hypochlorite has already been discussed (p. 10–14).

Sodium Hypochlorite (NaOCl) is formed when chlorine is passed into a solution of sodium hydroxide or sodium carbonate (which is cheaper).

$$\left.\begin{array}{l} 2NaOH + Cl_2 \rightarrow NaOCl + NaCl + H_2O \\ Na_2CO_3 + Cl_2 \rightarrow NaOCl + NaCl + CO_2 \end{array}\right\} \qquad (67)$$

Sodium hydroxide and chlorine are obtained as the products of the electrolysis of salt brine. By mixing the two directly as they are formed, sodium hypochlorite is obtained according to the above reaction. Dilute sodium hypochlorite is known as Javelle water and is used in laundry work. At higher temperatures hypochlorites are converted into chlorates. Thus

$$3NaOCl \rightarrow 2NaCl + NaClO_3 \qquad (68)$$

Sodium Chlorate (NaClO_3) is formed in electrolytic cells similar to those used to produce sodium hypochlorite but operated at a temperature between 70 and 100 deg cent. The hypochlorite is converted directly to chlorate. Sodium and potassium chlorates are used in matches and explosives, and as oxidizing agents.

Bromine

Bromides occur in natural brines in small concentrations associated with much larger amounts of chlorides. Bromine is liberated when such solutions are treated with chlorine.

$$2NaBr + Cl_2 \rightarrow 2NaCl + Br_2 \qquad (69)$$

Recently such a process has been devised and operated for extracting the bromine content of sea water. Bromine is used extensively in the manufacture of the anti-knock compound, tetraethyl lead. Bromides are used in photography and in medicine.

Iodine

Iodine is found in the form of iodates in the mother liquor of Chile saltpeter. It is obtained by treatment with sodium sulfite and bisulfite.

$$2NaIO_3 + 3Na_2SO_3 + 2NaHSO_3 \rightarrow 5Na_2SO_4 + I_2 + H_2O \qquad (70)$$

The iodine is then purified by sublimation. It is also obtained from sodium iodide which is leached from the ashes of seaweeds by treatment of the solution with chlorine, a process similar to that used for the preparation of bromine. Iodine and its compounds are used in medicine and, to a very small extent, in photography. Iodine at room temperatures is a gray, submetallic, crystalline solid.

Fluorine

Fluorine differs somewhat from the other halogens in its extraordinary reactivity. It attacks all the metals except gold and platinum. Copper forms an adherent protective coating of copper fluoride. It is obtained chiefly from fluorite (CaF_2), or fluorspar, although it is a constituent of cryolite (NaF·AlF_3) and of phosphate rock.

Hydrofluoric Acid (H_2F_2) is obtained by treating fluorite with sulfuric acid.

$$CaF_2 + H_2SO_4 \rightarrow CaSO_4 + H_2F_2 \qquad (71)$$

Hydrofluoric acid reacts with silica to form the volatile silicon tetrafluoride or, in the presence of water, fluosilicic acid or metallic fluosilicates.

$$SiO_2 + 2H_2F_2 \rightarrow SiF_4 + 2H_2O \qquad (72)$$

Hydrofluoric acid and the fluorides also attack silicates such as glass, producing an etch. They are accordingly used for etching as well as for cleaning. Hydrofluoric acid differs from the other halogen acids in being dibasic. It may therefore form acid fluorides such as sodium bifluoride (NaHF_2) which is obtained by treating the normal fluoride with hydrofluoric acid. The fluorides are used as insecticides; the bifluorides are used in laundering. Fluorine is a pale yellow-green gas.

The simple ions of all the halogens are colorless.

19. SULFUR, SELENIUM, AND TELLURIUM

Sulfur

Sulfur is obtained from extensive deposits of the native element and from the metallic ores.

Sulfur Dioxide (SO_2) is obtained as the gaseous product of the combustion of sulfur in air. It is also obtained in the roasting of ores. Its chief importance is in the fact that it is an intermediate product in the manufacture of sulfuric acid.

Sulfuric Acid (H_2SO_4) is obtained from sulfur dioxide by two important processes. In the chamber process, sulfur dioxide, air, and water are allowed to react to form the acid. The reaction is ordinarily very slow, but in the presence of oxides of nitrogen it is considerably catalyzed. The following intermediate reactions are believed to occur.

$$\left.\begin{array}{l} SO_2 + NO_2 \rightarrow SO_3 + NO \\ SO_3 + H_2O \rightarrow H_2SO_4 \\ 2NO + O_2 \rightarrow 2NO_2 \quad \text{(to be re-used)} \end{array}\right\} \tag{73}$$

The nitrogen compounds continue through a cycle and remain unchanged except for plant losses.

In the second method, known as the contact process, the sulfur dioxide and air are passed over a catalyst which may be platinum or vanadium compounds, to form sulfur trioxide. This is then dissolved in strong sulfuric acid, water being added to maintain the dilution. A solution of sulfur trioxide in anhydrous sulfuric acid is sold as oleum, or fuming sulfuric acid. It may be regarded as sulfuric acid which has been partially dehydrated. Sulfuric acid is manufactured in enormous quantities. It is the basic material of the chemical industries, and its uses are more extensive and widespread than those of any other chemical.

Hydrochloric and nitric acid plants are generally closely associated with sulfuric acid producing units and constitute an important outlet. The sodium sulfate produced as a by-product (see p. 10–12) is then marketed, to the glass industry in particular, or is converted to sodium sulfide as will be described below.

Most of the sulfuric acid produced is sold as 66 deg Bé acid, known as oil of vitriol, containing 93.195 per cent pure sulfuric acid. Weaker and stronger grades are also available. Oil of vitriol and, more especially, stronger acids and oleum, are strongly dehydrating and will char organic materials which contain water, such as cellulose. It is also a fairly strong oxidizing agent and a strong acid.

Sulfurous Acid (H_2SO_3) is produced when sulfur dioxide is passed into water.

$$SO_2 + H_2O \leftrightarrows H_2SO_3 \tag{74}$$

It is a weak, unstable acid which tends to dehydrate back to its anhydride, sulfur dioxide.

Sodium Sulfite (Na_2SO_3) and **sodium bisulfite** ($NaHSO_3$) are formed by passing sulfur dioxide into solutions of sodium carbonate. They are used as reducing agents, in tanning, paper-making, and the manufacture of dyestuffs.

Sodium Thiosulfate ($Na_2S_2O_3 \cdot 5H_2O$), or hypo, is produced by boiling a solution of sodium sulfite with sulfur.

$$Na_2SO_3 + S \rightarrow Na_2S_2O_3 \tag{75}$$

It is used as a reducing agent, particularly in photography.

Hydrogen Sulfide (H_2S) is a gas with an odor of rotten eggs. It is an undesirable impurity in industrial gases. It has very weakly acidic properties.

Sodium Sulfide (Na_2S) is produced by heating sodium sulfate with coke.

$$Na_2SO_4 + 4O \rightarrow Na_2S + 4CO \tag{76}$$

Solutions of sodium sulfide are strongly alkaline. It is used for removing hair from animal hides, in paper manufacture, and in the making of dyestuffs.

Elementary sulfur is usually obtained as the yellow amorphous brimstone. As a fine yellow crystalline powder, obtained by chilling sulfur vapor, it is known as flowers of sulfur; finely ground brimstone is called flour of sulfur.

Selenium and Tellurium

These elements are obtained in considerable quantity, particularly as by-products of the recovery of copper and nickel from their ores. Thus far the demand for them has not been commensurate with their availability. Selenium has been used in photoelectric cells and in glass. Both elements are similar to sulfur in their chemical properties.

20. CARBON, BORON, AND SILICON

Carbon and silicon are tetravalent in all their compounds, with very rare exceptions; boron is trivalent.

Carbon

The most important source of mineral carbon is coal. Carbon is an important constituent of all solid, liquid, and gaseous fuels and of all organic compounds as well as of the mineral carbonates of which limestone is the most important. In fuels it is either free as in charcoal or combined with hydrogen, oxygen, and small quantities of other elements. The carbon and the hydrogen combine, in burning, with the oxygen of the air, yielding, on complete combustion, carbon dioxide and water vapor.

$$C_x H_y O_z + NO_2 \rightarrow x CO_2 + \tfrac{1}{2} y H_2 O \tag{77}$$

This will be discussed in greater detail under Combustion and Fuels.

Carbon Dioxide (CO_2) is a constituent of the atmosphere and a product of the complete combustion of fuels. It dissolves to a slight extent in water at ordinary pressures and quite considerably when the pressure is raised. It is readily soluble in alkalis, forming carbonates and bicarbonates which, on the addition of acid, are converted back to carbon dioxide.

Carbon dioxide gas is readily converted to a liquid by the application of pressure and moderate cooling. When the pressure is released the expansion of a portion of this liquid will cool the remaining material to a solid, which is an increasingly popular refrigerant known as "dry ice." Many chemical industries which produce carbon dioxide as a by-product now find it profitable to convert the gas to the liquid or solid form.

Carbon Disulfide (CS_2) is produced by the reaction of coke and sulfur at a high temperature. It is used as a solvent for rubber, waxes, and fats, and as an insecticide.

Carbon Tetrachloride (CCl_4) is made by the reaction of carbon disulfide and chlorine gas. It is a solvent for many organic materials and is used for cleaning fabrics and as a fire extinguisher.

Boron

Boron is found in the minerals sassolite, borax, ulexite, and colemanite.

Boric Acid (H_3BO_3) is found as sassolite and is also produced by acidifying a solution of borax. It is a slightly soluble weak acid and is used as an antiseptic and preservative.

Borax ($Na_2B_4O_7 \cdot 10H_2O$) is found in nature and is also prepared by boiling ulexite ($CaNaB_5O_9 \cdot 8H_2O$) and colemanite ($Ca_2B_6O_{11} \cdot 5H_2O$) with sodium carbonate solution. It is used as a detergent and in the manufacture of glass and vitreous enamels.

Silicon

Silicon is the chief constituent, other than oxygen, of the earth's crust. It forms an endless variety of silicates, widely distributed.

Silicon Dioxide (SiO_2), or silica, is found as sand, quartz, opal, and chalcedony. It is dissolved by strong alkali, particularly at elevated temperatures.

Sodium Silicate ($xNa_2O \cdot ySiO_2$), of variable composition, is called water glass. It is prepared by fusing sand with sodium carbonate and dissolving in water. It is generally sold as a viscous liquid, but also as a soluble solid. Its solutions are used for the fireproofing and weighting of textiles, to cement glass, and as detergents.

Numerous metallic silicates may be formed by fusing salts or bases with silica. Most of them crystallize with difficulty. Certain compositions of mixed silicates may be melted to form glasses and vitreous enamels which are amorphous solids of variable composition and of a wide variety of properties.

Silicic Acid ($xSiO_2 \cdot yH_2O$), of variable hydration, is formed as a gelatinous precipitate by the acidification of water glass. It may be partially dehydrated, after carefully washing free of salts, to form a glassy solid, known as silica gel, which has remarkable absorptive and catalytic properties.

Silicon Carbide (SiC), or Carborundum, is produced by the reaction of coke and sand at a high temperature.

$$SiO_2 + 3C \rightarrow SiC + 2CO \tag{78}$$

It is a hard substance used as an abrasive.

QUALITATIVE ANALYSIS

This outline has been taken from Qualitative Analysis by Treadwell and Hall (John Wiley); the reader is referred to this book for detailed directions regarding these procedures as well as numerous others.

21. PRELIMINARY EXAMINATION

This should never be omitted, for it often shows how the subsequent analysis may be considerably shortened, and in some cases makes the further examination unnecessary. It consists only of making the following few simple tests:

Heating in the Closed Tube

By a closed tube is understood a small glass tube about 10 cm long and 0.5 cm in diameter sealed at one end. Place a little of the substance in the tube so that none of it remains adhering to the sides, hold the tube in a nearly horizontal position, and cautiously heat in a flame, noting carefully whether any change takes place.

The Substance is Volatile: (a) *The substance sublimes completely* without any deposition of water; it contains no non-volatile substance.

The sublimate is white. The halogen compounds of ammonium,* mercuric and mercurous chloride and bromide, mercuric aminochloride, arsenic trioxide, and arsenic pentoxide may be present.

Arsenic pentoxide melts before being changed into the trioxide.

The sublimate is colored—

Gray: all oxygen compounds of mercury, cyanide of mercury, free iodine, and arsenic.

Mercuric cyanide leaves a brown mass, paracyanide, which only disappears after long-continued heating.

Yellow: arsenic sulfide, sulfur, mercuric iodide.

Mercuric iodide becomes red immediately on being rubbed with a glass rod.

Grayish black: mercuric sulfide.

(b) *The substance is completely volatile, with separation of water* and gaseous products: most ammonium compounds (with the exception of those of the halogens) and free oxalic acid.

By very cautious heating, oxalic acid may be sublimed; it usually decomposes, however, into water, carbon monoxide, and carbon dioxide.

The Substance is Only Partly Volatile. In this case gases and vapors may be evolved: *Oxygen* from peroxides, nitrates, chlorates, iodates, etc.

Carbon dioxide from carbonates and organic substances; in the latter case it is usually accompanied with the separation of carbon and evolution of empyreumatic, combustible vapors.

Chlorine from chlorides of platinum, gold, copper, iron, etc.

Iodine from iodides, in the presence of oxidizing substances.

Sulfur from many sulfides and thiosulfates.

Arsenic from arsenites and arsenates, in the presence of carbon or organic substances.

Arsenites are reduced without the aid of charcoal.

$$10K_3AsO_3 = 6K_3AsO_4 + 6K_2O + As_4$$

Water from substances containing water of crystallization, from acid salts, organic substances, or from the phosphate, borate, chromate, vanadate, and tungstate of ammonium.

The water given off condenses in the cooler part of the tube and should be tested with litmus paper. If it reacts alkaline, it comes from ammonium compounds; if acid, it results from easily decomposable salts of the stronger acids.

Many fluorides when heated with water give off hydrofluoric acid, which etches the glass.

If a sublimate is formed, make the following experiment:

Mix a little of the substance with three times as much calcined sodium carbonate and heat in the closed tube. If *ammonium salts* are present, the smell of ammonia can be detected.

---

* In the case of ammonium salts, e.g., NH_4Cl, this is not a true sublimation. When heated NH_4Cl gives NH_3 and HCl gases which combine again when chilled.

Mercury compounds give a deposit of gray metal; *arsenic* and its oxygen compounds also usually yield the gray metal (but no globules), accompanied by a garlic odor.

The oxygen compounds of arsenic do not give the metal when heated with pure sodium carbonate. Commercial sodium carbonate, however, is usually contaminated with enough paper fibers to cause the reduction.

Test the Substance in the Bead

Make a borax or sodium phosphate bead in the loop of a very thin platinum wire, introduce it with a little of the substance into the oxidizing flame, observe the color of the bead both when it is hot and when it is cold, and then heat it in the reducing flame. Borax is usually used for this experiment, except when it is desired to test for silicic or titanic acids, or when the substance is white, in which case the salt of phosphorus is used. Only colored oxides are capable of coloring the borax bead.

Some oxides are reduced to metal, so that the bead appears gray in the reducing flame (see following table). $CuSO_4$ is white when anhydrous, but becomes blue immediately on the addition of water.

The following substances impart a characteristic color to the bead: iron, manganese, nickel, cobalt, chromium, uranium, copper, didymium, cerium, vanadium, titanium, and tungsten.

Since the coloration varies with the temperature and with the amount of substance used, the results to be expected, with the necessary conditions, are summarized in the table given below. The following abbreviations are used: h = hot; c = cold; h-c = hot and cold; s.s. = slightly saturated; sat. = saturated.

Color of the Bead	With Borax		With Salt of Phosphorus	
	In the Oxidizing Flame	In the Reducing Flame	In the Oxidizing Flame	In the Reducing Flame
Colorless	SiO₂ (without skeleton), alkaline earths, Hg, Pb, Bi, Sb, Cd, Zn, Sn, Ti	SiO₂ (without skeleton), alkaline earths and earths, Mn, Di, Ce, Cu (s.s.)	SiO₂ (usually with skeleton), alkaline earths and earths (sat. = turbid)	SiO₂ (usually with skeleton), alkaline earths and earths, Mn, Di, Ce, Cu (s.s.)
	W, Mo, Fe (s.s.–c)		W, Ti	
Gray		Ag, Pb, Bi, Sb, Cd, Zn, Ni		Ag, Pb, Bi, Sb, Cd, Zn, Ni
Yellow (or brown)	Fe (s.s.–h), Ag (h), Ce (h), U (h), V (h–sat.), Ni (c) (brown)	Ti (h), W (h), V (h), Mo (h)	Fe (s.s.–h), Ag (h), Fe (sat.–c), Ce (h), V (h), U (h), Ni (c) (brown)	Fe (h), Ti (h)
Green	Cr (c), Cu (h)	Fe (h–c), U, Cr, V (h)	Cr (c), Cu (h), Mo (h), U (c–sat.)	Cr (c), U (c), V (c), Mo (c)
Blue	Co (h–c), Cu (c)	Co (h–c)	Co (h–c), Cu (c)	Co (h–c), W (c)
Violet	Mn (h–c), Di (h–c), Ni (with cobalt)		Mn (h–c), Di (h–c)	Ti (c)
Red	Fe (h–sat.), Ce (h)	Cu (sat.), opaque; when very slightly saturated and with a trace of Sn, ruby red and transparent	Fe (h–sat.), Ce (h)	Cu as in the borax bead; Ti and W in the presence of iron = blood red

Heat a Little of the Substance upon Charcoal before the Blowpipe

If deflagration takes place a nitrate, nitrite, chlorate, iodate, etc., may be present.

Heat the Substance with Soda upon Charcoal before the Blowpipe

Mix as much of the substance as can be taken up on the end of a knife-blade with twice as much sodium carbonate, place it in a cavity on a piece of charcoal, and heat in the reducing flame of the blowpipe.

There is obtained:

(a) Metal without incrustation.............
- As malleable button: **Au, Ag, Sn, Cu,** which can be pressed flat in an agate mortar.
- As gray metallic particles: **Pt, Fe, Ni,** and **Co. Pt** may be pressed flat in an agate mortar; **Fe, Ni,** and **Co** are magnetic and are attracted by a magnet.

(b) Metal with incrustation..............
- As a brittle metallic button: **Sb** (white incrustation), **Bi** (yellow incrustation). The button may be reduced to a powder by grinding in an agate mortar.
- As a malleable button: **Pb** (yellow incrustation).

(c) Incrustation without metal............
- White, yellow when hot: **Zn.**
- Brown: **Cd.**
- White: **As** (garlic odor).

(d) White, infusible, strongly luminous mass. **Ca, Sr, Mg, Al,** and rare earths.

(e) **Sulfur** compounds are reduced to sulfides. If the melt is placed on a bright silver coin and moistened with water, the silver is blackened (Hepar reaction).

Test the Substance to See Whether It Imparts Any Color to the Non-luminous Flame

Introduce a little of the substance on a platinum wire into the base of the flame, and then into the fusion zone. Afterwards moisten it with dilute hydrochloric acid and repeat the experiment. The following indications may be obtained:

Sodium gives a yellow monochromatic flame; a piece of sealing-wax or a crystal of potassium dichromate appears yellow when illuminated by this flame.

Potassium (cesium and rubidium) gives a violet flame which is completely obliterated by the sodium flame. If the flame is observed through cobalt glass, the sodium flame disappears and the potassium flame appears pink.

Lithium gives a carmine-red flame (or a red line in the spectroscope).

Strontium also gives a carmine-red flame (which the spectroscope shows to consist of several lines in the orange, and a bright line in the blue).

Calcium gives a brick-red flame (in the spectroscope an orange and a green line are seen, both about an equal distance away from the sodium line).

Barium gives a greenish-yellow flame.

In the case of barium sulfate the green flame is either indistinct or not visible. In order to detect barium in this case, heat a small portion of the substance in the upper reducing flame, cool, moisten with hydrochloric acid (odor of hydrogen sulfide), and again heat, when the barium flame can be easily seen.

Thallium gives an emerald-green flame.

If a green flame is obtained, test another portion of the substance for boric acid, by treating with concentrated sulfuric acid and bringing near the flame. A green color indicates the presence of boric acid, but if copper is present this test is not reliable.

By heating the solid substance with potassium ethyl sulfate in a test-tube, boric acid is converted into $B(OC_2H_5)_3$, which is volatile and burns with a green flame. Copper chloride does not interfere with this test.

Lead, Arsenic, Antimony color the flame light blue, and **copper** compounds color the flame either green or blue.

22. SYSTEMATIC ANALYSIS OF THE METALS
Table I. General Scheme for Separating the Metals into Groups

Solution may contain all the common basic constituents. *Add HCl in slight excess.*			
Precipitate: Group I. *Examine as outlined in Table II.*	Filtrate: Groups II, III, IV, and V. *Saturate with H_2S.*		
	Precipitate: Group II. *Examine as outlined in Table III.*	Filtrate: Groups III, IV, and V. Test for phosphoric acid. If found present modify the following procedure as indicated in Table VI. *Add NH_4OH and $(NH_4)_2S_2$.*	
		Precipitate: Group III. *If phosphate is absent examine as outlined in Table VII. If phosphate is present examine by Table VI.*	Filtrate: Groups IV and V. *Add $(NH_4)_2CO_3$.*
			Precipitate: Group IV. *Examine as outlined in Table VIII.*
			Filtrate: Group V. *Examine as outlined in Table IX.*

Table II. Analysis of the Silver Group (Group I)

Solution may contain all the metals. *Add 6-normal HCl, filter, and examine the filtrate for succeeding groups. Treat with hot water.*

Residue: AgCl, Hg$_2$Cl$_2$. *Pour ammonia through the filter*		Solution: Pb^{++}. *Test for lead with H$_2$SO$_4$.*
Residue: Hg(NH$_2$)Cl + Hg.	Solution: [Ag(NH$_3$)$_2$]$^+$. *Add HNO$_3$: white precipitate shows the presence of Ag.*	*Filter off PbSO$_4$ and treat the precipitate with hot NH$_4$C$_2$H$_3$O$_2$ solution. Add K$_2$CrO$_4$; a yellow precipitate of PbCrO$_4$ shows presence of Pb.*

Table III. Separation of the Copper and Tin Groups (Group II)

Solution may contain cations of all the metals except silver and mercurous mercury. *Make the solution 0.3-normal in HCl and saturate with H$_2$S. Filter and examine the filtrate for Groups III, IV, and V. Treat the precipitate with Na$_2$S$_2$ solution.*

Residue: PbS, Bi$_2$S$_3$, CuS, CdS. *Examine by Table IV.*	Solution: [HgS$_2$]$^{--}$, [AsS$_4$]$^{---}$, [SbS$_4$]$^{---}$, [SnS$_3$]$^{--}$. *Add HCl.*	
	Precipitate: HgS, As$_2$S$_5$, Sb$_2$S$_5$, SnS$_2$, S.	Filtrate: NaCl. *Reject.*

Table IV. Analysis of the Copper Group

Residue from Table III: PbS, Bi$_2$S$_3$, CuS, CdS. *Boil with 3-normal HNO$_3$ and filter.*

Residue: S usually contaminated with negligible quantities of sulfides. *Reject.*	Solution: Pb^{++}, Bi^{+++}, Cu^{++}, Cd^{++}. *Add H$_2$SO$_4$, evaporate, dilute and filter.*			
	Precipitate: PbSO$_4$. *Dissolve in NH$_4$OAc and add K$_2$CrO$_4$. A yellow precipitate of PbCrO$_4$ shows the presence of lead.*	Filtrate: Bi^{+++}, Cu^{++}, Cd^{++}. *Add NH$_4$OH in excess and filter.*		
		Precipitate: Bi(OH)$_3$. *Add Na$_2$SnO$_2$. Black residue is Bi.*	Filtrate: [Cu(NH$_3$)$_4$]$^{++}$, [Cd(NH$_3$)$_4$]$^{++}$.	
			A blue solution shows Cu. *If in doubt, add HC$_2$H$_3$O$_2$ and K$_4$[Fe(CN)$_6$] to a small portion. Red precipitate is Cu$_2$[Fe(CN)$_6$].*	*To the larger part of the solution add H$_2$SO$_4$ and Fe. Filter and saturate the filtrate with H$_2$S. Yellow precipitate shows Cd.*

Table V. Analysis of the Arsenic-Tin Group

Precipitate from Table III. As$_2$S$_5$, Sb$_2$S$_5$, SnS$_2$, S. *Warm with 12-normal HCl.*

Residue: As$_2$S$_5$. *Dissolve in 6-normal HCl and KClO$_3$. Evaporate, dilute, neutralize with NH$_4$OH, and add MgCl$_2$·NH$_4$Cl solution. A white precipitate of MgNH$_4$AsO$_4$ indicates As. Dissolve in 6-normal HCl, and treat with H$_2$S. Yellow precipitate of As$_2$S$_5$ or As$_2$S$_3$ shows As.*	Solution: SbCl$_4^-$, SnCl$_6^{--}$. *Evaporate to small volume, pour upon clean platinum foil, and place a clean piece of zinc in the solution; a black spot on the platinum indicates Sb. When the evolution of hydrogen has ceased, remove the zinc and, if any tin deposit adheres to the platinum, rub it off and dissolve it, with the remaining zinc, in a small test-tube in one or two drops of concentrated hydrochloric acid. Dilute with water and add a few drops of mercuric chloride solution. A white or gray precipitate shows that Sn is present.*

Test for Phosphate. Boil a little of the filtrate from Group II until the hydrogen sulfide is expelled, pour into a mixture of 5 cc 6-normal nitric acid and 5 cc of ammonium molybdate reagent, heat to 60 deg, and allow to stand for 10 minutes. If a yellow precipitate of ammonium phosphomolybdate is obtained, members of Group IV are likely to precipitate as phosphates upon the neutralization of the solution by ammonia and ammonium sulfide.

Table VI. Analysis of Groups III and IV in Presence of Phosphate

Tin Method

Remove H$_2$S and HCl from filtrate from Group II, and evaporate repeatedly with HNO$_3$. Add tinfoil, concentrate, dilute, and allow the precipitate to settle.

Precipitate: (H$_2$SnO$_3$)x·(P$_2$O$_5$)y. *Reject.*	Solution: Groups III, IV, and V. *Saturate with H$_2$S and filter.*	
	Precipitate: CuS, PbS from impurities in tinfoil. *Reject.*	Solution: Groups III, IV, and V. *Add NH$_4$OH and (NH$_4$)$_2$S and continue as in Table I.*

Table VII. Analysis of Group III

Solution may contain Fe^{++}, Fe^{+++}, Al^{+++}, Cr^{+++}, Mn^{++}, Zn^{++}, Co^{++}, Ni^{++}, and Groups IV and V.
Add NH_4OH *and* $(NH_4)_2S$. *Filter and examine filtrate for Groups IV and V.*
Dissolve precipitate in HCl and $KClO_3$. *Evaporate, treat with NaOH and* Na_2O_2, *and filter.*

Precipitate: Fe(OH)$_3$, H$_2$MnO$_3$, Co(OH)$_3$, Ni(OH)$_2$, Zn(OH)$_2$. *Dissolve in* HNO_3 *and* H_2O_2. *Evaporate and boil with concentrated* $HNO_3 + KClO_3$.	Filtrate: AlO$_2^-$, CrO$_4^{--}$, HZnO$_2^-$. *Acidify with HCl and add* NH_4OH.

(Left branch — Precipitate: Fe(OH)$_3$, etc.)

Precipitate: MnO$_2$. *Dissolve in* $HNO_3 + H_2O_2$ *and test for Mn with* $NaBiO_3$.	Filtrate: Fe^{+++}, Co^{++}, Ni^{++}, Zn^{++}. *Add* NH_4OH.		
	Precipitate: Fe(OH)$_3$. *Test for Fe with* $K_4Fe(CN)_6$.	Filtrate: Co(NH$_3$)$_6^{++}$, Ni(NH$_3$)$_6^{++}$, Zn(NH$_3$)$_6^{++}$. *Saturate with* H_2S *and treat precipitate with cold, normal HCl.*	
		Residue: CoS, NiS. *Dissolve in HCl and* $KClO_3$ *and evaporate just to dryness. Add* $HC_2H_3O_2$ *and* KNO_2 *to precipitate cobalt as yellow* $K_3[Co(NO_2)_6]$. *Filter and test the filtrate with dimethylglyoxime. Red precipitate of* Ni[(CH$_3$C-NO)$_2$H]$_2$ *shows the presence of nickel.*	Solution: Zn^{++}, traces of Co^{++} and Ni^{++}. *Add NaOH and* Na_2O_2.
			Precipitate: Co(OH)$_3$ Ni(OH)$_2$. *Add to residue of CoS, NiS.*
			Filtrate: Na$_2$ZnO$_2$. *Acidify with* $HC_2H_3O_2$ *and saturate with* H_2S. *Confirm Zn by the Rinmann's green test.*

(Right branch — Filtrate: AlO$_2^-$, etc.)

Precipitate: Al(OH)$_3$. *Dissolve in HCl and test with aluminon or dissolve in* HNO_3, *add* Co(NO$_3$)$_2$ *solution, filter, and ignite the residue. A red precipitate with aluminon or the formation of Thénard's blue by ignition shows the presence of aluminum.*	Filtrate: CrO$_4^{--}$. *Boil with* Na_2CO_3, *till all NH$_3$ is expelled.*	
	Precipitate: Zn$_2$(OH)$_2$-CO$_3$. *Dissolve in a little HCl, add* NH_4OH *and* $HC_2H_3O_2$ *and test with* H_2S. *White precipitate: ZnS.*	Filtrate: CrO$_4^{--}$. *Add* $HC_2H_3O_2$ *and* Pb-$(C_2H_3O_2)_2$. *Yellow precipitate:* PbCrO$_4$.

Table VIII. Analysis of Group IV

Solution may contain: Ba^{++}, Sr^{++}, Mg^{++}, K$^+$, Na$^+$, NH$_4^+$. *Concentrate to 10 ml; add 15 ml* $(NH_4)_2CO_3$ *reagent, or more if necessary, and an equal volume of* C_2H_5OH. *Stir, let stand 30 minutes and filter. Test filtrate for Na$^+$ and K$^+$ according to Table IX. Dissolve the precipitate, which may contain* BaCO$_3$, SrCO$_3$, CaCO$_3$, *and* MgCO$_3 \cdot (NH_4)_2CO_3 \cdot 4H_2O$, *in 6-normal* $HC_2H_3O_2$, *add* $NH_4C_2H_3O_2$ *and* K_2CrO_4.

Precipitate: BaCrO$_4$. *Dissolve in HCl. Evaporate to dryness. Test residue in flame, treat with 3 ml of 6-normal* $HC_2H_3O_2$, *20 ml of 3-normal* $NH_4C_2H_3O_2$, *and 15 ml of water. Heat to boiling and test with* K_2CrO_4 *solution. Yellow precipitate is* BaCrO$_4$.	Filtrate: Sr^{++}, Ca^{++}, Mg^{++}. *Add* NH_4OH. *Dilute to 65 ml and add 50 ml* C_2H_5OH. *Shake the solution with filter paper pulp and filter.*	
	Precipitate: SrCrO$_4$. *Boil with* $(NH_4)_2CO_3$ *and* $K_2C_2O_4$. *Filter and reject the filtrate. Dissolve residue in 5 ml of normal* $HC_2H_3O_2$ *and add 2 ml of normal* Na_2SO_4 *solution. White precipitate of* SrSO$_4$ *shows Sr is present.*	Dilute with 50 ml of water, add 3 ml of 3-normal $K_2C_2O_4$. *If a precipitate forms, add more* $K_2C_2O_4$ *if necessary, heat and filter.*
		Precipitate: CaC$_2$O$_4$. *Dissolve in 5 ml of 6-normal* H_2SO_4 *and add 20 drops of* C_2H_5OH. *White precipitate is* CaSO$_4$.
		Filtrate: Mg^{++}. *Add* NH_4OH *and* Na_2HPO_4. *Dissolve in 5 ml of 2-normal* H_2SO_4, *add 10 ml* C_2H_5OH *and filter if necessary. Add* NH_4OH *and* Na_2HPO_4. *Precipitate is* MgNH$_4$PO$_4$.

Table IX. Analysis of Group V

Filtrate from Group IV may contain NH_4^+, K^+, and Na^+. *Evaporate and ignite the residue. Dissolve in water, add $BaCl_2$ (to remove SO_4^{--}), and then $(NH_4)_2CO_3$ (to remove Ba^{++}). Evaporate and ignite again.*

Vapor: NH_4 salts. *Test the original substance for NH_4^+.*	Residue: KCl, NaCl. *Add $HClO_4$, evaporate, cool, and add alcohol.*		
	Residue: $KClO_4$. *Dissolve in hot water, add $Na_3Co(NO_2)_6$ to precipitate yellow $K_2NaCo(NO_2)_6$.*	Solution: $NaClO_4$. *Saturate with HCl gas.*	
		Precipitate: NaCl. *Dissolve in water and add KH_2SbO_4 to precipitate white crystalline NaH_2SbO_4.*	Filtrate: *Reject.*

ELECTROCHEMISTRY

The close relationship between all chemical and electrical phenomena has already been indicated. Certain of the chemical industries, however, are so dependent upon the consumption of electrical energy, or upon its production or utilization, that they are conveniently classified as electrochemical. The subject may be divided into the electrochemistry of solutions, aqueous and non-aqueous; electrothermics; and thermionics and electronics.

23. ELECTROCHEMISTRY OF SOLUTIONS

Aqueous Solutions

The dissociation of electrolytes in solution to ions has already been discussed. Such solutions have the property of conducting an electric current through the migration of ions which bear charges of positive or negative electricity. Obviously, if a direct current is used, the ions can pass only as far as the electrodes, where their charges will be neutralized with the release of uncharged, electrically neutral matter. The quantity of matter discharged or deposited will be proportional to the quantity of electricity supplied by the electrodes (in coulombs). The total flow of current must be proportional to the number of ions which are neutralized and to the number of charges borne by each of them. The number of ions then is proportional to the number of gram-mols of the substance: 96,494 coulombs is sufficient to release a gram-mol of a monovalent radical, half a gram-mol of a bivalent radical, one-third gram-mol of a trivalent radical, etc. *This unit of charge is known as a faraday,* and the principle is known as Faraday's law.

In order to pass a current through a solution a certain voltage is required. The solution itself will have an ohmic resistance proportional to the length of the path between the electrodes and inversely proportional to the effective area. In addition there will be a potential drop across the thin film surrounding each electrode due to evolution of gas or a sharp concentration gradient. This may be reduced to some extent by efficient agitation. Finally, there will be the potential necessary to deposit the material which would be present at equilibrium even though no current were flowing. This is the minimum for deposition. Of course, if the solution is very dilute and the ions comparatively scarce, the required potential will be very high, and at high concentrations the reverse will be true. By Nernst's law,

$$E = \frac{0.058}{n} - \log C \text{ (at } 18° \text{ C)} \tag{1}$$

where E is the electrode voltage drop.

C is the ion concentration in mols per liter.

n is the number of charges on the ion.

The law is strictly valid only for very dilute solutions but may serve as a convenient approximation for most practical cases. E_0, the voltage drop when $C = 1$, is a constant for each kind of ion and is called the electrode potential. The actual electrode potentials are impossible to measure accurately in absolute units, therefore, they are expressed relative to the potential of the hydrogen ion which is assumed to have a reference potential of zero volts. The more active a metal, the lower will be the deposition potential of its ions. Conversely, the electrode potential may serve as a measure of the activity of a metal.

Table I. Measured Values of Electrode Potentials

Lithium	-3.02	Tin (against Sn^{++})	-0.14
Potassium	-2.92	Lead (against Pb^{++})	-0.13
Sodium	-2.71	Iron (against Fe^{+++})	-0.04
Calcium	-2.5	Hydrogen	0.00
Magnesium	-1.86	Antimony (against Sb^{+++})	$+0.01$
Aluminum	-1.34	Bismuth	$+0.2$
Manganese (against Mn^{++})	-1.0	Copper (against Cu^{++})	$+0.34$
Zinc	-0.76	(against Cu^{+})	$+0.52$
Chromium (against Cr^{++})	-0.6	Mercury (against Hg^{+})	$+0.80$
(against Cr^{+++})	-0.5	Silver	$+0.80$
Iron (against Fe^{++})	-0.43	Palladium	$+0.82$
Cadmium	-0.40	Mercury (against Hg^{++})	$+0.86$
Cobalt (against Co^{++})	-0.29	Gold (against Au^{+++})	$+1.3$
Nickel (against Ni^{++})	-0.22	(against Au^{+})	$+1.5$

This table may be considered the activity series of the metals, those highest in the table being the most active.

Every chemical reaction may, theoretically, be represented as being separated into two electrode reactions, and the difference in potential (algebraically) between the two will be a measure of the reactivity. A highly negative potential difference would represent a spontaneous reaction which might be utilized to generate a current, whereas a high positive potential difference would represent a reaction which requires energy to drive it forward.

Electrowinning. Ores of copper, zinc, cadmium, and others are sometimes leached with sulfuric acid to give solutions of metallic sulfates from which the metals may be recovered by electrolytic deposition. Copper is quite low in the electromotive series and so it may be deposited at a very low voltage while the more active metals such as iron, which may be present as impurities, remain in solution. The positively charged copper ions are charged at the negative electrode, called the cathode, while oxygen is evolved at the positive electrode, called the anode.

Zinc and cadmium are more difficult to deposit and require higher voltages. Salts of metals lower in the electromotive series must not be allowed to accumulate if a pure and smooth deposit is desired.

Electrorefining. Copper, nickel, lead, tin, silver, gold, and other metals produced by smelting or electrowinning may be further purified in order to be more useful commercially. Electrodeposition is the most effective means of accomplishing this end. The principles are similar to those of electrowinning except that the anode, instead of consisting of an inert material which liberates oxygen, is formed of the impure metal which dissolved and is reprecipitated on the cathode while the impurities generally are made to settle in the form of a mud which may then be further treated to recover valuable by-products.

Electroplating is similar to electrorefining in principle but the anodes are made of pure metals or desired alloys while the composition of the electrolytic solution, temperature, current density, etc., are adjusted to give a smooth, attractive, adherent, and useful plate.

Electrolytic Caustic Soda and Chlorine. Solutions of sodium chloride brines may be electrolyzed to give hydrogen and caustic soda at the cathode and chlorine at the anode. Thus

$$\left. \begin{array}{l} (2Na^{+}) + 2H_2O \xrightarrow{\text{at cathode}} (2Na^{+}) + 2OH^{-} + H_2 \\ 2Cl^{-} \xrightarrow{\text{at anode}} Cl_2 \end{array} \right\} \tag{2}$$

The products of the anode and of the cathode would react if allowed to mix so that it becomes necessary to keep them separated by means of a semi-permeable diaphragm or by some mechanical scheme. Numerous cells have been designed to achieve this end. In the manufacture of sodium hypochlorite and sodium chlorate the chlorine and alkali are purposely allowed to mix.

Electric Cells and Batteries. Numerous combinations of electrolytes and electrodes may be used for converting chemical to electrical energy. Practically, the most useful of these are the lead storage and the Edison alkali cells.

In the lead storage cell, lead dioxide reacts with sulfuric acid at the anode to produce a positive charge.

$$\underset{\text{+Plate}}{PbO_2} + 2H_2SO_4 + \underset{\text{−Plate}}{Pb} \rightleftarrows \underset{\text{+Plate}}{PbSO_4} + 2H_2O + \underset{\text{−Plate}}{PbSO_4} \tag{3}$$

At the cathode, metallic lead reacts with the acid to produce a negative charge. The lead ions formed at both electrodes combine with the sulfate to produce the sparingly soluble lead sulfate. Both electrode reactions are reversible so that, by impressing a current, the initial conditions may be restored and the cell will be recharged.

Nevertheless, owing to the energy dissipated by internal resistance, including polarization effects at the electrodes and some inevitable short-circuiting of current within the cells, called local action, the output of electrical energy is never quite equal to the input. The ratio of the two is known as the efficiency of a battery or cell.

The voltage of a cell on charging or discharging is the resultant or algebraic sum of the open-circuit emf due to the Nernst electrical potential and the voltage drop due to the internal resistance. For very low rates of charge or discharge the voltage approaches that of open circuit, but it is always somewhat greater on charging and lower on discharging. The internal resistance voltage drop may be considered to be the product of the current and the resistance by Ohm's law, but this resistance depends, in general, upon the rate and direction of the flow, the strength of the acid electrolyte, and the condition of the electrodes as well as the temperature. The acid gains in strength (usually measured by its specific gravity) on charging, and loses it on discharging, while the electrodes become coated with lead sulfate, on discharging, which disappears as the cell is charged. Fig. 1

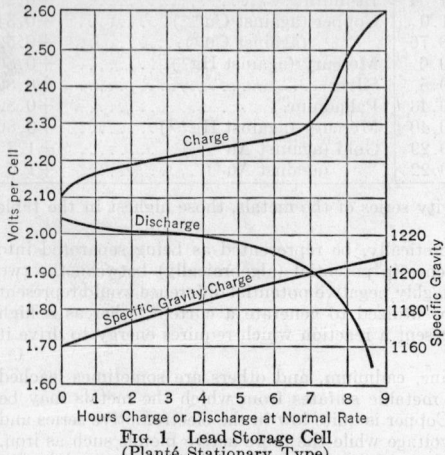

Fig. 1 Lead Storage Cell
(Planté Stationary Type)

shows typical cell voltage on charging and discharging as a function of the time. On changing the rate of current flow these curves will, of course, be greatly modified. The open-circuit voltage of a storage cell varies only from about 2.05 to 2.15 volts, the greater part of the voltage changes being due to the internal resistance factor.

The sp gr varies from 1.150 to 1.300. An approximate lower limit is shown in Fig. 1.

The Capacity of a cell is defined as the number of ampere-hours which it will supply when fully charged at some rate of discharge which must be specified.

The most important specifications for lead storage cells as well as for other cells are the following:

The energy efficiency, which is the ratio of the energy output to the input under specified conditions.

The capacity, as already defined.

The ampere-hour efficiency, which is the ratio of the number of ampere-hours output to the number of ampere-hours input under specified conditions.

The ampere rating, which is the number of amperes that may safely be passed through a cell for an appreciable time. For brief intervals considerably greater currents may be handled.

Certain rules must be observed for the proper care of lead storage batteries:

The cells should not be made to carry a greater current than that at which they are rated lest there be excessive temperature and gassing at the electrodes.

If the strength of the electrolyte is allowed to remain low for a considerable period, as when the battery is fully discharged, the lead sulfate which acts as a binder for the lead peroxide will disappear, with accompanying disintegration of the cell.

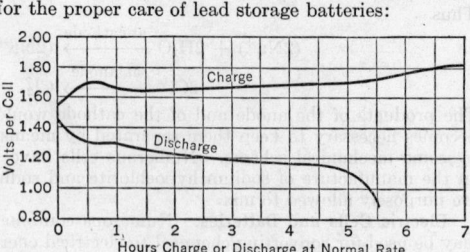

Fig. 2. Edison Storage Cell

If, on the other hand, the strength becomes too high, there will be excessive sulfating with injurious effects. The correct range of specific gravity for the acid is from 1.140 to 1.285, although it should not be allowed to remain at the lower extreme for very long.

In order to avoid corrosion at the liquid level, the plates should be kept fully covered at all times by adding distilled water occasionally. Tap water and other sources of impurιty should be avoided, and the original acid should be of high purity to avoid disintegrating effects.

The batteries should be overcharged once every month to form enough sulfate to keep the deposit on the plates intact. The gassing so produced also helps to overcome the tendency of the stronger acid to settle to the bottom of the cells.

Finally, the electrolyte should occasionally be removed and replaced by fresh acid.

The Edison Cell is similar in principle to the lead storage cell. Nickel peroxide replaces the lead peroxide at the anode; iron replaces lead at the cathode; and potassium hydroxide replaces sulfuric acid as the electrolyte. The principal reaction is

$$5Fe + 5Ni_2O_3 \cdot 6H_2O + 9H_2O \rightleftarrows 10Ni(OH)_2 + 5Fe(OH)_2 \tag{4}$$

Non-aqueous Solutions

The only important non-aqueous solutions used in the electrochemical industries are the fused salts. These are used only where the same result cannot be attained in an aqueous solution. The metals, aluminum, magnesium, calcium, sodium, and others, are prepared in this way.

Aluminum is produced from purified bauxite (Al_2O_3) dissolved in fused cryolite ($AlF_3 \cdot 3NaF$). Molten aluminum is deposited at the carbon cathodes while oxygen is liberated at the carbon anodes, reacting to form carbon monoxide so that the electrode is gradually consumed and must be replaced. In this way, the bauxite is decomposed proportionally to the metal produced while the cryolite remains substantially unaffected.

Magnesium is deposited from a fused bath of magnesium chloride to which a small amount of sodium chloride is added to lower the melting point. The cast-steel pot in which the bath is held acts as the cathode upon which the molten metal is deposited. Later the metal floats to the top. Chlorine is liberated at the graphite anodes.

24. ELECTROTHERMICS

In Electrothermic Processes, electric energy is supplied for the sole purpose of producing a high temperature. Several types of furnaces are used.

In the Resistor Type of Furnace a bed of solid granular material, usually carbon or graphite, is used. An electric current, alternating or direct, is passed through, liberating heat. The furnace charge itself may constitute the resistance. Thus, in the manufacture of silicon carbide (Carborundum), a mixture of sand and coke is placed between two graphite electrodes. (See Art. 20.) In graphite manufacture a similar construction is used but the charge is generally anthracite coal.

In the Arc Type of Furnace, electrodes, usually of graphite, are brought into contact and then drawn apart. The heat generated by the resistance of the air gap vaporizes the carbon across the arc, and a current continues to flow. Details of design vary widely. These furnaces are used extensively in the alloying of steel and in the manufacture of calcium carbide. In this process lime is made to react with coke at a high temperature.

$$CaO + 3C \rightarrow CaC_2 + CO \tag{5}$$

Calcium carbide is extensively used in the manufacture of acetylene, from which numerous organic chemical products are derived.

Finely ground calcium carbide is made to react with nitrogen in a resistance-type furnace to form calcium cyanamid.

$$CaC_2 + N_2 \rightarrow CaCN_2 + C \tag{6}$$

This is a useful method of nitrogen fixation since the cyanamid reacts with hot water in the presence of alkalis to form ammonia.

$$CaCN_2 + 3H_2O \rightarrow CaCO_3 + 2NH_3 \tag{7}$$

Calcium cyanamid is mixed with carbon and salt in an arc furnace to yield sodium cyanide.

$$CaCN_2 + C + 2NaCl \rightarrow CaCl_2 + 2NaCN \tag{8}$$

Induction Furnaces depend upon the production of heat directly in a metal charge by an electric current generated by a-c coil windings. Such furnaces are used for the refining of high-grade iron and steel. Temperatures are subject to very close control in this type of furnace.

25. ELECTRONICS AND THERMIONICS

These subjects in their relation to gas and vacuum tubes are discussed in Section 8. The phases most directly concerning the chemical industries are electrostatic precipitation and the manufacture of ozone and nitric oxide.

The electrostatic precipitator usually consists of a vertical cylindrical metal chamber; an electrode of wire or metal chain passes axially through the center of the chamber and receives a high potential electrostatic charge. The cylinder wall is grounded, and an electric discharge passes radially outward. The gas in the cylinder is thus ionized, as are the particles of dust or fog which are suspended in it. These are attracted to the grounded wall and are thus precipitated and recovered while the pure air or gas passes on.

Such installations are in use for the recovery of solid fumes in the cement and phosphate industries and for cleaning the gases in contact sulfuric acid manufacture.

Ozone (O_3) is produced by the silent electric discharge through air at room temperature.

$$3O_2 \rightarrow 2O_3 \qquad\qquad (9)$$

Ozone is a highly active form of oxygen and is used for sterilization.

Nitric Oxide is produced by passing air across a high-temperature arc. The nitrogen and oxygen then combine to form nitric oxide, which is converted to nitric acid.

$$N_2 + O_2 \rightarrow 2NO \qquad\qquad (10)$$

BIBLIOGRAPHY ON CHEMISTRY

1. ALLMAND, A. J., and ELLINGHAM, H. J. T., Principles of Applied Electrochemistry, New York, Longmans, Green, second edition, 1934.
2. BRINKLEY, S. R., Principles of General Chemistry, New York, Macmillan Co., 1926.
3. BRISCOE, H. T., General Chemistry for Colleges, Boston, Houghton Mifflin Co., 1935
4. BROCKMAN, C. J., Electrochemistry; Principles and Practice, New York, D. Van Nostrand, 1931.
5. CREIGHTON, H. J., and KOEHLER, W. A., Principles of Electrochemistry, New York, John Wiley & Sons, Vol. I, third edition, 1935: Vol. II, 1935
6. CONANT, J. B., Chemistry of Organic Compounds, New York, Macmillan, 1933.
7. CONANT, J. B., Organic Chemistry, New York, Macmillan, 1928.
8. CURTMAN, L. J., Qualitative Chemical Analysis, New York, Macmillan, 1931.
9. DEMING, H. G., General Chemistry, New York, John Wiley & Sons, fourth edition, 1935.
10. DANA, E. S., and FORD, W. E., Textbook of Mineralogy, New York, John Wiley & Sons, fourth edition, 1932.
11. ENGELDER, C. J., Textbook of Elementary Qualitative Analysis, New York, John Wiley & Sons, second edition, 1933.
12. GETMAN, F. H., and DANIELS, F., Outlines of Theoretical Chemistry, New York, John Wiley & Sons, fifth edition, 1931.
13. HAMMETT, L. P., Solutions of Electrolytes, New York, McGraw-Hill, 1929.
14. HILDEBRAND, J. H., Principles of Chemistry, New York, Macmillan, third edition, 1932.
15. HOLMES, H. N. General Chemistry, New York, Macmillan Co., 1930.
16. HOPKINS, B. S., Essentials of College Chemistry, Boston, Heath, 1932.
17. KENDALL, J., Smith's College Chemistry, New York, Appleton-Century, third edition, 1935.
18. KRAUS, C. A., Properties of Electrically Conducting Systems, A.C.S., Monograph, Chemical Catalog, Reinhold, 1922.
19. LOWY, A., HARROW, B., Introduction to Organic Chemistry, New York, John Wiley & Sons, fourth edition, 1936.
20. McPHERSON, W., and HENDERSON, W. E., Course in General Chemistry, New York, Ginn & Co., fourth edition, 1933.
21. McPHERSON, W., and HENDERSON, W. E., An Elementary Study of Chemistry, New York, Ginn & Co., 1934.
22. MELLOR, J. W., Modern Inorganic Chemistry, New York, Longmans, Green, eighth edition, 1933.
23. MILLARD, E. B., Physical Chemistry for Colleges, New York, McGraw-Hill, third edition, 1931.
24. MOORE, F. J., A History of Chemistry, New York, McGraw-Hill, second edition, 1931.
25. NORRIS, J. F., Principles of Organic Chemistry, New York, McGraw-Hill, third edition, 1931.
26. NOYES, W. A., Elements of Qualitative Analysis, New York, Henry Holt & Co., seventh edition, 1923.
27. REEDY, J. H., Elementary Qualitative Analysis, New York, McGraw-Hill, 1932.
28. READ, W. T., Industrial Chemistry, New York, John Wiley & Sons, 1933.
29. ROGERS, A., Elements of Industrial Chemistry, New York, D. Van Nostrand, second edition, 1926.
30. ROGERS, A., Manual of Industrial Chemistry, New York, D. Van Nostrand, fifth edition, 1931.
31. ROGERS, A. F., Introduction to Study of Minerals and Rocks, New York, McGraw-Hill, second edition, 1921.
32. SMITH, E. F., Old Chemistries, New York, McGraw-Hill, 1927.
33. TREADWELL, F. P., and HALL, W. T., Analytical Chemistry, Vol. I, New York, John Wiley & Sons, eighth edition, 1932.
34. WEEKS, MARY, Discovery of the Elements, Journal of Chemical Education.
35. WILLIAMS, R. J., Introduction to Organic Chemistry, New York, D. Van Nostrand, third edition, 1935.

SECTION 11

METALLIC MATERIALS

METALLIC MATERIALS

1. GENERAL PROPERTIES OF METALS AND ALLOYS

By Bradley Stoughton

Price must always be an important factor in the choice of materials for engineering construction. The wide-spread use of iron and steel for many purposes is due largely to this feature. From the technical standpoint, however, the two properties of metals and alloys which most influence their selection as the chief materials of construction in our modern civilization are, first, strength combined with ductility, and, second, the ready ability to be shaped, i.e., to be changed in size or form. Illustrations of this latter property are: casting while liquid, die-casting during solidification, extrusion, rolling or forging while hot and very plastic, and (at atmospheric temperature), rolling, wire drawing, flanging, spinning, etc. In the category of shaping should be included machining, which can also be applied to some non-metallic bodies, as well as welding and soldering, which are unique for metal joining. Besides these two properties of most frequent importance there are special properties each of which is of prime importance in individual activities or industries, for example: hardenability, including the property of doing efficient cutting work at specified temperatures; electrical conductivity; magnetic permeability; magnetic retentivity; resistance to corrosion, staining, or rusting, although this property is often lacking in metals and is valued in them only when combined with some other useful feature. The same may be said of a metal's resistance to the effect of heat tending toward: loss of strength, "creep," grain growth, softening, melting. An instance of a useful combination of several properties producing a valuable result is found in tungsten, with its ability to be drawn into very fine wire, its strength, its toughness, and its high melting point, achieving together a new art in electric lighting. Other properties of metals of great value are: high melting temperature as in points in spark plugs; low melting temperature, as in fusible plugs for boilers, fire sprinklers, and electric fuses; reactivity to light, as in photoelectric cells, television parts; heat conductivity, as in radiators, cook stoves, cooking utensils, etc.; low coefficient of expansion, as in surveyors' tapes and clock pendulums; wide divergence in expansion and contraction with temperature changes, as in bimetallic thermostats; strength combined with denseness, as in food containers, pressure gas bottles; color for decorative purposes; colors of metallic oxides, or other compounds, for paint pigments, glass, porcelain, china; mere weight, as window sash weights, fillers for rubber tires; resilience.

The Nature of Metal. Metals are chemical elements. Of the known chemical elements more than half are admittedly metals, while about 20 elements have combinations of chemical and physical properties which leave them in dispute. All the admittedly metallic elements are solid, crystalline bodies except the liquids, mercury (quicksilver) and gallium. A crystalline body is composed of crystals so small that normally there are several million crystals to each cubic inch of volume, and the crystals are composed of several million space lattices per crystal. The space lattices, in turn, are geometrical arrangements of atoms, of which the cube and the octahedron are the commoner forms. The atom nuclei are held together in space lattices by hypothetical atomic bonds, which resist both tension and compression, thus giving solidity to the mass. Electrons are situated among the atomic nuclei and have a limited amount of freedom of motion, upon which is predicated a theory of heat and electrical conductivity, and, perhaps, of magnetism in the ferromagnetic metals, iron, nickel, and cobalt, and the ferromagnetic alloy of paramagnetic metals, aluminum, manganese, and copper. The nature of the atomic bonds would seem, by inference, to be a basis of strength, elasticity, resilience, hardness, expansion with temperature, and perhaps even of fusibility. The ability of atomic bonds to re-establish themselves after slip would seem to be the basis of plasticity. The lengths of atomic bonds range from 10 to 38 billionths of an inch and are several times greater than the diameter of the atomic nuclei, with the result that the latter are held so widely apart that short rays of the x-ray type pass between them and penetrate a body which will totally reflect the visible light rays and give the appearance of being composed of closely packed particles.

Physical Metallurgy. About 80 years ago metallurgists began to use the microscope for the examination of polished surfaces of metals. This form of research has been followed extensively during the past 50 years, and much has been learned of the structure of metallic bodies, especially as to the size, form relations, and (in connection with chemical and other types of investigation) the kinds of crystals. This study of structure is known as metallography. Next came a disclosure by physicists of the structure of atoms. The third step in the development of the modern science of physical metallurgy was the introduction of the use of the x-ray spectrometer to disclose the structure of space lattices—specifically their form, their size, and the arrangement in them of atoms. The most important results have been obtained not with pure metals, but with alloys.

Alloys. An alloy is a union of two or more metals, or of metals with a subordinate amount of a non-metal, as in the case of the most-used of all alloys, namely: steel, which is an alloy of iron with a small proportion of carbon. The specific requirement of an alloy is that, when melted, its components dissolve in each other. Metals which will not dissolve in each other cannot be made to form alloys together. In the liquid mass the atoms move freely until the body cools to the freezing temperature; thereupon the atoms begin to unite themselves into space lattices with atomic bonds. Sometimes the atoms of a metal may enter freely, and without limit in proportion, into the space lattices of the other metal, forming solid solutions of any proportion of either metal. In other cases the atoms of each metal segregate to form space lattices of and by themselves, which space lattices then form crystals of the individual elements. Again, a limited number of atoms of one metal enter into the space lattices of another metal, forming thereafter crystals of what are called "solid solutions." The freezing of a liquid solution of any proportion of two metals into a solid solution of the same proportions is known as freezing of Type I, and is expressed diagrammatically in Fig. 1. The complete decomposition of a liquid solution of two metals into two pure solid metals is known as Type II, Fig. 2. The freezing which results in only limited solubility in the solid state is called Type III, Fig. 3. There still remains the formation of structures when metallic compounds are present, such as Fe$_3$C, Cu$_2$Zn$_3$, etc., a discussion of which may be found in any reference book on physical metallurgy.

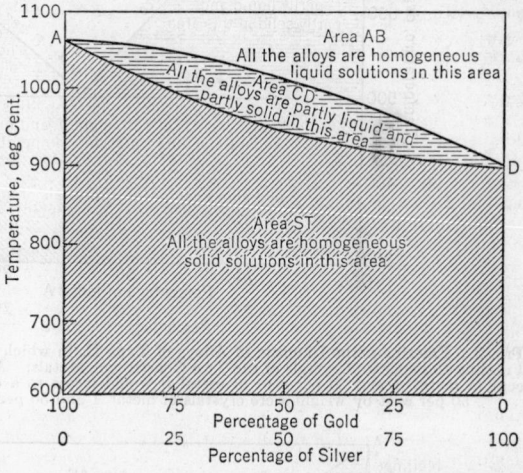

FIG. 1. Freezing-point Diagram of Alloys of Type I, in which a Homogeneous (Liquid) Solution Changes to a Solid Homogeneous Solution. The point A is the freezing point of pure gold; the point D is the freezing point of pure silver. Any solution in area AB will freeze to a corresponding solution in area ST. For example, a solution of 50 per cent gold in 50 per cent silver in liquid solution will freeze to crystals, each of which will be a solid solution of 50 per cent gold and 50 per cent silver. In this connection, it should be noted that, whereas the crystals may not all be alike on first freezing, the atoms of one element frequently migrate or diffuse through the space lattices of a solid crystal until equilibrium is established, that is to say, until all the crystals are alike.

Phase Changes in Solid Solutions. In the alloys of Type I, the crystals of solid solution, after formation, ordinarily cool to atmospheric temperature without further change. In the very limited number of alloys which form according to Type II there also seem to be no revolutionary changes after freezing is complete. But the solid solutions formed in Type III do not persist in unaltered form on cooling. Almost all limited solid solutions decrease their solubility with fall in temperature. In other words, the proportion of metal B which can be held in metal A in solid solution at a temperature of, say, 1000 deg cent, will be greater, and sometimes much greater, than the proportion which will saturate the same metal at 500 deg cent. Therefore, the structure of an alloy which exists immediately after freezing may be altered on cooling, and is then said to have undergone a phase change.

Influence of Structure on Properties. Some properties of metallic bodies are greatly dependent on their structure. The structure of a metallic body at a given temperature is due, first, to the formation of space lattices; second, the aggregation of space lattices

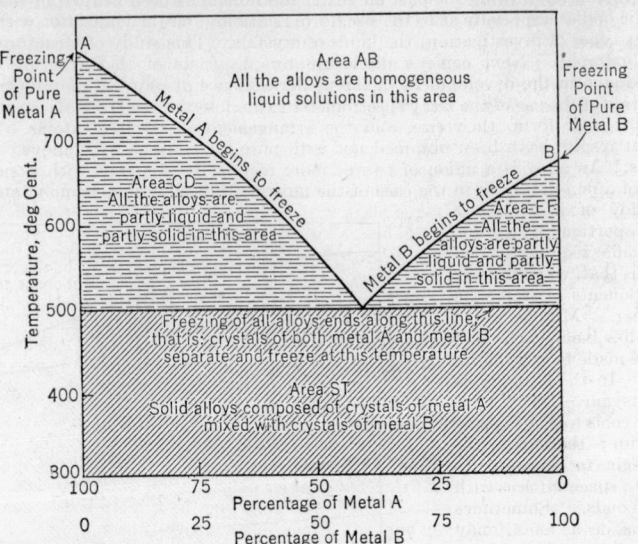

Fig. 2. Freezing-point Diagram of Alloys of Type II, in which Any Liquid Solution Changes on Freezing to Separate Crystals of the Two Constituent Metals. A liquid solution containing 50 per cent of metal *A* and 50 per cent of metal *B* would freeze to a conglomerate of crystals of which 50 per cent by weight were crystals of metal *A* and 50 per cent by weight of metal *B*.

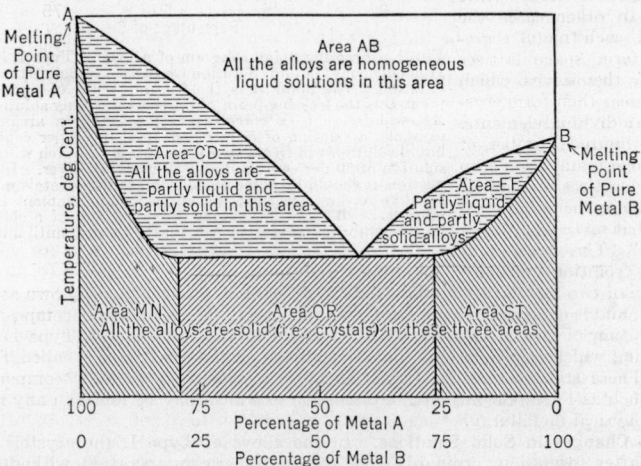

Fig. 3. Equilibrium Diagram of the Freezing of Alloys of Type III, in which Each Liquid Solution Changes into Either One or Two Solid Solutions. In area *MN* there is only one solid solution in each alloy. In area *ST* there is only one solid solution in each alloy. In area *OR* there are two solid solutions in each alloy, solid solutions consisting of a saturated solution of metal *B* in metal *A* and of metal *A* in metal *B*. Most of our commercial alloys are of this type, namely, those in which solid solutions of *B* in *A* form up to the limit of saturation, and, on the opposite end of the percentage scale, alloys of metal *A* in *B* up to the limit of saturation. Between these two saturation limits, the alloys consist of crystals of saturated solution of *A* in *B* and saturated solution of *B* in *A*.

into crystals; and third, changes which take place in the nature of the crystals on cooling after freezing. The nature of the crystal depends not only on its composition but also on its size. And finally, some of the properties of metallic bodies depend upon the nature of the extremely thin envelopes between crystals, sometimes called the "intercrystalline cement."

Allotropic Modifications. Some metals abruptly change their properties when heated above a critical temperature. On cooling again below this critical temperature, they revert to their former properties. For example, iron above its critical temperature range will dissolve carbon in any amount up to an upper limit of 1.7 per cent; below this critical range, it will not hold more than 0.03 per cent of carbon in solid solution. Other physical properties are in a somewhat marked degree coincident with the change in the power of dissolving carbon. In the case of iron, this change is known to be a change in space lattice: below 890 deg cent the pure iron crystal is made up of body-centered cubic space lattices, having 9 atoms per space lattice; above 900 deg cent the space lattice is face-centered, having 13 atoms to each space lattice. This change of number and position of atoms in the space lattice takes place within the solid crystal, and the change in the metal is said to be an allotropic change. Tin and several other metals undergo allotropic changes in the solid state. The temperature at which the change occurs is different for each individual metal.

CORROSION OF METALS
By Frank N. Speller

2. PRINCIPLES OF CORROSION

Corrosion of Metals. Corrosion of metals may be defined broadly as the chemical action of their environment, often resulting in their deterioration or destruction. In many conditions, most metals are unstable and tend to revert to a more stable combination, i.e., the metallic ores found in nature. Under most ordinary conditions of exposure, the corrosion products comprise mainly oxides (more or less hydrated), carbonates, and sulfides. At high temperatures the product may consist largely of oxides, although indications are that corrosion of this type also progresses more rapidly when some moisture is present. Corrosion may be entirely superficial or may attack the intercrystalline boundaries and cause disintegration in the metal, as dezincification of brass or so-called caustic embrittlement in boiler steel.

Recent work (1932) in the fundamentals of corrosion shows that the essential phenomena are the same for all metals and alloys, differing only in degree but not in kind. The discussion may be simplified, therefore, by considering the mechanism of corrosion with reference to iron.

It may be taken as established that in nearly all cases of corrosion at ordinary temperatures, comprising those most important in practice, the driving force of the corrosion reaction between metal and environment is electrochemical. The resultant electrochemical potential varies with the environment and the metal, and determines the tendency of the reaction to proceed. The rate of corrosion is determined mainly by the resistance to the continued progress of the reaction set up by certain of the corrosion by-products.

Established Facts Regarding Corrosion. *a.* In most cases both moisture and oxygen are necessary for corrosion. *b.* The initial rate of corrosion is usually comparatively rapid, slowing as protective films form. *c.* Surface films are important in controlling the rate and distribution of corrosion. *d.* Increased rate of motion increases corrosion in water up to a certain velocity; the rate may then drop where strong protective films are formed. *e.* Dissimilar metals in electrical contact accelerate corrosion of the one that happens to be anodic. Galvanic action is a most active agent of corrosion. It occurs when two metals, one electronegative to the other, are placed in contact and exposed to moisture. *f.* The composition of ordinary iron and steel has little or no effect on their relative rates of corrosion under water or underground. Under these conditions, the particular kind of metal is not usually so important as environment. *g.* Variation in the concentration of a solution in contact with a metal tends to localize corrosion. Where this is due to oxygen in solution, the surface to which the oxygen diffuses most readily is cathodic to the area that is protected from diffusion of oxygen. The smaller the anodic areas in relation to cathodic areas the greater is the rate of penetration at anodic points. *h.* Corrosion, like other chemical reactions, proceeds more rapidly with increase in temperature.

Corrosion in the Presence of Water. The above, and other facts (see F. N. Speller, Corrosion—Causes and Prevention, McGraw-Hill Book Co., 1926), are the basis of the electrochemical mechanism of corrosion, which is generally accepted to explain corrosion in the presence of water.

Iron, like all other metals, when in contact with water or a solution has a definite inherent tendency to enter the solution in the form of electrically charged particles (iron ions). The solution must remain electrically neutral, and these positive ions can enter it only if an equivalent number of positive ions of another element are displaced. Thus, iron immersed in a solution of copper sulfate begins to go into solution. Simultaneously, an equivalent amount of copper is plated out on the surface of the iron, and protects it somewhat from further action. Similarly, when iron is immersed in water, hydrogen is plated out and forms a thin invisible film on the iron surface.

The general mechanism of the corrosion processes is expressed in the following chemical equations. The typical primary reaction is

$$(1) \qquad \underset{\text{metal}}{Fe} + \underset{\text{ions}}{2H^+} \rightarrow \underset{\text{ion}}{Fe^{++}} + \underset{\text{atoms}}{2H}$$

The primary reaction is followed by either

$$(2)\ (a) \qquad \underset{\text{atoms}}{2H} + \underset{\text{dissolved}}{1/2\ O_2} \rightarrow \underset{\text{liquid}}{H_2O} \qquad \text{(the destruction of the hydrogen film)}$$

$$\text{or}\ (b) \qquad \underset{\text{atoms}}{2H} \rightarrow \underset{\text{gas}}{H_2} \qquad \text{(its removal as bubbles of gas)}$$

These permit reaction (1) to proceed with the accumulation in the solution of Fe^{++} which is oxidized and precipitated as rust by

$$(3) \quad 2Fe^{++} + 1/2\ O_2 + H_2O \rightarrow 2Fe^{+++} + 2OH^- \rightarrow \text{Insoluble ferric hydroxide (rust)}$$

Factors Controlling Corrosion. Primary factors are those having to do with the initial tendency toward solution (reaction 1) and are mainly associated with the metal itself. Secondary factors are those that influence the subsequent rate of corrosion, and usually are more important than primary factors. They depend mainly upon the environment of the metal. The main factors influencing corrosion are listed below, regardless of their relative importance, which changes materially with the environment.

Primary Factors Having to Do Mainly with the Metal or Alloy.

1. Effective electrode potential of the metal in the solution.
2. Chemical and physical homogeneity and texture of its surface.
3. Its inherent ability to form an insoluble protective film.
4. Overvoltage of hydrogen on the metal surface.

Factors Which Vary with the Environment.

5. Hydrogen-ion concentration (pH) in the solution.
6. Effective supply of oxygen in the solution adjacent to the metal.
7. Distribution of available oxygen on the metal surface.
8. Specific nature, concentration, and distribution of other ions in the solution.
9. Effective rate of flow of the liquid past the metal surface.
10. Presence of solid particles (dirt), or of a coating of any kind as mill scale, on the metal surface, or contact with other conducting material in the presence of an electrolyte.
11. Temperature.
12. Whether the metal is under static stress conditions or exposed to cycles of alternating stress (the so-called corrosion fatigue).
13. Ability of environment to build up protective films on the metal.

In different environments the order of importance of the above factors changes materially. The standard electrode potentials of the elements as given in textbooks have little significance, except that they indicate the relative tendency of the metal to enter solution under certain specific conditions. If the concentration of the solution is changed, the order of standing of metals that lie close together in the electrochemical series, e.g., iron and cadmium, actually may be reversed. The relative influence of the important factors on corrosion of steel in water of different acidities is illustrated by the following table.

In Alkaline Zone ($pH > 10$) Corrosion slow	In Neutral Zone (pH 4.3 to 10) Corrosion medium	In Acid Zone ($pH < 4.3$) Corrosion rapid
Protective films	Oxygen concentration	Hydrogen-ion concentration
Oxygen concentration	Protective films	Hydrogen overvoltage
Composition of metal	Hydrogen-ion concentration	Composition of metal
Hydrogen-ion concentration	Composition of metal	Oxygen concentration
Hydrogen overvoltage	Hydrogen overvoltage	Metal-ion concentration
Metal-ion concentration	Metal-ion concentration	Protective films

Factors that head the list dominate others in their influence and are termed controlling factors. Thus, in the alkaline zone protective films are much more influential than any other factor; in the acid zone they form with difficulty and are readily removed, and have little influence under acid conditions.

A lesser but often considerable amount of corrosion is found in the absence of oxygen. The dominant reaction then is reaction 2 b (see above), accompanied by the evolution of hydrogen. This may be due to acid conditions, the presence of hydrogen sulfide, or to a high concentration of chloride. The mechanism of corrosion at high temperatures is not so well understood. It probably is due mainly to direct chemical attack, and may be accelerated by some electrochemical action where moisture is present.

Though all the above factors are important under some conditions, the following deserve special attention and should be more clearly recognized.

Oxygen. In most cases the oxygen concentration and the rate at which oxygen diffuses to the metal is a controlling factor when metal is immersed in water or buried in soil. The part to which the oxygen diffuses most readily is cathodic to the adjacent areas that are shielded by protective coatings or other material. That is, the points that are less accessible to oxygen corrode more rapidly than areas to which the oxygen has freer access. This principle, and the galvanic effect from contact between dissimilar materials, generally cause local corrosion or pitting.

Surface Films. Clean metallic surfaces exposed to air quickly acquire a film of oxide, which, at ordinary temperatures, is thin and invisible. At higher temperatures it is thick enough to give well-known characteristic colors, varying with the temperature. The nature and properties of the film depend upon the composition of the metal itself and its environment. Aluminum and stainless steels, for instance, owe their high durability in certain environments to the formation of a continuous and permanent film that is stable under the conditions of exposure. In other environments the film may not form or may be quickly dissolved. The metal, therefore, has short life under such conditions. The addition of 0.25 per cent copper to ordinary steel increases its life in atmosphere two to four times, owing to the formation of a dense adherent film, apparently consisting of iron oxide with a little copper oxide, on the surface of the metal. When copper steel is immersed in water or buried in soil the protective film does not form. Under such conditions, copper steel has been no more durable than ordinary steel without copper.

If the metal has no inherent power to form a protective film in solution, a film may be built up by adding film-forming reagents, as the chromates or alkalies, to the water. When the metal is removed from the solution, however, these films are only temporary. To secure permanent protection it is necessary to maintain in the water the proper concentration of chromate, or other material, used for this purpose. Films when formed should be self-healing, so that, if they are injured or removed in any way, a new film will form immediately to protect the metal. Chromium will form a very resistant invisible film under oxidizing conditions, but in dilute hydrochloric acid, where such films cannot exist, chromium dissolves even more rapidly than pure iron. Metals which acquire a stable film by contact with an oxidizing solution are termed passive. In this condition they are, at least, temporarily resistant to corrosion when removed from the film-forming solution. The presence of thin invisible oxide films on passive material has been determined by the change in potential of the metal and by the removal of the films from the surface by selective dissolution of the underlying metal. (See U. R. Evans, Thin Films in Relation to Corrosion Problems, *J. Inst. Metals*, Vol. 46, pp. 7–23, 1931.) Where the corrosion products form spongy layers of irregular thickness, they do not protect, and may even accelerate the normal action by interfering with the rate of diffusion of oxygen to the surface of the metal.

Corrosion Fatigue. Metals subjected to repeated application of stress fail at considerably below their static ultimate tensile strength. However, the metal may be cyclically stressed indefinitely, without apparent injury, below the so-called fatigue or endurance limit. For carbon steels, this endurance limit is about one-half the tensile strength. Even a small amount of corrosion present with cyclic stress will considerably reduce the endurance limit. Concentrated stress tends to accelerate the rate of corrosion. A notch is soon formed at the point of maximum stress, and after this reaches a certain depth, the metal under cyclic stress fails by ordinary fatigue. The combined action of stress and corrosion is termed " corrosion fatigue." The amount of cyclic stress that a metal will stand under these conditions depends on the character of the corrosion and on the nature of the protective films formed by the metal or its environment. Hence, it is difficult to conceive of a fixed corrosion fatigue limit for any metal under all conditions of exposure. Corrosion factors predominate in corrosion fatigue. Therefore if there is a so-called corrosion fatigue limit, it is independent of the tensile strength. Heat treatment of steel raises the tensile strength and the air endurance limit, but if it does not increase resistance to corrosion it will have no material influence on the resistance to corrosion fatigue. Even 18 per cent chromium steel and 18–8 per cent chromium-nickel steel show a considerable reduction in their endurance limit in corrosive environment. Carbon steels in the as-rolled condition may fail at less than one-half of their air-endurance limit when kept continuously wet, depending upon the composition of the water and the amount of oxygen present.

An exceedingly small amount of corrosion is sufficient to depress the endurance limit of the metal under stress. In practice, therefore, it is important to prevent contact between stressed portions of metal and corrosive solutions. When inhibitors have been added to water that ordinarily causes failure at a relatively low stress by corrosion fatigue, the endurance of the steel has been maintained at the same stress as in dry air. This apparently is due to the formation and maintenance of a protective film on the surface of the metal under stress.

3. PRINCIPLES OF CORROSION TESTING

Relative Corrosion. Difference of opinion regarding the relative corrosion of iron and steel and other metals apparently is due to failure to appreciate that different factors control in different environment. Factors external to the metal usually determine the corrosion rate; they vary considerably with environment. The relative rate, therefore, may vary under different conditions of exposure. This should be the basis on which all corrosion tests (laboratory or service) are designed. Thus, in a study of metals under atmospheric conditions, the dominant factor should be an excess of oxygen. If the endurance of metal under water is in question, the test should be made in that environment alone. It is a mistake to take the results of tests made under one type of corrosion, e.g., in the atmosphere or in acids, and to apply the conclusions to conditions in which entirely different factors control. An extreme instance is the well-known acid test, made by exposing the metals to dilute sulfuric acid. A thorough investigation of this test in comparison with results of corrosion of the same metals under atmospheric and water conditions led to the following conclusions: An acid test conducted by the procedure followed by the committee is not capable of consistent repetition; further, the data from such an acid test should not be used to forecast the relative life of ordinary ferrous materials in the atmosphere. (See Report of Sub-committee V on Total Immersion Tests, *Proc. A.S.T.M.*, Vol. 31, Pt. I, p. 180, 1931.)

Clearly, the subject of relative corrosion should be studied on the basis of type of service. The service test is the final criterion of the value of the metal, although judiciously made laboratory tests, with proper consideration given to the factors involved, will show under accelerated conditions a fair approximation of results in service. Three common types of service to be considered are atmospheric, water, and soil corrosion.

4. PREVENTION OF CORROSION

Deterioration of metals may be prevented or reduced in three ways: (1) By using a more resistant metal. (2) By the application of a suitable protective coating. (3) By making the environment less corrosive. The amount of protection depends specifically upon the corrosive nature of the environment and must be chosen to suit the conditions and with a view to economy.

Protective Coatings. To obtain protection against corrosion three methods are in general use:

1. Applying impervious coatings such as paints, varnishes, lacquers, vitreous enamels, etc.

2. Applying coatings of protective metals which either mechanically exclude moisture and corroding materials from the metal surface, or which, being electronegative to iron, are themselves corroded in preference to the surface beneath.

3. Producing inert or non-corrodible coatings by heat or chemical treatment of the metal surface.

Protection from Atmospheric Corrosion

Paints, Varnishes, etc. A large variety of paints, lacquers, and similar protective materials has been developed. See Sec. 12 for a brief treatment of these. See also publications of American Paint and Varnish Mfrs. Assoc., distributed by the Institute of Paint and Varnish Research Laboratory, Washington, D.C.

Cast-iron water pipes are usually coated by dipping in a hot mixture of coal-tar and coal-tar pitch; riveted or welded steel pipes by dipping in hot asphalt. Ships' bottoms are coated with red lead or other inhibitive primer and a varnish paint to prevent rusting. Over this is a similar paint containing poison, as mercury chloride or a copper compound, or a greasy copper soap is applied hot, to tend to prevent the accumulation of marine growths. Galvanized iron and tin surfaces should be thoroughly cleaned with benzine and scrubbed before painting. When new, they are partly covered with grease and chemicals. These must be removed or paint will not adhere. Weathering for six months prior to painting serves the same purpose in preparing galvanized steel surfaces.

Galvanizing is a method of coating steel or iron articles with zinc, the product being known as galvanized steel or iron. For a discussion of various galvanizing processes and the corrosion resistance of galvanized surfaces, see pp. 11–54 and 11–55.

Lead Coatings. Lead is very resistant to some types of corrosion, and lead coatings on steel have been somewhat used. Lead, however, is difficult to apply, either by electroplating or hot dipping, in a coating sufficiently free from pinholes to be effective when submerged in corrosive water. The atmospheric resistance of such coatings is usually quite good. Hot-dipped lead sheets, known as terne plates, are extensively used.

Wrought steel or iron pipes protected on the interior by thick lead tubes mechanically applied, when carefully installed with suitable fittings and valves, are effective for carrying corrosive acids and similar liquids.

Electroplating with Other Metals is a method of depositing impervious and adherent metallic coatings on conductive surfaces by electrolysis. The following metals are most commonly used for this purpose:

Copper. Because of its resistance to corrosive influences, copper is widely used as a protective metal coating, frequently being the base coating for subsequent nickel or chromium deposits.

Nickel. Nickel is harder than copper and has excellent resistance to corrosive atmospheric conditions. Because of its lustrous gray-white color, it is often used as a metal coating where appearance is a factor as well as durability.

Chromium. Chromium is a hard, white metal which is non-tarnishing and which has good light-reflecting properties. Chromium deposits are difficult to obtain, but excellent coatings are produced under closely controlled electroplating conditions.

Silver. Silver has excellent resistance to oxidation and corrosive atmospheric conditions. It is used as an electrodeposited metal coating chiefly because of its efficiency as a carrier of electricity and as a reflector of light rays. Because it is susceptible to tarnishing from sulfur compounds in the air, it is frequently protected by a coating of lacquer, when used for reflectors.

Cadmium. Cadmium is a white metal which, being electronegative to iron is widely used for the protection of iron and steel parts against atmospheric corrosion. A thin layer gives good protection and is useful in protecting threaded parts where tolerances are close.

Tin. A tin coating, being electropositive to iron, must be free from pinholes, or accelerated corrosion will set in where the steel is exposed. Tin itself is resistant to corrosion.

Oxide Coatings. Oxide coatings for the protection of steel are obtained by oxidizing the metal by heat or chemical treatments. The oxide coatings are always oiled, which probably accounts for their resistance to corrosion.

One method is to heat the metal to about 400 deg cent, in the presence of steam and hydrocarbons, until a heavy black coating is produced.

Another method is to apply solutions of chemical reagents until a heavy rust film is obtained. The rust is then removed by scraping, leaving a thin adherent coat of oxide on the metal. The process is repeated until the desired depth of color is obtained. The surface is then oiled.

Burned Oil Finish. A deep black oxide coating is obtained by heating steel in volatilized oil vapors at a temperature of about 400 deg cent, or by first coating the steel with oil and then heating. In other processes the steel is heated in oil and sawdust, or in burned bone and charcoal to obtain the black oxide.

Coslettizing. Phosphate coatings are used extensively for the rust proofing of steel and to serve as base coatings for paints and lacquers. The Coslettizing process consists of immersing the steel in a hot ferric phosphate solution containing some phosphoric acid. The grayish white coating becomes black when oiled.

Parkerizing. The Parkerizing process of producing durable phosphate coatings on steel uses a patented mixture containing manganese and iron phosphates. It is otherwise similar to the Coslettizing process.

Bonderizing. Bonderizing is a modification of the Parkerizing process used to produce a base coating for finishing with paints and lacquers.

Granodizing. In the Granodizing process the article is made the cathode in a hot solution of zinc phosphate and phosphoric acid. A dense black coating is produced on iron, zinc, cadmium, and other metals, which is resistant to weathering. An immersion Granodizing bath, without application of voltage, is also in use.

Anodizing. Aluminum and its alloys are treated by the anodizing process which produces adherent oxide films for protection against corrosion, for electrical insulation, and for decorative effects.

Rust-resisting Metals. No metal or alloy has so far been produced that is equally durable under all conditions. The development of the alloy of chromium and iron, with and without nickel, has made available for industrial purposes a class of materials combining unusual resistance to corrosion with desirable physical properties. See p. 11-37. Copper-steel has found a wide commercial application on account of its slow rusting properties under atmospheric and similar conditions of exposure. See p. 11-37. These steels, copper, Monel metal, aluminum, and their alloys afford the engineer a wide choice of material. The selection of the most suitable metal for any particular condition will depend upon economic and structural conditions. (For the corrosion-resistant properties of specific metals, see discussion under each metal.)

Protection against Underwater Corrosion

The main factors controlling the rate of corrosion in water are dissolved oxygen, temperature, rate of motion, and the composition of the water. The chemical composition of ferrous metals, within rather wide limits, seems not to have a marked influence on the character or amount of corrosion. The high-chromium series of steels are an exception to this. With cold water the rate of corrosion is usually slow, but in hot water the corrosive action is accelerated according to the temperature, the rate being doubled for every 25 deg fahr increase in temperature.

Localized corrosion or pitting is usually much deeper near mill scale, especially where the scale is thick and firmly adherent, undoubtedly owing to the electronegative character of the scale with respect to the iron. Old rust acts somewhat similarly but is less harmful. Removal of the mill scale and rust greatly reduces the tendency to pitting, provided the metal itself is fairly homogeneous and free from strains. Surface finish is a greater controlling factor in corrosion than is the variation in the composition of the metal itself.

Within certain limits, corrosion varies directly with the temperature and the rate of flow and also with the composition of the water. Corrosion is likely to be more rapid on unprotected metal with increasing velocity of the water. The amount of corrosion is almost directly proportional to the amount of oxygen in solution in the water. Hot water heating systems show practically no corrosion after 35 or 40 years of use, whereas hot water supply systems, operating at the same temperatures, have deteriorated in from 6 to 8 years. The only difference between the two is that the heating system carries no oxygen whereas the water in the supply system is usually saturated with it.

In some cases it is more economical to prevent internal corrosion by removing dissolved oxygen from the water, especially hot water. Oxygen removal may be accomplished: (1) By mechanical deaeration, for which two or three satisfactory designs of apparatus are in use. (2) By the chemical combination of the oxygen with some material such as scrap and sheet iron. The two methods may be combined by using mechanical deaeration to remove the major portion of the oxygen and chemical treatment for the residual oxygen.

It is now generally recognized that no one metal will meet all requirements of service. Ordinary brass pipe (70 Cu, 30 Zn) is adequate where the water is fairly pure and almost free from chlorides; red brass (85 Cu, 15 Zn) is much more durable where the water carries considerable amounts of soluble salts and is less likely to suffer dezincification. This grade is preferable for sea water. Copper pipe is usually more durable than brass for practically all domestic water service.

Protection against Undersoil Corrosion

Soil Corrosion is highly localized and usually is caused by electrochemical action resulting from variations in the soil and solutions therein. Low alloy steels, e.g., steels with less than 10 per cent chromium, do not show enough advantage under severe soil corrosion to warrant their use from an economic standpoint, and solution of the problem of longer life of underground pipe is practically limited to a selection of suitable protective coatings.

Soil corrosion varies considerably from point to point on pipe lines. On long lines serious damage is confined to 5 per cent or less of the line as a rule. (See W. T. Smith, Economy in Wider Use of Protective Coatings on Pipes, *Eng. News-Rec.*, April 21, 1932.) It is therefore advantageous to survey the soil of the territory through which the pipe line will run, before deciding upon the type of protective coating, if any, to be used. Much progress has been made in the study of soil factors at the U. S. Bureau of Standards, so that a careful survey, judiciously interpreted, with regard to all the factors involved, should give an approximate idea as to the corrosivity of the soil. (See U. S. Bureau of Standards Research Papers Nos. 95, 298, 329, 359, 363, and 638.) This, with experience on pipe lines situated in similar soils, affords a fairly sound basis for selecting the most economical coating for a particular location.

Bituminous Coatings have been mostly used for underground protection up to now. These consist of the well-known coal-tar and asphalt dip coatings, preferably applied, after removing all grease, dirt, and loose mill scale, by vertically dipping the pipe in a bituminous bath at about 350 deg fahr. The melting point of the asphalt mixture can be varied between 140 and 190 deg fahr to suit climatic conditions. Coatings of this type, properly applied at the mill, are suitable only for mild corrosive conditions, but afford good protection on the inside of water mains. Often, in wet, marshy places, or in alkaline or acid soils, more substantial protection is required. A thicker coating may be applied at the trench, but, to prevent rusting in transit, the pipe should either receive an asphalt or coal-tar dip coating, or a coating of suitable bituminous primer, applied cold at the plant before shipment. Bituminous coatings are now usually reinforced with fabric or with saturated felt wound spirally on the pipe over the dip coat. Asbestos base reinforcement is preferable. In certain soils, unless these bituminous coatings have a high melting point and are unusually rigid, they are subject to soil stress; that is, some soils have a tendency to cling to the coating and pull it away from the pipe when the soil shrinks by drying, or irregular pressure in the trench may distort the bitumen and cause thin spots in the coating. In such soils a shielding material should be used to prevent damage to the coating by soil stress. Experience shows that many bituminous coatings that would otherwise have afforded adequate protection have been destroyed or rendered ineffective in this way. Thin, stiff, rolled-steel sheet (26 gage) or copper foil may be used as a shield. Other materials are being tried for this purpose. Asphalt mastics consisting of 30 per cent bitumen and 70 per cent of a graded sand have been used with good results, especially for protection of pipe conveying hot oil through very corrosive soils. These mixtures are applied about $3/8$ in. thick, but are too expensive for ordinary use.

In soils where the electrical conductivity is high and fairly uniform, as in New Orleans, it has been found practicable to maintain the coated pipe lines at a lower potential than the soil by imposing a current on the pipe to prevent the destruction of the coating wherever it happens to be broken.

Portland Cement Concrete has been used for about 40 years for protecting pipe in highly corrosive soil. It has a record as one of the most practical means of affording permanent protection. The minimum thickness is usually about 1 in., the mixture being applied in a wooden box, or more recently, a portable steel form, surrounding the pipe. Concrete coatings offer some resistance to stray electric currents but should not be relied upon to protect pipe against electrolysis. Where pipe lines pass under electric railways, or in situations where complete electrical insulation is necessary, the line has been effectively protected by boxing and coating with hot asphalt with a minimum thickness of about 1 in. for a distance of 100 ft on each side of the track.

Electrolysis is caused by current leaving the pipe directly to the ground when the potential of the pipe or other underground steel structure is higher than the earth. Two primary factors of electrolysis mitigation are: (1) The reduction of the flow of current through the earth and the metallic structures buried in the earth. (2) The reduction of the anodic portions of such structures to a minimum, where the current is not substantially eliminated, in order to reduce the area of destructive corrosion as far as possible. Damage from this cause may be lessened so far as underground pipe is concerned by: (1) Use of insulated joints to prevent the current entering or flowing on the pipe line. (2) Use of insulating coatings. (3) Reversal or neutralization of the polarity of pipe by bonding the structures to a negative bus-bar to secure suitable electrical drainage, insuring that the potential of the metal is lower than that of the ground. A discussion of the details of this problem will be found in Corrosion—Causes and Prevention, by F. N. Speller, Chapter XV, and in the Report of the American Committee of Electrolysis, 1921, A.I.E.E.

For the protection of cast-iron and lead pipe, use the methods recommended for steel except that Portland cement or lime should not be used in contact with lead. Drainage of the trench should be provided where practicable by filling in around the pipe with sand or laying it on broken stone or gravel. This is particularly recommended where the soil carries irregular patches of soluble salts (alkali) that tend to set up local differences of concentration, tending to cause pitting.

IRON AND STEEL

By Bradley Stoughton

5. METHODS OF MANUFACTURE

" Iron and Steel." The term " iron and steel " embraces a series of industrial alloys of iron and carbon, extending from 99.9 per cent iron and zero carbon, to 94 per cent iron and 5 per cent carbon, with traces of other elements, and sometimes other alloying metals, such as manganese, nickel, tungsten, etc., when the iron may fall to 65 per cent.

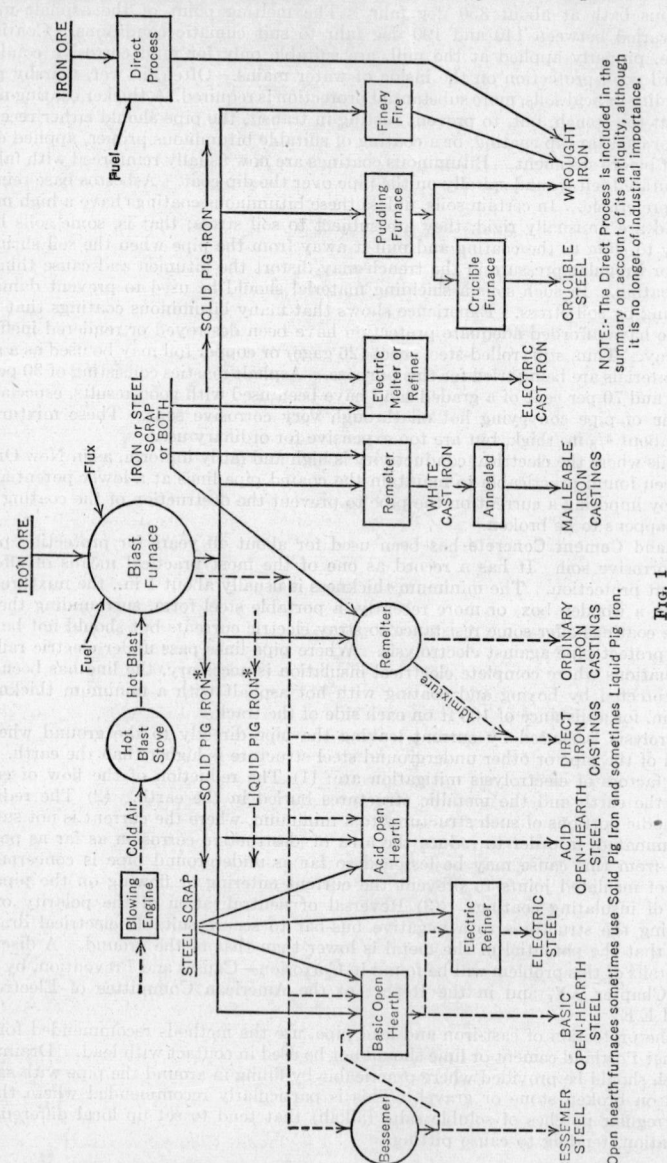

NOTE:- The Direct Process is included in the summary on account of its antiquity, although it is no longer of industrial importance.

FIG. 1

* Open hearth furnaces sometimes use Solid Pig Iron and sometimes Liquid Pig Iron.

Iron is a chemical element, and excepting aluminum, is the commonest metal in the earth's crust. The magnetism of the earth is explained on the supposition that it is essentially an iron ball. On the exterior, or crust, iron rarely occurs in metallic form, but usually is combined with oxygen. The rare deposits of unoxidized metal are supposed to be the remains of meteorites.

Steel is iron containing less than 1.7 per cent carbon. It is produced in a fluid state by either the open-hearth, Bessemer, electric, crucible, or duplex process. It is distinguished from cast iron by containing less carbon; from wrought iron by being produced in a fluid condition, and therefore free from slag, except for rare traces of less than 0.10 per cent.

Manufacture of Iron and Steel. Iron ore is mined from the earth and smelted in blast furnaces to produce pig iron. Pig iron is an impure product, weak as to tensile strength, and non-malleable. It is easily melted and may be cast into a great variety of useful forms. A somewhat malleable casting may be made by annealing a specific variety of iron casting in oxides (see Malleable Castings). However, if a malleable product of high tensile strength is desired, the pig iron must be refined and purified. This is accomplished by oxidizing the carbon and other impurities out of the pig iron, in a basic or acid open-hearth, a Bessemer, an electric, or a puddling furnace, the iron being charged to the furnace either in liquid or solid form. This converts it into a metal which can be rolled or forged, and which has toughness, strength, ductility, and other qualities lacking in pig iron or cast iron. This metal is called steel, except only the product of the puddling furnace, which is called wrought iron. Wrought iron is sometimes cut up into bars, remelted in crucibles, and used as "crucible steel." These, in brief, are the processes whereby practically all iron and steel of commerce are made. Fig. 1 is a skeleton outline, for easy reference.

6. PIG IRON

Pig Iron is the product of the iron blast furnace. It contains $2\frac{1}{2}$ to 5 per cent of carbon, 94 per cent and over of iron, and small amounts of silicon, sulfur, phosphorus, and manganese. Table I gives the analyses of various grades of pig iron.

Table I. Analyses of Pig Irons or Cast Irons

Figures in bold-faced type indicate essential constituents; figures in light-faced type are approximately correct, but are not the determining factor for the grade in question.

Trade Name	Total C, per cent	Si, per cent	S, per cent	P, per cent	Mn, per cent
No. 1 soft.......	3.00 ±	**2.75 to 3.25**	0.05 and under	0.30 to 1.50	0.10 to 1.00
No. 1 foundry....	3.25 ±	**2.25 to 2.75**	0.05 and under	0.30 to 1.50	0.10 to 1.00
No. 2 foundry....	3.50 ±	**1.75 to 2.25**	0.06 and under	0.30 to 1.50	0.10 to 1.00
No. 3 foundry....	3.75 ±	**1.25 to 1.75**	0.065 and under	0.30 to 1.50	0.10 to 1.00
Gray forge......	3.50 ±	**0.75 to 1.75**	0.07 and under	Under 1.00	0.10 to 1.00
Standard acid.. ⎱ Bessemer pig... ⎰	3.50 to 4.00	**1.00 to 1.50**	Under 0.08	**Under 0.09**	0.20 to 1.00
Basic pig........	3.50 to 4.00	**Under 1.25**	Under 0.08	0.10 to 1.50	**1.50 to 2.00**
Malleable...... ⎱ Bessemer...... ⎰	3.50 ±	0.75 to 2.00	Under 0.07	Under 0.20	0.50 ±
Ferrosilicon *....	0.50 to 2.00	**10.00 to 50.00**	Under 0.04	Under 0.10	0.20 ±
Silicospiegel.....	1.00 ±	**5.00 to 15.00**	Under 0.02	Under 0.10	**15.00 to 25.00**
Ferromanganese..	6.00 to 7.00	0.50 to 1.00	Under 0.03	....	**40.00 to 80.00**
Ferrophosphorus .	1.00 ±	1.50 ±	Under 0.05	**10.00 to 25.00**	....
Spiegeleisen ...	4.50 to 6.00	1.00 ±	Under 0.04	....	**15.00 to 35.00**

* Ferrosilicon of 10 per cent grade, ferromanganese, silicospiegel, and spiegeleisen are made in blast furnaces, by variations of the usual practice and by using special ores. Ferrosilicon of 20 to 50 per cent grades, and several other so-called *ferroalloys*, are made in electric furnaces. These include ferrochrome, ferrotungsten, ferromolybdenum, ferrotitanium, ferrovanadium, etc. They are all practically iron pigs with large amounts of the alloying metal. When these alloys are free from, or low in, carbon, they are made by the thermit and other processes.

Chemistry of Pig-iron Manufacture. Iron ore may be considered simply as oxide of iron, Fe_2O_3 or Fe_3O_4, mixed with a small amount of gangue, usually silica. When heated in contact with carbon and reducing gases the ore loses oxygen and is reduced to a spongy form of metallic iron. If this is heated in contact with carbon, it dissolves the latter to the extent of 1 or 2 per cent. Finally, if it be melted, it dissolves carbon up to 4 or 5 per cent, in direct ratio to the temperature attained; it will also dissolve, at the same time, any reduced silicon, manganese, or phosphorus, and any iron sulfide available.

The gangue requires some flux with which it may unite, in order that it may become fusible at the temperature of the blast furnace. The actual manufacturing unit is a brick lined steel shell roughly 30 ft outside diameter and 150 ft to top of charging apparatus. The other essential features are: 3 or 4 hot blast stoves roughly 110 ft high by 22 ft diameter; blowing engines of sufficient capacity to compress 60,000 to 75,000 cu ft of atmospheric air per minute to 30 lb per sq in. pressure; mechanical devices for handling, etc. The necessary heat is obtained by burning fuel (usually coke) with red hot air blown into the furnace through tuyères which are situated around its circumference a few feet from the bottom.

These data are summarized in the diagram, Fig. 2,* which is a skeleton outline of a section through the furnace stack, showing the temperatures and the chemical reactions normally occurring at each level. The stack is filled with a bed of solid fuel, extending from the bottom to the widest portion, located about 22 ft from the bottom. This lowest portion is the smelting zone; its temperature is from 2500 to 3000 deg fahr; only the fuel can remain unmelted in this zone. The temperature there is produced by burning the fuel with the air driven in through the tuyères, whose location is indicated. Above the smelting zone are alternate layers of ore and fuel, with which the flux, consisting of limestone, is mixed. As the iron is melted it trickles down through the smelting zone, dissolving carbon from the coke, all the phosphorus which has entered the furnace with the raw materials, all the manganese

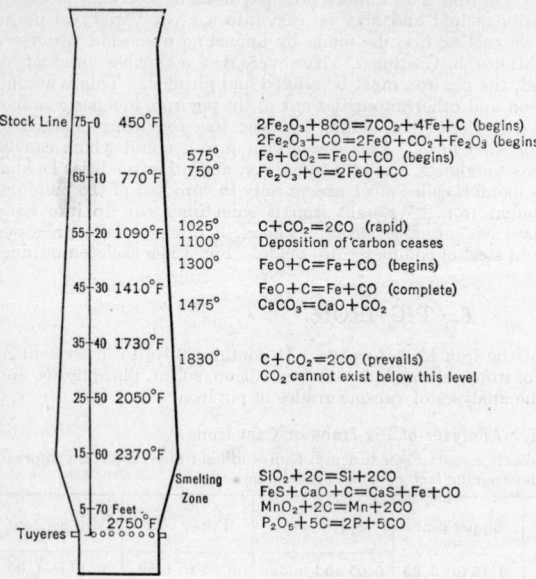

and silicon which have been reduced by carbon and heat, and also all the sulfur which has not been converted to CaS. In practice, as a rule, the hotter the smelting zone, the more silicon will be reduced and the more CaS will be formed; therefore a " hot " iron is usually relatively high in silicon and low in sulfur.

At the top of the smelting zone the gangue and flux dissolve in each other, thus forming a fusible " slag " or " cinder," which trickles down, dissolving ash of the burned fuel, and any CaS that may be present, and floats in a liquid layer on top of the melted pig iron in the hearth. It is drawn off at intervals through a " slag hole " in the side of the hearth. The pig iron collects in the hearth in the interstices between the fuel, and is " tapped " about 4 to 6 times in 24 hours, through a tap hole in the front of the hearth, at its lowest level. From 125 to 200 tons of pig iron are obtained from a modern furnace at each tap.

Foundry Pig Iron. Pig iron intended for foundry uses is made with an abundance of fuel and flux (e.g., limestone); therefore the temperature of the smelting zone is hot and the slag is rich in lime. The high temperature tends to produce iron with high silicon content, and the high temperature and limey slag both tend to give iron low in sulfur. The amount of phosphorus will depend on the amount that goes into the furnace with the ores, and the same is true to a large extent of manganese, except that a slag rich in silica will tend to absorb some manganese away from the iron.

Charcoal Pig Iron. This is pig iron made in blast furnaces using charcoal for fuel. The furnaces must be small, because the strength of charcoal is not sufficient to bear the weight of many layers of material above the fuel bed. The smelting practice differs in the very important respect that elimination of sulfur is not the controlling factor. Char-

---

coal contains only 0.05 per cent of sulfur, as compared with 1 per cent of sulfur in coke. This permits operation with a much colder furnace and an acid slag, thus getting low sulfur and low silicon at the same time. Some charcoal furnaces are run with cold blast, producing " cold-blast charcoal iron." Low-silicon iron is often wanted for chilling purposes; if made in a coke furnace, it is likely to run somewhat high in sulfur, which injures its strength. Therefore, charcoal iron is often preferred for chilled railroad car wheels, for chilled iron rolls, etc. It brings a price about 25 per cent higher than coke iron, and it costs more to make, under like conditions of supply. Some attribute the higher reputation of charcoal iron to tradition only; others, to the presence of strengthening oxide of iron;* still others, to differences in practice.

Acid Pig Iron is a trade name given to iron suitable for the acid steel-making processes, that is, the Bessemer (only the acid Bessemer process is employed in America) and the acid open-hearth processes. It must be low in phosphorus, because the acid steel-making processes cannot purge metal of phosphorus, and steel must contain less than 0.10 per cent phosphorus or it is likely to be exceedingly brittle.

Basic Pig Iron is the trade name given to pig iron containing too much phosphorus for the acid steel-making processes, and not enough silicon for foundry pig iron. It may carry a little sulfur also, as the basic steel-making processes will remove some sulfur, and also remove as much phosphorus as commercial considerations indicate. Basic pig iron also commonly contains from 1.75 to 2 per cent of manganese, because this assists in the operation.

Forge Pig Iron is pig iron suitable for refining in the puddling furnace.

Electric Pig Iron is pig iron made from ore in electric furnaces.

" **Synthetic** " **Pig Iron** is pig iron made from melted scrap by dissolving in it the desired proportions of carbon, silicon, etc.

Manufacture of Ferroalloys. Ferrosilicon of 10 per cent grade, silicospiegel, ferromanganese, and ferrophosphorus are made in the blast furnace, by adopting variations of the usual pig-iron practice, and by using special ores. Ferrosilicon of 20 to 50 per cent grade, ferrochrome, ferrotitanium, ferrotungsten, ferrovanadium, etc., are made in electric furnaces of special types. These same alloys, free from carbon, are made by the thermit and other processes.

Direct Iron Castings. By this is meant castings poured from liquid pig iron direct from a blast furnace. This practice has been in vogue for years for making ingot molds for use in steel works, and for other purposes. It requires a regular and uniform operation of the blast furnace, so that the iron may be suitable at all times. The normal blast-furnace operation produces cast iron which varies greatly in quality. Direct casting also requires supervision by one whose eye is trained to distinguish the quality of the iron, and determine approximately the percentages of silicon and sulfur therein, by its appearance as it runs from the furnace. An important American manufacturer of automobiles makes engine castings by partly filling a ladle with pig iron at the blast furnace, and then adding iron melted in a nearby cupola. The cupola metal is adjusted to correct or modify the metal coming from the blast furnace.

7. CAST IRON

Ordinarily, pig iron is not a finished industrial product. (See Direct Iron Castings above for exception.) It is converted into iron castings by mixing various grades of iron, to obtain the desired quality, analysis, and properties. This mixture is then melted and cast into the desired form, ready for immediate use, or for machining. In its restricted sense, cast iron is the form assumed after pig iron has been again melted and cast into its finished form.

The Cupola is the usual means for remelting pig iron to produce cast iron in its more restricted sense, namely, the finished castings. It consists of a cylindrical shaft provided with one or two rows of tuyères near the base, through which air is forced at a pressure of about $1/2$ lb per sq in. The charge consists of pig iron and coke in the proportion of about 200 lb of coke for each ton of metal. A little limestone is usually also introduced as a flux. The molten metal drawn off at the bottom is poured into the molds by means of cup-shaped ladles fitted with long handles, one of which has a cross bar for tipping the ladle in pouring, or, for larger work, by means of ladles carried on wheels or by cranes and tipped by gears.

Mixing Iron for Foundry Cupolas. Almost all foundry mixtures are made up of new iron with varying proportions of cheaper metal, such as the " return scrap " from the foundry, cast-iron or steel scrap purchased outside, etc. The uncertainty of analysis of

---

* See p. 481 of J. E. Johnson's The Principles, Operation, and Products of the Blast Furnace.

outside scrap, and the circumstance that it has undergone at least once the chemical changes due to melting, is the chief bar to its use in greater proportions. From 10 to 90 per cent of iron scrap is commonly used in foundry cupolas, depending upon market prices and the grade of iron to be made. Perhaps 25 per cent of scrap will approximate the average proportion used in America. The proportion of steel scrap will depend on the grade of iron to be made. The more the steel, the closer the grain of the castings made, and the greater the strength. The analysis of steel may be taken as about 0.15 per cent Si, 0.08 per cent S, 0.08 per cent P, and negligible proportions of other elements. Scrap from alloy steels, such as nickel, manganese, chromium, etc., should be avoided. In cupola melting, the sulfur content of the metal will increase from 0.025 to 0.065 per cent, depending upon the proportion of coke used in the charges and the percentage of sulfur in the coke; that is, a mixture estimated to contain 0.030 per cent S may contain after melting from 0.055 to 0.095 per cent. On the other hand, the silicon in the mixture will decrease by from 0.25 to 0.40 per cent during melting, so that a mixture estimated to contain 2.25 per cent Si will have only 2.00 to 1.85 per cent after melting. The better the practice, the less will be the silicon loss.

Mixing is customarily regulated by the silicon and sulfur desired in the castings. From the analyses of the pig iron available for use (see Table I), from the estimated analysis of the scrap, and from known experience of the increase of sulfur and loss of silicon during melting (which each foundry must determine for itself), the charges are made up to produce the desired result.

Addition of Ferrosilicon in the Ladle. The silicon content of the castings may be increased by adding some 50 per cent ferrosilicon to the metal in the ladle, which must have a slight excess of heat to melt the ferrosilicon. The full amount of silicon thus added will not necessarily be found in the castings, as some is oxidized by the oxygen of the air and some by the oxide in the metal.

Addition of Soda Ash in the Ladle. Beginning about 1929, iron foundries began the use of soda ash in the ladle of melted iron. By means of this flux the sulfur may be reduced as much as from 0.10 to 0.05 per cent in the cast iron.

Addition of Calcium Silicide in the Ladle. A commercial alloy of calcium and silicon may be used instead of ferrosilicon. It is said that the calcium will carry away some sulfur and oxygen while the silicon will help to remove oxygen and then increase the silicon in the metal. The vendors furnish the analysis of the alloy.

Air Furnace Melting. Castings very low in sulfur cannot be made from cast iron melted in cupolas, and the analysis also is likely to vary from hour to hour. Cast iron of the most delicate specifications, therefore, customarily is melted in a so-called air furnace which is similar to a puddling furnace. This is especially true of iron for chilling purposes, which must be closely limited in composition, and of iron for making malleable-iron castings. Also, for a very large casting, required to be of exactly the same chemical composition throughout, the metal is melted in the air furnace, and all tapped out at one time, instead of in a thin and continuous stream of some hours' duration, as from the cupola.

Innovations in Furnaces. Better control of the cupola operation has done much to prolong its activity in foundry practice, but it is not, at best, a perfect melting instrument. Its chief claim to usefulness is its low cost of installation and operation. Only in those rare cases when it is operated with judgment and skill does it perform satisfactorily as to temperature, uniformity of composition of product, and control. As a means of producing the new type of cast iron with very high strength, and of producing alloy cast irons, it is only partially and occasionally successful. One method of meeting this situation has been by supplanting the cupola with an electrically heated "forehearth" into which the cupola metal is tapped, and in which the metal is heated to the desired temperature for casting. Desulfurizing with soda ash, or a similar flux, is also sometimes practised in the forehearth. Many foundries have abandoned the cupola for making the best quality of cast iron and do all this work in electric furnaces, of which the Detroit rocking furnace is one of the commonest installations. Superheating cast iron just previous to casting into molds seems to produce a greater number of small and widely disseminated particles of graphite which give the metal 50 to 100 per cent greater strength than the same metal having the graphite in the usual type of flakes. It is thought that this result is brought about by the graphite precipitating in the freezing mass on a large number of nuclei. It is claimed by the Detroit Furnace Co. that the agitation given to the iron in the rocking furnace has the effect of still further increasing the number of nuclei for precipitation. The electric furnace, or the electric forehearth, seems to be almost essential for the manufacture of alloy cast irons, which are non-uniform in composition if the alloying metal or metals are added in the cupola, and are chilled too much if they are added in the ladle.

Definitions Relating to Cast Iron. *Fracture.* A freshly broken surface.

Gray Iron. Pig iron or cast iron whose fracture has a gray color due to precipitated carbon, e.g., graphite.

White Iron. Pig iron or cast iron whose fracture is white.

Mottled Iron. Pig iron or cast iron whose fracture is white with gray spots, or gray with white spots.

Chilled Iron. Pig iron or cast iron which would be gray if slowly cooled, but which has been rapidly cooled, so that the chilled surfaces are white and the interior and other surfaces are gray in color. The white surfaces are very hard, and resist wear and abrasion; the gray parts are relatively tough, and soft so that they may be machined, if desired.

"Black-Heart" Iron. Malleable cast iron whose fracture had a very dark gray, or black, color in the center, due to precipitated carbon in particles of very small size. The outer rim may be white in color, owing to removal of carbon in the annealing process.

Effect of Carbon on Cast Iron. The amount of carbon in cast iron is largely dependent on the presence of other elements. While 4 per cent is the ordinary maximum, the carbon may run as high as 7 per cent if much manganese is present. The presence of silicon in large proportions, on the other hand, may reduce the solubility of the carbon to as low as 1 per cent. The percentage of carbon present in cast iron in the combined form influences very largely the physical properties of the cast iron; thus, to get the maximum tensile strength, the combined carbon should be about 0.47 per cent; for the maximum transverse strength it should be about 0.70 per cent; and for the maximum crushing strength it should be above 1 per cent. The hardness of cast iron increases regularly with the increase in the percentage of combined carbon. In gray iron the carbon exists almost wholly as graphite, having been precipitated as such in the process of solidifying. The graphite, known as "kish," gives the iron a somewhat spongy nature and a dark color. The condition is brought about in part by slow cooling, which tends to produce large crystals as well as graphite carbon. In white iron the carbon is almost wholly combined and the iron has a more homogeneous texture and lighter appearance, and is composed of smaller crystals. Rapid cooling in solidifying tends to produce white iron. In mottled iron the proportions of combined and graphite iron are nearly equal, the fracture having, as the name indicates, a mottled appearance, due to the dark gray portions in the white matrix. Graphite decreases strength, increases porosity, and increases permeability to gases or liquids under pressure, but too much lowering of graphite means increasing the combined carbon to the point where strength is lowered and brittleness becomes dangerous.

Effect of Silicon on Cast Iron. A few tenths of 1 per cent of silicon has a direct effect of its own in increasing the strength and density of iron, but usually there must be from 0.75 to 2.50 per cent of silicon in iron castings, not for its direct effect, but for its effect on promoting the presence of graphite. Without this amount of silicon most of the carbon in the cast iron would be in the combined form. The rôle of silicon, therefore, is that of a graphite-producer. But, after the silicon exceeds about 3.0 to 3.5 per cent, its effect in promoting graphite seems to decrease, and cast iron with 4 or 5 per cent of silicon is nearer white again.

Effect of Sulfur on Cast Iron. The action of sulfur on the carbon is almost exactly opposite to that of silicon, but some 15 times as powerful, so that 0.01 per cent of sulfur will counteract the graphite-producing effect of 0.15 per cent of silicon. Sulfur also has a bad effect on cast iron in that it increases "dirtiness," segregation, and liability to "checking" in cooling. It also causes "red shortness," i.e., brittleness when in a heated condition. If possible the sulfur content should be below 0.05 per cent. Sulfur comes from the fuel and increases in the cast iron every time it is melted. The necessary use of scrap tends to build up sulfur in castings, and cast iron of second quality often contains above 0.10 per cent of sulfur. This means that more silicon must be used to keep combined carbon down and promote graphite formation.

Effect of Phosphorus on Cast Iron. The effect of phosphorus is to increase the fusibility and fluidity of the metal. It also causes the iron casting to retain for some time the pasty stage during solidification. This has the effect of decreasing density, bringing the graphite out in relatively large flakes, and of decreasing shrinkage by increasing the expansion during solidification. It is therefore used up to 1.5 per cent in castings which need to be very fluid when poured, as for example in ornamental castings where well-defined impressions are wanted. Phosphorus also tends to increase the brittleness of the iron.

Effect of Manganese on Cast Iron. Manganese must always be present in cast iron to the extent of at least twice the sulfur, in order that all the sulfur shall be in the form of MnS, rather than FeS. This lessens the bad effects of sulfur. Beyond this point the manganese in excess of that present as MnS makes harder and more brittle white cast iron.

It tends to fine the grain, slightly strengthen the casting, and keep carbon in the combined form. *Spiegeleisen*, so called on account of its white, glistening fracture, is a pig iron containing a large proportion of manganese (see Table I, p. 11–13). It is very hard, resisting cutting by cast-steel tools. If the proportion of manganese rises above 20 per cent, reaching sometimes as high as 80 per cent, it is known as *ferromanganese*.

Shrinkage of Cast Iron During Cooling. In cooling, white cast iron and steel shrink about twice as much as gray cast iron. Gray cast iron shrinks the same as the others in one respect, but its shrinkage is counteracted by an expansion which occurs because of the separation of graphite. Thus, during the solidification period, graphite separates and makes room for itself by pushing the crystals of metal apart. A decided expansion of gray iron castings is therefore noted during freezing. Subsequently the iron contracts, but, on cooling to the line *PSK* (Fig. 3), more graphite separates, and temporarily the contraction is much lessened. On this account, pattern-makers are accustomed to allow a shrinkage of $1/8$ in. per ft for gray cast iron, and $1/4$ in. per ft for white cast iron and steel.

"Chilling" Cast Iron. Cast iron rapidly cooled will retain the carbon in solution, unless the silicon be too high. This gives white cast iron instead of gray cast iron. Advantage is taken of this by using metal molds, thus producing a sudden cooling of the hot metal as it comes in contact with the comparatively cold surface of the mold. Such castings will have a white surface and gray interior. The less brittle interior protects the casting from breaking under shock, which it would do if it were white throughout, while the hardness of the surface resists wear. In this way is obtained a chilled tread on railroad freight-car wheels, to resist the wear against the rails, with a less brittle flange to resist the shocks of service. Likewise, a chilled surface on crushing rolls, with a less brittle interior, is obtained. The silicon must be high enough to give gray iron in the part which is cooled slowly through the range of solidification (freezing), but not high enough to cause the formation of graphite in the chilled surfaces.

"Growth" of Cast Iron. Cast iron subjected to long-continued temperatures of 500 deg fahr or above tends to separate out graphite. This causes an expansion of the casting, and, if repeated many times, will deform and ruin it. This becomes serious when using cast-iron fittings for superheated steam, which is often above 500 deg fahr. Any influence in the iron, such as the presence of silicon, which tends to cause graphite precipitation, will increase the difficulty; steel, and white cast iron low in silicon, which do not easily precipitate graphite, are relatively free from it.

Properties of Cast Iron. The strength of cast iron depends chiefly on the strength of the metallic matrix of the iron and the resistance which the metal part opposes to strain. If the graphite flakes are almost continuous, fracture will occur by splitting apart the graphite sheets; on the other hand, if the matrix structure is so built as to oppose strain with the maximum proportion of metallic part of the iron, and if the metallic portion is strong by virtue of containing 0.85 per cent of combined carbon, then high strength is obtained. On the basis of this reasoning, there was first developed in Germany a so-called " pearlitic cast iron " (pearlite is that structure in steel consisting of all small crystals of Fe_3C and containing 0.85 per cent of carbon). In this and other " high-strength " cast irons, ease of fracture through graphite flakes was lessened by:

1. Reducing the amount of total carbon in the iron.
2. Reducing the size of the graphite flakes by increasing their number. This is done chiefly by superheating the iron before casting. This apparently results in the graphite precipitating during freezing, and later, around a large number of isolated nuclei, instead of a few widely separated nuclei upon which the flakes continue to grow. The superheating may be done in a cupola, or, better, in an electric furnace. It is said that agitating the iron before casting further increases the number of nuclei.
3. Distributing the graphite as uniformly as possible.

By these methods there has been developed a " high-strength carbon cast iron " which has a tensile strength of 35,000 to 55,000 lb per sq in., as compared with a previous maximum of about 30,000 lb. This cast iron also has a slight ductility as measured by the elongation before rupture.

Table IV, p. 11–25, gives some of the properties of gray cast iron and high-strength cast iron.

Alloy Cast Iron. The same result in a more intense degree has been achieved by adding nickel up to 1.50 per cent and chromium up to 0.50 per cent or else molybdenum from 0.50 to 1.50 per cent. By these alloying elements cast iron having uniformly tensile strengths of 70,000 lb per sq in. can be made. The chief objections to them is not the cost of the alloy additions, but the difficulty of using a cupola for melting them (unless an electric " forehearth " receives the cupola metal and superheats it when the alloying elements are added), and the presence of the alloying metals in the " return scrap."

Non-magnetic Cast Iron. By adding at least 7 per cent of manganese, or 20 per cent of nickel, or a corresponding amount of some other alloying element, or elements, a cast iron may be produced which is a solid solution at atmospheric temperature. It is sometimes called "austenitic cast iron," because austenite is the name given to the solid solution of iron and carbon. It is approximately as non-magnetic as copper, and is used for parts of electrical machinery.

Heat-treated Cast Iron. Cast iron is heat-treated to make it soft even when the combined carbon is as high as 0.85 per cent. For this purpose it is best to use a long anneal at a low temperature (in the neighborhood of 500 deg fahr), or it may be much lessened in strength. On the other hand, it may be cooled with moderate rapidity from a yellow heat, in order to make the grains of the metallic part very small, or it may even be quenched (if the shape permits) to make it hard.

Malleable Cast Iron. For many years, cast iron with small, isolated graphite flakes has been manufactured by the so-called malleable cast-iron process. In this process, iron castings, usually thin, are first cooled so as to produce white cast iron with the carbon all in combination. This white iron is hard, not easily worked, and brittle. The castings are then heated to about 1650 deg fahr and " soaked " there for several hours, or even for several days, and then cooled slowly. By this operation the combined carbon is reduced almost to zero, and the graphite is precipitated from Fe_3C as small flakes of what is called " temper carbon." This is the fundamental mechanism of the process, but it may be further refined by packing the white castings in iron oxide, so that the carbon when it is precipitated from Fe_3C is oxidized to CO and separates from the metal, reducing the total carbon from perhaps 3.50 per cent to perhaps 2.50 per cent. On the skin of the castings the carbon may be almost completely removed, leaving tiny holes or pores in the metal. The castings have a tensile strength of at least 50,000 lb per sq in. and an elongation of at least 10 per cent in 2 in. Some of the properties of a representative cast iron are given in Table IV, p. 11–25. They are easily machined, may be deformed without rupture, will withstand heavy blows, and the skin will endure much battering without cracking.

Use of Cast Iron and Malleable Cast Iron. The improvement in the manufacture of steel castings has limited the field of commercial employment of iron and malleable-iron castings, but cast iron is still employed wherever weight or compressive strength of a casting is the controlling factor, and where as a structural part for a machine or building it does not have to withstand shock, tensile stress, or bending. Iron castings have the advantage of being capable of manufacture with simple apparatus right in the field, remote from centers of civilization. Malleable cast iron was losing some of its trade, but recent great improvements in qualities have enabled it to hold its own and even extend its field for castings of small size, where moderate tensile strength, small ductility, and slight bending are required. It has the advantage over steel of better resistance to shocks within the limit of its strength. For pipe fittings, household hardware, and many small or thin articles, it can excel steel castings in price, and give all that is necessary in service. Chilled cast iron is the cheapest very hard material that is made; for resisting wear and affording a useful amount of strength it is unexcelled, and it finds a large field in railroad freight-car wheels, rolls with hard surface, parts of crushing machinery, inserts in brake shoes, etc.

8. WROUGHT IRON

If commercial iron is mechanically mixed with a suitable amount of slag there results a malleable material called wrought iron which does not harden when suddenly cooled. It melts at a full white heat, but becomes pasty at a lower temperature, in which condition it can be readily welded. It is ductile when cold.

Process of Manufacture. Practically all wrought iron is produced from pig iron by indirect processes, although direct processes for production from the ore exist. The direct process has always proved a commercial failure, although tried in almost every conceivable manner and locality. The indirect processes may be divided into two general classes based upon the type of furnace used: (a) reverberatory or puddling furnaces; and (b) charcoal hearths. The best iron is made upon hearths, but puddling furnaces produce the larger quantity. The essential difference between the two processes is that in hearths the chief source of oxidation is atmospheric air, and the fuel is burned in contact with the iron, whereas in puddling furnaces the chief source of oxygen is magnetic oxide of iron, and the fuel is burned in a chamber separate from that containing the iron. A description of these processes follows.

Puddling. This method consists of melting pig iron in a reverberatory furnace heated either by coal or natural gas. The furnace hearth is lined with oxide of iron. The pig is exposed for about 2 hours to the continuous action of a flame hot enough to melt it but not hot enough to keep pure iron in a molten state. When purified by the iron oxide and the oxidizing flame, the molten iron becomes less fusible and finally pasty. After reaching this condition it is puddled by being worked into balls by hand labor. It is then taken from the furnace and squeezed or hammered into blooms, and then rolled into small bars, about $3/4$ in. thick and from 2 to 6 in. wide, called " muck bars." After cooling, these muck bars are cut into short pieces about 2 ft in length, piled into bundles, fastened by iron wire, reheated to welding heat, and rerolled into merchant bars. If the iron is subjected to a second piling, heating, and rerolling, it is called " double refined iron."

Charcoal Hearths. The following are the more important hearth processes.

1. *Finery Process.* Charcoal fineries produce " knobbled " iron of a high degree of softness which is much used for boiler tubes.

In the finery process the pig iron is first melted down in a coke or charcoal refinery to remove the silicon, phosphorus, and sulfur, and is then transferred in a molten condition to a charcoal hearth which is still hot from its previous charge. Damp charcoal is thrown in, a low-pressure, unheated blast turned on, and the metal agitated to keep it in contact with the blast. After an hour or more the metal is collected into a ball and hammered to remove some of the slag, cut up, and reheated in piles. Gray iron may be used in this process.

2. *Walloon Process.* The Walloon process was formerly used in Sweden for producing wrought iron from Dannemora pig iron, the resulting product being shipped to England, particularly to Sheffield, for conversion into blister steel for use in fine toolmaking.

In the Walloon process long pigs are melted gradually by being pushed forward into a charcoal fire. The molten iron drops through the blast, becoming decarburized, and collects in a pasty mass at the bottom of the furnace. The partially refined iron is then raised to the top of the charcoal fire, and melted down with the addition of rich slag and hammer scale. The metal is then balled, reheated, and hammered.

3. *Lancashire Process.* The Lancashire process is used principally in Sweden, but was formerly used in the United States.

The Lancashire process somewhat resembles the Walloon process. Pig iron is melted between two layers of charcoal, the liquid dropping down through the blast and becoming oxidized. The molten metal collects in a pasty mass at the furnace bottom where it is allowed to remain for 20 or 25 minutes; it is then mixed with decarburizing slag and remelted in a similar manner. Finally the pasty mass is removed from the hearth and hammered.

4. *Aston Process.* A newer method of manufacturing wrought iron on a large scale has been developed in which refined iron is poured into molten slag. A sponge ball is formed which is compressed and worked by mechanical devices until the right consistency is obtained. The sponge ball is then formed into the usual wrought-iron shapes. The process lends itself to control of quality and more uniformity of product.

Grades. Wrought iron may be graded as follows: (1) charcoal iron, the purest grade of wrought iron; (2) puddled iron, classified according to quality into stay-bolt (grade A) and merchant iron, grades B and C; (3) busheled scrap, a heterogeneous product made from iron scrap—steel is frequently mixed with the iron scrap, causing considerable irregularity in the resulting product.

Properties. Wrought iron possesses the important qualities of toughness, ductility, malleability, and weldability, but its properties are only slightly changed by tempering.

Coefficient of expansion............ 0.00000648 per deg fahr (Clarke)
Electrical conductivity......... 0.16 (Cu=1.00) (Lazare Weiler)
Melting temperature.......... 2732 to 2912 deg fahr (Pouillet, Claudel, Wilson)
Specific heat................. 0.1138 g-cal per g per deg cent, Btu per lb per deg fahr (Röntgen)
Specific gravity............... 7.4 to 7.9 (Kent)

Tension. The average results of a great many tensile tests made at the Testing Laboratory of Columbia University on good wrought iron for general purposes are as follows:

Yield point, lb per sq in.................................... 31,000
Ultimate strength, lb per sq in............................. 51,000
Elongation in 8 in., per cent................................ 21
Reduction in area, per cent................................. 30
Modulus of elasticity, lb per sq in.......................... 28,200,000

Shear and Torsion. J. Platt and R. F. Hayward (*Proc. Inst. C.E.*, Vol. 90) give the following values for " crown " best wrought iron which had an ultimate tensile strength of 48,400 lb per sq in.:

Ultimate strength in single shear, lb per sq in................ 42,050
Elastic limit in torsion, lb per sq in........................ 20,530
Modulus of elasticity in torsion, lb per sq in................ 12,800,000

Compression. The ultimate compressive strength of good wrought iron is not well defined. Practically, its yield point in compression should be considered as the ultimate for compression. This yield point is about the same as the yield point in tension.

The strength of wrought iron is affected by its chemical composition and the mechanical work and heat treatment it has undergone, and it also varies for different temperatures. Wrought iron has a well-defined yield point in both tension and compression, which is from 2000 to 4000 lb per sq in. higher than the elastic limit. Beyond the yield point wrought iron is a plastic material which flows rapidly as the maximum strength is approached. The ultimate strength in tension increases with the amount of carbon, which, however, is rarely greater than $1/10$ of 1 per cent. The strength of iron entirely free from carbon and phosphorus is probably between 39,000 and 40,000 lb per sq in.

Effect on Wrought Iron of Its Common Ingredients. Carbon, sulfur, phosphorus, and oxygen all reduce the softness, malleability, and resistance to rusting of wrought iron. Slag is believed to protect the enveloped grains of wrought iron from rusting, but its presence increases the differences of electric potential between the microscopic particles and, to this extent, increases the rate of rusting. This is presumably the reason why wrought iron corrodes faster in acid waters than does low-carbon steel free from solid particles.

Effect of Reheating and Rerolling. Within limits, puddled iron is much improved in quantity by being cut up, piled, reheated, and rerolled or hammered. However, it is found that only in special cases is it advantageous to reheat puddled iron more than twice. The following figures (Johnson) show the effect of reheating and rerolling on the tensile strength: The original bar had a tensile strength of 43,900 lb per sq in.; after the second working this rose to 52,860 lb per sq in., and after the sixth working it became 61,820 lb per sq in.; the tensile strength then diminished with the number of workings until after the twelfth working it became the same as that of the original bar.

Effect of Work on Wrought Iron. Mechanical treatment is important for wrought iron not only to refine the grain, but also to distribute the metal and slag and produce the so-called fibrous structure characteristic of wrought iron.

9. HIGH-PURITY IRON

Iron containing less than 0.10 per cent of total impurities has been produced by two chief methods: namely, electrolysis and extensive refinement in an open-hearth furnace. Representative analyses of these products are given in Table II.

Manufacture of Armco Ingot Iron. Using selected raw materials, the usual basic open-hearth process is employed, with the addition of a final period of superpurification during which additions of pure iron oxide to the slag reduce the carbon and manganese to below 0.02 per cent each. The resulting iron is heavily charged with oxide, which is reduced by the use of pig iron in the furnace and aluminum in the ladle.

Table II. Analyses of High-purity Iron

	Armco Ingot Iron %	Electrolytic Iron %
Carbon.............	0.012 *	0.006 *
Manganese.........	0.017 *	0.000 *
Phosphorus........	0.005 *	0.005 *
Sulfur.............	0.025 *	0.004 *
Silicon............	Trace *	0.005 *
Iron (about)........	99.9	99.95

* National Metals Handbook, 1933 Edition, p. 367.

Manufacture of Electrolytic Iron. Anodes are commonly ingot iron, soft steel, or pig iron. Electrolytes are usually ferrous chloride, with sometimes calcium chloride, and a trace of free acid, at a temperature of 15 to 90 deg cent, and either circulated or mechanically stirred. The cathodes are generally rotating mandrels or moving plates. The current density is variously from 12 to 75 amp per sq ft and the voltage drop about 3 to 4 volts per cell. The deposited metal is usually annealed to remove hydrogen and chlorides, which latter, if present, cause rusting. It is often vacuum melted.

Properties and Uses. See Table IV, p. 11–25, for some of the properties of electrolytic and ingot irons. High-purity iron is valued for its toughness, ductility, lessened activity in rusting, and high electrical and magnetic properties. Application of these advantages has been made in the use of Armco ingot iron for holding or transporting water, both hot and cold, as in factory and house boilers and heating systems, culverts, fumes, gutters, wire fences, welding electrodes of high ductility, etc. Attempts to make and sell iron of greater purity than Armco ingot iron have been successful technically, and commercially for a time, but have endured only in a few special cases, because the increase in usefulness as superior properties are achieved is not sufficient to command an adequate market at the higher price necessary. For some years the improved magnetic properties of iron of 99.9 per cent purity over that of only 99.80 per cent were sufficient to support the manufacture of electrolytic iron at more than double the price. Table III gives some comparative figures. But, after the introduction of permalloy and similar alloys of very high permeability, the commercial manufacture of electrolytic iron for this purpose ceased. Electrolytic iron, because of its softness, can be used in place of copper for projectile bands, etc., and was so used in Germany during the World War. It is still used for iron plates of great toughness, which are plated first with nickel and then with chromium, for printing plates in the U. S. Bureau of Engraving. At one time it was made commercially for the production of very thin-walled tubes with high heat conductivity. Ingot iron stands severe bending, and lends itself to rapid and economical fabrication. Hot working of steel can in many cases be displaced by cold working of pure iron. It constitutes an excellent base for vitreous enameling. Its electrical properties of high conductivity, high permeability, and low retentivity have made it useful in the electrical field for pole-pieces, magnet cores and shoes, and in the form of wire for solenoids, induction coils, telephone repeater coils, audio transformers, vibrator coils, rail bonds, and transmission lines.

Table III. Magnetic Properties of High-purity Iron
National Metals Handbook, 1933 Edition, p. 387

	Maximum Permeability	Coercive Force, oersted	Hysteresis Loss, ergs per cu cm per cycle	Residual Induction, gauss	Saturation, gauss
Iron A............	180,000	0.025 †	190 †		
Iron B............	9,500	0.9 *	2690 *		
Iron C............	20,000	0.08 *		6000 *	22,000
Iron D ‡.........	61,000	0.09 *	300 *		

Iron A, hydrogen annealed ingot iron; Iron B, annealed ingot iron; Iron C, iron by the carbonyl process; Iron D, annealed vacuum fused electrolytic iron.

* For B_m 10,000.
† For B_m 14,000.
‡ From The Metal Iron, by H. E. Cleaves and J. G. Thompson, 1935, McGraw-Hill.

10. KINDS OF STEEL

Steel was originally produced by the action of a hot fire directly on iron ore and the addition of carbon to the iron so produced. The modern processes, however, involve the fusion of the ore. The United States law defines steel as iron which is produced by fusion by any process, and which is malleable when first produced. The technical definition is that steel is iron containing up to 1.7 per cent of carbon and not containing admixed slag. The following is a rough comparison of properties of cast iron, steel and wrought iron.

	Per Cent of Carbon	Specific Gravity	Properties
Cast iron........	5 to 2	7.2	Not malleable, not temperable
Steel...........	1.50 to 0.02	7.8	Malleable and temperable
Wrought iron....	0.15 to 0.05	7.7	Malleable, not temperable, contains slag

It should be observed that the percentage of carbon alone is not sufficient to distinguish steel from wrought iron; also, that the mean values of specific gravity stated are in each case subject to considerable variation; further, only the hard steels (carbon above 0.50 per cent) are much affected by tempering, the softer grades resembling wrought iron.

Manufacture. The three principal methods of manufacturing steel are the Bessemer process, the open-hearth process, and the electric-furnace process. A combination method known as the *duplex process* is sometimes used. In this process the refining action is started in a Bessemer converter, and after partial refining the molten steel is transferred to an open-hearth furnace, where the refining process is finished. Formerly, a method known as the crucible process was commonly used.

Bessemer Steel is made in a Bessemer furnace or converter, which is a pear-shaped vessel lined with firebrick or its equivalent, and which can be rotated on trunnions, to receive and discharge metal. It will hold from 10 to 25 tons of liquid iron in the lower end, in a bath about 20 in. deep. During the " blow," the converter stands vertically, the melted pig iron lying in a pool at the lower end. Through this pool several thousand cubic feet of unheated, atmospheric air is blown per minute. The oxygen of the air first burns away the silicon and manganese, then the carbon, and before the carbon is entirely burned away, begins to burn the iron. Spiegeleisen or ferromanganese is then added to deoxidize the metal and to give it the amount of carbon desired in the finished steel. In the ordinary or "acid" Bessemer process the lining of the converter is a silicious material. This necessitates using an acid (silicious) slag in the process, so that phosphorus cannot be removed from the charge. In the "basic," or Thomas-Gilchrist, process, the lining is of magnesium limestone, and limestone additions are made to the bath, thereby producing and maintaining a basic slag, into which phosphorus will enter if oxidized. Basic Bessemer steel is not made in the United States.

Open-hearth Steel may be made from either: all steel scrap, or all pig iron from which the silicon, manganese, carbon, with perhaps phosphorus and some sulfur, are removed by oxidation with iron ore. In most cases, a mixture of steel scrap with pig iron and iron ore is used as raw material. The furnace is a reverberatory furnace heated by preheated air and by the burning of preheated gas, oil (or tar), or, rarely, pulverized coal. Because of the preheated flame producer, the furnace can melt, or keep melted, the purest forms of iron. After the charge is melted and brought to the proper temperature for casting, its chemical composition is adjusted with suitable additions of carbon, manganese, and silicon, together with alloying elements, such as nickel, chromium, vanadium, etc., when ordered. It is then tapped into a ladle and thence into molds. The raw steel scrap of the process is added in the solid condition, but pig iron is often added molten from a nearby blast furnace. In the Talbot modification of the process, melted blown metal from a Bessemer converter is used instead of cold steel scrap. The blown metal is chemically about the same as steel scrap. In this case the furnace is not drained of metal when tapped, but a reservoir of liquid steel is left for a foundation for a new charge of melted pig iron and melted blown metal. In the so-called Duplex process, blown metal from an acid Bessemer converter is poured into a basic-lined open-hearth furnace. In the Bessemer converter, the silicon, manganese, and carbon are oxidized out of the pig iron, after which the phosphorus, and some sulfur, are removed in the basic open-hearth furnace. The open-hearth process may be either basic or acidic, according to the character of the lining, which also determines the character of the slag utilized in the process. Phosphorus will be oxidized in either type of furnace, but only a basic slag will absorb phosphorus; therefore the basic process is the type usually employed, since raw material either high or low in phosphorus may be purified. The basic slag has the objection that it leaves more oxygen in the finished steel, with the result that basic steel may contain more dissolved oxygen and oxides (so-called "inclusions"); acid steel is often preferred, especially where service under "fatigue" conditions is anticipated.

Electric Furnace Steel is made either in an arc or resistance type of furnace. The resistance type of furnace generates a current of electricity in the steel bath either with a "primary" alternating current using an iron core in the conventional method, or with a high-frequency alternating current without a core. In either case, the liquid metal is heated by virtue of the resistance of the metal to the passage of the current induced in it. The greatest tonnage of steel is made in the arc type of furnace, but the high-frequency induction type makes much of the alloy steel. Some large steel-making furnaces are of the cored induction type.

Electric-arc Furnace. The operation and design of the electric arc furnaces are similar to those of fuel-fired furnaces, except that the arc, instead of a flame, heats the charge. One great advantage of electric heat is that, since the charge is out of contact with products of combustion, the furnace atmosphere may be neutral or reducing, if desired, whereas the atmosphere of a combustion furnace is always oxidizing. Heat from an electric arc can be used more economically at very high temperatures, e.g., the refining stages of steel production, than at low temperatures. The electric arc furnace is therefore sometimes used for "super-refining," that is, for the final stages of desulfurization and deoxidation of liquid steel from a basic open-hearth furnace.

The High-frequency Electric Furnace consists of a crucible in sizes from 600 lb to 5 tons each, in whose contents is induced a "secondary" current by a primary current of relatively high frequency traversing a coil encircling the crucible. This has all the advantages of the old crucible process and two advantages in addition: It may be made in sizes larger than the 100-lb maximum of the crucible process, and the "motor effect" produced by the current gives to the bath a stirring action which is almost invaluable in steel manufacture. This type of furnace is used very largely for the melting of alloy steel scrap. Stainless steel, high-speed steel, and even steel containing vanadium may be melted with loss of none, or very little, of the costly alloying elements. In Europe it is used somewhat for the refining of pig iron, giving a rapid reaction on account of the stirring action, which promotes extensive contact between metal and oxidizing slag. The electrical efficiency of this type of furnace is lower than that of the arc type, but, on the other hand, its loss of heat by radiation is less.

Crucible Steel is commonly made in pots or crucibles holding about 100 lb of metal. The raw material should be wrought iron with charcoal, or pure cast iron. Other mixtures which will produce a steel having the desired chemical composition make inferior crucible steel. Manganese in some form is usually added to remove oxides from the iron. Some silicon is usually absorbed from the crucible, and carbon also if the crucible is made of graphite and clay. The crucible being covered, the steel is not affected by the oxygen or sulfur in the flame. The quality of crucible steel depends on the freedom from objectionable elements, such as phosphorus, on the complete removal of oxide, slag, and blowholes by "dead-melting" or "killing" before pouring, and on the kind and quantity of different elements, such as carbon, manganese, chromium, tungsten, and vanadium, which are added in the mixture, or after melting, to give particular qualities to the steel. Only minor amounts of crucible steel are produced in the United States today (1936).

How to Distinguish between Acid and Basic Steel. (This does not include acid and basic electric steel.) Acid open-hearth or Bessemer steel may be distinguished from basic steel by being lower in manganese, sonims, and oxygen, but higher in silicon, phosphorus, and sulfur. It also dissolves more slowly in dilute sulfuric and hydrochloric acids. Comparisons should be made by experts, because the exact figures will depend on the country of manufacture and the purpose for which the steel is supplied.

How to Distinguish between Basic Open-hearth and Acid Bessemer Steel. Basic open-hearth steel has lower manganese, silicon, phosphorus, and sulfur and higher sonims and oxygen than acid Bessemer steel. It dissolves more rapidly in dilute acids. For the same tensile strength the ductility of basic open-hearth steel will exceed that of Bessemer steel, except sometimes in castings.

How to Distinguish between Acid Open-hearth and Bessemer Steel. Acid open-hearth steel will have fewer sonims, less oxygen and manganese than acid or basic Bessemer steel, and less phosphorus than acid Bessemer steel.

How to Identify Electric Steel. Electric steel may easily be distinguished from open-hearth and Bessemer steels. It has fewer sonims, manganese is under 0.40 per cent, usually less sulfur (e.g., under 0.03 per cent); it has higher elongation and reduction of area for the same tensile strength than any steel except crucible, and it dissolves much more slowly in dilute sulfuric and hydrochloric acid than basic open-hearth steel, which alone equals it in low phosphorus.

11. EFFECT OF COMMON INGREDIENTS ON THE PROPERTIES OF STEEL

The Properties of Steel most commonly desired are strength and ductility. Unfortunately there is more or less incompatibility between these two. That is to say, as the strength of steel increases, the ductility usually decreases; and, conversely, as the ductility increases, the strength usually decreases. Other properties of steel that are likewise of importance, either because they are desired or not desired, are hardness, ability to be machined, brittleness, electric conductivity, magnetic permeability, magnetic hysteresis, permanent magnetism, and weldability. Table IV gives some of the properties of hot-worked carbon steel. Pure iron has a tensile strength of about 40,000 lb per sq in., when in its softest condition, at which the ductility is great, being approximately equal to that of copper, and the malleability is equal to or greater than that of copper. The strength of iron is increased by the presence of several ingredients customarily accompanying it in industrial use, but the most important strengthener is carbon, because this will increase its strength with the least decrease in ductility.

Effect of Carbon. The effect of increasing percentages of carbon on the physical properties of steel can be seen from Table IV.

Effect of Manganese. Manganese increases strength and hardness, decreases the content of oxygen, and lessens the bad effect of any oxygen or sulfur left in the steel.

Effect of Phosphorus. Phosphorus increases strength, brittleness, segregation, and fluidity when molten, and greatly decreases resistance to shock. It increases crystal size with normal heating.

Effect of Sulfur. Sulfur slightly increases the strength of steel, but it also makes it dirty, oxidized, segregated, brittle under shock, and with a tendency to crack at red heat, either when cooling (as in a casting), or when being rolled or forged. Sometimes the cracks are microscopic, but nevertheless they weaken the steel. When the manganese is at least twice the sulfur, the bad effect of the latter is lessened because then the sulfur is in a compound, MnS, instead of FeS.

Table IV. Some Properties of Hot-worked Steel and of Cast Irons

Name	Approximate Per Cent Carbon	Specific Gravity	Weight, lb per cu ft	Melting Point, deg fahr	Boiling Point, deg fahr	Average Coefficient of Expansion, per deg fahr $\times 10^{-6}$		Brinell Hardness
						68 to 572° F	68 to 1112° F	
Iron, 99.97% Fe......	0.01	7.87	491	2795	5792	7.4	8.2	50–90
Armco ingot iron *...	0.03	7.86	491	2790		7.17	8.17	58
Soft steel...........	0.10	7.85	490	2780 †		6.6 §		120
Structural steel.......	0.25	7.85	490	2765 †		7.22		150
Machinery steel......	0.40	7.84	489	2740 †		6.7	7.94	180
Spring steel..........	0.75	7.83	489	2700 †		6.47 §		240
Tool steel...........	0.90	7.82	488	2695 †		6.39 §		260
Gray cast iron.......	3.50	7.00 to 7.22	437 to 451	2000±‡		5.6 §		120–190
Strong gray cast iron.	3.50	7.22±	451	2050±		5.55 to 5.92		
High-strength cast iron	3.00	7.30±	456	2100±		5.6 to 5.92		
Alloy cast iron.......	2.75	7.35±	459	2100 to 2200		5.55 to 5.92		
Malleable cast iron...	2.50	7.42	463	2050		6.6		

Name	Approximate Per Cent Carbon	Ultimate Strength, lb per sq in.	Yield Strength, lb per sq in.	Elongation in 2 in., per cent	Reduction of Area, per cent	Modulus of Elasticity, lb per sq in	Brinell Hardness
Iron, 99.97% Fe......	0.01	40,000	20,000	40	80	29,700,000	50–90
Armco ingot iron *....	0.03	44,000‖	27,500‖	46		29,500,000	58
Soft steel...........	0.10	50,000	30,000	35	70	29,100,000	120
Structural steel.......	0.25	60,000	38,000	30	52	28,900,000	150
Machinery steel......	0.40	80,000	50,000	25	40	28,600,000	180
Spring steel..........	0.75	100,000	60,000	12	22	28,300,000	240
Tool steel...........	0.90	130,000	75,000	8	12	28,000,000	260
Gray cast iron.......	3.50	22,000	17,000±			13,000,000	120–190
Strong gray cast iron..	3.50	30,000	25,000±	**	**	14,000,000	
High-strength cast iron	3.00	50,000	42,000±	**	**	15,000,000	
Alloy cast iron.......	2.75	70,000		**	**	18,000,000	
Malleable cast iron...	2.50	54,000	36,000	18	22	25,000,000	

NOTE. The figures in this table are representative of the properties of steel in commercial shapes. Variations may be expected relative to size and shape. The values given are not suitable as a basis for purchase specifications as they are not assured minima.

* Contains less than 0.1 per cent total of carbon, manganese, sulfur, phosphorus, and silicon.
† Completion of melting.
‡ The melting point of cast iron varies greatly with its composition. It begins to melt at about the temperatures given, but is not completely melted until a temperature 200 to 300 deg fahr higher is reached.
§ Coefficient per deg fahr at 60 deg fahr.
‖ Figures supplied by manufacturer.
** Some of the strong cast irons (including alloy cast irons) have a measurable permanent elongation and reduction of area before breaking, such as a fraction of 1 per cent.

Effect of Copper. A small percentage of copper dissolves in steel and forms a solid solution. Copper increases the hardness of steel, and less than 1 per cent of copper is used to lessen the rusting or corrodibility of steel. It seems also to decrease segregation and make the grain size finer.

Effect of Silicon. Silicon increases strength and hardness and decreases ductility. The chief purpose of having silicon in steel is to increase the solvent power of the metal for gases, especially oxygen and carbon monoxide. This influence decreases the blow-holes in soft steel, but increases the volume of the pipe in ingots and castings. In castings, silicon of 0.20 to 0.40 per cent is often added for strength. Silicon increases crystal size.

Iron Oxides. Oxygen occurs in steel in three forms: CO, FeO, and, perhaps, Fe_2O_3. In any form its presence is harmful, producing brittleness in both hot and cold steel, besides causing liability to blowholes. There is probably no constituent more harmful to steel than oxygen, but unfortunately no satisfactory method has as yet been found (1936) of rapidly determining small traces of this gas. The effect of oxygen is somewhat similar to that of sulfur and, in common parlance, makes the steel " rotten."

Nitrogen and Hydrogen. Both nitrogen and hydrogen occur in steel, and one of the theories to explain the superiority of electric and crucible steels is based upon the relative freedom of these materials from the two gases. The amount of nitrogen and hydrogen present is usually very small. Hydrogen dissolves very easily in iron at a high temperature but is evolved in part as the metal cools. In order to obtain entire freedom, however, it is necessary to heat and cool several times in vacuo. Nitrogen is important in connection with arc welding, when a needle-like constituent appears, which is thought to be a crystal of iron nitride.

12. METALLOGRAPHY OF IRON AND STEEL

Microscopic Constituents of Iron and Steel. Iron and steel are not simple, homogeneous substances, like glass, but, like the crystalline rocks (granite, for example), are composed of grains and crystals of different constituents. Thus, there may be, in slowly cooled iron castings: crystals of graphite, cementite, ferrite, and pearlite. The strongest simple steel made (excluding alloy steels, etc.) consists entirely of pearlite. Not only the kinds of metaral, but also the size of the crystals in which they occur has a very important effect on the qualities of the material which they compose. Thus, large crystals of graphite, etc., indicate weak and non-ductile metal. There are also other constituents which appear under the microscope, such as silicide of iron, nitride of iron, and also minute particles of slag, oxides of iron, manganese, and silicon, sulfide of iron or manganese, carbide of manganese, etc.

Ferrite is pure iron. It is soft, ductile, malleable; it can stand a great amount of cold work without annealing; it is not strong. It has a tendency to form in rather large crystals during cooling from solidification, or from a high temperature. It will not harden on rapid cooling, and can be formed of small-sized crystals if heated to a bright red heat and cooled very rapidly. This greatly increases its strength. Wrought iron is some 90 per cent ferrite crystals enveloped in slag; ingot iron is 90 per cent ferrite and over; pure iron is 100 per cent ferrite. Some ferrite often occurs in cast iron, apparently by precipitation of cementite into graphite and ferrite. This precipitation is the normal reaction of the malleable cast-iron annealing process.

Ferrite has a greater electric conductivity than any of the other metarals in iron or steel. It is about 6 times as resistant as copper. Alpha ferrite is the most magnetic substance known, having the greatest magnetic force, greatest permeability, and lowest hysteresis, when measured at high, as well as low, magnetizing forces. Alpha ferrite has a body-centered cubic space lattice. At 1400 deg fahr it becomes paramagnetic. At 1670 deg fahr it changes to a face-centered cubic space lattice and is known as gamma iron, whose most distinguishing characteristic is that it will dissolve carbon up to a limit of 1.7 per cent. At 2550 deg fahr the space lattice again becomes body-centered and the iron is often called delta iron.

Cementite is carbide of iron, Fe_3C. Its hardness is 6 to 6.5 on Moh's scale, and U on the mineralogical scale. It will scratch glass, but not quartz. It is magnetic below 400 deg fahr. It occurs in flat crystals which decrease the tensile strength of iron and steel, but increase their hardness and cutting properties. It is present in goodly quantities in white cast iron.

Graphite is a great weakener, because it occurs in flat plates, themselves made up of smaller plates, which separate under strain and allow the piece to break. The larger the crystals of graphite the less the tensile strain it will withstand. When a piece of gray cast iron is broken, only the separated flakes of graphite along which the piece has broken, and which give the fracture its gray color, are seen.

Pearlite is an aggregate made of alternate crystals of ferrite and cementite. Its chief characteristic is the minute crystal size of the components. Pearlite has about 7 parts by weight of ferrite to 1 part of cementite, and therefore contains about 0.85 per cent of carbon. Steel of this carbon is the strongest simple steel known, doubtless because of the absence of large crystals of ferrite or of cementite. The reason for the occurrence of pearlite in steel is explained on p. 11–28 and Fig. 3.

Austenite is a solid solution of ferrite and cementite in each other. It forms when the metal solidifies, and remains a solution until it cools to about 1350 deg fahr. Theoretically the solution would remain if the iron or steel were cooled instantaneously from a bright red heat to atmospheric temperature, but, in practice, this degree of rapidity is impracticable, and only a portion of the austenite is preserved by rapid cooling. But 10 per cent of manganese and above in the steel will preserve austenite to temperatures below 0 deg fahr, as will 12 to 25 per cent of nickel. Austenite is non-magnetic; it resists wear, but is not brittle.

Martensite is the chief constituent of rapidly cooled steel. It is the imperfectly preserved austenite, which cannot be cooled rapidly enough to prevent some decomposition, but was not slowly cooled, so as to precipitate into pearlite with or without some excess ferrite or cementite. It is a common constituent of hardened steels, and may occur in cast iron which is cooled rapidly through the range of red heat. It is strong, hard, and brittle. It differs from austenite in being magnetic, but is not as much so as the same steel slowly cooled.

Sorbite is imperfectly resolved pearlite. That is, it is a step beyond martensite in the decomposition of the solid solution. The ferrite and cementite are not fully formed, but may be said to be in a preliminary state of precipitation. Sorbite has some of the strength of martensite and some of the ductility of fully precipitated steel. It is obtained by cooling steel with medium rapidity from the temperature where it is a solid solution to atmospheric temperature, or accomplishing a similar result by other means.

Sonims is the name given to solid, non-metallic impurities in iron and steel, including slag particles, sulfides of iron or manganese, oxides of iron, manganese, silicon, aluminum, etc., or dirt from ladle or furnace linings. Just as muddy water will not clear itself without standing quietly for a time, so these sonims will remain suspended in some steel baths or ingots until caught in the solidifying mass. The crucible and electric processes give the best opportunity for the metal to clarify itself. Sonims occur to a very harmful extent only as a result of bad practice in steel making, such as lack of care in adding oxidizing agents too near the end of the process, or adding deoxidizers in the ingots when the steel is too cold to allow oxide of aluminum, for example, to rise to the surface, etc.

Equilibrium Diagram of Iron and Steel. The constituents present in the form of crystals or grains in any series of alloys can be learned from a study of the so-called equilibrium diagram, such as that shown in Fig. 3. The iron-carbon alloys (like every other series of alloys) are in a condition of chemical solubility when liquid. Upon freezing, the first crystals are born as small solids within the liquid mass. These crystals may still preserve the condition of chemical solubility present in the liquid, or they may form as crystals of the individual metals in the alloy, or as chemical compounds of these metals. For example, all the liquid iron-carbon alloys up to as much as 1.7 per cent of carbon will preserve the chemical solubility of the liquid. They will form crystals of solid solution. That is why all alloys having carbon from zero to 1.7 per cent are known as steel (except when they also contain particles of intermingled slag, when they are known as wrought iron). But if the alloy contains more than 1.7 per cent carbon, then, when it freezes, two kinds of crystals will form in it: one a saturated solid solution containing 1.7 per cent of carbon, the other Fe_3C, called cementite. This is white cast iron. Fig. 3 does not show how gray cast iron is obtained since the iron-carbon alloys all freeze to crystals of solid solution and cementite, but no graphite. If about 0.75 to 2.50 per cent silicon is present, however, then some or all of the cementite breaks down into iron and graphite, both during the freezing and during the subsequent cooling.

Decomposition of Crystals of Solid Solution. Whatever their carbon content, the crystals of solid solution formed during freezing break down upon further cooling. If the carbon content is near the saturation value (1.7 per cent), the solid solution crystals lose carbon in the form of Fe_3C, while for a very low carbon content, crystals lose iron in the form of ferrite crystals. The separation of Fe_3C is shown by the line ES in Fig. 3, and the separation of Fe is shown by the line GS. Consider the following three cases of iron-carbon alloys, cooled slowly:

1. An alloy containing 98.5 per cent iron and 1.5 per cent carbon. Within a solid solution crystal in this alloy, cooling from 1875 deg fahr, there might be seen, under a microscope (if the appropriate conditions could be obtained), crystals of Fe_3C beginning to appear. The mass is plastic because hot. Some of the Fe_3C crystals migrate to the

outer boundaries of the crystal; others remain imbedded in the inside. The residual solid solution, in which the crystals of Fe_3C are appearing, gradually loses its carbon and approaches a composition of 0.85 per cent of carbon. When this amount of carbon is left dissolved in the solid steel, and simultaneously the temperature has dropped to 1350 deg fahr, the residual solid solution entirely * breaks up into crystals of Fe_3C and of Fe, in the form of pearlite. See p. 11–27. This final precipitation requires a few seconds of time and continues while the temperature is falling through a few degrees, but is not a continuing action like the gradual separation of the Fe_3C from the initial solid solution.

2. An alloy containing 99.65 per cent iron and 0.35 per cent carbon. As this alloy cools from a temperature of about 1510 deg fahr, there begin to appear, in the midst of the crystals of solid solution, microscopic particles of iron, which migrate to the boun-

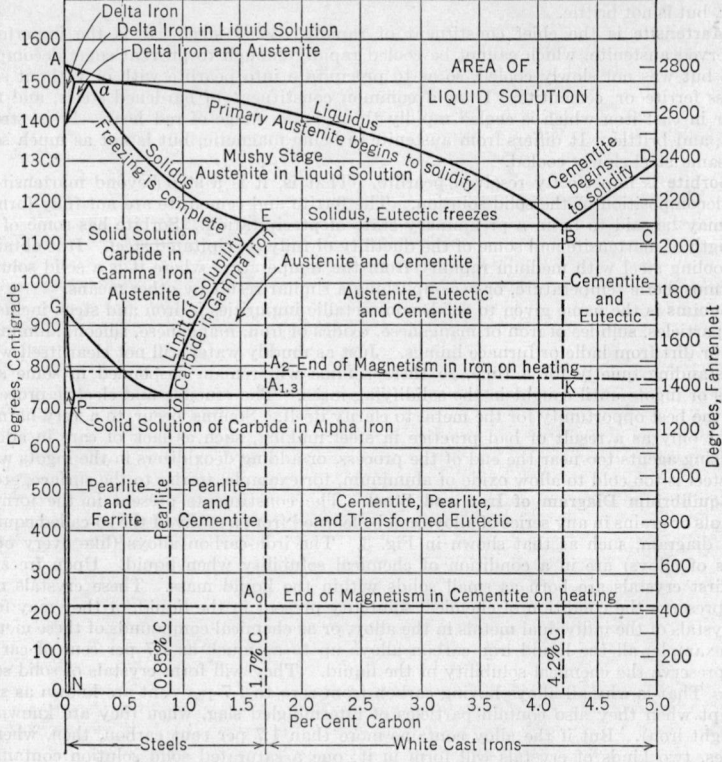

FIG. 3. Equilibrium Diagram of Iron-carbon Alloys

daries of the crystal and appear in larger and larger proportions until the metallic body remaining as a solid solution is deprived of iron down to 99.15 per cent iron and 0.85 per cent carbon. Simultaneously the temperature has fallen to 1350 deg fahr because the solid solution always retains amounts of iron and carbon in chemical solubility in exact relation to the temperature, and always comes to 99.15 per cent iron and 0.85 per cent carbon when the temperature has fallen to 1350 deg fahr. At this temperature, the 0.85 per cent solid solution undergoes a complete separation into crystals of iron and Fe_3C, associated together as pearlite, as in the previous case.

3. An alloy containing 99.15 per cent iron and 0.85 per cent carbon. Since the lines GS and SE in Fig. 3 intersect at 1350 deg fahr for an alloy of 0.85 per cent carbon, the

---

* The trace of carbon which remains in solution to lower temperatures is intentionally disregarded, because this is so small (0.03 to 0.015 per cent) that it does not affect the principle here involved.

solid solution crystal of this alloy will not lose iron or Fe$_3$C upon cooling. The resultant steel therefore at atmospheric temperature consists of 100 per cent pearlite.

Every known slowly cooled alloy of iron and carbon will contain pearlite, since every alloy from 0.01 to 6.6 per cent carbon will have crystals of solid solution in it when it has frozen, and every one of these solid solutions will drop out of itself either Fe or Fe$_3$C as it cools until the temperature has dropped to about 1350 deg fahr, when the solid solution will completely separate into crystals of Fe and Fe$_3$C, combined in a pearlitic mixture. The Fe or Fe$_3$C crystals which drop out in the cooling process are much larger crystals than the Fe or Fe$_3$C crystals which compose the pearlitic mixture. The 0.85 per cent carbon alloy is the strongest of all single steels since it has no large crystals of Fe or Fe$_3$C in its crystal boundaries to weaken it.

" Critical-point " Curves of Iron and Steel. The curves in Fig. 3 are the so-called " critical-point " curves, and the changes occurring at these points are second in importance only to the actual manufacture of the iron and steel itself. The effect of elements (carbon, silicon, etc.) on iron and steel, of heat treatment, etc., can best be discussed by relating it to these " critical points." The effect of other elements, including those entering into alloy steels, is discussed on pp. 11–24, 11–26.

Effect of Manganese on Critical-point Curves. The curves in Fig. 3 represent the changes occurring in iron-carbon alloys. If manganese be added to the alloys, the line *PSK* will occur at lower temperatures, depending on the amount of manganese. When the manganese content is as high as 7 per cent, this line will be reduced below the temperature of the earth's atmosphere. That is, the changes represented by these lines will never occur during cooling to atmospheric temperatures. This is the basis of the alloy steel known as manganese steel, which is discussed on p. 11–37.

Effect of Nickel on Critical-point Curves. Nickel, like manganese, reduces the temperature at which the changes represented by the lines *PSK* occurs. When the nickel content of steel is 12 per cent, the temperature at which these changes occur is below that of the atmosphere. At 25 per cent nickel, however, the temperatures begin to rise again. This leads to the most extraordinary alloys, such as nickel-steel bars which are magnetic at one end and non-magnetic at the other, and also alloys with unusual coefficients of dilation.

Effect of Chromium on Critical-point Curves. Chromium added to steel has the effect of slightly raising the line *PSK*, and slightly lowering the line *GS*. The maximum effect is with 5 per cent of chromium. However, these effects of chromium are not so important as its influence in reducing the speed at which the transformations (changes) represented by these lines occur. That is, if steel of, say, 0.50 per cent carbon be cooled from 1600 to 1100 deg fahr, at a moderately slow rate, the normal changes will occur. But, if a few per cent of chromium be present, the cooling must proceed very slowly. Conversely, if the cooling is rapid, for the purpose of suppressing the change as much as possible, the suppression will be more complete if a few per cent of chromium are present. Chromium thus intensifies the effect of rapid cooling on steels that are hardened by heat treatment.

13. THE MECHANICAL WORKING OF STEEL

Effect of Work on Iron and Steel. All work breaks up the crystals of iron or steel. This is more noticeable in wrought iron and low-carbon steel, for the grain of properly heated high-carbon steel is always smaller than that of low-carbon material. But if the mechanical work is stopped while the steel is still hot, the crystals will grow again to some extent. Work should, therefore, be continued to a low red heat, and extended to every part of the steel. This is difficult when rolling or forging thick pieces, whose interior is almost always of coarser grain than the surface.

The more work given to steel, the better will be the grain, provided that the finishing temperature is near the line *PSK* in Fig. 3. This, however, reaches a limit when the steel is finished at a moderate thinness. In other words, railroad rails rolled from 18-in. ingots have as good a grain as if they were rolled from ingots twice as large, but rails rolled from ingots 6 in. square would not have sufficient mechanical kneading. Six-inch ingots will, however, give a good crystalline structure to 7/8-in. wire rods, or 1-in. bars for concrete reinforcement.

Working Steel at a Blue Heat is Injurious. Not only are wrought iron and steel much more brittle at a blue heat (see p. 11–31), but, though they are probably not seriously affected by even prolonged simple exposure to blueness, if they be worked in this range of temperature they remain brittle after cooling.

Rolling vs. Forging. Rolling is the quickest and cheapest method of shaping, but it does not give quite so good a crystalline structure as either forging or hot pressing, and is more likely to tear the hot metal. It has less control over the finishing temperature, but finishes the steel more truly to form.

Cold Rolling gives more accurate and finished shape than hot rolling, and a better crystalline structure, with consequently greater strength and higher elastic limit. The hardness, as measured by the weight required to produce equal indentation, is increased by 50 per cent. Unless cold rolling is followed by annealing, it leaves the metal with strains and internal stresses. It gives the steel a better surface and brighter appearance. Only the final operations are done cold, and the steel is pickled and freed from scale before cold rolling begins. If annealed afterwards, it is protected from oxidation. High-carbon steel should not be rolled cold because the hardening and embrittling effect is too great.

Effect of Finishing Temperature in Rolling. The strength and ductility of steel depend to a high degree upon the fineness of grain, and this may be obtained by having the temperature of the steel rather low, say at a red heat, 1300 to 1400 deg fahr, during the finishing stage of rolling. In the manufacture of steel rails a great improvement in quality has been obtained by so finishing.

Hot Pressing. When it is desired that the kneading effect of mechanical work shall extend into the interior of large pieces, the shaping is performed by pressing hot under a press exerting a pressure of a few hundred to several thousand tons. Armor plate and other large pieces are shaped in this way.

Cold Pressing. Thin plate for structural purposes, automobiles, etc., is formed by pressing cold, sometimes in one operation and sometimes in several progressive ones, depending on the extent of distortion. The effect of this cold pressing is about the same as that of cold rolling, but leaves more intense strains in the metal. Often the shape is such that it is impossible to prevent the plate from springing back to an intermediate form, unless iron of more than 99 per cent purity is used.

Cold Punching, Deformation, etc. When steel is punched and sheared cold, bent, or otherwise deformed, severe strains are set up which ruin the strength of the metal immediately adjacent to the deformation. By punching or shearing the edges are cracked, and the metal should be cut away if reliance is to be placed on the edge to withstand strain.

Surface Decarbonization of Steel. When steel is rolled or heated, a coating of oxide forms on the surface. On subsequent heating this oxide reacts in the solid with the layer of steel underneath and deprives it of a part, or all, of its carbon. Thus, all hot-rolled steel has a film of decarbonized metal between the oxide coating and the unaffected steel. This layer is softer and, moreover, will not be hardened by heat treatment.

14. THE EFFECT OF HEAT ON STEEL

There are seven ways in which heat affects most metals, including steel:
1. The properties are different at different temperatures.
2. An oxide or scale forms above certain temperatures.
3. Some temperatures cause an increase or growth in grain size.
4. When the temperature approaches the melting point of the steel, a new damage known as "burning" occurs. (Burning is sometimes erroneously confused with the phenomenon of grain growth.)
5. Rapid cooling from certain temperatures develops hardness and brittleness in steel entirely different from the softness and ductility of the same steel when slowly cooled.
6. Rapid cooling from other temperatures increases the strength of the metal over its strength when slowly cooled.
7. In heating or cooling steel, there may be unequalized strains existing in the metal which will be released, producing shrinkage or warpage, or else the cooling through given ranges of temperature may produce strains which manifest themselves in warped material. Sometimes the distortion may result in the formation of a crack. In extreme cases, the change in volume may result in actual bursting with explosive violence.

Variation of Properties with Temperature

A few properties of steel are at their highest point at very low temperatures and decrease with temperature rise. The relation is not uniform and regular, however, but sudden changes, or even temporary reversals of trend, occur at certain temperatures, especially at points of allotropic or other critical change. The most important properties which are at their highest at lowest temperatures are strength, elasticity, hardness, brittleness, electric conductivity, and magnetism. Other properties are at their lowest point at low temperatures and rise with temperature, but, again, the relation is not uniform. The most important of these crescendo properties are ductility and malleability.

Strength and Ductility. Fig. 4 gives a general idea of the relative strength and ductility of steel at all temperatures from that of liquid air to that near the melting point. Average steel is relatively very strong and brittle at the temperature of liquid air, but both these properties decrease greatly to atmospheric temperature. Then both strength

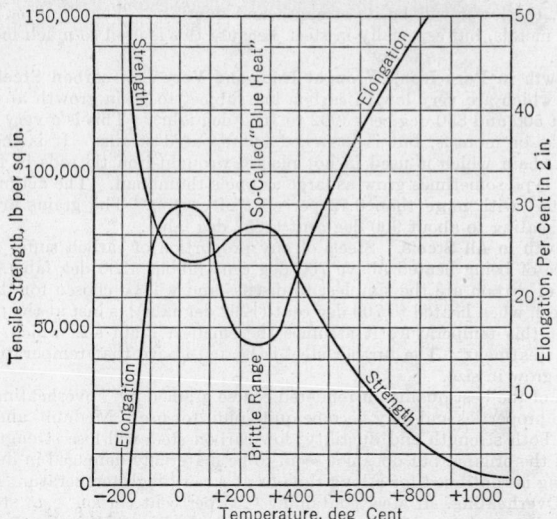

FIG. 4. Approximate Tensile Strength and Elongation in 2 in. of Structural Steel at Various Temperatures from that of Liquid Air to the Usual Rolling Temperatures

and brittleness increase again, reaching a maximum at about 260 deg cent (500 deg fahr). This is called the " blue heat," because a blue oxide will cover steel if it be left a few minutes at this temperature. Iron and steel must not be worked or strained at this temperature. They will crack even under light blows, and their toughness and ductility are very low. These properties again improve as red heat is approached.

Impact Resistance. The resistance of steel to shock decreases very much with lowered temperature, so that some steels are too brittle to use in impact service even in cold climates, although they would give satisfaction at all temperatures not far below freezing.

Creep (see p. 5–07) is most important at temperatures where a metal has a low combination of strength and ductility, e.g., 500 deg cent for steel. The action is illustrated graphically in Fig. 5. Part *ab* of the curve in Fig. 5 represents elongation which occurs within the yield point of the metal when the load is first applied. The load is unvarying and continuous. During passage of time, there is a slow permanent

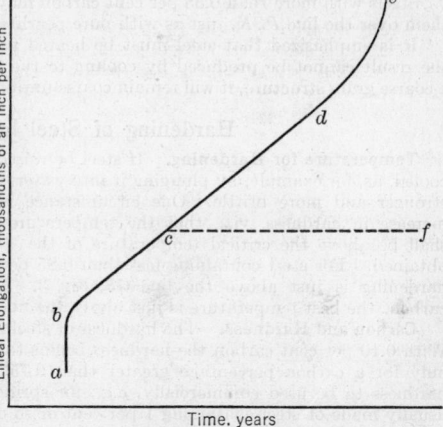

FIG. 5. Illustrating "Creep" in Metals

elongation of the specimen as indicated by *bcde*. At *e* the specimen fractures, because of the weakening due to deformation. To strain a metal beyond its yield point and then to allow it to rest results in what is called a "strain hardening," i.e., an increase in the value of the yield point. The same action occurs in extremely slow straining, so that sometimes an alloy after months of creep will become strengthened by the operation to the point where it will no longer yield to the strain. This is indicated in the line *cf* in Fig. 5.

Grain Growth

Grain Growth is caused by the elimination of grain boundaries and the merging of two or more grains into one large grain. Some grains grow to large size in a few minutes, and others require months. Everything else being equal, the larger the grains in a metallic body, the lower will be its strength and ductility. Therefore, large grains are dreaded in all metals, but especially in steel, because this is used so much more for structural purposes.

Grain Growth in Pure Iron, Wrought Iron, and Very Low-carbon Steel. The iron-carbon alloys which are very low in carbon are subject to grain growth at temperatures between about 500 and 850 deg cent (932 to 1562 deg fahr). This is a very slow growth, requiring weeks or months, but is hastened by repeated strains. It is therefore to be feared in iron chain which is used in hot places, wrought-iron tie rods in furnaces, etc. Grains of this type sometimes grow as large as one's thumbnail. The action is not to be expected in steel with more than 0.12 per cent of carbon. The grains are restored to small size by heating to about 900 deg cent (1652 deg fahr).

Grain Growth in All Steels. Steels of any proportion of carbon suffer grain growth in consequence of being heated above 700 deg cent (about 1300 deg fahr). Steels with 0.85 per cent of carbon are the simplest to discuss and will be chosen for this brief summary: this steel, when heated to 700 deg cent (1292 deg fahr), is just at the point of the V in Fig. 3. At this temperature it assumes the smallest grain size which can be given to it by heat treatment. The further steel is heated above that temperature, the more the grain will grow in size.

Even steel of the best quality, if rendered coarse grained by " overheating," will suffer in its valuable properties and may become quite unfit for use. Medium- and high-carbon steel will lose both strength and ductility; low-carbon steel will lose strength even up to 50 per cent of the original but does not seem to be materially damaged in ductility unless the overheating is continued for a long time or at a very high temperature.

Cure for Overheating. If steel containing 0.85 per cent carbon, e.g., steel consisting entirely of pearlite, be heated from some point below the line PSK in Fig. 3 to some point above that line, a new crystallization will occur and will largely obliterate previous crystallization. It seems as if dissolving the ferrite and cementite in each other produces forces which obliterate almost all existing crystalline forms. This process is known as " restoring " or, by some writers, " refining " the steel.

The cure for coarse crystallization in steel with less than 0.85 per cent carbon is to reheat it from below the line PSK to above the line GS, at which the last of the ferrite goes into solution (see Fig. 3).

Steels with more than 0.85 per cent carbon may be restored in every case by reheating them over the line PSK, just as with pure pearlite.

It is emphasized that steel must be heated to the appropriate temperature, because the result cannot be produced by cooling to the temperature. Once steel has acquired a coarse grain structure, it will remain coarse until heated through the critical temperature.

Hardening of Steel by Quenching

Temperature for Hardening. If steel be raised to a bright-red heat and then rapidly cooled, as, for example, by plunging it into water, it becomes harder and at the same time stronger and more brittle. One circumstance is absolutely necessary to produce the increase in hardness, viz., that the temperature from which rapid cooling takes place shall be above the critical temperature of the steel so that the best grain structure is obtained. For steel containing less than 0.85 per cent carbon, the best temperature for hardening is just above the line GS, Fig. 3. For steel with 0.85 per cent or more of carbon, the best temperature is just above the line SK.

Carbon and Hardness. The hardness of steel increases with every increase of carbon. With 0.10 per cent carbon the hardness begins to be perceptible by crude tests, but it is only for a carbon percentage greater than 0.75 that ordinary steel acquires sufficient hardness to be used commercially, e.g., for springs, saws, etc. Metal-cutting tools are usually made of steel containing 1 per cent or so of carbon; very hard implements, such as files, will contain 1.5 per cent or slightly more.

Rate of Cooling and Hardness. The degree of hardness of steel also varies with the speed of cooling from above the critical range of temperature. When the cooling is very slow, e.g., when it takes several days to cool, the steel will be as soft as it is possible to make it. When it is taken out of the furnace at a bright-red heat and plunged into a heavy oil with a low conducting power for heat, it becomes quite hard and springy, provided its carbon is in the neighborhood of 0.8 per cent or above. Quenching in water makes it harder still, and so on, the degree of hardness increasing with quenching liquids of greater heat-removing ability, such as ice water, ice brine, ice-sodium chloride solution, and mercury near its freezing point (-39 deg cent, -38 deg fahr).

Critical Hardening Speed. Every steel has what is called its critical hardening speed. This may be taken to be the speed at which steel should be cooled to produce the maximum amount of martensite.

Theory of Hardening of Steel. To get hardened steel, it must first be heated until it has become a solid solution of cementite in iron. This solid solution is not very hard. But if it be cooled rapidly to atmospheric temperature it becomes very hard, whereas, if it had been cooled slowly, it would be soft. The theories of hardness may be summarized as follows:

1. Slip is prevented by submicroscopic particles of cementite.
2. Slip is prevented by extreme fineness of grain.
3. Slip is prevented by intralattice carbon atoms.
4. Hardness is due to internal stress, because of:
   a. Lattice distortion.
   b. Suppression of expansion at about 350 deg fahr.
5. Hardness is a characteristic of a supersaturated solid solution.

The first theory is the one which seems to have the largest amount of support at present (1936). In other words, the solid solution decomposed enough, even in spite of the rapid cooling, to separate out particles of cementite too small to be seen even by the microscope but hard enough and numerous enough to wedge the mass tightly together so that it will not yield to slip or strain until it breaks.

Tempering. Hardened steel is too brittle to be used without some degree of tempering, except for a small variety of purposes, such as the points of armor-piercing projectiles and the face of armor plate. If it be heated to about 200 deg cent (392 deg fahr), quite a little of the brittleness and a part of the hardness will be lost. It is then in condition to be used for steel engraving tools, lathe tools, and other implements to cut metals. If it be heated to 250 deg cent (480 deg fahr), it would be tempered still further, and so on.

Heating for Annealing, etc. Annealing has for its object the treble purpose of (1) relieving any strains put upon the metal during its cooling, or by mechanical treatment or otherwise; (2) restoring the grain of the metal to that minute size which gives it the best possible qualities; or (3) softening it after hardening. These three objects may be accomplished in one annealing operation. The usual temperatures of true annealing lie between 700 and 1000 deg cent (1290 and 1830 deg fahr). Temperatures from 200 to 700 deg cent (1292 deg fahr) are sufficient to relieve strains in the metal and to soften it after mechanical treatment or hardening. This operation, using low temperatures, is known as "lonealing." To produce a new grain size, however, the steel must be heated slightly above the critical temperature and cooled slowly from that point so as to be in a soft condition. If, because of cold rolling, wire drawing, or other mechanical work, in the cold, a small grain size is already present, it is bad practice to form a new grain size. In this case the steel should be lonealed.

15. USES OF CARBON STEELS

Crucible Steel and Electric Steel. Crucible steel and electric steel excel all others in price and quality. Their high quality is due to freedom from gases, oxides, and defects other than metallic impurities. These steels may be used only for purposes which warrant the high price. Authorities differ as to whether crucible or electric steel is superior. In America, electric steel is made at the rate of more than a million tons per year, whereas the production of crucible steel has decreased from 20,000 to 1700 tons per year.

Bessemer Steel. The Bessemer product is losing ground, not so much on account of the limited field for which it is adapted, but because low-phosphorus pig iron from which it is made is becoming yearly more rare and costly, owing to the exhaustion of low-phosphorus ores. For small railroad rails, small structural shapes (angles, channels, standard beams, etc.), pipe, wire, and tin plate, Bessemer steel is as good as any obtainable provided the phosphorus be kept at a moderately low figure.

Basic Open-hearth Steel. For more important structural members, for large railroad rails, which must be relatively high in carbon, and, therefore, low in phosphorus, so as to be strong yet not brittle in cold weather, the basic open-hearth steel is especially appropriate. The same is true for structural plate, boiler plate, etc. Most modern steel, therefore, is made by the basic open-hearth process.

Acid Open-hearth Steel. It is easier to get low-phosphorus material for melting in the acid open-hearth than for the Bessemer converter, since in the former 75 to 90 per cent of the material usually consists of steel scrap. Therefore, acid open-hearth steel low in phosphorus and in sulfur is obtainable, and is the highest quality of steel in the market, next to crucible and electric. It excels basic open-hearth steel because of its relative freedom from oxygen, to which basic steel is liable on account of its highly oxidized basic slag. For steel castings this freedom from oxygen is especially valuable, as oxygen and oxides in steel tend to produce " blowholes " in castings. The acid open-hearth is not universal, but is generally preferred, for steel casting work. It is also preferred for fatigue members of important bridge and other structural work, on account of the smaller content of oxides which lower the resistance of the steel to this type of stress.

16. ALLOY STEELS

Alloy Steel. Steel is an alloy of iron and carbon. An alloy steel is a steel to which has been added, in addition to the carbon, an amount of some element sufficient to produce a distinguishing effect. The alloying element is usually a metal, and its effect must be such as to alter the properties of the steel so as to put it into a slightly different class from ordinary carbon steel. For example, manganese and silicon are contained in practically all carbon steels in small amount. But, if the proportion of manganese or silicon is sufficiently large to give properties to the steel which do not ordinarily occur in carbon steel, then the steel is classed as an alloy steel.

Nickel and chromium are the two alloying elements most often used. The weight of these two metals used in alloy steels exceeds the weight of all other alloying elements taken together.

The best alloy steels are made in the electric furnace or crucible, but 75 to 80 per cent of the tonnage comes from basic open-hearth furnaces. The greatest amount of alloy steel is used because of combined strength and ductility (95 per cent of all steel is important because of its strength). In some cases, however, other properties of alloy steels, such as hardness, heat resistance, corrosion resistance, etc., may be most important.

Binary Alloy Steels. If an alloy steel contains one alloying element besides the steel, it is called a " binary " alloy steel. Examples of these are: nickel, chromium, tungsten, vanadium, silicon, manganese, and molybdenum steels.

Ternary Alloy Steels. Very often, alloy steels are made up of steel and two alloying elements. These are called " ternary " alloy steels. Examples are: chrome-vanadium, chrome-nickel, silicon-manganese, and chrome-molybdenum steels.

S.A.E. Specification Numbering System. A numeral index system is used for numbering S.A.E. steels, in which the first figure indicates the class to which the steel belongs: thus " 1– " indicates a carbon steel, " 2–," a nickel steel; and " 3–," a nickel-chromium steel. In the case of the alloy steels, the second figure generally indicates the approximate percentage of the predominant alloying element. Usually the last two or three figures indicate the average carbon content in " points," or hundredths of 1 per cent. Thus " 2340 " indicates a nickel steel of approximately 3 per cent nickel (3.25 to 3.75), and 0.40 per cent carbon (0.35 to 0.45); and " 71360 " indicates a tungsten steel of about 13 per cent tungsten (12 to 15) and 0.60 per cent carbon (0.50 to 0.70). The basic numerals for the various qualities of steels specified are:

Carbon steels...............	1	Chromium steels.............	5
Nickel steels...............	2	Chromium-vanadium steels....	6
Nickel-chromium steels......	3	Tungsten steels.............	7
Molybdenum steels..........	4	Silico-manganese steels.......	9

S.A.E. steels are purchased on the basis of requirements as to chemical composition. Requirements as to physical properties and finish have been omitted for all steels except steel castings because the majority of steels for automotive purposes are either worked or given special heat treatment by the purchaser.

Binary Alloy Steels for Strength

Nickel. Nickel decreases the crystal size of steels, and especially the size of crystals of pure iron. For this reason, the addition of nickel to structural steel results in an increase of strength, without a proportionately great decrease of ductility. Through the same cause it increases the hardness of steel, and, therefore, is used for such purposes as railroad rails on curves. It is valuable in steel that is to be case-hardened, because it decreases the crystal size of the " core." The full benefit of nickel is obtained only when the steel is heat-treated for strength in the usual way, namely: it is heated to the lowest possible temperature to get all the iron and carbon in solid solution, quenched in oil or water to prevent precipitation of iron crystals in large size, and then reheated to some point below the line *PSK*, Fig. 3, to restore ductility to the steel. Nickel steel of

3.5 per cent nickel is superior to carbon steel which has been treated in this way, and excels especially in elastic limit.

Silicon. Many bridges have been built in the past five years using what is called " silicon structural steel." This is stronger than carbon steel of equal ductility. The silicon is usually between 0.50 and 1.05 per cent, and it is customary to raise the manganese of structural steel from about 0.50 to between 0.67 and 0.95 per cent. By this analysis the silico-manganese steels, much used for springs, are approached.

Silicon has the effect of decreasing the solubility of carbon in iron, both in the liquid and the solid state. In the solid solution, therefore, the end of the V in Fig. 3 is found occurring at a less amount of carbon than the usual 0.85 per cent. With 1 per cent of silicon, the solid solution will have its maximum solubility at about 0.45 instead of 0.85 per cent carbon. Since the point of the V is always the strongest steel, a stronger steel with less carbon in it is obtained in this way, and therefore, greater ductility, because the less the carbon, the greater the ductility.

Medium Manganese Structural Steel. The manganese in ordinary carbon steel is between 0.40 and 1 per cent. Increasing the manganese to about 1.50 to 1.75 per cent results again in a steel with much higher strength and without loss of ductility. The steel also withstands the shock test excellently. For this reason it is being used for railroad rails, which thus less easily develop transverse fissures in the heads, probably caused chiefly by blows from the driving wheels of locomotives. The steel is also being used in place of nickel steel in structural parts of some bridges.

Comparison of Nickel, Silicon, and Manganese Structural Steels. It is possible to secure a little better combination of strength and ductility in 3.5 per cent nickel steel than in silicon or medium manganese structural steels. Nickel steel has also had a long service in important structures, as compared with the length of time during which the others have been used. But 3.5 per cent nickel steel costs about twice as much as does either of the others. All three of these alloy steels are generally used in large members of structures without any heat treatment. In this respect, nickel steel has the advantage, because it can be improved to a greater extent by quenching and reheating. All three of the steels, when in the unheat-treated condition, have similar properties.

Vanadium. Vanadium is one of the most powerful scavengers that can be added to liquid steel for the special purpose of removing oxygen. After the removal of all the oxygen that can be eliminated by means of manganese and silicon, the addition of 0.25 per cent of vanadium will result in further oxygen elimination, leaving about 0.15 per cent vanadium in the steel. This vanadium has the effect of increasing the strength and hardness of the metal. In fact, the hardness is increased so much that ordinary alloy steel is not used with more than 0.2 per cent of vanadium remaining in it. Vanadium, like nickel, decreases the grain size of steel, but vanadium acts on the Fe_3C as well as the Fe grains. Vanadium also acts apparently during the phase when steel is freezing, so that it is especially beneficial in steel castings, whose properties it improves materially. Except for castings, not very much vanadium binary steel is made, but vanadium is added in extremely small doses to make ternary and quarternary alloy steels, some of which have great strength or hardness.

Molybdenum Structural Steel. From 0.25 to 0.75 per cent of molybdenum added to ordinary steel, which is then heat-treated, produces a structural steel which has increased elastic limit without correspondingly decreased ductility. Molybdenum resembles vanadium in not being used extensively in binary steels, but in being added in small doses to improve the properties of other alloy steels, such as the important chrome-molybdenum steel used in airplane structures, and also nickel-molybdenum steel.

Ternary Alloy Steels for Strength

Chromium in Ternary Alloy Steels. Chromium intensifies the effect of rapid cooling on steel. Tool steel which has been quenched for hardness is much harder for the presence of 0.5 to 2 per cent of chromium than steel of the same analysis in carbon and other elements which contains no chromium. Therefore, chromium is used only in steels which are to be heat-treated.

Chrome-nickel Steel. Thus a steel which contains about 1.5 per cent of nickel and 0.6 per cent of chromium will have, after heat treatment, almost the same strength and ductility as 3.5 per cent nickel steel which has also been heat-treated, but it will not cost as much. Table V gives data for the comparison of all these binary and ternary structural steels. The heat treatment of chrome-nickel steel is based on the principle already given: heat the steel until the solid solution is complete; then quench in oil or water; and, finally, reheat to some temperature below the line PSK in Fig. 3 to restore ductility. The best temperature for first quenching must be determined by experiment for all steels of different analysis; the temperature for reheating will depend on how much ductility

Table V. Some Mechanical Properties of Some Structural Alloy Steels

Steel	Analysis, per cent								Ultimate Strength, lb per sq in.	Yield Point, lb per sq in.	Elongation, per cent in 2 in.	Reduction of Area, per cent	Izod Value	Heat Treatment	
	C	Mn	Si	Ni	S	Cr	V	Mo						Quench in	Then draw at
Silicon	0.10	0.60§	1.00						72,000	52,000	27‡‡	59		As rolled	
Silicon	0.40§	1.00§	0.40§						93,000	55,000	18‡‡‡	>35		As rolled	
Silicon-manganese	0.55	0.90	1.80						242,000	230,500	4‡‡‡‡	21		Oil, 1742° F	842° F
Silicon-manganese									162,400	142,200	13‡	31		Oil, 1742° F	1112° F
Medium manganese	0.29	1.60							93,000	40,500*	31	68		Normalized	
Medium manganese	0.38	1.75			0.103				209,000	158,700*	11	45	45	Water, 1475° F	625° F
Nickel	0.35			3.50					245,000	220,000	11	38	56	Oil, 1450° F	400° F
									180,000	180,000	13	46		Oil, 1450° F	600° F
									160,000	138,000	16	53		Oil, 1450° F	800° F
									126,000	103,000	21	59		Oil, 1450° F	1000° F
									104,000	71,000	25	64		Oil, 1450° F	1200° F
									95,000	65,000	27	65		Oil, 1450° F	1300° F
Chrome-nickel	0.35			1.25		0.60			240,000	214,000	8	28		Oil, 1500° F	400° F
									220,000	195,000	9	30		Oil, 1500° F	600° F
									180,000	151,000	12	49		Oil, 1500° F	800° F
									135,000	110,000	17	58		Oil, 1500° F	1000° F
									108,000	86,000	21	63		Oil, 1500° F	1200° F
									96,000	74,000	22	65		Oil, 1500° F	1300° F
Chrome-vanadium	0.26					0.92	0.20		132,000	110,000	19	52		As rolled	
									83,700	61,000	35	66		Annealed	
									173,900	149,800	13	57		Oil, 1560° F	750° F
									157,500	147,150	15	61		Oil, 1560° F	840° F
									137,500	112,750	21	65		Oil, 1560° F	1020° F
									131,000	100,000	17	67		Oil, 1560° F	1155° F
Vanadium steel casting	0.34						0.25		90,750	67,500	10	28	10.88†	Water, 1650° F	1200° F
Molybdenum	0.35							0.76	228,000	212,000	11	43		Oil, 1550° F	600° F
									160,000	136,000	16	49		Oil, 1550° F	800° F
									140,000	125,000	21	61		Oil, 1550° F	1000° F
									120,000	106,000	14	66		Oil, 1550° F	1200° F
Chrome-molybdenum	0.35					1.06		0.36	205,000	189,000	15	50	49	Oil, 1550° F	600° F
									176,000	153,000	15	61	60	Oil, 1550° F	800° F
									152,000	132,000	23	66	60	Oil, 1550° F	1000° F
									127,000	112,000	18	57	49	Oil, 1550° F	1200° F
Stainless iron	0.11					12.5			202,000	57,000	18	62		Oil, 1800° F	500° F
									193,000	94,000	18	63		Oil, 1800° F	700° F
									186,000	114,000	18	62	31	Oil, 1800° F	900° F
									155,000	112,000	20	67	102	Oil, 1800° F	1100° F
									103,000	82,500	26	70	31	Oil, 1800° F	1300° F
									143,000	63,000	18	55		Oil, 1800° F	1500° F
Chrome	0.36					0.57			81,000	31,500	36	75	118	Annealed 1600° F	
									103,200	76,000	27	62		Oil, 1600° F	1200° F

* Proportional limit.   † Charpy.   ‡ In 8 in.   § Maximum.

is estimated to be necessary, always remembering that the greater the ductility the lower the elastic limit.

Chrome-vanadium Steel. Heat treatment and general mechanical properties of chrome-vanadium steel compare with those for chrome-nickel steel. Table V indicates some of the differences.

Silicon-manganese Steel. Silicon-manganese steel greatly resembles chrome-vanadium in strength and for service in springs. It is widely used in Europe for automobile springs, and to some extent in this country, although many American makers favor chrome-vanadium as being less brittle.

Chrome-molybdenum Steel. Chrome-molybdenum steel has not as good a combination of strength and ductility as nickel, chrome-nickel, and chrome-vanadium steels, but it is quite easy to roll and draw into tubes, to fabricate, and to weld, so that it is very popular for airplane structural parts.

Alloy Steels for Hardness

Effect of Chromium on Hardness. Chromium intensifies the effect of rapid cooling; consequently it greatly increases the hardness of quenched steel, if the carbon is high enough to produce hardness on quenching. Chromium is almost universally added to increase the hardness of cutting tools, the amount being usually about 1.50 up to 2.50 per cent for protective armor plate, etc. It is also used to decrease the wear in parts of crushing machinery. For simple abrasion hardness, high-manganese steel is also very commonly used.

High-manganese Steel. Steel, when it contains manganese in excess of 7 per cent, acquires an entirely new property which reaches its maximum efficiency when the manganese is about 13 per cent. This property consists in a toughness so great that the steel may be tied cold into a knot without producing any cracks, and a resistance to wear which makes it commercially unmachinable with the usual cutting tools. The toughness is developed only if the steel is heated above 1000 deg cent (1800 deg fahr) and cooled as rapidly as possible by quenching in water. The steel is made in the form of castings and can be shaped a little on the surface by grinding with emery wheels. Unfortunately, its elastic limit is too low to permit its being used as a cutting tool.

High-speed Steel. When carbon steel is quenched and then tempered, it begins to lose its hardness at 200 deg cent (400 deg fahr). This makes it impossible to use this steel for metal cutting at high speeds, because the friction of cutting warms the cutting tool to the temperature where it loses its hardness (sometimes called its " temper "). By the addition of about 18 per cent of tungsten to such steel it acquires the property of " red hardness," that is, of remaining hard even when at a low red heat (535 deg cent = 1000 deg fahr). Before it will have this characteristic of resisting tempering it must be heated to about 1150 deg cent (2100 deg fahr) and cooled in oil or in an air blast. In practice chromium is usually added up to 4 per cent and vanadium up to 2.5 per cent to this " high-speed steel," for the sake of further adding to its hardness and cutting power. Cobalt is now (1936) often added to intensify its properties. Nine per cent of molybdenum will replace the 18 per cent of tungsten to give this " red hardness " characteristic.

Super-speed Cutting Tools. The new " super-speed cutting tools " are not alloy steels, but often take the place of alloy-steel tools. Their base is the carbide of tungsten, WC, the hardest substance known next to the diamond. See p. 11-81.

Corrosion-resistant Steels

Steels and Cast Iron Which Resist Corrosion. Nickel steel rusts less than carbon steel, especially if the nickel is 25 per cent and higher. Alloys of iron with not more than 0.50 per cent of copper rust less than plain carbon steel, especially in slightly acidulated waters, such as the rivers which flow from coal-mining districts. Alloys with nitrogen (e.g., nitrided surfaces) also seem by recent studies to have a powerful resistance. The alloys of iron with silicon, beginning about 11 per cent silicon, not only do not rust at all, but even offer great resistance to acid attack which dissolves iron readily. Iron castings with 13 per cent of silicon are made for chemical purposes. But the material which is of most extensive industrial and household importance is the so-called stainless steel.

Stainless Steels. Stainless steel is a general term given to certain alloys of iron, chromium, and nickel that have high resistance to heat and corrosion. They are generally designated by the percentage of chromium; an 18-8 stainless is understood to be an alloy containing 18 per cent Cr and 8 per cent Ni. The composition and physical properties of the commonly used alloys are given in Table VI.

General properties of the alloys in Table VI are as follows: Tensile strength is higher than that of ordinary steels of equal carbon content, and fabricating and forming methods,

Table VI. Chemical and Physical Properties of Stainless Steels
(Allegheny Steel Company, Brackenridge, Pa., 1935)
Analyses of Standard Grades of Stainless Steels

Type No.	C, per cent, max.	Cr, per cent	Ni, per cent	Type No.	C, per cent, max.	Cr, percent	Ni, per cent	Other Elements, per cent	Type No.	C, per cent, max.	Cr, per cent	Other Elements, per cent
302	0.08–0.20*	17–19	7–9	309	0.20	22–26	11–13	....	410	0.12	12–14	
303	0.08–0.20†	17–19	7–9	310	.25	24–26	19–21	....	416	.12	12–15	‖
304	0.11*	17–19	7–9	316	.11*	17–19	7–11	Mo 2–4	418	.12	12–15	W, 2.5–3.5
305	0.08–0.20*	18–20	8–10	320	.20	17–19	7–9	Ti = 4C	425	.12	14–16	
306	0.11*	18–20	8–10	321	.20	18–20	8–10	Ti = 4C	430	.12	16–18	
307	0.08–0.20*	19–22	9–12	403	.12	11.5–13.0	.....	.....	438	.12	15–18	W, 2.5–3.5
308	0.11*	19–22	9–12	405	.08	11.5–13.5	.....	Al, 0.10–0.20‡	442	.35	18–23	
				406	.12	12–14	.....	Al, 4–4.05 §	446	.35	23–30	

* Carbon may be specified to a 4-point range within these limits. † Free machining quality. Phosphorus, sulfur, selenium, min. 0.15 per cent. ‡ Non-hardening quality. § High electrical resistance. ‖ Free machining quality. Contains sulfur, selenium, molybdenum.

Tensile Properties of Stainless Steels at Elevated Temperatures
(Average Values)

	Temperature, deg fahr								
	100	200	500	1000	1200	1400	1600	1800	2000
Cr, 18–20; Ni, 8–10; C, 0.08–0.20									
Ultimate strength, 1000 lb per sq in.....	89.4	82.4	74.4	70.6	64.5	50.2	30.0		
Proportional limit, 1000 lb per sq in.....	28.0	28.0	26.9	25.2	23.6	18.0			
Elongation in 2 in., per cent............	61.0	57.4	49.2	46.2	42.0	34.1	34.6		
Reduction of area, per cent............	75.2	75.8	71.1	70.2	69.9	54.8	55.5		
Cr, 22–26; Ni, 11–13; C, 0.20									
Ultimate strength, 1000 lb per sq in.....	98.8	92.4	85.0	77.0	69.4	56.4	36.0	20.9	13.4
Elongation in 2 in., per cent............	59.4	57.2	49.2	46.2	35.1	24.8	17.1	22.6	33.4
Reduction of area, per cent............	68.2	68.1	67.3	57.5	42.2	30.9	24.6	39.0	46.4
Cr, 12–15; C, 0.12									
Ultimate strength, 1000 lb per sq in.....	75.0	75.1	70.0	30.3	23.2	11.5	9.6	7.8	4.3
Elongation in 2 in., per cent...........	45.8	44.9	37.0	46.0	40.0	39.0	42.0	60.0	64.0
Reduction of area, per cent............	70.6	69.7	71.9	85.4	88.3	94.1	90.4	64.9	93.1
Cr, 16–18; C, 0.12									
Ultimate strength, 1000 lb per sq in.....	84.5	82.6	76.5	47.5	30.0	18.1	9.6	4.0	
Cr, 23–30; C, 0.25									
Ultimate strength, 1000 lb per sq in.....		116.0	102.2	84.5	43.1	24.3	14.4	7.3	5.5

Physical Properties of Stainless Steels
(Average Values)

	Cr, 18–20 Ni, 8–10 C, 0.08–0.20	Cr, 22–26 Ni, 11–13 C, 0.20	Cr, 12–15 C, 0.12	Cr, 16–18 C, 0.12	Cr, 23–30 C, 0.35
Specific gravity......................	7.97–8.07* / 7.86–7.94†	7.86–7.94	....	7.65–7.75	7.58–7.62
Average weight, lb per cu in...........	0.2985* / 0.285†	0.285	....	0.274	0.274
Melting point, deg fahr...............	2606–2679	2552–2597	2723	2714	
Thermal conductivity, cal per cm per deg cent 20–100° C	0.069	0.039	0.096	0.082	0.059
Specific heat, cal per gm per deg cent ...	....	0.142	0.159		
Coefficient linear expansion per deg fahr × 10^5					
at 54–212° F......................	0.961	0.900	0.567	0.583	0.567
at 54–1832° F.....................	1.112	1.112	0.711	0.733	0.744
Electrical resistivity, microhms per cu cm					
at 400° F........................	92	92	78	83	88
at 1200° F.......................	117	115	109	115	116

* Cold-rolled, annealed. † Hot-rolled, annealed.

hot or cold, should be modified accordingly. Heat treatment does not harden them appreciably but cold working does. As the heat conductivity is lower than that of steel, a longer time is required for heating heavy sections for forging, etc. All the above alloys resist oxidation at high temperatures, this quality being more pronounced in some than in others. The highest resistance to corrosion is obtained only when the sheets are entirely free from foreign matter, e.g., are highly polished. Polished stainless steels are resistant to corrosion in atmosphere at ordinary temperatures, and to many chemical solutions used in the industries. Manufacturers of the material should be consulted as to the alloy to be selected for resistance to corrosion by any particular liquid or gas.

Heat-resisting Alloy Steels

Tungsten steel is the strongest material known at the temperature of exhaust valves in gas engines, but it has a tendency to scale. High-chromium steels do not scale at this temperature, but they lack strength. Chromium up to 38 per cent has been used, but the most popular combination is steel with about 18 per cent chromium and 8 per cent nickel. See Table VI. This heat-resisting steel is sold under many trade names which give no indication of its analysis.

COPPER AND COPPER-BASE ALLOYS *
By the members of the staff of The American Brass Co. and W. M. Corse

17. COPPER

Composition of Commercial Copper. The composition requirements of the A.S.T.M. specifications for copper are almost universally accepted by the trade. These standard specifications cover *lake copper, electrolytic copper,* and *fire-refined copper* other than *lake.* In order to be classed as lake, copper must originate on the northern peninsula of Michigan, U.S.A. Lake copper is further divided into low-resistance lake, offered for electrical purposes, and high-resistance lake. Low-resistance lake, whether fire or electrolytically refined, shall have a purity of at least 99.900 per cent, silver being counted as copper. Low-resistance lake copper wire bars shall have a resistivity not to exceed 0.15436 international ohm (meter, gram) at 20 deg cent (annealed), while ingots and ingot bars shall have a resistivity not to exceed 0.15694 international ohm (meter, gram) at 20 deg cent (annealed). Lake copper having a resistivity greater than 0.15694 international ohm (meter, gram) at 20 deg cent (annealed) shall be known as high-resistance lake copper. Its purity shall be at least 99.900 per cent, copper, silver, and arsenic being counted together. The A.S.T.M. specifications for purity and electrical resistivity of electrolytic copper are the same as those for low-resistance lake copper. Fire-refined copper, other than lake, is intended for use in rolling into sheets and shapes for mechanical purposes and is not intended for electrical purposes nor wrought alloys. Its chemical composition shall be as follows:

		Per Cent
Copper plus silver, minimum		99.7000
Arsenic, maximum		0.1000
Antimony,	"	0.0120
Bismuth,	"	0.0020
Iron,	"	0.0100
Lead,	"	0.0100
Nickel,	"	0.1000
Oxygen,	"	0.0750
Selenium,	"	0.0400
Tellurium,	"	0.0140
Tin,	"	0.0500

Physical and Mechanical Properties of Copper. Average physical properties of copper are given in Table I. The mechanical properties of cast and rolled copper are given in Tables II and III, respectively. For electrical properties of copper conductors, see p. 11–93.

Corrosion. Copper is dissolved by the common acids, especially in the presence of air or other oxidizing agents, and it usually does not give satisfactory service in resisting

* The material on Copper and Wrought Copper-base Alloys was prepared by The American Brass Company, Waterbury, Conn., and that on Sand-cast Copper-base Alloys, by Mr. W. M. Corse.

the action of ammonia or most sulfur compounds. Some of the principal uses are in the shipbuilding industry where its property of resisting the action of corroding sea waters is valuable; in buildings, to resist the action of atmospheric corrosion particularly in industrial centers and upon the seacoast. In case of doubt, engineers not familiar with the corrosion-resisting properties of copper should consult manufacturers of the material, giving complete information as to the conditions under which the metal is to be used.

Table I. Physical Properties of Copper

Physical Properties	Value
Density, 20° C	8.90 g per cu cm, or 0.322 lb per cu in.
Melting point	1981 deg fahr
Specific heat, 25° C	0.0919 { g-cal per g per deg cent / Btu per lb per deg fahr
Linear coefficient of expansion (av. 25 to 300° C)	0.0000177 per deg cent
Thermal conductivity, 20° C	0.923 g-cal per sec per sq cm per deg cent per cm
Electrical resistivity, 20° C	1.699 microhm-cm
Temperature coefficient of resistivity, 20° C	0.00393 per deg cent
Magnetic susceptibility	0.085×10^6
Optical properties	Selectively reflecting
Modulus of elasticity	16,000,000 lb per sq in.

Oxygen-free High-conductivity Copper. A copper of special grade, made under carefully controlled conditions, is available. The atmosphere of the furnace and the method of casting prevent the entrance of oxygen and the formation of copper oxide. Wire and other shapes made from this material exhibit much superior characteristics in two respects. The ductility, as evidenced in elongation, torsion, and bending, is made greater. OFHC wire may be twisted two or three times as many turns as regular copper. This copper also may be subjected to the action of reducing gases at elevated temperatures (as in brazing) without the usual danger of embrittlement. Conductivity and tensile strength are the same as for tough pitch electrolytic copper. The fatigue resistance is apparently unchanged.

Because of the superior ductility of oxygen-free copper, it is useful in difficult operations of deep drawing, spinning, and edge bending. Where the embrittlement hazard must be avoided in welding, brazing, or hot-working operations, this copper may be used to advantage, in spite of the higher cost.

Fabrication. Copper may be hot or cold forged, hot or cold rolled, hot extruded, hot pierced, and drawn, stamped, or spun cold. It can be silver soldered, brazed, and welded, the last by the electric arc or oxyacetylene method. For welding, deoxidized copper is recommended instead of the usual electrolytic or lake copper because it gives more satisfactory welds. Copper cannot be cut by the oxygen jet as can iron or steel, because of the high heat conductivity of the metal. It is annealed at 480 to 1400 deg fahr, depending upon the properties desired, and in a slightly oxidizing atmosphere. For ordinary commercial annealing 1100 deg fahr is considered good practice. A reducing atmosphere will injure the copper, making it brittle and unfit for use. Copper is easily electrodeposited from the alkaline cyanide solution, or more usually from the acid sulfate solution.

Hardening of Copper. The search for the so-called lost art of hardening copper is still popular with many inventors, as evidenced by the number of inquiries on this subject and the applications in the Patent Office. Two ways of hardening copper are: by cold working, or by alloying with other elements such as zinc, tin, silicon, aluminum, or nickel.

Electrical Uses of Copper. See p. 11–92.

18. COPPER-BASE ALLOYS

Brasses and Bronzes. Brass is essentially a copper and zinc alloy, whereas bronze is primarily a copper and tin alloy. However, there is no sharp dividing line between the two. Many brasses contain tin, and bronzes often contain zinc. The term " bronze " is also applied to certain copper-base alloys that contain no tin, as, for example, aluminum bronze and silicon bronze. Since the same commercial name frequently applies to widely varying compositions, care should be taken to specify the chemical composition of a com mercial alloy.

Fabrication. Nearly all the copper-base alloys are readily machined. Some of the stronger alloys, such as aluminum-bronze and manganese-bronze, are tough and difficult to machine, but with proper tool angles and machine conditions it is entirely possible to machine even these. These alloys as a class are not readily welded by any of the com-

Table II. Sand-cast Copper-base Alloys

Name	Analysis, per cent						Tension †				Compression		Brinell Hard-ness	Impact Strength, Izod., ft-lb	Remarks and Uses
	Cu	Al	Zn	Si	Mn	Fe	1000 lb per sq in.		Elongation in 2 in., %	Reduction in Area, %	Deformation Limit, 1000 lb per sq in.*	Reduction in Height, % Load = 100,000 lb per sq in.			
							Yield Point	Ultimate Strength							
CAST COPPER															
Pure copper	99.6–99.9	..	..	..	..	..	...	20–25	20–25	75	...	...	40	...	Deoxidized with Si, B₂C₃ or carbon free Mn. Electrical uses, if pure.
HIGH TENSILE BRONZES AND BRASSES															
Aluminum bronze	90.6	9.4	..	..	..	..	21.7 46.6‡ 24.0s	67 85‡ 52.5s	36 9.5‡ 17.3s	47 20‡ 32s	...	...	...	...	Aluminum-bronzes. These alloys should not be slowly cooled from a high temperature if they are to be stressed at ordinary temperatures. Resistant to cold dilute H₂SO₄, cold weak HCl, sea water, etc. Pipe fittings valves and other equipment for chemical industry.
Aluminum bronze	89	10	..	..	..	1	20–30 54‡	60–75 90‡	24 10‡	27 12‡	18–20	13–15	92–120 175‡	...	
Aluminum bronze	88	9	..	..	..	3	30–45 40‡	70–80 84‡	25–45 30‡	20–40 25‡	14–18	...	95–120 125‡	...	
Everdur	94.4	..	..	4.5	1.1	..	20–30	50–60	10–25	15–22	...	...	92	22	Everdur. Resistant to H₂SO₄, HCl (in absence of air), sea water, caustic soda, phenol, etc.
Silicon brass	81.5	..	14	4.5	..	..	...	65–75	9–10	...	...	...	130–150	50	Silicon-brass, for hardness.
Manganese bronze	68.5	4	22	..	3.0	2.5	40–45	85–100	15–20	20–30	60–70	...	150–180	...	Manganese-bronze. For strength, toughness, and hardness.
Manganese bronze	58	..	39	..	0–1	0.75‡	30–45	65–75	20–40	...	12–16	...	90–110	...	Manganese-bronze. Propellers, engine frames, parts requiring strength and toughness. Resistant to sea water and acids.

Table II. Sand-cast Copper-base Alloys—*Continued*

Name	Analysis, per cent						Tension †				Compression		Brinell Hardness	Impact Strength, Izod, ft-lb	Remarks and Uses
	Cu	Sn	Pb	Zn	Ni	Fe	Yield Point	Ultimate Strength (1000 lb per sq in.)	Elongation in 2 in., %	Reduction in Area, %	Deformation Limit, 1000 lb per sq in.*	Reduction in Height, % Load = 100,000 lb per sq in.			
Silicon brass	59.7	..	39.7	0.6	..	..	...	50-55	12-15	...	...	...	...	25	Silicon-brass.
Nickel bronze	60	..	Ni, 30	..	Sn, 8	2	...	67	0	...	...	...	240	...	Nickel-bronze. Valve facing for severe conditions. Abrasion resistant. For hardness.

BRONZE AND RED BRASS FOR GENERAL ENGINEERING WORK ‡‡

Name	Analysis, per cent						Tension				Compression		Brinell Hardness	Impact Strength	Remarks and Uses
	Cu	Sn	Pb	Zn	Ni	P	Yield Point	Ultimate Strength	Elongation in 2 in., %	Reduction in Area, %	Deformation Limit	Reduction in Height, %			
Bronze	89	8	2	3	..	0.03‡	16-18	30-40	15-30	15-35	12.5-13	33-34	45-60	...	Bronze for valves and fittings for steam, gas, etc.
Bronze	88	8	1.0‡	4	0.75‡	0.05‡	20-25	30-45	15-40	25-35	...	...	55-75	...	Bronze for water-tight castings, underwater fittings, machine parts. Non-corrosive.
Gear bronze	89	11	..	..	..	0.3‡	18-20	30-35	5-15	6-8	16	25-27	65-85	...	Gear bronze. Very resistant to abrasion. For heavy-duty gears and worm wheels.
Bronze	86	8	3	3	..	0.03‡	...	30-35	25-30	25-30	...	...	55-65	...	Steam fittings. Machines well.
Bronze	86	13	1	..	..	Trace	20-35	30-45	1-8	...	16-22	...	85-120	...	Valve bodies subject to high pressure and vibration.
Red brass	85	5	5	5	..	..	15-19	27-33	16-20	15-20	11.5-12	36	50-60	...	Red brass for pump bodies, valves, steam fittings, bearing backs, and metal patterns.

Various Wrought Copper-base Alloys—*Continued*

expected in practice)

Shearing Strength, lb per sq in.		Brinell Hardness No. 10-mm Ball, 500-kg Load		Rockwell Hardness No. "B" 1/16-in. Ball, 100 kg		Bend Test, deg		Melting Point, deg cent	Specific Gravity †	Density, lb per cu in.	Coefficient of Expansion ×10^7 (j)	Resistivity, ohms (mil, ft)	Conductivity, per cent I.A.C.S.	Thermal Conductivity (u)	Uses—Remarks
Hard*	Soft	Hard*	Soft	Hard*	Soft	Hard*	Soft								
......	......	155	80	87	42	...	180	905x	8.396	0.303	208	36.25	28.60	0.300	For bolts, nuts, sheathing, pin wire, etc.
......	......											24.63	42.10	......	For caps and electrical parts.
......	......	158	52	90	15				8.495b	0.307	....	38.68	26.8		Pipe and tube.
				85	15										For hinges, etc. Also for threading and similar operations.
35,000		104	...	58					8.830d	0.319	183	25.61y	40.50y	0.432	For hardware, jewelry, etc. Free cutting.
									8.698d	0.314	192	35.87y	28.91y		For rivets, etc. Free cutting.
									8.562d	0.309	200	37.65	27.55	......	For special shapes where high lead is detrimental to the bending or working of the stock.
		142	54	87	13										For clock and meter parts, pinions, and other articles where free milling is required.
		122	82	...			120		8.44d	0.305		39.10‡	26.5‡	0.258	For hot forging. Machines easily.
36,000	28,000	120	54	77	16	120	180	885b	8.489d	0.307	204	41.46	25.0	0.258	For automatic machine work. Drills and turns easily.
							180	935b	8.535b	0.308	202	42.07	24.65	0.263	For condenser tubes. Resists action of sea water.
37,000	33,000						180				214				For piston rods, propeller shafts, nuts, bolts, plates, etc. Welding rod.
45,000	33,000	100	89	75				885b	8.404b	0.304	211	41.60	24.93	0.279	
......	33,000	165	90	93	55										
				71			180		8.712d	0.315			32.20	0.341	For Fourdrinier wire.
							180	1075z	8.89h	0.321		24.1	43.0	0.520	For flexible metal hose.
							180	1070z	8.89b	0.321		29.62	35.0	0.350	For electrical purposes.
54,000	33,000	175	60	90	30		180	1050z	8.88b	0.321	190	82.18‡	12.62‡	0.150	For springs, electric switches, etc.
......		190	60	96	30		180	1050z	8.87b	0.320	178	56.46	18.37	0.195	For window weight chain. Bronze chain in general.
				...	75		180		8.929b	0.322	....	56.46	18.37	0.199	Phosphor bronze with good machining properties.
60,000		200	70	99	38		180	1025z	8.815b	0.318	182	79.8	13.00	0.150	For electric switches, contact fingers, diaphragms, radio parts, etc.
64,000		200	74	100	52		180	1000z	8.78b	0.317	183	93.10	10.6	0.121	For very stiff resilient springs (flat or coiled). Also for chain.
35,000		120	...	75					8.86b	0.320	....	......	12.2	0.133	For good machining properties.
							180	1022b				86.43	12.0	......	For electrical purposes.

h Jenkins and Hanson constitution diagram.
j Average linear coefficient per deg cent from 25 to 300 deg cent. Tests on rod. Scientific Paper 410, U. S. Bureau of Standards.
k At 18.1 deg cent.
m Cold worked and heat-treated.
n Guertler-Tammann constitution diagram.
p Annealed, quenched, and heat-treated.

r Smith constitution diagram.
t Stockdale constitution diagram.
u G-cal, per sec per sq cm per deg cent per cm at 20 deg cent.
v Tafel constitution diagram.
x Bauer and Hansen constitution diagram.
y Hard at 25 deg cent.
z Heycock-Neville constitution diagram.

Table III. Chemical and Physical Properties of
(Variations must be

Material	Form	Copper	Zinc	Nickel			Tensile Strength, lb per sq in. Hard*	Soft	Elongation in 2 in., per cent Hard*	Soft	Yield Point, (g) lb per sq in. Hard*	Soft	Johnson's Elastic Limit, lb per sq in. Hard*	Soft	Modulus of Elasticity, lb per sq in.×10⁻⁶, Hard*
Super-nickel	T	70.00	....	30.00	....			65,000	....	30					
20% cupro-nickel	S	80.00	....	20.00			85,000	50,000	2	30					
15% cupro-nickel	S	85.00	....	15.00			70,000	45,000	3	30	51,000				
30% nickel silver	S	47.00	23.00	30.00			130,000	72,000	2	35					
	W	47.00	23.00	30.00			160,000	75,000	1e	35e					
Ambrac B	S	65.00	5.00	30.00			105,000	65,000	2	30					
	R	65.00	5.00	30.00			85,000	65,000	10	30					
	W	65.00	5.00	30.00			130,000	65,000	2e	30					20.0
25% nickel silver	S	55.00	20.00	25.00			110,000	72,000	4	30					
Ambrac A	S	75.00	5.00	20.00			85,000	50,000	5	35	77,000	23,000	57,000	10,000	
	R	75.00	5.00	20.00			80,000	55,000	10	50	70,000	18,000	52,000	13,000	
	W	75.00	5.00	20.00			115,000	55,000	2e	30e					19.0‡
18% nickel silver	S	65.00	17.00	18.00			90,000	58,000	3	40	83,000		72,000		18.0
18% nickel silver	S	56.00	26.00	18.00			100,000	60,000	2	40					
	W	56.00	26.00	18.00			143,000	60,000	1e	40e			103,000		14.1
15% nickel silver	S	64.00	21.00	15.00			93,000	58,000	5.5	40			75,000	22,000	
15% nickel silver	S	57.00	28.00	15.00			95,000	55,000	2	35					
Leaded nickel silver	S	61.00	25.00	12.50	Lead 1.50		90,000		5						
10% nickel silver	S	65.00	25.00	10.00			90,000	50,000	3	45			11,000		17.5‡
5% nickel silver	W	63.00	32.00	5.00			135,000		2e						
5% aluminum bronze	S	95.00			Al 5.00		105,000	52,000	5	70					
8% aluminum bronze	S	92.00			8.00		120,000	60,000	4	60	60,000				15.0
	R	92.00			8.00		100,000	60,000	4	60					
8% aluminum bronze with iron	R	89.50			8.00	Iron 2.50	125,000	72,000	5	50	80,000	35,000			
10% aluminum bronze	R	90.00			10.00		125,000 m	78,000	5m	36	67,000	41,000			
Avialite	R	90.00			9.50	0.50	88,000		35		43,000				

* For some alloys the figures given are for a temper slightly different from that commonly known as "hard."
† Compared to water at 4 deg cent.
‡ Soft.
R Rod.
S Sheet.
T Tube.
W Wire.

a Temper not known.
b Determination.
c Circular 73, U. S. Bureau of Standards.
d Scientific Paper 410, U. S. Bureau of Standards.
e Elongation of wire, per cent in 10 in.
f Corning Glass Works.
g Yield point taken as the load producing an extension under stress of 0.75 per cent.

Various Wrought Copper-base Alloys—*Continued*

expected in practice)

Shearing Strength, lb per sq in.		Brinell Hardness No. 10-mm Ball, 500-kg Load		Rockwell Hardness No. "B" 1/16-in. Ball, 100 kg		Bend Test, deg		Melting Point, deg cent	Specific Gravity †	Density, lb per cu in.	Coefficient of Expansion $\times 10^f$ (j)	Electrical Properties at 20° C		Thermal Conductivity (u)	Uses—Remarks
Hard*	Soft	Hard*	Soft	Hard*	Soft	Hard*	Soft					Resistivity ohms (mil, ft)	Conductivity, per cent I.A.C.S.		
.....	.....	...	...	...	...	...	...	1225n	8.950	0.323	162f	218.4	4.75	0.069	For condenser tubes.
.....	.....	...	../	85	37.5	...	180	1200n	.....	...	....	160.2	6.47	0.087	For turbine blades and parts where resistance to corrosion and erosion is required.
.....	.....	...	...	...	...	...	180	1175n	8.95b	0.323	....	127.0	8.17	0.112	For bullet jackets.
.....	.....	...	...	...	61	...	180	1140v	8.74b	0.316	....	290.0	3.58	.....	Has comparatively high electrical resistance. Used in electrical instruments.
55,000		195	63	96	32	...	180	1220b	8.86b	0.320	162f	231.8a	4.47a	0.068	For resistance to corrosion and atmospheric action; also for ornamental purposes.
.....		208	89	...	60	...	180	1135v	8.72b	0.315	....	259.0a	4.00a	.....	For tableware, plated and unplated.
50,000	33,000	160	58	88	25	...	180	1150b	8.860	0.320	164f	172.0	6.2	0.092	For resistance to corrosion and atmospheric action; also for ornamental purposes.
.....		170	70	91	40	...	180	1110v	8.752b	0.316	....	175.0	5.91	0.080	For silver-plated forks, spoons, knives, hollow ware, etc.
65,000		190	70	95	40			1055v	8.68b	0.314	....	186.5‡	5.56‡	0.071	Similar to 30% nickel silver but of lower resistance.
.....						180	180					185.0	5.61	0.071	
.....		...	73	92	33	...	180	1075v	8.691b	0.314	....	165.6	6.26	0.081	For silver-plated ware, spinning, drawing, and for work where a low percentage of nickel is required.
.....		...	74	...	...	...	180	1030b	8.631b	0.312					For white metal tubes, sheets, wire, etc. Also in plumbing and decorations.
.....		166	...	88	...	...	180								For watch parts, etc. Free cutting.
.....	34,000	...	...	82	32	...	...	1010	8.675b	0.313	....	125.5	8.27	0.110	For cheaper grades of silver-plated ware.
.....								960v				86.5	11.99	0.140	
.....		176	67	93	20	...	...	1060t	8.176b	0.295	....	58.61	17.69	0.198	For diaphragms to withstand pressure; also for its color.
.....		185	60	99	30	.....	...	1040t	7.80b	0.281	179	70.08k	14.80k	0.173	For diaphragms to withstand pressure; also for resistance to ordinary corrosion and wear.
.....		190	70	100	52	...	...		7.74b	0.280		95.10	10.9	.....	For strength and resistance to ordinary corrosion and wear.
.....		190	100	100	65	.....	...	1040t	7.57b	0.273		76.80	13.5	0.157	For strength and resistance to ordinary corrosion and wear.
45,000		140	...	...	...	.....	...	1042b	7.585b	0.274	169	82.25	12.61	0.144	For valve seats in airplane engines and at elevated temperatures.

h Jenkins and Hanson constitution diagram.
j Average linear coefficient per deg cent from 25 to 300 deg cent. Tests on rod. Scientific Paper 410, U. S. Bureau of Standards.
k At 18.1 deg cent.
m Cold worked and heat-treated.
n Guertler-Tammann constitution diagram.
p Annealed, quenched, and heat-treated.

r Smith constitution diagram.
t Stockdale constitution diagram.
u G-cal per sec per sq cm per deg cent per cm at 20 deg cent.
v Tafel constitution diagram.
x Bauer and Hansen constitution diagram.
y Hard at 25 deg cent.
z Heycock-Neville constitution diagram.

Table III. Chemical and Physical Properties of
(Variations must be

Material	Form	Copper	Zinc	Nickel				Tensile Strength, lb per sq in. Hard*	Soft	Elongation in 2 in., per cent Hard*	Soft	Yield Point, (g) lb per sq in. Hard*	Soft	Johnson's Elastic Limit, lb per sq in. Hard*	Soft	Modulus of Elasticity, lb per sq in. ×10⁻⁶, Hard*
Calsun bronze	W	95.50	....	Man-ga-nese	Al 2.50	Iron	Tin 2.00	135,000	50,000	4e	35e	....	....	81,000	......	....
Manganese bronze	R	57.00	40.00	0.10	.....	1.45	1.45	90,000	65,000	15	45					
Manganese bronze	R	59.00	39.00	0.50	.....	0.80	0.70	85,000	60,000	20	45					
Everdur (A) 1010	S	96.00	.....	1.00	Si 3.00	....		113,000	55,000	5	48	75,000	20,000	72,000	9,300	.....
	R	96.00	.....	1.00	3.00	....		95,000	55,000	15	85	75,000	20,000	67,000	......	15.0
	W	96.00	.....	1.00	3.00	....		145,000	59,000	5e	50e	95,000	25,000	90,000	......	
Everdur (B) 1015	T	98.25	.....	0.25	1.50	....		65,000	40,000	15	60	60,000	10,000	.....		
	R	98.25	.....	0.25	1.50	....		70,000	40,000	6	60	....	10,000			
	S	98.25	.....	0.25	1.50	....		70,000	40,000	6	46	65,000	10,000	38,000		
Hitenso A	W	99.35	....	Cadmium 0.65				75,000	....	3e	....	47,000		45,000	......	15.6
	S	99.35	....	0.65				54,000	....	5						
Hitenso BB	S	99.00	....	1.00				60,000	35,000	3	50			36,000	......	
	W	99.00	....	1.00				92,000	35,000	3e	50e			55,000		
Hitenso C	S	98.60	....	0.80		0.60		....	36,000	....	50			15,000	......	
	W	98.60	....	0.80		0.60		99,000	40,000	4e	45e			59,000		
Tempaloy 917	R	81.90	Iron 2.50	Ni 5.00	Al 9.60	Mn 1.00	....	100,000	....	10		50,000		....		
Extruded architectural bronze shapes		57.00	Zinc 40.00	Lead 2.50	Tin 0.34	Iron 0.16	....	70,000	50,000	10	20	....				
Beryllium copper	S	97.40	.....	Be 2.25 Ni 0.35	....			118,000	70,000	4.3	45	105,000	31,000	79,000	18,000	17.2
	S	97.40	.....	2.25 Ni 0.35	....			192,000 m	175,000 p	2 m	6.3p	138,000 m	114,000 p	130,000 m	87,000 p	18.4 m

* For some alloys the figures given are for a temper slightly different from that commonly known as "hard."
† Compared to water at 4 deg cent.
‡ Soft.
R Rod.
S Sheet.
T Tube.
W Wire.

a Temper not known.
b Determination.
c Circular 73, U. S. Bureau of Standards.
d Scientific Paper 410, U. S. Bureau of Standards.
e Elongation of wire, per cent in 10 in.
f Corning Glass Works.
g Yield point taken as the load producing an extension under stress of 0.75 per cent.

Various Wrought Copper-base Alloys—*Continued*

expected in practice)

Shearing Strength, lb per sq in.		Brinell Hardness No. 10-mm Ball, 500-kg Load		Rockwell Hardness No. "B" 1/16-in. Ball, 100 kg		Bend Test, deg		Melting Point, deg cent	Specific Gravity †	Density, lb per cu in.	Coefficient of Expansion $\times 10^7$ (j)	Electrical Properties at 20° C		Thermal Conductivity (u)	Uses—Remarks
Hard*	Soft	Hard*	Soft	Hard*	Soft	Hard*	Soft					Resistivity, ohms (mil, ft)	Conductivity, per cent I.A.C.S.		
......	......	..	..	..	......	..	...	1054b	8.540b	0.308	....	61.0	17.0	......	For electrical uses where corrosion resistance is important.
......	......	170	..	..	......	..	...								For structural work due to strength and resistance to corrosion.
......	......	..	..	..	90	..	...		8.370b	0.302	....	42.15	24.6	0.241	For structural work due to strength and resistance to corrosion.
......	......	200	70	95	40	...	180	1019b	8.539b	0.308	180	155.	6.7	0.078	For strength and resistance to corrosion. Has strength of mild steel and corrosion resistance of copper. Welding rod.
56,000	33,000	190	60	..	..										
75,000	35,000	..	..												
......	......	..	..	75	20	...	180	1055r	8.740b	0.316					For strength and resistance to corrosion, bolt stock, and sheet metal requiring high ductility.
......	......			..	..		180					86.4	12.0	0.129	
......	......			80	3	...	180								
......	......			95	...	62	180	1080h	8.89b	0.3212		12.20	85.0	......	For electrical wire and cable, etc.
......	......			98	...	65	180	1076h	8.89b	0.3212		12.95y	80.0y	0.824	For electrical wire and cables, contact fingers, commutator segments, etc.
......	......											12.95y	80.0y	......	
......	......						180	1070b	8.89b	0.3212	....	18.85y	55.0y	0.556	For electrical wire and cables, etc.
......	......											18.85y	55.0y		
......	......							1054b	7.569	0.273					For strength and resistance to corrosion.
......	......							884b	8.432b	0.305					For architectural shapes.
......	......	..	..	102	65 to 73	...		955b	......	0.297 ±.01	170	......	17±p	......	For springs, diaphragms, low duty bushings and bearings, and Bourdon tubes. High resistance to fatigue.
......	......	m	p	114	112.5	..				0.297 ±.01		......	18 to 25m	0.25p / 0.20m	
				m	p										

h Jenkins and Hanson constitution diagram.
j Average linear coefficient per deg cent from 25 to 300 deg cent. Tests on rod. Scientific Paper 410, U. S. Bureau of Standards.
k At 18.1 deg cent.
m Cold worked and heat-treated.
n Guertler-Tammann constitution diagram.
p Annealed, quenched, and heat-treated.

r Smith constitution diagram.
t Stockdale constitution diagram.
u G-cal per sq cm per deg cent per cm at 20 deg cent.
v Tafel constitution diagram.
x Bauer and Hansen constitution diagram.
y Hard at 25 deg cent.
z Heycock-Neville constitution diagram.

mercial methods. Because of their high heat conductivity they dissipate the heat so rapidly that it is difficult to make a proper weld. The classes that can most readily be welded are the yellow brasses, manganese-bronze, and the proprietory alloys, Everdur and Ambrac.

Corrosion. Certain alloys resist corrosion better than others, and under the heading " Remarks " in Tables II and III this condition is noted in some cases. As a class these alloys are considered non-corrosive with reference to atmospheric conditions, but they vary widely when exposed to chemical agents, or even to the same agent under different conditions. For this reason, it is difficult to predict resistance to corrosion. In nearly every instance a trial under service conditions is necessary where a new alloy is to be used. Laboratory tests are unreliable for comparing different types of material, although they are valuable as acceptance tests for material of the same type. Where corrosion resistance is of importance, the manufacturer of the alloy should be consulted as to its suitability under the proposed conditions, or tests made on samples of the alloy in question.

Sand-cast Copper-base Alloys. The common copper-base alloys containing more than 50 per cent copper are given in Table II which has been compiled from about twelve authorities. The composition and physical properties given are average and should not be used for specification limits. For many of these alloys, the physical properties will vary more owing to changes in casting and cooling conditions than to wide changes in composition. The relative value of these alloys for mechanical purposes varies with temperature, and information on this point should be secured before subjecting them to high-temperature use.

Wrought Copper-base Alloys. Table III gives the composition and physical properties of some of the common wrought copper-base alloys. The values given are average and should not be used for specification limits. Almost any physical properties between the figures for " hard " and " soft " may be obtained by appropriate working. Higher values for tensile strength or hardness may be obtained by a greater amount of working. The physical properties also vary with the temperature, and hence, if they are to be subjected to high-temperature use, information should be obtained from the manufacturers on this point. For copper-base bearing alloys, see p. 11–84.

ZINC AND ZINC-BASE ALLOYS
By W. M. Peirce

19. CHEMICAL AND PHYSICAL PROPERTIES

Chemical Characteristics. Zinc is a chemically active metal. Its chemical properties are the reason for its use in primary cells, for cyaniding and in the production of nascent hydrogen. It forms both basic and acid radicals, and is soluble both in acids and strong alkalies.

Physical Constants. The more important physical constants of zinc are given in Table I.

Metallography. The common impurities in zinc are lead, cadmium, and iron. See Table II, p. 11–54. Their importance varies individually with the use to which the metal is put. These metals, as well as copper, magnesium, and aluminum, which are the more common elements used in zinc alloys, are discussed below.

Lead, which does not enter into solid solution, has no great effect in unalloyed zinc. Its effect on the properties of certain zinc alloys, however, is enormous.

Cadmium, in the amounts present in commercial zinc, is completely in solid solution, and exerts an important hardening effect. It also raises the recrystallization temperature, and whereas pure zinc recrystallizes at so little above room temperature that it cannot be appreciably work hardened, zinc containing cadmium can be given a considerable degree of work hardening by cold rolling.

Iron has a limited solid solubility of the order of 0.001 to 0.003 per cent. Attention must be given to the iron content of zinc for rolling.

Copper is the alloying element most frequently added to zinc. It enters into solid solution in zinc to about the same extent (approximately 1 per cent), and with about the same effect, as cadmium, except that the copper-zinc alloys are more ductile and easier to roll.

Magnesium has a solid solubility of 0.01 or 0.02 per cent in zinc, but even these amounts exert a remarkable influence on its properties. When magnesium is added in the presence of copper, its effect is even more striking. Some of the most important zinc alloys contain both copper and magnesium.

Table I. Physical Properties of Zinc

(Compiled from various sources)

	Metric Units	English Units
Atomic weight	65.38	65.38
Density (rolled), (see Note 1)	7.14 g per cu cm	445.8 lb per cu ft
Melting point	419.45° C	787° F
Boiling point	905 ± 2° C	1661 ± 4° F
Mean specific heat (20°–100° C)	0.0931 g-cal per g per deg cent	....
Latent heat of fusion	26.6 g-cal per g	47.88 Btu per lb
Latent heat of vaporization	426.8 g-cal per g	768.2 Btu per lb
Coefficient of linear expansion		
Cast	39.5 × 10^{-6} ⎫ Per	21.9 × 10^{-6} ⎫ Per
Rolled, with grain	32 × 10^{-6} ⎬ deg	17.8 × 10^{-6} ⎬ deg
Rolled, across grain	23 × 10^{-6} ⎭ cent	12.8 × 10^{-6} ⎭ fahr
Thermal conductivity	1.13 watts per sq cm per deg cent per cm 0.270 g-cal per sec per sq cm per deg cent per cm	
Electrical resistivity (see Note 2)	5.916 microhm-cm	2.33 microhm-in.
Temperature coefficient of resistance (0°–100° C)	0.00419 per deg cent	0.00233 per deg fahr
Resonance	See Note 3	

NOTES. 1. Solid zinc (rolled) is about 3 per cent heavier than liquid zinc at the melting point.
2. Based on soft rolled zinc strip 99.99 per cent pure. Resistivity of strip zinc may vary 3 per cent, depending on the rolling treatment, and in commercial grades about the same amount, depending on the purity.
3. Rolled zinc has extremely low resonance, which permits its use in various sound apparatus.

Aluminum is the other important element used in zinc alloys. Its use is limited entirely to casting alloys, as usually zinc alloys containing aluminum are unstable when rolled. In the cast form, however, several per cent of aluminum can be used to improve greatly the physical properties, particularly the tensile and impact strength of zinc. The alloys, if properly formulated, are stable.

Corrosion

Atmospheric Corrosion. In pure distilled water zinc forms a loosely adherent film of hydroxide which affords little protection. This film, dried in the presence of oxygen and the traces of carbon dioxide always present in the atmosphere, forms a protective layer or film believed to be a zinc oxide-hydroxide-carbonate mixture. This is quite insoluble in rainwater, affords effective protection against further attack, and makes zinc a satisfactory roofing and flashing material. The presence of sulfur gases in industrial atmospheres increases the solubility of this film, accounting for the higher rate of weathering in industrial than in rural atmospheres.

Resistance to Organic Substances. Zinc is inert to such common organic substances as gasoline, kerosene, oil, and grease free from water. Soap and soap paste do not attack it, though in dilute soap solutions there is a tendency to form zinc soaps. Zinc is entirely inert toward anhydrous alcohol, but is oxidized by mixtures of alcohol and water. Sugar solutions in hard water do not attack zinc when totally immersed at room temperature, but distilled-water solutions at any temperature or hard-water solutions at elevated temperatures attack it.

Certain organic acids dissolve the atmospheric corrosion film on zinc, for example, acids formed by decomposition of red and white cedar at ordinary temperatures, and of other woods at higher temperatures (as in steam). Hence zinc and some other common metals cannot be safely used in contact with certain moist wood, or the drainage from them.

Toxicity. Excepting the salts of strong acids, which are corrosive, or zinc compounds containing other poisonous elements or radicals, the compounds of zinc are not strongly toxic. Zinc is a normal constituent in many foods and considerable excesses of zinc taken into the body are readily eliminated without ill effects. Excess zinc content in foods or beverages may cause unpleasant but not serious symptoms. Drinking water should not contain above 40 mg per liter.

Effect of Carbon Dioxide and Steam. Very high carbon dioxide concentrations appear to aid the solution of the corrosion film. Increased temperature may sometimes have such an effect. Live steam destroys the protective film and also attacks the metallic zinc at an increased rate. Hence unalloyed zinc is unsuitable for use when exposed to live steam.

Effect of Oxygen Concentration. See p. 11–07. Severe corrosion of zinc occasionally occurs in the presence of a water film without free access of oxygen to all portions of it. An example is a zinc roof, laid over an absorbent sheathing and building paper, on a building having high humidity inside. If the roof is unprotected from condensation on the under side, rapid corrosion of the zinc may occur. The preventive is building paper, saturated and coated on both sides with asphalt, under the metal roofing.

20. SLAB ZINC

Chemical Composition of Slab Zinc. According to the A.S.T.M. Standard Specifications for slab zinc (Spelter) (B6–33), the composition should conform to the maximum values of Table II.

Table II.   Standard Specifications of Slab Zinc

Grade		Maximum Allowable Per Cent of			Lead+Cadmium +Iron not to Exceed
		Lead	Cadmium	Iron	
1	Special high grade *†....	0.010	0.005	0.005	0.010
2	High grade *............	0.07	0.07	0.03	0.10
3	Intermediate *..........	0.20	0.50	0.03	0.50
4	Brass special *..........	0.60	0.50	0.03	1.00
5	Selected *..............	0.80	0.75	0.04	1.25
6	Prime western..........	1.60	....	0.08	....

* All grades except prime western must be free from aluminum.
† Tentative standard.

Uses of Slab Zinc

Galvanizing. The process of coating iron or steel with zinc as a protection against corrosion is known as galvanizing, and the product is known as galvanized iron or steel. This use is the largest single outlet for metallic zinc. Zinc coatings are desirable not only because the zinc corrodes more slowly than iron but also because at cut edges or similar discontinuities in the coating, the zinc, being anodic to the iron, affords galvanic protection and the iron is not dissolved until the zinc has been completely removed by corrosion.

The suitability of galvanized coatings for use under any particular service conditions is governed by the factors discussed above under corrosion.

The life of zinc coatings, regardless of the method of application, has been shown to be directly proportional to the thickness or weight of the coating. The proportion of pure zinc to iron-zinc alloys in the coating does not have any significant effect.

Specifications and Tests for Galvanized Coatings. Galvanized coatings usually are specified as a given weight of zinc per unit area, for example, ounces of zinc per square foot of surface. For details of methods of determining the weight of the coating see Standard Methods of Determining Weight of Coating on Zinc Coated Articles, A.S.T.M. Specification A–90–33.

Specifications for most commercial products covering weight of coating and bend tests when required are available in A.S.T.M. Standards, 1933, Part I, Metals, pp. 278–312, and A.S.T.M. Tentative Standards, 1933, pp. 583–586.

On sheets, coating weights are given as weight per square foot of sheet, i.e., 2 sq ft of coated surface. Ordinary coatings on sheets range from 0.75 to 2.75 oz per sq ft of sheet coated on both sides. The weight of zinc per single covered surface would be one-half this amount. Zinc coatings on pipe, structural shapes, hardware, etc., generally range between 1.15 and 3.5 oz per sq ft of covered surface. The weight of coating on wire varies with the size of wire and process of coating, and, except in fine sizes, will range from 0.15 to 1.25 oz per sq ft of covered surface.

Methods of Application. Galvanized coatings are applied: (a) by dipping the article in molten zinc, (b) by electroplating, (c) by heating in contact with zinc dust.

Hot Dip Galvanizing. In the process, the iron or steel is cleaned by pickling, usually in hot sulfuric acid. A rinse and a dip in cold hydrochloric usually follow, but better practice involves removal of iron salts from the pickled material by vigorous rinsing and scrubbing if necessary, followed by dipping in 25 per cent zinc chloride (slightly acidulated). After partial drying, the material enters the bath of molten zinc, sometimes through a flux of zinc ammonium chloride. Wetting of the iron by the zinc and the formation of a solid layer of iron-zinc alloy on the iron surface occur in a matter of seconds. The longer the immersion, the thicker the alloy layers.

The material is withdrawn from the zinc bath through rolls kept clean by zinc ammonium chloride flux in the case of sheet or through a charcoal sand or asbestos wipe in the case of wire. The speed of withdrawal and character of the wipe influence the thickness of the layer of molten zinc adhering to the work.

The behavior of the coating on bending is influenced largely by the purity of the zinc, high-grade zinc being used where bending properties are important, as in the case of telephone wire. Factors in the operation tending to produce a thin uniform alloy layer also have an important beneficial effect on bending. A common practice is to wipe off practically all the molten zinc, leaving only the alloy layer which dusts rather than flakes on bending, the loss of coating being thus less conspicuous. Exposure tests have shown that a heavy coating which flakes lasts longer than a thin " tight wiped " coating which dusts at a bend.

A patent process known as " galvannealing," in commercial use, converts the pure zinc layer to alloy by heating, imparting some of the bending characteristics of tight wiped material and a type of surface somewhat similar to sherardizing.

Another patented process known as the " Crapo Process " involves special pretreatment of the iron surface before galvanizing to improve adherence.

Tin may be added to the zinc bath to produce a sheet with bright spangle (which has no merit except appearance). Aluminum may be added in hand dip galvanizing of pipe, shapes, and hardware to produce a smooth coating. The vapor of burning sulfur or ammonium chloride dust is sometimes blown over the surface of sheets to improve brightness.

Electrogalvanizing. Zinc coatings are also applied to wire, conduit, and hardware by electroplating. The only distinguishing feature of this process, as compared to other electroplating processes, lies in the attention given to methods of rapidly depositing heavy coatings (e.g., the patented Tainton Process), since the serviceability of the coatings depends on their thickness and the thickness ordinarily desirable is greater than in purely decorative plating.

This method of zinc coating has the merit of avoiding changes in the base steel due to heat and of not producing excessive deposits in recesses such as the base of threads which would affect dimensional tolerances.

Sherardizing. Zinc and iron alloy very readily, and coatings can therefore be produced by heating iron or steel in a closed vessel with zinc dust (sometimes termed blue powder) for several hours. The vapor pressure of the zinc is sufficient at the temperatures used, 600–700 deg fahr, to cause a reaction of zinc vapor with the iron, and this is probably supplemented by actual contact. (It has been demonstrated that alloying will occur by diffusion at only slightly elevated temperatures.) The resulting coating is almost entirely iron zinc alloy (richer in iron near the base metal) with some mechanically held zinc dust in the outer layers.

This process may result in some heat treatment of the base metal. The thickness of coating produced is quite uniform over all parts of the surface. Sherardized coatings like coatings of iron-zinc alloy produced by other methods afford an excellent base for paints or enamels. The coating itself is a matte gray and can be polished. Like other coatings consisting almost entirely of iron-zinc alloys, sherardized coatings dust rather than flake on bending. Also in common with such coatings the protection afforded by a given thickness is, under the average normal service conditions, equal to the protection afforded by an equal thickness of pure zinc.

The zinc dust used may be the by-product blue powder from spelter furnaces or may be expressly manufactured for the purpose, attention being given to a suitable particle size and metallic zinc content (the balance being largely ZnO).

Brass. See p. 11–40. The second largest use of zinc is in brass. This constitutes a separate field, and will not be discussed here except to state that, since lead is objectionable in brass for drawing operations, grades of zinc low in lead are largely used in brass manufacture.

Die Casting. The most rapidly growing use of zinc is for die casting. Suitable alloys for this process have been found to require zinc of exceptional purity, and the " Special High-grade " specification listed above is drawn primarily to define a suitable grade for use in zinc die-casting alloys. Freedom from lead, tin, and cadmium is the primary requirement.

By alloying with about 4 per cent aluminum, a few hundredths magnesium, and in some cases 1 to 3 per cent copper, alloys amenable to die casting, and having in the diecast condition radically improved properties as compared with unalloyed zinc, are obtained.

These alloys and their properties are further described on p. 11–82.

Slush Casting. High grade slab zinc is used in slush castings, largely used for lighting fixtures and other ornamental parts. High grade unalloyed zinc is used as well as alloyed zinc containing small percentages of aluminum, and sometimes of copper.

21. ROLLED ZINC

Classification of Rolled Zinc. Rolled or wrought zinc is divided by the A.S.T.M. (see A.S.T.M. Standard Specifications for Rolled Zinc, B 69–29) into the following types:

Type A. Ribbon zinc and sheets or strips cut from ribbon zinc which has been rolled from a single bar in one continuous direction.

Type B. Sheet zinc or strips cut from sheet zinc that has been rolled by the pack rolling method.

Type C. Boiler and hull plates, which may be rolled either from a single bar or by the pack rolling method.

Zinc Gage. Table III compares the standard zinc gage and the American or Brown and Sharpe gage and the U. S. Standard gage. The use of this special zinc gage is discouraged and, in order to avoid errors, the actual thickness expressed in thousands of an inch is preferable.

Table III.   Comparison of Zinc Gage and Other Gages

Brown & Sharpe Gage, Approximate Thickness		Rolled Zinc Gage			U. S. Standard Gage, Approximate Thickness	
No.	In.	No.	Weight of 1 Sq Ft, lb	Thickness In.	No.	In.
34	0.0063	3	0.22	0.006	38	0.0062
..	....	..	.....	.....	37	.0066
33	.0070	..	.....	.....	36	.0070
32	.0079	4	.30	.008	35	.0078
31	.0089	..	.....	.....	34	.0086
..	.....	..	.....	.....	33	.0093
30	.0100	5	.37	.010	32	.0101
29	.0112	..	.....	.....	31	.0109
28	.0126	6	.45	.012	30	.0125
27	.0141	7	.52	.014	29	.0140
26	.0159	8	.60	.016	28	.0156
25	.0179	..	.....	.....	27	.0171
24	.0201	9	.67	.018	26	.0187
23	.0225	10	.75	.020	25	.0218
22	.0253	11	.90	.024	24	.0250
21	.0284	12	1.05	.028	23	.0281
20	.0319	13	1.20	.032	22	.0312
19	.0353	14	1.35	.036	21	.0343
18	.0403	15	1.50	.040	20	.0375
17	.0452	16	1.68	.045	19	.0437
16	.0508	17	1.87	.050	18	.0500
15	.0570	18	2.06	.055	17	.0562
14	.0640	19	2.25	.060	16	.0625
13	.0719	20	2.62	.070	15	.0703
12	.0808	21	3.00	.080	14	.0781
11	.0907	22	3.37	.090	13	.0937
10	.1018	23	3.75	.100	12	.1093
9	.1144	24	4.70	.125	11	.1250
8	.1284	..	.....	.....	10	.1406
7	.1442	..	.....	.....	9	.1562
6	.1620	..	.....	.....	8	.1718
5	.1819	..	.....	.....	7	.1875
4	.2043	..	.....	.....	6	.2031
3	.2294	..	.....	.....	5	.2187
..	.....	..	.....	.....	4	.2343
2	.2576	25	9.40	.250	3	.2500
..	.....	..	.....	.....	2	.2656
1	.2893	..	.....	.....	1	.2812
0	.3249	..	.....	.....	0	.3125
3/0	.4096	26	14.00	.375	3/0	.3750
..	.....	27	18.75	.500	7/0	.5000
..	.....	28	37.50	1.000	..	.....

Mechanical Properties of Rolled Zinc. A standard specification (A.S.T.M., B 69–29) calls for temper and dynamic ductility (cupping) tests. These are considered the only ones sufficiently reproducible and valuable for specification purposes. *Temper* is measured by a testing machine which wraps a specimen tightly around a mandrel to which one end of the specimen is clamped. The degree to which the free end springs away from the mandrel is measured on an arbitrary scale, ranging from 0, representing no spring whatever, to 100, representing material that returns to its original straight condition. *Dynamic ductility* is determined by forming a series of cups by forcing a spherical-ended plunger into a test strip, the plunger being adjustably mounted in a drawing press to permit varying the depth of the cup. The maximum depth of the cup, in inches, which can be formed before visible " necking down " occurs is the dynamic ductility.

The three types of rolled zinc are classified according to temper as follows: Type A: dead soft, soft, half hard, and hard; Type B: commercial; Type C: no classification. It should be noted that the terms soft, dead soft, etc., serve to designate certain specific ranges of properties regardless of the combination of composition and rolling treatment by which the properties are obtained.

Where tensile tests are used the A.S.T.M. standard tensile specimen (see p. 5–84) for thin sheet metal is entirely suitable for zinc. A pulling speed as near to 0.25 in. per min as can be obtained on the testing machine should be used. Under these conditions, rolled zinc will have a " with-grain " tensile strength varying from 18,000 lb per sq in. for soft-temper high-grade zinc to 35,000 lb per sq in. for hard-temper prime western zinc. The elongation will vary from 5 per cent for the hardest to 65 per cent for the softest metal. The " across-grain " strength in every case will be a few thousand pounds higher and the elongation somewhat lower. By alloying, considerably higher tensile strengths can be obtained, although this is usually at the expense of ductility. The percentage elongation in the tensile test is of little significance since the rate of loading is far below the rate of deformation in commercial drawing or fabrication, and is no index to ductility in these operations.

The Modulus of Elasticity of zinc lies between 10,000,000 and 20,000,000, depending on the rolling treatment. Approximately 12,000,000 is a representative value for soft-rolled high-grade zinc.

The Shearing Strength of high-grade zinc plates is reported as 17,000 to 19,000 lb per sq in.

Static Tensile Tests. Of much greater importance than the ordinary tensile test, from a practical standpoint, is the static tensile or creep test which determines the resistance of various grades of zinc to elongation or flow at different temperatures under static tensile load. This information has been correlated with actual loading tests on corrugated zinc roofing sheets. (See Tables IV and V.)

Table IV. Safe Span for Corrugated Zinc Roofing Sheets at 70° F (21.1° C)
Corrugations 7/8 in. deep × 2 1/2 in.

Gage	C. to C. of Purlins	
	30 lb per sq ft Load	40 lb per sq ft Load
13 ga. 0.032 in. thick	39.5 in.	36 in.
14 ga. 0.036 in. thick	41	38
15 ga. 0.040 in. thick	42	39
16 ga. 0.045 in. thick	43.5	40

Table V. Safe Span for Zilloy* Roofing Sheets at 70° F (21.1° C)
Under a Uniform Load of 40 lb per sq ft

Corrugations 1 in. deep × 2 1/2 in.	Safe Span, C. to C. of Purlins	Corrugations 7/8 in. deep × 2 1/2 in.	Safe Span, C. to C. of Purlins
12 ga. 0.028 in. thick	50.5 in.	13 ga. 0.032 in. thick	48 in.
13 ga. 0.032 in. thick	54	14 ga. 0.036 in. thick	51
14 ga. 0.036 in. thick	57	15 ga. 0.040 in. thick	54
15 ga. 0.040 in. thick	60	16 ga. 0.045 in. thick	57
16 ga. 0.045 in. thick	64		

* Trade Mark, Reg. U.S. Patent Office. A zinc-copper-magnesium alloy patented and sold by The New Jersey Zinc Co.

Fabrication. The ductility of zinc falls off rapidly at temperatures below 70 deg fahr. All drawing and bending operations, therefore, should be performed at temperatures above that point. Frequently an operation which is just too severe to be successful at temperatures near the lower limit may be successfully accomplished by warming the

Table VI.   Safe Loads in lb per sq ft for Zilloy Roofing Sheets
Corrugations 1 in. deep $\times$ 2 1/2 in.

Gage	Span C. to C. of Purlins								
	39 in.	42 in.	45 in.	48 in.	51 in.	54 in.	57 in.	60 in.	63 in.
12 ga. 0.028 in.	67	58	50	44	39	Rigidity when			
13 ga. 0.032 in.	76	65	57	50	44	40	roof is walked		
14 ga. 0.036 in.	86	74	64	56	50	45	40	on question-	
15 ga. 0.040 in.	96	83	72	63	56	50	45	40	able beyond
16 ga. 0.045 in.	108	93	81	71	63	56	50	45	41	this line

zinc and tools, for example to 100 deg fahr. In any type of extrusion, it is necessary to use an elevated temperature in order to operate with reasonable pressures.

For certain ornamental sheet metal work heavy gage zinc is hand formed at temperatures as high as 480 deg fahr. Shop methods in drawing zinc vary considerably from one plant to another, but in general, brass practice is followed with departures in detail depending upon the particular operation. It is, of course, unnecessary to anneal pure zinc between operations, and the work-hardening alloys require fewer annealings than brass.

Reductions in diameter from blank to the first cup should not exceed 45 per cent. A somewhat lower per cent reduction is usually preferable practice.

It is possible to reduce the wall thickness 25 to 33 per cent in redrawing operations in which the cup diameter is reduced 20 per cent.

There are many satisfactory lubricants for drawing zinc, the one chosen usually depending upon the succeeding operations. In using soap solutions it is usually necessary to wash the fabricated article within a short time to prevent spotting.

A vital factor in bending is the grain direction. Wherever possible, rolled zinc should be so used as to bring bends at right angles to the grain or rolling direction. When this can be done, proper bending is easy without sacrifice of hardness and stiffness. Zinc is successfully extruded into any of the forms commonly produced in this way. Tubing and rod have been produced, but in the United States development has been limited principally to the production of cups, buttons, nails, etc. In machining zinc, it is common practice to employ tools with a greater rake than normal for brass, and to use soapy water as a lubricant.

Welding of zinc requires some care, because of the low melting point and the tenacious character of the oxide. The best welding is accomplished with a gas flame, but zinc may also be spot-welded electrically. Zinc cannot be welded without seriously weakening areas adjacent to the weld by annealing. If strength is important, some cold-working operation to refine the grain should follow welding.

Zinc is easily soldered. A low soldering temperature is necessary to avoid excessive grain growth in areas adjacent to the joint. This is best secured by using a large iron hot enough to accomplish the soldering with a single pass. Half and half solder is generally used, although a low-melting-point solder is also of advantage. A solder composed of Pb 55 per cent, Sn 30 per cent and Cd 15 per cent is suitable for zinc. It has a low melting point and high tensile strength. Acidulated zinc chloride or killed hydrochloric acid makes an excellent flux, although much zinc is soldered without a flux.

ALUMINUM AND ALUMINUM ALLOYS

By Junius D. Edwards and Zay Jeffries

22. PROPERTIES AND COMMERCIAL FORMS

Aluminum is one of the lightest of the structurally used metals. In the period of less than 50 years during which aluminum has been commercially available, its annual production has increased from a few thousand pounds to more than 500,000,000 lb.

Bauxite, a hydrated oxide of aluminum, is the principal source of the metal, and is found widely distributed in many parts of the world. For the production of aluminum, the ore is refined by treatment with caustic soda, and pure aluminum hydrate is precipitated from the resulting solution. After calcination, the pure alumina (Al_2O_3) is sent to the electrolytic reduction works. Here it is dissolved in a bath of molten cryolite and electrolytically reduced to metallic aluminum. Any impurities in the alumina, such as oxides of iron and silicon, are reduced and appear in the aluminum. Commercially pure aluminum is generally understood to be 99 to 99.5 per cent pure, although grades up to 99.8 per cent or even higher are available. Aluminum having a purity of 99.98 per cent ᴄᴀn be produced by electrolytic refining of the lower grades of metal.

Table I gives the properties of aluminum.

Table I.   Properties of Aluminum
· A.S.T.M. Proceedings, Vol. 34, 1934, p. 299

		Sample Purity, per cent
Atomic weight......................................	26.97	......
Boiling point, deg cent.............................	1800	......
Crystal form.......................................	Face centered cubic	......
Mean coefficient of expansion { 20° to 300° C..........	0.0000257	99.95 (cast)
{ 20° to 500° C..........	0.0000277	99.95 (cast)
Density at 20° C (68° F), g per cu cm..........	2.70	99.971 (wrought-annealed)
Density at melting point (solid), g per cu cm..........	2.55	......
Density at melting point (liquid), g per cu cm..........	2.38	......
Electrical resistivity at 20° C:		
Microhm-cm.....................................	2.688	99.968 (hard drawn)
Ohms (mil, ft) (A.I.E.E. Standard).................	17.01	Commercial
Temperature coefficient at 20° C (A.I.E.E. Standard)....	0.00403	Commercial
Electrical conductivity at 20° C:		
Mass, per cent International Annealed Copper Standard	212.9	......
Volume, per cent International Annealed Copper Standard..	64.6	
Freezing point, deg cent.............................	659.8	......
Heat of vaporization, g-cal per g......................	1950 to 2000	......
Latent heat of fusion { g-cal per g..................	93	......
{ Btu per lb...................	169.16	......
Mechanical properties:		
Tensile strength, lb per sq in.......................	9000	Annealed
Yield strength, lb per sq in (set = 0.2 per cent).......	3000	sheet
Elongation in 2 in., per cent.......................	60	99.95
Brinell hardness, 10-mm ball, 500-kg load.............	15	......
Modulus of elasticity, lb per sq in....................	10,000,000	......
Modulus of rigidity (torsion), lb per sq in............	3,870,000	Commercial
Poisson's ratio.....................................	0.33	......
Total reflectivity, per cent for white light.............	87	......
Mean specific heat, g-cal per g per deg cent (0°–100° C)..	0.226	......
Thermal conductivity, cgs units.......................	0.52	99.66
Watts per sq cm per deg cent per cm.................	2.17	99.66
Btu per hr per sq ft per deg fahr per in..............	1509	......

Commercial Forms. Pure aluminum is soft and ductile but can be hardened by cold working and alloying; certain of the alloys can also be hardened by heat treatment. Both pure aluminum and its alloys are available in wrought form, as plate, sheet, rod, wire, tubing, and rolled and extruded sections. It can also be worked by forging, drawing, stamping, spinning, and other metal-working methods. Alloys are available in cast form, produced by sand, permanent mold, or die-casting processes.

Corrosion-resistant Characteristics of Aluminum. Aluminum is resistant to most atmospheric influences, especially inland industrial atmospheres, but although it is relatively more resistant to seacoast atmospheres than many other commonly used metals, paint or other protection is generally advisable for permanent structures in such locations. As examples of the resistance of unpainted aluminum and its alloys to a variety of atmospheric conditions, may be cited the very satisfactory performance of relatively high-purity aluminum in transmission lines and outside bus-bar installations, of aluminum-silicon alloy castings used in many large buildings as spandrels and other ornamental parts, and of wrought products as window frames and store fronts. Aluminum is used to handle distilled water, many food products, fruit juices, milk, beer, and atmospheric nitric and glacial acetic acids. It is readily dissolved, however, by hydrochloric and hydrofluoric acids and caustic solutions.

This metal, in common with many other corrosion-resistant metals, owes its high resistance to the protective effect of the ever-present oxide coating. Aluminum of the highest purity, in general, possesses the highest corrosion resistance. The presence of most other metals, either as impurities or alloying elements, tends to lower corrosion resistance. Of the common alloying elements, manganese, chromium, and magnesium produce the most corrosion-resistant alloys. Silicon affects the corrosion resistance slightly, and yet, since it conveys other beneficial effects, such as good casting characteristics, it is either the major or one of the minor alloying constituents of some of the most corrosion-resistant alloys. Iron and copper lower the corrosion resistance in the order named, although properly heat-treated aluminum-copper alloys have a sufficiently high corrosion resistance to be used for many applications without paint protection.

The formation of a resistant film or coating under corrosive conditions consumes some of the aluminum and may result in complete perforation of thin sheet or foil, but in heavier sections the same amount of attack will have no appreciable effect on the mechanical integrity of the part. In aircraft, where the sections are of necessity very thin and the consequences of deterioration serious, the strong aluminum alloys are protected from corrosion by one of the several commercially available methods. For such service, the wrought Alclad products, consisting of a heat-treatable strong alloy core covered by a surface layer of high-purity aluminum, or corrosion-resistant alloy, offers an excellent combination of mechanical strength and corrosion resistance. The surface layer not only covers the strong alloy core and so protects it from corrosion, but also, because of its higher solution potential, offers an electrolytic protection over cut edges and abraded areas and also prevents penetration into the core, even under severely corrosive conditions. Ordinarily 17S rivets used to join Alclad sheet are likewise afforded considerable protection because of this electrolytic effect. Other non-heat-treatable Alclad products, employing the principle of a coating of higher solution potential than the core, are available. They resist destructive perforation to a remarkable extent.

Owing to the high solution potential of aluminum and its alloys, contact with many of the commonly used metals in the presence of a corrosive medium results in the rapid deterioration of the aluminum, with a corresponding protection of the metal of lower solution potential. For this reason, metallic contacts with other metals are generally avoided. Electrical insulation between the two dissimilar metals is of considerable help, although salts formed by the solution of the other metal are likely to be plated out on the aluminum surface and thus set up electrolytic action. In spite of the rapid action in severely corrosive media, little action is found to take place in ordinary atmosphere, unless there is an accumulation of a solution of relatively low electrical resistance. On the other hand, in some assemblies used in contact with strong electrolytes, it is advisable even to consider the relative solution potentials of various aluminum alloys which are in contact.

Bright surfaces produced by rolling or extrusion, or highly polished surfaces, tend to become darkened and slightly roughened through exposure to the weather, unless periodically cleaned. Similarly, regular cleaning of cooking utensils and similar articles will prevent pitting, which is often caused by the plating out of particles of heavy metals which have been dissolved in the liquids being handled.

23. ALUMINUM CASTINGS

Very little pure or commercially pure aluminum is fabricated directly into castings of commerce. The pure metal does not cast easily, nor are the properties of a casting made of pure aluminum attractive for most commercial purposes. The aluminum casting industry is therefore largely one of casting various aluminum alloys. There are three distinct casting arts; namely, sand casting, permanent mold casting, and pressure die casting. These arts are sufficiently different to warrant the inclusion of a list of alloys for each. The composition and properties of the more common alloys used for sand castings, permanent mold castings, and pressure die castings are given in Tables II, III, and IV, respectively. Aluminum alloy castings are so widely used at present that it is not possible to list the many specific uses here; nor is it possible to mention the particular combinations or properties leading to the selection of a particular alloy for a specific use.

Sand Castings are made by the ordinary methods of molding. The sand process is used for most large castings, such as crankcases for internal-combustion motors, oil pumps, manifolds, transmission housings, motor frames, architectural castings, etc. Green sand molds with either green or baked sand cores are used. The core binders are usually oil, pitch, or resin, the last two being used for soft and the first for hard cores. The crystallization shrinkage of aluminum alloys being high, ample gates and risers must be provided. Iron, aluminum, or copper chills are also used frequently to prevent cracks or shrinks. In making the molds, care must be taken to obtain the proper temper of the sand and uniform ramming. Aluminum does not " lay " well against a hard-rammed

Table II. Composition and Properties of Sand-cast Aluminum Alloys *

Alloy †	Nominal Chemical Composition	Tension,‡ Typical Values — Yield Strength,§ lb per sq in.	Ultimate Strength, lb per sq in.	Elongation, % in 2 in.	Compression,¶ Typical Values — Yield Strength,§ lb per sq in.	Ultimate Strength, lb per sq in.	Hardness, Typical Values — Brinell 10-mm ball 500-kg load	Rockwell 1/8-in. ball 100-kg load	Shear, Typical Values — Shearing Strength,∥ lb per sq in.	Fatigue — Endurance Limit,** lb per sq in.	Density — Typical Values, lb per cu in.
12 and 212, ASTM-B, SAE-30	Cu 8%	14,000	22,000	2.0	16,000	38,000	65	E-75	20,000	7,500	0.102
43, ASTM-J, SAE-35	Si 5%	9,000	19,000	4.0	9,000	25,000	40	E-41	15,000	6,500	0.096
47, ASTM-K, SAE-37	Si 12.5%	11,000	26,000	8.0	12,000	28,000	50	E-59	18,000	6,000	0.095
108	Si 4%, Cu 3%	17,000	21,000	2.0	21,500	43,000	60	E-70	20,000	8,500	0.099
109, ASTM-E, SAE-32	Cu 12%	18,000	24,000	1.5	23,500	45,000	75	E-82	20,000	10,000	0.105
112, ASTM-C, SAE-33	Cu 7%, Zn 2%, Fe 1.2%	14,000	22,000	2.0	24,000	44,000	75	E-79	20,000	8,500	0.103
122-T2	Cu 10%, Fe 1.2%, Mg 0.2%	21,000	25,000	1.0	33,500	54,000	75	E-82	25,500	9,500	0.106
122-T61 } ASTM-F, SAE-34.		30,000	36,000	1.0	40,500	80,000	100	E-96	29,500	......	0.106
142	Cu 4%, Ni 2%, Mg 1.5%	24,000	28,000	1.0	34,000	52,000	85	E-88	24,000	8,000	0.101
142-T61 } ASTM-H, SAE-39.		30,000	37,000	0.5	58,000	70,000	100	E-96	32,000	8,000	0.101
195-T4	Cu 4.5%	16,000	31,000	8.0	27,000	43,000	65	E-70	28,000	6,000	0.100
195-T6 } ASTM-G, SAE-38		22,000	36,000	4.0	29,000	48,000	80	E-82	30,000	6,500	0.100
195-T62		27,000	40,000	2.0	45,500	56,000	95	E-92	31,000	7,000	0.100
214	Mg 3.7%	12,000	25,000	9.0	12,000	50,000	50	E-59	19,000	5,500	0.095
216	Mg 6%	16,000	27,000	6.0	15,000	57,000	60	E-70	23,500	......	0.094
220-T4	Mg 10%	26,000	44,000	13.0	23,500	72,500	75	E-82	33,500	7,500	0.092
A-334	Cu 3%, Si 4%, Mg 0.3%	20,000	26,000	1.5	20,000	70,000	65	E-79	24,000	......	0.099
355-T4 }	Cu 1.2%, Si 5%, Mg 0.5%	20,000	30,000	4.0	25,000	65,000	60	E-70	30,000	......	0.097
355-T6 }		27,000	35,000	2.0	29,000	68,000	80	E-86	30,000	......	0.097
A-355-T51 }	Cu 1.4%, Si 5%, Mn 0.7% Ni 0.7%, Mg 0.5%	24,000	28,000	1.5	24,000	54,000	65	E-70	21,000	8,000	0.099
A-355-T59 }		21,000	25,000	2.0	21,000	52,000	60	E-66	20,000	8,000	0.099
356-T4 }	Si 7%, Mg 0.3%	16,000	28,000	6.0	16,000	46,000	55	E-70	22,000	......	0.095
356-T6 }		22,000	32,000	4.0	21,000	48,000	70	E-82	23,000	8,000	0.095
645	Zn 11%, Cu 2.5%, Fe 1.5%	22,000	29,000	4.0	34,000	50,000	70	E-82	22,500	7,500	0.106

* Modulus of elasticity approximately 10,300,000 lb per sq in. for these alloys.

† Alloy numbers, except ASTM and SAE, refer to alloys of Aluminum Co. of America. "T" suffix indicates heat-treated alloys.

‡ Tension values determined from standard ½-in. diameter tensile test specimens cast in green sand molds and tested without machining off the surface.

§ Stress at which stress-deformation curve departs 0.2 per cent from the initial modulus line produced.

¶ Results of tests on specimens having an l/r ratio of 16-20. All specimens failed by lateral bending.

∥ Single-shear strength values obtained from double-shear tests.

** Endurance limit based on 500,000,000 cycles, using R. R. Moore type of rotating-beam machine.

Table III. Composition and Properties of Permanent Mold Casting Alloys

Alloy *	Approximate Composition	Typical Values		Brinell Hardness 500-kg 10-mm ball ‡	Approximate Density, lb per cu in.
		Tensile Strength,† lb per sq in.	Elongation, % in 2 in.		
43	Si 5%..................	24,000	4.0	45– 55	0.097
A–108	Cu 4.5%, Si 5.5%............	26,000	1.5	65– 80	0.099
112	Cu 7%, Zn 2%, Fe 1.2%......	27,000	2.0	70– 90	0.106
B–113	Cu 7%, Si 1.5%, Fe 1.2%.....	29,000	1.0	70– 90	0.104
122		32,000	0.4	85–110	0.106
122-T 52		32,000	0.5	95–125	0.106
122-T551	Cu 10%, Fe 1.2%, Mg 0.25%...	35,000	....	125–150	0.106
122-T552		33,000	....	100–125	0.106
122-T 62		42,000	....	125–150	0.106
132	Si 14%, Cu 1%, Fe 1%, Mg 1%	32,000	0.5	85–110	0.098
132-T541	Ni 2%.....................	34,000	....	90–115	0.098
132-T 7		36,000	0.5	95–120	0.098
142		35,000	0.5	90–115	0.100
142-T571	Cu 4%, Ni 2%, Mg 1.5%......	38,000	....	90–120	0.100
142-T 61		44,000	....	100–130	0.100
144	Cu 10%, Si 4%, Mg 0.25%....	32,000	....	85–110	0.104
144-T4		40,000	0.5	100–130	0.104
B–195–T4	Cu 4.5%, Si 3%..............	38,000	6.0	70– 90	0.100
D–195–T4	Cu 5.5%....................	40,000	8.0	60– 80	0.102
A–214	Mg 3.75%, Zn 2%...........	24,000	4.5	50– 65	0.096
355-T4	Si 5%, Cu 1.2%, Mg 0.5%....	35,000	5.0	70– 85	0.097
355-T6		43,000	4.0	85–100	0.097

* Alloy numbers referred to are those of the Aluminum Co. of America. Prefixed letters denote changes in composition of standard alloy. Suffixed "T" and number designate heat-treated alloys.
† Properties obtained from standard 1/2-in. diameter test specimens, individually cast in permanent molds and tested without machining off surface.
‡ Hardness limits are based on casting Brinell tests. In the case of 122 and 142 alloys, the Brinell is that obtained on the heads of permanent mold pistons 1/2 in. or less in thickness, and at a point 1/2 in. from outer edge and 1/2 in. from gate. For heavier castings, semi-permanent and sand-cast pistons, the hardness decreases proportionally with increased section, the maximum decrease being approximately 20.

Table IV. Composition and Properties of Aluminum-base Die-casting Alloys

Alloy Numbers *	Desired Composition, per cent				Typical Values	
	Copper	Silicon	Nickel	Aluminum	Tensile Strength, lb per sq in.	Elongation, % in 2 in.
IV	....	5	....	95	29,000	3.5
V	....	12	....	88	33,000	1.5
VI	2	3	....	95	30,000	3.5
VII	4	5	....	91	32,000	2.0
VIII	1.5	1	2.25	95.25	29,000	4.0
IX	4	1.75	4	90.25	31,000	1.5
XII	8	1.5	....	90.50	33,000	1.0

* The alloy designations correspond to numbers used in the investigation on aluminum-base die-casting alloys carried out under the jurisdiction of Committee B-6 on Die Cast Metals and Alloys (formerly Subcommittee XV on Die Cast Metals and Alloys of Committee B-2 on Non-Ferrous Metals and Alloys of the American Society for Testing Materials); the alloy numbers omitted correspond to alloy compositions which were investigated by the Committee, but which were not considered desirable for inclusion in these specifications. See *Proc. A.S.T.M.*, Vol. 29, Part I, p. 192, 1929.

mold. The metal must be stirred thoroughly to insure uniformity of composition. Melting is usually done in iron pots, non-metallic crucibles, or reverberatory furnaces. The metal should preferably be kept below about 1500 deg fahr during melting, and an oxidizing atmosphere is preferable to a reducing one. Unclean melting practice is largely responsible for so-called hard spots which usually consist of foreign matter entrapped in the liquid alloy. These hard spots may cause much trouble in machining. The pouring temperature should, in general, be the lowest one at which the mold can be filled without danger of misruns. Such practice will usually produce the strongest and most ductile as well as the most leak-proof castings. Low pouring temperature can often be secured by judicious arrangement of gates and risers.

Permanent Mold Castings are poured by gravity or other low pressure into metal molds. The permanent mold process imparts unusual properties to the metal as a result of the rapid chilling in the metal molds. Gates and risers are provided to insure compensation for crystallization shrinkage so that the permanent mold castings are sound and non-porous. They may be made very nearly to size and usually machine easily. Large numbers of permanent mold castings are used in cooking utensils, washing machines, vacuum sweepers, cylinder heads, and the like. It will be noted that certain permanent mold castings can be produced with a hardness up to 150 Brinell. The permanent mold process is conducive to the production of castings of high hardness, and moreover, such hardness may be combined with relatively great toughness. The benefits of the permanent mold process can be obtained to a marked degree and greater latitude of design enjoyed by using sand cores in conjunction with metal mold parts. Parts made in this way are called " semi-permanent mold " castings.

Pressure Die Castings are made in metal dies by forcing liquid metal quickly into the dies at high pressure, which is applied by means of a piston or with compressed air. The casting solidifies so rapidly that there is no opportunity for complete compensation for crystallization shrinkage or for elimination of all the entrapped air. Although the interior of the casting is sometimes quite porous, the outside shell is usually very sound and strong. Comparisons of tensile strengths of pressure die castings, as shown in Table IV, with other types of aluminum alloy castings indicate that the average strength of the die castings is high, notwithstanding a certain amount of porosity. Aluminum die castings may be made with thinner sections than those fabricated by other processes, and they may be made so nearly to size as to eliminate all or many of the machining operations.

Silicon is now perhaps the most important alloying element in aluminum-base die castings. It will be noted that all the alloys listed in Table IV have silicon specified. The combination of copper and silicon also occurs in five of the seven alloys.

Maximum and Minimum Weights of Castings. Aluminum sand castings weighing more than 7000 lb and as little as 1 oz have been made in production. So far as experience goes, there is no inherent reason for any limitation on the weight of a sand casting. In the permanent mold process, castings weighing as much as 750 lb each have been made and castings weighing less than $1/2$ lb have been made in production. The usual weight of permanent mold castings, however, is between 20 lb and $1/2$ lb. A 12-lb casting is considered large for a pressure die casting, and castings weighing as little as $1/32$ lb are made.

Section Thickness. The minimum section thickness for sand castings is usually kept at about $1/8$ in., that for permanent mold castings about $3/32$ in., and for pressure die castings $1/16$ in. There is no limit on the high side.

Finish. On large sand castings, $3/16$ to $3/4$ in. should be allowed for finish, depending on design, and on small bench work castings, $1/8$ in. For disk grinding, $1/32$ in. should be allowed. On permanent mold castings, for example, pistons up to 3-in. diameter, 0.075 in. on the diameter should be allowed. On pistons up to 5-in. diameter, about 0.10 in. should be allowed. Pressure die castings often require no finish if tolerances ±0.0025 in. per in. are permitted.

Tolerances on Dimensions and Weights. A tolerance of $1/32$ in. in thickness of sand castings, and ± 0.010 in. per in. on permanent mold castings, should be allowed. Plus or minus 5 per cent in weight with wood patterns and ± 3 per cent with metal patterns should be allowed on sand castings and ± 2 per cent on permanent mold castings. On pressure die castings a section tolerance of ± 0.0025 in. per in. should be allowed and a weight tolerance of ± 2 per cent.

Properties of Aluminum Alloy Castings at Elevated Temperatures. Commercial aluminum has a Brinell hardness number of only about 25 and a tensile strength of about 12,000 lb per sq in. at ordinary temperature, and its strength and hardness decrease progressively with rising temperature. Table V shows some of the tensile properties of certain of the aluminum alloys which are used commercially at elevated temperatures. So marked is the effect of alloying that one alloy has a strength at 600 deg fahr higher than that of commercial aluminum at ordinary temperature. The values shown, however, for the temperatures 400, 500, and 600 deg fahr are considerably lower than those usually associated with such temperatures. This results from the stabilization of the alloys at the temperature of test prior to the test itself. Except for the values given at 500 deg fahr for 132 alloy, the minimum time of exposure at the temperature of test prior to testing was 75 days. The profound effect on the material is indicated by the hardness values. These hardness tests were made at room temperature after the test piece had been stabilized

Table V. Properties of Cast Aluminum Alloys at Elevated Temperatures after Stabilization at the Temperature of Testing

Alloy			Temperature, deg fahr				
Designation from Tables II and III	Condition	Property	75	300	400	500	600
112 ASTM–C SAE–33	Sand cast	T.S.* Y.S.† Elong.‡ B.H.§	23,400 14,800 1.8 74	25,500 22,750 1.5 91	17,150 .... 1.5 72	14,860 9,700 3.5 65	6,300 19.0 49
122–T551 SAE–34	Permanent mold cast	T.S. Y.S. Elong. B.H.	35,000 34,000 0.0 130	34,910 33,500 0.5 112	23,300 .... 8.5 87	18,770 10,750 2.0 74	9,070 .... 10.0 54
132–T541	Permanent mold cast	T.S. Y.S. Elong. B.H.	34,000 24,000 0.5 105	17,500 8,000 2.0	17,940 .... 1.0 76	18,970 ‖ 8,660 ‖ 2.0 ‖ 75 ‖	9,610 .... 3.0 61
142–T571 ASTM–H SAE–39 "Y"	Permanent mold cast	T.S. Y.S. Elong. B.H.	38,000 31,000 0.5 110	40,930 38,000 0.5 111	28,100 .... 2.5 78	15,520 8,000 8.0 56	9,080 .... 41.0 50
A–355–T59	Sand cast	T.S. Y.S. Elong. B.H.	25,000 21,000 2.0 55	21,560 14,750 2.0 65	14,940 .... 2.5 52	11,050 6,700 8.0 51	8,720 .... 10.0 48
195–T4 ASTM–G SAE–38	Sand cast	T.S. Y.S. Elong. B.H.	31,000 16,100 8.0 60	27,590 19,750 4.0 78	15,900 9,750 16.5 55	9,820 6,100 24.0 49	4,050 .... 61.0 39
254	Sand cast	T.S. Y.S. Elong. B.H.	27,000 22,000 2.0 75	27,000 18,000 2.0 78	20,970 12,750 3.0 71	17,700 10,000 3.5 74	14,700 11.5 76

* Tensile strength, lb per sq. in.
† Yield strength, lb per sq in.
‡ Elongation, per cent in 2 in.
§ Brinell hardness at room temperature after stabilization and testing at elevated temperatures.
‖ Properties after 18 days at temperature; not completely stabilized.

at the testing temperature. For example, in the 132 alloy, the room temperature hardness was changed from 130 to 54 by holding at 600 deg fahr for 75 days.

24. WROUGHT ALLOYS OF ALUMINUM

Alloy Composition and Nomenclature. The wrought alloys of aluminum may be grouped in two divisions, the first containing those alloys in which various tempers are produced by cold working, and the second containing those alloys which are subjected to heat treatment in order to obtain the desired mechanical properties. The latter are frequently called "the strong alloys," and, in general, their mechanical properties have higher values than those of the alloys in the first group.

Each of the wrought alloys is designated by a number, indicating the composition, followed by the letter " S," indicating that it is in the wrought condition or is capable of being wrought. The compositions of the commercial alloys are given in Table VI; other alloys have been used to a limited extent.

Temper Designations. To indicate an alloy in the soft or annealed condition, the alloy designation is followed by the letter "–O"; e.g., 2S–O, 17S–O. The hard temper is designated by "–H" (2S–H, 4S–H), and the intermediate cold-worked tempers by fractions before the "H" (2S–3/4H, 4S–1/2H).

In the strong alloys the letter "T" indicates that the material is in the fully heat-treated condition and has the maximum strength developed by heat treatment. This condition is obtained by a solution heat treatment, which consists of heating to the

Table VI.   Nominal Composition of Wrought Aluminum Alloys

Alloy	Per Cent of Alloying Element. Aluminum and normal impurities constitute remainder						
	Copper	Silicon	Manganese	Magnesium	Lead	Nickel	Bismuth
2S							
3S			1.25				
4S			1.25	1.0			
11S	5.0				0.5		0.5
14S	4.4	0.8	0.75	0.35			
Duralumin or 17S	4.0		0.5	0.5			
A17S	2.5			0.3			
18S	4.0					2.0	
24S	4.2		0.6	1.5			
25S	4.5	0.8	0.8				
32S		12.0		1.0		0.8	
51S		1.0		0.6			
52S				2.5			Chromium 0.25
53S		0.7		1.25			0.25

proper temperature and quenching in cold water, followed by aging. Some of the strong alloys age at room temperature; others must be subjected to higher temperatures to cause precipitation of certain constituents (aging). These latter alloys are designated 25S-W, 51S-W, and 53S-W when they have been quenched but not subjected to the precipitation treatment, although 51S-W undergoes some spontaneous aging at room temperature.

In order to produce material with higher yield strengths than can be obtained by heat treatment alone, some of the alloys are cold worked after heat treatment, by an amount carefully controlled so as to retain suitable ductility in the resulting product. This produces material in the " RT " condition.

Alclad Products.   In order to provide exceedingly high corrosion resistance, a composite material is produced in which this quality is imparted by means of a surface of high corrosion resistance, alloyed and integral with the strong alloy core. The thickness of the surface metal is so chosen as to retain the maximum physical properties consistent with adequate protection of the core.

Aluminum Foil.   Aluminum sheet 0.005 in. and less in thickness is termed foil. The ductility and malleability of aluminum permits the rolling of foil commercially to gages as thin as 0.00025 in. Most extensively used thicknesses, however, are 0.0003 to 0.0007 in. For these extremely thin gages a special grade of pure metal is used. For certain uses, however, where additional strength is required, such as for diaphragms and shims, alloys of aluminum are used. The alloy foils, being less ductile, are usually of the gages of 0.001 in. and heavier.

The " film-forming " characteristic of aluminum has resulted in an extensive use of foil in electrolytic condensers for radio equipment, power factor condensers, etc. Aluminum foil is also used in foil and paper type condensers, in contacts for burglar alarm systems, as protecting tape for underground cables, etc. Its attractive appearance and non-toxic qualities have resulted in its being used extensively for wrapping food products and manufactured articles, such as photographic films and typewriter ribbons.

Effects of Cold Working on the Physical Properties of Aluminum and Its Alloys. The formulas given below are taken from R. L. Templin in The Aluminum Industry, Vol. II, Chap. 19, p. 396, and the American Institute of Mining and Metallurgical Engineers, Institute of Metals Division, p. 466, 1930.

Cold working is here defined as meaning the change in cross-sectional area of the metal which occurs as a result of rolling, forging, drawing, or extrusion at temperatures in the neighborhood of room temperature, that is, 60 to 80 deg fahr. In most cases the change in cross-sectional area of the metal amounts to a reduction in area. In the rolling of wide sheet, a reduction in cross-sectional area of the product may, without sensible error, be considered as resulting solely from the reduction in thickness of the product. When aluminum and its alloys are worked at temperatures above room temperature, the effects of cold working are less in proportion to the amount of working done than when they are worked at room temperature. Conversely, the working done at lower than room temperature becomes more effective than the same amount of work at room temperature.

In general, the cold working is expressed as the percentage change in the original cross-sectional area (commonly called " reduction ") as follows: $C = \dfrac{A - a}{A} \times 100$, wherein C = amount of cold working in percentage, A = initial area of the material in the properly annealed condition, a = area of the cold-worked material. For sheet, this formula becomes: $C = \dfrac{T - t}{T} \times 100$, wherein T = initial thickness of the material, and t = the final thickness. Aluminum sheet is usually rolled so as to conform to the Brown and Sharpe gage system.

The nominal amounts of cold working, together with the approximate B. & S. gage numbers' reduction for the various tempers, are given in Table VII.

Table VII.   Relation of Cold Working to Temper

Temper of Metal	Approximate Amount of Cold Working *	Approximate B. & S. Gage Numbers' Reduction	
		Sheet	Wire
Soft..........	0	0	0
1/4 Hard.........	21	2	1
1/2 Hard.........	37	4	2
3/4 Hard.........	60	8	4
Hard.........	80	14	7

* Percentage reduction in cross-sectional area.

The effect of cold working on the tensile strength of aluminum and its alloys in the wrought condition is shown by the following formula: $T = T_0(1 + 0.9R)$, wherein T = tensile strength, lb per sq in., T_0 = tensile strength of the properly annealed material, R = reduction in area expressed as a decimal.

The yield strength of aluminum and its alloys is the stress corresponding to a limiting permanent set of 0.2 per cent. For properly annealed wrought metal this value will be approximately one-third of the ultimate tensile strength. For all the other tempers of a cold-worked product, the yield strength will vary from 80 to 95 per cent of the ultimate tensile strength.

The elongation value is affected to a considerable extent by both the size and shape of the test specimen, as well as by the ductility of the material. Cold working decreases the ductility and therefore the elongation.

The relation between the tensile strength and the Brinell hardness of wrought aluminum and its alloys may be expressed approximately by the formula:

$$BHN = T/575$$

Effects of Heat Treatment on the Physical Properties of Aluminum Alloys. The change in properties resulting from heat treatment of aluminum alloys is usually associated with a change in solubility of one or more of the alloying ingredients in aluminum with change in temperature. More than 5 per cent copper, for example, is soluble in solid aluminum just below the melting point of the eutectic, whereas at room temperature the solubility is well below 1 per cent. By heating aluminum alloys containing about 4 per cent or more of copper to a temperature slightly below the melting point of the eutectic, allowing the copper to dissolve in the aluminum at that temperature, and cooling quickly to a low temperature, the alloy becomes supersaturated in copper at the lower temperature. Such a treatment is known as a " solution heat treatment." In certain of the alloys, like 17S or duralumin, this supersaturated solid solution breaks down, at least in part, even at ordinary temperatures. This change, referred to as " aging," changes the physical properties. In certain of the alloys, because the changes produced at ordinary temperatures are insufficient for the requirements, elevated temperatures are used to effect the desired results. Such a treatment is known as the " precipitation heat treatment," or as " artificial aging." The general effect of aging is to increase hardness and strength of aluminum alloys, and the same is true of the precipitation heat treatment if it is not carried too far. This treatment, assuming prior solution heat treatment, is capable of producing a wide range of properties, without change in the composition of the alloy.

Since the alloys which age at room temperature do not acquire the full properties of the " T " condition until about four days have elapsed after quenching, the practice of forming immediately after quenching is frequently followed, particularly with strong alloys which are to be subjected to difficult forming operations. Room temperature aging can also be effectively retarded by holding the material at a low temperature after quenching. This can be accomplished by packing in ice or in frozen carbon dioxide (dry ice).

Heat treatment of aluminum alloys may be used to produce other effects, such as the removal of internal strains, stabilization of dimensions of parts used or processed at elevated temperatures, and change in particle size of constituents such as silicon, which may be present in amounts greater than can be dissolved in solid aluminum even at the eutectic temperature.

In carrying out the solution heat treatment, it is necessary to have close control of

Table VIII. Specific Gravity and Weight of Alloys

Alloy	Specific Gravity	Weight, lb per cu in.	Alloy	Specific Gravity	Weight, lb per cu in.
Pure Al (99.97%)	2.70	0.0976	24S	2.76	0.100
2S	2.71	0.098	25S	2.79	0.101
3S	2.73	0.099	51S	2.69	0.097
4S	2.72	0.098	52S	2.67	0.096
17S	2.79	0.101	53S	2.69	0.097

Table IX. Typical Mechanical Properties of Wrought Aluminum Alloys *

Alloy and Temper	Tension			Hardness		Shear	Fatigue
	Yield Strength,† lb per sq in.	Ultimate Strength, lb per sq in.	Elongation ‡ per cent in 2 in.	Brinell (500-kg– 10-mm ball)	Shore (Magnifier Hammer)	Shearing Strength,§ lb per sq in.	Endurance Limit, ‖ lb per sq in.
2S–O	4,000	13,000	35	23	7	9,600	5,000
2S–1/4 H	13,000	15,000	12	28	11	10,000	6,000
2S–1/2 H	14,000	17,000	9	32	13	11,000	7,000
2S–3/4 H	17,000	20,000	6	38	15	12,000	8,000
2S–H	21,000	24,000	5	44	18	13,000	8,500
3S–O	5,000	16,000	30	28	10	11,000	7,000
3S–1/4 H	15,000	18,000	10	35	14	12,000	8,000
3S–1/2 H	18,000	21,000	8	40	16	14,000	9,000
3S–3/4 H	21,000	25,000	5	47	19	15,000	9,500
3S–H	25,000	29,000	4	55	23	16,000	10,000
4S–O	10,000	26,000	20	45	15	16,000	14,000
4S–1/4 H	25,000	31,000	6	55	22	17,000	14,500
4S–1/2 H	31,000	35,000	5	65	23	19,500	15,000
4S–3/4 H	35,000	39,000	3	73	26	21,000	15,500
4S–H	38,000	42,000	3	80	30	23,000	16,000
52S–O	14,000	29,000	25	45	....	18,000	17,000
52S–1/4 H	26,000	34,000	12	62	....	20,000	18,000
52S–1/2 H	29,000	37,000	10	67	....	21,000	19,000
52S–3/4 H	34,000	39,000	8	74	....	23,000	20,000
52S–H	36,000	41,000	7	85	....	24,000	20,500
11S–T	35,000	55,000	23	100	30	39,000	....
17S–O	10,000	26,000	20	45	15	18,000	11,000
17S–T	35,000	58,000	20	100	30	35,000	15,000
17S–RT	46,000	61,000	13	110	35	36,000	....
Alclad 17S–T	32,000	55,000	18	....	....	32,000	....
Alclad 17S–RT	40,000	57,000	11	....	....	32,000	....
A17S–O	8,000	22,000	24	38	11	15,000	....
A17S–T	24,000	43,000	24	70	22	25,000	13,500
24S–O	10,000	26,000	20	42	....	18,000	....
24S–T	43,000	65,000	20	105	....	40,000	14,000
24S–RT	53,000	68,000	13	116	....	41,000	14,500
Alclad 24S–T	40,000	60,000	18	....	....	39,000	....
Alclad 24S–RT	49,000	62,000	11	....	....	39,000	....
25S–O	10,000	26,000	20	45	15	18,000	9,000
25S–W	25,000	48,000	18	80	23	30,000	14,500
25S–T	35,000	58,000	20	100	30	35,000	15,000
27S–T	50,000	60,000	9	115	....	37,000	13,000
51S–O	6,000	16,000	30	28	10	11,000	6,500
51S–W	20,000	35,000	24	64	20	24,000	10,500
51S–T	38,000	48,000	14	95	28	30,000	10,500
53S–O	7,000	16,000	25	26	9	11,000	7,500
53S–W	20,000	33,000	22	65	21	22,000	10,000
53S–T	32,000	38,000	14	80	26	26,000	11,000

* Modulus of elasticity is approximately 10,300,000 lb per sq in.
† Stress at which stress-deformation curve departs 0.2 per cent from the initial modulus line produced. The yield strength in compression is substantially equal to the yield strength in tension for wrought alloys.
‡ Values for 14-gage sheet; for heavier sections the elongations are higher.
§ Single-shear strength values obtained from double-shear tests.
‖ R. R. Moore type of rotating-beam machine; endurance limit based on 500,000,000 cycles.

temperature. Thin pieces of wrought metal may be heated to the proper temperature and held there only a short time before cooling, with good results. This operation may be carried on in a hearth or pit furnace or in a bath of fused niter. Castings and large wrought pieces, however, must be held at the solution heat-treating temperature for considerable periods of time, and hence automatic control of temperature is a practical necessity of such operations. Cooling after the proper heating cycle may be done in cold or hot water, in oil, or in a blast of air.

The precipitation heat treatment may be effected by heating in pressure vessels with steam, or in baths such as oil, or in hearth or pit furnaces. The temperature should be well controlled for best results, and if an ordinary furnace is used, air circulation is desirable. The rate of cooling after the precipitation heating is not usually an important factor.

Specific Gravity. The specific gravity of aluminum alloys differs only slightly from that of the parent metal. The greatest increase is only about 3 per cent, and three of the alloys (51S, 52S, and 53S) are actually lighter than aluminum. The specific gravities are shown in Table VIII; the weights in pounds per cubic inch are obtained by multiplying the specific gravities by 0.03613.

Mechanical Properties. The mechanical properties of the wrought aluminum alloys are shown in Table IX. Although these properties are actually for sheet, they are generally applicable to all products except that the elongation values depend to some extent upon the size and shape of test specimen, and in certain products, such as heavy bar and plate, the amount of reduction may not be sufficient to permit development of the maximum properties of the alloy on subsequent heat treatment. All properties reported have been determined in accordance with the Standard Methods of Tension Testing of Metallic Materials (E8–33) prescribed by the American Society for Testing Materials.

Design Stresses for Aluminum Alloys. In Table X are given the stresses considered safe for ordinary structural design at temperatures below 100 deg fahr. Where temperatures above that point are to be considered, the values of Table X should be multiplied by the factors in Table XI.

Table X. Design Stresses for Aluminum Alloys

Values below are considered safe for ordinary structural design. When temperatures above 100° F are to be considered, multiply these values by factors of Table XI.

	Alloy and Temper	Tension, lb per sq in.	Compression, lb per sq in.	Bearing, lb per sq in.	Shear, lb per sq in.
Wrought	3S–O	4,000	4,000	7,000	3000
	3S–1/2 H	6,000	6,000	9,000	3500
	3S–H	8,000	8,000	13,000	4000
	4S–O	6,000	6,000	11,000	4000
	4S–1/4 H	9,000	9,000	14,000	4500
	4S–1/2 H	10,000	10,000	15,000	5000
	4S–H	13,000	13,000	19,000	6000
	17S–T	15,000	15,000	26,000	9000
	51S–W	9,000	9,000	15,000	6000
	51S–T	14,000	14,000	21,000	7500
Sand Cast	12	5,000	9,000	9,000	5000
	43	5,000	6,000	18,000	4000
	195–T62	11,000	15,000	18,000	7000
	220–T4	11,000	15,000	18,000	8000
	356–T6	10,000	12,000	15,000	6000

Table XI. Factors for Design Stresses at Elevated Temperatures

	Alloy and Temper	100° F	200° F	300° F	400° F	500° F
Wrought	3S–O	1.0	0.85	0.70	0.60	0.40
	3S–1/2 H	1.0	0.75	0.60	0.45	0.30
	3S–H	1.0	0.75	0.60	0.35	0.25
	4S–O	1.0	0.90	0.80	0.50	0.40
	4S–1/2 H	1.0	0.90	0.65	0.30	0.25
	4S–H	1.0	0.80	0.55	0.25	0.20
	17S–T	1.0	0.90	0.60	0.30	0.15
	51S–W	1.0	1.00	0.80	0.30	0.15
	51S–T	1.0	0.75	0.55	0.20	0.10
Sand Cast	220–T4	1.0	0.85	0.70	0.50	0.30

25. FABRICATION

Machining Aluminum. Aluminum and its alloys may be machined readily. Cutting tools for aluminum resemble in many respects those for cutting hard wood. The cutting edges must be ground to a sharp included angle, must be keen, and should be provided with smoothly finished surfaces. Such tools differ materially from brass-cutting tools. In many instances, satisfactory results may be obtained using tools ordinarily used for steel, provided they are sharp and in good condition. Steel tools for machining aluminum may be either high-carbon or high-speed types. Cemented tungsten carbide tools have been found indispensable, especially for machining aluminum alloys with high silicon content.

Forging. Forgings are produced from several of the strong aluminum alloys. The alloys are forged hot either under a hammer or in a forging press. For the general class of forgings including connecting-rods, aircraft propellers, and crankcases, the alloy 25S-T is used because of its superior hot working characteristics. Crankcases and nose pieces of more intricate design for radial aircraft engines are made from 51S-T since it is even more easily forged into the large, thin sections. For a more limited class of forgings 17S is also used. Forged pistons are commonly manufactured from 32S, which has a low coefficient of expansion, or from 18S. These alloys retain their physical properties at elevated temperatures better than some of the other aluminum alloys.

Welding. Aluminum and its alloys may be welded by the torch, arc, or electric resistance processes, by a technique that varies slightly from that applicable to steel. The equipment used in fusion welding is the same as that required for welding steel. In electric resistance welding, however, machines of greater electrical capacity and slightly different design are necessary.

A flux is used in the fusion welding processes to remove the oxide from the base metal and improve weld fusion. In metal arc welding this flux is most suitably supplied as a heavy coating on the electrode.

A 5 per cent silicon (95 per cent aluminum) alloy is used for metal arc electrodes and as a filler rod for torch welds in the strong aluminum alloys. Torch welds in common alloys (2S and 3S) are often made using a pure aluminum filler rod, especially where a polished surface is desired.

The heat of welding produces an annealing action in the common aluminum alloys and a complex—and somewhat deleterious—heat-treating effect in the strong alloys. For this reason a welded joint, except in fully annealed material, will not have mechanical properties equal to the unwelded material. In some cases, too, the heating has an adverse effect on the corrosion resistance. The metal arc will generally produce welds of greater strength than those made with the torch, but the process is not applicable to metal less than $1/16$ in. thick. Heat-treating the strong alloys after welding will improve the properties of the joint. Where the joint must develop maximum efficiency, torch welding and, in some cases, arc welding, cannot be considered equal to a well-designed mechanical type of joint.

Soldering. The soldering of aluminum presents a number of difficulties not met with in the soldering of other non-ferrous metals. The very tenacious oxide film on aluminum prevents wetting the metal when ordinary soldering technique is employed. Furthermore, many of the solders used in the past have not made corrosion-resistant joints when applied to aluminum. The situation has, however, been recently changed by development of a variety of solders and fluxes adapted to nearly all soldering requirements. By the use of the proper solder and the proper flux, and with a simple technique, aluminum parts can be joined in much the same way and for about the same type of service as solder is employed with other metals.

Finishing of Aluminum. Aluminum articles may be painted, lacquered, electroplated, oxide-coated, sand-blasted, given a frosted finish, given a satin finish by means of a wire scratch brush, or polished by suitable buffing wheels and polishing compounds.

For painting or lacquering, all that is required normally is a cleaning for grease and dirt by wiping the surface with mineral spirits or other solvent, though in the case of castings, improved adhesion may be obtained by means of a light sand blasting. Sheet or extruded shapes provide exceptionally good adhesion when they are given either an electrolytic or chemical oxide coating; the latter type of surface preparation is important in painting for protection against salt-water corrosion.

In electroplating aluminum, the surface is roughened by special etching procedures, which depend on the alloy being coated, and then plated with nickel. Any desired metal may then be plated over the nickel. For certain special applications, zinc or chromium may be applied directly to the aluminum surface. Zinc will electrochemically protect the aluminum, while chromium is of value in resisting abrasion or chemical attack by mild alkalies.

Electrolytic or anodic oxide coatings may be obtained on aluminum by making the article to be finished the positive electrode in a special electrolyte. This type of coating forms a hard, abrasion-resistant coating of superior protective value. It is usually white to light gray in appearance, but on the aluminum-silicon alloys it forms a dark gray coating, which is of artistic value, particularly on sand-blasted castings.

A frosted finish is usually obtained by etching the aluminum in a hot solution of sodium hydroxide (usually 2–5 per cent), followed by a treatment of strong nitric acid (usually 2 parts of concentrated acid to 1 part water). The nitric acid removes the colored film left on the surface by the caustic dip, but has little solvent action on the aluminum.

26. STRUCTURAL USES OF ALUMINUM ALLOYS

Although almost all the alloys mentioned in the preceding tables have been used structurally, certain ones are more important than others. These are listed below, together with a brief description of their uses.

3S Alloy. 3S is used in structural work where strength is not of primary importance or where welding is necessary. It is used for tank cars, storage containers, car and bus body plates, corrugated roofing, and the like. It is generally used in the hardest temper suitable to the necessary shop work.

4S Alloy. 4S, like 3S, is supplied in the annealed and in various cold-worked tempers. For any given temper, however, 4S has considerably higher tensile and yield strength than 3S. In the harder tempers the yield strength is comparable to that of the heat-treated alloys, although the ultimate strength is lower and the amount of forming which can be done is limited. Its uses are similar to those of 3S alloy.

52S Alloy. 52S combines mechanical properties comparable with those of 4S, with forming characteristics comparable with those of 3S alloy, and hence is developing a wide field of use. Rolled or extruded shapes of 52S, however, in common with those of 3S and 4S, cannot be cold worked sufficiently to obtain the properties of the harder tempers, the properties of such shapes usually being intermediate between those of the annealed and $1/4$ H tempers. Largely because of this fact, 52S is used structurally mostly in the form of sheet and plate.

17S Alloy. Since 17S ages naturally at room temperatures following heat treatment, it does not have a stable as-quenched condition. 17S–T has tensile and yield strengths comparable with those of ordinary structural steel and is used for important strength members. When cold worked after heat treatment, the alloy is called 17S–RT and has higher properties as indicated in the foregoing tables.

51S Alloy. 51S in the as-quenched or "W" condition is very workable and hence is adapted to severe forming operations. 51S–W is used in body framing of railway cars and buses and in various welded constructions where 3S is not strong enough. As pointed out elsewhere, it can be artificially aged to 51S–T after forming, thereby gaining additional strength. 51S–T has the same yield strength as 17S–T, but its other mechanical properties are somewhat lower, as indicated in Table IX.

53S. Alloy. 53S is very similar to 51S, having slightly lower mechanical properties, somewhat greater ductility, and better resistance to corrosion, especially when compared with 51S–T. Its uses are similar to those of 51S alloy and, in addition, it is widely used for window sash, railings, store fronts, and various other architectural trim.

Casting Alloys. No. 12 alloy can be used structurally to about the same extent as cast iron. When a tight, leak-proof casting is needed, No. 43 is recommended.

Alloys 195–T6, 220–T4, and 356–T6 are heat-treated to obtain the maximum mechanical properties and are used to replace malleable-iron castings and, in some cases, steel castings. In choosing between these three alloys, it is advisable to consult the foundry to determine which is best suited to the specific conditions.

NICKEL AND NON-FERROUS NICKEL ALLOYS
By Robert Worthington

27. COMMERCIAL GRADES AND PHYSICAL PROPERTIES

Nickel is a white metal, commercially available as ingot and shot for the manufacture of alloys, anodes for electroplating, and in malleable mill products. The commercial grades of nickel produced in the United States and Canada are listed in Table I.

Malleable Nickel is available in castings and in the usual mill forms: plate, sheet, and strip; bar, rod, and wire; forgings; tubing. The metal is ductile and lends itself to ordinary fabricating operations, as drawing, stamping, spinning, machining. The strength of nickel is improved by cold-working, or by forging in the lower range of temperatures where the strains of working are not relieved, e.g., 1000–1200 deg fahr. Strengths ranging from 60,000 to 115,000 lb per sq in. are regularly furnished; spring wire carries strengths of 150,000 lb per sq in. with correspondingly low ductility.

Table I.   Commercial Grades of Nickel Produced in the United States and Canada

Grades	Typical Composition							Uses
	Ni + Co	Fe	Cu	C	Si	Mn	S	
Malleable.............	99.00+	0.30	0.25	0.10	0.10	0.25	0.010	Rolling, forging, drawing.
Malleable, 5% man-ganese	94.00–95.50	0.40	0.25	0.15	0.10	4.25–5.25	0.010	Spark-plug wire, high-temperature applications,etc.
Malleable, 2% man-ganese	97.00–98.00	0.40	0.25	0.15	0.10	1.75–2.25	0.010	Electrical resistance wire; spark-plug wire.
Anodes; rolled and cast	99.00+	......	......	......	......	......	......	Electroplating.
Electrolytic, cathodes 27 by 36 in. and smaller cuttings therefrom	99.95	0.01–0.04	0.01–0.03	Trace	Trace	......	Trace	Highest-grade material for alloying in steel and non-ferrous metals in electric, open-hearth, or crucible furnaces.
Ingot (10, 25, 50 lb) made by remelting electrolytic cathodes	99.55	0.15	0.15	0.06	0.08	......	0.010	For alloying of ferrous metals, particularly where this form is more adapted to the process involved.
Shot, made by remelting electrolytic cathodes	99.55	0.15	0.15	0.06	0.08	......	0.010	Principally used for crucible charges in ferrous and non-ferrous alloys involving small amounts of nickel.
"F" shot and ingot (5 lb), low melting point	92.00	2.00	0.25	0.25	5.00–6.00	......	0.05	For cupola and ladle additions of nickel to gray iron.

Table II.   Physical Properties of Nickel

(Typical Values)

Density, g per cu cm...	8.85
Melting point, deg cent..	1440
Magnetic transformation, deg cent...	340
Specific heat, mean, 20° C to melting point, g-cal per g per deg cent...............	0.134
Coefficient of expansion, per deg cent:	
25–100°..	0.0000132
25–300°..	0.0000144
25–600°..	0.0000155
Thermal conductivity, mean, 0–100° C, g-cal per sec per sq cm per deg cent per cm...	0.14
Electrical resistivity at 20° C, ohm (mil, ft)...................................	64
Temperature coefficient of resistivity, 20–100° C, per deg cent.....................	0.00537
Modulus of elasticity, lb per sq in...	30,000,000
Modulus in torsion, lb per sq in..	10,000,000

Table III.   Mechanical Properties of Nickel

	Hot-rolled; Forged	Cold-rolled and Cold-drawn					Cast
		Annealed	Sheet, full-hard	Strip, full-hard	Rod, normalized	Tubing, as drawn	
Tensile strength, lb per sq in.	70–85,000	70–85,000	95–110,000	95–115,000	80–95,000	100–105,000	60–70,000
Yield point, lb per sq in.....	30–40,000	20–30,000	90–100,000	90–105,000	70–80,000	85–95,000	20–30,000
Elastic limit, lb per sq in....	20–30,000	17–23,000	....	....	40–50,000	....	
Elongation, per cent (2 in.)..	40–50	43–53	2–8	2–5	25–35	15–20	15–35
Reduction in area, per cent..	55–65	65–75	....	....	40–60	....	30–50
Brinell (500 kg)............	105–125	85–105	....	....	215–240	....	75–95
Brinell (3000 kg)...........	125–140	115–130	....	....	200–240	....	80–100
Shore scleroscope...........	15–19	11–14	35–40	35–40	35–45	30–35	....
Rockwell "B"..............	60–70	55–65	95–100	95–100	90–100	85–90	51–59
Endurance limit, lb per sq in.	....	26–30,000	....	....	....	....	....
Izod impact, ft-lb..........	95–100	80–85	....	....	....	....	....

Corrosion resistance accounts for the use of malleable nickel in caustic evaporators and in food-processing and chemical equipment; high temperature oxidation resistance accounts for its use as automotive spark-plug wire and furnace equipment; appearance and toughness account for its use as coinage. Another important use, as elements in vacuum tubes, is based on several characteristics such as high melting point, fabricability, purity.

Physical and Mechanical Properties. Physical and mechanical properties of nickel are given in Tables II and III, respectively. Table IV gives the technological properties of nickel.

Table IV. Technologic Properties of Nickel

Process	Deg Cent	Deg Fahr
Pouring (castings)................................	1590–1650	2894–3002
Forging..	870–1260	1598–2300
Annealing:		
Open anneal....................................	900– 950	1652–1742
Box anneal.....................................	760	1400

Nickel-clad Steel is mild steel clad on one side with 10–20 per cent nickel. The bond is permanent under conditions of pressure, vacuum, temperature, and deformation in forming. The material is used for tanks, tank cars, and miscellaneous heavy plate construction.

28. ALLOYS OF NICKEL AND COPPER

Copper and Nickel in all proportions form solid solutions. The alloys are malleable, both hot and cold, throughout the entire range. As the nickel content increases, the alloys become stronger and tougher up to 70–80 per cent Ni. The alloys of the high copper end of the series, characterized by relative softness and high ductility, are easily and cheaply fabricated. Alloys low in nickel show a characteristic pink color, which disappears at 20 to 25 per cent nickel. Alloys with about 25 per cent nickel have a white color, such that nickel appears slightly yellow in comparison.

The nickel-copper alloys are hardened and strengthened by cold work, the high-nickel-content alloys to a considerably greater extent than the low-nickel. The tensile strength of spring temper Monel metal runs around 150,000 lb per sq in., whereas 80/20 cupro-nickel runs around 85,000 lb per sq in. Typical values of the physical and mechanical properties of copper-nickel alloys are given in Tables V and VI, respectively.

Table V. Physical Properties of Copper-nickel Alloys

(Typical values)

Property	Per Cent Nickel			
	20	30	45	70
Density, g per cu cm......................	8.96	8.93	8.90	8.80
Melting point, deg cent..................	1160	1185	1210	1350
Thermal expansion, per deg cent at 35° C...	0.0000156	0.0000152	0.0000149	0.0000140
Thermal conductivity, g-cal per sec per sq cm per deg C per cm......................	0.082	0.071	0.055	0.06
Electrical resistivity, ohm (mil, ft)..........	164	242	290	268
Coefficient of resistivity per deg cent, 20–100° C.............................	....	0.0001	0.0000	0.0019
Modulus of elasticity, lb per sq in	20,000,000	....	....	26,000,000

Table VI. Mechanical Properties of Annealed Copper-nickel Alloys

(Typical values)

Nickel Content, per cent	Tensile Strength, lb per sq in.	Proportional Limit, lb per sq in.	Elongation in 2 in., per cent	Reduction in Area, per cent	Brinell Hardness No.
2	34,000	......	50	..	..
15	46,000	11,900	47	83	65
20	48,000	13,800	46	79	72
40	59,000	11,900	44	71	88
70	75,000	25,000	42	70	120

Monel Metal

Monel Metal * is a nickel-copper alloy of the following composition: Ni, 65–70 per cent; Cu, 26–30 per cent; Fe, to 3.0 per cent; Mn, to 1.5 per cent; Si, to 0.25 per cent; C, to 0.25 per cent. Spring wire sometimes carries a higher silicon (to 1.25 per cent) or manganese (to 2.5 per cent) content, and high-strength castings higher copper (to 34 per cent) and silicon (to 4 per cent) content.

Physical and Mechanical Properties. In appearance and in physical and mechanical properties Monel metal closely resembles malleable nickel. It is white, malleable, and ductile, both hot and cold, and corrosion resistant. The physical and mechanical properties of Monel metal are given in Tables VII and VIII, respectively. The effect of temperature on the tensile properties of hot-rolled Monel metal is given in Table IX.

" K " Monel Metal. A special grade of Monel metal, designated as " K " Monel metal, carries about 3.75 per cent aluminum. This modification is hardened and strengthened by heat-treatment, as well as by cold-working. The properties are given in Table X. Softening is effected by quenching in water from 1400–1500 deg fahr; hardening by slow furnace cooling from 1000–1100 deg fahr, with or without previous cold-working.

Table VII.   Physical Properties of Monel Metal

(Typical values)

Density, g per cu cm	8.80
Melting point, deg cent	1350
Magnetic transformation, deg cent	95
Specific heat, mean, 20–1270° C, g-cal per g per deg cent	0.128
Coefficient of expansion per deg cent:	
25–100°	0.0000140
25–300°	0.0000150
25–600°	0.0000163
Thermal conductivity, mean, 0–100° C, g-cal per sec per sq cm per deg cent per cm	0.06
Electrical resistivity at 20° C, ohm (mil ft)	268
Temperature coefficient of resistivity, 20–100° C per deg cent	0.00196
Modulus of elasticity, lb per sq in	26,000,000
Modulus in torsion, lb per sq in	9,000,000

Table VIII.   Mechanical Property Ranges of Monel Metal

Product	Tensile Strength, lb per sq in.	Yield Point, lb per sq in.	Proportional Limit, lb per sq in.	Elongation in 2 in., per cent	Reduction in Area, per cent
Rod and Bar:					
Cold-drawn, annealed	70,000– 85,000	25,000– 35,000	20,000–30,000	35–50	65–75
" as drawn	85,000–125,000	60,000– 95,000		15–35	50–65
Hot-rolled	80,000– 95,000	40,000– 65,000	25,000–40,000	30–45	50–65
Forged	80,000–105,000	60,000– 85,000	45,000–65,000	20–40	.....
Wire:					
Cold-drawn, annealed	70,000– 85,000			.....	.....
" No. 1 temper	95,000–110,000			.....	.....
" regular	110,000–140,000			.....	.....
" spring	140,000–175,000			.....	.....
Plate, hot-rolled	60,000– 75,000	25,000– 30,000		25–35	.....
Sheet and Strip:					
Full-finished sheet	65,000– 80,000	25,000– 35,000	20,000–30,000	.....	.....
Cold-rolled, annealed	65,000– 80,000	25,000– 35,000	20,000–30,000	.....	.....
" full-hard sheet	100,000–120,000	90,000–110,000		.....	.....
" full-hard strip	100,000–125,000	90,000–115,000		.....	.....
Tubing, cold-drawn:					
Annealed	65,000– 80,000	25,000– 35,000	20,000–30,000	.....	.....
As drawn	90,000–105,000	60,000– 75,000		15–25	.....
Castings	65,000–100,000	30,000– 60,000		5–35	5–35

Fabrication. *Hot-working.* Monel metal responds to all hot-working operations within the temperature range of 1900 to 2100 deg fahr. With care, the temperature of the metal may be extended to 2150 deg fahr, but it loses all malleability at about 2200 deg fahr. Hot forging should not be attempted between 1200 and 1600 deg fahr, and only where

* Trade mark of International Nickel Co., Inc.

Table IX. Effect of Temperature on Tensile Properties of Hot-rolled Monel Metal

Temperature, deg		Tensile Strength, lb per sq in.	Limiting Creep Stress,* lb per sq in.	Yield Point, lb per sq in.	Elongation in 2 in., per cent
Cent	Fahr				
Room	Room	85,000	......	45,000	45
315	600	80,000	......	34,000	44
426	800	70,000	45,000	30,000	40
538	1000	55,000	15,000	27,000	30
648	1200	36,000	2,500	23,000	18
760	1400	22,000	......	......	22
871	1600	12,000	......	......	31
981	1800	7,500	......	......	42
1093	2000	5,000	......	......	55

* Maximum stress that will not cause fracture over indefinitely long period of time.

Table X. Mechanical Property Ranges of " K " Monel Metal

Grade	Tensile Strength, lb per sq in.	Yield Point, lb per sq in.	Proportional Limit, lb per sq in.	Elongation in 2 in., per cent	Reduction of Area, per cent	Brinell Hardness (3000-kg load)
Soft....................	to 120,000	to 80,000	to 60,000	40+	50+	to 215
Intermediate hardness....	120,000–160,000	80,000–120,000	60,000–100,000	20+	25+	215–315
Hard.................	160,000 and over	120,000 and over	100,000 and over	15+	20+	over 315

necessary for special conditions between 1600 and 1900 deg fahr. Sulfur-free fuel should be used for heating furnaces, and a definitely reducing atmosphere is desirable.

Table XI gives the temperature ranges for hot working of Monel metal.

Table XI. Technologic Properties of Monel Metal

Process	Deg Cent	Deg Fahr
Pouring (castings)...............................	1540–1565	2804–2849
Forging...	1000–1175	1832–2147
Annealing:		
Open anneal......................................	925– 980	1697–1796
Box anneal......................................	750	1382

Cold-working. Monel metal is similar in many respects to mild steel in mechanical cold working, as in cupping, drawing, swaging, die forging, power hammering, bending, and forming. The elastic limit is higher; hence more power is required. Annealing for further cold work is accomplished by either box or open annealing methods. Sulfur-bearing atmosphere must be avoided and a reducing temperature is desirable.

Machining. Best results are obtained with cutting tools having slightly sharper cutting angles than required for steel. Cutting tools, where possible, are ground to a 15–20 deg rake back from the cutting edge. Self-opening die heads are necessary for successful thread chasing, and high-speed cutting tools are imperative. Sulfur-base oil, cut with a paraffin-base oil, is a better coolant than straight paraffin-base oil. For automatic work a free machining quality rod is available.

Welding. Monel metal welds readily by the several electric and gas methods. In arc welding, a special deoxidizing flux gives the best results. The flame, in gas welding, must be on the reducing side, close to neutral, and the work must be done rapidly and without rewelding. Fused boric acid is used as a flux.

Soldering. Soft solders, either high or low in tin, work well with Monel metal. Lead fillets are used for special purposes, and brazing and silver solders for strong joints where special corrosive substances are being handled.

Pickling. In commercial pickling, the oxide is first reduced by heating and cooling in a definitely reducing atmosphere, then the metal is submerged in a solution of 6 lb sodium nitrate, 3 lb sodium chloride, 1 gal concentrated sulfuric acid per 40 gal water, held at 180–200 deg fahr. Where reducing treatment cannot be applied, the metal is dipped in a hot moderately strong solution of hydrochloric acid and scrubbed with abrasive.

Uses. Because of its corrosion resistance and appearance, Monel metal is used for sheet-metal work of kitchens, restaurants, and soda fountains; architectural trim: and containers for handling acids, alkalies, salt solutions, food products, etc. Its strength and toughness make it useful for turbine blading, valves, marine propeller shafting, springs, etc.

Other Nickel-copper Alloys

Nickel 40-45 Per Cent. Alloys with 40-45 per cent nickel have a low temperature coefficient of electrical resistance, combined with relatively high resistivity (see Table V, 11-72) and thus are used for rheostats and resistances of all kinds which run at black heat. This alloy is used also for low-temperature heaters, bed warmers, etc.

The thermoelectric force developed between the 40-45 per cent nickel-copper alloy and either iron, copper, or nickel-chromium is high, and for that reason these combinations are used in thermocouples for pyrometric work.

Cupro-nickel Tubing. Copper-nickel alloys with 20 and 30 per cent nickel, both with and without zinc, are used as tubes for the more severe air impingement conditions of marine and stationary condensers handling sea water or corrosive inland waters at high velocity.

Coinage. The alloy with 25 per cent nickel is used for coinage by several countries, a use depending on appearance and toughness.

High Ductility Cupro-nickel. Copper-nickel alloys with 15-20 per cent nickel will stand excessive cold work in drawing and forming, without intermediate anneals. For this reason these alloys are used as bullet envelopes and deep drawings.

2-4 Per Cent Nickel. Small amounts of nickel improve the strength of copper in the elevated temperature range, and for that reason such alloys are used as heat interchanger tubes and particularly in locomotive work for stay rods and boiler and flue tubes.

29. ALLOYS OF COPPER, NICKEL, AND ZINC

Alloys of Copper, Nickel, and Zinc are known commercially as nickel-silver or german silver. It is usual to designate an alloy by the nickel content, e.g., 18 per cent nickel-silver.

In composition, the nickel-silvers range from about 10 to 25 per cent Ni and from 3 to 40 per cent Zn. In these ranges fall the common casting and cold-working compositions. Alloys with 10 per cent Ni or less and high Zn are regularly extruded. In some cases alloys with 10 to 15 per cent Ni are extruded, at least in simpler shapes. Alloys with Zn less than 10 per cent can be hot-worked, though not hot-extruded.

The strength of the nickel-silver alloys is improved only by cold working. Thus spring temper sheet and strip of an 18 per cent Ni and 27 per cent Zn alloy carries a tensile strength of 100,000 lb per sq in., and spring temper wire a tensile strength of 143,000 lb per sq in.

Cast and wrought alloys of nickel, copper, and zinc and their properties are given in Tables II, III, respectively, pp. 11-41 to 11-51.

30. ALLOYS OF NICKEL AND CHROMIUM

Nickel-chromium Alloys with 20 per cent or less of chromium have been used for years as elements in resistance heating devices, a use depending on both high resistivity and very good resistance to deterioration up to temperatures as high as 2100-2150 deg fahr. Data on these alloys are given in the section on conductor materials, pp. 11-92 to 11-101.

Nickel and chromium alloys, particularly when carrying iron, are used very extensively in high-temperature service aside from electrical resistance applications, and in handling corrosive substances. For nickel-chromium-iron alloys, see pp. 11-35 to 11-36.

MAGNESIUM AND MAGNESIUM ALLOYS
By John A. Gann

31. PROPERTIES AND USES OF MAGNESIUM

Magnesium is a silver-white metal and is the basis of the lightest structural alloys. It is produced by the electrolysis of molten anhydrous magnesium chloride. Domestic magnesium averages 99.94 per cent pure. Table I gives the properties of magnesium. A special product containing nominally 99.99 per cent magnesium is produced in small quantities by sublimation of the regular commercial grade. The more important uses are: (1) Chemical, based on its chemical reactivity when in a finely divided form or at high temperatures. These uses include pyrotechnics, flares, Grignard reaction, and desulfurization of nickel and nickel alloys. (2) Alloying ingredient: the addition of small amounts of magnesium to certain types of alloys gives marked improvement in physical properties, as in aluminum alloys and zinc die-casting alloys. (3) Structural material, as ultra-light alloys, castings, and wrought shapes. The structural stability and engineering properties of magnesium alloys adapt them to a wide variety of service conditions.

Table I. Properties of Magnesium
Proc. A.S.T.M., Vol. 34, p. 299, 1934

		Sample Purity,* per cent
Atomic weight..	24.32	....
Boiling point, deg cent.................................	1097	....
Crystal form..	Close packed, hexagonal	....
Mean coefficient of expansion { 20° to 300° C............	0.0000283	....
{ 20° to 500° C............	0.0000299	....
Density at 20° C (68° F), g per cu cm....................	1.74	....
Density at melting point (solid), g per cu cm.............	1.64	....
Density at melting point (liquid), g per cu cm............	1.57	....
Electrical resistivity at 20° C:		
Microhm per cu cm..................................	4.4611	....
Ohms (mil, ft) (A.I.E.E. Standard)....................	26.83	....
Temperature coefficient at 20° C (A.I.E.E. Standard)......	0.0040	....
Electrical conductivity at 20° C:		
Mass, per cent International Annealed Copper Standard..	197.7	....
Volume, per cent International Annealed Copper Standard.	38.6	....
Freezing point, deg cent................................	651	....
Heat of vaporization, g-cal per g........................	1300 to 1500	....
Latent heat of fusion { g-cal per g......................	70	....
{ Btu per lb......................	126	....
Mechanical properties:		
Tensile strength, lb per sq in...........................	27,000	Commercial
Yield strength, lb per sq in. (set = 0.2 per cent)	10,000	annealed
Elongation in 2 in., per cent...........................	15	sheet
Brinell hardness, 10-mm ball, 500-kg load..............	37	99.8 to 99.9
Modulus of elasticity, lb per sq in.....................	6,250,000	....
Mean reflectivity, per cent for white light..............	73	....
Mean specific heat, g-cal per g per deg cent (0–100° C).....	0.249	....
Thermal conductivity, cgs units.........................	0.37	....
Watts per sq cm per deg cent per cm..................	1.55	....
Btu per hr per sq ft per deg fahr per in..............	1102	....

* Unless otherwise noted, the magnesium used in the determination of many of the above properties had a purity of 99.9 to 99.99 per cent. Metal of approximately the same purity was probably used in the determination of the other properties, although the literature is silent on this point.

32. MAGNESIUM ALLOYS

Composition, and Physical and Mechanical Properties. Present (1936) commercial alloys, as Dowmetal, AM Alloys, and Bohnalite " X," contain between 88 and 99 per cent Mg. Tables II and III give the nominal compositions, uses, and physical and mechanical properties of these alloys.

Lightness is the most outstanding characteristic of magnesium alloys and is responsible for many of their present uses. Aluminum alloys are 1 1/2 times as heavy, cast iron and steel are approximately 4 times as heavy, and brass and bronze 5 times as heavy.

Strength characteristics, as tensile properties, toughness, and fatigue endurance, recommend magnesium alloys for a wide variety of applications. The cast alloys have properties substantially the same as those of cast aluminum alloys, when compared on an equal volume basis. On an equal weight basis, magnesium alloys have strength properties equal, or superior, to those of most other metals. (See Table IV.) Strength decreases with rise in temperature. In general, magnesium alloys are not recommended for use at temperatures above 400 deg fahr.

Available Forms. Magnesium alloys are available in a wide variety of cast and wrought forms. Sand castings vary in weight from a few ounces to approximately 700 lb. Die castings can be made in sizes having projected areas up to 100 sq in. and weighing up to 3 lb. Forgings range in size from small resonator horn disks to aircraft propellers. Sheet is available in sizes up to 20 ft long by 4 ft wide. Structural shapes, produced by extrusion, cover a complete range of sizes of round, square, and hexagonal bars, angles, I-beams, channels, and special sections.

Corrosion. Magnesium alloys are stable under ordinary exposure conditions, the surface gradually darkening with no decrease in strength. In heavy industrial areas, or in humid atmospheres along the seacoast, surface roughening may occur, and some protection may be desirable. Aqueous salt and acid solutions corrode magnesium alloys, with the exception of pure chromic acid, pure concentrated hydrofluoric acid, and alkali metal fluorides, chromates, and bichromates. The alloys are resistant to attack by most alkalies and many organic chemicals, including hydrocarbons, phenols, and oils.

Table II. Trade Designations, Analyses, and Uses of Magnesium Alloys

A.S.T.M. Alloy No.	U. S. Army Designation	U. S. Navy Designation	Dow Chem. Co., Dowmetal	Amer. Magnesium Corp.	Bohn Aluminum and Brass Corp., Bohnlite	Al	Mn	Zn	Sn	Mg	Uses
1 *	57–741b Grade 1	M-112c Alloy 1	A	AM-241	X-5	8.0	0.2	......	......	91.8	Sand castings. Heat treatment not required for general use. Heat-treated for highly stressed parts requiring good impact toughness.
2 *	57–741b Grade 2	M-112c Alloy 2	G	AM-240	X-2	10.0	0.1	......	......	89.9	Die castings. Heat-treated sand castings requiring high yield strength with moderate toughness.
3 *	......	......	B	AM-246	X-7	12.0	0.1	......	......	87.9	Heat-treated sand castings requiring maximum yield strength and hardness. Impact toughness relatively low.
4 *	......	M-112c Alloy 5	H	AM-265	X-8	6.0	0.2	3.0	.....	90.8	Sand castings with improved salt-water corrosion resistance. Heat-treated castings combine high yield and ultimate strength with good impact toughness.
6†, ‡, §	......	M-111b Alloy 1	F	AM-53S	X-1s	4.0	0.3	......	......	95.7	Forgings, sheet and plate, extruded shapes, bars, rods, and tubes.
8 ‡, §	......	M-126a Grade 2	J	AM-57S	......	6.5	0.3	0.75	.....	92.45	Forgings and extruded bars, rods and shapes.
9 ‡, §	......	M-126a Grade 3	......	AM-58S	......	8.5	0.2	0.5	.....	90.8	Hot-pressed forgings for highly stressed parts. More difficult to forge than other alloys.
10 ‡	......	M-126a Grade 1	......	AM-61S	X-11s	.....	1.0	.....	6.0	93.0	Extruded rods and shapes. Hammer forgings for moderately stressed parts.
11 †, §	......	M-111b Alloy 2	M	AM-3S	X-6	.....	1.5	......	......	98.5	Sheet, plate, and rod for moderately stressed parts requiring resistance to salt water.

* Tentative specifications for magnesium-base alloy sand castings (B80–36T).
† Tentative specifications for magnesium-base alloy sheet (B90–36T).
‡ Tentative specifications for magnesium-base alloy forgings (B91–36T).
§ Tentative specifications for magnesium-base alloy bars, rods, and shapes.

Table III. Typical Physical and Mechanical Properties of Magnesium Alloys

Modulus of elasticity = 6,500,000, lb per sq in.

A.S.T.M. Designation	Condition *	Treatment †	Tensile ‡	Yield (set = 0.2 per cent) §	Compressive	Shearing	Elongation, per cent in 2 in.	Brinell ¶	Rockwell E Scale	Charpy Impact, ft-lb	Endurance Limit, 1000 lb per sq in.‖	Thermal Conductivity, cgs units, 100 to 300° C	Electrical Resistivity, microhm-cm at 20° C	Specific Gravity	Weight, lb per cu in.
1	SC	....	25	11	46	17	4	48	55	0.9	7	0.18	13.0	1.80	0.065
	SC	H.T. 1	34	12	46	17	9	48	55	2.2	7	......	15.0	1.80	0.065
2	DC	....	29	20	......	......	1	63	75	......	......	0.17	15.0	1.81	0.066
	SC	H.T. 1	33	12	51	20	7	51	61	2.0	11.5	......	17.5	1.81	0.066
	SC	H.T. 2	33	16	51	21	3	60	72	1.0	10.	......	16.0	1.81	0.066
	SC	H.T. 3	33	19	55	22	1	69	80	0.7	10.5	......	14.0	1.81	0.066
3	SC	H.T. 3	29	21	....	......	0.5	75	84	......	9.	0.16	14.0	1.82	0.066
4	SC	....	28	11	46	17	5	48	55	1.0	10.	....		1.84	0.066
	SC	H.T. 1	35	12	46	17	10	51	61	2.0	10.	....		1.84	0.066
	SC	H.T. 3	40	20	50	18	5	68	79	1.0	10.	....		1.84	0.066
6	Ex**	....	40	29	58	20	15	48	55	2.2	14	0.23	10.0	1.77	0.064
	F	....	38	23	....	......	12	50	60	......	12	....		1.77	0.064
	Sh	....	43	30	....	......	8	65	76	....				1.77	0.064
	Sh	annealed	35	19	....	......	14	55	66	....				1.77	0.064
8	Ex**	....	43	28	54	22	15	55	66	2.0	16	....		1.81	0.065
	F	....	42	28	....	......	9	59	71	2.2	......	....		1.81	0.065
9	F	....	45	32	40	23	6	72	82	1.4	16	....		1.83	0.066
10	F	....	35	19	....	......	5	45	49	2.0	9	....		1.85	0.067
11	Ex**	....	42	26	57	19	7	42	40	......	7	0.30	5.0	1.76	0.064
	Sh	....	33	21	....	......	6	50	60	....				1.76	0.064

* SC = sand cast. DC = die cast. Ex = extruded. F = forged. Sh = sheet.
† H.T. 1 = solution heat treatment. H.T. 2 = solution heat treatment + partial aging. H.T. 3 = solution heat treatment + complete aging.
‡ Standard A.S.T.M. tension specimens.
§ Yield strength is defined as the stress at which the stress-deformation curve deviates 0.2 per cent from the modulus line.
¶ Obtained with 500-kg load, 10-mm ball.
‖ R. R. Moore type rotating beam machine, 500 million cycles.
** Properties of extruded material for round and square up to 1 1/2 in.

Table IV. Comparative Mechanical Properties of Structural Material

	Specific Gravity	Tensile Strength, lb per sq in.	Yield Strength, lb per sq in.	Endurance Limit, lb per sq in.	Specific Tensile Strength §	Specific Yield Strength §	Specific Endurance Limit §
Cast:							
Dowmetal A, H.T.1 *	1.80	34,000	12,000	7,000	18,900	6,700	3,900
Dowmetal H, H.T.3†	1.83	40,000	20,000	10,000	21,800	10,900	5,500
Aluminum alloy S.A.E. 30.........	2.83	22,000	14,000	7,500	7,800	5,000	2,700
Aluminum alloy S.A.E. 38, H.T.‡...	2.77	36,000	22,000	6,000	13,000	7,900	2,200
Cast iron (Gray)....	7.2	40,000	.....	20,000	5,600	.....	2,800
Wrought:							
Dowmetal F........	1.77	40,000	29,000	14,000	22,600	16,400	7,900
Aluminum sheet 1/2 hard..........	2.71	17,000	14,000	.....	6,300	5,200	.....
Duralumin.........	2.79	58,000	35,000	15,000	20,800	12,500	5,400
Mild steel..........	7.85	60,000	36,000	35,000	7,600	4,600	4,500
Cr-Mo steel, H.T.‡.	7.85	122,000	86,000	68,000	15,600	11,000	8,700

* H.T. 1 = solution heat treatment.
† H.T. 3 = solution heat treatment + complete aging.
‡ H.T. = heat treated.
§ Specific strength values are the normal strength values divided by the specific gravity.

Protection. Paints, varnishes, lacquers, and enamels of all types can be applied to magnesium alloys, although many paint materials, within a class, vary considerably in quality and service performance. Synthetic resin varnishes and enamels are the best all-round coatings, both for protection and high-grade finish. Baked finishes combine speed of finish with excellent adhesion, hardness, and toughness of film. Prior to painting, the metal should be cleaned free of dirt and grease, and then chrome-pickled. This consists of a short-time dip in a bath of 1.5 lb $Na_2Cr_2O_7$ and 1.5 pt concentrated HNO_3 per gallon of solution, followed by a thorough wash and rapid drying. Properly applied, this treatment produces a dull, iridescent bronze finish, combining a mechanical " tooth " and chemically inhibitive film, which greatly improves the adhesion and protective value of the paint coating.

Fabrication and Use

Foundry. Sand castings may be made in dry sand but are normally made in green sand to which has been added small amounts of fluorides, sulfur, boric acid, or other materials which inhibit the action of water vapor on the hot metal. Shrinkage factors are: $3/16$ in. per ft for castings of moderate size or with unrestrained shrinkage, $5/32$ in. per ft for large castings. Pattern equipment designed for aluminum work usually is satisfactory for magnesium alloys. Heat treatment effects pronounced improvement of the properties of most of the alloys, and is used where service conditions are severe. The properties of the as-cast metal are satisfactory for many industrial applications. Magnesium alloy die castings possess all the advantages of other types of die castings, plus light weight.

Machinability of magnesium alloys is superior to that of any other common metal. Both speed and depth of cut can be increased. Sharpness and proper clearance of cutting tools are essential for best results. The alloys finish exceptionally smooth with no tendency to tear or drag. Cutting compounds are recommended in certain high-speed operations, such as screw machine work.

Hot and Cold Working. Most plastic deformation operations on magnesium alloys are performed between 400 and 800 deg fahr. At these temperatures the alloys may be extruded, rolled, forged, and formed. Best results are obtained by working at moderate speeds and allowing generous bend radii. The alloys work-harden at or near room temperature more rapidly than many metals, and cold-working operations usually are limited to simple steps with small changes in shape or cross-section.

Joining. Magnesium alloy parts are joined by riveting or welding. Aluminum-alloy rivets, preferably containing no nickel or copper, should be used. Rivet holes should be $1/64$ to $1/32$ in. larger than shank diameter. The bearing strength of magnesium alloy sheet is approximately 50 per cent greater than its tensile strength. Galvanic corrosion in riveted assemblies is minimized by bitumastic paint or reinforced red lead between contacting, dissimilar metals.

Oxyacetylene, Electric Spot, and Seam Welding are feasible with magnesium alloys using technique similar to that used with aluminum. Acetylene welds have the strength of as-cast metal. A filler rod, of the same approximate composition as the base metal, and a flux are used. After welding, complete removal of flux is essential to prevent corrosion. It is removed by washing in hot water, followed by the chrome-pickle treatment (see above). Electric spot and seam welds are made on machines with water-cooled electrodes. Welds on $1/8$-in. sheet have a strength of approximately 1800 lb per spot, or 20,000 lb per linear foot of seam.

Uses. Magnesium alloys are standard materials of construction for many airplane parts, including crankcases, starting equipment, instrument housings, and landing and tail wheels. Sheet, plate, and structural shapes are used to increase the ratio of payload to dead load in trucks and trailers. Used in portable tools and equipment, these alloys reduce human fatigue, and in high-speed automotive equipment they improve operating efficiency.

TUNGSTEN

By Zay Jeffries

33. PROPERTIES AND USES OF TUNGSTEN

Tungsten, a metallic element, is very important, although the total amount produced seems insignificant as compared with some of the other metals. Because of several peculiar properties, tungsten is irreplaceable for some important uses.

Manufacture of Tungsten. Until 1904, pure tungsten had been produced only in the form of a powder or a non-coherent sponge. It was not used, except for alloying with other metals, until the invention of the tungsten incandescent lamp filament, in 1904, by Just and Hannaman. The filaments were of the squirted or pressed type, prepared by mixing tungsten powder with a binder, squirting the mixture through a die, and subsequently removing the binder or the greater portion of it by passing electric current through the filament, which also served to sinter or consolidate the tungsten into a coherent and fairly dense condition. Such filaments were brittle and fragile but were used in incandescent lamps until about 1911. In 1908, the General Electric Co. succeeded in producing ductile tungsten. Strong wrought tungsten, not ductile when cold, was also produced.

Tungsten ingots for working are pressed from dry powder and heated to a temperature near the melting point to consolidate. The resulting ingots are brittle when cold but somewhat malleable when hot.

In swaging an ingot from about $1/4$ in. square, the work all being done at a high temperature, the rod is brittle cold and malleable hot until the swaged rod is about 50 mils diameter. At a size near 50 mils diameter, above or below as the working temperature is low or high respectively, the swaged rod becomes ductile cold.

Physical and Mechanical Properties. The properties of tungsten are: atomic weight, 184.0; melting point, 3382 deg cent (highest of all metals and among the elements exceeded only by carbon); coefficient of linear expansion, 0.000,004,44 per deg cent at 27 deg cent (Worthing); electrical resistivity at 0 deg cent, 0.000,004,91 ohm-cm for pure single crystal wire, 0.000,005,05 for ordinary polycrystalline wire; at 20 deg cent, 0.000,005,50. Very fine wire as drawn may have a value as high as 0.000,008, which is reduced to about 0.000,006 or somewhat less by heating to a high temperature. The average temperature coefficient of resistivity between 0 and 100 deg cent is about 0.0047 per deg. Resistance at 2100 deg cent is about 12 times and at 2400 deg cent about 15 times the resistance at room temperature. Modulus of elasticity is 40,000 kg per sq mm or about 57,000,000 lb per sq in. Poisson's ratio is 0.17, independent of temperature. The thermal conductivity is 1.17 watts per sq cm per deg cent per cm at 2000 deg cent, 1.66 at 0 deg cent, 2.32 at −190 deg cent, and 34.3 at −252 deg cent. It is weakly paramagnetic. The electronic work function is 4.54 volts. Tungsten crystallizes with a body-centered cubic space lattice, the length of a side of the unit cube being 3.155 Angstrom units and the nearest approach of atom centers 2.732 Angstrom units. Fine tungsten wire is stronger than any other material known. The remarkable improvement in tensile strength by working is shown in Table I.

Table I.   Tensile Strength of Tungsten

Kind of Material	Diameter, mils	Tensile Strength, lb per sq in.	Kind of Material	Diameter, mils	Tensile Strength, lb per sq in.
Sintered tungsten ingot	200 × 250	18,000	Drawn wire.......	5.78	366,000
Swaged rod..........	216	50,000	" "	5.50	378,000
" "	125	107,000	" "	3.96	483,000
" "	80	176,000	" "	1.14	590,000
" "	26	215,000	" "	1.00	650,000
Drawn wire..........	18	264,000	" "	0.50	700,000
" "	7.23	340,000			

Drawn tungsten can be treated to a higher temperature than any other metal without removing the effects of working (strain hardening). A 25-mil drawn wire had a tensile strength of 101,000 lb per sq in. at 890 deg cent, a value not equaled by any other metal.

Drawn tungsten wire has some peculiar properties. When ductilized by the swaging and drawing process, it is typically ductile. That is, it can be drawn further cold, but it is not typically malleable; it splits into many fibers when hammered on an anvil. When ordinary drawn metals are heated so as to cause the strain-hardened grains to recrystallize, the ductility, largely lost because of the drawing, is restored. Ductile tungsten so treated becomes brittle at ordinary temperature, and to make it again ductile it must be further worked hot, but below the recrystallization temperature

Corrosion. Tungsten metal in the powdered state is black when finely divided and gray when coarse. In air at ordinary temperatures, the coherent and dense metal slowly oxidizes on the surface until a thin film of oxide stops further action. It is rapidly dissolved by fused alkali nitrates and nitrites and slowly attacked by hot aqua regia or strong hydrogen peroxide.

Tungsten is scarcely attacked by hydrochloric, nitric, or sulfuric acids owing to the formation of a protective film or tungstic acid. It is rapidly dissolved by hydrofluoric acid containing nitric acid, giving a clear solution. When heated above a red heat it oxidizes fairly rapidly. Exposed at high temperatures to carbon monoxide or hydrocarbon gases two tungsten carbides (reported to be WC and W_2C) form.

Cemented Carbides. Tungsten is the most important element in the so-called cemented carbides now used extensively for cutting tools, wire drawing and other dies, and wearing parts of machinery. The cemented tungsten carbide is made by producing very fine tungsten carbide powder approximating the composition of WC. This is mixed with metallic cobalt from about 3 to 20 per cent by weight according to the hardness and wearing properties desired, and sintered at a temperature far below the melting point of the tungsten carbide. This material has remarkable cutting and wear-resisting properties. It is relatively expensive as compared with the common cutting tools, and tools are therefore usually made by attaching a small tip of the cemented carbide to a steel shank by copper brazing. In a similar manner the drawing dies are usually made by mounting a relatively small piece of the cemented carbide in a steel casing. Other carbides such as tantalum carbide and titanium carbide have been used to add to the tungsten carbide, principally for the purpose of enhancing the steel-cutting qualities.

Uses. Wrought and ductile tungsten are now used for many purposes. Drawn wire has supplanted the pressed filaments for incandescent lamps. Tungsten is also used for talking-machine needles, filaments for radio and rectifier tubes, electric furnace resistors, and lamp filament supports. The wrought tungsten has been made in rods up to about $3/4$-in. diameter, and in sheet. Wrought tungsten is used principally for x-ray targets and contacts for internal-combustion ignition appliances such as Delco.

By far the greater part of the tungsten produced is used in making alloy steel, principally into high-speed steel, which contains about 18 per cent tungsten, and into magnet steel. The use of small percentages of tungsten in some structural steels seems assured. Tungsten is added to steel either in the form of tungsten powder or preferably as ferrotungsten containing at least 75 per cent tungsten.

MOLYBDENUM

By Zay Jeffries

34. PROPERTIES AND USES OF MOLYBDENUM

Molybdenum is a hard, silvery-white metallic element. Its use as a metal followed that of tungsten. It was prepared by squirting into small wires which were used for filament supports in incandescent lamps. It is still used for this purpose but the wires are drawn.

Manufacture. Wrought and drawn molybdenum were developed by the General Electric Co. about 1908. Wire is made by hot drawing, at least in the early stages of drawing. The ingots are prepared by pressing powdered metal and consolidating below the melting point. These are brittle when cold and must be worked hot. After the hot working has progressed to a certain point, the rod becomes ductile cold.

Physical and Mechanical Properties. Some of the properties of molybdenum are: atomic weight, 96.0; density, 10.21 g per cu cm; coefficient of linear expansion, 0.000,005,00 per deg cent at 27 deg cent (Worthing); electrical resistivity at 0 deg cent, 0.000,005,08 ohm–cm; at 2000 deg cent, 0.000,006,15; average temperature coefficient of resistivity between 0 and 100 deg cent, 0.0047; thermal conductivity is 1.43 watts per sq cm per deg cent per cm at 0 deg cent. It is weakly paramagnetic. The electronic work function is 4.41 volts. Molybdenum crystallizes with a body-centered cubic space lattice, the length of a side of the unit cube being 3.142 Angstrom and the nearest approach of atom centers 2.720 Angstrom.

Table I gives typical mechanical properties of molybdenum wire, 25 mils diameter, treated in various ways.

Table I. Mechanical Properties of Molybdenum

Description	Tensile Strength, lb per sq in.	Elongation in 2 in., per cent	Reduction of Area, per cent
Swaged and drawn hot (1000–1300° C) from 25 to 125 mils	148,000	4.7	68
Swaged and drawn hot (black heat–800°) from 25 to 125 mils	154,000	5.7	65
Annealed to produce large grains......................	42,500	3.15	None
Annealed to produce very small grain size...............	125,000	20.0	66

Brittle molybdenum can be ductilized like tungsten by working below the recrystallization temperature. Unlike tungsten, drawn wire can be recrystallized with an increase in ductility if the annealing temperature is low, say 1050 deg cent, so as to produce a fine-grained structure. Higher annealing temperatures produce larger grains, causing a diminution in cold ductility.

Corrosion. In air at ordinary temperatures, dense and coherent molybdenum, like tungsten, slowly oxidizes superficially, the action stopping with the formation of a protective film of oxide. At red heat, the oxidation proceeds rapidly with the formation and volatilization of molybdenum trioxide. It is attacked or dissolved by nearly all reagents which attack tungsten. It is soluble in nitric acid, sulfuric acid, and hydrogen peroxide.

Uses. Molybdenum is used mostly as an alloying element in steel. Although it imparts characteristics to steel somewhat similar to those imparted by tungsten, the two metals are not interchangeable, volume for volume. Molybdenum has never been as successful in high-speed steel as tungsten. It is used chiefly in structural steels for automobiles in amounts less than 1 per cent. The wrought metal is used for x-ray targets, the wavelength being quite suitable for the study of crystal structure.

DIE-CASTING ALLOYS
By J. C. Fox

35. TYPES OF DIE-CASTING ALLOYS

Die-casting alloys may be classified into six main groups:
1. Tin-base alloys: tin, alloyed with copper, antimony, and lead.
2. Lead-base alloys: lead, alloyed with antimony or antimony and tin.
3. Zinc-base alloys: zinc, alloyed with aluminum, magnesium, and/or copper.
4. Aluminum-base alloys: aluminum, alloyed with copper, nickel, silicon, iron, and manganese.
5. Copper-base alloys: the brasses and bronzes, copper, alloyed with zinc, tin, lead, aluminum, nickel, manganese, etc.
6. Magnesium-base alloys: magnesium, alloyed with aluminium, manganese and nickel.

Tin-base Alloys. Table I gives the composition of typical tin-base alloys used in die casting.

Alloy No. 1, of Table I, is the highest quality "babbitt" mixture corresponding to S.A.E. specification No. 10 Babbitt. It is used for main shaft and connecting-rod bearings in the automotive and aircraft industries. No. 2 also is used for bearings and other applications requiring a high-class tin-base alloy. It fulfils S.A.E. specification No. 11. No. 3 is a special automotive bearing composition.

Table I. Typical Tin-base Die-casting Alloys

Alloy No.	Copper, per cent	Antimony, per cent	Lead, per cent	Tin, per cent
1	4.50	4.50	......	90.0
2	6.0	8.0	......	86.0
3	7.75	7.75	1.75	82.75
4	3.0	10.50	25.0	61.50

No. 4 (S.A.E. Specification No. 12), because of the lead content, is of lower cost than the others.

Although tin-base alloys are used mostly for automotive bearings, they also are used in parts of soda fountains, milking machines, syrup pumps, and similar apparatus where resistance to the action of acids, alkalies, and moisture is essential. They are also used to some extent for surgical instruments, dental appliances, etc., because of their resistance to corrosion.

Lead-base Alloys. The compositions of typical lead-base alloys used in die castings are given in Table II.

Lead-base alloys are used where a cheap non-corrosive metal is required and where strength, hardness, and other mechanical properties are unimportant. Parts which must resist strong mineral acids as in the chemical industry are made of lead-base die alloys. X-ray apparatus parts are made of lead-base alloys, because of the opacity of lead to the x-rays. The high density or unit weight of lead is another factor in its use.

Table II. Typical Lead-base Die-casting Alloys

Alloy No.	Antimony, per cent	Tin, per cent	Lead, per cent
5	5	..	95
6	10	..	90
7	17	..	83
8	15	5	80

Zinc-base Alloys. The zinc-base die-casting alloys in most common use today are those conforming to the A.S.T.M. Tentative Standard B86–34T and the S.A.E. Standards 921 and 903.* Chemical composition limits for these alloys are given in Table III.

Table III. Composition of Zinc-base Die-casting Alloys

Composition	A.S.T.M. Alloy XXI S.A.E. Alloy 921	A.S.T.M. Alloy XXIII S.A.E. Alloy 903
Copper, per cent	2.50–3.50	0.10 max.
Aluminum, per cent	3.50–4.30	3.50–4.30
Magnesium, per cent	0.02–0.10	0.03–0.08
Iron (max.), per cent	0.100	0.100
Lead (max.), per cent	0.007	0.007
Cadmium (max), per cent	0.005	0.005
Tin, per cent	0.005	0.005
Zinc	Remainder	Remainder

The percentages of lead, tin, and cadmium given in this table should not be exceeded if stability of properties, dimensions, and corrosion resistance are to be expected. This makes necessary the use of the highest purity metals: zinc of the 99.99+ per cent purity grade; electrolytic copper; 99+ per cent aluminum; 99.9+ per cent magnesium. Precaution must also be taken to insure against contamination with injurious metals in the melting and casting operations.

The A.S.T.M. and S.A.E. Standards call for the minima of physical properties of die-castings of these alloys, as given in Table IV.

Table IV. Minimum Physical Properties of Zinc-base Die-casting Alloys

Property	Alloy XXI	Alloy XXIII
Tensile strength, lb per sq in	44,000	35,000
Charpy impact, ft-lb	6.0	12
Elongation in 2 in., per cent	2.0	3

Average physical and mechanical properties of these two alloys, as determined from die-cast test bars, made in accordance with the A.S.T.M. specifications, are given in Table V. Though the A.S.T.M. Alloy XXI possesses higher tensile strength and hardness than the Alloy XXIII, the latter alloy, because of its greater dimensional stability, and higher impact strength which remains unchanged even under the severest conditions of use, is usually favored for applications requiring strict maintenance of properties and dimensions.

Table V. Physical and Mechanical Properties of Zinc-base Die-casting Alloys

Property	Alloy XXI	Alloy XXIII
Density, g per cu cm	6.7	6.64
Melting point, deg fahr	734°	728°
Specific heat, g-cal per g per deg cent	0.10	0.10
Thermal conductivity, g-cal per sec per sq cm per deg cent per cm	0.25	0.27
Thermal expansion per deg cent	27.7×10^{-6}	27.4×10^{-6}
Electrical conductivity, mho-cm at 25 deg cent	144,000	155,000
Tensile strength, lb per sq in	48,000	40,000
Elongation in 2 in., per cent	5	5
Compressive strength, lb per sq in	93,000	60,000
Shearing strength, lb per sq in	45,800	31,000
Transverse deflection, in	0.22	0.27
Brinell hardness number	83	74
Charpy impact strength, ft-lb (1/4" × 1/4" bar)	19	20

Pressure die-castings made from these alloys have high strength, high ductility, resistance to impact, and good corrosion resistance, and they are easily machined. Practically every type of commercial finish may be satisfactorily applied. Zinc-base die-castings are widely used for automotive parts, household and office appliances, and miscellaneous objects such as toys, novelties, and ornaments.

Aluminum-base Alloys, see p. 11–60.

Copper-base Alloys. Until recently (1932), commercial die-casting practice was limited to the casting of alloys of comparatively low melting points. Progress developed

* These alloys also conform to the "Zamak" series of the New Jersey Zinc Co. (U. S. Patents 1596761, 1779525, 1852441.)

along the line of higher melting points. Tin and lead alloys of casting temperatures up to 650 deg fahr were first used, followed by zinc-base alloys with casting temperatures up to 800 deg fahr, in turn followed by aluminum-base alloys with casting temperatures up to 1300 deg fahr. Difficulties in the manufacture of die castings multiply rapidly with the rise in the melting points of the alloys. The life of the die decreases with ascending casting temperatures. The Doehler Die Casting Co. perfected (1931) a process for the pressure die casting of copper-base alloys. Typical die-casting alloys of this group are given in Table VI. Mechanical properties of these alloys are given in Table VII.

Table VI. Nominal Composition of Copper-base Die-casting Alloys

Composition	Alloy 1	Alloy 2	Alloy 3
Copper, per cent	57.0–59.0	63.0–66.0	80.0–81.5
Zinc, per cent	40.0–42.0	32.0–34.0	13.5–15.0
Tin, per cent	0.5–1.50		
Silicon, per cent		0.75–1.25	4.0–5.0
Lead, per cent			
Nickel, per cent			
Manganese, per cent			

Table VII. Mechanical Properties of Copper-base Die-casting Alloys

Property	Alloy 1	Alloy 2	Alloy 3
Tensile strength, lb per sq in	55,000–65,000	65,000–75,000	85,000–95,000
Yield point, lb per sq in	35,000–40,000	35,000–40,000	65,000–70,000
Elongation in 2 in., per cent	15–20	15–20	10–15
Brinell hardness	120–130	110–120	160–180

Magnesium Base Alloy (see also p. 11–76). Although at present only a few magnesium-base alloy die-castings are being produced, it is interesting to note that a subcommittee of committee B–6–A.S.T.M. is functioning on this type of alloy. This committee has prepared tentative specifications (A.S.T.M. Tentative Standard B94–36T) covering "Alloy 12" as follows:

    Aluminum, per cent .... 10.0 ± 1.0
    Silicon, per cent .... 0.5 ± 0.5
    Manganese, min. per cent 0.10
    Copper, max. per cent 0.05
    Nickel, max. per cent 0.03
    Magnesium, per cent .... Remainder

BEARING METALS
By Christopher H. Bierbaum

36. PROPERTIES AND USES OF BEARING METALS

Bearing Metals are alloys composed of two or more metals in proportions in which they do not enter into a solid solution. They consist of relatively hard and soft microscopic particles or crystals intimately mixed. The function of the hard particles or bearing crystals is to support the load and resist the wear at times when actual metallic contact exists between the bearing surfaces. The softer particles, in a measure, owing to their plasticity, allow the harder particles to adjust themselves to the surface requirements of the journal. The softer particles also wear down lower than the harder particles and thus form slight depressions on the apparently smooth bearing surface. These depressions retain some of the lubricant and thereby effect a residuary lubrication, sufficient to prevent scoring or cutting during metallic contact. The property of a metal to retain lubrication upon a "run-in" bearing surface characterizes it as a bearing metal, and its capacity for doing so largely determines its value as such. A bearing metal, therefore, may be defined as an alloy that is capable of retaining a lubricant upon a bearing surface. Heretofore a run-in bearing surface could be produced only under service conditions, wherein it was necessary that all the disturbed metal on the surface, incident to tooling, should first be worn off; this was tedious and often caused bearing surface inaccuracies before a run-in condition was obtained. Recently (1928), however, a high state of perfection of diamond tooling has enabled the production of bearing surfaces that approach insensibly close to those run-in in service.

This effects a twofold economy: it reduces the time for fitting and running-in; and it enormously prolongs the life of bearings. Nevertheless, journal and bearing should mutually polish each other. Bearing and journal therefore should bear some relation to each other, e.g., their hardest particles, for best results, should be of the same order of hardness. These requirements would not be imperative, were the journal to possess infinite hardness and the cylindrical surface to be ideally true. A highly accurate, ground and polished journal surface of chromium plate, nitrided nitralloy steel, or hardened tooled steel closely approaches this ideal state. The mating member, nevertheless, should have the microstructure of a bearing metal.

It is essential that, with two surfaces bearing together, one, say the journal, should have the highest possible microscopic homogeneity, and the other a heterogeneity corresponding to that of a bearing metal.

Babbitt Metals. The alloys in Table I are from A.S.T.M., 1933 Standards, Part 1, p. 845. These alloys cover the field very completely and can be recommended for the uses outlined below:

No. 1 is suited for crankpin service in steam and internal-combustion engines. It should be well confined in its backing or be used as a thin layer sweated onto bronze or steel. It is the least likely to crack and the most plastic of the tin-base alloys.

No. 2 is suited for substantially the same service as No. 1. It has, however, a higher bearing value, and is less likely to pound out. Like No. 1, it is especially suited for sweating on, owing to its high tin content.

No. 3 is the hardest babbitt and has the highest bearing value. When allowed to cool and solidify very slowly, it develops the SnCu$_4$ crystal, which is the hardest copper-tin constituent; it should therefore never be mated with the softest steels. It is ideal for the highest service requirements when well seated and not subjected to loose pounding.

No. 4 alloy has excellent bearing value for engine main bearings and general machinery, machine tools, and the like. It will withstand severe punishment and give general satisfaction. It is the most economical tin-base babbitt.

Nos. 5 and 6 are intermediate alloys, neither tin nor lead base. They are alloys in which the soft matrix contains the tin-lead eutectic, for which reason they become mushy at a relatively low temperature. They are not to be recommended for either service or economy, as compared with Nos. 4 and 7.

No. 7 is the most economical of the lead-base alloys. Its entire tin content is combined with antimony, giving a high percentage of bearing crystal; for that reason it is very serviceable. It is even suitable for use in many places where the high-tin babbitts are now specified.

Nos. 8, 9, and 10 are all lead-base babbitts belonging to the same general class. Their bearing value decreases with a decrease of tin content. They are serviceable with relatively light loads; with good workmanship they stand high speeds and are suitable for mating with the softer steels.

Nos. 11 and 12 are antimonial lead alloys and constitute the cheapest grade of babbitt. They should be used for the lightest service only, such as line shafting and less important bearings; they are suited to mate with the softest steels.

Bronze Alloys. Up to the present time (1936) a vast number of bronze bearing formulas have been evolved, many of them even of doubtful value. The whole range of engineering work, however, can be covered satisfactorily by a comparatively small number of alloys. Those given in Table II are an approved list, from which the engineer can select a bearing for any and all requirements encountered in practice. This table is the result of selections and rejections of bearing formulas, during a period of more than 39 years, in an effort to reduce this entire field of alloys to an efficient minimum number.

The phosphorus content of a bronze, be it a trace or an amount not in excess of 0.25 per cent, has no appreciable effect, either upon the physical properties or bearing value of the resulting bronze; it is important, however, that deoxidation with phosphorus be effected. Hence, deoxidation with phosphorus should be specified and a trace of it required in the resulting alloy.

Considerable work and research have been done on casting bearing bronzes centrifugally; so far, however (1936), there is no proved advantage either as to physical properties or bearing value of any centrifugally cast material. The advantages claimed are entirely due to the chill effect incident to the process, and the question is one of economic production. Chilling, however, can best be controlled in stationary molds.

The importance of high-class workmanship cannot be overestimated, especially with the harder bearing metals and their harder mating journals. Grinding or lapping is ideal for the production of accurate surfaces, but, owing to the microconstituents of bearing metals, great care should be taken not to leave grinding particles embedded in the softer constituents of the bearing surface.

Table I. Composition and Physical Properties * of White Metal Bearing Alloys

Alloy Number	Specified Composition of Alloys, per cent †				Specific Gravity	Compositions of Alloys Tested, per cent				Yield Point, lb per sq in.‡		Johnson's Apparent Elastic Limit, lb per sq in.§		Ultimate Strength, lb per sq in.‖		Brinell Hardness ¶		Melting Point	Temperature of Complete Liquefaction	Proper Pouring Temperature
	Copper	Tin	Antimony	Lead		Copper	Tin	Antimony	Lead	At 68° F	At 212° F	At 68° F	At 212° F	At 68° F	At 212° F	At 68° F	At 212° F	Deg F	Deg F	Deg F
1	4.5	91.0	4.5	.....	7.34	4.56	90.9	4.52	None	4400	2650	2450	1050	12,850	6950	17.0	8.0	433	.....	825
2	3.5	89.0	7.5	.....	7.39	3.1	89.2	7.4	0.03	6100	3000	3350	1100	14,900	8700	24.5	12.0	466	669	795
3	8 1/3	83 1/3	8 1/3	.....	7.46	8.3	83.4	8.2	0.03	6600	3150	5350	1300	17,600	9900	27.0	14.5	464	792	915
4	3.0	75.0	12.0	10.0	7.52	3.0	75.2	11.6	10.2	5550	2150	3200	1550	16,150	6900	24.5	12.0	363	583	710
5	2.0	65.0	15.0	18.0	7.75	2.0	65.5	14.1	18.2	5050	2150	3750	1500	15,050	6750	23.0	12.0	358	565	690
6	1.5	20.0	15.0	63.5	9.33	1.5	19.8	14.5	63.7	3800	2050	3550	1800	14,550	8050	21.0	10.5	358	531	655
7	.....	10.0	15.0	75.0	9.73	0.11	10.2	14.9	75.0	3550	1600	2500	1350	15,650	6150	22.5	10.5	464	514	640
8	.....	5.0	15.0	80.0	10.04	0.14	5.2	14.5	79.4	3400	1750	2650	1200	15,600	6150	22.5	9.5	459	522	645
9	.....	5.0	10.0	85.0	10.24	0.06	5.0	9.9	84.6	3350	1550	2400	950	14,700	5850	20.0	8.5	459	493	620
10	.....	2.0	15.0	83.0	10.07	0.12	2.05	15.7	82.0	3350	1850	2250	1200	15,450	5750	19.0	9.0	468	507	630
11	.....	.....	15.0	85.0	10.28	0.19	0.09	14.8	84.7	3050	1400	2750	1100	12,800	5100	17.5	7.0	471	504	630
12	.....	.....	10.0	90.0	10.67	0.12	0.11	9.9	89.4	2800	1250	2250	950	12,900	5100	14.5	6.5	473	498	625

* The compression test specimens were cylinders 1 1/2 in. long and 1/2 in. in diameter, machined from chill castings 2 in. long and 3/4 in. in diameter. The Brinell tests were made on the bottom face of parallel machined specimens cast in a 2-in. diameter by 5/8-in. deep steel mold at room temperature.

† Permissible variations in percentages of the desired elements are as follows:

Percentage of element specified......	not over 2	2-5	5-10	over 10
Permissible variation, units of per cent.	0.25	0.50	0.75	1.0

‡ The values for yield point were taken from stress-deformation curves at a deformation of 0.125 per cent reduction of gage length.

§ Johnson's apparent elastic limit is taken as the unit stress at the point where the slope of the tangent to the curve is 1 1/2 times its slope at the origin.

‖ The ultimate strength values were taken as the unit load necessary to produce a deformation of 25 per cent of the length of the specimen.

¶ These values are the average Brinell number of three impressions on each alloy using a 10-mm ball and a 500-kg load applied for 30 sec.

Two distinct tendencies during the last 15 years (1936), for the improvement of bearing service, apply to both bearing alloys and their steel journals: a large number of the more suitable alloys are now being produced, not only as sand cast, but also in a preferred chill cast condition; and there is a very general tendency to increase the hardness of journals

Table II. Composition and Properties of Bronze Bearing Alloys

Properties	T-1 *	T-1 †	T-2 *	T-2 †	T-3 *	T-3 †	T-4 *	T-4 †	T-5 *
Composition:									
Percentage of copper	88.75	88.75	87.50	87.50	85.0	85.0	84.0	84.0	84.00
" aluminum									
" tin	11.00	11.00	11.00	11.00	10.00	10.00	10.00	10.00	16.00
" lead	0.25	0.25	1.50	1.50	5.0	5.0	2.5	2.5	
" nickel							3.5	3.5	
" phosphorus	‡	‡	‡	‡	‡	‡	‡	‡	‡
Tensile properties:									
Ultimate strength, thousands of pounds	30-40	33-40	32-43	33-36	29-34	31-36	40-49	40-48	23-32
Yield point, " " "	20-23	25-27	20-22	21-25	19-22	21-22	25-28	25-28	19-27
Elastic limit, " " "	11-16		11-15		15-16	6-9	18-21		13-19
Elongation in 2 in., per cent	5-10	4-8	5-15	4-8	5-12		7-20	8-14	1-2
Reduction of area, per cent	5-10		5-15		4-10		7-20		0.8-1.2
Compression load, thousands of pounds to produce compression of 0.001 in..	15-17	22	15-17	17-19	13-14	16	20-24	24	18-25
0.1 in.	53-54	72	44-51	60-67	40-48	50	58-64	66	
0.15-0.17 in.		100							
0.1 -0.2 in.				100			100	100	100
0.22-0.25 in.	100				100	100			
0.23-0.28 in.			100						
0.27-0.30 in.									
0.3 -0.33 in.									
Brinell hardness No	63-77	75-90	45-54	70-80	50-61	65-74	80-93	83-93	83-93
Specific gravity	8.5	8.8	8.7		8.8		8.8		8.6
Weight, lb per cu in	0.307		0.316		0.314		0.318		0.310
Patternmaker's shrinkage, in. per ft	3/16	1/8	3/16	1/8	3/16	1/8	3/16	1/8	1/8
Electrical conductivity	10.1		10.2		11.3		9.6		7.3
Impact test (Izod)	3-7		3-6		4-7		2-4		1-1.3
Endurance (Landgraf Turner)	48-584		32-142		40-690		14-42		0
Modulus of elasticity × 10^{-5}	124		124		108		125		97

Properties	T-6 *	T-7 *	T-7 †	T-8 *	T-8 †	T-9 *	T-10 *	T-11 *
Composition:								
Percentage of copper	80.0	80.0	80.0	78.0	78.0	70.00	70.0	10.0
" aluminum								4.0
" tin	20.00	10.0	10.0	8.0	8.0	9.0	4.0	
" lead		10.0	10.0	14.0	14.0	21.0	26.0	
" nickel								
" phosphorus	‡	‡	‡	‡	‡	‡	‡	Zn86.0
Tensile properties:								
Ultimate strength, thousands of pounds	26-33	25-30	30-35	27-32	29-34	27-29	18-23	32-36
Yield point, " " "	18-21	18-20	20-22	16-18	18-20	17-19	12-16	32-36
Elastic limit, " " "	17-18	9-11		6-13				32-36
Elongation in 2 in., per cent	0.5	6-8	2-6	12-15	10-15	14-17	12-20	0
Reduction of area, per cent	0.4	5-7		11-15				0
Compression load, thousands of pounds to produce compression of 0.001 in..	24-28	13-15	18-20	13-15	17-18	12	8	25
0.1 in.	100	45-47	50-54	38-48	46-55			75
0.15-0.17 in.						50		
0.1 -0.2 in.								
0.22-0.25 in.			100		100			
0.23-0.28 in.		100						
0.27-0.30 in.							50	
0.3 -0.33 in.				100				
Brinell hardness No	130-143	46-50	65-73	48-54	61-65	59-63	41-45	114-119
Specific gravity	8.7	8.9		9.4		9.5	9.7	6.9
Weight, lb per cu in	0.314	0.322		0.339		0.346	0.376	0.250
Patternmaker's shrinkage, in. per ft	1/8	3/16	1/8	3/16	1/8	3/16	3/16	1/8
Electrical conductivity	6.7	9.2		11.2				25.7
Impact test (Izod)		2-4		4-5				
Endurance (Landgraf Turner)		24-116		30-306				
Modulus of elasticity × 10^{-5}		85		88				

* Sand cast   † Chill cast.   ‡ Deoxidized with phosphorus.

and shafts. Both conditions have aided materially in improving serviceability of bearings. It therefore has become a more exacting engineering problem to specify the most efficient combinations of bearings and journals. For this reason rather full comments are made on the following list of bronzes and their application.

Furthermore, the mere selection of the proper alloy for any particular service does not insure that the bearing will be satisfactory. Many factors, including design, quality of workmanship, accuracy of fitting, clearance, oil grooving, etc., still enter the problem.

Alloy T–1 is a high-quality, worm gear bronze. As such it may be designated an international standard. It should not be used with very soft or low-carbon steel. In the sand-cast condition it is specified as: S.A.E., 65; A.S.T.M., B22–21 – grade D; A.R.E.A., grade D. Chill casting increases its physical properties. In this condition it has the widest application for motor car, truck, and bus worm gear drives. It also is widely applied in worm gear speed reducers. For best service it should mate with hardened steel, accurately finished and well polished.

Alloy T–2 is a high-grade gear bronze. Its lead content does not detract from its physical properties, yet is sufficient to permit tooling to be done with greater accuracy than on T–1. It is suitable for elevator worm gear, worm gear speed reducers, spur gears meshing with small steel pinions, where quiet running and the wearing quality of a bronze is essential, feed nuts for working tools, and like service. When sand cast it is specified as S.A.E., 63. Chill casting increases its physical properties, making it an exceptionally high-grade bearing bronze for very high speeds, as in steam turbine worm wheels. With fair workmanship, at lower speeds it will support relatively heavy loads.

Alloy T–3, an intermediate bronze between T–1 and T–7, is a favorite composition for machine tool bearings. It is well adapted for worm gears where the softer steels are used, and also is suitable for steel mill bronze inserts and segmental bearing sections, feed nuts, bushings, and general machinery bearings. Its lead content permits easy and accurate tooling. Chill casting increases the physical properties, especially compressive strength, making it more serviceable for use with heavier loads.

Alloy T–4 is a new nickel-phosphor-bronze. It has the lowest coefficient of thermal expansion of all the copper-tin bearing and phosphor bronzes. It is suitable for heavy punishment when the bearing surface of its mating member is either hardened steel, nitrided nitralloy, or chromium plated, accurately finished and polished, and is also suitable for valve stem guides for internal-combustion engines. The lead content gives it an accurate tooling quality. Chill casting increases its density and refines the grain. It then has wide application for the highest requirements of worm wheel service and speed reducers, both in the largest and smallest sizes. It is favored for small worm wheels in portable tools. For hard bronzes in Diesel engines and like service, if combined with corresponding workmanship and mating material, it is unsurpassed.

Alloy T–5 is especially adapted to service requiring high compressive strength. It is suitable for low-speed and heavy-pressure journals, not exceeding 1500 lb per sq in. It is well adapted for thrust bearings, thrust washers, and step bearings, pivot bearings, dies, and trunnions, and is suitable for bascule and lift bridges. With light loads and accurate workmanship it will support an exceedingly high speed. It is specified as: A.S.T.M., B22–21, grade B; and A.R.E.A., grade B.

Alloy T–6 is adapted to very heavy duty on thrust and pivot bearings for lift and swing bridges and the like, with very high pressures and comparatively low speeds. For this purpose it is second only to Alloy T–11. It should be used only against hardened-steel surfaces. Accurately fitted, it will withstand bearing pressures in excess of 1500 lb per sq in. It is specified as: Federal Specification Board, Q–Q–B–691, composition 10; U. S. Navy, 46–B22, grade 4; U. S. Army Ordnance Dept., 57–702, grade 10; A.S.T.M., B22–21, grade A; A.R.E.A., grade A.

Alloy T–7 is a leaded phosphor-bronze, an old standard for general machine construction, suitable for crosshead and crankpin bearings and for general machinery, lathes, grinders, etc., for relatively high speeds and journals, not heat-treated. When sand cast, it is specified as: U. S. Navy, 46–B22, grade 2; U. S. Army Ordnance Dept., 57–70B, grade 8; S.A.E., 64. Chill casting increases its physical properties materially, causing a finer and more perfect distribution of the lead with a general refinement of grain, making a superior bearing metal for severe punishment.

Alloy T–8 is a relatively high-lead bronze suitable for brass and copper rolling mill neck bearings and bushings, where the spindles are of soft steel and the speed relatively high. In general, it is adapted for the intermediate or softer grades of steel journals, with intermediate or light pressures and relatively high speeds. It is substantially the famous Penn. R. R. alloy known as Ex. B metal. When sand cast it is specified as: U. S. Navy, 46–B22, grade 1; U. S. Army Ordnance Dept., 57–70B, grade 7; S.A.E., 67. Chill casting increases its physical properties materially, owing to the finer distribution of the lead and a general grain refinement, with the result that in the chilled condition this alloy is capable of resisting greater punishment with higher bearing and wearing qualities.

Alloy T-9 is a relatively high-lead bronze. It is serviceable for bearings where the danger of melting babbitts exists. It fills a field where the harder babbitts are otherwise especially serviceable. On account of its lead content and resulting plasticity, it is serviceable with poor workmanship and a soft steel mating member, in that the copper-tin crystal is hard enough to produce a mutual polishing effect between the bearing and its journal.

Alloy T-10 is a very high-lead alloy, representing the probable limit of usefulness of high lead content. Its composition and serviceability are substantially those of the old plastic bronzes. It is suitable for poor workmanship, and competes with the intermediate and cheaper grades of babbitt, having the advantage of not melting out when heating.

Alloy T-11, Lumen bronze, is a unique hard zinc-base alloy. Its capacity for holding an oil film after it has once been established is unequaled by any other alloy. It is hard and unyielding, and therefore requires care in fitting. It is especially serviceable for use where high compressive strength is required, and has an enviable record for all kinds of bridge bearings, for pivots, thrust collars, bascule trunnion bushings, and bearings in draw, swing, and lift bridges. It is suitable for turntable pivots, cold neck rolling mill table bearings, crane bearings, etc. In electrical and in general machine tool service it has phenomenally long life, and is well suited for fractional-horsepower motors. It must not be subjected to excessive pounding and impact.

Thermal Expansion of Bearing Bronzes. Table III gives the linear coefficient of thermal expansion for the bearing bronzes. It supplies exact data for computing expansions and clearance of bearings at different temperatures. The expansion of these alloys is rather irregular, and therefore, it is necessary that these data be given in each case for several temperature intervals.

Table III. Linear Coefficient of Thermal Expansion of Bearing Bronzes

(In. per in. per deg fahr)

Made on Sand-cast Specimens

Alloy No.	Between 70 deg fahr and				
	200 deg fahr	300 deg fahr	400 deg fahr	500 deg fahr	600 deg fahr
T- 1	0.000 009 63	0.000 009 74	0.000 010 02	0.000 010 31	0.000 010 58
T- 2	.000 009 67	.000 009 89	.000 010 13	.000 010 40	.000 010 61
T- 3	.000 009 83	.000 009 98	.000 010 25	.000 010 48	.000 010 67
T- 4	.000 009 48	.000 009 69	.000 009 87	.000 010 15	.000 010 44
T- 5	.000 009 79	.000 009 98	.000 010 18	.000 010 46	.000 010 72
T- 6	.000 010 08	.000 010 14	.000 010 37	.000 010 61	.000 011 02
T- 7	.000 009 92	.000 010 04	.000 010 23	.000 010 40	.000 010 69
T- 8	.000 010 13	.000 010 21	.000 010 33	.000 010 54	.000 010 67
T-11	.000 014 17	.000 015 30	....	....	....

WELDING, BRAZING, AND SOLDERING MATERIALS

By Bradley Stoughton and D. F. Miner

37. METAL JOINING

Joining Metallic Bodies. If two metals are brought into such close contact that there is actual union of the interatomic bonds, they will be completely joined. Thus, if two pieces of a very soft metal like lead or gold be pressed together for a considerable period of time at atmospheric temperature, mutual diffusion will produce a firm bond between the space lattices. In the case of iron, however, the pieces of metal must be heated to a point where they are very soft (actually near the melting point) and forced together, care being taken that no oxide of iron intervenes in the joint. The process of welding wrought iron is very old, but has now been much improved by electric methods of heating. Another means of accomplishing the same result is to bring melted metal in contact with the pieces to be joined. The processes of soldering, brazing, and " burning on " are examples of this method.

Pressure Processes

Hammer Welding is the original and old-fashioned method, slow in operation and low in efficiency.*

Electric Welding without Full Fusion. This includes butt (or " flash"), spot, seam, and percussive welding. All these are rapid and high in efficiency.*

Pressure after Heating by the "Thermit" Reaction. This is also high in efficiency.*

Fusion Processes

In all fusion processes, the structure of the deposited metal has the characteristics of cast metal which has not been worked. Its properties will depend on what metal (or alloy) is deposited. It may be strong, or it may be ductile, but it never can be both as strong and as ductile as the same metal after rolling or forging.

Soldering. Deposited metal has very low melting point and very low strength.

Brazing or Bronzing. Deposited metal has low melting point and low strength.

Fusion of " Welding Rod " by Burning Gas. (a) Oxy-hydrogen gas, or else city gas with oxygen. These gases serve for welding with lead, brass, bronze, etc., but do not give high enough temperature for fusing steel welding rods and others of high melting point. Usually the welding-rod alloys which have high melting points have also higher strength. (b) Oxy-acetylene gas. Gives temperatures up to 3500 deg cent.

Fusion of Welding Rod by Electric Arc. (c) " Carbon arc," i.e., using a carbon electrode for the arc. (d) " Metal arc," i.e., using the welding rod itself as an electrode. (e) " Shielded arc." The electric arc is surrounded with a gas which keeps the deposited as well as the heated metal from becoming oxidized.

Fusion by Combination of Gas and Electric Arcs. (f) Atomic hydrogen arc welding. Especially valuable for small-sized work; easy to operate; oxidation of metals is avoided; gives higher temperature than the ordinary electric arc.

Fusion by the " Thermit " Reaction. This process is especially adapted to very large welds, and to repair work in place, such as welding stern posts of ships and side frames on locomotives without dismantling the broken machine.

General Discussion of Joining

A joint may be made which is 100 per cent as strong as the parent metal, but two very important considerations must here be noted:

1. If the metal is heated to get it plastic, its properties may be injured by the high temperature necessary, because all metals are injured within certain ranges which are peculiar to the metals concerned.

2. When metals freeze and cool slowly, they assume a coarse grain size which gives less strength and less ductility than the same metal with smaller grain size.

Expertness in welding takes into account these two circumstances, and also two more:

3. The molten pool must be free from oxide, dirt, gases, and other foreign matter.

4. In planning the operation, provision must be made for taking care of the expansion and contraction stresses which are set up in the structure.

38. ARC WELDING ELECTRODE MATERIALS

Bare Wire Electrodes.

Representative Composition of Wire

C	Mn	S	Si	P
max	max	max	max	max
0.18	0.60	0.04	0.04	0.04

So-called bare wire usually has a residual coating of iron oxide (sulcoat) resulting from acid left from the pickling operation and a thin coating of lime applied after pickling. These materials are purposely applied, and they serve to stabilize the arc.

Weld metal deposited with bare wires has the following average properties:

Ultimate tensile strength.................... 50,000–60,000 lb per sq in.
Elongation in 2 in. (weld metal test piece).... 5–10 per cent
Free bend elongation...................... 15 per cent
Density.................................. 7.60–7.65 g per cu cm
The usual sizes of wire cover the range....... $1/8$ in. to $5/16$ in.

* By efficiency is meant the strength, as well as the ductility, of the joint, as compared to the same two properties of the pieces welded.

Coated Wire Electrodes. Where easier manipulation, better arc stability, and better control of melting rate are desired, lightly coated electrodes are widely used. These coatings, approximately 0.002 to 0.005 in. thick, applied by dipping, dusting, or wiping, usually consist of metal oxides and carbonates. The physical properties of the deposited metal are practically the same as for bare electrodes.

Covered Wire Electrodes. Heavy coatings (10 to 25 per cent of wire diameter) are applied by extrusion or other methods to electrodes to be used where better physical properties of the weld are desired. These coatings improve the strength, ductility, density, and resistance to corrosion by excluding oxygen and nitrogen from the arc stream and pool of molten metal. They also serve to maintain the composition of the metal, replacing elements lost in melting of the wire. The resistance to corrosion of metal thus deposited is often greater than the structural plate on which it is used, whereas bare electrode metal rusts very easily.

Heavy coatings fall into two classes: (a) inorganic coatings which contain primarily metal oxides and silicates, and (b) organic coatings which contain as high as 30 per cent carbohydrates, the remainder being inorganic, slag-forming constituents. Some successful coatings are combinations of the two types. The quality of a weld depends as much on the skill of the welder as upon the particular brand of covered electrode he uses. Weld wire deposited with covered wire electrodes has the following average properties:

Ultimate tensile strength	60,000–75,000 lb per sq in.
Elongation in 2 in. (weld metal test piece)	25–35 per cent
Free bend elongation	30–50 per cent
Density	7.80–7.85 g per cu cm

39. SOLDERING

Solders. Many special solders are on the market, which have complex compositions and exhibit some advantages for special work. The most generally used materials are of two types: (a) lead and tin solders, and (b) silver solders. Where high operating temperatures are to be encountered, or high-strength joints are required, silver solder should be used in preference to the lead and tin solders. Silver solder can be used on metals other than copper and is recommended for stainless steel. Brazing alloys containing copper and phosphorus are used successfully for copper and copper alloys, the cost being less than that of silver solder.

Lead-tin Solders. Table I (from A.S.T.M. Standard Specifications B32–21) gives the composition and melting points of several lead-tin alloys used for solder metal and commercially known as soft solder. Melting points of lead and tin are included for comparison. The A.S.T.M. specifies that those designated by an A (Class A) shall be made of new or virgin metal while those designated by a B (Class B) shall be made from at least one-half virgin metals, the balance being recovered or secondary metals. For galvanized iron and zinc only Class A solders should be used.

It is to be noted that the alloys are completely solid below the lower point given, designated "melting point," and completely liquid only above the higher point given, designated "complete liquefaction point." In the range of temperature between these two points the alloys are partly solid and partly liquid. In Grade 1 the amount of solid portion is so small, in the range given, that it is practically unnoticeable. In Grade 4 the proportion of solid and fluid metal in the range given makes this alloy suitable for use as a wiping solder. The choice of the class and grade of solder for any specified purpose depends on the material in connection with which it is to be used and the method of applying. It is recommended that the grade of solder metal be selected which contains the least amount of time required to give suitable flowing and adhesive qualities for the work in hand.

Silver Solders. Table II gives the composition, melting point, flow point, and color of eight grades of silver-copper-zinc alloys used for brazing purposes and commercially known as silver solders (from A.S.T.M. Standard Specifications B 73–29).

Solders of Grades 1, 2, and 3 are suitable for brazing purposes which require a solder that flows more readily than the ordinary copper-zinc brazing solders. Grades 4 and 5 flow freely at a still lower temperature and are recommended for use where strong joints are required, and where heating to a sufficiently high temperature to flow Grades 1, 2, or 3 would be injurious to the article being soldered. Grades 6, 7, and 8 are high-grade silver solders and are recommended for special cases where a high degree of malleability and ductility is required.

Soldering Fluxes are rated according to activity. The neutral fluxes, particularly rosin or rosin in alcohol, are not corrosive and are used where corrosive action is to be avoided

Table I. Composition and Melting Points of Lead-tin Solders

Grade	Formula			Melting Point		Complete Liquefaction Point	
	Tin, per cent	Lead, per cent	Antimony, per cent	Deg Cent	Deg Fahr	Deg Cent	Deg Fahr
Tin	100.00	.....	.....	232	449.6	232	449.6
OA	63.00	37.00	0.12	181	357.8	181	357.8
1 A	50.00	50.00	0.12	181	357.8	213	415.4
1 B	49.25	50.00	0.75	185	365.0	208	397.4
2 A	45.00	55.00	0.12	181	357.8	225	437.0
2 B	43.50	55.00	1.50	188	370.4	220	428.0
3 A	40.00	60.00	0.12	181	357.8	237	458.6
3 B	38.00	60.00	2.00	188	370.4	228	442.4
4 A	37.50	62.50	0.12	181	357.8	241	467.6
4 B	35.50	62.50	2.00	188	370.4	231	411.8
5 A	33.00	67.00	0.12	181	357.8	252	485.6
5 B	31.00	67.00	2.00	188	370.4	235	455.0
Lead	.....	100.00	....	327	620.6	327	620.6

Table II. Composition and Properties of Silver Solders

Grade No.	Composition					Melting Point		Flow Point		Color
	Silver, per cent	Copper, per cent	Zinc, per cent	Cadmium, per cent	Impurities, max, per cent	Deg Fahr	Deg Cent	Deg Fahr	Deg Cent	
1	10	52	38	*	0.15	1510	820	1600	870	Yellow
2	20	45	35	*	0.15	1430	775	1500	815	Yellow
3	20	45	30	5	0.15	1430	775	1500	815	Yellow
4	45	30	25	Nil	0.15	1250	675	1370	745	Nearly white
5	50	34	16	Nil	0.15	1280	695	1425	775	Nearly white
6	65	20	15	Nil	0.15	1280	695	1325	720	White
7	70	20	10	Nil	0.15	1335	725	1390	755	White
8	80	16	4	Nil	0.15	1360	740	1460	795	White

* The addition, not to exceed 0.50 per cent, of cadmium to assist in fabricating Grades 1, 2 shall not be considered as a harmful impurity.

or where washing is not practicable. They are mild in cleaning action, however, and difficult to use on oxidized surfaces.

The more active fluxes usually contain zinc chloride, ammonium chloride, or both, either in a water solution or in a petrolatum paste. Various proportions of these materials are used, depending on how much cleaning action is required. To prevent corrosion, the joints should be washed in hot water after soldering. Powdered borax is the most widely used flux for silver solder and brazing alloys.

ELECTRICAL CONDUCTOR MATERIALS
By H. C. Knutson and D. F. Miner

The terms conductor and insulator are only relative. There is no sharp dividing line between them. For practical purposes, however, conducting materials are those selected to carry current in an electrical circuit and insulating materials are those chosen to restrict the current in the conductor to desired paths.

Conductors are mostly all metals, but there is a wide difference in conductivity (as much as 70 to 1 ratio in metals). They are usually separated into:

(a) Good conductors such as copper, aluminum, silver.

(b) Poor conductors (resistors) such as iron; alloys of nickel, iron, copper, and chromium; and carbon products.

40. COPPER CONDUCTORS

Conductivity of Copper. The Bureau of Standards (1914) made measurements of a large number of representative samples of copper and established standard values of resistivity and temperature coefficients, which have been adopted by the International Electrotechnical Commission.

The following rules of the International Electrotechnical Commission have been adopted by the American Institute of Electrical Engineers.

The following shall be taken as normal values for standard annealed copper:

1. At a temperature of 20 deg cent the resistance of a wire of standard annealed copper 1 meter in length and of a uniform section of 1 sq mm is $1/58$ ohm = 0.017241..... ohm.

2. At a temperature of 20 deg cent the density of standard annealed copper is 8.89 grams per cubic centimeter.

3. At a temperature of 20 deg cent the constant " mass " temperature coefficient of resistance of standard annealed copper, measured between two potential points rigidly fixed to the wire, is $0.00393 = 1/254.45$ .... per deg cent.

Table I.   Wire Table, Standard Annealed Copper
American Wire Gage (B. & S.).   English Units

Gage No. A.W.G.	Diameter in Mils at 20° C	Cross-section at 20° C		Ohms per 1000 ft * at 20° C (= 68° F)	Pounds per 1000 ft	Feet per Pound	Feet per Ohm † at 20° C (= 68° F)	Ohms per Pound at 20° C (= 68° F)	Pounds per Ohm at 20° C (= 68° F)
		Circular Mils	Square Inches						
0000	460.0	211 600.	0.1662	0.049 01	640.5	1.561	20 400.	0.000 076 52	13 070.
000	409.6	167 800.	.1318	.061 80	507.9	1.968	16 180.	.000 1217	8219.
00	364.8	133 100.	.1045	.077 93	402.8	2.482	12 830.	.000 1935	5169.
0	324.9	105 500.	.082 89	.098 27	319.5	3.130	10 180.	.000 3076	3251.
1	289.3	83 690.	.065 73	.1239	253.3	3.947	8070.	.000 4891	2044.
2	257.6	66 370.	.052 13	.1563	200.9	4.977	6400.	.000 7778	1286.
3	229.4	52 640.	.041 34	.1970	159.3	6.276	5075.	.001 237	808.6
4	204.3	41 740.	.032 78	.2485	126.4	7.914	4025.	.001 966	508.5
5	181.9	33 100.	.026 00	.3133	100.2	9.980	3192.	.003 127	319.8
6	162.0	26 250.	.020 62	.3951	79.46	12.58	2531.	.004 972	201.1
7	144.3	20 820.	.016 35	.4982	63.02	15.87	2007.	.007 905	126.5
8	128.5	16 510.	.012 97	.6282	49.98	20.01	1592.	.012 57	79.55
9	114.4	13 090	.010 28	.7921	39.63	25.23	1262.	.019 99	50.03
10	101.9	10 380.	.008 155	.9989	31.43	31.82	1001.	.031 78	31.47
11	90.74	8234.	.006 467	1.260	24.92	40.12	794.0	.050 53	19.79
12	80.81	6530.	.005 129	1.588	19.77	50.59	629.6	.080 35	12.45
13	71.96	5178.	.004 067	2.003	15.68	63.80	499.3	.1278	7.827
14	64.08	4107.	.003 225	2.525	12.43	80.44	396.0	.2032	4.922
15	57.07	3257.	.002 558	3.184	9.858	101.4	314.0	.3230	3.096
16	50.82	2583.	.002 028	4.016	7.818	127.9	249.0	.5136	1.947
17	45.26	2048.	.001 609	5.064	6.200	161.3	197.5	.8167	1.224
18	40.30	1624.	.001 276	6.385	4.917	203.4	156.6	1.299	0.7700
19	35.89	1288.	.001 012	8.051	3.899	256.5	124.2	2.065	.4843
20	31.96	1022.	.000 802 3	10.15	3.092	323.4	98.50	3.283	.3046
21	28.46	810.1	.000 636 3	12.80	2.452	407.8	78.11	5.221	.1915
22	25.35	642.4	.000 504 6	16.14	1.945	514.2	61.95	8.301	.1205
23	22.57	509.5	.000 400 2	20.36	1.542	648.4	49.13	13.20	.075 76
24	20.10	404.0	.000 317 3	25.67	1.223	817.7	38.96	20.99	.047 65
25	17.90	320.4	.000 251 7	32.37	0.9699	1031.	30.90	33.37	.029 97
26	15.94	254.1	.000 199 6	40.81	.7692	1300.	24.50	53.06	.018 85
27	14.20	201.5	.000 158 3	51.47	.6100	1639.	19.43	84.37	.011 85
28	12.64	159.8	.000 125 5	64.90	.4837	2067.	15.41	134.2	.007 454
29	11.26	126.7	.000 099 53	81.83	.3836	2607.	12.22	213.3	.004 688
30	10.03	100.5	.000 078 94	103.2	.3042	3287.	9.691	339.2	.002 948
31	8.928	79.70	.000 062 60	130.1	.2413	4145.	7.685	539.3	.001 854
32	7.950	63.21	.000 049 64	164.1	.1913	5227.	6.095	857.6	.001 166
33	7.080	50.13	.000 039 37	206.9	.1517	6591.	4.833	1364.	.000 7333
34	6.305	39.75	.000 031 22	260.9	.1203	8310.	3.833	2168.	.000 4612
35	5.615	31.52	.000 024 76	329.0	.095 42	10 480.	3.040	3448.	.000 2901
36	5.000	25.00	.000 019 64	414.8	.075 68	13 210.	2.411	5482.	.000 1824
37	4.453	19.83	.000 015 57	523.1	.060 01	16 660.	1.912	8717.	.000 1147
38	3.965	15.72	.000 012 35	659.6	.047 59	21 010.	1.516	13 860.	.000 072 15
39	3.531	12.47	.000 009 793	831.8	.037 74	26 500.	1.202	22 040.	.000 045 38
40	3.145	9.888	.000 007 766	1049.	.029 93	33 410.	0.9534	35 040.	.000 028 54

* Resistance at the stated temperatures of a wire whose length is 1000 ft at 20 deg cent.
† Length at 20 deg cent of a wire whose resistance is 1 ohm at the stated temperatures.

4. As a consequence it follows from (1) and (2) that, at a temperature of 20 deg cent, the resistance of a wire of standard annealed copper of uniform section, 1 meter in length and weighing 1 gram, is $(1/58) \times 8.89 = 0.15328$ ohm.

Paragraphs 1 and 4 define what are sometimes called "volume resistivity" and "mass resistivity," respectively. These may be expressed in other units as follows: Volume resistivity = 1.7241 microhm-cm (or microhms in a centimeter cube) at 20 deg cent = 0.67879 microhm-in. at 20 deg cent and mass resistivity = 875.20 ohms (mile, pound) at 20 deg cent.

The new value is known as the International Annealed Copper Standard, and is equivalent to

$$0.017241 \text{ ohm (meter, mm}^2\text{) at 20 deg cent.}$$

The units of mass resistivity and volume resistivity are interrelated through the density; this was taken as 8.89 grams per cu cm at 20 deg cent by the International Electrotechnical Commission. The International Annealed Copper Standard, in various units of mass resistivity and volume resistivity is:

0.15328	ohm (meter, gram) at 20 deg cent
875.20	ohms (mile, pound) at 20 deg cent
0.017241	ohm (meter, mm²) at 20 deg cent
1.7241	microhm-cm at 20 deg cent
0.67879	microhm-in. at 20 deg cent
10.371	ohms (mil, ft) at 20 deg cent

Table II. Specifications for Hard-drawn and Medium Hard-drawn Copper Wire

Diameter, in.	Area, cir mils	Hard-drawn Copper Wire*		Medium Hard-drawn† Copper Wire		
		Tensile Strength, lb per sq in.	Elongation, per cent in 60 in.	Tensile Strength, lb per sq in.		Elongation, per cent in 60 in.
				Minimum	Maximum	
0.460	211,600	49,000	3.75 ‡	42,000	49,000	3.75 ‡
0.410	168,100	51,000	3.25 ‡	43,000	50,000	3.6 ‡
0.365	133,225	52,800	2.80 ‡	44,000	51,000	3.25 ‡
0.325	105,625	54,500	2.40 ‡	45,000	52,000	3.0 ‡
0.289	83,520	56,100	2.17 ‡	46,000	53,000	2.75 ‡
0.258	66,565	57,600	1.98 ‡	47,000	54,000	2.5 ‡
0.229	52,440	59,000	1.79 ‡	48,000	55,000	2.25 ‡
0.204	41,615	60,100	1.24	48,330	55,330	1.25
0.182	33,125	61,200	1.18	48,600	55,660	1.20
0.165	27,225	62,000	1.14	....	....	....
0.162	26,245	62,100	1.14	49,000	56,000	1.15
0.144	20,735	63,000	1.09	49,330	56,330	1.11
0.134	17,956	63,400	1.07	....	....	....
0.128	16,385	63,700	1.06	49,660	56,660	1.08
0.114	12,995	64,300	1.02	50,000	57,000	1.06
0.104	10,815	64,800	1.00	....	....	....
0.102	10,404	64,900	1.00	50,330	57,330	1.04
0.092	8,464	65,400	0.97	....	....	....
0.091	8,281	65,400	0.97	50,660	57,660	1.02
0.081	6,561	65,700	0.95	51,000	58,000	1.00
0.080	6,400	65,700	0.94	....	....	....
0.072	5,184	65,900	0.92	51,330	58,330	0.98
0.065	4,225	66,200	0.91	....	....	....
0.064	4,096	66,200	0.90	51,660	58,660	0.96
0.057	3,249	66,400	0.89	52,000	59,000	0.94
0.051	2,601	66,600	0.87	52,330	59,330	0.92
0.045	2,025	66,800	0.86	52,660	59,660	0.90
0.040	1,600	67,000	0.85	53,000	60,000	0.88
		Maximum resistivity at 20 deg cent: for diameters 0.460 to 0.325 in., 900.77 lb per mile-ohm (10.674 ohms (mil, ft)); for diameters 0.324 to 0.040 in., 910.15 lb per mile-ohm (10.785 ohms (mil, ft)).		Maximum resistivity at 20 deg cent: for diameters 0.460 to 0.325 in., 896.15 lb per mile-ohm (10.619 ohms (mil, ft)); for diameters 0.324 to 0.040 in., 905.44 lb per mile-ohm (10.729 ohms (mil, ft)).		

* A.S.T.M. Standard B1–27; A.S.A. Standard H14–1929.
† A.S.T.M. Standard B2–27.
‡ Elongation per cent in 10 in.

Table III. Specifications for Soft or Annealed Copper Wire, and Tinned Soft or Annealed Copper Wire for Rubber Insulation

Diameter, in.	Soft or Annealed Copper Wire *			Tinned Soft or Annealed Copper Wire for Rubber Insulation †		
	Tensile Strength, lb per sq in.	Elongation in 10 in., per cent	Maximum Resistivity,‡ lb per mile-ohm	Tensile Strength, max, lb per sq in.	Elongation in 10 in., min, per cent	Maximum Resistivity,‡ lb per mile-ohm
0.460 to 0.290	36,000	35	891.58	36,000	30	896.15
0.289 to 0.103	37,000	30	891.58	37,000	25	900.77
0.102 to 0.021	38,500	25	891.58	38,500	20	910.15
0.020 to 0.012	40,000	20	891.58	39,000	15	929.52
0.011 to 0.003	40,000	20	891.58	40,000	10	939.51

 * A.S.T.M. Standard B3–27; A.S.A. Standard H4–1928 and C862–1928; A.I.E.E. Standards 60, 61–1928.
 † A.S.T.M. Standard B33–21; A.S.A. Standard H16–1928 and C861–1928; A.I.E.E. Standards 60, 61–1928.
 ‡ At 20 deg cent (68 deg fahr).

Table IV. Allowable Carrying Capacities of Copper Wires *
(National Electrical Code)

Gage No. A.W.G.	Diameter of Solid Wires, mils	Area, cir mils	Rubber Insulation, amp	Varnished Cambric Insulation, amp	Other Insulation, amp
18	40.3	1,624	3	....	5 †
16	50.8	2,583	6	....	10 †
14	64.1	4,107	15	18	20
12	80.8	6,530	20	25	30
10	101.9	10,380	25	30	35
8	128.5	16,510	35	40	50
6	162.0	26,250	50	60	70
5	181.9	33,100	55	65	80
4	204.3	41,740	70	85	90
3	229.4	52,630	80	95	100
2	257.6	66,370	90	110	125
1	289.3	83,690	100	120	150
0	325.0	105,500	125	150	200
00	364.8	133,100	150	180	225
000	409.6	167,800	175	210	275
....	....	200,000	200	240	300
0000	460.0	211,600	225	270	325
....	....	250,000	250	300	350
....	....	300,000	275	330	400
....	....	350,000	300	360	450
....	....	400,000	325	390	500
....	....	500,000	400	480	600
....	....	600,000	450	540	680
....	....	700,000	500	600	760
....	....	750,000	525	630	800
....	....	800,000	550	660	840
....	....	900,000	600	720	920
....	....	1,000,000	650	780	1,000
....	....	1,100,000	690	830	1,080
....	....	1,200,000	730	880	1,150
....	....	1,300,000	770	920	1,220
....	....	1,400,000	810	970	1,290
....	....	1,500,000	850	1,020	1,360
....	....	1,600,000	890	1,070	1,430
....	....	1,700,000	930	1,120	1,490
....	....	1,800,000	970	1,160	1,550
....	....	1,900,000	1,010	1,210	1,610
....	....	2,000,000	1,050	1,260	1,670

 * Copper wires and cables of 98 per cent conductivity. For aluminum wire the allowable carrying capacities shall be taken as 84 per cent of those given in the table for the respective sizes of copper wire with the same kind of covering.
 † The allowable carrying capacities of No. 18 and No. 16 are 10 and 15 amp, respectively, when in cords for portable heaters, types HC and HPD.

Per Cent Conductivity of a material is computed on the basis of 100 per cent conductivity corresponding to the resistivity of the International Annealed Copper Standard at 20 deg cent, e.g., 0.15328 ohm (meter, gram).

Wire Tables. The values in Table I (abridged from Smithsonian Physical Tables) are for annealed copper of standard resistivity. For copper of other resistivity, a suitable correction factor must be applied. Hard-drawn copper may be taken as having about 2.7 per cent greater resistivity than annealed copper.

Tables II and III give the A.S.T.M. Standard Specifications for tensile strength, elongation, and maximum resistivity for various grades of copper wire.

Table IV gives the allowable continuous-current-carrying capacities of copper wires and and cables of 98 per cent conductivity, according to the National Electrical Code. For aluminum wire the allowable carrying capacities shall be taken as 84 per cent of those given given in the table for the respective sizes of copper wire, with the same kind of covering.

Temperature Coefficient of Resistivity of Copper. The temperature coefficient for the International Annealed Copper Standard is $\alpha_{20} = 0.00393$, and $\alpha_0 = 0.00427$ at 20 and 0 deg cent, respectively. The temperature coefficient of copper is proportional to the conductivity, so that where the conductivity is known the temperature coefficient may be calculated, and vice versa. A consequence of this relation is that the change of *resistivity* per degree is constant, independent of the sample of copper and of the temperature of reference. This resistivity-temperature constant, for volume resistivity and centigrade degrees, is 0.00681 microhm-cm, and for mass resistivity is 0.000597 ohm (meter, gram). Table V gives the temperature coefficients (αt_1) of copper having various percentages of standard conductivity. These are for use in the formula

$$R_t = R_{t_1}[1 + \alpha_{t_1}(t - t_1)],$$

where R_t is the resistance at the temperature t, and R_{t_1} is the resistance at the "initial temperature" t_1. Table V was calculated by means of the following formula, which holds for any per cent conductivity, n, within commercial ranges, and for centigrade temperatures. (n is considered to be expressed decimally: e.g., if per cent conductivity = 99 per cent, $n = 0.99$).

$$\alpha_{t_1} = \cfrac{1}{\cfrac{1}{n\,(0.00393)} + (t_1 - 20)}$$

Table V.   Temperature Coefficients of Copper for Different Initial Temperatures (Centigrade) and Different Conductivities

Ohms (meter, gram) at 20° C	Per Cent Conductivity	a_0	a_{15}	a_{20}	a_{25}	a_{30}	a_{50}
0.161 34	95	0.004 03	0.003 80	0.003 73	0.003 67	0.003 60	0.003 36
.159 66	96	.004 08	.003 85	.003 77	.003 70	.003 64	.003 39
.158 02	97	.004 13	.003 89	.003 81	.003 74	.003 67	.003 42
.157 53	97.3	.004 14	.003 90	.003 82	.003 75	.003 68	.003 43
.156 40	98	.004 17	.003 93	.003 85	.003 78	.003 71	.003 45
.154 82	99	.004 22	.003 97	.003 89	.003 82	.003 74	.003 48
.153 28	100	**.004 27**	**.004 01**	**.003 93**	.003 85	.003 78	.003 52
.151 76	101	.004 31	.004 05	.003 97	.003 89	.003 82	.003 55

41. ALUMINUM CONDUCTORS

Conductivity of Aluminum. The A.I.E.E. standard of conductivity for hard-drawn aluminum wire is 60.97 per cent of the International Annealed Copper Standard. On this scale the conductivity of commercial hard-drawn copper is usually taken at 97 per cent.

The electrical conductivity of annealed high purity (99.97 per cent) aluminum is 64.6 per cent, based on the International Annealed Copper Standard. The electrical conductivity is lowered by the addition of alloying elements, the reduction varying with the nature of the element and the amount added. Heat treatment and mechanical working also influence this property to a marked degree. See Table VI.

Wire Tables. Table VII for aluminum wire (from Smithsonian Physical Tables) is based on a figure for the conductivity of aluminum published by the U.S. Bureau of Standards, which is the result of many thousands of determinations by the Aluminum Co. of America. A volume resistivity of 2.828 microhm-cm and a density of 2.70 may be

Table VI. Electrical Conductivity

(Approximate Values)

Metal	Conductivity, Per Cent of International Annealed Copper Standard
Aluminum (99.97 per cent)....................................	64.6
Aluminum conductors (hard drawn)...........................	61.
2S–O...	57.
3S–O...	50.
3S–H...	40.
17S–T..	30.
51S–T..	45.

considered to be good average values for commercial hard-drawn aluminum. These values give:

Conductivity at 0° C, cgs electromagnetic units...........	38.36×10^{-6}
Mass resistivity, ohms (meter, gram) at 20° C.............	0.0764
" " " (mile, pound) at 20° C............	436.0
Mass per cent conductivity relative to copper.............	200.7
Volume resistivity, microhm-cm at 20° C..................	2.828
" " microhm-in. at 20° C..............	1.113
Volume per cent conductivity relative to copper..........	61.0
Density, g per cu cm....................................	2.70
Density, lb per cu in....................................	0.0975

For current-carrying capacity of aluminum wires, see Table IV.

Temperature Coefficient of Resistivity. The 20 deg cent temperature coefficient of 61 per cent conductivity annealed aluminum wire is 0.00403 per deg cent, corresponding to a 0 deg cent coefficient of 0.00444. Grassi found that the temperature coefficient of aluminum is proportional to its per cent conductivity (as is also true of copper).

Comparison of Copper and Aluminum Wires for Equal Resistance per Unit Length.

	Copper	Aluminum
Cross-section..............	1	1.61
Diameter..................	1	1.27
Weight....................	1	0.488
Breaking strength..........	1	0.64

Use of Aluminum Conductors. The largest use of aluminum conductors is for power transmission through cables having a high-strength steel reinforcing core. At very high potentials, such as 100,000 volts, aluminum conductors possess a marked advantage over copper in the lower corona loss due to their greater diameter for the same conductance. Aluminum cable steel reinforced (A.C.S.R.) is used for the messenger cables of overhead catenary railway lines. It is also used in the smaller sizes for signal circuits and for telephone lines supported on the same structures with power lines, where its high strength permits the use of as long spans as the transmission conductors. Large all-aluminum cables have frequently been installed for railway feeders where they carry heavy currents at relatively low voltages. Particularly in large conductors the use of aluminum effects a great saving in weight.

Aluminum may be used in bus-bar construction, both on switchboards and for the general transmission of power. The current rating of aluminum bus-bars may be conveniently taken as 80 per cent of the accepted values for copper of equal cross-section and similar shape.

Aluminum is used for the rotor windings of squirrel-cage induction motors and also for field windings in certain types of motors and high-speed turbo-generators. The windings must, however, either occupy more space or be operated at a higher temperature. The remarkable property of insulating aluminum wire by means of an electrolytically applied oxide film is of service in constructing windings for electrical machinery where space is limited, or where a heat-resistant insulation is necessary. The difficulty of making a satisfactory and permanent joint to other portions of the circuit, which may be of copper, has retarded the widespread use of aluminum conductors in machines.

Table VII. Wire Table, Aluminum

Hard-drawn aluminum wire at 20 deg cent (68 deg fahr)
American Wire Gage (B. & S.), English units

Gage No.	Diameter, mils	Cross-section		Ohms per 1000 ft	Pounds per 1000 ft	Pounds per Ohm	Feet per Ohm
		Circular mils	Square Inches				
0000	460.	212 000.	0.166	0.0804	195.	2420.	12,400.
000	410.	168 000.	.132	.101	154.	1520.	9860.
00	365.	133 000.	.105	.128	122.	957.	7820.
0	325.	106 000.	.0829	.161	97.0	602.	6200.
1	289.	83 700.	.0657	.203	76.9	379.	4920.
2	258.	66 400.	.0521	.256	61.0	238.	3900.
3	229.	52 600.	.0413	.323	48.4	150.	3090.
4	204.	41 700.	.0328	.408	38.4	94.2	2450.
5	182.	33 100	.0260	.514	30.4	59.2	1950.
6	162.	26 300.	.0206	.648	24.1	37.2	1540.
7	144.	20 800.	.0164	.817	19.1	23.4	1220.
8	128.	16 500.	.0130	1.03	15.2	14.7	970.
9	114.	13 100.	.0103	1.30	12.0	9.26	770.
10	102.	10 400.	.008 15	1.64	9.55	5.83	610.
11	91.	8230.	.006 47	2.07	7.57	3.66	484.
12	81.	6530.	.005 13	2.61	6.00	2.30	384.
13	72.	5180.	.004 07	3.29	4.76	1.45	304.
14	64.	4110.	.003 23	4.14	3.78	0.911	241.
15	57.	3260.	.002 56	5.22	2.99	.573	191.
16	51.	2580.	.002 03	6.59	2.37	.360	152.
17	45.	2050.	.001 61	8.31	1.88	.227	120.
18	40.	1620.	.001 28	10.5	1.49	.143	95.5
19	36.	1290.	.001 01	13.2	1.18	.0897	75.7
20	32.	1020.	.000 802	16.7	0.939	.0564	60.0
21	28.5	810.	.000 636	21.0	.745	.0355	47.6
22	25.3	642.	.000 505	26.5	.591	.0223	37.8
23	22.6	509.	.000 400	33.4	.468	.0140	29.9
24	20.1	404.	.000 317	42.1	.371	.008 82	23.7
25	17.9	320.	.000 252	53.1	.295	.005 55	18.8
26	15.9	254.	.000 200	67.0	.234	.003 49	14.9
27	14.2	202.	.000 158	84.4	.185	.002 19	11.8
28	12.6	160.	.000 126	106.	.147	.001 38	9.39
29	11.3	127.	.000 099 5	134.	.117	.000 868	7.45
30	10.0	101.	.000 078 9	169.	.0924	.000 546	5.91
31	8.9	79.7	.000 062 6	213.	.0733	.000 343	4.68
32	8.0	63.2	.000 049 6	269.	.0581	.000 216	3.72
33	7.1	50.1	.000 039 4	339.	.0461	.000 136	2.95
34	6.3	39.8	.000 031 2	428.	.0365	.000 085 4	2.34
35	5.6	31.5	.000 024 8	540.	.0290	.000 053 7	1.85
36	5.0	25.0	.000 019 6	681.	.0230	.000 033 8	1.47
37	4.5	19.8	.000 015 6	858.	.0182	.000 021 2	1.17
38	4.0	15.7	.000 012 3	1080.	.0145	.000 013 4	0.924
39	3.5	12.5	.000 009 79	1360.	.0115	.000 008 40	.733
40	3.1	9.9	.000 007 77	1720.	.0091	.000 005 28	.581

42. METALLIC RESISTOR MATERIALS

A large number of alloy wires used for resistance purposes are on the market. They cover a wide range of resistivities, operating temperature limits, physical properties, temperature coefficient of resistance, etc. For detailed description of these products the catalogs of manufacturers should be consulted. In general, the trade-name products can be grouped in approximately ten classes of alloys. Table VIII, naming a few products under each class name, gives the approximate composition and electrical characteristics of resistance wires commonly used. Tables of current-carrying capacities at various chosen operating temperatures are available in the manufacturers' catalogs.

Table VIII. Electrical Resistance Materials *

	Nominal Composition †							Resistivity, Ohms (mil, ft)	Temperature Coefficient of Resistance per deg cent	Coefficient of Linear Expansion per deg cent	Melting Point deg cent
	Ni	Cr	Fe	Mn	Cu	Zn	Al				
Nickel chromium......... Nichrome IV Chromel A Tophet A	80	20	....	....	....	....	....	650 (25° C)	0.0000937 (25 to 427° C)	0.000081 (20 to 500° C)	1320 (1100)‡
Nickel chromium......... Chromel C Nichrome Tophet C	60	15	25	....	....	....	....	675 (25° C)	0.000157 (25 to 427° C)	0.00015 (20 to 500° C)	1350 (1000)‡
Manganin...............	4		....	12	84			290 (20° C)	± 0.00001	....	....
Monel.................	69		....	28				268 (20° C)	0.00196 (20 to 100° C)	.000015 (25 to 300° C)	1350 (500)‡
Nickel silver............ Nickel silver German silver	18			65	17	....		175 (20° C)	.00027 (20 to 100° C)	....	1110 (250)‡
Copper nickel............ Advance, Cupron, Copel, Constantan, Ideal, etc.	45		....	55		....		294 (20° C)	± 0.00001	0.0000149 (35° C)	1210 (500)‡
Nickel-chromium-iron.....	36	11	51	1.5	....			601 (20° C)	......	0.0000136 (0 to 100° C)	1450
Aluminum-chromium-iron (Ohmalloy)	....	12.5	83	....	....	....	4.5	750 (20° C)	0.0003	....	(850)‡
Nickel, pure.............	100–	....		....	....	....		58 to 64 (20° C)	0.00537 (20 to 100° C)	0.0000144 (20 to 300° C)	1440 (500)‡
Iron, high-purity.........		....	99.97 †	....	....	....		9.8 (20° C)	0.0065 (0 to 100° C)	0.0000137 (0 to 400° C)	1535

* Properties may vary considerably with small variations in composition. Manufacturer's catalogs should be consulted for more specific information on any given material.
† Compositions given are approximate only; minor constituents and impurities have been omitted.
‡ Approximate values of maximum operating temperature in deg cent.

43. CARBON
Carbon Brushes

Types. The chief use of carbon in electrical manufacturing is for current collection. Carbon brushes form an important part of the electrical circuit in commutator machines, and many types have been developed to afford most satisfactory operation of motors and generators. The many grades of brushes on the market may be classified generally into five grades known as, (1) carbon graphite, (2) electro-graphite, (3) natural graphite, (4) resin bonded, (5) metal graphite.

Composition and Manufacture. The three purest forms of carbon are diamond, petroleum coke, and lampblack. The last two substances are extensively used in the manufacture of carbon brushes and other carbon products. Petroleum coke is the residue left on the side of a still after the refining of crude oil. For brush use, this green petroleum coke is first purified by subjecting it to an intense heat in a calcining furnace, and then ground to a fine powder, 200 mesh or finer. Lampblack is made by the incomplete combustion of oil or gas, depending upon the type of black desired.

The graphite brushes of highest grade are made by transforming pure carbon brushes to graphite by subjecting the material to an intense heat in an electric furnace.

The method of making carbon graphite and graphite brushes is as follows: (1) Calcined petroleum coke, lampblack, graphite, or other flours are mixed with a pitch or other binder in steam heated mixers. (2) After thoroughly mixing, material for molded brushes is permitted to cool and again reground and pulverized, after which the fine powder mix is molded under hydraulic pressure into plates. (3) The molded carbon graphite plates are then baked at various temperatures. (4) This completes the manufacturing process for carbon graphite and for natural graphite plates from which brushes of these two classes are cut. (5) In the case of electro-graphite material the carbon graphite plates are given an additional high-temperature treatment in an electric furnace which removes all impurities and in addition changes some of the carbon into graphite. From these plates are cut electro-graphite brushes.

Metal graphite grades are made by mixing fine-mesh copper, lead, zinc, tin, or other materials with graphite. This material is mixed, molded, and baked in a manner similar to carbon graphite material.

Resin bonded brushes contain a certain amount of resin of high electrical resistance such as a condensation product resulting from the reaction of formaldehyde upon phenol.

Properties. Plain carbon graphite brushes will carry between 35–50 amp per sq in., whereas the grade having the highest content of graphite will carry about 70 amp per sq in. continuously. High metal content grades are rated at 125–150 amp per sq in. but will carry 450–500 amp per sq in. momentarily without undue heating. The higher the metal content of brush material, the higher the current-carrying capacity of that material.

Table IX gives the U.S. Navy specifications for carbon brushes.

Table IX. Specifications for Carbon Brushes *
(U. S. Navy)

	Grade A	Grade B	Grade D	Grade E
Specific resistance at 30° C, ohm-in.........	0.00176 to 0.0021	0.0015 to 0.0019	0.0006 to 0.0012	0.000005 to 0.000025
Specific resistance at 250° C, ohm-in........	0.0013 to 0.0017	0.0011 to 0.0015	0.0004 to 0.0010	....
Contact drop, volts at rated current........	1.5 min 3.2 max	1.8 min 3.0 max	1.6 min 3.0 max	Low
Coefficient of friction (no current).........	0.50 max	0.55 max	0.60 max	0.40 max
Coefficient of friction (carrying current).....	0.35 max	0.40 max	0.45 max	....
Transverse strength, lb per sq in...........	2100 min	3000 min	1000 min	2500 min
Hardness, scleroscope.....................	43 to 58	50 to 65	8 to 16	8 to 20
Per cent ash	0.25 max	0.25 max	2.3 max	....
Density, lb per cu in.....................	0.054 to 0.058	0.058 to 0.065	0.042 to 0.050	....
Per cent graphite.........................	....	....	....	20 to 30

* A Grade C, formerly included in these specifications, has been discontinued by the Navy.

Uses. 1. Carbon graphite brushes are survivals of the original types and are used mostly on machines of older design where a cleaning action on the commutator is required. They are not suitable for high speeds and heavy currents.

2. Electro-graphite brushes have largely superseded the carbon graphite type. They have lower friction, higher current capacity, less ash, lower abrasive effect, and greater mechanical strength.

3. Natural graphite brushes are an improvement over the carbon graphite type where abrasive action is beneficial but where low friction is required for higher-speed operation.

4. Resin bonded brushes have a laminated structure whose distinctive characteristic is that the resistance across these laminations is from 5 to 8 times the resistance parallel to the laminations. This is effective in reducing short-circuit current in the face of the brush. They are particularly suited to machines with high commutating voltage.

5. Metal graphite brushes have replaced the early leaf copper types. They are used where high current capacity and low contact drop are important, as in electroplating generators or slip rings on a-c machines

Carbon Contact Material

Carbon and combinations of carbon and metal are often used as contact materials where current is frequently interrupted. The object is usually to provide terminals which will not melt and weld together, as metal contacts sometimes do. Relays, contactors, and various control devices use buttons or studs of this type, making contact with moving parts of metal, usually brass or copper. Where high conductivity is required, copper graphite or silver graphite material is used. These are similar to metal graphite brush material, giving non-sticking contacts with low contact drop and some degree of lubrication. Silver graphite, although more expensive, gives lower contact drop after long service than does copper graphite. It is therefore used in low-energy circuits, such as relays, where reliable operation, even after long periods of idleness, is important.

MAGNETIC MATERIALS

By J. B. Seastone

44. COMMERCIAL TYPES

Classes of Commercial Magnetic Materials. Magnetic materials may be divided into four groups for the sake of convenience of description, namely: (*A*) the *non-retentive* or magnetically " soft " materials; (*B*) *retentive* or magnetically " hard " materials; (*C*) those *special magnetic materials* having properties suited only to certain special applications; and (*D*) the *non-magnetic ferrous* alloys.

The Non-retentive or Magnetically " Soft " Materials are by far the most important, on the basis of the amount used. Materials falling in this class range from cast iron, which is one of the poorest, to Hipernik, which is one of the best, and include also cast steel, ordinary low-carbon sheet or plate, ingot iron, and the electrical (silicon) sheet materials. These materials are, in general, characterized by low coercive force, comparatively low hysteresis loss, relatively high permeability, and, usually, a fairly high saturation induction. They are used in the electromagnetic circuits of electrical apparatus.

The Retentive or Magnetically " Hard " Materials find application in the permanent magnets of meters and relays, sound-reproducing units, magnetos, and other equipment where a steady magnetic field is required and where it is not convenient to obtain this field electromagnetically. These materials are characterized by high coercive force, comparatively high hysteresis loss, and, usually, low permeability.

Special Alloys include those materials having special temperature-permeability relations, used in compensating for changes in flux in a magnetic circuit due to temperature changes; materials having unusually good properties only at low inductions; materials especially suited to operation at very high flux densities; and those materials which can be used at very high frequencies.

Non-magnetic Steels. Steel in the austenitic state is practically non-magnetic, having a permeability 1 to 2 per cent greater than air. It has been found that certain alloying elements, notably manganese, nickel, and carbon, lower the critical point so that steel can be made austenitic at room temperatures. In order to make a non-magnetic steel of reasonable cost and good machinability, certain compositions have been found most favorable. A typical non-magnetic steel composition contains 0.20 to 0.40 carbon, 10.0 to 11.5 manganese, 6.0 to 7.5 nickel.

45. NON-RETENTIVE MATERIALS

Effect of Impurities. Generally speaking, the magnetic properties of iron and its alloys are adversely affected by the presence of impurities. Carbon, sulfur, and oxygen tend to increase the hysteresis loss and to lower the permeability at all inductions. Manganese, phosphorus, and copper have little effect if present in small quantities, but, with the exception of cobalt, all additions to pure iron tend to lower the saturation induction and the permeability at high flux densities. Silicon, aluminum, and arsenic tend to decrease the hysteresis loss and to improve the permeability at moderate and low flux densities, largely because of the elimination of oxygen and other impurities, but even these elements impair the permeability at high flux densities. Silicon is also of considerable value because it increases the resistivity of the alloy, and, therefore, reduces the eddy current losses. (Aluminum and arsenic act in the same way, but are seldom used.)

Effect of Mechanical Strain. A strain beyond the elastic limit tends to increase the hysteresis loss and reduce the permeability of magnetic materials. This effect is apt to be

Table I. General Data on Magnetic Properties of Commercial Materials †

Figures represent approximate average properties; individual samples may differ somewhat

Property	Permalloy Western Electric ‡	Hipernik Westinghouse Electric §	Si Steel 0.60 Loss	Si Steel 0.66 Loss	Si Steel 0.72 Loss	Si Steel 0.82 Loss	Si Steel 1.01 Loss	Si Steel 1.17 Loss	Si Steel 1.30 Loss	Pure Iron Armco or Norway	Low-carbon Sheet or Shapes	Cast Steel Annealed	Cast Iron Annealed
Specific gravity, g per cu cm	8.6	8.3	7.5*	7.5*	7.5*	7.5*	7.5*	7.7*	7.7*	7.85	7.85	7.8	7.0
Sheet weight, lb per sq ft in 29 gage	0.63	0.60	0.54	0.54	0.54	0.54	0.54	0.55	0.55	0.56	0.56	0.56	....
Ultimate strength, lb per sq in	....	65,000	75,000	74,000	72,000	70,000	60,000	45,000	40,000	40,000	45,000	60,000	25,000
Yield point, lb per sq in	....	20,000	55,000	55,000	52,000	50,000	35,000	22,000	20,000	20,000	25,000	30,000	....
Per cent elongation (2 in.)	....	50	3	3	3.5	5	14	18	20	25	9	....	....
Erichsen draw mm (ductility index)	....	8	2.5	2.5	2.5	4.5	5	7	18	25	13	....	....
Resistivity, microhm-cm	.22	45	60	58	56	48	41	26	18	10.7	13	15	100
Steinmetz, hysteresis coefficient	0.0001	0.00015	0.00046	0.00051	0.00056	0.00065	0.00081	0.00088	0.001	0.002	0.003	0.005	0.012
Typical coercive force, oersteds	0.04	0.06	0.32	0.36	0.39	0.46	0.56	0.70	0.85	1.0	2.0	5	11
B (max) = 10,000 gausses													
W 10/60–29 gage iron loss in watts per lb ¶	....	0.25	0.60	0.66	0.72	0.82	1.01	1.17	1.30	....	....	....	....
Maximum aging core loss per cent		Nil	Nil	Nil	Nil	2	3	5	5				
Typical maximum permeability	100,000	90,000	8,000	8,000	6,500	6,000	5,500	5,200	5,000	4,500	2,500	1,500	500
Saturation (ferric induction)	11,000	15,500	19,500	19,800	19,800	20,200	20,500	21,000	21,200	21,600	21,200	21,000	14,000
Typical initial permeability	9,000	6,000	750	700	600	500	400	350	325	275	250	175	125
Typical applications	Telephone equipment, relays	High-quality audio and instrument transformers, relays	Distribution and power transformers	Distribution and power transformers	High-efficiency rotating machines and small transformers	High-efficiency rotating machines and small transformers	Small motors, a-c magnets, starting transformers	Small motors, a-c magnets, starting transformers	Small motors, a-c magnets, starting transformers	Pole pieces, relays	Fields and frames of d-c and synchronous machines	Frames and solid poles	Frames
Approximate relative cost, in per cent	....	2,500	100	93	80	73	64	50	43	36	32	20	17
Approximate per cent silicon			4.5	4.5	4.4	3.5	2.5	1.0	0.5	Low	Low	0.4	2.0

* A.S.T.M. Standard, not quite actual.
† Values for electrical sheet steels furnished in part by American Rolling Mill Co., Middletown, Ohio.
‡ 78 per cent nickel.
§ 50 per cent nickel.
¶ The guaranteed maximum loss at 10,000 gausses, 60 cycles, in 29 gage, is used to designate the grade of electrical sheet steel.

roughly proportional to the amount of distortion or strain, and usually the best magnetic materials are the most sensitive to mechanical abuse. Shearing or punching strains will increase the 10 kilogausses, 60-cycle loss of a 1 3/16-in. wide strip of silicon steel 10 or 15 per cent and will decrease the permeability at this induction more than 30 per cent. This effect is greater the thicker the material, and is apt to be more marked on the softer grades. The percentage effect of shearing or punching is an inverse function of the width of the piece sheared. It may be very large in the case of narrow sections such as are found in the teeth of small motors.

Stresses within the elastic limit will change the magnetic characteristics of materials. These changes may improve or impair the magnetic properties, depending on the kind and the amount of the stress, the induction at which the test is made, and the kind of material. Changes in magnetic conditions are likewise reflected in changes in the length, or, if confined, in the stress on such materials. These effects are usually small, but may become significant at low inductions or for very high-quality materials.

Effect of Direction of Grain. Electrical sheet or strip steels are apt to show an appreciable change in properties depending on the direction of the flux in the material relative to the final rolling direction. Usual sheet or strip material will show 10 per cent or 15 per cent higher loss when test strips are cut perpendicular to the direction of final rolling than when they are cut parallel to this direction, and the " cross-grain " samples will have 20 to 30 per cent lower permeability. Samples sheared at 45 degrees to the direction of rolling usually show loss and permeability characteristics not far different from the " straight-grain " specimens.

Effect of Temperature. The magnetic properties of iron and iron-silicon alloys are only slightly affected by ordinary temperature changes. In general, the permeability at low and moderate flux densities is improved, and the hysteresis loss is reduced, as the

Table II. Normal Induction Data (Average Figures)

Value of magnetizing force (oersteds) corresponding to induction

Induction in Gausses	Perm-alloy Western Electric Co.	Hipernik Westinghouse Electric Co.	High about 4 per cent Silicon Steel	Medium about 2.5 per cent Silicon Steel	Low about 1 per cent Silicon Steel	Commercially Pure Iron Annealed	Ordinary Low-carbon Steel Annealed	Cast Steel Annealed	Cast Iron Annealed	Induction Lines per sq in.
10	0.0010	0.0015	0.010	0.017	0.021	0.033	0.038	0.050	0.08	64
16	0.0017	0.0021	0.016	0.025	0.030	0.05	0.041	0.075	0.13	103
25	0.0026	0.0034	0.025	0.038	0.044	0.07	0.093	0.11	0.19	161
40	0.0039	0.0058	0.04	0.05	0.063	0.11	0.14	0.15	0.29	258
64	0.0057	0.0089	0.06	0.08	0.095	0.16	0.21	0.22	0.44	423
100	0.008	0.0107	0.09	0.12	0.14	0.21	0.29	0.30	0.65	645
160	0.011	0.0130	0.12	0.17	0.20	0.29	0.41	0.42	0.91	1,030
250	0.016	0.017	0.16	0.22	0.27	0.40	0.52	0.57	1.2	1,610
400	0.021	0.023	0.19	0.30	0.35	0.55	0.67	0.79	1.6	2,580
640	0.026	0.029	0.23	0.38	0.45	0.68	0.82	1.03	2.0	4,230
1,000	0.030	0.036	0.28	0.45	0.53	0.75	1.02	1.23	2.5	6,450
1,250	0.033	0.041	0.31	0.49	0.58	0.78	1.13	1.38	2.8	8,100
1,600	0.036	0.047	0.35	0.54	0.64	0.82	1.24	1.57	3.3	10,300
2,000	0.038	0.053	0.38	0.58	0.69	0.87	1.4	1.8	4.0	12,900
3,000	0.044	0.069	0.46	0.66	0.82	0.94	1.6	2.3	7.0	19,400
4,000	0.049	0.100	0.56	0.74	0.93	1.0	1.8	2.8	14.	25,800
5,000	0.060	0.137	0.64	0.85	1.06	1.15	2.1	3.3	25.	32,300
6,000	0.080	0.185	0.75	1.00	1.25	1.4	2.4	3.9	45.	38,700
7,000	0.12	0.25	0.90	1.19	1.50	1.6	2.8	4.5	70.	45,200
8,000	0.20	0.35	1.05	1.45	1.8	1.8	3.2	5.2	81.	51,600
9,000	0.50	0.50	1.22	1.8	2.2	2.0	3.8	6.2	160.	58,100
10,000	2.0	0.76	1.40	2.3	2.7	2.3	4.5	7.5	220.	64,500
11,000	20.0	1.40	1.80	3.2	3.6	2.8	5.3	9.5	310.	71,000
12,000	500.	2.50	2.6	4.5	5.0	3.3	6.6	12.5	410.	77,400
13,000	....	4.8	4.1	6.8	7.6	4.1	8.6	16.	620.	83,900
14,000	....	10.0	9.0	11.0	13.0	5.5	12.8	22.	1000.	90,300
15,000	....	40.	23.00	24.0	26.0	10.	17.	32.	....	96,800
16,000	....	400.	52.	47.0	41.0	20.	28.	50.	....	103,200
17,000	....	....	110.	93.	80.0	40.	52.	82.	....	109,700
18,000	....	....	200.	170.	140.0	80.	95.	130.	....	116,100
19,000	....	....	380.	300.	220.0	145.	165.	200.	....	122,600
20,000	....	....	900.	590.	360.0	230.	280.	380.	....	129,000
21,000	....	....	1800.	1250.	700.	360.	500.	800.	....	135,500
22,000	....	....	2800.	2100.	1400.	940.	1100.	1800.	....	141,900

NOTE. Permeability at any induction may be found from the relation $\mu = B/H$.

Table III (Part 1). Approximate Frequency and Induction Core Loss Factors for 29 Gage (0.014 in.) Material

Induction, gausses	Frequency					Induction, lines per sq in.
	15 Cycles	25 Cycles	40 Cycles	50 Cycles	60 Cycles	
10	0.35×10^{-6}	0.60×10^{-6}	0.10×10^{-5}	0.13×10^{-5}	0.16×10^{-5}	64
16	0.10×10^{-5}	0.17×10^{-5}	0.30×10^{-5}	0.36×10^{-5}	0.46×10^{-5}	103
25	0.29×10^{-5}	0.50×10^{-5}	0.80×10^{-5}	0.10×10^{-4}	0.12×10^{-4}	161
40	0.80×10^{-5}	0.14×10^{-4}	0.23×10^{-4}	0.28×10^{-4}	0.35×10^{-4}	258
64	0.22×10^{-4}	0.41×10^{-4}	0.65×10^{-4}	0.82×10^{-4}	0.10×10^{-3}	423
100	0.58×10^{-4}	0.10×10^{-3}	0.18×10^{-3}	0.22×10^{-3}	0.26×10^{-3}	645
160	0.15×10^{-3}	0.28×10^{-3}	0.44×10^{-3}	0.56×10^{-3}	0.66×10^{-3}	1,030
250	0.36×10^{-3}	0.64×10^{-3}	0.10×10^{-2}	0.13×10^{-2}	0.16×10^{-2}	1,610
400	0.90×10^{-3}	0.15×10^{-2}	0.26×10^{-2}	0.30×10^{-2}	0.38×10^{-2}	2,580
640	0.20×10^{-2}	0.35×10^{-2}	0.62×10^{-2}	0.75×10^{-2}	0.93×10^{-2}	4,230
1,000	0.43×10^{-2}	0.74×10^{-2}	0.13×10^{-1}	0.16×10^{-1}	0.22×10^{-1}	6,450
1,600	0.10×10^{-1}	0.16×10^{-1}	0.28×10^{-1}	0.36×10^{-1}	0.43×10^{-1}	10,300
2,000	0.14×10^{-1}	0.24×10^{-1}	0.40×10^{-1}	0.52×10^{-1}	0.62×10^{-1}	12,900
2,500	0.20×10^{-1}	0.34×10^{-1}	0.60×10^{-1}	0.75×10^{-1}	0.92×10^{-1}	16,100
3,000	0.29×10^{-1}	0.46×10^{-1}	0.81×10^{-1}	0.10	0.12	19,400
4,000	0.45×10^{-1}	0.73×10^{-1}	0.13	0.17	0.20	25,800
5,000	0.66×10^{-1}	0.11	0.19	0.25	0.29	32,300
6,000	0.90×10^{-1}	0.15	0.26	0.34	0.40	38,700
7,000	0.12	0.20	0.35	0.44	0.52	45,200
8,000	0.15	0.25	0.44	0.55	0.66	51,600
9,000	0.19	0.31	0.54	0.68	0.82	58,100
10,000	0.23	0.38	0.64	0.82	1.00	64,500
11,000	0.28	0.46	0.76	0.98	1.20	71,000
12,000	0.33	0.55	0.91	1.15	1.45	77,400
13,000	0.39	0.64	1.07	1.37	1.70	83,900
14,000	0.45	0.74	1.25	1.60	2.00	90,300
15,000	0.52	0.86	1.47	1.90	2.35	96,800

Induction, gausses	Frequency				Induction, lines per sq in.
	80 Cycles	100 Cycles	160 Cycles	250 Cycles	
10	0.22×10^{-5}	0.28×10^{-5}	0.47×10^{-5}	0.80×10^{-5}	64
16	0.64×10^{-5}	0.80×10^{-5}	0.14×10^{-4}	0.24×10^{-4}	103
25	0.18×10^{-4}	0.23×10^{-4}	0.40×10^{-4}	0.72×10^{-4}	161
40	0.51×10^{-4}	0.64×10^{-4}	0.12×10^{-3}	0.21×10^{-3}	258
64	0.15×10^{-3}	0.18×10^{-3}	0.32×10^{-3}	0.58×10^{-3}	423
100	0.38×10^{-3}	0.47×10^{-3}	0.80×10^{-3}	0.15×10^{-2}	645
160	0.92×10^{-3}	0.12×10^{-2}	0.21×10^{-2}	0.38×10^{-2}	1,030
250	0.22×10^{-2}	0.30×10^{-2}	0.50×10^{-2}	0.90×10^{-2}	2,580
400	0.56×10^{-2}	0.72×10^{-2}	0.12×10^{-1}	0.22×10^{-1}	2,580
640	0.13×10^{-1}	0.17×10^{-1}	0.30×10^{-1}	0.53×10^{-1}	4,230
1,000	0.28×10^{-1}	0.36×10^{-1}	0.61×10^{-1}	0.11	6,450
1,600	0.60×10^{-1}	0.78×10^{-1}	0.14	0.26	10,300
2,000	0.88×10^{-1}	0.11	0.20	0.38	12,900
2,500	0.13	0.16	0.29	0.55	16,100
3,000	0.18	0.22	0.37	0.74	19,400
4,000	0.28	0.36	0.64	1.25	25,800
5,000	0.41	0.54	0.96	1.80	32,300
6,000	0.56	0.72	1.30	2.50	38,700
7,000	0.72	0.96	1.70	3.30	45,200
8,000	0.92	1.20	2.10	4.1	51,600
9,000	1.14	1.48	2.60	5.1	58,100
10,000	1.40	1.80	3.3	6.2	64,500
11,000	1.70	2.25	4.0	7.7	71,000
12,000	2.05	2.8	4.9	9.5	77,400
13,000	2.5	3.3	5.9	11.3	83,900
14,000	2.90	3.9	7.1	13.0	90,300
15,000	3.40	4.6	8.5	15.0	96,800

NOTE. To find the approximate iron loss at any induction or frequency, multiply the loss, at 60 cycles, 10,000 gausses, by the factor shown in the table. Values are most accurate for about a 4 per cent silicon steel, are reasonably exact for lower silicon steels, and may be used to give approximate values for Hipernik.

Table III (Part 2). Approximate Frequency and Induction Core Loss Factors for 29 Gage (0.014 in.) Material

Induction, gausses	Frequency					Induction, lines per sq in.
	400 Cycles	640 Cycles	1000 Cycles	1600 Cycles	2500 Cycles	
10	0.14×10^{-4}	0.30×10^{-4}	0.56×10^{-4}	0.13×10^{-3}	0.39×10^{-3}	64
16	0.47×10^{-4}	0.95×10^{-4}	0.20×10^{-3}	0.43×10^{-3}	0.10×10^{-2}	103
25	0.14×10^{-3}	0.28×10^{-3}	0.58×10^{-3}	0.14×10^{-2}	0.32×10^{-2}	161
40	0.40×10^{-3}	0.85×10^{-3}	0.18×10^{-2}	0.44×10^{-2}	0.95×10^{-2}	258
64	0.11×10^{-2}	0.24×10^{-2}	0.51×10^{-2}	0.11×10^{-1}	0.27×10^{-1}	423
100	0.28×10^{-2}	0.59×10^{-2}	0.13×10^{-1}	0.29×10^{-1}	0.67×10^{-1}	645
160	0.70×10^{-2}	0.15×10^{-1}	0.32×10^{-1}	0.70×10^{-1}	0.16	1,030
250	0.17×10^{-1}	0.36×10^{-1}	0.74×10^{-1}	0.17	0.38	1,610
400	0.41×10^{-1}	0.86×10^{-1}	0.18	0.39	0.88	2,580
640	0.95×10^{-1}	0.20	0.42	0.90	2.2	4,230
1,000	0.22	0.45	0.94	2.2	5.0	6,450
1,600	0.48	1.0	2.15	4.9	11.5	10,300
2,000	0.71	1.5	3.2	7.4	17.0	12,900
2,500	1.10	2.2	4.6	11.0	25.0	16,100
3,000	1.40	3.1	6.4	15.0	35.0	19,400
4,000	2.30	5.0	11.0	26.0	58.0	25,800
5,000	3.50	7.7	16.0	38.0	82.0	32,300
6,000	5.0	10.0	22.0	50.0	....	38,700
7,000	6.6	14.0	29.0	65.0	....	45,200
8,000	8.5	18.0	37.0	....	....	51,600
9,000	10.9	22.0	46.0	....	....	58,100
10,000	13.4	27.0	58.0	....	....	64,500
11,000	16.0	32.0	....	....	....	71,000
12,000	19.0	38.0	....	....	....	77,400
13,000	22.0	....	....	....	....	83,900
14,000	25.0	....	....	....	....	90,300
15,000	29.0	....	....	....	....	96,800

Induction, gausses	Frequency				Induction, lines per sq in.
	4000 Cycles	6400 Cycles	10,000 Cycles	15,000 Cycles	
10	0.79×10^{-3}	0.16×10^{-2}	0.38×10^{-2}	0.80×10^{-2}	64
16	0.24×10^{-2}	0.56×10^{-2}	0.11×10^{-1}	0.30×10^{-1}	103
25	0.80×10^{-2}	0.19×10^{-1}	0.44×10^{-1}	0.10	161
40	0.24×10^{-1}	0.58×10^{-1}	0.14	0.31	258
64	0.64×10^{-1}	0.15	0.38	0.84	423
100	0.15	0.38	0.96	2.0	645
160	0.38	0.95	2.3	5.0	1,030
250	0.93	2.2	5.3	11.0	1,610
400	2.2	5.2	13.0	27.0	2,580
640	5.1	13.0	30.0	62.0	4,230
1,000	12.0	29.0	72.0	....	6,450
1,600	28.0	65.0	....	....	10,300
2,000	42.0	....	....	....	12,900
2,500	63.0	....	....	....	16,100
3,000	....	....	....	....	19,400
4,000	....	....	....	....	25,800
5,000	....	....	....	....	32,300
6,000	....	....	....	....	38,700
7,000	....	....	....	....	45,200
8,000	....	....	....	....	51,600
9,000	....	....	....	....	58,100
10,000	....	....	....	....	64,500
11,000	....	....	....	....	71,000
12,000	....	....	....	....	77,400
13,000	....	....	....	....	83,900
14,000	....	....	....	....	90,300
15,000	....	....	....	....	96,800

NOTE. To find the approximate iron loss at any induction or frequency, multiply the loss, at 60 cycles, 10,000 gausses, by the factor shown in the table. Values are most accurate for about a 4 per cent silicon steel, are reasonably exact for lower silicon steels, and may be used to give approximate values for Hipernik.

I—30

temperature is raised. These changes are greater at low flux densities but may usually be neglected in the commercial application of materials over ordinary temperature ranges. Iron and silicon-iron alloys become non-magnetic at about 750 deg cent, and the magnetic properties are in general more seriously impaired as temperatures of about 500 deg cent are exceeded. The magnetic properties of materials are sometimes impaired after being being held for some time at temperatures of the order of 100 deg cent. This " aging " effect used to be of considerable importance, but electrical steels produced today are not seriously affected.

Effect of Heat Treatment. It is usually possible to effect a marked improvement in the magnetic properties of materials by a proper heat treatment or annealing cycle. This heat treatment usually involves heating the material to a suitable temperature, holding at this temperature for a short time, and cooling slowly to several hundred degrees centigrade. The best annealing temperature, if only the release of punching strains is desired, will usually be about 725 deg cent. The punchings can be held at this temperature for several hours, and cooled at a rate of about 30 deg cent per hr. It is important that every precaution be taken to exclude oxidizing or carburizing gases from the material while it is above 600 deg cent. This is effected by either placing the material to be annealed under a tightly sealed metal box, or, if an electric furnace is used, by supplying an inert or reducing atmosphere to the annealing chamber.

If the material to be annealed has been given no other annealing treatment, the maximum temperature will range between 750 and 900 deg cent for such materials as cast iron,

Table IV. Loss of Electrical Sheets as a Function of Gage for Commercial Grades in Common Use

The grade is designated by the guaranteed maximum iron loss when tested at 10,000 gausses, 60 cycles, A.S.T.M. Method

Grade	Gage	Induction in gausses												
		3000	4000	5000	6000	7000	8000	9000	10,000	11,000	12,000	13,000	14,000	15,000
0.72	30	0.096	0.160	0.237	0.317	0.402	0.495	0.60	0.71	0.84	1.00	1.18	1.38	1.63
.72	29	.096	.160	.237	.317	0.402	0.495	0.60	0.71	0.84	1.00	1.18	1.38	1.63
.72	28	.104	.172	.250	.329	0.417	0.52	0.63	0.75	0.89	1.05	1.24	1.45	1.71
.72	27	.112	.184	.255	.344	0.438	0.54	0.66	0.79	0.94	1.11	1.31	1.53	1.80
.72	26	.124	.196	.271	.360	0.464	0.57	0.70	0.83	0.99	1.17	1.38	1.62	1.91
.72	25	.137	.214	.302	.392	0.492	0.61	0.74	0.89	1.06	1.25	1.48	1.74	2.05
.72	24	.152	.231	.320	.410	0.53	0.66	0.80	0.97	1.17	1.36	1.59	1.86	2.19
.82	30	.098	.158	.237	.318	0.415	0.53	0.64	0.78	0.94	1.10	1.27	1.47	1.68
.82	29	.098	.162	.242	.330	0.430	0.55	0.66	0.81	0.97	1.13	1.32	1.53	1.76
.82	28	.104	.173	.253	.347	0.450	0.57	0.69	0.85	1.01	1.18	1.38	1.61	1.85
.82	27	.112	.183	.264	.368	0.477	0.60	0.73	0.90	1.06	1.24	1.45	1.69	1.95
.82	26	.123	.198	.285	.390	0.51	0.64	0.77	0.96	1.11	1.30	1.52	1.78	2.07
.82	25	.137	.218	.313	.423	0.55	0.68	0.83	1.03	1.17	1.38	1.61	1.89	2.21
.82	24	.154	.240	.350	.468	0.60	0.74	0.89	1.10	1.26	1.48	1.72	2.02	2.38
1.01	30	.129	.209	.313	.423	0.54	0.66	0.81	0.98	1.16	1.36	1.58	1.86	2.15
1.01	29	.132	.214	.319	.435	0.56	0.69	0.84	1.01	1.19	1.40	1.62	1.91	2.20
1.01	28	.139	.224	.331	.452	0.58	0.72	0.87	1.06	1.24	1.47	1.70	1.99	2.30
1.01	27	.150	.237	.346	.475	0.61	0.75	0.91	1.12	1.30	1.54	1.79	2.08	2.42
1.01	26	.164	.253	.363	.498	0.64	0.79	0.96	1.18	1.37	1.62	1.89	2.20	2.56
1.01	25	.180	.271	.384	.53	0.68	0.84	1.01	1.24	1.45	1.71	2.02	2.34	2.72
1.01	24	.198	.293	.408	.56	0.73	0.90	1.09	1.30	1.55	1.82	2.16	2.51	2.91
1.17	30	.144	.247	.350	.450	0.58	0.74	0.91	1.10	1.31	1.55	1.82	2.11	2.50
1.17	29	.155	.258	.360	.460	0.61	0.76	0.93	1.15	1.34	1.58	1.86	2.16	2.55
1.17	28	.165	.268	.370	.480	0.63	0.78	0.96	1.17	1.37	1.62	1.90	2.22	2.61
1.17	27	.178	.285	.388	.50	0.65	0.80	1.00	1.21	1.43	1.69	2.00	2.35	2.74
1.17	26	.197	.308	.425	.53	0.70	0.87	1.07	1.28	1.52	1.82	2.18	2.55	2.98
1.17	25	.224	.342	.47	.60	0.78	0.97	1.19	1.43	1.70	2.04	2.43	2.84	3.31
1.17	24	.260	.385	.53	.72	0.91	1.15	1.39	1.65	1.96	2.33	2.78	3.32	3.96
1.30	30	.172	.280	.395	.53	0.68	0.85	1.03	1.24	1.49	1.77	2.10	2.47	2.91
1.30	29	.178	.290	.410	.55	0.71	0.88	1.07	1.28	1.53	1.81	2.15	2.55	3.00
1.30	28	.186	.305	.435	.58	0.74	0.92	1.12	1.33	1.58	1.88	2.22	2.67	3.14
1.30	27	.198	.325	.465	.62	0.79	0.98	1.19	1.41	1.67	2.00	2.37	2.86	3.38
1.30	26	.216	.350	.50	.67	0.85	1.06	1.28	1.53	1.82	2.18	2.60	3.11	3.67
1.30	25	.235	.375	.55	.75	0.95	1.17	1.41	1.69	2.02	2.42	2.90	3.47	4.10
1.30	24	.260	.420	.61	.85	1.09	1.37	1.68	2.03	2.44	2.94	3.54	4.25	5.10

cast steel, ordinary structural or low-carbon steel, "pure" iron, and low-silicon steel. High-silicon steel is annealed at temperatures ranging above 1000 deg cent, and Hipernik at temperatures above 1200 deg cent. The importance of proper atmospheric control increases as the annealing temperature is raised.

Curves and Data on Commercial Non-retentive Magnetic Materials. In using data on commercial magnetic materials it is important to remember that the magnetic properties of all such materials are apt to vary considerably, depending upon chemistry, kind and amount of mechanical work done on the material, heat treatment, and factors at present beyond control. It is impossible to give exact figures representing the various magnetic characteristics, and the values presented will be those corresponding to the average of good practice. In general, the range over which the values will fluctuate will be smaller for the materials of higher magnetic quality. Silicon steel sheets, for example, show variations in standard iron loss of less than 10 per cent, although permeability figures for this class of material will vary over a considerably wider range. In general, both hysteresis losses, and low and moderate flux density permeabilities, will vary over a considerably wider range than the permeabilities at high values of magnetizing force.

Although electrical sheets are usually marketed under the trade names of the various manufacturers, the number of grades and the loss characteristics of these grades have been fairly well standardized (the "radio" grades are essentially the same as the standard). Accordingly, the figure corresponding to the 29 gage (0.014) iron loss, expressed in watts per pound when tested at 10,000 gausses and 60 cycles, has been used to designate the grade of electrical sheet material.

Table V.　Apparent Incremental Permeability Standard E and I Laminations

Length of magnetic circuit = 5.6 in.　Two lap joints.　29 gage material, 0.66 grade

A-c induction	D-c Magnetizing Force, in Oersteds							
	0	0.5	1.0	1.5	2	3	4	5
10 gausses	650	600	480	390	330	260	220	210
100 gausses	1230	1000	750	580	475	360	300	280
1000 gausses	2400	1450	1070	850	700	560	500	480

Data by American Rolling Mill Co., Middletown, Ohio. Data shown are for 60 cycles; 1000 cycles shows almost identical result.

Table VI.　Incremental Permeability D-c Tests

29 gage material, 0.60 grade

	B = 10	B = 30	B = 100	B = 300	B = 1000	B = 3000
Steady magnetizing force = 0.0 oersted	1000	1440	1970	2770	4460	7320
Steady magnetizing force = 0.1 oersted	1000	1350	1910	2550	4030	6650
Steady magnetizing force = 0.3 oersted	840	1090	1470	1985	3120	5200
Steady magnetizing force = 1.0 oersted	578	740	934	1130	1570	2750
Steady magnetizing force = 3.0 oersteds	200	204	214	250	450	1000
Steady magnetizing force = 10.0 oersteds	62	63	65	70	100	310

Data from Westinghouse Electric tests. Ring samples, no air gaps. 60-cycle a-c tests with no air gaps have checked these figures closely.

46.　RETENTIVE MATERIALS

General Considerations. The magnetic properties and the application of the various retentive or permanent magnet materials, depend, in the main. on four factors, namely: (1) the physical dimensions of the magnetic current, (2) the heat treatment of the material, (3) the subsequent "stabilization," and (4) small variations in composition.

1. The relative lengths of the retentive material, of the air gap, and, if present of the non-retentive material, together with the cost and weight or size considerations, will determine, in general, the choice of magnetic material. If the air gap must be relatively large, or if weight or size are important considerations, materials having high coercive force will be used.

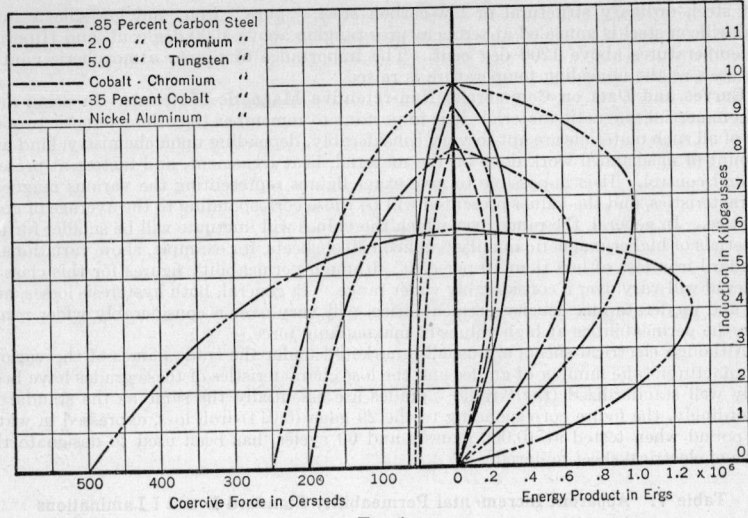

———	.85 Percent Carbon Steel
———	2.0 " Chromium "
———	5.0 " Tungsten "
———	Cobalt - Chromium "
———	35 Percent Cobalt "
———	Nickel Aluminum "

Coercive Force in Oersteds   Energy Product in Ergs

FIG. 1

2. The desired magnetic properties of these materials are not developed, as a rule, until a final heat treatment has been given. Usually, precautions must be taken to avoid cracking, excessive oxidation, decarburization, or overheating; the temperatures must be rather closely controlled; and it is ordinarily desirable to keep these materials at high temperatures as short a time as is practicable. Permanent magnet materials are ordinarily quite difficult to forge or machine.

Table VII. Properties of Permanent Magnet Materials, Approximate Values

Characteristic	0.85 Per Cent Carbon Steel	2.0 Per Cent Chromium Steel	5.0 Per Cent Tungsten Steel	Cobalt Chromium Steel	Cobalt Steel	Nickel Aluminum Steel
Per cent carbon.............	0.85	0.90	0.65	0.9	0.85 ¶	....
Per cent chromium...........	....	2.0	0.50	10.0	4.2	....
Per cent cobalt..............	....	....	....	15.0	37.0	....
Per cent tungsten...........	....	....	5.50	....	2.3	....
Per cent manganese..........	0.25	0.30	0.30	0.40	0.4	5.0 ‖
Per cent aluminum...........	....	....	....	....	....	10
Per cent nickel..............	....	....	....	....	....	25
Forging temperature..........	850° C	1000° C	1000° C	1000° C	1000° C	†
Annealing temperature........	875° C *	900° C *	850° C *	750° C *	§	‡
Hardening temperature.......	760° C	800° C	840° C	**	950° C	‡
Quenching medium...........	Oil	Oil	Oil	Oil	Oil	‡
Magnetizing force, oersteds.....	300	400	400	1000	1000	2000
Residual induction (B_r)........	8500	9500	10,000	8300	10,000	6000
Coercive force (H_c)...........	50	55	65	200	250	500
Maximum energy product ($B_r \times H_c$) max.............	180,000	230,000	300,000	650,000	1,000,000	1,300,000
Approximate relative cost in percentage....................	100	100	200	1000	1900	300
Approximate ergs per dollar (max)....................	1.8×10^6	2.3×10^6	1.5×10^6	0.65×10^6	0.52×10^6	4.2×10^6

* Cooled in air.
† Cannot be forged or machined, may be ground, and casts fairly well.
‡ Heat to 1200 deg cent, quench, and age 4 hr at 700 deg cent.
§ Annealing impairs the magnetic properties of this material and should be avoided. If necessary for machining hold at 830 deg cent for 1 hr, cool 30 deg cent per hr to 600 deg cent, cool in air.
¶ Carbon fairly critical.
‖ The manganese is not essential, but increases the coercive force from 350 to 500, and lowers the residual induction from 7500 to 6000.
** Heat rapidly to 1160 deg cent, cool in air, heat slowly to 725 deg cent, cool in air, heat to 1000 deg cent, cool in moving air to 300 deg cent, and quench in oil, according to Darwins, Ltd., Sheffield, England.

3. After the material has been heat-treated and magnetized it is frequently necessary to put the material in such condition that very little or no further change in magnetic properties will occur. This may be accomplished, but only by sacrificing a part of the initially available magnetic energy, by one or all of three methods.

(a) Prolonged " aging " at a slightly elevated temperature, usually about 100 deg cent for about 10 hours.

(b) Subjecting the material to mechanical shock or vibration, as by dropping it several feet to a hard surface.

(c) Applying a small negative, or alternating, demagnetizing force, as by introducing a slightly larger air gap than will later be used in the magnetic circuit.

4. Small amounts of various impurities will sometimes produce changes in the magnetic properties of retentive materials. Small percentages of sulfur, phosphorus, or oxygen are believed to be harmful, and loss of carbon in heat treatment may damage some grades considerably.

Data on Commercial Retentive Materials. Hysteresis loops are shown in Fig. 1. General data on permanent magnet materials are shown in Table VII.

47. SPECIAL MAGNETIC MATERIALS

Low-induction Materials. There are several magnetic materials which have remarkable magnetic characteristics at very low flux densities. These materials include those known as (1) " Conpernik " and (2) " Perminvar."

(1) *Conpernik* is characterized by a constant permeability of a little over 1000 at flux densities up to several hundred gausses, and by a very low hysteresis loss at those low inductions. The composition of Conpernik is the same as that of Hipernik, and the unusual properties are secured by a low-temperature heat treatment. The hysteresis loss of Conpernik is about 1.6×10^{-2} erg per cu cm per cycle at an induction of 100 gausses. The material may be used to advantage in several ways, for example, in producing reactors with a reactance to resistance ratio well over 150, at frequencies of about 500 cycles. In order to keep eddy current losses low, it is generally used in 0.005-in. thickness.

(2) *Perminvar*, characterized by somewhat similar properties, is an alloy of iron, nickel, and cobalt, in one of several proportions. The magnetic properties are developed by special heat treatment.

High-induction Materials. An alloy of iron and cobalt, preferably in the ratio of 65 per cent iron to 35 per cent cobalt, has remarkable properties at very high inductions. The saturation induction is about 12 per cent higher than that of pure iron, or a little over 24,000 gausses, and at magnetizing forces between 50 and 200 oersteds the inductions are about 25 per cent higher than for iron. The material is used only for special applications because of its relatively high cost.

Temperature Effects. (1) Alloys of copper and nickel, in the proportions of 70 per cent copper to 30 per cent nickel with the addition of small amounts of manganese and silicon, and alloys of iron and nickel in the ratio of 3 to 1 respectively, will show substantial and approximately linear changes in permeability with temperature, and are used as shunts for compensating the magnetic circuits of electrical instruments for changes in temperature.

(2) An alloy of iron and nickel, with about 35 per cent nickel (Invar composition), will become non-magnetic at a slightly elevated temperature and is used in magnetic-thermal relays.

High-frequency Materials. Powdered iron or powdered permalloy, with the particles of magnetic material insulated from each other, and the whole compressed into a solid mass, may be used for the cores of radio reactors, or in other applications where the frequency is very high. Such materials usually have low permeabilities (initial permeabilities of the order of 25) and high resistivity, one material having a resistivity of about 50 ohm-cm.

MISCELLANEOUS MATERIALS

48. MISCELLANEOUS METALLIC MATERIALS

Duriron is a corrosion-resisting material made by the Duriron Co., Dayton, Ohio, consisting of Si, 14.50 per cent; Mn, 0.35 per cent; C, 0.80 to 0.85 per cent; Fe, balance. The following are given as its physical properties: specific gravity, 7.0; weight per cubic inch, 0.253 lb; melting range, 2275 to 2375 deg fahr; coefficient of expansion, 0.000,015,65 per deg fahr from room temperature to the melting point, and 0.000,004 per deg fahr from room temperature to 212 deg fahr; electrical resistivity, microhm-cm at 32 deg fahr, 63.3; thermal conductivity (silver = 1.000), 125; Shore scleroscope hardness, 49–51; contraction allowance in casting, 1/4 in. per ft. The makers give the tensile strength as 15,000 to 20,000 lb per sq in., and the compressive strength as 95,000 lb per sq in. Duriron will not soften or materially alter its shape at temperatures below 2000 deg fahr, nor does it oxidize at temperatures below 1500 deg fahr.

Corrosiron is a cast-iron alloy, containing about 14.25 per cent silicon and other metalloids in small quantities. It melts at about 2400 deg fahr and weighs 0.263 lb per cu in. It is brittle with long flat crystals. A bar 1 by 2 in., 24 in. long, has a transverse strength of about 1200 lb, with the load applied at the center, the deflection being about 0.16 in. Shrinkage is about 3/16 in. per ft. In designing, flat surfaces should be avoided, all corners rounded, and sections of metal kept as even as possible.

Corrosiron is used in the construction of pipes, valves, pipe fittings, acid pumps, pans, etc. It is made by the Pacific Foundry Co., San Francisco.

Copper-aluminum-iron Bronze. Tests on copper-aluminum-iron bronze as an acid-resisting material, made at the Univ. of Wisconsin, were reported by O. L. Kowalke (*Chem. & Met. Engg.*, Jan. 7, 1920). Two bronzes of the following composition were tested:

	Copper	Aluminum	Iron Alloy	Specific Gravity
Bronze A	87.0	9.8	3.14	7.71
Bronze B	85.6	10.81	3.57	7.58

Bronze A is resistant particularly to sulfuric, lactic, phosphoric, tartaric and acetic acids and to caustic soda. Nitric acid attacks it readily, and hydrochloric acid and aqua ammonia both attack it too readily for commercial purposes. Bronze B is more resistant to sulfuric acid than Bronze A. It is less resistant to hydrochloric acid and more resistant to aqua ammonia than Bronze A, and is also attacked readily by nitric acid.

The corrosion of forged specimens of Bronze A in 35 per cent sulfuric acid was only about one-half that of cast or rolled specimens.

Illium (*Product. Engg.*, November, 1932). Illium is an alloy of nickel, chromium, and copper, developed by the Burgess-Parr Co., with the following average physical characteristics: tensile strength, 6000 lb per sq in.; elastic limit, 50,000 lb per sq in.; hardness, Brinell, 170–200; melting point, 2372 deg fahr; specific gravity, 8.3; weight per cubic inch, 0.3 lb; specific heat, 0.105 g-cal per g per deg cent; coefficient of expansion per deg cent (20–300 deg), 0.000,013,5; electrical resistance, 121.9 microhm-cm; contraction in casting, 5/16 in. per ft. Illium is readily machined, being slightly harder than cast steel, and may be welded to itself or other metals by acetylene or electric arc. It is resistant to the following: *acids*: acetic, butyric, citric, formic, hydrocyanic, lactic, nitric, oleic, oxalic, phosphoric, picric, sulfuric; *salts*: ammonium chlorate and sulfate, copper sulfate, ferric chloride, mercuric chloride, potassium alum, silver nitrate, sodium chloride and hydroxide, hypochlorite, and nitrite; *organic substances*: acid mine water, apple vinegar, carbolic acid, formaldehyde, fruit juices, malt vinegar; *miscellaneous*: bleaching powder, bromide solution, carbonated water, hydrogen sulfide, sulfur dioxide.

Fusible Alloys. A variety of compositions containing tin, lead, and bismuth or cadmium are used when a low melting point is required; some of these alloys are given in Table I.

Table I.   Composition of Fusible Alloys

Alloys	Melting Point deg fahr	Composition, per cent			
		Pb	Sn	Cd	Bi
Lipowitz	140	26	13	10	51
Wood's	158	26	13	12	49
Rose's	230	28	22	..	50
50 per cent plumbers' solder	358	50	50	..	..
Pure tin	450	..	100	..	..

SECTION 12

NON-METALLIC MATERIALS

NON-METALLIC MATERIALS

CEMENT, CONCRETE, LIME, MORTAR, AND PLASTER

By Theodore Crane

1. CEMENT

Cement. In engineering literature the term cement is understood to mean the finely pulverized product obtained by the burning of a suitable mixture of argillaceous and calcareous materials, or by an artificial mixture of such materials after burning, which will possess the property of hardening into a solid mass when mixed with water. The essential ingredients in the manufacture of cement are calcium carbonate ($CaCO_3$), silica (SiO_2), and alumina (Al_2O_3); the last two, combined in various proportions, constitute the argillaceous material. The characteristic property of cement is that of hardening by the addition of water, and therefore its ability to harden when excluded from the air.

The cements used in engineering and building construction in this country are portland, natural, puzzolan, and calcium aluminate cements.

Portland Cement is the finely pulverized product resulting from the calcination to incipient fusion of an intimate, artificial mixture of properly proportioned argillaceous and calcareous materials with no addition subsequent to calcination excepting water and calcined or uncalcined gypsum. It has a definite chemical composition varying within comparatively narrow limits. There are three distinct stages in the process of its manufacture: (1) the preparation of the correct mixture by the selection, proportioning, mixing, and grinding of the ingredients; (2) the burning of the mixture to a clinker; and (3) the pulverizing of the burned clinker to a fine powder.

Portland cement is almost universally used for reinforced-concrete construction. It is a highly uniform product sold under the standard specifications of the A.S.T.M.

Standard Specifications for Portland Cement. (A.S.T.M. Standards C 9-30.)

Chemical Properties. The following limits shall not be exceeded:

Loss on ignition, per cent.............................. 4.00
Insoluble residue, per cent.............................. 0.85
Sulfuric anhydride (SO_3), per cent...................... 2.00
Magnesia (MgO), per cent............................. 5.00

Physical Properties. 1. The residue on a standard No. 200 sieve shall not exceed 22 per cent by weight.

2. A pat of neat cement * shall remain firm and hard, and show no signs of distortion, cracking, checking, or disintegration in the steam test for soundness.

3. The cement shall not develop initial set in less than 45 minutes when the Vicat needle is used or 60 minutes when the Gillmore needle is used. Final set shall be attained within 10 hours.

4. The average tensile strength in pounds per square inch of not less than three standard mortar briquets composed of one part cement and three parts standard sand by weight, shall be equal to or higher than the following:

Age at Test, days	Storage of Briquets	Tensile Strength, lb per sq in.
7	1 day in moist air, 6 days in water............................	275
28	1 day in moist air, 27 days in water...........................	350

5. The average tensile strength of standard mortar at 28 days shall be higher than the strength at 7 days.

Natural Cement is the finely pulverized product resulting from the calcination of an argillaceous limestone at a temperature below fusion. The proportions of lime and clay

---

* Neat cement is portland cement mixed with water and no aggregate added. See A.S.T.M. Standard C77-32 for method of preparation of pat.

in the raw material may vary between much wider limits than in portland cement. Natural cement does not develop its strength as quickly nor is it as strong as portland cement.

Natural cement, mixed with three parts of sand, is widely used for laying brick, stone, or terra-cotta as it produces, without the addition of lime, a plastic mortar amply strong for masonry requirements. It is suitable for concrete placed in massive foundations and similar work where high structural strength is not required, and is also blended with portland cement to increase the workability of the latter.

Standard Specifications for Natural Cement. A.S.T.M. Standard C 10–09. 1. The residue on a standard No. 100 sieve shall not exceed 10 per cent, and on a standard No. 200 sieve shall not exceed 30 per cent, by weight.

2. Pats of neat cement about 3 in. in diameter, $1/2$ in. thick at center, tapering to a thin edge, shall be kept in moist air for a period of 24 hours.

(a) A pat shall then be kept in air at normal temperature.

(b) Another pat shall be kept in water maintained as near 70 deg fahr as practicable.

These pats shall be observed at intervals for at least 28 days, and, to pass the tests satisfactorily, shall remain firm and hard and show no signs of distortion, checking, cracking, or disintegrating.

3. The cement shall not develop initial set in less than 10 minutes, using the Vicat needle. Final set shall be attained in not less than 30 minutes nor more than 3 hours, using the Vicat needle.

4. The minimum requirements for tensile strength for briquets 1 sq in. in cross-section shall be as follows, and the cement shall show no retrogression in strength within the periods specified:

Neat Cement

Age	Strength
24 hours in moist air	75 lb
7 days (1 day in moist air, 6 days in water)	150 lb
28 days (1 day in moist air, 27 days in water)	250 lb

One part cement, three parts standard Ottawa Sand

7 days (1 day in moist air, 6 days in water)	50 lb
28 days (1 day in moist air, 27 days in water)	125 lb

Pending the revision of this specification, the neat cement tests have been practically eliminated from standard practice. Furthermore, the facilities for grinding natural cement have been so improved, since this standard was written, that the residue permitted on the No. 200 sieve may be reduced to 12 per cent by weight.

Puzzolan Cement is the finely pulverized product resulting from grinding a mechanical mixture of fused argillaceous material and hydrated lime. The argillaceous substance may consist of natural puzzolaric material, such as volcanic ash, trass or allied igneous material, or of an artificial material such as water-granulated blast-furnace slag.

The American puzzolan cements are manufactured from blast-furnace slag, granulated at the furnace by spraying with water, after which the cinder is very finely ground. The best grades of puzzolan will pass approximately 98 per cent through a No. 200 sieve. The chief use of puzzolan cement in this country is for non-staining mortars employed in laying fine masonry, particularly limestone and marble. It is also blended to some extent with portland cement for use in massive construction to reduce the amount of heat generated by hydration.

Lafarge and other grappier cements, by-products produced during the calcination of hydraulic lime, are no longer employed to any extent in this country. They were formerly imported from Europe and used in non-staining mortars. At present the white portlands, certain natural cements, and high-grade puzzolan cements have taken their place.

High, Early-strength Cements are now being widely used for work which requires speed or where cold-weather conditions demand costly protection during the curing period. There are: (1) The calcium-aluminate cements, in a class by themselves, producing a 28-day strength in 24 hours. These cements have a high resistance to corrosive sulfate solutions which makes them particularly suitable for work exposed to sea water and ground water containing calcium, magnesium, or sodium sulfates. They are also used as a binder for refractory materials. (2) A large number of high, early-strength portland cements which, when used in normal quantities, produce a 28-day strength at about 72 hours. Both these types of cements are more expensive than standard portlands. When used, they should be specified by name, and an abstract of the manufacturer's recommendations for their use should be written into the specifications.

2. CONCRETE

Concrete is a physicochemical mixture of cement and water combined with a fine and coarse aggregate. The hardening of the cement-water paste, resulting from the chemical reaction between the water and cement, binds together the particles comprising the aggregates. It requires only about $2\,1/2$ gal of water to hydrate 1 bag of cement, but it is necessary to use two or three times this amount for the purpose of obtaining a sufficiently plastic mixture to permit proper placement of the concrete. A certain amount of water, therefore, remains uncombined and distributed within the paste, causing minute water voids in the concrete, which tend to reduce its structural strength, impermeability, and resistance to exposure. The strength and other desirable qualities of concrete, as far as proportioning is concerned, depend upon the cement-water ratio and not upon the relative amounts of aggregate and cement, except in so far as the latter affect the cost and the workability of the concrete.

Designing a concrete mixture, therefore, comprises: (1) the selection of suitable materials meeting the requirements of good practice which are described in the Standard Specifications of the A.S.T.M.; (2) selecting a water-cement ratio which will produce concrete of the desired strength and resistance to exposure; (3) determining the most suitable quantities and combinations of aggregates which will give the necessary workability when mixed with cement and water of the chosen proportions.

Cement. Standard and high-early-strength portland cements, meeting the standard specifications of the A.S.T.M., should be used for all reinforced-concrete work except that calcium-aluminate cement may be used where rapid hardening is essential. Natural and puzzolan cements, with or without a blending of portland, are suitable for massive construction, but are not used to any extent for reinforced-concrete work. American cements are sold by the barrel (4 bags each weighing 94 lb and assumed to contain 1 cu ft) and delivered in jute or paper bags, except that for very large operations bulk delivery is employed.

Aggregates. Crushed stone or screened gravel are the principal materials used for coarse aggregates. Trap, granite, limestone, or quartz gravel are satisfactory; soft limestones, sandstones, and shale should be avoided. Quartz sand is almost universally used as a fine aggregate, although crushed cinders, crushed slag, and various light-weight materials are employed for special purposes.

The following is a summary of the Joint Standard Building Code * specification for concrete aggregates: They shall consist of natural sands and gravels, crushed rock, crushed air-cooled blast-furnace slag, or other inert material having clean, uncoated grains of strong and durable minerals; they must not contain more than 3 per cent soft, friable, thin, flaky, elongated, or laminated particles; or more than $1\,1/2$ per cent shale; or more than 2 per cent silt and crusher dust finer than No. 100 standard sieve (percentages to be based on the weight of the combined aggregate as used in the concrete). When all three groups of these deleterious substances are present in the aggregates, the combined amounts shall not exceed 5 per cent by weight of the combined aggregate. Aggregates shall not contain strong alkali or organic material which gives a color darker than standard when tested by the A.S.T.M. standards for organic impurities in sands for concrete (Serial Designation: C40–33).

The maximum size of the aggregate should not be larger than $1/5$ of the narrowest dimension between forms of the member for which the concrete is to be used nor more than $3/4$ of the minimum clear spacing between reinforcing bars. Maximum size here means the clear space between sides of the smallest square opening through which 95 per cent (by weight) of the material can pass.

Fine Aggregate. Fine aggregate should consist of uniformly graded sand, or the screenings of crushed stone or gravel. Material that appears satisfactory upon cursory inspection should have: (1) a colorimetric test to determine the amount of alkali or organic material, (2) a decantation test to determine the amount of silt, (3) a sieve analysis to determine the grading of the sand: particles should vary from fine (at least 5 per cent passing a 50-mesh sieve) up to a $1/4$-in. maximum. These tests are described in detail in the A.S.T.M. standards.

Mortar specimens, composed of the sand and cement to be used, should be made and tested for both tension and compression. The results at both the 7- and 28-day periods should at least equal tests on similar specimens of the same proportion and consistency, using graded Ottawa sand having a fineness modulus of 2.40 ± 0.10 mixed with the same cement.

* Published by the American Concrete Institute.

Coarse Aggregate. Coarse aggregate should consist of crushed stone or gravel retained on a screen with $1/4$-in. holes. It should be graded from the smallest to the largest particles. Though the strength and economy of concrete are favored by a larger, rather than a smaller, size of aggregate, some fine particles are necessary for workability, and the necessity of proper placement definitely limits the maximum size for any particular type of work. If the aggregate is not well graded from fine to coarse, the concrete will be harsh and subject to honeycomb. For most reinforced concrete in building construction, a size passing a 1-in. square opening is customary. For narrow walls or thin sections, as the ribs composing the structural members of a ribbed floor system, $5/8$-in. stone or gravel is desirable. A 2-in. or even 3-in. size may be used for thick walls, piers, or other massive work.

Admixtures are substances other than cement, aggregates, and water added to concrete mixtures to improve their quality. They may be used as integral waterproofing, to shorten the time of setting, to protect against the action of frost, to harden surfaces exposed to abrasion, or to increase workability. For waterproofing of concrete, see p. 12–10.

The use of admixtures to shorten the normal period required for hydration of the cement is generally accepted practice where job conditions demand the earliest possible employment of the structure. Certain chemicals, as calcium chloride, may be bought in the open market and safely added to the mixing water, and many proprietary compounds also will not injure the quality of the concrete. Such products should be specified by name, and the maker's recommendations for use should be included in the specifications.

Admixtures should not be relied upon to protect concrete against frost, except as insurance against a slight and temporary fall of temperature below freezing. Under such conditions, an accelerating compound may be used to shorten the period of extreme vulnerability, as the effect of freezing is most disastrous before the concrete has taken initial set. The use of admixtures to harden concrete surfaces is confined almost exclusively to interior floor finishes. Many excellent proprietary compounds are available. They should be specified by name, and the maker's recommendations written into the specifications.

Increased workability may be obtained: (1) by increasing the proportion of cement in the mixture; (2) by adding plasticizing agents, as hydrated lime or celite. Although many compounds are available, some of which are of material benefit, it is always desirable to proportion the concrete ingredients with the utmost care and to use a well-graded aggregate.

Water. The water used in mixing concrete should be free from oil, acid, alkali, or organic matter. The use of sea water for mixing is generally prohibited.

Proportionment. The amount of each ingredient is measured by volume or weight. Any appropriate method may be used for measurement, provided that accuracy is obtained. The concrete is designated by the proportion of each of the ingredients in the following order: cement, sand, stone or gravel. For example, a 1 : 2 : 4 mixture is one consisting of 1 part of cement, 2 parts of fine aggregate, and 4 parts of coarse aggregate. One bag of cement (94 lb) is considered to equal 1 cu ft.

Since the prime requisite for making good concrete is the strict control of the water-cement ratio, provided that the mixture is sufficiently plastic to insure proper placement without the danger of honeycomb, the proportion of cement paste to aggregate may be varied for the several portions of the work provided that the ultimate strength, assumed in the structural design, is held constant for all mixtures by strictly adhering to the water-cement ratio.

For example, massive work such as abutments or gravity retaining walls may have a mixture such as 1 : 3 : 5 or 1 : 3 : 6, whereas, for comparatively thin, heavily reinforced sections, such as the structural elements of a floor system, where greater workability is required, a mixture of 1 : 2 $1/2$: 3 $1/2$ or 1 : 1 $1/2$: 3 would be used. The proportions of aggregates to cement, however, should always be such as to produce a plastic mass that will work readily into the corners and angles of the forms and around the reinforcement without excessive puddling; there should be no segregation of materials, nor should free water collect upon newly poured surfaces. In general, the combined aggregate should be such that when separated by a $1/4$-in. sieve, the volume retained on the sieve is approximately 40 per cent of the total, nor should the amount of coarse material be such as to produce a harsh mixture. When forms are removed, the faces and corners of all members should appear smooth and free from honeycomb. In no case should the water-cement ratio exceed the limit given in Table I corresponding to the strength assumed in the design. The value upon which the working stresses are based is the ultimate compressive strength in pounds per square inch developed at an age of 28 days by standard cylinders prepared and tested according to the A.S.T.M. standards. During the progress of the work, at least one specimen of concrete should be tested for each 100 cu yd. If the strength of such samples falls below that assumed in the design, the engineer should require the application of heat and moisture to increase the strength of the concrete to the required minimum.

As it is often impracticable to await the result of a 28-day test, samples may be tested at an age of 7 days and the following equation applied:

$$\text{Probable 28-day strength} = f + 30\sqrt{f}$$

f = ultimate compressive strength at an age of 7 days.

Table I, taken from the Joint Standard Building Code, gives the assumed 28-day strength of various concrete mixtures. The water-cement ratios to be used for different degrees of exposure of concrete are presented in Table II. In Table III are listed trial mixtures for various water-cement ratios. The mixes are intended as a guide only. The first batch should be made with measured water content and the proportions thereafter adjusted to produce the desired workability, maintaining the specific water-cement ratio.

Table I. Assumed Strength of Concrete Mixtures (From Joint Standard Building Code)

Water-cement Ratio *	Plastic Concrete		Moderately Wet Concrete	
	Approximate Mixture †	Assumed 28-day Compressive Strength, lb per sq in.	Approximate Mixture †	Assumed 28-day Compressive Strength, lb per sq in.
8 1/4	1 : 7	1500	1 : 6 1/2	1500
7 1/2	1 : 6	2000	1 : 5 1/2	2000
6 3/4	1 : 5 1/4	2500	1 : 4 3/4	2500
6	1 : 4 1/2	3000	1 : 4	3000

NOTE.—In interpreting this table, surface water contained in the aggregate must be included as part of the mixing water in computing the water-cement ratio.

* U. S. gallon per 94-lb sack of cement.

† Volume of portland cement to sum of separate volumes of fine and coarse aggregate, measured dry.

Table II. Classes of Concrete for Different Degrees of Exposure

Type of Structure	Degree of Exposure	U. S. Gallon of Water * per Sack of Cement
Walls, dams, piers, and other structures exposed to sea or alkali waters.	Extreme	5 1/2
Walls, dams, piers, reservoir linings, etc., exposed to alternate wetting and drying in fresh water in northern climate. Watertight structures. Sewers, pressure pipe, tanks, piles, athletic stadia, pavements, all thin structural members exposed to severe weather and frost action.	Severe	6
Walls, dams, piers, reservoir linings exposed to fresh water in southern climate. Exterior columns and beams of reinforced-concrete buildings. Basement walls. Thin structural members of all types exposed to moderate weather and frost action.	Moderate	6 3/4
Ordinary enclosed structural members. Heavy piers and retaining walls in moderate exposure. Mass concrete, footings, etc., protected from alternate wetting and drying and from severe weather conditions.	Protected	7 1/2

* These quantities should not be exceeded even when resultant strength is higher than required for structural stability. Free water or moisture carried by the aggregate must be included as part of the mixing water.

Moisture Contained in Aggregates. The absorption of most aggregates can be neglected as it is very small except for porous sandstones. All aggregates, however, particularly the fine aggregates, retain more or less water in the form of surface moisture. As this becomes part of the mixing water, the amount should be determined and the quantity deducted from that otherwise required for the chosen water-cement ratio. An approximation from 1/4 to 1/2 gal of water per cu ft may be assumed for fine aggregates varying from moist to moderately wet. Very wet sand may contain from 3/4 to 1 gal per cu ft. Coarse aggregates retain less—from 1/8 to 1/4 gal. Accurate determination may be made by weighing a sample of the damp material, drying, and reweighing. The loss in weight is then converted to gallons of water per cubic foot of aggregate. Storage piles will retain a constant moisture content for two or three days, under settled weather conditions. Determination of water should, therefore, be made at such intervals or after a rain.

Table III.   Trial Mixtures for Various Water-cement Ratios

Water-cement Ratio, gallons per sack *	Slump, in.	Trial Mix, Dry Compact Volumes for Maximum Size of Aggregate †	
		1-in. Aggregate	2-in. Aggregate
5 1/2	1/2–1	1 : 2 : 3	1 : 2 : 3 1/2
	3–4	1 : 1 3/4 : 2 1/2	1 : 1 3/4 : 3
	5–7	1 : 1 1/2 : 2	1 : 1 1/2 : 2 1/2
6	1/2–1	1 : 2 1/4 : 3 1/4	1 : 2 1/4 : 4
	3–4	1 : 2 : 3	1 : 2 : 3 1/2
	5–7	1 : 1 3/4 : 2 1/2	1 : 1 3/4 : 3
6 3/4	1/2–1	1 : 2 1/2 : 3 1/2	1 : 2 1/2 : 4
	3–4	1 : 2 1/4 : 3 1/4	1 : 2 1/4 : 3 3/4
	5–7	1 : 2 : 3	1 : 2 : 3 1/2
7 1/2	1/2–1	1 : 3 : 4	1 : 3 : 4 3/4
	3–4	1 : 2 1/2 : 3 3/4	1 : 2 1/2 : 4 1/4
	5–7	1 : 2 1/4 : 3 1/2	1 : 2 1/4 : 3 3/4

* Water-cement ratios include moisture contained in the aggregate.
† Proportions are given by volume, aggregate dry and compact. For approximate proportions by weight add 15 per cent to proportions of aggregate shown in the table. If aggregates are measured in a damp and loose condition, they occupy a greater volume than when dry and compact. Amount should be determined by test. Approximate average value for sand 20 per cent, for coarse aggregate, 6 per cent.

Some aggregates, especially sand, increase in volume when wet. Fine sands may increase as much as 40 per cent on adding only 5 per cent by weight of water. To correct for bulking, the bulked aggregate should be increased a sufficient amount to obtain the desired volume based upon a dry, compact condition. The weight of a given volume, measured damp and loose, compared to the volume produced by the same weight dry and compact, gives the necessary factor for the correct field mix to correspond to the proportions stated in the specifications.

Slump Test. An approximate method of determining the relative consistency of concrete is that known as the slump test. Samples of concrete, taken at the mixer, are placed in a metal mold, which is the frustum of a cone, base 8 in. in diameter, upper surface 4 in. in diameter, height 12 in. The mold is filled in a specified manner and immediately removed by being raised vertically. The distance which the plastic concrete subsides from the 12-in. level is the "slump." For similar materials mixed under the same conditions this test gives a very fair indication of the consistency of the concrete. It should not be used to compare consistencies of batches made with aggregates of other than the same grading. See Table III.

Mixing. Concrete should be mixed in a standard type batch mixer or, for small operations, on a water-tight platform. Mixing should continue until all materials are thoroughly distributed and the mass is uniform in color and homogeneous, i.e., for at least 1 min and preferably for 2 min after all materials have been placed in the mixer. Each batch should be carefully voided from the mixer before recharging. All equipment used to mix or convey concrete should be thoroughly cleaned at completion of the day's run. Remixing partially hardened concrete with an additional amount of water, or water and cement, should not be permitted. Aggregates may be measured in loading hoppers or in calibrated buggies or wheel barrows. Automatic water control is desirable provided that the water contained in the aggregates can be accurately checked; in any case, a water-measuring device should be installed controlling the supply from the storage tank to the mixer.

Conveying. Concrete should be handled from the mixer to the place of deposit as rapidly as practicable. Any means such as two-wheel buggies, wheel barrows, trucks, chutes, or belt conveyors may be employed provided that the concrete is delivered to the point of final deposit in a thoroughly homogeneous condition and before the cement has commenced to harden.

Depositing. Before concrete is placed in excavated areas all water should, if possible be removed and under no consideration should a flow of water be permitted around the newly deposited material. Before concrete is placed within wood or steel forms, ice, snow, shavings, or other débris should be removed. When building structural floors composed of clay block or cement tile, against which concrete is poured, the tile or block should be thoroughly wet with water except in freezing weather.

Concrete should be deposited evenly in the forms, in uniform layers. When constructing walls, a depth of 1 or 2 ft should be carried in a continuous operation entirely around the building or around the unit that is being constructed. Columns and pilasters should be poured in one operation and the concrete allowed to settle for at least 2 hours before pouring superimposed elements. Floor construction should commence with the beams and girders, into which the concrete should be poured directly; if concrete is dumped on the floor forms and allowed to flow into the beams, segregation will result. Where chutes are used, the concrete should be received in a hopper and redistributed by buggy or wheel barrow.

Concrete should not be dropped from a height of more than 5 ft without the aid of a pipe or elephant-trunk. It should be placed as nearly as practicable in its final position to avoid rehandling, and it should be thoroughly compacted by spading or puddling so as to expel entrained air as well as to insure complete filling of the forms and thorough embedment of the reinforcement. Excessive spading against exterior surfaces should, however, be avoided, as such tends to cause a layer of laitance next to the forms. Either internal or external vibration is helpful for compacting the concrete in thin walls or sections which it is difficult to spade.

Construction joints should be located so as to least impair the strength of the structure. Where horizontal joints are made, the hardened surface should be cleaned and roughened before additional concrete is deposited. Beams, girders, brackets, and column capitals should be considered as part of the floor system and placed monolithically with the floor slab. Construction joints in floors should be located near the middle of the spans, slabs, beams or girders, unless a beam intersects a girder at this point, in which case the joints in the girders should be offset a distance equal to twice the width of the beam, and provision should be made for shear by use of inclined reinforcement.

Concrete should not be deposited during freezing weather without special precautions being taken, as freezing of the water before setting exerts a disruptive force which causes disintegration. Although concrete which has been frozen immediately after placement may, upon subsequent thawing, eventually gain its designed strength, good practice demands protection, as alternate thawing and freezing will completely destroy the best concrete.

On cold-weather operations, the materials should be sufficiently heated to produce a temperature in the concrete at the time of deposit between 50 deg fahr and 100 deg fahr. Sheet-iron pipe, buried in the aggregates and fired with wood, is the usual method for heating small quantities of aggregates. Large quantities may be heated by a network of steam pipes underlying the storage piles. Foundations and slabs resting upon the ground may then be sufficiently protected by covering with canvases or, at extreme temperatures, by canvases covered with earth. For multi-story buildings, it is necessary to enclose the entire structure for a height of several stories with canvases, the interior being heated to a temperature of at least 50 deg fahr for a period of not less than 72 hours by means of steam, or salamanders burning coke.

Curing. After concrete has obtained its initial set, the proper hardening requires the presence of heat and moisture. Surfaces such as sidewalks, pavements, and floors should be kept moist for a period of 10 days after laying. Such treatment greatly increases the strength, durability, and resistance to abrasion. Surfaces may be covered with damp sand, or soft-wood shavings, the day after they are laid, and kept damp by frequent sprinklings. Vertical surfaces such as walls and columns should be sprinkled twice daily for a period of one to two weeks after stripping, according to the length of time which the forms have remained in place. Thin sections and ornamental work should also be protected by burlap or canvases from the effect of hot sun or drying winds. It should be remembered that a concrete designed for a certain 28-day strength, which it would acquire if cured at a temperature of 70 deg fahr, will attain only about 82 per cent of that strength when cured at a period of 50 deg fahr, and that a temperature just above freezing might well result, at the end of 28 days, in a strength hardly more than one-half of that which an average 70 deg fahr temperature would have produced.

Forms may be made of steel, wood, or composition boards, as may be most practicable for the type of work. They should conform to the lines and dimensions of the member as described on the drawings; they should be substantially constructed and sufficiently tight to prevent leakage of mortar. Temporary openings should be provided to facilitate cleaning débris from the bottoms of columns, piers, and similar members. Forms should be so removed as to insure the complete safety of the structure. The surfaces of forms should be oiled or wet before placing concrete. Oils should not be used against surfaces which are to receive plaster, nor should water be used in freezing weather.

In order to permit the erection of multi-story buildings with one set of forms, stripping is performed panel by panel, reshoring immediately. The entire floor system is then supported by shores for a period of two or three weeks from the time that concrete is deposited. Under such conditions the following periods may be accepted as a guide in determining the approximate time that the forms for the various members should remain in place upon buildings which are conservatively designed and which are not subjected to excessive construction loads, provided, however, that the concrete is such as will develop, under good curing conditions, a compressive strength of 2000 lb per sq in. at an age of 28 days, and that the temperature of the surrounding air during the entire curing period has not fallen below 50 deg fahr.

Beam and Girder Construction: Columns, 1 day provided that girders are shored to prevent any appreciable load being transferred to columns; girders, 3 days provided that each girder is immediately reposted so that only one member at a time is left unsupported; beams, 4 days provided that the same procedure is followed as for girders; panels up to 7-ft span, any time after the beam forms are removed.

Girderless Construction: Columns as noted above; drops, 3 days provided that slabs are reshored to prevent any appreciable load being transferred to the unsupported sections; slabs, up to 20-ft span, 4 days provided that each slab is immediately reposted and permanent 6 by 6 in. shores left beneath the center of each bay and not disturbed at the time of stripping.

Wall Forms: The forms of low, non-bearing walls can often be removed one or two days after pouring. It is only necessary that the concrete be sufficiently hard to support its own weight and permit the shock and jar of stripping without crumbling or spalling.

If concrete has been subjected to low temperatures, it may have the appearance of adequate strength when actually frozen. If forms are removed, the structure or the part affected is likely to fall when thawed. Although the use of a blow-torch may prove the existence of frost in the concrete, a more reliable method is to obtain a sample of the material in question and to place it in warm water for a few hours. If frozen and not hardened, the concrete on the surface of the sample will disintegrate.

High Early-strength Concrete. Increased strength at early ages may be obtained either by the use of additional cement or by special cements made for this purpose. For example, a compression strength of 2000 lb per sq in. may be obtained at age 3 days by limiting the water to $4^1/_2$ gal per sack of cement and curing at a temperature of 70 deg fahr; a 1000-lb compression strength may be obtained at the same age by using 6 gal of water per sack and curing at the same temperature. It should be remembered that, if the curing temperature is lower, less water should be used per sack of cement. For example, if the temperature is 40 deg fahr, a little less than 5 gal of water would correspond to a strength of 1000 lb at age 3 days. As the water-cement ratios are reduced, the amount of cement required for any given quantity of aggregate must be increased to make the concrete sufficiently plastic or workable. Increasing the time of mixing also increases the strength of the concrete, if other conditions remain constant. This increase is quite rapid up to 2 min.

Many special portland cements are made to give high early strength, without increasing the amount per batch that normally would be required for standard construction. The calcium aluminate cements have also found wide application, although considerably more expensive. They may be used to obtain at age 24 hours a strength normally to be expected from a standard portland cement at age 28 days.

Light-weight Concrete. Stone concrete weighs approximately 144 lb per cu ft. A lighter material is often desirable for short-span floor slabs and roof slabs, which may be designed with concrete of low stress value. This is obtained by using light-weight aggregates of burnt clays, or by proprietary methods that produce light-weight concrete by aeration. Cinder concrete weighs about 120 lb per cu ft; burnt clay aggregate concrete, 100 lb per cu ft; aeration methods are controlled to meet any specification for weight down to approximately 40 lb per cu ft.

Colored Concrete. Only mineral pigments should be employed to color concrete. Several makers produce a wide range of colors especially designed for portland cement mortars. The weight of pigment ordinarily should not exceed 5 per cent of that of the cement; 10 per cent should be an absolute limit, as a greater amount is likely to cause deterioration of surfaces exposed to abrasion or weathering. Much smaller percentages of certain colors, as lampblack, injure the quality of the concrete. Only thoroughly accredited material should be used, and the effect upon the cement should be established by actual test. Common practice is to buy the powdered pigment, proportion by weight, and mix dry with the cement; but better results are obtained when the cement and pigment are ground together. It is recommended that cement and pigment be blended at the mill and not on the job.

Finishing Concrete Surfaces. Concrete surfaces may be finished by painting, rubbing with abrasive material, scrubbing to expose the aggregate, or tooling as for natural stone. It is necessary to remove all nails, wires, and bolts, or to cut them off a sufficient distance back of the surface to permit the application of protecting mortar, 1 in. thick, properly keyed into the surrounding concrete, and to repair stone pockets, honeycomb, or seams where laitance has settled. Such sections should be cut out, cleaned, wet, and pointed with a mortar of the same proportions as used in the concrete. When cutting out defective work, a $1/2$-in. shoulder should be left around the edges of the recess to avoid thin coatings of mortar spreading out over sound concrete, as these will invariably crack off.

A cheap method of finishing concrete surfaces not subject to abrasion is the application of a cement wash composed of 1 part white cement, 1 part finely screened sand, and 5 per cent hydrated lime, measured by volume of the cement. There are also many excellent proprietary paints for use on concrete surfaces. Such coatings resist the action of lime in the concrete and cover the same range of colors as that found in ordinary oil paints. Chemical solutions, some of which are colorless, may also be used to harden floor surfaces and prevent dusting; chief among these are the sodium silicate, aluminum sulfate, and zinc sulfate treatments.

A method of finishing vertical surfaces widely used on industrial buildings is to rub or grind with No. 20 Carborundum stone and plain water. The surfaces are rubbed until a thin paste develops, which is later removed by washing and brushing. Best results are obtained if the surfaces can be rubbed when the concrete is not more than 2 days old; if of greater age, a cement wash may be applied during rubbing to assist in the grinding. Excess material should invariably be removed later by brushing and washing.

The exposed aggregate finish is obtained by scrubbing concrete surfaces when only 1 or 2 days old with fiber or wire brushes and clean water. If the surfaces are too hard to be affected by this treatment, a solution of hydrochloric acid may be used. When the aggregates have been exposed, the surface should be thoroughly washed. This method is satisfactory for panels or other limited areas, but it is not suitable for extended work on monolithic buildings, owing to the difficulty of treating all surfaces at the same age, which is necessary for uniform results.

If thoroughly hardened before treatment, concrete may be finished by bush hammering, crandaling, or other methods employed for the finishing of natural stones. Tooling may be done by hand, compressed air, or electricity.

Quantities of Materials. Handbook tables, giving volumes of cement, sand, and coarse aggregates required for 1 cu yd of concrete of specified proportions, may serve as a rough guide, but may be somewhat misleading on account of the various gradings of the aggregates. An accurate determination of the quantities required for any given mixture can be made on the principle that the volume of concrete produced by any combination of materials, so long as the mixture is plastic, equals the sum of the absolute volumes of the cement, aggregates, and water. The absolute volume of a loose material is the actual total volume of solid matter comprising the particles.

Absolute volume = Unit weight ÷ (Apparent specific gravity × Unit weight of water).

Unit weight of the aggregate is determined for surface dry material; 1 cu ft of water is roughly 62.5 lb; 1 sack of cement = 1 cu ft = 94 lb; apparent specific gravity of cement = 3.1; specific gravity of aggregate = 2.65.

Assume that a batch consists of 1 sack of cement; 2.2 cu ft of dry, fine aggregate, at 110 lb per cu ft; 3.6 cu ft of dry, coarse aggregate at 100 lb per cu ft; and 7 gal of water. Then:

$$
\begin{aligned}
\text{Cement} &= 1 \text{ cu ft @ } 94/(3.1 \times 62.5) = 0.49 \text{ cu ft abs vol} \\
\text{Fine aggregate} &= 2.2 \text{ cu ft @ } 110/(2.65 \times 62.5) = 1.46 \text{ " " " "} \\
\text{Coarse aggregate} &= 3.6 \text{ cu ft @ } 100/(2.65 \times 62.5) = 2.18 \text{ " " " "} \\
\text{Volume of water} &= 7.0/7.5 = 0.93 \text{ " " " "}
\end{aligned}
$$

Total volume of concrete produced   5.06 cu ft

For these conditions, 1 sack of cement produces 5.06 cu ft of concrete, neglecting absorption or losses in manipulation. The cement required for 1 cu yd of concrete is $27/5.06 = 5.34$ sacks, or 1.33 bbl. The amount of fine aggregate is $(5.34 \times 2.2)/27 = 0.43$ cu yd; the amount of coarse aggregate is $(5.34 \times 3.6)/27 = 0.71$ cu yd.

For unusual materials, as blast-furnace slag or light-weight aggregates, the exact apparent specific gravity should be used. The value 2.65 is sufficiently accurate for sand, gravel, and limestone. The average value for granite is about 2.70, and for traprock 2.95.

Waterproofing Concrete. Concrete may be made practically impervious to water under moderate pressures if (1) the water-cement ratio is reduced to 5 $1/2$ or 6 gal per bag of cement; (2) the cement content is increased to give proper workability, i.e., the amount of combined aggregate, measured separately, reduced to between 3 $1/2$ and 5 parts by volume of the cement (aggregates measured dry and compact); if vibration is employed, a stiffer and consequently cheaper concrete can be used; (3) the aggregates, both fine and coarse, are carefully graded to obtain a minimum void content; (4) the methods of mixing, transporting, and depositing conform to good practice as defined in preceding paragraphs; (5) the concrete is cured under moist and warm conditions for a period of at least 10 days after placement.

The concrete comprising small units should be deposited as far as practicable in one continuous operation; when construction joints are necessary the old and new work should be joined by keys and the bond insured by roughing the surfaces already cast and slushing with a rich mortar before continuing work. If contraction joints are required by the design, they should be carefully placed so as to eliminate any possibility of the passage of water.

Concrete may also be waterproofed by either the membranous or surface coat method. The former consists of 3 to 5 layers of fabric laid in hot pitch or asphalt mastic, usually applied on the exterior and protected by a single course of brick or a heavy coating of cement mortar. The surface coat method generally consists of two coats of carefully proportioned cement mortar applied to the interior surface, which has previously been roughened and dampened to insure bond. Both methods require care in design and expert application, as their value depends upon obtaining a continuous, unbroken envelope on all surfaces exposed to hydrostatic pressure.

3. LIME

Quicklime is a calcined material, the major part of which is calcium oxide in natural association with a lesser amount of magnesium oxide, capable of slaking in water. Quicklime can never be used as such for structural purposes; it must always be slaked first. Quicklime is sold in several forms, such as crushed, granular, ground, lump, pebble, and pulverized lime. In many localities, well-supervised commercial plants have been established for the preparation of lime putty. Slaked and aged under proper conditions, it is delivered to the work as required.

Chemical Composition of Quicklime. (A.S.T.M. Tentative Specifications C5-34T.) All classes of quicklime shall conform to the following requirements as to chemical composition, calculated to the non-volatile basis:

	Calcium Lime	Magnesium Lime
Calcium oxide, min, per cent	75	..
Magnesium oxide, min, per cent	..	20
Calcium and magnesium oxides, min, per cent	95	95
Silica, alumina, and oxide of iron, max, per cent	5	5
Carbon dioxide, max, per cent:		
If sample is taken at the point of manufacture	3	3
If sample is taken at any other place	10	10

Classification of Quicklime According to Slaking Time. (A.S.T.M. Tentative Specifications C5-34T, Appendix 2.) In a bucket put two or three lumps of lime about the size of one's fist, or, if the lime is granular, an equivalent amount. Add sufficient water to just barely cover the lime, and note how long it takes for slaking to begin. Slaking has begun when pieces split off from the lumps or when the lumps crumble. Water of the same temperature should be used for the test and field practice.

If slaking begins in less than 5 min, the lime is quick slaking; from 5 to 30 min, medium slaking; after 30 min, slow slaking.

Slaking of Quicklime. For quick-slaking lime, the lime should always be added to the water. Sufficient water should be used at first to cover all the lime completely. The mass should be hoed thoroughly and quickly at the slightest appearance of escaping steam and enough water should be added to stop the steaming.

For medium-slaking lime, enough water should be added to the lime to about half submerge it. Occasional hoeing may be necessary if steam starts to escape. A little water may be added now and then if necessary to prevent the putty from becoming dry and crumbly. No more water than is required should be added, and not too much at a time.

For slow-slaking lime, sufficient water should be added to the lime to moisten it thoroughly, and the mass should be allowed to stand until the reaction has started. Water may then be added in such small quantities that the mass is not cooled. Hoeing should not be begun until the slaking is practically complete. Hot water is preferable in cold weather, or the mortar box may be covered so as to prevent loss of heat.

Preparation of Lime Putty or Paste. The time required for aging lime putty varies for different limes. The process should continue until all particles have been completely hydrated. In no case should the putty be used until thoroughly cold. The following procedure applies, under average conditions, to the preparation of lime putty after slaking. If desired, a part or all of the sand may be added immediately after slaking, but the present practice, except on small operations, is to postpone the addition of sand until the mortar is desired for use.

(a) *Plaster White Coat.* After the action has ceased, the putty should be run through a No. 10 sieve and stored in bins for a minimum of 2 weeks, except for quick-slaking pulverized limes which may be used 24 hours after slaking is completed.

(b) *Plaster Brown Coat.* After the action has ceased, the putty should be run through a No. 8 sieve and stored in bins for 2 weeks except as noted above. When desired for use, 1 part of lime putty is combined with 3 parts of sand by volume, together with the required quantity of hair or fiber, the whole being thoroughly mixed in a drum type of mixer.

(c) *Plaster Scratch Coat.* The procedure is the same as for the brown coat except that the proportions should be 1 part of lime putty to 2 parts of sand by volume.

(d) *Mason's Mortar.* After the action has ceased, the putty should be stored until cold, the length of time depending upon the character of the lime, and mixed in the appropriate proportions as given for lime or cement-lime mortars.

Hydrated Lime is a dry powder obtained by treating quicklime with enough water to satisfy its chemical affinity under the conditions of hydration. It consists essentially of calcium hydroxide or a mixture of calcium hydroxide and magnesium oxide and magnesium hydroxide. It is more convenient, particularly for masonry mortars, but does not give a plasticity equal to that of well slaked quicklime and is less economical where the volume of work warrants the slaking of lime at the site.

Classes of Hydrated Lime. A.S.T.M. Tentative Specification C6-34T covers the following two classes of limes: mason's hydrated lime, used for scratch or brown coat of plaster, for stucco, for mortar, and for addition to portland cement concrete; and finishing hydrated lime, used for any of the purposes enumerated above under mason's hydrated lime, and in addition, as an ingredient in the final or white coat of plaster. Finishing plaster shall have a plasticity figure of not less than 200, as determined in accordance with method given in A.S.T.M. Tentative Specification C110-34T.

Air-slaked Lime. Quicklime slakes when exposed to the air, by absorbing moisture from the atmosphere; and lime that is thoroughly air-slaked is as good as that slaked in the usual way. In general, however, air-slaked lime is not thoroughly slaked, and is therefore unsuitable for construction purposes inasmuch as it contains injurious amounts of oxides and carbonates in addition to the hydroxides of calcium and magnesium.

4. MORTAR

General Requirements. All materials should conform to the latest standard specifications of the A.S.T.M. Sand should be thoroughly screened, well graded from fine to coarse, the width of the joints determining the maximum size of particle, which is usually that passing a screen with 8 meshes to the linear inch. Except for this limitation on size, sands used for mortars should conform to the requirements given above for fine aggregates. Mineral pigments, thoroughly incorporated with the cement before mixing the other ingredients, may be employed to obtain the desired color, but the amounts used should be limited as specified for concrete work. Integral waterproofing compounds, hardeners, or accelerators may also be incorporated where conditions warrant their use. Such admixtures should be used in strict conformity with the manufacturers' recommendations.

All dry materials should be thoroughly mixed before the addition of water. The amount of water is controlled by the requirements of the work. In general, the consistency for laying brick, stone, and tile should be such as to facilitate thorough embedment of the masonry units and yet stiff enough to permit proper pointing and to furnish support for superimposed courses. Mortar applied as a finish over floor slabs, or fills, should be placed with merely enough water to permit screeding. This is not only for the purpose of permitting more speedy finishing, but also to increase the abrasive resistance and diminish dusting of the wearing surface. The consistency of mortar applied as stucco, to the exteriors or interiors of wall surfaces, is determined by the requirements of application and surface texture.

Portland Cement Mortar, mixed in the proportion of 1 part cement to 2 1/2 or 3 parts of sand, is customarily used for the surfacing of concrete slabs such as sidewalks and floors. Wherever possible, such finishes should be placed monolithically with the base course; hard, metallic surfaces may be obtained by the use of various admixtures, the mortar being surfaced with a steel trowel. For exterior work, exposed to the elements, a steel trowel finish is not only inappropriate but causes disintegration; sidewalks, for example, should be finished by means of a wood float. Cement mortars, usually containing integral waterproofing compounds, are also used in the surface-coat method of waterproofing and occasionally in place of lime plaster for interior finishes where a particularly hard surface is required.

Lime Mortar, generally composed of 1 part of either hydrated lime or lime paste and 3 parts of sand by volume, is now seldom used except for plastering purposes as noted below.

Portland Cement—Lime Mortar, composed of 1 part portland cement, an equal volume of either hydrated lime or lime paste, and 5 or 6 parts of sand, makes a satisfactory mortar for all ordinary masonry purposes. The use of portland cement and sand in the proportions of about 1:3, with the addition of only 10 or 15 per cent of lime by volume, is good practice only for masonry structures subjected to heavy loads where strength is a prime requisite. In the field of building construction, where it is necessary to construct weather-tight walls, the addition of a quantity of lime equal in volume to that of the portland cement produces a much more plastic mortar and one which will greatly facilitate the proper laying of masonry units.

Natural Cement Mortar, mixed in the proportion of 1 part cement to 3 parts of sand, is suitable for all types of masonry used in building construction, as the natural cements produce, without the addition of lime, a more plastic mortar than that obtained with portland cement.

Puzzolan Cement—Lime Mortar, mixed in the proportions of 1 part of puzzolan cement, 1 part lime paste, and 6 parts of sand, produces an excellent mortar which is also widely used for masonry.

Non-staining Mortar. Owing to the fact that many of our light-colored building stones, such as marble and limestone, are discolored when brought into contact with ordinary portland cement, it is necessary to use a so-called non-staining cement for such work. At present there are several white portland cements, natural cements, and puzzolan cements which are specially manufactured to meet this requirement. These cements may be used with varying amounts of hydrated lime or, preferably, in order to gain greater plasticity, lime paste. To avoid the possibility of efflorescence only the better grades of cement and lime should be used.

Table IV.   Quantities of Material for 1000 Cu Ft of Mortar

Mortar	Lump Lime, 180-lb. bbl, number of bbl	Hydrated Lime, 50-lb. Sacks, number of sacks	Cement, 94-lb Sacks, number of sacks	Sand, cu yd
Lime mortar:				
1 : 2 1/2	57	350	....	37
1 : 3	47	292	....	37
Cement-lime mortar:				
1 : 1 : 6	24	146	130	37
Cement mortar:				
1 : 2	16	92	442	34
1 : 3	12	69	331	39
1 : 4	10	55	264	41

(Based on use of good-quality lime. Lime quantities are approximate and will vary with the grade of lime and the size of particles composing the sand. In cement-mortars, $1/10$ of the cement by weight is replaced by dry hydrated lime or its equivalent in lump-lime paste.)

5.   PLASTER

Plasters are made from gypsum, which is composed of 1 part calcium sulfate and 2 parts of chemically combined water of crystallization. Gypsum plaster is produced by the calcination or dehydration of gypsum at a temperature which varies from 325 deg fahr to 350 deg fahr. At this temperature calcination removes approximately 1 1/2 parts of the chemically combined water, resulting in calcined gypsum or plaster of Paris. When gypsum is dehydrated by complete calcination at high temperatures, it is called calcined gypsum. Hard-finish plasters such as Keene's cement are made from this material by the addition of a catalyzer, such as alum.

Portland Cement Plaster is made from limestone and clay, which have been heated to a temperature above 1200 deg cent, and then ground to a fine powder and mixed with a small amount of gypsum to retard its setting time. Lime plaster is made by mixing quicklime, which is obtained by heating limestone to a temperature above 900 deg cent. Plaster used for finishing coats may be a specially prepared gypsum plaster or a mixture of lime plaster and calcined gypsum.

Neat Gypsum Plaster is composed of calcined gypsum, fibered or unfibered, and materials to control the working quality and setting time. Gypsum ready-sanded plaster is sanded at the mill in the proper proportions of calcined gypsum and sand, water being added only on the job. Gypsum bond plaster is a specially prepared gypsum plaster for use on concrete surfaces, it is not sanded. Gypsum wood fibered plaster, containing usually between 1 and 2 per cent of wood fiber, and other gypsum plasters to which sand is added, should be mixed as follows:

First or scratch coat on wood, metal or gypsum lath: 1 part plaster to 2 parts of sand by weight.

First or scratch coat on clay tile, gypsum tile, or brick, and for all second or browning coats: 1 part plaster to 3 parts of sand by weight.

The final coat may be a sand float finish, employing ready-sanded plaster, or texture work with color as desired. The universally used hard white finish is produced by combining approximately 1 part of gypsum gaging plaster with 3 parts of lime putty by volume, or 1 part of lime putty with 1 part of Keene's cement by volume where a more resistant surface is desired. Only gypsum mortar should be used for setting precast gypsum units, and when gypsum construction is plastered, gypsum plaster should be employed. Gypsum mortar is composed of 1 part of unfibered gypsum neat plaster and not more than 3 parts of clean, well-graded sand by weight.

STONE, BRICK, AND TERRA-COTTA

By Jasper O. Draffin

6. STONE *

Classification. Building stones are classified according to origin (igneous, sedimentary and metamorphic), and subdivided according to mineral and chemical composition, texture and structure, and geologic age. The most common granular crystalline-igneous rocks are granites, diorites, and gabbros or diabases; the more common dense varieties of volcanic origin are rhyolite, andesite, and basalt. Igneous rocks that have conspicuous crystals disseminated through a fine-grained to dense ground mass are called porphyries (e.g., granite-porphyry, rhyolite-porphyry). Sedimentary rocks include conglomerates (consolidated gravel), sandstones and many quartzites, shales (consolidated clays), limestones, and dolomites. The more common metamorphic rocks are gneisses, schists, slates, some quartzites, and marbles.

Igneous Rocks. The most abundant of the granular crystalline rocks is *granite*, which consists mainly of feldspars and quartz with minor quantities of mica or hornblende, and minute quantities of certain other minerals. Commercially, however, other granular igneous rocks, like *diorite* and *gabbro*, which consist mainly of soda-lime feldspar and hornblende or pyroxene, are referred to as " black granite." These rocks are commonly massive, although closely spaced fractures or joints parallel to the surfaces of some quarries resemble a bedded or stratified structure. *Gneisses* (granular metamorphic rocks similar to granites in mineral composition but distinguished by a foliated arrangement of mineral grains) are also called granite commercially. Granites as a whole are composed mainly of hard minerals that are extremely resistant to chemical weathering and are so firmly welded together by crystallization under great pressure that they make by far the strongest stone in common use. Granites that contain unusually large percentages of mica are comparatively soft, but are resistant to weathering if free from alteration. Gray and light-red granites are generally more durable, as they consist of minerals which are more resistant to weathering. True granite generally has the advantage of breaking with regularity and is readily formed into simple shapes, but is so much harder and tougher than most sedimentary rocks that the elaborate finishing of blocks is comparatively expensive; however, in structures of monumental character and those subjected to severe conditions of physical and chemical weathering it may be ultimate economy to use granite.

Sedimentary Rocks. *Limestone* is widely distributed and is more widely used for building and crushing that any other kind of stone. It includes many varieties, which differ in color, composition, and adaptability for engineering and building purposes. Many limestones are dull gray or bluish gray and unattractive from an architectural standpoint.

* Largely from G. F. Loughlin.

Some of these are massive and suitable for crushing, and sufficiently free from impurities to be used in metallurgical and chemical industries; but others contain so many shaly streaks and are so impure that they are of no value unless situated where they can be used with other material in the manufacture of portland cement. The famous Indiana oölitic limestone, which contributes more than half of the building stone quarried annually in the United States, is a light buff to gray, porous, granular stone, similar to sandstone in mode of origin, although its " sand " grains are practically all minute shells or shell fragments. It is very easily quarried and worked, and is adapted for architectural and engineering uses where chemical weathering is not too severe.

Most limestones and marbles consist mainly of the mineral calcite which is slightly soluble in rainwater and in other waters or vapors containing acids and certain salts, especially ferric sulfate. Dolomite stone, or high magnesium limestone, which consists mainly of the mineral dolomite, is similarly affected but much more slowly. The effect of this corrosion is to roughen the surfaces of unevenly grained stones and gradually to remove small details of finish; but the rate of corrosion on the most exposed parts of buildings in the larger eastern cities of the United States is only about 1 in. in 600 to 800 years. It is much faster where attack by acid waters is more concentrated and continuous. The texture of limestones and dolomites varies from very porous to impervious, and their strength and resistance to weathering vary accordingly; but resistance to freezing depends not so much upon the degree of porosity as upon the size and distribution of the pores and the presence of impurities, especially certain varieties of clay minerals, that readily absorb and give off water with changing climatic conditions.

Sandstones vary greatly in color, texture, and usefulness. Their more common colors include light gray, buff, pink, red, and brown. Siliceous sandstones consist almost entirely of quartz grains cemented by silica, and the impervious variety of this composition, called quartzite, is extremely hard and difficult to work; but it is used especially in the manufacture of silica brick and occasionally as crushed stone and building stone. Calcareous sandstones contain calcite (calcium carbonate) as the principal cementing material; like limestones they are noticeably affected by severe or prolonged chemical weathering. Argillaceous sandstone contains clayey material as its chief cementing constituent; it is subject to relatively rapid disintegration, especially if certain of the clay minerals are concentrated along layers. Ferruginous sandstone contains considerable red, brown, or yellow iron oxide in its matrix. Its durability depends mainly upon whether the stone is otherwise siliceous, calcareous, or argillaceous.

Metamorphic Rocks are igneous and sedimentary rocks which have been acted upon by heat, water, or pressure, or combinations of these agents, to the extent that the original rock structures have been altered. Gneiss, marble, slate, and schist are the more common varieties; they are generally characterized by a foliated or laminated appearance, and some have pronounced cleavage planes. Marble occurs in all colors from pure white to black and is used chiefly for buildings, especially as interior finish; slate is employed for roofing purposes, the common colors being " slate," red, green, and purple. Mica and hornblende schists sometimes occur in such thin layers that they are of little value except for low-grade rubble or riprap, but the thicker layers of the more compact varieties are used for masonry and for concrete aggregate.

Strength of Stone. The strength varies according to the kind of stone, type of stress, and the locality where the stone is found. Table I gives average values for the principal varieties employed in engineering and architectural construction.

Table I. Average Strength of Stone
(U. S. Bureau of Standards, *Tech. Paper*, 349)

Kind	Range of Strength Properties, lb per sq in.				Modulus of Elasticity, millions of pounds per square inch
	Compression	Tension	Modulus of Rupture	Shear	
Granite.................	10,000–40,000	600–1000	1300–2400	2000–4300	5.7– 9.6
Syenite.................	14,000–28,000	....	....	....	....
Diorite.................	16,000–35,000	....	....	....	....
Quartzite.............	16,000–45,000	....	....	....	....
Limestone.............	2,500–28,400	280– 890	600–2200	1200–3000	3.0–10.4
Marble.................	8,000–27,000	400–2300	600–3500	1300–6500	7.2–14.5
Basalt.................	28,000–67,000	....	....	....	....
Serpentine.............	11,000–28,000	800–1600	....	2600–5000	4.8– 9.6
Sandstone.............	5,000–20,000	280– 500	500–1000	300–3000	1.9– 7.7
Slate..................	7,000–31,000	3000–4300	4000–9000	2000–3600	9.0–15.0

Durability of stone is a relative term and depends upon the climate, character of atmosphere, and amount of exposure of the stone in the structure. On the basis of a degree of disintegration so great that repairs are necessary because the building becomes unsightly, the U. S. Bureau of Standards (*Tech. Paper*, 123, 1919) gives the following estimates for the life of stone:

Coarse brownstone	5 to 15 years
Laminated fine brownstone	20 to 50 years
Compact fine brownstone	100 to 200 years
Bluestone	Untried, probably centuries
Nova Scotia stone	Untried, probably 50 to 200 years
Ohio sandstone, best siliceous variety	Perhaps 1 to many centuries
Limestone, coarse fossiliferous	20 to 40 years
Limestone, fine oölitic (French)	30 to 40 years
Marble, coarse dolomitic	40 years
Marble, fine	50 to 200 years
Granite	75 to 200 years
Gneiss	50 years to many centuries

7. BRICK

Brick. Until about 1900 the word brick always meant a prism of burned clay; but at about that date bricks composed of sand and lime were put upon the market, and at present many such brick are used annually, although their number is very small in comparison with that of ordinary clay brick. Ordinarily the word brick means a burned-clay brick, and a brick composed of sand and lime is called a sand-lime brick.

Clay Brick is made by submitting clay which has been prepared properly and molded into shape to a temperature which converts it into a semi-vitrified mass. Building brick are usually made from surface clay, and paving brick from shale (a fine-grained and indurated clay), since shale gives a tougher, denser, and stronger brick.

Classification of Clay Brick according to Method of Molding. *Soft-mud brick:* one molded from clay which has been reduced to a soft mud by adding water. It may be either hand- or machine-molded. *Stiff-mud brick:* one molded from clay in the condition of stiff mud. It is always machine-molded. *Pressed brick:* one molded from dry or semi-dry clay. *Re-pressed brick:* usually a stiff-mud brick which has been subjected to an enormous pressure to render the form more regular and to increase its strength and density. It is doubtful whether the re-pressing increases either the strength or the density. Occasionally in the East, and more formerly than at present, a soft-mud brick, after being partially dried, is re-pressed, which process greatly improves the form and also the strength and the density. A re-pressed brick is sometimes, but inappropriately, called a pressed brick. *Slop brick:* in molding brick by hand, the molds are sometimes dipped into water just before being filled with clay, to prevent the mud from sticking to them. Brick molded by this process is known as slop brick. It is deficient in color, and has a comparatively smooth surface, with rounded edges and corners. This kind of brick is now seldom made. *Sanded brick:* ordinarily, in making soft-mud brick, sand is sprinkled into the molds to prevent the clay from sticking; the brick is then called sanded brick. The sand on the surface is of no serious advantage or disadvantage. In hand-molding, when sand is used for this purpose, it is certain to become mixed with the clay and occurs in streaks in the finished brick, which is very undesirable; and owing to details of the process, which it is here unnecessary to explain, every third brick is especially bad. *Machine-made brick:* brick is frequently described as "machine-made," but this is very indefinite, since all grades and kinds are made by machinery.

Classification of Clay Brick According to Firing. When bricks were usually burned in the old-style up-draft kiln, the classification according to position was important; but with the new styles of kilns and improved methods of burning, the quality is so nearly uniform throughout the kiln that the classification is less important. Three grades of brick are taken from the old-style kiln: arch brick, body brick, and salmon brick. *Arch* or *clinker bricks:* those which form the tops and sides of the arches in which the fire is built. Being overburned and partially vitrified, they are hard, brittle, and weak. *Body, cherry,* or *hard bricks:* those taken from the interior of the pile. The best bricks in the kiln. *Salmon, pale,* or *soft bricks:* those which form the exterior of the mass. Being underburned, they are too soft for ordinary work, unless it is for filling. The terms "salmon" and "pale" refer to the color of the brick, and hence are not applicable to a brick made of a clay that does not burn red. Although nearly all brick clays burn red, yet the localities where the contrary is true are sufficiently numerous to make it desirable to use a different term in designating the quality.

Classification of Clay Brick According to Form. The form of the brick gives rise to the following terms. *Compass brick:* one having one edge shorter than the other. *Feather-edge brick:* one having one edge thinner than the other. Used in arches; and more properly, but less frequently, called voussoir brick. *Face brick:* those which, owing to uniformity of size and color, are suitable for the face of the wall of buildings. Sometimes face bricks are simply the best ordinary brick; but generally the term is applied only to re-pressed or pressed brick made specially for this purpose. *Sewer brick:* ordinary hard brick, smooth, and regular in form. *Paving brick:* very hard, ordinary brick. A vitrified clay block, very much larger than ordinary brick, is sometimes used for paving, and is called a paving brick, but more often a brick paving-block. *Vitrified brick:* the introduction of brick for street pavements about 1890 led to a new grade, one burned to the point of vitrifaction and then annealed or toughened by slowly cooling. Vitrified brick and paving blocks, though originally made for paving purposes, are now much used in building and engineering structures. Standard sizes of clay brick are given in Table III.

Classification of Clay Brick According to Strength. Table II gives the A.S.T.M. classification of clay brick according to strength. The compressive test is made on a half-brick tested flatwise and properly bedded in plaster of paris to provide an even bearing. The bending test is made with the brick flatwise, span 7 in., and the load applied at mid-span. Table IV gives the result of strength tests made on bricks from different parts of the United States. Tests of brick piers are reported in Table V.

Table II. Grades of Clay or Sand-lime Building Brick

(According to A.S.T.M. Standard Specifications C62–30, C73–30)

Name of Grade	Compressive Strength (bricks flatwise), lb per sq in., mean gross area		Modulus of Rupture (bricks flatwise), lb per sq in., gross area	
	Mean of 5 tests	Individual minimum	Mean of 5 tests	Individual minimum
Grade A.....................	4500 or over	3500	600 or over	400
Grade B.....................	2500–4500	2000	450 or over	300
Grade C.....................	1250–2500	1000	300 or over	200

The above classifications are based on strength and do not necessarily measure weather resistance.

Table III. Standard Sizes for Clay and Sand-lime Building Brick

(According to A.S.T.M. Standard Specifications C62–30, C73–30)

Types	Standard Sizes, in.			Permissible Variations, in.		
	Depth	Width	Length	Depth	Width	Length
Common clay brick.................	2 1/4	3 3/4	8	±1/16	±1/8	±1/4
Rough-face clay brick...............	2 1/4	3 3/4	8	±1/16	±1/8	±1/4
Smooth-face clay brick..............	2 1/4	3 7/8	8	±1/16	±1/8	±1/4
Sand-lime brick....................	2 1/4	3 3/4	8	±1/16	±1/8	±1/4

Sand-lime Brick consist of a mass of sand cemented together with lime. There are two classes of sand-lime brick: one in which the binding material is carbonate of lime, and the other in which it is silicate of lime.

The first is virtually a brick made of ordinary lime mortar, molded as are soft-mud clay brick, and hardened in the open air or in an atmosphere rich in carbon dioxide (CO_2), either with or without pressure. This form may properly be called a lime-mortar brick. It is the older form of sand-lime brick, and was formerly made in a small way where sand and lime were cheap and clay and fuel were expensive; but the brick is so weak and friable that it has not given satisfaction, and needs no further consideration here.

The second kind is made from a mixture of sand and lime which is molded in a press and hardened by being subjected to steam under pressure. The binding material consists chiefly of hydrosilicate of lime. Probably part of the lime is converted into carbonate by absorbing carbon dioxide; but the most of the lime combines with the silica of the sand and forms hydrosilicate of lime, a stable and comparatively strong cementing material. This form is the only one to which the term sand-lime brick is now applied; but in con-sulting the past literature on the subject, a careful distinction should be made between the two forms of so-called sand-lime brick. This form of sand-lime brick was first manufactured in Germany about 1880, and was introduced into America about 1900.   There are localities where this form of brick is an important factor in building operations.

Sand-lime brick are made which in appearance and quality are the equal of dry-clay (pressed) brick.   The average sand-lime brick will be equivalent in strength to medium clay-brick.   When sand-lime bricks are manufactured under standard specifications they may be used as a substitute for clay-brick in masonry construction.   Table II gives the A.S.T.M. classification of sand-lime brick according to strength.   Table III gives the standard sizes of sand-lime brick.

Table IV.   Strength of Clay or Shale Building Bricks

(From "Report of Committee C-3 *Proc. A.S.T.M.*, Pt. I, 1915)

Each lot consisted of 5 samples, and the maximum and minimum values refer to lots and not to individual tests.

Place of Manufacture	No. of Lots Tested	Compressive Strength, lb per sq in.			Modulus of Rupture, lb per sq in.			Average Absorption, per cent
		Max.	Min.	Av.	Max.	Min.	Av.	
Birmingham, Ala..........	5	14,964	4482	9428	1926	733	1499	4.74
Fresno, Cal..............	4	8,636	2442	4496	1031	434	594	12.00
San Francisco, Cal........	4	3,294	1951	2730	908	501	763	16.14
Chicago, Ill..............	8	3,470	1687	2620	1618	462	832	20.88
Crawfordsville, Ind........	4	14,766	2502	7750	1383	337	842	16.65
Mason City, Iowa.........	4	5,984	4564	5476	1440	1028	1273	14.43
Brewer, Me..............	8	9,295	3304	6889	1456	570	1028	10.80
W. Barnstable, Mass.......	4	5,302	1564	3541	851	281	561	14.61
Detroit, Mich.............	4	2,398	1846	2167	....	....	....	.....
Ganic, N. H.............	8	6,024	3092	4563	1522	627	1035	10.93
Scranton, Pa.............	4	9,728	4758	7314	2705	1609	2077	6.35
Spokane, Wash...........	4	7,480	4156	6336	1105	564	827	13.57

Table V.   Tests of Brick Piers

(U. S. Bureau of Standards, *Tech. Paper*, 111, 1918)

Construction Data				Test Data		Brick Test Data		
All Piers 10 ft High				Max. Load, lb per sq in.	Modulus of Elasticity	Average Compressive Strength, Flat	Average Compressive Strength on Edge	Average Transverse Strength, Modulus of Rupture
Serial No.	Grade of Brick	Courses	Area, sq in.					
Cement mortar { 1	1	46	930	2710	2,500,000	11,990	8,900	1945
4	2	45	856	2000	2,500,000	7,880	6,450	1375
7	3	41	1024	510	700,000	1,659	1,350	345
Cement and lime mortar { 10	1	45	841	3800	3,500,000	11,965	10,050	2775
13	2	45	908	1760	1,550,000	7,880	6,450	1370
Lime mortar { 16	1	45	940	1450	725,000	11,990	8,900	1945
19	2	44	906	840	620,000	7,880	6,450	1370
22	3	41	1024	210	300,000	1,659	1,350	345

8. TERRA-COTTA

Terra-cotta is a burnt-clay product made in the same general way as brick.   Hard terra-cotta blocks and tile are made by burning clay at a very high temperature.   Porous or soft terra-cotta, sometimes called terra-cotta lumber, is made by burning a mixture of clay and straw or sawdust.   The straw or sawdust burns out, leaving a light, porous material.   Nails and screws can be driven into porous terra-cotta, and it can be cut with a wood saw.   Terra-cotta lumber is weaker than hard terra-cotta.   Terra-cotta building blocks are made hollow with walls 3/4 in. to 1 in. thick.

Strength.   The A.S.T.M. specifications for structural clay hollow tile list three types: floor, non-load-bearing, and load-bearing wall tile.   Each of these types is divided into

Table VI. Size and Weight of Hollow Clay Wall Tile
(From A.S.T.M. Tentative Specifications C34–34T, C56–34T)

Dimensions or Horizontal Thickness. Tile as Laid in Wall, in.	Minimum Number of Cells		Average Weight per sq ft of Tile, lb	
	In unit	In wall thickness	Minimum	Maximum
Non-load-bearing Partition Tile				
2 × 12 × 12	3	1	14	16
3 × 12 × 12	3	1	15	17
4 × 12 × 12	3	1	16	18
6 × 12 × 12	3	1	22	25
6 × 12 × 12	4	2	25	28
8 × 12 × 12	4	2	30	34
10 × 12 × 12	4	2	35	40
12 × 12 × 12	4	2	40	45
Split Furring Tile				
1 1/2 × 12 × 12	3	...	7 1/2	8 1/2
2 × 12 × 12	3	...	8	9
Load-bearing Wall Tile				
4	...	1	20	23
6	...	2	30	35
8	...	2	36	41
10	...	2	42	48
12	...	3	52	60

Table VII. Size and Weights of Hollow Clay Floor Tile
(From A.S.T.M. Tentative Standards C57–34T)

Depth of Arch or Thickness of Unit, in.	Minimum Number of Cells in Arch or Tile Thickness			Average Dry Weight, lb per sq ft		
	Flat arch	Segmental arch	Tile-concrete construction	Flat arch	Segmental arch	Tile-concrete construction
3	...	...	1	...	...	15
4	...	...	1	...	...	16
5	...	...	1	...	...	19
5	...	...	2	...	...	23
6	1	...	1	26	...	22
6	...	2	2	...	30	25
7	1	...	1	30	...	24
7	...	...	2	...	...	27
8	...	...	1	...	...	27
8	2	2	2	32	36	29
9	2	...	2	33	...	31
9	...	...	3	...	...	36
10	2	...	2	35	...	33
10	...	...	3	...	...	38
11	2	...	...	38	...	...
12	2	...	2	40	...	40
12	...	...	3	...	...	45
13	...	...	...	43	...	...
14	3	...	...	46	...	...
15	3	...	...	47	...	...
16	3	...	...	52	...	...

two grades on the basis of absorption and compressive strength. Table VIII gives the classification. The specified absorption for non-load-bearing tile is the same as given in the table for the other two types but there are no strength requirements.

Tests of terra-cotta columns built of hollow blocks laid with portland cement mortar were made in 1908 by Talbot and Abrams and reported in *Bull*. 27, Eng. Exp. Sta., Univ.

Table VIII. **Absorption and Strength Requirements for Floor and Wall Tile**

(From A.S.T.M. Tentative Specifications C57–34T, C34–34T)

Class	Absorption			Compressive Strength, lb per sq in.* †			
	Average of 5 tests	Individual		End-construction Tile		Side-construction Tile	
		Max.	Min.	Average of 5 tests	Individual minimum	Average of 5 tests	Individual minimum
Floor Tile *							
5–16	5 to 16	19	4	3200 or more	2250	1600 or more	1100
16–25	25 or less	28	4	2000 or more	1400	1200 or more	850
Load-bearing Wall Tile †							
5–16	5 to 16	19	4	1400 or more	1000	700 or more	500
16–25	25 or less	28	4	1000 or more	700	700 or more	500

* For floor tile the strength is based on the net area, which is taken as the area of solid material in shells and webs carrying stresses in a direction parallel to the direction of loading.

† For load-bearing wall tile the strength is based on the gross area, which includes total area of section including area of cells perpendicular to direction of loading.

of Ill. The compressive strength of blocks loaded on end ranged from 3472 to 5170 lb per sq in. Transverse tests of the blocks gave a modulus of rupture of 562 to 1440 lb per sq in. The strength of the columns varied from 64 per cent of the compressive strength of the blocks for those poorly laid to 86 per cent for those well laid.

REFRACTORIES

By J. Spotts McDowell and E. B. Guenther

9. COMMON TYPES OF REFRACTORY BRICK

Refractories, generically classed as fire brick, are structural materials used at high temperatures in industrial furnaces. The life of refractories is affected by the high temperatures to which they are subjected, and usually by one or more of the following influences: abrasion; corrosion through chemical action by slags and fluxes; erosion by mechanical action of molten metal or slag, or by dust-laden gases moving at high velocity; spalling of various types; the effect of various gases. The principal types of refractories are fireclay, high-alumina, silica, magnesite, and chrome. Refractories of other types have less extensive application. The term " firebrick " when used alone is generally understood to mean fireclay brick. It should be here noted that the data given in the following discussion refer to current practice in the United States which differs in various respects from that abroad.

Fireclay Brick. The most widely used refractory brick are those made from flint fire clays and plastic fire clays, the essential components of which are hydrous alumina silicates of the general type formula $Al_2O_3 \cdot 2SiO_2 \cdot 2H_2O$. Kaolinite is probably the most common member of this group. Until recent years this mineral was regarded as the essential constituent or " clay base " of all clays. However, it is now believed that it may not be the predominating mineral in all refractory fire clays.

The manufacture of fireclay brick consists in blending the raw materials, flint clay, plastic clay, and calcined clay or grog, either by grinding them together in a wet pan, or by grinding together or separately in a dry pan, then mixing and tempering them with the addition of water. The brick are molded by hand or mechanically; dried, either on hot floors or in dryers; and fired in periodic downdraft kilns or in continuous tunnel kilns. Various grades of fireclay brick are available and are referred to as super-duty, high heat duty, intermediate heat duty, moderate heat duty, and low heat duty fireclay brick. See Table IX for Pyrometric Cone Equivalents.

High-alumina Brick. In many parts of furnaces where the requirements are severe, high-alumina brick may be used to decided advantage.

High-alumina raw materials include bauxite, diaspore, diasporitic clays, cyanite, andalusite, sillimanite, and crystalline alumina or corundum. In manufacturing high-alumina brick (i.e., brick containing 50 per cent or more of alumina), these materials are used singly, in combination, or blended with flint and plastic clays according to the properties and percentage of alumina desired in the finished product. High-alumina brick which are manufactured by methods similar to those used in manufacturing fire-clay brick are available in the 50, 60, 70, and 80 per cent alumina classes. Other high-alumina brick may be considered as special refractories.

Silica Brick. The raw material of the silica refractories industry is quartzite or ganister. Silica brick is manufactured by the same general processes used for fireclay brick. However, grinding is usually done in a wet pan with approximately 2 per cent of lime added in the form of milk of lime or an equivalent amount of hydrated lime. The lime bonds and gives strength to the green or unfired brick. It also reacts chemically with the quartzite during firing, imparting strength and toughness to the finished product.

The true specific gravity of silica brick depends both upon the character of the quartzite used in its manufacture and upon the temperature and duration of firing, and should lie between 2.28 and 2.40.

In the firing process a permanent expansion occurs from the green brick size to the fired size. It is desirable that this permanent expansion be completed in the firing, but as the final increments of permanent expansion take place slowly under high temperature, silica brick will show a slight permanent expansion in service.

When subjected to heat, silica brick, like other refractories, exhibit a temporary or purely thermal expansion, which disappears upon cooling. The linear thermal expansion of well-burned brick amounts to 1.2 to 1.6 per cent, the greater part of which occurs below 600° C.

In laying silica brick, it is important to provide for expansion at the rate of $1/8$ to $3/16$ in. per ft. Expansion joints should be kept free from mortar by packing to a depth of about $1 1/2$ in., with a filler which will burn out, such as sawdust, cardboard, or strips of wood. Silica brick are sensitive to rapid temperature change, and should be heated and cooled slowly and evenly; otherwise cracking or spalling will occur.

Magnesite Brick. The chief use of magnesite is in the manufacture of refractory materials. Its chemical properties and high refractoriness make it very suitable for furnace linings for metallurgical operations. For refractory purposes, it is sold in the form of brick, of finely ground furnace magnesite for brick-laying, and of dead-burned grains for making and repairing furnace bottoms. The grains are a mixture of granules varying from $5/8$ in. diameter to very fine but gritty particles.

For brick-making, the crude magnesite (essentially $MgO \cdot CO_2$) must be dead-burned, i.e., calcined at a temperature that will not merely drive off nearly all carbon dioxide, but will also cause sintering of the particles. During this process, the pieces shrink considerably and become hard, dense, and inert to atmospheric moisture and carbon dioxide. The material is ground dry to the desired size, then mixed and tempered in a wet pan with a small amount of water. The brick are usually molded under heavy pressure and dried in tunnel dryers. Usually magnesite brick are fired at cone 18 to 20. Cooling must be slow to avoid cracking. Magnesite brick bonded chemically instead of by firing, are also available.

Metal encased magnesite brick consist of round or square soft steel containers filled with ground dead-burned magnesite, or with chemically bonded magnesite brick. They are used for the back walls, bulkheads, and ends of basic open-hearth furnaces and side walls of electric furnaces. Their special advantage lies in the fact that the metal containers fuse for 1 or 2 in. back from the surface exposed to the heat, impregnate the magnesite, and bind the entire face of the wall. Joints, which are usually a source of weakness, are thus eliminated and the life of the wall is extended.

Chrome Brick. Chromite, $FeO \cdot Cr_2O_3$, is the most nearly chemically neutral of all the common refractories. However, it is acted upon either by strong acids or by strong bases. Because of its chemical character and high refractoriness it is an important refractory in metallurgical furnaces. The important sources of chrome ore for refractories are Greece, Cuba, Southern Rhodesia, and the Transvaal.

In American practice, it is not customary to use bonding material in the manufacture of fired chrome brick. It is therefore essential that the ore used should bond strongly together at kiln temperatures, but without deforming or squeezing out of shape. The ground ore is mixed and tempered with a small amount of water in a wet pan to the consistency of damp sand. The brick are usually molded in a power press at high pressure and dried in tunnel dryers. They are fired in either rectangular downdraft periodic kilns or continuous tunnel kilns, at a firing temperature of cone 18 to 20. Kilns must be cooled slowly to avoid cracking of the brick. Chrome brick, bonded chemically instead of by firing, are also available.

10   PROPERTIES OF REFRACTORIES

(Arranged alphabetically)

Abrasion, Resistance to. Tests for resistance to abrasion have been rather unsatisfactory. No method so far devised has been generally regarded as sufficiently reliable to warrant adoption as standard.

Analyses, Chemical. There is considerable variation in analyses of the various types of refractories. The figures given in Table I represent approximate mean values.

Table I.   Approximate Chemical Analyses of Refractories

Type of Brick	SiO_2	Al_2O_3 $+ TiO_2$*	Fe_2O_3	FeO	CaO	MgO	Cr_2O_3 $+ Al_2O_3$	Alkalies
Fireclay								
Super-duty..............	51.0	45.0	2.2	....	0.3	0.4	......	1.0
High heat duty (Aluminous)..	55.0	41.0	2.2	....	0.3	0.4	......	1.2
Intermediate heat duty......	61.0	34.0	3.0	....	0.3	0.4	......	1.5
High heat duty (Siliceous)....	75.0	23.0	1.4	....	0.2	0.2	......	0.2
High-alumina								
50% Alumina Class..........	43.0	53.0	1.8	....	0.2	0.5	......	1.4
70% Alumina Class..........	23.0	74.0	1.7	....	0.1	0.3	......	0.9
Silica.......................	95.5	1.2	1.0	....	2.1	0.2	......	0.2
Magnesite (fired)..............	3	1		7	3	85	......	
Chrome (fired)...........	5		....	16	....	15.5	63 †	......

* The TiO_2 content will average about 5 per cent of the combined $Al_2O_3 + TiO_2$. Thus for a brick with 53 per cent $Al_2O_3 + TiO_2$, the TiO_2 content is about 2.7 per cent and the Al_2O_3 is about 50.3 per cent.
† In brick made from different raw materials, the Al_2O_3 content will vary from 12 to 30 per cent and the Cr_2O_3 will vary from 33 to 44 per cent.

Cold Crushing Strengths of various types of refractories are given in Table II.

Table II.   Cold Crushing Strength of Refractories

Cold Crushing Strength in Pounds per Square Inch; Average Values—Bricks Tested on Flat

Fireclay Brick				High-alumina Brick 70% Al_2O_3	Silica Brick	Magnesite Brick	Chrome Brick
Super-duty	High Heat Duty (Aluminous)	Moderate Heat Duty	High Heat Duty (Siliceous)				
4000	1000–4000	Up to 5000	1500	4000	2000–4000	4500	4000

Conductivity, Thermal. Table III gives the approximate thermal conductivities of various refractories over a wide range of temperatures.

Table III.   Approximate Thermal Conductivity of Refractories

Modern Refractory Practice, Published by Harbison-Walker Refractories Company, Pittsburgh, Pa.

Btu per hr per sq ft per deg fahr for a thickness of 1 in.

Temp. deg fahr	Kind of Brick				Temp. deg fahr	Kind of Brick			
	Fire-clay	Silica	Mag-nesite	Chrome		Fire-clay	Silica	Mag-nesite	Chrome
0	5.0	6.0	39.5	9.0	1400	9.0	11.3	26.9	12.5
200	5.6	6.8	37.2	9.5	1600	9.6	12.0	25.9	13.0
400	6.1	7.5	35.4	10.0	1800	10.1	12.8	25.0	13.5
600	6.7	8.3	33.3	10.5	2000	10.7	13.5	24.0	14.0
800	7.3	9.0	31.5	11.0	2200	11.3	14.3	23.5	14.5
1000	7.8	9.8	30.0	11.5	2400	11.8	15.0	23.2	15.0
1200	8.4	10.5	28.3	12.0	2600	12.4	15.8	23.0	15.5

Expansion, Thermal. The linear expansion of refractory brick in per cent, for various types of refractories, is given in Table IV. The figures given represent average values for total expansion of brick from room temperature to the temperatures indicated.

Table IV.   Thermal Expansion of Various Types of Refractory Brick
(Expressed in linear per cent)

Temp. deg fahr	Type of Brick				Temp. deg fahr	Type of Brick			
	Fireclay 40% Al_2O_3	Silica	Mag- nesite	Chrome		Fireclay 40% Al_2O_3	Silica	Mag- nesite	Chrome
400	0.10	0.54	0.28	0.23	1600	0.47	1.34	1.18	0.96
800	0.23	1.12	0.56	0.47	2000	0.57	1.38	1.59	1.33
1200	0.34	1.28	0.86	0.70	2400	0.50	1.38	1.97	1.71

Load, Resistance to, at High Temperature.   The behavior of refractory brick of various types under load at high temperature is indicated in Table V.

Table V.   Behavior of Refractory Brick Under Load at High Temperature

Type of Brick	Linear subsidence, per cent *	Temperature of failure, deg fahr †
Fireclay—Super-duty	4–5	....
Fireclay—High heat duty (Aluminous)	3–10	....
Fireclay—High heat duty (Siliceous)	2–4	....
High-alumina—70% Alumina	1–3	....
Silica	....	2800–2900
Magnesite	....	2400–2800
Chrome	....	2400–2550

* Standard Load Test, A.S.T.M. Designation C16–20.   Under a load of 25 lb per sq in. on end, the specimen is heated according to a prescribed heating schedule to 1350 deg cent (2462 deg fahr) and held at that temperature for 90 min.
† Standard Load Test, A.S.T.M. Designation C16–20.   Under a load of 25 lb per sq in. on end, the specimen is heated according to a prescribed heating schedule until failure occurs.

Modulus of Rupture.   Average values of modulus of rupture of various types of refractory brick are given in Table VI.

Table VI.   Modulus of Rupture at Atmospheric Temperature
(A.S.T.M. Method C67–31, 7-in. span on flat)

Type of Brick	Modulus of Rupture, lb per sq in.	Type of Brick	Modulus of Rupture, lb per sq in.
Fireclay		High-alumina	
Super-duty	400	50% Alumina	750
High heat duty (Aluminous)	600–1200	70% Alumina	1200
Intermediate heat duty	800–1400	Silica	500–1000
High heat duty (Siliceous)	400	Magnesite	1500
		Chrome	1600–2000

Porosity.   The porosity of refractories depends upon various factors, among them the character and quality of the raw material, the grind, the water content at the time of molding, the pressure of molding, and the time and temperature of firing.   The porosity in turn affects the resistance of the brick to temperature change, the rigidity under load at high temperatures, the thermal conductivity, and the resistance of the brick to abrasion and slag action.   See A.S.T.M. Standard C20–33 for method of determining porosity of refractory materials.   Porosity of various types of refractory brick is given in Table VII.

Table VII.   Porosities by Volume, Average Values

Type of Brick	Process of Manufacture	Porosity, per cent	Type of Brick	Process of Manufacture	Porosity, per cent
Fireclay			High-alumina		
Super-duty	Machine	12–16	50% Alumina	Machine	20–25
High heat duty (Aluminous)	Hand	20–30	70% Alumina	Machine	28–31
High heat duty (Aluminous)	Machine	15–24	Silica	Hand or machine	24–32
Intermediate heat duty	Machine	17–21	Magnesite	Machine	20–30
High heat duty (Siliceous)	Hand or machine	30	Chrome	Machine	20–30

Pyrometric Cone Equivalent (P.C.E.) is defined, in reference to refractories, as the number of that standard cone whose tip would touch the supporting plaque simultaneously with a cone of the material being investigated, when tested in accordance with the standard method of test for softening point of fire brick. See A.S.T.M. Standard C24–33. The determination of the P.C.E. consists in testing cones made of the ceramic material by comparing them with standard pyrometric cones, all heated together in the same furnace. The softening points of standard pyrometric cones used in connection with refractories are given in Table VIII. Table IX presents the pyrometric cone equivalents of various types of refractory brick.

Table VIII. Softening Point * of Standard Pyrometric Cones Used in Connection with Refractories †

A.S.T.M. Proc., Vol. 34, Part I, 1934, p. 1264

Cone No.	Softening Point		Cone No.	Softening Point		Cone No.	Softening Point		Cone No.	Softening Point	
	Deg cent	Deg fahr		Deg cent	Deg fahr		Deg cent	Deg fahr		Deg cent	Deg fahr
15	1435	2615	20	1530	2786	29	1640	2984	34	1760	3200
16	1465	2669	23	1580	2876	30	1650	3002	35	1785	3245
17	1475	2687	26	1595	2903	31	1680	3056	36	1810	3290
18	1490	2714	27	1605	2921	32	1700	3092	37	1820	3308
19	1520	2768	28	1615	2939	33	1745	3173	38	1835	3335

* These temperatures, which were determined by Fairchild and Peters for a heating rate of 150 deg cent per hr for cones 15 to 20, and of 100 deg cent per hr for cones 23 to 38, other conditions being the same as specified, apply satisfactorily for all the conditions of this test method, but do not apply to conditions of the commercial firing and use of refractory materials.

† Fairchild and Peters, Characteristics of pyrometric cones, *Journal, Am. Ceramic Soc.*, Vol. 9, No. 11, p. 701, Nov., 1926.

Table IX. Pyrometric Cone Equivalents (P.C.E.) for Various Types of Refractory Brick

Type	P.C.E.	Temperature	
		Deg fahr	Deg cent
Fireclay			
Super-duty..................................	33–34	3173–3200	1745–1760
High heat duty (Aluminous)..................	31–33	3056–3173	1680–1745
Intermediate heat duty......................	28–31	2939–3056	1615–1680
Moderate heat duty.........................	26–28	2903–2939	1595–1615
High heat duty (Siliceous)..................	28–31	2939–3056	1615–1680
High-alumina			
50% Alumina...............................	34–35 (av.)	3200–3245	1760–1785
60% Alumina...............................	36 (av.)	3290	1810
70% Alumina...............................	37 (av.)	3308	1820
80% Alumina...............................	38 (av.)	3335	1835
Silica....................................	31–32	3092	1700
Magnesite.................................	Above 38	3335+	1835+
Chrome....................................	Above 38	3335+	1835+

Refractoriness. The terms fusion point, softening point, and melting point are indefinite when applied to ceramic materials, which soften over a wide temperature range. No definite temperature marks the transition from the distinctly solid to the distinctly liquid state. Instead, the pyrometric cone equivalent (P.C.E.) is generally used.

Resistance to Slagging. This property is of primary importance in selection of refractory brick for service in furnaces where they are subjected to chemical corrosion by molten slags or fluxes. The resistance of a refractory brick to slag action depends upon its chemical composition, density and porosity, the prevailing temperature, and the chemical characteristics of the slag or flux. For resistance to siliceous slags or fluxes, fireclay brick, high-alumina brick or silica brick are serviceable. Where basic slags or fluxes are present, either fireclay, high-alumina, magnesite, or chrome brick are serviceable, the selection depending upon conditions stated above. Various simulative service tests have been devised, but since slagging depends on many factors, no test as yet developed (1936) has proved sufficiently reliable to warrant its adoption as standard.

Spalling, Resistance to. Spalling is defined as the breaking or cracking or crushing of refractory brick in service to such an extent that pieces are separated or fall away, leaving new surfaces of the brick exposed.

According to the A.S.T.M. Designation C71-31 the causes of spalling may be classified under three main headings as follows:

Thermal: (a) *Factors Related to Service.* Rapidity in range of thermal fluctuation; contamination by slags and fluxes; tightness of joints; previous vitrification.

(b) *Factors Related to Refractories.* Degree and uniformity of reversible thermal expansion; heat transfer; elasticity; plastic flow.

Mechanical: (a) *Factors Related to Service.* Rapid heating of wet brick; abuse in removing clinker and slags; unequal and excessive stresses; pinching; no provision for expansion; thin joints.

(b) *Factors Related to Refractories.* Mechanical strength; toughness; accuracy of shape.

Structural: (a) *Factors Related to Service.* Slags and fluxes; character of the material in joints; insulation of refractories.

(b) *Factors Related to Refractories.* Vitrification; shrinkage; nature of bond; structure; degree of burning.

Under the heading " Structural " the slags and fluxes referred to may cause a change in the texture or mineral constitution of the hot end of the brick or the high temperature prevailing may produce a like change; either or both of these may result in the formation of differing zones between inner and outer brick surfaces with consequent spalling.

Experience has shown that " Structural " spalling may also occur as the result of improper design of brick shapes, also because of faulty design or construction of the furnace.

Of the various types of refractory brick most widely used, super-duty fireclay brick have the greatest resistance to thermal spalling. Both super-duty fireclay brick and high-alumina brick may be considerably more resistant to textural spalling than other types of fireclay brick in the presence of certain types of slag, owing to their high refractoriness and chemical composition which enable them to resist change in texture due to high temperature or slag action. Silica brick are extremely sensitive to temperature change in the range of 400-1100 deg fahr. Magnesite and chrome brick are also very sensitive to temperature change, although changes in manufacturing methods are improving this characteristic. No single method for determining resistance to spalling can be applied to all types of refractory brick. A tentative method of panel test for resistance of refractory brick to thermal and structural spalling is covered by the A.S.T.M. Tentative Standard C38-34T. It has been found to be satisfactory for testing all classes of fireclay brick including super-duty.

Specific Gravity of various types of refractories is given in Table X.

Table X. Specific Gravity of Various Types of Refractories

Type of Brick	Specific Gravity			Type of Brick	Specific Gravity		
	High	Low	Average		High	Low	Average
Fireclay Super-duty........	2.80	2.70	2.75	High-alumina......	Somewhat higher than for super-duty fireclay		
High heat duty (Aluminous)........	2.75	2.65	2.70	Silica.............	2.40	2.28	2.35
High heat duty (Siliceous)..........	Somewhat lower than for aluminous fireclay			Magnesite.........	3.60	3.44	3.52
				Chrome..........	4.4	3.7	4.05

Specific Heat. The figures given in Table XI appear to be the most probable values of the specific heats of refractory materials. They are based upon the work of various observers, whose data do not check with exactness.

Table XI. Specific Heats of Refractory Materials

Temperature, deg cent	0	100	200	300	400	500	600	700	800	900	1000	1100	1200	1300
Fireclay brick..........	.193	.199	.205	.211	.218	.225	.231	.238	.244	.249	.254	.258	.261	.265
Silica brick.............	.169	.189	.210	.230	.236	.245	.248	.253	.258	.262	.266	.269	.272	.275
Magnesite brick.........	.208	.220	.232	.241	.248	.254	.260	.265	.269	.274	.278	.282	.287	.292
Chrome brick...........	.170	.177	.182	.188	.193	.198	.202	.206	.210	.213	.217	.220	.222	.224

Thermal Resistivity is the reciprocal of thermal conductivity.

11. MORTARS FOR LAYING REFRACTORY BRICK

Fireclay brick are generally laid with fireclay mortar. Silica fireclay usually serves for laying silica brick; finely ground dead-burned magnesite, known as furnace magnesite, for magnesite brick, and finely ground chrome ore, known as furnace chrome, for chrome brick. Depending upon service conditions these materials are replaced to advantage by other materials known as " refractory bonding mortars."

Fireclay Mortars. The fireclay mortars used in laying fireclay brick are generally composed of clays of the same quality and characteristics as those of the clays used in the manufacture of the brick with which the mortars are used. Ground fireclay, used for laying brick, should be sufficiently plastic to have good working properties when mixed with water. For high temperature service, its refractoriness should closely approximate that of the brick. It may be as much as but not more than 3 cones lower.

Refractory Bonding Mortars. Until recently the term high-temperature cement designated various refractory products now known as high-temperature bonding mortars, used in furnace masonry to bond refractory brick. Some of these will set and develop great strength merely upon air drying. Others bond only when heated; some of these require very high temperature to develop their bond fully. There is also considerable variation in the refractoriness of bonding mortars on the market. They include a wide range of base materials, with considerable variation in their properties. Care is necessary in selection in order that satisfactory results may be secured.

Certain advantages over fireclay are secured by the use of high-temperature bonding mortars, as follows: (1) increased resistance to erosion by mechanical action of molten metal, slag or dust-laden gases moving at high velocity; (2) greater resistance to chemical corrosion by slags and fluxes; (3) increased resistance to abrasion; (4) decreased permeability to gases, liquid metal, and slag; (5) more rigid construction; (6) greater resistance to spalling.

12. OTHER REFRACTORY MATERIALS

Acid-resisting Brick. Chemical process industries, and other industries where various acids are manufactured or are used in large quantities, require storage tanks, towers, and other types of equipment for which linings and packing material with acid-resisting properties are necessary. Lead, wood, asphalt, ordinary vitrified brick, chemical stoneware, and special acid-resisting refractory brick have wide application, especially acid-resisting refractory brick. Such brick are serviceable both in contact with acids and other liquid solvents, and also in conjunction with nascent gases and acid fumes at high temperatures. The best materials of this type are dense, vitreous, non-absorbent, of low porosity, and strongly resistant to the action of solvents. They are manufactured from materials of extremely low flux content. The brick are fired at temperatures sufficiently high to convert the constituents largely into crystalline minerals which are insoluble in acids and corrosive acid chemical solutions and highly resistant to concentrated alkali solutions.

Digester Brick. The largest source of raw materials for the manufacture of paper pulp is soft wood, although other materials are used. Wood is transformed into paper pulp by either mechanical or chemical methods. One of the latter, known as the sulfite process, comprises boiling wood chips in sulfite liquor, which consists mainly of calcium and magnesium bisulfates dissolved in sulfurous acid. This process is accomplished in steel tanks called digesters. Formerly, digesters were lead lined, but in most modern practice the lining consists of two courses of acid-resisting brick separated by a 1-inch space which is filled with a mixture of Portland cement and sand. Between the brick lining and the shell is a 2-inch space, also filled with the cement-sand mixture.

Various types of acid-resisting brick are used for lining the digesters. One type is exceedingly dense and impervious; another is of a slightly more open texture. The dense vitreous brick is often preferred for the back lining, with the more open-texture brick for the face. The face brick becomes readily impregnated with solids and after a short time in service is quite impervious. The open-texture type is more resistant to spalling conditions, but under certain conditions of practice, the dense impervious brick is frequently used to good advantage for both the face and back linings. For certain digester conditions, a third type of brick, of still more open texture, is made. This is exceptionally resistant to spalling but can be used to advantage only in operations where the pores readily become filled with organic constituents and the salts formed therefrom.

Forsterite Brick. Forsterite refractories are made from olivine rock to which magnesia is added in the process of manufacture. Their chief constituent is the mineral forsterite ($2MgO \cdot SiO_2$), the brick analyzing about 57 per cent MgO, 32 per cent SiO_2, 6 per cent FeO, 5 per cent other oxides. Forsterite refractories are considered to be semi-basic. They excel in stability of volume at high temperatures. Their thermal conductivity is less than that of magnesite brick and approximates that of silica brick. Steam or aqueous acids will attack them.

Forsterite brick find application in ports, bridge walls, division walls, uptakes and bulkheads of basic open-hearth steel furnaces, and in exposed sections of side walls in copper reverberatory and refining furnaces. Their ability to carry load at relatively high temperatures has made them suitable within a certain temperature range for the construction of suspended and sprung arch roofs on copper reverberatory and refining furnaces and on copper holding furnaces.

Forsterite is a new type of refractory which is undergoing development, and it is highly probable that its field of application will be extended.

Insulating Materials. Within recent years an increasing amount of attention has been paid to thermal insulation as a means of increasing the operating efficiency of industrial furnaces. The materials available for this purpose may be classified as (1) bulk insulation, (2) insulating brick, (3) insulating refractory brick.

1. Bulk insulation, in the form of diatomaceous earth powder or expanded vermiculite, is used as an insulating backing to refractory settings, especially for irregular surfaces where brick cannot be readily fitted.

2. Insulating brick have high insulating values but are not suitable for use where they may be exposed to flame or products of combustion. They are manufactured from diatomaceous earth or other materials having inherently low thermal conductivities and are used mainly as a backing for refractory brick settings to reduce heat losses.

3. Insulating refractory brick are usually made from selected fire clays, to which an open porous structure is imparted during manufacture by means of " chemical bloating," or by the addition of organic materials which burn out during the firing process. Insulating refractory brick can be used in contact with flame or combustion gases, but will not withstand slag action or mechanical abrasion.

Insulation of a refractory setting reduces the heat flow and raises the mean temperature of the wall. This may necessitate the use of a more refractory material for the setting and always increases the amount of heat stored in it. Where high heat capacity is undesirable a lining of insulating refractory brick may be used in place of a combination of refractory brick and an insulating backing. Insulating refractory brick ordinarily weigh only 30 to 40 per cent as much as refractory fireclay brick of the usual density, and their heat capacity is only 30 to 40 per cent as great. Therefore, when conditions permit their use, they promote maximum thermal efficiency in intermittently operated furnaces.

Silicon Carbide Brick. Silicon carbide is composed of carbon and silicon, the chemical formula being SiC. It is made in the electric resistance furnace and sold under various trade names. The crystalline product forms at 3340 deg fahr and dissociates into its elements at 4060 deg fahr. No softening or fusion occurs below the dissociation temperature. Its hardness is 9.6 on the Moh scale, giving a remarkable resistance to abrasion. It is inert to all acids, liquid or gaseous, excepting a mixture of hydrofluoric and nitric acids, but may be decomposed by alkali when subjected to high temperature. Silicon carbide reacts with basic slags and molten iron and steel. It is made into refractory brick and shapes of two types known as bonded and recrystallized.

Bonded SiC refractories comprise silicon carbide crystals, with small percentages of permanent binders, depending on the type of service. The standard 9 by 4 1/2 by 2 1/2 in. brick weighs approximately 9.25 lb. A wide variety of special shapes are made for use in boiler, heat-treating, malleable-iron annealing, forge and melting furnaces, soaking pits, recuperators, electric furnaces, zinc retorts, coking and calcining retorts, gas producers, water-gas generators, porcelain enameling furnaces, periodic and tunnel kilns, glass lehrs, rotary kilns, roasting furnaces, etc. SiC refractories are especially resistant to the destructive action of clinker formed from coal ash. Thermal conductivity of the higher grades of SiC refractories is high, averaging 108 Btu per sq ft for a thickness of 1 in. per deg fahr per hr in the temperature range 1200–2800 deg fahr, making them suitable for indirect heating, as in muffles, retorts, recuperators, etc. Other average physical properties are: modulus of rupture, up to 900 lb per sq in. at 2460 deg fahr; crushing strength at 2460 deg fahr up to 10,000 lb per sq in., at 68 deg fahr approximately 15,000 lb per sq in.; specific heat, 0.18; spalling resistance, exceedingly high.

Recrystallized SiC refractories consist of a dense mass of SiC crystals bonded together by a recrystallization process. Since these bricks contain no added bonds they have essentially the same refractoriness as silicon carbide itself. They have little tendency to crack and spall and are used in extremely high temperature ranges where great load-carrying capacity is essential.

13. APPLICATION OF THE COMMON TYPES OF REFRACTORY BRICK AND OF INSULATION, IN FURNACE CONSTRUCTION *

Legend

1. Fireclay Brick
   - 1–A Super-duty
   - 1–B High heat duty
   - 1–C Intermediate heat duty
   - 1–D Moderate heat duty
   - 1–E Low heat duty
2. High-alumina Brick
   - 2–A 50% alumina class
   - 2–B 60% alumina class
   - 2–C 70% alumina class
   - 2–D 80% alumina class

3. Silica Brick
4. Magnesite Brick
5. Chrome Brick
6. Insulation
   - 6–A Insulating refractory brick
   - 6–B Insulating brick

Table XII

Type of Furnace	Application	Kinds of Brick Used (alone or in combination)
Air furnace	Bottom	1–A, 1–B
	Side walls	1–A, 1–B
	Roof	1–A, 1–B
	Stack base	1–B
	Stack	1–C, 1–D, 1–E
Annealing furnace	Lining	1–B, 1–C, 1–D, 6–A
	Combustion chamber	1–A, 1–B, 2
	Backing	1–C, 1–D, 1–E, 6–B
Arches, sprung	Complete	1, 2, 3, 6–A
Arches, suspended	Complete	1–A, 1–B, 2, 3, 4, 6–A
Bake oven	Combustion chamber	1–A, 1–B, 2
	Lining	1–B, 1–C
	Backing	1–C, 1–D, 1–E
Blast furnace		
Copper	Crucible	1–B, 1–C, 1–D, 4, 5
	Shaft	1–B, 1–C, 1–D
	Settlers	4, 5
Iron	Hearth and bosh	1–B
	Inwall	1–B
	Top	1–B
	Piping	1–C
Lead	Crucible and shaft	1–B, 1–C, 1–D
Blast furnace stove		
Iron	Lining	1–B
	Well wall	1–A, 1–B, 2
	Checkers	1–A, 1–B, 2
Boiler setting	Combustion chamber	1–A, 1–B, 2
	Arches and side walls	1–A, 1–B, 2
	Bridge walls	1–A, 1–B, 2
	Baffles	1–B
	Second pass	1–B, 1–C, 1–D
	Backing	1–C, 1–D, 1–E
Carbon baking furnace	Lining	1–B
Carbureter		
Oil gas	Lining	1–B
	Checkers	1–A, 1–B, 1–C
Water gas	Lining	1–B
	Checkers	1–A, 1–B, 1–C, 2
Coal gas benches	Retorts	3
	Settings	1–B

* In some cases the applications given may appear to be conflicting. It must be borne in mind that both furnace designs and operating conditions vary considerably; consequently the refractories requirements vary correspondingly.

Table XII—*Continued*

Type of Furnace	Application	Kinds of Brick Used (alone or in combination)
Coke oven		
By-product	Above floor	3, 6–A, 6–B
	Below floor	1–B
	Regenerators	1–B
	Checkers	1–B, 3
	Flues	1–B, 1–C, 1–D
	Doors	1–B, 1–C, 1–D
	Backing	1–D, 6–B
Beehive	Floors and doors	1–B
	Walls and crown	3
Converter		
Copper	Lining	4
Steel	Lining	3
Crucible furnace	Lining	1–A, 1–B, 2
Cupola	Lining (except melting zone)	1–B, 1–C
	Melting zone	1–A, 1–B, 1–C, 3
	Backing	1–C, 1–D
Distillation furnace		
Zinc	Outer walls	1–A, 1–B
	Center walls	1–B, 3
	Roof	1–A, 1–B
Dross furnace (non-ferrous)	Bottoms	1–A, 1–B
	Side walls	1–A, 1–B, 2
	Side walls (at slag line)	2, 4
	Roof	1–A, 1–B, 2
Electric furnace		
Brass	Complete lining	1–A, 1–B, 2
Steel (acid)	Bottom	3
	Side walls	3
	Door jambs	1–A, 1–B, 3
	Roof	1–A, 1–B, 3
Steel (basic)	Bottoms	4
	Side walls	3, 4
	Door jambs	1–A, 1–B, 3
	Roof	1–A, 1–B, 3
Enameling furnace	Complete lining	1–A, 1–B
	Piers	1–A, 1–B, 2
Enamel frit furnace	Complete lining	1–A, 1–B
Forge furnace	Lining	1–A, 1–B, 2–A, 2–B
Generator		
Oil gas	Complete lining	1–A, 1–B
Producer gas	Complete lining	1–B
Water gas	Complete lining	1–B
	Wall (at clinker line)	2–A
Glass lehrs	Complete lining	1–B, 6–A
	Backing	6–B
Glass pot furnace	Lining	1–A, 1–B, 2
	Crowns	1–B, 3
Glass tank (continuous and day)	Regenerators	1–A, 1–B
	Checkers	1–A, 1–B, 2
	Ports	1–A, 1–B, 2, 3
	Breast walls	3
	Roof	3
	Bottoms and side walls	Flux blocks
Gypsum kettle	Complete lining	1–A, 1–B
	Backing	1–C, 1–D, 6–A, 6–B
Heating furnace	Bottoms and several courses in side walls	1–A, 1–B, 4, 5
	Side walls	1–A, 1–B, 2, 6–A
	Roof	1–A, 1–B, 2, 6–A

Table XII—*Continued*

Type of Furnace	Application	Kinds of Brick Used (alone or in combination)
Incinerator		
Municipal	Complete lining	1–A, 1–B
	Backing	1–C, 1–D, 1–E
Paper mill	Lining	1–B
Kilns		
Cement, rotary	Burning zone	1–B, 2, 4
	Intermediate zone	1–B
	Cold zone	1–B, 1–C, 1–D
	Coolers	1–C, 1–D
Ceramic, periodic	Lining	1–A, 1–B
	Combustion chambers	1–A, 1–B, 2
	Backing	1–C, 1–D, 1–E, 6–A, 6–B
Ceramic, continuous	Lining	1–A, 1–B
	Burning zone (walls and arch)	1–A, 1–B, 2, 3
	Backing	1–C, 1–D, 1–E, 6–A, 6–B
Dolomite, rotary	Burning zone	1–B, 2, 4
	Intermediate zone	1–B
	Cold zone	1–B, 1–C, 1–D
	Coolers	1–C, 1–D
Lime, rotary	Burning zone	1–B, 2, 4
	Intermediate zone	1–B
	Cold zone	1–B, 1–C, 1–D
	Coolers	1–C, 1–D
Lime, vertical shaft and pot type	Lining	1–B
	Top lining	1–B, 1–C, 1–D
	Hot zone and arches	1–A, 1–B, 2, 3
	Piers	1–A, 1–B, 2, 3
Ladles		
Steel, tapping	Complete lining	1–B, 1–C, 1–D, 1–E
Treadwell	Complete lining	1–B
Litharge furnace	Bottom	4
	Lower walls	4
	Upper walls	1–B
	Roof	1–B
Locomotive firebox	Complete lining	1–B
Malleable-iron furnace	Bottom	1–A, 1–B
	Side walls	1–A, 1–B
	Bungs	1–A, 1–B
	Stack base	1–B
	Stack	1–C, 1–D, 1–E
Metal mixer	Complete lining	1–B
Muffle furnace	Complete lining	1–B
	Muffle	3
Open-hearth furnace		
Steel (acid)	Furnace lining	3
	Checker chamber lining	1–A, 1–B
	Checkers	1–A, 1–B
	Top course checkers	1–A, 1–B, 2
	Backing checker chambers	1–C, 1–D, 1–E, 6–A, 6–B
	Stack	1–C, 1–D, 1–E
Steel (basic)	Bottom	4, 5
	Bottom walls to slag line	4
	Slopes	4, 5
	Upper front walls	3, 4, 5
	Upper back walls	3, 4, 5
	Upper end walls	3, 4, 5
	Corner walls	4, 5
	Ports	4, 5
	Water-cooled ports	2
	Bulkheads	3, 4, 5
	Checker chamber lining	1–A, 1–B
	Checkers	1–A, 1–B
	Top courses checkers	1–A, 1–B, 2, 3
	Backing checker chambers	1–C, 1–D, 1–E, 6–A, 6–B
	Stack	1–C, 1–D, 1–E

Table XII—*Continued*

Type of Furnace	Application	Kinds of Brick Used (alone or in combination)
Puddle furnace...................	Complete lining.................	1–A, 1–B
Recuperators....................	Complete lining...............	1–B
Refining furnace (non-ferrous)......	Bottom......................	1–B, 4
	Side walls to slag line..........	4
	Side walls, upper..............	1–A, 1–B, 2, 3
	Roof........................	1–A, 1–B, 2, 3
Regenerators....................	Complete lining...............	1–A, 1–B
	Checkers....................	1–A, 1–B, 2, 3
	Backing.....................	1–C, 1–D, 1–E, 6–A, 6–B
Reverberatory furnace		
Copper.......................	Side walls....................	3, 4
	Roof........................	3, 4
	Taps........................	4, 5
Lead.........................	Bottom......................	1–B
	Side walls...................	1–B, 2
	Side walls at slag line..........	4
	Roof........................	1–B, 2
Roasters........................	Complete lining...............	1–B
Silicate of soda furnace...........	Bottom......................	1–B
	Side walls...................	1–A, 1–B
	Roof........................	1–A, 1–B, 2, 3
Soaking pits (steel)...............	Bottom......................	4, 5
	Lower side walls...............	4, 5
	Side walls...................	1–A, 1–B
	Roof........................	1–A, 1–B
	Backing.....................	1–C, 1–D, 1–E, 6–A, 6–B
Soda recovery furnace (Paper mill)..	Bottom......................	5
	Walls.......................	1–B, 5
	Backing.....................	1–C, 1–D, 1–E, 6–A, 6–B
Softening furnace. *See* Reverberatory furnace, lead.		
Stacks, chimneys.................	Stack base...................	1–B, 1–C, 1–D
	Lining......................	1–C, 1–D, 1–E
Stills (oil refining)...............	Lining......................	1–A, 1–B, 6–A, 6–B
	Combustion chamber, particularly at slag line.............	1–A, 1–B, 2
	Bridgewall...................	1–A, 1–B, 2
	Backing.....................	1–C, 1–D, 1–E
Superheater (water gas)...........	Complete lining...............	1–B
	Checkers....................	1–B, 1–C, 1–D
Welding furnace.................	Complete lining...............	1–A, 1–B, 2
	Bottom......................	1–B, 4, 5
Zinc distillation furnace. *See* Distillation furnace, zinc.		
Zinc oxide furnace................	Complete lining...............	1–A, 1–B, 3

THERMAL INSULATING MATERIALS

14. HEAT TRANSFER

By Radiation. The energy radiated per unit area per unit time from a substance is approximately proportional to the fourth power of the absolute temperature. (For a black body the proportionality is exact.) The net loss per unit of time depends on the surroundings, being the difference between the energy radiated and the energy received by radiation from surrounding bodies.

By Convection. Transfer of heat by convection occurs in liquids and gases, the transfer being accomplished by the motion of the fluid from a locality where it receives heat to a locality where it gives up heat.

By Conduction. Transfer of heat by conduction occurs through continuous materials in which energy is transferred directly between adjacent molecular aggregates without mass motion of the materials.

When heat flows in a solid, homogeneous body in only one direction, the time rate of heat flow, after a steady state has been reached, across a given area will be proportional to the temperature drop per unit length in the direction of the flow of heat. The factor of proportionality is, by definition, the thermal conductivity.

If $\frac{dQ}{d\tau} = q =$ the time rate of heat flow;

$A =$ the area measured perpendicular to the direction of low;

$\frac{dT}{dx} =$ the temperature gradient;

and $k =$ the thermal conductivity;

$$q = \frac{dQ}{d\tau} = kA\frac{dT}{dx} \tag{1}$$

for a steady state where $\frac{dT}{d\tau} = 0$ at all points.

15. THERMAL CONDUCTIVITY

The Heat Conductivity of a material is a measure of the insulating value of that material: the lower the conductivity, the greater the insulating value. Obviously the best conductor of heat is the poorest heat insulator. The customary measure of the conductivity k of a material is the amount of heat in Btu (British thermal units) which will flow in 1 hr through a layer of the material 1 sq ft in area when the temperature difference between the surfaces of the layer is 1 deg fahr per in. of thickness.

The thermal conductivity k is a property of a material itself, and does not depend upon the size or shape of a particular piece of the material in question.

Thermal Conductance per Unit Area, or Unit Conductance, C_a, depends directly upon the conductivity and inversely upon the thickness of a given material, or

$$C_a = \frac{k}{x} \tag{2}$$

The Internal Resistance to heat flow or resistance of a unit area of a flat layer of any material is:

$$RA = \frac{1}{C_a} = \frac{x}{k} \tag{3}$$

where R is the thermal resistance, in degrees, per unit of heat transferred per unit of time; A is the area; and $1/k$ the resistivity.

Insulation. The same principles are involved in what is sometimes called "insulation against cold" as in "insulation against heat." The only difference is the point of view, with regard to the direction of heat flow. The insulation of a building against the outside cold is merely a question of reducing the heat flow from the inside to the outside. The insulating value of a material depends somewhat upon the temperature of the material, but this effect is small over the small temperature ranges occurring in buildings. The same layer of material would be somewhat more effective as house insulation than as oven insulation.

Coefficients of Transmission may be determined experimentally * or they may be calculated from fundamental constants. The *overall coefficient of heat transfer, U,* or heat transferred per unit time per unit area, per degree overall, for a compound wall of several materials having thicknesses x_1, x_2, x_3, etc., is

$$U = \frac{1}{\dfrac{1}{f_i} + \dfrac{x_1}{k_1} + \dfrac{1}{a} + \dfrac{x_2}{k_2} + \dfrac{1}{f_o} + \text{etc.}} \tag{4}$$

where a is the unit conductance of the air space; f_i and f_o the inside and outside coefficients for the two materials in contact with air,† and k_1, k_2, etc., the thermal conductivity of the separate materials.

Conductances of Air Spaces at various mean temperatures and for several widths between ordinary building materials are given in Table I. These results were obtained at the University of Minnesota under a cooperative research agreement with the American Society of Heating and Ventilating Engineers.

Conductances of Building Materials and Insulators are given in Table II. This table, published with the permission of the American Society of Heating and Ventilating Engineers, was compiled from the published values of various investigators. It should be noted that the figures in the table depend upon the mean temperatures for which they were determined.

16. THERMAL COEFFICIENTS

Table I. Conductances of Air Spaces‡ at Various Mean Temperatures

Mean Temperature, deg fahr	Conductances of Air Spaces for Various Width in Inches						
	0.128	0.250	0.364	0.493	0.713	1.00	1.500
20	2.300	1.370	1.180	1.100	1.040	1.030	1.022
30	2.385	1.425	1.234	1.148	1.080	1.070	1.065
40	2.470	1.480	1.288	1.193	1.125	1.112	1.105
50	2.560	1.535	1.340	1.242	1.168	1.152	1.149
60	2.650	1.590	1.390	1.295	1.210	1.195	1.188
70	2.730	1.648	1.440	1.340	1.250	1.240	1.228
80	2.819	1.702	1.492	1.390	1.295	1.280	1.270
90	2.908	1.757	1.547	1.433	1.340	1.320	1.310
100	2.990	1.813	1.600	1.486	1.380	1.362	1.350
110	3.078	1.870	1.650	1.534	1.425	1.402	1.392
120	3.167	1.928	1.700	1.580	1.467	1.445	1.435
130	3.250	1.980	1.750	1.630	1.510	1.485	1.475
140	3.340	2.035	1.800	1.680	1.550	1.530	1.519
150	3.425	2.090	1.852	1.728	1.592	1.569	1.559

* See A.S.H.V.E. Guide 1936, Chapter 43.
† See Surface Conductances as Affected by Air Velocity, Temperature and Character of Surface, by F. B. Rowley, H. B. Algren, and J. L. Blackslaw, *A.S.H.V.E. Trans.*, vol. 36, 1930.
‡ Thermal Resistance of Air Spaces, by F. B. Rowley and A. B. Algren, *A.S.H.V.E. Trans.*, vol. 35, 1929.

Table II. Conductivities (k) and Conductances (Cₐ) of Building Materials and Insulators[a]

The coefficients are expressed in Btu per hour per square foot per degree fahrenheit per 1-in. thickness, unless otherwise indicated.

(Copyright, American Society of Heating and Ventilating Engineers. From A.S.H.V.E. Guide 1936)

Material	Description	Density (lb per cu ft)	Mean Temp. (deg fahr)	Conductivity (k) or Conductance (C_a)	Resistivity ($\frac{1}{k}$) or Resistance (R)	Authority
Masonry Materials						
Brick...............	Common...............................	.....	...	5.00*	0.20	..
	Face.................................	.....	...	9.20*	0.11	..
Brickwork...........	Damp or wet..........................	.....	...	5.00 ^{b}	0.20	(2)
Cement mortar.......	Typical..............................	.....	...	12.00*	0.08	..
Cinder concrete......	Typical..............................	110.0	75	5.20*	0.19	(3)
Cinder blocks ^{c}......	Typical (8 in.)......................	.....	...	0.62†*	1.61	..
	" (12 in.)......................	.....	...	0.51†*	1.96	..
Concrete.............	Typical..............................	.....	...	12.00*	0.08	..
	1-2-4 mix........... ^{d}	143.0	69	9.46	0.11	(4)
	Various ages and mixes ^{d}	.....	...	11.35 to 16.36	....	(5)
	Cellular.............................	40.0	75	1.06	0.94	(3)
	"	50.0	75	1.44	0.69	(3)
	"	60.0	75	1.80	0.56	(3)
	"	70.0	75	2.18	0.46	(3)
	Typical gypsum fiber concrete, 87.5% gypsum and 12.5% wood chips........	51.2	74	1.66*	0.60	(4)
	Special concrete made with an aggregate of hardened clay—1-2-3 mix...........	101.0	70	3.98	0.25	(3)
Concrete blocks ^{c}......	Typical (8 in.)......................	.....	...	1.00†*	1.00	..
	" (12 in.)......................	.....	...	0.80†*	1.25	..
	Special concrete block made with an aggregate of hardened clay—4 × 8 × 16 in., 3 cores, 18% voids....................	74.0	...	0.66†	1.51	(3)
	Special concrete block made with an aggregate of hardened clay—8 × 8 × 16 in., 4 cores, 35% voids....................	74.5	...	0.30†	3.33	(3)
Stone...............	Typical..............................	.....	...	12.50*	0.08	..
Stucco..............	....	.....	...	12.00*	0.08	..
Tile................	Typical hollow clay (4 in.) ^{e}	.....	...	1.00†*	1.00	..
	" " " (6 in.) ^{e}	.....	...	0.64†*	1.57	..
	" " " (8 in.) ^{e}	.....	...	0.60†*	1.67	..
	" " " (10 in.) ^{e}	.....	...	0.58†*	1.72	..
	" " " (12 in.) ^{e}	.....	...	0.40†*	2.50	..
	" " " (16 in.) ^{e}	.....	...	0.31†*	3.23	..
	Hollow clay (2 in.) 1/2-in. plaster both sides	120.0	110	1.00†	1.00	(2)
	Hollow clay (4 in.) 1/2-in. plaster both sides	127.0	100	0.60†	1.67	(2)
	Hollow clay (6 in.) 1/2-in. plaster both sides	124.3	105	0.47†	2.13	(2)
	Hollow gypsum (4 in.).................	.....	...	0.46†*	2.18	..
	Solid gypsum.........................	51.8	70	1.66	0.60	(4)
	Solid gypsum.........................	75.6	76	2.96	0.34	(4)
Tile or terrazzo.......	Typical flooring......................	.....	...	12.00*	0.08	..

Authorities:
[1] U. S. Bureau of Standards, tests based on samples submitted by manufacturers.
[2] A. C. Willard, L. C. Lichty, and L. A. Harding, tests conducted at the University of Illinois.
[3] J. C. Peebles, tests conducted at Armour Institute of Technology, based on samples submitted by manufacturers.
[4] F. B. Rowley, tests conducted at the University of Minnesota.
[5] A.S.H.V.E. Research Laboratory.
[6] E. A. Allcut, tests conducted at the University of Toronto.
[7] Lees and Chorlton.
* Recommended conductivities and conductances for computing heat transmission coefficients.
† For thickness stated or used on construction, not per 1-in. thickness.
[a] For additional conductivity data see Table 14, page 63, 1934 *A.S.R.E. Data Book*.
[b] Recommended value. See Heating, Ventilating and Air Conditioning, by Harding and Willard, revised edition, 1932.
[c] One air cell in the direction of heat flow.
[d] See A.S.H.V.E. Research Paper, Conductivity of Concrete, by F. C. Houghten and Carl Gutberlet, *A.S.H.V.E. Trans.*, vol. 37, 1931.
[e] The 6-in., 8-in., and 10-in. hollow tile figures are based on two cells in the direction of heat flow. The 12-in. hollow tile is based on three cells in the direction of heat flow. The 16-in. hollow tile consists of one 10-in. and one 6-in. tile, each having two cells in the direction of heat flow.
[f] Not compressed.
[g] Roofing, 0.15-in. thick (1.34 lb per sq ft), covered with gravel (0.83 lb per sq ft), combined thickness assumed 0.25.

Table II—*Continued*

Material	Description	Density (lb per cu ft)	Mean Temp. (deg fahr)	Conductivity (k) or Conductance (C_a)	Resistivity $\left(\frac{1}{k}\right)$ or Resistance (R)	Authority
Insulation—Blanket or Flexible Types Fiber..............	Typical...........	.....	...	0.27*	3.70	..
	Chemically treated wood fibers held between layers of strong paper...	3.62	70	0.25	4.00	(3)
	Eel grass between strong paper...	4.60	90	0.26	3.85	(1)
	" " " " "	3.40	90	0.25	4.00	(1)
	Fabric with non-metallic reflective surface (1/32 in. thick)...........	.....	70	0.33†	3.03	(3)
	Flax fibers between strong paper...	4.90	90	0.28	3.57	(1)
	Chemically treated hog hair between kraft paper...	5.76	71	0.26	3.85	(3)
	Chemically treated hog hair between kraft paper and asbestos paper...	7.70	71	0.28	3.57	(3)
	Hair felt between layers of paper...	11.00	75	0.25	4.00	(3)
	Kapok between burlap or paper...	1.00	90	0.24	4.17	(1)
	Jute fiber...	6.70	75	0.25	4.00	(3)
Insulation—Semi-rigid Type Fiber..............	Felted cattle hair...	13.00	90	0.26	3.84	(1)
	" " "	11.00	90	0.26	3.84	(1)
	Flax...	12.10	70	0.30	3.33	(3)
	Flax and rye...	13.60	90	0.32	3.12	(1)
	Felted hair and asbestos...	7.80	90	0.28	3.57	(1)
	75% hair and 25% jute...	6.30	90	0.27	3.70	(1)
	50% hair and 50% jute...	6.10	90	0.26	3.85	(1)
	Jute...	6.70	75	0.25	4.00	(3)
	Felted jute and asbestos...	10.00	90	0.37	2.70	(1)
	Compressed peat moss...	11.00	70	0.26	3.84	(3)
Insulation—Loose Fill or Bat Type Fiber..............	Made from ceiba fibers...	1.90	75	0.23	4.35	(3)
	" " " "	1.60	75	0.24	4.17	(3)
	Fibrous material made from dolomite and silica...	1.50	75	0.27	3.70	(3)
Glass wool............	Fibrous material made from slag...	9.40	103	0.27	3.70	(1)
Granular.............	Fibrous material 25 to 30 microns in diameter, made from virgin bottle glass.....	1.50	75	0.27	3.70	(3)
	Made from combined silicate of lime and alumina...	4.20	72	0.24	4.17	(3)
Gypsum.............	Made from expanded aluminum-magnesium silicate...	6.20	42	0.32	3.12	(3)
	Cellular, dry...........	30.00	90	1.00	1.00	(1)
	" "	24.00	90	0.77	1.30	(1)
	" "	18.00	90	0.59	1.69	(1)
	Flaked, dry and fluffy	12.00	90	0.44	2.27	(1)
	" " "	34.00	90	0.60	1.67	(1)
	" " " "	26.00	90	0.52	1.92	(1)
	" " " "	24.00	75	0.48*	2.08	(3)
	" " " "	19.80	90	0.35	2.86	(1)
Mineral wool..........	All forms, typical........	18.00	75	0.34	2.94	(3)
Regranulated cork.....	About 3/16-in. particles........	.....	...	0.27*	3.70	..
Rock wool............	Fibrous material made from rock......	8.10	90	0.31	3.22	(1)
	" " " "	21.00	90	0.30	3.33	(1)
	" " " " "	18.00	90	0.29	3.45	(1)
	" " " " "	14.00	90	0.28	3.57	(1)
	Rock wool with a binding agent.......	10.00	90	0.27*	3.70	(1)
	Rock wool with flax, straw pulp, and binder	14.50	77	0.33	3.03	(1)
	Rock wool with vegetable fibers......	14.50	75	0.38	2.63	(3)
Sawdust..............	Various..............	11.50	72	0.31	3.22	(3)
Shavings.............	Various from planer.........	12.00	90	0.41	2.44	(1)
	From maple, beech and birch (coarse).....	8.80	90	0.41	2.44	(1)
	Redwood bark...........	13.20	90	0.36	2.78	(1)
		3.00	90	0.31	3.22	(1)
Insulation—Rigid Corkboard............	Typical...........	.....	...	0.30*	3.33	..
	No added binder...........	14.00	90	0.34	2.94	(1)
	" " "	10.60	90	0.30	3.33	(1)
	" " "	7.00	90	0.27	3.70	(1)
	" " "	5.40	90	0.25	4.00	(1)

For notes see page 12-34.

Table II—*Continued*

Material	Description	Density (lb per cu ft)	Mean Temp. (deg fahr)	Conductivity (k) or Conductance (Ca)	Resistivity ($\frac{1}{k}$) or Resistance (R)	Authority
Insulation—Rigid—*Cont.*						
Corkboard...........	Asphaltic binder........	14.50	90	0.32	3.12	(1)
Fiber...............	Typical............	.....	...	0.33*	3.03	..
	Core of fiber board coated two sides with non-metallic reflective surface (3/8 in. thick).	23.4	70	0.27†	3.70	(3)
	Fiber board coated one side with non-metallic reflective surface (3/16 in. thick).....	.....	75	0.49†	2.04	(3)
	Made from chemically treated wood fiber..	20.00	70	0.36	2.78	(3)
	Made from chemically treated wood and vegetable fibers.................	25.00	75	0.38	2.63	(3)
	Chemically treated hog hair covered with film of asphalt................	10.00	75	0.28	3.57	(3)
	Made from corn stalks............	15.00	71	0.33	3.03	(3)
	" " exploded wood fiber...........	17.90	78	0.32	3.12	(4)
	" " hard wood fibers............	15.20	70	0.32	3.12	(3)
	Insulating plaster 9/10-in. thick applied to 3/8-in. plaster board base.............	54.00	75	1.07†	0.93	(3)
	Made from licorice roots............	16.10	81	0.34	2.94	(3)
	Made from 85% magnesia and 15% asbestos	19.30	86	0.51	1.96	(1)
	Made from shredded wood and cement....	24.20	72	0.46	2.17	(3)
	" " sugar cane fiber.............	13.50	70	0.33	3.03	(3)
	Sugar cane fiber insulation blocks encased in asphalt membrane.................	13.80	70	0.30	3.33	(3)
	Made from wheat straw...........	17.00	68	0.33	3.03	(3)
	" " wood fiber...........	15.90	72	0.33	3.03	(3)
	" " " "	15.00	70	0.33	3.03	(3)
	" " " "	....	52	0.33	3.03	(6)
	" " " "	8.50	72	0.29	3.45	(3)
	" " " "	15.20	...	0.33	3.03	(3)
	" " " "	16.90	90	0.34	2.94	(1)
Building Boards						
Asbestos.............	Compressed cement and asbestos sheets....	123.00	86	2.70	0.37	(1)
	Corrugated asbestos board............	20.40	110	0.48	2.08	(2)
	Pressed asbestos mill board............	60.50	86	0.84	1.19	(1)
	Sheet asbestos................	48.30	110	0.29	3.45	(2)
Gypsum.............	Gypsum between layers of heavy paper....	62.80	70	1.41	0.71	(3)
	Rigid, gypsum between layers of heavy paper (1/2-in. thick)................	53.50	90	2.60†	0.38	(1)
	Gypsum mixed with sawdust between layers of heavy paper (0.39-in. thick)........	60.70	90	3.60†	0.28	(1)
Plaster Board.........	(3/8 in.)................	.....	...	3.73†*	0.27	..
	(1/2 in.)................	.....	...	2.82†*	0.35	..
Roofing Construction						
Roofing..............	Asphalt, composition or prepared.........	70.00	75	6.50†*	0.15	(3)
	Built up—3/8-in. thick............	.....	...	3.53†*	0.28	..
	Built up, bitumen and felt, gravel or slag surfaced 8...........	.....	...	1.33†	0.75	(2)
	Plaster board, gypsum fiber concrete and 3-ply roof covering.............	52.40	76	0.58†	1.72	(4)
Shingles.............	Asbestos................	65.00	75	6.00†*	0.17	(3)
	Asphalt................	70.00	75	6.50†*	0.15	(3)
	Slate................	201.00	...	10.37*	0.10	(7)
	Wood................	.....	...	1.28†*	0.78	..
Plastering Materials						
Plaster..............	Cement................	.....	...	8.00	0.13	(2)
	Gypsum, typical................	.....	...	3.30*	0.30	..
	Thickness 3/8 in................	.....	73	8.80†	0.11	(4)
Metal lath and plaster..	Total thickness 3/4 in................	.....	...	4.40†*	0.23	(4)
Wood lath and plaster...	3/8-in. plaster, total thickness 3/4 in........	.....	70	2.50†*	0.40	(4)
Building Constructions						
Frame...............	1-in. fir sheathing and building paper......	.....	30	0.71†*	1.41	(4)
	1-in. fir sheathing, building paper, and yellow pine lap siding................	.....	20	0.50†*	2.00	(4)
	1-in. fir sheathing, building paper and stucco	.....	20	0.82†*	1.22	(4)
	Pine lap siding and building paper—siding 4 in. wide................	.....	16	0.85†*	1.18	(4)
	Yellow pine lap siding................	.....	...	1.28†*	0.78	..
Flooring.............	Maple—across grain................	40.00	75	1.20	0.83	(3)
	Battleship linoleum (1/4 in.)............	.....	...	1.36†*	0.74	..

For notes see page 12-34.

Table II—*Continued*

Material	Description	Density (lb per cu ft)	Mean Temp. (deg fahr)	Conductivity (k) or Conductance (C_a)	Resistivity ($\frac{1}{k}$) or Resistance (R)	Authority
Air Space and Surface Coefficients						
Air spaces............	Over 3/4-in. faced with ordinary building materials...........................	.....	40	1.10†*	0.91	(4)
Surfaces, ordinary......	Still air (f_i)............................	...	...	1.65†*	0.61	(4)
	15 mph—(f_o)........................	...	...	6.00†*	0.17	(4)
Surface, bright aluminum	Still air (f_i)............................	...	60	1.18†	0.85	..
Air Spaces Faced with Bright Aluminum Foil						
	Air space, faced one side with bright aluminum foil, over 3/4-in. wide............	.....	50	0.46†*	2.17	(4)
	Air space, faced one side with bright aluminum foil, 3/8-in. wide............	.....	50	0.62†	1.61	(4)
	Air space, faced both sides with bright aluminum foil, over 3/4-in. wide.........	.....	50	0.41†*	2.44	(4)
	Air space, faced both sides with bright aluminum foil, 3/8-in. wide............	.....	50	0.57†	1.75	(4)
	Air space divided in two with single curtain of bright aluminum foil (both sides bright)					
	Each space over 3/4-in. wide..........	.....	50	0.23†*	4.35	(4)
	Each space 3/8-in. wide..........	.....	50	0.31†	3.23	(4)
	Air space with multiple curtains of bright aluminum foil, bright on both sides, curtains more than 3/4-in. apart, in standard construction					
	2 curtains, forming 3 spaces..........	.....	50	0.15†*	6.78	(4)
	3 curtains, forming 4 spaces...........	.....	50	0.11†*	9.22	(4)
	4 curtains, forming 5 spaces..........	.....	50	0.09†*	11.66	(4)
Woods (across grain)						
Balsa.................		20.0	90	0.58	1.72	(1)
		8.8	90	0.38	2.63	(1)
		7.3	90	0.33	3.03	(1)
California redwood.....	0% moisture.	22.0	75	0.66	1.53	(4)
	0% "	28.0	75	0.70	1.43	(4)
	8% "	22.0	75	0.70	1.43	(4)
	8% "	28.0	75	0.75	1.33	(4)
	16% "	22.0	75	0.74	1.35	(4)
	16% "	28.0	75	0.80	1.25	(4)
Cypress............		28.7	86	0.67	1.49	(1)
Douglas fir...........	0% moisture.	26.0	75	0.61	1.64	(4)
	0% "	34.0	75	0.67	1.49	(4)
	8% "	26.0	75	0.66	1.52	(4)
	8% "	34.0	75	0.75	1.33	(4)
	16% "	26.0	75	0.76	1.32	(4)
	16% "	34.0	75	0.82	1.22	(4)
Eastern hemlock.......	0% moisture.	22.0	75	0.60	1.67	(4)
	0% "	30.0	75	0.76	1.32	(4)
	8% "	22.0	75	0.63	1.59	(4)
	8% "	30.0	75	0.81	1.23	(4)
	16% "	22.0	75	0.67	1.49	(4)
	16% "	30.0	75	0.85	1.18	(4)
Hard maple...........	0% moisture.	40.0	75	1.01	0.99	(4)
	0% "	46.0	75	1.05	0.95	(4)
	8% "	40.0	75	1.08	0.93	(4)
	8% "	46.0	75	1.13	0.89	(4)
	16% "	40.0	75	1.15	0.87	(4)
	16% "	46.0	75	1.21	0.83	(4)
Longleaf yellow pine....	0% moisture.	30.0	75	0.76	1.32	(4)
	0% "	40.0	75	0.86	1.16	(4)
	8% "	30.0	75	0.83	1.21	(4)
	8% "	40.0	75	0.95	1.05	(4)
	16% "	30.0	75	0.89	1.12	(4)
	16% "	40.0	75	1.03	0.97	(4)
Mahogany...........		34.3	86	0.90	1.11	(1)
Maple.............		44.3	86	1.10	0.91	(1)
Maple or oak.........	0% moisture.	.....	...	1.15*	0.87	..
Norway pine...........	0% "	22.0	75	0.62	1.61	(4)
	8% "	32.0	75	0.74	1.35	(4)
	8% "	22.0	75	0.68	1.47	(4)
	16% "	32.0	75	0.83	1.21	(4)
	16% "	22.0	75	0.74	1.35	(4)
		32.0	75	0.91	1.10	(4)

For notes see page 12-34

Table II—*Continued*

Material	Description	Density (lb per cu ft)	Mean Temp. (deg fahr)	Conductivity (k) or Conductance (C_a)	Resistivity ($\frac{1}{k}$) or Resistance (R)	Authority
Woods—*Continued*.......						
Red cypress...........	0% moisture........................	22.0	75	0.67	1.49	(4)
	0% "	32.0	75	0.79	1.27	(4)
	8% "	22.0	75	0.71	1.41	(4)
	8% "	32.0	75	0.84	1.19	(4)
	16% "	22.0	75	0.74	1.35	(4)
	16% "	32.0	75	0.90	1.11	(4)
Red oak..............	0% moisture........	38.0	75	0.98	1.02	(4)
	0% "	48.0	75	1.18	0.85	(4)
	8% "	38.0	75	1.03	0.97	(4)
	8% "	48.0	75	1.24	0.81	(4)
	16% "	38.0	75	1.07	0.94	(4)
	16% "	48.0	75	1.29	0.78	(4)
Shortleaf yellow pine....	0% moisture....	26.0	75	0.74	1.35	(4)
	0% "	36.0	75	0.91	1.10	(4)
	8% "	26.0	75	0.79	1.27	(4)
	8% "	36.0	75	0.97	1.03	(4)
	16% "	26.0	75	0.84	1.19	(4)
	16% "	36.0	75	1.04	0.96	(4)
Soft elm..............	0% moisture....	28.0	75	0.73	1.37	(4)
	0% "	34.0	75	0.88	1.14	(4)
	8% "	28.0	75	0.77	1.30	(4)
	8% "	34.0	75	0.93	1.08	(4)
	16% "	28.0	75	0.81	1.24	(4)
	16% "	34.0	75	0.97	1.03	(4)
Soft maple...........	0% moisture....	36.0	75	0.89	1.12	(4)
	0% "	42.0	75	0.95	1.05	(4)
	8% "	36.0	75	0.96	1.04	(4)
	8% "	42.0	75	1.02	0.98	(4)
	16% "	36.0	75	1.01	0.99	(4)
	16% "	42.0	75	1.09	0.92	(4)
Sugar pine...........	0% moisture....	22.0	75	0.54	1.85	(4)
	0% "	28.0	75	0.64	1.56	(4)
	8% "	22.0	75	0.59	1.70	(4)
	8% "	28.0	75	0.71	1.41	(4)
	16% "	22.0	75	0.65	1.54	(4)
	16% "	28.0	75	0.78	1.28	(4)
Virginia pine........		34.3	86	0.96	1.04	(1)
West Coast hemlock....	0% moisture....	22.0	75	0.68	1.47	(4)
	0% "	30.0	75	0.79	1.27	(4)
	8% "	22.0	75	0.73	1.37	(4)
	8% "	30.0	75	0.85	1.18	(4)
	16% "	22.0	75	0.78	1.28	(4)
	16% "	30.0	75	0.91	1.10	(4)
White pine..........	....	31.2	86	0.78	1.28	(1)
Yellow pine..........	....	.....	...	1.00	1.00	(3)
Yellow pine or fir......	....	.....	...	0.80*	1.25	..

For notes see page 12–34.

TIMBER

By H. C. Knutson and Herbert F. Moore

17. COMMON TIMBER TREES

Classes of Timber Trees. Wood as a building material is produced by the Spermatophyta or seed-bearing trees, which may be divided botanically into two groups, the Gymnosperms, or conifers and the Angiosperms. The Angiosperms have two subclasses, the Dicotyledons and Monocotyledons. The Dicotyledons are the two seed leaved, broad-leaved trees such as ashes, elms, maples, walnuts, etc. The Monocotyledons have single seed leaves. Bamboos, palms, and yuccas belong to this subclass.

The conifers and broad-leaved trees produce the structurally valuable timbers. The conifers are generally called the softwoods while the broad-leaved trees are referred to as hardwoods. The terms softwood and hardwood as used here have no reference to the actual hardness of the wood. Many hardwoods are actually softer than the average softwood.

The conifers and the broad-leaved trees are known as the outward-growing or exogeneous trees. The structure consists of three parts, the bark. the sapwood, and the heartwood. On the outside of the tree trunk is found from 1/4 to 2 in. or more of bark or protective tissue. As a structural material this is valueless and is always removed soon after the tree is felled, as it hastens the decay of the wood. Inside of the bark there is a portion made up of thin-walled cells which constitute the living portion of the tree, called the sapwood. Arranged in a circle inside of this sapwood are many fibrous bundles making up the middle of the stem, giving it strength and stiffness and known as the heartwood. As the stem grows, new and branching bundles of these hollow fibers appear under the bark and form each season an annular ring. At the end of the season growth stops, to be resumed the following spring; and the rapid open growth of the spring against the slow and condensed growth of the summer gives rise to the peculiar marking in the bundles which indicates each year's increase. The last few rings formed constitute the sapwood, usually from 1/2 to 4 in. in thickness and light in color. The rings inside of the sapwood form the heartwood. The rings are interrupted by plates of tissue or radial cells communicating between the pith at the center of the tree and the soft tissue on the outside. These form the medullary rays. In the pine, the sapwood constitutes 40 to 60 per cent of the cross-section of the tree. The time required for sapwood to transform into heartwood varies from a few years for the fir to many years for the oak tree. The approximate composition of all woods when dry is nearly uniform and consists by weight of the following elements: 49 per cent of carbon, 6 per cent of hydrogen, 44 per cent of oxygen, and 1 per cent of ash.

Green Ash. Heavy, hard, and coarse-grained; brittle. Color, brown, with lighter sapwood. Used as a substitute for white ash.

Red Ash. Heavy, compact, and coarse-grained but brittle. Color, rich brown, with sapwood a light brown sometimes streaked with yellow. Used as a substitute for the more valuable white ash.

White Ash. Heavy, hard, very elastic, coarse-grained, and compact. Tendency to become decayed and brittle after a few years. Color, reddish-brown, with sapwood nearly white. Used for interior and cabinet work, but unfit for structural work.

Balsa. Extremely light, about half the strength of white pine. Appearance like poplar. Used for heat insulation and, when waterproofed, for life preservers.

Butternut (White Walnut). Light, soft, coarse-grained, compact, and easily worked. Polishes well. Color, light brown, turning dark on exposure. Used for interior finish.

Red Cedar. Strong pungent odor repellent to insects. Very durable and compact, but easily worked and brittle. Color, dull brown tinged with red. Used as posts, sills, ties, fencing, shingles, and lining for chests, trunks, and closets.

White Cedar. Soft, light, fine-grained, and very durable in contact with the soil; lacks strength and toughness. Color, light brown, darkening with exposure. Sapwood very thin and nearly white. Used for water tanks, shingles, posts, fencing, cooperage, and boat building.

Chestnut. Light, moderately soft, stiff, and of coarse texture. Shrinks and checks considerably in drying; works easily. Durable when exposed to weather. Color, heartwood dark and sapwood light brown. Used for cabinet work, cooperage, railway ties, telegraph poles, and exposed heavy construction.

Cypress. One of the most durable of woods, light, hard, close-grained but brittle. Easily worked, polishes highly and gives a satiny gloss. Color, bright clear yellow with nearly white sapwood. Used for interior finish and cabinet work, but used as extensively in the South as pine is in the North.

Douglas Fir. Hard, strong, varying greatly with age, conditions of growth, and amount of sap. Durable but difficult to work. Of two varieties, red and yellow, of which yellow is the more valuable. Color, light red to yellow, with white sapwood. Used in all kinds of construction.

White Elm. Heavy, hard, strong and tough, and very close-grained. Difficult to split and shape, but warps badly in drying. Capable of high polish. Color, light clear brown often tinged with red and gray, with broad whitish sapwood. Used for car, wagon, boat, and shipbuilding, bridge timbers, sills and ties, and furniture, also barrel staves.

Greenheart. Very heavy, strong, durable heartwood, dark green to dark chestnut color, free from knots. Used for shipbuilding, docks, implements, rollers.

Gum. Heavy, hard, tough, compact, and close-grained. Tendency to shrink and warp badly in seasoning. Not durable if exposed. Takes high polish. Color, bright brown tinged with red. Used in the manufacture of furniture, wagon hubs, hat blocks.

Hemlock. Brittle, splits easily and likely to be shaky. Soft, light, not durable, with coarse and uneven grain. Color, light brown tinged with red and often nearly white. Used for cheap rough framing timber, crates, and packing boxes.

Hickory. Medullary rays very numerous and distinct. Heaviest, hardest, toughest, and strongest of American woods. Very flexible. Color, brown, with very thin but valuable sapwood nearly white. Used for carriages, sleighs, handles, and bent-wood implements. Unfit for building material because of extreme hardness and liability to attack of boring insects.

Lignum Vitæ. Exceedingly heavy, hard, resinous, difficult to split and work, and has a soapy feeling. Color, rich yellow brown varying to almost black. Used for small turned articles, tool handles, and sheaves of block pulleys.

Locust. Heavy, hard, strong, and close-grained. Very durable in contact with ground. Hardness increases with age. Color, brown and rarely light green, with yellow sapwood. Used for posts and turned ornaments.

Mahogany. Strong, durable, and flexible when green, but brittle when dry. Free from shakes and less liable than most other woods to attacks of dry rot or worms. Rapid seasoning causes deep shakes. Color, red-brown of various shades and degrees of brightness, often varied and mottled. Inferior qualities contain large numbers of gray specks. Used for interior finish, handrails, patterns, etc.

Hard Maple. Heavy, hard, strong, tough, and close-grained. Medullary rays small but distinct. Curly and circular inflexion of fibers gives rise to " curly maple " and " bird's-eye maple." Susceptible of good polish. Color, very light brown to yellow. Used for flooring, interior finish, and furniture.

White Maple. Fine-grained, hard, strong, and heavy. Characteristics of grain the same as hard maple and more marked. Light colored. Used for flooring and furniture.

Chestnut Oak. Very durable in contact with soil. Color, dark brown. Used for railroad ties.

Live Oak. Very heavy, hard, tough, and strong. Difficult to work. Color, light brown or yellow, with sapwood nearly white.

Red and Black Oak. More porous than white oak and softer. Color, darker and redder than white oak. Used for interior finish and furniture, and railway ties.

White Oak. Heavy, strong, hard, tough, and close-grained. Checks if not carefully seasoned Well-known silver grain and capable of receiving high polish. Color, brown, with lighter sapwood. Used for framed structures, shipbuilding, interior finish, carriage, furniture making, and railway ties.

Palmetto. Light but difficult to work when dry. Very durable under water and less subject to attacks of the teredo. Color, light brown, with dark-colored fibers. Used for wharf piles, canes and handles.

Red Pine (Norway Pine). Light, hard, coarse-grained, compact, with few resin pockets. Color, light red, with a yellow or white sapwood. Used for all purposes of construction.

White Pine. Light, soft and straight-grained and easily worked, but not very strong. Color, light yellowish brown often slightly tinged with red. Used for interior finish and pattern making.

Yellow Pine (Long-leaf). Heavy, hard, strong, coarse-grained, and very durable when dry and well ventilated. Cells are dark colored and very resinous. Color, light yellowish red or orange. Cannot be used in contact with ground. Used for heavy framing timbers and floors. As house sills, sleepers, or posts it rapidly decays.

Yellow Pine (Short-leaf Pine). Varies greatly in amount of sap and quality. Cells broad and resinous, with numerous large resin ducts. Medullary rays well marked. Color, orange, with white sapwood. Used as a substitute for a long-leaf pine.

Yellow Poplar (Whitewood). Moderately light in weight, straight-grained, moderately soft, moderately weak, comparatively uniform in texture. Sapwood white, heartwood yellowish brown with greenish tinge. Easily worked. Finishes smoothly. Used in carpentry and joinery.

Redwood (California). Light, soft, coarse-grained, and easily worked. Durable in contact with soil, but brittle. " Shrinks lengthwise as well as crosswise." Color, dull red, resembling pine. Used for railroad ties, fence posts, telegraph poles, and general building material.

Red Spruce. Light, soft, close and straight-grained and satiny. Color, light red and often nearly white. Used for piles, lumber, and framing timber, submerged cribs and coffer dams, as it resists the destructive action of crustaceans.

Sitka Spruce. Light, soft, medium strength. Heartwood, light, reddish brown; sapwood, white; trees very large. Used for general structural purposes; also for airplane frame-work.

White Spruce. Similar to red variety, but not so common. Color, light yellow; sapwood indistinct. Used as lumber for construction.

Tamarack. Wood like pine in appearance, quality, and uses. Used for telegraph poles, railway ties, and in shipbuilding.

Black Walnut.—Heavy, hard, strong, and checks if not carefully seasoned. Coarse-grained but easily worked. Color, rich dark brown, with light sapwood. Used for interior finish and cabinet work.

18. SAWING AND SEASONING

Sawing. The manner in which the stick of lumber is sawed from the tree has a remarkable influence upon its qualities and behavior, and the selection of cutting is determined by the character of the wood and the purpose for which it is destined. *Flat sawing* consists in cutting the timber tangential to the annular rings. *Rift sawing* is cutting the boards out of the log in such a manner that the annular rings are cut through as nearly as possible in a radial direction. Rift sawing and flat sawing give rise in the lumber trade to the terms edge grain and flat grain, respectively. Rift sawing is done for the sake of the beauty of the grain thus obtained, as well as to expose the edge of the hard bands of summer wood. Edge-grain lumber shrinks and checks less, does not sliver, and wears more evenly and smoother than flat-grain lumber.

Air Seasoning. In the preparation of lumber for construction purposes, it is necessary to expel the moisture from the pores of the wood by the process of seasoning. The drier the timber, the less likely it is to shrink and decay. Natural seasoning consists in exposing the planks and boards, after sawing, to a free circulation of the air. The lumber is placed on skids in large square piles under shelter in a dry place, the layers being separated by three or four narrow strips or boards laid in the opposite direction. The lowest layer should be at least 2 ft from the ground. The time required for thorough seasoning varies from one to three years, depending upon the character of the wood, the purpose to which it is to be adapted, and the dimensions. Green wood contains from 30 to 35 per cent of water. Air seasoning reduces this to 12 to 15 per cent.

Artificial Seasoning or Kiln-drying hastens the evaporation of the moisture but at the same time tends to cause a rapid drying of the surface and ends of the material and a slow or imperfect drying of the interior. This may impair both the strength and elasticity of the wood. The timber is stacked in a drying kiln and exposed to a current of hot air, the temperature depending on the kind and the dimension of the stack. Sometimes the heat is supplemented by the employment of vacuum pumps. The best temperature to be employed depends on the kind and dimensions of the lumber, and varies from 100 deg fahr for oak to 200 deg fahr for pine. The time required depends on the thickness of the stack. About four days is necessary for 1-in. pine, spruce, or cedar boards. Hardwoods are usually dried in air from three to six months and then placed in the drying kiln from six to ten days. Kiln drying reduces the moisture content of wood to less than 10 per cent.

19. SHRINKAGE AND DEFECTS

Shrinkage. The concentric annular zones of wood are made up of pores or cells enclosed by walls of cellulose and are pierced at right angles by plates of similar fibers. As the average width of cell is 1/100 of the length, the greatest shrinkage will take place in the cross-section of the fibers or tangentially to the annular rings. This is known as the circumferential shrinkage. By rift sawing the medullary rays are cut across the length, in which direction shrinkage is least. Flat sawing produces lumber which checks and cracks to a greater extent in shrinking. The average values for shrinkage in width are:

Hardwoods: radial, 2–5%; tangential, 4–7%
Softwoods: radial, 1–4%; tangential, 2–6%

The longitudinal shrinkage is usually less than 0.1 per cent. The change in volume is therefore due to radial and tangential shrinkage, and expressed in percentage is approximately twice the figures given, as shrinkage takes place in two directions by approximately equal amounts.

The harder timbers are more compact in structure, with thicker cell walls, and therefore produce the greater shrinkage. The opposite effect to shrinkage is produced by the absorption of moisture, and protective checks must be resorted to in applying timber to construction; the expansion joints in wooden block pavement serve as checks. A roadway 40 ft wide has been observed to expand 8 in. in rainy weather.

Definitions of Standard Defects. The following definitions of standard defects are from the A.S.T.M. Standard D9–30.

Defect. Any irregularity occurring in or on the wood that may lower its strength. *Blemish.* Anything, not necessarily a defect, marring the appearance of the wood.

Bark Pocket. Bark partially or wholly enclosed in wood.

Check. A separation along the grain of wood, the greater part of which occurs across the rings of annual growth. *End check.* A check occurring at the end of a piece. *Heart check.* A check starting near the pith and extending toward but not to the surface of a piece. Several of these occurring together are called a star check. *Surface check.* A check occurring at the surface of a piece. *Through check.* A check extending through the piece from one surface to an opposite or to an adjoining surface.

Collapse. A caving at a surface of a piece of wood. It sometimes occurs in streaks, giving the surface a corrugated appearance and often is due to the flattening of the cells when wet wood is dried quickly. *Honeycombing.* Checks that occur in the interior of a piece of wood, often not visible at the surface. On a cross-section they usually appear as slits or pockets the width of which may be very large relative to the radial length. *Cross break.* A separation of the wood cells across the grain. Such breaks may be due to internal strains resulting from unequal shrinkage or to external forces.

Cross-grained Wood. Wood in which the fibers are not parallel with the axis of the piece. *Curly grained wood.* Wood in which the fibers are distorted so that they afford a curled appearance, as in " bird's-eye " wood. Areas showing curly grain may vary up to several inches in diameter. *Diagonal-grained wood.* Wood in which fibers are at an angle with (that is, diagonal to) the axis of a piece as a result of sawing at an angle with the axis of the tree. It may appear on either the radial or flat-grain surface. *Dip-grained wood.* Wood which has single waves or undulations of the fibers, such as occur around knots and pitch pockets. *Interlocked-grained wood.* Wood in which fibers are inclined in one direction in a number of rings of annual growth, then gradually reverse and are inclined in an opposite direction in succeeding growth rings, then later again reverse, etc. *Spiral-grained wood.* Wood in which the fibers take a more or less winding or spiral course, as in a twisted tree. It may be detected on the flat grain surface. *Wavy-grained wood.* Wood in which the fibers collectively take the form of waves or undulations. It may appear on either the radial or flat-grained surface and is indicated by the wavy surface of a split piece.

Decay. Destruction of the wood substance due to the action of wood-destroying fungi. " Dote " and " rot " are synonymous with " decay "; they are any form of decay, which may be evident either as dark red discolorations not found in the sound wood, or as white or red rotten spots. *Advanced (or typical) decay.* The older stage of decay in which the destruction is readily recognized because the wood has become punky, soft and spongy, stringy, ring-shaked, pitted, or crumbly. Decided discoloration or bleaching of the rotted wood is often apparent as, for example, brown and white rots, pocket rots. *Incipient decay.* The early stages of decay which has not proceeded far enough to soften or otherwise perceptibly impair the hardness of the wood. It is accompanied by a slight discoloration or bleaching of the wood as instanced by the " firm red heart " in softwoods and the " water-soaked " stage in certain types of decay. *Firm red heart.* A stage of incipient decay in wood characterized by a reddish color produced in the heartwood, which does not, however, make the wood unfit for the majority of yard purposes. It is caused by the fungus *Trametes pini* and occurs chiefly in the pines. *Water-soak (or stain)*. A term applied to a generally water-soaked area in heartwood, which is usually interpreted as the incipient stage of certain wood decays. It occurs in hemlock and possibly in other woods.

Knot.* That portion of a branch which has become incorporated in the body of a tree. *Pin knot.* A knot not more than $1/2$ in. in diameter. *Small knot.* A knot more than $1/2$ in. but no more than $3/4$ in. in diameter. *Medium knot.* A knot more than $3/4$ in. but not more than $1\ 1/2$ in. in diameter. *Large knot.* A knot more than $1\ 1/2$ in. in diameter. *Encased knot.* A knot whose rings of annual growth are not intergrown and homogeneous with those of the surrounding wood. The encasement may be partial or complete; if intergrown partially or so fixed by growth or position that it will retain its place in the piece, it shall be considered a tight knot; if completely intergrown on one face, it is a watertight knot. *Intergrown knot.* A knot whose rings of annual growth are completely intergrown with those of the surrounding wood. *Loose knot.* A knot not firmly held in place by growth or position. *Tight knot.* A knot so fixed by growth or position that it will firmly retain its place in the piece. *Pith knot.* A sound knot with a pith hole not more than $1/4$ in. in diameter in the center. *Round knot.* A knot whose sawn section is oval or circular. *Spike knot.* A knot sawn in a lengthwise direction. *Decayed knot.* A knot which owing to advanced decay is not as hard as the surrounding wood. *Sound knot.* A knot which is solid across the face and which is as hard as the surrounding wood. Red or black knots may be sound.

Pitch Pocket. An opening between the grain of the wood, containing more or less pitch. Pitch pockets are classified as small, medium, and large. *Small pitch pocket.* A pocket not more than $1/8$ in. in width or 4 in. in length, or not more than $1/4$ in. in width or 2 in. in length. *Medium pitch pocket.* A pocket not more than $3/8$ in. in width or 4 in. in length, or not more than $1/8$ in. in width or 8 in. in length. *Large pitch pocket.* A pocket more than $3/8$ in. in width and more than 4 in. in length, or more than $1/8$ in. in width and more than 8 in. in length. *Pitch streak.* A well-defined accumulation of pitch at one point in the piece. When not sufficient to develop a well-defined streak, or where the fiber between grains, that is, the coarse-grained fiber, usually termed " springwood," is not saturated with pitch, it is not considered a defect.

Shake. A separation along the grain of wood, the greater part of which occurs between the rings of annual growth. *Through shake.* A shake which extends between any two faces of a timber.

Wane. Bark or lack of wood, from any cause, on edges of timbers.

Molds, Stains and Decays in wood are caused by fungi, which are microscopic plants that must have organic material on which to live, and for some of them wood offers the required food supply. Their growth, however, is dependent upon suitable surroundings of mild temperature and dampness, the latter being aggravated by sluggish circulation of air. Most decay occurs in wood having moisture above the fiber-saturation point. Wood that is continuously water-soaked or continuously dry (below 20 per cent moisture) will not decay. Under proper conditions, wood has proved itself good for centuries of service.

Molds and Stains, which are confined largely to the sapwood, are characterized by cottony or powdery surface growths of various colors. Little direct staining of the wood is caused by molds. Such blemishes are easily brushed or surfaced off. Stains penetrate into the sapwood (not heartwood) and cannot be removed by surfacing. The discoloration of the wood occurs as specks, spots, streaks, or patches of varying intensities of color. Stains should not be considered a stage of decay, since staining fungi do not attack the wood substance appreciably. Ordinarily, they affect the strength of the wood only slightly.

Decay (see also Decay, p. 12-41). Decay-producing or wood-destroying fungi may, under conditions that favor their growth, attack either heartwood or sapwood, causing a condition of the wood that is variously designated as decay, rot, or dote. The fresh surface growths of decay fungi are usually fluffy or cottony, and only seldom powdery as the molds are. Some wood-destroying fungi live largely on the cellulose whereas others use the lignin more than the cellulose.

Every brown, crumbly rot is commonly called "dry rot," but since no wood will rot while it is dry, the term "dry rot" is a misnomer. There are a few fungi that have water-conducting strands and are therefore capable of carrying water from some source, usually in the soil, up into buildings or lumber piles, where they moisten and rot wood that would otherwise be dry. After these fungi cease to work, the decayed wood commonly becomes dry again; the term "dry rot," if used at all, is probably best limited to the work of these fungi.

In living trees the sapwood is less subject to fungus attack than the heartwood. The sapwood of logs or products, on the other hand, decays more readily than the heartwood; this may be due to the more available food supply in the sapwood, or to the presence in the heartwood of certain extractives that are toxic to the fungus.

Incipient decay induced by fungi is not always reflected immediately in pronounced weakening of the wood. In the later stages of decay serious reduction in strength will always occur.

---

* For methods of measurement of size of knots or holes, see A.S.T.M. Standard D245-33.
† Excerpts from Wood Handbook by the Forest Products Laboratory, pp. 249 to 250.

20. PRESERVATION OF TIMBER

Preservative Processes. The average life of timber used in the United States, which is subject to decay, is about 8 years; its life can be extended to 12 years either by a chemical impregnation of the wood cells or by an exterior application of a preservative coating which will penetrate the fibers. Creosote oil is the preservative in most common use.

Preservation. The general method followed in the commercial treatment of timber with creosote involves the following steps: (1) seasoning the timber, (2) steaming the timber in a large cylinder to soften the wood fiber, (3) removal of air and moisture from the wood fibers by means of a vacuum pump, (4) admission of creosote oil to the evacuated chamber—the oil penetrates some distance into the timber, (5) the application of pressure forcing the preservative into the innermost fibers of the timber, and (6) the removal of pressure, after which the excess of creosote is allowed to drip off the timber and run into a tank.

In the best non-pressure process, the timber is heated and cooled in an open tank of creosote. The contraction of gases upon cooling draws the creosote into the timber. The penetration of creosote is less in this process than in the pressure-vacuum process.

Since creosote is rather expensive, other preservatives have been tried. Zinc chloride, which is violently poisonous to timber-destroying bacteria, can be forced into the inner fibers of wood; it is cheaper than creosote. However, zinc chloride is soluble in water, whereas creosote is not, and zinc chloride is an effective preservative only in extremely dry regions.

The following table gives approximate weights of creosote required per cubic foot of timber for various services.

Railroad ties:
    Hardwood...................................... 6–14 lb per cu ft
    Softwood...................................... 13–20 lb per cu ft
Dimension timbers............................... 15–20 lb per cu ft
Piles.. 20–30 lb per cu ft
Poles and posts, treated by open tank method for a length
    of 7 ft:
    Chestnut poles................................... 21 lb per pole
    Western pine poles.............................. 65 lb per pole

21. CLASSIFICATION AND GRADING OF LUMBER

Classification of Lumber (Simplified Practice Recommendation 16, U. S. Department of Commerce). Lumber is defined as the product of the saw and planing mill not further manufactured than by sawing, resawing, and passing lengthwise through a standard planing machine, cross-cut to length and matched.

Use Classification

Yard Lumber. Lumber that is less than 6 in. in thickness, and is intended for general building purposes.
Structural Timbers. Lumber that is 6 in. or over in thickness and width.
Factory or Shop Lumber. Lumber intended to be cut up for further manufacture.

Size Classification

Strips. Yard lumber less than 2 in. thick and less than 8 in. wide.
Boards. Yard lumber less than 2 in. thick, 8 in. or over in width.
Dimension Lumber. All yard lumber except boards, strips, and timbers; that is, yard lumber not less than 2 and under 6 in. thick, and of any width; this includes (1) planks, yard lumber not less than 2 and under 4 in. thick and 8 in. or more wide; (2) scantlings, yard lumber not less than 2 and under 6 in. thick and under 8 in. wide; (3) heavy joists, yard lumber not less than 4 and under 6 in. thick and 8 in. or over wide.
Timbers. Lumber 6 in. or larger in least dimension.

Manufacturing Classification

Rough Lumber. Undressed as it comes from the saw.
Surfaced Lumber. Lumber that is dressed by running through a planer. It may be surfaced on one side (S1S), two sides (S2S), one edge (S1E), two edges (S2E), or a combination of sides and edges, (S1S1E), (S2S1E), (S1S2E), or (S4S).
Worked Lumber. Lumber which has been run through a matching machine, sticker, or molder. Worked lumber includes: (1) matched lumber, which is edge dressed and shaped to make a close tongued and grooved joint at the edges or end when laid edge to edge or end to end; (2) shiplapped lumber, which is edge dressed to make a close rabbeted or lapped joint; (3) patterned lumber, which is shaped to a patterned or molded form.

Table I. Strength Properties of Some Commercially Important Woods Grown in the United States

(From Wood Handbook, U. S. Department of Agriculture, prepared by Forest Products Laboratory, Madison, Wis.)

(Results of tests on small,[1] clear specimens in the green and air-dry condition[2])

Commercial and Botanical Name of Species	Moisture Content (Per Cent)	Specific Gravity[3]	Static Bending — Fiber Stress at Proportional Limit (Lb per sq in.)	Modulus of Rupture (Lb per sq in.)	Modulus of Elasticity (1000 lb per sq in.)	Work to Proportional Limit (In.-lb per cu in.)	Work to Maximum Load (In.-lb per cu in.)	Impact Bending — Fiber Stress at Proportional Limit (Lb per sq in.)	Impact Bending — Height of Drop Causing Complete Failure (50-lb Hammer) (Inches)	Compression Parallel to Grain — Fiber Stress at Proportional Limit (Lb per sq in.)	Compression Parallel to Grain — Maximum Crushing Strength (Lb per sq in.)	Compression Perpendicular to Grain — Fiber Stress at Proportional Limit (Lb per sq in.)	Shear Parallel to Grain — Maximum Shearing Strength (Lb per sq in.)	Hardness — End — Load Required to Embed a 0.444-in. Ball to ½ Its Diameter (Lb)	Hardness — Side (Lb)
	2	3	4	5	6	7	8	9	10	11	12	13	14	15	16
Alder, red (Alnus rubra)	98	0.37	3,800	6,500	1170	0.70	8.0	8,000	20	2620	2960	310	770	550	440
	12	.41	6,900	9,800	1380	1.85	8.4	11,600	22	4530	5820	540	1080	980	590
Ash, black (Fraxinus nigra)	85	.45	2,600	6,000	1040	.41	12.1	.....	33	1690	2300	430	860	590	.....
	12	.49	7,200	12,600	1600	1.57	14.9	.....	35	4520	5970	940	1570	1150	.....
Ash, commercial white[4] (Fraxinus sp.)	43	.54	5,300	9,500	1400	1.14	14.7	12,800	37	3360	4060	860	1350	1010	940
	12	.58	8,900	14,600	1680	2.68	17.0	17,000	40	5580	7280	1510	1920	1680	1260
Ash, Oregon (Fraxinus oregona)	48	.50	4,200	7,600	1130	.92	15.6	8,900	39	2760	3510	650	1190	850	790
	12	.55	7,000	12,700	1360	2.08	12.2	13,300	33	4100	5680	1540	1790	1430	1160
Aspen (Populus tremuloides)	94	.35	2,100	5,100	1180	.69	6.4	7,000	22	1670	2140	220	660	280	300
	12	.38	5,600	8,400	860	1.53	7.6	9,000	21	3040	4250	460	850	510	350
Basswood (Tilia glabra)	105	.32	2,500	5,000	1040	.40	5.3	6,300	16	1690	2220	210	600	290	250
	12	.37	5,500	8,700	1460	1.37	7.2	9,800	16	3800	4730	450	990	520	410
Beech (Fagus grandifolia)	54	.56	4,300	8,600	1380	.85	11.9	11,500	43	2550	3550	670	1290	970	850
	12	.64	8,700	14,900	1720	2.63	15.9	16,000	41	4880	7300	1250	2010	1590	1300
Birch[5] (Betula sp.)	62	.57	4,400	8,700	1560	.79	15.8	11,100	48	2640	3510	550	1160	910	910
	12	.63	10,100	16,700	2070	2.83	19.8	20,000	52	6200	7510	1250	2020	1660	1340
Birch, paper (Betula papyrifera)	65	.48	3,000	6,400	1170	.45	16.0	12,400	49	1640	2360	340	840	470	560
	12	.55	5,700	12,300	1590	1.80	16.2	.....	34	3610	5690	740	1210	890	910
Butternut (Juglans cinerea)	104	.36	2,900	5,400	970	.52	8.2	7,300	24	2020	2510	270	760	410	390
	12	.38	5,700	8,100	1180	1.59	9.4	9,100	24	4200	5110	570	1170	570	490
Cedar, Alaska (Chamaecyparis nootkatensis)	38	.42	4,100	6,400	1140	.77	10.4	12,200	27	2500	3050	430	840	540	440
	12	.44	6,000	11,100	1420	2.06	15.0	.....	29	5210	6310	770	1130	790	580
Cedar, eastern red (Juniperus virginiana)	35	.44	3,400	7,000	650	1.01	8.3	7,500	35	2540	3570	860	.....	760	650
	12	.47	3,800	8,800	880	.94	6.4	8,500	22	.....	6020	1140	1010	900	.....
Cedar, incense (Libocedrus decurrens)	108	.35	3,900	6,200	840	.....	5.4	7,300	17	2940	3150	460	830	570	390
	12		5,900	8,000	1040	1.67		9,600	17	4760	5200	730	880	830	470

Species	Tests[1]	Sp. gr.[3]	C3	C4	C5	C6	C7	C8	C9	C10	C11	C12	C13	C14	C15
Cedar, northern white (*Thuja occidentalis*)	55	.29	2,600	4,200	640	.60	5.7	5,300	15	1490	1990	290	620	320	230
	12	.31	4,900	6,500	800	.72	4.8	7,100	12	2630	3960	380	850	450	320
Cedar, Port Orford (*Chamaecyparis lawsoniana*)	43	.40	4,000	6,200	1420	.65	7.4	9,200	22	2770	3130	350	830	460	400
	12	.42	7,000	11,500	1730	.97	9.1	13,500	28	5890	6470	760	1080	730	560
Cedar, southern white (*Chamaecyparis thyoides*)	35	.31	2,500	4,700	750	.51	5.9	6,000	18	1660	2390	300	690	400	290
	12	.32	4,800	6,800	930	.46	4.1	7,600	13	2740	4700	500	800	520	350
Cedar, western red (*Thuja plicata*)	37	.31	3,200	5,100	920	.63	5.0	6,900	17	2470	2750	340	710	430	270
	12	.31	5,300	7,700	1120	.44	5.8	8,600	17	4360	5040	610	860	660	350
Cherry, black (*Prunus serotina*)	55	.47	4,200	12,300	1310	.80	12.8	10,200	33	2940	3540	440	1130	750	660
	12	.40	9,000	5,600	1490	3.11	7.0	13,200	29	5960	7110	850	1700	1470	950
Chestnut (*Castanea dentata*)	122	.40	3,100	5,300	930	.59	6.5	7,900	24	2080	2080	380	800	530	420
	11	.37	6,100	8,500	1010	.78	7.3	10,700	19	3780	2470	760	1080	720	540
Cottonwood, eastern (*Populus deltoides*)	132	.40	2,900	4,800	1370	.49	7.4	7,200	21	1740	5320	240	930	580	340
	12	.32	5,700	8,300	1070	.39	5.0	7,300	20	3490	2280	470	680	580	430
Cottonwood, northern black (*Populus trichocarpa hastata*)	91	.35	5,300	10,600	1260	.44	6.7	6,800	22	1760	2160	200	600	600	250
	12	.42	8,500	11,700	1180	1.25	6.6	9,800	25	3270	4420	370	1020	540	350
Cypress, southern (*Taxodium distichum*)	36	.46	2,900	3,600	1440	.91	8.2	8,800	24	3100	3580	500	810	440	590
	12	.45	4,800	6,800	1550	2.15	8.6	10,400	24	4740	6360	900	1000	510	510
Douglas fir (coast region) (*Pseudotsuga taxifolia*)	42	.48	4,200	11,300	1920	.85	8.9	9,800	30	3410	3890	510	930	660	480
	12	.41	6,600	6,400	1340	.96	6.6	12,700	22	6450	7420	910	1140	760	670
Douglas fir ("Inland Empire" region) (*Pseudotsuga taxifolia*)	38	.44	4,800	9,600	1610	.55	8.6	8,700	27	2460	3240	500	870	720	470
	12	.43	8,100	7,200	1180	.91	6.8	11,800	26	5520	6700	950	1190	450	630
Douglas fir (Rocky Mountain region) (*Pseudotsuga taxifolia*)	89	.46	3,600	11,800	1400	.65	6.4	9,100	38	2460	3000	450	720	740	400
	12	.50	6,800	9,500	1110	1.60	11.8	12,100	39	2540	2910	820	880	680	630
Elm, American (*Ulmus americana*)	48	.57	7,400	14,800	1340	.81	13.0		54	4660	5520	440	1070	1110	
	12	.63	11,300	8,000	1190	1.05	19.2		47	1920	3780	850	1510	980	
Elm, rock (*Ulmus racemosa*)	85	.48	6,300	13,000	1540	2.53	19.8	9,200	45	4030	7050	750	1270	1510	660
	12	.53	9,600	4,900	1230	2.45	15.4	5,300	16	2970	3320	510	1920	750	860
Elm, slippery (*Ulmus fulva*)	117	.34	3,900	7,600	1490	.82	4.7	6,900	20	4700	6360	1010	1110	1120	290
	12	.36	7,200	5,800	960	2.35	5.1	7,800	22	2790	2400	210	1630	290	400
Fir, balsam (*Abies balsamea*)	108	.36	4,600	9,300	1230	.52	5.3	8,300	20	4760	4530	380	610	510	460
	12	.38	11,800	7,000	1120	1.23	7.0	11,200	30	2080	2810	360	710	390	340
Fir, commercial white (*Abies sp.*)[6]	55	.46	8,000	9,600	1470	.75	6.2	1,200	22	3970	5380	610	750	710	640
	12	.50	14,800	11,900	1030	1.55	9.4	4,500	33	2470	3040	930	930	790	810
Gum, black (*Nyssa sylvatica*)	81	.44	7,700	7,300	1150	.91	11.3	14,500	32	3870	5520	600	1100	1240	520
	12	.49	13,000	9,600	1490	2.54	8.3	16,800	30	2490	2230	1150	1340	630	690
Gum, red (*Liquidambar styraciflua*)	97	.46	3,000	11,000	1050	.81	8.9		23	3470	5800	460	1070	690	710
	12	.46	4,900	6,400	1260	2.57	14.5	2,500	48	2230	3370	860	1610	800	880
Gum, tupelo (*Nyssa aquatica*)	65	.50	5,200	8,900	950	.98	12.8	2,900	43	4700	5920	590	1190	1200	700
	12	.49	7,600		1190	2.41	6.7	13,700	21	2690	2650	1070	1590	760	880
Hackberry (*Celtis occidentalis*)	111	.53	3,800	6,300	1070	.58	6.8	7,900		4280	5440	490	1070	1110	400
	12	.38	6,100	8,900	1190	1.22		10,700		2070	3080	1100	1590	760	500
Hemlock, eastern (*Tsuga canadensis*)		.40			1200	.76				2600	5410	440	850	1110	
						1.79				4020		800	1060	810	

[1] Test specimens 2 by 2 in. in section. Bending specimens 30 in. long; others shorter depending on kind of test.

[2] The values in the first line for each species are from tests of green material; those in the second line are from tests of seasoned material adjusted to an average air dry condition of 12 per cent moisture.

[3] Based on weight when oven dry and volume when green or at 12 per cent moisture content.

[4] Average of Biltmore white ash (*Fraxinus biltmoreana*), blue ash (*F. quadrangulata*), green ash (*F. pennsylvanica lanceolata*), and white ash (*F. americana*).

[5] Average of sweet birch (*Betula lenta*) and yellow birch (*B. lutea*).

[6] Average of lowland white fir (*Abies grandis*) and white fir (*A. concolor*).

Table I. Strength Properties of Some Commercially Important Woods Grown in the United States—*Continued*

(From Wood Handbook, U. S. Department of Agriculture, prepared by Forest Products Laboratory, Madison, Wis.)

(Results of tests on small, clear specimens in the green and air-dry condition)

Commercial and Botanical Name of Species	Moisture Content	Specific Gravity	Static Bending — Fiber Stress at Proportional Limit	Static Bending — Modulus of Rupture	Static Bending — Modulus of Elasticity	Work to — Proportional Limit	Work to — Maximum Load	Impact Bending — Fiber Stress at Proportional Limit	Impact Bending — Height of Drop Causing Complete Failure (50-lb Hammer)	Compression Parallel to Grain — Fiber Stress at Proportional Limit	Compression Parallel to Grain — Maximum Crushing Strength	Compression Perpendicular to Grain — Fiber Stress at Proportional Limit	Shear Parallel to Grain — Maximum Shearing Strength	Hardness — End (Load Required to Embed a 0.444-in. Ball to ½ Its Diameter)	Hardness — Side
1	2	3	4	5	6	7	8	9	10	11	12	13	14	15	16
	Per Cent		Lb per sq in.	Lb per sq in.	1000 lb per sq in.	In.-lb per cu in.	In.-lb per cu in.	Lb per sq in.	Inches	Lb per sq in.	Lb per sq in.	Lb per sq in.	Lb per sq in.	Lb	Lb
Hemlock, western (*Tsuga heterophylla*)	74	0.38	3,400	6,100	1220	0.57	6.8	8,100	22	2480	2990	390	810	520	430
	12	.42	6,800	10,100	1490	1.82	7.5	12,400	26	5340	6210	680	1170	940	580
Hickory, pecan [7] (*Hicoria sp.*)	68	.59	5,300	9,900	1380	1.18	19.3	14,200	60	3810	4320	980	1260	1274	1308
	12	.65	9,100	16,300	1780	2.61	18.8	15,700	57	6360	8230	2040	1770	1930	1820
Hickory, true [8] (*Hicoria sp.*)	57	.65	6,100	11,300	1570	1.34	28.5	21,800	88	3650	4570	1080	1360	.....	.....
	12	.73	10,900	19,700	2180	3.07	27.2	.....	75	.....	8970	2310	2140	.....	.....
Honey locust (*Gleditsia triacanthos*)	63	.60	5,600	10,200	1290	1.40	12.6	15,400	47	3330	4420	1420	1660	1440	1390
	12	.....	8,800	14,700	1630	2.74	13.3	.....	47	5250	7500	2280	2250	1860	1580
Larch, western (*Larix occidentalis*)	58	.48	4,600	7,500	1350	1.01	8.0	9,400	24	3250	3800	560	920	470	450
	12	.52	7,900	11,900	1710	2.46	15.4	15,100	32	5950	7490	1080	1360	1110	760
Locust, black (*Robinia pseudoacacia*)	40	.66	8,800	13,800	1850	2.36	18.0	18,300	44	6120	6800	1430	1760	1640	1570
	12	.69	12,800	19,400	2050	4.62	18.4	21,100	57	6800	10,180	2260	2480	1580	1700
Magnolia, cucumber (*Magnolia acuminata*)	80	.44	4,200	7,400	1560	.66	12.4	14,700	35	2810	3140	410	990	600	520
	12	.48	8,000	12,300	1820	.98	15.2	.....	54	4840	6310	710	1340	950	700
Magnolia, evergreen (*Magnolia grandiflora*)	105	.46	3,600	6,800	1110	.67	12.7	13,600	23	2160	2700	570	1040	780	740
	12	.50	6,800	11,200	1400	1.02	12.8	8,500	23	3420	5460	1060	1530	1280	1020
Maple, bigleaf (*Acer macrophyllum*)	72	.44	4,400	7,400	1100	.70	8.7	10,200	28	2510	3240	550	1110	630	620
	12	.48	6,600	10,700	1450	1.66	7.8	.....	48	4790	5950	930	1730	850	850
Maple, black (*Acer nigrum*)	65	.52	4,100	7,900	1330	.71	12.8	13,500	40	2800	3270	740	1130	940	840
	12	.57	8,300	13,300	1620	2.39	12.5	.....	32	4600	6680	1250	1820	1180	1180
Maple, red (*Acer rubrum*)	63	.49	3,800	7,700	1390	.61	11.4	6,800	32	2360	3280	500	1150	700	.....
	12	.54	8,700	13,400	1640	2.84	11.0	.....	29	4650	6540	1240	1850	950	910
Maple, silver (*Acer saccharinum*)	66	.44	3,100	5,800	940	.....	.....	12,400	25	1930	2490	460	1050	670	590
	12	.47	6,200	9,400	1140	.90	.....	.....	40	4360	5220	910	1480	1140	700
Maple, sugar (*Acer saccharum*)	58	.56	5,100	9,400	1550	1.03	13.3	12,200	39	2850	4020	800	1460	1070	970
	12	.63	9,500	15,800	1830	2.76	16.5	20,600	39	5390	7830	1810	2330	1840	1450

Species	Moisture (%)	Sp. gr.	C3	C4	C5	C6	C7	C8	C9	C10	C11	C12	C13	C14	C15
Oak, red [9] (Quercus sp.)	80	.57	4,400	8,500	1360	.85	12.6	10,800	43	2590	3520	800	1220	1050	1036
	12	.63	8,400	14,400	1810	2.30	15.0	17,000	43	4610	6920	1260	1830	1490	1300
Oak, white [10] (Quercus sp.)	70	.59	4,700	8,100	1200	1.08	11.3	10,900	42	2940	3520	850	1270	1420	1070
	12	.67	7,900	14,700	1620	2.31		17,400	39	4350	7040	1190	1890		1330
Pine, lodgepole (Pinus contorta)	65	.38	3,000	5,500	1080	.49	5.6	7,400	20	2110	2610	1410	680	520	1070
	12	.41	6,700	9,400	1340	1.97	8.2	10,900	20	4310	5370	750	880	550	520
Pine, northern white (Pinus strobus)	68	.34	3,100	5,000	1020	.54	6.8	7,400	17	2060	2490	290	660	850	440
	12	.36	5,700	8,600	1340	1.59	10.8	9,600	19	3680	4840	550	880	530	310
Pine, Norway (Pinus resinosa)	54	.44	3,400	6,800	1380	.59	5.7	7,100	28	2410	3080	360	780	860	500
	12	.48	6,200	11,000	1800	2.78	10.9	9,500	25	5330	7340	830	1230	670	360
Pine, ponderosa (Pinus ponderosa)	91	.38	3,100	6,300	970	.59	5.5	6,800	20	2070	2400	360	680	300	340
	12	.40	6,300	9,200	1260	1.85	6.6	9,800	17	4060	5270	740	1160	550	580
Pines, southern yellow:															
Loblolly (Pinus taeda)	81	.47	4,100	7,300	1410	.68	8.2	8,900	30	2550	3490	480	850	420	450
	12	.51	7,800	12,800	1800	1.92	10.4	12,100	30	4820	7080	980	1370	750	690
Longleaf (Pinus palustris)	63	.54	5,200	8,700	1600	.95	8.9	10,100	35	3430	4300	590	1040	550	590
	12	.58	9,300	14,700	1990	2.44	10.0	12,100	34	6150	8440	1190	1500	920	870
Shortleaf (Pinus echinata)	81	.46	3,900	7,300	1390	.63	8.2	8,600	30	2500	3430	440	850	410	490
	12	.49	7,700	12,800	1760	1.93	11.0	13,600	33	5090	7070	1000	1310	710	690
Pine, sugar (Pinus lambertiana)	137	.35	3,400	5,100	940	.70	5.6	7,600	17	2330	2530	350	680	320	310
	12	.36	5,700	8,000	1190	1.53	7.6	10,700	18	4140	4770	590	1050	530	370
Pine, western white (Pinus monticola)	54	.36	3,400	5,200	1200	.56	5.7	7,600	19	2430	2650	290	640	320	310
	12	.38	6,200	9,500	1510	1.47	8.8	11,900	23	4480	5620	540		440	340
Poplar, yellow (Liriodendron tulipifera)	64	.38	3,400	5,400	1090	.62	8.4	8,600	18	1930	2420	330	740	390	340
	12	.40	6,100	9,200	1500	1.43	7.4	13,500	18	3550	5290	520	1100	560	450
Redwood (virgin) (Sequoia sempervirens)	112	.38	4,800	7,500	1180	1.18	6.4	8,900	21	3700	4200	860	800	570	410
	12	.40	6,900	10,000	1340	2.04	6.5	10,200	19	4560	6150	290	940	790	480
Spruce, eastern [11] (Picea sp.)	46	.38	3,300	5,000	1440	.57	6.1	7,400	21	2120	2600	290	710	390	340
	12	.40	6,500	10,100	1180	1.68	8.4	11,400	22	2600	5590	590	1070	630	490
Spruce, Engelmann (Picea engelmannii)	100	.31	2,500	4,200	830	.43	4.9	5,800	14	1680	1980	240	590	390	240
	12	.33	6,000	8,500	1160	1.64	6.4	9,000	15	3580	4580	340	1010	450	310
Spruce, Sitka (Picea sitchensis)	42	.37	3,300	5,700	1230	.53	6.3	8,400	24	2240	2670	290	760	430	350
	12	.40	6,700	10,200	1570	1.62	9.4	11,400	25	4780	5610	640	1150	760	510
Sugarberry (Celtis laevigata)	62	.47	3,200	6,600	810	.78	12.2	8,200	33	1990	2800	340	1050	840	740
	12	.51	6,900	9,900	1140	2.18	11.0	11,600	36	3970	5620	710	1280	1280	960
Sycamore (Platanus occidentalis)	83	.46	3,300	6,500	1060	.60	7.5	8,800	26	2400	2920	580	1000	700	610
	12	.49	6,400	10,000	1420	1.66	8.5	10,500	28	3710	5380	1240	1280	610	770
Tamarack (Larix laricina)	52	.49	4,200	7,200	1240	.84	7.2	7,800	23	2930	3480	450	860	920	380
	12	.53	8,000	11,600	1640	2.19	7.1	12,500	28	4780	7160	860	1470	400	590
Walnut, black (Juglans nigra)	81	.51	5,400	9,500	1420	1.16	14.6	11,900	37	3520	4300	480	1220	670	900
	12	.55	10,500	14,600	1680	3.70	10.7	16,400	34	5780	7580	600	1370	960	1010

[7] Average of bitternut hickory (Hicoria cordiformis), nutmeg hickory (H. myristicaeformis), water hickory (H. aquatica), and pecan (H. pecan).

[8] Average of bigleaf shagbark hickory (Hicoria laciniosa), mockernut hickory (H. alba), pignut hickory (H. glabra), and shagbark hickory (H. ovata).

[9] Average of black oak (Quercus velutina), laurel oak (Q. laurifolia), pin oak (Q. palustris), red oak (Q. borealis), scarlet oak (Q. coccinea), southern red oak (Q. rubra), swamp red oak (Q. rubra pagodaefolia), water oak (Q. nigra), and willow oak (Q. phellos).

[10] Average of bur oak (Quercus macrocarpa), chestnut oak (Q. montana), post oak (Q. stellata), swamp chestnut oak (Q. prinus), swamp white oak (Q. bicolor), and white oak (Q. alba).

[11] Average of black spruce (Picea mariana), red spruce (P. rubra), and white spruce (P. glauca).

Grades of Softwood Yard Lumber. The term " yard lumber " as here used means lumber that is manufactured and classified into those sizes, shapes, and qualities required for ordinary construction and general-purpose uses. Heavy timbers for structural purposes, softwood factory lumber, and other special-use materials are not considered yard stock. In the rules of the American Lumber Association, finish, siding, flooring, ceiling, partition, common boards and strips, shiplap, D. & M. (dressed and matched), grooved roofing, dimension and lath are considered yard lumber.

On the basis of quality, yard lumber is divided into two main divisions: (*a*) select lumber and (*b*) common lumber. Each of these is again divided into two classes: select lumber into (1) that suitable for natural finishes, and (2) that suitable for paint finishes; common lumber into (1) that which can be used without waste, and (2) that which permits some waste. Each of these four classes is further divided into quality classes or grades as hereinafter described.

The following diagram shows the general characteristics of, and the relationship existing between, the various grades of lumber:

Diagrammatic Summary of the Basic Grades for Yard Lumber

Select (Lumber of good appearance and finishing qualities)	Suitable for natural finishes	Grade B and better—Allows a few small defects or blemishes
	Suitable for paint finishes	Grade C—Allows a limited number of small defects or blemishes that can be covered with paint
		Grade D—Allows any number of defects or blemishes which do not detract from a finish appearance, especially when painted
Common (Lumber containing defects or blemishes which detract from a finish appearance but which is suitable for general utility and construction purposes)	Lumber suitable for use without waste	No. 1 Common—Sound and tight knotted stock; size of defects and blemishes limited; may be considered watertight lumber
		No. 2 Common—Allows large and coarse defects; may be considered graintight lumber
	Lumber permitting waste	No. 3 Common—Allows larger and coarser defects than No. 2 and occasional knot holes
		No. 4 Common—Low-quality lumber admitting the coarsest defects such as rot and holes
		No. 5 Common—Must hold together under ordinary handling

Grades of Hardwood Lumber. (From Rules of the National Hardwood Lumber Association, 1934.) The standard grades of hardwood lumber shall consist of firsts, seconds, selects, No. 1 common, No. 2 common, sound wormy, No. 3A common, and No. 3B common. Firsts and seconds are combined as one grade, and the percentage of firsts in the combined grade shall not be less than as follows: poplar and Philippine mahogany, 40 per cent; African and Mexican mahogany, 35 per cent; tupelo, sycamore, plain oak, chestnut, red gum, sap gum, black gum, cottonwood, magnolia, locust, hackberry, willow and aspen, 33 1/3 per cent; cherry, soft elm, buckeye, box elder, quartered oak and quartered gum, 25 per cent; hard maple, soft maple, red alder, white ash, beech, birch, black ash and basswood, 20 per cent.

Selects and No. 1 common may be combined as one grade, except in mahogany, walnut, and cherry, and when so combined and specified shall be understood to include all selects that the logs produce.

No. 3A common and No. 3B common may be combined as one grade, No. 3 common, and when so combined and specified shall be understood to include all the No. 3A common that the logs produce.

For details concerning each grade, see the rules published by the National Hardwood Lumber Association.

22. PROPERTIES OF TIMBER

Mechanical Properties of Timber. Table I gives the mechanical properties of some important woods grown in the United States. For allowable safe loads on timbers see pp. 12–44 and 12–47.

Time Element in the Strength of Wood. Under long-continued steady load wood will fail under stresses much lower than those found at the ultimate strength in laboratory tests, which cover only a few moments. Under longtime loading test pieces of wood have broken under stresses only a little above 50 per cent of the ultimate as given by short-time laboratory tests. This very pronounced time effect is one of the reasons why working stresses for timber are low as compared with ultimate strength.

Effect of Moisture on Strength of Wood. Up to a moisture content of about 25 per cent for softwoods, the fibers absorb water and are weakened and softened by it. For moisture content above this " fiber saturation point " water no longer affects the strength and stiffness of wood.

Increase in Strength Due to Seasoning. The increase in strength of woods due to drying is more uniform in small test specimens than in the large sizes used in construction. However, if the seasoning is done carefully so as to avoid the formation of checks, there should be a marked increase in the strength of structural timber after drying.

23. PLYWOOD

Manufacture. Plywood is made by gluing together thin layers of wood. The grain in one layer is at right angles to the grain in the next layer. An odd number of layers is used. It is important that the layers of wood are all split or sawed the same way from a stick of timber, and that the moisture content is approximately the same for all layers. If these precautions are not taken the plywood will tend to warp owing to uneven stresses in the different layers.

Strength of Plywood. A limitation of the use of large boards is the difference in strength of wood in various directions. The tensile strength of wood parallel to the grain may be as much as twenty times the strength perpendicular to the grain, and the shearing strength parallel to the grain is much lower than the shearing strength across the grain, In plywood the strength is approximately equal in all directions and is equal, approximately, to the mean of the strength with and the strength across the grain. As plywood is built up of thin layers it becomes feasible to use a high grade of wood in its manufacture. The tensile strength of plywood is given in Table II.

Woods Available for Plywood. Basswood, redwood, poplar, maple, birch, and red gum are domestic woods which can be cut into the thin sheets necessary for making plywood. Basswood, redwood, and poplar are not often used for the face layers.

Plywood is used mainly in the shape of thin sheets, and is of importance in manufacture of automobiles, street and railway cars, airplanes, and boats.

Table II. Tensile Strength of Plywood
Based on test data from the U. S. Forest Products Laboratory, Madison, Wis.

Species	Weight of Plywood, Kiln-dry, lb per cu ft	Moisture at Test, per cent	Tensile Strength of 3-ply Plywood Parallel to Grain of Faces, lb per sq in.	Tensile Strength of Single-ply Veneer, Parallel to Grain, lb per sq in.
Basswood...............	28	9.2	6,900	10,300
Yellow birch............	45	8.5	13,200	19,800
Maple, soft.............	38	8.9	8,200	12,300
hard.............	46	8.0	10,200	15,300
Yellow poplar...........	34	3.4	7,400	11,100
Red gum...............	36	8.7	7,800	11,800
Redwood...............	28	9.7	4,800	7,200

PAINTS, ENAMELS, VARNISHES, AND LACQUERS

By Joseph Mattiello

24. PAINTS AND ENAMELS

Paints and Enamels. Paint, technically a plastic solid, covers a wide variety of pigmented coatings designed for the purpose of protecting and decorating the surface to which they are applied.

There are various types of paints, such as: exterior house paints, interior flat wall paints, enamels, semi-gloss finishes, primers and undercoaters, floor enamels, anti-corrosive and metal-preservative paints, heat-resisting paints, and hundreds of others. Each type is formulated to give the best results for its specific use. For instance, house paint is formulated with three major properties in mind—protection, durability, and beautification; flat wall paint is formulated primarily for decorative value; floor paints, for wear and resistance to abrasion, etc.

In general, paints are mechanical mixtures of pigments and vehicles (oils, varnishes, thinners, and driers). The paint technologist selects the proper vehicle combination to give specific results according to the type of paint being formulated. The proper pigment or pigment combination is then selected, again according to the purpose for which the paint is to be used. Extensive tests have proved that the volume of pigment present is of great importance. From 28 to 30 per cent pigment volume concentration, based on the non-volatile vehicle, gives greater durability and protection than lesser amounts of pigment.

Exposure tests have shown that primers for new wood should contain a pigment volume of about 35 per cent rather than 28 to 30 per cent as in finishing coats.

Flat wall paints are very high in pigment volume (about 60 per cent based on the non-volatile vehicle) and the vehicles which produce a flat finish are low in non-volatile content (30 to 37 per cent non-volatile content, 70 to 63 per cent volatile thinner). Enamels are low in pigment content and higher in non-volatile vehicle, producing a gloss finish. Enamels are usually made of pigments and varnishes.

Manufacture. The pigments are first mixed to a paste consistency with a portion of the total vehicle. This paste is ground through either a roller mill, consisting of steel rolls, one of which goes faster than another, or a stone mill, one stone of which is stationary and the other revolving. This grinding action breaks down the agglomerates of the pigment and disperses them throughout the vehicle. After grinding, the paste is thinned to the proper consistency with the balance of the vehicle, stored, and filled.

In a variation of this process, the pigment and vehicles are "loaded" without pre-mixing, in a pebble mill, which is a revolving barrel half filled with flint pebbles. The drum is revolved for many hours. The pebbles falling through the paint disperse the pigment agglomerates. This mill grinds paint in the "ready-mixed" or liquid form so that it does not require a separate thinning operation after grinding, but may be canned directly from the mill.

Vehicles. The vehicles used in the formulation of paints may be any of the drying oils (linseed, tung, perilla, etc.), or semi-drying oils (soya, fish, etc.) with or without the addition of resin varnishes, or straight resin varnish, the manufacture of which is treated under varnishes, thinners, and driers.

Pigments. The pigments may be divided into the following three general classes:

1. The white opaque pigments shown in Table I.
2. The extender pigments: asbestine, whiting, silica, barites, clay, etc.
3. The colored opaque pigments:
    - *a.* The earth colors: ochers, siennas, umbers, red oxides, etc.
    - *b.* The chemical color pigments: chrome yellows, chrome and nitrate greens, blues, etc.
    - *c.* The lake colors: precipitated dyes.
    - *d.* The blacks, gasblack, lampblack, boneblack, etc.
    - *e.* Numerous others.

The principal difference between the white opaque pigments and the extender pigments is in opacity. The extender pigments are white in the dry form, but they become transparent when mixed or wetted with paint oils or vehicles. This phenomenon is due to the fact that there is very little difference between the refractive indices of the extender pigments (1.53–1.60) and those of the oils (media) with which they are wetted (1.47–1.53).

Any pigment used to increase opacity must have a high refractive index; and the difference between its refractive index and that of the vehicle media should be as great as possible. The refractive indices of the opaque pigments vary from 1.84 for lithopone to 2.55 for titanium dioxide. The relative tinting strength and hiding power of the white opaque pigments are given in Table I.

Table I. Properties of White Opaque Pigments

(From Handbook published by the Titanium Pigment Co., Inc., and other sources)

	Tinting Strength	Hiding Power, sq ft per lb	Hiding Units	Refractive Indices
Basic lead sulfate	85	13	0.87	
Basic lead carbonate	100	15	1.00	2.02
Zinc oxide	200	20	1.33	2.01
Lithopone	260	27	1.80	1.84
Titanox B (titanium barium pigment)	380	40	2.67	1.90
High-strength lithopone	400	44	2.93	
Titanated lithopone	400	44	2.93	
Titanox C (titanium calcium pigment)	450	48	3.20	1.91
Zinc sulfide	540	58	3.87	2.34
Titanox A (titanium dioxide pigment)	1150	115	7.67	2.55

Properties and Uses of the Important White Opaque Pigments. The choice of pigments, and oils, and varnishes for vehicles depends upon the serviceability expected of the particular paint or enamel. Protective coatings made from a good combination of mixed pigments are more durable than those containing one single pigment. Some of the characteristics of important white pigments are:

Basic Carbonate White Lead in a paint exhibits excellent durability and freedom from cracking and scaling, but fails by chalking. (Chalking is an advantage for repainting.)

Zinc Oxide imparts hardness to the paint film and improves gloss, but it fails by cracking and scaling. Being opaque to ultraviolet rays, it retards chalking to a greater extent than white lead. Zinc oxide has good color retention. Its greatest use is in interior enamels.

Zinc Sulfide has excellent hiding power and color.

Titanox B (titanium barium pigment: 25 per cent titanium oxide, 75 per cent barium sulfate) is used for both exterior and interior paints and enamels. In exterior house paints, it adds greatly to the hiding power of the paint, reduces the tendency to crack and scale, but fails by chalking.

Titanox C (30 per cent titanium oxide, 70 per cent calcium sulfate) is used principally in interior paints and enamels. It has excellent hiding power and brightness. Its low specific gravity produces high bulking.

Titanium Oxide is the most opaque pigment known to science. It is particularly valuable in low pigment content and fume-resistant paint. It is also used in high-grade interior and exterior enamels. It chalks badly on exterior exposure when used alone.

Lithopone (28 per cent zinc sulfide, 72 per cent barium sulfate) is generally used for interior paints. It has good hiding power and color.

Preparation of Surface. The preparation of the surface to be painted is important. The surface should be dry and free from grease and dirt. A metal surface should also be free from rust and scale. If it is to be used for exterior exposure, metal should first be primed with a pure red lead or specially prepared primer which may contain zinc chromate as part of the pigment. Galvanized iron should be treated with copper sulfate or copper acetate before the first coat of paint is applied. Wooden surfaces, as on frame houses, should be thoroughly dry and all knot holes shellacked before the priming coat is applied. Three thin, well-brushed-out coats give greater durability than two heavy coats. Common practice calls for three coats on new work and two coats on old work.

Plaster walls should be well pointed, dry, and primed or sealed before the finish coats are applied.

Application. Paints for either exterior or interior use are applied either by brush or by air spraying; enamels for industrial use are applied by brushing, spraying, roller-coating, dipping, tumbling, etc. The formulation of the paint or enamel is varied according to the method used. If the paint is to be brushed, careful attention must be given its brushing qualities, flow, etc. If it is to be sprayed it must be formulated to work well in the air gun without clogging, and to atomize easily and properly.

Some industrial finishes are baked. In such finishes the pigment and vehicle must be carefully selected to dry hard in a given time and to resist wrinkling, gas effects, discoloration at baking temperature, etc.

Properties of Paint Films. Air-dry paint films dry, initially, by evaporation of the thinners, and finally by oxidation of the drying oils. The initial setting period is complete within several hours, but from six hours to several days are required for the final drying.

Baking paint films or enamels dry, initially, by evaporation of the thinner, then slightly by oxidation of the drying oils, but finally and mainly by the polymerization of the oil and resin content.

Exterior paints are effected by various rays of the sun. The ultraviolet rays probably disintegrate the oils, thus producing chalking. The disintegrating effects of sunlight, atmospheric gases, and moisture are such that repainting is usually necessary after two or three years of outdoor exposure.

Aluminum Paint. Aluminum paint is made by mixing aluminum powder with a suitable vehicle. Aluminum powder is composed of minute flake-like particles of metallic aluminum produced by a stamping process. It is supplied either as a dry powder or in paste form mixed with mineral spirits. Aluminum paint, mixed in the proportion of 2 lb of powder to 1 gallon of vehicle, gives a coating of high moisture-proofing resistance and superior protective qualities. By proper choice of vehicle it can be used on metal, wood, plaster, or concrete, and is particularly recommended for the painting of aluminum and its alloys.

25. OLEORESINOUS VARNISHES

Varnishes. A varnish is partly a solution, but mainly a colloid. It is a combination of resins and thinners; or resins, oils, driers, and thinners; and of such fluidity that it can readily be applied to a surface. After the thinners evaporate, the remaining material dries to a solid film either by oxidation, or oxidation and polymerization, or by simple evaporation. This solid film protects, preserves, and beautifies the surface.

There are two types of varnish, oleoresinous and spirit. The oleoresinous varnishes dry to a solid film by oxidation (air drying), or by oxidation and polymerization (baking). The spirit varnishes dry purely by evaporation.

General Composition. The four general constituents of oleoresinous varnishes are resins, drying and semi-drying vegetable and animal oils, driers, and thinners or solvents. These are illustrated diagrammatically in Table II.

Table II. Composition of Oleoresinous Varnishes

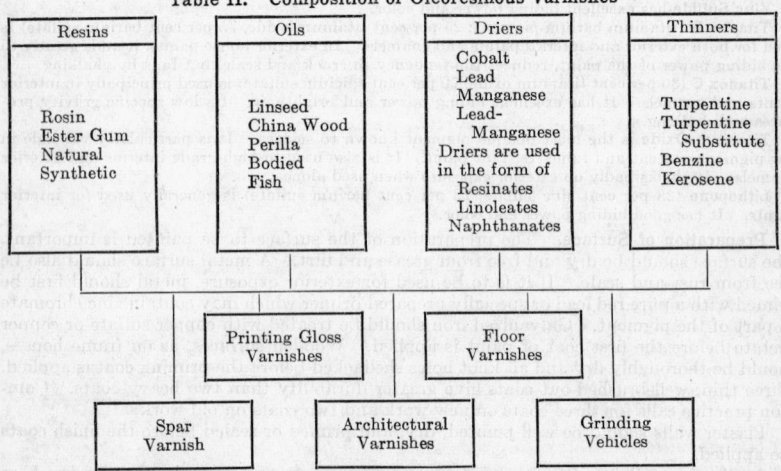

Courtesy Joseph Mattiello, Technical Director: Hilo Varnish Corp., Brooklyn, N. Y.

Function of Each Constituent. *The resins* provide the elements of hardness, resistance to wear, and waterproofness; they also impart gloss and slightly accelerate drying. The synthetic phenol-formaldehyde resins definitely improve durability.

The oils supply the elements of toughness, adhesion, durability, and waterproofness. China wood (tung), has better waterproofness than linseed oil, both give good durability.

Driers. The only important function of the drier is to accelerate drying. For example, linseed oil requires eight days to air-dry by itself when flowed out to a thin film, but with the proper combination and amount of drier it will dry within as brief a time as eight hours. The most effective driers are cobalt, manganese, and lead. They are used in the form of resinates, linoleates, tungates, or naphthanates. Cobalt, the most efficient of the three, is a "surface" drier, lead is a "bottom" drier, and manganese is a "through" drier. Zinc, as a naphthanate, is used to retard wrinkling.

In the formulation of a paint, varnish, or other protective coating, great care must be exercised in the choice of driers. A combination of lead with small amounts of manganese is an ideal drier for colored enamels. Manganese has a tendency to discolor white paints or enamels, causing a very bad after-yellow. The best drier to use for white paints or enamels is a lead or cobalt combination in the form of linoleates, naphthanates, etc.

There is an optimum amount of drier which can be added to paint above which the drier not only becomes ineffective, but actually retards drying. Too much drier also causes the loss of gloss in enamels. It reduces the durability of protective coatings.

Representative figures for the amount of cobalt and lead to be used as a drier for white paint are:

	1	2	3
Lead metal	None	0.20%	0.25%
Cobalt metal	0.025%	0.015%	0.005%

and for a drier composed of lead, manganese, and cobalt:

Lead metal	0.20%
Manganese metal	0.03%
Cobalt	0.01%

All percentages are based on the non-volatile content of the vehicle.

Thinners or Solvents. The most important function of the solvent is to reduce viscosity or increase fluidity so as to permit easy application of the coating to the surface. When vegetable oils are cooked with resins, a very heavy viscous substance is obtained, which may be considered a new resin. As in this state it cannot be applied to a surface, the reduction of viscosity with solvents is necessary. Driers in any form have but slight influence on viscosity.

Formulation of Varnish. Which particular resin or resins, oil or oils, are used in a varnish depends upon the application for which it is being formulated. A varnish may be composed of one resin, one oil, several driers, and one thinner, but most are composed of several resins, oils, driers, and thinners. Varnishes are usually called long or short oil, but more specifically, by the number of gallons of oils used for each 100 lb of resins. Table III illustrates a 35-gallon varnish which is of the usual spar varnish type, and an 18-gallon varnish of the usual floor varnish type.

Table III

35-gallon varnish

Basis: 100 lb resin
35 gallons oil
x gallons drier } varies from 45 to 60% non-volatile
y gallons thinner varies from 55 to 40% volatile
Yield: 100% by weight

18-gallon varnish

Basis: 100 lb resin
18 gallons oil
x' gallons drier } varies from 45 to 50% non-volatile
y' gallons thinner varies from 55 to 50% volatile
Yield: 100% by weight

Manufacture of Oleoresinous Varnishes. Natural hard resins, such as Congo, are insoluble in linseed oil. It is necessary to heat the resin to a temperature above the softening point, whereupon decomposition and depolymerization take place. This causes a loss in weight of 15 to 30 per cent, depending upon the hardness of the natural resin. The resulting fused mass has a lower acid value and a higher iodine number,* and is readily soluble in drying oils. The oil is now added in either the raw or bodied state. With many of the synthetic resins, the oil and resin are added together. In many cases, a definite amount of oil (usually linseed oil) is held out to be used as a chill-back. The varnish is cooked or boiled until the oil and resin are thoroughly miscible in each other. A definite chemical reaction takes place, probably forming a new resin with a higher softening point than the original resin. This mass becomes very viscous if permitted to

---

* The iodine number is a measure of the unsaturation of the oil. Generally, the higher the iodine number is, the better are the drying properties of the oil.

cool. Driers are usually added on the down heat, after which the varnish is thinned, clarified by filtering or centrifuging, stored, and, wherever necessary, natured.

Application. Varnishes are applied either by brushing (mainly for painting homes and buildings), or by spraying or dipping (mainly for commercial use).

Uses. Varnish is used on interior and exterior woodwork, on furniture, on enamels to give added gloss, and on many hundreds of industrial articles.

Resins

Natural Resins. The natural resins are found in nearly all the tropical and semitropical countries. They are the hardened sap of trees, ancient or living. The most important natural varnish resins used are Kauri, Congo, Pontianok, East India, Dammar and Manila. There are many other resins, but their use is limited.

Synthetic Resins constitute an extremely numerous and heterogeneous class of products. They have been studied since the middle of the nineteenth century, when Beyer investigated the reaction products of phenols and aldehydes. Since Baekeland's commercial success with Bakelite, an increasing amount of research has been devoted to the utilization of these products in oleoresinous varnishes.

Phenol-formaldehyde Resins. When phenol and formaldehyde are caused to give a series of condensation products, and these in turn polymerize, the resulting product is a synthetic resin. If an acid catalyst is used during the condensation reactions, the so-called Novelack resin is obtained, which remains fusible and soluble under all conditions. With an alkali catalyst, the so-called Bakelite or reactive type is obtained. In the early stages of condensation, this resin is fusible, and soluble in alcohol and in certain other petroleum solvents, but on further heating or under heat and pressure as in a molding press the substance changes to resins of a very great hardness and complete insolubility. These are not the resins that have found extensive use in the varnish industry, since *they are not oil-reactive resins*.

Oil-reactive Synthetic Resins. When phenol and formaldehyde are condensed and polymerized in the presence of a natural resin, ester gum, or rosin, oil-reactive synthetic resins are obtained. These are the resins that have become increasingly important to the varnish industry since 1925. Compounded with China wood and a small amount of linseed oil used as a chill-back, they are used to make the so-called *four-hour varnishes*.

The term phenol-formaldehyde is now used somewhat loosely, because many resins are made in which phenol is replaced by one of its homologues, such as creosol and other more complex phenols. Formaldehyde can also be replaced by its homologues.

Alkyd (Glyptal) was first made by the General Electric Co. It is produced by condensation reactions between phthalic anhydride and glycerin or modifications of these substances. The simple phthalic anhydride and glycerin resins, during the early part of the condensation, are soft and soluble in certain solvents, such as the esters. Then, as condensation proceeds, the resins increase in hardness and decrease in solubility, until an extremely hard, insoluble product is obtained. These simple forms have not found wide use because the soluble ones have lacked hardness and waterproofness, while the harder ones have lacked solubility.

The modified forms of these resins which are being adopted by the protective coating industry are those in which part of the phthalic anhydride or acid is replaced by the fatty acids of either linseed, China wood, or castor oil, etc., or by mixtures of several of the fatty acids. The simpler resins in which the phthalic anhydride or acid is replaced by acids of castor oil or oleic acid are insoluble, as a rule, in drying oils and hydrocarbons. Those resins in which the phthalic acid is replaced by the fatty acid of the drying oils are soluble in thinners used in oleoresinous varnishes, thereby allowing many of these resins to be incorporated in oil varnishes, particularly the baking type. Many of the alkyd resins have found considerable use in lacquers.

From a chemical point of view, practically any dibasic acid will react with any polyhydroxy alcohol to give resinous materials. The phthalic acid can be replaced by dibasic acids of the aliphatic series, such as succinic, tartaric, citric, etc., or by aromatic polybasic acids. On the other hand, glycerin can be wholly or partly replaced by other polyhydroxy alcohols, for example, glycol.

Cumarone and Indene Resins. These resins are derived from the unsaturated hydrocarbons such as cumarone and indene, which occur in certain fractions of coal-tar naphtha. Their use has been limited, however, because they show a marked tendency to yellow under the action of sunlight. It has been stated that this yellowing tendency is caused by the presence of traces of iron resulting from the use of acid catalysts in iron equipment, and the use of alkalies in washing out the traces of the acid catalyst. Lately, improved forms of these resins have been offered. In the improved forms, polymerization agents are used which considerably reduce the yellowing tendency. Varnishes made from these resins are practically unaffected by alkalies.

Vinyl Resins are obtained by the polymerization of esters, particularly the acetates of the unsaturated vinyl alcohol. These resins are flexible, and compatible with nitrocellulose. The vinyl resins are harder, less soluble, and less compatible with oils than other synthetic resins. The vinyl ester resins may be used by themselves, without oil or nitrocellulose. They are soluble in special solvents, particularly of the type of ketones.

Urea-formaldehyde Resins are not used to any great extent in the varnish industry.

The Petroleum Industry is now producing synthetic resins from the residue of the distillation process.

Ester Gum. Ester was the first synthetic resin to be widely used in varnish production. Curiously enough, ester gum was not considered a synthetic resin until the phenol-formaldehyde and alkyd resins were introduced. Ester gum is a glycerin ester of rosin. Rosin, chemically speaking, consists for the most part of a complex acid known as abietic acid. Up to the present (1936), only the glycerin esters of rosin have received any practical attention. They are used extensively in oleoresinous varnishes, and nitrocellulose (pyroxylin) lacquers.

Many other rosin esters of the monohydroxy alcohols, both aliphatic and aromatic, have been prepared but have not found any practical use. Polyhydroxy alcohols containing four hydroxy groups and of higher molecular weight than glycerin have been described as giving esters of higher melting point. These would unquestionably find wide commercial application, but unfortunately, the commercially available quantities are very limited. Research will undoubtedly find new sources of these materials.

Recently (about 1931), modified ester gums, such as mixed esters, have appeared in the lacquer industry. Mixed esters are those in which the glycerin, or even a dihydroxy alcohol such as glycol, is esterified partly with rosin and partly with another acid. An example of such an ester is the one resulting from esterification of glycerin with rosin and phthalic acid.

An ester gum varnish is more durable than a limed rosin varnish, in which the acidity of rosin is partly neutralized by means of calcium oxide. Before synthetic resins appeared, ester gum was used extensively in the making of spar varnishes.

Oils

Linseed Oil is obtained from the seeds of the flax plant (*Linum usitatissimum*). The principal flaxseed-producing countries are Argentina, Russia, India, the United States, and Canada.

Linseed oil is essentially a mixture of mixed triglycerides of unsaturated acids, oleic, linolenic, linolic, and small amounts of saturated stearic and palmitic acids. A series of analyses made by many investigators varied as

Saturated acids—Stearic and palmitic	4.8 to 9.0%
Unsaturated acids { Oleic	13.3 to 14.5%
Linolenic	38.9 to 40.3%
Linolic	37.9 to 41.6%
Unsaponifiable matter	1.05 to 1.4%
Combined with glycerin radical	4.6%

Raw linseed oil has a golden yellow color with a pleasant odor. Its iodine number usually varies from 175 to 181. It is (1) acid refined by means of concentrated sulfuric acid, (2) alkali refined by means of sodium hydroxide. The acid-refined oil is used as a grinding medium, particularly for basic carbonate white lead; the alkali-refined oil is used for oeloresinous and lithographic varnishes.

Perilla Oil is obtained from the seeds of *Perilla ocymoides*, a plant found in China, Japan, and southeastern Asia. Perilla oil is closely similar to linseed oil, but its degree of unsaturation as indicated by the iodine number, which is above 200, is greater. According to J. S. Long, this oil has a higher percentage of linolenic and linolic acid. The available quantity of this oil is much smaller than that of linseed.

Tung, or China Wood Oil, is a nut oil. It is mainly a glyceride of the fatty acid known as oleostearic acid, which is supposed to be isomeric with linolic acid. It contains about 10 per cent of glyceride of oleic acid, and from 2 and 3 per cent of the glyceride of saturated fatty acids, mainly palmitic and stearic. This oil has decidedly better waterproofness than linseed. The iodine number of Tung oil varies from 163 to 170.

Menhaden Oil (Fish Oil). Many different oils are produced from fish. A kind much used is menhaden oil which has an iodine number varying from 139 to 180. It may be used in varnishes and other protective coatings.

Semi-drying Oils

Soya bean oil..................... iodine number 124 to 143
Hempseed....................... iodine number 140 to 166
Lumbang....................... iodine number 140 to 164
Walnut......................... iodine number 140 to 158

Other semi-drying oils are on the market.

Special Varnishes

Crystallizing and Wrinkle Varnishes are representative of certain special varnishes on the market for producing unusual decorative surface effects. In the crystallizing varnish, the crystals are formed when the freshly painted article is placed in an atmosphere deprived of oxygen at a temperature of about 110 deg fahr. The usual method is to have a yellow flame burning in the oven with the draft closed until the crystals appear. The film is then made hard and durable by baking at higher temperatures in the oven with the draft opened. These crystal effects can also be obtained in colors.

A wrinkle or shrivel finish may be obtained on an article by baking it at temperatures ranging from 150 to 300 deg fahr after application of the special " wrinkle varnish."

The formation of these effects appears to be due to the rapid oxidation at the surface, forming a skin over the less oxidized material beneath. The surface increases in volume during the continued drying, and the less viscous material in the interior flows to the hilly or high surfaces.

Rubbing Varnishes are so compounded that they generally dry in 48 hr, some in 24 hr, to a hard film which may be rubbed to a dull, smooth finish with pumice and oil or water. After being rubbed, they may be polished to a high gloss with rotten stone and crude oil, or other polishing compounds which are on the market.

26. SPIRIT VARNISHES

Spirit Varnishes are simple solutions of resins in volatile solvents. They dry entirely by evaporation of the solvent which leaves the original resin in a thin film.

These varnishes dry rapidly, generally within 10 or 20 min. They form hard films of limited elasticity which are somewhat impervious to moisture. These hard films are readily removed by abrasion and by solvents.

Manila Copal Spirit Varnish. The greatest quantity of spirit varnish is made by dissolving Manila copal (spirit-soluble resin) in industrial ethyl alcohol. Sometimes rosin and a limited quantity of petroleum solvent are added for cheapening. A small proportion (usually 1 per cent) of castor oil (plasticizer) is added to give elasticity to the film.

Spirit varnishes are prepared by placing the resin in a churn provided with a stirrer. The solvent is added and the resin dissolved by stirring action. The solution is run into another container, allowed to settle to deposit dirt, and clarified by filtering and centrifuging.

These varnishes are used mainly for coating paper, including wallpaper, and for sealing packages.

Shellac Spirit Varnish. Shellac is a resinous material of animal origin. This resinous substance is a natural exudation from the tree on which it is found, actually produced by the larvae of insects feeding on the sap. Shellac comes mainly from India, although large quantities are produced in Siam. It is found on a large variety of trees, the most important of which is the dhak tree (*Butea frondosa*).

Shellac is soluble in ethyl alcohol and methylated spirits, forming a turbid solution. The turbidity is due to the presence of insoluble wax. In ether, chloroform, and turpentine, shellac is partially soluble. It is insoluble in petroleum solvents and oils. Sometimes a limited quantity of butyl or amyl alcohol is used to give greater flow to the shellac varnish.

Because of the partial insolubility in turpentine, and complete insolubility in oils and petroleum solvents, shellac is largely used as a sealing coat on the knots of uncoated wood before painting, to prevent resin in the knots from bleeding into the oil of the applied paint, thereby avoiding glossy and unsightly patches.

Shellac is mainly employed for the preparation of spirit varnishes. Its alcohol solution dries by the evaporation of the solvent to a hard film which takes a high polish. The film is fairly durable but it is not resistant to moisture. Shellac varnishes are used for general decorative purposes, such as *brown hard varnishes* for polishing furniture, and also to make colored spirit and colored matt stains. The largest quantity of the shellac is used for floors and as a sealer coat for stain in furniture and other articles. In nitrocellulose lacquers it imparts adhesion.

Shellac Water Varnishes are made of shellac, borax, and water. These varnishes are used as a vehicle for water colors, and as a wallpaper varnish.

Turpentine Varnishes are made by dissolving dammar, mastic, or sandarac in turpentine. Rosin is sometimes added as a cheapening agent. The Dammar varnish is largely used for varnishing wallpapers; mastic varnish, mainly for varnishing oil paintings and maps.

27. LACQUERS

Lacquers, at the present time (1936), are composed mainly of nitrocellulose (pyroxylin), plasticizers, resins, and thinners. The thinner consists of a mixture of solvents, latent solvents, and diluents. Table IV illustrates diagrammatically types of lacquers and their compositions.

Table IV. Composition of Nitrocellulose Lacquers

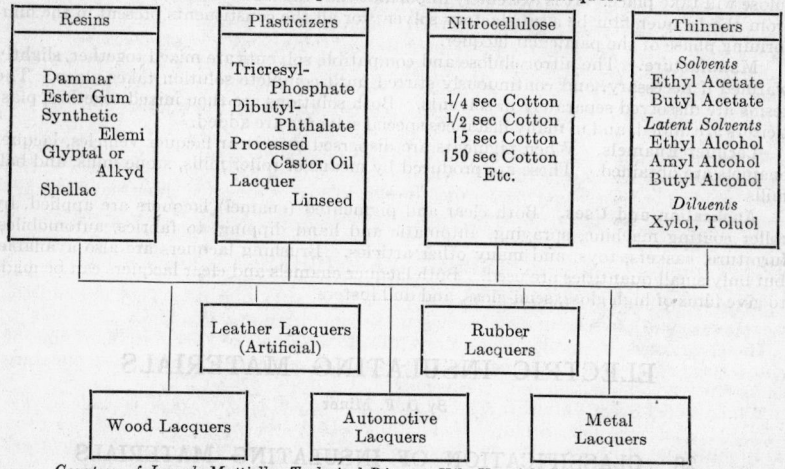

Resins	Plasticizers	Nitrocellulose	Thinners
Dammar	Tricresyl-	1/4 sec Cotton	*Solvents*
Ester Gum	Phosphate	1/2 sec Cotton	Ethyl Acetate
Synthetic	Dibutyl-	15 sec Cotton	Butyl Acetate
Elemi	Phthalate	150 sec Cotton	*Latent Solvents*
Glyptal or	Processed	Etc.	Ethyl Alcohol
Alkyd	Castor Oil		Amyl Alcohol
Shellac	Lacquer		Butyl Alcohol
	Linseed		*Diluents*
			Xylol, Toluol

Leather Lacquers (Artificial)   Rubber Lacquers

Wood Lacquers   Automotive Lacquers   Metal Lacquers

Courtesy of Joseph Mattiello, Technical Director Hilo Varnish Corp., Brooklyn, N. Y.

Nitrocellulose (Pyroxylin) provides the element of toughness, and assists in making a continuous film. The nitrocellulose solutions offered on the market vary in viscosity from 1/2-sec to 150-sec. For example, the term 1/2-sec nitrocellulose is used commercially to indicate a 12 1/2 per cent solution of dry cotton dispersed in a definite solvent mixture, whose final viscosity, measured at 20 deg fahr by the falling-ball method, is 1/2 sec. Viscosity, the most important physical property, is of great value in controlling the finished product.

Resins. The resins mainly used in lacquers are ester gum, dammar, elemi, alkyd, some modified phenol-formaldehydes, and shellac. In a particular lacquer, one or more resins may be used. The resin imparts adhesion, gloss, and hardness; it improves the rubbing and polishing qualities, increases the solid content (non-volatile), accelerates drying, and with some of the glyptal or alkyd resin, imparts some plasticizing action and gives greater durability.

Plasticizers (Softeners). The plasticizers impart the elements of elasticity, durability, and adhesion. They are either solid or difficultly volatile, high-boiling liquids. They improve the flowing properties of lacquers, inhibit blushing, and enhance the luster of the dry film. Camphor was the earliest plasticizer used. The other important plasticizers are given in Table IV.

Solvents, Latent Solvents, and Diluents. The important function of these is solvency, and reduction of the viscosity of the viscous mass, which is composed of nitrocellulose, resin, and plasticizer, to that fluidity which will permit the spreading of lacquers.

The esters, such as ethyl, butyl acetate, etc., are good solvents for nitrocellulose. Other organic liquids, such as acetone, other ketones, and glacial acetic acid, are also good solvents for nitrocellulose.

The alcohols, ethyl, butyl, and amyl, are latent solvents. That is, alone they are not good solvents for nitrocellulose, but in the presence of esters act as good solvents.

Diluents are non-solvents, and the proportion of these which a lacquer will tolerate without destroying quality, or without causing the precipitation of nitrocellulose, is of importance in reducing the cost of a lacquer. Diluents extensively used are: coal-tar thinners such as toluol, xylol, high-flash naphthas; petroleum hydrocarbons such as benzine, gasoline, and, more recently, hydrogenated petroleum hydrocarbons, whose solvency is the same as that of coal tar but whose evaporation rate is slower.

Evaporation of Non-volatile Content and Character of Film Obtained. In order to get perfectly smooth lacquer film, without an orange peel (wrinkled surface), or precipitation of nitrocellulose, or bloom, an evaporation equilibrium must exist between the solvents and non-solvents. The rate of evaporation of various organic solvents depends primarily upon the vapor pressure of the solvents and non-solvents, and only secondarily upon the boiling point. If the evaporation rates of the solvent and non-solvent used in the lacquer are roughly the same, a satisfactorily dried film will be obtained. If in a solvent mixture the solvents evaporate first, leaving behind only the diluent, precipitation of the nitrocellulose will take place. It is extremely important that the last volatile portion evaporating from the lacquer film be a satisfactory solvent for all the constituents present in the film-forming phase of the particular lacquer.

Manufacture. The nitrocellulose and compatible solvents are mixed together, slightly warmed if necessary, and continuously stirred until complete solution takes place. The resins are dissolved separately in solvents. Both solutions are then mixed together, plasticizers are added, and in many instances special solvents are added.

Lacquer Enamels. When pigments are dispersed into clear lacquer vehicles, lacquer enamels are obtained. These are produced by means of roller mills, stone mills, and ball mills.

Application and Uses. Both clear and pigmented (enamel) lacquers are applied, by roller coating machine, spraying, automatic and hand dipping, to fabrics, automobiles, furniture, caskets, toys, and many other articles. Brushing lacquers are also available, but only small quantities are used. Both lacquer enamels and clear lacquers can be made to give films of high gloss, semi-gloss, and dull lusters.

ELECTRIC INSULATING MATERIALS

By D. F. Miner

28. CLASSIFICATION OF INSULATING MATERIALS

Thermal Classification as defined in the A.I.E.E. standards.

CLASS   DESCRIPTION OF MATERIAL

O   Class O insulation consists of cotton, silk, paper, and similar organic materials when neither impregnated* nor immersed in oil.

A   Class A insulation consists of cotton, silk, paper, and similar organic materials when impregnated* or immersed in oil; also enamel as applied to conductors.

B   Class B insulation consists of inorganic materials such as mica and asbestos in built-up form combined with binding substances. If Class A material is used in small quantities in conjunction for structural purposes only, the combined material may be considered as Class B, provided the electrical and mechanical properties of the insulated winding are not impaired by the application of the temperature permitted for Class B material. (The word " impair " is here used in the sense of causing any change which could disqualify the insulating material for continuous service.)

C   Class C insulation consists of inorganic materials such as pure mica, porcelain, quartz, etc.

Physical Classification. Insulation material may be divided according to physical state into four general major classes each of which may be further subdivided as shown on the top of the next page.

* Impregnated cotton, paper, or silk. An insulation is considered to be impregnated when a suitable substance replaces the air between its fibers, even if this substance does not completely fill the spaces between the insulated conductors. The impregnating substance, in order to be considered suitable, must have good insulating properties; must entirely cover the fibers and render them adherent to each other and to the conductor; must not produce interstices within itself as a consequence of evaporation of the solvent or through any other cause; must not flow during the operation of the machine at full working load or at the temperature limit specified; must not unduly deteriorate under prolonged action of heat.

1. Solid. Natural; vitreous; fibrous; organic; rubber and substitutes.
2. Plastics. Synthetic resins; waxes; gums.
3. Liquids. Natural oils; mineral oils; varnishes; solvents.
4. Gases.

Electrical Classification according to dielectric properties. Table I gives the electrical properties of various insulating materials.

29. SOLID INSULATING MATERIALS

Insulating materials are often described in general terms without specific data. A material is said to be " heat proof " which may mean that it will not deteriorate when used continuously at some temperature within the range of 30 to 250 deg cent. Dielectric strength is sometimes quoted without reference to the thickness of the test specimen. If the test has been made on a very thin specimen, the dielectric strength obtained will be misleading to those who are not aware of the law of the increase of dielectric strength with the decrease of the thickness of the test specimen. Claims may be made that an insulating material is insoluble in certain solvents and is weatherproof. Such claims are not absolute. They are only general and refer to ordinary conditions found in the use of insulations. If the working conditions are unusual and severe, specific information should be obtained on the appropriateness of the insulation under consideration.

Natural Solid Insulating Materials

Asbestos is a mineral consisting chiefly of silica, magnesia, lime, alumina, water, and oxide of iron. The structure is of fibers, the ultimate fiber of which is thought to be a single row of the molecular structure of the crystal. The fibers are exceedingly smooth and glossy and have very little friction to hold them together when they are spun into yarn, thus resulting in a low tensile strength. This difficulty, however, has been partly overcome so that now threads are made which have fair tensile strength. The more important varieties, amianthus and amphibole, are used in the form of asbestos paper, cardboard, yarn, cloth, tape, and as a filler in molding mixtures.

Asbestos contains small particles of iron oxide or grit which cannot be entirely removed and which affect to a slight degree its insulating qualities. It is hygroscopic and should therefore not be used on high voltage, in general not over 3300 volts. It is unaffected by oils, acids, and alkalies, and it withstands very high temperatures. Above 500 deg cent it loses its mechanical strength; it melts at about 1300 deg cent. It has extensive applications as a heat insulator.

Lava is a mineral talc, machined in its natural condition and then baked at a temperature of 1100 deg cent to a condition of extreme hardness. It is then unaffected by any subsequent temperature short of its baking temperature. It is slowly attacked by hydrochloric acid but is not affected by other acids or alkalies.

Marble is the name given to any limestone which is sufficiently compact to admit of a polish. Pure marble is white, but the presence of iron oxide or other impurities gives it different colors. It is used principally for switchboard work and should not contain metallic veins, which reduce its insulating qualities. If used on circuits of 1000 volts or more, it should be saturated with an insulating varnish and baked. It shows oil spots and for that reason it is sometimes stained black and given a so-called marine finish. Very little marble is now used except to match old installations.

Slate is a microgranular crystalline stone, derived from argillaceous sediments by regional metamorphism and characterized by a perfect cleavage entirely independent of original bedding, which cleavage has been induced by pressure within the earth. The essential mineral constituents are white mica (chiefly sericite) and quartz. Prominent accessory constituents are black mica (biotite), chlorite, and hematite. Minor accessory constituents are carbonates, magnetite, apatite, clay, andalusite, barite, rutile, pyrite, graphite, feldspar, zircon, tourmaline, and carbonaceous matter. Slate is hygroscopic. It is often permeated by metallic veins, making it unfit for use unless the electrical connections are insulated by bushings. It is useful for switchboard and switch-base work owing to its desirable mechanical and fireproof qualities. Its dielectric strength decreases rapidly as the temperature increases, and at a high temperature slate becomes a conductor. When a high voltage is impressed upon a piece of slate for some time, the slate usually is not punctured but, owing to the consequent rise in temperature, the slate acts as a short circuit to the impressed voltage. The breakdown is thus only apparent as the specimens regain their dielectric properties after cooling.

Purple slate from Vermont and vicinity is considered superior to black slate from Pennsylvania. The use of slate for electrical purposes is rapidly declining.

Table I. Electrical Properties of Insulating Materials

Material	Dielectric Strength			Resistivity				Specific Inductive Capacity	
	Specimen thickness, mm	Kv per mm*	Authority	Volume, ohm-cm	Authority	Surface † Ohms, 30%	Ohms, 90%	Air unity	Authority
Asbestos paper	1.2	4.2	3	1.6×10^{11}	24			2.7	25
Asphalt (Byerlyte)	3.6	14.0	4					4.5 to 5.5	5
Bakelite, wood molding mixture		17.7 to 21.6	5	1×10^{12}	5			5	6
Bakelite, asbestos molding mixture		up to 9.8	5	4×10^{11}	5			8	6
Bakelite, Micarta-213	0.022	up to 31.4	6	5×10^{11}				5	6
Cellophane	0.25	51 to 66	7	2×10^{10}	26	8×10^{10}	2×10^{9}		
Celluloid (clear)	.019	12 to 28	1			8×10^{16}	8×10^{16}		
Cellulose acetate		48.0	6	over 5×10^{18}	26				
Ceresin, muslin	.38			5 to 20×10^{9}	26	3×10^{10}	1×10^{7}	5	25
Empire cloth, muslin		48.0	9	5 to 20×10^{9}	26	3×10^{10}	1×10^{7}	5	25
Fiber, vulcanized, including hard fiber, all colors	3.2 / 6.4	4.9 to 10.8 / 3.9 to 8.9	12	9×10^{13}	27	3×10^{13}	2×10^{7}	5.5 to 9.1	28
Glass (ordinary)	6	8 to 9	13	2×10^{13}	26			5.5 to 9.1	
Glass (plate)				2×10^{10}	26			3 to 4	
Jute (impregnated)		1.2	14						
Lava		3 to 10	15	1 to 100×10^{9}	26	6×10^{11}	1×10^{8}	8.3	29
Marble	1.6	6.5	13	.04 to 200×10^{15}	26	8×10^{10}	1×10^{7}	5 to 7	40
Mica	.6	21 to 28	13	5×10^{14}	26	2×10^{13}	3×10^{9}		
Micabond, plate	2.54	37.5	17	1×10^{16}				2.5	40
Micabond, flexible	0.13	23.1	17	3×10^{14}				2.6	31
Oil, insulating		10–16	40					2.1	21
Paper	20	8.7	13	5×10^{16}				4.4	32
Paraffin (parowax)	1.58	11.5	21	1×10^{16}				5.0	32
Porcelain	1.58	8.0	40	3×10^{14}	26			3	38
Pressboard (oiled)		29.2	40	5×10^{16}		1.5×10^{16}	5×10^{15}	2.5	30
Pressboard (varnished)		15.5	40	1×10^{18}		4×10^{13}	5×10^{8}	2.0 to 3.5	39
Rosin	0.5		37	1×10^{16}	26	8×10^{14}	2×10^{14}	3.0 to 3.7	35
Rubber (hard)		70		1×10^{18}	26	6×10^{15}	6×10^{9}	6.6 to 7.4	39
Shellac	10.3	1.3	22	1×10^{17}	26	2×10^{8}	1×10^{8}	2.9 to 3.2	39
Slate									
Sulfur	15.2	4.6	32	3×10^{10}	26	1×10^{14}	1×10^{12}	4.1	32
Wood (maple), paraffined						3×10^{10}	2×10^{9}		

* To obtain volts per mil per millimeter multiply kilovolts per millimeter by 25.4

† At 30 per cent and 90 per cent relative humidity.

Authorities for Table I: (1) Hobart and Turner. (2) Physicalische Technische Reichsanstalt. (3) Steinmetz. (4) Byerly & Sons, Manufacturers. (5) General Bakelite Co. (6) Westinghouse. (7) Continental Fiber Co. (8) Electrical Testing Laboratory. (9) Mica Insulator Co. (10) Bittlemann. (11) Formica Insulation Co. (12) William Eves, 3d. (13) Walter. (14) Baur. (15) American Lava Corporation. (16) Symons. (17) Chicago Mica Co. (18) Mica Insulation Co. (19) Minerallac Electric Co. (20) Canfield & Robinson. (21) The Locke Insulator Mfg. Co. (22) Massachusetts Institute of Technology. (23) *Electrician.* (24) Whittaker's Pocket Book. (25) Pirani. (26) Curtis. (27) Table of French Physical Society. (28) Coyne & Howe. (29) Schmidt. (30) Various. (31) Zietkowsky. (32) Hendrick. (33) Kinzbrunner. (34) Stadt Lab., Munich. (35) Schulze. (36) E. Müller. (37) C. C. Paterson, E. H. Raynor, A. Kinnes. (38) Boltzmann. (39) Wüllner. (40) Peek.

Quartz, a form of silica, naturally formed into hexagonal crystals, has a density of about 2.7. It may be fused and cast into usable shapes and is sometimes used as a ceramic type of insulation for high temperatures.

Soapstone, a form of talc or steatite, is gray in color and feels smooth and soapy. It is very easily machined and is sometimes used as an insulator and structural part where resistance to heat and chemicals is desired. It is weak mechanically, and hygroscopic.

Mica is an anhydrous silicate of aluminum and potassium or sodium. It crystallizes in a laminated mass, some grades of which may be subdivided down to a thickness of 0.0008 mm. The ultimate thickness of cleavage layers is unknown and may be finally but one layer of the molecular structure. It is useful as an insulator because of its high insulating qualities and its ability to withstand high temperatures. Owing to its impurity, lack of flexibility and excessive surface leakage in the natural state, the laminae are separated and sorted into various grades of purity and are then cemented together to form plate or flexible reconstructed mica of any thickness or purity.

Two kinds of mica are in common use, muscovite (white mica) and phlogopite (amber mica). The former is usually obtained from India and the latter from Madagascar.

Mica can be built into various useful forms, including plate, flexible mica, tape, coil wrappers, and tubing. Mica is combined with thin paper or cloth as a backing when made into tape or wrappers. The bond is frequently shellac, although asphalts, synthetic resins, and other materials are preferred for special purposes.

White mica is hard and is used in building segment mica for undercut commutators. The maximum safe temperature for white mica is 500 deg cent.

Amber mica is softer and is used in mica plate for flush commutators. It is also used in making plate for heating appliance insulation. It will withstand temperatures up to 800 deg cent.

Flexible mica or molding mica may be made for hot or cold molding. White mica is generally used with a bond which is plastic at the molding temperature. Shellac bond may be made flexible with castor oil.

Sheet insulation is made with mica and some other insulation, such as fish paper, rope paper, Kraft paper, etc., for special purposes.

30. VITREOUS SOLID INSULATING MATERIALS

Glass is essentially a mixture of silicates of sodium, potassium, calcium, or barium. A given specimen may contain one or more of these silicates, the composition being chosen so as to produce the desired properties. Metallic oxides are often added, and if a low-expansion, heat-resisting glass is desired, boron trioxide is used, to make the boro-silicate glass.

At normal temperatures glass is a good insulator, but at red heat it is a fair conductor. It resists most chemicals except hydrofluoric acid. Most glass is brittle and weak on heat shock. Newer glasses of the borosilicate type (Pyrex) have lower coefficients of expansion and do not shatter with wide temperature variations. Successful line insulators have been placed on the market, competing with porcelain.

Porcelain is distinguished from other forms of earthenware by a vitrified and non-porous structure. It is composed of china clay, ball clay, flint, and feldspar. China clay, sometimes called kaolin, is slightly plastic whereas ball clay is very tough and plastic. By a proper combination of the two the desired plasticity is obtained. Flint is in the form of pure sand or quartz ground so finely as to be entirely free from any gritty feeling. Feldspar is a natural rock and is ground as fine as the flint. These four ingredients are mixed in proper proportions and passed through the manufacturing processes which require very skillful care and experience.

Such articles as knobs, cleats, and lamp sockets are made by a dry process. Dry-process porcelain is porous and not usually suitable for high-voltage outdoor applications. It is of value because of the accuracy with which intricate pieces can be molded, and is applicable for indoor or low-voltage purposes.

High-voltage insulators are made by a wet process and are non-porous, which is necessary for high-voltage use. The glaze is provided to protect the porcelain from dust and deterioration in the weather, and it should have the same temperature coefficient of expansion as the porcelain itself. In the wet process, the ingredients are thoroughly ground in a ball mill and then mixed with water to a consistency about the same as that of paint. After several hours of stirring (blunging), this liquid (slip) is pumped through a filter press, where the water is extracted and press cakes left. These are stacked in bins for use, being kept moist. The press cake material is thoroughly mixed by a screw type of mixer called a pug mill. The wet clay is extruded in cylindrical form, and sections are cut off for forming into insulators or other parts. Forming is usually done either by hot pressing the plastic clay soon after it leaves the pug mill, or by turning operations performed after the clay has partially dried. Wet-process material may also be cast in plaster of paris molds, a special liquid body being prepared for this purpose. Porcelain is fired for several days at temperatures ranging from 1250 to 1300 deg cent.

The mechanical strength of porcelain depends upon the flint content, the heat resistance upon the clay, and the dielectric strength upon the feldspar which unfortunately also adds brittleness. In a special type of porcelain for spark plugs, magnesia is added to promote mechanical strength at high temperatures. Porcelain, because of its low tensile strength, should be used under a compressive strain. It is comparatively inexpensive, chemically inert, and not sensitive to changes of temperature. The fracture of good porcelain is conchoidal, fine grained, white, and bright.

31. FIBROUS ORGANIC SOLID INSULATING MATERIALS

Cotton occurs as an insulator in many forms, such as cloth, tape, and yarn. These products serve as mechanical supports or separators of conductors and are usually impregnated with an insulating liquid or compound. The insulating value of cotton is considered equivalent only to the same thickness of air, reliance being placed usually on the impregnation for dielectric strength and moisture proofing. Cloth is used in making varnished " cambric " of various types. Tape is employed largely in insulating coils of all types, and yarn, in covering wires or insulating layers of enameled wire in "universal" wound magnet coils.

Silk infrequently serves as an insulator, except where space is an important factor. It is sometimes used as a varnished fabric or as wire covering for appearance and because it can easily be obtained thinner than cotton materials. The cost is higher, however. Its insulating properties are approximately the same as those of cotton.

Linen thread or twine is valuable for fastening the coils of rotating machines because of its high unit strength.

Insulating Papers. The principal papers used in electrical apparatus are described below.

Absorbent Papers made of 100 per cent purified sulfite wood pulp are used in making laminated phenolic products. The paper has a soft fiber, thoroughly cleaned of natural resin, and takes the impregnating phenolic varnishes readily. A " high ratio " plate can be made with absorbent papers. A common thickness is 0.10 in.

Another type of absorbent paper is made from 100 per cent cotton rag stock and it is used in filter presses employed in purifying insulator oils. It is very porous, in order to absorb water readily, and yet let oil through. The sheets are approximately 0.025 in. thick.

Asbestos Paper is not all asbestos fiber, the usual grades containing not more than 80 per cent asbestos, the remainder being sulfite wood pulp fibers. Papers from 0.005 to 0.010 in. thick are used in insulating heavy copper in field coils, and in tape form as a covering for wire. Certain grades of heat-resisting laminated phenolic plate are made of asbestos paper impregnated with materials like Bakelite. Asbestos papers are not high-grade insulators owing to conducting particles and moisture absorption.

Rag Base Papers. (a) Tough insulating papers, used where resistance to mechanical damage, as in motor and generator slots, is important, are manufactured from 100 per cent cotton rags. Most of them are identified by trade names, such as Duro, Capacio, and Armco papers.

(b) Fish paper is a special type of rag paper made wholly from old cotton rags. The paper during manufacture is treated with zinc chloride which partially dissolves the cellulose. A paper is obtained without a definite fiber structure. It is hard, tough in both directions, and does not dislaminate. Fish paper may be obtained in thicknesses from 0.007 to 0.056 in., it is used for slot insulation, layer insulation of coils, and as switch barriers. Paraffin impregnation or varnish treatments are frequently applied to overcome the inherent hygroscopic property of fish paper.

Fullerboard (or Pressboard). (a) Rag fullerboard is composed of 75 per cent rag stock and 25 per cent sulfite wood pulp. It is made on a cylinder machine, cut off, dried, and pressed in sheets. It may be obtained in thickness from 0.007 to $1/2$ in. and in sheets as large as 84 in. by 120 in. Fullerboard is particularly adapted for oil impregnation and is extensively used in transformer construction for barriers, coil sides, and washers. It may be formed into angles and channels. Shrinkage and distortion are low.

(b) Kraft fullerboard, made of 100 per cent sulfite wood pulp in the same general manner as rag fullerboard, is a cheaper type of material and is valuable for many applications for which rag fullerboard was once used. It is used for barriers, coil spacers, washers, etc., for electrical machinery. It has much greater shrinkage and warping tendencies than rag material. Forming is not so readily done. These limitations result in the continued use of both rag and Kraft types. Varnish treatment is frequently applied when fullerboard is to be exposed to air.

(c) A similar material in thin papers with a highly calendered surface is called express paper. It is used in making varnish treated papers where only a surface coating and not impregnation is desired.

Kraft Papers contain 100 per cent sulfite wood pulp and may be obtained in a range of thickness from 0.0005 in. to fullerboard thicknesses. It is brown in color, is readily impregnated, and is one of the most useful electrical papers. Many grades of laminated resin (phenolic or other) plate and tubing are made with Kraft paper. It is also used, shellac coated, in making rolled paper bushings and terminals. Very thin Kraft tissue (0.0005 in.) now largely replaces the linen and cotton tissue formerly used in capacitors.

Linen Paper. So-called linen papers are part, sometimes as much as 60 per cent cotton. They are strong and tough, and the very thin grades have been employed for condenser (capacitor) insulation. The use of linen in all forms (cloth, paper, and twine) is not nearly so extensive as it once was. Cheaper satisfactory substitutes have been found.

Japanese Paper is imported from Japan and is made of mulberry pulp fiber. The particular feature of this fiber is the great length, giving good strength, although the paper looks frail and not dense. Tissue (0.001 in.) finds use as a backing for mica tape, and as wire insulation. It is not suitable for capacitors because of small holes and lack of uniform structure.

Rope Paper may be manufactured either from manila hemp fiber or from old manila hemp rope. It is very strong, resisting tear better than cotton paper. It is frequently impregnated with varnish and used in combination insulations such as mica and rope paper. Paper made from old rope frequently contains metal particles. For this reason, other papers are usually preferred for high insulation duty. Rope paper can be folded and crimped. It is thus used in holding wires in some types of coils where flanges are omitted.

Cellophane is a pure cellulose product made from wood pulp by chemical treatment. It is transparent. It is obtainable in sheet, tubing, and tape forms. The dielectric strength and specific inductive capacity are high, and its inflammability is no greater than that of paper. Because of its purity it has much promise as an insulator and has been used as wire insulation and coil taping. Some varieties termed "flame proof" and "moisture proof" are now available. Moisture proofing is accomplished by a lacquer coating. Some grades of cellophane are flexibilized with the addition of glycerin.

Cellulose Acetate is obtained by acetic anhydride treatment of cotton fiber or purified wood pulp. It has high dielectric properties and uniformity of characteristics. It can be obtained in the same forms as cellophane and has similar applications. It is comparable in inflammability to paper. It is not so hygroscopic as regular cellophane.

Varnish-treated Cloth, usually muslin, is widely used as an insulating material. It is sometimes known as varnished cambric or empire cloth. It enters the manufacture of cloth insulated cables, is used as coil wrappings, especially on end turns of rotating machines, and in combination with paper as lining for coil slots. Coil terminals on large transformers are taped with varnished cloth.

The fabric is most commonly an unbleached cotton cloth of 60 by 64 threads per inch and in various thickness from 0.005 to 0.015 in. Treatment consists of impregnating and coating with varnish. This is done in a tower through which the cloth passes continuously. It passes through successive varnish baths and is dried by heat between dips. When it emerges it has had from two to four dips and bakes. The varnishes used are generally natural oil varnishes of two types, tan cloth varnish or black. The tan is somewhat more oil proof and less moisture proof than the black. The black is usually asphaltic but can be made satisfactorily oil proof. The dielectric properties of black cloth are generally superior to those of tan. Black cloth finds extensive application in cable manufacture. For this purpose it must possess low power factor and small losses. The surface coat of varnish may be made: relatively hard and smooth; tacky so that, in taping, successive layers will stick together; or greasy so that layers of tape on irregular forms will slip into place easily. Table II gives the dielectric strengths of some treated insulating fabrics and papers.

Wood. Dry wood is a good dielectric and possesses the advantages of low cost, light weight, and strength with toughness. Probably the most frequently used woods are maple and hickory. White pine is a good insulator, especially when oil treated, but is not strong. Wood is generally treated with oil (linseed, tung, or transformer) or some wax or gum to fill the pores and keep out moisture. For use in air it is frequently given a finish of baking varnish.

Table II.   Dielectric Strength of Some Insulating Fabrics and Papers

	Thickness, inches	Breakdown Volts	
		1 Layer	Per mil
Treated Cloths			
Asbestos cloth, varnished........................	0.047	3,780	80
Asbestos tape, varnished.........................	.037	3,145	85
Cambric tape, varnished, black, bias...............	.010	13,640	1364
Cambric tape, varnished, tan, bias.................	.010	11,515	1151
Cambric, rolls, varnished, black, straight...........	.010	13,320	1332
Cambric, rolls, varnished, tan, straight.............	.007	7,850	1121
Drilling, rolls, varnished, black, flexible...........	.020	9,250	462
Duck, rolls, varnished, black, flexible..............	.030	8,947	298
Friction, cloth tape, commercial...................	.015	3,290	219
Friction, cloth tape, bias.........................	.015	1,480	99
Friction cloth..................................	.024	1,815	76
Silk, oiled.......................................	.004	4,450	1112
Surgical tape, varnished..........................	.023	1,240	54
Treated Papers			
Asbestos paper, shellac 1 side.....................	.010	2,120	212
Asbestos paper, shellac 1 side.....................	.029	2,610	90
Express paper, paraffin 2 sides....................	.008	5,370	671
Fishpaper, shellac 1 side.........................	.003	1,710	570
Fishpaper, paraffin 1 side........................	.010	8,840	884
Fullerboard, shellac 2 sides.......................	.013	3,390	260
Fullerboard, varnish 2 sides......................	.035	13,130	375
Japanned paper, shellac 2 sides...................	.003	1,136	379
Kraft paper, tan, shellac 1 side...................	.0045	1,270	282
Rope cement paper, varnish 2 sides................	.008	9,746	1218
Rope cement paper, shellac 2 sides................	.016	8,850	553

Cloths and papers tested flat between 2-in. circular electrodes. Average of 10 breaks. (60 cycles.)

Tapes tested by wrapping on 1-in. diameter rod in half lapped layers. Average of 10 breaks. (60 cycles.)

Fiber is pure cotton cellulose chemically treated to form a hard bone-like material. It is known by various trade names such as Fiber, Vulcanized Fiber, Hard Fiber, Horn Fiber. Fiber of best quality has its origin in old rags because the natural oil of the virgin cotton fiber is deleterious and cannot be easily removed by chemical processes. This oil is removed in the wearing and washing of the garment. All dirt and grit must be removed from the rags. The quality also depends on the softness of the rags.

" Vulcanized Fiber sheets are made by passing cotton rag paper through a strong acid or zinc chloride bath and rolling it up on a large drum where each layer of paper sticks to the layer beneath it. When the proper thickness is obtained the acid-soaked material is cut from the drum and cut in half, forming two sheets of raw fiber. These sheets are put through a soaking process in large wooden tubs, each subsequent tub containing a weaker solution, the last tub containing pure water." (Catalogue of the Continental Fiber Co.)

The soaking process requires from one week to one year depending on the thickness of the sheet. A very small amount of acid or chloride will remain in spite of all the soaking. The sheets are air dried and seasoned at a constant temperature. During the drying, they warp and shrink to one-half the original thickness. They are flattened in a steam-heated hydraulic press and then calendered to exact thickness.

According to Almy, the mechanical and physical properties of fiber vary between wide limits according to the manipulation of the chemical treatment and the varying quality of the original paper or rags. A fiber for a particular use should therefore be selected with great care.

Fiber is not waterproof. Dilute acids and alkalies cause no other effects than water, but concentrated acids cause disintegration. Organic solvents and oils have no effect whatever. At a sustained temperature of 80 to 100 deg cent it loses its water of condition and becomes brittle and it chars in a short period of time at 200 deg cent.

Fiber is widely used because of its strength, toughness, and comparatively high insulating values when dry. It is easily formed and machined. It resists the action of arcs on the surface to a great degree.

Table III gives the N.E.M.A. specifications for hard fiber.

Table III. N.E.M.A. Specifications for Hard Fiber

Minimum Tensile Strength at 20° C
(Lb per sq in.)

Grades Thickness, in.	Bone		Commercial	
	Cross-wise	Length-wise	Cross-wise	Length-wise
Up to 1/8 incl.	6500	8500	6000	8000
1/8 to 1/2	6000	8000	5500	7500
Over 1/2	. . . .	. . . .	5500	7000

Minimum Transverse Strength
(Lb per sq in.)

Commercial Grade	Crosswise	Lengthwise
Load applied on. . . . 1/2 in. thick and over	Face or edge 11,000	Face or edge 13,000

Adopted Standard 9–24–1926.

Minimum Dielectric Strength

All Grades, in.	Volts per Mil
Up to 1/16 incl.	175
Over 1/16 to 1/8 incl	150
Over 1/8 to 3/8 incl	100
Over 3/8 to 1/2 incl.	50
Over 1/2 at least.	25,000 total

Minimum Dielectric Strength for Thin-weight Fiber and Fish Paper

Thickness, in.	Volts per Mil
0.004 to 0.005 incl. . . .	200
Over 0.005 to 0.015 incl. . . .	300
Over 0.015 to 0.040 incl. . . .	250

Adopted Standard 10–22–1930.

Maximum Water Absorption, Percent Change in Weight After 1-hour Immersion

Thickness, in.	Bone	Commercial
Up to 1/16 incl.	45.0	65.0
Over 1/16 to 1/8	20.0	35.0
Over 1/8 to 3/8	10.0	15.0
Over 3/8	5.0	10.0

Minimum Brinell Hardness

Thickness, in.	Bone	Commercial
1/4 in. and over.	15.0	10.0

Minimum Specific Gravity

Thickness, in.	Bone	Commercial
Up to 1/16	1.30	1.05
1/16 to 1/2 incl.	1.30	1.10
1/2 to 1	. . . . .	1.05
1 and over. .	. . . . . .	1.01

Adopted Standard 12–9–1930.

32. RUBBER AND RUBBER SUBSTITUTES

Rubber is derived from the milky secretion or latex of certain tropical trees, creepers, and shrubs found chiefly in America, Africa, Ceylon, and Malacca. When these plants are tapped, a thick milky-looking fluid or latex exudes from them. This latex is composed of very minute oil-like refractive globules, varying in size, which are in a state of rapid Brownian movement in a clear transparent liquid, called the serum. Besides these *caoutchouc* globules, or rubber-gum proper, the serum contains resins, protein, enzymes, and various organic and inorganic compounds. Rubber or India rubber is the dried-up or coagulated latex. The best rubber is from a tree known as the *Hevea brasiliensis*, and is known as hevea rubber. It grows wild in Brazil and is cultivated in Ceylon and the Malay Peninsula. In Brazil coagulation is effected principally by dry heat or smoking. A wooden paddle is dipped in the latex and held over a smoky fire until the latex has coagulated. This process is repeated until the caoutchouc layers have become sufficiently thick, when the lump of raw rubber is cut off, dried for several days, and dispatched usually as " fine Para biscuits " to a trading center. The plantation rubber is coagulated in sheets by means of acetic acid. If subsequently smoked it is known as *smoked sheets*. Para enterfine, Negro Heads and Sernamby are usually prepared from fine Para rubber which adheres to the tree during tapping or to the vessels containing the latex. A relatively recent development is the shipping of the preserved latex in the liquid form. This may then be treated to precipitate the rubber particles, or used directly for impregnation of cords or fabrics.

Manufacture of Rubber Insulation. The washed, dried rubber is passed between heavy rollers and flattened into thin sheets. It is then cut into small pieces and again passed through the rollers with a large proportion of fine powder consisting usually of inert mineral substances, waxy hydrocarbons, and sulfur. The mixture is thus masticated until all its constituents are thoroughly mixed and a smooth homogeneous paste obtained. This process is known as compounding.

Fillers Used in Compounding Rubber. Experience has shown that 60 or 70 per cent of mineral filler, or even a greater proportion of rubber substitute, may be added to rubber gum, before the essential qualities of the rubber cease to predominate. The majority of commercial 30 per cent insulating compounds have compositions which fall within the following limits.

Ingredient	Percent
Rubber	30–32
Whiting	0–30
Zinc oxide	28–67
Litharge	1–12
Ozokerite or paraffin	2– 4

In addition to the above fillers, from 2 to 4 per cent of sulfur is added to the compound, the greater part of which combines with the rubber in the vulcanizing process (see below).

Barium sulfate, sublimed white lead, lead carbonate, lampblack, talc, magnesium carbonate, red lead, barium carbonate, and other substances are also used in small quantities. Talc is often objected to, as making the compound porous, and lampblack, as rendering analysis difficult.

Applying the Rubber Compound to Wires. The rubber compound is applied to the wire by " tubing " machines, or is applied in strips, and the wire thus covered with the compound is coiled up ready for vulcanizing.

Vulcanizing Rubber. If exposed for a long time to air and sunlight, rubber loses its elasticity and finally oxidizes completely into resinous matter soluble in acetone. By vulcanization, however, rubber is rendered more or less immune from deterioration by weathering. Vulcanization is the chemical union of rubber gum with sulfur. It takes place at a temperature of 248 to 302 deg fahr.

The coils of wire, covered with the compound as above described, are placed in a suitable chamber to which steam at the proper temperature is admitted. The time required for vulcanization depends upon the thickness of the insulation, the nature of the compound, the temperature and pressure of the steam, etc., ranging from 2 to 8 hours.

Sulfur Required for Vulcanization of Rubber. The amount of sulfur required to produce vulcanization varies with the brand of rubber and the nature of the compounding materials with which it is mixed. The ratio of the weight of combined sulfur to the weight of caoutchouc, which is insoluble in acetone, is called the vulcanization coefficient. The highest grades of 30 per cent hevea insulation usually have a coefficient between 5 and 10 per cent.

The vulcanization of some brands of rubber cannot be accomplished without either an excess of sulfur or the presence of excessive quantities of some mineral accelerator, such as red lead. Such rubber is to be avoided where permanency is an important consideration. It does not follow from this that red lead in reasonable amounts is a detrimental ingredient.

Certain classes of organic compounds are used in small amounts to accelerate the cure greatly, thus largely decreasing the investment in molds and ovens for a given production. Anti-oxidants such as aniline and related compounds, are often added to the mix to resist the action of corona, thus increasing the useful life of the article made from the mix.

Specific Resistance of Rubber. The specific resistance of 30 per cent hevea rubber compounds is exceedingly variable, depending largely upon the success with which steam is prevented from condensing in the insulation during vulcanization. The megohm-miles are usually computed from the following formula:

$$M = K \log_{10} \frac{D}{d}$$

where M = insulation resistance of a cable, megohm-miles.
d = diameter of cylindrical conductor.
D = diameter of cable over its insulation.
K = 5.8 × (millions of megohms per inch cube at 60 deg fahr).

The value of K varies from 3000 to 7000, the usual specification value being 4000 for 30% hevea compounds.

The specific resistance is not an indication of the quality of rubber insulation as it depends more upon the dryness, the proportion of mineral wax, and the degree of vulcanization, than upon the quality of the ingredients. When the megohms are low they can almost invariably be raised by drying the insulation in a desiccator. The specific resistance of very poor-quality rubber compound, however, sometimes is so low that, when a cable lies in damp earth, sufficient leakage current may flow to permit the passage of water by endosmose, when the conductor is negative to the ground.

Dielectric Strength of Rubber. The disruptive strength of rubber insulation is generally given as between 350 and 450 kv per in. or about 140 to 180 kv per cm effective a-c values. The pressures which should be used in commercial testing do not depend entirely upon the dielectric strength of the rubber, as air in the rubber or between the rubber and conductor or between the rubber and ground becomes ionized at a pressure of about 30 kv per cm with consequent generation of ozone, which rapidly oxidizes and destroys the rubber. This does not occur with paper insulation because the impregnating oil precludes the possibility of air spaces; and no harm results in the case of varnished cambric because it is not seriously attacked by ozone. Hence test pressures for rubber insulation must be based upon experience rather than upon theory and, if sufficiently high to permit ionization of the air, should not last long enough to permit the formation of an appreciable amount of ozone.

Specific Inductive Capacity of Rubber. The specific inductive capacity of pure rubber is about 2.3 (Floy), but the vulcanized compounds used for insulation have specific capacities ranging between 3 and 5, the latter value being nearer the average. The specific capacities of several compounds of stated composition are given by E. Jona (St. Louis, 1904), but they cannot be considered as representative of American practice.

Gutta-percha is derived from the milky secretion or latex of the bark of certain trees of the order of Sapotaceæ, especially the Dichopsia Gutta, found chiefly in the Straits Settlements and Malaccan Archipelago. The trees are felled immediately after the rainy season, and the gutta or gum collected as it exudes from incisions in the bark. Latex is also extracted from the leaves by digesting them in toluol. However it may be extracted, the latex is boiled in water and it is then ready for export. Gutta-percha is becoming quite scarce, and practically the whole available supply is used by British cable makers.

The chemical composition of gutta-percha is represented by the formula C_1C_{16}. It resembles dark brown leather at temperatures between 0 and 27 deg cent. At higher temperatures it softens, and at 65 deg cent it is plastic and capable of being molded or rolled. On cooling it returns to the non-plastic condition.

Gutta-percha oxidizes when exposed to the air, changing from dark brown or black to yellowish gray and becoming brittle.

Preparation of Gutta-percha Insulation. For insulating purposes gutta-percha is shredded and squeezed in warm water. It is then kneaded and strained through fine wire gauze and rolled into sheets. Its further refinement is carried on differently by various manufacturers, the processes being more or less trade secrets. Like rubber it is applied to the wire either by a tubing machine or by strips. Unlike rubber it is used in the pure state without mixture with minerals. Gutta-percha is less porous than rubber and therefore more waterproof, a quality which makes it the best material for submarine cables. Its specific gravity is just above unity.

Specific Resistance of Gutta-percha. The constant K in the formula

$$M = K \log \frac{D}{d}$$

has the value 900 approximately, at 75 deg fahr after 1 min electrification.

Temperature Coefficient of Resistance of Gutta-percha is of the same nature as that of rubber, i.e.,

$$R_T = R_{75}\,\epsilon^{(75-T)C},$$

where R_{75} is the resistance at 75 deg fahr, R_T the resistance at T degrees fahrenheit, and C a constant which varies from 0.065 to 0.085.

Effect of Pressure upon Resistance of Gutta-percha. Gutta-percha being used principally for submarine cables, the effect of pressure is important. Resistance and permittance decrease somewhat with increase in pressure, substantially in proportion to the change in density with pressure.

Duprene is a synthetic rubber developed by the Dupont Co. It is a chlorinated derivative of acetylene, and is similar in molecular structure to rubber. The advantages of Duprene are its resistance to age brittleness and to the action of oil. The material is permanently flexible and in accelerated aging at high temperature shows superiority to rubber. Light mineral oils soften Duprene somewhat but not as seriously as they do rubber. It may be obtained in sheets and is used chiefly for gaskets.

Thiokol, chemically olein polysulfide, derived from natural gas, is an oil proof rubber substitute made by the Thiokol Corp. It is unaffected by oil, gasoline, or similar materials. In accelerated aging tests, its life compares with that of high-grade long-life rubber. The "cold flow" under pressure (as in a gasket) is greater than that of either rubber or Duprene. Because of the composition, Thiokol produces corrosion in contact with copper; and with transformer oil, sludging and acid formation result. It cannot be used as transformer gaskets with ordinary designs. The chief application is for oil and gasoline hose. It may be used as a surface layer over rubber for gaskets on lubricating oil and gasoline containers. Also, an outside coating of thiokol on rubber-insulated cables is valuable where cables are subjected to oily conditions.

33. PLASTIC INSULATING MATERIALS

Synthetic Resin Products

Synthetic Resin Products. (See also Resins under Paints, Enamels, Varnishes, Lacquers, pp. 12–54, et seq.) In recent years great advances have been made in the manufacture of countless varieties of insulating products using some organic filler (cloth, paper, or other fiber) bonded with some type of synthetic resin. The first important material of this type was Bakelite, developed by Dr. Bakeland. This is a condensation product resulting from the combination of phenol and formaldehyde under certain conditions. The resin in its initial state is thermoplastic and soluble in alcohol-benzol solvent or acetone. Further heat will polymerize the resin and render it insoluble and infusible. In treating materials with Bakelite, the first stage is used in varnish form and the impregnated filler is then pressed with accompanying heat to cause polymerization.

Many other resins have been introduced since Bakelite was developed. Some are modifications of the phenolic class, but many are of other distinct types. A useful series of resins is known as Glyptal. These are made of glycerin and phthalic anhydride. Other types are resorcinal-formaldehyde, furfural-formaldehyde, vinyl resins, and urea resins. Some are permanently thermoplastic; others are infusible. The urea resins have the advantage of being more nearly colorless, so that light shades of color for decorative purposes are possible.

Synthetic resin products are usually water and oil proof and resist mild acids and alkalies well. Their electrical properties are in general good, being dependent to an extent on the type of filler used.

The physical forms of resin products are many:

(a) Resin alone can be molded for ornamental objects such as umbrella handles. It is clear or translucent and can be colored, if desired, by dyes or pigments.

(b) Paper or cloth, impregnated with resin and molded in layers, is used for making plate, tubing, angles, channels, etc.

(c) Essentially homogeneous fillers such as wood flour, asbestos fiber, chopped cloth may be mixed with dry resin and molded into intricate shapes. The mixture (filler and dry resin) is usually called a molding powder.

Synthetic resin varnishes are also used for impregnating coils and other parts in a manner similar to regular varnishes. Baking completes the polymerization.

Low-grade molding compositions are used for parts not highly stressed either mechanically or electrically. They made be made of a large variety of finely divided materials mixed with shellac, gums, pitch, sodium silicate, etc.

Properties of laminated phenolic sheet and laminated tubing are given in Tables IV and V, respectively.

Table IV. Properties of Laminated Phenolic Sheet Materials (N.E.M.A. Standards, 1931)

Grade	Description	Average Tensile Strength, lbs per sq in.	Average Flexural Strength, lbs per sq in.	Average Dielectric Strength, volts per mil		1,000,000 Cycles			Moisture Absorption, % in 24 hr
				Short Time	Step by Step	Power Factor %	s.i.c.	Dielectric Loss Factor	
X	Paper base	12,000	21,000	700	500	...	...	...	4.0
P	Paper base	8,000	15,000	600	400	...	...	...	4.0
XX	Paper base	8,000	16,000	700	500	4.5	5.5	0.25	1.3
XXX	Paper base	7,000	15,000	650	450	3.5	5.0	0.18	1.0
C	Heavy fibre base for mechanical purposes	10,000	20,000	150	100	10.0	7.0	0.70	1.7
CE	Heavy fabric base electrical and mechanical	9,500	19,000	425	275	5.5	5.5	0.30	1.5
L	Fine weave fabric mechanical	10,000	20,000	150	100	10.0	7.0	0.70	2.0
LE	Fine weave fabric electrical and mechanical	9,000	19,000	500	300	4.5	5.0	0.22	1.2

Table V. Properties of Typical Laminated Tubing

Description	Color	Specific Gravity	Water Absorption, % Increase in Weight After 24 hr	Ultimate Strength, lb per sq in. Axial Stresses		Dielectric Strength 1/16 Wall, volts per mil	
				Tensile	Compression	In Oil	In Oil After 24 hr in Water
Kraft paper and synthetic resin. Applications where machining qualities are desirable. Superior mechanical and electrical properties. Special tools for shapes other than round.	Dark tan	1.29	3	11,000	20,000	1000	800
Kraft paper and shellac. For general use (except brush holder tubes) under 75 deg. cent. Will collapse at 100 deg. cent., unless mechanically supported. Resists arcing slightly more than phenolic materials. Made in round and other shapes. Not baked.	Brown	1.12	55	8,000	7,000	800	...
Fine weave fabric and synthetic resin. Where extra strength and high impact are desired. Has lowest moisture absorption of any grade, and is preferred for most chemical applications.	Tan	1.25	2	5,800	22,000	350	300
Kraft paper and synthetic resin.	Black	1.29	3	11,000	20,000	650	500

Waxes

Several waxes, mostly of mineral origin, are used as impregnating materials. They have the advantage when melted of penetrating fibrous insulation and making it moisture proof. Since they are made liquid by heating, no difficulty is presented in the evaporation of solvent, as with varnishes. Most waxes are not oil proof. Natural waxes are composed of carbon, hydrogen, and oxygen. The mineral waxes differ in having no oxygen. Some of the most useful waxes are described below.

Montan Wax is a mineral wax derived from lignite. It has a sharp melting point (75–80 deg cent) and is very fluid when melted. Density at 25 deg cent is 0.90 to 1.00. Frequently, when used for coil impregnation, it is mixed with asphalt gums to give increased fluidity without lowering the melting point.

Mineral Wax (petroleum) has a melting point of 37.5 deg cent and resembles a very viscous petrolatum. It is used as a substitute for beeswax in the impregnation of radio coils and capacitors. It gives good moisture proofing and low dielectric losses.

Beeswax, sometimes mixed with rosin, is used for the impregnation of radio coils and various wire coverings. It has the advantage of avoiding solvents, is very fluid when melted, and has excellent dielectric properties. Density is 0.96 to 0.97 at 15 deg cent. Melting point is 62 to 64 deg cent.

Halowax, a halogenated naphthalene, is an excellent wax dielectric used widely for capacitor insulation. It is also flame resisting and enters the composition of preparations applied to insulation such as cable braid.

Paraffin. The grade of paraffin most common for impregnation has a melting point 50–52 deg cent. It is used to exclude moisture from fish paper, wood, cotton insulation on coils, and other applications where the operating temperature is low. Paraffin, being usually a petroleum product is not oil proof. Specific gravity 0.85 to 0.95, and s.i.c. 1.9 to 2.3.

Ozokerite is a natural mineral wax, related to petroleum products. It may vary from white to brown in color, depending on degree of purification. One purified form is called ceresine wax. The specific gravity at 25 deg cent is 0.85–1.00, and the melting point is 60–95 deg cent. Some impregnating compounds contain this type of material.

Gums, Asphalts, Etc.

Fossil Gums. A numerous group of so-called "fossil gums" have found considerable application both in insulating compounds and as major constituents of varnishes. Among these may be mentioned acroides, dammar, and copal as typical. Gum acroides is soluble in alcohol and sometimes serves as a substitute for shellac, but is more brittle. Copal is used in a variety of compounds. It is also a shellac substitute, being cheaper but having less adhesion. It does possess the advantage, however, of resisting change in flow with continued heating. It does not polymerize as readily as shellac, and is frequently used with powdered shellac to provide good flow properties for coating mica. For other forms of mica products, copal is employed in the compounding of "sticking" varnishes.

A common type of oil-proof impregnating compound consists largely of copal gum, castor oil, and sometimes rosin. It is amber in color and is used for transformer coils, magnet coils, and other apparatus where varnish is not suitable.

Asphaltic gums, both natural (gilsonite) and that made from distillation of petroleum, are very valuable as insulating materials. They range in consistency from viscous tarlike substances to hard, glossy black brittle grades. They may be combined with oils, other gums, or resins in many impregnating compounds. Asphaltic materials are quite moisture resistant, are unaffected by ordinary acids or alkalies, but are generally oil soluble. They cannot be used, therefore, with transformer oil but are excellent for coils operated in air. Natural asphalt is a mixture of hydrocarbons, brown to black in color, with a density 1.04 to 1.40 and s.i.c of 2.7. It starts to soften at about 70 deg cent and is liquid at 90–100 deg cent. Asphalt impregnating compounds give more complete filling of deep coils than varnish, and being melted for use, require no removal of solvents.

Stearin Pitch. This material has a high melting point, 110 deg cent, and is very low in volatile matter. It also possesses flame-resisting characteristics. It is an ingredient in mica bonding compounds.

Pine Tar, derived from yellow pine distillation, is permanently plastic and is therefore very valuable as a flexibilizer. It is a component in spirit and sticking varnishes and in filling and sealing compounds.

Solventless Varnishes. A recent addition to impregnating compounds of a semisolid type is made in the same manner as insulating varnish (see Insulating Varnishes) except that the final dilution with solvents is omitted. The material is about the consistency of medium asphalt, will just flow at room temperature, and is considered 100 per cent solid. Impregnation is done by heating, to increase fluidity. The difficulty of evaporating solvents, which is a problem with usual varnishes, is thus eliminated.

Shellac (see shellac under Liquid Insulating Materials) obtained from a natural resin, secreted by insects, is used both as a spirit varnish and as a gum. Powdered shellac is used in a number of hot-molding compounds when mixed with a filler. Liquid or powdered shellac is also coated on paper for making insulating bushings and tubing. When rolled, heat is applied to melt the shellac and drive off any residual solvent. Melted shellac is sometimes used for impregnation. It changes to an infusible state if heated for long periods, however, and cannot be readily used in large vats kept hot for impregnating work unless replenished frequently.

34. LIQUID INSULATING MATERIALS

Natural Oils

Linseed Oil, an impregnating material and a major constituent of paints and varnishes, comes from flaxseed. The specific gravity at 15 deg cent is 0.934. Linseed oil dries principally by atmospheric oxidation, finally to a hard gum. With "raw" linseed this process in air is quite slow. "Boiled" oil will oxidize fairly rapidly in air. The action is accelerated by heat or chemical driers. Linseed oil is frequently employed to impregnate wood, making it moisture proof and capable of withstanding exposure to the weather. Impregnation is usually done hot (60 deg cent) to aid in penetration. Baking oxidizes the oil to give a satisfactory surface coat.

Tung Oil (China wood oil) comes from the nuts of an oriental tree, and its main application is in the manufacture of varnishes. It hardens chiefly by polymerization rather than oxidation, thus differing from linseed oil. It may be used for impregnating coils or wood.

Non-drying Oils, such as castor, rosin, or olive oil, are good insulators, but are almost always combined with other materials.

Mineral Oils are used mainly in transformers, induction regulators, and circuit breakers. In transformers and induction regulators, the oil provides an electrical insulating medium which also will carry the heat away from the windings. In circuit breakers, the oil serves primarily as an electrical insulating medium which interrupts the arc when the circuit breaker operates. The requirements for insulating oil for transformers and induction regulators are not inconsistent with those for oil for service in circuit breakers, and hence a single oil will often meet all requirements satisfactorily. Some special switches require a different grade of oil with respect to viscosity, but the properties in general are not materially different.

The Primary Requirements for Transformer and Induction Regulator Oils are as follows:

High dielectric strength; freedom from inorganic acid, alkali, and corrosive sulfur to prevent injury to insulation or conductors; low viscosity to provide good heat transfer; good resistance to emulsion, so that the oil will throw down any moisture entering the apparatus instead of holding it in suspension. (Water in suspension is a menace to safe operation.)

The Primary Requirements for Circuit Breaker Oils are as follows:

High dielectric strength; freedom from inorganic acid, alkali, and corrosive sulfur, to prevent injury to insulation or conductors; low viscosity to aid in dissipating the arc when the circuit is interrupted; low freezing point to insure proper fluidity at all operating temperatures; good resistance to emulsion so that any moisture entering the apparatus or carbon formed by arcing will settle to the bottom of the tank.

Properties of Mineral Oils. It has not been found feasible to cover the performance of an insulating oil completely by specification. Changes in oil with temperature and time cannot always be foretold from physical or chemical tests on the oil. Certain characteristics, however, are indicative of satisfactory oil as far as laboratory tests can determine. The following values may be taken as representative of acceptable unused transformer oil which is also suitable for most circuit breakers.

Specific gravity............................ 0.898 at 15.5 deg cent
Flash point................................ 132 deg cent
Fire point................................. 149 deg cent
Viscosity (Saybolt)........................ 57 sec at 40 deg cent
                                            280 sec at 0 deg cent
Pour test.................................. −45.6 deg cent
Demulsibility (resistance to emulsion value).... 25 sec
Neutralization value....................... 0.03 mg. of KOH per g

Insulating Varnishes. See also Paints, Varnishes, Enamels, and Lacquers, p. 12-50.

A Varnish is generally considered as a solution of gums (fossil or synthetic) in (1) volatile solvents, e.g., spirit varnishes, or (2) drying oils, e.g., oleoresinous varnishes.

Spirit Varnishes are generally those composed of shellac (various grades) or synthetic resins dissolved in alcohol or other volatile solvents. They are valuable for rapid air-drying applications and are better for finishes or surface coatings than for impregnating purposes. They commonly possess low flexibility and good cementing properties.

Oil and Asphaltic Varnishes consist of varnish gums or resins, such as copal, succin, dammar, or mastic, combined with a vehicle compounded from linseed oil and tung oil. In black varnishes, clear gums are replaced by asphaltic materials or pitches. The drying time is governed by the proportion of gums and oils and by the quantity of oxidizing agents or driers in the varnish. The greater the proportion of oils, the longer the drying time.

Some of the quick air-drying black varnishes may contain no drying oil. Such varnishes are of neither the oil nor the spirit type and may be termed "asphaltic varnishes." They may consist of an asphaltic base and solvent derived from petroleum or coal tar.

For most electrical work the following varnishes cover the requirements satisfactorily; a clear and a black varnish for both air drying and baking, and a plastic coil impregnation varnish, making five varieties. These varnishes are useful as well for finishing apparatus (metal and insulation) or to provide good appearance and a surface easily kept clean.

Air-drying varnishes do not produce so hard a moisture-resistant coating as baking varnishes under usual conditions but are necessary for apparatus that cannot be baked or for repairs away from the factory. The black varnishes are generally more moisture resistant than the clear but are less oil resistant. The dielectric properties of the black varnishes are somewhat superior to those of clear varnishes. Table VI gives the properties of the common insulating varnishes.

Table VI. Insulating Varnishes

Varnish	Drying Time, hours	Moisture Resistance Rating	Oil Resistance Rating	Acid Resistance, Seconds till Failure		Dielectric		Life at 110° C, hours	Chemical Analysis, Percent										Applications
				H$_2$SO$_4$	HNO$_3$	Dry	Wet		Rosin	Asphaltum	Lime	Linseed Oil	China Wood Oil	Lead and Manganese	Iron Oxide Drier	Benzine 50° to 60°	Heavy Benzine	Turpentine	
Black plastic baking	4	90	65	72	150	1923	947	770	6.1	14.9		23	11.5	0.77		44			Plastic insulator for coils and stators
Black coil baking	5	90	80	128	65	1890	610	528									54		For coils, armatures and wound apparatus. Also finish
Clear coil baking	1	55	100	61	40	1722	403	600	9.4		.51		43.3	1.02		46			For wound armatures and cloth finish
Black air dry	4	65	0	107	141	1642	527	24		29		13			.43	59			General use where baking cannot be done
Clear air dry	4	75	100	27	22	1128	246	675	8.2			3	27	1.4		55		6.1	General use where baking cannot be done

Specific gravity of all varnishes, 0.835 or 0.850.   Thinner for all varnishes, benzine.

Requirements for Insulating Varnishes. Varnishes to be satisfactory must possess desirable properties in all three states—as a liquid, during drying, and when solid. The most important characteristics to consider are:

Liquid	While Drying	Solid
Color	Spreading	Hardness
Viscosity	Draining	Toughness
Specific gravity	Drying time	Cementing ability
Per cent solids	Relation of surface to subsurface drying	Dielectric strength
Nature of solvent		Softening temperature
Penetration	Chemical action on metals or insulating materials	Resistance to water, oil, chemicals
Flow		
Tendency to skin in tanks		

It is not possible to combine in one varnish the maximum degree of all desirable attributes. There are, therefore, a number of useful types of insulating varnish, adapted for particular needs. For example, it is not yet (1936) possible to make a quick-drying varnish that has the ultimate degree of flexibility and heat life. Further, a plastic varnish is not considered the best for a hard surface finishing material.

Application of Varnishes. Varnishes may be applied by brushing, dipping, or spraying. Coils are usually dipped for sufficient time to drive out air, then drained, and then baked. The temperature of baking depends on many factors such as time allowable, type of material, etc. Short time baking (15 min) may be done up to 200 deg cent. A more usual temperature for baking time of 1 to 3 hr is 150 deg cent. Good oven circulation to remove solvent and thus hasten drying is important. Vacuum drying of coils is frequently employed to remove moisture and air. The impregnating material may be admitted to the tank while under vacuum to prevent entrapping air.

Wire Enamels. Certain special insulating varnishes, called wire enamels, are used in coating wires with an insulating film. Most of them are composed of fossil gums combined with drying oils. They differ from usual insulating varnishes in containing less oil (linseed and tung) and are thinned with coal-tar solvents quite similar to kerosene.

In the coating operation, the wire is passed successively through the tank of liquid enamel (" dope pan ") and vertically through a baking chamber, over sheaves, and then the cycle is repeated. From three to six layers are applied, depending on size of wire and service required. Baking is best done by controlled electric heat in the range 400–500 deg cent. The speed of wire travel depends on height of baking oven, temperature, and size of wire. Heavy wires (No. 10 B. & S.) may travel 12 ft per min, whereas fine wire (Nos. 40–44 B. & S.) may pass through at 80 ft per min.

Common American enamels are mahogany red in color when properly baked. Color is a fair indicator of degree of bake or cure, but it is not infallible since it changes with time. Underbaked wire (copper red) is tougher and will elongate without rupture of enamel, but may be less resistant to abrasion and not oil proof. On the other hand, a black wire (overbaked) will probably be brittle but harder and more oil resistant. A good wire enamel properly baked should:

(a) Produce a uniform coating, no beading, and no thin spots; (b) be flexible to withstand elongation in coil winding and show no breaks when wire is stretched to breaking point; (c) be resistant to abrasion; (d) have reasonably high dielectric strength (1500 volts per mil); (e) withstand hot oil and varnish, e.g., withstand varnish at 80 deg cent for 16 hr without softening; (f) have long life. Elongation should not decrease appreciably when wire is stored for 6 months.

Solvents

Solvents. It is important to know the insulating characteristics of ordinary solvents, since some quantity of solvent is usually still present after coils are baked or insulating structures finished.

Because of its high affinity for water, alcohol must be thoroughly removed from spirit varnish impregnation. In deep coils this is difficult, and drying must be done carefully.

Turpentine, benzine, toluol, benzol, and related solvents do not mix with water and are good insulators. It is not, therefore, required for insulating reasons that all solvent be completely removed in impregnation processes. Evaporation will continue for some time. For mechanical reasons (to prevent throwing of " wet " varnish or distortion of coils) it is important to carry evaporation far enough to produce a hardening of the varnish or compound. Under some conditions, organic acids develop in " wet " varnish.

Gases

Gases, when stressed below rupturing gradients, are excellent insulators. Their s.i.c. under normal atmospheric conditions is nearly the same as that in a vacuum, being less than 1 per cent greater. Dielectric strength is rather low, being 31 kv (crest) per cm for air in a uniform electrostatic field. Where the field is non-uniform, local breakdown (corona) induces complete rupture at much lower values. The dielectric strength increases directly with pressure.

Air occurs as an insulator on every piece of electrical apparatus. The distance externally between live parts or between terminals and a grounded part must be great enough to prevent breakdown or excessive leakage in an air path. It is true that frequently the effect of a solid insulation creepage surface is important, but in many cases air is the effective external dielectric. In solid insulation, air is a detriment. Its low s.i.c. causes concentration of voltage gradient on the air layers or pockets (inversely proportional to s.i.c.) and may lead to corona and progressive breakdown.

The dielectric strength of air gaps depends largely on the type of electrodes with their local electrostatic fields. Needle-point gaps have a fairly uniform strength of approximately 4 kv per cm. Sphere gaps or gaps between large curved surfaces have much higher unit breakdown strength, especially at spacings less than the diameter of the spheres. With most types of air gaps, humidity, air density, and frequency greatly influence the dielectric strength.

Carbon Dioxide. Compressed carbon dioxide has been employed as an insulator in high-voltage condensers for apparatus used in measurement of power factor and capacitance. It is an inert gas, obtainable in a relatively pure state.

Nitrogen. There is little difference in the dielectric properties of the common gases. The choice for any application is usually determined by cost or chemical properties. Nitrogen is inert and finds application as an atmosphere in sealed transformers. It prevents absorption of oxygen by the oil and thus eliminates formation of organic acids and sludge. ("Inertaire" type of transformer.)

Hydrogen. Because of its high specific heat (3.41 compared to 0.237 for air) hydrogen is useful as a dielectric to absorb heat from electrical machinery. It is used in a closed system for cooling large generators. Care must be taken to keep a positive gas pressure in the system to prevent influx of sufficient air to produce an explosive mixture.

Relative Dielectric Strength of Gases. Although the dielectric strength of gases varies roughly as the pressure, there are small differences in behavior of the different common gases. Considering the strength of air as 1.00 at the various pressures, Table VII shows the relative dielectric strengths as a factor of the air values.

Table VII. Relative Dielectric Strengths of Gases (Air = 1.00)
(Wolf)

Atmospheres Pressure	Carbon Dioxide	Nitrogen	Hydrogen
1	1.20	1.16	0.87
2	1.10	1.15	0.76
3	1.05	1.15	0.72
4	1.03	1.14	0.69
5	1.02	1.14	0.68

BIBLIOGRAPHY

MINER, D. F., Oil Breakdown at Large Spacings. *A.I.E.E. Proc.*, May, 1927.
HARVEY, Dean, Testing Paper for Electrical Insulation. *Elec. J.*, October, 1932.
HARVEY, Dean, Tests of Molded Material. *Elec. J.*, July, 1932.
HARVEY, Dean, Tests of Insulation Varnishes. *Elec. J.*, May, 1932.
HARVEY, Dean, Methods of Test for Phenolic Resin Laminated Materials. *Elec. J.*, February, 1933.
JACKSON, H. P., Electrical Insulating Materials. *Elec. J.*, August, 1919.
ARNOLD, R. H., and FROST, L. E., Service Requirements of Insulating Varnishes. *Ind. & Eng. Chem.*, February, 1933.
FINDLEY, HARVEY, and RODGERS, Electrical Insulating Varnishes. *A.S.T.M. Proc.*, 1923.
N.E.M.A. Standards for Fiber, 1931.
N.E.M.A. Standards for Laminated Phenolic Sheet Materials, 1931.
W. E. & M. Co. Instruction Book on Oil, No. I.B.5336.C.
BENEDICT, F. R., Dielectric Power Factor. *Elec. J.*, April, 1934.

LUBRICANTS

By D. F. Miner

35. CLASSES OF LUBRICANTS

Classification of Lubricants. There are three general classes of lubricants: (1) mineral oils, (2) animal and vegetable oils, and (3) greases.

1. Mineral oils may be of either naphthenic (asphaltic) or paraffin base origin, the former being fluid at low temperatures, and the latter being more highly resistant to oxidation. They cover the range from light spindle oils to heavy cylinder oils.

2. Animal or vegetable oils, though occasionally employed for lubricating purposes, either straight or blended with mineral oils, are not considered primarily as lubricants. Their use is sometimes justified to increase lubricity or oiliness. They are subject to the general characteristics of their class, i.e., tendency to oxidize and to gum in the vegetable oils, and to rancidify in animal oils.

3. The term grease is applied to a mixture of mineral oil and fats which have been saponified with an alkali. Grease is available, either with or without fillers, in three general classes: (a) hard grease, (b) soft grease, and (c) non-fluid oil. More definite classification is being sponsored by the A.S.T.M. by standardizing penetration values.

Source of Lubricants. (a) Animal oils are made by rendering the fatty parts of animals, usually with steam. The resulting material is chilled and the oil pressed out. Some of the varieties are: tallow from cattle or sheep, lard oil from cattle, neatsfoot oil from bones of cattle feet, whale oil, and porpoise oil.

(b) Most vegetable oils come from the seeds of various plants, by crushing or by chemical extraction. Examples are: castor oil, cottonseed oil, rapeseed oil, corn oil, olive oil.

(c) Mineral oils result from the distillation of crude petroleum. One method of refining is to treat by agitation with sulfuric acid, followed by washing with water and caustic soda. In the last few years, laboratory methods of purification have been applied to installations of commercial size. Oils are now being refined by means of aluminum chloride and by use of special selective solvents, which remove the naphthene and aromatic portions from mid-continent and western crudes, the products having essentially the properties of Pennsylvania oils (high heat resistance and flat viscosity curve). Catalytic hydrogenation of oils is being practiced, with the production of very desirable oils having a flat viscosity curve. Accurate temperature control of distillation by means of heat-transfer media such as mercury and diphenyl is being employed to give uniform high-quality products.

36. PROPERTIES OF LUBRICANTS

Definitions and Tests Pertaining to Lubricants. (a) *Viscosity* is the term used to signify the body or degree of fluidity of an oil at a given temperature. Measurement is made by means of a viscosimeter, such as the Standard Saybolt Universal in this country, or the Engler, Barbier, and Redwood in Europe. The values obtained by these instruments, that is, the time required for a given amount of oil to flow through an orifice at a given temperature, are purely relative. However, actual measurement may be made in cgs units and is known as absolute viscosity.

(b) *Flash Point* is the lowest temperature at which the lubricant will give off sufficient vapor to ignite momentarily when a flame is applied to the vapor.

(c) *Fire Point* is the lowest temperature at which the vapors given off will burn continuously.

(d) *The Evaporation Test* indicates the quantity of oily vapor an oil will give off on heating under definite conditions of test. It gives an indication of the volatility of oils used in such applications as in the lubrication of vacuum pumps, and serves as an additional check on fire hazard.

(e) *Test for Acidity* indicates the amount of uncombined acid in the oil. Since modern refining methods of mineral oils have practically eliminated the danger of contamination from inorganic acids such as sulfuric, the acidity, due to organic acids, is usually referred to as the acid number or neutralization number. It is expressed as the number of milligrams of potassium hydroxide required to neutralize 1 g of oil. However, the vegetable or mineral oils, which are sometimes used for lubricating purposes, are tested for what is termed "free fatty acids," and the acidity is expressed in terms of oleic acid. The acid number divided by 1.99 will give the acidity in terms of oleic acid. The permissible amount of oleic acid varies according to the application.

(*f*) *Saponification Value* is used to determine if an animal or vegetable oil has been mixed with a mineral oil, as well as the degree of oxidation of the mineral oil.

(*g*) *Specific Gravity* of oils is sometimes expressed as a decimal relation to the specific gravity of water. Another method of expression is the number on the Baumé hydrometer scale.

(*h*) *Pour Test* is the lowest temperature at which the oil will just flow, an indication of its usefulness in cold weather.

Properties of Oils. A satisfactory oil should have:

1. Low cohesion to facilitate spreading an adequate oil film between a shaft and its bearing.

2. High adhesion to prevent the oil film from being squeezed out of the bearing contacts and from running freely away from parts to be lubricated.

3. Resistance to oxidation on continued exposure to high temperatures, thus maintaining its original properties over long periods.

4. Freedom from foreign matter. Water may emulsify the oil and ruin its lubricating value. Dirt, metal particles, etc., injure bearings or restrict flow of lubricant in small passages.

Properties of Greases. Grease should have the proper consistency and the ability to resist heat in certain applications, should not turn rancid nor permit the separation of the oil from the soap, and should have the ability to cling to bearings and not break down under violent churning. The amount and kind of soap used in preparing the grease, as well as the type of oil with which it is compounded, have a bearing on these requirements. Relatively higher melting points can be obtained through the use of a given amount of sodium soap, but, in contact with water, such a grease has a greater tendency to disintegrate than grease with a calcium or lime soap base. Therefore, the choice of a grease necessitates a definite knowledge of the requirements for a given application.

37. USES OF LUBRICANTS

Suggestions for Selection of Lubricants. 1. The flash point should be as high as possible, and still be consistent with other characteristics, particularly viscosity. A safe minimum may be taken as 300 deg fahr.

2. For light pressures and high speeds, mineral oils having viscosities of about 150 sec at 100 deg fahr may be used.

3. For general-purpose machinery, mineral oils having a viscosity of 175 to 225 sec at 100 deg fahr will give satisfactory results. Such oils have a flash point of around 370 deg fahr. In some instances animal and vegetable oils are employed, but usually straight-run mineral oils are preferable.

4. For heavy duty, industrial heavy mineral oils having a viscosity range of about 300 to 1200 sec at 100 deg fahr are recommended.

5. For internal-combustion engines, mineral oils having viscosities of 200 to 600 sec are used in winter and 400 to 1500 sec in summer. Pour tests of +20 deg fahr maximum are imperative in cold climates.

6. For steam cylinder or extra heavy duty, cylinder oils, either straight-run oils or oils compounded with several per cent of acidless tallow, are in general use. Their flash point is about 600 deg fahr, and their viscosity is 2500 to 3000 sec at 100 deg fahr and 150 to 175 sec at 210 deg fahr.

7. For watches and fine machinery several oils are in use, including, highly refined water-white mineral oils having low pour tests, specially refined low pour test black fish " melon " oil, and other less efficient fish oils.

8. For very high pressure and slow speed, or where ordinary oils will not stay in position, greases give satisfactory results. Roller and ball bearings are frequently lubricated with greases.

Automotive Oils. The viscosity of oils used for automotive purposes has been standardized, and a list of S.A.E. numbers used for identification is as follows:

S.A.E. No.	Saybolt Viscosity
10	90–120 at 130 deg fahr
20	120–185 at 130 deg fahr
30	185–255 at 130 deg fahr
40	255 at 130 deg fahr, not less than 75 at 210 deg fahr
50	75–105 at 210 deg fahr
60	105–125 at 210 deg fahr
70	125–150 at 210 deg fahr

FUELS AND EXPLOSIVES *

38. FUELS

Carbon and Hydrogen are the principal constituents of solid, liquid, and gaseous fuels. In burning, the carbon and hydrogen combine with oxygen from the air, yielding, when combustion is complete, carbon dioxide and water, respectively. When insufficient air is admitted over the bed of fuel, or into the firebox when liquid or gaseous fuels are used, much of the fuel may be lost, either as solids (smoke, soot) and tars, or in the form of unburned gases, especially carbon monoxide. It is almost impossible to attain complete combustion of solid fuels by forcing air under the grate and through the bed of coals, because part of the carbon dioxide formed near the grate is reduced to carbon monoxide on passing through the overlying layers of hot fuel. This monoxide, which has a high heating value, can be burned completely only when a plentiful supply of air is available over the bed of fuel. The blue flames seen when anthracite, coke, or charcoal is burned are due to carbon monoxide.

Wood consists mainly of lignin and cellulose, compounds of carbon with hydrogen and oxygen, together with varying amounts of water and mineral matter. The last largely remains behind in the ash.

Charcoal is made by piling wood into heaps which are covered with earth, leaving a few small openings to admit a limited amount of air and allow the products of combustion to escape when the wood is ignited. When sufficient wood has burned to insure thorough charring (" destructive distillation ") of the remainder, the openings are closed and the pile allowed to cool completely. By this method of making charcoal only a little tar is obtained and all the volatile constituents are allowed to escape. When wood is heated in closed retorts, large amounts of tar, creosote, wood or methyl alcohol, acetone, and pyroligneous (acetic) acid, etc., are obtained. The yield of charcoal is also nearly doubled. Charcoal consists mainly of carbon and the mineral matter of the wood. Its value in metallurgy is due to its low content of phosphorus and sulfur. The calorific value of charcoal is about 95 per cent that of anthracite.

Peat is the result of the partial decay of mosses and other bog plants under water. Even when compressed and dried it contains much water and its mineral content may be high. Its calorific value is 3000 to 4000 cal per kg in air-dried condition.

Lignite, or brown coal, is a stage beyond peat in the formation of coal. It contains much moisture and is often high in ash. Its calorific value as mined is 3500 to 4500 cal per kg. Owing to its large amount of volatile matter, lignite burns with a long, smoky flame.

Bituminous Coal was formed by the further transformation of lignite by heat and pressure. It comprises many varieties, including gas, coking, steam, and cannel coals. They differ principally in their content of volatile matter, the " fat " coals having at times as high as 50 per cent of the compounds of carbon and hydrogen, which are readily driven off by heating. The length of flame of burning bituminous coal depends on the percentage of volatile matter.

Anthracite Coal was produced by the further action of heat and pressure upon bituminous coal, whereby nearly all the volatile constituents were driven off, leaving mainly carbon and mineral matter. These coals burn with little flame and no visible smoke, and do not cake. Their calorific value may be 6500 to 7500 cal per kg.

Coke. As charcoal is the residue left by heating wood in retorts or partially burning it with a limited air supply, so coke is made by heating bituminous coals. In the older types of coke ovens the gaseous and liquid products formed by the destructive distillation are allowed to escape into the air; with modern types of ovens this loss is not permitted and valuable by-products are obtained, such as ammonia, fuel and illuminating gas, and coal tar. Coke is mainly carbon but contains also the mineral constituents of the coal. It is low in volatile matter and sulfur. Upon this and its infusibility and resistance to crushing depends its value as a fuel in blast furnaces. Its calorific value is about 90 per cent that of anthracite.

Chemical Examination of Coal and Coke. The heating value of any fuel can be determined conveniently by means of one of the numerous forms of bomb calorimeters. But this leaves unanswered many questions which have a very practical bearing, for example, the percentages of volatile matter, sulfur, and ash, and the amount of coke the coal will yield. In general, the lower the percentage of ash the better the quality of the

* Written by C. E. Waters, Chemist, National Bureau of Standards, in 1930, for the American Civil Engineers' Handbook by Merriman and Wiggin and reviewed in 1935 by engineers of the U. S. Bureau of Mines.

fuel. The only mineral constituent that has any heating value is the sulfur of pyrites. But as sulfur is injurious in practically all metallurgical operations and the oxides of sulfur have a corroding effect upon boiler tubes, etc., a coal high in either pyritic or organic sulfur is undesirable. Coals for use in stoker-fired boiler plants operating at high ratings should have high ash fusion temperatures. Coals which are to be burned in pulverized form under boilers should be easily pulverized and have either high or low ash fusion temperatures for plants designed for dry bottom or slag tap operation, respectively. Gas coals and coal for use in certain metallurgical operations requiring long reducing flames should be high in volatile matter. Coals that are to be worked economically for coke may be low in volatile matter but must possess the property of partially fusing or caking together when heated in the ovens.

Samples for calorimetric determinations or for chemical analysis should be collected by the American Standard method promulgated by the American Society for Testing Materials. In sampling at the mine, the coal should be cut from a freshly exposed face, and the sample, after quartering to suitable size, should fairly represent not only the actual coal but also the interpenetrating veins of shale, etc., if these are regularly mined with the coal. It is very important to prepare the sample, not only with great care but also as rapidly as possible, to minimize the inevitable loss of moisture in breaking up the lumps. This explains the necessity of placing the fuel sample in air-tight receptacles, such as fruit jars with rubber rings.

39.　LIQUID AND GASEOUS FUELS

Crude Petroleum is the most important of the liquid fuels. It owes its importance not only to its comparative cheapness but also to the ease with which it is handled and its high efficiency, which is two or more times that of anthracite. It is usually burned in the form of a spray obtained by means of a blast of air or superheated steam. Petroleum residues and coal-tar residues are also burned to some extent. Their calorific value is not as great as that of crude petroleum, but may run as high as 10,000 cal per kg.

Gasoline is the lowest-boiling distillate from crude petroleum, or from the " cracking " of the higher-boiling fractions by high temperature, usually under excess pressure, and sometimes in the presence of catalysts which facilitate the breaking down of the more complex hydrocarbon molecules into simpler ones. *Casinghead gasoline* is condensed from natural gas by compression and cooling, before the gas enters the mains through which it is distributed. It is too volatile to be used alone for ordinary purposes, but large quantities of it are mixed with the other forms of gasoline. Each of the kinds of gasoline is a mixture of hydrocarbons containing different percentages of carbon and hydrogen. When mixed with the proper amount of air the vapors form a mixture which is readily ignited and burns with explosive violence. If the vapor is largely in excess of the proportion needed for complete combustion the force of the explosion is weakened, so that, apart from the actual loss of unburned gases, the full power of the engine is not developed. There is a similar loss in power when too much air is present. For the complete combustion of 1 cu ft of the vapor of the hydrocarbon hexane, C_6H_{14}, 45.2 cu ft of air are required, whereas the same volume of heptane, C_7H_{16}, vapor requires 52.4 cu ft of air, or 16 per cent more.

The chief use for gasoline is as the fuel for internal-combustion engines. Most of it is used without the addition of anything else, but various mixtures of gasoline with benzol from coal tar, and with alcohol, are on the market. The value of a motor fuel depends not only upon its volatility and calorific value, but also upon its " anti-knocking " characteristics, upon the degree to which the mixture of its vapor with air can be compressed without pre-ignition, upon its relative freedom from sulfur compounds, which yield sulfuric acid when burned, and upon other factors.

Natural Gas consists mainly of methane, CH_4, with 10 per cent or less of ethane and other gases. Methane is also known as marsh gas, from its abundant formation when vegetable matter decays under water. The name fire damp refers to its occurrence in coal mines, where it is one of the causes of explosions.

Coal Gas, which is made by distilling bituminous coal in retorts, contains 80 to 85 per cent of a mixture of nearly equal parts of hydrogen and methane, and ethane, with much smaller amounts of oxygen, nitrogen, carbon monoxide and dioxide, etc. It is used to some extent in gas engines and as a fuel.

Water Gas is formed by the action of superheated steam upon white-hot coal or coke. The steam gives up its oxygen to the carbon of the fuel, forming carbon monoxide, CO, and leaving hydrogen, thus: $C + H_2O = CO + H_2$. The reaction is endothermic, that is, it requires the addition of heat, so that it is necessary to cut off the steam every few minutes and reheat the fuel by an air blast. Water gas consists of about 45 per cent each of hydrogen and carbon monoxide, with small percentages of oxygen, nitrogen, carbon dioxide, etc. The first two gases burn with very hot, non-luminous flames. For use as an illuminant it must be " enriched " with oil gas.

Producer Gas is made in much the same way as water gas, except that only air and no steam is passed through the incandescent coal or coke. The carbon is burned to carbon monoxide, which makes about 25 per cent of the gas. Smaller amounts of hydrogen, methane, and carbon dioxide are present. There is also nearly 65 per cent of nitrogen from the air which is used. This is unavoidable, though the presence of such a large amount of inert gas reduces the thermal efficiency.

The reaction whereby carbon is burned to carbon monoxide is accompanied by the evolution of about one-third the total heating value of the fuel. It is evident that, if the gas can be burned without allowing it to cool, a great saving of heat can be effected. This is not always feasible, and it is the practice, with some forms of producers, to pass some steam with the air, thus making a mixed water-producer gas. The heat which would otherwise be lost is used up in forming water gas, and the resultant fuel gas has an increased fuel value. It is much more economical to convert the fuel into producer gas and use it in explosion engines than to burn it under steam boilers.

40. EXPLOSIVES

The Fundamental Property of an explosive is that when ignited or subjected to a sudden shock it shall decompose, or its components react, suddenly yielding a relatively large volume of highly heated gas. This definition includes not only gunpowder, nitroglycerin, and similar substances, but also mixtures of inflammable gases and vapors with air; or even coal dust, fine sawdust, or flour suspended in the air. The last three have all been the cause of disasters, the reason being that when some of the particles are ignited the flame is rapidly communicated to adjacent ones, yielding large volumes of highly heated gaseous products of combustion, in addition to which the surrounding air is also heated. Thus, 1 g of anthracite, of specific gravity 1.5, occupies a volume equal to only 2/3 cc. If it contains 95 per cent of carbon, it will yield when burnt about 1761 cc, or 2642 times its own volume, of carbon dioxide measured at 0 deg cent and 760 mm pressure. If suspended as dust in a large volume of air and burned in a fraction of a second, it is evident that the large amount of hot gases must expand with explosive violence.

Gunpowder is a mixture of 75 parts by weight of saltpeter, or potassium nitrate, 15 parts of charcoal, and 10 parts of sulfur, made by grinding the ingredients together with enough water to moisten the mass. It is then compressed into a cake and broken into grains, which are glazed by revolving with graphite and sorted into sizes by sieves. The larger grains are used for blasting, and the smaller ones for small arms. *Blasting powder* is frequently made with the cheaper Chile saltpeter, or sodium nitrate, which produces a cheaper and less powerful powder than that made from ordinary saltpeter. Chile saltpeter, however, has the disadvantage of absorbing moisture from the air, and powder made from it cannot be kept too long nor stored in a damp place. The proportions used are 73 parts of Chile saltpeter, 16 parts of charcoal, and 11 parts of sulfur.

Guncotton, Nitrocellulose, typical of another class of explosives, is made by the action of a mixture of nitric and sulfuric acids upon cotton. When only moderately strong acids are allowed to act on the cotton for a short time, the product is pyroxylin, or soluble nitrocellulose, used for making collodion and celluloid. By longer action with more concentrated acids, guncotton is formed. It is then washed in a machine of the kind used for making paper pulp to remove all traces of acids that might cause spontaneous explosions. While still moist, it is compressed into blocks or sticks. Guncotton is usually stored and transported in a moist condition, and can be exploded without drying. It is comparatively safe to handle, as ordinary shocks do not explode it readily. In the open, it burns with extreme rapidity.

Nitroglycerin is made by the cautious addition of glycerin to a well-stirred and cooled mixture of the strongest nitric and sulfuric acids. The oily product is washed to remove all traces of acids that might cause spontaneous explosion. Under the most favorable conditions, nitroglycerin is not safe to handle. The fact that it is a liquid with consequent liability to leakage from containers greatly increases the danger of transportation and storage. For this reason, it is commonly mixed with some absorbent or transformed into a gelatinous mass.

Dynamite is a mixture of nitroglycerin with infusorial earth, powdered " rottenstone," or similar porous material, known as " dope." Instead of these inactive dopes that take no part in the explosion, explosive mixtures are generally used to absorb the nitroglycerin. Gunpowder is one of these. Dynamite, consisting of 40 per cent nitroglycerin, 44 per cent sodium nitrate, 15 per cent wood pulp, and 1 per cent calcium carbonate, is an example of dynamite with an active dope.

Explosive gelatin is a jelly-like mass made from a solution of soluble nitrocellulose in nitroglycerin. Too powerful for common work, it is used with success for very hard rock in tunnels. Gelatin dynamite is a mixture of explosive gelatin with a dope such as sodium nitrate and wood pulp; it is not so powerful as the straight gelatin. Smokeless powder is a general term covering many modifications of explosive gelatin and mixtures of nitrocellulose with nitrobenzene, etc.; they are usually given fanciful names, as ballistite, cordite, indurite, and so forth. Nitroglycerin and mixtures containing it are all likely to freeze at moderately low temperatures. They cannot be used satisfactorily in that condition, and should not be thawed by placing them near a fire or on steam pipes but by leaving them in a warm chamber kept at a temperature not above 90 deg fahr.

Picric Acid, or trinitrophenol, is made by the action of nitric and sulfuric acids upon phenol (carbolic acid). It is a yellow, crystalline substance, formerly used only as a dye for silks, and so forth. For years it was not known as an explosive, but it is now known that it will explode with great violence when detonated. If ignited, it usually burns without exploding and is not very susceptible to shock. Lyddite, melinite, and shimose are composed of picric acid. Some of the salts, or picrates, are exploded by slight blows.

Nitrocellulose, Nitroglycerin, and Nitrostarch are true nitrates, as they all contain the atomic group NO_3. They are chemically quite different from the true nitro-compounds, such as picric acid, which contain the atomic group NO_2. Benzene, toluene, naphthalene, and other substances obtained from coal tar yield nitro-compounds when treated with nitric acid. The best known of these is trinitrotoluene, or "TNT," which was used in such enormous quantities in the Great War. They are used as components of explosives, mixed with either ammonium nitrate or other nitrates, or with chlorates, which are good oxidizing agents, or they may be used in dynamite because they lower the freezing point of the nitroglycerin. Rack-a-rock, roburite, bellite, and securite are typical of the explosives made from these nitro-compounds and oxidizing agents.

A Detonator contains a high explosive, too powerful and sensitive to be employed alone, which by its sudden disruptive force brings about the instantaneous explosion of a large amount of a less sensitive explosive. The ones commonly in use consist of copper capsules containing a definite amount of a mixture of chlorate of potash and mercury fulminate, which is exploded either by a fuse or a wire heated electrically. The fulminate is made by mixing a solution of mercury in strong nitric acid with alcohol. The gray crystalline powder which is precipitated must be well washed to remove all acid. It is sensitive to shock and may explode even when wet.

Explosives must be selected with reference to the character of the work. For quarrying building stone, those that act slowly, with little shattering effect, must be chosen. When the stone is to be crushed after quarrying, or for breaking up rock so that it can be handled by a steam shovel, a quick shattering effect is desired. Generally in open work, the character of the gases arising from the explosion may be disregarded, but in tunnels or mines, especially if not well ventilated, this factor is of great importance. No explosive is absolutely safe in this respect. In coal mines, where the presence of fire damp (methane) is a menace, no explosive giving a long flame or a high heat of detonation should be used. Even in the absence of gas, there is danger of igniting the coal dust.

Explosives should be stored in a dry place so that the sodium or ammonium nitrates will not take up enough moisture to lessen their power. But if in too dry a place, they may lose the moisture they naturally contain, which will change their speed of explosion and thus modify the character of the results obtained. Explosives should not be stored for a longer time than absolutely necessary, on account of the possibility of chemical changes taking place in such mixtures.

ADHESIVE MATERIALS

By D. F. Miner

41. TYPES OF ADHESIVES

Spirit Solutions consist of alcoholic solutions of shellac, resins, gums, or combination of similar organic materials. A filler is sometimes added to give body. Shellac, copal, gum, rosin, pine tar, and castor oil are commonly constituents of these cements. Pine tar and castor oil are used as plasticizers to reduce brittleness. Spirit cements are employed on gaskets and on coil spacers. They are thermoplastic and fairly moisture proof.

Benzine or Benzol Solutions. These adhesives are generally solutions of resins, quite similar to varnishes. The resins include Bakelite, other synthetic resins, fossil gums, pitch, copal, and rubber compounds. Varnish types of cements are oil and moisture proof, but are more brittle than spirit cements. They are used on gaskets and for sticking insulating materials to metal.

Cellulose Cements. A series of lacquer cements, with cellulose nitrate or acetate base and lacquer thinner solvent, has proved to be of considerable value when a quick-drying, strong adhesive is required. They are used for cementing celluloid and leather and for fastening instrument parts.

Solids, melted for use. Several kinds of pitches, asphalts, and gums are used hot as adhesives. They are suitable where there is little chance for evaporation of solvent, and for high operating temperatures. Most of these adhesives are not oil proof but are water proof.

Water Solutions. The ordinary glues are water soluble and cover a variety of materials, such as casein, fish glue, hide glue, sodium silicate, and dextrin. Table I gives the properties of various glues.

Table I. Properties of Various Glues

Technical Note 207, U. S. Forest Products Laboratory, Madison, Wis.

Point of Comparison	Animal Glue	Casein Glue	Vegetable Glue	Blood Glue	Liquid Glue
Source of principal ingredient	Animal hides, bones, etc.	Casein from milk	Starch, generally cassava	Soluble dried blood	Animal glue, or skins, bones, etc., of fish
Spread* Extremes reported Common range	20 to 50 25 to 35	30 to 80 35 to 55	35 to 70 35 to 55	30 to 100	No data
Mixing	Soaked in water, then melted	Mixed cold	Mixed with alkali and water, with or without heat; can be made without alkali	Mixed cold	Requires no preparation
Application	Applied warm with brush or mechanical spreader	Applied cold with brush or mechanical spreader	Applied cold with mechanical spreader	Applied cold by hand or with mechanical spreader	Applied cold or warm, usually by hand
Temperature of press	Cold; hot cauls frequently used	Cold	Cold	Hot or cold, depending on formula used	Cold
Strength (block shear test)	High grade; has greater shear strength than strongest American woods; medium grades, slightly lower	Similar to medium grade animal glue	Similar to medium grade animal glue	Similar to or slightly less than medium grade animal glue	Good grades similar to medium grade animal glue; some brands very weak
Water resistance	Naturally low, but can be increased by chemical treatment	High or low, as required	Low	High	Low
Staining	Does not stain	Stains wood of some species	If mixed with caustic soda, stains wood of some species	Does not stain, but the glue is very dark and may show through thin veneer	Does not stain
Uses in woodworking	High grade, where a strong joint is desired; low grade sometimes used for veneering, especially where it is desired to prevent staining	Mainly where water resistance is desired in veneered or joint work	To some extent for joint work, but mainly in veneered work where good strength at low cost is desired	Almost entirely for water-resistant plywood for aircraft or automobiles and for articles to be molded after boiling in water	Mainly for repair work and gluing small articles by hand

* For veneer work, expressed in square feet of single glue line per pound of dry glue.

MISCELLANEOUS MATERIALS

42. CORK

Cork is the spongy outer bark of the cork oak tree, which grows principally in Spain, Portugal, and northern Africa. It is of cellular structure, each cell comprising a strong impenetrable skin, enclosing air. As many as 80 distinct grades of corkwood are recognized.

Natural Cork. The uses of natural cork are limited by the variability of the raw material, by structural flaws, which are uncontrollable in a natural material, and by the irregularity in size, thickness and shape. These limitations can be overcome by laminating the corkwood to produce a material of greater uniformity and structural strength.

Cork Compositions.—Finely ground cork combined with various binders forms materials having all the desirable basic qualities of natural cork. Compositions can be made to provide for expansion or contraction, or to be fabricated into sheets, disks, tubes, blocks, rings, strips, balls, wheels, rods, and irregularly shaped articles. It also can be molded directly to a desired pattern. Composition cork is laminated with cloth, vulcanized fiber, or other material to increase the tensile strength. Cork has also been combined with rubber and synthetic resins.

Properties of Cork. 1. *Resistance to Liquid Penetration.* Cork is highly resistant to penetration by liquids. Since it is not fibrous, liquids are not drawn through it by capillarity.

2. *Compressibility.* Prolonged compression, under heavy loads, will cause little permanent deformation. Eight small pieces of cork composition $7/8$ in. thick, used as cushions between journal box and the car body of railway cars, supporting approximately 120,000 lb, after one year showed a reduction of total thickness of only $1/8$ in. and were still resilient.

3. *Resilience.* Long subjection to pressure does not destroy the structure or resilience of cork. It will not harden or deteriorate under normal conditions.

4. *Frictional Properties.* The coefficient of friction of natural cork and compositions is higher than that of most materials used for friction. This coefficient is not materially decreased by the presence of moisture, oil, or grease. Compositions are more extensively used, as it is possible to control, within reasonable limits, their coefficient of friction. The softer compositions have the higher coefficients of friction, but dense materials for severe conditions have a sufficiently high coefficient for ordinary work.

5. *Buoyancy.* Natural cork, with a specific gravity of 0.15 to 0.20, is generally used for floats and other devices requiring buoyancy.

6. *Low Thermal Conductivity.* The air-cell structure of cork makes it an excellent insulator. It is highly resistant to charring and ignition. At about 250 deg fahr slow distillation begins and the cork discolors slightly. It does not ignite except in contact with flame, and it burns only as long as flame is applied from an external source. Combustion produces a carbonized coating which retards further burning.

7. *Chemical Inertness.* Cork resists chemical action better than most natural materials, and can be safely used in contact with most chemicals. In industrial processes it does not corrode, discolor, or deteriorate and is not affected by oil, grease, gasoline, or other petroleum products. Alkalies and certain acids and organic solvents have a destructive action, and in general, cork should not be used in contact with them. Iron solutions sometimes react with the natural tannin in the cork to cause surface discoloration which, however, does not affect the properties of the cork.

8. *Stability.* Cork retains its initial properties practically unimpaired under all temperature, humidity, or other atmospheric conditions. Its compressibility and resilience enable it to withstand abrasive wear.

Uses. *Seals.* Gaskets for sealing and cushioning, and for sealing anti-friction bearings. Cork closures are sometimes made as split rings, but the continuous ring is generally used. Cork seals should not be distorted either in assembling or in use. They are not recommended for assembly in internal grooves and must be lubricated before assembly, with graphite grease thinned with lubricating oil to the consistency of vaseline. Cork gaskets should not be used on steam or other high-temperature connections or in contact with strong alkaline solutions such as ammonia. *Cushioning* between adjoining surfaces of metal and glass; metal and porcelain or similar combinations; automobile bodies; to deaden vibration in machinery. *Friction.* In the textile industry for drawing yarn and cloth through machines; friction drives; clutches; feed rolls for machines handling paper, cloth, foil, etc. *Floats.* Gage mechanisms for carburetors; dispensing pumps for oil and gasoline. *Insulation.* Under roofs to reduce heat losses, to lessen condensation, and to eliminate ceiling drip; pipe covering for drinking water, brine, and ammonia lines and cold lines in the oil-refining and chemical industries. *Natural Cork Products.* Bottle corks; wheels for polishing glass; floats for carburetors and gages; handles for tools and instruments; disks, washers, and gaskets for various applications; life preservers; yacht fenders; cork balls and paper.

43. LEATHER

Leather as an engineering material is mostly applied in the manufacturing of belting for transmission trains. The best quality of well-tanned ox hide is cut into strips of 4 to 6 ft long and usually about $3/16$ in. in thickness, which are scarfed, spliced, or cemented end to end to make the desired length of belt. According to the strength required, these are in turn cemented or riveted together in thickness to form "single" or "double" belts. Under light loads, the "single belt" gives the greater adhesion, but under heavy loads the "double belt" proves the more satisfactory. The "flesh side" or inside of the belt is customarily placed next to the pulley, as it gives the best wear, although when placed grain side to the pulley the belt is less likely to slip.

The weight of a hard well-tanned belt leather is about 62 $1/2$ lb per cu ft and the tensile strength of a good quality is about 650 lb per in. of width of single belt. When spliced or riveted, the tenacity is about one-half of the above figure, and when laced about one-third of the strength is developed. A safe working tension may be taken at about 50 lb per in. of width.

Rawhide, or untanned leather, finds many applications in textile machinery connections, looms, ships' tiller ropes, etc., and also in the manufacture of high-speed gear wheels. When sound, it is much stronger than tanned leather and gives greater resistance to violent impact. Its tensile strength may be taken as one-half greater than that of tanned leather.

44. GASKETS AND PACKINGS

Packing Materials, used to prevent entrance or exit of liquids or gases between metal parts, may be classified according to materials or application. They embrace metals, inorganic, and organic materials. The following list, arranged by type of application, may be found convenient:

Purpose	Materials	Apparatus
a. Splash proof	1. Square flax	Liquid tanks
	2. Folded asbestos tape	Circuit breakers Transformers
b. Dust proof	1. Felt cemented with shellac	Control boxes Bearing housings
c. Gas and moisture proof	1. Fiber (vellumoid) sheet laminated with cork sheet	Mine apparatus Manhole circuit breakers
	2. Rubber sheet	
d. Oil proof	1. Cork cemented with synthetic resin cements	Static condenser tanks Transformer tanks Circuit breaker tanks
	2. Oil proof rubber	
	3. Rubber substitute (Duprene)	
e. Heat proof For machined surfaces (high pressure)	1. Lead (where flow is required)	Compressors Engine heads
	2. Copper (takes less "set" than lead)	
	3. Aluminum (for high pressures where copper flows too much)	
For rough surfaces	1. Asbestos with rubber binder	Solder pots Furnaces Steam lines
f. Moving parts	1. Asbestos with graphite 2. Rubber and duck	Pumps, motor shafts Pump and ram plungers

45. ICE

Ice at 32 deg fahr weighs 57.5 lb per cu ft, its specific gravity being 0.922 (water at 62 deg fahr = 1).   Its volume relative to water is 1.0855.   Its melting point decreases from 32 deg fahr at the rate of 0.0133 deg fahr for each additional atmospheric pressure. Its specific heat is 0.504 (water = 1).   Some German experiments made in 1885 gave a tensile strength of 142 to 223 lb per sq in.   Tests made by the U. S. Engineer Corps on 6- and 12-in. cubes, gave crushing strengths varying from 100 to 1000 lb per sq in. depending on the structure of the ice and the purity of water from which it was formed. Before crushing, ice in cubes will compress from 6 to 30 per cent.   The sustaining capacity of ice is not definitely determined; 2-in. ice is considered safe for infantry, 4-in. ice for cavalry or light guns, 6-in. ice for heavy field guns, and 8-in. ice for loads not over 1000 lb per sq ft on sledges.   Railway trains have been run across ice which was 15 in. thick.

The expansive force of ice is given by Trautwine as probably not less than 30,000 lb per sq ft. The coefficient of expansion, as given by Ganot, is 0.000052.   By its expansion a sheet of ice 150 ft in width has been known to tip a masonry bridge pier weighing 1000 tons 2 in. out of plumb, and in another instance to move masonry piers on pile foundations from 2 to 12 in. out of line.   The expansive effect in river or lake ice, however, does not make itself felt until the ice is at least 5 in. thick.

Freshly fallen snow weighs from 5 to 12 lb per cu ft; compacted or wet snow weighs from 15 to 50 lb per cu ft.

SECTION 13

CONTRACTS

BY

R. L. SACKETT

CONTRACTS

1. CONDITIONS OF CONTRACTUAL RELATIONSHIP

A **Contract** is an agreement to do or to refrain from doing a specified lawful act.

In order that a contract may be enforceable at law, it must fulfil certain conditions, as follows:

1. There must be at least two parties to a contract.
2. The parties signing a contract must be competent in the eyes of the law.
3. They must agree, or there must be " a meeting of the minds."
4. The subject matter of the contract must be legal.
5. There must be a consideration, except that in certain documents a seal is adequate.

Certain contracts are required by statute to be in writing, but with those exceptions an oral contract is as legal as a written instrument. However, oral contracts are more susceptible of misunderstandings and may be the cause of litigation. In case of doubt reduce the agreement to writing.

1. Two or More Parties

A principal cannot contract with himself since he cannot sue himself to secure enforcement or to obtain damages. A person cannot be both plaintiff and defendant.

Neither can a party acting as principal have a major interest, or an official position of importance, in a company or corporation which is the second party.

Being a stockholder or holding a position of minor importance in a corporation does not prevent a person from contracting as a principal with such a corporation. A city official may contract for the municipality with a corporation provided that his position with the latter does not create a strong suspicion that he influenced the contract for his personal profit. A municipal, state, or federal officer should resign an official position with a corporation which would create a suspicion of dual interest.

A party cannot act for himself and at the same time act as agent for another.

2. Competence

Minors. Legally, a contract cannot be enforced against a minor, although a moral obligation may exist, except that a minor may compel a principal to perform especially where the necessities of life are involved and can himself be held therefor. Contracts with minors are said to be voidable rather than void; i.e., the minor may enforce fulfilment but the other party cannot. When a contract is void, neither party can enforce it. If a contract with a minor continues until he is of age, he may then ratify the contract and enforce it if he elects, where otherwise it would be voidable at the instance of the other party.

The parents of a minor are entitled to his services or to the income from his work. The parent may contract for the employment of his child; such a contract is enforceable during the minority of the child, but becomes void when the infant comes of age. See Agent.

Persons of Unsound Mind are incompetent to sign a contract. The infirmities of age or illness may render one incompetent. A confirmed drunkard is also incapable of contracting, but degrees of drunkenness are such as to make the boundary between competency and incompetency a matter to be decided by the evidence.

Women are coming by statute to have the same status before the law as men in contracting. In cases involving a woman as party to a contract, an attorney should be consulted to be certain of the right of women to contract in that state.

Partnerships. The duly authorized representative of a partnership may contract for the partnership, and in so doing he binds the partners individually to the limit of their resources.

A Corporation may enter into a contract when duly authorized by action of the board of directors designating an official or officials to sign contracts. By-laws and minutes of the board of directors should establish the legality of the proceedings by which a corporation binds itself.

In the case of contracts with a municipal corporation, certain legal procedures should be examined by a competent attorney, such as the law, actions of the municipal council, minutes of their proceedings, advertisement, hearing, etc., as technicalities may make the contract void. John C. Waite states: " If the contract is ultra vires, the contractor will not only be unable to recover on the contract but he will even be precluded from getting back the value of his labor and materials on a quantum meruit and will lose everything he has put into the structure."*

3. Agreement

The parties to a contract must have a common understanding of the terms of the agreement; in other words, "There must be a meeting of their minds."

Even though an oral contract is legal, memory may fail, misunderstandings may creep in, and evidence may be conflicting concerning intent. The more complicated the terms of the agreement, the more important it is to have them written and witnessed.

Statute of Frauds. In order to prevent fraud, English law provided that certain contracts, to be enforceable at law, must be in writing; the states of the United States have adopted similar statutes. Two sections of the English law are as follows:

Section 4. No action shall be brought to charge any executor or administrator on any special promise to answer damages out of his own estate; (2) or to charge the defendant upon any special promise to answer for the debt, default, or miscarriage of another person; (3) or to charge any person upon any agreement made upon consideration of marriage; (4) or upon any contract or sale of lands or any interest therein; (5) or upon any agreement that is not to be performed within one year of the making thereof; unless the agreement or some memorandum or note thereof shall be in writing and signed by the party to be charged, or by some person thereunto by him lawfully authorized.

Section 17. No contract for the sale of any goods, wares, and merchandises for the price of ten pounds sterling, or upwards, shall be allowed to be good, except the buyer shall accept part of the goods so sold, and actually receive the same, or give something in earnest to bind the bargain, or in part payment, or that some note or memorandum in writing of the said bargain be made and signed by the party to be charged, or their agents thereunto lawfully authorized.

The adjudication of cases under the Statute of Frauds is often complicated. The major questions are: Does the transaction in question come under the statute? Was there a written memorandum signed by the parties? What was their intent?

For illustration, it is necessary to determine whether a certain contract is for a completed article or for the labor and materials necessary to make it. In the latter case, no writing is necessary; in the former, it depends on the price stipulated, the time required for delivery, the acceptance of part delivery or of part payment, or the presence of a signed memorandum.

Contracts for the sale of land or options on land must be in writing. Growing crops and portable tools are goods, and no writing is necessary to convey them. Standing timber is part of the land.

A lease of land or an easement for the use of land for specific purposes and for a specified time requires a writing.

Offer and Acceptance. The usual steps in making a contract are for one party to make an offer of so much goods or labor for a given sum. The offer may be made orally, by letter, telephone, telegraph, or other means of communication. The offer may be made subject to acceptance within a given time; if no time limit is set then it must be accepted within "a reasonable length of time " as the courts may decide how long is reasonable.

An offer may be withdrawn by any means of communication. An offer made by letter can be canceled by wire. An acceptance mailed before the offer is withdrawn constitutes a contract even though it had not been received at the time the offer was canceled. An acceptance, to be binding, must be unequivocal.

To answer, " I will accept your offer provided that you pay the costs of delivery " when no such offer was made is not an acceptance but a new offer. Thus one offer after another may be made until there is an agreement on all details. Not until then is there a contract.

An order for goods is a contract to pay a reasonable price—unless the price was specified. Be careful to specify price, quality, time and kind of delivery, and other items open to misunderstanding.

Mistakes may render a contract void. They include mistakes as to the person when one is contracting for personal, skilled services. A mistake about the person with whom one was contracting would not necessarily be void if the goods tendered were of the quality specified.

---

* John C. Waite, Engineering and Architectural Jurisprudence, p. 36.

Carelessness in reading or neglect to read a contract is not a ground on which to plead for the voiding of a contract. A mistake as to the nature of a contract not due to neglect may cause a contract to be declared void.

A contract made for the sale of a stack of hay was void when it was discovered that the hay had burned *before* the contract was made. If the contract was signed before the hay burned, the purchaser would suffer the loss unless there were other stipulations, such as delivery at a given place, which had not been fulfilled.

In interpeting a contract, the usual meaning of words and local customs will prevail.

Besides mistakes, contracts may be illegal because of fraud, duress, or undue influence.

Fraud. The reality of consent may be affected by a spoken or acted falsehood designed to induce one, and whereby one is induced, to agree to terms which are definitely detrimental. In other words:

There must be a misrepresentation or a false representation of pertinent facts, with intent to deceive.

The other party must be ignorant of the truth after using reasonable diligence in finding the facts.

The party claiming the contract to be void because of fraud must have suffered material injury as a result of such falsifications.

It is extremely difficult to prove intent to defraud.

In case of fraud the injured party may:

   (a) plead the fraud as a defense against action taken to compel the injured party to perform his part of the contract; or
   (b) proceed in court to have the contract declared void; or
   (c) sue to recover damages caused him by the fraud.

Duress. Duress exists when compulsion by force or by threat is used to induce a party to sign a contract. Duress by force includes the use of actual physical force to a person or to a near relative, thus influencing a party to pay ransom, deliver property, or perform acts to obtain release or release of a relative, which acts would not normally be agreed to.

Duress by threat may consist of demands made on threat of bodily harm, exposure of illegal acts, or prosecution for crime.

The party intimidated may:

   (a) ask the court to declare the agreement void; or
   (b) plead duress as a defense if sued for performance; or
   (c) sue for recovery of moneys or property transferred under duress.

Undue Influence is the misuse of mental power by one to change the purposes of another. In contesting wills, it is sometimes charged that a relative, a nurse, or other person in intimate and confidential relations with the ill or aged has used undue influence.

4. The Subject Matter Must Be Lawful

The courts can enforce only legal obligations. An agreement having an illegal object as its purpose cannot be enforced or is void. An illegal contract is not a contract in the eyes of the law.

An agreement in violation of a statutory law is illegal. Gambling is illegal; hence a contract to enforce payment of a gambling debt is void. A contract to commit a crime is likewise null.

In some states, an agreement entered into on Sunday or to be performed on Sunday is made illegal by statute. There are exceptions, such as acts of charity, to preserve property or life.

Licenses. For certain professions a license is required before a person may legally practice. In order to protect life and property, it is common to require physicians, lawyers, dentists, architects, and engineers to be licensed and registered. A contract requiring such licensed professional services is illegal if the party in question is not duly licensed. In states requiring architects and engineers to be licensed they may employ unlicensed designers, inspectors, and resident engineers, but the contracting principal for whom they work must be licensed except in certain governmental positions.

Public Policy. A contract against public interest may be declared illegal by the courts. As an illustration, suppose that a town council proceeds legally to buy or build a public utility or to sell a municipally owned plant. Citizens may ask for an injunction to forbid such act on the ground that it is against public policy, i.e., the best interests of the citizens, as expressed by their opinions and through expert opinion. The court may dissolve the injunction or make it permanent after due hearings.

It may be against public policy to let a contract for a public building or for repairs to the same to other than the lowest bidder.

Suppressing Competition. The common law (and statutes also) recognize competition in trade, and any contract in restraint of trade is illegal. Recent powers delegated by Congress to the President of the United States are amendatory to and in contradiction to English Common Law, the Clayton Act, and the Sherman Anti-Trust Law.

An agreement not to bid on a contract or to bid higher or lower than another or any form of collusion is illegal. In addition, parties to such illegal proceedings are liable under the criminal law.

5. Consideration

In deeds for the conveyance of lands, the price may be stated correctly or as "One Dollar and other considerations, receipt of which is hereby acknowledged." In land contracts, options on the purchase of real estate, and similar documents, including all executory contracts, it is customary to state the exact amount to be paid.

There must be a valuable consideration in a legal contract, but the courts are not concerned with adequacy of the consideration unless fraud is claimed.

The consideration may be something done, forborne, or suffered, or a promise to do, forbear, or suffer, or it may be money, goods, or real estate. The market value of the goods or land may be little under the common law injunction "Let the buyer beware"; that is, the buyer should take all reasonable means to inform himself that the exchange is to his advantage or that he is satisfied even though he will suffer a loss as a result of the bargain or contract.

The consideration should be something which the law esteems of value. A promise to pay the debt of a third party may create a moral obligation, but if there is no consideration, the law will not require the promisor to fulfil his promise. On the other hand, to say to a merchant, "Send A this bill of goods and if he does not pay for it, I will" is enforceable at law. The loss which would be suffered by the merchant in conveying the goods is sufficient consideration for the promise to pay for them. A promise to A that I will make him a gift of a bill of goods is a promise without a consideration and hence is not legal.

Sealed Instruments. A seal is a very old device for giving solemnity to a contract where there is no consideration. A promise to do or to refrain from doing a certain legal act is enforceable when it is a sealed contract. The seal serves notice on the parties to give the contract special consideration as the court will not "go behind the seal" to inquire into the justice of the bargain unless fraud is charged.

Wills, benefactions, trust fund agreements, freehold surety bonds, and similar documents should be sealed.

Originally, a seal ring impression was made in melted wax. The seal may now be made by sticking a piece of a stamp or writing the word "seal" or by a scroll following the signatures to a sealed instrument.

2. THE DISCHARGE OF A CONTRACT

The usual method of terminating a contract is to fulfil the terms of the same, and is called, 1, *performance*. But a contract may also be discharged by

2, breach of contract,
3, " impossibility " of performance,
4, a new agreement or consent, or
5, operation of law.

Performance is the normal method of discharging a contract, but in engineering and construction contracts it is rare for the original terms of the agreement to be carried out without change. All modifications of plans and extras call for supplementary contracts and a change in the consideration.

Where slight changes have been made and something "just as good" has been substituted, the courts will not usually interfere to require the substitution of that which may have been specified. The remedy is to prevent the substitution of other than that specified—unless the substitute is acceptable.

The meaning of a contract is a question of law, although the intent of the parties may be shown by evidence. Whether the contract has been completed is a question of fact for a jury to decide according to the evidence. "Substantial performance" will usually be accepted as full performance in litigation over that question.

Tender. If one party to a contract is obstructed by the other party in his purpose to perform, the obstructed party may "tender" the amount due in "legal tender," i.e., in bank notes (unless objected to at the time), U. S. Treasury notes, and coin, or he may offer to deliver the goods or do the labor as the contract specifies. Refusal to accept when the tender has been made in good faith and in accordance with the terms of the contract relieves the party making the tender of obligation under the contract.

Breach of Contract. Refusal or failure of a party to perform his part of a contract according to its terms constitutes a breach of contract and relieves the offended party of further obligations under the contract. The refusal must be absolute and unconditional. Mere objection or argument is not construed as refusal.

Failure to perform is sometimes difficult to establish. If a time is set for completion, the courts will often take into consideration weather conditions, strikes affecting the supply of or transportation of materials, the effect of fire, and the necessity for completion by a specific date.

The remedy for failure to complete the work on time may be by suit for damages *if* actual loss can be established and the amount of it can be determined. Otherwise the court will rarely enforce damages for non-completion by the specified time. See Liquidated Damages, page 16.

If no time for the completion of the contract is stated then the court will permit "a reasonable length of time" for performance. What is reasonable may depend on the factors of weather, etc., mentioned above.

The remedy for breach of contract may be a suit by the injured party for damages. Establishing by evidence the amount of damage suffered is usually difficult and expensive. It is therefore to be avoided so far as possible by requiring the contractor on engineering and construction work to provide a surety bond. The surety is usually a well-established bonding company, and in effect the bond ensures the completion of the contract by the bonding company if the contractor fails or refuses to perform. Litigation may follow to compel the bonding company to complete the work, or a settlement may be agreed to out of court. This involves a new contract.

There is another remedy for breach of contract called

Specific Performance. Specific performance, as a rule, deals only with lands or specific goods in existence where like goods cannot be acquired in the open market if money damages were awarded. If a person or contracting firm was engaged because of his or their particular skill and experience, and if the contract cannot be completed equally well by another contractor, then a court of equity might consider a suit for specific performance. If the court agrees that the particular skill and experience of the contractor were important considerations and that equal skill and experience cannot be obtained by reasonable effort, then the contractor may be required to perform the contract, but this is rare.

Impossibility of performance is the term applied when the conditions imposed were not contemplated in the contract and are onerous. It does not mean that it is actually impossible in the literal sense but that the difficulties and expense are much greater than was known or than existed when the contract was let. Ordinary difficulties do not comprise impossibility in the legal sense. The usual hazards of contracting are a part of the undertaking although they may involve extra work. Fire is a well-known danger, and insurance will save the contractor from a major part of the loss he would suffer. But a flood which washes away the site of a building which the contractor had agreed to build is an example of legal impossibility.

Acts of Providence. Certain catastrophies called "Acts of God," such as extremely high floods, tornadoes, earthquakes, and similar unforeseen acts of nature, are the basis of defense when contracts cannot be performed without much greater difficulty, time, and expense than was contemplated by the contracting parties. Such so-called Acts of God may create legal impossibility.

A contract for personal services is discharged by the death or incapacity of the party.

Contract Discharged by Agreement. Supplementary contracts to cover changes in the amount of work to be done and to cover extra work are usually provided for in the original contract. These do not affect the legality of the agreement.

Conditions may become such that changes greater than those contemplated by the contract may be necessary. The work may be abandoned at an uncompleted stage and the contract be discharged by a new contract which is in effect an amicable settlement of the case out of court.

Contract Discharged by Law. A legal contract cannot contain requirements or prohibitions contrary to law. A contract may have been entered into in good faith to perform a legal act. Subsequently, and before completion, a law may have been passed by a state or an ordinance by a city council which makes the contract illegal. It is discharged by law. A decision by the courts may have the same effect.

A contract to build a frame addition to a store may be made illegal by the passage of a zoning ordinance prescribing that frame buildings shall not be built in that zone.

3. AGENCY

An employee is one who is hired by the hour, day, week to perform such tasks as he may be directed to do in the way he is told. He may be employed on piece work.

An agent is given authority to act for and in the place of the principal in executing certain business transactions where he has more latitude than the employee as to the time, place, and manner in which he shall act. An employee may also be an agent when he performs certain specific acts.

The nature of the act will determine whether one was acting as employee or agent at the time.

An agent is one who acts for a principal within the powers expressly granted him and those which may reasonably be implied. An engineer for a railroad who is instructed to design and build a bridge has the authority delegated to him to carry out the usual steps customary with that railroad in contracting for materials and hiring the necessary force, or in advertising, receiving bids, accepting an offer, obtaining surety bond, and other details ready for the prescribed officers to sign the contract.

In addition to the authority which may be delegated to an agent in writing and the implied powers which follow as a consequence, there are cases where the courts have protected the third party from loss by holding the principal liable. Such are acts which might reasonably be expected to be within the powers of the agent. The test is thus stated: "Would a reasonably prudent person in like circumstances have been justified in assuming that the agent had the power to enter into the contract in behalf of his principal?"

The above does not apply to an agent of a public corporation. As in a contract with a municipality, it is necessary to observe strictly the powers granted by the government, and its agent has no *apparent* powers—only those specifically granted and those necessary to carry out the grant.

When a principal has ratified or has accepted by implication a contract not within the authority granted an agent, the principal is held liable.

When a principal promptly repudiates an unauthorized act of an agent and so notifies the third party, the principal is not liable.

The principal is liable for torts committed by the agent when carrying out the instructions of his principal and within the authority granted the agent. See Torts. The principal is not liable for criminal acts committed by an agent.

A minor may act as agent and thus bind his principal when he could not act as the principal because of being under twenty-one years of age.

When an agent has acted within the powers delegated to him or when the principal has ratified the contract executed by an agent, the third party is now liable to the principal the same as if he had negotiated directly with the principal.

It is the duty of the agent to carry out the instructions of his principal unless illegal, impossible, or unreasonable. He should exercise due care, act in good faith, and make regular accounting of his acts, receipts, and disbursements. The agent may not act for opposing interests or as principal when carrying out a commission.

The principal is bound by his contract with an agent and is liable to his agent as in any other contract.

4. LIENS AND LIABILITIES

Statutes in the majority of states provide that mechanics employed on building repairs or construction of a substantial character may file a mechanic's lien in a prescribed manner within a limited time. The owner is liable and the property may be sold to satisfy such claims.

Similar protection has also been provided for those supplying materials for such improvements even though the materials have not been used.

In some states a minimum cost of perhaps $100 is stipulated below which cost liens may not be legal.

The architect or engineer who prepares plans and specifications cannot recover under a mechanic's lien unless he has also supervised and inspected the work, in which latter case he may come under the law. The statute should be examined to determine its scope.

The only evidence admissible that the right to file a lien has been waived is a written agreement, known as a Release of Mechanic's Lien, which, properly signed and witnessed, becomes a quit claim against the property.

In large contracts the owner may require that the contractor furnish a bond with a proper surety company to indemnify against mechanic's and material dealer's liens.

If the owner has provided in the contract that amounts may be retained by him sufficient to meet all liens, the usual procedure is to file the lien in the prescribed manner.

The owner satisfies the lien, obtains an affidavit to that effect, withholds the sum or sums so paid, and in the final settlement with the contractor subtracts such sum or sums from the balance due. The prescribed procedure should be rigorously observed.

The lapse of time after the work in question is completed and within which a lien must be filed is usually not over ninety days. The contract may therefore provide for the withholding of sufficient funds until the expiration of the legal period within which liens must be filed. Such liens take precedence over all other claims.

The Lien of Wages is the term applied to statutes which provide for the payment of wages through a lien on the property of the employer or his interest in a property. There is usually a limit of $100 or $200 on the amount of each individual lien for wages.

5. WORKMEN'S COMPENSATION

Workmen's Compensation refers to statutes which provide for the recovery of damages for personal injury suffered while employed and while engaged on duties assigned by the employer or reasonably connected therewith.

Under the common law, the employer was expected to provide safe conditions and proper tools to employees. If a workman was injured, the recovery of damages depended on whether negligence of the employer could be proven and if negligence or contributory negligence could be proven against the employee, usually he could not recover.

Safety appliances were next specified and required with factory inspection by the state in order to improve working conditions.

Employer's Liability Acts were designed to remove the old defence of contributory negligence by the injured employee or that the act of a fellow employee such as foreman or superintendent, or some one to whom the injured employee was bound, was the act of a vice-principal and therefore relieved the employer of liability. There remained only the defense of culpable, intentional, or criminal neglect on the part of the injured.

The major weaknesses of the earlier acts were that no insurance was required by the employing company and that the amount of compensation to be received in case of an injury was not specified. In order to remedy these defects workmen's compensation acts were passed in most states.

Workmen's Compensation Acts provide that the employer, if he elects to operate under the statute, must carry insurance with the state, with an authorized company, or give evidence of financial ability to carry his own insurance and must receive permission so to do.

Under this act the defense is not admissible

  (a) that the employee was negligent;
  (b) that the injury was caused by the negligence of a fellow employee; or
  (c) that the employee had assumed the risks and hazards of the task.

The statutes specify the amount of insurance to be received in case of temporary disability, the permanent loss of a member, and in case of death. Compensation is paid unless it can be proven that there was fraud, i.e., intent on the part of the workman to injure himself or to be injured and thereby obtain compensation.

6. THE ENGINEER'S LEGAL RELATIONS

The engineer may be an employee and as such should have a clear understanding of his duties, salary, and responsibilities. Correspondence, a memorandum signed by his employer, or a contract is desirable. If he is an employee on a day, week, or month basis, he may be given notice a day or two or a week or two before his time expires. Practices differ, but usually a two weeks' notice is given engineers on a monthly pay basis.

The engineer may be an agent either occasionally on special assignments or as a full-time job. He should observe strictly his instructions and the law of agency.

The engineer may be an employer and should then observe the law concerning safety devices, sanitary requirements, and workmen's compensation insurance; he should keep accurate records of all contracts, account for all receipts and disbursements, and prepare the necessary reports and legal statements required by law.

As a contractor he may contract to prepare plans and specifications on a percentage basis of about 5 per cent of the estimated cost for average buildings and more or less for structures of greater or less complexity. An additional charge is made for supervision and inspection.

He will not enter into collusion, nor will he prepare plans on a contingent fee which depends on his receiving the contract award or on whether the building is built.

He will observe the ethics of his profession—a moral not a legal obligation.

The engineer who contracts to prepare plans and specifications, supervise the construction, and inspect materials and workmanship agrees to bring to the job such skill as is usual and is necessary to prepare the designs so that the structure will be safe and equal to the loads and forces which it may reasonably be expected to carry or which are specified. Details should conform to all laws, building codes, and ordinances which may apply.

Although absolute accuracy is not required, neglect of plain duty renders him liable. The engineer who undertakes a contract for services agrees in the eyes of the law to supply reasonable knowledge, skill, and experience related to that specialty. He also agrees to use due care and diligence and to employ his best judgment. To receive commissions on materials, devices, or inventions used without the knowledge and consent of his principal is unfair, and absolute honesty is required in all relations with his principal and the contractor.

If the independent, practicing engineer also holds a public office such as city engineer —on a fee basis—or member of a board of public works, it is important that private and public business do not get mixed. It is necessary that they be kept strictly separate in order that he may not be charged with letting self-interest influence his judgment.

The engineer who prepares plans, like the architect, cannot obtain his compensation through a mechanic's lien unless he has also performed the labor of supervising and inspecting on something like a full-time basis similar to that of a mechanic.

7. ENGINEER AS EXPERT WITNESS

The engineer who accepts employment as an expert witness in cases involving contention over the quality of work, the quantity of work done, or the valuation of public utilities, or in other cases involving special knowledge and skill, must first be prepared to show by his education and experience that he can qualify as a specialist in the field in question. A recital of works designed or built by him similar to those under consideration or of valuations made is necessary. The opposing attorney may question his ability. The judge decides whether the witness qualifies as an expert.

Preparation for a case should include independent surveys, measurements, tests, computations, and such other steps as will provide full information concerning the facts at issue.

His estimates, judgments, and findings should be unswayed by the opinions of others. It is necessary that he be familiar with the evidence which is offered so far as it bears on the technical problems involved. Witnesses who are too anxious to help may do more harm than good if they have not been questioned carefully concerning the points at issue.

In preparation for the case, such maps, photographs, and plans as will be clear to the jury should be chosen for exhibit. Special drawings should be prepared to help make explanations clear to the jury. All pertinent facts upon which the engineer is asked to give testimony should be explained in language which is easily understood by the layman. Opinions should be fortified by illustrations drawn from similar cases.

The hypothetical case is used to introduce the opinion of an expert, for opinion evidence is looked upon askance, in fact, is admitted only under special circumstances in the ordinary case at law. The hypothetical question relates the facts of a similar but imaginary case and then asks the witness what, in his judgment, was the cause or effect.

Notes, computations, and tables of data may be used by the engineer acting as an expert witness in order to refresh his memory. He may also present as exhibits standard works of technology and may read from them in support of his method of analysis.

The witness should be prepared for an extensive, incisive cross-examination. That which is factual should be admitted. If differences arise the opposing attorney may insist on a "Yes" or "No" answer where neither is adequate in the judgment of the engineer. An appeal to the judge may be necessary in order to obtain the privilege of making an answer which is free from possible misinterpretation.

As a rule, engineers object to accepting a contingent fee for services as an expert witness and usually require a definite agreement concerning compensation.

8. TORT

A Tort has been defined as "An act or omission which unlawfully violates a person's right created by law, and for which the appropriate remedy is a common law action for damages by the injured person."

Torts are wrongs committed by one person against the person, property, business, or reputation of another. The liability which results from a tort is due either to intent or negligence; it is not based on contract or on a positive obligation such as is involved in a breach of contract.

Torts Are Classified as (1) those against the person; (2) those against personal property; and (3) those against real property.

The torts which most concern the engineer are, under (1), fraud, negligence, procuring breach of contract, slander, and libel. Under (2) or (3) there are infringement of patents, copyright, and trademark; violation of right of support; violation of water rights; nuisance.

Negligence

Negligence is a breach of duty which requires one to use due care, skill, diligence, and proper caution to avoid injury to another.

The owner or tenant of property must keep it in such repair that those who may lawfully enter may not suffer injury. There is an obligation to barricade pitfalls, trenches, and other excavations against the injury of those who may have the right to enter.

If a city permits the use of a part of a street or sidewalk for private improvements, the owner becomes liable if proper lights by night or barriers by day are not placed for the protection of the public.

The Engineer in the course of his practice must be reasonably prudent and careful in the exercise of his skill to protect property and life against damage due to his acts. The degree of skill which may be demanded depends on the difficulties and requirements of the situation.

If the injured party was negligent or was guilty of contributory negligence he may not recover.

Negligence on the part of the party sued for damages must be the primary cause of the accident and not an incidental circumstance.

Since the burden of proof is on the injured party it is necessary for him to show the conditions preceding, accompanying, and following the accident with a chain of evidence establishing the cause of weakness of the structure, the defect of its design or construction, and the usual good practice in such cases.

The determination of the cause of failure of complicated structures requires a special knowledge of the theory of design, the usual shop practice or method of construction, and a highly analytical skill in obtaining evidence.

Slander and Libel are torts against the reputation. Slander is oral defamation of character; and libel is a written communication designed to injure the name, business, or public estimate of the character of the party libeled.

Infringement of Patent Rights

The inventor or the party to whom rights have been assigned or a licensee may sue to recover damages for the use of a patented device for which rights have not been obtained or if the article has been manufactured by a party having no license. Infringement must be proven, and the prosecution or defense of patent suits is expensive and usually delays the use of the article.

Engineering contracts ordinarily require that the contractor shall provide the necessary license to use and shall be liable for damages for the use of patented devices and for infringement of patented devices, instruments, or machines.

Violation of Right of Support

By virtue of title to real estate the owner has the right to the lateral support of his land and thereby has the duty imposed on him to preserve the support of adjoining property. Excavations for walls, sewers, or basements which weaken the support of adjoining land renders liable the party who causes the excavation.

Support of the soil only is required. The owner of an adjoining building is obligated to shore, underpin, or otherwise protect his building. Otherwise the excavator may enter and protect at the owner's expense or proceed with his excavation, using ordinary care under the circumstances.

The Supreme Court of Massachusetts stated in one case: " If the owner of land makes an excavation in it so near to the adjoining of another proprietor that the soil of the latter breaks away and falls into the pit, he is responsible for all the damage thereby occasioned. Few principles of the law can be traced to an earlier or to a more constant recognition."

In Gildersleeve *vs.* Hammond, the Supreme Court of Michigan 1896, the court in summation said:

1. "While a landowner has the undoubted right to excavate close to the boundary line, he must take reasonable precautions to prevent his neighbor's soil from falling.

2. "If he has taken such reasonable precautions, and yet the soil falls from its own pressure, he is still liable for injury to the soil, but not for any injury to the superstructures.

3. "If the pressure of the superstructure causes the land to fall, he is not liable either for injury to the land or superstructure.

4. "If he fails to take such reasonable precautions to protect his neighbor's soil, and to preserve it in its natural state, he is liable for the injury to both the land and the superstructure if the pressure of the superstructure did not cause the land to fall, and it fell in consequence of the failure to take such reasonable precautions."

Good practice requires cooperation of adjoining owners, the engineers, and legal advisers to provide a proper contract covering shoring and other protective measures to save the interests of all concerned.

The lowering of the water table in the course of excavation may cause settlement. If due care has been used it is unlikely that damages can be obtained, but the problems of water rights and support of the soil may introduce legal complications.

Riparian Rights

The owner of lands adjoining a water course is entitled to the reasonable use of such water so long as he does not damage other riparian owners by the pollution of the stream or by damming it in such manner as to affect the interests above or so store and discharge the water as to injure those below.

The boundary of properties on non-navigable streams is often the streambed or thread of the stream, and the streambed is real property. The boundary may change as the stream slowly erodes and deposits, thus increasing or decreasing the area of a tract bounded by a stream. When land is made by deposit or by change of the channel of a stream or river, boundaries between adjoining properties are legally extended on lines at right angles to the water line, though in fact more frequently by extending the boundaries by mutual consent or custom.

If a lake recedes, the boundaries of adjoining properties are extended normally to the receding line, which action preserves a proportional water frontage and cuts off no one.

Irrigation. In the western states a different practice has grown up and is now recognized by statute in some of them. Prior use constitutes a right, and amounts of water are assigned to new projects according to need. See the law in such states. Congress has recognized priority of possession on public lands.

Pollution. Many of the industrial states have laws against pollution by city or trade wastes, but the laws were not passed until conditions under the common law had become so bad that the remedy is most difficult. Where statutes require it, plans for water supply and sewerage must be submitted for approval to the state board of health or similar authority. Plans not submitted or not approved, in those states, cannot be legally financed by bonds. The bonds are void. It is important that the engineer be familiar with the law and observe it. Failure to adopt changes suggested by the approving authority or to satisfy the same only delays the work.

Manufacturing Wastes constitute a serious source of pollution in the industrial states. Numerous cases have been carried through the courts with conflicting decisions, but the tendency is to view streams and rivers not as natural sewers but as property in which the public has an interest—especially on navigable streams—and to impose greater responsibility on the company contributing to serious pollution by requiring that screens, detention tanks, and treatment works be installed and operated.

Surface Waters is the term applied to run-off from storms, which is seeking a lower level in natural flow over lands on its way to recognized streams. The law of riparian rights does not apply, and in general an owner of lands may appropriate surface waters, but this is not true in all western states. In California a decision was against the storage of flood water to the detriment of users downstream.

The accumulation of excessive amounts of surface water added to normal stream flow produces floods. Floods overflow and damage farm lands and cities, and wash away bridges, railway embankments, and highways. Damages cannot be recovered for such losses unless it can be proven that dams have raised the water above its normal height for such volumes of flow or bridges have reduced the normal waterway and thus have raised the level artificially. Natural causes do not constitute a basis for action to recover damages.

Well Waters are the result of rainfall or surface waters percolating through the soil to porous strata above impervious strata of rock, hardpan, or other material where underground streams are formed.

In the construction of sewers such underground streams may be intercepted and wells rendered worthless. No recovery under such circumstances has been noted, but cities have been enjoined from pumping from wells which damaged private wells. No private owner has been prevented by law from sinking and using wells which interfered with the yield of neighboring wells.

Nuisance

A Nuisance is an offense which does harm or damage or creates inconvenience to private parties or to the public. Private parties are entitled to the comfortable use and enjoyment of their rights. The public likewise may be annoyed, inconvenienced, or damaged by the wrongful conduct of an owner, tenant, or trespasser who creates a material annoyance, offense, or damage. The pollution of streams; the dumping of offal on the banks of streams or in parks; smoke, odor, noise, and vibration caused by private acts, by utilities, or by cities may be the basis of suits by the public to abate or to pay damages.

Garbage incinerators, sewage treatment works, abattoirs, garbage disposal by feeding to hogs are sources of contention in which engineers are concerned.

Damages may be recovered by a private party if he can show depreciation of his property, injury to health, definite discomfort, or other real rather than prospective damages.

Trespass

" Trespass to real property is an unlawful entry upon the land of another, or unlawful acts committed subsequent to a lawful entry. The interest protected is that of possession, free from interference by physical intrusions of persons or things."

"Squatter's right" is established by continued, unchallenged possession of the real estate of another for a period of fifteen to twenty years. Such neglect by the owner may lead to loss of title through adverse possession, i.e., possession against the rights of the former owner who held title to the land in question. Numerous examples exist of title to valuable public or private lands being obtained in this manner.

Cattle roaming at large or breaking out of enclosures into the lands of others may do damage for which the owner may be sued.

The right to enter public buildings, parks, and other public places is granted so long as nuisance is not created or possession is not adverse.

The public has certain license to enter private property in the ordinary course of business, but permission may be revoked.

The law permits entry to control a conflagration and to destroy buildings to prevent loss to other property.

Surveyors and engineers who enter private property to lay out highways, sewers, or other public works, before easements, license, or title has been obtained, should obey the owner's instructions to get off, as otherwise trespass may be charged. The mere act of entry under those conditions is, in fact, trespass, but prompt respect for the rights of contestants or objecting owners rarely leads to suit.

In emergency, a temporary right of way may be established if a highway is blocked or impassable and several vehicles have already followed a specific path or route through a field and around such obstruction. Other vehicles may follow without trespassing until the condition has been cured and fences have been restored.

The engineer should see to it that license, easement, or other right to enter, construct, or repair a sewer, water main, or other public work crossing private property is obtained before entering thereon, unless by verbal agreement a temporary permit is obtained until such legal right has been consummated. A license is usually temporary, whereas an easement provides a permanent right to enter, perhaps for specific purposes.

9. PRELIMINARY STEPS IN LETTING A CONTRACT

1. Business Investigations. The engineer is frequently called upon to prepare reports covering the facts, estimates of cost, estimates of probable income, future prospects for business, probable competition, expected rate of income based on population growth, increase in usage, saturation point, and methods of financing.

In the last connection it is important that the engineer and his clients be thoroughly familiar with the Securities Act of 1933 and its amendments, if amended. Misrepresentation of facts or failure to obtain and divulge all facts related to the issue of securities is a serious offense.

2. Land Rights. The engineer may be called upon to obtain rights of way, options for the purchase of lands, or easements in order that power plants, water lines, transmission lines, highways, railways, sewers, or other constructions may be carried to completion.

Proper land rights should be obtained which will provide for the right to enter to repair or maintain such works.

3. Titles and Records. With the aid of legal advice, it will be necessary to prepare options, easements, deeds, and licenses for the use of patents, and other documents. It is necessary to see that transfers of title are properly "signed, sealed, and delivered" in order to consummate the act, and also to see that they are recorded in the correct office of record.

The engineer's records or the company records should show when deeds are submitted for legal record, at what office or offices, and by whom. Fees must be paid.

4. Issue of Securities. Incorporation of a corporation requires a specific legal procedure depending on the statutes of the state in which incorporation is proposed. Legal services are usually necessary in order to ensure full compliance with the law.

Certain business meetings, election of officers, and records are necessary before the company is in legal operation.

The issue of stocks and bonds involves the preparation of statements of facts and of necessity. Such prospectus must conform to the Securities Act of 1933 in full and with exactness in order that those making the statements may be free from liability.

5. Plans and Specifications must be prepared and made a part of the contract. Such plans and specifications constitute a description of the work to be done, the quality of the materials to be used, the quality of workmanship required, the time within which the work is to be done, the method of payment, provision for extra work, and protection for the contractor and for the owner against liens, suits, and disagreements.

6. Surety Bond. Provision should be made (*a*) for the deposit of a certified check to ensure that the contractor will sign the contract if awarded the same and (*b*) that he will indemnify the owner by a surety bond against loss in case of breach of contract by the contractor.

7. Instructions to Bidders define the basis on which bids must be submitted, i.e., whether on a unit cost basis for each class of material and work or by lump sum with a unit cost for extra work of each kind or a cost plus percentage of one type or another.

The time and place of receiving and opening bids will be stated. The amount of the certified check required from each bidder and the manner of returning the same to successful and unsuccessful bidders will also be stated. The amount and type of surety bond required will be stated.

The address where plans and specifications can be obtained and the cost of same will be given.

It is usual to state that any and all bids may be rejected.

The following is a short form of "Instructions to Bidders" which could be extended to meet the needs of more complicated jobs:

Sealed bids addressed to the Board of Public Works, ..., Pa., and endorsed "Bids for Sewers" will be received at their office in the City Building until 12 o'clock noon on February 5, 1935, and at that time all such bids will be publicly opened and read.

All bids must be on the blank forms provided for the purpose by the Board of Public Works.

A certified check for $...... must accompany the bid or bids submitted by each bidder.

Certified checks of unsuccessful bidders will be returned within three days after the contract has been signed and a satisfactory surety bond is provided.

The surety bond of a satisfactory bonding company must be provided in the sum of $...... within 10 days after the contractor is notified of the award or his certified check will be declared forfeited for failure to fulfil the terms of the contract. Likewise, the contract must be signed within the same ten days or the certified check may be declared forfeited.

The Board of Public Works reserves the right to reject any bid or all bids or to accept any bid which it deems for the best interests of the city.

Each bidder shall submit with his bid the names and addresses of parties for whom he has performed work of similar character to that on which he submits a bid.

The quantities of the various classes of work to be done are only approximate and may be increased or decreased by the Board of Works by an amount not to exceed 10 per cent, the increase or decrease to be made at the unit prices bid.

The contractor shall begin work within 30 days after the award of the contract, and the same shall be completed within 90 days after the award of the contract.

Where statutes or ordinances specify the maximum number of hours per day of work permitted or make other conditions, reference to or quotation from the statute should be included.

The instructions to bidders should be signed by a responsible officer such as the clerk or the engineer of the Board of Public Works.

Portions of the above do not apply verbatim where a private party or corporation is proposing to receive bids.

8. The Advertisement. In order to bring the letting of a contract to the attention of prospective bidders, a statement may be sent to a preferred list of bidders, as is often done by architects, or an advertisement may be inserted in a journal which appeals to the desired clientele.

Such notice or advertisement should contain certain pertinent facts, such as when, where, and by whom bids will be received; where plans and specifications can be obtained; conditions of bid such as certified check and surety bond required; the statement that "The right is reserved to refuse any or all bids or to let the contract to other than the lowest bidder."

Advertisements for bids by the U. S. Government may be brief, as in the following, taken from the *Engineering News-Record*, Dec. 13, 1934, p. 47.

UNITED STATES ENGINEER OFFICE, Room 710, Army Building, 39 Whitehall St., New York, N. Y. Sealed bids will be received until 12 m., December 18, 1934, and then publicly opened, for furnishing all labor and materials and performing all work for *dredging* approximately 10,830 cubic yards, place measurement, of material (maintenance) from Port Chester Harbor, N. Y. (225)

Longer and more detailed instructions may be seen in that and other engineering journals.

The following, from the *Engineering News-Record*, Nov. 29, 1934, p. 69, is a good example of a detailed statement designed to protect the state:

Bids: December 4.

State Highway Work

STATE DEPARTMENT OF PUBLIC WORKS—
DIVISION OF HIGHWAYS, ALBANY, N. Y.

Sealed proposals will be received by the undersigned at the State Office Building, 13th Floor, Albany, N. Y., until one o'clock p.m. on Tuesday, December 4, 1934, for the construction and reconstruction of highways and bridges in the following Counties, in accordance with the provisions of the National Industrial Recovery Act and Section 1 of the Act of June 18, 1934 (H.R. 8781):

Construction	Deposit Required
CLINTON..	$5,000
(18' Gravel Bituminous Treated, including 65' Girder: 3.34 miles)	
COLUMBIA..	1,700
(18' Gravel Surfacing: 2.85 miles)	
DELAWARE..	3,600
(18' Gravel Surfacing: 5.13 miles)	
FRANKLIN..	1,900
(18' Gravel Surfacing, including 55' I-Beam: 2.88 miles)	
KINGS & QUEENS...	33,000
(Prelim. Grading, including 56'–67', 87.5' Rigid Frame Structures: 0.82 mile)	
MONROE..	2,100
(18' Gravel Surfacing: 5.06 miles)	
ORANGE..	2,500
(18' Gravel Surfacing: 6.22 miles)	
ORLEANS...	2,000
(18' Gravel Surfacing: 4.38 miles)	
ST. LAWRENCE...	2,500
(18' Gravel Surfacing, including one 42' and one 50' Timber bridge: 5.53 miles)	
SCHOHARIE..	4,000
(Broken stone—Bit. Treated: 4.25 miles)	
Reconstruction	
ORANGE..	3,500
(30' Concrete 8" and 65.5' Beam Elim. Structure: 0.27 mile)	
OSWEGO..	4,500
(85.5' Girder: 30' Concrete Arch and Concrete Appr.: 0.12 mile)	
ULSTER..	10,000
(Bit. Mac. M.M.O. & Concrete incl. 75' Girder: 2.63 miles)	
SCHENECTADY & ALBANY...	21,000
(Concrete: 7.58 miles)	

Maps, plans, specifications, and estimates may be seen and proposal forms obtained at the office of the Division of Highways in Albany, N. Y., and at the office of the District Engineers in whose districts the roads are located, upon the payment of Five Dollars ($5.00) for plans and proposal forms. Standard specifications are Two Dollars ($2.00) per copy. No refund will be made on plans, specifications, or proposal forms. Plans and proposal forms may also be seen at the office of the State Department of Public Works, State Office Building, Worth & Center Streets, New York City. The addresses of the District Engineers and counties in each district will be furnished upon request.

Attention of Bidders is called to "General Information for Bidders" in the proposal, specifications, and contract agreement. The attention of bidders is also directed to the special provisions covering sub-letting or assigning the contract and to the use of domestic materials, when financed wholly or in part from funds apportioned under the National Industrial Recovery Act and

Section 1 of the Act of June 18, 1934 (H.R. 8781), and especially called to the fact that the funds for NRH, NRM, NRS (1935) projects were obtained from the provisions of the National Industrial Recovery Act, and Section 1 of the Act of June 18, 1934 (H.R. 8781), for the purpose of providing employment and hastening industrial recovery.

Proposals must be submitted in separate sealed envelopes with the name and number of contract plainly endorsed on the outside of the envelope. Each proposal must be accompanied by cash, draft or certified check payable to the New York State Department of Public Works, Division of Highways, for a sum of at least five per centum and not more than six per centum of the estimate accompanying the plans and specifications, and as specified in the advertisement for proposals and the proposal itself. The retention and disposal of such cash, draft or check by the State Division of Highways shall conform with Subdivision 2 of Section 130 of the Highway Law, as amended. The successful bidder will be required to execute the contract and comply in all respects with Section 130 of the Highway Law, as amended. The amount of the certified check accompanying the proposal of the bidder to whom the contract is awarded will be returned when ten per centum of the work under the contract has been completed. If Surety Bond is dispensed with, pursuant to the Highway Law, the amount of the bidding check will be returned when fifteen per centum of the contract work has been completed.

A certificate of compliance on the prescribed form which will be furnished for that purpose shall be signed and submitted by all bidders, in accordance with Executive Order No. 6646, issued by the President on March 14, 1934. Only bids accompanied by such certificate shall be considered or accepted. The contractor to whom award is made shall require subcontractors and dealers furnishing equipment, materials, and supplies to sign similar certificates before making awards to or purchases from such subcontractors or dealers, copies of which shall be furnished to the contracting officer.

On Federal Aid Contracts, when optional types are permitted for any one item of work, contractors must state in the space provided in the proposal for this purpose the exact designation of the optional type upon which the proposal is predicated. No one proposal shall contain more than one bid for an optional item. The award, if made, will be on the basis of the responsible proposal which for all items of work gives the lowest total cost for the project and the contract will call for the type designated in such proposal.

Skilled, intermediate grade, and unskilled labor on projects under the National Industrial Recovery Act, and Section 1 of the Act of June 18, 1934 (H.R. 8781) shall receive the minimum wage rate per hour as follows:

In New York City: skilled labor, eighty cents per hour; intermediate grade labor, sixty-five cents per hour; unskilled labor, fifty-five cents per hour; in the Counties of Nassau, Rockland, Suffolk, and Westchester, skilled labor, seventy-five cents per hour; intermediate grade labor, sixty cents per hour; unskilled labor, fifty-five cents per hour; in counties other than Nassau, Rockland, Suffolk, and Westchester, and New York City, skilled labor, seventy-five cents per hour; intermediate grade labor, fifty-five cents per hour; unskilled labor, forty-five cents per hour. The minimum hourly rate for the various types of operations and trades shall be set forth in the itemized proposal for each project.

The right is reserved to reject any or all bids.

A. W. BRANDT,
Commissioner of Highways.

9. Receiving Bids. A record should be prepared and kept of the time when each bid was received; the person, partnership, or corporation submitting it; and by whom submitted.

The bids should be opened by the duly authorized official in the case of a municipality, county, state, or federal unit of government.

The engineer should prepare on forms provided for the purpose a comparison of the bids submitted in order to determine the lowest bidder. The law recognizes the right of parties receiving bids to investigate the reliability, experience, and reputation of each bidder and to use their best judgment in selecting the "lowest and best bid," which may not be the lowest. All governmental authorities may be required to show that judgment without prejudice was used. Other things being equal, the courts have required that the lowest bid for public works shall be accepted.

This does not apply to private parties or corporations which may, barring fraud, award the contract as they see fit and usually without recourse on the part of disappointed bidders.

10. Awarding the Contract consists in formally accepting a bid and officially informing the bidder. The contract must be signed within a specified time or the certified check becomes the property of the owner, and he may proceed to notify another party that his bid has been accepted, or the certified check may be held pending the determination of damages sustained by accepting the next higher bid.

In addition to signing the contract, the successful bidder must provide a surety bond of approved form.

It is usual to hold in reserve a second or even a third best bid until the contract has been signed and a satisfactory bond has been submitted. When and if all details are satisfactory, then the certified checks are returned to the unsuccessful bidders.

If the contractor receiving the award in the first instance fails to sign the contract and/

or to supply a satisfactory bond, his certified check may be declared forfeited and another contractor may be notified that his bid is accepted. Or all bids may be rejected, changes may be made in conditions, and new bids advertised for.

10. FORM OF AGREEMENT

The following "Standard Form of Agreement between Contractor and Owner for Construction of Buildings" has received the approval of the National Association of Builders Exchanges, the Associated General Contractors of America, the Joint Conference on Construction Contracts, the National Association of Master Plumbers, and several other organizations. It is used with the approval of the American Institute of Architects. Comments, additions, and suggestions by the author are in smaller type.

"THIS AGREEMENT made the...

day of..............in the year Nineteen Hundred and...........................

by and between...

hereinafter called the Contractor, and...

....hereinafter called the Owner, WITNESSETH, that the Contractor and the Owner for the considerations herein-after named agree as follows:

" **Article 1. Scope of the Work**—The Contractor shall furnish all of the materials and perform all of the work shown on the Drawings and described in the Specifications entitled

"(*Here insert the caption descriptive of the work as used on the Drawings and in the other Contract Documents.*) "

prepared by...

acting as and in these Contract Documents entitled the Architect; and shall do everything required by this Agreement, the General Conditions of the Contract, the Specifications and the Drawings."

The word "Engineer" or "Chief Engineer" may be substituted for "Architect" where desirable.

" **Article 2. Time of Completion**—The work to be performed under this Contract shall

be commenced..
and shall be substantially completed...

" (*Here insert stipulation as to liquidated damages, if any.*)"

An alternative form is: The contractor shall begin active work not later than......days after the contract is signed. The work shall be substantially completed on or before.............

It was customary to provide a penalty of $...... per day for each day thereafter that the work remained uncompleted.

The courts held that if no equal bonus was provided for completion before the specified date, the imposing of a penalty was an assumption of a legal authority which lay only in the courts. It was further required that the owner show that damages of the amount of the penalty was suffered. In many instances this was impossible.* Consequently resort has been made to a paragraph entitled " Liquidated Damages."

Whereas, time is of the essence of this contract and whereas the specific amount of damage suffered for each day that the work remains uncompleted after the specified date for completion is difficult or impossible of determination, it is hereby agreed between the Owner and the Contractor that the latter shall pay the sum of $...... per day for each day of delay, not as a penalty, but as liquidated damages for such delay except that the agreed shall not be due if the delay is caused by the owner, nor shall liquidated damages be paid for Sundays or legal holidays.

A " time charge " of similar import has been used by the Delaware State Highway Department.†

" **Article 3. The Contract Sum**—The Owner shall pay the Contractor for the perform-

---

* See The Elements of Specification Writing by Kirby, 1935, pp. 112 et seq.
† Ibid.

ance of the Contract, subject to additions and deductions provided therein, in current
funds as follows:. . . . .

" (*State here the lump sum amount, unit prices, or both, as desired in individual cases.*) "

Where the quantities originally contemplated are so changed that application of the
agreed unit price to the quantity of work performed is shown to create a hardship to the
Owner or the Contractor, there shall be an equitable adjustment of the Contract to
prevent such hardship."

The above article should contain the total of the contract, the agreed unit prices for extras such
as excavation, concrete, etc.

Where the contract is on a unit basis the details of amounts of work to be done and unit costs
should be given. If the owner supplies certain materials or equipment, this should be clearly stated.

If the contract is on a cost-plus basis, the details should be definite in order to avoid disputes.

" **Article 4. Progress Payments**—The Owner shall make payments on account of the
Contract as provided therein, as follows:

On or about the. . . . . .day of each month. . . . . .per
cent of the value, based on the Contract prices, of labor and materials incorporated in the
work and of materials suitably stored at the site thereof up to the. . . . . .day of
that month, as estimated by the Architect, less the aggregate of previous payments; and
upon substantial completion of the entire work, a sum sufficient to increase the total
payments to. . . . . .per cent of the contract price. . . . .
. . . .

" (*Insert here any provision made for limiting or reducing the amount retained after the work
reaches a certain stage of completion.*) "

On contracts for large sums it is usual to include two items under " Payments for Work in
Progress." First, estimate the value of the work completed during the preceding month, and
second, specify the payment of 75 or some other per cent of the estimated value of the work done.

If a payment is also made on the value of materials delivered during that month and not yet
incorporated in the work, then a deduction will be made of the previous payments on materials *now*
in the work completed. This requires careful bookkeeping, checking of bills of lading, and inven-
tories of materials on hand. It is also necessary to check the amounts paid on materials received
in order to ensure that payments do not exceed the agreed percentage of work done *and paid for*.
It is important that the books of the contractor, bills, and receipts be open to inspection by the
owner. See Art. 24.

" **Article 5. Acceptance and Final Payment**—Final payment shall be due. . . . .
days after substantial completion of the work provided the work be then fully completed
and the Contract fully performed.

Upon receipt of written notice that the work is ready for final inspection and acceptance,
the Architect (or Engineer) shall promptly make such inspection, and when he finds the
work acceptable under the Contract and the Contract fully performed he shall promptly
issue a final certificate, over his own signature, stating that the work provided for in this
Contract has been completed and is accepted by him under the terms and conditions
thereof, and that the entire balance found to be due the Contractor, and noted in said
final certificate, is due and payable.

Before issuance of final certificate the Contractor shall submit evidence satisfactory to the
Architect (or Engineer) that all payrolls, material bills, and other indebtedness connected
with the work have been paid.

If after the work has been substantially completed, full completion thereof is materially
delayed through no fault of the Contractor and the Architect (or Engineer) so certifies,
the Owner shall, upon certificate of the Architect (or Engineer) and without terminating
the Contract, make payment of the balance due for that portion of the work fully completed and accepted. Such payment shall be made under the terms and conditions
governing final payment, except that it shall not constitute a waiver of claims.

" **Article 6. The Contract Documents**—The General Conditions of the Contract, the
Specifications and the Drawings, together with this Agreement, form the Contract, and
they are as fully a part of the Contract as if hereto attached or herein repeated. The
following is an enumeration of the Specifications and Drawings:

" **IN WITNESS WHEREOF,** the parties hereto have executed this Agreement, the
day and year first above written.

" . . . .

" . . . . "

11. ARTICLES OF THE GENERAL CONDITIONS

Index

" **Art. 1. Definitions.**

"(a) The Contract Documents consist of the Agreement, the General Conditions of the Contract, the Drawings and Specifications, including all modifications thereof incorporated in the documents before their execution. These form the Contract.

"(b) The Owner, the Contractor and the Architect are those mentioned as such in the Agreement. They are treated throughout the Contract Documents as if each were of the singular number and masculine gender.

"(c) The term Subcontractor, as employed herein, includes only those having a direct contract with the Contractor and it includes one who furnishes material worked to a special design according to the plans or specifications of this work, but does not include one who merely furnishes material not so worked.

"(d) Written notice shall be deemed to have been duly served if delivered in person to the individual or to a member of the firm or to an officer of the corporation for whom it is intended, or if delivered at or sent by registered mail to the last business address known to him who gives the notice.

"(e) The term 'work' of the Contractor or Subcontractor includes labor or materials or both.

"(f) All time limits stated in the Contract Documents are of the essence of the Contract.

"(g) The law of the place of building shall govern the construction of this Contract.

" **Art. 2. Execution, Correlation and Intent of Documents.**—The Contract Documents shall be signed in duplicate by the Owner and the Contractor. In case the Owner and the Contractor fail to sign the General Conditions, Drawings or Specifications, the Architect shall identify them.

"The Contract Documents are complementary, and what is called for by any one shall be as binding as if called for by all. The intention of the documents is to include all labor and materials, equipment and transportation necessary for the proper execution of the work. It is not intended, however, that materials or work not covered by or properly inferable from any heading, branch, class or trade of the specifications shall be supplied unless distinctly so noted on the drawings. Materials or work described in words which so applied have a well-known technical or trade meaning shall be held to refer to such recognized standards.

" **Art. 3. Detail Drawings and Instructions.**—The Architect shall furnish with reasonable promptness, additional instructions, by means of drawings or otherwise, necessary for the proper execution of the work. All such drawings and instructions shall be consistent with the Contract Documents, true developments thereof, and reasonably inferable therefrom.

"The work shall be executed in conformity therewith and the Contractor shall do no work without proper drawings and instructions.

"The Contractor and the Architect, if either so requests, shall jointly prepare a schedule, subject to change from time to time in accordance with the progress of the work, fixing the dates at which the various detail drawings will be required, and the Architect shall furnish them in accordance with that schedule. Under like conditions, a schedule shall be prepared, fixing the dates for the submission of shop drawings, for the beginning of manufacture and installation of materials and for the completion of the various parts of the work."

In engineering work it is customary to submit all detail drawings with the general drawings to bidders. This paragraph may be omitted or a specific item can be incorporated where it is appropriate.

" Art. 4. Copies Furnished.—Unless otherwise provided in the Contract Documents the Architect will furnish to the Contractor, free of charge, all copies of drawings and specifications reasonably necessary for the execution of the work.

" Art. 5. Shop Drawings.—The Contractor shall submit with such promptness as to cause no delay in his own work or in that of any other Contractor, two copies of all shop or setting drawings and schedules required for the work of the various trades, and the Architect shall pass upon them with reasonable promptness. The Contractor shall make any corrections required by the Architect, file with him two corrected copies and furnish such other copies as may be needed. The Architect's approval of such drawings or schedules shall not relieve the Contractor from responsibility for deviations from drawings or specifications, unless he has in writing called the Architect's attention to such deviations at the time of submission, nor shall it relieve him from responsibility for errors of any sort in shop drawings or schedules."

This paragraph may be omitted from engineering work where detail and shop drawings are submitted to bidders. Where shop drawings are to be provided by the contractor, the paragraph should make clear that they are to be satisfactory to the engineer and approved by him when satisfactory.

" Art. 6. Drawings and Specifications on the Work.—The Contractor shall keep one copy of all drawings and specifications on the work, in good order, available to the Architect and to his representatives.

" Art. 7. Ownership of Drawings and Models.—All drawings, specifications and copies thereof furnished by the Architect are his property. They are not to be used on other work and, with the exception of the signed Contract set, are to be returned to him on request, at the completion of the work. All models are the property of the Owner.

" Art. 8. Samples.—The Contractor shall furnish for approval all samples as directed. The work shall be in accordance with approved samples.

" Art. 9. Materials, Appliances, Employes.—Unless otherwise stipulated, the Contractor shall provide and pay for all materials, labor, water, tools, equipment, light, power, transportation and other facilities necessary for the execution and completion of the work.

"Unless otherwise specified, all materials shall be new and both workmanship and materials shall be of good quality. The Contractor shall, if required, furnish satisfactory evidence as to the kind and quality of materials.

"The Contractor shall at all times enforce strict discipline and good order among his employes, and shall not employ on the work any unfit person or any one not skilled in the work assigned to him."

On engineering work it is usual to specify that workmanship shall be satisfactory in quality to the engineer. If any workman is judged by the engineer to be unfit for the work which is assigned him, he shall be discharged from that position upon written notice by the engineer to the contractor and shall not again be employed on this contract without the consent of the engineer.

" Art. 10. Royalties and Patents.—The Contractor shall pay all royalties and license fees. He shall defend all suits or claims for infringement of any patent rights and shall save the Owner harmless from loss on account thereof, except that the Owner shall be responsible for all such loss when a particular process or the product of a particular manufacturer or manufacturers is specified, but if the Contractor has information that the process or article specified is an infringement of a patent he shall be responsible for such loss unless he promptly gives such information to the Architect or Owner.

" Art. 11. Surveys, Permits and Regulations.—The Owner shall furnish all surveys unless otherwise specified. Permits and licenses of a temporary nature necessary for the prosecution of the work shall be secured and paid for by the Contractor. Permits, licenses and easements for permanent structures or permanent changes in existing facilities shall be secured and paid for by the Owner, unless otherwise specified.

"The Contractor shall give all notices and comply with all laws, ordinances, rules and regulations bearing on the conduct of the work as drawn and specified. If the Contractor observes that the drawings and specifications are at variance therewith, he shall promptly notify the Architect in writing, and any necessary changes shall be adjusted as provided in the Contract for changes in the work. If the Contractor performs any work knowing it to be contrary to such laws, ordinances, rules and regulations, and without such notice to the Architect, he shall bear all costs arising therefrom."

Engineering specifications often require the contractor to protect all grade stakes and bench marks. If they are damaged or removed by the contractor or his employees, the contractor shall be charged with the cost of replacing the same and shall be responsible for delays and expense caused thereby.

" **Art. 12. Protection of Work and Property.**—The Contractor shall continuously maintain adequate protection of all his work from damage and shall protect the Owner's property from injury or loss arising in connection with this Contract. He shall make good any such damage, injury or loss, except such as may be directly due to errors in the Contract Documents or caused by agents or employes of the Owner. He shall adequately protect adjacent property as provided by law and the Contract Documents. He shall provide and maintain all passage ways, guard fences, lights and other facilities for protection required by public authority or local conditions.

"In an emergency affecting the safety of life or of the work or of adjoining property, the Contractor, without special instruction or authorization from the Architect or Owner, is hereby permitted to act, at his discretion, to prevent such threatened loss or injury, and he shall so act, without appeal, if so instructed or authorized. Any compensation, claimed by the Contractor on account of emergency work, shall be determined by agreement or Arbitration.

" **Art. 13. Inspection of Work.**—The Architect and his representatives shall at all times have access to the work wherever it is in preparation or progress and the Contractor shall provide proper facilities for such access and for inspection.

"If the specifications, the Architect's instructions, laws, ordinances or any public authority require any work to be specially tested or approved, the Contractor shall give the Architect timely notice of its readiness for inspection, and if the inspection is by another authority than the Architect, of the date fixed for such inspection. Inspections by the Architect shall be promptly made, and where practicable at the source of supply. If any work should be covered up without approval or consent of the Architect, it must, if required by the Architect, be uncovered for examination at the Contractor's expense.

"Re-examination of questioned work may be ordered by the Architect and if so ordered the work must be uncovered by the Contractor. If such work be found in accordance with the Contract Documents the Owner shall pay the cost of re-examination and replacement. If such work be found not in accordance with the Contract Documents the Contractor shall pay such cost, unless he shall show that the defect in the work was caused by another Contractor, and in that event the Owner shall pay such cost.

" **Art. 14. Superintendence: Supervision.**—The Contractor shall keep on his work, during its progress, a competent superintendent and any necessary assistants, all satisfactory to the Architect. The superintendent shall not be changed except with the consent of the Architect, unless the superintendent proves to be unsatisfactory to the Contractor and ceases to be in his employ. The superintendent shall represent the Contractor in his absence and all directions given to him shall be as binding as if given to the Contractor. Important directions shall be confirmed in writing to the Contractor. Other directions shall be so confirmed on written request in each case.

"The Contractor shall give efficient supervision to the work, using his best skill and attention. He shall carefully study and compare all drawings, specifications and other instructions and shall at once report to the Architect any error, inconsistency or omission which he may discover, but he shall not be held responsible for their existence or discovery.

" **Art. 15. Changes in the Work.**—The Owner, without invalidating the Contract, may order extra work or make changes by altering, adding to or deducting from the work, the Contract Sum being adjusted accordingly. All such work shall be executed under the conditions of the original contract except that any claim for extension of time caused thereby shall be adjusted at the time of ordering such change.

"In giving instructions, the Architect shall have authority to make minor changes in the work, not involving extra cost, and not inconsistent with the purposes of the building, but otherwise, except in an emergency endangering life or property, no extra work or change shall be made unless in pursuance of a written order from the Owner signed or countersigned by the Architect, or a written order from the Architect stating that the Owner has authorized the extra work or change, and no claim for an addition to the contract sum shall be valid unless so ordered.

"The value of any such extra work or change shall be determined in one or more of the following ways:

(a) By estimate and acceptance in a lump sum.
(b) By unit prices named in the contract or subsequently agreed upon.
(c) By cost and percentage or by cost and a fixed fee.

"If none of the above methods is agreed upon, the Contractor, provided he receives an order as above, shall proceed with the work. In such case and also under case (c), he shall keep and present in such form as the Architect may direct, a correct account of the net cost of labor and materials, together with vouchers. In any case, the Architect shall certify to the amount, including reasonable allowance for overhead and profit, due to the Contractor. Pending final determination of value, payments on account of changes shall be made on the Architect's certificate.

" **Art. 16. Claims for Extra Cost.**—If the Contractor claims that any instructions by drawings or otherwise involve extra cost under this contract, he shall give the Architect written notice thereof within a reasonable time after the receipt of such instructions, and in any event before proceeding to execute the work, except in emergency endangering life or property, and the procedure shall then be as provided for changes in the work. No such claim shall be valid unless so made.

" **Art. 17. Deductions for Uncorrected Work.**—If the Architect and Owner deem it inexpedient to correct work injured or done not in accordance with the Contract, an equitable deduction from the contract price shall be made therefor.

" **Art. 18. Delays and Extension of Time.**—If the Contractor be delayed at any time in the progress of the work by any act or neglect of the Owner or the Architect, or of any employe of either, or by any other Contractor employed by the Owner, or by changes ordered in the work, or by strikes, lockouts, fire, unusual delay in transportation, unavoidable casualties or any causes beyond the Contractor's control, or by delay authorized by the Architect pending arbitration, or by any cause which the Architect shall decide to justify the delay, then the time of completion shall be extended for such reasonable time as the Architect may decide.

"No such extension shall be made for delay occurring more than seven days before claim therefor is made in writing to the Architect. In the case of a continuing cause of delay, only one claim is necessary.

"If no schedule or agreement stating the dates upon which drawings shall be furnished is made, then no claim for delay shall be allowed on account of failure to furnish drawings until two weeks after demand for such drawings and not then unless such claim be reasonable.

"This article does not exclude the recovery of damages for delay by either party under other provisions in the contract documents.

" **Art. 19. Correction of Work Before Final Payment.**—The Contractor shall promptly remove from the premises all materials condemned by the Architect as failing to conform to the Contract, whether incorporated in the work or not, and the Contractor shall promptly replace and re-execute his own work in accordance with the Contract and without expense to the Owner and shall bear the expense of making good all work of other contractors destroyed or damaged by such removal or replacement.

"If the Contractor does not remove such condemned work and materials within a reasonable time, fixed by written notice, the Owner may remove them and may store the material at the expense of the Contractor. If the Contractor does not pay the expenses of such removal within ten days' time thereafter, the Owner may, upon ten days' written notice, sell such materials at auction or at private sale and shall account for the net proceeds thereof, after deducting all the costs and expenses that should have been borne by the Contractor.

" **Art. 20. Correction of Work After Final Payment.**—Neither the final certificate nor payment nor any provision in the Contract Documents shall relieve the Contractor of responsibility for faulty materials or workmanship and, unless otherwise specified, he shall remedy any defects due thereto and pay for any damage to other work resulting therefrom, which shall appear within a period of one year from the date of substantial completion. The Owner shall give notice of observed defects with reasonable promptness. All questions arising under this article shall be decided by the Architect subject to arbitration.

" **Art. 21.** **The Owner's Right to Do Work.**—If the Contractor should neglect to prosecute the work properly or fail to perform any provision of this contract, the Owner, after three days' written notice to the Contractor may, without prejudice to any other remedy he may have, make good such deficiencies and may deduct the cost thereof from the payment then or thereafter due the Contractor, provided, however, that the Architect shall approve both such action and the amount charged to the Contractor.

" **Art. 22.** **Owner's Right to Terminate Contract.**—If the Contractor should be adjudged a bankrupt, or if he should make a general assignment for the benefit of his creditors, or if a receiver should be appointed on account of his insolvency, or if he should persistently or repeatedly refuse or should fail, except in cases for which extension of time is provided, to supply enough properly skilled workmen or proper materials, or if he should fail to make prompt payment to subcontractors or for material or labor, or persistently disregard laws, ordinances or the instructions of the Architect, or otherwise be guilty of a substantial violation of any provision of the contract, then the Owner, upon the certificate of the Architect that sufficient cause exists to justify such action, may, without prejudice to any other right or remedy and after giving the Contractor seven days' written notice, terminate the employment of the Contractor and take possession of the premises and of all materials, tools and appliances thereon and finish the work by whatever method he may deem expedient. In such case the Contractor shall not be entitled to receive any further payment until the work is finished. If the unpaid balance of the contract price shall exceed the expense of finishing the work including compensation for additional managerial and administrative services, such excess shall be paid to the Contractor. If such expense shall exceed such unpaid balance, the Contractor shall pay the difference to the Owner. The expense incurred by the Owner as herein provided, and the damage incurred through the Contractor's default, shall be certified by the Architect.

" **Art. 23.** **Contractor's Right to Stop Work or Terminate Contract.**—If the work should be stopped under an order of any court, or other public authority, for a period of three months, through no act or fault of the Contractor or of anyone employed by him, or if the Architect should fail to issue any certificate for payment within seven days after it is due, or if the Owner should fail to pay to the Contractor within seven days of its maturity and presentation, any sum certified by the Architect or awarded by arbitrators, then the Contractor may, upon seven days' written notice to the Owner and the Architect, stop work or terminate this contract and recover from the Owner payment for all work executed and any loss sustained upon any plant or materials and reasonable profit and damages.

" **Art. 24.** **Applications for Payments.**—The Contractor shall submit to the Architect an application for each payment, and, if required, receipts or other vouchers, showing his payments for materials and labor, including payments to subcontractors as required by Art. 37.

" If payments are made on valuation of work done, such application shall be submitted at least ten days before each payment falls due, and, if required, the Contractor shall, before the first application, submit to the Architect a schedule of values of the various parts of the work, including quantities, aggregating the total sum of the contract, divided so as to facilitate payments to subcontractors in accordance with Article 37 (e), made out in such form as the Architect and the Contractor may agree upon, and, if required, supported by such evidence as to its correctness as the Architect may direct. This schedule, when approved by the Architect, shall be used as a basis for certificates of payment, unless it be found to be in error. In applying for payments, the Contractor shall submit a statement based upon this schedule, and, if required, itemized in such form and supported by such evidence as the Architect may direct, showing his right to the payment claimed.
" If payments are made on account of materials delivered and suitably stored at the site but not incorporated in the work, they shall, if required by the Architect, be conditional upon submission by the Contractor of bills of sale or such other procedure as will establish the Owner's title to such material or otherwise adequately protect the Owner's interest.

" **Art. 25.** **Certificates of Payments.**—If the Contractor has made application as above, the Architect shall, not later than the date when each payment falls due, issue to the Contractor a certificate for such amount as he decides to be properly due.
" No certificate issued nor payment made to the Contractor, nor partial or entire use or occupancy of the work by the Owner, shall be an acceptance of any work or materials not in accordance with this contract. The making and acceptance of the final payment shall constitute a waiver of all claims by the Owner, other than those arising from unsettled liens, from faulty work appearing after final payment or from requirement of the specifications, and of all claims by the Contractor, except those previously made and still unsettled.

"Should the Owner fail to pay the sum named in any certificate of the Architect or in any award by arbitration, upon demand when due, the Contractor shall receive, in addition to the sum named in the certificate, interest thereon at the legal rate in force at the place of building.

" **Art. 26. Payments Withheld.**—The Architect may withhold or, on account of subsequently discovered evidence, nullify the whole or a part of any certificate to such extent as may be necessary to protect the Owner from loss on account of:

    (a) Defective work not remedied.

    (b) Claims filed or reasonable evidence indicating probable filing of claims.

    (c) Failure of the Contractor to make payments properly to subcontractors or for material or labor.

    (d) A reasonable doubt that the contract can be completed for the balance then unpaid.

    (e) Damage to another Contractor.

"When the above grounds are removed payment shall be made for amounts withheld because of them.

" **Art. 27. Contractor's Liability Insurance.**—The Contractor shall maintain such insurance as will protect him from claims under workmen's compensation acts and from any other claims for damages for personal injury, including death, which may arise from operations under this Contract, whether such operations be by himself or by any subcontractor or anyone directly or indirectly employed by either of them. Certificates of such insurance shall be filed with the Owner, if he so require, and shall be subject to his approval for adequacy of protection.

" **Art. 28. Owner's Liability Insurance.**—The Owner shall be responsible for and at his option may maintain such insurance as will protect him from his contingent liability for damages for personal injury, including death, which may arise from operations under this contract.

" **Art. 29. Fire Insurance.**—The Owner shall effect and maintain fire insurance upon the entire structure on which the work of this contract is to be done and upon all materials, in or adjacent thereto and intended for use thereon, to at least eighty per cent of the insurable value thereof. The loss, if any, is to be made adjustable with and payable to the Owner as Trustee for whom it may concern.

"All policies shall be open to inspection by the Contractor. If the Owner fails to show them on request, or if he fails to effect or maintain insurance as above, the Contractor may insure his own interest and charge the cost thereof to the Owner. If the Contractor is damaged by failure of the Owner to maintain such insurance, he may recover as stipulated in the contract for recovery of damages.

"If required in writing by any party in interest, the Owner as Trustee shall, upon the occurrence of loss, give bond for the proper performance of his duties. He shall deposit any money received from insurance in an account separate from all his other funds and he shall distribute it in accordance with such agreement as the parties in interest may reach, or under an award of arbitrators appointed, one by the Owner, another by joint action of the other parties in interest, all other procedure being as provided elsewhere in the contract for Arbitration. If after loss no special agreement is made, replacement of injured work shall be ordered and executed as provided for changes in the work.

"The Trustee shall have power to adjust and settle any loss with the insurers unless one of the Contractors interested shall object in writing within three working days of the occurrence of loss, and thereupon arbitrators shall be chosen as above. The Trustee shall in that case make settlement with the insurers in accordance with the directions of such arbitrators, who shall also, if distribution by arbitration is required, direct such distribution.

" **Art. 30. Guaranty Bonds.**—The Owner shall have the right, prior to the signing of the Contract, to require the Contractor to furnish bond covering the faithful performance of the Contract and the payment of all obligations arising thereunder, in such form as the Owner may prescribe and with such sureties as he may approve. If such bond is required by instructions given previous to the submission of bids, the premium shall be paid by the Contractor; if subsequent thereto, it shall be paid by the Owner."

It is customary to require the deposit of a certified check, payable to the owner, by each bidder to ensure that the contract if awarded to a bidder will be signed by him, and also to ensure that a satisfactory bond is submitted by a surety company covering the completion of the contract. A bond by freeholders, i.e., individual holders of real estate, is not usually acceptable except on small contracts awarded to local bidders. Even then a bond supplied by material dealers may not be desirable.

" **Art. 31. Damages.**—If either party to this Contract should suffer damage in any manner because of any wrongful act or neglect of the other party of or anyone employed by him, then he shall be reimbursed by the other party for such damage.

"Claims under this clause shall be made in writing to the party liable within a reasonable time at the first observance of such damage and not later than the time of final payment, except as expressly stipulated otherwise in the case of faulty work or materials, and shall be adjusted by agreement or arbitration.

" **Art. 32. Liens.**—Neither the final payment nor any part of the retained percentage shall become due until the Contractor, if required, shall deliver to the Owner a complete release of all liens arising out of this Contract, or receipts in full in lieu thereof and, if required in either case, an affidavit that so far as he has knowledge or information the releases and receipts include all the labor and material for which a lien could be filed; but the Contractor may, if any subcontractor refuses to furnish a release or receipt in full, furnish a bond satisfactory to the Owner, to indemnify him against any lien. If any lien remain unsatisfied after all payments are made, the Contractor shall refund to the Owner all moneys that the latter may be compelled to pay in discharging such a lien, including all costs and a reasonable attorney's fee.

" **Art. 33. Assignment.**—Neither party to the Contract shall assign the Contract or sublet it as a whole without the written consent of the other, nor shall the Contractor assign any moneys due or to become due to him hereunder, without the previous written consent of the Owner.

" **Art. 34. Mutual Responsibility of Contractors.**—Should the Contractor cause damage to any other contractor on the work the Contractor agrees, upon due notice, to settle with such contractor by agreement or arbitration, if he will so settle. If such other contractor sues the Owner on account of any damage alleged to have been so sustained, the Owner shall notify the Contractor, who shall defend such proceedings at the Owner's expense and, if any judgment against the Owner arise therefrom, the Contractor shall pay or satisfy it and pay all costs incurred by the Owner.

" **Art. 35. Separate Contracts.**—The Owner reserves the right to let other contracts in connection with this work. The Contractor shall afford other contractors reasonable opportunity for the introduction and storage of their materials and the execution of their work, and shall properly connect and coordinate his work with theirs.

"If any part of the Contractor's work depends for proper execution or results upon the work of any other contractor, the Contractor shall inspect and promptly report to the Architect any defects in such work that render it unsuitable for such proper execution and results. His failure so to inspect and report shall constitute an acceptance of the other contractor's work as fit and proper for the reception of his work, except as to defects which may develop in the other contractor's work after the execution of his work.

"To insure the proper execution of his subsequent work the Contractor shall measure work already in place and shall at once report to the Architect any discrepancy between the executed work and the drawings.

" **Art. 36. Subcontracts.**—The Contractor shall, as soon as practicable after the signature of the contract, notify the Architect in writing of the names of subcontractors proposed for the principal parts of the work and for such others as the Architect may direct and shall not employ any that the Architect may within a reasonable time object to as incompetent or unfit.

"If the Contractor has submitted before signing the contract a list of subcontractors and the change of any name on such list is required in writing by the Owner after signature of agreement, the contract price shall be increased or diminished by the difference in cost occasioned by such change.

"The Architect shall, on request, furnish to any subcontractor, wherever practicable, evidence of the amounts certified on his account.

"The Contractor agrees that he is as fully responsible to the Owner for the acts and omissions of his subcontractors and of persons either directly or indirectly employed by them, as he is for the acts and omissions of persons directly employed by him.

"Nothing contained in the contract documents shall create any contractual relation between any subcontractor and the Owner.

" **Art. 37. Relations of Contractor and Subcontractor.**—The Contractor agrees to bind every Subcontractor and every Subcontractor agrees to be bound by the terms of the Agreement, the General Conditions, the Drawings and Specifications as far as applicable to his work, including the following provisions of this article, unless specifically noted to the contrary in a subcontract approved in writing as adequate by the Owner or Architect.

"This does not apply to minor subcontracts.

"The Subcontractor agrees—

"(a) To be bound to the Contractor by the terms of the Agreement, General Conditions, Drawings and Specifications, and to assume toward him all the obligations and responsibilities that he, by those documents, assumes toward the Owner.

"(b) To submit to the Contractor applications for payment in such reasonable time as to enable the Contractor to apply for payment under Article 24 of the General Conditions.

"(c) To make all claims for extras, for extensions of time and for damages for delays or otherwise, to the Contractor in the manner provided in the General Conditions for like claims by the Contractor upon the Owner, except that the time for making claims for extra cost is one week.

"The Contractor agrees—

"(d) To be bound to the Subcontractor by all the obligations that the Owner assumes to the Contractor under the Agreement, General Conditions, Drawings and Specifications, and by all the provisions thereof affording remedies and redress to the Contractor from the Owner.

"(e) To pay the Subcontractor, upon the issuance of certificates, if issued under the schedule of values described in Article 24 of the General Conditions, the amount allowed to the Contractor on account of the Subcontractor's work to the extend of the Subcontractor's interest therein.

"(f) To pay the Subcontractor, upon the issuance of certificates, if issued otherwise than as in (e), so that at all times his total payments shall be as large in proportion to the value of the work done by him as the total amount certified to the Contractor is to the value of the work done by him.

"(g) To pay the Subcontractor to such extent as may be provided by the Contract Documents or the subcontract, if either of these provides for earlier or larger payments than the above.

"(h) To pay the Subcontractor on demand for his work or materials as far as executed and fixed in place, less the retained percentage, at the time the certificate should issue, even though the Architect fails to issue it for any cause not the fault of the Subcontractor.

"(j) To pay the Subcontractor a just share of any fire insurance money received by him, the Contractor, under Article 29 of the General Conditions.

"(k) To make no demand for liquidated damages or penalty for delay in any sum in excess of such amount as may be specifically named in the subcontract.

"(l) That no claim for services rendered or materials furnished by the Contractor to the Subcontractor shall be valid unless written notice thereof is given by the Contractor to the Subcontractor during the first ten days of the calendar month following that in which the claim originated.

"(m) To give the Subcontractor an opportunity to be present and to submit evidence in any arbitration involving his rights.

"(n) To name as arbitrator under arbitration proceedings as provided in the General Conditions the person nominated by the Subcontractor, if the sole cause of dispute is the work, materials, rights or responsibilities of the Subcontractor; or, if of the Subcontractor and any other subcontractor jointly, to name as such arbitrator the person upon whom they agree.

"The Contractor and the Subcontractor agree that—

"(o) In the matter of arbitration, their rights and obligations and all procedure shall be analogous to those set forth in this contract.

"Nothing in this article shall create any obligation on the part of the Owner to pay to or to see to the payment of any sums to any Subcontractor.

" **Art. 38. Architect's Status.**—The Architect shall have general supervision and direction of the work. He is the agent of the Owner only to the extent provided in the Contract Documents and when in special instances he is authorized by the Owner so to act, and in such instances he shall, upon request, show the Contractor written authority. He has authority to stop the work whenever such stoppage may be necessary to insure the proper execution of the Contract.

"As the Architect is, in the first instance, the interpreter of the conditions of the Contract and the judge of its performance, he shall side neither with the Owner nor with the Contractor, but shall use his powers under the contract to enforce its faithful performance by both.

"In case of the termination of the employment of the Architect, the Owner shall appoint a capable and reputable Architect, whose status under the contract shall be that of the former Architect.

" Art. 39. Architect's Decisions.—The Architect shall, within a reasonable time, make decisions on all claims of the Owner or Contractor and on all other matters relating to the execution and progress of the work or the interpretation of the Contract Documents.

" The Architect's decisions in matters relating to artistic effect, shall be final, if within the terms of the Contract Documents.

"Except as above or as otherwise expressly provided in the Contract Documents, all the Architect's decisions are subject to arbitration.

" Art. 40. Arbitration.—All questions subject to arbitration under this Contract shall be submitted to arbitration at the choice of either party to the dispute.

"The Contractor shall not cause a delay of the work during any arbitration proceedings, except by agreement with the Owner.

"The demand for arbitration shall be filed in writing with the Architect, in the case of an appeal from his decision, within ten days of its receipt and in any other case within a reasonable time after cause thereof and in no case later than the time of final payment, except as otherwise expressly stipulated in the Contract. If the Architect fails to make a decision within a reasonable time, an appeal to arbitration may be taken as if his decision had been rendered against the party appealing.

"No one shall be nominated or act as an arbitrator who is in any way financially interested in this Contract or in the business affairs of either the Owner, Contractor or Architect.

"Unless otherwise provided by controlling statutes, the parties may agree upon one arbitrator; otherwise there shall be three, one named in writing, by each party to this Contract, to the other party and to the Architect and the third chosen by these two arbitrators, or if they fail to select a third within fifteen days, then he shall be chosen by the presiding officer of the Bar Association nearest to the location of the work. Should the party demanding arbitration fail to name an arbitrator within ten days of his demand, his right to arbitration shall lapse. Should the other party fail to choose an arbitrator within said ten days, then such presiding officer shall appoint such arbitrator. Should either party refuse or neglect to supply the arbitrators with any papers or information demanded in writing, the arbitrators are empowered by both parties to proceed ex parte.

"If there be one arbitrator his decision shall be binding; if three the decision of any two shall be binding. Such decision shall be a condition precedent to any right of legal action, and wherever permitted by law it may be filed in Court to carry it into effect.

"The arbitrators, if they deem that the case demands it, are authorized to award to the party whose contention is sustained such sums as they shall deem proper for the time, expense and trouble incident to the appeal and, if the appeal was taken without reasonable cause, damages for delay. The arbitrators shall fix their own compensation, unless otherwise provided by agreement, and shall assess the costs and charges of the arbitration upon either or both parties.

"The award of the arbitrators shall be in writing and it shall not be open to objection on account of the form of the proceeding or the award, unless otherwise provided by the controlling statutes.

"In the event of such statutes providing on any matter covered by this article otherwise than as hereinbefore specified, the method of procedure throughout and the legal effect of the award shall be wholly in accordance with the said statutes, it being intended hereby to lay down a principle of action to be followed, leaving its local application to be adapted to the legal requirements of the jurisdiction having authority over the arbitration."

Arbitration is increasingly recognized as a quicker way of settling disputes than resort to court action. It is also cheaper and as just. It should apply to all disagreements such as those which may arise under Arts. 15 and 17.

New York, in 1920, was the first state to recognize arbitration and " made agreements to arbitrate irrevocable. New Jersey, Pennsylvania, Massachusetts, California, Oregon, Louisiana, Connecticut, New Hampshire, Rhode Island, and Arizona have similar laws while all the other states have passed arbitration laws of one kind or another." The American Arbitration Association, organized in 1926 by Chief Justice Hughes and others, was designed to speed justice and reduce the cost of litigation. See *Harper's Magazine*, December, 1931.

It is generally accepted that the engineer should have power " to reject or condemn any work or material which does not conform to the contract."

The clause formerly specifying that " the decision of the chief engineer shall be final " is less frequently used.

" Art. 41. Cash Allowances.—The Contractor shall include in the contract sum all allowances named in the Contract Documents and shall cause the work so covered to be done by such contractors and for such sums as the Architect may direct, the contract sum being adjusted in conformity therewith. The Contractor declares that the contract sum includes such sums for expenses and profit on account of cash allowances as he deems proper. No demand for expenses or profit other than those included in the contract sum shall be allowed. The Contractor shall not be required to employ for any such work persons against whom he has a reasonable objection.

" Art. 42. Use of Premises.—The Contractor shall confine his apparatus, the storage of materials and the operations of his workmen to limits indicated by law, ordinances, permits or directions of the Architect and shall not unreasonably encumber the premises with his materials.

"The Contractor shall not load or permit any part of the structure to be loaded with a weight that will endanger its safety.

"The Contractor shall enforce the Architect's instructions regarding signs, advertisements, fires and smoking.

" Art. 43. Cutting, Patching and Digging.—The Contractor shall do all cutting, fitting or patching of his work that may be required to make its several parts come together properly and fit it to receive or be received by work of other contractors shown upon, or reasonably implied by, the Drawings and Specifications for the completed structure, and he shall make good after them as the Architect may direct.

"Any cost caused by defective or ill-timed work shall be borne by the party responsible therefor.

"The Contractor shall not endanger any work by cutting, digging or otherwise, and shall not cut or alter the work of any other contractor save with the consent of the Architect.

" Art. 44. Cleaning Up.—The Contractor shall at all times keep the premises free from accumulations of waste material or rubbish caused by his employees or work, and at the completion of the work he shall remove all his rubbish from and about the building and all his tools, scaffolding and surplus materials and shall leave his work 'broom clean' or its equivalent, unless more exactly specified. In case of dispute the Owner may remove the rubbish and charge the cost to the several contractors as the Architect shall determine to be just."

ADDITIONAL CLAUSES which should be given consideration if the character of the work to be done suggests their fitness:

Contractor's Understanding.—The Contractor agrees that he by careful examination satisfied himself as to the nature and location of the work, the conformation of the ground, the character, quality, and quantity of the materials to be excavated and moved, and the conditions affecting all the work to be done, and that his conclusion to execute this contract is based on such investigation, and not on the estimates of the quantities or other information supplied by the Engineer, and that the Contractor will make no claim against the Owner because of any estimates, tests, borings, or representations of any kind affecting the work to be done which have been or may be made by any agent of the Owner and which may prove to be in error.

Rejected Material.—" Any materials condemned or rejected by the Engineer as not conforming to the specifications may be (so) branded or otherwise marked, and shall, on demand, be at once removed by the Contractor (at his expense) to a satisfactory distance from the work."

Report Errors and Discrepancies.—" If the Contractor, in the course of the work, finds any discrepancy between the plans (specifications) and the physical conditions of the locality, or any errors on plans or in the layout as given by said points and instructions, it shall be his duty to immediately inform the Engineer, in writing, and the Engineer shall promptly verify the same. Any work done after such discovery shall be done at the Contractor's risk."

If the Engineer's decision concerning the responsibility for the error and the cost of correction, if any, is refused by the Contractor, the question at issue shall be referred to the Board of Arbitration.

"Indemnity.—The Contractor shall indemnify and save harmless the Company from and against all losses and all claims, demands, payments, suits, actions, recoveries, and judgments of every nature and description brought or recovered against it, by reason of any act or omission of the said Contractor, his agents, or employees, in the execution of the work or in consequence of any negligence or carelessness in guarding the same.*

"Liens.—If at any time there shall be evidence of any lien or claim for which the Company might become liable and which is chargeable to the Contractor, the Company shall have the right to retain out of any payment then due or thereafter to become due, an amount sufficient to completely indemnify the Company against such lien or claim, and if such lien or claim be valid, the Company may pay and discharge the same, and deduct the amount so paid from any moneys which may be or become due and payable to the Contractor."†

Legal Restrictions.—Specifications should contain clauses calling the attention of the contractor to, or quoting, statutes which may require citizenship to be established, restrict hours of labor, or stipulate minimum wage rates.

Unforeseen Difficulties.—The justice of such clauses should be carefully studied as any attempt to make the contractor responsible for the damage resulting from so-called " Acts of God " will defeat

---

* Business Law for Engineers, by Allen, 1929, pp. 16–38.
† Ibid., pp. 16–40.

itself—and should. Ordinary risks are covered by the article entitled " Contractor's Understanding." The following may be inserted if it makes clearer the legitimate risks which the Contractor assumes. "All loss or damages arising out of the nature of the work to be done under this contract on account of unforeseen obstructions or difficulties, from the action of the elements, from strikes, lockouts, or from incumbrances on the work, shall be at the expense of the Contractor."

Intoxicating Liquors Prohibited.—" The Contractor, in so far as his authority extends, shall not permit the sale, distribution or use of intoxicating liquors upon or adjacent to the work, or allow any such to be brought upon, to or near the property of the Company."

Note. Neither the above contract nor any other form should be used without examining each clause to see if it is pertinent and adequate.

In order to ensure the completeness of the specifications, especially on complicated or unusual jobs, additional or substitute clauses should be examined as they are presented in

Business Law for Engineers, by C. F. Allen, published by McGraw-Hill Book Company, New York.

Elements of Specification Writing, by R. S. Kirby, published by John Wiley & Sons, New York.

Specification details can best be studied from office copies which represent good practice. All construction firms have files of specifications designed to meet general and particular cases.

INDEX

Note: The double folios refer to both section and page numbers. For example, **13–09** indicates page **09** of Section **13**.

1

12 INDEX

Entropy, saturated steam, 7–33 to 7–35
   superheated steam, 7–36 to 7–39
   temperature-, diagram, 7–09
   units of, 3–15
Epicycloid, 2–53, 2–68
   mensuration formulas for, 2–40
Epitrochoid, 2–68
Epsom salt, 10–16
Equalities, symbols for, 1–02
Equations, 2–12 to 2–16
   application of $\frac{dP}{dh} = pg$, 6–11 to 6–13
   Bernoulli, 2–100
   biquadratic, 2–14
   chemical, 10–04
   cubic, 2–13, 2–14
   differential, *see* Differential equations
   dimensional, 3–04
   Euler's homogeneous, 2–103
   graphical solution of, 2–16
   Laplace's, 2–106
   linear, 2–12, 2–17, 2–18
   Navier-Stokes, 6–15
   nth degree, 2–14 to 2–16
      special systems of, 2–19
   physical, 3–03, 3–13
      dimensional homogeneity of, 3–36, 3–37
      style of writing, 3–37
   quadratic, 2–12, 2–13
   Riccati's, 2–101
   unitary homogeneous, 3–37
   writing of the electromagnetic, 3–35
Equiangular spiral, 2–69
Equilateral triangle, 2–32
Equilibrant, 4–03
Equilibrium, conditions of, 5–20
   diagram of iron and steel, 11–27 to 11–29
   principles of, 4–10, 4–11
   problems, 4–11 to 4–15
Equipment, air-conditioning, 7–94
   materials testing, 5–81 to 5–84
Equipotential surfaces, electric, 8–35
   magnetic, 8–26
Equivalent sinusoidal current, 8–46
Erg, 3–25, 3–28
Erichsen draw, non-retentive magnetic materials, 11–102
Errors, 2–05
   and observations, 2–123
   probable, 2–123 to 2–126
      applications, 2–126 to 2–128
      interpretation of, 2–127, 2–128
Ester gum, 12–55
Ethane, properties of, 1–121, 7–82
Ether, density of, 6–06
Ethyl acetate, properties of, 1–123
   alcohol, density of, 6–06
      index of refraction of, 9–15
      magneto-optic rotation of, 9–18
      properties of, 1–123
      surface tension of, 6–09
   bromide, properties of, 1–123
   chloride, properties of, 1–121, 1–123, 7–82
   ether, index of refraction of, 9–15
   iodide, properties of, 1–123
Ethylene bromide, properties of, 1–123
   chloride, properties of, 1–123
   properties of, 1–121, 7–82
Euler's column formula, 5–38
   homogeneous equation, 2–103
Evaporation and rainfall, 9–58, 9–59
   test (lubricants), 12–75
Everdur, properties of, 11–41, 11–50

Evergreen magnolia, properties of, 12–46
Exact differential equation, 2–10
   simple interest on $1000, 2–23
Exchange (magnetism), 8–19
Excitation of line spectra, 9–20
Expansion, actual, of a vapor, 7–49
   of functions, series, 2–79 to 2–85
   ratio (Otto cycle), 7–74
   thermal coefficient of, aluminum, 11–59
      bearing bronzes, 11–89
      copper, 11–40
      copper-base alloys, wrought, 11–45 to 11–51
      copper-nickel alloys, 11–72
      electrical resistance materials, 11–99
      gases, 1–121, 1–122
      iron, 11–20, 11–25
      magnesium, 11–76
      metals, 1–125, 1–126
      molybdenum, 11–81
      Monel metal, 11–73
      nickel, 11–71
      non-metallic solids, 1–129
      refractories, 12–22, 12–23
      stainless steel, 11–38
      steel, 11–25
      tungsten, 11–80
      zinc, 11–53
      zinc-base die-casting alloys, 11–83
Expert witness, engineer as, 13–09
Explosives, 12–79, 12–80
Exponential charge, 8–52
   current, 8–52
   emf, 8–52
   horn, 9–47
   impedance, 8–53
   values and logarithms, 1–102 to 1–112
Extensometers, 5–83
External shear, reinforced concrete, 5–66
Eye, 9–26
Eyelet brass, properties of, 11–44
Eyepieces, optical instruments, 9–13
Eyring's formula, 9–50

Fabrication aluminum and aluminum alloys, 11–69
   copper, and copper alloys, 11–40
   of rolled zinc, 11–57
Fabrics, insulating, dielectric strength of, 12–64
Factor, integrating, 2–101
   of safety, 5–10, 5–11
   shape (wind pressure), 9–66 to 9–69
Factorials, 1–11, 2–03
Factoring (algebra), 2–08
Factors (arithmetic), 2–03
   conversion, tables of, 1–130 to 1–147
Factory lumber, 12–43
Fahrenheit temperature scale, 3–27
Failure, character of (repeated stress), 5–12
Fan, characteristics of, 6–46
   drag, 6–37
   and propellers, 6–44
   propeller-type, 6–46
Farad, 3–33, 8–40
   international, 3–34
Faraday, 3–34, 10–36
   effect, 9–18
Faraday's induction law, 3–20
   law, 10–36
Fatigue, corrosion, 5–16, 11–07
   of metals, 5–12
Fechner's law, 9–26
Feedwater heaters, 7–70
Fermat's principle, 9–10
Fermi-Dirac statistics, 8–64

Rule, slide, 2–11, 2–12
Rupture from impact, 5–18
  modulus of, 5–22
    brick, 12–17, 12–18
    refractories, 12–23
    stone, 12–15
    wood, 12–44 to 12–47
  point of, 5–04, 5–05
  work required for, 5–08
Rust-resisting metals, 11–10
Ruthenium, 10–19
Rydberg constant, 9–20

Sabine's formula, 9–50
SAE numbering system of steel alloys, 11–34
Safety, factor of, 5–10, 5–11
Salts, acid, 10–13
  acids and bases, 10–06 to 10–08
  properties of various, 10–11
  solubility of, in water, 10–09
Samples, contractor's, 13–19
Sand-cast aluminum alloys, 11–60 to 11–63
  copper-base alloys, 11–41 to 11–43
Sand-lime brick, 12–17
Sandstone, 12–15, 12–16
Saponification value of lubricants, 12–76
Saturated liquid and vapor, 7–32
  line, 7–41
  steam, pressure table, 7–33 to 7–35
Saturation of a color, 9–27
  magnetic, iron, 11–22
    non-retentive magnetic materials, 11–102
  region of vapors, 7–41
  and solubility, 10–08
  temperature of emission, 8–06
  voltage of emission, 8–05
Sawdust, thermal conductivity of, 12–35
Sawing timber, 12–40
Saybolt Universal viscosimeter, formula for,
  6–08
  viscosity, 6–03
  of lubricants, 12–76
Scalar product, 2–113
Scale effect (fluid dynamics), 6–17
  factors (models), 3–44
Scales, musical, 9–49, 9–50
Scattering of radiation, 9–03
  sound, 9–40
  x-rays, 8–08
Scavenger blower, 7–73
Schiller's value, 6–29
Scleroscope hardness, aluminum alloys, **11–67**
  carbon brushes, 11–100
  nickel, 11–71
  testing machine, 5–90
Screw-power, compound-lever testing machine,
  5–81
  threads, standard, 1–166
Sealed instruments (contracts), 13–05
Seasoning timber, 12–40, 12–41
Secant, 2–54
  of a circle, 2–33
  formula, column, 5–38
    eccentric loads, 5–45
    transverse loads, 5–46
  hyperbolic, 2–59
Second law energy balance, 7–60
  of thermodynamics, 7–07
  unit of angle measurement, 2–32
  unit of time, 3–23
Section, dangerous, of beams 5–21
  modulus, 5–22
    beam sections, 5–22

Section, modulus, steel sections, 1–153 to 1–163
  yard lumber, 1–167, 1–168
  repeating, riveted joints, 5–58
Sections of beams, properties of, 5–22
  conic, 2–64 to 2–66
  method of, analysis by, 4–14
  structural aluminum, 1–153
    steel, 1–153 to 1–163
  wing, 6–41
Sector of a circle, 2–33
  circular, mensuration formulas for, 2–39
    properties of, 4–22
  spherical, 2–36
    mensuration formulas for, 2–42
    properties of, 4–25
Securities, issue of, 13–13
Sedimentary rocks, 12–14, 12–15
Seebeck effect, 8–10
Segments, circular, 1–28, 1–29
  mensuration formulas for, 2–39
    properties of, 4–22
  of a curve, 2–33
  parabolic, properties of, 4–22
  spherical, 2–36
    mensuration formulas for, 2–43
    properties of, 4–25
Select lumber, 12–48
Selenium, 10–29
Self-inductance, 8–28, 8–50
Semicircle, mensuration formulas for, 2–39
  properties of, 4–22
Semi-Diesel cycle, 7–73
Semi-drying oils, 12–56
Semi-red brass, properties of, 11–42
Sense of a force, 4–02
Series circuits, 8–14
  expansion of functions, 2–79 to 2–84
  -parallel circuits, 8–15
  special, 2–19, 2–20
Serpentine, average strength, 12–15
Set method, determination of yield strength,
  5–87
Shafts, 5–48 to 5–52
Shake (wood), 12–42
Shale building brick, strength of, 12–18
Shape factor (wind pressure), 9–66 to 9–69
Shavings, thermal conductivity of, 12–35
Shear, 5–02
  allowable unit stress, reinforced concrete, 5–62
    riveted joints, 5–58
    structural steel, 5–24
    timber, 5–31
  due to axial stress, 5–09
  combined with tension or compression, 5–10
  deflection due to, 5–23
  diagram, 5–20
  external, reinforced concrete, 5–66
  horizontal, 5–21
    example in beam design, 5–30
    in timber beams, 5–25
  modulus of elasticity in, 5–06
  due to normal stress at right angles, 5–09
  resisting, 5–20
  tensile or compression stress due to, 5–09
  vertical, 5–20
    of beams of uniform cross-section, 5–26 to
    5–28
  web, in beams, 5–23
Shearing modulus, metals, 1–127
  strength, aluminum sand-cast alloys, 11–61
    aluminum wrought alloys, 11–67
    copper-base wrought alloys, 11–45 to 11–51
    magnesium alloys, 11–78
    stone, 12–15

WILEY ENGINEERING HANDBOOK SERIES

HANDBOOK OF ENGINEERING FUNDAMENTALS

EDITED BY OVID W. ESHBACH. 1081 PAGES

SECTION

1. MATHEMATICAL AND PHYSICAL TABLES: SYMBOLS AND ABBREVIATIONS; MATHEMATICAL TABLES; PHYSICAL PROPERTIES OF MATERIALS; TABLES OF CONVERSION FACTORS—UNITS OF WEIGHTS AND MEASURES; GAGES; STANDARD STRUCTURAL SIZES; by Ovid W. Eshbach in collaboration with J. L. Barnes, J. G. Brainerd, R. T. Kent, and H. C. Knutson.

2. MATHEMATICS: ARITHMETIC; ALGEBRA; MATHEMATICS OF FINANCE; GEOMETRY; TRIGONOMETRY; PLANE ANALYTIC GEOMETRY; SOLID ANALYTIC GEOMETRY; DIFFERENTIAL CALCULUS; INTEGRAL CALCULUS; DIFFERENTIAL EQUATIONS; SOLUTION OF LINEAR CONSTANT-COEFFICIENT INTEGRO-DIFFERENTIAL EQUATIONS BY THE LAPLACIAN TRANSFORMATION (OPERATIONAL CALCULUS); FUNCTIONS OF COMPLEX VARIABLES; VECTOR ANALYSIS; ALIGNMENT CHARTS (NOMOGRAMS); PRECISION OF MEASUREMENTS; by J. L. Barnes in collaboration with J. G. Brainerd, C. Eisenhart, M. J. Fish, and J. M. Rice.

3. PHYSICAL UNITS AND STANDARDS: DIMENSION SYSTEMS; UNIT SYSTEMS; UNITS AND STANDARDS; DIMENSIONAL ANALYSIS; by Ernst Weber.

4. THEORETICAL MECHANICS: STATICS; KINEMATICS; KINETICS; by Janvier M. Rice.

5. MECHANICS OF MATERIALS: SIMPLE STRESSES; BEAMS; COLUMNS; SHAFTS; CYLINDERS, PLATES, ROLLERS, AND RIVETED JOINTS; TESTING OF MATERIALS; by Jasper O. Draffin. REINFORCED CONCRETE; by Theodore Crane.

6. MECHANICS OF FLUIDS: PROPERTIES OF FLUIDS, DIVISIONS OF FLUID MECHANICS; FLUID STATICS; FLUID DYNAMICS; by P. E. Hemke.

7. ENGINEERING THERMODYNAMICS: PRINCIPLES OF THERMODYNAMICS; GASES; LIQUIDS AND VAPORS; THE STEAM POWER PLANT; THE INTERNAL-COMBUSTION ENGINE; REFRIGERATION; GAS AND VAPOR MIXTURES, HUMIDITY, AND AIR CONDITIONING; by Milton C. Stuart and Paul J. Kiefer.

8. ELECTRICITY AND MAGNETISM: ELECTRON THEORY; DIRECT-CURRENT CIRCUITS; ELECTROKINETICS AND THE MAGNETIC CIRCUIT; ELECTROSTATICS AND THE DIELECTRIC CIRCUIT; ALTERNATING-CURRENT CIRCUITS; TRANSIENTS; CONDUCTION OF ELECTRICITY IN SOLIDS AND FLUIDS; by Charles Weyl and Irven Travis.

9. RADIATION AND LIGHT: THEORY OF RADIATION; GEOMETRY OF RADIATION; PHYSICS OF RADIATION; PHYSIOLOGY OF RADIATION; by Ernst Weber. ACOUSTICS; by R. B. Lindsay. METEOROLOGY; by Edgar W. Woolard, R. J. Martin, and H. L. Dryden.

10. CHEMISTRY: GENERAL CHEMISTRY; INDUSTRIAL CHEMISTRY; QUALITATIVE ANALYSIS; ELECTROCHEMISTRY; by Joseph Mattiello and Sidney B. Tuwiner.

11. METALLIC MATERIALS: CORROSION OF METALS; by Frank N. Speller. IRON AND STEEL; by Bradley Stoughton. COPPER AND COPPER-BASE ALLOYS; by members of the staff of the American Brass Co. and W. M. Corse. ZINC AND ZINC-BASE ALLOYS; by W. M. Peirce. ALUMINUM AND ALUMINUM ALLOYS; by Junius D. Edwards and Zay Jeffries. NICKEL AND NON-FERROUS NICKEL ALLOYS; by Robert Worthington. MAGNESIUM AND MAGNESIUM ALLOYS; by John A. Gann. TUNGSTEN; MOLYBDENUM; by Zay Jeffries. DIE-CASTING ALLOYS; by J. C. Fox. BEARING METALS; by Christopher H. Bierbaum. WELDING, BRAZING, AND SOLDERING MATERIALS; by Bradley Stoughton and D. F. Miner. ELECTRICAL CONDUCTOR MATERIALS; by H. C. Knutson and D. F. Miner. MAGNETIC MATERIALS, by J. B. Seastone. MISCELLANEOUS MATERIALS.

12. NON-METALLIC MATERIALS: CEMENT, CONCRETE, LIME, MORTAR, AND PLASTER; by Theodore Crane. STONE, BRICK, AND TERRA-COTTA; by Jasper O. Draffin. REFRACTORIES; by J. Spotts McDowell and E. B. Guenther. THERMAL INSULATING MATERIALS. TIMBER; by H. C. Knutson and H. F. Moore. PAINTS, ENAMELS, VARNISHES, AND LACQUERS; by Joseph Mattiello. ELECTRIC INSULATING MATERIALS; LUBRICANTS; ADHESIVE MATERIALS; by D. F. Miner. FUELS AND EXPLOSIVES. MISCELLANEOUS MATERIALS.

13. CONTRACTS. By R. L. Sackett.

MECHANICAL ENGINEERS' HANDBOOK

POWER

Edited by Robert Thurston Kent

1226 PAGES

SECTION

1. AIR: PROPERTIES OF AIR. COMPRESSED AIR, by Robert Peele. FANS AND BLOWERS, by Robert T. Kent.

2. WATER: PROPERTIES OF WATER. HYDRAULICS, by William P. Creager. HYDRAULIC TURBINES, by R. E. V. Sharp. PUMPS AND PUMPING ENGINES, by Robert T. Kent. CENTRIFUGAL PUMPS, by V. deP. Gerbereux.

3. HEAT: MEASUREMENT OF HEAT. HEAT TRANSMISSION, by W. J. King. EVAPORATORS AND EVAPORATION, by W. L. Badger. DRYERS AND DRYING, by Francis E. Finch. KILN DRYING OF LUMBER, by L. V. Teesdale. HEAT INSULATION, by P. Nicholls. THERMODYNAMICS, by A. G. Christie.

4. COMBUSTION AND FUELS: COMBUSTION AND SOLID FUELS, by Robert T. Kent. LIQUID FUELS, by Harry L. Tapp. GASEOUS FUELS. ILLUMINATING GAS, by Alfred E. Forstall.

5. STEAM: PROPERTIES OF STEAM; THE MOLLIER DIAGRAM, by A. G. Christie. FLOW OF STEAM IN PIPES, by Robert K. Behr. STEAM PIPING. STRESSES IN PIPE LINES, by A. S. McCormick. COMMERCIAL PIPE AND FITTINGS. STEAM VALVES.

6. THE STEAM BOILER: BOILER CONSTRUCTION; SUPERHEATERS, ECONOMIZERS AND AIR HEATERS; UTILIZATION OF WASTE HEAT; MOISTURE IN STEAM. BOILER FEEDING. FEEDWATER FOR STEAM BOILERS. By D. S. Jacobus, Robert K. Behr and Robert T. Kent. BOILER FURNACES; STOKERS; GAS AND OIL BURNERS, by W. S. Carter. CHIMNEYS AND DRAFT. SMOKE.

7. THE STEAM ENGINE: CAPACITY OF ENGINES; By W. Trinks. COMPOUND AND TRIPLE-EXPANSION ENGINES; STEAM ENGINE ECONOMY; OPERATION OF ENGINES; VALVE GEARS; OPERATING DATA; STEAM ENGINE PARTS; SELECTION OF TYPE OF ENGINE; COST OF ENGINES.

8. THE STEAM TURBINE: By A. G. Christie. TYPES OF TURBINES. STEAM TURBINE CYCLES. NOZZLES. BLADING. STEAM SUPPLY. ROTORS. TURBINE DETAILS. REDUCTION GEARING. LUBRICATION. TURBINE GOVERNORS. CASINGS. ERECTION AND OPERATION. CORRECTION FACTORS. TURBINE PERFORMANCE. TURBINE CALCULATIONS. REHEATING TURBINES. ECONOMIC SELECTION OF OPERATING CONDITIONS. MERCURY TURBINES.

9. CONDENSING AND COOLING EQUIPMENT: By Robert T. Kent. DIRECT CONTACT CONDENSERS. PROPERTIES OF SATURATED STEAM BELOW ATMOSPHERIC PRESSURE. SURFACE CONDENSERS. AIR PUMPS. COOLING TOWERS. COOLING PONDS.

10. REFRIGERATION AND ICE MAKING: By Louis A. Harding. REFRIGERATION. COLD STORAGE. HEAT TRANSMISSION. THE AMMONIA ABSORPTION MACHINE. VAPOR CONDENSERS. BRINE CIRCULATING SYSTEM. ICE MANUFACTURE.

11. HEATING, VENTILATING AND AIR CONDITIONING: By Louis A. Harding. ESTIMATING HEATING REQUIREMENTS OF BUILDINGS. HEATING SYSTEMS. RATING OF HEATING BOILERS. DESIGN OF AIR DUCTS. VENTILATION. AIR CONDITIONING.

12. INTERNAL COMBUSTION ENGINES: DIESEL ENGINES, by E. J. Kates. GAS ENGINES, by H. A. Gehres. GASOLINE ENGINES.

13. GAS PRODUCERS: By John Blizard. GENERAL DESIGN AND OPERATION OF GAS PRODUCERS. PROPERTIES OF PRODUCER GAS. DESIGN OF FURNACES FOR PRODUCER GAS.

14. TRANSPORTATION: RAILROAD ENGINEERING, by G. E. Rhoads. AUTOMOTIVE VEHICLES, by Ralph A. Richardson. AERONAUTICS, by Edward P. Warner and S. Paul Johnston.

15. ELECTRIC POWER: By E. S. Dibble. PURCHASED POWER. GENERATED POWER. CONVERSION EQUIPMENT. SWITCHBOARD EQUIPMENT. BATTERIES. POWER FACTOR. POWER DISTRIBUTION.

16. POWER TEST CODES: INSTRUMENTS AND APPARATUS. TEST CODES.

17. MATHEMATICAL TABLES.

DESIGN. SHOP PRACTICE
Edited by Robert Thurston Kent

1378 PAGES

HANDBOOK FOR ELECTRICAL ENGINEERS
ELECTRIC POWER

EDITED BY HAROLD PENDER, WILLIAM A. DEL MAR, AND KNOX MCILWAIN

1300 PAGES

SECTION

1. MATHEMATICS, UNITS, AND SYMBOLS: MATHEMATICS; by Carl C. Chambers. MATHEMATICAL TABLES. UNITS AND CONVERSION FACTORS; by J. G. Brainerd and Carl C. Chambers. SYMBOLS AND ABBREVIATIONS. CONSTANTS; by Carl C. Chambers.

2. PROPERTIES OF MATERIALS: WEIGHTS OF MATERIALS; CONDUCTOR MATERIALS; INSULATING MATERIALS; MAGNETIC MATERIALS; THERMAL PROPERTIES OF MATERIALS; by D. F. Miner.

3. ELECTRIC CIRCUITS AND ELECTRIC LINES: ALTERNATING CURRENTS; LINEAR CIRCUITS; NON-LINEAR CIRCUITS; POLYPHASE SYSTEMS AND SYMMETRICAL COMPONENTS; ELECTRICAL MACHINES; TRANSMISSION LINES; STABILITY OF POWER SYSTEMS; by Irven Travis.

4. RESISTORS, REACTORS, MAGNETS: RESISTORS, RHEOSTATS; CAPACITORS— CONDENSERS; INDUCTORS; MAGNETS, MAGNETIC DEVICES; by A. Dexter Hinckley.

5. MEASUREMENTS AND MEASURING APPARATUS: by H. B. Brooks.

6. PRINCIPLES OF ELECTROCHEMISTRY: by H. M. Goodwin, revised by Martin Kilpatrick and Mary L. Kilpatrick.

7. BATTERIES: PRIMARY BATTERIES; by C. F. Burgess. LEAD-ACID STORAGE BATTERIES; by J. Lester Woodbridge. ALKALINE-TYPE STORAGE BATTERIES; by E. W. Allen and F. Brehme.

8. DIRECT-CURRENT MACHINES: DIRECT-CURRENT GENERATORS; DIRECT-CURRENT MOTORS; by Walter I. Slichter.

9. ALTERNATING-CURRENT MACHINES: ALTERNATING-CURRENT GENERATORS; SYNCHRONOUS MOTORS; POLYPHASE INDUCTION MOTORS; SINGLE-PHASE INDUCTION MOTORS; ALTERNATING-CURRENT COMMUTATOR MOTORS; by Walter I. Slichter.

10. TRANSFORMERS; by Walter I. Slichter.

11. CONVERTERS AND RECTIFIERS: ENERGY CONVERTERS; FREQUENCY CONVERTERS; PHASE CONVERTERS AND BALANCERS; RECTIFIERS; by Walter I. Slichter.

12. SWITCHING, CONTROL, AND PROTECTION: CIRCUIT ELEMENTS; CIRCUIT BREAKERS; CONTROLLERS AND REGULATORS; PROTECTION; STATION EQUIPMENT; STATION STRUCTURES AND LAYOUT; by Stephen Q. Hayes.

13. POWER STATIONS AND SUBSTATIONS: STEAM POWER STATIONS; by F. S. Bennett. HYDROELECTRIC POWER STATIONS; by R. A. Hopkins and A. G. Cherry. INTERNAL-COMBUSTION POWER STATIONS; by W. A. Sloan. SUBSTATIONS; by W. I. Slichter. POWER STATION CIRCUITS; by R. A. Hopkins.

14. POWER TRANSMISSION AND DISTRIBUTION: SYSTEMS; CAPACITANCE AND INDUCTANCE TABLES; UNDERGROUND CONDUITS; DISTRIBUTION; BARE WIRES AND CABLES; INSULATED WIRES AND CABLES; ELECTROLYSIS OF UNDERGROUND STRUCTURES; by W. A. Del Mar. ELECTRICAL DESIGN OF TRANSMISSION AND DISTRIBUTION SYSTEMS; by W. A. Del Mar, J. H. Palmer, F. W. Peek, and R. A. Philip. POLE AND TOWER LINES; by Howard Enos. WIRING OF BUILDINGS; by G. W. Zink. GROUNDING OF ELECTRIC CIRCUITS AND ACCESSORIES; by R. F. Abele.

15. LIGHTING AND HEATING: LIGHTING; by F. C. Caldwell. HOUSEHOLD HEATING APPLIANCES AND COOKING; by Frank Thornton, Jr. WATER HEATING; by C. J. Fay and J. F. Reifenberg. HEATING AND AIR CONDITIONING OF BUILDINGS; by Otto W. Walter.

16. INDUSTRIAL APPLICATIONS OF MOTORS; by Francis A. Westbrook.

17. TRANSPORTATION: ELECTRIC TRACTION; by H. A. Currie and Robert S. Rhodes. ELECTRICAL EQUIPMENT OF INTERNAL-COMBUSTION AUTOMOBILES; by H. Chase. ELECTRIC AUTOMOBILES; by W. P. Kennedy. ELECTRIC PROPULSION OF SHIPS; by W. N. Zippler.

18. ELECTROCHEMICAL AND ELECTROTHERMAL INDUSTRIES: ELECTROCHEMICAL PROCESSES; ELECTRIC FURNACES AND THEIR PRODUCTS; by M. de K. Thompson. ELECTRIC RESISTANCE HEATING; by Frank Thornton. Jr. ELECTRICAL PRECIPITATION OF SUSPENDED PARTICLES; by N. W. Sultzer. ELECTRIC WELDING; by H. M. Hobart.

19. ELECTRICITY ON THE FARM; by Lee C. Prickett.

HANDBOOK FOR ELECTRICAL ENGINEERS

COMMUNICATION. ELECTRONICS

EDITED BY HAROLD PENDER AND KNOX McILWAIN.   1022 PAGES

SECTION

1. MATHEMATICS, UNITS, AND SYMBOLS: MATHEMATICS; by Carl C. Chambers. MATHEMATICAL TABLES. UNITS AND CONVERSION FACTORS; by J. G. Brainerd and Carl C. Chambers. SYMBOLS AND ABBREVIATIONS. CONSTANTS; by Carl C. Chambers.

2. PROPERTIES OF MATERIALS: CONDUCTING MATERIALS; INSULATING MATERIALS; LUMINESCENT MATERIALS; MAGNETIC MATERIALS; SPECIAL PROPERTIES OF DIELECTRICS; by William F. Diehl with W. R. Dohan, H. W. Leverenz, D. G. C. Luck, and C. R. Nelson.

3. ELECTRIC CIRCUITS, LINES, AND FIELDS: LINEAR ELECTRIC CIRCUITS; GENERAL NETWORK THEORY; RECURRENT NETWORKS; NON-LINEAR ELECTRIC CIRCUITS; ELECTROMAGNETIC RADIATION; ELECTROMECHANICAL SYSTEMS; by Knox McIlwain.

4. RESISTORS, INDUCTORS, CAPACITORS: RESISTORS AND RHEOSTATS; INDUCTORS WITH AIR CORES; FERROUS-CORED INDUCTORS; CAPACITORS, CONDENSERS; by A. Dexter Hinckley.

5. ELECTRON TUBES: THERMIONIC VACUUM TUBES; by B. J. Thompson with J. M. Stinchfield, Bernard Salzberg, and E. W. Herold. GASEOUS CONDUCTION TUBES; by O. W. Livingston. CATHODE-RAY OSCILLOGRAPH TUBES; by G. F. Metcalf. X-RAY TUBES; by S. Reid Warren, Jr. PHOTORESPONSIVE DEVICES; by H. E. Ives.

6. ELECTROMECHANICAL-ACOUSTIC DEVICES: EFFECTS OF THE ACOUSTIC MEDIUM; LOUD SPEAKERS AND TELEPHONE RECEIVERS; MICROPHONES; by Hugh S. Knowles. MECHANICAL RECORDING AND REPRODUCING OF SOUND; OPTICAL RECORDING AND REPRODUCING; MAGNETIC RECORDING AND REPRODUCING; by H. A. Frederick and A. C. Keller.

7. CIRCUIT ELEMENTS: SINGLE MESH AND COUPLED CIRCUITS; by Vernon D. Landon and Knox McIlwain. TRANSFORMERS WITH IRON CORES; by J. I. Cornell and A. J. Rohner. ELECTRICAL WAVE FILTERS; by T. E. Shea and C. E. Lane. RADIO ANTENNAS; by G. C. Southworth. VACUUM-TUBE AMPLIFIERS; by Loy E. Barton. MODULATORS; POWER SUPPLY; RADIO TRANSMITTERS; by J. E. Young. DETECTORS; RADIO RECEIVERS; by Vernon D. Landon. OSCILLATORS; by Carl C. Chambers.

8. HIGH-FREQUENCY TRANSMISSION: WIRE TRANSMISSION LINES; by Knox McIlwain. TRANSMISSION IN SPACE; by John C. Schelleng. MECHANICAL FEATURES OF TRANSMISSION LINES; by C. H. MacDonald. COORDINATION OF COMMUNICATION AND POWER SYSTEMS; by C. H. MacDonald and H. A. Dambly.

9. ACOUSTICS: THE SENSE OF HEARING; SPEECH AND MUSIC; EFFECTS OF DISTORTION ON SPEECH AND MUSIC; by John C. Steinberg. ACOUSTIC PROPERTIES OF ROOMS; SOUND INSULATION; ACOUSTIC DESIGN OF AUDITORIUMS; by Vern O. Knudsen.

10. ELECTRICAL MEASUREMENTS: FREQUENCY MEASUREMENTS; by W. A. Marrison. MEASUREMENT OF PRIMARY ELECTRICAL QUANTITIES; by W. J. Shackelton and J. G. Ferguson. WIRE TRANSMISSION MEASUREMENTS; by F. H. Best. MEASUREMENTS OF TRANSMISSION THROUGH SPACE; by R. K. Potter. WAVE ANALYSIS; by E. Peterson and T. G. Castner.

11. TELEGRAPHY: ELEMENTS OF TELEGRAPH SYSTEMS; D-C TELEGRAPH SYSTEMS; A-C TELEGRAPH SYSTEMS; PRINTING TELEGRAPH SYSTEMS; LOCAL EQUIPMENT; SUBMARINE CABLE TELEGRAPHY; by Allison A. Clokey. RADIO TELEGRAPH SYSTEMS; by J. L. Finch.

12. SOUND-REPRODUCTION SYSTEMS: ACOUSTO-ELECTRIC EQUIPMENT; RADIO TELEPHONE BROADCASTING; by Howard A. Chinn. ELECTRO-ACOUSTIC EQUIPMENT; by W. H. Bohlke and Knox McIlwain. PUBLIC ADDRESS SYSTEMS; SOUND PICTURES; by Knox McIlwain. POLICE RADIO SYSTEMS; by Loren F. Jones.

13. TELEPHONY: SUBSTATION EQUIPMENT AND CIRCUITS; CENTRAL OFFICE SYSTEMS; by Knox McIlwain. TELEPHONE LINES; by C. H. MacDonald. RADIO TELEPHONE SYSTEMS; by A. A. Oswald.

14. FACSIMILE TRANSMISSION AND RECEPTION: SCANNING SYSTEMS; RECORDING SYSTEMS; TRANSMISSION AND SYNCHRONIZATION; COMPLETE FACSIMILE SYSTEMS; by Maurice Artzt.

15. TELEVISION: TRANSMITTING POINT ANALYZER; TRANSMISSION CHANNEL; RECEIVING POINT REPRODUCER; SCANNING SYSTEMS (ELECTRICAL); COMPLETE TELEVISION SYSTEMS; CIRCUIT ELEMENTS PECULIAR TO TELEVISION SYSTEMS; by H. Branson and R. L. Campbell.

16. ELECTRONIC CONTROL AND NAVIGATION EQUIPMENT: FUNDAMENTAL ELECTRONIC CONTROL CIRCUITS; LIGHT-SENSITIVE CONTROL EQUIPMENT; THYRATRON CONTROL EQUIPMENT; by W. R. King. RADIO AIDS TO AIR AND MARINE NAVIGATION; by W. E. Jackson and J. C. Hromada.

17. MEDICAL APPLICATIONS OF ELECTRICITY: ELECTROTHERAPY; DIATHERMY AND HIGH-FREQUENCY SURGERY; ULTRA-VIOLET-RAY THERAPY; PHYSIOLOGICAL ELECTROMOTIVE FORCES; ELECTRO-ACOUSTIC DEVICES; ROENTGEN THERAPY; ROENTGENOGRAPHY AND ROENTGENOSCOPY; HIGH-VOLTAGE SHOCK AND X-RAY BURN; by Charles Weyl.

MINING ENGINEERS' HANDBOOK

Edited by the late Robert Peele. 2442 Pages. In Two Volumes

Volume I

OTHER WILEY HANDBOOKS

THE ENGINEERS' MANUAL

By RALPH G. HUDSON, assisted by the late JOSEPH LIPKA, DEAN
PEABODY, and HOWARD B. LUTHER. Second edition. 340
pages. 5 by 7¾. 227 figures. Flexible binding.

ARCHITECTS' AND BUILDERS' HANDBOOK

By the late FRANK E. KIDDER. HARRY PARKER, Editor-in-chief,
with the collaboration of a staff of 18 specialists. 18th
edition. 2315 pages. 4½ by 7. Flexible binding.

MERRIMAN'S AMERICAN CIVIL
ENGINEERS' HANDBOOK

THADDEUS MERRIMAN, the late Editor-in-chief; THOMAS H.
WIGGIN, Associate Editor-in-chief; with a staff of 21
specialists. Fifth revised edition. 2263 pages. 4¼ by 7.
One volume, atholeather; two volumes, real leather.

CHEMICAL ENGINEERS' MANUAL

By D. B. KEYES and A. G. DEEM. 221 pages. 4¼ by 6¼. Flexible binding.

HANDBOOK OF ORE DRESSING

By ARTHUR F. TAGGART and 7 contributors. 1679 pages. 5 by
7¾. Flexible binding.

VEST-POCKET HANDBOOK OF MATHEMATICS
FOR ENGINEERS

By the late L. A. WATERBURY with special sections by the late
G. A. GOODENOUGH and H. H. HIGBIE. Third edition,
enlarged. 278 pages. 3 by 5½. Flexible binding.